# MusicMaster

# MUSIC MASTER
# SOUL CATALOGUE
# 1st EDITION

Edited by

Chris Wells

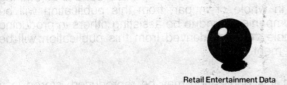

Retail Entertainment Data

Retail Entertainment Data Publishing Ltd,
Paulton House, 8 Shepherdess Walk, London, N1 7LB
Tel: 0171 490 0049    Fax: 0171 253 1308

1st edition published by Retail Entertainment Data Publishing Ltd., 1994.

**Editor:** Matthew Garbutt. **Researcher:** Gary Ford.
**Editorial Team:** Jane Scarratt, Bruno MacDonald, Howard Richardson.
**Product Manager:** Chris Spalding.
**Sales Manager:** Marie-Clare Murray.
**Senior Sales Executive:** Anna Sperni. **Sales Executive:** Adrian Pope.
**Publisher:** Brenda Daly.


*All enquiries:*
**Retail Entertainment Data Ltd.**
**Paulton House, 8 Shepherdess Walk**
**London N1 7LB**


Telephone: 0171-490 0049 Fax: 0171-253 1308


Cover artwork and design by IIIIi, London.
Cover photo of Shure Model 55SH supplied by
H.W. International, London

Database typeset in Great Britain by B.P.C. Whitefriars, Tunbridge Wells.

Printed and bound by B.P.C. Wheatons Ltd, Exeter, Devon.

ISBN 0 904520 85 4

# CONTENTS

iv

# HOW TO USE THE SOUL CATALOGUE

Welcome to Music Master's 1st edition of the Soul Catalogue.

The **Main Section** contains the majority of the recording information. It is divided into 26 separate chapters from A through to Z. The 'black strip' headings are the key to finding the artist you want, and are listed alphabetically by name. Recordings under each 'black strip' heading are listed in alphabetical order. Where a recording has a sub-title, this appears in brackets after the recording title. Tracks are listed, where available, after the recording title. Format and catalogue numbers are shown in bold on the same line to make them easier to read and are sorted chronologically where appropriate. This is followed by the record label, release date and the distributor. Deleted recordings are marked with a solid black square.

In the **Compilation Section** recordings are listed alphabetically by title and thereafter the format and layout are as for the Main Section of the catalogue.

There is a **Useful Address Section** at the back of the catalogue which contains information on record companies, dealers and magazines.

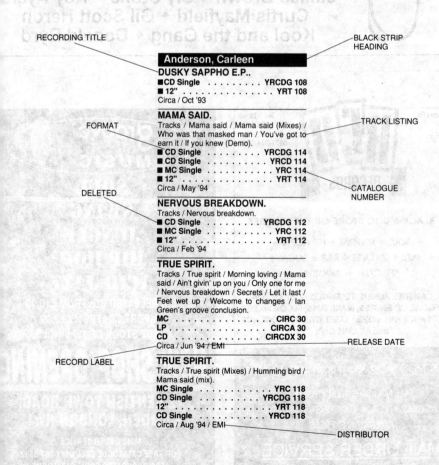

RECORDING TITLE

BLACK STRIP HEADING

### Anderson, Carleen
**DUSKY SAPPHO E.P..**
■ CD Single . . . . . . . . . YRCDG 108
■ 12" . . . . . . . . . . . . . YRT 108
Circa / Oct '93

FORMAT

TRACK LISTING

**MAMA SAID.**
Tracks / Mama said / Mama said (Mixes) / Who was that masked man / You've got to earn it / If you knew (Demo).
■ CD Single . . . . . . . . . YRCDG 114
■ CD Single . . . . . . . . . YRCD 114
■ MC Single . . . . . . . . . YRC 114
■ 12" . . . . . . . . . . . . . YRT 114
Circa / May '94

DELETED

CATALOGUE NUMBER

**NERVOUS BREAKDOWN.**
Tracks / Nervous breakdown.
■ CD Single . . . . . . . . . YRCDG 112
■ MC Single . . . . . . . . . YRC 112
■ 12" . . . . . . . . . . . . . YRT 112
Circa / Feb '94

**TRUE SPIRIT.**
Tracks / True spirit / Morning loving / Mama said / Ain't givin' up on you / Only one for me / Nervous breakdown / Secrets / Let it last / Feet wet up / Welcome to changes / Ian Green's groove conclusion.
MC . . . . . . . . . . . . . . . CIRC 30
LP . . . . . . . . . . . . . . . CIRCA 30
CD . . . . . . . . . . . . . . . CIRCDX 30
Circa / Jun '94 / EMI

RELEASE DATE

RECORD LABEL

**TRUE SPIRIT.**
Tracks / True spirit (Mixes) / Humming bird / Mama said (mix).
MC Single . . . . . . . . . . YRC 118
CD Single . . . . . . . . . YRCDG 118
12" . . . . . . . . . . . . . YRT 118
CD Single . . . . . . . . . YRCD 118
Circa / Aug '94 / EMI

DISTRIBUTOR

# INTRODUCTION

Soul music. Only the British still refer to it by name as a description of a strand of contemporary black culture. The Americans who invented it largely see soul in historical terms; something that happened in the sixties and early seventies, and has now gone the way of all fads. Looking at today's American R&B charts, one can see why. If you'd like a proper dissection of the demise of 'traditional' soul music, a good place to start would be Nelson George's book, 'The Death Of Rhythm & Blues'. The essence of George's argument is this: that as American blacks assimilated into the white cultural and business mainstreams - the American equivalent of our class system - many of their indigenous creative attributes began to be blurred by the process. Add into the equation the centralisation of the (largely white owned) record business in these technology obsessed times, and the result has been a planing down of nearly all the rough edges. (Hip hop? Nice try, but just count the number of its biggest stars signed to major labels.)

Yet soul does still exist and, occasionally, flourish. While the likes of Luther Vandross and Whitney Houston wander embarrassingly about music's middle of the road like over-dressed extras from 'Day Of The Triffids', here in Britain we're still doing it differently. Jhelisa Anderson, for example, was thrown out of Motown's LA offices when they discovered her secretarial position to be mere cover for her musical ambitions, but in London some three years later she is guesting with pop groups, recording an excellent first solo album (for Dorado Records) and generally being regarded with awe in even the trendiest circles. Likewise her cousin Carleen, also rejected in America, now recording for Circa after a chart-topping sojourn with The Young Disciples. Still more impressive, our home-grown acts, like Brand New Heavies, Incognito, Soul II Soul, Caron Wheeler, Sade, Jamiroquai and Mica Paris have all been enjoying healthy sales and profile over in the States - taking back to the Americans what they gave us in the first place.

So all in the British soul garden is rosy? Not quite. When Omar released his 'For Pleasure' album last summer, RCA were delighted to sell 20,000 copies during the first two weeks - but crushed not to see such sales reflected in the pop album chart. How could this happen? Because many of the people who bought Omar's album did so from specialist shops not connected to the Chart Information Network (CIN) chart return system. The effect of this is to mask the very existence of artists like Omar - and if they have no profile, the major labels will soon lose interest and cease to sign what are perceived as unsuccessful acts. Fortunately Ray Hayden of Opaz Productions, chairman of the newly formed British R&B Association, may have come up with a solution: the first official UK R&B singles and albums chart. Launched in January '95 and compiled with the assistance and technological (and, one hopes, financial) backing of the British Phonographic Industry (BPI) as well as CIN, the UK R&B chart will be sourced directly from specialist shops and so ought to reflect more accurately the true sales figures for R&B/soul music in this country. Positive knock on effects for the future of R&B/soul artists - major label investment, increased capacity to export, higher all-round profile - may ensure that the music has a future as well as a glittering past.

And so to this book. The MusicMaster Soul Catalogue is aimed at both consumers and professionals and seeks to provide a list of all soul music released in the UK. By definition, then, it does not include imports - with a few exceptions that would be too distressing to leave out: to compile such a listing would prove an impossible task. Having said that, there may, of course, be omissions. If you spot one then please write to me at R.E.D. and the next edition will include your suggestions. Equally, if you think we've got something wrong, then feel free to speak up: we won't bite. As to any opinions expressed herein, your agreement or otherwise is a matter for yourself and your record collection.

Chris Wells

# THE EDITOR

Chris Wells has been a soul fan since the early seventies and is currently the Editor of 'Echoes', where he has worked in various editorial capacities since 1984. He also makes frequent contributions to 'The Guardian' and 'Top' magazine, and is in constant demand as a sleevenote compiler and record company biographer. Graduating with an Upper-Second Class Honours Degree in Law from the University Of Sheffield, he has a daughter aged three and an insatiable desire to support Leeds United. At 37 he really should know better.

# NUMERICAL

## 5th Dimension

### 6 TRACK HITS.
**Tracks:** Puppet man / Never my love / One less bell to answer / Carpet man / Save the country / Last night I didn't get to sleep at all.
- **EP** . . . . . . . . . . . . . . . . . . . 7SR 5025
- **MC** . . . . . . . . . . . . . . . . . . . 7SC 5025
Scoop 33 / Sep '83.

### AGE OF AQUARIUS.
**Tracks:** Aquarius / Let the sunshine in / Blowing away / Skinny man / Wedding bell blues / Don't cha hear me callin' to ya / Hideaway / Workin' on a groovy thing / Let it be me / Sunshine of your love / Winds of heaven / Those were the days.
- **LP** . . . . . . . . . . . . . . . . . . . LBS 83205
Liberty / Jul '69.

### ANOTHER DAY ANOTHER HEARTACHE.
**Tracks:** Another day another heartache / Rosecrans Blvd.
7" . . . . . . . . . . . . . . . . . . . . . LIB 12056
Liberty / May '67 / EMI.

### AQUARIUS - LET THE SUNSHINE IN.
**Tracks:** Aquarius.
- **7"** . . . . . . . . . . . . . . . . . . .LBF 15198
Liberty / Apr '69.

### BEST OF THE FIFTH DIMENSION, THE.
**Tracks:** (Last night) I didn't get to sleep at all / One less bell to answer / Aquarius / Let the sunshine in / Wedding bell blues / Save the country / Love's lines, angles and rhymes / Puppet man / Up, and away / Never my love / Together let's find love / Light sings / If I could reach you / Go where you wanna go / Sweet blindness / Working on a groovy thing / MacArthur Park (live).
- **CD** . . . . . . . . . . . . . . . .74321 22545-2
Arista / Oct '94 / BMG.

### FANTASTIC.
**Tracks:** Magic garden / Up up and away / Carpet man / California my way / Worst that could happen / Good news / Sweet blindness / Stoned soul picnic / California soul / Go where you wanna go / Ticket to ride / I guess I'll have to learn to fly.
- **LP** . . . . . . . . . . . . . . . . . . . LBS 83228
Liberty / Jun '70.

### GO WHERE YOU WANNA GO.
**Tracks:** Go where you wanna go / Too poor to die.
- **7"** . . . . . . . . . . . . . . . . . . . LIB 12051
Liberty / Feb '67.

### HIGH ON SUNSHINE.
**Tracks:** High on sunshine / Tdrn my love away / Everybody's got to light it up / Magic man / Children of tomorrow / Sway / Skyway / Can't get you / You're my star.
- **LP** . . . . . . . . . . . . . . . . . . .STML 12106
Motown / '79.

### INDIVIDUALLY & COLLECTIVELY.
**Tracks:** Not Advised.
- **LP** . . . . . . . . . . . . . . . . . . . BELLS 211
Bell / '72.

### LIGHT SINGS.
**Tracks:** Light sings / Love's lines, angles and rhymes.
- **7"** . . . . . . . . . . . . . . . . . . . BLL 1161
Bell / Jun '71.

### LOVE'S LINES, ANGLES AND RHYMES.
**Tracks:** Time and lover / Love's lines, angles and rhymes / What does it take / Guess who / Viva Tirado / Light sings / Rainmaker / He's a runner / Singer / Every night.
- **LP** . . . . . . . . . . . . . . . . . . . SBLL 144
Bell / Aug '71.

### MAGIC GARDEN.
**Tracks:** Not Advised.
- **LP** . . . . . . . . . . . . . . . . . . . BELLS 215
Bell / '72.

### ONE LESS BELL TO ANSWER.
**Tracks:** One less bell to answer / Feelin' alright.
- **7"** . . . . . . . . . . . . . . . . . . . BLL 1137
Bell / Jan '71.

## PORTRAIT.
**Tracks:** Puppet man / One less bell to answer / Feelin' alright / This is your life / Love like ours / Save the country / Declaration / Change is gonna come / People gotta be free / Dimension 5IVE.
- **LP** . . . . . . . . . . . . . . . . . . . SBLL 135
Bell / Jul '70.

### STAR DANCING.
**Tracks:** You are the reason / Hold me / Going through the motions / You are the most important person in your life / Star dancing / You're my lifetime opera / Slipping into something new / We could fly / Good love.
- **LP** . . . . . . . . . . . . . . . . . . .STML 12077
Motown / Apr '78.

### STONED SOUL PICNIC.
**Tracks:** Sweet blindness / I'll never be the same again / Sailboat song / It's a great life / Stoned soul picnic / California soul / Lovin' stew / Broken wing bird / Good news / Bobbie's blues / 11th song.
- **LP** . . . . . . . . . . . . . . . . . . . LBS 83155
Liberty / Oct '68.

### SURRENDER.
**Tracks:** Surrender / Fantasy.
- **12"** . . . . . . . . . . . . . . . . . . . BDSL 502
- **7"** . . . . . . . . . . . . . . . . . . . BDS 502
Buddah / Jul '83.

### UP UP AND AWAY.
**Tracks:** Up, up and away.
- **CD Single** . . . . . . . . . . . . . . . . . .162064
Arista / Jun '89.

### WEDDING BELL BLUES.
**Tracks:** Wedding bell blues.
- **7"** . . . . . . . . . . . . . . . . . . . LBF 15288
Liberty / Jan '70.

### YOU ARE THE REASON.
**Tracks:** You are the reason / Slipping into something new.
- **7"** . . . . . . . . . . . . . . . . . . . TMG 1101
Motown / Mar '78.

## 8th Day

### CALL ME UP.
**Tracks:** Call me up / Body buddy.
- **12"** . . . . . . . . . . . . . . . . . . . USAF 1228
- **7"** . . . . . . . . . . . . . . . . . . . USA 1228
Funk America / Apr '83.

### EIGHTH DAY.
**Tracks:** Call me up / It ain't funny no more / In the valley / Right mood / I've got my heart in the right place / Body buddy / Last night made my day / Hot on the heels of love / Don't blow it.
- **LP** . . . . . . . . . . . . . . . . . . . AMLH 64942
A&M / Apr '83.

### SHE'S NOT JUST ANOTHER WOMAN.
**Tracks:** She's not just another woman / I can't fool myself.
- **7"** . . . . . . . . . . . . . . . . . . . INV 514
Invictus / Jul '71.

### TOO MANY COOKS (SPOIL THE BROTH).
**Tracks:** Too many cooks (spoil the broth) / Can't fool myself.
- **7"** . . . . . . . . . . . . . . . . . . .HDH 456
HDH / Jun '84.

## 24 Carat Black

### GHETTO: MISFORTUNE'S WEALTH.
**Tracks:** Synopsis One: In the Ghetto / God save the world / Poverty's paradise / Brown-baggin' / Synopsis Two: Mother's Day / Mother's Day / Foodstamps / Ghetto: Misfortune's wealth / 24 Carat Black / God save the world.
- **CD** . . . . . . . . . . . . . . . . . . . CDSXE 090
Stax / Sep '93 / Pinnacle.

## 52nd Street

### ARE YOU RECEIVING ME.
**Tracks:** Make up your mind / Are you receiving me (On 7" only) / Are you receiving me? (extended remix) (On 12" only) / Are you receiving me? (over and out mix) (On 12" only).
- **12" Remix** . . . . . . . . . . . . . . . . TENR 163
10 / '87.
- **7"** . . . . . . . . . . . . . . . . . . . TEN 163
- **12"** . . . . . . . . . . . . . . . . . . . TENT 163
10 / Aug '87.

### CAN'T AFFORD.
**Tracks:** Can't afford.
- **12"** . . . . . . . . . . . . . . . . . . . FAC 118T
Factory / Nov '84.

### CHILDREN OF THE NIGHT.
**Tracks:** Tell me (how it feels) / Never give up on you / You're my last chance / Abandon love / Children of the night / Look I've heard / I can't let you go / Smiling eyes / I'm available / Let's celebrate.
- **LP** . . . . . . . . . . . . . . . . . . . XID 10
- **MC** . . . . . . . . . . . . . . . . . . . CXID 10
- **CD** . . . . . . . . . . . . . . . . . . . DIXCD 25
10 / Jun '88.

### COOL AS ICE.
**Tracks:** Cool as ice.
- **7"** . . . . . . . . . . . . . . . . . . . FBN 20
Factory Benelux / Mar '83.

### I CAN'T LET YOU GO.
**Tracks:** I can't let you go / Tell me (how it feels).
- **7"** . . . . . . . . . . . . . . . . . . . TEN 114
- **12"** . . . . . . . . . . . . . . . . . . . TEND 114-12
10 / Feb '86.

### I'LL RETURN.
**Tracks:** I'll return / Jamaica boy.
- **7"** . . . . . . . . . . . . . . . . . . . TEN 136
- **12"** . . . . . . . . . . . . . . . . . . . TENT 136
10 / Jun '87.

### LOOK INTO MY EYES.
**Tracks:** Look into my eyes.
- **7"** . . . . . . . . . . . . . . . . . . . FAC 59
Factory / Aug '82.
- **12"** . . . . . . . . . . . . . . . . . . .FAC 59T
Factory / Jan '82.

### SAY YOU WILL.
**Tracks:** Say you will / Say you will (radio edit) (Only on TENX 215) / I will wait (NOT on TENR 215) / I will wait (radio edit) (Only on TENX 215) / I will wait (version) (Only on 7") / I will wait for you (Only on TENR 215) / Something's going on (Only on TENR215) / Tell me (how it feels) (Only on TENR 215).
- **12" Remix** . . . . . . . . . . . . . . . . TENR 215
- **CD Single** . . . . . . . . . . . . . . . . TENCD 215
10 / '88.
- **12"** . . . . . . . . . . . . . . . . . . . TENX 215
- **7"** . . . . . . . . . . . . . . . . . . . TEN 215
10 / May '88.

### SOMETHING'S GOING ON.
**Tracks:** Not Advised.
- **CD** . . . . . . . . . . . . . . . . . . . DIXCD 60
- **LP** . . . . . . . . . . . . . . . . . . . DIX 60
- **MC** . . . . . . . . . . . . . . . . . . . CDIX 60
10 / '88 / EMI.

### TELL ME HOW IT FEELS.
**Tracks:** Tell me how it feels (On TEN 7412 only) / Tell me how it feels (extended) / Tell me how it feels (dub) / Tell me how it feels (M + M style) (On TEN 7413 only).
- **12" Remix** . . . . . . . . . . . . . . . . TEN 74-13
10.
- **12"** . . . . . . . . . . . . . . . . . . . TEN 74-12
- **7"** . . . . . . . . . . . . . . . . . . . TEN 74
10 / Oct '85.

### TELL ME HOW IT FEELS (OLD GOLD).
**Tracks:** Tell me how it feels / You're my last chance.
- **12"** . . . . . . . . . . . . . . . . . . .OG 4110
Old Gold / Mar '89.

■ DELETED

1

### WHAT IT FEELS LIKE LOVING ME.
**Tracks:** What it feels like loving me / What it feels like loving me (Andersons mix) (Only on 3" CD single.) / Always seem to cry.
- CD Single . . . . . . . . . . . . . . . . TENCD 272
- MC Single. . . . . . . . . . . . . . . . . TENC 272
10 / '90.

### YOU'RE MY LAST CHANCE.
**Tracks:** You're my last chance / I'm available.
- 12" . . . . . . . . . . . . . . . . . . . . . TEN 89-12
- 12" Remix. . . . . . . . . . . . . . . TEND 89-12
- 7" . . . . . . . . . . . . . . . . . . . . . . . TEN 89
10 / Jan '86.

## 80's Ladies

### TURNED ON TO YOU.
**Tracks:** Turned on to you / Turned on to you (alternative mix).
- 12" . . . . . . . . . . . . . . . . . . . . . . . MOLIF 6
- 7" . . . . . . . . . . . . . . . . . . . . . . . . MOL 6
Music Of Life / Aug '86.

## 94 East

### MINNEAPOLIS GENIUS.
**Tracks:** If you feel like dancin' / Lovin' cup / Just another sucker / Dance to the music of the world / One man jam.
- CD . . . . . . . . . . . . . . . . . . . . . CLACD 132
- LP . . . . . . . . . . . . . . . . . . . . . . CLALP 132
- MC . . . . . . . . . . . . . . . . . . . . . CLAMC 132
Castle Classics / '87.

## 100 Proof (Aged In Soul)

### 100 PROOF AGED IN SOUL.
**Tracks:** Somebody's been sleeping in my bed / Love is sweeter / One man's leftovers / I've come to save you / Ain't that lovin' you / Not enough love to satisfy / Age ain't nothing but a number / She's not just another woman / Too many cooks (spoil the soup) / I can't sit and wait / Backtrack / If I could see the light in the window / Driveway / 90 day freeze (on her love) / Everything good is bad / I'd rather fight than switch / Don't scratch (where it don't itch) / Nothing sweeter than love / Since you been gone / Never my love.
- CD . . . . . . . . . . . . . . . . . . . . HDHCD 504
HDH / Apr '92 / Pinnacle.

### SOMEBODY'S BEEN SLEEPING IN MY BED.
**Tracks:** Somebody's been sleeping / Love is sweeter / One man's leftovers / I've come to save you / Ain't that lovin' you / Not enough love to satisfy / Age ain't nothing but a number / She's not just another woman / Too many cooks / I can't sit and wait / Backtrack.
- LP . . . . . . . . . . . . . . . . . . . . . . SHW 5003
Hot Wax / Apr '71.

### SOMEBODYS BEEN SLEEPING IN MY BED.
**Tracks:** Somebody's been sleeping in my bed.
- 7" . . . . . . . . . . . . . . . . . . . . . . . HDH 455
HDH / May '84.

## 100% Pure Poison

### YOU KEEP COMING BACK.
**Tracks:** You keep coming back.
- 7" . . . . . . . . . . . . . . . . . . . . . . . INT 501
EMI / Aug '74.

## 7669

### EAST FROM A BAD BLOCK.
**Tracks:** Here ah cumm / Session (interlude) / 69 ways to love a (black) man / Ma, I luv him (interlude) / Joy / Shoot the M.F. in his kneecap (interlude) / R.M.A. (Will you remember me) / Crossover message (interlude) / Last song / Who dez bytches anyway (interlude) / So high / Tic away / By your side / Cabaret (interlude) / Cloud 69 / 1-800-Dial F. (interlude) / King size bed / Shmoken' em up y'all (interlude) / Phillies, 40's & 69.
- CD . . . . . . . . . . . . . . . . . . . . . .532842-2
- MC . . . . . . . . . . . . . . . . . . . . . .532842-4
Motown / Mar '94 / PolyGram.

### HERE AH CUMM.
**Tracks:** Here ah cumm (Mixes).
- 12" . . . . . . . . . . . . . . . . . TMGX 1425
- 7" . . . . . . . . . . . . . . . . . . . . TMG 1425
- MC Single. . . . . . . . . . . . . TMGMC 1425
- CD Single. . . . . . . . . . . . . TMGCD 1425
Motown / Apr '94.

# A

## Aaliyah

### AGE AIN'T NOTHING BUT A NUMBER.
**Tracks:** Throw your hands up / Back & forth / Age ain't nothing but a number / Down with the clique / At your best (you are love) / Me quite like you do / I'm so into you / Street thing / Young nation / Old scool / I'm down / Back and forth.

| | |
|---|---|
| CD | CHIP 149 |
| LP | HIP 149 |
| MC | HIPCD 149 |

Jive / Jul '94 / BMG.

### AT YOUR BEST YOU ARE LOVE.
**Tracks:** At your best you are love (Mixes).

| | |
|---|---|
| 12" | JIVET 359 |
| CD Single | JIVECD 359 |
| MC Single | JIVEC 359 |

Jive / Oct '94 / BMG.

### BACK AND FORTH.
**Tracks:** Back and forth (mixes).

| | |
|---|---|
| 12" | JIVET 357 |
| 7" | JIVE 357 |
| CD Single | JIVECD 357 |
| MC Single | JIVEC 357 |

Jive / Jun '94 / BMG.

## Abbott, Gregory

### I GOT THE FEELING.
**Tracks:** Rhyme and reason / I got the feeling.

| | |
|---|---|
| ■ 12" | ABBT 2 |
| ■ 7" | ABB 2 |

CBS / Feb '87.

### I'LL PROVE IT TO YOU.
**Tracks:** Back to stay / Prisoner of love / I'll prove it to you / Runaway / Unfinished business / Crazy over you / Let me be your friend / Take me back / Two of a kind / She's an entertainer.

| | |
|---|---|
| ■ LP | 4606911 |
| ■ CD | 4606912 |
| ■ MC | 4606914 |

CBS / Jun '88.

### SHAKE YOU DOWN.
**Tracks:** I got the feelin' / Say you will / Shake you down / You're my angel / Magic / Wait until tomorrow / Rhyme and reason / I'll find a way.

| | |
|---|---|
| ■ CD | 450061 2 |
| ■ LP | 450061 1 |
| ■ MC | 450061 4 |

CBS / '86.

| | |
|---|---|
| ■ CD | 4609502 |
| ■ LP | 4609501 |
| ■ MC | 4609504 |

CBS / Aug '90.

| | |
|---|---|
| CD | 983310 2 |

Pickwick/Sony Collector's Choice / Oct '93 / Pickwick / Pinnacle.

### SHAKE YOU DOWN.
**Tracks:** Shake you down / Shake you down (ext. version) (On 12" only) / Wait until tomorrow.

| | |
|---|---|
| ■ 12" | TA 7326 |
| ■ 7" | A 7326 |

CBS / Sep '86.

### YOU'RE MY ANGEL.
**Tracks:** You're my angel.

| | |
|---|---|
| ■ 12" | ABBT 3 |
| ■ 7" | ABB 3 |

CBS / May '87.

## Abdul, Paula

### (IT'S JUST) THE WAY THAT YOU LOVE ME.
**Tracks:** (It's just) the way that you love me (7" only).

| | |
|---|---|
| ■ 7" | SRN 101 |
| ■ MC Single | SRNC 101 |
| ■ 12" | SRNT 101 |
| ■ CD Single | SRNCD 101 |

Siren / Nov '88.

### CAPTIVATED - THE VIDEO COLLECTION '92.
**Tracks:** Opposites attract / Knocked out / Rush rush / Promise of a new day / Blowing kisses in the wind.

| | |
|---|---|
| VHS | VVD 994 |

Virgin Vision / Feb '92 / Gold & Sons / THE.

### COLD HEARTED.
**Tracks:** Cold hearted snake.

| | |
|---|---|
| ■ 12" | SRNT 117 |
| ■ 7" | SRN 117 |

Siren / Sep '89.

| | |
|---|---|
| ■ CD Single | VUSCD 27 |
| ■ 12" | VUST 27 |
| ■ 12" P.Disc. | VUSTX 27 |
| ■ 7" | VUS 27 |
| ■ MC Single | VUSC 27 |

Virgin / Sep '90.

### COMPILATION.
**Tracks:** Not Advised.

| | |
|---|---|
| VHS | VVD 639 |

Virgin Vision / '88 / Gold & Sons / THE.

### FOREVER YOUR GIRL.
**Tracks:** Way that you love me / Knocked out / Opposites attract (Duet with the Wild Pair) / State of attraction / I need you / Forever your girl / Straight up / Next to you / Cold hearted / One or the other.

| | |
|---|---|
| ■ LP | SRNLP 19 |
| ■ MC | SRNMC 19 |

Siren / Oct '88.

| | |
|---|---|
| CD | CDSRN 19 |
| MC | OVEDC 400 |

Siren / Apr '92 / EMI.

### FOREVER YOUR GIRL.
**Tracks:** Forever your girl / Next to you / Straight up (12" version) (Only on 12" single.).

| | |
|---|---|
| ■ 12" | SRNT 112 |
| ■ 12" Remix | SRNX 112 |
| ■ 7" | SRN 112 |
| ■ MC Single | SRNC 112 |
| ■ CD Single | SRNCD 112 |

Siren / May '89.

### KNOCKED OUT.
**Tracks:** Knocked out (Not on 12") / Knocked out (instrumental) (On 7" only) / Knocked out (round 1-extended mix) (On CD & 12" only) / Knocked out (round 2-instrumental) (On CD & 12" only) / Knocked out (TKO dub) (On CD & 12" only).

| | |
|---|---|
| ■ 7" | SRN 92 |
| ■ 12" | SRNT 92 |

Siren / Sep '88.

| | |
|---|---|
| ■ 7" | SRNS 92 |
| ■ CD Single | SRNCD 92 |
| ■ MC Single | SRNC 92 |

Siren / Sep '88.

| | |
|---|---|
| ■ 12" | VUST 23 |
| ■ 7" | VUS 23 |
| ■ MC Single | VUSC 23 |
| ■ CD Single | VUSCD 23 |

Virgin / Jul '90.

### OPPOSITES ATTRACT.
**Tracks:** Opposites attract (Only on 7" formats.) / One or the other (LP version) (Only on 7" formats.) / Opposites attract (street mix) (Only on 12" and CD single.) / Opposites attract (party dub) (Only on 12" and CD single.) / Megamix (Only on 12" and CD single.) / Way that you love me, The medley (Only on 12" and CD single.) / Opposites attract (club mix) (Only on CD single.).

| | |
|---|---|
| ■ 12" | SRNTG 124 |
| ■ CD Single | SRNCD 124 |
| ■ MC Single | SRNC 124 |

Siren / Apr '90.

| | |
|---|---|
| ■ 12" | SRNT 124 |
| ■ 7" | SRN 124 |

Siren / Apr '90.

### RUSH RUSH.
**Tracks:** Rush rush.

| | |
|---|---|
| ■ 12" | VUST 38 |
| ■ MC Single | VUSC 38 |
| ■ 7" | VUS 38 |
| ■ CD Single | VUSCD 38 |

Virgin / Jun '91.

### SHUT UP AND DANCE (THE DANCE REMIXES).
**Tracks:** Cold hearted / Straight up / One or the other / Forever your girl / Knocked out / Way that you love me / Opposites attract / Medley / State of attraction.

| | |
|---|---|
| ■ Double LP | VUSLP 28 |
| ■ MC | VUSMC 28 |

Virgin / Oct '90.

| | |
|---|---|
| CD | CDVUS 28 |

Virgin / Apr '92 / EMI.

### SKAT STRUT/OPPOSITES ATTRACT.
**Tracks:** Not Advised.

| | |
|---|---|
| ■ VHS | VVC 981 |

Virgin / Nov '91.

### SPELLBOUND.
**Tracks:** Not Advised.

| | |
|---|---|
| CD | CDVUS 33 |
| ■ LP | VUSLP 33 |
| ■ MC | VUSMC 33 |

Virgin / Jul '91 / EMI.

### STRAIGHT UP.
**Tracks:** Straight up / Cold hearted / Straight up (power mix) / Straight up (Kevin Saunderson house mix) / Straight up (Marley Marl mix) / Straight up (house mix).

| | |
|---|---|
| ■ 7" | SRNN 111 |
| ■ 7" | SRN 111 |
| ■ 12" | SRNT 111 |
| ■ CD Single | SRNCD 111 |

Siren / Feb '89.

### VIBEOLOGY.
**Tracks:** Vibeology.

| | |
|---|---|
| ■ 12" | VUST 53 |
| ■ 7" | VUS 53 |
| ■ CD Single | VUSCD 53 |
| ■ MC Single | VUSC 53 |

Virgin / Jan '92.

### WAY THAT YOU LOVE ME, THE.
**Tracks:** Way that you love me, The (UK remix) / Megamix / Way that you love me, The (drums all the way).

| | |
|---|---|
| ■ 12" | SRNX 101 |

Siren / '90.

### WILL YOU MARRY ME.
**Tracks:** Will you marry me / Goodnight my love (pleasant dreams) / Promise of a new day (Only on 12" and CD single).

| | |
|---|---|
| ■ 12" | VUST 58 |
| ■ 7" | VUS 58 |
| ■ CD Single | VUSCD 58 |
| ■ MC Single | VUSC 58 |

Virgin / Jul '92.

## Abrams, Colonel

U.S. singer best remembered for 1985 smash *Trapped*, and whose final U.K. chart entry, *How Soon We Forget*, proved prophetic. Previously, Abrams' closest brush with success was involvement with mid-70's also-rans 94 East, who briefly numbered Prince among their ranks. Abrams' last notable release was 1990 single *Bad Timing*, produced by Cameo's Larry Blackmon.

### ALBUM, THE.
**Tracks:** Truth / Speculation / Never change / Picture me in love with you / Trapped / I'm not gonna let / Over and over / Margaux / Table for two.

| | |
|---|---|
| ■ LP | MCG 6001 |
| ■ MC | MCGC 6001 |

MCA / Mar '86.

### HOW SOON WE FORGET.
**Tracks:** How soon we forget / How soon we forget (dub).

| | |
|---|---|
| ■ 12" | MCAX 1179 |
| ■ 7" | MCA 1179 |

MCA / Jul '87.

### I'M NOT GONNA LET YOU (GET THE BEST OF ME).
**Tracks:** I'm not gonna let you / I'm not gonna let you (percapella mix) / I'm not gonna let you (ext) (On ext. 12" only) / I'm not gonna let you (ext dub) (On ext. 12" only).

| | |
|---|---|
| ■ 12" | MCAX 1031 |
| ■ 12" | MCAT 1031 |
| ■ 7" | MCA 1031 |

MCA / Mar '86.

### MUSIC IS THE ANSWER.
**Tracks:** Music is the answer.

| | |
|---|---|
| ■ 12" | 12P 336 |
| ■ 7" | 7P 336 |

PRT / Nov '85.

## OVER AND OVER.
Tracks: Over and over / Speculation.
- 12" . . . . . . . . . . . . . . . . . . . . MCAT 1041
- 7" . . . . . . . . . . . . . . . . . . . . .MCA 1041
MCA / Aug '86.

## TRAPPED.
Tracks: Trapped.
- 7" . . . . . . . . . . . . . . . . . . . . . MCA 997
MCA / Aug '85.
- 12" . . . . . . . . . . . . . . . . . . . .MCAT 997
- 12" . . . . . . . . . . . . . . . . . . . .MCAX 997
MCA / Sep '85.

## YOU AND ME EQUALS US.
Tracks: How soon we forget / We live a memory /
Nameless / Can't stay away / Soon you'll be gone /
You and me equals us / Caught in the middle / When
a man loves / Running / Fame and fantasy.
- LP . . . . . . . . . . . . . . . . . . . . MCF 3388
- MC. . . . . . . . . . . . . . . . . . . MCFC 3388
- CD . . . . . . . . . . . . . . . . . DMCF 3388
MCA / Jul '87.

## YOU DON'T KNOW.
Tracks: You don't know.
- 12" . . . . . . . . . . . . . . . . . . . . URBX 89
Urban / Jan '92.

## Absolute

### INTRODUCE ME TO LOVE.
Tracks: Introduce me to love.
- 12" . . . . . . . . . . . . . . . . . . . . FEFT 003
Feet First / Apr '92.

## Ace, Buddy

### GOT TO GET MYSELF TOGETHER.
Tracks: Got to get myself together / Darling depend
on me.
- 7" . . . . . . . . . . . . . . . . . . . . . ACT 4504
Action / Mar '68.

## Ace, Johnny

### MEMORIAL ALBUM FOR JOHNNY ACE.
Tracks: Pledging my love / Ace's wild / Anymore /
Yes baby / My song / Never let me go / Clock / No
money / Angel / Follow the rule / Burley cutie /
Please forgive me / You've been gone so long.
- LP . . . . . . . . . . . . . . . . . . . . . CH 40
Ace / Oct '81.

## Acklin, Barbara

Following unsuccessful releases on the St.
Lawrence label under both her own name
and as Barbara Allen, she co-wrote the
Jackie Wilson hit *Whispers*, and was consequently signed to Brunswick. Initial releases dueting with Gene Chandler
achieved only limited success but in 1968
she reached the U.S. Top 20 with *Love
Makes A Woman*, a song co-written with
Eugene Record of the Chi-Lites. Further
chart success followed with *Just Ain't
Enough Love* and *Am I The Same Girl*. The
writing partnership with Eugene Record
continued and created various hits for the
Chi-lites, including *Have You Seen Her*,
reaching No. 3 in both the U.S. and U.K.
charts. A move to Capitol Records saw Acklin back in the charts in 1974 with the Willie
Henderson produced *Raindops* but she was
dropped from the label the following year.

### AM I THE SAME GIRL.
Tracks: Am I the same girl / Love makes a woman.
7" . . . . . . . . . . . . . . . . . . . . .MU 1071
MCA / '69 / BMG.
- 12" . . . . . . . . . . . . . . . . . . . DEBTX 3024
- 7" . . . . . . . . . . . . . . . . . . . DEBT 3024
Debut (1) / May '87.

### FROM THE TEACHER TO THE PREACHER (see under Chandler, Gene).

### GROOVY IDEAS.
Tracks: I'll bake me a man / I call it trouble / I'm
living with a memory / It's a groovy idea / I did it /
Portrait of a broken heart / Seven days of night /
More ways than one / Love makes a woman / Be by
my side / Just ain't no love / Here is a heart / I've got
you baby / After you / Am I the same girl / Come and
see my baby.
- LP . . . . . . . . . . . . . . . . . . . KENT 072
Kent / Sep '87.

## LOVE MAKES A WOMAN.
Tracks: What the world needs now is love / Look of
love / Old matchmaker / Come and see me baby /
I've got you baby / Love makes a woman / Please
sunrise, please / Your sweet loving / Yes I see the
love / To sir, with love / Be by my side.
- LP . . . . . . . . . . . . . . . . . . . .MUPS 366
MCA / May '69.

## LOVE MAKES A WOMAN.
Tracks: Love makes a woman.
7" . . . . . . . . . . . . . . . . . . . . . . 55379
Brunswick / Oct '68.

## SEVEN DAYS OF NIGHT.
Tracks: Raggedy ride / Go with love / Seven days of
night / Just ain't no love / Where would I go / Am I
the same girl / Until you return / This girl's in love
with you / Here is a heart / Mr. Sunshine / Love had
come to stay.
- LP . . . . . . . . . . . . . . . . . . . .MUPS 410
MCA / Feb '71.

## SOMEONE ELSE'S ARMS.
Tracks: Someone else's arms / After you / Quiet
nights / What's it gonna be / Is it me / More / He's
just a little guy / More today than yesterday / Spinning wheel / More ways than one / You've been in
love too long.
- LP . . . . . . . . . . . . . . . . . . . .MUPS 416
MCA / Mar '71.

## SPECIAL LOVING.
Tracks: Special loving / You give him everything, but
I give him love.
- 7" . . . . . . . . . . . . . . . . . . . . . CL 15807
Capitol / Feb '75.

## Act Of Faith

### LITE UP YOUR LIFE.
Tracks: Lite up your life (mixes) / Fly.
- 12" . . . . . . . . . . . . . . . . . . 12BRW 306
- 7" . . . . . . . . . . . . . . . . . . . BRW 306
- CD Single . . . . . . . . . . . . . . . . BRCD 306
- MC Single. . . . . . . . . . . . . . . . BRCA 306
4th & Broadway / May '94.

### LOVE NOT LOVE.
Tracks: Love not love (Mixes) / Looking at the world /
All over now / Dream about you / Be Mine (On CD
only).
12" . . . . . . . . . . . . . . . . . . .12 BRW 310
7" . . . . . . . . . . . . . . . . . . . BRW 310
CD Single . . . . . . . . . . . . . . . . BRCD 310
MC Single . . . . . . . . . . . . . . . BRCA 310
4th & Broadway / Oct '94 / PolyGram.

### WHOLE THING, THE.
Tracks: Not Advised.
- 12" . . . . . . . . . . . . . . . . . . . EZY 1203
One Vision / Nov '92.

## Act One

### TOM THE PEEPER.
Tracks: Tom the peeper.
- 7" . . . . . . . . . . . . . . . . . . . .6008 005
Mercury / May '74.

## Active Force

### GIMME YOUR LOVE.
Tracks: Gimme your love / My sunshine.
- 12" . . . . . . . . . . . . . . . . . . . AMX 150
- 7" . . . . . . . . . . . . . . . . . . . AM 150
A&M / Sep '83.
- 12" . . . . . . . . . . . . . . . . . . . AMY 345
- 7" . . . . . . . . . . . . . . . . . . . AM 345
A&M / Aug '86.

## Ad Libs

### NEW YORK IN THE DARK.
Tracks: New York in the dark / Boy from New York
City.
- 7" . . . . . . . . . . . . . . . . . . . HEAT 1
Inferno (1) / May '79.

## Adams, Anita

### FOR YOUR LOVE.
Tracks: For your love.
- 12" . . . . . . . . . . . . . . . . . . . PWLT 86
PWL / May '91.

## Adam's Apples

### DON'T TAKE IT OUT ON THIS WORLD.
Tracks: Don't take it out on this world / Don't you
want me home.
- 7" . . . . . . . . . . . . . . . . . . . . BR 42
Brunswick / Jun '77.
- 7" . . . . . . . . . . . . . . . . . . TOWN 101
Kent / Apr '85.

## Adams, Arthur

### YOU GOT THE FLOOR.
Tracks: You got the floor / Stay with me tonight.
- 12" . . . . . . . . . . . . . . . . . . RCAT 146
- 7" . . . . . . . . . . . . . . . . . . .RCA 146
RCA / Oct '81.

## Adams, Faye

### I'M GONNA LEAVE YOU.
Tracks: You ain't been true / I'm gonna leave you /
Johnny Lee / Shake a hand / It hurts me to my heart /
Look around / I'm so happy / Cry you crazy heart.
- LP . . . . . . . . . . . . . . . . . . . RB 110
Mr.R&B (Sweden) / '89.

### SHAKE A HAND.
Tracks: Witness to the crime / Teenage heart / Takin'
you back / Don't forget to smile / Tag along / Angels
tell me / Your love (has my heart burnin') / Anything
for a friend / Shake a hand / I've gotta leave you /
Everyday / I'll be true / Say a prayer / Hurts me to
my heart / I owe my heart to you / Love ain't nothing
to play with.
- LP . . . . . . . . . . . . . . . . . . . OFF 6027
Official / '88.

## Adams, Gayle

### BABY I NEED YOUR LOVING.
Tracks: Baby I need your loving / Don't jump to
conclusions.
- 12" . . . . . . . . . . . . . . . . . EPCA 132167
- 7" . . . . . . . . . . . . . . . . . EPCA 2167
Epic / Apr '82.

### GAYLE ADAMS.
Tracks: Baby I need your loving / Don't blame it on
me / You don't owe me nothing / Let's go all the way
/ Love fever / I can't get enough of you / Don't jump
to conclusions / I loved every minute of it.
- LP . . . . . . . . . . . . . . . . . . . EPC 85687
Epic / May '82.

### I'M WARNING YOU.
Tracks: I'm warning you.
- 7" . . . . . . . . . . . . . . . . . . . BRW 16
- 12" . . . . . . . . . . . . . . . . . 12 BRW 16
4th & Broadway / Oct '84.

### LOVE FEVER.
Tracks: Love fever / I don't want to hear it anymore.
- 7" . . . . . . . . . . . . . . . . . . .A 1881
Epic / Dec '81.

### STRETCHIN' OUT.
Tracks: Stretchin' out.
- 7" . . . . . . . . . . . . . . . . . . . EPC 8791
Epic / Jul '80.

### YOUR LOVE IS A LIFE SAVER.
Tracks: Your love is a life saver / For the love of my
man.
- 7" . . . . . . . . . . . . . . . . . . . EPC 8987
Epic / Sep '80.

## Adams, Johnny

Nicknamed 'The Tan Nightingale', Johnny
Adams began singing for the Ric & Ron
label in the late 50's before moving to SSS
International where he enjoyed his greatest
sucess. Hits like *I Can't Be All Bad* and
*Release Me, Reconsider Me* in 1969, led to
a deal with Atlantic but the expected success failed to materialise. After short spells
on many smaller labels Adams has now
found more stability with the label Rounder,
where his material has been sympatheti-
cally recorded and subsequently well
received.

### AFTER DARK.
Tracks: Not Advised.
- LP . . . . . . . . . . . . . . . . . . . REU 1008
Rounder Europa (USA) / Feb '87.
CD. . . . . . . . . . . . . . . . . . . CD 2049
- LP . . . . . . . . . . . . . . . . . . ROUNDER 2049
MC. . . . . . . . . . . . . . . .ROUNDER 2049C

■ DELETED

Rounder / '88 / Roots Records / C.M. Distribution / Topic Records / A.D.A. Distribution / Direct Distribution.

## CHRISTMAS IN NEW ORLEANS.
**Tracks:** Silent night / O little town of Bethlehem / Lord's prayer / Silver bells / Christmas song / Little boy that Santa forgot / This Christmas / Lonesome Christmas / Bells of St. Mary's / White Christmas / Please come home for Christmas.

■ **LP** . . . . . . . . . . . . . . . . . . . . . . 1023
**MC.** . . . . . . . . . . . . . . . . . . . . . 1023 TC
Maison De Soul / '88 / Swift.

## FROM THE HEART.
**Tracks:** I feel like breaking up somebody's home / Why do I / Laughin' and clownin' / If I ever had a good thing / Scarred knees / From the heart / Your love is so doggone good / We don't see eye to eye / Roadblock / Teach me to forget.

■ **LP** . . . . . . . . . . . . . . . . . . . FIEND 26
Demon / Sep '84.
■ **LP** . . . . . . . . . . . . . . . . . . . . . OLD 3
Old Bean / Aug '85.
**MC.** . . . . . . . . . . . . . . . . .ROUNDER 2044C
■ **LP** . . . . . . . . . . . . . . . . . ROUNDER 2044
Rounder / '88 / Roots Records / C.M. Distribution / Topic Records / A.D.A. Distribution / Direct Distribution.
**CD.** . . . . . . . . . . . . . . . . . . . CDROU 2044
Rounder / Dec '90 / Roots Records / C.M. Distribution / Topic Records / A.D.A. Distribution / Direct Distribution.
**CD.** . . . . . . . . . . . . . . . . . . . . FIENDCD 26
Demon / Mar '92 / Pinnacle / A.D.A. Distribution.

## GOOD MORNING HEARTACHE.
**Tracks:** Not Advised.
**CD.** . . . . . . . . . . . . . . . . . . . ROU 2125CD
**MC.** . . . . . . . . . . . . . . . . . . . . ROU 2125C
Rounder / Oct '93 / Roots Records / C.M. Distribution / Topic Records / A.D.A. Distribution / Direct Distribution.

## RECONSIDER ME.
**Tracks:** I won't cry / Losing battle / Release me / You made a new man out of me / Reconsider me / If I could just see you one more time / I can't be all bad / In a moment of weakness / Proud woman / Real live living hurtin' man / Georgia morning dew / Living on your love / Lonely man / Too much pride / I want to walk through this life with you / Down by the river / I don't worry myself / I have no one / South side of Soul Street / Something worth leaving for / You can depend on me / Let me be myself.
**CD.** . . . . . . . . . . . . . . . . . . . CDCHARLY 89
Charly / Apr '87 / Charly.

## RELEASE ME, RECONSIDER ME.
**Tracks:** Release me, reconsider me / If I could see you one more time.
**7"** . . . . . . . . . . . . . . . . . . . . . BM 56775
Polydor / '69 / PolyGram.

## ROOM WITH A VIEW OF THE BLUES.
**Tracks:** Room with a view / I don't want to do wrong / Not trustworthy / Neither one of us / Body and fender man / I owe you / Wished I'd never loved you at all / Hunt is on / World I never made.
**CD** . . . . . . . . . . . . . . . . . . . . . CD 2059
■ **LP** . . . . . . . . . . . . . . . ROUNDER 2059
**MC.** . . . . . . . . . . . . . . . . . ROUNDER 2059 C
Rounder / '88 / Roots Records / C.M. Distribution / Topic Records / A.D.A. Distribution / Direct Distribution.
■ **LP** . . . . . . . . . . . . . . . . . .FIEND 111
Demon / Feb '88.
**CD.** . . . . . . . . . . . . . . . . . . FIENDCD 111
Demon / Sep '91 / Pinnacle / A.D.A. Distribution.

## SINGS DOC POMUS - THE REAL ME.
**Tracks:** Imitation of love / Still in love / There is always one more time / My baby's quit me / She's everything to me / I underestimated you / Blinded by love / Prisoner of love / Night is a hunter / No one / Real me.
■ **CD** . . . . . . . . . . . . . . . . . . . .ZS 119
Zensor (Germany) / Jan '92.

## TAN NIGHTINGALE, THE.
**Tracks:** Release me / You made a new man out of me / How can I prove I love you / You depend on me / Real live living hurtin' man / I won't cry / Losing battle / I have no one / Love me now / Proud woman / Reconsider me / Something worth leaving for / Let me be myself / It's got to be something / Hell yes, I cheated.
■ **LP** . . . . . . . . . . . . . . . . . . . CRB 1058
Charly R&B / '84.

## WALKING ON A TIGHTROPE.
**Tracks:** Not Advised.
**CD.** . . . . . . . . . . . . . . . . . . . . CDZS 89
**LP.** . . . . . . . . . . . . . . . . . . . . . . ZS 89

Zensor (Germany) / Mar '90 / New Note / A.D.A. Distribution / Direct Distribution / Topic Records / C.M. Distribution.

## WHEN I NEED YOU.
**Tracks:** When I need you / Cry cry darlin'.
■ **7"** . . . . . . . . . . . . . . . HEPME 45-180
Hep Me / Oct '83.

# Adams, Oleta

Adams was 'discovered' by Roland Orzabel and Curt Smith of Tears For Fears singing in a hotel bar in 1985 and they invited her to sing on the track *Woman In Chains*, from the album *Sowing The Seeds Of Love*. When it was released as a single her profile rock- eted and the ensuing publicity landed her a solo deal with Phonogram (home of Tears For Fears). Her debut album *Circle Of One* was produced by Orzabel, who also penned the first single *Rhythm Of Life* but the big breakthrough came with *Get Here* in 1991. Since then she has released her second album *Evolution* which included a cover of James Taylor's *Don't Let Me Be Lonely* but so far it has not had the impact or sales of her impressive debut.

## CIRCLE OF ONE.
**Tracks:** Rhythm of life / Get here / Circle of one / You've got to give me room / I've got to sing my song / I've got a right / Will we ever learn / Everything must change.
**CD.** . . . . . . . . . . . . . . . . . . . 8427442
**MC.** . . . . . . . . . . . . . . . . . . . 8427442
■ **LP.** . . . . . . . . . . . . . . . . . . . 8427441
Fontana / May '90 / PolyGram.
**CD.** . . . . . . . . . . . . . . . . . . . 8487402
**MC.** . . . . . . . . . . . . . . . . . . . 8487404
Fontana / Aug '91 / PolyGram.
**DCC** . . . . . . . . . . . . . . . . . 848 740-5
Fontana / Jan '93 / PolyGram.

## CIRCLE OF ONE.
**Tracks:** Circle of one / Think again / Watch what happens (Only on 12" and CD single.).
■ **12"** . . . . . . . . . . . . . . . . OLETA 212
■ **7"** . . . . . . . . . . . . . . . . . OLETA 2
■ **CD Single** . . . . . . . . . . . . . OLECD 2
■ **MC Single.** . . . . . . . . . . . . OLEMC 2
Fontana / Jun '90.
■ **12"** . . . . . . . . . . . . . . . . OLETA 512
■ **7"** . . . . . . . . . . . . . . . . . OLETA 5
■ **CD Single** . . . . . . . . . . . . . OLECD 5
■ **MC Single.** . . . . . . . . . . . . OLEMC 5
Fontana / Jun '91.

## DON'T LET THE SUN GO DOWN ON ME.
**Tracks:** Don't let the sun go down on me / I've got to sing my song / Get here (Only on CD Single.).
■ **12"** . . . . . . . . . . . . . . . . TRIMC 1
■ **CD Single** . . . . . . . . . . . . . TRICD 1
■ **7"** . . . . . . . . . . . . . . . . . TRIBO 1
Fontana / Sep '91.

## EVOLUTION.
**Tracks:** Not Advised.
**CD.** . . . . . . . . . . . . . . . . . . . 5149652
**DCC** . . . . . . . . . . . . . . . . . . . 5149655
**LP.** . . . . . . . . . . . . . . . . . . . 5149651
**MC.** . . . . . . . . . . . . . . . . . . . 5149654
Phonogram / Jun '93 / PolyGram.

## GET HERE.
**Tracks:** Get here / I've got to sing my song / Birdland (Available on MC and CD single.).
■ **12"** . . . . . . . . . . . . . . . . OLETA 312
■ **7"** . . . . . . . . . . . . . . . . . OLETA 3
■ **CD Single** . . . . . . . . . . . . . OLECD 3
■ **MC Single.** . . . . . . . . . . . . OLEMC 3
Fontana / Dec '90.

## I JUST HAD TO HEAR YOUR VOICE.
**Tracks:** I just had to hear your voice.
■ **7"** . . . . . . . . . . . . . . . . . OLETA 6
■ **CD Single** . . . . . . . . . . . . . OLECD 6
■ **MC Single.** . . . . . . . . . . . . OLEMC 6
Fontana / Jul '93.

## RHYTHM OF LIFE.
**Tracks:** Rhythm of life / Don't look too closely / Rhythm of life (Full version) (12" only) / Rhythm of life (Twilight version) (CD single only.)
■ **12"** . . . . . . . . . . . . . . . . OLETA 112
■ **7"** . . . . . . . . . . . . . . . . . OLETA 1
■ **CD Single** . . . . . . . . . . . . . OLECD 1
Fontana / Mar '90.
■ **MC Single.** . . . . . . . . . . . . OLEMC 1
Fontana / Oct '90.
■ **12"** . . . . . . . . . . . . . . . . OLETA 412
■ **7"** . . . . . . . . . . . . . . . . . OLETA 4
■ **CD Single** . . . . . . . . . . . . . OLECD 4

■ **MC Single.** . . . . . . . . . . . . OLEMC 4
Fontana / Apr '91.

# Adeva

Born Patricia Patterson, Adeva earned her name with her impressive vocal range and was dubbed 'A Diva'; the name stuck. A self-proclaimed New Jersey Baptist girl, Adeva was brought up on gospel music and was a leading light in the local choir where her father was minister. In later years she coached the choir and taught in a school for physically handicapped and emotionally disturbed children. She left, reluctantly, to pursue her singing career with the release of *In And Out Of My Life* for Easy Street, before signing with Cool Tempo. Her first major hit was a club rendition of Aretha Franklin's *Respect* and was followed with the equally stirring *Musical Freedom*. In 1990 Adeva collaborated with British rapper Monie Love; the result was the hugely suc- cessful House/Rap anthem *Ring My Bell*. A Greatest Hits package was released in 1992.

## ADEVA.
**Tracks:** Respect / I thank you / In and out of my life / I don't need you / Musical freedom / Treat me right / So right / Warning / Promises.
■ **LP** . . . . . . . . . . . . . . . . . . .CTLP 13
■ **LP P.Disc.** . . . . . . . . . . . . CTLPD 13
■ **CD** . . . . . . . . . . . . . . . . . . CCD 1719
■ **MC** . . . . . . . . . . . . . . . . . ZCTLP 13
Cool Tempo / Aug '89.

## BEAUTIFUL LOVE.
**Tracks:** Beautiful love.
■ **7"** . . . . . . . . . . . . . . . . . .COOL 195
■ **CD Single** . . . . . . . . . . . . COOLCD 195
■ **12"** . . . . . . . . . . . . . . . . COOLX 195
■ **12" Remix** . . . . . . . . . . . . COOLXR 195
■ **MC Single.** . . . . . . . . . . . . COOLMC 195
Cool Tempo / Dec '89.

## DON'T LET IT SHOW ON YOUR FACE.
**Tracks:** Don't let it show on your face / Independent woman.
■ **12"** . . . . . . . . . . . . . . . . . COOLX 248
■ **12" Remix.** . . . . . . . . . . . . COOLXR 248
■ **7"** . . . . . . . . . . . . . . . . . .COOL 248
■ **CD Single** . . . . . . . . . . . . COOLCD 248
Cool Tempo / Feb '92.

## HITS.
**Tracks:** Respect / I thank you / Warning / Beautiful love / It should've been me / Independent woman / Musical freedom (With Paul Simpson) / I'm the one for you / Don't let it show on your face / Until you come back to me / You've got the best of my love / Ring my bell (With Monie Love).
**CD.** . . . . . . . . . . . . . . . . . . . CTCD 30
**MC.** . . . . . . . . . . . . . . . . . . . CTTC 30
■ **LP** . . . . . . . . . . . . . . . . . . . CTLP 30
Cool Tempo / Oct '92 / EMI.
**MiniDisc.** . . . . . . . . . . . . . . . CTMD 30
EMI / Jan '93 / EMI.

## I THANK YOU.
**Tracks:** I thank you.
■ **7"** . . . . . . . . . . . . . . . . . .COOL 192
■ **CD Single** . . . . . . . . . . . . COOLCD 192
■ **12"** . . . . . . . . . . . . . . . . . COOLX 192
■ **12" Remix.** . . . . . . . . . . . . COOLXR 192
Cool Tempo / Oct '89.

## I'M THE ONE FOR YOU.
**Tracks:** I'm the one for you / Megamix (Feat:Respect/ Warning/Musical freedom/I thank you/Don't let it show on your face).
■ **12"** . . . . . . . . . . . . . . . . 12COOL 264
■ **7"** . . . . . . . . . . . . . . . . . .COOL 264
■ **CD Single** . . . . . . . . . . . . CDCOOL 264
■ **MC Single.** . . . . . . . . . . . . TCCOOL 264
Cool Tempo / Oct '92.

## IT SHOULD'VE BEEN ME.
**Tracks:** It should've been me / It should've been me (mixes).
■ **12"** . . . . . . . . . . . . . . . . . COOLX 236
■ **7"** . . . . . . . . . . . . . . . . . .COOL 236
■ **CD Single** . . . . . . . . . . . . COOLCD 236
■ **MC Single.** . . . . . . . . . . . . COOLMC 236
Cool Tempo / Oct '91.

## LIVE AT THE TOWN & COUNTRY CLUB.
**Tracks:** Warning / Treat me right / Respect / Beauti- ful love / Musical freedom.
**VHS** . . . . . . . . . . . . . . . . . . CVHS 5047
Chrysalis Music Video / '91 / EMI.

## LOVE OR LUST.
**Tracks:** It should've been me / Don't let it show on your face / Undercover lover / Until you come back to me / You've got the best (of my love) / (No need to get) emotional / Try me love / Who do you love / Be there / Ring my bell.
- **LP** . . . . . . . . . . . . . . . . . . . . . CTLP 22
Cool Tempo / Oct '91.
- **CD** . . . . . . . . . . . . . . . . . . . . . CCD 1866
- **MC** . . . . . . . . . . . . . . . . . . . . . ZCTLP 22
Cool Tempo / Feb '94.

## RESPECT.
**Tracks:** Respect.
- **12"** . . . . . . . . . . . . . . . . . . . 4 V 943329
- **12"** . . . . . . . . . . . . . . . . . . . COOLX 179
- **12" Remix** . . . . . . . . . . . . . . COOLXR 179
- **7"** . . . . . . . . . . . . . . . . . . . . COOL 179
Cool Tempo / Dec '88.

## RESPECT '93.
**Tracks:** Respect.
- **12"** . . . . . . . . . . . . . . . . . . . NWKT 79
- **CD Single** . . . . . . . . . . . . . . . NWKCD 79
- **MC Single** . . . . . . . . . . . . . . . NWKMC 79
Network / Dec '93.

## TREAT ME RIGHT.
**Tracks:** Treat me right.
- **7"** . . . . . . . . . . . . . . . . . . . . COOL 200
- **CD Single** . . . . . . . . . . . . . . . COOLCD 200
- **12"** . . . . . . . . . . . . . . . . . . . COOLX 200
- **12" Remix** . . . . . . . . . . . . . . COOLXR 200
- **MC Single** . . . . . . . . . . . . . . COOLMC 200
Cool Tempo / Apr '90.

## UNTIL YOU COME BACK TO ME.
**Tracks:** Until you come back to me / You've got the best (of mylove) / Musical freedom (Only available on 12" Single.).
- **7"** . . . . . . . . . . . . . . . . . . . . COOL 254
- **12"** . . . . . . . . . . . . . . . . . . . COOLX 254
- **CD Single** . . . . . . . . . . . . . . . COOLCD 254
- **MC Single** . . . . . . . . . . . . . . COOLMC 254
Cool Tempo / May '92.

## VIDEO HITS!.
**Tracks:** Respect / I thank you / Warning / Beautiful love / It should've been me / Musical freedom / Don't let it show on your face / Until you come back to me / Ring my bell.
- **VHS** . . . . . . . . . . . . . . . . . . MVR 4900013
PMI / Nov '92 / EMI / Gold & Sons / THE.

## WARNING!.
**Tracks:** Warning / Respect.
- **12"** . . . . . . . . . . . . . . . . . . . COOLX 185
- **MC Single** . . . . . . . . . . . . . . COOLMC 185
- **7"** . . . . . . . . . . . . . . . . . . . . COOL 185
- **CD Single** . . . . . . . . . . . . . . . COOLCD 185
Cool Tempo / Jul '89.

## ALL THE TIME IN THE WORLD.
**Tracks:** All the time in the world / All the time in the world (version).
- **12"** . . . . . . . . . . . . . . . . . . . PANTX 1201
Pantrax / Oct '90.

## ARE YOU READY.
**Tracks:** Are you ready (Mixes).
- 12" . . . . . . . . . . . . . . . . . . . . 12 BRW 297
- CD Single . . . . . . . . . . . . . . . . BRCD 297
4th & Broadway / Aug '94 / PolyGram.

## JUST CAN'T GET ENOUGH.
**Tracks:** If only you could be mine / Are you ready / Just can't get enough / Way we are / This man of mine / Something for nothing / Think it over / Take my love / I'm standing still / Wherever you are.
- CD . . . . . . . . . . . . . . . . . . . . BRCD 596
- LP . . . . . . . . . . . . . . . . . . . . . BRLP 596
- MC . . . . . . . . . . . . . . . . . . . . . BRCA 596
4th & Broadway / Sep '94 / PolyGram.

## WAY WE ARE, THE.
**Tracks:** Way we are / Way we are (mixes).
- **12"** . . . . . . . . . . . . . . . . . . . 12EMH 5
Intimate / Jul '93.
- **12"** . . . . . . . . . . . . . . . . . . . 12 BRW 286
- **7"** . . . . . . . . . . . . . . . . . . . . BRW 286
- CD Single . . . . . . . . . . . . . . . . BRCD 286
- **MC Single** . . . . . . . . . . . . . . . BRCA 286
4th & Broadway / Sep '93 / PolyGram.

## PLEASE DON'T BREAK MY HEART.
**Tracks:** Please don't break my heart.
- **12"** . . . . . . . . . . . . . . . . . . . TEN 53-12
- **7"** . . . . . . . . . . . . . . . . . . . . TEN 53
10 / Jun '85.

## AFTER 7.
**Tracks:** Don't cha think / In the heat of the moment / Can't stop / My only woman / Love's been so nice / One night / Ready or not / Sayonara.
- CD . . . . . . . . . . . . . . . . . . . . CDVUS 7
- LP . . . . . . . . . . . . . . . . . . . . . VUSLP 7
- **MC** . . . . . . . . . . . . . . . . . . . . VUSMC 7
Virgin / Sep '89 / EMI.

## CAN'T STOP.
**Tracks:** Can't stop.
- **7"** . . . . . . . . . . . . . . . . . . . . VUS 31
- **MC Single** . . . . . . . . . . . . . . . VUSC 31
- **12"** . . . . . . . . . . . . . . . . . . . VUST 31
- **CD Single** . . . . . . . . . . . . . . . VUSCD 31
Virgin / Oct '90.

## HEAT OF THE MOMENT.
**Tracks:** Heat of the moment / Sayonara.
- **CD Single** . . . . . . . . . . . . . . . VUSCD 7
- **12"** . . . . . . . . . . . . . . . . . . . VUST 7
- **7"** . . . . . . . . . . . . . . . . . . . . VUS 7
- **CD Single** . . . . . . . . . . . . . . . VUSCX 7
Virgin / '90.

## FADE TO GREY.
**Tracks:** Fade to grey.
- **12"** . . . . . . . . . . . . . . . . . . . TOT 5
Jumpin' & Pumpin' / Apr '90.

## SLAVE TO THE VIBE.
**Tracks:** Slave to the vibe.
- **12"** . . . . . . . . . . . . . . . . . . . VUST 75
- **CD Single** . . . . . . . . . . . . . . . VUSCD 75
- **MC Single** . . . . . . . . . . . . . . . VUSC 75
Virgin / Aug '93.

## L.A. NIGHTS.
**Tracks:** L.A. nights.
- **12"** . . . . . . . . . . . . . . . . . . . BRT 26
Blue Bird (2) / Jun '89.

## SHINE.
**Tracks:** Shine.
- **12"** . . . . . . . . . . . . . . . . . . . EXPAND 22
Expansion / Feb '92.

## BIRDS AND THE BEES.
**Tracks:** Birds and the bees / Fenderman.
- **7"** . . . . . . . . . . . . . . . . . . . . HLN 9954
London-American / Mar '65.

## EVERY DAY I HAVE TO CRY.
**Tracks:** Every day I have to cry / I don't want to cry / My heart cries for you / I cried all the way home / Cry me a river / I wake up crying / Cry / She cried / Don't cry / Cry of the wild goose / Cry myself to sleep / Don't let the sun catch you crying.
- **LP** . . . . . . . . . . . . . . . . . . . . GCH 8100
Chess (Charly) / '89.

## SO MUCH LOVE.
**Tracks:** So much love / Truer than true.
- **7"** . . . . . . . . . . . . . . . . . . . . POP 1531
H.M.V. / May '66.

## BERMUDA NIGHTS.
**Tracks:** When you say you love me / In the mood / Bermuda nights / Hook / Feeling inside / Still in love / Truth / Too cool.
- **CD** . . . . . . . . . . . . . . . . . . . . K 781 919 2
- **LP** . . . . . . . . . . . . . . . . . . . . K 781 919 1
- **MC** . . . . . . . . . . . . . . . . . . . . K 781 919 4
Atlantic / Dec '88.

## JUST BETWEEN US.
**Tracks:** New girl on the block / Trying to find a way / So amazing / King Boulevard / Come back to me /

You're my no. 1 / Just between us / You don't even know / Softly at sunrise.
- **LP** . . . . . . . . . . . . . . . . . . . . 781 813-1
- **MC** . . . . . . . . . . . . . . . . . . . . 781 813-4
Atlantic / Dec '87.

## SMOOTH.
**Tracks:** Don't worry about it / I surrender / Sweet baby / This is for the lover in you / G & Lee / Just 2 b with u / Anniversary / Passion / Sedona / Say it with feeling.
- **CD** . . . . . . . . . . . . . . . . . . . . .756782552-2
- **LP** . . . . . . . . . . . . . . . . . . . . .756782552-1
- **MC** . . . . . . . . . . . . . . . . . . . . .756782552-4
WEA / Mar '94 / WEA.

Identical twin brothers Taharqa and Tunde-Ra Aleem along with vocalist Leroy Burgess formed Aleem in New York during the early 80's. After writing a batch of tunes they formed their own label, Nia Records, in an attempt to get their songs out to the clubs where they thought they would create quite a stir. The brothers had started their recording career with Jimi Hendrix on the album *Cry Of Love* as The Ghetto Fighters, this experience along with the strength of material such as *Hooked On Your Love* and *Confusion* made the expected impact on the New York club scene and Aleem were signed by Atlantic Records in 1985. Their debut album *Casually Formal* , although critically well received, failed to sell and the brothers now work primarily as producers.

## CASUALLY FORMAL.
**Tracks:** Love's on fire / Two faces / Confusion / Stay / More than a million / Think / Fine young tender / Dance to the groove.
- **LP** . . . . . . . . . . . . . . . . . . . . 781 622-1
- **MC** . . . . . . . . . . . . . . . . . . . . 781 622-4
Atlantic / Apr '86.

## FINE YOUNG TENDER (Aleem & Leroy Burgess).
**Tracks:** Fine young tender / Two faces.
- **7"** . . . . . . . . . . . . . . . . . . . . A 9401
- **12"** . . . . . . . . . . . . . . . . . . . A 9401 T
Atlantic / Jul '86.

## GET LOOSE.
**Tracks:** Get loose.
- **12"** . . . . . . . . . . . . . . . . . . . MKHAN 61
Streetwave / Dec '85.

## RELEASE YOURSELF.
**Tracks:** Release yourself.
- **12"** . . . . . . . . . . . . . . . . . . . MKHAN 26
Streetwave / Oct '84.

Southern country-soul pioneer born in Alabama, 1940. First hit *You Better Move On* gave Muscle Shoals Studio its first success. Other Alexander penned songs: *Anna*, *Go Home Girl* and *A Shot Of Rhythm & Blues*, although selling in relatively low numbers, have been widely covered by the like of the Beatles, Johnny Kidd, Tina Turner, Elvis Presley etc. Sadly, he recorded only sporadically from the early 1960's and slid into obscurity. Alexander died in June '93, just after release of proposed comeback album *Lonely Just Like Me*. 1994 tribute album, *Adios Amigos*, boasted diverse cast, including Chuck Jackson, Gary 'U.S.' Bonds and Robert Plant.

## ARTHUR ALEXANDER.
**Tracks:** I'm comin' home / Go home girl / Burning love / Lover please / Down with the back roads / Come along with me / Thank God he came / It hurts to want it so bad / In the middle of it all / Rainbow Road / Love's where life begins / Call me honey / Call me in Tahiti / They'll do it every time.
- **LP** . . . . . . . . . . . . . . . . . . . . CH 270
Ace / May '89.

## EVERYDAY I HAVE TO CRY SOME.
**Tracks:** Everyday I have to cry some / Everybody needs somebody to love.
- **7"** . . . . . . . . . . . . . . . . . . . . BDS 439
Buddah / Jan '76.

## FOR YOU.
**Tracks:** For you / Other woman.
- **7"** . . . . . . . . . . . . . . . . . . . . HLU 10023
London-American / Feb '66.

■ DELETED

## GREATEST, THE.
Tracks: Anna / Soldier of love / You don't care / Call me lonesome / Where have you been / Don't you know / All I need is you / Keep her guessing / In the middle of it all / Without a song / Black night / You're the reason / I hang my head and cry / Dream girl / Are you / Shot of rhythm and blues / You better move on / Detroit City / Go home girl / Whole lot of trouble / I wonder where you are tonight.
CD . . . . . . . . . . . . . . . . . . . . . . . CDCHD 922
Ace / Jun '89 / Pinnacle / Complete Record Co. Ltd.

## LONELY JUST LIKE ME.
Tracks: If it's really got to be this way / Go home girl / Sally Sue Brown / Mr. John / Lonely just like me / Every day I have to cry / In the middle of it all / Genie in the jug / Johnny Heartbreak / All the time / There is a road / I believe in miracles.
CD . . . . . . . . . . . . . . . . . . . . . .755961475-2
Elektra / Jul '93 / WEA.

## SHOT OF RHYTHM & SOUL, A.
Tracks: Anna / Sally Sue Brown / You're the reason / Dream girl / Go home girl / Shot of rhythm and blues / Pretty girls everywhere / I wonder where you are tonight / You better move on / Girl that radiates that charm / Black night / Soldiers of love / I hang my head and cry / Where have you been / You don't care / Old John Amos.
■ LP . . . . . . . . . . . . . . . . . . . . . . . CH 66
■ MC . . . . . . . . . . . . . . . . . . . . . .CHC 166
Ace / Jan '85.

## SOLDIER OF LOVE.
Tracks: Don't you know / Call me lonesome / Detroit City / After you / Love letters / Keep her guessing / Hey baby / Soldiers of love / All I need is you / Whole lot of trouble / In the middle of it all / Funny how time slips away / Without a song / Love me warm and tender.
■ LP . . . . . . . . . . . . . . . . . . . . . . CH 207
Ace / Apr '87.

## YOU BETTER MOVE ON.
Tracks: Not Advised.
CD . . . . . . . . . . . . . . . . . . . . . . MCLD 19251
MC . . . . . . . . . . . . . . . . . . . . . . MCLC 19251
MCA / Oct '94 / BMG.

## YOU BETTER MOVE ON.
Tracks: You better move on.
■ 7" . . . . . . . . . . . . . . . . . . . . . . HLD 9523
London / '62.

## Alexander, David

### COME HOME RHONDA BOY.
Tracks: Green green grass of home / Come home Rhonda boy.
■ 7" . . . . . . . . . . . . . . . . . . . . . . DB 9078
Columbia / Mar '80.

### DAVID ALEXANDER.
Tracks: Anyone who isn't me tonight / For no reason at all / Can't stop lovin' you / Sylvia's mother / She thinks I still care / Answer to everything / I know / Lay down beside me / Love or something like it / For the first time in my life / Funny face / You and the looking glass.
■ LP . . . . . . . . . . . . . . . . . . . . . . OU 2230
One-Up / May '80.

### IF I COULD SEE THE RHONDDA ONE MORE TIME.
Tracks: If I could see the Rhondda one more time / Emerald green.
■ 7" . . . . . . . . . . . . . . . . . . . . . . DB 9044
Columbia / Jun '75.

## Alexander, Margie

### KEEP ON SEARCHIN'.
Tracks: Keep on searchin'.
■ 7" . . . . . . . . . . . . . . . . . . . . . . STAX 2016
Stax / Jul '78.

## Alice Street Gang

### BAIA.
Tracks: Baia / Brazilian hustle.
■ 7" . . . . . . . . . . . . . . . . . . . . . . CS 2106
Contempo (1) / Jan '77.

## All 4 One

### ALL 4 ONE.
Tracks: Not Advised.
CD . . . . . . . . . . . . . . . . . . . . . .756782588-2
MC . . . . . . . . . . . . . . . . . . . . . .756782588-4
Atlantic / Apr '94 / WEA.

---

### I SWEAR.
Tracks: I swear (Mixes).
7" . . . . . . . . . . . . . . . . . . . . . . .A 7255
CD Single . . . . . . . . . . . . . . . . . . .A 7255CD
MC Single . . . . . . . . . . . . . . . . . . .A 7255C
Atlantic / Jun '94 / WEA.

### SO MUCH IN LOVE.
Tracks: So much in love (Mixes).
■ 7" . . . . . . . . . . . . . . . . . . . . . .A 7261
■ CD Single . . . . . . . . . . . . . . . . . .A 7261CD
■ MC Single . . . . . . . . . . . . . . . . . .A 7261C
Atlantic / Mar '94.
12" . . . . . . . . . . . . . . . . . . . . . .A 7253T
7" . . . . . . . . . . . . . . . . . . . . . . .A 7253
CD Single . . . . . . . . . . . . . . . . . . .A 7253CD
MC Single . . . . . . . . . . . . . . . . . . .A 7253C
Atlantic / Sep '94 / WEA.

## Alldis, Dominic

### NIGHT MUSIC.
Tracks: Not Advised.
■ CD . . . . . . . . . . . . . . . . . . . . . .LUMCD 4
■ MC . . . . . . . . . . . . . . . . . . . . . .LUMCA 4
Lumina / Dec '89.

## Allen, Debbie

### SPECIAL LOOK.
Tracks: Not Advised.
■ CD . . . . . . . . . . . . . . . . . . . . . .MCAD 6317
MCA / Oct '89.

## Allen, Donna

### CAN WE TALK.
Tracks: Can we talk / Can we talk (version).
■ 12" . . . . . . . . . . . . . . . . . . . . . BCM 277 X
■ 7" . . . . . . . . . . . . . . . . . . . . . . BCM 277
■ CD Single . . . . . . . . . . . . . . . . . . BCM 277 CD
BCM / Aug '89.

### HEAVEN ON EARTH.
Tracks: Can we talk / Come for me / Heaven on Earth / Joker's wild / Hot seat (of my car) / We're smokin' now / You move, you lose / Joy and pain / Renew the love / Make it my night.
CD . . . . . . . . . . . . . . . . . . . . . .BCM 260CD
■ LP . . . . . . . . . . . . . . . . . . . . . .BCM 260LP
MC . . . . . . . . . . . . . . . . . . . . . .BCM 260MC
BCM / Aug '89 / Pinnacle.

### JOY AND PAIN.
Tracks: Joy and pain.
■ 12" . . . . . . . . . . . . . . . . . . . . . BCM 257 X
■ 7" . . . . . . . . . . . . . . . . . . . . . . BCM 257
■ CD Single . . . . . . . . . . . . . . . . . . BCM 257 CD
BCM / Aug '89.

### PERFECT TIMING.
Tracks: Serious / Sweet somebody / Satisfied / Day-dreams / Wild nights / Perfect timing / Bit by bit / Another affair / Bad love.
■ LP . . . . . . . . . . . . . . . . . . . . . .450888 1
MC . . . . . . . . . . . . . . . . . . . . . .450888 4
■ CD . . . . . . . . . . . . . . . . . . . . . .450888 2
Portrait / May '87 / Sony.

### SATISFIED.
Tracks: Satisfied / Another affair.
■ 12" . . . . . . . . . . . . . . . . . . . . . XXX T1
■ 7" . . . . . . . . . . . . . . . . . . . . . . XXX 1
Portrait / Jun '87.

### SATISFIED (BLUE MIX).
Tracks: Satisfied (blue mix) / Satisfied (acappella version) / Another affair / Serious.
■ 7" . . . . . . . . . . . . . . . . . . . . . . XXXQT 1
Portrait / Jul '87.

### SERIOUS.
Tracks: Serious.
■ 12" . . . . . . . . . . . . . . . . . . . . . 650744 6
■ 7" . . . . . . . . . . . . . . . . . . . . . . 650744 7
Portrait / Mar '87.

### SWEET SOMEBODY.
Tracks: Sweet somebody / Bit by bit / Sweet some-body (version).
■ 12" . . . . . . . . . . . . . . . . . . . . . XXT 2
■ 7" . . . . . . . . . . . . . . . . . . . . . . XX2
■ 7" . . . . . . . . . . . . . . . . . . . . . . XXX 2
Portrait / Sep '87.

---

## Allen, Rance

One of four Allen brothers that made up the Detroit based Rance Allen Band. Best known for their religious re-working of soul tunes which included *Just My Salvation*, an interpretation of the Temptations *Just My Imagination*. They were initially signed to the Truth label, a gospel subsidiary of Stax, before moving to Capitol where they worked with producer Ronnie McNeir. More successful releases included *See What You Done* a song documenting a mothers grief as her son returns from Vietnam a junkie, and *Where Have All Our Friends Gone* from 1979's *Smile* album.

### SMILE (Allen, Rance Group).
Tracks: Smile / I belong to you.
■ 7" . . . . . . . . . . . . . . . . . . . . . . STAX 506
Stax / Sep '79.

## Alpert, Herb

### 40 GREATEST (Alpert, Herb & Tijuana Brass).
Tracks: Not Advised.
■ LP . . . . . . . . . . . . . . . . . . . . . .NE 1005
K-Tel / Nov '77.

### AFRICAN SUMMER.
Tracks: African Summer.
■ 7" . . . . . . . . . . . . . . . . . . . . . .AMS 7307
A&M / Aug '77.

### AMERICA (Alpert, Herb & Tijuana Brass).
Tracks: Not Advised.
■ LP . . . . . . . . . . . . . . . . . . . . . .AMLB 1000
A&M / Nov '71.

### BEAT OF THE BRASS (Alpert, Herb & Tijuana Brass).
Tracks: Not Advised.
■ LP . . . . . . . . . . . . . . . . . . . . . .AMLS 916
A&M / Jun '68.

### BEST OF HERB ALPERT.
Tracks: Not Advised.
CD . . . . . . . . . . . . . . . . . . . . . . CDMID 170
MC . . . . . . . . . . . . . . . . . . . . . . CMID 170
A&M / Oct '92 / PolyGram.

### BEYOND.
Tracks: Kamalie / Continental / Reach for the stars / Interlude / Red hot / Beyond / That's the way of the world / Keep it going.
■ LP . . . . . . . . . . . . . . . . . . . . . .AMLK 63717
A&M / Aug '80.

### BLOW YOUR OWN HORN.
Tracks: Red hot / True confessions / Blow your own horn / Gently / Midnight tango / Garden party / Paradise cove / Latin lady / Oriental eyes / Sundown.
■ LP . . . . . . . . . . . . . . . . . . . . . .AMLX 64949
■ MC . . . . . . . . . . . . . . . . . . . . . .CXM 64949
A&M / Sep '83.
CD . . . . . . . . . . . . . . . . . . . . . . CDA 64949
A&M / Jun '84 / PolyGram.

### BRASS ARE COMIN' THE (Alpert, Herb & Tijuana Brass).
Tracks: Not Advised.
■ LP . . . . . . . . . . . . . . . . . . . . . .AMLS 962
A&M / Mar '70.

### BULLISH.
Tracks: Bullish / Always have a dream / Make a wish / Maniac / Struttin on five / Love without words / Passion play / Life is my song.
■ LP . . . . . . . . . . . . . . . . . . . . . .AMLX 65022
■ MC . . . . . . . . . . . . . . . . . . . . . .CXM 65022
A&M / Sep '84.

### BULLISH (Alpert, Herb & Tijuana Brass).
Tracks: Bullish / Oriental eyes.
■ 7" . . . . . . . . . . . . . . . . . . . . . . AM 211
A&M / Sep '84.

### CASINO ROYALE.
Tracks: Casino royale.
■ 7" . . . . . . . . . . . . . . . . . . . . . . AMS 700
A&M / Apr '67.

### CLASSICS: HERB ALPERT.
Tracks: Not Advised.
■ CD . . . . . . . . . . . . . . . . . . . . . .CDA 2501
A&M.

### CLOSER YOU GET.
Tracks: Not Advised.
■ LP . . . . . . . . . . . . . . . . . . . . . .PL 84663

**■ MC.** . . . . . . . . . . . . . . . . . **PK 84663**
RCA / Jan '81.

## COMPACT HITS: HERB ALPERT.
**Tracks:** Keep your eye on me / Diamonds / Rise / Rotation.
**■ CD Single.** . . . . . . . . . . . . . . . **AMCD 910**
A&M / Apr '88.

## DIAMONDS.
**Tracks:** Diamonds / Rocket to the moon.
**■ MC Single.** . . . . . . . . . . . . . . . **USATC 605**
**■ 12".** . . . . . . . . . . . . . . . . . **USAT 605**
**■ 7".** . . . . . . . . . . . . . . . . . . **USA 605**
Breakout / May '87.

## DIAMONDS (COOL SUMMER MIX).
**Tracks:** Diamonds (cool summer mix) / Diamonds (12" dance mix) / Rocket to the moon.
**■ 12".** . . . . . . . . . . . . . . . . . **USAF 605**
Breakout / Jun '87.

## DOWN MEXICO WAY (Alpert, Herb & Tijuana Brass).
**Tracks:** Not Advised.
**■ LP** . . . . . . . . . . . . . . . . . . **AMLS 974**
A&M / Jun '70.

## FANDANGO.
**Tracks:** Fandango / Margarita / Push and pull / California blues / Quiereme tal como soy / Route 101 / Coco loco / Aria / Angel / Sugarloaf / Latin (medley) / Bahia / Moliando cafe.
**■ LP** . . . . . . . . . . . . . . . . . . **AMLK 63731**
**■ MC.** . . . . . . . . . . . . . . . . . **CKM 63731**
A&M / Jun '82.

## GARDEN PARTY.
**Tracks:** Garden party / Sundown.
**■ 12".** . . . . . . . . . . . . . . . . . **AMX 148**
**■ 7".** . . . . . . . . . . . . . . . . . . **AM 148**
A&M / Sep '83.

## GOING PLACES (Alpert, Herb & Tijuana Brass).
**Tracks:** Not Advised.
**■ LP** . . . . . . . . . . . . . . . . . **NPL 28065**
Pye International / Jan '66.

## GREATEST HITS: HERB ALPERT (Alpert, Herb & Tijuana Brass).
**Tracks:** Lonely bull / Spanish flea / My favourite things / If I were a rich man / Up Cherry Street / Marjorine / Wade in the water / Cabaret / Taste of honey / Tijuana taxi / Hello Dolly / A banda / Lollipops and roses / So whats new / Zorba the Greek.
**■ LP** . . . . . . . . . . . . . . . . . . **AMLS 980**
A&M / May '70.
**■ LP** . . . . . . . . . . . . . . . . . . **AMID 111**
**■ MC.** . . . . . . . . . . . . . . . . . **CMID 111**
A&M / Mar '82.
**■ LP** . . . . . . . . . . . . . . . . . . **SHM 3143**
MC. . . . . . . . . . . . . . . . . . . . . **HSC 3143**
Hallmark / May '84 / Pickwick.

## I NEED YOU.
**Tracks:** I need you / Lady in my life.
**■ 12".** . . . . . . . . . . . . . . . . . **AMY 464**
**■ 7".** . . . . . . . . . . . . . . . . . . **AM 464**
A&M / Sep '88.

## JERUSALEM.
**Tracks:** Jerusalem.
**■ 7".** . . . . . . . . . . . . . . . . . . **AMS 810**
A&M / Dec '70.

## JUMP STREET.
**Tracks:** Jump Street.
**■ 12".** . . . . . . . . . . . . . . . . . **AMY 750**
A&M / Jun '91.

## KEEP YOUR EYE ON ME.
**Tracks:** Keep your eye on me / Our song / Hotshot / Pillow / Diamonds / Stranger on the shore / Traffic jam / Rocket to the moon / Making love in the rain.
CD. . . . . . . . . . . . . . . . . . . . . **CDA 5125**
MC. . . . . . . . . . . . . . . . . . . . . **AMC 5125**
**■ LP** . . . . . . . . . . . . . . . . . . **AMA 5125**
A&M / Mar '87 / PolyGram.

## KEEP YOUR EYE ON ME.
**Tracks:** Keep your eye on me / Our song.
**■ 12".** . . . . . . . . . . . . . . . . . **AMY 387**
**■ 7".** . . . . . . . . . . . . . . . . . . **AM 387**
A&M / Mar '87.

## LONELY BULL, THE.
**Tracks:** Lonely bull.
**■ 7".** . . . . . . . . . . . . . . . . . . **SS 138**
Stateside / Jan '63.

## MAGIC MAN.
**Tracks:** Magic man / Manhattan melody / I get it from you / Secret garden / Besame mucho / This one's for me / Fantasy island / You smile, the song begins.
**■ LP** . . . . . . . . . . . . . . . . . . **AMLK 63728**
A&M / Sep '81.
**■ MC.** . . . . . . . . . . . . . . . . . **CKM 63728**
A&M / '87.

## MAIN EVENT (LIVE) (Alpert, Herb & Hugh Masekela).
**Tracks:** Foreign natives / People make the world go 'round / Besame mucho / I'm comin' home / Shebeen / Kalahari nights / Shame the devil / Mama way.
**■ LP** . . . . . . . . . . . . . . . . . . **AMLH 64727**
A&M / Jan '79.

## MAKING LOVE IN THE RAIN.
**Tracks:** Making love in the rain.
**■ 12".** . . . . . . . . . . . . . . . . . **USAT 608**
**■ 7".** . . . . . . . . . . . . . . . . . . **USA 608**
Breakout / Aug '87.

## MIDNIGHT SUN.
**Tracks:** Midnight sun / All the things you are / Someone to watch over me / In the wee small hours / Friends / Taste of honey / Mona Lisa / I've grown accustomed to her face / Silent tears and roses / Smile.
**■ CD.** . . . . . . . . . . . . . . . . . **395 391 2**
A&M / Jun '92.

## MY ABSTRACT HEART.
**Tracks:** Not Advised.
CD. . . . . . . . . . . . . . . . . . . . . **CDA 5273**
**■ LP** . . . . . . . . . . . . . . . . . . **AMA 5273**
MC. . . . . . . . . . . . . . . . . . . . . **AMC 5273**
A&M / Sep '89 / PolyGram.

## NINTH (Alpert, Herb & Tijuana Brass).
**Tracks:** Not Advised.
**■ LP** . . . . . . . . . . . . . . . . . . **AMLS 905**
A&M / Feb '68.

## NORTH ON SOUTH STREET.
**Tracks:** Jump street / It's the last dance / Passion lady / North on South Street / Paradise 25 / Na na na / Funky reggae / Where's Tommy / City terrace / I can't stop thinking about you.
CD. . . . . . . . . . . . . . . . . . . . . **3953452**
MC. . . . . . . . . . . . . . . . . . . . . **3953454**
**■ LP** . . . . . . . . . . . . . . . . . . **3953451**
A&M / Apr '91 / PolyGram.

## RED HOT.
**Tracks:** Red hot / Interlude.
**■ 7".** . . . . . . . . . . . . . . . . . . **AMS 7557**
A&M / Sep '80.
**■ 7".** . . . . . . . . . . . . . . . . . . **AM 165**
A&M / Nov '83.

## RISE.
**Tracks:** 1980 / Rise / Behind the rain / Rotation / Street life / Love is / Angelina / Aranjuez mon amour.
**■ LP** . . . . . . . . . . . . . . . . . . **AMLH 64790**
A&M / Nov '79.
**■ CD.** . . . . . . . . . . . . . . . . . **CDA 64790**
A&M / Apr '84.
CD. . . . . . . . . . . . . . . . . . . . . **CDMID 107**
MC. . . . . . . . . . . . . . . . . . . . . **CMID 107**
A&M / Oct '92 / PolyGram.

## RISE.
**Tracks:** Rise.
**■ 7".** . . . . . . . . . . . . . . . . . . **AMS 7465**
A&M / Oct '79.

## RISE.
**Tracks:** Not Advised.
**■ LP** . . . . . . . . . . . . . . . . . . **SHM 3163**
MC. . . . . . . . . . . . . . . . . . . . . **HSC 3163**
Hallmark / Feb '85 / Pickwick.
CD. . . . . . . . . . . . . . . . . . . . . **PWKS 542**
Pickwick / Sep '89 / Pickwick.

## RISE (SINGLE)(OLD GOLD).
**Tracks:** Rise / This guy's in love with you.
**■ 7".** . . . . . . . . . . . . . . . . . . **OG 9540**
Old Gold / Sep '85.

## ROTATION.
**Tracks:** Rotation / Behind the rain.
**■ 7".** . . . . . . . . . . . . . . . . . . **AMS 7500**
A&M / Jan '80.

## ROUTE 101.
**Tracks:** Route 101 / Angel.
**■ 7".** . . . . . . . . . . . . . . . . . . **AMS 8248**
A&M / Aug '82.

## S.R.O.
**Tracks:** Not Advised.
**■ LP** . . . . . . . . . . . . . . . . . . **NSPL 28088**
Pye International / Feb '67.

## SOLID BRASS.
**Tracks:** Work song / This guy's in love with you / Shadow of your smile / Maltese melody / South of the border / Jerusalem / Flamingo / What now my love / Without her / Casino Royale / Darlin' / Acapulco 1922 / Walk in the Black Forest / Summertime.
**■ LP** . . . . . . . . . . . . . . . . . . **AMLS 68103**
A&M / Aug '72.

## SOUNDS LIKE HERB ALPERT (Alpert, Herb & Tijuana Brass).
**Tracks:** Not Advised.
**■ LP** . . . . . . . . . . . . . . . . . . **AMLS 900**
A&M / Jul '66.

## SPANISH FLEA.
**Tracks:** Spanish flea.
**■ 7".** . . . . . . . . . . . . . . . . . . **7N 25335**
Pye International / Dec '65.

## STREET LIFE.
**Tracks:** Street life / 1980.
**■ 12".** . . . . . . . . . . . . . . . . . **AMSP 7511**
**■ 7".** . . . . . . . . . . . . . . . . . . **AMS 7511**
A&M / Mar '80.

## THIS GUY'S IN LOVE WITH YOU.
**Tracks:** Not Advised.
**■ LP** . . . . . . . . . . . . . . . . . . **MFP 50432**
MFP / '79.

## THIS GUY'S IN LOVE WITH YOU.
**Tracks:** This guy's in love with you.
**■ 12".** . . . . . . . . . . . . . . . . . **AMY 836**
**■ 7".** . . . . . . . . . . . . . . . . . . **AM 836**
**■ MC Single.** . . . . . . . . . . . . . . **AMMC 781**
A&M / Oct '91.

## THIS GUY'S IN LOVE WITH YOU.
**Tracks:** This guy's in love with you.
**■ 7".** . . . . . . . . . . . . . . . . . . **AMS 727**
A&M / Jul '68.

## TIJUANA TAXI.
**Tracks:** Tijuana taxi.
**■ 7".** . . . . . . . . . . . . . . . . . . **7N 25352**
Pye International / Mar '66.

## TIME FOR TIME.
**Tracks:** Time for time / This guy's in love with you / Rise.
**■ 12".** . . . . . . . . . . . . . . . . . **AMY 284**
**■ 7".** . . . . . . . . . . . . . . . . . . **AM 284**
A&M / Oct '85.

## UNDER A SPANISH MOON.
**Tracks:** Fragile / My song / I need you / Under a Spanish moon / Rumba flamenca / Lamento / Pachanga / Ancient source / Zamba / Hidden angel.
CD. . . . . . . . . . . . . . . . . . . . . **CDA 5209**
MC. . . . . . . . . . . . . . . . . . . . . **AMC 5209**
**■ LP** . . . . . . . . . . . . . . . . . . **AMA 5209**
A&M / Aug '88 / PolyGram.

## VERY BEST OF HERB ALPERT.
**Tracks:** Lonely bull / Taste of honey / Tijuana taxi / Spanish flea / Zorba the Greek / What now my love / Casino Royale / This guy's in love with you / Without her / Jerusalem / Rise / Rotation / Keep your eye on me / Diamonds / Jump Street.
CD. . . . . . . . . . . . . . . . . . . . . **397165 2**
**■ LP** . . . . . . . . . . . . . . . . . . **397165 1**
MC. . . . . . . . . . . . . . . . . . . . . **397165 4**
A&M / Oct '91 / PolyGram.

## VERY BEST OF HERB ALPERT.
**Tracks:** Ode to the sun / Lonely bull / The (el solo toro) / Spanish flea / Great manolete, The (la virgen de la Macarena) / Magic trumpet / Tijuana taxi / Banda / Taste of honey / Mame / Struttin' with Maria / Casino Royale / Jerusalem / Getting sentimental over you / Whipped cream / Without her / This guy's in love with you / Rotation / Rise / Keep your eye on me / Diamonds / What now my love.
VHS . . . . . . . . . . . . . . . . . . . . **0898823**
Polygram Music Video / '92 / PolyGram.

## WARM (Alpert, Herb & Tijuana Brass).
**Tracks:** Not Advised.
**■ LP** . . . . . . . . . . . . . . . . . . **AMLS 937**
A&M / Aug '69.

## WHAT NOW MY LOVE (Alpert, Herb & Tijuana Brass).
**Tracks:** Not Advised.
**■ LP** . . . . . . . . . . . . . . . . . . **NPL 28077**
Pye International / Apr '66.

### WHERE'S TOMMY.
Tracks: Where's Tommy.
- 12". . . . . . . . . . . . . . . . . . . . . AMY 633
- 7". . . . . . . . . . . . . . . . . . . . . . AM 633
- CD Single. . . . . . . . . . . . . . . AMCD 633
- MC Single. . . . . . . . . . . . . . AMMC 633

A&M / Jul '91.

### WHIPPED CREAM AND OTHER DE-LIGHTS (Alpert, Herb & Tijuana Brass).
Tracks: Not Advised.
- LP . . . . . . . . . . . . . . . . . . . NPL 28058

Pye International / Apr '66.

### WHISTLE SONG.
Tracks: Whistle song / Carmine.
- 7". . . . . . . . . . . . . . . . . . . . AMS 7207

A&M / Jan '76.

### WILD ROMANCE.
Tracks: "8" ball / You are the one / Lady love / It's all for you / Catch me / African flame / Dancin' in the light / No time for time.
- CD. . . . . . . . . . . . . . . . . . . . CDA 5082
- LP . . . . . . . . . . . . . . . . . . . . AMA 5082
- MC. . . . . . . . . . . . . . . . . . . . AMC 5082

A&M / Sep '85 / PolyGram.

### WITHOUT HER.
Tracks: Without her.
- 7". . . . . . . . . . . . . . . . . . . . . AMS 755

A&M / Jun '69.

## Alston, Gerald

Alston spent seventeen years as leader of Manhattans, winning Grammy for vocals on 1980 hit *You Are My Shining Star*. Emerging from chart wilderness with eponymous solo debut in '88, he was entrusted with revitalising Motown's fortunes; however, his career has yet to set world alight. 1993 album *Always In The Mood* included cover of Al Green's 1973 classic *Love And Happiness*.

### ACTIVATED.
Tracks: Activated / Activated (version).
- 12". . . . . . . . . . . . . . . . . . . . ZT 42682
- 7". . . . . . . . . . . . . . . . . . . . . ZB 42681
- CD Single . . . . . . . . . . . . . . . ZD 42682

Motown / Mar '89.

### ALWAYS IN THE MOOD.
Tracks: Not Advised.
- CD. . . . . . . . . . . . . . . . . . . . . 5301342
- LP. . . . . . . . . . . . . . . . . . . . . 5301341
- MC. . . . . . . . . . . . . . . . . . . . . 5301344

Motown / Jan '93 / PolyGram.

### GERALD ALSTON.
Tracks: Take me where you want to / Stay a little while / I come alive when I'm with you / Let's try love again / Midnight angel / You laid your love on me / I can't tell you why / I've waited all night / Activated / We've only just begun / Still in love with loving you (Only on cassette and CD.) / You laid your love on me (extended version) (Only on cassette and CD.).
- CD . . . . . . . . . . . . . . . . . . . ZD 72651
- LP . . . . . . . . . . . . . . . . . . . . ZL 72651
- MC. . . . . . . . . . . . . . . . . . . . ZK 72651

Motown / Dec '88.

### NOTHING CAN CHANGE (THE LOVE WE SHARED BEFORE).
Tracks: Nothing can change (the love we shared before) / Almost there (instrumental).
- 12". . . . . . . . . . . . . . . . . . . . ZT 44946
- 7". . . . . . . . . . . . . . . . . . . . . ZB 44945
- CD Single . . . . . . . . . . . . . . . ZD 44946

Motown / Sep '91.

### OPEN INVITATION.
Tracks: Slow motion / Getting back into love / Don't you know how I feel / I'll go crazy / Nothing can change (the love we shared before) / Never give up / Tell me this night won't end / Open invitation / Still in love / Any day now / Almost there.
- CD . . . . . . . . . . . . . . . . . . . ZD 72725
- LP . . . . . . . . . . . . . . . . . . . . ZL 72725
- MC. . . . . . . . . . . . . . . . . . . . ZK 72725

Motown / Oct '90.
- CD . . . . . . . . . . . . . . . . . . . 530 027 2

Motown / Feb '93.

### SLOW MOTION.
Tracks: Slow motion (radio edit) / Slow motion (instrumental) / Slow motion (full version) (Only on 12" and CD single.).
- 12". . . . . . . . . . . . . . . . . . . . ZT 44102
- 7". . . . . . . . . . . . . . . . . . . . . ZB 44101
- CD Single . . . . . . . . . . . . . . . ZD 44102

Motown / Apr '91.

### STAY A LITTLE WHILE.
Tracks: Stay a little while (radio edit) / Stay a little while (Quiet storm) (Not on 7".) / Activated (Radio edit of re-activated club mix) / Activated (Re-activated club mix) (Not on 7".).
- 12". . . . . . . . . . . . . . . . . . . . ZT 43086
- 7". . . . . . . . . . . . . . . . . . . . . ZB 43085
- CD Single . . . . . . . . . . . . . . . ZD 43086

Motown / Nov '89.

### TAKE ME WHERE YOU WANT TO.
Tracks: Take me where you want to / Still in love with loving you.
- 12". . . . . . . . . . . . . . . . . . . . ZT 42578
- 7". . . . . . . . . . . . . . . . . . . . . ZB 42577

Motown / Dec '88.

## Alton & Johnny

### HANG ON IN THERE BABY.
Tracks: Hang on in there baby.
- 7". . . . . . . . . . . . . . . . . . . . . POSP 118

Polydor / Jan '80.

## Always, Billy

### BACK ON TRACK.
Tracks: Back on track / Back on track (club version) / Back on track (hip hop mix) (Only on 12".) / Back on track (inst) (Only on 12".).
- 12". . . . . . . . . . . . . . . . . . . . . 6531138
- 7". . . . . . . . . . . . . . . . . . . . . . 6531137

Epic / Oct '88.

## Amazing Dance Band

### DEEP BLUE TRAIN.
Tracks: Deep blue train / Simon Smith and his amazing dancing bear.
- 7". . . . . . . . . . . . . . . . . . . . . . VS 567

Verve / '67.

## Ambrose, Sammy

### MONKEY SEE, MONKEY DO.
Tracks: Monkey see, monkey do / Welcome to Dreamsville.
- 7". . . . . . . . . . . . . . . . . . . . . . SS 399

Stateside / '64.

### THIS DIAMOND RING.
Tracks: This diamond ring / Bad night.
- 7". . . . . . . . . . . . . . . . . . . . . . SS 385

Stateside / '64.

## American Poets

### SHE BLEW A GOOD THING.
Tracks: She blew a good thing / Out to lunch.
- 7". . . . . . . . . . . . . . . . . . . . HLC 10037

London-American / Apr '66.

## Amoo, Chris

### NO CHOIR OF ANGELS (Amoo, Chris & Debby Bishop).
Tracks: No choir of angels / Love talk.
- 7". . . . . . . . . . . . . . . . . . . . . EMI 5455

EMI / Mar '84.

### THIS MUST BE LOVE.
Tracks: This must be love / You'll never know what you're missing.
- 7". . . . . . . . . . . . . . . . . . . . . PAR 118

Precision (1) / Apr '81.

## Anderson, Carl

### ABSENCE WITHOUT LOVE.
Tracks: Not Advised.
- LP . . . . . . . . . . . . . . . . . . . . FE 38063

Columbia (USA) / Jun '88.

### BUTTERCUP.
Tracks: Buttercup (radio edit) / Amour / Buttercup / Magic.
- 12". . . . . . . . . . . . . . . . . . . MKHAN 45
- 7". . . . . . . . . . . . . . . . . . . . KHAN 45

Streetwave / '87.

### BUTTERCUP (OLD GOLD).
Tracks: Buttercup / Magic.
- 12". . . . . . . . . . . . . . . . . . . OG 4026

Old Gold / Nov '87.

### CARL ANDERSON.
Tracks: Friends and lovers / C'est la vie / First time on a ferris wheel / Buttercup / Can't stop this feeling

/ Mr. V.J. / You are my shining star / Just a little love / Woman in love.
- LP . . . . . . . . . . . . . . . . . . . . 4500811
- MC. . . . . . . . . . . . . . . . . . . . 4500814

Epic / Sep '86 / Sony.

### FANTASY HOTEL.
Tracks: I will be there / If not for love / Once in a lifetime love / Love will follow / Enough said / All I wanna do / Closest thing to love / Lover's mask / I'm no stranger / Wish I could stay (Fantasy Hotel).
- CD . . . . . . . . . . . . . . . . . . . GRP 96712
- MC. . . . . . . . . . . . . . . . . . . GRP 96714

GRP / Jun '92 / BMG / New Note.

### FRIENDS AND LOVERS (see under Loring, Gloria).

### HEAVY WEATHER SUNLIGHT AGAIN.
Tracks: I can't stop the rain / I'm all about you / I need your love / Love'll hold my baby tonight / Gather ye rosebuds / Heavy weather / Baby's gift to the world / Feel the night / Always come running / Black rain (Miles to go).
- CD . . . . . . . . . . . . . . . . . . . GRP 97782

GRP / May '94 / BMG / New Note.

### LET'S TALK.
Tracks: Let's talk / Light me.
- 12". . . . . . . . . . . . . . . . . . . . TA 6439
- 7". . . . . . . . . . . . . . . . . . . . . A 6439

Epic / Jul '85.

### PIECES OF A HEART.
Tracks: My love will / Baby my heart / How deep does it go / You're the reason / Hot coffee / Pieces of a heart / If I could / Children of a lesser god / Life's lessons / Dance of the seven veils / Maiden voyage.
- LP . . . . . . . . . . . . . . . . . . . GRP 96121
- MC. . . . . . . . . . . . . . . . . . . GRP 96124
- CD . . . . . . . . . . . . . . . . . . . GRP 96122

GRP / Jun '90.

### PROTOCOL.
Tracks: Can't stop this feeling / Let's talk / Still thinking of you / What will happen now / Buttercup / Somebody up there likes me / One more time with feeling / Love on ice / Girl I won't take no / Saving my love for you.
- LP . . . . . . . . . . . . . . . . . . . EPC 26591
- MC. . . . . . . . . . . . . . . . . . . .40 26591

Epic / Aug '85 / Sony.

## Anderson, Carleen

Daughter of Vicki Anderson and step-daughter to Bobby Byrd (both members of James Brown's backing band The JB's), Carleen Anderson performed so impressively at the JB's 1988 show at London's Town & Country Club, that DJs Femi Williams and Marco Nelson invited her to join their new band, The Young Disciples. Signed by Talkin' Loud, Phonogram's in-house funky jazz label, the group hit immediately with the single *Apparently Nothin'* and followed up with an acclaimed album, *Road To Freedom*, Carleen writing six of the tracks thereon. Leaving the band amicably the following year, Anderson signed to Circa Records as a solo artist and released her first, again widely approved album, *True Spirit* in late '93. Two top 30 hits, *Mama Said* and *Nervous Breakdown*, were followed by the title track, which made the top 40.

### DUSKY SAPPHO E.P.
Tracks: Mama said / By any means / Pick up the pieces / Ain't giving up on you.
- 12". . . . . . . . . . . . . . . . . . . . YRT 108
- CD Single . . . . . . . . . . . . . . YRCDG 108

Virgin / Oct '93.

### MAMA SAID.
Tracks: Mama said / Mama said (Mixes) / Who was that masked man (Features on MCS & YRCDG 114 only.) / You've got to earn it (Features on YRCDG 114 only.) / If you knew (Demo) (Features on YRCDG 114 only.).
- 12". . . . . . . . . . . . . . . . . . . . YRT 114
- CD Single . . . . . . . . . . . . . . YRCDG 114
- CD Single . . . . . . . . . . . . . . . YRCD 114
- MC Single. . . . . . . . . . . . . . . . YRC 114

Circa / May '94.

### NERVOUS BREAKDOWN.
Tracks: Nervous breakdown.
- 12". . . . . . . . . . . . . . . . . . . . YRT 112
- CD Single . . . . . . . . . . . . . . YRCDG 112
- MC Single. . . . . . . . . . . . . . . . YRC 112

Circa / Feb '94.

**TRUE SPIRIT.**
Tracks: True spirit / Morning loving / Mama said / Ain't givin' up on you / Only one for me / Nervous breakdown / Secrets / Let it last / Feet wet up / Welcome to changes / Ian Green's groove conclusion.
CD...................................CIRCDX 30
LP....................................CIRCA 30
MC....................................CIRC 30
Circa / Jun '94 / EMI.

**TRUE SPIRIT.**
Tracks: True spirit (Mixes) / Humming bird (On YRC 118/YRCDG 118 only) / Mama said (mix) (On YRCD 118 only).
12".....................................YRT 118
CD...................................YRCDG 118
CD Single...........................YRCD 118
MC Single............................YRC 118
Circa / Aug '94 / EMI.

## Anderson, Carol

**SAD GIRL.**
Tracks: Sad girl.
■ 7"....................................GRP 133
Grapevine (Northern Soul) / Oct '79.

## Anderson, Ernestine

**BE MINE TONIGHT.**
Tracks: Sunday in New York / In a mellow tone / I'm comin' home again / Christopher Columbus / London by night / Little bird / Be mine (tonight) / Lend me your life / Sack full of dreams.
CD...................................CCD 4319
■ LP....................................CJ 319
MC....................................CJC 319
Concord Jazz / Jul '87 / New Note.

**BIG CITY.**
Tracks: All I need is you / 59th Street Bridge song / Spring is here / I'll never pass this way again / Big city / All blues / Welcome to the club / I didn't know what time it was.
■ LP.....................................CJ 214
MC....................................CJC 214
Concord Jazz / May '83 / New Note.
■ CD...................................CCD 4214
Concord Jazz / '89.

**BOOGIE DOWN (Anderson, Ernestine & Clayton Hamilton Jazz Orchestra).**
Tracks: Boogie down / That Sunday that Summer / Love walked in / Only trust your heart / Day by day / Nothing ever changes my love for you / Wait till you see him / One mint julep / Le blues (instrumental).
MC....................................CJ 407C
■ CD...................................CCD 4407
Concord / Apr '90 / New Note.

**GREAT MOMENTS WITH ERNESTINE ANDERSON.**
Tracks: I love being here with you / Day by day / Tain't nobody's bizness if I do / As long as I live / Don't get around much anymore / Please send me someone to love / Skylark / In mellow tone / Someone else is steppin' in / Time after time / Body and soul / Never make your move too soon.
CD...................................CCD 4582
Concord / Nov '93 / New Note.

**HELLO LIKE BEFORE.**
Tracks: Hello like before / Yes sir, that's my baby / T'ain't nobody's bizness if I do / Send in the clowns / Bird of beauty / Time for love / Soft shoe / It don't mean a thing / I am his lady.
■ CD...................................CCD 4031
Concord Jazz / Jun '89.

**LATE AT NIGHT.**
Tracks: Skylark / What a difference a day made / Someone to watch over me / My funny valentine / Poor butterfly / As long as I live / My way / Ill wind / As time goes by / Summertime.
■ CD...................................KICJ 113
King/Paddle Wheel / Nov '92.

**LIVE AT THE 1990 CONCORD JAZZ FESTIVAL (3RD SET).**
Tracks: Blues in the closet / I let a song go out of my heart / I should care / There is no greater love / Skylark / On my own / Never make your move too soon.
CD...................................CCD 4454
MC....................................CJ 454 C
Concord / May '91 / New Note.

**LIVE FROM CONCORD TO LONDON.**
Tracks: Don't get around much any more / Days of wine and roses / Stormy Monday / Am I blue / Take the 'A' Train / My romance / Ellington medley.

■ CD...................................CCD 4054
Concord / Nov '90.

## MISS ERNESTINE ANDERSON.
Tracks: Let's get away from it all / End of a love affair / So nice / Funny how time slips away / Talk to me baby / Tears have to fall / Big spender / What did I have that I don't have / On a clear day / I fall in love too easily / Feeling good / Make it another old fashioned please.
■ MC..................................TCEMS 1141
■ LP..................................EMS 1141
Capitol / Jan '86.

**NEVER MAKE YOUR MOVE TOO SOON.**
Tracks: Never make your move too soon / What a difference a day made / As long as I live / Old folks / Just one more chance / My shining hour / Why did I choose you / Poor butterfly.
■ LP.....................................CJ 147
Concord Jazz / May '81.
■ CD...................................CCD 4147
Concord Jazz / Jun '90.

**SOMEBODY TOLD ME.**
Tracks: Somebody told me.
■ 7"....................................SS 455
Stateside / '65.

**SUNSHINE.**
Tracks: Love / Summertime / Time after time / God bless' the child / I've got the world on a string / I'm walkin' / I want a little boy / You are my sunshine / Satin doll / Sunny.
CD...................................CCD 4109
Concord / Jan '92 / New Note.

**WHEN THE SUN GOES DOWN.**
Tracks: Someone else is steppin' in / In the evening / I love being here with you / Down home blues / I'm just a lucky so and so / Alone on my own / Mercy, mercy, mercy / Goin' to Chicago blues.
■ LP.....................................CJ 263
MC....................................CJC 263
Concord Jazz / Apr '85 / New Note.
CD...................................CCD 4263
Concord Jazz / '88 / New Note.

**YOU CAN'T BUY LOVE.**
Tracks: You can't buy love / Jerk and twine.
■ 7"....................................MF 912
Mercury / '65.

## Anderson, Jhelisa

**ALL I NEED.**
Tracks: All I need / All I need (instrumental).
■ 12"...................................DOR 014
Dorado / Aug '93.

**FRIENDLY PRESSURE.**
Tracks: Not Advised.
12"....................................DOR 25
CD Single.............................DOR 25CD
Dorado / Sep '94 / RTM / Pinnacle.

**GALACTICA RUSH.**
Tracks: Not Advised.
CD...................................DOR 026CD
LP....................................DOR 026LP
MC....................................DOR 026MC
Dorado / Sep '94 / RTM / Pinnacle.

**SALL'S KNOCKING.**
Tracks: Sall's knocking.
■ 12"...................................DOR 005
Revolver / Aug '92.

## Anderson, Kip

**YOU'LL LOSE A GOOD THING.**
Tracks: You'll lose a good thing / I'm out of love.
7"......................................PT 163
President / Oct '67 / Grapevine Distribution / Target / Jazz Music / BMG.

## Anderson, Roshell

**NATURE'S WAY.**
Tracks: Not Advised.
■ LP..................................ICH 1021
MC..................................ZCICH 1021
Ichiban / Apr '88 / A.D.A. Distribution / Pinnacle / ACD Trading Ltd. / Koch International / Direct Distribution.

**OUTLAWWH CASANOVA, THE.**
Tracks: Wild thang in the rain / Groove thang / Outlawwh Casanova / I'm still in love with you / I love you more than you'll ever know / Sunshine lady / Shell shockin' body / Eye for eye.
LP..................................ICH 1113

MC..................................ICH 1113MC
Ichiban / Jul '91 / A.D.A. Distribution / Pinnacle / ACD Trading Ltd. / Koch International / Direct Distribution.
CD..................................CDICH 1113
Ichiban / Oct '93 / A.D.A. Distribution / Pinnacle / ACD Trading Ltd. / Koch International / Direct Distribution.

**ROLLING OVER.**
Tracks: Not Advised.
CD..................................ICH 1142CD
MC..................................ICH 1142MC
Ichiban / Feb '94 / A.D.A. Distribution / Pinnacle / ACD Trading Ltd. / Koch International / Direct Distribution.

**STEPPING OUT.**
Tracks: Twilight state / Bodies talking / Peace / Victim of a system / Better love / Passionate transition / Stepping out / Broken heart.
CD..................................CDICH 1053
LP..................................ICH 1053
MC..................................MCICH 1053
Ichiban / Mar '90 / A.D.A. Distribution / Pinnacle / ACD Trading Ltd. / Koch International / Direct Distribution.

**SWEET 'N' SOUR RHYTHM 'N' BLUES.**
Tracks: Come on back / Leaving me / Chokin' kind / Grapevine will lie sometimes / Dearest darling / What do you expect from me / You wouldn't believe / Stop doggin' me.
CD..................................CDICH 1035
■ LP..................................ICH 1035
MC..................................ZCICH 1035
Ichiban / Jun '89 / A.D.A. Distribution / Pinnacle / ACD Trading Ltd. / Koch International / Direct Distribution.

## Andrews, Ernie

**FROM THE HEART.**
Tracks: On Broadway / Don't let the sun catch you crying / I cover the waterfront / If you could see me now / Again.
■ LP..................................DS 825
Discovery (USA) / '88.

**NO REGRETS.**
Tracks: When they ask about you / Don't you know I care / I'll never be free / You call it madness / Hunt is on / Until the real thing comes along / When did you leave heaven / Sweet Lorraine / Sweet slumber.
CD..................................MCD 5484
Muse / Nov '93 / New Note / Jazz Horizons / C.M. Distribution.

**TRAVELLIN' LIGHT.**
Tracks: Not Advised.
■ LP..................................GNPS 10008
GNP Crescendo / May '89.

**WHERE WERE YOU.**
Tracks: Where were you / What do I see in the girl.
■ 7"....................................CL 15407
Capitol / Jul '65.

## Andrews, John

**IT'S JUST LOVE (Andrews, John & The Lonely Ones).**
Tracks: It's just love / Rose growing in the ruins.
■ 7"....................................R 5455
Parlophone / May '66.

## Andrews, Ruby

**I GOT A BONE TO PICK WITH YOU.**
Tracks: I got a bone to pick with you / I don't know how to love you.
■ 7"....................................ABC 4156
ABC Records / Dec '76.

**KISS THIS.**
Tracks: I want to rock with you baby no.2 / Since I met you / Que pasa / To the other woman (I'm the other woman) / Kiss this / Lovey dovey / Throw some more dirt on me (the shacking song) / Loving you no.44 / I got what I want at home / As in always.
LP..................................ICH 1104
MC..................................ICH 1104 MC
Ichiban / Apr '91 / A.D.A. Distribution / Pinnacle / ACD Trading Ltd. / Koch International / Direct Distribution.

■ DELETED

CD. . . . . . . . . . . . . . . . . . . . . .CDICH 1104
Ichiban / Oct '93 / A.D.A. Distribution / Pinnacle / ACD Trading Ltd. / Koch International / Direct Distribution.

## Anuforo

### MR. BEAUTIFUL.
Tracks: Mr. Beautiful.
12". . . . . . . . . . . . . . . . . . . . . . .ANJT 12
Ram Jam / Jan '94 / Jetstar.

## Any Day Now

### I'LL BE WAITING.
Tracks: I'll be waiting / Under your spell.
■ 7". . . . . . . . . . . . . . . . . . . . . . . AM 355
A&M / Oct '86.

### SHOW ME THE WAY (GRAND GROOVE).
Tracks: Show me the way (Grand groove) / Shock tactics / Show me the way (No Derek) (On 12" version only).
■ 12". . . . . . . . . . . . . . . . . . . . . . .AMY 310
■ 7". . . . . . . . . . . . . . . . . . . . . . . AM 310
A&M / Apr '86.

## APB

### CHAIN REACTION.
Tracks: Chain reaction.
■ 7". . . . . . . . . . . . . . . . . . . . . .SLICK 6
Oily / Jul '81.

### CURE FOR THE BLUES.
Tracks: Not Advised.
■ LP. . . . . . . . . . . . . . . . . . .YTHANLP 4
Red River / Apr '86.

### DANCEABILITY.
Tracks: Danceability / Crazy day rainy day / Palace filled with love.
■ 12". . . . . . . . . . . . . . . . . . . .12ION 160
Albion / Apr '84.

### MISSING YOU ALREADY.
Tracks: Missing you already / Best of our love / Boy, you're not so great.
■ 7". . . . . . . . . . . . . . . . . . . . . . YTHAN 6
Red River / Oct '87.
■ 12". . . . . . . . . . . . . . . . . . . .YTHANT 6
Red River / Apr '89.

### ONE DAY.
Tracks: One day.
■ 12". . . . . . . . . . . . . . . . . . .SLICK 1210
■ 7". . . . . . . . . . . . . . . . . . . . SLICK 10
Oily / Aug '83.

### OPEN YOUR EYES.
Tracks: Open your eyes / Sunset song.
■ 12". . . . . . . . . . . . . . . . . . . .YTHANT 3
■ 7". . . . . . . . . . . . . . . . . . . . .YTHAN 3
Red River / Apr '86.

### PALACE FILLED WITH LOVE.
Tracks: Palace filled with love / All your life with me.
■ 7". . . . . . . . . . . . . . . . . . . . . .SLICK 8
Oily / Apr '82.

### RAINY DAY.
Tracks: Rainy day.
■ 7". . . . . . . . . . . . . . . . . . . . . .SLICK 9
Oily / Oct '82.

### SHOOT YOU DOWN.
Tracks: Shoot you down.
■ 7". . . . . . . . . . . . . . . . . . . . . .SLICK 7
Oily / Oct '81.

### SOMETHING TO BELIEVE IN.
Tracks: Something to believe in / So many broken hearts.
■ 12". . . . . . . . . . . . . . . . . . . .YTHANT 2
■ 7". . . . . . . . . . . . . . . . . . . . .YTHAN 2
Red River / Oct '85.

### SOMETHING TO BELIEVE IN.
Tracks: Not Advised.
■ LP. . . . . . . . . . . . . . . . . .YTHANLP 005
Red River / '88.

### SUMMER LOVE.
Tracks: Summer love / Is the music loud enough.
■ 12". . . . . . . . . . . . . . . . . . . .YTHANT 1
■ 7". . . . . . . . . . . . . . . . . . . . .YTHAN 1
Red River / Jul '85.

### WHAT KIND OF GIRL.
Tracks: What kind of girl.
■ 7". . . . . . . . . . . . . . . . . . . . . .ION 160
Albion / Jun '84.

## Apollonia 6

### APOLLONIA 6.
Tracks: Happy birthday, Mr. Christian / Sex shooter / Blue limousine / Million miles / Ooo she she wa wa / Some kind of lover / In a Spanish villa.
■ LP. . . . . . . . . . . . . . . . . . . . .925108 1
WEA / Oct '84.

### BLUE LIMOUSINE.
Tracks: Blue limousine / Some kind of lover.
■ 12". . . . . . . . . . . . . . . . . . . .W 9092T
■ 7". . . . . . . . . . . . . . . . . . . . W 9092
WEA / Mar '85.

### SEX SHOOTER.
Tracks: Sex shooter / In a Spanish villa.
■ 7". . . . . . . . . . . . . . . . . . . . .9291827
WEA / Oct '84.

## Aquarian Dream

### AQUARIAN DREAM.
Tracks: Phoenix / Once again / Treat me like the one you love / Guitar talk / East 6th Street / Let me be the one / Look ahead / I'll always love you.
■ LP. . . . . . . . . . . . . . . . . . . . . DISC 08
Buddah / Feb '80.

### DISCO JUICE.
Tracks: Disco juice / Chance to dance.
■ 7". . . . . . . . . . . . . . . . . . . . .K 12378
Elektra / Sep '79.

### FANTASY.
Tracks: You're a star / Friends / It ain't watcha say / Yesterday / Play it for me / Fantasy / gentle thoughts / Do you realize.
■ LP. . . . . . . . . . . . . . . . . . . . .K 52109
Elektra / Dec '78.

### PHOENIX.
Tracks: Phoenix / East of 6th Street.
■ 7". . . . . . . . . . . . . . . . . . . . .BDS 488
Buddah / Aug '79.

### YOU'RE A STAR.
Tracks: You're a star / Play it for me.
■ 7". . . . . . . . . . . . . . . . . . . . . . LV 7
Elektra / '88.

## Armenta

### I WANNA BE WITH YOU.
Tracks: I wanna be with you.
■ 12". . . . . . . . . . . . . . . . . . . .FAIT 005
■ 7". . . . . . . . . . . . . . . . . . . .FAIS 005
Savoir Faire / Nov '83.

## Armstrong, Vanessa

Vanessa Bell Armstrong began her recording career on the Onyx label with strictly gospel titles such as *Peace Be Still* before signing with Jive Records where she moved onto more secular material. Her first album for Jive, *Vanessa Bell Armstrong*, included the single *You Bring Out The Best In Me* which created a lot of interest in the States. She is perhaps best known over here for her 1988 duet with the South African musician Jonathan Butler, *True Love Never Fails* which, although heavily played, failed to chart. Although she has yet to make a big mark on the charts she is highly regarded by critics on both sides of the Atlantic.

### FOLLOWING JESUS.
Tracks: Not Advised.
■ LP. . . . . . . . . . . . . . . . . . .MSSG 8001
Malaco / Oct '87.

### I'M COMING BACK.
Tracks: I'm coming back.
■ 12". . . . . . . . . . . . . . . . . . . .JIVET 230
■ 7". . . . . . . . . . . . . . . . . . . . .JIVE 230
■ CD Single. . . . . . . . . . . . . . .JIVECD 230
Jive / Nov '89.

### PRESSING ON.
Tracks: Pressing on.
■ 12". . . . . . . . . . . . . . . . . . . .JIVET 168
■ 7". . . . . . . . . . . . . . . . . . . . .JIVE 168
Jive / May '88.

### TRUE LOVE NEVER FAILS (see under Butler, Jonathan).

### VANESSA BELL ARMSTRONG.
Tracks: Not Advised.
■ LP. . . . . . . . . . . . . . . . . . . . .HIP 52
■ MC. . . . . . . . . . . . . . . . . . . . .HIPC 52

CD. . . . . . . . . . . . . . . . . . . . . . .CHIP 52
Jive / Nov '87.

### WONDERFUL ONE.
Tracks: Not Advised.
CD. . . . . . . . . . . . . . . . . . . . . . .CHIP 78
■ LP. . . . . . . . . . . . . . . . . . . . .HIP 78
MC. . . . . . . . . . . . . . . . . . . . . .HIPC 78
Jive / Nov '89 / BMG.

## Arnie's Love

### I'M OUT OF YOUR LIFE.
Tracks: I'm out of your life.
■ 7". . . . . . . . . . . . . . . . . . . . .WAVE 9
Streetwave / Nov '83.

### NATURAL WISH.
Tracks: Natural wish / Natural wish (inst).
■ 12". . . . . . . . . . . . . . . . . . . .12P 351
■ 7". . . . . . . . . . . . . . . . . . . . .7P 351
PRT / Mar '86.

## Arnold, Calvin

### FUNKY WAY.
Tracks: Funky way / Snatchin' back.
■ 7". . . . . . . . . . . . . . . . . . .MGM 1378
MGM (Polydor) / '67.

## Arnold, P.P.

### (IF YOU THINK YOU'RE) GROOVY.
Tracks: (If you think) you're groovy.
■ 7". . . . . . . . . . . . . . . . . . . . .IM 061
Immediate / Jan '68.

### ANGEL.
Tracks: Not Advised.
■ LP. . . . . . . . . . . . . . . . . . . .SHLP 157
MC. . . . . . . . . . . . . . . . . . . . .SHTC 157
Castle Showcase / '88 / Arabesque Ltd.

### ANGEL OF THE MORNING.
Tracks: Angel of the morning.
■ 7". . . . . . . . . . . . . . . . . . . . .IM 067
Immediate / Apr '82.

### BEST OF P.P. ARNOLD (Kafunta/First Lady Of Immediate).
Tracks: (If you think you're) groovy / Something beautiful happened / Born to be together / Am I still dreaming / First cut is the deepest / Everything is gonna be alright / Treat me like a lady / Would you believe / Speak to me / God only knows / Eleanor Rigby / Yesterday / Angel of the morning / It'll never happen again / As tears go by / To love somebody / Dreamin' / If you see what I mean / Though it hurts me badly (Available on CD only) / Welcome home (Available on CD only) / Life is but nothing (Available on CD only) / Time has come (Available on CD only).
CD. . . . . . . . . . . . . . . . . . . .SEECD 235
■ LP. . . . . . . . . . . . . . . . . . . .SEE 235
See For Miles / Oct '88 / Pinnacle.

### BEST OF P.P. ARNOLD - THE FIRST CUT IS THE DEEPEST, THE.
Tracks: Not Advised.
CD. . . . . . . . . . . . . . . . . . . . .CSL 6035
Immediate / Nov '93 / BMG.

### DREAMING (see under Pressure Point).

### DYNAMITE.
Tracks: Dynamite / Dynamite (version).
■ 12". . . . . . . . . . . . . . . . . . . .PPX 2
■ 7". . . . . . . . . . . . . . . . . . . .7PPX 2
Full Circle / Mar '90.

### ELECTRIC DREAMS.
Tracks: Electric dreams.
■ 12". . . . . . . . . . . . . . . . . . .TEN 29-12
■ 7". . . . . . . . . . . . . . . . . . . .TEN 29
10 / Aug '84.

### EVERYTHING'S GONNA BE ALRIGHT.
Tracks: Everything's gonna be alright / Life is but nothing.
■ 7". . . . . . . . . . . . . . . . . . . . .IM 040
Immediate / '67.

### FIRST CUT IS THE DEEPEST, THE.
Tracks: First cut is the deepest / Speak to me.
■ 7". . . . . . . . . . . . . . . . . . . . .IM 047
Immediate / Apr '67.
■ 7". . . . . . . . . . . . . . . . . . . .IMS 1109
Immediate / May '77.
■ 7". . . . . . . . . . . . . . . . . . . .IMS 047
Immediate / Dec '82.

■ DELETED

11

## FIRST CUT IS THE DEEPEST, THE (OLD GOLD).
Tracks: First cut is the deepest / Angel of the morning.
■ 7" . . . . . . . . . . . . . . . . . . . . . OG 9464
Old Gold / Jan '85.

## GREATEST HITS: P P ARNOLD.
Tracks: First cut is the deepest / Dreaming / Would you believe / To love somebody / Born to be together / Eleanor Rigby / Angel of the morning / As tears go by / Am I still dreaming / Though it hurts me badly / Speak to me / If you think you're groovy.
■ LP . . . . . . . . . . . . . . . . . . . . . IML 2006
Immediate / Jan '78.

## LITTLE PAIN, A.
Tracks: Little pain / Smile.
■ 12" . . . . . . . . . . . . . . . . . . . . TEN 70-12
■ 7" . . . . . . . . . . . . . . . . . . . . . TEN 70
10 / Sep '85.

## TIME HAS COME, THE.
Tracks: Time has come / If you see what I mean.
■ 7" . . . . . . . . . . . . . . . . . . . . . IM 055
Immediate / Aug '67.

# Arnold, Wayne

## TOUGH LIFE.
Tracks: Not Advised.
CD . . . . . . . . . . . . . . . . . . . . . CD 013
About Time / Sep '92 / BMG.

# Arrington, Steve

Unlikely as it may seem for band whose best-remembered number was *Stellar Fungk*, U.S. funk act Slave were torn apart by 'musical differences'. Steve Arrington, singer with band since 1978, formed more accessible Hall Of Fame; although break-through 1985 hits *Feel So Real* and *Dancin' In The Key Of Life* bore his name only. Having established solo career, Arrington promptly turned back on pop and took up gospel. Celestial Fungk presumably ensued.

## DANCIN' IN THE KEY OF LIFE.
Tracks: Feel so real / Dancin' in the key of life / She just don't know / Willie Mae / Gasoline / Stand with me / Brown baby boy / Turn up love.
■ LP . . . . . . . . . . . . . . . . . . . 781 245-1
■ MC . . . . . . . . . . . . . . . . . . . 781 245-4
Atlantic / May '85.

## DANCIN' IN THE KEY OF LIFE.
Tracks: Dancin' in the key of life / Turn up the love.
■ 7" . . . . . . . . . . . . . . . . . . . . . A 9534
■ 12" . . . . . . . . . . . . . . . . . . . . A 9534 T
Atlantic / Jun '85.

## FEEL SO REAL.
Tracks: Feel so real / Willie Mae.
■ 7" . . . . . . . . . . . . . . . . . . . . . A 9576
■ 12" . . . . . . . . . . . . . . . . . . . . A 9576 T
Atlantic / Apr '85.

## FEEL SO REAL (OLD GOLD).
Tracks: Feel so real / Dancing on the key of life.
12" . . . . . . . . . . . . . . . . . . . . OG 4207
Old Gold / Jun '91 / Pickwick.

## GASOLINE.
Tracks: Gasoline / She just don't know.
■ 12" . . . . . . . . . . . . . . . . . . . . A 9500T
■ 7" . . . . . . . . . . . . . . . . . . . . . A 9500
Atlantic / Nov '85.

## HALL OF FAME.
Tracks: Nobody can be you / You meet my approval / Last nite-nite before / Strange / Speak with your body / Week at the knees / Way out.
■ LP . . . . . . . . . . . . . . . . . . . . . A 0049
Atlantic / Apr '83.

## HUMP TO THE BUMP.
Tracks: Hump to the bump / Nobody can be you.
■ 12" . . . . . . . . . . . . . . . . . . . A 6963 T
Atlantic / Mar '84.

## JAM PACKED.
Tracks: Jam packed (at the wall) / Stone love / Let it loose / True love always / I just wanna be with you / Kelly 16-33 / Never take your love / Trouble / What I do for you.
■ CD . . . . . . . . . . . . . . . . . . CDMTL 1015
■ LP . . . . . . . . . . . . . . . . . . . MTL 1015
■ MC . . . . . . . . . . . . . . . . . . TCMTL 1015
EMI-Manhattan / Oct '87.

## JAMMIN' NATIONAL ANTHEM, THE.
Tracks: Jammin' National Anthem / Holiday / Tee-nage jazz / One of a kind / Paradise / Everybody's got to be free / Home boy / Like it loud / Have a heart.
■ LP . . . . . . . . . . . . . . . . . . . . . WX 58
■ MC . . . . . . . . . . . . . . . . . . . WX 58 C
Atlantic / May '86.

## JAMMIN' NATIONAL ANTHEM, THE.
Tracks: Jammin' National Anthem / Racial jammin'.
■ 12" . . . . . . . . . . . . . . . . . . . A 9428 T
■ 7" . . . . . . . . . . . . . . . . . . . . . A 9428
Atlantic / Apr '86.

## POSITIVE POWER.
Tracks: 15 rounds / Money on it / Sugar momma baby / What do you want from life / Young and ready / Mellow as a cello / Hump to the bump / Positive power.
■ LP . . . . . . . . . . . . . . . . . . . 780 127-1
Atlantic / Feb '84.

## STONE LOVE.
Tracks: Stone love / Trouble.
■ 7" . . . . . . . . . . . . . . . . . . . . . MT 30
■ 12" . . . . . . . . . . . . . . . . . . . 12MT 30
EMI-Manhattan / Oct '87.

# Artistics

## GIRL I NEED YOU.
Tracks: Girl I need you / Glad I met you.
■ 7" . . . . . . . . . . . . . . . . . . . . Q 72492
Coral / Apr '67.

# Ashford & Simpson

This U.S. duo are perhaps best-known to the wider public for their 1985 hit *Solid*, they are better known in soul circles for their songwriting genius. After performing to-gether in a choir in Harlem, they joined forces with fellow writer Jo Armstead and the trio penned songs for Ray Charles, Ron-nie Milsap and Maxine Brown amongst others. Having parted company with Arm-stead the duo moved to Motown, composing classics such as *Ain't No Mountain High Enough*, *Reach Out And Touch* and *You're All I Need To Get By* thereby cementing their reputation as songwriters of the highest calibre. Their own recordings have enjoyed mixed fortunes, although a switch to Capitol in late '70s showed a marked upswing. The results are helpfully compiled on the '93 *Best Of* set.

## ASHFORD AND SIMPSON VIDEO, THE.
Tracks: Not Advised.
VHS . . . . . . . . . . . . . . . . . TVE 90 0985 2
EMI / Nov '82 / EMI.

## BABIES.
Tracks: Babies / Outta the world.
■ 12" . . . . . . . . . . . . . . . . . . . 12CL 355
■ 7" . . . . . . . . . . . . . . . . . . . . . CL 355
Capitol / Apr '85.

## BEST OF ASHFORD & SIMPSON, THE.
Tracks: Street corner / Love it away / Highrise / It's much deeper / I'm not that tough / Solid / Outta the world / Babies / Count your blessings / How does it fit / Real love / Noboby walks in L.A. / I'll be there for you / Love or physical / It seems to hang on / Found a cure.
MC. . . . . . . . . . . . . . . . . . . C4 50815
■ CD . . . . . . . . . . . . . . . . . . C2 80515
Capitol / Aug '93 / EMI.

## COME AS YOU ARE.
Tracks: It'll come, it'll come, it'll come / One more try / Believe in me / Caretaker / Somebody told a lie / Tell it all / Sell the house / It came to me.
■ LP . . . . . . . . . . . . . . . . . . . . K 56159
WEA / Nov '78.

## COUNT YOUR BLESSINGS.
Tracks: Count your blessings / Side effect.
■ 12" . . . . . . . . . . . . . . . . . . . 12CL 422
■ 7" . . . . . . . . . . . . . . . . . . . . . CL 422
Capitol / Aug '86.

## DON'T COST YOU NOTHING.
Tracks: Don't cost you nothing / Let love use me.
■ 7" . . . . . . . . . . . . . . . . . . . . K 17096
WEA / '78.

## FOUND A CURE.
Tracks: Found a cure / You always could.
■ 7" . . . . . . . . . . . . . . . . . . . . K 17422
WEA / '79.

## HAPPY ENDING.
Tracks: Happy ending / Handkerchief.
■ 7" . . . . . . . . . . . . . . . . . . . . K 17738
WEA / Jan '81.

## HIGH RISE.
Tracks: High rise / Side effect / Experience / It's a rush / My kinda pick me up / I'm not that tough / It's much deeper / Still such a thing.
■ LP . . . . . . . . . . . . . . . EST 712 282 1
Capitol / Sep '83.

## HIGH RISE.
Tracks: High rise.
■ 12" . . . . . . . . . . . . . . . . . . . 12CL 304
■ 7" . . . . . . . . . . . . . . . . . . . . . CL 304
Capitol / Aug '83.

## IS IT STILL GOOD TO YA.
Tracks: Not Advised.
■ LP . . . . . . . . . . . . . . . . . . . . K 56547
MC . . . . . . . . . . . . . . . . . . . K4 56547
WEA / '80 / WEA.

## IT SEEMS TO HANG ON.
Tracks: It seems to hang on.
■ 7" . . . . . . . . . . . . . . . . . . . . K 17237
WEA / Nov '78.

## LOVE DON'T MAKE IT RIGHT.
Tracks: Love don't make it right / Bourgie bourgie.
■ 7" . . . . . . . . . . . . . . . . . . . . K 17679
WEA / Sep '80.

## LOVE OR PHYSICAL.
Tracks: Love or physical / I'll be there for you / Comes with the package / Till we get it right / Something to you / In your arms / Cookies and cake / Timing.
■ LP . . . . . . . . . . . . . . . . . . EST 2085
■ MC . . . . . . . . . . . . . . . . . TCEST 2085
■ CD . . . . . . . . . . . . . . . . . CDEST 2085
Capitol / Mar '89.

## MAIN LINE.
Tracks: Main line / Don't fight it.
■ 7" . . . . . . . . . . . . . . . . . . . . K 16441
WEA / Jul '74.

## MUSICAL AFFAIR, A.
Tracks: Love don't make it right / Rushing to / I ain't asking for your love / Make it to the sky / We'll meet again / You never left me alone / Get out your handkerchief / Happy ending.
■ MC . . . . . . . . . . . . . . . . . K4 56840
WEA / Sep '80.

## REAL LOVE.
Tracks: Count your blessings / Real love / Nobody walks in L.A. / How does it fit / Relations / What becomes of love / Way ahead / Tenth round.
■ LP . . . . . . . . . . . . . . . . . . EST 2019
■ MC . . . . . . . . . . . . . . . . . TCEST 2019
Capitol / Aug '86.
■ CD . . . . . . . . . . . . . . . CDP 736 368 2
Capitol / Jan '87.

## SOLID.
Tracks: Solid / Jungle / Honey I love you / Babies / Closest to love / Cherish forever more / Tonight we escape (we make love) / Outta the world.
■ LP . . . . . . . . . . . . . . . . . . EJ 2402501
MC. . . . . . . . . . . . . . . . . . EJ 2402504
Capitol / Nov '84 / EMI.
■ LP . . . . . . . . . . . . . . . . . . . . SASH 1
Capitol / Feb '85.
■ CD . . . . . . . . . . . . . . . CDP 746 466 2
Capitol / Apr '87.
CD . . . . . . . . . . . . . . . . . . MUSCD 501
MC . . . . . . . . . . . . . . . . . MUSMC 501
Music Collection International / Sep '94 / THE / Jazz Music.

## SOLID.
Tracks: Solid / Street corner.
■ 12" . . . . . . . . . . . . . . . . . . . 12CL 345
■ 7" . . . . . . . . . . . . . . . . . . . . . CL 345
Capitol / Oct '84.
■ 12" . . . . . . . . . . . . . . . . . . . 12CLX 345
Capitol / Mar '85.

## SOLID.
Tracks: Not Advised.
VHS . . . . . . . . . . . . . . . . . . . PM 0012
Video Collection / May '87 / Gold & Sons / Video Collection / THE.

## SOLID (OLD GOLD).
Tracks: Solid / Babies.
12" . . . . . . . . . . . . . . . . . . . . OG 4235
Old Gold / Jun '92 / Pickwick.

■ DELETED

## STAY FREE.
**Tracks:** Found a cure / Stay free / Dance forever / Nobody knows / Crazy / Finally got to me / Follow your heart.
■ LP . . . . . . . . . . . . . . . . . . . . . K 56703
WEA / '88.

## STREET CORNER.
**Tracks:** Street corner / Make it work again.
■ 12" . . . . . . . . . . . . . . . . . . . 12CL 242
■ 7" . . . . . . . . . . . . . . . . . . . . .CL 242
Capitol / Nov '82.

## STREET OPERA.
**Tracks:** Not Advised.
■ LP . . . . . . . . . . . . . . . . . . .EST 12207
Capitol / May '82.

## TIME TALKING.
**Tracks:** Time talking / Time talking (ext mix) (Extra track on 12" only) / Flying / Flying (inst).
■ 12" . . . . . . . . . . . . . . . . . .12EMI 5555
■ 7" . . . . . . . . . . . . . . . . . . . EMI 5555
EMI / Mar '86.

# Ashley, Tyrone

## DON'T STOP DANCING.
**Tracks:** Don't stop dancing / Put your finger on the trigger.
■ 7" . . . . . . . . . . . . . . . . . . UP 36431
United Artists / Sep '78.

## FEET START MOVING.
**Tracks:** Feet start moving / Moving on.
■ 7" . . . . . . . . . . . . . . . . . 7N 25504
Pye International / May '76.

## JUST ANOTHER RUMOUR.
**Tracks:** Just another rumour (inst).
■ 12" . . . . . . . . . . . . . . . . . . .NGR 5
Nightmare Gold / Feb '87.

## LOOKS LIKE LOVE IS HERE TO STAY.
**Tracks:** Looks like love is here to stay / Surround me.
■ 7" . . . . . . . . . . . . . . . . . . UP 36371
United Artists / Mar '78.

# Asia Blue

## BOY IN THE MOON.
**Tracks:** Boy in the moon / Hope / Hope (mixes) (On 12"/CDs only) / Boy in the moon (mixes) (On 12"/CDs only).
■ 12" . . . . . . . . . . . . . . . . .WNRT 188
■ 7" . . . . . . . . . . . . . . . . . WNR 188
■ CD Single . . . . . . . . . . . . .WNRCD 188
Atomic / Mar '93.

## CONNECT.
**Tracks:** Connect / This journey.
■ 12" . . . . . . . . . . . . . . . . . WNRT 0025
■ 7" . . . . . . . . . . . . . . . . . WNR 0025
■ CD Single . . . . . . . . . . . . WNRCD 0025
■ MC Single . . . . . . . . . . . . WNRMC 0025
Atomic / Oct '92.

## ESCAPING.
**Tracks:** Escaping / I want the right (to be wrong).
■ 12" . . . . . . . . . . . . . . . . . WNR 882 T
■ 7" . . . . . . . . . . . . . . . . . WNR 882
■ CD Single . . . . . . . . . . . . .WNRCD 882
■ MC Single . . . . . . . . . . . . WNRMC 882
A&M / Jun '92.

# Astors

## CANDY.
**Tracks:** Candy / I found out.
■ 7" . . . . . . . . . . . . . . . . . . AT 4037
Atlantic / Jul '65.

# Atlantic Soul Machine

## COAST TO COAST.
**Tracks:** Not Advised.
■ CD . . . . . . . . . . . . . . . . . QSECD 2
■ MC . . . . . . . . . . . . . . . . QSEMC 2
Kadence / Nov '92.

## WHAT'S WRONG WITH ME.
**Tracks:** Not Advised.
■ CD . . . . . . . . . . . . . . . . QSECDS 1
QSE / Mar '93.

# Atlantic Starr

East Coast brothers David, Jonathon and Wayne Lewis moved to LA in mid-'70s and recruited six associates for Atlantic Starr. Group enjoyed modest success until 1984, when singer Sharon Bryant quit for solo career (her subsequent projects included album with Jam & Lewis). When Bryant rejected propsed tracks, producers recycled them for Janet Jackson's *Control*. Starr's stock rose in 1985, when self-produced *As the Band Turns* spawned four hits, including classic *Secret Lovers*. Newly-signed to Warner Brothers from A&M, band enjoyed another smash with *Always*, though this remained peak of six years with label. 1994 found Starr on Arista; line-up was trimmed to Lewis brothers plus singer Aisha Tanner - their third since Bryant's departure.

## ALL IN THE NAME OF LOVE.
**Tracks:** One lover at a time / You belong with me / Females / Don't take me for granted / Always / Let the sun in / Thankful / All in the name of love (Only on 12" version.) / My mistake / Interlude.
■ CD . . . . . . . . . . . . . . . . . .925560 2
WEA / May '86.
■ LP . . . . . . . . . . . . . . . . . . . WX 115
■ MC . . . . . . . . . . . . . . . . . WX 115C
WEA / Apr '87.

## ALWAYS.
**Tracks:** Always / Always (inst).
■ 12" . . . . . . . . . . . . . . . . . .W 8455T
■ 7" . . . . . . . . . . . . . . . . . . W 8455
WEA / May '87.

## AS THE BAND TURNS.
**Tracks:** Freak-a-ristic / Cool, calm, collected / One love / In the heart of passion / If your heart isn't in it / Silver shadow / Let's start it over / Secret lovers / Thank you.
■ LP . . . . . . . . . . . . . . . . . AMA 5019
■ MC . . . . . . . . . . . . . . . . AMC 5019
A&M / Jun '85.
■ CD . . . . . . . . . . . . . . . . CDA 5019
A&M / '88.

## ATLANTIC STARR.
**Tracks:** Stand up / Keep it comin' / Visions / Being in love with you is so much fun / Love I never had / Gimme you luvin' / With your love I come alive / We got it together / Don't abuse my love / Where there's smoke there's fire.
■ LP . . . . . . . . . . . . . . . . AMLH 64711
A&M / Oct '78.

## BEST OF ATLANTIC STARR, THE.
**Tracks:** Circles / Silver shadow / Send for me / Secret lovers / Love me down / Stand up / When love calls / Am I dreaming / Touch a four leaf clover / One love / Gimme your lovin' / If your heart isn't in it.
■ LP . . . . . . . . . . . . . . . . AMA 5141
■ MC . . . . . . . . . . . . . . . . AMC 5141
A&M / Oct '86.

## BRILLIANCE.
**Tracks:** Not Advised.
■ LP . . . . . . . . . . . . . . . . AMLH 64883
A&M / Jun '82.

## CIRCLES.
**Tracks:** Circles / Does it matter.
■ 7" . . . . . . . . . . . . . . . . AMS 8218
A&M / Nov '82.

## CLASSICS:ATLANTIC STARR.
**Tracks:** Not Advised.
■ CD . . . . . . . . . . . . . . . . CDA 2508
A&M.

## COMPACT HITS: ATLANTIC STARR.
**Tracks:** Secret lovers / Circles / Touch a four leaf clover / Silver shadow.
■ CD Single . . . . . . . . . . . AMCD 907
A&M / Apr '88.

## EVERYBODY'S GOT SUMMER.
**Tracks:** Everybody's got Summer (Mixes).
12" . . . . . . . . . . . . . . . . 7432122807-1
7" . . . . . . . . . . . . . . . . . 7432122807-7
CD Single . . . . . . . . . . . . . 7432122807-2
MC Single . . . . . . . . . . . . . 7432122807-4
Arista / Aug '94 / BMG.

## FOUR LEAF CLOVER.
**Tracks:** Four leaf clover / Circles.
■ 12" . . . . . . . . . . . . . . . . . AMX 155
■ 7" . . . . . . . . . . . . . . . . . AM 155
A&M / Nov '83.

## FREAK-A-RISTIC.
**Tracks:** Freak-a-ristic / Island dreams.
■ 12" . . . . . . . . . . . . . . . . . AMY 245
■ 7" . . . . . . . . . . . . . . . . . AM 245
A&M / Apr '85.

## GIMME YOUR LOVIN'.
**Tracks:** Gimme your lovin' / With your love I come alive / Don't abuse my love.
■ 7" . . . . . . . . . . . . . . . .AMS 7380
A&M / Sep '78.

## HEADLINES (OLD GOLD).
**Tracks:** Headlines / Wet my whistle.
■ 12" . . . . . . . . . . . . . . . . .OG 4125
Old Gold / '89.

## IF YOUR HEART ISN'T IN IT.
**Tracks:** If your heart isn't in it / Let's start it over / Stand up (Extra track on 12" only).
■ 12" . . . . . . . . . . . . . . . . . AMY 319
■ 7" . . . . . . . . . . . . . . . . . AM 319
A&M / May '86.
■ MC Single. . . . . . . . . . . . . AMC 319
A&M / Aug '88.

## LET THE SUN IN.
**Tracks:** Let the sun in / Females / All in the name of love (12" only).
■ 12" . . . . . . . . . . . . . . . . . W 8145 T
■ 7" . . . . . . . . . . . . . . . . . W 8145
WEA / Oct '87.

## LETS ROCK AND ROLL.
**Tracks:** Lets rock and roll / Bullseye.
■ 7" . . . . . . . . . . . . . . . .AMS 7452
A&M / Nov '79.

## LOVE CRAZY.
**Tracks:** Not Advised.
CD . . . . . . . . . . . . . . . . 7599265452
■ LP . . . . . . . . . . . . . . . . 7599265454
WEA / Nov '91 / WEA.

## LOVE ME DOWN.
**Tracks:** Love me down / You're the one.
■ 7" . . . . . . . . . . . . . . . USAF 1224
A&M / Aug '82.

## ONE LOVE.
**Tracks:** One love / Four leaf clover.
■ 12" . . . . . . . . . . . . . . . . . AMY 273
■ 7" . . . . . . . . . . . . . . . . . AM 273
A&M / Aug '85.

## ONE LOVER AT A TIME.
**Tracks:** I'm in love / One lover at a time.
■ 12" . . . . . . . . . . . . . . . . . W 8327 T
■ 7" . . . . . . . . . . . . . . . . . W 8327
WEA / Aug '87.

## RADIANT.
**Tracks:** When love calls / Does it matter / Think about that / Send for me / Mystery girl / Am I dreaming / Under pressure / My turn now.
■ LP . . . . . . . . . . . . . . . . AMLH 64833
A&M / Mar '81.

## SECRET LOVERS.
**Tracks:** When love calls / Secret lovers.
■ 12" . . . . . . . . . . . . . . . . . AMY 307
■ 7" . . . . . . . . . . . . . . . . . AM 307
A&M / Feb '86.

## SECRET LOVERS (OLD GOLD).
**Tracks:** Secret lovers / Silver shadow.
■ 12" . . . . . . . . . . . . . . . . .OG 4089
Old Gold / Nov '88.

## SILVER SHADOW.
**Tracks:** Silver shadow / Cool, calm, collected / Cool, calm, collected (LP version remix) / Cool, calm, collected (US club mix).
■ 12" . . . . . . . . . . . . . . . . .AMYE 260
■ 7" . . . . . . . . . . . . . . . . . AM 260
A&M / Sep '85.
■ 12" . . . . . . . . . . . . . . . . . AMY 336
■ 7" . . . . . . . . . . . . . . . . . AM 336
A&M / Aug '86.

## STAND UP.
**Tracks:** Stand up / Being in love with you is so much fun.
■ 7" . . . . . . . . . . . . . . . .AMS 7401
A&M / Nov '78.

## STRAIGHT TO THE POINT.
**Tracks:** Rock 'n' roll / Kissin' power / Let the spirit move ya / Straight to the point / Bullseye / What'cha feel inside / Fallin' in love with you / Losin' you.
■ LP . . . . . . . . . . . . . . . . AMLH 64764
A&M / '79.

## VERY BEST OF, THE.
Tracks: Not Advised.
CD.................................CDMID 152
MC.................................CMID 152
A&M / Oct '92 / PolyGram.

## WE'RE MOVIN' UP.
Tracks: Not Advised.
■ CD.................................925849 2
WEA / '89.

## YOURS FOREVER.
Tracks: Yours forever / Four leaf clover / More, more, more / I want your love / Second to none / Island dreams / Who could love you better / More time for me / Trying.
■ LP.................................AMLX 64948
■ MC.................................CXM 64948
A&M / Nov '85.

# Atmosfear

## DANCING IN OUTER SPACE.
Tracks: Dancing in outer space / Dancing in outer space (version).
■ 12"................................MCAT 543
■ 7"................................MCA 543
MCA / Nov '79.

## DANCING IN SPACE/PLANET MENTAL.
Tracks: Dancing in space / Planet mental.
■ 12"................................12CHIL 15
Jam Today / Sep '89.

## FIRST/FOURMOST.
Tracks: Not Advised.
■ LP.................................ATM 33
Elite Records / Jan '84.

## INTERPLAY.
Tracks: Interplay.
■ 12"................................DAZZ 8
Elite Records / Oct '81.

## INVASION.
Tracks: Invasion.
■ 12"................................MCAT 734
■ 7"................................MCA 734
MCA / Jul '81.

## MOTIVATION.
Tracks: Motivation / Extract.
■ 7"................................MCA 580
MCA / Mar '80.

## PERSONAL COLUMN.
Tracks: Personal column / Dancing in outer space.
■ 12"................................DAZZ 47
Elite Records / Mar '86.

## RE ENTRY - BEST OF ATMOSFEAR.
Tracks: Dancing in outer space / Extract / Alternative II / Interplay / Xtra special / Face tonight.
■ LP.................................CHEMXP 02
Chemical Discs (2) / Sep '93.

## TELEPATHY.
Tracks: Telepathy.
■ 12"................................DAZZ 35
Elite Records / Dec '84.

## TRANCE PLANTS.
Tracks: Not Advised.
CD.................................CUTUPCD 004
LP.................................CUTUPLP 004
Jump Cut / Apr '94 / New Note / Total.

## WHAT DO WE DO.
Tracks: What do we do / What do we do (club mix) / Xtra special.
■ 12"................................CHS 122730
■ 7"................................CHS 2730
Chrysalis / Aug '83.

## WHAT'S HAPPENING.
Tracks: What's happening.
■ 12"................................12CHIL 10
Jam Today / Jan '89.

## WHEN TONIGHT IS OVER.
Tracks: When tonight is over.
■ 7"................................DAZZ 317
Elite Records / Jun '84.
■ 12"................................DAZZ 31
Elite Records / Mar '84.

## XTRA SPECIAL.
Tracks: Xtra special.
■ 12"................................DAZZ 12
Elite Records / Apr '82.

# August & Duneen

## WE GOT TOGETHER.
Tracks: We go together / Like Adam and Eve.
■ 7"................................ABC 4181
ABC Records / Jun '77.

# Augustin, Nat

## EGO.
Tracks: Ego / I'll rescue you.
■ 12"................................AMY 329
■ 7"................................AM 329
A&M / Aug '86.

## SUMMER IS HERE AGAIN.
Tracks: Summer is here again / All my love.
■ 12"................................DEBT 06(12)
■ 7"................................DEBT 06
Debut (1) / Jul '85.

## THAT GIRL.
Tracks: That girl / Underneath the sheets.
■ 12"................................USAT 609
Breakout / Apr '87.
■ 7"................................USA 609
Breakout / Aug '87.

## TOO BUSY THINKING ABOUT MY BABY.
Tracks: Too busy thinking about my baby / You are the one.
■ 12"................................12EMI 5453
■ 7"................................EMI 5453
EMI / Mar '84.

# Aurra

## DREAM.
Tracks: Too much / Who are you / When I come home / In the mood / You're the only one / Got to get my lady back.
■ LP.................................SALP 3
Salsoul / Oct '80.

## HAPPY FEELING.
Tracks: Happy feeling.
■ 12"................................TEN 54-12
■ 7"................................TEN 54
10 / Jul '85.

## IN THE MOOD.
Tracks: In the mood / You're the only one.
■ 12"................................SAL 12 3
Salsoul / Jun '80.

## LIKE I LIKE IT.
Tracks: You and me tonight / Keep on dancing / Hooked on you / Talking in your sleep / Bedtime story / Like I like it (remixed version) / Living inside yourself / Happy feelings (remixed version) / I'll keep waiting / I love myself.
■ LP.................................DIX 12
10 / Nov '86.
■ LP.................................XID 7
■ MC.................................CXID 7
10 / Jun '88.

## LIKE I LIKE IT.
Tracks: Like I like it.
■ 12"................................TEN 45-12
■ 7"................................TEN 45
10 / '85.

## LIKE I LIKE IT (REMIX).
Tracks: Like I like it (remix) / I love myself.
■ 7"................................TEN 126
10 / Jun '86.

## LITTLE LOVE, A.
Tracks: Little love / Make up your mind / Checking out.
■ 12"................................BATTL 1
Battersea / Jun '82.

## LIVE AND LET LIVE.
Tracks: Live and let live / Such a feeling / Coming to get you / Undercover lover / Baby love / You can't keep on walking / One more time / Positive.
■ LP.................................SA 8559
Salsoul / Mar '83.

## NASTY DISPOSITION.
Tracks: Nasty disposition / Are you single.
■ 12"................................SALT 9
Salsoul / May '81.

## SEND YOUR LOVE.
Tracks: Nasty disposition / Send your love / Kingston lady / Forever / Are you single / Keep doin' it / Living too fast / Party time.
■ LP.................................SALP 6
Salsoul / Jun '81.

## WHEN I COME HOME.
Tracks: When I come home / Who are you.
■ 7"................................SALT 5 12
Salsoul / Sep '80.

## YOU AND ME TONIGHT.
Tracks: You and me tonight / You and me tonight (inst) / Keep on dancing (On TEN 7112 only) / You and me tonight (midnight mix) (On TEN 7113 only).
■ 12"................................TEN 71-13
■ 12"................................TEN 71-12
■ 7"................................TEN 71
10 / Apr '86.

## YOU AND ME TONIGHT (OLD GOLD).
Tracks: You and me tonight / Like I like it.
■ 12"................................OG 4106
Old Gold / Mar '89.

# Austin, Dennis

## I'LL SHINE FOR YOU.
Tracks: I'll shine for you / Best friend / I need your help.
■ 12"................................EXPAND 41
Expansion / Jul '93.

# Austin, Patti

## ARE WE READY FOR LOVE.
Tracks: Are we ready for love / Now that I know what loneliness is.
■ 7"................................CBS 7180
CBS / Apr '71.

## BABY COME TO ME (Austin, Patti & James Ingram).
Tracks: Baby come to me / Solero.
■ 12"................................K 15005T
■ 7"................................K 15005
WEA / Feb '83.

## BODY LANGUAGE.
Tracks: Body language / Another nail in my heart / S.O.S. / We've got tonite / He's killing me / I can't stop / Love me again / Soar me like an eagle flies / People In love / I want you tonight.
■ LP.................................240 601 3
CTI (1) / Oct '81.

## CARRY ON.
Tracks: Carry on / Givin' in to love / I will remember you / How can I be sure / Why did she come in with you / I just can't let go / Monday, Monday / More I thing about it / Nobody to dance with / I'll be waiting for you / (Don't know) Whether to laugh or cry.
CD.................................GRP 96602
■ LP.................................GRP 96601
■ MC.................................GRP 96604
GRP / Oct '91 / BMG / New Note.
■ DCC.................................GRX 96605
GRP / Jan '93.

## DO YOU LOVE ME.
Tracks: Do you love me / Solero.
■ 7"................................K 17838
Qwest / Aug '81.

## END OF A RAINBOW.
Tracks: Say you love me / You don't have to say you're sorry / In my life / More today than yesterday / Give it time / There is no time / What's at the end of the rainbow / This side of heaven / Sweet Sadie the saviour.
■ LP.................................CTI 5001
CTI (1) / Jan '77.

## EVERY HOME SHOULD HAVE ONE.
Tracks: Do you love me / Love me to death / Way I feel / Every home should have one / Baby, come to me / Genie / Stop look listen / Symphony of love / Oh no, Margerita / Island.
CD.................................K2 56931
■ LP.................................K 56931
MC.................................K4 56931
Qwest / WEA.

## EVERY HOME SHOULD HAVE ONE.
Tracks: Every home should have one / Genie.
■ 7"................................K 17874
Qwest / May '80.

## GETTIN' AWAY WITH MURDER.
Tracks: Talking about my baby / Big bad world / Heat of heat / If I believe / Honey for the bees / Anything can happen here / Only a breath away / Summer is the coldest time of year.
■ LP.................................925276 1
■ MC.................................925276 4
Qwest / Oct '85.

14                                                          ■ DELETED

### GIRL WHO USED TO BE ME, THE.
Tracks: Girl who used to be me / Shirley Valentine end title.
- 7" . . . . . . . . . . . . . . . . . . . . GRP 3027
GRP / Oct '89.

### HAVANA CANDY.
Tracks: Havana candy / That's enough for me / Little baby / I just want to know / Golden oldies / I need somebody / We're in love / Lost in the stars.
- LP . . . . . . . . . . . . . . . . . . . CTI 5006
CTI (USA) / Jan '78.

### HEAT OF HEAT, THE.
Tracks: Heat of heat / Hot in the heat of love / All behind us now (Extra track on 12" only).
- 12" . . . . . . . . . . . . . . . . . . W 8798T
- 7" . . . . . . . . . . . . . . . . . . . W 8798
WEA / Mar '86.

### HOW DO YOU KEEP THE MUSIC PLAYIN' (Austin, Patti & James Ingram).
Tracks: How do you keep the music playin'.
- 12" . . . . . . . . . . . . . . . . . . W 9681T
- 7" . . . . . . . . . . . . . . . . . . . W 9618
WEA / May '83.

### I CAN'T STOP.
Tracks: I can't stop / Body language.
- 7" . . . . . . . . . . . . . . . . . . .CTSP 11
CTI (1) / Sep '80.

### I'LL KEEP YOUR DREAMS ALIVE (see under Benson, George).

### LIVE AT THE BOTTOM LINE.
Tracks: Not Advised.
- MC . . . . . . . . . . . . . . . . . . . CTK 9501
CTI (Musidisc France) / Feb '84.
- CD . . . . . . . . . . . . . . . . . . . 4679222
- MC . . . . . . . . . . . . . . . . . . . 4679224
Sony Music / Jun '91 / Sony.

### LOVE IS GONNA GETCHA.
Tracks: Through the test of time / Too soon to know / In my life / Love is gonna getcha / Ooh-whee (the carnival) / Believe the children / Good in love / Wait for me / First time love / In my dream / Girl who used to be me (Available on CD only).
- CD . . . . . . . . . . . . . . . . . . GRP 96032
- LP . . . . . . . . . . . . . . . . . . GRP 96031
- MC . . . . . . . . . . . . . . . . . . GRP 96034
GRP / Mar '90 / BMG / New Note.

### PATTI AUSTIN.
Tracks: It's candy be special / Rhythm of the street / All behind us now / Hot in flames of love / Change your attitude / Shoot the moon / I've got my heart set on you / Fine fine fella / Starstruck / Any way you can.
- CD . . . . . . . . . . . . . . . . . . .923974 2
- MC . . . . . . . . . . . . . . . . . . .923974 4
- LP . . . . . . . . . . . . . . . . . . .923974 1
Qwest / Feb '84 / WEA.

### PATTI AUSTIN LIVE.
Tracks: I can cook too / Love is gonna getcha / It might be you / Baby come to me / How do you keep the music playing / Do you love me / We're all in this together / Through the test of time / (Don't know) whether to laugh or cry.
- MC . . . . . . . . . . . . . . . . . . GRP 98624
- CD . . . . . . . . . . . . . . . . . . GRP 96822
GRP / Aug '92.

### REAL ME, THE.
Tracks: I can cook too / Stockholm sweetnin' / Smoke gets in your eyes / True love / Across the valley from the Alamo / How long has this been going on / Mood indigo / Cry me a river / Someone is standing outside / Spring can really hang you up the most.
- CD . . . . . . . . . . . . . . . . . K 925696 2
- LP . . . . . . . . . . . . . . . . . K 925696 1
- MC . . . . . . . . . . . . . . . . . K 925696 4
Qwest / Jul '88.

### RHYTHM OF THE STREET.
Tracks: Rhythm of the street / It's gonna be special.
- 12" . . . . . . . . . . . . . . . . . . W 9266 T
- 7" . . . . . . . . . . . . . . . . . . . W 9266
WEA / Aug '81.

### SAY YOU LOVE ME.
Tracks: Say you love me / In my life.
- 7" . . . . . . . . . . . . . . . . . . . CTSP 9
CTI (1) / Mar '77.

### SHOOT THE MOON.
Tracks: Shoot the moon / Solero.
- 12" . . . . . . . . . . . . . . . . . . W 9281T
- 7" . . . . . . . . . . . . . . . . . . . W 9281
Qwest / May '84.

### THAT SECRET PLACE.
Tracks: That's enough for me / Ability to swing / Somebody make me laugh / Broken dreams / Rock steady / That secret place / Hurry home / Reach / Stars in your eyes.
- CD . . . . . . . . . . . . . . . . . . GRM 40232
GRP / May '94 / BMG / New Note.

### WE'RE IN LOVE.
Tracks: We're in love / Little baby.
- 7" . . . . . . . . . . . . . . . . . . . CTSP 011
CTI (1) / Jan '78.

## Average White Band

Scottish sextet formed in 1972 who cracked U.S. with eponymous second album. Produced by Arif Mardin, and pushed by band's new label Atlantic, album produced funk classic *Pick Up The Pieces*. By early '75, both album and single were giant U.S. charts. Band survived loss of drug casualty Robbie McIntosh to produce another big-seller, *Cut The Cake* and collaborate with Ben E. King on *Benny And Us*. Subsequent, somewhat formulaic career, was rejuvenated by 1980's *Shine* album and *Let's Go Round Again* single, but band split in '82. Guitarist Hamish Stuart wrote songs for George Benson, Jeffrey Osborne, the Temptations and Diana Ross, before teaming up with Paul McCartney; drummer Steve Ferrone (McIntosh's replacement) worked with Duran Duran and Eric Clapton. Neither were involved with relaunched AWB, which boasted guitarist Onnie McIntyre, keyboardist Roger Ball and bassist Alan Gorrie from original line-up (remaining member, saxophonist Malcolm Duncan, formed funk act Contraband). Consequent album, '89's *Aftershock*, sunk without trace, although best-of collection returned AWB to chart in '93.

### AFTER SHOCK.
Tracks: Spirit of love / Aftershock / I'll get over you / Let's go all the way / Stocky sachoo a shun / Sticky situation / Love at first sight / Later we'll be greater / We're in too deep.
- MC . . . . . . . . . . . . . . 839 466-4
- LP . . . . . . . . . . . . . . 839 466-1
- CD . . . . . . . . . . . . . . 839 466-2
Polydor / Aug '89 / PolyGram.

### ATLANTIC AVENUE.
Tracks: Atlantic Avenue / She's a dream.
- 7" . . . . . . . . . . . . . . . . . . . XB 1061
RCA / Jan '79.

### AVERAGE WHITE BAND.
Tracks: You got it / Got the love / Pick up the pieces / Person to person / Nothing you can do / Work to do / Just want to love you tonight / Keepin' it to myself / I just can't give you up / There's always someone waiting.
- LP . . . . . . . . . . . . . . . . . . . K 50058
Atlantic / Mar '75.
- LP . . . . . . . . . . . . . . . . . . . INTS 5049
RCA / Nov '80.
- LP . . . . . . . . . . . . . . . . . . . FA 3157
- MC . . . . . . . . . . . . . . . . . . TCFA 3157
Fame / Jun '86 / EMI.
- CD . . . . . . . . . . . . . . . . . . . 7815152
Atlantic / '87.

### BENNY AND US (Average White Band & Ben E. King).
Tracks: Get it up for love / Fool for your anyway / Star in the ghetto / Message / What is soul / Someday we'll be free / Imagine / Keepin' it to myself.
- LP . . . . . . . . . . . . . . . . . . . K 50384
- MC . . . . . . . . . . . . . . . . . . K4 50384
Atlantic / Jul '77.

### BEST OF THE AVERAGE WHITE BAND.
Tracks: Pick up the pieces / Cut the cake / Queen of my soul / Love of your own / Person to person / I heard it through the grapevine / Walk on by / You got it / Cloudy / Work to do / Atlantic Avenue / We will you be mine.
- LP . . . . . . . . . . . . . . . . . . . NL 89091
- MC . . . . . . . . . . . . . . . . . . NK 89091
RCA / '84.

### CUPID'S IN FASHION.
Tracks: You're my number one / Easier said than done / You wanna belong / Cupids in fashion / Theatre of excess I believe / Is it love that you're running from / Reach out I'll be there / Isn't it strange / Love's a heartache.
- LP . . . . . . . . . . . . . . . . . . RCALP 6052
- MC . . . . . . . . . . . . . . . . . . RCAK 6052
RCA / Sep '82.

### CUT THE CAKE.
Tracks: Cut the cake / School boy crush / It's a mystery / Groovin' the night away / If I ever lose this heaven / Why / High flyin' woman / Cloudy / How sweet can you get / When they bring down the curtain.
- LP . . . . . . . . . . . . . . . . . . . K 50146
Atlantic / Jun '75.

### CUT THE CAKE.
Tracks: Cut the cake.
- 7" . . . . . . . . . . . . . . . . . . . K 10605
Atlantic / Jun '75.

### FEEL NO FRET.
Tracks: When will you be mine / Please don't fall in love / Walk on by / Feel no fret / Stop the rain / Atlantic Avenue / Ace of hearts / Too late to cry / Fire burning / Cut the cake / School boy crush / It's a mystery / Groovin' the night away / If I ever lose this heaven / Why / High flyin' woman / Cloudy / How sweet can you get / When they bring down the curtain.
- LP . . . . . . . . . . . . . . . . . . . XL 13063
RCA / Mar '79.
- LP . . . . . . . . . . . . . . . . . . INTS 5140
- MC . . . . . . . . . . . . . . . . . . INTK 5140
RCA / Sep '81.

### FOR YOU FOR LOVE.
Tracks: For you for love / Help is on the way.
- 12" . . . . . . . . . . . . . . . . . . AWB 12 2
- 7" . . . . . . . . . . . . . . . . . . . AWB 2
RCA / Jun '80.

### GOING HOME.
Tracks: Going home / I'm the one.
- 7" . . . . . . . . . . . . . . . . . . . K 10912
Atlantic / Mar '77.

### HOW CAN YOU GO HOME.
Tracks: How can you go home / Twilight zone.
- 7" . . . . . . . . . . . . . . . . . . . MCA 186
MCA / Apr '75.

### I BELIEVE.
Tracks: I believe.
- 12" . . . . . . . . . . . . . . . . . . RCAT 274
- 7" . . . . . . . . . . . . . . . . . . . RCA 274
RCA / Sep '82.

### LET'S GO ROUND AGAIN (PT 1).
Tracks: Let's go around again (Pt 1) / Love of your own.
- 12" . . . . . . . . . . . . . . . . . . AWB 12 1
- 7" . . . . . . . . . . . . . . . . . . . AWB 1
RCA / Apr '80.

### LET'S GO ROUND AGAIN - THE BEST OF THE AVERAGE WHITE BAND.
Tracks: Not Advised.
- CD . . . . . . . . . . . . . . . . . . AHLCD 15
- MC . . . . . . . . . . . . . . . . . . AHLMC 15
Hit Label / Mar '94 / PolyGram.

### LIVE ON THE TEST.
Tracks: Put it where you want it / If I ever lose this heaven / Cloudy / Pick up the pieces / Person to person / I heard it through the grapevine / Star in the ghetto / When will you be mine / Please don't fall in love / Atlantic Avenue / Show your hand.
- CD . . . . . . . . . . . . . . . . . . WHISCD 005
Windsong / Aug '94 / Pinnacle / A.D.A. Distribution.

### ONE LOOK OVER MY SHOULDER.
Tracks: One look over my shoulder / Big city lights.
- 12" . . . . . . . . . . . . . . . . . . XC 9270
- 7" . . . . . . . . . . . . . . . . . . . XB 9270
RCA / '79.

### PERSON TO PERSON.
Tracks: Person to person / Cut the cake / If I ever lose this heaven / Cloudy / T.L.C. / I'm the one / Pick up the pieces / Love you life / School boy crush / I heard it through the grapevine.
- Double LP . . . . . . . . . . . . . . . K 60127
- MC Set . . . . . . . . . . . . . . . . K4 60127
Atlantic / Jan '77.

### PICK UP THE PIECES.
Tracks: Pick up the pieces / You've got it.
- 7" . . . . . . . . . . . . . . . . . . . K 10489
Atlantic / Jul '84.

### PICK UP THE PIECES (OLD GOLD).
Tracks: Pick up the pieces.
- 7" . . . . . . . . . . . . . . . . . . .GOLD 514
RCA Golden Grooves / Jul '81.

### PUT IT WHERE YOU WANT IT.
Tracks: Not Advised.
- LP . . . . . . . . . . . . . . . . . . . MCL 1650
MCA / Feb '82.

## QUEEN OF MY SOUL.
Tracks: Queen of my soul.
■ 7" . . . . . . . . . . . . . . . . . . . . . K 10825
Atlantic / Sep '76.

## SHINE.
Tracks: Catch me / Let's go round again / Whatch' gonna do for me / Help is on the way / Shine / For you, for love / Into the night / Our time has come / If love only lasts for one night.
■ LP . . . . . . . . . . . . . . . . . . . XL 13123
RCA / May '80.

## SHOW YOUR HAND.
Tracks: Jugglers / This world has music / Twilight zone / Put it where you want it / Show your hand / Back in '67 / Reach out / T.L.C.
■ LP . . . . . . . . . . . . . . . . . . MCF 2514
MCA / '73.
■ LP . . . . . . . . . . . . . . . . . . . FA 3062
MC. . . . . . . . . . . . . . . . . . . TCFA 3062
Fame / May '83 / EMI.

## SOUL SEARCHING TIME.
Tracks: Overture / Love your life / I'm the one / Love of your own / Queen of my soul / Soul searching / Going home / Everybody's darling / Would you stay / Sunny days / Digging deeper.
■ LP . . . . . . . . . . . . . . . . . . K 50272
Atlantic / Jan '76.
■ LP . . . . . . . . . . . . . . . . . INTS 5058
■ MC. . . . . . . . . . . . . . . . . INTK 5058
RCA / Nov '80.

## SPIRIT OF LOVE, THE.
Tracks: Spirit of love.
■ CD Single . . . . . . . . . . . . . . 889 308-3
Polydor / Nov '89.
■ 12" . . . . . . . . . . . . . . . . . . . PZ 56
■ 7" . . . . . . . . . . . . . . . . . . . PO 56
Polydor / Oct '89.

## STAR IN THE GHETTO.
Tracks: Star in the ghetto / Keeping it to myself.
■ 7" . . . . . . . . . . . . . . . . . . K 10977
Atlantic / Jul '77.

## WALK ON BY.
Tracks: Walk on by / Too late to cry.
■ 7" . . . . . . . . . . . . . . . . . . XB 1087
RCA / Jun '79.

## WARMER COMMUNICATIONS.
Tracks: Your love is a miracle / Same feeling, different song / Daddy's all gone / Big city lights / She's a dream / Sweet and sour / One look over my shoulder (is this really).
■ LP . . . . . . . . . . . . . . . . . . XL 13053
■ MC. . . . . . . . . . . . . . . . . . XK 13053
RCA / '78.

## WHEN WILL YOU BE MINE.
Tracks: When will you be mine / Ace of hearts.
■ 12" . . . . . . . . . . . . . . . . . . XC 1096
■ 7" . . . . . . . . . . . . . . . . . . XB 1096
RCA / Jul '79.

## YOU'RE MY NUMBER 1.
Tracks: You're my number 1 / Theater of excess.
■ 12" . . . . . . . . . . . . . . . . . RCAT 250
■ 7" . . . . . . . . . . . . . . . . . . RCA 250
RCA / Jul '82.

## Ayers, Roy

Ayers was born in L.A. in 1940 and was encouraged from an early age to study music, he was a piano student but discovered a love for the vibes when he attended a Lionel Hampton concert at the tender age of 5. Having mastered both instruments Ayers began to play professionally in the early 60's, eventually landing a solo deal with Atlantic in 1967 where he recorded three jazz albums. After forming Roy Ayer's Ubiquity in 1970 he moved onto Polydor and began incorporating elements of R&B and jazz-funk fusion into his work. With a star studded assortment of sidemen, such as Herbie Hancock and George Benson, Ubiquity pioneered the jazz-funk crossover that peaked with the track *Evolution* in 1975 and the 1977 album *Lifeline* with its classic single *Running Away*. He then entered a more mellow soul influenced period which gave him his first Top 50 hit *Get On Up, Get On Down*. As he entered the 80's Ayers seemed anxious to move on, and during a tour of Africa he found fresh purpose and direction. Incorporating African rhythms into his work and persuading percussionist Fela Kuti to tour and record with him, Ayers surfaced with the album *Africa, Center Of The World*,

pre-empting the Afrocentric direction adopted by many contemporary dance/soul/ rap acts. Although his recorded output has slowed considerably his influence has become more visible over the last decade with covers, samples and downright steals of his work by Loose Ends, The Chimes and Galliano etc.

## AFRICA, CENTER OF THE WORLD.
Tracks: Africa, center of the world / River Niger / I'll just keep trying / Destination motherland / Third eye / Land of fruit and honey / Mo nise si E / There's a master plan.
■ LP . . . . . . . . . . . . . . . . . 2391 517
Polydor / Aug '81.
CD. . . . . . . . . . . . . . . . . . PD 1627
Polydor / Jun '88 / PolyGram.

## AT RONNIE SCOTT'S 1988.
Tracks: Not Advised.
■ VHS . . . . . . . . . . . . . . . . . HEN 2162
Hendring Video / Sep '89.

## BEST OF ROY AYERS.
Tracks: Heat of the beat / Can't you see me / Fever / Love will bring us together / Running away / Get on up, get on down / Freaky deaky / You send me.
■ LP . . . . . . . . . . . . . . . . . 2391 429
Polydor / Dec '79.
■ MC. . . . . . . . . . . . . . . . . 3177 429
Polydor / Nov '79.

## CAN'T YOU SEE ME.
Tracks: Can't you see me / Love will bring us together / Sweet tears.
■ 12" . . . . . . . . . . . . . . . . . URBX 6
■ 7" . . . . . . . . . . . . . . . . . . URB 6
Urban / Sep '87.

## CRACK IN THE MIRROR (WAKE UP).
Tracks: Crack in the mirror (wake up) / Spirit of dodo 89.
■ 12" . . . . . . . . . . . . . . . . . 12 PO 33
Ichiban / Sep '89.

## CRYSTAL REFLECTIONS (Ayers, Roy & B.Williams).
Tracks: Not Advised.
■ LP . . . . . . . . . . . . . . . . . MR 5101
Muse / Jun '77.
MC. . . . . . . . . . . . . . . . . . MC 5430
■ CD . . . . . . . . . . . . . . . . . MCD 5430
Muse / Sep '92 / New Note / Jazz Horizons / C.M. Distribution.

## DON'T STOP THE FEELING.
Tracks: Don't stop the feeling / Don't hide your love.
■ 12" . . . . . . . . . . . . . . . . . STEPX 9
■ 7" . . . . . . . . . . . . . . . . . . STEP 9
Polydor / Jan '80.

## DRIVE.
Tracks: Not Advised.
LP . . . . . . . . . . . . . . . . . ICH 1028
MC. . . . . . . . . . . . . . . . . ZZICH 1028
Ichiban / Sep '88 / A.D.A. Distribution / Pinnacle / ACD Trading Ltd. / Koch International / Direct Distribution.
CD . . . . . . . . . . . . . . . . . CDICH 1028
Ichiban / Mar '94 / A.D.A. Distribution / Pinnacle / ACD Trading Ltd. / Koch International / Direct Distribution.

## DRIVIN' ON UP.
Tracks: Drive / Everybody / And then we were one / Black family / Chicago.
■ LP . . . . . . . . . . . . . . . . . UMLP 2
Uno Melodic / Nov '83.

## EASY MONEY (Live At Ronnie Scott's).
Tracks: Spirit of do do / I wanna touch you / Everybody loves the sunshine / Fast money / Battle of the vibes / Can't you see me / Running away / Don't stop the feeling.
■ CD . . . . . . . . . . . . . . . . . ESMCD 017
■ MC. . . . . . . . . . . . . . . . . ESMMC 017
Essential / Feb '90.

## EVERYBODY LOVES THE SUNSHINE.
Tracks: Hey u / Golden rod / Keep on walking / You and me my love / Third eye / It ain't your sign / People and the world / Everybody loves the sunshine / Tongue power / Lonesome cowboy.
■ LP . . . . . . . . . . . . . . . . . UMID 1
MC. . . . . . . . . . . . . . . . . . UMIDC 1
Urban / Apr '88 / PolyGram.

## FAST MONEY.
Tracks: Fast money / Black family.
■ 12" . . . . . . . . . . . . . . . . . 12 PO 14
Ichiban / Sep '88.

## FEELIN' GOOD.
Tracks: Our time is coming / Fire up the funk / Let's stay together / Ooh / Turn me loose / Knock knock / Stairway to the stars / Feeling good.
■ LP . . . . . . . . . . . . . . . . . 2391 539
Polydor / '83.

## FEVER.
Tracks: Love will bring us together / Simple and sweet / Take me out to the ball game / I wanna feel it (I wanna dance) / Fever / Is it too late to try / If you love me / Leo.
■ LP . . . . . . . . . . . . . . . . . 2391396
Urban / '79.
■ CD . . . . . . . . . . . . . . . . . UMIDD 2
■ MC. . . . . . . . . . . . . . . . . UMIDC 2
■ LP . . . . . . . . . . . . . . . . . UMID 2
Urban / Feb '88.

## FEVER.
Tracks: Fever / Is it too late to try.
■ 12" . . . . . . . . . . . . . . . . . POSPX 53
■ 7" . . . . . . . . . . . . . . . . . . POSP 53
Polydor / May '79.

## FREAKY DEE JAY.
Tracks: Freaky dee jay / You came into my life.
■ 7" . . . . . . . . . . . . . . . . . . 2066896
Polydor / Feb '78.

## GET ON UP, GET ON DOWN.
Tracks: Get on up, get on down / And don't you say no.
■ 7" . . . . . . . . . . . . . . . . . . 2066982
Polydor / Sep '78.

## GET ON UP, GET ON DOWN (OLD GOLD).
Tracks: Get on up, get on down / Heat of the beat.
12" . . . . . . . . . . . . . . . . . OG 4176
Old Gold / May '90 / Pickwick.

## GET ON UP, GET ON DOWN - BEST OF ROY AYERS.
Tracks: Turn me loose / Get on up get on down / Sweet tears / What you won't do for love / Rhythm / You send me / This side of sunshine / Vibrations.
CD . . . . . . . . . . . . . . . . . 519918-2
■ LP . . . . . . . . . . . . . . . . . 519918-1
■ MC. . . . . . . . . . . . . . . . . 519918-4
Polydor / Aug '93 / PolyGram.

## GET UP, GET DOWN (see under Fishbelly Black).

## GOOD VIBRATIONS.
Tracks: Everybody loves the sunshine / Easy to move / Mission / Wrapped up in your love / X marks the spot / Poo poo la la / Ivory tower.
CD . . . . . . . . . . . . . . . . . JHCD 028
Ronnie Scott's Jazz House / Jan '94 / THE / Jazz Music / New Note / Magnum Music Group.

## HEAT OF THE BEAT (Ayers, Roy & Wayne Henderson).
Tracks: Heat of the beat / No deposit, no return.
■ 7" . . . . . . . . . . . . . . . . . . POSP 16
Polydor / Jan '79.

## HOT.
Tracks: Can't you see me / Running away / Love will bring us together / Lots of love / Everyone loves the sunshine / Hot / Pete King / Sweet tears / Philadelphia mambo / We live in London baby.
LP . . . . . . . . . . . . . . . . . JHR 021
Ronnie Scott's Jazz House / Aug '92 / THE / Jazz Music / New Note / Magnum Music Group.
CD . . . . . . . . . . . . . . . . . JHCD 021
MC. . . . . . . . . . . . . . . . . JHMC 021
Ronnie Scott's Jazz House / Jan '94 / THE / Jazz Music / New Note / Magnum Music Group.

## I'M THE ONE (FOR YOUR LOVE TONIGHT).
Tracks: I'm the one / Don't you ever turn away / Blue summer / I once had your love (and I can't let go) / I really want to be with you / Let me love you / Marion / Word / Crack attack.
■ LP . . . . . . . . . . . . . . . . . 4505971
■ MC. . . . . . . . . . . . . . . . . 4505974
CBS / Nov '87.

## IN THE DARK.
Tracks: In the dark / Sexy, sexy, sexy / I can't help it / Compardre / Goree Island / Poo poo la la / Blast the box / Love is in the feel.
■ LP . . . . . . . . . . . . . . . . . 26199
CBS / Jan '85.

■ DELETED

## IN THE DARK.
**Tracks:** In the dark.
- 12"................................. TA 4855
- 7"..................................A 4855

CBS / Nov '84.

## LET'S DO IT.
**Tracks:** Let's do it / Melody maker / When is real real / Sweet tears / You came into my life / Freaky deaky / Kiss.
- LP................................. 2490145

CD...................................... UMIDD 4
- LP.................................... UMID 4
- MC................................... UMIDC 4

Urban / Feb '88 / PolyGram.

## LET'S DO IT.
**Tracks:** Let's do it / Melody maker.
- 7".................................. 2066930

Polydor / Jun '78.

## LET'S STAY TOGETHER.
**Tracks:** Let's stay together / Knock, knock.
- 12"................................. POSPX 474
- 7".................................. POSP 474

Polydor / Jul '82.

## LIFELINE (Ayers, Roy Ubiquity).
**Tracks:** This side of sunshine / Running away / Gotta find a lover / I still love you / Lifeline / Cincinnati growl / Fruit / Sanctified feeling / Stranded in the jungle / Together.
- LP................................. 2391292

Polydor / Sep '77.

## LOVE FANTASY.
**Tracks:** Rock your roll / Betcha gonna / Sometimes believe in yourself / Love fantasy / Sigh / Baby Buba.
- LP.................................... UMID 6
- MC................................... URBMC 6

Urban / Apr '88.

## MYSTIC VOYAGE.
**Tracks:** Not Advised.
CD...................................... 5195672

Polydor / Aug '93 / PolyGram.

## NO STRANGER TO LOVE.
**Tracks:** Don't stop the feeling / What you won't do for love / Shack up, pack up / It's up / Slyde / No stranger to love / Don't let our love slip away / Don't hide your love.
- LP................................. .2391 438
MC...................................... .3177 438

Polydor / Jan '80 / PolyGram.

## POO POO LA LA.
**Tracks:** Poo poo la la / Compadre / Running away (on 12" only).
- 7".................................. .A 6087
- 12"................................. TA 6087

CBS / Feb '85.

## PRIME TIME (Ayers, Roy & Wayne Henderson).
**Tracks:** You make me feel like / Thank you thank you / Weekend lover / Tell me what you want / Can you dance / It ain't your sign / Have your way / Million dollar baby.
- LP................................. .2391 455

Polydor / Jul '80.

## RARE.
**Tracks:** Evolution / Love from the sun / Magic lady / Fikisha (to help somebody arrive) / 2000 black / Mystic voyage / Tear to a smile / For real / Change up the groove / Time and space / It's so sweet / Life is just a moment / Show us a feeling / Des nude soul.
- CD................................. 841 416-2
- LP................................. 841 416-1
- MC................................. 841 416-4

Polydor / Feb '90.

## RARE VOLUME II.
**Tracks:** Brother Louie / Don't you worry about a thing / When is real, real / Ebony blaze / Funky motion / Sensitize / Ain't got time / Ain't no sunshine / Sweet tears / Red, black and green / Hummin' / Feel like makin' love / Wee bit / Raindrops keep falling / On my head.
- CD................................. 843 758-2
- LP................................. 843 758-1
- MC................................. 843 758-4

Polydor / Aug '90 / PolyGram.

## RUNNING AWAY.
**Tracks:** Running away / Can't you see me.
- 12"................................. POSPX 135

Polydor / Mar '80.

## SEARCHIN'.
**Tracks:** Searchin' / Yes / You send me / Mystic voyage (CD only) / Love will bring us together (CD only) / Spirit of the Do-Do / Long time ago / Can you see me (CD only).
LP................................. JHR 013

Ronnie Scott's Jazz House / May '91 / THE / Jazz Music / New Note / Magnum Music Group.
CD................................. JHCD 013
MC................................. JHMC 013

Ronnie Scott's Jazz House / Jan '94 / THE / Jazz Music / New Note / Magnum Music Group.

## SHINING SYMBOL - THE ULTIMATE COLLECTION, A.
**Tracks:** Not Advised.
CD................................. .519378-2
LP................................. .519378-1
MC................................. .519378-4

Polydor / May '93 / PolyGram.

## SILVER VIBRATIONS.
**Tracks:** Not Advised.
- LP................................. UMLP 1
MC................................. UMC 1

Uno Melodic / Jul '83 / Pinnacle.

## SILVER VIBRATIONS.
**Tracks:** Silver vibrations / Fast money.
- 12"................................. UM 1 T
- 7".................................. UM 1

Uno Melodic / Jul '83.

## SLIP'N'SLIDE.
**Tracks:** Slip'n'slide / Can't see you.
- 12"................................. TA 6604
- 7".................................. .A 6604

CBS / Sep '85.

## SOMETIMES BELIEVE IN YOURSELF.
**Tracks:** Sometimes believe in yourself / Can you dance / Thank you, thank you.
- 12"................................. POSPX 186

Polydor / Oct '80.

## STEP INTO OUR LIFE.
**Tracks:** Not Advised.
- LP................................. POLS 1004

Polydor / Jan '79.

## SUAVE.
**Tracks:** Suave / And then we were one.
- 12"................................. 12 PO 23

Ichiban / May '89.

## TURN ME LOOSE.
**Tracks:** Turn me loose / Ooh.
- 12"................................. POSPX 427
- 7".................................. POSP 427

Polydor / Apr '82.

## VIBRANT.
**Tracks:** Not Advised.
CD................................. VSOPCD 179
MC................................. VSOPMC 179

Connoisseur Collection / Feb '93 / Pinnacle.

## VIBRATIONS (Ayers, Roy Ubiquity).
**Tracks:** Domelo (give it to me) / Baby I need your love / Higher / Memory / Come out and play / Better days / Searching / One sweet love to remember / Vibrations / Moving, grooving / Baby you give me a feeling.
- LP................................. .2391 256

Polydor / Feb '77.
- LP................................. UMID 5
- MC................................. UMIDC 5

Urban / Apr '88.

## WAKE UP.
**Tracks:** Midnight after dark / Suave / Sweet talk / Spirit of dodo '89 / Crack is in the mirror (wake up) / You've got the power / Mystic vibrations.
LP................................. ICH 1040
MC................................. ZCICH 1040

Ichiban / Jun '89 / A.D.A. Distribution / Pinnacle / ACD Trading Ltd. / Koch International / Direct Distribution.
CD................................. CDICH 1040

Ichiban / Oct '93 / A.D.A. Distribution / Pinnacle / ACD Trading Ltd. / Koch International / Direct Distribution.

## YOU MIGHT BE SURPRISED.
**Tracks:** Hot / Programmes for love / Virgo / You might be surprised / Night flyte / Can I see you / For you / Slip 'n' slide.
- MC................................. .40 26653
- LP................................. CBS 26653

CBS / Oct '85.

## YOU SEND ME.
**Tracks:** You send me / I wanna touch you baby / Can't you see me / Get on up, get on down / Every

time I see you / Rhythm / And don't you say no / It ain't your sign / It's your mind.
- LP................................. .2391 365

Spring / Oct '78.
CD................................. UMID 3
- LP................................. UMID 3
MC................................. UMIDC 3

Urban / Feb '88 / PolyGram.

# AZ One

## ALL OF MY HEART.
**Tracks:** All of my heart.
- 12"................................. PROFT 278

Profile (USA) / Mar '90.

# Azymuth

## AZIMUTH.
**Tracks:** Not Advised.
CD Set................................. 5230102

ECM / Jul '94 / New Note.

## AZYMUTH '85.
**Tracks:** Adios Iony / Dream - lost song / Who are you / Breathtaking / Potion 1 / February daze / Til bakeblikk / Potion 2.
CD................................. 8275202
- LP................................. ECM 1298

ECM / Dec '85 / New Note.

## BEST OF AZYMUTH, THE.
**Tracks:** Club Morrocco / Cascades of the seven waterfalls / Textile factory / Right on / Somewhere in Brazil / Outubro / 500 miles high / Dear Limmertz / Song of the jet / Areiras / All the carnaval / Maracana.
CD................................. .MCD 9160-2

Ace / Apr '94 / Pinnacle / Complete Record Co. Ltd.

## CARIOCA.
**Tracks:** Not Advised.
CD................................. .MCD 9169

Milestone / Oct '93 / Jazz Music / Pinnacle / Cadillac.

## CRAZY RHYTHM.
**Tracks:** Not Advised.
CD................................. .MCD 9156

Milestone / Oct '93 / Jazz Music / Pinnacle / Cadillac.

## DEAR LIMMERTZ.
**Tracks:** Dear Limmertz / Papa song.
- 12"................................. MRC 102
- 7".................................. MSP 102

Mile Stone / Nov '80.

## DEPART (Azymuth with Ralph Towner).
**Tracks:** Not Advised.
- LP................................. .ECM 1163

ECM / Nov '80.

## EARLY YEARS.
**Tracks:** Not Advised.
CD................................. 963 84

Crusader / '88.

## FLAME.
**Tracks:** Not Advised.
- LP................................. M 9128

Milestone / Sep '84.

## JAZZ CARNIVAL.
**Tracks:** Jazz carnival.
- 7".................................. MRC 101

Milestone / Jan '80.

## JAZZ CARNIVAL - BEST OF AZYMUTH.
**Tracks:** Jazz carnival / Dear Limmertz / Estreito de taruma / Cascade of the seven waterfalls / Missing doto / Maracana / Samba da barra / Textile factory / Turma do samba / Papaia / Partido alto / Pantanal il swamp.
CD................................. CDBGP 1007
- MC................................. BGPC 1007
- LP................................. BGP 1007

BGP / Mar '88 / Pinnacle.

## OUTUBRO.
**Tracks:** Papsong / 500 miles high / Pantanal / Dear Limmertz / Carta pro airto / Outubro / Maracana / Un amigo.
- LP................................. M 9097

Milestone / Nov '80.

## RAPID TRANSIT.
**Tracks:** Make mine guarana / Afternoon / Missing doto / Somewhere in Brazil / I'm just looking around / Montreux / Gate of time.
- LP................................. M 9118

Milestone / Mar '84.
CD................................. 815 441 2

Metronome / '88 / Jazz Music.

## SPECTRUM.
**Tracks:** Not Advised.
CD.......................... 98170
Carrere (France) / Apr '87.

## TELECOMMUNICATION.
**Tracks:** Not Advised.
CD.......................... 813 558 2
Metronome / '88 / Jazz Music.

## TUDO BEN.
**Tracks:** Not Advised.
CD.......................... CDENV 533
■ LP ........................ ENVLP 533
Enigma (EMI) / Jul '89 / EMI.

# B

## B & B

**XMASOUL (MEDLEY).**
Tracks: Xmasoul (medley).
- 12"................................WDRX 5
- 7"..................................WDR 5

World Dance / Dec '90.

## B B & Q Band

**(I'M A) DREAMER.**
Tracks: (I'm a) dreamer / (I'm a) dreamer (instrumental).
- 12"..............................COOLX 132
- 7"................................COOL 132

Cool Tempo / Aug '86.

**ALL NIGHT LONG.**
Tracks: All night long / Imagination / Things we do in love / Desire / Hanging out / Hard to get around / It's over / Children of the night.
- LP................................EST 12212

Capitol / Oct '82.

**GENIE.**
Tracks: Genie / Main attraction / Won't you be with me tonight / Don't force it / Minutes away / On the shelf / Dreamer / Ricochet.
- LP................................CHR 1509
- MC..............................ZCHR 1509

Cool Tempo / Jul '85.

**GENIE.**
Tracks: Genie.
- 12"..............................COOLX 110
- 7"................................COOL 110

Cool Tempo / Jun '85.

**I'LL CUT YOU LOOSE.**
Tracks: I'll cut you loose / Starlette.
- 12"..............................12CL 220

Capitol / Sep '81.

**IMAGINATION.**
Tracks: Imagination / Hard to get around.
- 7"..................................CL 257

Capitol / Jul '82.

**MINUTES AWAY (Brooklyn Bronx & Queens).**
Tracks: Minutes away.
- 12"..............................COOLX 112
- 7"................................COOL 112

Cool Tempo / Aug '85.

**ON THE BEAT.**
Tracks: On the beat / Don't say goodbye / Love is what we should do.
- 12"..............................12CL 202
- 7"..................................CL 202

Capitol / Jul '81.

**RICOCHET.**
Tracks: Genie / Dreamer/ Genie.
- 7"................................COOL 154
- 12"..............................COOLX 154

Cool Tempo / Sep '87.

## B.T. Express

**1980.**
Tracks: Takin' off / Heart of fire / Does it feel good / Give up the funk / Closer / Have some fun / Better late than never / Funk theory.
- LP..............................CABLP 5002

Calibre / Sep '80.

**DEPEND ON YOURSELF.**
Tracks: Depend on yourself / Energy level.
- 7"..................................INT 527

EMI International / Jan '77.

**DOES IT FEEL GOOD.**
Tracks: Does it feel good / Give up the funk.
- 7"..................................CAB 503

Calibre / Jul '80.

**EXPRESS.**
Tracks: Express / Express (Mixes).
- 7"..................................7N 25674

Pye International / Mar '75.
- 12"..............................PWLT 285

---

**FUNCTION AT THE JUNCTION.**
Tracks: Funky music / Expose yourself / Scratch my itch / Eyes / We got it together / Sunshine / Door to my mind / Star gazer / How big can you dream.
- LP..................................INS 3009

EMI / Jul '77.

**FUNKY MUSIC (DON'T LAUGH AT MY FUNK).**
Tracks: Funky music (don't laugh at my funk) / We got it together.
- 7"..................................INT 537

EMI International / Sep '77.

**MIDNIGHT BEAT.**
Tracks: Midnight beat.
- 12"..............................EXCL 508
- 7"................................EXC 508

Excaliber / Mar '81.

**OLD GOLD FUTURE GOLD.**
Tracks: Stretch / Peace pipe (remix) / Shout it out (remix) / Let me be the one / Express (remix) / Do it (till you're satisfied) / I wanna hold you / Midnight beat.
- LP..............................EXCLP 5001

Excaliber / Jan '81.

**SHOUT.**
Tracks: Shout it out / What you do in the dark / Put it in / I want you with me / Shake it off / You got something / Look at the people / It's in your blood / Ride on B.T.
- LP..................................INS 3016

EMI / May '78.

**SHOUT IT OUT.**
Tracks: Shout it out / Ride on B.T.
- 7"..................................INT 548

EMI International / Jan '78.

**THIS MUST BE THE NIGHT.**
Tracks: This must be the night / It's got to be you.
- 12"..............................SOHOT 3
- 7"................................SOHO 3

Record Shack / Feb '83.

## B.V.S.M.P.

**ANY TIME.**
Tracks: Any time (inst) / Any time.
- 12"..............................DEBTX 3056
- 7"................................DEBT 3056
- CD Single........................BC 50-2160

Debut (1) / Sep '88.

**BEST BELONG TOGETHER, THE.**
Tracks: Anytime / Can we go on / Rock bottom / Grad dat botre / I need you / Gentle memory.
- CD................................CDDB 503
- LP................................DBLP 503
- MC..............................ZCDB 503

Debut (1) / Sep '88 / Pinnacle.

**HOLD ME.**
Tracks: Hold me.
- 12"..............................12PUM 003
- 7"................................PUM 003
- CD Single......................CDPUM 003
- MC Single......................TCPUM 003

Pump Records / Jul '91.

**I NEED YOU.**
Tracks: I need you / I need you (radio instrumental) / I need you (extended vocal version) (Track on 12" version.) / I need you (radio mix) (Track on 12" version.).
- 12"..............................DEBTX 3044
- 7"................................DEBT 3044

Debut (1) / Jul '88.

**I NEED YOU.**
Tracks: I need you / Be gentle.
- VHS................................VC 4063

Wienerworld Video / Oct '88 / VCI Distribution / THE.

---

## B.Y.O.B.

**B.Y.O.B.**
Tracks: Too good to let go / Ramifications of shaking one's ass / Change it / Distances / Go jazz go / Outerspacegethithang / Ramblifications of getting and saying high / Rackett / Day off in the life / Where ya going to.
- CD................................RCD 10310
- MC..............................RAC 10310

Rykodisc / Oct '94 / Vital Distribution / Topic Records / Direct Distribution / C.M. Distribution / A.D.A. Distribution.

## Baby Ray

**ELVIRA.**
Tracks: Elvira / Just because.
- 7"................................LIB 66232

Liberty / May '67.

## Babyface

Best known as half of LA & Babyface, Kenny Edmonds could afford to leave four years between 1989 solo debut *Tender Lover* and follow-up *For The Cool In You*. Antonio 'LA' Reid and his partner first tasted success with Ohio quintet The Deele, on whose 1988 hit *Two Occasions* Babyface sang lead, then split for production career. Originally dismissed as cut-price Jam & Lewis, they established own successful and influential 'Sunset sound' - notably with Bobby Brown, Karyn White and Whitney Houston - and launched own La Face label in '91. By '94, Babyface could boast songwriting credits on U.S. hits by, among many others, Boyz II Men, Toni Braxton, Tevin Campbell, El De-Barge and Gladys Knight. He also won a Grammy for his work on *The Bodyguard* soundtrack.

**FOR THE COOL IN YOU.**
Tracks: For the cool in you / Lady, lady / Never keeping secrets / Rock bottom / And our feelings / Saturday / When can I see you / Illusions / Bit old fashioned / You are so beautiful / I'll always love you / Well alright.
- CD................................473949 2
- LP................................473949 1
- MC..............................473949 4

Epic / Jan '94 / Sony.

**IT'S NO CRIME.**
Tracks: It's no crime / It's no crime (instrumental).
- 12"..............................MCAT 1366
- 7"................................MCA 1366
- CD Single......................DMCAT 1366

MCA / Aug '89.

**LOVERS.**
Tracks: Not Advised.
- LP................................ST 72552

Solar / Dec '88.

**MY KINDA GIRL.**
Tracks: My kinda girl / My kinda girl (instrumental) / My kinda girl (scratch mix) (Not available on 7" format.) / My kinda girl (album version) (Available on 12" format.) / My kinda girl (Raquet Gass dub) (Not available on 7" format.).
- 12"..............................6564946
- 7"................................6564947
- CD Single......................6564942
- MC Single......................6564944

Epic / Feb '91.

**ROCK BOTTOM.**
Tracks: Rock bottom (mixes).
- 12"..............................660183 6
- CD Single......................660183 2
- MC Single......................660183 4

Epic / Jun '94 / Sony.

**TENDER LOVER.**
Tracks: It's no crime / Tender lover / Let's be romantic / Can't stop my heart / My kinda girl / Where will you go (prelude) / Whip appeal / Soon as I get home / Given a chance / Sunshine / Where will you go.
- LP..............................MCG 6064
- CD..............................DMCG 6064

---

■ DELETED

19

■ MC. . . . . . . . . . . . . . . . . . MCGC 6064
MCA / Aug '89.
CD. . . . . . . . . . . . . . . . . . . . . 4657629
■ LP . . . . . . . . . . . . . . . . . . . . 4657621
MC. . . . . . . . . . . . . . . . . . . . . 4657628
Epic / Mar '91 / Sony.

## TENDER LOVER.
Tracks: Tender lover.
■ 12" . . . . . . . . . . . . . . . . . MCAT 1389
■ 7" . . . . . . . . . . . . . . . . . . MCA 1389
■ CD Single . . . . . . . . . . . . DMCAT 1389
MCA / Jan '90.

## WHEN CAN I SEE YOU.
Tracks: When can I see you (mixes).
12" . . . . . . . . . . . . . . . . . . . .660659 6
CD Single. . . . . . . . . . . . . . . .660659 2
MC Single . . . . . . . . . . . . . . .660659 4
Epic / Sep '94 / Sony.

# Backman, Nila

## EVEN IF YOU SAY.
Tracks: Even if you say (remix) / I believe in music.
12" . . . . . . . . . . . . . . . . . . . .LBAY 19
Loading Bay / Jan '93 / Loading Bay Records.

# Bad Boys

## LET'S MOVE, LET'S GROOVE.
Tracks: Let's move, let's groove.
■ 12". . . . . . . . . . . . . . . . . . WAR 053
Idlers (USA) / Sep '89.

# Badarou, Wally

## BACK TO SCALES TONIGHT.
Tracks: Not Advised.
■ LP . . . . . . . . . . . . . . . . . .1091 065
Polydor / May '82.

## CHIEF INSPECTOR.
Tracks: Chief inspector.
■ 12" . . . . . . . . . . . . . . . 12 BRWX 37
■ 7" . . . . . . . . . . . . . . . . . BRW 37
■ 12" . . . . . . . . . . . . . . . 12 BRW 37
4th & Broadway / Oct '85.
■ 12" . . . . . . . . . . . . . . . .12BRW 213
■ 7" . . . . . . . . . . . . . . . . . BRW 213
■ CD Single . . . . . . . . . . . . . BRCD 213
■ MC Single . . . . . . . . . . . . . BRCA 213
4th & Broadway / Mar '91.

## ECHOES.
Tracks: Keys / Hi life / Mambo / Voices / Canyons / Endless race / Chief inspector / Waltz / Jungle / Rain.
CD. . . . . . . . . . . . . . . . . . . . CID 104
■ MC. . . . . . . . . . . . . . . . . .ICT 9822
Island / May '85 / PolyGram.
■ LP . . . . . . . . . . . . . . . . . ILPS 9822
Island / Mar '88.

## ECHOES.
Tracks: Countryman theme / Chief inspector.
■ 7" . . . . . . . . . . . . . . . . . WIP 6759
Island / Apr '82.

## HI-LIFE.
Tracks: Hi-life (radio edit.) / Hi-life.
■ 7" . . . . . . . . . . . . . . . . . . BRW 53
4th & Broadway / Oct '86.

## NOVELA DAS NOVE.
Tracks: Novela das nove / Chief inspector (precinct 13) / Endless race (extra track on 12" only).
■ 7" . . . . . . . . . . . . . . . . . BRW 44
■ 12" . . . . . . . . . . . . . . . 12 BRW 44
4th & Broadway / Mar '86.

## WORDS OF A MOUNTAIN.
Tracks: Not Advised.
■ LP . . . . . . . . . . . . . . . . . ILPS 9897
■ MC. . . . . . . . . . . . . . . . . .ICT 9897
■ CD . . . . . . . . . . . . . . . . . CID 9897
Island / Apr '89.

# Bailey, Philip

## CHILDREN OF THE GHETTO (Reissue).
Tracks: Children of the ghetto / Show you the way to love / Photogenic memory.
■ 12" . . . . . . . . . . . . . . . . . TA 4857
■ 7" . . . . . . . . . . . . . . . . . .A 4857
CBS / Nov '84.
■ 12" . . . . . . . . . . . . . . . . . TA 6433
■ 7" . . . . . . . . . . . . . . . . . .A 6433
CBS / Jul '85.

## CHINESE WALLS.
Tracks: Photogenic memory / I go crazy / Walking on the Chinese wall / For every heart that's been broken / Go / Easy lover / Show you the way to love / Time is a woman / Woman / Children of the ghetto.
■ LP . . . . . . . . . . . . . . . . . CBS 26161
CBS / Mar '85.
■ LP . . . . . . . . . . . . . . . . . . 4500891
■ MC. . . . . . . . . . . . . . . . . . 4500894
CBS / Nov '86.
■ CD . . . . . . . . . . . . . . . . CD 26161
CBS / Apr '87.
CD. . . . . . . . . . . . . . . . . . .983282 2
Pickwick/Sony Collector's Choice / Mar '94 / Pickwick / Pinnacle.

## CONTINUATION.
Tracks: I know / It's our time / Desire / I'm waiting for your love / Vaya (go with love) / Good guys are supposed to get the girl / Your boyfriend's back / Trapped.
MC. . . . . . . . . . . . . . . . . . .40 25550
■ LP . . . . . . . . . . . . . . . . . CBS 25550
CBS / Sep '83 / Sony.
■ LP . . . . . . . . . . . . . . . . . CBS 32680
■ MC. . . . . . . . . . . . . . . . . .40 32680
CBS / Feb '86.

## EASY LOVER (Bailey, Philip & Phil Collins).
Tracks: Easy lover / Woman.
■ 7" . . . . . . . . . . . . . . . . . .A 4195
■ 12" . . . . . . . . . . . . . . . . . TA 4195
CBS / Mar '85.

## ECHO MY HEART.
Tracks: Echo my heart / Take this with you / Walking on the Chinese wall (extra track on 12" only) / Children of the ghetto (extra track on 12" only).
■ 12" . . . . . . . . . . . . . . . . . TA 7293
■ 7" . . . . . . . . . . . . . . . . . .A 7293
CBS / Jul '86.

## FAMILY AFFAIR.
Tracks: Not Advised.
■ CD . . . . . . . . . . . . . . . MYRCD 6877
■ LP . . . . . . . . . . . . . . . . MYRR 6877
■ MC. . . . . . . . . . . . . . . . MYRC 6877
Myrrh / Feb '90.

## I KNOW.
Tracks: I know / Good guys are supposed to get the girl.
■ 12" . . . . . . . . . . . . . . . . . TA 3686
■ 7" . . . . . . . . . . . . . . . . . .A 3686
CBS / Aug '83.

## I'M WAITING FOR YOUR LOVE.
Tracks: I'm waiting for your love / Caya.
■ 7" . . . . . . . . . . . . . . . . . .A 3862
CBS / Oct '83.

## INSIDE OUT.
Tracks: Welcome to the club / State of the heart / Long distance love / Echo my heart / Don't leave me baby / Special effect / Because of you / Back it up / Take this with you / Day will come.
■ LP . . . . . . . . . . . . . . . . . CBS 26903
■ MC. . . . . . . . . . . . . . . . . .40 26903
CBS / May '86.
■ CD . . . . . . . . . . . . . . . . CD 26903
CBS / May '87.

## STATE OF THE HEART.
Tracks: State of the heart / Take this with you.
■ 12" . . . . . . . . . . . . . . . . . TA 7086
■ 7" . . . . . . . . . . . . . . . . . .A 7086
CBS / May '86.

## TRIUMPH.
Tracks: All soldiers / Thank you / Love of God / Marvellous / Same way (you've always been) / Other side / Bring it to Jesus / Triumph / Came before his presence.
■ CD . . . . . . . . . . . . . . . MYRCD 1226
■ LP . . . . . . . . . . . . . . . . MYR R 1226
■ MC. . . . . . . . . . . . . . . . MYR C 1226
Myrrh / Nov '86.

## TWINS (Bailey, Philip & Little Richard).
Tracks: Twins / Twins (instrumental) / Twins (extended mix) (Only on 12" and CD single.) / Twins (acapella) (Only on 12" and CD single.) / Twins (dub mix) (Only on 12" and CD single.)
■ 12" . . . . . . . . . . . . . . . . . 6545196
■ 7" . . . . . . . . . . . . . . . . . 6545197
■ CD Single . . . . . . . . . . . . . 6545192
Epic / Apr '89.

## WALKING ON THE CHINESE WALL.
Tracks: Walking on the Chinese wall / Woman I know / Trapped.
■ 12" . . . . . . . . . . . . . . . . . TA 6202

■ 7" . . . . . . . . . . . . . . . . . .A 6202
CBS / May '85.

## WONDERS OF HIS LOVE, THE.
Tracks: I will no wise cast you out / I want to know you / God is love / Sing a new song / Safe in God's love / I am gold / He don't lie / Make us one / Wonders of his love.
■ LP . . . . . . . . . . . . . . . . MYR 1181
■ MC. . . . . . . . . . . . . . . . .MC 1181
Myrrh / Feb '85.
■ CD . . . . . . . . . . . . . . . MYRCD 1181
Myrrh / Jul '88.

# Baker, Anita

Detroit vocalist Baker emerged from local band Chapter 8 at the end of the '70s to become one of the most copied solo artists of the next decade-and-a-half. Spotted by LA record executive Otis Smith performing at the Total Experience Club, Anita signed to Smith's Beverly Glen indie in '82, achieving R&B hits with her singles No More Tears and Angel and an enviable reputation for her debut album, Songstress, produced by Patrick Moten. Like labelmates Bobby Womack and Johnnie Taylor, however, Baker fell out permanently with Smith, two years later signing to Elektra and restoring her career with Rapture, one of the most successful albums of the '80s. Perfecting her slurred, jazzy-soul stylings through Giving You The Best That I've Got and the even more impressive Compositions, Baker then took a three year break from the business to raise a family. She returned to both stage and chart-tops in '94, the single Body And Soul and the album Rhythm Of Love both topping and American R&B charts inside a month of release.

## BODY & SOUL.
Tracks: Body & soul / Baby / Sweet love (On CDs only).
7" . . . . . . . . . . . . . . . . . . .EKR 190
CD Single . . . . . . . . . . . . . EKR 190CD
MC Single . . . . . . . . . . . . . .EKR 190C
Elektra / Sep '94 / WEA.

## CAUGHT UP IN A RAPTURE.
Tracks: Mystery / Caught up in the rapture.
■ 12" . . . . . . . . . . . . . . . . EKR 49 T
■ 7" . . . . . . . . . . . . . . . . . EKR 49
Elektra / Jan '87.

## COMPOSITIONS.
Tracks: Talk to me / Whatever it takes / Lonely / More than you know / Fairy tales / Perfect love affair / Soul inspiration / No one to blame / Love you to the letter.
CD. . . . . . . . . . . . . . . . . . .EKT 72CD
■ LP . . . . . . . . . . . . . . . . . . EKT 72
MC. . . . . . . . . . . . . . . . . . .EKT 72C
Elektra / Jul '90 / WEA.

## GIVING YOU THE BEST THAT I GOT.
Tracks: Giving you the best that I got / Good enough / Sweet love (live) (Only on 12") / Watch your step (live) (Only on CD single.).
■ 12" . . . . . . . . . . . . . . . . .EKR 79T
■ 7" . . . . . . . . . . . . . . . . . EKR 79
■ CD Single . . . . . . . . . . . . .EKR 79CD
Elektra / Sep '88.

## GIVING YOU THE BEST THAT I GOT.
Tracks: Priceless / Lead me into love / Giving you the best that I got / Good love / Rules / Good enough / Just because I love you / You belong to me.
CD. . . . . . . . . . . . . . . . . . . 9608272
■ LP . . . . . . . . . . . . . . . . . EKT 49
MC. . . . . . . . . . . . . . . . . . .EKT 49C
Elektra / Oct '88 / WEA.

## JUST BECAUSE.
Tracks: Just because / Moondance / Sweet love (Only on 12" single.).
■ 12" . . . . . . . . . . . . . . . . EKR 87 T
■ 7" . . . . . . . . . . . . . . . . . EKR 87
■ CD Single . . . . . . . . . . . . .EKR 87CD
Elektra / Jan '89.

## ONE NIGHT OF RAPTURE.
Tracks: Mystery / Caught up in the rapture / Same ole love / You bring me joy / You've changed / Watch your step / Sweet love / Been so long / No one in the world.
VHS . . . . . . . . . . . . . . . . . .940105-3
WEA Music Video / Jan '89 / WEA / Gold & Sons.

## RAPTURE.
Tracks: Sweet love / You bring me joy / Caught up in the rapture / Been so long / Mystery / No one in the world / Same ole love / Watch your step.

■ DELETED

MC. . . . . . . . . . . . . . . . . . . . . . EKT 37 C
■ LP . . . . . . . . . . . . . . . . . . . . . . EKT 37
Elektra / Apr '86 / WEA.
CD. . . . . . . . . . . . . . . . . . . . . . . 9604442
Elektra / Aug '86 / WEA.
CD . . . . . . . . . . . . . . . . . . . . 7559604445
Elektra / Nov '92 / WEA.

**RHYTHM OF LOVE.**
Tracks: Not Advised.
CD . . . . . . . . . . . . . . . . . . . .755961555-2
LP . . . . . . . . . . . . . . . . . . . .755961555-1
MC. . . . . . . . . . . . . . . . . . . .755961555-4
Elektra / Sep '94 / WEA.

**SAME OLE LOVE.**
Tracks: Same ole love / Been so long.
■ 12" . . . . . . . . . . . . . . . . . . . EKR 57 T
■ 7" . . . . . . . . . . . . . . . . . . . . . EKR 57
Elektra / May '87.

**SONGSTRESS.**
Tracks: Angel / You're the best thing yet / Feel the need / Squeeze me / No more tears / Sometimes / Will you be mine / Do you believe me.
CD. . . . . . . . . . . . . . . . . . . . 7559611162
MC. . . . . . . . . . . . . . . . . . . . . EKT 100C
■ LP . . . . . . . . . . . . . . . . . . . . EKT 100
Elektra / Nov '91 / WEA.

**STAR PORTRAITS: ANITA BAKER.**
Tracks: Not Advised.
VHS . . . . . . . . . . . . . . . . . . . GEMV 5007
Gemini Vision / Sep '94 / Sony / THE.

**SWEET LOVE.**
Tracks: Sweet love / No one in the world / Watch your step (Extra track on 12" only) / Same ole love (live) (Extra track on Double-pack only) / You bring me joy (live) (Extra track on Double-pack only) / Watch your step (inst) (Extra track on Double-pack only).
■ 12". . . . . . . . . . . . . . . . . . . . EKR 44 T
■ 7" . . . . . . . . . . . . . . . . . . . . . EKR 44
■ 7" Set . . . . . . . . . . . . . . . . . EKR 44 TX
Elektra / Oct '86.

**SWEET LOVE.**
Tracks: Sweet love / Rapture / Same old love / No one in the world.
CD Video . . . . . . . . . . . . . . . . . 964 001 2
WEA Music Video / Jan '89 / WEA / Gold & Sons.

**TALK TO ME.**
Tracks: Talk to me.
■ 12". . . . . . . . . . . . . . . . . . . . EKR 111 T
■ 7" . . . . . . . . . . . . . . . . . . . .EKR 111
■ CD Single . . . . . . . . . . . . . . . EKR 111CD
Elektra / Jun '90.

## Baker, Arthur

**GIVE IN TO THE RHYTHM.**
Tracks: Give in to the rhythm / Let there be love / IOU / Leave the guns at home / (Rock me in the) house of love / C'mon c'mon / Kiss the ground (you walk on) / Meaning of life / 2 can play this game / Inspiration / If love had a heart / Surrender (trance like us) / Feels like the first time / Season of love.
CD. . . . . . . . . . . . . . . . . . . . . . 262 097
RCA / Oct '91 / BMG.
■ LP . . . . . . . . . . . . . . . . . . . . PL 90613
■ MC. . . . . . . . . . . . . . . . . . . . PD 90613
RCA / Feb '92.

**IT'S YOUR TIME.**
Tracks: It's your time.
■ MC Single . . . . . . . . . . . . . . . USATC 654
■ 7" . . . . . . . . . . . . . . . . . . . . USA 654
■ 12" . . . . . . . . . . . . . . . . . . . USAT 654
■ CD Single . . . . . . . . . . . . . . . USACD 654
Breakout / May '89.

**LEAVE THE GUNS AT HOME (Baker, Arthur/Backbeat Disciples featuring Al Green).**
Tracks: Leave the guns at home.
■ 12" . . . . . . . . . . . . . . . . . . . . PT 49148
RCA / Feb '92.

**LET THERE BE LOVE.**
Tracks: Let there be love.
■ 12" . . . . . . . . . . . . . . . . . . . .614421
■ 7" . . . . . . . . . . . . . . . . . . . . .114421
Arista / Aug '91.

**MERGE (Baker, Arthur & The Backbeat Disciples).**
Tracks: Talk it over / Willin' to be chillin' / Last thing on my mind / Mythical girl / I believe in love / Message is love / Walk away / It's your time / Count to ten / 2 x 1 / All I ever wanted / Silly games.

CD. . . . . . . . . . . . . . . . . . . . . CDA 5262
■ LP . . . . . . . . . . . . . . . . . . . . AMA 5262
■ MC. . . . . . . . . . . . . . . . . . . . AMC 5262
A&M / Aug '89.

**MESSAGE IS LOVE, THE.**
Tracks: Message is love / Message is love, The (version).
■ 12" . . . . . . . . . . . . . . . . . . . USAT 668
■ 7" . . . . . . . . . . . . . . . . . . . . USA 668
■ CD Single . . . . . . . . . . . . . . . USACD 668
Breakout / Sep '89.

**TALK IT OVER.**
Tracks: Talk it over / Talk it over (midnight mix).
■ 7" . . . . . . . . . . . . . . . . . . . . USA 655
■ 12" . . . . . . . . . . . . . . . . . . . USAT 655
■ CD Single . . . . . . . . . . . . . . . USACD 655
A&M / Jul '89.

**WE GOT TO COME TOGETHER.**
Tracks: We got to come together.
■ 12" . . . . . . . . . . . . . . . . . . . . CR 7877
Minimal 4 / Jul '88.

## Baker, LaVern

Spotted by bandleader Fletcher Henderson she was signed to OKeh Records before recording on the King and Columbia labels. A move to Atlantic led to a decade of chart hits including gold discs for *Tweedle Dee* in 1955 and *Jim Dandy* two years later. Reaching her chart peak with 1958's U.S. no.6 *I Cried A Tear* Baker was one of the first R&B artists to attract a large white audience. Her last chart entry came in 1966 dueting with Jackie Wilson on *Think Twice* but as the Motown sound became dominant her distinctly R&B style became less popular. Having spent 22 years living in the Philippines she attempted to revive her career in the early nineties but the response was disappointing.

**HITS AND RARITIES.**
Tracks: Jim Dandy / Tweedle dee / So high so low / Soul on fire / Romance in the dark / Tomorrow night / Humpty dumpty heart / Manana / Harbour lights / Fool that I am / I can't love you enough / I'm living my life for you / I can't hold out any longer / I'll do the same for you / Game of love / Help each other romance.
■ LP . . . . . . . . . . . . . . . . . . . . OFF 6042
Official.

**I'M GONNA GET YOU.**
Tracks: Love is ending / Born to lose / I need you so / Play it fair / Baby / One monkey don't stop no show / Batman to the rescue / Think twice / Call me darling / Nothing like being in love / I'm gonna get you / Pledging my love to you / Let me belong to you / I'm the one to do it / Baby you do it / Please dont hurt me.
■ LP . . . . . . . . . . . . . . . . . . . .C5-510
MC. . . . . . . . . . . . . . . . . . . . C5K-510
C5 / Nov '87 / Pinnacle.

**LAVERNE BAKER SINGS BESSIE SMITH/THAT'S JAZZ.**
Tracks: Gimme a pigfoot and a bottle of beer / Baby doll / On revival day / Money blues / I ain't gonna play no second fiddle / Back water blues / Empty bed blues / There'll be a hot time in the old town tonight / Nobody knows you (when you're down and out) / After you've gone / Young woman's blues / Preachin' the blues.
■ LP . . . . . . . . . . . . . . . . . . . . K 50241
Atlantic / '88.

**REAL GONE GAL.**
Tracks: How can you leave a man like this / Jim Dandy / My happiness for ever / Fee fi fo fum / Jim Dandy got married / Substitute / Whipper snapper / Voodoo voodoo / I cried a tear / He's a real gone guy / I waited too long / Tiny Tim / Shake a hand / Bumble bee / Hey Memphis / c.c. rider.
■ LP . . . . . . . . . . . . . . . . . . . . CRB 1072
■ MC. . . . . . . . . . . . . . . . . . . . TCCRB 1072
Charly R&B / Apr '84.

**SEE SEE RIDER.**
Tracks: You better stop / Real gone guy / Story of my love / You said / See see rider / I'm leavin' you / Don't let the stars get in your eyes / Trying / Half of your love / Little bird told me so / Endless love / All the time.
■ LP . . . . . . . . . . . . . . . . . . . . 588 133
Atlantic / Feb '69.

**SOUL ON FIRE.**
Tracks: Not Advised.
CD . . . . . . . . . . . . . . . . . . . .756782311-2
WEA / Mar '93 / WEA.

**TWEEDLE DEE.**
Tracks: Tweedle dee / Jim Dandy / Bumble bee.
■ EP . . . . . . . . . . . . . . . . . . . . REV 6007
Revival / Jul '82.

## Baker, Michael

**DON'T YOU WANT MY LOVIN.**
Tracks: Don't you want my lovin'.
■ 12". . . . . . . . . . . . . . . . . . . . PASH 23(12)
Passion (1) / Mar '84.

## Baker, Sam

**BRINGING YOU SOME SOUL.**
Tracks: Coming to bring you some soul / Hold back girl / I love you / I can't breakaway / Let me come on home / Sometimes you have to cry / What did sister do / Don't feel rained on / Sugarman / I believe in you / I'm number one / It's all over / Strange sensation / Something tells me / You can't see the blood / Sunny.
■ LP . . . . . . . . . . . . . . . . . . . . CRB 1137
Charly R&B / Oct '86.

**I'M NUMBER ONE.**
Tracks: I'm number one / I believe in you.
■ 7" . . . . . . . . . . . . . . . . . . . .MON 1009
Monument / Oct '67.

## Baldwin, Bob

**DREAM, THE.**
Tracks: Not Advised.
CD. . . . . . . . . . . . . . . . . . . . . MJCD 1501
■ LP . . . . . . . . . . . . . . . . . . . . MJ 1501
MC. . . . . . . . . . . . . . . . . . . . MJC 1501
Malaco / '89 / C.M. Distribution / Charly / Pinnacle.

**LONG WAY TO GO.**
Tracks: Not Advised.
CD. . . . . . . . . . . . . . . . . . . . . MALCD 1501
Malaco / Mar '93 / C.M. Distribution / Charly / Pinnacle.

## Ballard, Florence

**IT DOESN'T MATTER HOW I SAY IT.**
Tracks: It doesn't matter how I say it / Goin' out of my head.
■ 7" . . . . . . . . . . . . . . . . . . . . SS 2113
Stateside / '67.

## Ballard, Hank

**DANCE ALONG (Ballard, Hank & The Midnighters).**
Tracks: Not Advised.
CD. . . . . . . . . . . . . . . . . . . . .KCD 759
King / Mar '90 / New Note / Koch International.

**HANK BALLARD & THE MIDNIGHTERS (Ballard, Hank & The Midnighters).**
Tracks: Not Advised.
■ LP . . . . . . . . . . . . . . . . . . . . BID 8003
Bellaphon / Jul '88.

**LET 'EM ROLL.**
Tracks: Work with me Annie / It's love baby / Tore up over you / Annie had a baby / In the doorway crying / Twist / Rock and roll wedding / Kansas city / Teardrops on your letter / Sexy ways / Let 'em roll / Crazy lovin' / Deep blue sea / Hoochie coochie coo / Let's go / Sugaree / Look at little sister / Switch-a-roo / I'm gonna miss you / Daddy Rolling Stone.
■ CD . . . . . . . . . . . . . . . . . . . . CDCHARLY 240
Charly / Oct '90.

**LET'S GO, LET'S GO, LET'S GO (Ballard, Hank & The Midnighters).**
Tracks: Twist, The (ext.version) / Let's go, let's go, let's go.
■ 12". . . . . . . . . . . . . . . . . . . . CYZ 113
Charly / Jul '85.

**LIVE AT THE PALAIS (Ballard, Hank & The Midnighters).**
Tracks: Lucille (Instrumental) / Hoochie coochie coo / Work with Annie / Tore up over you / Teardrops on your letter / Look at little sister / Annie had a baby / My girl / Girl's alright with me / You're all I need to get by / I'll try something new / Stand by me / Hold on I'm coming / Soul man / Sky is crying / Sugaree / It's love baby / Sexy ways / Deep blue sea / Baby workout / Your love keeps lifting me higher and higher / Christmas time for everyone but me / Finger poppin' time / Let's go, let's go, let's go / Twist (The).
CD. . . . . . . . . . . . . . . . . . . . . CDCHARLY 88
■ Double LP. . . . . . . . . . . . . . . . CDX 16

■ MC. . . . . . . . . . . . . . . . . . . . .TCCDX 16
Charly / Apr '87 / Charly.

**MR RHYTHM & BLUES (Ballard, Hank & The Midnighters).**
**Tracks:** Not Advised.
CD. . . . . . . . . . . . . . . . . . . .KCD 000700
King / Dec '92 / New Note / Koch International.

**NAKED IN THE RAIN (Ballard, Hank & The Midnighters).**
**Tracks:** Not Advised.
CD. . . . . . . . . . . . . . . . . . . . .AFT 4137CD
MC. . . . . . . . . . . . . . . . . . . . .AFT 4137MC
Ichiban / Feb '94 / A.D.A. Distribution / Pinnacle / ACD Trading Ltd. / Koch International / Direct Distribution.

**ONE AND ONLY, THE.**
**Tracks:** Sugaree / Rain down tears / Cute little ways / House without windows / Everybody does wrong some time / So good to be home / Kansas City / I'll keep you happy / I'm crying mercy, mercy / She's got a whole lot of soul / I'll pray for you / Move, move, move.
■ LP. . . . . . . . . . . . . . . . . . . . .SING 674
Sing / '88.
CD. . . . . . . . . . . . . . . . . . . . . .KCD 674
King / May '93 / New Note / Koch International.

**SING 24 SONGS (Ballard, Hank & The Midnighters).**
**Tracks:** Not Advised.
CD. . . . . . . . . . . . . . . . . . . . . .KCD 950
King / Mar '90 / New Note / Koch International.
CD. . . . . . . . . . . . . . . . . . . . . .KCD 0950
King / Mar '93 / New Note / Koch International.

**SINGIN' AND SWINGIN' (Ballard, Hank & The Midnighters).**
**Tracks:** Teardrops on your letter / Ring-a-ling-a-ling / Let me hold your hand / Don't say your last goodbye / Whatsoever you do / Stingy little thing / Ashamed of myself / Twist / That house on the hill / Sweet mama do right / Ooh ooh baby / Tell them / Rock 'n' roll wedding / I'll be home someday.
■ LP. . . . . . . . . . . . . . . . . . . . .SING 618
Sing / '88.
■ CD. . . . . . . . . . . . . . . . . . . . .KCD 618
King / Mar '90.
CD. . . . . . . . . . . . . . . . . . .KCD 000618
King / Dec '92 / New Note / Koch International.

**SPOTLIGHT ON BALLARD.**
**Tracks:** Not Advised.
CD. . . . . . . . . . . . . . . . . . . . . .KCD 740
King / Mar '90 / New Note / Koch International.

**THEIR GREATEST JUKE BOX HITS (Ballard, Hank & The Midnighters).**
**Tracks:** Work with me Annie / Moonrise / Sexy ways / Get it / Switchie witchie titchie / It's love baby / Annie had a baby / She's the one / Annie's Aunt Fannie / Crazy loving / Henry's got flat feet / Tore up over you.
■ LP. . . . . . . . . . . . . . . . . . . . .SING 541
Sing / Jul '88.
CD. . . . . . . . . . . . . . . . . . . . . .KCD 541
King / Mar '90 / New Note / Koch International.

**TWENTY ORIGINAL HITS:HANK BALLARD (Ballard, Hank & The Midnighters).**
**Tracks:** Not Advised.
■ LP. . . . . . . . . . . . . . . . . . . . .K 5003
King (USA) / Mar '88.

**WHAT YOU GET WHEN THE GOING GETS GOOD (Ballard, Hank & The Midnighters).**
**Tracks:** Sexy ways / Don't change your pretty ways / Rock 'n' roll wedding / Open up the back door / Rock, granny, roll / Tore up over you / Is your love for real / Twist / Teardrops on your letter / Kansas City / Sugaree / Finger poppin' time / Let's go, let's go, let's go / What is this I see / I'm gonna miss you / Work with me Annie.
■ LP. . . . . . . . . . . . . . . . . . . . .CRB 1090
MC. . . . . . . . . . . . . . . . . . . .TCCRB 1090
Charly R&B / Jul '85 / Charly.
■ CD. . . . . . . . . . . . . . . . . .CDCHARLY 29
Charly / Oct '86.

## Ballin, Chris

**DO IT RIGHT.**
**Tracks:** Do it right.
■ 12". . . . . . . . . . . . . . . . . . . . .12EMH 6
Intimate / Dec '93.

**STAY AWAY FROM YOU.**
**Tracks:** Stay away from you / Starlite / Give me all your love.

---

■ 12". . . . . . . . . . . . . . . . . . . . .EXPAND 33
Expansion / Jul '93.

## Banbarra

**SHACK UP.**
**Tracks:** Shack up.
■ 12". . . . . . . . . . . . . . . . . . . .12STATES 1
■ 7". . . . . . . . . . . . . . . . . . . . .STATES 1
Stateside / Jul '85.

## Band AKA

**BAND AKA.**
**Tracks:** Funkdown / Grace / When you believe in love / Steppin' out / Homeward bound / New beginning / Funny kind of love.
■ LP. . . . . . . . . . . . . . . . . . . . .EPC 85887
Epic / Jul '82.

**GRACE.**
**Tracks:** Grace / Grace (part 2).
■ 12". . . . . . . . . . . . . . . . . . .EPCA 132376
■ 7". . . . . . . . . . . . . . . . . . . .EPCA 2376
Epic / May '82.

**IF YOU WANT TO HEAR.**
**Tracks:** If you want to hear / Men of the music.
■ 12". . . . . . . . . . . . . . . . . . . .TA 3370
■ 7". . . . . . . . . . . . . . . . . . . . .A 3370
Epic / Apr '83.

**JOY.**
**Tracks:** Joy.
■ 12". . . . . . . . . . . . . . . . . . .EPCA 133145
■ 7". . . . . . . . . . . . . . . . . . .EPCA 3145
Epic / Mar '83.

**JOY (OLD GOLD).**
**Tracks:** Joy / Grace.
■ 12". . . . . . . . . . . . . . . . . . . . .OG 4070
Old Gold / Jul '88.

**MEN OF THE MUSIC.**
**Tracks:** If you want to know / Joy / Men of the music / Work me all over / You got it all / It must be love / It's you that I need (loneliness made me realise).
■ LP. . . . . . . . . . . . . . . . . . . . .EPC 25415
MC. . . . . . . . . . . . . . . . . . . . .40 25415
Epic / Apr '83 / Sony.

**WHEN YOU BELIEVE IN LOVE.**
**Tracks:** When you believe / Funk on.
■ 7". . . . . . . . . . . . . . . . . . . . .A 2602
Epic / Jul '82.

## Band Of Angels

**ACCEPT MY INVITATION.**
**Tracks:** Accept my invitation / Michael the lover / Our love is getting stronger.
■ 12". . . . . . . . . . . . . . . . . . . . .12SS 101
■ 7". . . . . . . . . . . . . . . . . . . . .7SS 101
Soul Supply / Oct '83.

## Banda Black Rio

**MISS CHERYL.**
**Tracks:** Miss Cheryl / Nelissa / Subindo o morro / Amor natural.
■ 12". . . . . . . . . . . . . . . . . . . . .PC 9637
■ 7". . . . . . . . . . . . . . . . . . . . .PB 9637
RCA / Dec '80.

## Banks, Bessie

**GO NOW.**
**Tracks:** Go now / It sounds like my baby.
■ 7". . . . . . . . . . . . . . . . . . . . .CYZ 7120
Charly / May '87.

**I CAN'T MAKE IT.**
**Tracks:** I can't make it / Need you.
■ 7". . . . . . . . . . . . . . . . . . . . .VS 563
Verve / Nov '67.

## Banks, Darrell

**ANGEL BABY (DON'T YOU LEAVE ME).**
**Tracks:** Angel baby (don't you leave me) / Look into the eyes of a fool.
■ 7". . . . . . . . . . . . . . . . . . . . .584120
Atlantic / Jul '67.
■ 7". . . . . . . . . . . . . . . . . . . . .K 10879
Atlantic / Feb '77.

**DARRELL BANKS IS HERE.**
**Tracks:** Here come the tears / I've got that feelin' / Gonna hang my head / Look into the eyes of a fool /

---

Our love / Open the door to your heart / Angel baby / Somebody / Baby what'cha got.
■ LP. . . . . . . . . . . . . . . . . . .ATCO 33216
Atlantic / Nov '67.

**HERE TO STAY.**
**Tracks:** Just because your love has gone / Forgive me / Only the strong survive / Don't know what to do / When a man loves a woman / We'll get over / Beautiful feeling / I could never hate her / Never alone / No one blinder / My love is strictly reserved for you.
■ LP. . . . . . . . . . . . . . . . . . . .SXATS 1011
Stax / Nov '69.

**OPEN THE DOOR TO YOUR HEART.**
**Tracks:** Open the door to your heart / Our love (is in the pocket).
■ 7". . . . . . . . . . . . . . . . . . . . .SS 536
Stateside / Dec '66.
■ 7". . . . . . . . . . . . . . . . . . . .HL 10070
London-American / Nov '66.

**OPEN THE DOOR TO YOUR HEART.**
**Tracks:** Open the door to your heart / Angel baby.
■ 7". . . . . . . . . . . . . . . . . . . . .CS 8005
Contempo (1) / Mar '78.

## Banks, Homer

**60 MINUTES OF YOUR LOVE.**
**Tracks:** 60 minutes of your love / Do you know what.
■ 7". . . . . . . . . . . . . . . . . . . . .LIB 12047
Liberty / Jan '67.

**HOOKED BY LOVE.**
**Tracks:** Hooked by love / Lady of stone.
■ 7". . . . . . . . . . . . . . . . . . . . .LIB 12060
Liberty / Jun '67.

**LOT OF LOVE, A.**
**Tracks:** Lot of love / Fighting to win.
■ 7". . . . . . . . . . . . . . . . . . . . .LB 12028
Liberty / '66.

## Banks, Larry

**I DON'T WANNA DO IT.**
**Tracks:** I don't wanna do it / I'm comin' home.
■ 7". . . . . . . . . . . . . . . . . . . . .SS 579
Stateside / Jan '67.

## Bar-Kays

**AS ONE.**
**Tracks:** Boogie body land / Say it through love / Work it out / Bodyfever / Take the time to love somebody / Open your heart / Deliver us / As one.
■ LP. . . . . . . . . . . . . . . . . . . . .6337 108
Mercury / Feb '81.
■ LP. . . . . . . . . . . . . . . . . . .SRM 13844
Mercury / Aug '88.

**BAR-KAYS.**
**Tracks:** Not Advised.
■ MC. . . . . . . . . . . . . . . . . . . .SRC 14028
Mercury / Sep '89.

**BLACK ROCK.**
**Tracks:** Baby I love you / I've been trying / You don't know like I know / Dance to the music / Piece of your peace / Six o'clock news report / How sweet it would be / Montego Bay.
■ LP. . . . . . . . . . . . . . . . . . . . .2362003
Stax / May '71.

**BOOGIE BODY LAND.**
**Tracks:** Boogie body land / Running in and out of my life.
■ 12". . . . . . . . . . . . . . . . . . . .MERX 56
■ 7". . . . . . . . . . . . . . . . . . . . .MER 56
Mercury / Jan '81.

**CONTAGIOUS.**
**Tracks:** Not Advised.
CD. . . . . . . . . . . . . . . . . . . . .830 305-2
■ LP. . . . . . . . . . . . . . . . . . . . .8303051
MC. . . . . . . . . . . . . . . . . . . . .8303054
Mercury / Nov '87 / PolyGram.

**DANGEROUS.**
**Tracks:** Dangerous / Dirty dancer / Make believe lover / Dance party / Freakshow on the dance floor / Lovers should never fall in love / Loose talk / Sexomatic.
■ LP. . . . . . . . . . . . . . . . . . . . .818 478 1
Mercury / Jul '84.

**FLYING HIGH ON YOUR LOVE.**
**Tracks:** Attitudes / Can't keep my hands off you / Flying high on your love / Let's have some fun / Shut the funk up / Standing on the outside / Whatever it is / Woman of the night / You can't run away.

■ DELETED

■ **LP** . . . . . . . . . . . . . . . . . . . 9100048
Mercury / Mar '78.

### GOTTA GROOVE.
**Tracks:** Don't stop dancing / If this world was mine / In the hole / Funky thing / Jiving round / Grab this thing / Street walker / Yesterday / Humpin' / Hey Jude.
■ **LP** . . . . . . . . . . . . . . . . . . .SXATS 1009
Stax / Nov '69.
■ **LP** . . . . . . . . . . . . . . . . . . . 2363007
Stax / Aug '71.

### GOTTA GROOVE BLACK ROCK.
**Tracks:** Don't stop dancing (to the music) part 1 / If this world was mine / In the hole / Funky thang / Jivin' 'round / Grab this thing / Don't stop dancing (to the music) part II / Street walker / Yesterday / Humpin' / Hey Jude / Baby I love you / I've been trying / You don't know like I know / Dance to the music / Piece of your peace / Six o'clock news report / How sweet it would be / Montego Bay.
CD . . . . . . . . . . . . . . . . . . CDSXD 962
Stax / Nov '90 / Pinnacle.

### HOLY GHOST.
**Tracks:** Holy ghost / Monster.
■ **12"** . . . . . . . . . . . . . . . . .12STAX 505
■ **7"** . . . . . . . . . . . . . . . . . STAX 505
Stax / Mar '79.

### LET'S HAVE SOME FUN.
**Tracks:** Let's have some fun / Attitudes.
■ **7"** . . . . . . . . . . . . . . . . . .6167 649
Mercury / Mar '78.

### MONEY TALKS.
**Tracks:** Holy ghost / Feelin' alright / Monster / Money talks / Mean mistreater / Holy ghost (reborn).
■ **LP** . . . . . . . . . . . . . . . . . . . STX 3023
Stax / Mar '79.
CD . . . . . . . . . . . . . . . . . . CDSXE 023
LP . . . . . . . . . . . . . . . . . . .SXE 023
Stax / Jan '90 / Pinnacle.

### NIGHTCRUISING.
**Tracks:** Nightcruising / Hit and run.
■ **12"** . . . . . . . . . . . . . . . . . MERX 89
■ **7"** . . . . . . . . . . . . . . . . . MER 89
Mercury / Jan '82.

### PROPOSITIONS.
**Tracks:** Propositions / Tripping out / Anticipations (busted) / Do it (let me shake you) / She talks to me with her body / I can't believe you're leaving me / You made a change in my life.
■ **LP** . . . . . . . . . . . . . . . . . SRM 14065
Mercury / May '89.

### SEXOMATIC.
**Tracks:** Sexomatic.
■ **12"** . . . . . . . . . . . . . . . . .JABX 10
Club / Nov '84.
■ **7"** . . . . . . . . . . . . . . . . . JAB 10
Club / Jan '85.

### SEXOMATIC (OLD GOLD).
**Tracks:** Sexomatic / Shake your rump to the funk.
■ **12"** . . . . . . . . . . . . . . . . .OG 4082
Old Gold / Oct '88.

### SHAKE YOUR RUMP TO THE FUNK.
**Tracks:** Shake your rump to the funk / Summer of our love.
■ **7"** . . . . . . . . . . . . . . . . . .6167 417
Mercury / Jan '77.

### SOUL FINGER.
**Tracks:** Soul finger / Knucklehead.
■ **7"** . . . . . . . . . . . . . . . . . 601 014
Stax / Aug '67.

### SOUL FINGER.
**Tracks:** Knucklehead / Soul finger / With a child's heart / Bar-kays boogaloo / Hells Angels / You can't sit down / House shoes / Pearl high / I want someone / Hole in the wall / Don't do that.
■ **LP** . . . . . . . . . . . . . . . . . . VOLT 417
Atlantic / Nov '67.
■ **LP** . . . . . . . . . . . . . . . . . 228030
Atco / Jan '70.
CD . . . . . . . . . . . . . . . . . 8122702982
WEA / Jul '93 / WEA.

### SOUL FINGER (OLD GOLD).
**Tracks:** Soul finger / Last night.
■ **7"** . . . . . . . . . . . . . . . . . .OG 9906
Old Gold / '89.

### YOUR PLACE OR MINE.
**Tracks:** Your place or mine / Sex-o-matic.
■ **12"** . . . . . . . . . . . . . . . . .JABX 22
Club / Sep '85.

---

## Barnes, Dena

### IF YOU EVER WALKED OUT OF MY LIFE.
**Tracks:** If you ever walked out of my life / Who am I.
■ **7"** . . . . . . . . . . . . . . . . . .GRP 141
Grapevine (Northern Soul) / Jun '80.

### ZOLA.
**Tracks:** Zola.
■ **7"** . . . . . . . . . . . . . . . . . . SUE 1
Suemi / '74.

---

## Barnes, J.J.

### COMPETITION AIN'T NOTHING.
**Tracks:** Competition ain't nothing / Double cookin' / Bok to Bach.
■ **7"** . . . . . . . . . . . . . . . . . . BURN 7
■ **7" P.Disc** . . . . . . . . . . . . . PICBURN 7
Inferno / Jul '84.

### ERROL FLYNN.
**Tracks:** Errol Flynn / Love cookin'.
■ **7"** . . . . . . . . . . . . . . . . . . CX 16
Contempo (2) / Dec '76.

### GROOVESVILLE MASTERS, THE.
**Tracks:** Baby please come back home / Your love is gone / Chains of love / I need a change / To an early grave / Time has come / Now I got you back / Sweet sherry / Help me / Welcome to the club / Cloudy days.
■ **LP** . . . . . . . . . . . . . . . . . . .CLP 520
Contempo (1).

### GUESS I'LL TRY IT AGAIN.
**Tracks:** Guess I'll try it again.
■ **12"** . . . . . . . . . . . . . . . . .12 BURN 15
Inferno (1) / Mar '85.

### HOW LONG.
**Tracks:** How long / I can't seem to hold you.
■ **7"** . . . . . . . . . . . . . . . . . .CC 9
Casino Classics / Jun '79.

### HOW LONG (ORIGINAL).
**Tracks:** How long / I'm the one who loves you.
■ **7"** . . . . . . . . . . . . . . . . . CS 2123
Contempo (1) / Aug '77.

### RARE STAMPS (Barnes, J.J. & Steve Mancha).
**Tracks:** Baby, please come back home / Chains of love / Now that I got you back / Easy living / Sweet sherry / Don't make me a storyteller / Love like yours / Keep the faith / I don't wanna lose you.
■ **LP** . . . . . . . . . . . . . . . . .SXATS 1012
Stax / Nov '69.

### SARA SMILE.
**Tracks:** Errol Flynn / Sara smile / She's mine / If you move I'll fall / Errol Flynn (reprise) / Let me feel the funk / We can't hide it any more / How long / I'm the one who loves you / Let me feel the funk (reprise).
■ **LP** . . . . . . . . . . . . . . . . . .CLP 604
Contempo (1).

### SWEET SHERRY.
**Tracks:** Sweet sherry.
■ **7"** . . . . . . . . . . . . . . . . . . BURN 3
Inferno (1) / Dec '83.

### TRY IT ONE MORE TIME.
**Tracks:** Not Advised.
■ **CD** . . . . . . . . . . . . . . . . . MOTCCD 69
Motor City / Oct '92.

---

## Barnes, Johnny

### FANCY OUR MEETING.
**Tracks:** Samba rossi / Blue horizon / Boko's bounce / Hawk / Moonlight becomes you / Fascinating rhythm / Falling in love with you.
CD . . . . . . . . . . . . . . . . . . CLGCD 019
■ **LP** . . . . . . . . . . . . . . . . . CLGLP 019
MC . . . . . . . . . . . . . . . . . ZCLG 019
Calligraph / Feb '89 / Cadillac / Wellard / Jazz Music.

### JAZZ MASTERS (Barnes, Johnny & Bruce Turner).
**Tracks:** Not Advised.
■ **LP** . . . . . . . . . . . . . . . . . SGC 1005
Cadillac / Feb '77.

---

## Barnum, H.B.

Although he recorded two albums for RCA during the 60's, H.B. Barnum is better known in soul circles for his arranging, songwriting and producing abilities. In terms of arrangement he has worked with The Temptations, The Jackson 5, Aretha Franklin and Lamont Dozier. Of the dozens of songs he arranged perhaps his finest was the masterful interpretation of Kris Kristofferson's *Help Me Make It Through The Night* for Gladys Knight & The Pips, and the classic *When I Think About You* with Aretha Franklin. He has also written material for Jimmy Norman , *I Just Wanna Make Love To You* and more recently *From The Heart* for Gloria Bare.

### RECORD, THE (BABY I LOVE YOU).
**Tracks:** Record.
■ **7"** . . . . . . . . . . . . . . . . . CL 15391
Capitol / '65.

---

## Barrett, Marcia

### YOU.
**Tracks:** You / I'm lonely.
■ **7"** . . . . . . . . . . . . . . . . . K 11578
Atlantic / Apr '81.

---

## Barrow, Keith

### MISTER MAGIC MAN.
**Tracks:** Mr. Magic Man / We've got a right to be wrong.
■ **7"** . . . . . . . . . . . . . . . . . CBS 5141
CBS / May '77.

### PRECIOUS.
**Tracks:** Precious / Precious (part 2).
■ **7"** . . . . . . . . . . . . . . . . . CBS 4662
CBS / Oct '76.

### TURN ME UP.
**Tracks:** Turn me up / Joyful music.
■ **7"** . . . . . . . . . . . . . . . . . CBS 7090
CBS / Mar '79.

---

## Barry, Claudja

### (I DON'T KNOW IF YOU'RE) DEAD OR ALIVE.
**Tracks:** (I don't know if you're) dead or alive.
■ **12"** . . . . . . . . . . . . . . . . . BLUM 1
■ **7"** . . . . . . . . . . . . . . . . . 7 BLUM 1
Blue Moon (1) / Jun '88.

### CAN'T YOU HEAR MY HEARTBEAT.
**Tracks:** Can't you hear my heartbeat.
■ **12"** . . . . . . . . . . . . . . . . . 6504456
■ **7"** . . . . . . . . . . . . . . . . . 6504457
Epic / Apr '87.

### CLAUDJA BARRY.
**Tracks:** Dancin' fever / Every beat of my heart / Johnny, Johnny please come home / Love machine / Open the door / Sweet dynamite / Take it easy / Take me in your arms / Why must a girl like me.
■ **LP** . . . . . . . . . . . . . . . . . 6306105
Lollipop / Sep '78.

### DANCIN' SHOES.
**Tracks:** Dancin' shoes / Boogie tonight.
■ **7"** . . . . . . . . . . . . . . . . . .LOLLY 5
Lollipop / Jan '79.

### DANCING FEVER.
**Tracks:** Dancing fever / Take it easy.
■ **7"** . . . . . . . . . . . . . . . . . .LOLLY 1
Lollipop / Jun '78.

### DOWN AND COUNTING.
**Tracks:** Down and counting.
■ **12"** . . . . . . . . . . . . . . . . . .350047-6
■ **7"** . . . . . . . . . . . . . . . . . 6500477
Epic / Oct '86.

### DOWN BY THE WATER.
**Tracks:** Down by the water / Boogie tonight.
■ **7"** . . . . . . . . . . . . . . . . . .LOLLY 3
Lollipop / Oct '78.

### FREAK DYNAMITE.
**Tracks:** Freak dynamite / Johnny Johnny please come home.
■ **7"** . . . . . . . . . . . . . . . . . .6198 168
Mercury / Sep '77.

### I WANNA BE LOVED BY YOU.
**Tracks:** Boogie tonight / Cold fire / Dancin' shoes / Down by the water / Give it up / Heavy makes you happy / I wanna be loved by you / Love of the hurtin' kind / Nobody but you / Way you are dancing.
■ **LP** . . . . . . . . . . . . . . . . . 630 610 7
Lollipop / Mar '79.

### I WILL FOLLOW HIM.
**Tracks:** I will follow him / Work me over.
■ **12"** . . . . . . . . . . . . . . . . . EXCL 528

---

■ 7" . . . . . . . . . . . . . . . . . . .EXC 528
Excaliber / '83.

## I, CLAUDJA.
Tracks: Down and counting / Can't you feel my heartbeat / Dance for your life / Give me a sign / Hot to the touch / Dead or alive (I don't know if you are) / Secret affair / You've got me jumpin' / Change of heart / Show me another way.
■ LP . . . . . . . . . . . . . . . . . . . 4510451
MC . . . . . . . . . . . . . . . . . . . 4510454
Epic / Aug '87 / Sony.

## IF I DO IT TO YOU.
Tracks: If I do it to you / Up all night.
■ 12" . . . . . . . . . . . . . . . . . . ENYT 223
■ 7" . . . . . . . . . . . . . . . . . . .ENY 223
Ensign / Feb '82.

## JOHNNY JOHNNY.
Tracks: Johnny Johnny / Long lost friend.
■ 7" . . . . . . . . . . . . . . . . . . 6198188
Mercury / Feb '78.

## TRIPPIN' ON THE MOON.
Tracks: Trippin' on the moon / Trippin' on the moon (version).
■ 12" . . . . . . . . . . . . . . . . 12 PER 103
■ 7" . . . . . . . . . . . . . . . . . . PERS 103
Personal / '84.

## WHY MUST A GIRL LIKE ME.
Tracks: Why must a girl like me / Love for the sake of love.
■ 7" . . . . . . . . . . . . . . . . . .6198 126
Mercury / May '77.

# Bartley, Chris

## I FOUND A GOODIE.
Tracks: I found a goodie.
■ 12" . . . . . . . . . . . . . . . . . . MIS 004
Not Advised / '88.

# Bartz, Gary

## MUSIC.
Tracks: Music / Give it your best shot.
■ 12" . . . . . . . . . . . . . . . . ARIST 12355
■ 7" . . . . . . . . . . . . . . . . .ARIST 355
Arista / Jun '80.

## SHADOWS.
Tracks: Not Advised.
■ CD . . . . . . . . . . . . . . . . CDJSP 379
JSP / Oct '92.

## SHAKE YOUR BODY.
Tracks: Shake your body / Penelope.
■ 12" . . . . . . . . . . . . . . . 12CL 15999
Capitol / Oct '78.

## THERE GOES THE NEIGHBORHOOD.
Tracks: Not Advised.
CD . . . . . . . . . . . . . . . . . . CCD 79506
Candid / Oct '93 / Cadillac / Jazz Music / Wellard / Koch International.

## WEST 52ND STREET (Live at Birdland 1990).
Tracks: West 52nd Street / Speak low / It's easy to remember / Cousins / Night has a thousand eyes.
CD . . . . . . . . . . . . . . . . . . CCD 79049
Candid / Jan '90 / Cadillac / Jazz Music / Wellard / Koch International.

# Bas Noir

## AH..BAS NOIR.
Tracks: Superficial love / Shoe-b-doo / Patiently / Addicted 2 luv / Get u back / Love high / Out in the rain / I'm glad you came to me / We'll find love / If I / Yearn'n.
CD . . . . . . . . . . . . . . . . 7567823602
■ LP . . . . . . . . . . . . . . . . 7567823601
MC . . . . . . . . . . . . . . . . 7567823604
Atlantic / Mar '92 / WEA.

## I'M GLAD YOU CAME TO ME.
Tracks: I'm glad you came to me / I'm glad you came to me (version).
■ 7" . . . . . . . . . . . . . . . . . TENK 282
■ 12" . . . . . . . . . . . . . . . . TENX 282
■ 12" Remix . . . . . . . . . . . . . . TENR 282
■ 7" . . . . . . . . . . . . . . . . . TEN 282
■ CD Single . . . . . . . . . . . . TENCD 282
10 / Sep '89.

## MY LOVE IS MAGIC.
Tracks: My love is magic.
■ 12" . . . . . . . . . . . . . . . . TENX 257
■ 7" . . . . . . . . . . . . . . . . . TEN 257
10 / Dec '88.

# Basic Black

## BASIC BLACK.
Tracks: She's mine / Give your love to me / What ever it takes / Nothing but a party / Special kind of fool / It's a man's thang / Don't make me fall in love / Baby can we talk / Now or never / Stupid.
■ LP . . . . . . . . . . . . . . . . . ZL 72723
■ CD . . . . . . . . . . . . . . . . . ZD 72723
■ MC . . . . . . . . . . . . . . . . . ZK 72723
Motown / Sep '90.

## NOTHING BUT A PARTY.
Tracks: Nothing but a party / Nothing but a party (dub) / Nothing but a party (12" version) (Ony on 12" and CD single).
■ 12" . . . . . . . . . . . . . . . . ZT 44058
■ 7" . . . . . . . . . . . . . . . . ZB 44057
■ CD Single . . . . . . . . . . . . . ZD 44058
Motown / Sep '90.

## WHATEVER IT TAKES.
Tracks: Whatever it takes (European mix) / Whatever it takes (European radio edit) / Whatever it takes (house mix).
■ 12" . . . . . . . . . . . . . . . . ZT 44548
Motown / May '91.

# Bass, Fontella

## FREE.
Tracks: To be free / Hold on this time / I want everyone to know / I need to be loved / Talking about freedom / I need love / Wiping tears / Now that I've found a good thing / Who you gonna blame my God, my freedom, my home.
■ LP . . . . . . . . . . . . . . . . . 2916018
Mojo / Nov '72.

## NEW LOOK, THE.
Tracks: Our day will come / How glad I am / Oh no,not my baby / Rescue me / Gee whiz / I'm a woman / Since I fell for you / Impossible / You've lost that lovin' feelin' / Soul of the man / Come and get these memories / I know.
■ LP . . . . . . . . . . . . . . . . CRL 4517
Chess / Feb '66.
■ LP . . . . . . . . . . . . . . . . GCH 8048
MC . . . . . . . . . . . . . . . . GCHK 78048
Chess (Charly) / Jun '88 / Charly.

## RECOVERY.
Tracks: Recovery.
■ 7" . . . . . . . . . . . . . . . . . CRS 8027
Chess / Jan '66.

## RESCUE ME.
Tracks: Rescue me / Soul of the man / Recovery / I can't rest.
■ 7" . . . . . . . . . . . . . . . . . CRS 8023
Chess / Dec '65.
■ 7" . . . . . . . . . . . . . . . . . CHES 4002
Chess (PRT) / Jul '85.

## RESCUE ME (OLD GOLD).
Tracks: Rescue me / Soul of a man.
■ 7" . . . . . . . . . . . . . . . . . .OG 9412
Old Gold / Jul '84.

## RESCUE ME (OLD GOLD) (2).
Tracks: Rescue me / Recovery.
■ 7" . . . . . . . . . . . . . . . . . .OG 9844
Old Gold / Jan '89.

## RESCUED.
Tracks: Not Advised.
CD . . . . . . . . . . . . . . . . .CHLD 19252
MC . . . . . . . . . . . . . . . . .CHLC 19252
Chess (MCA) / Oct '94 / BMG.

## SISTERS OF SOUL (Bass, Fontella & Sugar Pie Desanto).
Tracks: Not Advised.
CD . . . . . . . . . . . . . . . . . RTS 33024
MC . . . . . . . . . . . . . . . . . RTS 43024
Roots / Nov '90 / Pinnacle / Target.

# Bataan, Joe

## MISTIZO.
Tracks: Mistizo / Rap o, clap o / Sadie / Latin lover / Rock me all night long / I see your hiney / Rap o, dance o / Always and forever.
■ LP . . . . . . . . . . . . . . . . . SALP 1
Salsoul / Jul '80.

## MR. NEW YORK.
Tracks: Purto rico me illama / Special girl / Muneca / What good is a castle (part 1) / Magic rose / Subway Joe / Chilli beans / Young gifted and black / Uptown / Auguanta la lengua / Mambo de Bataan / My opera / Riot (it's a good feeling) / Gypsy woman / Shaft, Theme from / What good is a castle (part 2).

CD . . . . . . . . . . . . . CDCHARLY 166
■ LP . . . . . . . . . . . . . . . .HOT 122
MC . . . . . . . . . . . . . . . TCHOT 122
Caliente / Apr '89 / Charly / Cadillac / Projection.

## RAP-O, CLAP-O.
Tracks: Rap-o, clap-o / Rap-o, clap-o (part 2).
■ 12" . . . . . . . . . . . . . . . .RAP12-1
■ 7" . . . . . . . . . . . . . . . . RAP 1
RCA / Feb '80.

## SADIE.
Tracks: Sadie / Rap o clap o.
■ 12" . . . . . . . . . . . . . . . . SALT 7
■ 7" . . . . . . . . . . . . . . . . . SAL 7
Salsoul / Oct '80.

# Battle, Jean

## LOVE MAKING.
Tracks: Love making / When a man loves a woman
■ 7" . . . . . . . . . . . . . . . .2027 010
Mojo / Jun '72.

# Baylor, Helen

## LOOK A LITTLE.
Tracks: Not Advised.
CD . . . . . . . . . . . . . . DAYCD 4215
Word (UK) / May '93 / Word Records (UK) / Sony.

## OASIS.
Tracks: Oasis.
■ 12" . . . . . . . . . . . . . . . EXPAND 20
Debut (2) / Nov '91.

## THERE'S NO GREATER LOVE.
Tracks: There's no greater love.
■ 12" . . . . . . . . . . . . . . . EXPAND 19
Expansion / Sep '90.

## VICTORY.
Tracks: Victory.
■ 12" . . . . . . . . . . . . . . . EXPAND 26
Debut (1) / Mar '92.

# Beasley, Walter

## I'M SO HAPPY.
Tracks: I'm so happy / On the edge / Call me / Jump on it / Back in love again / Tenderness / Nothin' but a thang / Where / I'm so happy (12" remix).
■ LP . . . . . . . . . . . . . . . . URBLP 6
Urban / Feb '88.
■ CD . . . . . . . . . . . . . . . 833 866-2
Urban / Mar '88.

## I'M SO HAPPY.
Tracks: I'm so happy / Jump on it.
■ 12" . . . . . . . . . . . . . . . URBX 14
■ 7" . . . . . . . . . . . . . . . . URB 14
Urban / Jan '88.

## JUST KICKIN' IT.
Tracks: Just kickin' it / Good love / I would never go / Get loose / Don't say goodbye / You are the one / Muriel's lament / In time / Have you seen my girl / Mancy.
CD . . . . . . . . . . . . . . . . 838 912 2
■ LP . . . . . . . . . . . . . . . 838 912 1
■ MC . . . . . . . . . . . . . . . 838 912 4
Mercury / Nov '89 / PolyGram.

# Beat System

## DON'T HOLD BACK ON THE LOVE.
Tracks: Don't hold back on the love.
■ 7" . . . . . . . . . . . . . . . . BRW 189
■ 12" . . . . . . . . . . . . . .12 BRW 189
4th & Broadway / Jul '90.

## TO BRIGHTER DAY.
Tracks: To a brighter day.
■ 12" . . . . . . . . . . . . . . . . .FX 217
■ CD Single . . . . . . . . . . . . .FCD 217
FFRR / Aug '93.

## WALK ON THE WILD SIDE.
Tracks: Walk on the wild side / Walk on the wild side (inst).
■ 12" . . . . . . . . . . . . . .12 BRW 163
■ 7" . . . . . . . . . . . . . . . BRW 163
4th & Broadway / Jan '90.

# Beavers, Jackie

## MR. BUMP MAN.
Tracks: Mr. Bump man / Somebody help the bigger man.
■ 7" . . . . . . . . . . . . . . . .BDS 423
Buddah / Feb '75.

■ DELETED

## Beck, Kenny

**SHUT YOUR CRACK.**
Tracks: Shut your crack.
■ 12"......................12BECK 5
White / Mar '89.

## Beck, Robin

**FIRST TIME, THE.**
Tracks: First time.
■ 12"........................MERX 270
■ 7".........................MER 270
Mercury / Jul '88.

**SAVE UP ALL YOUR TEARS.**
Tracks: Save up all your tears / Jealous hearts / First time.
■ CD Single............MERCD 278
■ 12".................MERX 278
■ 7"..................MER 278
Mercury / Feb '89.

**TEARS IN THE RAIN.**
Tracks: Tears in the rain / Heart for you / In a crazy world like this (On 12" and CD single only).
■ 12"......................MERX 303
■ 7".......................MER 303
■ CD Single............MERCD 303
■ MC Single.............MERMC 303
Mercury / Jan '90.

**TROUBLE OR NOTHING.**
Tracks: Hide your heart / If you were a woman (and I was a man) / Save up all your tears / Tears in the rain / Sleepin' with the enemy / Don't lose any sleep / Hold back the night / In a crazy world like this / Heart for you / First time.
■ LP.......................838 768 1
■ MC......................838 768 4
■ CD......................838 768 2
Mercury / Jan '90.

## Beggar & Co

**ANYBODY SEE MY TRIAL.**
Tracks: Anybody see my trial.
■ 12"....................POSPX 615
■ 7".....................POSP 615
Polydor / Jul '83.

**LIFE.**
Tracks: Life / Life (instrumental).
■ 12"...................12TOCO 9
■ 7"....................TOCO 9
Total Control / Jun '86.

**MONUMENT.**
Tracks: You need love / Laughing on / Somebody help me out / Mule (chant no.2) / Break it up / Got to get away / Bahia de palma / I tried to write a song / That's life / Keep on writing.
■ LP.....................RCALP 6024
■ MC....................RCAK 6024
RCA / Dec '81.

**MULE (CHANT NO.2).**
Tracks: Mule (chant no.2).
■ 7"......................RCA 130
RCA / Sep '81.

**SOMEBODY HELP ME OUT.**
Tracks: Somebody help me out / Rising sun.
■ 12"....................ENYT 201
■ 7"....................ENY 201
Ensign / Feb '81.

**WE ALL WORK OUT.**
Tracks: We all work out / Got to get away.
■ 12"....................RCAT 233
■ 7"....................RCA 233
RCA / Jun '82.

## Beginning Of The End

**FUNKY NASSAU.**
Tracks: Funky nassau.
■ 7"......................209 1097
Atlantic / Jul '71.
■ 12"...................K 10021 T
■ 7"....................K 10021
Atlantic / Feb '74.

## Bell, Archie

**ANY TIME IS RIGHT.**
Tracks: Any time is right / Harder and harder.
■ 12"....................BKSL 1
■ 7"....................BKS 1
Beckett / Aug '81.

**ARTISTS SHOWCASE: ARCHIE BELL.**
Tracks: Not Advised.
■ LP......................MUSIC 8
■ MC.....................ZCMUS 8
Street Sounds / Oct '86 / BMG / Total.

**DISCO SHOWDOWN.**
Tracks: Disco showdown / I've been missing you.
■ 7".....................PIR 5580
Philadelphia Int / Aug '77.

**DON'T LET LOVE GET YOU DOWN (Bell, Archie & The Drells).**
Tracks: Don't let love get you down / Where will you go when the party's over.
■ 7"......................A 7254
Portrait / Jun '86.

**EVERYBODY HAVE A GOOD TIME (Bell, Archie & The Drells).**
Tracks: Everybody have a good time / I bet I can do that dance you're doing.
■ 7"......................PIR 5179
Philadelphia Int / Jun '77.

**HERE I GO AGAIN (Bell, Archie & The Drells).**
Tracks: Here I go again.
■ 7"......................K 10210
Atlantic / Sep '72.

**HERE I GO AGAIN (Bell, Archie & The Drells).**
Tracks: I love my baby / Houston, Texas / Showdown / Giving up dancing / Girl you're too young / Mama didn't teach me that way.
■ LP.....................K 40454
Atlantic / Feb '73.

**HERE I GO AGAIN (OLD GOLD) (Bell, Archie & The Drells).**
Tracks: Here I go again / Tighten up.
■ 7"......................OG 9096
Old Gold / Jul '72.

**I COULD DANCE ALL NIGHT (Bell, Archie & The Drells).**
Tracks: I could dance all night / King of the castle.
■ 7"......................PIR 3851
Philadelphia Int / Jan '76.

**I NEVER HAD IT SO GOOD.**
Tracks: Don't wait for the world / Anytime is right / I never made love I never had it so good / Why didja do me / Good guys / Harder and harder / Without you.
■ LP.....................BKLP 1002
Beckett / Jul '81.

**LOOK BACK OVER YOUR SHOULDER (Bell, Archie & The Drells).**
Tracks: Look back over your shoulder / Look back over your shoulder(Instrumental version).
■ 12"....................MARE 16
■ 7"....................MARES 16
Nightmare / Mar '87.

**SOUL CITY WALK (Bell, Archie & The Drells).**
Tracks: Soul city walk.
■ 7"......................PIR 4250
Philadelphia Int / May '76.

**STRATEGY (Bell, Archie & The Drells).**
Tracks: Strategy / We got 'em dancin'.
■ 7"......................PIR 7842
Philadelphia Int / Sep '79.

**THERE'S GONNA BE A SHOWDOWN (Bell, Archie & The Drells).**
Tracks: There's gonna be a showdown.
■ 7"......................K 10263
Atlantic / Jan '73.

**WHERE WILL YOU GO WHEN THE PARTY'S OVER (Bell, Archie & The Drells).**
Tracks: Where will you go when the party's over / I swear you're beautiful.
■ 7"......................PIR 4803
Philadelphia Int / Jan '77.

**WHERE WILL YOU GO WHEN THE PARTY'S OVER (Bell, Archie & The Drells).**
Tracks: Don't let love get you down / Where will you go when the party's over / Right here is where I want to be / Dancin' man / Everybody have a good time / I swear you're beautiful / Nothing comes easy / I bet I can do that dance you're doing.
■ LP.....................PRT 57121

■ MC......................40 57121
Portrait / Aug '86.

## Bell Biv Devoe

Rising from ashes of New Edition, BBD immediately hit with 1990's Poison, spurring debut album on to 3.5 million U.S. sales. Band were rougher than antecedants, though Michael Bivins' clean-cut side found outlet as manager of Boyz II Men. Despite acclaimed albums, band have not consolidated first flush of international success, but returned to U.K. charts with old Edition cohort Ralph Tresvant on Janet Jackson/ Luther Vandross-led hit Best Things In Life Are Free in 1992.

**B.B.D. I THOUGHT IT WAS ME.**
Tracks: B.B.D. I thought it was me.
■ 12"....................MCST 1511
■ 12" Remix............MCSX 1511
■ 7"....................MCS 1511
MCA / Feb '91.

**DO ME.**
Tracks: Do me / Do me (mixes).
■ 12"....................MCAT 1440
■ 12" Remix............MCAX 1440
■ 7"....................MCA 1440
■ CD Single............DMCAT 1440
■ MC Single.............MCAC 1440
MCA / Sep '90 / BMG.

**HOOTIE MACK.**
Tracks: Nickel / Above the rim / Lovely / Ghetto booty / Hootie mack / Gangsta / From the back / Show me the way / Situation / Something in your eyes / Please come back / Lost in the moment (Available on CD only).
CD......................MCD 10853
■ LP.....................MCA 10853
■ MC....................MCC 10853
MCA / Jun '93 / BMG.

**MENTAL VIDEO.**
Tracks: Not Advised.
■ VHS...................MCAV 10218
MCA Video / Apr '91.

**POISON.**
Tracks: Poison.
■ 12"....................MCAT 1414
■ 12" Remix............MCAX 1414
■ 7"....................MCA 1414
MCA / May '90.

**POISON.**
Tracks: Dope / B.B.D. (I thought it was me) / Let me know something / Do me / Ronnie, Bobby, Ricky, Mike / Ralph and Johnny (word to the Mutha) / Poison / Ain't nut'in changed / When will I see you smile / Again / I do need you.
CD......................DMCG 6094
■ LP.....................MCG 6094
■ MC....................MCGC 6094
MCA / Jun '90 / BMG.

**POISON.**
Tracks: Not Advised.
■ DCC....................MCX 06387
MCA / Jan '93.

**WBBD - BOOT CITY.**
Tracks: Not Advised.
■ LP.....................MCA 10345
■ MC....................MCAC 10345
■ CD....................MCAD 10345
MCA / Sep '91.

**WORD TO THE MUTHA.**
Tracks: Word to the mutha.
■ 12"....................MCST 1587
■ 7"....................MCS 1587
■ CD Single............MCSTD 1587
MCA / Nov '91.

## Bell, Madeline

**CLIMB EVERY MOUNTAIN.**
Tracks: Climb every mountain / It makes no difference now.
■ 7"......................BF 1596
Philips / Aug '67.

**DANCE DANCE DANCE.**
Tracks: Dance, dance, dance / It happened overnight.
■ 7"......................7N 45576
Pye / Feb '76.

## DOIN' THINGS.
Tracks: Help yourself / After all is said and done / Together with you / It's up to you / For your pleasure / To sir with love / Hold it / Step inside love / Gotta get away from here / No sun today / Ain't gonna cry anymore / Finding you, loving you.
■ LP . . . . . . . . . . . . . . . . . . . . . . SBL 7865
Philips / Feb '69.

## EAST SIDE, WEST SIDE (Bell, Madeline & David Martin).
Tracks: Eastside, Westside / Love finds a way to get through.
■ 7" . . . . . . . . . . . . . . . . . . . . . . . DEB 104
Deb / Apr '82.

## I'M NOT REALLY ME WITHOUT YOU (Bell, Madeline & David Martin).
Tracks: I'm not really me without you / Without you.
■ 7" . . . . . . . . . . . . . . . . . . . . . . . DEB 102
Deb / Jan '82.

## ONE STEP AT A TIME.
Tracks: One step at a time / You won't see me.
■ 7" . . . . . . . . . . . . . . . . . . . . . . BF 1526
Philips / Jan '67.

## PICTURE ME GONE.
Tracks: Picture me gone / Go ahead on.
■ 7" . . . . . . . . . . . . . . . . . . . . . . BF 1611
Philips / Oct '67.

## STAR TRACKS.
Tracks: Picture me gone / You don't love me no more / Soul time / I'm gonna make you love me / Mercy mercy mercy / Help yourself / After all is said and done / For your pleasure / Hold it / Step inside love / Gotta get away from here / Thinkin' / How much do I love you / I'm gonna leave you / No sun today / We're so much in love.
■ LP . . . . . . . . . . . . . . . . . . . . . . 6308066
Philips / Sep '71.

## THIS IS ONE GIRL.
Tracks: Not Advised.
■ LP . . . . . . . . . . . . . . . . . . . NSPL 18483
PRT / Feb '76.

# Bell, William

Born in Memphis, William Bell was early signing to Stax label. He scored several hits throughout '60s but tended to live in shadow of famous labelmate, Otis Redding (latter the subject of Bell's U.K. chart debut, Tribute To A King). Career nonetheless threw up several classics; including '68 duet with Judy Clay Private Number and Albert King-fronted Born Under A Bad Sign, both of which Bell wrote with regular collaborator Booker T. Jones. He later recorded for Mercury (making U.S. Top 10 in 1977 with Trying To Love Two) before forming own labels to continue his R&B-charting career into next decade.

## BEDTIME STORIES.
Tracks: Not Advised.
CD . . . . . . . . . . . . . . . . . . . WIL 4128CD
MC . . . . . . . . . . . . . . . . . . . WIL 4128MC
Wilbe / Mar '94 / ACD Trading Ltd. / Koch International.

## BOUND TO HAPPEN.
Tracks: I forgot to be your lover / Hey, Western Union man / My whole world is falling down / Everyday people / Johnny, I love you / All God's children got soul / Happy / By the time I get to Phoenix / Bring the curtain down / Smile can't hide a broken heart / Born under a bad sign / I got a sure thing.
■ LP . . . . . . . . . . . . . . . . . . SXATS 1016
Stax / Nov '69.
■ LP . . . . . . . . . . . . . . . . . . . 2363002
Stax / May '71.

## BOUND TO HAPPEN/WOW.
Tracks: I forgot to be your lover / Hey Western union man / My whole world is falling down / Everyday people / Johnny, I love you / All God's children got soul / Happy / By the time I get to Phoenix / Bring the curtain down / Smile can't hide a broken heart / Born under a bad sign / I got a sure thing / I can't make it (all by myself) / 'Til my back ain't got no bone / All for the love of a woman / My door is always open / Penny for your thoughts / You'll want diamonds / Winding winding road / Somebody's gonna get hurt / I'll be home.
CD . . . . . . . . . . . . . . . . . . . CDSXD 970
Stax / Apr '91 / Pinnacle.

## COMING BACK FOR MORE.
Tracks: I absolutely, posulutely love you / Coming back for more / I wake up cryin' / If sex was all we

had / Just another way to feel / Malnutrition / Relax / Tryin' to love two / You don't miss your water / You've really got a hold on me.
■ LP . . . . . . . . . . . . . . . . . . . 9100038
Mercury / Jul '77.

## DO RIGHT MAN.
Tracks: You don't miss your water / Any other way / I'm waiting on you / Somebody mentioned your name / I'll show you / Don't stop now / Crying all by myself / Share what you got / Never like this before / Everybody loves a winner / Do right woman, do right man / Then you can tell me goodbye / Eloise / It's happening all over / Everyday will be like a holiday / Tribute to a king.
■ LP . . . . . . . . . . . . . . . . . . . CRB 1076
■ MC . . . . . . . . . . . . . . . . . TCCRB 1076
Charly R&B / Apr '84.

## ELOISE.
Tracks: Eloise / One plus one.
7" . . . . . . . . . . . . . . . . . . . . . .601019
Stax / Sep '67 / Pinnacle.

## FEELING GUILTY.
Tracks: Feeling guilty / Headline news.
■ 12" . . . . . . . . . . . . . . . . . 12LUTE 10
■ 7" . . . . . . . . . . . . . . . . . . . LUTE 10
Tout Ensemble / Feb '87.

## GETTING OUT OF YOUR BED.
Tracks: Getting out of your bed / Short circuit.
■ 7" . . . . . . . . . . . . . . . . . WILBE 89508
Wilbe / Nov '89.

## HAPPY.
Tracks: Happy / Bring the curtain down.
■ 7" . . . . . . . . . . . . . . . . . STXS 2038
Stax / Feb '76.

## HEADLINE NEWS.
Tracks: Headline news.
■ 12" . . . . . . . . . . . . . . . . . 12 204
Ichiban / '86.
■ 7" . . . . . . . . . . . . . . . . . . LUTE 1
Absolute / Apr '86.

## I FORGOT TO BE YOUR LOVER.
Tracks: I forgot to be your lover.
■ 7" . . . . . . . . . . . . . . . . . . STAX 818
Stax / Oct '87.

## LITTLE SOMETHING EXTRA, A.
Tracks: She won't be like you / All that I am / Let's do something together / Forever wouldn't be too long / You got me where you want me / Quittin' time / That's my love / You need a little something extra / There's a love / Never let me go / We got something good / Will you love me tomorrow / Love will find a way / What did I do wrong / Sacrifice / Love is after me / Life I live / Wait / You're never too old.
CD . . . . . . . . . . . . . . . . . . . CDSXD 037
Stax / Sep '91 / Pinnacle.

## NEVER LIKE THIS BEFORE.
Tracks: Never like this before.
■ 7" . . . . . . . . . . . . . . . . . . K 10598
Atlantic / Aug '75.

## NEVER LIKE THIS BEFORE.
Tracks: Never like this before / Soldiers goodbye.
■ 7" . . . . . . . . . . . . . . . . . . .584076
Atlantic / Jan '67.

## ON A ROLL.
Tracks: Getting out of your bed / If you don't use it / I need your love so bad / When you've got the best / On a roll / I'm ready / I can do it / Short circuit / Holding on to love.
CD . . . . . . . . . . . . . . . . . . WIL 3007CD
LP . . . . . . . . . . . . . . . . . . . WIL 3007
MC . . . . . . . . . . . . . . . . . WIL 3007MC
Wilbe / Nov '89 / ACD Trading Ltd. / Koch International.

## PASSION.
Tracks: Not Advised.
■ LP . . . . . . . . . . . . . . . . . . LPLUTE 1
Absolute / Aug '86.
MC. . . . . . . . . . . . . . . . . . . LUTEC 1
Tout Ensemble / Aug '86 / Pinnacle.
■ LP . . . . . . . . . . . . . . . . . . WIL 3001
WRC / '88.

## PASSION.
Tracks: Passion.
■ 12" . . . . . . . . . . . . . . . . .12 LUTE 3
Absolute / Jun '86.
■ 7" . . . . . . . . . . . . . . . . . . LUTE 3
Tout Ensemble / Jun '86.

## PHASES OF REALITY.
Tracks: Save us / True love don't come easy / Fifty dollar habit / What I don't know won't hurt me /

Phases of reality / If you really love him / Lonely fc your love / Man in the street.
■ LP . . . . . . . . . . . . . . . . . . 236202
Stax / '72.
CD. . . . . . . . . . . . . . . . . . CDSXE 05
Stax / Jul '92 / Pinnacle.

## PRIVATE NUMBER.
Tracks: Private number / Love-eye-tis / My bab specializes / Left over love.
■ 7" . . . . . . . . . . . . . . . . . STAX 100
Stax / Mar '82.
■ 12" . . . . . . . . . . . . . . . . STAT 80
Stax / Oct '87.

## SOUL OF A BELL, THE.
Tracks: Everybody loves a winner / You don't mis your water / Do right woman, do right man / I'v been loving you too long / Nothing takes the place c you / Then you can tell me goodbye / Eloise (hang c in there) / Any other way / It's happening all over Never like this before / You're such a sweet thing.
■ LP . . . . . . . . . . . . . . . . . . .71
Stax / Nov '67.
CD. . . . . . . . . . . . . . . . . . 756782252
MC. . . . . . . . . . . . . . . . . . 756782252
Atlantic / Jul '91 / WEA.

## TRIBUTE TO A KING.
Tracks: Tribute to a king.
■ 7" . . . . . . . . . . . . . . . . . . 601 03
Stax / May '68.

## TRIBUTE TO A KING.
Tracks: Tribute to a king / Everybody loves a winne / You don't miss your water / Do right woman / I'v been loving you too long / Nothing takes the place c you / Then you can tell me goodbye / Every ma oughta have a woman / Eloise / Any other way / It' happening all over / Never like this before / You'r such a sweet thing.
■ LP . . . . . . . . . . . . . . . . . . 228 00
Atco / Apr '69.

## WINDING WINDING ROAD.
Tracks: Winding winding road / I forgot to be you lover.
■ 7" . . . . . . . . . . . . . . . . . . DJS 24
DJM / Apr '71.

## WOW.. WILLIAM BELL.
Tracks: I can't make it / 'Til my back ain't got no bone / All for the love of a woman / My door is alway open / Penny for your thoughts / You'll want dia monds / Winding, winding road / Somebody's gonna get hurt / I forgot to be your lover / I'll be home.
■ LP . . . . . . . . . . . . . . . . . . 236200
Stax / Jun '71.

# Belle, Jenny

## I CAN LOVE YOU BETTER.
Tracks: I can love you better.
■ 12" . . . . . . . . . . . . . . . . . 12BR
White / Feb '89.

# Belle, Regina

Belle made star-studded entrance, duetting with Manhattans on 1986 Bobby Womack produced Where Did We Go Wrong. Her 1987 debut All By Myself sparked rash c (favourable) Anita Baker comparisons, and led to cameos with Surface and James 'J.T. Taylor. However, follow-up Stay With M demonstrated that Belle lacked Baker's ver satility, and third album Passion, released in '93, was no more remarkable. However she did score hit duet with Peabo Bryson o Whole New World, from Disney's Aladdin.

## ALL BY MYSELF.
Tracks: Show me the way / Take your love away Please be mine / After the love has lost its shine Intimate relations / You got the love / How could yo do it to me / Gotta give it up / So many tears.
CD. . . . . . . . . . . . . . . . . . 450998
■ LP . . . . . . . . . . . . . . . . . 450998
MC. . . . . . . . . . . . . . . . . . 450998
CBS / Jul '87 / Sony.
■ CD . . . . . . . . . . . . . . . . . 467017
■ LP . . . . . . . . . . . . . . . . . 467017
■ MC . . . . . . . . . . . . . . . . . 467017
CBS / Oct '90.

## BABY COME TO ME.
Tracks: Baby come to me / Forever eyes / Bab come to me (LP version) / Show me the way (ext mix) / So many tears.
■ 12" . . . . . . . . . . . . . . . . . 655122
■ 12" . . . . . . . . . . . . . . . . . 655564
■ 7" . . . . . . . . . . . . . . . . . . 655122

■ CD Single . . . . . . . . . . . . . . 6551225
CBS / Jan '90.

## GOOD LOVIN'.
**Tracks:** Good lovin' / This is love / You got the love / Show me the way / So many tears.
■ 12" . . . . . . . . . . . . . . . . . . . . 6552308
■ 7" . . . . . . . . . . . . . . . . . . . . 6552307
■ CD Single . . . . . . . . . . . . . . 6552302
■ MC Single . . . . . . . . . . . . . . 6552304
CBS / Sep '89.

## PASSION.
**Tracks:** Interlude / Passion / Quiet time / If I could / Do you wanna get serious / Dream in colour / My man (mon homme).
■ CD . . . . . . . . . . . . . . . . . . . .472301 2
■ LP . . . . . . . . . . . . . . . . . . . .472301 1
■ MC . . . . . . . . . . . . . . . . . . . .472301 4
Columbia / Mar '93 / Sony.

## SHOW ME THE WAY.
**Tracks:** Show me the way / Show me the way (inst) / How could you do it to me (Extra track on 12" only) / Show me the way (extended mix).
■ 12" . . . . . . . . . . . . . . . . . . . . 6509388
■ 12" . . . . . . . . . . . . . . . . . . . . 6509386
■ 7" . . . . . . . . . . . . . . . . . . . . 6509387
CBS / Jun '87.
■ CD Single . . . . . . . . . . . . . . 6509382
CBS / Mar '88.

## SHOW ME THE WAY (OLD GOLD) (Belle, Regina featuring J.T. Taylor).
**Tracks:** Show me the way / All I want is forever.
12" . . . . . . . . . . . . . . . . . . . .OG 4231
Old Gold / Jun '92 / Pickwick.

## STAY WITH ME.
**Tracks:** Baby come to me / When will you be mine / Dream lover / What goes around / Make it like it was / Good livin' / It doesn't hurt / This is love / (It's gonna take) all our love / Someday we'll all be free / Save the children.
■ CD . . . . . . . . . . . . . . . . . . . . 4651322
■ LP . . . . . . . . . . . . . . . . . . . . 4651321
■ MC . . . . . . . . . . . . . . . . . . . . 4651324
CBS / Aug '89.

## WHOLE NEW WORLD, A (Belle, Regina & Peabo Bryson).
**Tracks:** Whole new world (Aladdin's theme) / Love.
■ 7" . . . . . . . . . . . . . . . . . . . .659900 7
■ 7" . . . . . . . . . . . . . . . . . . . .659900 0
■ MC Single . . . . . . . . . . . . . .659900 4
■ CD Single . . . . . . . . . . . . . .659900 2
Columbia / Nov '93.

## WITHOUT YOU (see under Bryson, Peabo).

## YOU GOT THE LOVE.
**Tracks:** You got the love / Gotta give it up / You got the love (dub version) / You got the love (7" version) / Show me the way (extended mix).
■ 12" . . . . . . . . . . . . . . . . . . REBE QT1
■ 12" . . . . . . . . . . . . . . . . . . REBE T1
■ 7" . . . . . . . . . . . . . . . . . . . . REBE 1
CBS / Sep '87.

# Bendeth, David

## ADRENALIN.
**Tracks:** Breakdown / Easy ridin' / Lock stock and barrel / Dr. Dimento / Feel the real / Copycat / Bozonoknowz / Adrenalin / Count me out / Turbo charger / Calm.
■ LP . . . . . . . . . . . . . . . . . . . .SWK 2004
Sidewalk / Oct '79.

## BETTER BELIEVE IT.
**Tracks:** Better believe it / Make it play.
■ 12" . . . . . . . . . . . . . . . . . . ENYT 210
Ensign / Apr '81.

## FEEL THE REAL.
**Tracks:** Feel the real / Make it pop / Feel the real (again).
■ 7" . . . . . . . . . . . . . . . . . . . . SID 113
Sidewalk / Sep '79.
■ 7" . . . . . . . . . . . . . . . . . . . .ENY 210
Ensign / May '81.

## JUST DESSERT.
**Tracks:** Make it pop / Goldmine / I was there / Love collects / Rollin' / Feel the real (again) / Colourful dream / Risque rock / Better believe it / Acapulco.
■ MC . . . . . . . . . . . . . . . . . . ENCAS 502
■ LP . . . . . . . . . . . . . . . . . . . .ENVY 502
Ensign / Mar '81.

## LOVE COLLECT.
**Tracks:** Love collect / Gold mine.
■ 12" . . . . . . . . . . . . . . . . . . ENYT 203
■ 7" . . . . . . . . . . . . . . . . . . . .ENY 203
Ensign / Feb '81.

# Benoit, David

## BENOIT/FREEMAN PROJECT (Benoit, David & Russ Freeman).
**Tracks:** Reunion / When she believed in me / Mediterranean nights / Swept away / End of our season / After the love is gone / Smartypants / It's the thought that counts / Mirage / That's all I could say.
CD . . . . . . . . . . . . . . . . . . . . GRP 97392
GRP / Feb '94 / BMG / New Note.

## EVERY STEP OF THE WAY.
**Tracks:** Every step of the way / Shibuya Station / Key to you / Remembering what you said / Painted desert / ReBach / Sao Paulo / No worries / I just can't stop loving you / Once running free.
■ LP . . . . . . . . . . . . . . . . . . . . GRP 91047
■ MC . . . . . . . . . . . . . . . . . GRPM 91047
■ CD . . . . . . . . . . . . . . . . . . GRP 95582
GRP / May '88.

## FREEDOM AT MIDNIGHT.
**Tracks:** Freedom at midnight / Along the Milky Way / Kei's song / Man with the panama hat / Pieces of time / Morning sojourn / Tropical breeze / Passion walk / Del sasser / Last goodbye (On CD Only).
■ LP . . . . . . . . . . . . . . . . . . . . GRP 91035
■ MC . . . . . . . . . . . . . . . . . GRPM 91035
■ CD . . . . . . . . . . . . . . . . . . . GRD 9545
GRP / May '87.
■ CD . . . . . . . . . . . . . . . . . . GRP 95452
GRP / Jul '92.

## INNER MOTION.
**Tracks:** M.W.A. (musicians with attitude) / Coconut Roads / Every corner of the world / 6 string poet / Houston / Along love's highway / Deep light / El camino real / South East Quarter / Last request.
■ LP . . . . . . . . . . . . . . . . . . . . GRP 96211
■ MC . . . . . . . . . . . . . . . . . . GRP 96214
■ CD . . . . . . . . . . . . . . . . . . GRP 96212
GRP / Oct '90.

## LETTER TO EVAN.
**Tracks:** Letter to Evan / Waiting for love / On golden pond / Island / Looking for eastlake / Knit for Mary F / Kathy's waltz / Things are getting better / Spring can really hang you up the most / Take six / Blues at sunset.
CD . . . . . . . . . . . . . . . . . . . . GRP 96872
GRP / Oct '92 / BMG / New Note.

## LIFE IS A SAMBA.
**Tracks:** Life is a samba.
■ 12" . . . . . . . . . . . . . . . . . . .AVISL 103
■ 7" . . . . . . . . . . . . . . . . . . . . AVIS 103
AVI (USA) / Nov '79.

## SHADOWS.
**Tracks:** Overture / Over the edge / Have you forgotten (interlude) / Shadows / Saudade / Moments / Already there / Still standing / Castles / Have you forgotten / Reprise.
■ MC . . . . . . . . . . . . . . . . . . GRP 96544
■ CD . . . . . . . . . . . . . . . . . . GRP 96542
GRP / Oct '91.
■ DCC . . . . . . . . . . . . . . . . . GRX 96545
GRP / Jan '93.

## SHAKEN, NOT STIRRED.
**Tracks:** Wailea / I went to bat for you / Any other time / Carmel / Sparks flew / Shaken, not stirred / Chi Chi's eyes / Days of old / Jacqueline / Sarah's theme.
CD . . . . . . . . . . . . . . . . . . . . GRP 97872
GRP / Oct '94 / BMG / New Note.

## THIS SIDE UP.
**Tracks:** Beach trails / Stingray / Land of the loving / Linus and Lucy / Sunset Island / Hymn for Aquino / Santa Barbara / Waltz for Debbie.
CD . . . . . . . . . . . . . . . . . . GRD 9541
■ LP . . . . . . . . . . . . . . . . . . GRP 91031
GRP / Mar '87 / BMG / New Note.
■ CD . . . . . . . . . . . . . . . . . . GRP 95412
GRP / Nov '91.

## URBAN DAYDREAMS.
**Tracks:** Sailing through the city / Urban daydreams / Snow dancing / Wild kids / Seattle morning / Cloud break / When the winter's gone / Safari / Looking back / As if I could reach rainbows.
■ LP . . . . . . . . . . . . . . . . . . . . GRP 95871
■ CD . . . . . . . . . . . . . . . . . . GRP 95872
■ MC . . . . . . . . . . . . . . . . . . GRP 95874
GRP / Apr '89.

## WAITING FOR SPRING.
**Tracks:** Not Advised.
■ LP . . . . . . . . . . . . . . . . . . GRP 95951
■ CD . . . . . . . . . . . . . . . . . . GRP 95952
GRP / Oct '89.

# Benson, George

Born in Pennsylvania in 1943, George Benson began learning the guitar at the age of eight. Having moved to New York, he began to make his mark during the sixties and early seventies with his jazz flavoured guitar work, culminating in 1973's much praised *White Rabbit* album. Under the name George 'Bad' Benson, he scored his first British hit single in the autumn of '75 with *Supership*. His breakthrough came in 1976 with the jazz-funk LP *Breezin'*, when it became apparent that his skilful guitarist was a strong singer too. *This Masquerade*, a remake of the Leon Russell song became the first US Top 10 hit for Benson and 1977's *In Flight* continued the success, giving Benson another US Top 10 album and his first UK album placing. The Stevie Wonder-ish vocals of Benson were pushed to the forefront on the next hit *The Greatest Love Of All*, the theme from the Mohammed Ali movie *The Greatest*. In 1980 Benson teamed up with the Quincy Jones who, fresh from his massive success with Michael Jackson's *Off The Wall*, made *Give Me The Night* a major commercial triumph. The producer's jazz-tinged, soul-inflected but ever commercial sound was just what the artist needed to complete his long-term move into the pop market. In the UK the LP reached No. 3 with 40 weeks on the chart, while the title track was Benson's first Top 10 single in the UK. Stateside it was his biggest ever 45, reaching No. 4. The follow-up *Love X Love* was the second UK Top 10 hit from the album, consolidating his position as a major vocal artist. This success with it's financial rewards gave Benson the kind of security needed to tempt him back to jazz with 1989's *Tenderly* and 1990's *Big Boss Band* with the Count Basie Orchestra. Benson has managed to build himself a considerable fanbase with his big sellers while keeping the critic's respect with his obvious musical ability, the jazz apprenticeship has given him a credibility and longevity that is rare amongst his peer group.

## 20/20.
**Tracks:** No one emotion / Please don't walk away / I just wanna hang around you / Nothing's gonna change my love for you / La mer / New day / You are the love of my life / Hold me / Stand up / 20/20 / Shark bite.
MC . . . . . . . . . . . . . . . . . . .925178 4
■ LP . . . . . . . . . . . . . . . . . . .925178 1
WEA / Jan '85 / WEA.

## 20/20.
**Tracks:** 20/20 / Shark bite.
■ 12" . . . . . . . . . . . . . . . . . . . W 9120 T
■ 7" . . . . . . . . . . . . . . . . . . . . W 9120
WEA / Jan '85.

## BEST OF GEORGE BENSON.
**Tracks:** White rabbit / Somewhere in the East / Body talk / Take five / California dreamin' / Full compass.
■ LP . . . . . . . . . . . . . . . . . . . . AMID 115
■ MC . . . . . . . . . . . . . . . . . . CMID 115
A&M / Mar '82.

## BEST OF GEORGE BENSON (EPIC).
**Tracks:** California dreamin' / Gentle rain / One rock don't make no boulder / Take five / Summertime / Theme from good king bad / Bodytalk / Theme from summer of '42 / My latin brothers / Ode to a Kudu / I remember Wes / From now on.
CD . . . . . . . . . . . . . . . . . . . . 4654052
MC . . . . . . . . . . . . . . . . . . . . 4654054
Epic / Oct '92 / Sony.

## BEYOND THE SEA.
**Tracks:** Beyond the sea / Breezin' / This masquerade (on 12" only).
■ 12" . . . . . . . . . . . . . . . . . . WN 014 T
■ 7" . . . . . . . . . . . . . . . . . . . . W 9014
WEA / Apr '85.

## BIG BOSS BAND (Featuring The Count Basie Orchestra).
**Tracks:** Without a song / How do you keep the music playing / Baby workout / Portrait of Jennie / Skylark / Ready now that you are / On Green Dolphin Street / I only have eyes for you / Walkin' my baby back home / Basie's rag.
CD . . . . . . . . . . . . . . . . . . . . 7599262952

■ LP . . . . . . . . . . . . . . . 7599262951
MC . . . . . . . . . . . . . . . . 7599262954
WEA / Sep '90 / WEA.

## BLUE BENSON.
Tracks: Billie's bounce / Low down and dirty / That lucky old sun / Thunder walk / Doobie, doobie blues / What's new / I remember Wes.
■ LP . . . . . . . . . . . . . . . . . .2486 272
MC . . . . . . . . . . . . . . . . . . . .3186 098
Polydor / Jun '83 / PolyGram.

## BODY TALK.
Tracks: Not Advised.
MC . . . . . . . . . . . . . . . . . . CTK 9503
CTI (Musidisc France) / Feb '84.
CD . . . . . . . . . . . . . . . . . . . .239206
Musidisc / Dec '86 / Vital Distribution / Discovery / A.D.A. Distribution / Harmonia Mundi (UK).

## BREEZIN'.
Tracks: This masquerade / Six to four / Breezin' / So this is love / Lady / Affirmation.
CD . . . . . . . . . . . . . . . . . . K2 56199
■ LP . . . . . . . . . . . . . . . . . K 56199
■ MC . . . . . . . . . . . . . . . . K4 56199
WEA / Jun '89 / WEA.

## COLLABORATION (Benson, George & Earl Klugh).
Tracks: Mt. Airy road / Mimosa / Brazilian stomp / Dreamin' / Since you're gone / Collaboration / Jamaica / Romeo and Juliet love theme.
CD . . . . . . . . . . . . . . . . . .925580 2
■ MC . . . . . . . . . . . . . . . . .WX 91 C
■ LP . . . . . . . . . . . . . . . . . . WX 91
WEA / Jul '87 / WEA.

## COLLECTION: GEORGE BENSON.
Tracks: Not Advised.
CD . . . . . . . . . . . . . . . . . DVCD 2076
■ LP . . . . . . . . . . . . . . . DVLP 2076
MC . . . . . . . . . . . . . . . . DVMC 2076
Deja Vu / Nov '88 / Jazz Music / Music Collection International.

## COMPACT JAZZ: GEORGE BENSON.
Tracks: Billie's bounce / What's new / Thunder walk / Low down and dirty / That lucky old sun / Song for my father / Sack o' woe / Doobie doobie blues / Tuxedo Junction / I remember Wes.
CD . . . . . . . . . . . . . . . . . 833 292-2
■ MC . . . . . . . . . . . . . . . 833 292-4
Verve / Mar '88 / PolyGram.

## DETROIT'S GEORGE BENSON.
Tracks: Not Advised.
■ LP . . . . . . . . . . . . . . PARKWOOD 107
Parkwood / Jul '88.

## EARLY YEARS.
Tracks: White rabbit / Somewhere in the East / Take five / California dreamin' / Body talk / Full compass.
■ LP . . . . . . . . . . . . . . .CTI 2409219
CTI (1) / Jul '82.
■ LP . . . . . . . . . . . . . . . . SPELP 53
MC . . . . . . . . . . . . . . . . . . SPEMC 53
■ CD . . . . . . . . . . . . . . . . .8136 592
CTI (1) / Nov '83 / New Note.

## ELECTRIFYING GEORGE BENSON, THE (Benson, George Quartet).
Tracks: All the things you are / Love for sale / Oleo / All blues / Masquerade is over / Invitation / Li'l darlin'.
■ Double LP . . . . . . . . . . . . . AFFD 140
Affinity / May '85.
CD . . . . . . . . . . . . . . . .CDCHARLY 9
Charly / Mar '86 / Charly.
■ CD . . . . . . . . . . . . . . . . . 500 064
Intertape / Jul '87.

## EXCLUSIVE BENSON.
Tracks: I am the walrus / You make me feel like a natural woman / Doobie doobie blues / Along comes Mary / Billie's bounce / Groovin' / Sunny / I remember Wes / Low down and dirty / Sack o' woe / Walk on by / Julie / What's new / That lucky old sun / Giblet gravy / Windmills of your mind / People get ready / Thunder walk / Song for my father / Carnival joys.
■ Double LP . . . . . . . . . . . . VSOPLP 109
MC . . . . . . . . . . . . . . . . VSOPMC 109
Connoisseur Collection / Nov '87 / Pinnacle.

## FEEL LIKE MAKIN' LOVE.
Tracks: Feel like makin' love / Use me.
■ 12" . . . . . . . . . . . . . . . . W 9551 T
■ 7" . . . . . . . . . . . . . . . . . W 9551
WEA / Jul '83.

## GENIUS OF GEORGE BENSON.
Tracks: California dreamin' / Shell of a man / Summer knows / Summertime / Cast your fate to the

wind / No sooner said than done / Changing world / Take five.
MC . . . . . . . . . . . . . . . . . . HSC 3129
■ LP . . . . . . . . . . . . . . . . SHM 3129
Hallmark / Nov '83 / Pickwick.

## GEORGE BENSON AND JACK MCDUFF (Benson, George & Jack McDuff).
Tracks: Shadow dancers / Sweet Alice blues / I don't know / Just another Sunday / Will you still be mine / Easy living / Rock a bye / Hot barbecue / Party's over / Briar patch / Hippy dip / 601 1/2 No. Poplar / Cry me a river / Three day thang.
■ Double LP . . . . . . . . . . . . PR 24072
Prestige / Jul '77.

## GEORGE BENSON COLLECTION, THE.
Tracks: Turn your love around / Love all the hurt away / Give me the night / Cast your fate to the wind / Love ballad / Nature boy / Last train to Clarksville / Livin' inside your love / Never give up on a good thing / On Broadway / White rabbit / This masquerade / Here comes the sun / Breezin' / Moody's mood / We got the love / Greatest love of all.
CD . . . . . . . . . . . . . . . 7599 23577 2
■ Double LP . . . . . . . . . . . . . K 66107
MC . . . . . . . . . . . . . . . . . K4 66107
WEA / Nov '81 / WEA.
CD . . . . . . . . . . . . . . . . . K2 66107
WEA / Jul '88 / WEA.

## GEORGE BENSON COOKBOOK, THE.
Tracks: Cooker / Benny's back / Bossa rocka / All of me / Big fat lady / Benson's rider / Ready and able / Borgia stick / Return of the prodigal son / Jumpin' with symphony Sid.
CD . . . . . . . . . . . . . . . . .476903 2
Columbia / Sep '94 / Sony.

## GEORGE BENSON IN CONCERT.
Tracks: Love for sale / Witch craft / Love walked in / Dahlin's delight (on cassette only) / Masquerade is over / All the things you are / There will never be another you / All blues (on cassette only).
MC . . . . . . . . . . . . . . . . KCBR 1029
■ LP . . . . . . . . . . . . . . . . CBR 1029
Premier (Sony) / May '85 / Sony / Pinnacle.

## GEORGE BENSON LIVE IN CONCERT.
Tracks: Not Advised.
■ LP . . . . . . . . . . . . . . . . DELD 309
■ MC . . . . . . . . . . . . . . . . CELD 309
Design / Apr '84.

## GIVE ME THE NIGHT.
Tracks: What's on your mind / Dinorah Dinorah / Love dance / Star of the story / Midnight love affair / Turn out the lamplight / Love x love / Off Broadway / Moody's mood / Give me the night.
■ LP . . . . . . . . . . . . . . . . K 56823
■ MC . . . . . . . . . . . . . . . K4 56823
WEA / Jul '80.
CD . . . . . . . . . . . . . . . . K 256823
WEA / Apr '84 / WEA.

## GIVE ME THE NIGHT.
Tracks: Give me the night / Red lights.
■ 7" . . . . . . . . . . . . . . . . K 17673
WEA / Aug '80.

## GRAFFITI COLLECTION.
Tracks: Not Advised.
CD . . . . . . . . . . . . . . . . . GRCD 05
MC . . . . . . . . . . . . . . . . GRMC 05
Graffiti Collection / Aug '90 / THE.

## GREATEST LOVE OF ALL.
Tracks: Greatest love of all.
■ 7" . . . . . . . . . . . . . . . .ARIST 133
Arista / Nov '80.

## GREATEST LOVE OF ALL (OLD GOLD).
Tracks: Greatest love of all / Funkin' for Jamaica.
7" . . . . . . . . . . . . . . . . . OG 9454
Old Gold / Mar '90 / Pickwick.

## GUITAR GIANTS.
Tracks: Love for sale / Masquerade is over / There will never be another you / All bless / Witchcraft / Blue bossa / Oleo / Lil' darlin'.
CD . . . . . . . . . . . . . . . . SMS 055
Pickwick / Oct '92 / Pickwick.

## HEY GIRL.
Tracks: Hey girl / Welcome to my world.
■ 7" . . . . . . . . . . . . . . . . K 17472
WEA / Nov '79.

## I'LL KEEP YOUR DREAMS ALIVE (Benson, George & Patti Austin).
Tracks: I'll keep your dreams alive.
■ 12" . . . . . . . . . . . . . . 12AMMI 101
■ 7" . . . . . . . . . . . . . . . AMMI 101
■ CD Single . . . . . . . . . . . . CDAMMI 101

■ MC Single . . . . . . . . . . . . MCAMMI 101
Ammi / Dec '92.

## IN CONCERT - CARNEGIE HALL.
Tracks: Gone / Take 5 / Octane / Summertime.
■ LP . . . . . . . . . . . . . . . .CTI 6072
CTI (1) / May '77.

## IN FLIGHT.
Tracks: Nature boy / Wind and I / World is a ghetto / Gonna love you more / Valdez in the country / Everything must change.
■ LP . . . . . . . . . . . . . . . . K 56327
■ MC . . . . . . . . . . . . . . . K4 56327
WEA / Jan '77.
CD . . . . . . . . . . . . . . . . .256327
WEA / '86 / WEA.

## IN YOUR EYES.
Tracks: Feel like makin' love / Inside love (so personal) / Lady love me (one more time) / Love will come again / In your eyes / Never too far to fall / Being with you / Use me / Late at night / In search of a dream.
MC . . . . . . . . . . . . . . . .923744 4
■ LP . . . . . . . . . . . . . . .923744 1
WEA / Jun '83 / WEA.
CD . . . . . . . . . . . . . . . .923744 2
WEA / Jul '88 / WEA.

## IN YOUR EYES.
Tracks: In your eyes / Being with you.
■ 7" . . . . . . . . . . . . . . . . W 9487
■ 12" . . . . . . . . . . . . . .W 9487T
WEA / Sep '83.

## INSIDE LOVE (SO PERSONAL).
Tracks: Inside love (so personal).
■ 7" . . . . . . . . . . . . . . . . W 9427
WEA / Dec '83.

## INVITATION.
Tracks: Not Advised.
CD . . . . . . . . . . . . . . . . . RC 83111
■ MC . . . . . . . . . . . . . . . . . 82111
Royal Collection / Mar '93 / BMG.

## IT'S UPTOWN WITH THE GEORGE BENSON QUARTET (Benson, George Quartet).
Tracks: Clockwise / Summertime / Ain't that peculiar / Jaguar / Willow weep for me / Foggy day / Hello birdie / Bullfight / Stormy weather / Eternally / Myna bird blues.
CD . . . . . . . . . . . . . . . . .476902 2
Columbia / Sep '94 / Sony.

## IT'S UPTOWN/GEORGE BENSON COOKBOOK.
Tracks: Clockwise / Summertime / Ain't that peculiar / Jaguar / Willow weep for me / Foggy day / Hello birdie / Bullfight / Stormy weather / Eternally / Myna bird blues / Cooker / Benny's back / Bossa rocka / All of me / Big fat lady / Benson's rider / Ready and able / Borgia stick / Return of the prodigal son / Jumpin' with symphony Sid.
■ Double LP . . . . . . . . . . . . CBS 22187
MC Set . . . . . . . . . . . . .40 22187
CBS (Blue Diamond) / Jun '85 / Sony.

## KISSES IN THE MOONLIGHT.
Tracks: Kisses in the moonlight / Open your eyes (instrumental).
■ 12" . . . . . . . . . . . . . . . W 8640 T
■ 7" . . . . . . . . . . . . . . . . W 8640
WEA / Jul '86.

## LADY BLUE.
Tracks: Lady blue / Down here on the ground.
■ 7" . . . . . . . . . . . . . . . K 17172
WEA / May '78.

## LADY LOVE ME (ONE MORE TIME).
Tracks: Lady love me (one more time) / In search of a dream.
■ 12" . . . . . . . . . . . . . . . W 9614 T
■ 7" . . . . . . . . . . . . . . . . W 9614
WEA / May '83.

## LATE AT NIGHT.
Tracks: Late at night / Love will come again / Welcome into my world (On 12" only).
■ 12" . . . . . . . . . . . . . . .W 9325T
■ 7" . . . . . . . . . . . . . . . W 9325
WEA / Mar '84.

## LEGENDS IN MUSIC - GEORGE BENSON.
Tracks: Not Advised.
CD . . . . . . . . . . . . . . . .LECD 068
Wisepack / Jul '94 / THE / Conifer Records.

■ DELETED

## LET'S DO IT AGAIN.
Tracks: Let's do it again / Let's go.
- 12" ............................. W 7780 T
- 7" .............................. W 7780

WEA / Aug '88.

## LIL' DARLIN'.
Tracks: Witchcraft / Blue bossa / Oleo / Li'l darlin'.
CD ............................... CDTB 078
LP ............................... THBL 078

Thunderbolt / Sep '90 / THE / Jazz Music.

## LIVE AT CASA CARIBE (Benson, George Quartet).
Tracks: Not Advised.
CD ............................... COD 011

Jazz View / Mar '92 / Harmonia Mundi (UK).

## LIVE AT CASA CARIBE VOL.2 (Benson, George Quartet).
Tracks: Not Advised.
CD ............................... COD 035

Jazz View / Jun '92 / Harmonia Mundi (UK).

## LIVE AT THE CASA CARIBE (VOL.3) (Benson, George Quartet).
Tracks: Not Advised.
CD ............................... COD 036

Jazz View / Aug '92 / Harmonia Mundi (UK).

## LIVIN' INSIDE YOUR LOVE.
Tracks: Before you go / Welcome into my world / Love is a hurtin' thing / You're never too far from me / Love ballad / Change is gonna come / Prelude to fall / Soulful strut / Nassau day / Hey girl.
- Double LP ....................... K 66085
- MC ............................. K4 66085

WEA / Mar '79.
- CD ............................. K2 66085

WEA / Jun '89.

## LOVE ALL THE HURT AWAY.
Tracks: Love all the hurt away / Whole lot of me / Hold on I'm coming.
- 12" ........................... ARIST 12428
- 7" ............................ ARIST 428

Arista / Aug '81.

## LOVE BALLAD.
Tracks: Love ballad / You're too far from me.
- 7" ............................ K 17333

WEA / Mar '79.

## LOVE OF MY LIFE.
Tracks: Love of my life / Give me the night / Never give up on a good thing (Available on 12"/CDS only) / Love ballad (Available on 12"/CDS only).
- 12" ............................ W 0199T
- 7" ............................. W 0199
- CD Single ...................... W 0199CD

Warner Bros. / Sep '93.

## LOVE REMEMBERS.
Tracks: I'll be good to you / Got to be there / My heart is dancing / Love of my life / Kiss and make up / Come into my world / Love remembers / Willing to fight / Somewhere Island / Lovin' on borrowed time / Lost in love / Calling you.
CD ............................... .759926685-2
MC ............................... .759926685-4

Warner Bros. / Jun '93 / WEA.

## LOVE SONGS: GEORGE BENSON.
Tracks: Give me the night / Lady love me (one more time) / Love X love / New day / Feel like makin' love / 20/20 / Never give up on a good thing / Inside love (so personal) / No one emotion / In your eyes / Turn your love around / Greatest love of all.
- LP ............................. NE 1308
- MC ............................. CE 2308

K-Tel / Oct '85.

## LOVE WALKED IN.
Tracks: All the things you are / Invitations / Love walked in / Dahlin's delight.
- LP ............................. PLP 36
MC. ............................. PMC 36

Platinum (W.Germany) / Oct '85.
CD ............................... CDTB 088

Thunderbolt / Dec '90 / THE / Jazz Music.

## LOVE X LOVE.
Tracks: Love x love / Off Broadway.
- 12" ............................ LV 41
- 7" ............................. K 17699

WEA / Sep '80.

## MASQUERADE.
Tracks: Love for sale / Masquerade is over / There will never be another you / All blues.
CD ............................... CDTB 072
- LP ............................. THBL 072

Thunderbolt / Oct '89 / THE / Jazz Music.

---

## NATURE BOY.
Tracks: Nature boy / Wind and I.
- 7" ............................. K 16921

WEA / Jun '77.

## NEVER GIVE UP ON A GOOD THING.
Tracks: Never give up on a good thing / California p.m.
- 12" ............................ K 17902 T
- 7" ............................. K 17902

WEA / Jan '82.

## NO ONE EMOTION (Benson, George & Roberta Flack).
Tracks: No one emotion / You are the love of my life.
- 12" ............................ W 8863T
- 7" ............................. W 8863

WEA / Oct '85.

## ON BROADWAY.
Tracks: On Broadway / We as love.
- 7" ............................. K 17120

WEA / Mar '78.

## ON BROADWAY.
Tracks: On Broadway / Love will come again.
- 12" ............................ W 9427 T

WEA / Nov '83.

## PAR EXCELLENCE.
Tracks: Not Advised.
LP Set ........................... CDMT 501

Magnum Music / Sep '93 / Magnum Music Group / THE.

## QUARTET ALL BLUES.
Tracks: Not Advised.
CD ............................... CDSGP 034

Prestige / Jul '92 / Total / BMG.

## QUARTET BLUE BOSSA.
Tracks: Not Advised.
CD ............................... CDSGP 035

Prestige / Jul '92 / Total / BMG.

## REPLAY ON GEORGE BENSON.
Tracks: Not Advised.
- LP ............................. FEDB 5019
MC. .............................. CFEDB 5019

Sierra / Aug '85.

## SHAPE OF THINGS TO COME.
Tracks: Footin' it / Face it boy it's over / Shape of things that are and were / Chattanooga choo choo / Don't let me lose this dream / Last train to Clarksville / Shape of things to come.
- LP ............................. AMLS 945

A&M / Sep '69.
- CD ............................. CDA 0803

A&M / Nov '88.

## SHIVER.
Tracks: Shiver / Love is here tonight.
- 12" ............................ W 8523T
- 7" ............................. W 8523

WEA / Nov '86.

## SILVER COLLECTION, THE.
Tracks: Billie's bounce / Low down and dirty / Thunder walk / Doobie doobie blues / What's new / I remember Wes / Windmills of your mind / Song for my father / Carnival joys / Giblet gravy / Walk on by / Sack o' woe / Groovin'.
- CD ............................. 823 450-2

Verve / Nov '85.

## SPACE.
Tracks: Hold on I'm coming / Summertime / Son of sky dive / Gone / Octane.
- LP ............................. CTI 7085

CTI (1) / '79.

## SPOTLIGHT ON GEORGE BENSON.
Tracks: Witchcraft / Love for sale / There will never be another you / All blues / L'il darlin' / Oleo.
CD ............................... HADCD 102
MC. .............................. HADMC 102

Javelin / Feb '94 / THE.

## STAND UP.
Tracks: Not Advised.
- CD ............................. .925178 2

WEA / Dec '84.

## STORMY WEATHER.
Tracks: Clockwise / Big fat lady / Hammond's bossa nova / Stormy weather / Slow scene / Jumpin' with symphony Sid / Cooker / Push push / Bullfight / Ready 'n' able / Bossa rocka / Flamingo.
- MC ............................. .40 31689
- LP ............................. 31689

CBS / Oct '78.

---

## SUMMERTIME.
Tracks: Not Advised.
- LP ............................. EPC 32191
- MC ............................. .40 32191

Epic / Sep '82.

## SUPERSHIP.
Tracks: Supership.
- 7" ............................. CTSP 002

CTI (1) / Oct '75.

## TEASER.
Tracks: Did you hear the thunder / Teaser.
- 12" ............................ W 8437T
- 7" ............................. W 8437

WEA / Jan '87.

## TENDERLY.
Tracks: You don't know what love is / Stella by starlight / Stardust / At the mambo inn / Here, There and Everywhere / This is all I ask / Tenderly / I could write a book.
CD ............................... 9259072
- LP ............................. WX 263
- LP ............................. 9259071
- MC ............................. WX 263C

WEA / Jul '89 / WEA.

## TURN YOUR LOVE AROUND.
Tracks: Turn your love around / Nature boy.
- 7" ............................. K 17877

WEA / Nov '81.

## TWICE THE LOVE.
Tracks: Twice the love / Starting all over / Good habit / Everybody does it / Living on borrowed love / Let's do it again / Stephanie / Tender love / You're still my baby / Until you believe.
CD ............................... .925705 2
- LP ............................. WX 160
- MC ............................. WX 160C

WEA / Aug '88 / WEA.

## TWICE THE LOVE.
Tracks: Twice the love (guitar love mix) / Love is here tonight.
- CD Single ...................... W 7665 CD
- 12" ............................ W 7665 T
- 7" ............................. W 7665

WEA / Nov '88.

## UNCHAINED MELODY.
Tracks: Unchained melody / Before you go.
- 7" ............................. K 17409

WEA / '79.

## WEEKEND IN LA.
Tracks: Greatest love of all / Down here on the ground / Ode to a Kudu / We as love / California pm / Lady blue / We all remember Wes / Windsong / On Broadway / It's all in the game / Weekend in LA.
- Double LP ...................... K 66074
- MC ............................. K4 66074

WEA / Jan '78.

## WHAT'S ON YOUR MIND.
Tracks: What's on your mind / Turn out the lamplight.
- 12" ............................ K 17748 T
- 7" ............................. K 17748

WEA / Feb '81.

## WHILE THE CITY SLEEPS.
Tracks: Shiver / Love is here tonight / Teaser / Secrets in the night / Too many times / Did you hear the thunder / While the city sleeps / Kisses in the moonlight.
CD ............................... .925475 2
- LP ............................. WX 55
- MC ............................. WX 55 C

WEA / Sep '86 / WEA.

## WHITE RABBIT.
Tracks: White rabbit / Summer of '42 theme / Little train / California dreaming / El mar.
- LP ............................. CTL 6

Creed Taylor / '72.

## WITCHCRAFT.
Tracks: Not Advised.
CD ............................... JHR 73523

Jazz Hour / Sep '93 / Target / Jazz Music.

## WONDERFUL YEARS, THE.
Tracks: Not Advised.
- LP ............................. PENALP 2

Proto / Mar '84.

## YOU ARE THE LOVE OF MY LIFE.
Tracks: You are the love of my life / I just wanna hang around you.
- 12" ............................ W 8985 T
- 7" ............................. W 8985

WEA / Jul '85.

---

■ DELETED

## Benson, Jo Jo

**I THANK YOU (see under Scott, Peggy).**

**LOVERS' HOLIDAY (Benson, Jo Jo & Peggy Scott).**
Tracks: Lover's holiday / Picking wild mountain berries.
■ 7" . . . . . . . . . . . . . . . . . . . . . . . . . . . CTD 108
Charly / Jul '80.

**SOUL SHAKE (see under Scott, Peggy).**

## Benton, Brook

**20 GOLDEN PIECES: BROOK BENTON.**
Tracks: Bayou baby / Sunshine / Endlessly / Old-fashioned proud / Soft / Trust me to do what you want me to do (and I'll do it) / Pulling me down / Makin' love is good for you / Love is best of all / Tribute to "Mamam" / Let the sun come out / We need what we need / Better times / Lover's question / Let me in your world / I love her / Lord, you know how men are / Till I can't take it anymore / I keep thinking to myself / There's still a little love left for me.
■ LP . . . . . . . . . . . . . . . . . . . . . . . . . . BDL 2039
Bulldog Records / Mar '84.

**20 GREATEST HITS.**
Tracks: Not Advised.
CD . . . . . . . . . . . . . . . . . . . . . . . . RMB 75041
MC . . . . . . . . . . . . . . . . . . . . . . . . RMB 45041
Remember / Nov '93 / Midland Records / BMG.

**20 GREATEST HITS: BROOK BENTON.**
Tracks: Not Advised.
CD . . . . . . . . . . . . . . . . . . . . . . . . . . CD 1032
Gusto (USA) / '88.

**40 GREATEST HITS: BROOK BENTON.**
Tracks: Not Advised.
CD . . . . . . . . . . . . . . . . . . . . . . . . . . 8367552
Philips / Jan '90 / PolyGram.

**BEST BALLADS OF BROADWAY.**
Tracks: Once upon a time / Make someone happy / I've never been in love before / Long before I knew you / Till there was you / Hello young lovers / As long as she needs me / Soon / I'll know / If ever I would leave you / Love look away / Sweetest sounds.
■ LP . . . . . . . . . . . . . . . . . . . . . . . . . MVL 307
Mercury / Nov '67.

**BEST OF BROOK BENTON.**
Tracks: Fools rush in / Kiddio / Hotel happiness / Sill waters run deep / Shadrack / Think twice / Frankie and Johnny / Rockin' good way / Hit record / Boll weevil song / Revenge / Endlessly / Lie to me / So many ways / It's just a matter of time / Walk on the wild side / Baby (you've got what it takes).
■ LP . . . . . . . . . . . . . . . . . . . . . . . . TIME 01
■ MC . . . . . . . . . . . . . . . . . . . . . . . TIMEC 01
Philips (Timeless) / Jul '84.
■ CD . . . . . . . . . . . . . . . . . . . . . . . 830 772 2
Philips / Jan '90.

**BEST OF BROOK BENTON (K-TEL).**
Tracks: Not Advised.
■ MC . . . . . . . . . . . . . . . . . . . . . . . GM 0229
K-Tel / Aug '84.
■ CD . . . . . . . . . . . . . . . . . . . . . . . NCD 3418
K-Tel / '90.

**BEST OF BROOK BENTON, VOL 1.**
Tracks: It's just a matter of time / Kiddio / Same one / It's just a house without you / My true confession / Fools rush in / Think twice / Hotel happiness / Thank you pretty baby / Boll weevil song.
■ LP . . . . . . . . . . . . . . . . . . . . . . . . PHX 1019
Phoenix (2) / Oct '82.

**BLACK VELVET (Brook Benton's Hot Millions Of The 1950's & 60's).**
Tracks: Baby (You've got what it takes) / Boll weevil song / Endlessly / Fools rush in / frankie and johnny / Hit record / Hotel happiness / It's just a matter of time / Kiddio / Lie to me / Rainy night in Georgia / Revenge / Rockin' good way / Shadrack / So many ways / Still waters run deep / Think twice / Walk on the wild side.
■ LP . . . . . . . . . . . . . . . . . . . . . . . . 6336268
■ MC . . . . . . . . . . . . . . . . . . . . . . . 7175095
Mercury / Sep '77.

**BOLL WEEVIL SONG.**
Tracks: Boll weevil song.
■ 7" . . . . . . . . . . . . . . . . . . . . . . . . AMT 1148
Mercury (EMI) / Jul '61.

**BROOK BENTON.**
Tracks: Not Advised.
MC . . . . . . . . . . . . . . . . . . . . . . . ZCGAS 722
Audio Fidelity / Oct '84 / Telstar/Ronco.

**BROOK BENTON SINGS THE STANDARDS.**
Tracks: Hey there / That old feeling / Nightingale sang in Berkeley Square / Love is a many splen-doured thing / Once in love with Amy / Try a little tenderness / Call me irresponsible / Blue moon / Second time around / Moon river / Hawaiian wedding song / More / There, I've said it again / I only have eyes for you / Unforgettable / There goes my heart.
■ LP . . . . . . . . . . . . . . . . . . . . . . NL 89092
■ MC . . . . . . . . . . . . . . . . . . . . . . NK 89092
RCA / '84.

**DIAMOND SERIES: BROOK BENTON.**
Tracks: That old feeling / Nightingale sang in Berke-ley Square / Love is a many splendoured thing / Try a little tenderness / Hey there / Call me irrespon-sible / Peg o' my heart / Mother Nature, Father Time / I wanna be with you / More time to be with you / Cold, cold heart / Funny how time slips away / He's got you / I really don't want to know / Hello walls / Gone.
■ CD . . . . . . . . . . . . . . . . . . . . . . . CD 90109
Diamond Series / Apr '88.

**DO YOUR OWN THING.**
Tracks: Touch 'em with love / Nothing takes the place of you / Destination heartbreak / Woman with-out love / Break out / She knows what to do for me / Set me free / With pen in hand / Hiding behind the shadow of a dream / I just don't know what to do with myself / Oh Lord, why Lord / Do your own thing.
■ LP . . . . . . . . . . . . . . . . . . . . . . . . 588 187
Atlantic / Sep '69.

**ENDLESSLY.**
Tracks: It's just a matter of time / Boll weevil song / Baby you've got what it takes / Lie to me / So many ways / Hotel happiness / Kiddio / Endlessly / Revenge / Same one / Think twice / Rockin' good way.
MC . . . . . . . . . . . . . . . . . . . . . . . GM 0208
K-Tel Goldmasters / Aug '84 / C.M. Distribution / Arabesque Ltd. / Ross Records / PolyGram.
■ LP . . . . . . . . . . . . . . . . . . . . . . . TOP 158
MC . . . . . . . . . . . . . . . . . . . . . . . KTOP 158
Topline / Jan '87 / Charly.

**ENDLESSLY.**
Tracks: Endlessly.
■ 7" . . . . . . . . . . . . . . . . . . . . . . . AMT 1043
Mercury (EMI) / Aug '59.

**FOOLS RUSH IN.**
Tracks: Fools rush in.
■ 7" . . . . . . . . . . . . . . . . . . . . . . . AMT 1121
Mercury (EMI) / Feb '61.

**GOLDEN HITS.**
Tracks: Endlessly / Hither and thither and yon / How many times / Hurtin' inside / It's just a matter of time / Kiddio / Same one / So close / So many ways / Thank you pretty baby / Ties that bind / With all of my heart.
■ LP . . . . . . . . . . . . . . . . . . . . . . SMCL 20060
Mercury / Aug '69.

**GOLDEN HITS - VOL. 2.**
Tracks: Boll weevil song / Fools rush in / Frankie and Johnny / Hit record / Hotel happiness / It's just a house without you / Lie to me / Revenge / Shadrack / Still waters run deep / Think twice / Walk on the wild side.
■ LP . . . . . . . . . . . . . . . . . . . . . . SMCL 20184
Mercury / May '70.

**GOSPEL TRUTH.**
Tracks: Let us all get together with the Lord / Oh happy day / Heaven help us all / Going home in his name / Take a look at your hands / If you think God is dead / I dreamed of a city called Heaven / Doing the best I can / Precious Lord.
■ LP . . . . . . . . . . . . . . . . . . . . . . . 2400202
Atlantic / Feb '72.

**GREAT LOVE SONGS.**
Tracks: Not Advised.
CD . . . . . . . . . . . . . . . . . . . . . . . . 15 102
MC . . . . . . . . . . . . . . . . . . . . . . . . 79 549
Laserlight / Aug '91 / THE / BMG / Target.

**HIS GREATEST HITS.**
Tracks: Not Advised.
■ LP . . . . . . . . . . . . . . . . . . . . . . . 822321 1
MC . . . . . . . . . . . . . . . . . . . . . . . 822321 4
Mercury / Aug '87 / PolyGram.

**HIS TOP HITS.**
Tracks: Not Advised.
MC . . . . . . . . . . . . . . . . . . . . . . . . . . 808
Timeless Treasures / Jul '86 / THE.

**HOME STYLE.**
Tracks: Whoever finds this - I love you / For Lee Ann / Willie and Laura Mae Jones / It's all in the game / Don't make you wanta go home / Aspen Colorado / Don't think twice, it's alright / Born under a bad sign / Are you sincere / Let me fix it.
■ LP . . . . . . . . . . . . . . . . . . . . . . . 2400 024
Atlantic / Apr '71.

**INCOMPARABLE BROOK BENTON, THE.**
Tracks: It's just a matter of time / Kiddio / Same one / It's just a house without you / My true confession / Fools rush in / Think twice / Hotel happiness / Thank you pretty baby / Boll weevil song / Rainy night in Georgia / So close / Frankie and Johnny / Revenge / Lie to me / So many ways / I got what I wanted / Ties that bind / Shadrack / For my baby.
■ LP . . . . . . . . . . . . . . . . . . . . . . AFEMP 1024
Audio Fidelity / Oct '82.

**IT'S JUST A MATTER OF TIME.**
Tracks: Nearness of you / I can't begin to tell you / You tell me your dream / I'm in the mood for love / But beautiful / When I fall in love / I'll string along with you / Bold me / More I see you / It's just a matter of time / Love me or leave me / I could have told you.
■ LP . . . . . . . . . . . . . . . . . . . . . . SMWL 21013
Mercury / Dec '68.

**KIDDIO.**
Tracks: Kiddio.
■ 7" . . . . . . . . . . . . . . . . . . . . . . . AMT 1109
Mercury (EMI) / Oct '60.

**MAGIC MOMENTS WITH BROOK BENTON.**
Tracks: That old feeling / My darling, my darling / Nightingale sang in Berkeley Square / Love is a many splendoured thing / Once in love with Amy / Try a little tenderness / Hey there / Call me irrespon-sible / Peg o' my heart / Blue moon / Second time around / Moon river / While there's life (there's still hope) / Mother Nature, Father Time / I still wanna be with you (everywhere you go) / Life is too short (for me to stop loving you) / You're so wonderful / It's a crime / Boy I wish I was in your place / Since you've been gone / Song I heard last night, The (play it again) / Foolish enough to try / You're mine (and I love you) / More time to be with you.
■ MC . . . . . . . . . . . . . . . . . . . . . . NK 89623
RCA / May '85.

**MISTER BARTENDER.**
Tracks: All in love is fair / Can't take my eyes off you / I had to learn / It started all over again / Mr. Bartender / My funny valentine / Nightingale sang in Berkeley Square / Now is the time / Taxi / Weekend with feathers / You were gone.
■ LP . . . . . . . . . . . . . . . . . . . . . . . 9109303
■ MC . . . . . . . . . . . . . . . . . . . . . . . 7208405
Mercury / Jan '76.

**MY FUNNY VALENTINE.**
Tracks: My funny valentine / You were gone.
■ 7" . . . . . . . . . . . . . . . . . . . . . . . 6146 315
All Platinum / Apr '76.

**MY TRUE CONFESSION.**
Tracks: Lie to me / Got you on my mind / Take good care of her / My true confession / It's just a house without you / Tomorrow night / Endlessly / But beautiful / Hold me thrill me kiss me / I'll string along with you / I could have told you / More I see you.
■ LP . . . . . . . . . . . . . . . . . . . . . . . SFJL 951
Fontana / Jan '69.

**MY WAY.**
Tracks: My way / Shoes/Rainy night in Georgia.
■ 7" . . . . . . . . . . . . . . . . . . . . . . . 2091 050
Atlantic / Jan '71.

**ON THE COUNTRYSIDE.**
Tracks: Going going gone / Faded love / I'd trade all my tomorrows / All over again / Everytime I'm kiss-ing you / My shoes keep walkin' back to you / etc.
■ LP . . . . . . . . . . . . . . . . . . . . . . . MVL 308
Mercury / Dec '67.

**PORTRAIT OF A SONG STYLIST.**
Tracks: Not Advised.
■ CD . . . . . . . . . . . . . . . . . . . . . . HARCD 109
■ MC . . . . . . . . . . . . . . . . . . . . . . HARMC 109
Masterpiece / Oct '89.

■ DELETED

## RAINY NIGHT IN GEORGIA.
Tracks: Not Advised.
CD . . . . . . . . . . . . . . . . . . . . . CDSGP 033
MC . . . . . . . . . . . . . . . . . . . CASSGP 033
Prestige / Sep '92 / Total / BMG.

## RAINY NIGHT IN GEORGIA, A.
Tracks: Not Advised.
CD . . . . . . . . . . . . . . . . . . . . 260 422 2
MC . . . . . . . . . . . . . . . . . . . . 260 422 4
Mainline (2) / Jan '90.

## RAINY NIGHT IN GEORGIA, A.
Tracks: Rainy night in Georgia / It's just a matter of time / Boll weevil song / Baby you got what it takes / Rockin' good way / Lie to me / So many ways / Hotel happiness / Kiddio / Endlessly / Revenge / Same one / Think twice.
CD . . . . . . . . . . . . . . . . . . . CDCD 1047
Charly / Mar '93 / Charly.

## SEND FOR ME.
Tracks: Chains of love / Pledging my love / Hither and thither / Will you love me tomorrow / Send for me / Still waters run deep / I got what I wanted / How many times / Revenge / Call me / Valley of tears / Shadrack.
■ LP . . . . . . . . . . . . . . . . . . . . SFJL 970
Fontana / Feb '69.

## SONGS I LOVE TO SING.
Tracks: Moonlight in Vermont / It's been a long long time / Lover come back to me / If you are but a dream / Why try to change me now / September song / Oh what it seemed to be / Baby won't you please come home / They can't take that away from me / I'll be around / I don't know enough about you / Fools rush in.
■ LP . . . . . . . . . . . . . . . . . . . MOIR 112
■ MC . . . . . . . . . . . . . . . . . CMOIR 112
Memoir / Dec '85.

## SPOTLIGHT ON BROOK BENTON.
Tracks: Not Advised.
■ Double LP . . . . . . . . . . . . . . . . .6612 116
Philips / Jun '77.

## STORY TELLER.
Tracks: Movin' day / Willoughby Grove / Shoes / Poor make believer / Please send me someone to love / Big Mable Murphy / Save the last dance for me / Sidewalks of Chicago / Country comfort.
■ LP . . . . . . . . . . . . . . . . . . . K 40314
Atlantic / Apr '72.

## THAT OLD FEELING.
Tracks: That old feeling / My darling my darling / Nightingale sang in Berkley Square / Once in love with Amy / Try a little tenderness / Hey there / Call me irresonsible / Peg o' my heart / Call me responsible / Moon river / Second time a round / Blue moon.
■ LP . . . . . . . . . . . . . . . . . . . RD 7797
RCA / Sep '66.

## TODAY.
Tracks: Rainy night in Georgia / My way / Life has its little ups and downs / Can't take my eyes off you / We're gonna make it / Little bit of soap / Where do I go from here / Desertion / I've gotta be me.
■ LP . . . . . . . . . . . . . . . . . . . .2465 004
Atlantic / Jul '70.

## UNFORGETTABLE: BROOK BENTON (16 Golden Classics).
Tracks: Kiddio / It's just a matter of time / My true confession / Frankie and Johnny / Think twice / Hotel happiness / Thank you pretty baby / Boll weevil song / Rainy night in Georgia / Lie to me / Revenge / So many ways / I got what I wanted / Ties that bind / Shadrack / For my baby.
■ LP . . . . . . . . . . . . . . . . . . . UNLP 010
MC . . . . . . . . . . . . . . . . . . . UNMC 010
Unforgettable / Dec '86 / BMG.
CD . . . . . . . . . . . . . . . . . . . UNCD 010
Unforgettable / '88 / BMG.

## Bernard, Kenny

### I DO.
Tracks: I do / Isn't that a good idea.
■ 7" . . . . . . . . . . . . . . . . . . . 7N 17284
Pye / Mar '67.

### PITY MY FEET.
Tracks: Pity my feet / Somebody.
■ 7" . . . . . . . . . . . . . . . . . . . . . 2936
CBS / '67.

## Berry, Richard

### GET OUT OF THE CAR.
Tracks: Mad about you / Angel of my life / Yama yama pretty mama / Next time / Rockin' man / Oh, oh, get out of the car / Crazy lover / I'm still in love with you / Jelly roll / Big John / One little prayer / Big break.
■ LP . . . . . . . . . . . . . . . . . . . CH 59
Ace / Aug '87.
CD . . . . . . . . . . . . . . . . . . .CDCH 355
Ace / Mar '92 / Pinnacle / Complete Record Co. Ltd.

### LOUIE LOUIE.
Tracks: Not Advised.
■ LP . . . . . . . . . . . . . . . . . . . .JD 901
Earth Angel (Sweden) / Aug '87.

## Beverly, Frankie

### THAT'S WHAT'S YOU WANTED (Beverly, Frankie & The Butlers).
Tracks: If that's what you wanted / Love, your pain goes deep.
■ 7" . . . . . . . . . . . . . . . . . . . HEAT 4
Inferno (1) / '83.

## Biddu

### BLACKER THE BERRY (Biddu Orchestra).
Tracks: Blacker the berry / James Bond disco theme.
■ 7" . . . . . . . . . . . . . . . . . . EPC 6230
Epic / Mar '78.

### DANCE OF SHIVA (Biddu Orchestra).
Tracks: Not Advised.
CD . . . . . . . . . . . . . . . . . 290 07 082
Bellaphon / Dec '86 / New Note.

### DAUGHTER OF LOVE.
Tracks: Daughter of love / Look out here I come.
■ 7" . . . . . . . . . . . . . . . . . . . RZ 3002
Regal Zonophone / Sep '67.

### FOUNDATION OF LOVE (Biddu Orchestra featuring Erica).
Tracks: Foundation of love / Humanity (latin house mix).
■ 12" . . . . . . . . . . . . . . . . . .12TX 10
■ 7" . . . . . . . . . . . . . . . . . . .7TX 10
Trax / Jul '89.

### GIRL YOU'LL BE A WOMAN SOON (Biddu Orchestra).
Tracks: Girl you'll be a woman soon / Boogie song.
■ 7" . . . . . . . . . . . . . . . . . . EPC 5823
Epic / Feb '77.

### GROOVY KIND OF LOVE.
Tracks: Groovy kind of love.
■ 7" . . . . . . . . . . . . . . . . . . . GT 48
GTO / Feb '76.

### HUMANITY (Biddu Orchestra).
Tracks: Humanity.
■ 12" . . . . . . . . . . . . . . . . . .12TX 5
■ 7" . . . . . . . . . . . . . . . . . . . 7TX 5
Trax / Apr '89.

### I COULD HAVE DANCED ALL NIGHT (Biddu Orchestra).
Tracks: I could have danced all night / Jump for joy.
■ 7" . . . . . . . . . . . . . . . . . . EPC 3708
Epic / Nov '75.

### JOURNEY TO THE MOON (Biddu Orchestra).
Tracks: Journey to the moon / Journey in the rain.
■ 7" . . . . . . . . . . . . . . . . . . EPC 5910
Epic / Feb '78.

### NIRVANA.
Tracks: Not Advised.
■ LP . . . . . . . . . . . . . . . . . . . HEAV 1
MC . . . . . . . . . . . . . . . . . .HEAVTC 1
Heaven / Oct '84.

### RAIN FOREST (Biddu Orchestra).
Tracks: Rain forest.
■ 7" . . . . . . . . . . . . . . . . . . EPC 4084
Epic / Apr '76.

### SERENADE FOR LOVERS (Biddu Orchestra).
Tracks: Un homme et une femme / Rain forest / Girl you'll be a woman soon / Summer of '42 / Lover's serenade / Blue eyed soul / Couldn't we be friends / I could have danced all night / Bionic boogie / Journey to the moon / Blacker the berry / Soul coaxing.
■ LP . . . . . . . . . . . . . . . . . . SHM 3054

### MC . . . . . . . . . . . . . . . . . . HSC 3054
Hallmark / Mar '81.

### SOUL COAXING (Biddu Orchestra).
Tracks: Soul coaxing / Nirvana.
■ 7" . . . . . . . . . . . . . . . . . . EPC 5416
Epic / Jul '77.

### SOUL SERENADE (Biddu Orchestra).
Tracks: Soul serenade / Bionic boogie.
■ 7" . . . . . . . . . . . . . . . . . . EPC 4506
Epic / Aug '76.

### STUD (THEME FROM) (Biddu Orchestra).
Tracks: Stud (Theme from) / Unfinished journey.
■ 7" . . . . . . . . . . . . . . . . . . EPC 6317
Epic / Apr '78.

### SUMMER OF '42 (Biddu Orchestra).
Tracks: Summer of '42 / Northern dancer.
■ 7" . . . . . . . . . . . . . . . . . . EPC 3318
Epic / Aug '75.

### VOODOO MAN (Biddu Orchestra).
Tracks: Voodoo man / Voodoo man (version).
■ 12" . . . . . . . . . . . . . . . . . EPC 12 7311
■ 7" . . . . . . . . . . . . . . . . . . EPC 7311
Epic / May '79.

## Big Maybelle

'Mother of soul', Big Maybelle Smith emerged as an R'n'B 'shouter' in the early 1950's. Signing with OKeh, a subsidiary of CBS in 1952, she had her first hit single with *Gabbin' Blues*. She was also the first person to record *Whole Lotta Shakin' Goin' On* but as she entered the 60's her style began to change. After recording for Brunswick, Chess and Scepter where she recorded the classic *Don't Let The Sun Catch You Cryin'* Big Maybelle moved to Epic and released *Pure Soul* cementing her reputation as an inspirational soul singer. This success encouraged her to cover recent pop hits like the Beatles' *Don't Pass Me By* giving her a minor chart hit. But her career was cut tragically short when she died in January 1972, finally succumbing to a drugs-related illness.

### MAYBELLE SINGS THE BLUES.
Tracks: Not Advised.
CD . . . . . . . . . . . . . . . . . . . CDRB 14
Charly / Nov '94 / Charly.

### OKEH SESSIONS, THE.
Tracks: Just want your love / So good to my baby / Gabbin blues / My country man / Rain down rain / Way back home / Stay away from my Sam / Jinny Mule / Maybelle's blues / I've got a feeling / You'll never know / No more trouble out of me / My big mistake / Ain't no use / I'm getting 'long alright / You'll be sorry / Hairdressin' women / One monkey don't stop no show / Don't leave poor me / Ain't to be played with / New kind of mambo / Whole lotta shakin' goin' on.
■ CD . . . . . . . . . . . . . . . CDCHARLY 108
■ Double LP . . . . . . . . . . . . . . . CDX 27
■ MC . . . . . . . . . . . . . . . . . TCCDX 27
Charly / Sep '88.

### ROOTS OF ROCK'N'ROLL AND EARLY SOUL.
Tracks: Not Advised.
■ LP . . . . . . . . . . . . . . . . . . SJL 1143
Savoy Jazz (USA) / Mar '85.

## Big Tony

### BUST THE BEAT (Big Tony & The T.F. Crew).
Tracks: Not Advised.
LP . . . . . . . . . . . . . . . . . . . RTT 3
Rhythm Attack (Germany) / Apr '90 / Charly.

### CAN'T GET ENOUGH OF YOUR LOVE BABE.
Tracks: Can't get enough of your love babe / I miss you.
■ 12" . . . . . . . . . . . . . . . . . DOLEQ 3
■ 7" . . . . . . . . . . . . . . . . . . DOLE 3
Lisson / Jul '86.

## Birdsong, Cindy

### DANCING ROOM.
Tracks: Dancing room.
■ 12" . . . . . . . . . . . . . . . . . .CIND 1T
■ 7" . . . . . . . . . . . . . . . . . . CIND 1
Hi-Hat / Dec '87.

■ 12"..................... CIND 1TR
Hi-Hat / Jan '88.

## Bishop, Eddie

**CALL ME.**
**Tracks:** Darkest days (Jackie Lee) / Call me.
■ 7"..................... TOWN 107
Kent / Apr '85.

## Bishop, Elvin

**BEST OF ELVIN BISHOP.**
**Tracks:** Travelin' shoes / Yes sir / Struttin' my stuff /
Give it up / Fooled around and fell in love / Juke joint
jump / Spend some time / Good times roll / Change
is gonna come / Bring it on home / Love medley.
■ LP..................... 2429189
Capricorn / Nov '79.

**BIG FUN.**
**Tracks:** Not Advised.
■ LP..................... AL 4767
Alligator / Oct '88.
MC..................... ALCS 4767
Alligator / Aug '92 / Topic Records / Direct Distribu-
tion / C.M. Distribution / A.D.A. Distribution / Jazz
Music.
CD..................... ALCD 4767
Alligator / Apr '93 / Topic Records / Direct Distribu-
tion / C.M. Distribution / A.D.A. Distribution / Jazz
Music.

**DON'T LET THE BOSSMAN GET YOU
DOWN.**
**Tracks:** Fannie Mae / Don't let the bossman get you
down / Murder in the first degree / Kissing in the
dark / My whiskey head buddies / Stepping up in
class / You got to rock 'em / Come on in this house /
Soul food / Rollin' with my blues / Devil's slide / Just
your fool.
MC..................... AC 4791
Alligator / Apr '91 / Topic Records / Direct Distribu-
tion / C.M. Distribution / A.D.A. Distribution / Jazz
Music.
CD..................... ALCD 4791
Alligator / May '93 / Topic Records / Direct Distribu-
tion / C.M. Distribution / A.D.A. Distribution / Jazz
Music.

**FOOLED AROUND AND FELL IN LOVE.**
**Tracks:** Fooled around and fell in love.
■ 7"..................... 2089 024
Capricorn / May '76.

**HOMETOWN BOY MAKES GOOD.**
**Tracks:** Sugar dumplin' / Sidelines / Twist & shout /
Yes sir / Spend some time / Give it up / Keep it cool /
Graveyard blues / Once in a lifetime / D.C. strut.
■ LP..................... 2429 147
Capricorn / Jan '77.

**IS YOU IS OR IS YOU AIN'T MY BABY.**
**Tracks:** Is you is or is you ain't my baby / Midnight
hour blues / Honest I do / Drunk / Sweet cocaine /
Good good rockin' / We must go on / Big diamonds /
Red hot / Another mule / Catfish.
CD..................... LICD 900 253
Line / Jan '89 / C.M. Distribution / Grapevine Distri-
bution / A.D.A. Distribution / Conifer Records.

**JUKE JOINT JUMP.**
**Tracks:** Juke joint jump / Arkansas line.
■ 7"..................... 2089014
Capricorn / Jul '75.

**TULSA SHUFFLE - BEST OF ELVIN
BISHOP.**
**Tracks:** Tulsa shuffle / How much more / Things
(That) I used to do / Sweet potatoe / Honey bee /
Prisoner of love / Party till the cows come home /
Hogbottom / Be with me / So fine / Don't fight it (Feel
it) / As the years go passing by / So good / Rock my
soul / Rock bottom / Stomp / Stealin' watermelons /
Last mile.
CD..................... 476722 2
MC..................... 476722 4
Legacy / May '94 / Sony.

**TWIST AND SHOUT.**
**Tracks:** Twist and shout / Sidelines.
■ 7"..................... 2089 044
Capricorn / Mar '77.

## Black, Bill

**DON'T BE CRUEL (Black, Bill Combo).**
**Tracks:** Don't be cruel.
■ 7"..................... HLU 9212
London-American / Nov '60.

**GOES WEST & PLAYS (Black, Bill
Combo).**
**Tracks:** Not Advised.
CD..................... HIUKCD 124
Demon / Jun '93 / Pinnacle / A.D.A. Distribution.

**GREATEST HITS: BILL BLACK'S COM-
BO (Black, Bill Combo).**
**Tracks:** Do it rat / Josephine / Rollin' / Hearts of
stone / Yogi / White silver sands / Blue tango / Willie
/ Ole butter milk sky / Royal blue / Don't be cruel /
Smokie, part 2 / School days / Sweet little sixteen /
Roll over Beethoven / Maybellene / Carol / Little
queenie / Brown-eyed handsome man / Nadine /
Thirty days / Johnny B. Goode / Reelin' and rockin' /
Memphis, Tennessee.
CD..................... HIUKCD 115
Hi / '91 / Pinnacle.

**LET'S TWIST HER (Black, Bill Combo).**
**Tracks:** Not Advised.
CD..................... HIUKCD 131
Hi / Jun '92 / Pinnacle.

**MEMPHIS ROCK 'N' SOUL PARTY
(Black, Bill & Willie Mitchell).**
**Tracks:** Don't be cruel / Honky tonk / Blueberry Hill /
Hearts of stone / Movin' / Hey Bo Diddley / Work with
me annie / Twist-her / My girl Josephine / Night train
/ So what / Do it - rat now / Monkey shine / School
days / Memphis, Tennessee / Little queenie / Secret
home / Buster Browne / At the woodchopper's ball /
That driving beat / Everything is gonna be alright /
Champion / Bad eye / Sugar T / Mercy / Up-hard /
30-60-90 / Who's making love / Come see about me /
My babe / I'm a midnight mover / Set free.
CD..................... HIUKCD 102
Hi / Jul '89 / Pinnacle.

**MOVIN' (Black, Bill Combo).**
**Tracks:** Movin' / Honky train.
■ 7"..................... HLU 9436
London-American / '61.

**SOLID AND RAUNCHY AND MOVIN'
(Black, Bill Combo).**
**Tracks:** Don't be cruel / Singing the blues / Blue-
berry Hill / I almost lost my mind / Cherry pink /
Mona Lisa / Honky Tonk / Tequila / Raunchy / You
win again / Bo Diddley / Mack the knife / Movin' /
What'd I say / Hey Bo Diddley / Witchcraft / Work
with me Annie / Be bop a lula / My babe / 40 miles of
bad road / Ain't that lovin' you baby / Honky train /
Walk / Torquay.
CD..................... HIUKCD 112
Hi / '91 / Pinnacle.

**THAT WONDERFUL FEELING (Black, Bill
Combo).**
**Tracks:** Not Advised.
CD..................... HIUKCD 145
Demon / Aug '94 / Pinnacle / A.D.A. Distribution.

**UNTOUCHABLE SOUND OF BILL
BLACK'S COMBO.**
**Tracks:** White silver sands / Smokie part 2 / Movin' /
Monkey-shine / Don't be cruel / Little Queenie /
Josephine / Willie / Turn on your lovelight / Mem-
phis, Tennessee / Hearts of stone / Twist-her / Honky
train / Little Jasper / Do it-rat now / So what.
■ LP..................... HIUKLP 410
Hi.

**WHITE SILVER SANDS (Black, Bill
Combo).**
**Tracks:** White silver sands.
■ 7"..................... HLU 9090
London-American / Sep '60.

## Black Is Beautiful

**BLACK IS BEAUTIFUL.**
**Tracks:** Not Advised.
CD..................... 013 710 62
Compact Leisure / Aug '89.

## Black Ivory

**BLACK IVORY.**
**Tracks:** Big apple rock / Get down / Peace and
harmony / Mainline / Rest inside my love / Hustlin' /
You turned my whole world around.
■ LP..................... BDLP 4060
Buddah / Dec '79.

**YOU TURNED MY WHOLE WORLD
AROUND.**
**Tracks:** You turned my whole world around / Push
comes to shove.
■ 7"..................... PX 277
Power Exchange / Jun '78.

## Black Nasty

**CUT YOUR MOTOR OFF.**
**Tracks:** Cut you motor off / Keep on stepping.
■ 7"..................... GRP 140
Grapevine (Northern Soul) / May '80.

**TALKING TO THE PEOPLE.**
**Tracks:** Talking to the people / I must be in love /
Nasty soul / Getting funky round here / Black nasty
boogie / We're doin' our thing / I have no choice / It's
not the world / Rushin' sea / Booger the hooker.
CD..................... CDSXE 091
Stax / Nov '93 / Pinnacle.

## Black Russian

**BLACK RUSSIAN.**
**Tracks:** Move together / 'Cause I love you / Love's
enough / Leave me now / Mystified / New York City /
Life is too short / Emptiness.
■ LP..................... STML 12142
Motown / Oct '81.

**LEAVE ME NOW.**
**Tracks:** Leave me now / Move together.
■ 7"..................... TMG 1220
Motown / Jan '81.

**MYSTIFIED.**
**Tracks:** Mystified / Love's enough.
■ 7"..................... TMG 1199
Motown / Aug '80.

## Blackbyrds

**ACTION.**
**Tracks:** Supernatural feeling / Lookin' ahead / Mys-
terious vibes / Something special / Street games /
Soft and easy / Dreaming about you.
■ LP..................... FT 534
Fantasy / Dec '77.

**ACTION/BETTER DAYS.**
**Tracks:** Supernatural feeling / Lookin' ahead / Mys-
terious vibes / Something special / Street games /
Soft and easy / Dreaming about you / Dancin' dan-
cin' / Lonliness for your love / Better days / Do it girl
/ Without your love / Do you wanna dance / Love
don't strike twice / What's on your mind / Don't know
what to say / What we have is right.
CD..................... CDBGPD 090
Beat Goes Public / Nov '94 / Pinnacle.

**BEST OF THE BLACKBYRDS VOL.1.**
**Tracks:** Do it fluid / Love don't strike twice / Walking
in rhythm / Mysterious vibes / Baby / Gut level /
Funkie junkie / Dreaming about you.
■ LP..................... BGP 1012
BGP / Jun '88.

**BEST OF THE BLACKBYRDS VOL.2.**
**Tracks:** Rock creek park / Time is movin' / Don't
know what to say / Blackbyrds' theme / Happy music
/ Supernatural feeling / Soft and easy.
■ LP..................... BGP 1014
BGP / Oct '88.

**BEST OF THE BLACKBYRDS, THE.**
**Tracks:** Blackbyrds' theme / Rock creek park / Time
is movin' / Don't know what to say / Love don't strike
twice / Supernatural feeling / Soft and easy / Do it
fluid / Walking in rhythm / Happy music / Something
special / Baby / Gut level / Dreaming about you /
Mysterious vibes.
CD..................... CDBGP 918
MC..................... BGPC 918
Ace / Jun '88 / Pinnacle / Complete Record Co. Ltd.

**BETTER DAYS.**
**Tracks:** Dancin' dancin' / Lonelies for your love /
Better days / Do it girl / Without your love / Do you
wanna dance / Love don't strike twice / What's on
your mind / Don't know what to say / What we have
is right.
■ LP..................... F 9602
Fantasy / Feb '81.

**BLACKBYRDS/FLYING START.**
**Tracks:** Do it, fluid / Gut level / Reggins / Runaway /
Funkie junkie / Summer love / Life styles / Hot day
today / I need you / Baby / Love is love / Blackbyrds'
theme / Walking in rhythm / Future children, future
hopes / April showers / Spaced out.

32                                                      ■ DELETED

CD Set . . . . . . . . . . . . . . . . . . .CDBGPD 86
Beat Goes Public / Jul '94 / Pinnacle.

## BLACKBYRDS: GREATEST HITS.
**Tracks:** Happy music / Gut level / Walking in rhythm / Do it fluid / Rock Creek Park / Supernatural feeling / Soft and easy.
- ■ LP . . . . . . . . . . . . . . . . . . . . .FT 555
Fantasy / Feb '79.

## CITY LIFE/UNFINISHED BUSINESS.
**Tracks:** Rock creek park / Thankful 'bout yourself / City life / All I ask / Happy music / Love so fine / Flying high / Hash and eggs / Time is movin' / In life / Enter in / You've got that somwthing / Party land / Lady / Unfinished business.
- CD . . . . . . . . . . . . . . . . . . .CDBGPD 089
Beat Goes On / Sep '94 / Pinnacle.

## DON'T KNOW WHAT TO SAY.
**Tracks:** Don't know what to say / Rock creek park.
- ■ 12" . . . . . . . . . . . . . . . . . . .FTCT 194
- ■ 7" . . . . . . . . . . . . . . . . . . .FTC 194
Fantasy / Feb '81.

## HAPPY MUSIC.
**Tracks:** Happy music / Love so fine.
- ■ 7" . . . . . . . . . . . . . . . . . . .FTC 129
Fantasy / Apr '76.

## STREET GAMES.
**Tracks:** Street games / Soft and easy.
- ■ 7" . . . . . . . . . . . . . . . . . . .FTC 150
Fantasy / Jan '78.

## TIME IS MOVIN'.
**Tracks:** Time is movin' / Lady.
- ■ 7" . . . . . . . . . . . . . . . . . . .FTC 141
Fantasy / May '77.

## UNFINISHED BUSINESS.
**Tracks:** Time is movin' / In life / Enter in / You've got that something / Party land / Lady / Unfinished business.
- ■ LP . . . . . . . . . . . . . . . . . . .FTA 3007
Fantasy / Jan '77.

## WALKING IN RHYTHM.
**Tracks:** Walking in rhythm / Rock park week.
- ■ 7" . . . . . . . . . . . . . . . . . . .FTC 114
Fantasy / May '75.
- ■ 7" . . . . . . . . . . . . . . . . . . .SWAVE 3
Streetwave / Sep '85.

## Blackfoot, J.

After a troubled adolescence spent in and out of jail, Blackfoot (a.k.a. John Colbert), joined the new line-up of The Bar-Kays as lead singer, formed after the tragic plane crash that had killed the original members along with Otis Redding. In 1968 he was approached by Isaac Hayes and David Porter and offered the role of lead singer in The Soul Children at Stax Records, working closely with Hayes and Porter they released two albums *Soul Children* in '69 and *Best Of Two Worlds* in '71 before breaking through with the singles *I Want To Be Loved* and *Herseay* from the 1972 album *Genesis*. After two more well received albums Blackfoot quit the group to pursue a solo career which can best be described as patchy.

## CITY SLICKER.
**Tracks:** Way of the city / Taxi / Street girl / One of those parties / Where is love / I stood on the sidewalk / City slicker / All because of what you did to me / Can you hang.
- ■ LP . . . . . . . . . . . . . . . . . . .ALE 5602
- MC . . . . . . . . . . . . . . . . . . .ZCALE 5602
Allegiance / Mar '84.

## TAXI.
**Tracks:** Taxi / Where is love.
- ■ 7" . . . . . . . . . . . . . . . . . . .ALES 2
Allegiance / Feb '84.

## WHAT YOU DID TO ME LAST NIGHT.
**Tracks:** What you did to me last night / I stood on the sidewalk.
- ■ 12" . . . . . . . . . . . . . . . . . . .ALES 126
- ■ 7" . . . . . . . . . . . . . . . . . . .ALES 6
Allegiance / Aug '84.

## Blackgirl

## 90'S GIRL.
**Tracks:** 90's Girl.
- ■ 12" . . . . . . . . . . . . . . . . .74321 217881
- ■ CD Single . . . . . . . . . . . . .74321 217882
- ■ MC Single . . . . . . . . . . . . .74321 217884
Arista / Jul '94.

## TREAT U RIGHT.
**Tracks:** Krazy / Treat U right / Can U feel it / Where did we go wrong / Chains / Ooh yeh (Smooth) / 90's Girl / Nubian prince / Things we used to do / Can't live without U / Let's do it again / Home.
- CD . . . . . . . . . . . . . . . . . . .7863 66359-2
- LP . . . . . . . . . . . . . . . . . . .7863 66359-1
- MC . . . . . . . . . . . . . . . . . . .7863 66359-4
Arista / Jul '94 / BMG.

## Blackman, Donald

## DON BLACKMAN.
**Tracks:** Yabba dabba do / Heart's desire / Holding you, loving you / Deaf hook-up connection / You ain't hip / Let your conscience be your guide / Since you been away so long / Never miss a thing.
- ■ CD . . . . . . . . . . . . . . . . . . .262582
- ■ LP . . . . . . . . . . . . . . . . . . .212582
- ■ MC . . . . . . . . . . . . . . . . . . .412582
Arista / Jun '92.

## Blacksmith

## DON'T LET THEM HOLD YOU BACK.
**Tracks:** Don't let them hold you back / Don't let them hold you back (version).
- ■ 12" . . . . . . . . . . . . . . . . . . .FX 130
- ■ 7" . . . . . . . . . . . . . . . . . . .F 130
- ■ CD Single . . . . . . . . . . . . . . .FCD 130
- ■ MC Single . . . . . . . . . . . . . . .FCS 130
FFRR / Mar '90.

## GET BACK TO LOVE.
**Tracks:** Get back to love (radio mix) / Get back to love (swing beat mix) (Not available on 12") / Blacksmith (Only on 12") / Get back to love (blaze club mixes) (Not on 12".) / Get back to love (blaze dub) (Only on 12".).
- ■ CD Single . . . . . . . . . . . . . . .FCD 111
- ■ MC Single . . . . . . . . . . . . . . .FCS 111
FFRR / Jul '89.
- ■ 12" . . . . . . . . . . . . . . . . . . .FX 111
- ■ 7" . . . . . . . . . . . . . . . . . . .F 111
FFRR / Jun '89.

## Blackstreet

## BABY BE MINE (Blackstreet & Teddy Riley).
**Tracks:** Baby be mine.
- ■ 12" . . . . . . . . . . . . . . . . . .MCST 1772
- ■ 12" Remix . . . . . . . . . . . . . .MCSX 1772
- ■ CD Single . . . . . . . . . . . . . .MCSTD 1772
- ■ MC Single . . . . . . . . . . . . . .MCSC 1772
MCA / Jun '93.

## BLACKSTREET.
**Tracks:** Intro (Blackstreet philosophy) / Baby be mine / U blow my mind / Hey love (keep it real) / I like the way you work / Good life / Physical thing / Make U wet / Booti call / Love's in need / Joy / Before I let you go / Confession (interlude) / Tonight's the night / Happy home / Wanna make love / Once in a lifetime / Givin' you all my lovin'.
- CD . . . . . . . . . . . . . . . . . .654492351-2
- LP . . . . . . . . . . . . . . . . . .654492351-1
- MC . . . . . . . . . . . . . . . . . .654492351-4
Warner Bros. / Jun '94 / WEA.

## BOOTI CALL.
**Tracks:** Booti call (Mixes).
- 12" . . . . . . . . . . . . . . . . . . .A 8250T
- CD Single . . . . . . . . . . . . . . .A 8250CD
- MC Single . . . . . . . . . . . . . . .A 8250C
Interscope / Aug '94 / WEA.

## Blackwell, Debbie

## ONCE YOU GOT ME GOING.
**Tracks:** Once you got me going.
- ■ 7" . . . . . . . . . . . . . . . . . . .TEN 151
- ■ 12" . . . . . . . . . . . . . . . . . .TENT 151
10 / Jul '86.

## Bland, Billy

## BLUES CHICKEN, FRIENDS AND RELATIVES.
**Tracks:** Fat man / Chicken in the basket / Oh, you for me / I Had A Dream / If I could be your man / What's That / Grandma give a party / Uncle Bud / Little boy / Chicken hop / My hearts on fire / Flo, open the door / Momma stole the chicken / Bug.
- ■ LP . . . . . . . . . . . . . . . . . . .CH 222
Ace / Jun '87.

## LET THE LITTLE GIRL DANCE.
**Tracks:** Let the little girl dance.
- ■ 7" . . . . . . . . . . . . . . . . . . .HL 9096
London-American / May '60.

## LET THE LITTLE GIRL DANCE.
**Tracks:** Let the little girl dance / Chicken hop / Grandma gave a party / Fat man / Pardon me / I had a dream / Chicken in the basket / You born to be loved / Harmony / Can't stop her from dancing / Momma stole the chicken / Flo - open the door / What's that / Oh, you for me / If I could be your man / Everything that shines ain't gold / Make believe lover / My heart is on fire / Steady kind / Uncle bud / Keep talkin' that sweet talk / You took my love for granted / Little boy blue / I cross my heart / I spend my life loving you / All I want to do is cry / How many hearts / Do the bug with me / Let the little girl dance (2).
- ■ CD Set. . . . . . . . . . . . . . . . .CHCHD 370
Ace / Sep '92.

## Bland, Bobby

Bobby 'Blue' Bland was raised in Memphis surrounded by the blues and gospel music, it was inevitable that this hotbed of musical activity would spawn a generation of musicians who would draw on both genres and Bland is perhaps the finest example of the fusion of both styles. In the late 40's Bland joined a gospel group, The Miniatures, shortly before meeting B.B. King and being recruited into the Beale Streeters, a loose collective of Memphis bluesmen, but it wasn't until 1954 that he landed a deal. His touring band at that time, featuring the tenor sax of Bill Harvey and trumpeter Joe Scott who co-wrote most of Bland's material, displayed a bolder and brassier edge than most of their contemporaries and were the blueprint for the rich sound of much 60's soul music. While never as commercially successful as B.B. King, Bland did clock up over 30 R&B hits including the superb *Turn On Your Love Light*, *That's The Way Love Is* and *I Pity The Fool* and his influence to modern soul music is immeasurable.

## AFTER ALL.
**Tracks:** Not Advised.
- ■ LP . . . . . . . . . . . . . . . . . . .MALP 009
Malaco / Dec '86.

## AIN'T NOTHING YOU CAN DO.
**Tracks:** Not Advised.
- ■ LP . . . . . . . . . . . . . . . . . . .DL 78
Duke / '77.

## ANGELS IN HOUSTON: LEGENDARY DUKE BLUES.
**Tracks:** Not Advised.
- ■ LP . . . . . . . . . . . . . . . . .ROUNDER 2031
- MC . . . . . . . . . . . . . . . . .ROUNDER 2031C
Rounder / '88 / Roots Records / C.M. Distribution / Topic Records / A.D.A. Distribution / Direct Distribution.

## BAREFOOT ROCK (Bland, Bobby & Junior Parker).
**Tracks:** Not Advised.
- ■ LP . . . . . . . . . . . . . . . . . . .DL 72
Duke / '77.

## BLUES IN THE NIGHT.
**Tracks:** Blue moon / If I hadn't called you back / Ask me 'bout nothing but the blues / Jelly, jelly / When you put me down / Blind man / Chains of love / Fever / Blues in the night / Loneliness hurts / Feeling is gone / I'm too far gone / Black night / Share your love with me.
- ■ LP . . . . . . . . . . . . . . . . . . .CH 132
- ■ MC . . . . . . . . . . . . . . . . . . .CHC 132
Ace / May '85.
- CD . . . . . . . . . . . . . . . . . . .CD 14531
Jazz Portraits / Jan '94 / Complete Record Co. Ltd.

## BLUES YEARS, THE.
**Tracks:** No blow, no show / Wise man's blues / Army blues / Lost lover blues / It's my life, baby / Honey bee / Time out / Little boy blue / Million miles from nowhere / Woke up screaming / You've got bad intentions / I can't put you down / You did me wrong / I lost sight on the world / You got me / Loan a helping hand / I smell trouble / Don't want no woman / I don't believe / Teach me how to love you / Bobby's blues / Wishing well / Last night / I learned my lesson / Farther up the road.
- CD . . . . . . . . . . . . . . . . . . .CDCHD 302
Ace / Nov '93 / Pinnacle / Complete Record Co. Ltd.

## BLUES YOU CAN USE.
**Tracks:** Not Advised.
- ■ LP . . . . . . . . . . . . . . . . . . .MAL 7444
Malaco / Oct '88.
- CD . . . . . . . . . . . . . . . . . . .MALCD 7444
Malaco / Apr '93 / C.M. Distribution / Charly / Pinnacle.

## BOBBY BLAND.
**Tracks:** Not Advised.
■ **LP** . . . . . . . . . . . . . . . . . . . MALP 7439
Malaco Gospel / '89.

## CALIFORNIA ALBUM.
**Tracks:** This time I'm gone for good / Up and down world / It's not the spotlight / (If loving you is wrong) I don't wanna be right / Going down slow / Right place at the right time / Help me through the day / Where baby went / Friday the 13th child / I've got to use my imagination.
■ **LP** . . . . . . . . . . . . . . . . . . . SPB 1088
Probe / '73.
■ **LP** . . . . . . . . . . . . . . . . . . BGOLP 64
Beat Goes On / Jan '89.
**CD** . . . . . . . . . . . . . . . . . . BGOCD 64
Beat Goes On / Jan '90 / Pinnacle.

## CALL ON ME.
**Tracks:** Not Advised.
■ **LP** . . . . . . . . . . . . . . . . . . . . DL 77
Duke / '77.

## COME FLY WITH ME.
**Tracks:** Come fly with me / Lady lonely / Night games / To be friends / I'm just your man / Love to see you smile / You can count on me / This bitter Earth / Ain't God something.
■ **LP** . . . . . . . . . . . . . . . . . . ABCL 5249
ABC Records / Jun '78.

## DREAMER.
**Tracks:** Ain't no love in the heart of the city / I wouldn't treat a dog (the way you treated me) / Lovin' on borrowed time / End of the road / I ain't gonna be the first to cry / Dreamer / Yolanda / Twenty four hour blues / Cold day in hell / Who's foolin' who.
**CD** . . . . . . . . . . . . . . . . . . BGOCD 63
■ **LP** . . . . . . . . . . . . . . . . . . BGOLP 63
Beat Goes On / Oct '89 / Pinnacle.

## FIRST CLASS BLUES.
**Tracks:** Not Advised.
**CD** . . . . . . . . . . . . . . . . . . MALCD 5000
Malaco / Mar '93 / C.M. Distribution / Charly / Pinnacle.

## FOOLIN' WITH THE BLUES.
**Tracks:** You got me (where you want me) / Loan me a helping hand / I pity the fool / Who will the next fool be / Two steps from the blues / Reconsider, baby / Bobby's blues / Cry, cry, cry / Touch of the blues / You're worth it all / Don't cry no more / I'm not ashamed / I'll take care of you / 36-22-36 / Ain't no telling / Yield not to temptation.
■ **LP** . . . . . . . . . . . . . . . . . . CRB 1049
Charly R&B / '83.

## GOOD TIME CHARLIE.
**Tracks:** Good time Charlie / Good time Charlie (working his groove bag).
■ **7"** . . . . . . . . . . . . . . . . . . VP 9273
Vocalion / '65.

## HERE'S THE MAN.
**Tracks:** Not Advised.
■ **LP** . . . . . . . . . . . . . . . . . . . . DL 75
Duke / '77.

## I WOULDN'T TREAT A DOG.
**Tracks:** I wouldn't treat a dog / I ain't gonna be the first to cry.
■ **7"** . . . . . . . . . . . . . . . . . . ABC 4030
ABC Records / Jan '75.

## I'M TOO FAR GONE.
**Tracks:** I'm too far gone / If you could read my mind.
■ **7"** . . . . . . . . . . . . . . . . . . VP 9262
Vocalion / Feb '66.

## INSTRUMENTAL ALBUM.
**Tracks:** Not Advised.
■ **LP** . . . . . . . . . . . . . . . . . . LP 8502
Rockhouse / Oct '85.

## INTROSPECTIVE OF THE EARLY YEARS.
**Tracks:** Not Advised.
■ **LP** . . . . . . . . . . . . . . . . . . . . DL 92
Duke / '77.

## LIKE 'ER RED HOT.
**Tracks:** Not Advised.
■ **LP** . . . . . . . . . . . . . . . . . . . . DL 73
Duke / '77.

## LIVE AT LONG BEACH.
**Tracks:** Not Advised.
**CD** . . . . . . . . . . . . . . . . . . CDBL 750
Charly / Nov '94 / Charly.

## MASTER OF THE BLUES.
**Tracks:** Not Advised.
**CD** . . . . . . . . . . . . . . . . . . NTRCD 025
**MC** . . . . . . . . . . . . . . . . . . NTRC 025
Quality / Jun '94 / Pinnacle.

## MEMBERS ONLY.
**Tracks:** Members only / In the ghetto / I've just got to know / Straight / From the shoulder / Sweet woman's love / Can we make love tonight / Sweet surrender / I need your love so bad / Heart open up again.
■ **LP** . . . . . . . . . . . . . . . . . . MAL 7429
Malaco / Nov '85.
■ **LP** . . . . . . . . . . . . . . . . . . MALP 004
Malaco / '88.
**MC** . . . . . . . . . . . . . . . . . . MALC 7429
Malaco / Mar '89 / C.M. Distribution / Charly / Pinnacle.

## MEMBERS ONLY.
**Tracks:** Members only / Straight from the shoulder / Sweet surrender.
■ **12"** . . . . . . . . . . . . . . . . . . MAL 12 031
Malaco / Mar '86.

## MIDNIGHT RUN.
**Tracks:** Not Advised.
■ **LP** . . . . . . . . . . . . . . . . . . MALP 7450
**MC** . . . . . . . . . . . . . . . . . . MALC 7450
Malaco / '89 / C.M. Distribution / Charly / Pinnacle.
**CD** . . . . . . . . . . . . . . . . . . MALCD 7450
Malaco / Mar '93 / C.M. Distribution / Charly / Pinnacle.

## PIECE OF GOLD.
**Tracks:** Back in the same old bag / Share your love with me / Poverty / If you could read my mind / Dust got in Daddy's eyes / These hands / Piece of gold / Save your love for me / Who will the next fool be / Yield not to temptation.
■ **LP** . . . . . . . . . . . . . . . . . . ACLP 6006
Action / Mar '69.

## PORTRAIT OF THE BLUES.
**Tracks:** Not Advised.
**CD** . . . . . . . . . . . . . . . . . . MALCD 7458
Malaco / Mar '93 / C.M. Distribution / Charly / Pinnacle.

## REFLECTIONS IN BLUE.
**Tracks:** Soul of a man / I'll be your fool once more / Sittin' on a poor man's throne / Intend to take your place / It ain't the real thing / It's all over / If I weren't a gambler / Five long years / I got the same old blues.
■ **LP** . . . . . . . . . . . . . . . . . . ABCL 5196
ABC Records / May '77.

## SHOES.
**Tracks:** Shoes / Call me / Getting used to the blues / Good time Charlie.
■ **7"** . . . . . . . . . . . . . . . . . . TOWN 108
Kent / Jun '85.

## SOUL OF A MAN.
**Tracks:** Soul of a man / If I weren't a gambler.
■ **7"** . . . . . . . . . . . . . . . . . . ABC 4186
ABC Records / Jul '77.

## SOUL OF THE MAN, THE.
**Tracks:** Not Advised.
■ **LP** . . . . . . . . . . . . . . . . . . . . DL 79
Duke / '77.

## SOUL WITH A FLAVOUR.
**Tracks:** Wishing well / St. James' infirmary / Ain't that lovin' you / Turn on your lovelight / You're the one (that I adore) / Stormy Monday blues / Your friends / Honky tonk / That's the way love is / These hands (small, but mighty) / Poverty / Driftin' blues / Sad feeling / Rockin' in the same old boat / Gotta get to know you / Soon as the weather breaks / You'd be a millionaire / Soul with a flavour / Real woman is what it takes / Try me I'm real / Recess in heaven / You're about to win / Is this the blues / Just because I love you / Looking back.
■ **Double LP** . . . . . . . . . . . . . . . . . . CDX 30
■ **MC** . . . . . . . . . . . . . . . . . . TCCDX 30
Charly / Nov '88.

## SOULFUL SIDE OF BOBBY BLAND, THE.
**Tracks:** Getting used to the blues / Yum yum tree / These hands (small, but mighty) / Back in the same old bag again / Keep on loving me / Honeychild / Wouldn't you rather have me / Call on me / Dear Bobby / How does a cheating woman feel / I ain't myself anymore / That did it / Ain't doing too bad / Love with a reputation / Good time Charlie / Ain't nothing you can do.
■ **LP** . . . . . . . . . . . . . . . . . . KENT 044
Kent / Oct '86.

## SPOTLIGHTING THE MAN B.B.
**Tracks:** Not Advised.
■ **LP** . . . . . . . . . . . . . . . . . . . . DL 89
Duke / '77.

## TELL MR. BLAND.
**Tracks:** Not Advised.
■ **LP** . . . . . . . . . . . . . . . . . . MCF 3181
MCA / Oct '83.

## THESE HANDS.
**Tracks:** These hands (small but mighty) / Today.
■ **7"** . . . . . . . . . . . . . . . . . . VP 9251
Vocalion / Oct '65.

## TOGETHER AGAIN - LIVE (Bland, Bobby & B.B. King).
**Tracks:** Let the good times roll / Strange things happen / Feel so bad / Mother in law blues / Mean old world / Everyday (I have the blues) / Thrill is gone / I ain't gonna be the first to cry.
■ **LP** . . . . . . . . . . . . . . . . . . IMPL 8027
Impulse Jazz / Jul '76.
■ **LP** . . . . . . . . . . . . . . . . . . IMCA 27012
MCA / Oct '87.
**CD** . . . . . . . . . . . . . . . . . . BGOCD 162
Pinnacle / Feb '93 / Pinnacle.

## TOUCH OF THE BLUES.
**Tracks:** Not Advised.
■ **LP** . . . . . . . . . . . . . . . . . . . . DL 88
Duke / '77.

## TWO STEPS FROM THE BLUES (Bland, Bobby & B.B. King).
**Tracks:** Cry, cry, cry / I pity the fool / I'll take care of you.
■ **LP** . . . . . . . . . . . . . . . . . . . . DL 74
Duke / '77.
■ **LP** . . . . . . . . . . . . . . . . . . MCA 4160
■ **CD** . . . . . . . . . . . . . . . . . . MCAD 4160
MCA / Jan '90.

## TWO STEPS FROM THE BLUES.
**Tracks:** Two steps from the blues / Cry, cry, cry / I'm not ashamed / Don't cry no more / Lead me on / I pity the fool / I've just got to forget you / Little boy blue / St. James infirmary / I'll take care of you / I don't want no woman / I've been wrong so long.
**CD** . . . . . . . . . . . . . . . . . . BGOCD 163
Beat Goes On / Feb '93 / Pinnacle.

## VOICE, THE.
**Tracks:** Who will the next fool be / I pity the fool / Don't cry no more / Ain't that loving you / I'm not ashamed / Cry, cry, cry / I'll take care of you / Call on me / Blue moon / Turn on your love light / Stormy Monday blues / Two steps from the blues / Ain't nothing you can do / Ain't doing too bad Part 1 / Sometimes you gotta cry a little / Ain't no telling / Yield not to temptation / I'm too far gone (to turn around) / These hands (small but mighty) / Good time Charlie Part 1 / Ask me 'bout nothin' (but the blues) / Share your love with me / That did it / Shoes / Back in the same old bag again / Chains of love.
**CD** . . . . . . . . . . . . . . . . . . CHCD 323
Ace / Nov '93 / Pinnacle / Complete Record Co. Ltd.

## WOKE UP SCREAMING.
**Tracks:** No blow, no show / Wise man blues / Army blues / Lost lover blues / It's my life baby / Honey bee / Time out / Little boy blue / Woke up screaming / You've got bad intentions / I can't put you down / I smell trouble / Don't believe / I learned my lesson / Farther up the road.
■ **LP** . . . . . . . . . . . . . . . . . . CH 41
Ace / Oct '81.

# Blast, C.L.

## BOOMERANG LOVE.
**Tracks:** Not Advised.
■ **LP** . . . . . . . . . . . . . . . . . . CRB 1145
Charly R&B / Nov '86.

## I WANNA GET DOWN.
**Tracks:** I wanna get down / If I had loved you more / I've got to make it on my own / Our love will last / Let's do something different tonight / If I could feel that old feeling again / Share your love with me / Love don't feel like love no more / Beautiful lover.
■ **CD** . . . . . . . . . . . . . . . . . . TLCD 407
■ **LP** . . . . . . . . . . . . . . . . . . TRPL 111
Timeless (Soul) / Jan '90.

## I WANNA GET DOWN.
**Tracks:** I wanna get down / Let's do something different tonight.
■ **7"** . . . . . . . . . . . . . . . . . . K 11531
Cotillion / Aug '80.

■ DELETED

## LAY ANOTHER LOG ON THE FIRE.
**Tracks:** Lay another log on the fire / Somebody shot my eagle.
- ■ 12" . . . . . . . . . . . . . . . . . . . . . .CYZ 117

Celluloid (USA) / Feb '87.

## Blaze

### 25 YEARS LATER.
**Tracks:** Get up / So special / Miss my love / You don't really love me / Anything for your lovin' / We all must live together / I wonder / Gonna make it work / All that I should know / Missing you / Loverman (Only on cassette.) / Love is forever (CD & cassette only.) / Broad and market / NWK (CD & cassette only.) / Hope song / Mission (CD & cassette only.).
- ■ CD . . . . . . . . . . . . . . . . . . . . . ZD 72713
- ■ LP . . . . . . . . . . . . . . . . . . . . . ZL 72713
- ■ MC . . . . . . . . . . . . . . . . . . . . . ZK 72713

Motown / Jun '90.

### CAN'T WIN FOR LOSIN'.
**Tracks:** Can't win for losin' / Can't win for losin' (remix) (Only on (LIC 004 R) 12" remix.).
- ■ 12" . . . . . . . . . . . . . . . . . . . . LIC 004 R
- ■ 7" . . . . . . . . . . . . . . . . . . . . . LICT 004

Republic / Oct '88.

### IF YOU SHOULD NEED A FRIEND.
**Tracks:** If you should need a friend (friendship mix) / If you should need a friend (movin mix) / If you should need a friend (stardust mix).
- ■ 12" . . . . . . . . . . . . . . . . . . DEBTX 3032
- ■ 7" . . . . . . . . . . . . . . . . . . . DEBT 3032

Debut (1) / Oct '87.

### SO SPECIAL.
**Tracks:** So special / Mission.
- ■ 12" . . . . . . . . . . . . . . . . . . . . ZT 43710
- ■ 7" . . . . . . . . . . . . . . . . . . . . ZB 43709
- ■ CD Single . . . . . . . . . . . . . . . . ZD 43710

Motown / Apr '90.

### WHATCHA GONNA DO.
**Tracks:** Whatcha Gonna Do / Whatcha gonna do (dub mix).
- ■ 7" . . . . . . . . . . . . . . . . . . . . CHAMP 36
- ■ 12" . . . . . . . . . . . . . . . . . . CHAMP 1236

Champion / Feb '87.

## Bleu, Mikki

### I PROMISE.
**Tracks:** I promise / Lock-n-key / Something real / Every little thing / Knocks me off my feet / Move your feet (let's dance) / Nothin' but the best / Until / Can he rock you like this / Stand.
- ■ CD . . . . . . . . . . . . . . . . . . CDMTL 1047
- ■ LP . . . . . . . . . . . . . . . . . . . . MTL 1047
- ■ MC . . . . . . . . . . . . . . . . . . TCMTL 1047

EMI-Manhattan / Jul '89.

### I PROMISE.
**Tracks:** I promise / I promise (inst.) (7" only.) / I promise (UK 12" mix) (Not on 7".) / I promise (5.30 AM dub) (12" only.) / I promise (street mix) (Not on 7".).
- ■ 12" . . . . . . . . . . . . . . . . . . . .12MT 78
- ■ 7" . . . . . . . . . . . . . . . . . . . . . . MT 78
- ■ CD Single . . . . . . . . . . . . . . . . CDMT 78

EMI-Manhattan / Jan '90.

## Blige, Mary J.

Swing diva whose 1992 debut *What's the 411?* disguised mostly-average material with Blige's gospel-trained voice; result went double platinum in U.S. Endless spin-off singles, remix of album, and badly-received U.K. shows demonstrated various limitations of scam. Among more well-travelled tracks was *You Remind Me*, which appeared on both versions of album and *Strictly Business* soundtrack as well as single in its own right. When remixers ran out of *..411* material, *You Don't Have to Worry* - Blige's contribution to 1993 *Who's The Man* soundtrack - was disinterred. Blige also appeared on former Brand Nubian rapper Grand Puba's debut album in late '92, (Puba having contributed to *..411*). Her own new album, largely self-penned *My Life*, is reported to improve on debut.

### MY LOVE.
**Tracks:** My love (Mixes).
- ■ 12" . . . . . . . . . . . . . . . . . . . . MCST 1972
- ■ 12" Remix . . . . . . . . . . . . . . . . MCSX 1972
- ■ CD Single . . . . . . . . . . . . . . . MCSTD 1972
- ■ MC Single . . . . . . . . . . . . . . . MCSC 1972

MCA / May '94.

---

## REAL LOVE.
**Tracks:** Real love.
- ■ 12" . . . . . . . . . . . . . . . . . . . MCST 1721
- ■ 7" . . . . . . . . . . . . . . . . . . . . MCS 1721
- ■ CD Single . . . . . . . . . . . . . . . MCSTD 1721
- ■ MC Single . . . . . . . . . . . . . . . MCSC 1721

MCA / Nov '92.
- ■ 12" . . . . . . . . . . . . . . . . . . . MCSX 1922
- ■ 12" . . . . . . . . . . . . . . . . . . . MCST 1922
- ■ CD Single . . . . . . . . . . . . . . . MCSTD 1922
- ■ MC Single . . . . . . . . . . . . . . . MCSC 1922

MCA / Aug '93.

## REMINISCE.
**Tracks:** Reminisce.
- ■ MC Single . . . . . . . . . . . . . . . MCSC 1731
- ■ 12" . . . . . . . . . . . . . . . . . . . MCSX 1731
- ■ 12" . . . . . . . . . . . . . . . . . . . MCST 1731
- ■ CD Single . . . . . . . . . . . . . . . MCSTD 1731

MCA / Feb '93.

## WHAT'S THE 411.
**Tracks:** Leave a message / Reminisce / Real love / You remind me / Intro' talk / Sweet thing / Love no limit / I don't want to do anything / Slow down / My love / Changes I've been going through / What's the 411.
- ■ CD . . . . . . . . . . . . . . . . . . . MCD 10681
- ■ MC . . . . . . . . . . . . . . . . . . . MCC 10681

MCA / Aug '92.
- ■ LP . . . . . . . . . . . . . . . . . . . MCA 10681

MCA / Mar '93.

## WHAT'S THE 411 - REMIX.
**Tracks:** Leave a message / You don't have to worry / My love / Real love / What's the 411 / Reminisce / Mary & Andre / Sweet thing / Love no limit / You remind me / Changes I've been going through / I don't want to do anything.
- CD . . . . . . . . . . . . . . . . . . . . MCD 10942
- MC. . . . . . . . . . . . . . . . . . . . MCC 10942
- ■ LP . . . . . . . . . . . . . . . . . . . MCA 10942

MCA / Dec '93 / BMG.

## YOU DON'T HAVE TO.
**Tracks:** You don't have to.
- ■ 12" . . . . . . . . . . . . . . . . . . . MCST 1948
- ■ CD Single . . . . . . . . . . . . . . . MCSTD 1948
- ■ MC Single . . . . . . . . . . . . . . . MCSC 1948

MCA / Nov '93.

## YOU REMIND ME.
**Tracks:** You remind me.
- ■ 12" . . . . . . . . . . . . . . . . . . . .MCST 177
- ■ CD Single . . . . . . . . . . . . . . . MCSTD 1770
- ■ CD Single . . . . . . . . . . . . . . . MCSXD 1770
- ■ MC Single . . . . . . . . . . . . . . . MCSC 1770

MCA / May '93.

## Blood, Sweat & Tears

### BLOOD, SWEAT & TEARS.
**Tracks:** Variations on a theme by Satie / Smiling phases / Sometimes in winter / More and more / And when I die / God bless the child / Spinning wheel / You've made me so very happy / Blues.
- ■ LP . . . . . . . . . . . . . . . . . . . . . . 63504

CBS / Apr '69.
- ■ CD. . . . . . . . . . . . . . . . . . . . CD 63504
- ■ CD. . . . . . . . . . . . . . . . . . . . 30DP 304

CBS / '88.

### BLOOD, SWEAT & TEARS.
**Tracks:** Sorry that i left you (I must have been blind) / God bless the child / Back up against the wall / You've made me so very happy / Down in the flood / Inner crisis / Empty pages / Maiden voyage / Snow queen / Over the hill / Sail away / And when I die.
- VHS . . . . . . . . . . . . . . . . . .7431 10667-30

BMG / Jan '94 / BMG.

### BLOOD, SWEAT & TEARS.
**Tracks:** Not Advised.
- CD . . . . . . . . . . . . . . . . . . . . BGOCD 28
- ■ LP . . . . . . . . . . . . . . . . . . . .BGOLP 28

Beat Goes On / Dec '88 / Pinnacle.

### BLOOD, SWEAT & TEARS 3.
**Tracks:** Not Advised.
- ■ LP . . . . . . . . . . . . . . . . . . . . . . 64024

CBS / Aug '70.

### BLUE STREET.
**Tracks:** Blue Street / Put on the light.
- ■ 7" . . . . . . . . . . . . . . . . . . . . ABC 4202

ABC Records / Feb '78.

### BRAND NEW DAY.
**Tracks:** Somebody I trusted / Dreaming as one / Same old blues / Lady put out the light / Womanizer / Blue street / Gimme that wine / Rock and roll queen / Don't explain.

---

- ■ LP . . . . . . . . . . . . . . . . . . . ABCL 5234

ABC Records / Feb '78.

## CHALLENGE, THE.
**Tracks:** Not Advised.
- ■ LP . . . . . . . . . . . . . . . . . . . . . . 20140
- MC. . . . . . . . . . . . . . . . . . . . . . 40140

Astan / Nov '84.

## CHILD IS FATHER TO THE MAN.
**Tracks:** Overture / I love you more than you'll ever know / Morning glory / My days are numbered / Without her / Just one smile / I can't quit her / Meagan's gypsy eyes / Somethin' goin' on / House in the country / Modern adventures of Plato, Diogenes and Freud / So much love / Underture.
- ■ LP . . . . . . . . . . . . . . . . . . . . . . 63296

CBS / Jul '68.
- CD. . . . . . . . . . . . . . . . . . . . 30DP 303

CBS / '88 / Sony.

## CLASSIC BLOOD SWEAT & TEARS.
**Tracks:** You've made me so very happy / I can't quit her / Go down gamblin' / Hi de ho / Sometimes in the winter / Without her / When I die / Spinning wheel / Lisa / Listen to me / Smiling phases / I love you more than you'll ever know / Lucretia MacEvil / God bless the child.
- ■ LP . . . . . . . . . . . . . . . . . . . CBS 31824

CBS / Jun '80.

## COLLECTION.
**Tracks:** Not Advised.
- CD . . . . . . . . . . . . . . . . . . . CCSCD 379

Castle / Sep '93 / BMG.

## GREATEST HITS: BLOOD, SWEAT & TEARS.
**Tracks:** Spinning wheel / I can't quit her / Go down gamblin' / God bless the child / Hi de ho / You've made me so very happy / Sometimes in winter / And when I die / Lisa listen to me / I love you more than you'll ever know / Lucretia mac evil.
- ■ LP . . . . . . . . . . . . . . . . . . . CBS 32159

CBS / Jul '83.
- ■ CD . . . . . . . . . . . . . . . . . . . CD 64803

CBS / Nov '87.

## LATIN FIRE.
**Tracks:** Not Advised.
- ■ LP . . . . . . . . . . . . . . . . . . . . . PLP 25
- MC. . . . . . . . . . . . . . . . . . . . . PMC 25

Platinum (W.Germany) / Oct '85.

## MIDNIGHT CONCERT.
**Tracks:** Not Advised.
- ■ LP . . . . . . . . . . . . . . . . . . . MA 25884

Masters (Holland) / '88.
- MC. . . . . . . . . . . . . . . . . . MAMC 925884

Masters (Holland) / Dec '88.

## NEW BLOOD.
**Tracks:** Down in the flood / Touch me / Alone / Velvet / I can't move no mountains / Over the hill / So long Dixie / Snow Queen / Maiden voyage.
- ■ LP . . . . . . . . . . . . . . . . . . . CBS 65252

CBS / Dec '72.

## NUCLEAR BLUES.
**Tracks:** Agitato / Nuclear blues / Manic depression / I'll drown in my own tears / Fantasy stage / Spanish wine / Latin fire / Challenge / Duel / Amor.
- ■ LP . . . . . . . . . . . . . . . . . . . MCF 3061

MCA / Apr '80.
- ■ LP . . . . . . . . . . . . . . . . . . . . 2215235
- MC. . . . . . . . . . . . . . . . . . . . . 2115235

Big Time / Sep '89.

## NUCLEAR BLUES.
**Tracks:** Nuclear blues / Agitato / Drowning in my own tears (Only on 12" single.).
- ■ 12" . . . . . . . . . . . . . . . . . . . .MCAT 569
- ■ 7" . . . . . . . . . . . . . . . . . . . . MCA 569

MCA / Mar '80.

## SMILING PHASES.
**Tracks:** Smiling phases / More and more / Fire and rain / Lonesome Susie / Somethin' comin' on / Cowboys and Indians / High on a mountain / Take me in your arms (rock me a little while) / Down in the flood / Touch me / Alone / Morning glory / Without her / Just one smile / Rollercoaster / Rosemary / Back up against the wall / Velvet.
- MC. . . . . . . . . . . . . . . . . . ELITE 005 MC

Elite (Pickwick) / May '91 / Pickwick.
- CD. . . . . . . . . . . . . . . . . . . ELITE 005CD

Elite (Pickwick) / Aug '93 / Pickwick.

## YOU'VE MADE ME SO VERY HAPPY.
**Tracks:** You've made me so very happy.
- ■ 7" . . . . . . . . . . . . . . . . . . . CBS 4116

CBS / Apr '69.
- ■ 7" . . . . . . . . . . . . . . . . . . . .A 4576

CBS / Jul '84.

---

■ DELETED

## Bloodstone

After working the West Coast as the Sinceres the band returned to their native Kansas and worked on a new style. They emerged as Bloodstone with a brand of rock-influenced soul and set off on a Brtish tour supporting Al Green in 1972. The reception they received was overwhelming and they were soon signed to Decca. The following year they released the Mike Vernon produced *Natural High* and achieved a transatlantic hit reaching no. 10 in the U.S and gaining a Top 40 hit in Britain. Unfortunately that same year Roger Durham died and Melvin Webb left and the band could not sustain their success. In 1975 Steve Ferrone left to join the Average White Band and despite a period at Motown the group were unable to repeat their earlier success.

### BLOODSTONE.
Tracks: Not Advised.
■ LP . . . . . . . . . . . . . . . . . . . . . TXS 110
Decca / '72.

### DON'T STOP.
Tracks: Don't stop / I'm just doing my job / Throw a little bit of love my way / It's all been said before / She wants to hear the words / Just wanna get the feel of it / You bring out the best in me / It's been a long time.
■ LP . . . . . . . . . . . . . . . . . . . .STML 12097
Motown / Mar '79.

### GO ON AND CRY.
Tracks: Go on and cry / Go on and cry (pt 2).
■ 7" . . . . . . . . . . . . . . . . . . . . . EPCA 2713
Epic / Sep '82.

### INSTANT LOVE.
Tracks: Instant love.
■ 7" . . . . . . . . . . . . . . . . . . . . . . . A 4574
Epic / Jun '84.

### NATURAL HIGH.
Tracks: Something / Natural high / Never let you go / Outside woman / Just like in the movies / Give me your heart / That's not how it goes / This is it / Little green apples / Sadie Mae / When we're doin' it / Shake the building / Everybody needs love / Do you wanna do a thing (1988 remix) / Stand up, let's party / My little lady.
■ CD . . . . . . . . . . . . . . . . . . . . . 8205712
London / Oct '88.

### NATURAL HIGH.
Tracks: Natural high.
■ 7" . . . . . . . . . . . . . . . . . . . . . F 13382
Decca / Aug '73.

## Blount, Tanya

### I'M GONNA MAKE YOU MINE.
Tracks: I'm gonna make you mine (mixes).
12" . . . . . . . . . . . . . . . . . . . . . . . PZ 315
7" . . . . . . . . . . . . . . . . . . . . . . . . PO 315
CD Single . . . . . . . . . . . . . . . . . PZCD 315
MC Single . . . . . . . . . . . . . . . . . POCS 315
Polydor / Jul '94 / PolyGram.

## Blow, Kurtis

### AMERICA.
Tracks: America / America (dub mix) / Super sperm / AJ meets Davy mix / Hello baby / If I ruled the world / Respect to the king / Summertime groove MC lullaby / Don't cha feel like making love.
■ LP . . . . . . . . . . . . . . . . . . . 826 141-1
MC. . . . . . . . . . . . . . . . . . . . . 826 141-4
Club / Dec '85 / PolyGram.

### BEST OF KURTIS BLOW, THE.
Tracks: Breaks / Christmas rappin / Hard times / Starlife / Tough / Daydreaming / Party time / One-two-five (main street Harlem, USA) / 8 Million stories / AJ Scratch / Basketball / America / If I ruled the world / I'm chillin'.
CD. . . . . . . . . . . . . . . . . . . . . 522 456-2
Mercury / Jun '94 / PolyGram.

### BEST RAPPER IN TOWN, THE.
Tracks: Party time / Do the do / Boogie blues / Breaks / One two five / Throughout your years.
■ LP . . . . . . . . . . . . . . . . . . . . 822 283 1
■ MC. . . . . . . . . . . . . . . . . . . . 822 283 4
Mercury / Oct '84.

### BREAKS, THE.
Tracks: Breaks.
■ 12" . . . . . . . . . . . . . . . . . . . BLOW 8-12
■ 7" . . . . . . . . . . . . . . . . . . . . . BLOW 8
Mercury / Oct '80.

### CHRISTMAS RAPPIN'.
Tracks: Christmas rappin' / Nervous.
■ 7" . . . . . . . . . . . . . . . . . . . . . BLOW 7
Mercury / Dec '79.
■ 12" . . . . . . . . . . . . . . . . . . . BLOW 13 12
■ 7" . . . . . . . . . . . . . . . . . . . . BLOW 13
Mercury / Dec '83.

### EGO TRIP.
Tracks: Eight million stories / AJ Scratch / Basketball / Under fire / I can't take it no more / Ego trip / Falling back in love again.
■ LP . . . . . . . . . . . . . . . . . . . . 8224201
MC. . . . . . . . . . . . . . . . . . . . . 8224204
Mercury / Nov '84 / PolyGram.

### I'M CHILLIN'.
Tracks: I'm chillin' / Don't cha feel like making love.
■ 12" . . . . . . . . . . . . . . . . . . . . JABX 42
■ 7" . . . . . . . . . . . . . . . . . . . . . JAB 42
Club / Oct '86.

### IF I RULED THE WORLD.
Tracks: If I ruled the world / If I ruled the world(dub) / If I ruled the world (instrumental) (Extra track on 12" only).
■ 12" . . . . . . . . . . . . . . . . . . . . JABX 26
■ 7" . . . . . . . . . . . . . . . . . . . . . JAB 26
Club / Dec '85.

### KINGDOM BLOW.
Tracks: Street rock / Bronx / Unity party jam / Sunshine / Magilla Gorilla / I'm chillin' / Kingdom blow / Reasons for wanting you.
■ CD . . . . . . . . . . . . . . . . . . . 830 215-2
■ LP . . . . . . . . . . . . . . . . . . . . JABH 22
■ MC. . . . . . . . . . . . . . . . . . . . JABHC 22
Club / Nov '86.

### KURTIS BLOW.
Tracks: Rappin' blow / Breaks / Way out west / Throughout your years / Hard times / All I want in this world / Takin' care of business.
■ LP . . . . . . . . . . . . . . . . . . . . . 6337137
Mercury / Dec '80.

### PARTY TIME.
Tracks: Party time / Breaks.
■ 12" . . . . . . . . . . . . . . . . . . . BLOW 1112
■ 7" . . . . . . . . . . . . . . . . . . . . BLOW 11
Mercury / Aug '83.
■ 7" . . . . . . . . . . . . . . . . . . . . . JAB 12
■ 12" . . . . . . . . . . . . . . . . . . . . JABX 12
Club / Feb '85.

### THROUGHOUT YOUR YEARS.
Tracks: Throughout your years / Christmas rappin'.
■ 12" . . . . . . . . . . . . . . . . . . . .BLOW 912
■ 7" . . . . . . . . . . . . . . . . . . . . . BLOW 9
Mercury / Dec '80.

### TOUGH.
Tracks: Tough / Juice / Daydreaming / Boogie blues / Baby you've got to go.
■ LP . . . . . . . . . . . . . . . . . . . . .MX 1505
MC. . . . . . . . . . . . . . . . . . . . . M4X 1505
Mercury / Oct '82 / PolyGram.

### TOUGH.
Tracks: Tough / Tough (pt 2).
■ 12" . . . . . . . . . . . . . . . . . . . BLOW 1012
■ 7" . . . . . . . . . . . . . . . . . . . . BLOW 12
Mercury / Oct '82.

## Blu, Peggi

### BLU BLOWIN'.
Tracks: Tender moments / Love's just a mystery / Once had your love (and I can't let go) / All the way with you (Duet with Bert Robinson.) / Over and over / Mesmorize me / Feels good to me / All and all / Two can play at that game / I believe in you.
■ LP . . . . . . . . . . . . . . . . . . . ESTV 2033
■ MC. . . . . . . . . . . . . . . . . . TCESTV 2033
Capitol / Jun '87.

### TWO CAN PLAY AT THAT GAME.
Tracks: Two can play at that game / Tender moment.
■ 12" . . . . . . . . . . . . . . . . . . . 12CL 460
■ 7" . . . . . . . . . . . . . . . . . . . . .CL 460
Capitol / Sep '87.

## Blue Feather

### LET IT OUT.
Tracks: Let it out / High up to the sky.
■ 12" . . . . . . . . . . . . . . . . . . . .MERX 136
■ 7" . . . . . . . . . . . . . . . . . . . . MER 136
Mercury / Mar '83.

### LET'S FUNK TONIGHT.
Tracks: Let's funk tonight / It's love.
■ 12" . . . . . . . . . . . . . . . . . . . .MERX 109

### 
■ 7" . . . . . . . . . . . . . . . . . . . . MER 109
Mercury / Jul '82.

## Blue Magic

### BLUE MAGIC.
Tracks: Sideshow / Look me up / What's come over me / Just don't want to be lonely / Stop to start / Welcome to the club / Spell / Answer to my prayer / Tear it down.
■ LP . . . . . . . . . . . . . . . . . . . . K 40532
Atlantic.

### FROM OUT OF THE BLUE.
Tracks: It's like magic / Couldn't get to sleep last night / Secret lover / We're gonna make it / I heard you're going away / From out of the blue / Romeo and Juliet / We ain't new to this / There's a song in my head / Tuesday heartbreak / More I get / Take a long last look / Break it out / Dancin' to the flag.
■ CD. . . . . . . . . . . . . . . . . . . . 4633922
■ LP . . . . . . . . . . . . . . . . . . . . 4633921
■ MC. . . . . . . . . . . . . . . . . . . . 4633924
CBS / Apr '89.

### GREATEST HITS: BLUE MAGIC.
Tracks: Sideshow / Stop to start / Spell / What's come over me / Three ring circus / Tear it down / Look me up / Welcome to the club / Chasin' rainbows / Just don't want to be lonely / Summer snow / Where have you been.
■ LP . . . . . . . . . . . . . . . . . . XXHAN 508
Streetwave / Nov '86.

### IN THE RAIN.
Tracks: In the rain / Magic / See through.
■ 12" . . . . . . . . . . . . . . . . . . . WAVEL 6
■ 7" . . . . . . . . . . . . . . . . . . . . WAVE 6
Streetwave / Aug '83.

### LOVE HAS FOUND IT'S WAY.
Tracks: Love has found it's way / When you're coming home.
■ 7" . . . . . . . . . . . . . . . . . . . . K 10588
Atlantic / May '75.

### MAGIC OF THE BLUE.
Tracks: Magic of the blue / Stop to start.
■ 7" . . . . . . . . . . . . . . . . . . . . K 10689
Atlantic / Nov '75.

### ROMEO AND JULIET.
Tracks: Romeo and Juliet.
■ 12" . . . . . . . . . . . . . . . . . . . 6547696
■ 7" . . . . . . . . . . . . . . . . . . . . 6547697
■ CD Single . . . . . . . . . . . . . . . 6547692
Def Jam / Mar '89.

### THREE RING CIRCUS.
Tracks: Three ring circus / Spell.
■ 7" . . . . . . . . . . . . . . . . . . . . K 10553
Atlantic / Jan '75.

### THREE RING CIRCUS.
Tracks: Three ring circus / Sideshow.
■ 7" . . . . . . . . . . . . . . . . . . . . K 10910
Atlantic / Mar '77.

## Blue Moderne

### DO THAT AGAIN.
Tracks: Do that again / Blue.
■ 7" . . . . . . . . . . . . . . . . . . . . .A 9045
■ 12" . . . . . . . . . . . . . . . . . . . A 9045 T
Atlantic / Sep '88.

### THROUGH THE NIGHT.
Tracks: Through the night.
■ 12" . . . . . . . . . . . . . . . . . . . SDT 2
■ 7" . . . . . . . . . . . . . . . . . . . . SD 2
Sure Delight / Jul '86.

## Blue Zone

### FINEST THING.
Tracks: Finest thing / Love will wait / Finest thing (US remix) (on 12" RHTX 109 only) / Finest thing (instrumental) (on 12" RHTX 109 only).
■ 12" . . . . . . . . . . . . . . . . . . . RHTX 109
■ 12" . . . . . . . . . . . . . . . . . . . RHT 109
■ 7" . . . . . . . . . . . . . . . . . . . . RH 109
Rockin' Horse / Jun '86.

### JACKIE.
Tracks: Jackie / There was I / Chance it (Only on 3" CD single.).
■ CD Single . . . . . . . . . . . . . . . .661548
■ 12" . . . . . . . . . . . . . . . . . . . .611548
■ 7" . . . . . . . . . . . . . . . . . . . . 111548
Arista / Sep '88.

■ DELETED

## LOVE WILL WAIT.
**Tracks:** Love will wait / There was I / Dirty tale (extra track on 12" RHTX 107 only).
| | |
|---|---|
| ■ 12" | RHTX 107 |
| ■ 12" | RHT 107 |
| ■ 7" | RH 107 |
Rockin' Horse / Mar '86.

## ON FIRE.
**Tracks:** On fire / Be the sugar.
| | |
|---|---|
| ■ 12" | RHT 116 |
| ■ 7" | RH 116 |
Arista / Oct '87.

## THINKING ABOUT HIS BABY.
**Tracks:** Thinking about his baby / Thinking about his baby (extended) (on 12" only) / Big thing (extended version) (Track on 12") / Big thing.
| | |
|---|---|
| ■ 7" | RH 115 |
| ■ 7" | RH 5115 |
| ■ 12" | RHT 115 |
| ■ CD Single | RHCD 115 |
Arista / Jan '88.

## Blues Brothers Band

### RED, WHITE AND BLUES.
**Tracks:** You got the bucks / Red, white and blues / Can't play the blues (in an air conditioned room) / Early in the morning / One track train / Boogie thing / Never found a girl / Trick bag / Take you and show you / Big bird.
| | |
|---|---|
| CD | 9031772842 |
| ■ LP | 9031772841 |
| MC | 9031772844 |
WEA / Jun '92 / WEA.

## Blues Busters

### ACCEPT NO SUBSTITUTE.
**Tracks:** Not Advised.
| | |
|---|---|
| ■ LP | LM LP 1009 |
| MC | LMC 1009 |
Landslide / Oct '86.

### CLOSER I GET TO YOU.
**Tracks:** Closer I get to you / Midnight.
| | |
|---|---|
| ■ 12" | SP 20 |
Spank / Sep '86.

### HOW SWEET IT IS.
**Tracks:** How sweet it is (to be loved by you).
| | |
|---|---|
| ■ 7" | WI 214 |
Island / '66.

### IN MEMORY OF.
**Tracks:** Not Advised.
| | |
|---|---|
| CD | JMC 200114 |
Creole / Sep '93 / THE / BMG.

### JUST DON'T WANT TO BE LONELY.
**Tracks:** Just don't want to be lonely / Baby I'm sorry.
| | |
|---|---|
| ■ 7" | DYN 135 |
Dynamic / Aug '77.

### PHILLIP AND LLOYD.
**Tracks:** Not Advised.
| | |
|---|---|
| ■ LP | DYLP 3007 |
Dynamic / Dec '76.

### SWEETEST THING.
**Tracks:** Sweetest thing / Keep on doing it.
| | |
|---|---|
| ■ 7" | DYN 117 |
Dynamic / Oct '76.

### THIS TIME.
**Tracks:** Not Advised.
| | |
|---|---|
| ■ LP | LD 1014 |
Landslide (USA) / Aug '87.

### TOP OF THE POPS.
**Tracks:** Monkey man / How sweet it is (to be loved by you) / Nice time.
| | |
|---|---|
| ■ LP | VSLP 2001 |
Vista Sounds / '83.

### TRUTH.
**Tracks:** Not Advised.
| | |
|---|---|
| LP | SARGE 001 |
Sarge / Jun '89 / Jetstar.

## Bob & Earl

### BOB & EARL.
**Tracks:** Your time is my time / Big brother / Land of 1000 dances / I can't get away / My little girl / I'll keep running back / Dancin' everywhere / Send for me / I'll be there / Ooh honey babe / Harlem shuffle.
| | |
|---|---|
| ■ LP | JSX 2004 |
Jay Boy / Apr '71.

## BOB & EARL.
**Tracks:** Your time is my time / Big brother / Duck / Baby it's over / Land of 1000 dances / Puppet on a string / Would you believe / My little girl / I'll keep running back / Ooh honey baby.
| | |
|---|---|
| ■ LP | BCB 1 |
B & C / Jun '69.

## HARLEM SHUFFLE.
**Tracks:** Harlem Shuffle / You don't know like I know / Let's go baby (where the action is) / Little piece of leather / Billy's bag / Justine.
| | |
|---|---|
| ■ LP | OLLP 5160 |
Line / Feb '84.

## HARLEM SHUFFLE.
**Tracks:** Harlem Shuffle.
| | |
|---|---|
| ■ 7" | CS 9016 |
Contempo (1) / May '75.
| | |
|---|---|
| ■ 10" | 10WIP 6599 |
| ■ 7" | WIP 6599 |
Island / Apr '80.

## HARLEM SHUFFLE (OLD GOLD).
**Tracks:** Harlem shuffle / Duck.
| | |
|---|---|
| ■ 7" | OG 9032 |
Old Gold / '82.

## HARLEM SHUFFLE (ORIGINAL).
**Tracks:** Harlem shuffle.
| | |
|---|---|
| ■ 7" | WIP 6053 |
Island / Mar '69.

## Bobo, Willie

### HELL OF AN ACT TO FOLLOW.
**Tracks:** Always there / Keep that same old feeling / Together / Pisces / Dindi / Snort of green / Fairy tales for two / Sixty two fifty.
| | |
|---|---|
| ■ LP | CBS 83160 |
CBS / Nov '79.

## Body

### MIDDLE OF THE NIGHT.
**Tracks:** Middle of the night / Middle of the night (inst).
| | |
|---|---|
| ■ 12" | MCAT 1203 |
| ■ 7" | MCA 1203 |
MCA / Feb '88.

### TOUCH ME UP.
**Tracks:** Touch me up.
| | |
|---|---|
| ■ 12" | MCA 24039 |
MCA (Import) / Jul '90.

## Bofill, Angela

Having been voted Best Latin Female Vocalist by the Latin New York magazine for her recording *My Friend* Bofill became involved in jazz and performed with the Brooklyn Academy Of Music before moving to the Dance Theatre Of Harlem Chorus. She was signed to GRP and released her first album *Angie* in 1978 which included her jazz suite *Under The Moon And Over The Sky*. Moving to Arista for her third album *Something About You* in 1981 she displayed a move from jazz to soul with production credits for this and her next two releases going to Narada Michael Walden. Three more Arista albums followed including 1984's *System* before she signed to Capitol in 1988 and released *Intuition* featuring Norman Connors amongst the producers. Bofill has also appeared on other artists recordings most notably Stanley Clarke's *Hideaway* album.

### ANGEL OF THE NIGHT.
**Tracks:** I Try / People make the world go round / Angel of the night / Rainbow child / What I wouldn't do / Feeling's love / Love to last / Voyage.
| | |
|---|---|
| ■ LP | SPART 1113 |
Chrysalis / '82.

### ANGIE.
**Tracks:** Under the moon and over they sky / This time I'll be sweeter / Baby I need your love / Rough times / Only thing I would wish for / Summer days / Share your love / Children of the world united.
| | |
|---|---|
| ■ LP | SPART 1084 |
Chrysalis / '82.

### BEST OF ANGELA BOFILL.
**Tracks:** I try / This time / I'll be sweeter / What I wouldn't do / Still in love / I'm on your side / Time to say goodbye / Something about you / Let me be the one / Tonight I give in / Call of the wild / Break it to me gently / Angel of the night.
| | |
|---|---|
| ■ MC | 407829 |

| | |
|---|---|
| ■ LP | 207829 |
Arista / Aug '86.

### BEST OF ANGIE, THE (Next Time I'll Be Sweeter).
**Tracks:** This time I'll be sweeter / People make the world go round / Still in love / I'm on your side / Break it to me gently / Song for a rainy day / Holdin' out for love / I try / Tonight I give in / Stop look listen / Ain't nothing like the real thing / Tropical love / What I wouldn't do (for the love of you) / Something about you / Time to say goodbye.
| | |
|---|---|
| ■ CD | 211516 |
| ■ MC | 411516 |
Arista / Jun '91.

### BREAK IT TO ME GENTLY.
**Tracks:** Break it to me gently / Time to say goodbye.
| | |
|---|---|
| ■ 12" | ARIST 12463 |
| ■ 7" | ARIST 463 |
Arista / '82.

### HEAVENLY LOVE.
**Tracks:** Heavenly love.
| | |
|---|---|
| ■ CD Single | JIVECD 334 |
Jive / May '93.

### HOLDING OUT FOR LOVE.
**Tracks:** Holding out for love / Only love.
| | |
|---|---|
| ■ 7" | ARIST 433 |
Arista / Jan '82.

### I WANNA LOVE SOMEBODY.
**Tracks:** Not Advised.
| | |
|---|---|
| CD | CHIP 134 |
| ■ MC | HIPC 134 |
Jive / Mar '93 / BMG.

### INTUITION.
**Tracks:** Love is in your eyes / Intuition / I just wanna stop / Long gone / For you and I / Fragile handle with care / In your lovers eyes / Lover overtime / Festival / Special lover / Everlasting love.
| | |
|---|---|
| ■ CD | CDP 748 335 2 |
| ■ LP | EST 2077 |
| ■ MC | TCEST 2077 |
Capitol / Nov '88.

### SOMETHING ABOUT YOU.
**Tracks:** Something about you / Break it to me gently / On and on / Tropical love / You should know by now / Only love / Holdin' out for love / Stop look listen / I do love you / Three blind mice / Time to say goodbye.
| | |
|---|---|
| ■ LP | SPART 1179 |
Arista / Feb '82.

### TELL ME TOMORROW.
**Tracks:** Generate love / Tell me tomorrow / Midnight shine / I don't wanna come down / First time / This change of yours / Still in love / Woman' intuition / If you wanna love me, you're on.
| | |
|---|---|
| ■ LP | 207443 |
| ■ MC | 407443 |
Arista / Nov '85.

### THIS TIME I'LL BE SWEETER.
**Tracks:** This time I'll be sweeter / Baby I need your love.
| | |
|---|---|
| ■ 7" | ARIST 238 |
Arista / Mar '79.

### TOO TOUGH.
**Tracks:** Too tough / Ain't nothing like the real thing / Tonight I give in / You could come take me home / Love you too much / Is this a dream / Song for a rainy day / I can see it in your eyes / Accept me / Rainbow inside my heart.
| | |
|---|---|
| ■ LP | 205273 |
| ■ MC | 405273 |
Arista / Feb '83.

### TOO TOUGH.
**Tracks:** Too tough / Rainbow inside my heart.
| | |
|---|---|
| ■ 12" | ARIST 12515 |
| ■ 7" | ARIST 515 |
Arista / Feb '83.

## Bohannon, Hamilton

### ANDRIA.
**Tracks:** Andria / Bohannon disco symphony.
| | |
|---|---|
| ■ 7" | 6167 565 |
Mercury / Aug '77.

### BOHANNON DRIVE.
**Tracks:** Rock your body / Wake up / Running from yourlove / Do it goo / Lets start the dance III / Tell me you'll wait / Enjoy your day.
| | |
|---|---|
| ■ LP | CLTLP 3 |
Compleat (USA) / Oct '83.

**BOHANNON MIX.**
Tracks: Bohannon mix / Disco stomp / South African man.
■ 12".....................PASH 17(12)
Passion (1) / Jan '84.

**BOHANNON'S BEST.**
Tracks: Stop and go / Keep on dancing / South African man / Disco stomp / Truck stop / Getting to the other side / Foot stompin' music / Happy feeling / Pimp walk / Have a good day.
■ LP.....................SHU 8522
London / Dec '78.

**CUT LOOSE.**
Tracks: At nightfall / Beat / Cut loose / Let me see how you do it / Mighty groovy / That's the way it goes.
■ LP.....................9100061
Mercury / Apr '79.

**CUT LOOSE.**
Tracks: Cut loose / At nightfall.
■ 7".....................6167 774
Mercury / '79.

**DANCE YOUR ASS OFF.**
Tracks: Dance your ass off / Stop and go.
■ 7".....................BR 36
Brunswick / Jul '76.

**DISCO STOMP.**
Tracks: Disco stomp.
■ 7".....................BR 19
Brunswick / May '75.

**DISCO STOMP (OLD GOLD).**
Tracks: Disco stomp / Foot stompin' music / South African man.
■ CD Single.....................OG 6110
Old Gold / Nov '88.
■ 12".....................OG 4122
Old Gold / Dec '89.

**ESSENTIAL DANCEFLOOR.**
Tracks: Not Advised.
CD.....................DGPCD 699
LP.....................DGPLP 699
Deep Beats / Jun '94 / BMG.

**FOOT STOMPIN' MUSIC.**
Tracks: Foot stompin' music.
■ 7".....................BR 21
Brunswick / Jul '75.

**HAPPY FEELING.**
Tracks: Happy feeling.
■ 7".....................BR 24
Brunswick / Sep '75.

**INSIDES OUT.**
Tracks: Foot stomping music / East coast groove / Keep on being my girl / Disco stomp / Love is fading / Thoughts and wishes / Happy feeling.
■ LP.....................SHU 8523
London / Dec '78.

**IT'S TIME TO JAM.**
Tracks: Let's start II dance again / Foot stompin' music / Throw down the groove / Let's start the dance / Rock and groove your soul / Dance fever.
CD.....................CDSEW 033
LP.....................SEW 033
■ MC.....................SEWC 033
South Bound / Oct '90 / Pinnacle.

**LET'S START THE DANCE.**
Tracks: Let's start the dance.
■ 7".....................6167 700
Mercury / Aug '78.
■ 12".....................CLTL 1
■ 7".....................CLT 1
Compleat (USA) / Jun '83.

**LET'S START TO DANCE AGAIN (2).**
Tracks: Let's start to dance again.
■ 12".....................HLX 10582
■ 7".....................HL 10582
London-American / Jul '83.

**LET'S START TO DANCE AGAIN (RAP).**
Tracks: Let's start to dance again(rap) / Let's start to dance again(party version).
■ 12".....................DOM T3
Domino (1) / Jul '86.

**MAKE YOUR BODY MOVE.**
Tracks: Make your body move / Wrong number / Don't leave me / B.T. is doing the reggae / School girl / Funkville / Come back my love / Make your body move (instrumental).
■ LP.....................CLTLP 1
Compleat (USA) / Aug '83.

**PHASE 2.**
Tracks: Andrea / Bohannon disco symphony / But what is a dream / Daddy's little son / Isn't it a beautiful morning / Just doing my thing / Moving fast / Heart 'n' soul.
■ LP.....................9100040
Mercury (EMI) / Oct '77.

**SOUTH AFRICAN MAN.**
Tracks: South African man.
■ 7".....................BR 16
Brunswick / Feb '75.

**WAKE UP.**
Tracks: Wake up / Enjoy your day.
■ 12".....................CLTL 2
■ 7".....................CLT 2
Compleat (USA) / Sep '83.

## Boiling Point

**LET'S GET FUNKTIFIED.**
Tracks: Let's get funktified / Let's get funktified (version).
■ 12".....................BANG 1312
■ 7".....................BANG 13
Bang / May '78.

## Bombers

**(EVERYBODY) GET DANCIN'.**
Tracks: (Everybody) get dancin' / Music fever.
■ 7".....................FM 1
Flamingo / May '79.

**LET'S DANCE.**
Tracks: Let's dance.
■ 7".....................FM 4
Flamingo / Aug '79.

## Bond, Isabel

**DON'T FORGET ABOUT ME.**
Tracks: Don't forget about me.
■ 7".....................MM 627
Major Minor / '69.

## Bond, Jacki

**HE SAY.**
Tracks: He say / Why can't I love him.
■ 7".....................JH 320
Strike (60's) / '66.

**TELL HIM TO GO AWAY.**
Tracks: Tell him to go away / Don't worry 'bout me.
■ 7".....................JH 302
Strike (60's) / '66.

## Bonds, Gary U.S.

**BEST OF GARY 'US' BONDS, THE.**
Tracks: Not Advised.
CD.....................MCCD 111
MC.....................MCTC 111
Music Club / Jun '93 / Gold & Sons / THE / Video Collection / C.M. Distribution.

**COLLECTION: GARY US BONDS.**
Tracks: Not Advised.
CD.....................IMCD 9.00715
Impact (import) / Nov '89.

**DANCE TIL QUARTER TO THREE WITH..**
Tracks: Not Advised.
■ LP.....................LG 1002
Legrand (USA) / Aug '87.

**DEDICATION.**
Tracks: Jolie blon / This little girl / Your love / Dedication / Daddy's come home / It's only love / Pretender / Way back when / From a Buick 6 / Just like a child.
■ LP.....................AML 3017
EMI-America / Aug '81.
■ LP.....................FA 4130751
MC.....................TCFA 41 30754
Fame / Nov '83 / EMI.
■ LP.....................ED 2606951
■ MC.....................ED 2606954
Capitol / Sep '85.

**GARY U.S. BONDS.**
Tracks: Not Advised.
MC Set.....................GM 0230
K-Tel Goldmasters / Aug '84 / C.M. Distribution / Arabesque Ltd. / Ross Records / PolyGram.

**GREATEST HITS: GARY U.S. BONDS.**
Tracks: New Orleans / Quarter to three / Not me / Dear lady twist / Mixed up faculty / School is out /

School is in / Having so much fun / Twist twist senora / Where did that naughty girl go / I dig this station / Take me back to New Orleans.
■ LP.....................ENGY 506
MC.....................ENCAS 506
Ensign / Sep '81 / EMI.

**GREATEST HITS: GARY U.S. BONDS (2).**
Tracks: Not Advised.
CD.....................TRLGCD 100
LP.....................TRLG 100
MC.....................TRLGCX 100
Timeless (Jazz) / Sep '90 / New Note / Jazz Music.

**IT'S ONLY LOVE.**
Tracks: It's only love / This little girl.
■ 7".....................EA 128
EMI-America / Oct '81.

**JOLE BLON.**
Tracks: Jolie blon.
■ 7".....................EA 127
EMI-America / Aug '81.

**NEW ORLEANS.**
Tracks: New Orleans / High time / Little bitty pretty one.
■ 7".....................JAR 527
Top Rank (1) / Jan '61.
■ 7".....................CR 181
Blast From The Past / Oct '80.
■ 7".....................ENY 219
Ensign / Oct '81.

**ON THE LINE.**
Tracks: Hold on / Out of work / Club soul city / Soul deep / urn the music down / Love's on the line / Rendezvous / Angelyne / All I need / Bring her back / Last time.
■ LP.....................AML 3022
EMI-America / Jul '82.

**QUARTER TO THREE.**
Tracks: Quarter to three.
■ 7".....................JAR 575
Top Rank (1) / Jul '61.

**RENDEZVOUS.**
Tracks: Rendezvous / Way back when.
■ 7".....................EA 145
EMI-America / Sep '82.

**SOUL DEEP.**
Tracks: Soul deep / Bring her back.
■ 7".....................EA 140
EMI-America / Jul '82.

**STANDING IN THE LINE OF FIRE.**
Tracks: Not Advised.
MC.....................CSPRAY 103
■ LP.....................SPRAY 103
Making Waves / Aug '85 / C.M. Distribution.

**STANDING IN THE LINE OF FIRE.**
Tracks: Standing in the line of fire / Wild nights.
■ 12".....................SURFT 106
■ 7".....................SURF 106
Making Waves / Jul '85.

**STAR, THE.**
Tracks: Star.
■ 7".....................CYX 200
Charly / Nov '81.

**TAKE ME BACK TO NEW ORLEANS.**
Tracks: Take me back to New Orleans / Send her to me / Shine on lover's moon / Please forgive me / Workin' for my baby / Give me one more chance / My little room / What a dream / Don't go to strangers / Food of love / Girl next door / What a crazy world / I'm that kind of guy / Call me for Christmas / Guida's Romeo & Juliet / One million tears / Time ol' story / My sweet Ruby Rose / I know why dreamers cry / I walk the line / Oh yeah oh yeah / Nearness of you / I love you so / I don't wanna wait (why wait 'til Saturday night).
CD.....................CDCHD 549
Ace / Aug '94 / Pinnacle / Complete Record Co. Ltd.

**THIS LITTLE GIRL.**
Tracks: This little girl.
■ 7".....................EA 122
EMI-America / May '81.

**TWIST UP CALYPSO.**
Tracks: Calypso / Scratch me back / Coconut woman / Day O / Twist twist senora.
■ LP.....................6.24794
Teldec (Germany) / Dec '81.

**U.S. BONDS GREATEST HITS.**
Tracks: Not Advised.
■ LP.....................LPS 1001
Legrand (USA) / Aug '87.

■ DELETED

**WARNING.**
Tracks: Not Advised.
■ LP . . . . . . . . . . . . . . . . . . . . . . . . LG 1004
Legrand (USA) / Aug '87.

## Boo, Betty

**SAY IT ISN'T SO.**
Tracks: Say it isn't so / Say it isn't so (inst.).
■ 7" . . . . . . . . . . . . . . . . . . . . . . . GRP 125
Grapevine (Northern Soul) / Aug '79.

## Booker, Chuckii

**CHUCKII.**
Tracks: Not Advised.
■ CD . . . . . . . . . . . . . . . . . . . . K 781947-2
■ MC . . . . . . . . . . . . . . . . . . . . 781 947-4
■ LP . . . . . . . . . . . . . . . . . . . . K 781947-1
WEA / May '89.

**NIICE N WIILD.**
Tracks: Spinnin / Love is medicine / Out of the dark / You don't know / With all my heart / I git around / Games / Deep c diiver / Soul trilogy 1 / Soul trilogy 11 / Soul trilogy 111 / Niice n wiild / I should have loved you.
CD . . . . . . . . . . . . . . . . . . . . . 7567824102
MC . . . . . . . . . . . . . . . . . . . . . 7567824104
WEA / Nov '92 / WEA.

**TURNED AWAY.**
Tracks: Turned away / Keep your guard up.
■ 12" . . . . . . . . . . . . . . . . . . . . . . A 8917T
■ 7" . . . . . . . . . . . . . . . . . . . . . . . A 8917
Atlantic / Oct '89.

## Booker T & The MG's

Booker T. Jones joined the Stax organisation in 1960 as a saxophonist, although he could play numerous other instruments as well, where he met the Mar-Keys guitarist Steve Cropper. The pair hit it off immediately and formed the MG's (short for Memphis Group) who became the principal Stax house band, architects of the lean Stax sound, as well as a hugely successful band in their own right. Hits like *Green Onions*, *My Sweet Potato* and *Hip Hug-Her* established the band's identity in the public mind but it was as the backing band for Otis Redding, Wilson Pickett, Albert King et al that cemented their reputation as one of the finest soul bands of all time. In addition to this embarrassment of riches they also had a brilliant songwriter in Cropper, who has writing credits on *In The Midnight Hour*, *Soul Man* and *(Sittin' On) The Dock Of The Bay* and his trebly Telecaster can be heard on literally hundreds of other soul classics. The informal nature of the band meant that their demise in 1971 was a sad but not unexpected event. Jones has mainly busied himself with production duties, while Cropper continued his session work before joining ex-MG 'Duck' Dunn in the Blues Brothers Band, appearing in the film and on the subsequent spin-off albums. In 1993 a re-formed MG's were the backing band for Neil Young on a tour that included a breathtaking show at Finsbury Park. Sadly illhealth cut short this unique partnership before any material was recorded.

**AND NOW.**
Tracks: Not Advised.
CD . . . . . . . . . . . . . . . . . . . . . 8122702972
WEA / Jul '93 / WEA.

**BE MY LADY.**
Tracks: Be my lady / Red beans and rice.
■ 7" . . . . . . . . . . . . . . . . . . . . . . . AT 4063
Atlantic / Jan '66.

**BEST OF BOOKER T AND THE MG'S.**
Tracks: Green onions / Slim Jenkins place / Hip hug her / Soul dressing / Summertime / Bootleg / Jellybread / Tic-tac-toe / Can't be still / Groovin' / Mo' onions / Red beans and rice.
■ LP . . . . . . . . . . . . . . . . . . . . . . 228 015
Atco / Nov '69.
■ LP . . . . . . . . . . . . . . . . . . . . . K 40072
MC . . . . . . . . . . . . . . . . . . . . . K4 40072
Atlantic / Jul '84 / WEA.
CD . . . . . . . . . . . . . . . . . . . . . FCD 60004
London / Apr '87 / PolyGram.

**BEST OF BOOKER T AND THE MG'S, THE.**
Tracks: Time is tight / Soul limbo / Heads or tails / Over easy / Hip hug-her / Hang 'em high / Johnny I

love you / Slum baby / Horse / Soul clap '69 / Sunday sermon / Born under a bad sign / Mrs Robinson / Something / Light my fire / It's your thing / Fuquawi / Kinda easy like / Meditation / Melting pot.

**BOOKER T AND THE MG'S.**
Tracks: Green onions / Rinky dink / I got a woman / Mo' onions / Twist and shout / Behave yourself / Stranger on the shore / Lonely avenue / One who really loves you / You can't sit down / Woman, a lover, a friend / Comin' home baby.
■ LP . . . . . . . . . . . . . . . . . . . . . SHM 3031
Pickwick / Jun '80.

**BOOKER T SET, THE.**
Tracks: Love child / Lady Madonna / Horse / Sing a simple song / Mrs. Robinson / This guy's in love with you / Light my fire / Michelle / You're all I need / I've never found a girl / It's your thing.
■ LP . . . . . . . . . . . . . . . . . . . . SXATS 1015
Stax / Nov '69.
■ LP . . . . . . . . . . . . . . . . . . . . . 2362012
Stax / Jun '71.
■ LP . . . . . . . . . . . . . . . . . . . . MPS 8531
MC . . . . . . . . . . . . . . . . . . . . MPS 58531
Stax / Dec '86 / Pinnacle.
CD . . . . . . . . . . . . . . . . . . . . CDSXE 026
■ LP . . . . . . . . . . . . . . . . . . . . SXE 026
Stax / May '90 / Pinnacle.

**DOIN' OUR THING.**
Tracks: I can dig it / Expressway to your heart / Doin' our thing / You don't love me / Never my love / Exodus song / Beat goes on / Ode to Billie Joe / Blue on green / You keep me hanging on / Let's go get stoned.
■ LP . . . . . . . . . . . . . . . . . . . . . 231 002
Stax / Jun '68.
■ LP . . . . . . . . . . . . . . . . . . . . 2464 011
Atlantic / Jun '70.

**GET READY.**
Tracks: Hip hug-her / Soul sanction / Get ready / More / Double or nothing / Carnaby Street / Slim Jenkins' joint / Pigmy / Groovin' / Booker's notion / Sunny.
■ LP . . . . . . . . . . . . . . . . . . . . . 228 004
Atco / Apr '69.

**GREATEST HITS.**
Tracks: Hang 'em high / Eleanor Rigby / Soul limbo / Over easy / Mrs Robinson / Something / Time is tight / Johnny I love you / Heads or tails / Meditation / Hip hug-her.
■ LP . . . . . . . . . . . . . . . . . . . . . 2362002
Stax / Mar '71.

**GREEN ONIONS.**
Tracks: Green onions / Chinese checkers / Memphis soul stew / Sock it to 'em JB.
■ 7" . . . . . . . . . . . . . . . . . . . . . . ATM 10
Atlantic / Apr '80.

**GREEN ONIONS.**
Tracks: Green onions / Bootleg.
■ 12" . . . . . . . . . . . . . . . . . . . . K 10109 T
Atlantic / Apr '80.
■ 7" . . . . . . . . . . . . . . . . . . . . . K 10109
Atlantic / Jun '86.

**GREEN ONIONS.**
Tracks: Green onions / Rinky dink / I got a woman / Mo' onions / Twist and shout / Behave yourself / Stranger on the shore / Lonely avenue / One who really loves you / You can't sit down / Woman, a lover, a friend / Comin' home baby.
■ LP . . . . . . . . . . . . . . . . . . . . . STAX 701
Stax / Mar '62.
■ LP . . . . . . . . . . . . . . . . . . . . HAK 8182
London-American / Jul '64.
■ LP . . . . . . . . . . . . . . . . . . . . . 588 033
Atlantic / Oct '69.
MC . . . . . . . . . . . . . . . . . . . . 756782255-4
Atlantic / Jun '91 / WEA.
CD . . . . . . . . . . . . . . . . . . . . 75678222552
Pickwick/Warner / Oct '94 / Pinnacle.

**GREEN ONIONS.**
Tracks: Green onions / Boot leg.
■ 7" . . . . . . . . . . . . . . . . . . . . . . 584088
Atlantic / Mar '67.

**GREEN ONIONS (OLD GOLD).**
Tracks: Green onions / Chinese crackers.
7" . . . . . . . . . . . . . . . . . . . . . . OG 9499
Old Gold / '92 / Pickwick.

**HANG 'EM HIGH.**
Tracks: Hang 'em high / Over easy.
■ 7" . . . . . . . . . . . . . . . . . . . . . STAX 813
Stax / Sep '87.

**HIP HUG HER.**
Tracks: Hip hug her / Slim Jenkin's place / Soul sanction / Get ready / More / Double or nothing / Carnaby St. / Slim Jenkins' joint / Pigmy / Groovin' / Booker's notion / Sunny.
■ LP . . . . . . . . . . . . . . . . . . . . . . . .717
Stax / Nov '67.

**HIP HUG HER.**
Tracks: Not Advised.
CD . . . . . . . . . . . . . . . . . . . . 8122710132
WEA / Jul '93 / WEA.

**HIP HUG HER.**
Tracks: Hip hug her / Summertime.
■ 7" . . . . . . . . . . . . . . . . . . . . . 601009
Stax / Apr '67.
■ 7" . . . . . . . . . . . . . . . . . . . . . K 11454
Atlantic / Mar '80.

**IN THE CHRISTMAS SPIRIT.**
Tracks: Not Advised.
CD . . . . . . . . . . . . . . . . . . . . 7567823382
Atlantic / Jul '93 / WEA.

**MCLEMORE AVENUE.**
Tracks: Golden slumbers / Here comes the sun / Come together / Because / Mean Mr Mustard / She came in through the bathroom window / Carry that weight / End / Something / You never give me your money / Polythene Pam / Sun king / I want you.
■ LP . . . . . . . . . . . . . . . . . . . . SXATS 1031
Stax / Jul '70.
■ LP . . . . . . . . . . . . . . . . . . . . . 2362016
Stax / Aug '71.
CD . . . . . . . . . . . . . . . . . . . . MFCD 835
Mobile Fidelity Sound Lab(USA) / '88.
CD . . . . . . . . . . . . . . . . . . . . CDSXE 016
■ LP . . . . . . . . . . . . . . . . . . . . . SXE 016
Stax / Nov '88 / Pinnacle.

**MELTING POT.**
Tracks: Melting pot / Back home / Chicken pox / Fuquawi / Kinda easy like / Hi ride / L.A. jazz song / Sunny Monday.
■ LP . . . . . . . . . . . . . . . . . . . . . 2325 030
Polydor / Mar '71.
CD . . . . . . . . . . . . . . . . . . . . CDSXE 055
Stax / Sep '92 / Pinnacle.

**MELTING POT.**
Tracks: Melting pot / Kinda easy.
■ 7" . . . . . . . . . . . . . . . . . . . . . 2025 026
Stax / Jul '71.

**MY SWEET POTATO.**
Tracks: My sweet potato / Booker-loo.
■ 7" . . . . . . . . . . . . . . . . . . . . . 584044
Atlantic / Oct '66.

**SOUL CHRISTMAS.**
Tracks: Jingle bells / Winter wonderland / Christmas song / Silver bells / Silent night / We three kings / etc.
■ LP . . . . . . . . . . . . . . . . . . . . . 589 013
Stax / Dec '67.

**SOUL CLAP '69.**
Tracks: Soul clap '69.
■ 7" . . . . . . . . . . . . . . . . . . . . . STAX 127
Stax / Aug '69.

**SOUL DRESSING.**
Tracks: Not Advised.
CD . . . . . . . . . . . . . . . . . . . . 756782337-2
WEA / Mar '93 / WEA.

**SOUL LIMBO.**
Tracks: Be young, be foolish, be happy / Hang 'em high / Over easy / Eleanor Rigby / Sweet sweet baby / Foxy lady / La la means I love you / Willow weep for me / Soul limbo / Heads or tails / Born under a bad sign.
■ LP . . . . . . . . . . . . . . . . . . . . SXATS 1001
Stax / Dec '68.
■ LP . . . . . . . . . . . . . . . . . . . . . SX 009
■ LP . . . . . . . . . . . . . . . . . . . . . SXE 009
Stax / Feb '88.
CD . . . . . . . . . . . . . . . . . . . . CDSXE 009
Stax / Apr '90 / Pinnacle.

**SOUL LIMBO.**
Tracks: Soul limbo / Soul clap '69.
■ 7" . . . . . . . . . . . . . . . . . . . . . STAX 102
Stax / Dec '68.
■ 7" . . . . . . . . . . . . . . . . . . . . STAX 1011
Stax / Aug '82.
■ 7" . . . . . . . . . . . . . . . . . . . . STAX 808
■ 7" P.Disc . . . . . . . . . . . . . . . . . STAP 808
■ 12" . . . . . . . . . . . . . . . . . . . . STAT 808
Stax / Aug '87.

## THAT'S THE WAY IT SHOULD BE.
**Tracks:** Slip slidin' / Mo' greens / Gotta serve somebody / Let's wait awhile / That's the way it should be / Juts my imagination (Running away with me) / Camel ride / Have a heart / Crusin' / I can't stand the rain / Sarasota sunset / I still haven't found what I'm looking for.
CD. . . . . . . . . . . . . . . . . . . . . . . . . . .474470 2
MC. . . . . . . . . . . . . . . . . . . . . . . . . . .474470 4
Columbia / Jun '94 / Sony.

## TIME IS TIGHT.
**Tracks:** Time is tight / Johnny, I love you.
■ 7″. . . . . . . . . . . . . . . . . . . . . . . . . STAX 119
Stax / May '69.
■ 7″. . . . . . . . . . . . . . . . . . . . . . . . STAX 2001
Stax / Mar '80.
■ 7″. . . . . . . . . . . . . . . . . . . . . . . . STAX 1003
Stax / Mar '82.
■ 7″. . . . . . . . . . . . . . . . . . . . . . . . . STAX 803
Stax / Jun '87.

## TIME IS TIGHT.
**Tracks:** Time is tight / Hip hug her / Mrs. Robinson / Soul clap / Slum baby / Hang 'em high / Soul limbo / Sugar cane / Melting pot / Soul man / I'd rather drink muddy water / Heads or tails / Crop dustin' / Jive man / Way I feel tonight / Funky Broadway / One with sugar / Land of a thousand dances.
■ LP . . . . . . . . . . . . . . . . . . . . . . . . STX 3007
Stax / May '80.

## TIME IS TIGHT (OLD GOLD).
**Tracks:** Time is tight / Soul limbo.
■ 7″. . . . . . . . . . . . . . . . . . . . . . . . .OG 9530
Old Gold / Sep '85.

## UNIVERSAL LANGUAGE.
**Tracks:** Sticky stuff / Grab bag / Space nuts / Love wheels / Moto cross / Last tango in Memphis / MG's salsa / Tie stick / Reincarnation.
■ LP . . . . . . . . . . . . . . . . . . . . . . . . . K 53057
Asylum / Mar '77.

# Boom, Taka

## BOOMERANG.
**Tracks:** To hell with him / Boomerang / Ride like the wind / Let it burn / Love party / Listen to your heart / Kiss it and make it better / I saw him first.
■ MC. . . . . . . . . . . . . . . . . . . . . . ZCCAB 1008
■ LP . . . . . . . . . . . . . . . . . . . . . CABLP 1008
Calibre / Jun '83.

## IN THE MIDDLE OF THE NIGHT.
**Tracks:** In the middle of the night.
■ 12″. . . . . . . . . . . . . . . . . . . . . POSPX 763
■ 7″. . . . . . . . . . . . . . . . . . . . . . POSP 763
Boiling Point / Jan '86.

## MIDDLE OF THE NIGHT.
**Tracks:** Not Advised.
■ CD . . . . . . . . . . . . . . . . . . . . . 827 613-2
■ LP . . . . . . . . . . . . . . . . . . . . . 827 613-1
■ MC. . . . . . . . . . . . . . . . . . . . . 827 613-4
Polydor / Mar '86.

## NIGHT DANCIN'.
**Tracks:** Night dancin' / Cloud dancer.
■ 12″. . . . . . . . . . . . . . . . . . . . . . AROD 172
■ 7″. . . . . . . . . . . . . . . . . . . . . . . ARO 172
Ariola / '79.

## TO HELL WITH HIM.
**Tracks:** To hell with him / Love party.
■ 12″. . . . . . . . . . . . . . . . . . . . . . CABL 113
■ 7″. . . . . . . . . . . . . . . . . . . . . . .CAB 113
Casablanca / May '83.

# Boone, Len

## LOVE WON'T BE DENIED.
**Tracks:** Love won't be denied / Living just to love you / Love won't be denied (instrumental) (Only on 12″ version.).
■ 12″. . . . . . . . . . . . . . . . . . . . .CHS 122227
■ 7″. . . . . . . . . . . . . . . . . . . . . . CHS 2227
Chrysalis / '83.

## THERE'S NO ME WITHOUT YOU.
**Tracks:** There's no me without you / Smile baby.
■ 12″. . . . . . . . . . . . . . . . . . . . .CHS 122317
■ 7″. . . . . . . . . . . . . . . . . . . . . . CHS 2317
Chrysalis / '79.

# Boothe, Patrick

## DANCE ALL NIGHT.
**Tracks:** Dance all night / Dance all night (part 2).
■ 12″. . . . . . . . . . . . . . . . . . . STRA 13 2213
■ 7″. . . . . . . . . . . . . . . . . . . . STRA 2213
Streetwave / May '82.

---

## NEVER KNEW LOVE LIKE THIS BEFORE.
**Tracks:** Never knew love like this before.
■ 12″. . . . . . . . . . . . . . . . . . STRA 132596
■ 7″. . . . . . . . . . . . . . . . . . . STRA 2596
Streetwave / Aug '82.

# Bowie, John

## CAN IT BE NOW.
**Tracks:** Can it be now.
■ 7″. . . . . . . . . . . . . . . . . . . . . . . .MER 6
Merben / '79.

# Box Tops

## BEST OF THE BOX TOPS.
**Tracks:** Letter / Neon rainbow / I pray for rain / Door you closed to me / Cry like a baby / Deep in Kentucky / Fields of clover / You keep me hangin' on / Choo choo train / I can dig it / Yesterday where's my mind / Soul deep / I shall be released / Together / I must be the devil / Sweet cream ladies forward march / Happy song.
■ LP . . . . . . . . . . . . . . . . . . . . . . . . LIK 41
Decal / Sep '88.

## BOX TOPS, THE.
**Tracks:** Not Advised.
CD. . . . . . . . . . . . . . . . . . . . . . . . .295591
MC. . . . . . . . . . . . . . . . . . . . . . . . .495591
Ariola / Apr '93 / BMG.

## CRY LIKE A BABY.
**Tracks:** Cry like a baby / Lightning strikes / Sugar shack.
■ 7″. . . . . . . . . . . . . . . . . . . . . . . CR 179
Blast From The Past / Aug '82.

## CRY LIKE A BABY.
**Tracks:** Deep in Kentucky / I'm the one for you / Weeping Analeah / Everytime / Fields of clover / Letter / Trouble with Sam / Lost / Good morning dear / 727 / You keep me hanging on / Cry like a baby / Door you closed to me.
■ LP . . . . . . . . . . . . . . . . . . . . . SBLL 105
Bell / Jun '68.

## CRY LIKE A BABY (ORIGINAL).
**Tracks:** Cry like a baby.
■ 7″. . . . . . . . . . . . . . . . . . . . . BELL 1001
Bell / Mar '68.

## LETTER, THE.
**Tracks:** Letter.
■ 7″. . . . . . . . . . . . . . . . . . . . . . SS 2044
Stateside / Sep '67.
■ 7″. . . . . . . . . . . . . . . . . . . . . .OG 9116
Old Gold / Jul '82.
■ CD Single. . . . . . . . . . . . . . . . .162071
Arista / Jun '89.

## LETTER, THE (RE-RELEASE).
**Tracks:** Letter / Cry like a baby.
■ 7″. . . . . . . . . . . . . . . . . . . . . . . JB 04
Juke Box (Re-issue) / Mar '82.

## NON-STOP.
**Tracks:** Choo choo train / Movin' on / Sandman / She shot a hole in my soul / People gonna talk / I can dig it / Met her in church / Rock me baby / If I let you in / Rollin' in my sleep / Yesterday / Where's my mind.
■ LP . . . . . . . . . . . . . . . . . . . . . SBLL 108
Bell / Nov '68.

## SOUL DEEP.
**Tracks:** Soul deep.
■ 7″. . . . . . . . . . . . . . . . . . . . . BELL 1068
Bell / Aug '69.

# Boys

## BOYS, THE.
**Tracks:** Dear fans (intro) / Crazy / Thing called love / Compton (interlude) / Funny / My love / What's for dinner (reprise) / I had a dream / Got to be there / Interview (interlude) / Sir Nose (interlude) / Thanx 4 the funk / Hey clown (interlude) / Bush / See ya / Strings'n'things (On CD only.).
■ CD . . . . . . . . . . . . . . . . . . . . . ZD 72718
■ LP . . . . . . . . . . . . . . . . . . . . . ZL 72718
■ MC. . . . . . . . . . . . . . . . . . . . . ZK 72718
Motown / Nov '90.

## CRAZY.
**Tracks:** Crazy.
■ 12″. . . . . . . . . . . . . . . . . . . . . ZT 44038
■ 7″. . . . . . . . . . . . . . . . . . . . . . ZB 44133
■ 7″. . . . . . . . . . . . . . . . . . . . . . ZB 44037
■ CD Single . . . . . . . . . . . . . . . . ZD 44038
■ MC Single . . . . . . . . . . . . . . . . ZK 44037
Motown / Sep '90.

---

## DIAL MY HEART.
**Tracks:** Dial my heart / Dial my heart (instrumental).
■ 12″. . . . . . . . . . . . . . . . . . . . . ZT 42246
■ 7″. . . . . . . . . . . . . . . . . . . . . . ZB 42245
■ 7″. . . . . . . . . . . . . . . . . . . . . . ZB 42571
■ CD Single. . . . . . . . . . . . . . . . ZD 42246
Motown / Oct '88.

## LUCKY CHARM.
**Tracks:** Lucky charm / Lucky charm (version).
■ 12″. . . . . . . . . . . . . . . . . . . . . ZT 42688
■ 7″. . . . . . . . . . . . . . . . . . . . . . ZB 42687
Motown / Mar '89.

## MESSAGES FROM THE BOYS.
**Tracks:** Dial my heart / Lucky charm / Little romance / Sunshine / Love gram / Just for the fun of it / Personality / Be my girl / Happy / Let's dance.
■ CD . . . . . . . . . . . . . . . . . . . . . ZD 72648
■ LP . . . . . . . . . . . . . . . . . . . . . ZL 72648
■ MC. . . . . . . . . . . . . . . . . . . . . ZK 72648
Motown / Nov '88.

## SAGA CONTINUES.
**Tracks:** Not Advised.
■ MC. . . . . . . . . . . . . . . . . . . .530069-4
Motown / Jan '93.

# Boystown Gang

## AIN'T NO MOUNTAIN HIGH ENOUGH.
**Tracks:** Ain't no mountain high enough / Cruisin' the streets.
■ 12″. . . . . . . . . . . . . . . . . . . . . DICK 1T
■ 7″. . . . . . . . . . . . . . . . . . . . . . DICK 1
Moby Dick / Sep '82.

## BRAND NEW ME.
**Tracks:** Brand new me.
■ 12″. . . . . . . . . . . . . . . . . . . . .12RNF 1
■ 7″. . . . . . . . . . . . . . . . . . . . . . 7RNF 1
Rich & Famous / Sep '84.

## CAN'T TAKE MY EYES OFF YOU.
**Tracks:** Can't take my eyes off you / Disco kicks.
■ 12″. . . . . . . . . . . . . . . . . . . . .ERCL 101
■ 7″. . . . . . . . . . . . . . . . . . . . . .ERC 101
ERC / Jul '82.

## CAN'T TAKE MY EYES OFF YOU (OLD GOLD).
**Tracks:** Can't take my eyes off you / Remember me / Ain't no mountain high enough suite (remix).
12″. . . . . . . . . . . . . . . . . . . . . .OG 4156
Old Gold / Feb '90 / Pickwick.

## CAST OF THOUSANDS, A.
**Tracks:** Good man is hard to find / Brand new me / In and out of love / Here I am waiting for you / I just can't help believin' / Dance trance medley / Yesterme, yester-you, yesterday / When will I see you again.
■ LP . . . . . . . . . . . . . . . . . . . . . RNF 7260
MC. . . . . . . . . . . . . . . . . . . . ZCRNF 7260
Rich & Famous / Oct '84.

## CRUISIN' THE STREETS.
**Tracks:** Remember me / Ain't no mountain high enough / Reprise / Finale / Cruisin' the streets / Cruisin' / Rejected / Pick up / Busted.
■ LP . . . . . . . . . . . . . . . . . . . . .BTG 231
Moby Dick / Aug '81.
■ LP . . . . . . . . . . . . . . . . . . . . . K 231
Moby Dick / Sep '81.

## DISCHARGE.
**Tracks:** Not Advised.
■ LP . . . . . . . . . . . . . . . . . . . . .ERCLP 101
MC. . . . . . . . . . . . . . . . . . . . ZCERC 101
ERC / Aug '82 / Jetstar.

## I JUST CAN'T HELP BELIEVING.
**Tracks:** I just can't help believin'.
■ 12″. . . . . . . . . . . . . . . . . . . . .ERCL 107
■ 7″. . . . . . . . . . . . . . . . . . . . . .ERC 107
ERC / Jul '83.

## REMEMBER ME.
**Tracks:** Remember me / Ain't no mountain high enough / Cruising in the streets / You do it for me.
■ 12″. . . . . . . . . . . . . . . . . . . . .SOHOT 69
Record Shack / Aug '86.

## SIGNED, SEALED, DELIVERED, I'M YOURS.
**Tracks:** Signed, sealed, delivered, I'm yours.
■ 12″. . . . . . . . . . . . . . . . . . . . .ERCL 102
■ 7″. . . . . . . . . . . . . . . . . . . . . .ERC 102
ERC / Sep '82.

■ DELETED

## YESTER-ME, YESTER-YOU, YESTERDAY.
**Tracks:** Yester-me, yester-you, yesterday / Dance trance medley.
■ 12" . . . . . . . . . . . . . . . . . . . . . . . . 12RNF 2
Rich & Famous / Dec '84.
■ 7" . . . . . . . . . . . . . . . . . . . . . . . . . 7RNF 2
Rich & Famous / Jan '85.

## Boyz II Men

Nate Morris, Michael McCary, Shawn Stockman and Wanya Morris became overnight-sensations when LA & Babyface production *End Of The Road* - from 1992 *Boomerang* soundtrack - spent record-breaking spell atop U.S. chart and also made U.K. no. 1, winning Grammy in process. Managed by Bell Biv Devoe's Michael Bivins and signed to Motown, group's debut *Cooleyhighhar-mony* sold millions, thus reviving label's fortunes. Boyz headlined 1993 U.S. tour with Jade, Shai and Wreckx-N-Effect; proving longevity when *II* album entered at top of U.S. chart, heralded by another transatlantic smash, *I'll Make Love to You*. Group's influence was demonstrated when swing quartet Silk attracted attention of Keith Sweat with medley of BIIM songs at 4th of July barbeque.

### CHRISTMAS INTERPRETATIONS.
**Tracks:** Not Advised.
CD . . . . . . . . . . . . . . . . . . . . . . . 530 257-2
Polydor / Nov '93 / PolyGram.

### COOLEYHIGHHARMONY.
**Tracks:** Please don't go / Lonely heart / This is my heart / Uhh ahh / It's so hard to say goodbye to yesterday / Motownphilly / Under pressure / Sympin' / Little things / Your love.
■ CD . . . . . . . . . . . . . . . . . . . . . . . ZD 72739
■ LP . . . . . . . . . . . . . . . . . . . . . . . ZL 72739
■ MC . . . . . . . . . . . . . . . . . . . . . . . ZK 72739
Motown / Jun '91.
CD . . . . . . . . . . . . . . . . . . . . . . . . 5300892
MC . . . . . . . . . . . . . . . . . . . . . . . . 5300894
■ LP . . . . . . . . . . . . . . . . . . . . . . . 5300891
Motown / Oct '92 / PolyGram.
DCC . . . . . . . . . . . . . . . . . . . . . . . 5300015
Motown / Jan '93 / PolyGram.

### END OF THE ROAD.
**Tracks:** End of the road.
■ 12" . . . . . . . . . . . . . . . . . . . . . TMGX 1411
■ 7" . . . . . . . . . . . . . . . . . . . . . . . TMG 1411
■ CD Single . . . . . . . . . . . . . . . . . TMGCD 1411
■ MC Single . . . . . . . . . . . . . . . . . TMGCS 1411
Motown / Aug '92.

### I'LL MAKE LOVE TO YOU.
**Tracks:** I'll make love to you.
12" . . . . . . . . . . . . . . . . . . . . . . TMGX 1431
7" . . . . . . . . . . . . . . . . . . . . . . . TMG 1431
CD Single . . . . . . . . . . . . . . . . . TMGCD 1431
MC Single . . . . . . . . . . . . . . . . . TMGCS 1431
Motown / Sep '94 / PolyGram.

### IN THE STILL OF THE NITE (I'LL REMEMBER).
**Tracks:** In the still of the nite / In the still of the nite (mixes).
■ 7" . . . . . . . . . . . . . . . . . . . . . . . TMG 1415
■ 12" . . . . . . . . . . . . . . . . . . . . . TMGX 1415
■ CD Single . . . . . . . . . . . . . . . . . TMGCD 1415
■ MC Single . . . . . . . . . . . . . . . . . TMGCS 1415
Motown / Mar '93.

### MOTOWNPHILLY.
**Tracks:** Motownphilly.
■ 12" . . . . . . . . . . . . . . . . . . . . . . ZT 45080
■ 7" . . . . . . . . . . . . . . . . . . . . . . . ZB 45079
■ CD Single . . . . . . . . . . . . . . . . . . ZD 45080
Motown / Nov '91.

## Bragg, Johnny

### THEY'RE TALKING ABOUT ME NOW.
**Tracks:** They're talking about me now / Is it you.
■ 7" . . . . . . . . . . . . . . . . . . . . . . . HEAT 2
Inferno (1) / '79.

## Braggs, Al 'TNT'

### AL 'TNT' BRAGGS.
**Tracks:** You're something else / Easy rock / We belong together / Cigarettes and coffee.
■ EP . . . . . . . . . . . . . . . . . . . . . VEP 170163
Vocalion / '66.

## EARTHQUAKE.
**Tracks:** Earthquake / How long do you hold on.
■ 7" . . . . . . . . . . . . . . . . . . . . . . . ACT 4506
Action / '68.

## Brainstorm

### FUNKY ENTERTAINMENT.
**Tracks:** Hot for you / Case of the boogie / Popcorn / Funky entertainment / You put a charge in my life / Don't let me catch you with your groove down.
■ LP . . . . . . . . . . . . . . . . . . . . . . TBU 83736
Tabu / '79.

### HOT FOR YOU.
**Tracks:** Hot for you / Don't let me catch you with your groove down.
■ 12" . . . . . . . . . . . . . . . . . . . . TBU12 7341
■ 7" . . . . . . . . . . . . . . . . . . . . . . TBU 7341
Tabu / May '79.

### LOVIN' IS REALLY MY GAME.
**Tracks:** Lovin' is really my game / Stormin'.
■ 7" . . . . . . . . . . . . . . . . . . . . . . . . . M 5
Miracle / Apr '79.

## Brainstorm

### ROCK THE HOUSE.
**Tracks:** Rock the house.
■ 12" . . . . . . . . . . . . . . . . . . . . 12YOBR 24
Yobro / Jul '91.

## Bramlett, Delaney

### YOU HAVE NO CHOICE.
**Tracks:** You have no choice / Liverpool Lou.
■ 7" . . . . . . . . . . . . . . . . . . . . . . . VN 9237
Vocalion / '65.

## Brand New Heavies

Initially shunned in homeland, London trio Jan Kincaid, Simon Boswell and Andrew Levy's 1990 eponymous debut LP - on Eddie Pillar's Acid Jazz label - prompted band to be signed by Delicious Vinyl in the States. BNH became first UK act since Soul II Soul to crack U.S. R&B chart. Adding permanent vocalist, N'Dea Davenport, they finally cracked UK singles chart in 1992 and debut LP was subsequently repackaged and re-promoted, taking the band's jazz-funk into charts on both sides of Atlantic. Success story has continued with 1994's *Brother Sister* LP. In between, Heavies diverted into rap for *Heavy Rhyme Experience*, featuring Gang Starr, Pharcyde and Main Source etc.

### BACK TO LOVE.
**Tracks:** Back to love (Mixes) / Baby don't use me (BNHCD 4 only.) / Never stop (BNCDP 4 only) / Dream come true (BNCDP 4 only).
12" . . . . . . . . . . . . . . . . . . . . . . . BNHX 4
CD Single . . . . . . . . . . . . . . . . . . BNCDP 4
CD Single . . . . . . . . . . . . . . . . . . BNHCD 4
MC Single . . . . . . . . . . . . . . . . . . BNHMC 4
FFRR / Sep '94 / PolyGram.

### BRAND NEW HEAVIES, THE.
**Tracks:** Dream come true / Stay this way / People get ready / Never stop / Put the funk back in it / Ride in the sky / Brand new heavies / Gimme one of those / Got to give / Sphynx / Dream come true (reality mix).
LP . . . . . . . . . . . . . . . . . . . . . JAZIDLP 023
Acid Jazz / Apr '90 / Vital Distribution.
CD . . . . . . . . . . . . . . . . . . . . . JAZIDCD 023
MC . . . . . . . . . . . . . . . . . . . . . JAZIDMC 023
Acid Jazz / Jun '90 / Vital Distribution.
CD . . . . . . . . . . . . . . . . . . . . . . 8283002
LP . . . . . . . . . . . . . . . . . . . . . . 8283001
MC . . . . . . . . . . . . . . . . . . . . . . 8283004
Acid Jazz / Mar '92 / Vital Distribution.

### BROTHER SISTER.
**Tracks:** Back to love / Ten ton take / Mind trips / Spend some time / Keep together / Snake hips / Fake / People giving love / World keeps spinning / Forever / Day break / Midnight at the Oasis / Dream on dreamer / Have a good time / Brother sister.
CD . . . . . . . . . . . . . . . . . . . . . .828557-2
LP . . . . . . . . . . . . . . . . . . . . . .828557-1
MC . . . . . . . . . . . . . . . . . . . . . .828557-4
FFRR / Apr '94 / PolyGram.

### DON'T LET IT GO TO YOUR HEAD.
**Tracks:** Don't let it go to your head.
■ 12" . . . . . . . . . . . . . . . . . . . . . . BNHX 1
■ 7" . . . . . . . . . . . . . . . . . . . . . . . BNH 1
■ CD Single . . . . . . . . . . . . . . . . . BNHCD 1

■ MC Single. . . . . . . . . . . . . . . . . BNHMC 1
Acid Jazz (Polygram) / Jul '92.

### DREAM COME TRUE.
**Tracks:** Dream come true / Stay this way.
CD . . . . . . . . . . . . . . . . . . . . . JAZIDCD 025
■ 12" . . . . . . . . . . . . . . . . . . . . JAZID 025 T
■ 7" . . . . . . . . . . . . . . . . . . . . . JAZID 025
Acid Jazz / Aug '90 / Vital Distribution.
■ 12" Remix. . . . . . . . . . . . . . . . . . .FX 180
■ 7" . . . . . . . . . . . . . . . . . . . . . . . F 180
■ CD Single . . . . . . . . . . . . . . . . . . FCD 180
■ MC Single. . . . . . . . . . . . . . . . . . FCS 180
FFRR / Feb '92.

### DREAM ON DREAMER.
**Tracks:** Dream on dreamer (Mixes).
■ 12" . . . . . . . . . . . . . . . . . . . . . . BNHX 3
■ 12" Remix. . . . . . . . . . . . . . . . . BNHXR 3
■ CD Single . . . . . . . . . . . . . . . . . BNHCD 3
■ MC Single. . . . . . . . . . . . . . . . . BNHMC 3
FFRR / Feb '94.

### GOT TO GIVE.
**Tracks:** Got to give (part 1) / Got to give (part 2).
■ 7" . . . . . . . . . . . . . . . . . . . . . . COOL 167
■ 12" . . . . . . . . . . . . . . . . . . . . . COOLX 167
Cool Tempo / May '88.

### HEAVY RHYME EXPERIENCE VOL.1.
**Tracks:** Bonafied funk / It's getting hectic / Who makes the loot / Wake me when I'm dead / Jump 'n' move / Death threat / State of yo / Do what I gotta do / Whatgabothat / Soul Flower / HRE Theme.
CD . . . . . . . . . . . . . . . . . . . . . .828335-2
■ LP . . . . . . . . . . . . . . . . . . . . . .828335-1
MC . . . . . . . . . . . . . . . . . . . . . .828335-4
Acid Jazz (Polygram) / Jul '92 / PolyGram.

### MIDNIGHT AT THE OASIS.
**Tracks:** Midnight at the Oasis (mixes).
12" . . . . . . . . . . . . . . . . . . . . . .857703-1
12" . . . . . . . . . . . . . . . . . . . . . .857697-1
CD Single . . . . . . . . . . . . . . . . . .857697-2
CD Single . . . . . . . . . . . . . . . . . .857702-2
FFRR / Aug '94 / PolyGram.

### NEVER STOP.
**Tracks:** Never stop.
■ 12" . . . . . . . . . . . . . . . . . . . . JAZID 39 T
■ CD Single . . . . . . . . . . . . . . . JAZID 039 CD
Acid Jazz / Sep '91.
■ 12" . . . . . . . . . . . . . . . . . . . . . . .FX 165
■ 12" Remix. . . . . . . . . . . . . . . . . . FXR 165
■ 7" . . . . . . . . . . . . . . . . . . . . . . . F 165
■ MC Single. . . . . . . . . . . . . . . . . . FCS 165
FFRR / Sep '91.

### PEOPLE GET READY.
**Tracks:** People get ready.
■ 12" . . . . . . . . . . . . . . . . . . . . . .JAZID 17T
Acid Jazz / Nov '89.

### REALITY.
**Tracks:** Rest of me / Put yourself in my shoes / Reality / Country funkin' / Got to give / Mother's tongue / Dream come true / Never stop / Head-hunters (live) / Day at the seaside.
CD . . . . . . . . . . . . . . . . . . . . . JAZIDCD 114
LP . . . . . . . . . . . . . . . . . . . . . JAZIDLP 114
MC . . . . . . . . . . . . . . . . . . . . . JAZIDMC 114
Acid Jazz / Jun '94 / Vital Distribution.

### SPEND SOME TIME.
**Tracks:** Spend some time.
12" . . . . . . . . . . . . . . . . . . . . . . . BNHX 6
CD Single . . . . . . . . . . . . . . . . . BNHCDP 6
CD Single . . . . . . . . . . . . . . . . . . BNHCD 6
MC Single . . . . . . . . . . . . . . . . . . BNHMC 6
FFRR / Oct '94 / PolyGram.

### ULTIMATE TRUNK FUNK (Brand New Heavies featuring N'Dea Davenport).
**Tracks:** Never stop / Stay this way / Mr. Tanaka.
■ 12" . . . . . . . . . . . . . . . . . . . . . . .FX 185
■ 7" . . . . . . . . . . . . . . . . . . . . . . . F 185
■ CD Single . . . . . . . . . . . . . . . . . . FCD 185
■ MC Single. . . . . . . . . . . . . . . . . . FCS 185
FFRR / Apr '92.

## Brass Construction

### ATTITUDES.
**Tracks:** Can you see the light / Funtimes / Attitudes / Do that thang / Forever love / E.T.C. / Hotdog.
■ LP . . . . . . . . . . . . . . . . . . . . . LBG 30348
Liberty / Jun '82.

## BRASS CONSTRUCTION.
**Tracks:** Not Advised.
- LP . . . . . . . . . . . . . . . . . . **UAS 29923**
United Artists / Mar '76.

## BRASS CONSTRUCTION 4.
**Tracks:** Get up / one to one / Perceptions / Pick yourself yp / Help yourself / Night chaser / Starting tomorrow / Sweet as sugar.
- LP . . . . . . . . . . . . . . . . . . **UAG 30210**
United Artists / Jan '79.

## BRASS CONSTRUCTION 5.
**Tracks:** Music makes you feel like dancing / Shake it / Get up to get down.
- LP . . . . . . . . . . . . . . . . . . **UAG 30285**
United Artists / Jan '80.

## BRASS CONSTRUCTION 6.
**Tracks:** Do ya / We can do it / I'm not gonna stop / How do you do / Working harder every day / We are brass / Don't try to change me.
- LP . . . . . . . . . . . . . . . . . . **UAG 30315**
United Artists / Oct '80.

## CAN YOU SEE THE LIGHT.
**Tracks:** Can you see the light / ETC.
- 12" . . . . . . . . . . . . . . . . . . **12UP 652**
- 7" . . . . . . . . . . . . . . . . . . **UP 652**
United Artists / Mar '82.

## CELEBRATE.
**Tracks:** Celebrate / Top of the world.
- 7" . . . . . . . . . . . . . . . . . . **UP 36389**
United Artists / May '78.

## CONQUEST.
**Tracks:** Goodnews / Modern touch / Give and take / Startin' all over again / Comeback / Zig zag / Secret lover / My place / Conquest.
- LP . . . . . . . . . . . . . . . . . . **BRASS 1**
- MC . . . . . . . . . . . . . . . . . . **TCBRASS 1**
Capitol / Aug '85 / EMI.

## CONQUEST.
**Tracks:** Conquest.
- 12" . . . . . . . . . . . . . . . . . . **12CL 371**
- 7" . . . . . . . . . . . . . . . . . . **CL 371**
Capitol / Aug '85.

## CONVERSATIONS.
**Tracks:** We can work it out / Walk the line / Physical atraction / Easy / Breakdown / I do love you / It's a shame / No communication.
- LP . . . . . . . . . . . . . . . . . . **EST 4001701**
Capitol / Jul '83.

## GIVE AND TAKE.
**Tracks:** Give and take / Vintage brass medley.
- 7" . . . . . . . . . . . . . . . . . . **CL 377**
- 12" . . . . . . . . . . . . . . . . . . **12CL 377**
Capitol / Oct '85.

## HA CHA CHA '88.
**Tracks:** Movin' / Ha cha cha.
- 12" . . . . . . . . . . . . . . . . . . **12 SYX 15**
- 12" . . . . . . . . . . . . . . . . . . **12 SYR 15**
- 12" . . . . . . . . . . . . . . . . . . **12 SY 15**
- 7" . . . . . . . . . . . . . . . . . . **SY 15**
- CD Single . . . . . . . . . . . . . . . . **CDSY 15**
Syncopate / Aug '88.

## HA CHA CHA (FUNKTION).
**Tracks:** Ha cha cha (funktion).
- 7" . . . . . . . . . . . . . . . . . . **UP 36205**
United Artists / Feb '77.

## HELP YOURSELF.
**Tracks:** Help yourself / Pick yourself up.
- 7" . . . . . . . . . . . . . . . . . . **UP 36474**
United Artists / Jan '79.

## INTERNATIONAL.
**Tracks:** International.
- 12" . . . . . . . . . . . . . . . . . . **12CL 341**
- 7" . . . . . . . . . . . . . . . . . . **CL 341**
Capitol / Oct '84.

## MOVIN'.
**Tracks:** Movin' / Changing.
- 7" . . . . . . . . . . . . . . . . . . **UP 36090**
United Artists / Apr '76.
- 12" . . . . . . . . . . . . . . . . . . **12UP 617**
United Artists / Mar '80.

## MOVIN' & CHANGIN' (The Best Of Brass Construction).
**Tracks:** Goodnews / Changin' / What's on your mind (expression) / Love / Ha cha cha (funktion) / Movin' / Wake up / Message (inspiration) / L-O-V-E-U / Help yourself / Perceptions (what's the right direction) / Get up to get down / Can you see the light / Walkin' the line / Give and take.

## MOVIN' (OLD GOLD).
**Tracks:** Movin' / Party line / Give and take (Only on CD single).
- 12" . . . . . . . . . . . . . . . . . . **OG 4234**
- CD Single . . . . . . . . . . . . . . . . **OG 6518**
Old Gold / Jun '92 / Pickwick.

## MOVIN' - 1988.
**Tracks:** Movin' (mix) / Movin' / Give and take.
- 12" . . . . . . . . . . . . . . . . . . **12SY 11**
- 12" Remix . . . . . . . . . . . . . . . . **12 SYX 11**
- 7" . . . . . . . . . . . . . . . . . . **SY 11**
- CD Single . . . . . . . . . . . . . . . . **CDSY 11**
Syncopate / May '88.

## MOVIN' 1988 (Best of).
**Tracks:** Movin' / Changing / Ha cha cha / Shakit / Music makes you feel like dancin' / Walkin' the line / Partyline / Give and take / Can't you see the light / International (Only on CD and cassette.) / Get up and get down (Extra tracks on cassette only.)
- LP . . . . . . . . . . . . . . . . . . **SYLP 6002**
- LP . . . . . . . . . . . . . . . . . . **SYLPX 6002**
- MC . . . . . . . . . . . . . . . . . . **SYTC 6002**
- CD . . . . . . . . . . . . . . . . . . **SYCD 6002**
Syncopate / Aug '88.

## MUSIC MAKES YOU FEEL LIKE DANCING.
**Tracks:** Music makes you feel like dancing / Shakit.
- 7" . . . . . . . . . . . . . . . . . . **UP 615**
United Artists / Jan '80.

## PARTYLINE.
**Tracks:** Partyline.
- 12" . . . . . . . . . . . . . . . . . . **12CL 335**
- 7" . . . . . . . . . . . . . . . . . . **CL 335**
Capitol / Jun '84.

## RENEGADES.
**Tracks:** International / Never had a girl / We can bring it back / Fascinating you / Partyline / Renegades / Dangerous / Closer to you / What is the law.
- LP . . . . . . . . . . . . . . . . . . **EJ 2401601**
Capitol / Jun '84.

## WALKIN' THE LINE.
**Tracks:** Walkin' the line / Forever love.
- 12" . . . . . . . . . . . . . . . . . . **12CL 292**
- 7" . . . . . . . . . . . . . . . . . . **CL 292**
Capitol / May '83.

## WE.
**Tracks:** We / Get it together.
- 7" . . . . . . . . . . . . . . . . . . **UP 36360**
United Artists / Feb '78.

## WE CAN WORK IT OUT.
**Tracks:** We can work it out / So that thang / Cha cha cha.
- 12" . . . . . . . . . . . . . . . . . . **12CL 299**
- 7" . . . . . . . . . . . . . . . . . . **CL 299**
Capitol / Jul '83.

## WHAT'S ON YOUR MIND.
**Tracks:** What's on your mind / Blame it on me.
- 7" . . . . . . . . . . . . . . . . . . **UP 36246**
United Artists / Apr '77.

# Brasseur, Andre

## HOLIDAY.
**Tracks:** Holiday / Kid.
- 7" . . . . . . . . . . . . . . . . . . **202557**
CBS / Feb '67.

## KID, THE.
**Tracks:** Kid / Holiday.
- 7" . . . . . . . . . . . . . . . . . . **CBS 202557**
CBS / '66.
- 7" . . . . . . . . . . . . . . . . . . **CBS 2557**
CBS / May '70.

# Braxton, Toni

## ANOTHER SAD LOVE SONG.
**Tracks:** Another sad love song.
- 12" . . . . . . . . . . . . . . . . . . **7432116350-1**
- 7" . . . . . . . . . . . . . . . . . . **7432116350-7**
- CD Single . . . . . . . . . . . . . . . . **7432116350-2**
- MC Single . . . . . . . . . . . . . . . . **7432116350-4**
Arista / Sep '93.
- 7" . . . . . . . . . . . . . . . . . . **74321 19668-7**
- CD Single . . . . . . . . . . . . . . . . **74321 19669-2**
- CD Single . . . . . . . . . . . . . . . . **74321 19668-2**
- MC Single . . . . . . . . . . . . . . . . **74321 19668-4**
Arista / Apr '94.

## CD . . . . . . . . . . . . . . . . . . **CZ 525**
EMI / Mar '94 / EMI.

## BREATHE AGAIN.
**Tracks:** Breathe again (mixes).
- 12" . . . . . . . . . . . . . . . . . . **7432118544-1**
- 7" . . . . . . . . . . . . . . . . . . **7432118544-7**
- CD Single . . . . . . . . . . . . . . . . **7432118544-2**
- MC Single . . . . . . . . . . . . . . . . **7432118544-4**
Arista / Jan '94.

## TONI BRAXTON.
**Tracks:** Another sad song / Breathe again / Seven whole days / Love affair / Candlelight / Spending my time with you / Love shoulda brought you home / I belong to you / How many ways / You mean the world to me / Best friend / Breathe again (Reprise).
- CD . . . . . . . . . . . . . . . . . . **.74321 16268-2**
- MC . . . . . . . . . . . . . . . . . . **.74321 16268-4**
- LP . . . . . . . . . . . . . . . . . . **.74321 16268-1**
Arista / Jan '94 / BMG.

## YOU MEAN THE WORLD TO ME.
**Tracks:** You mean the world to me (mixes) / Seven whole days (mixes).
- 12" . . . . . . . . . . . . . . . . . . **.7432121470-1**
- 7" . . . . . . . . . . . . . . . . . . **.7432121470-7**
- CD Single . . . . . . . . . . . . . . . . **.7432121470-2**
- MC Single . . . . . . . . . . . . . . . . **.7432121470-4**
Arista / Jun '94.

# Break Water

## SAY YOU LOVE ME GIRL.
**Tracks:** Say you love me girl / Work it out.
- 7" . . . . . . . . . . . . . . . . . . **.ARIST 674**
- 12" . . . . . . . . . . . . . . . . . . **ARIST 12674**
Arista / Sep '86.

## WORK IT OUT.
**Tracks:** Work it out / Feel your way.
- 7" . . . . . . . . . . . . . . . . . . **.ARIST 267**
Arista / May '79.

# Breakfast Band

## DOLPHIN RIDE.
**Tracks:** Tokyo shuffle / Jazzabel / Constant spring / Tuna / Trinidad / Hadeed / L.A. 14 / Prelude in steel / Broadside rhumba.
- LP . . . . . . . . . . . . . . . . . . **IOU 001**
Breakfast Music / Feb '82.

## FEELING THE FEELING.
**Tracks:** Feeling the feeling (version) / Feeling the feeling / Never going to leave.
- 12" . . . . . . . . . . . . . . . . . . **.TASSA 1T**
Cane / Jun '89.

## FUNKSTERS.
**Tracks:** Funksters / Such a feeling.
- 12" . . . . . . . . . . . . . . . . . . **12 BM 103**
Breakfast Music / Nov '83.

## SUCH A FEELING.
**Tracks:** Such a feeling / Dozen time dragon.
- 12" . . . . . . . . . . . . . . . . . . **12 BM 102**
- 7" . . . . . . . . . . . . . . . . . . **BM 102**
Breakfast Music / Sep '82.

## TOKYO SHUFFLE.
**Tracks:** Tokyo shuffle / Broadside rhumba.
- 12" . . . . . . . . . . . . . . . . . . **12 BM 101**
- 7" . . . . . . . . . . . . . . . . . . **BM 101**
Breakfast Music / Mar '82.

## WATER'S EDGE.
**Tracks:** Not Advised.
- LP . . . . . . . . . . . . . . . . . . **SPIN 501**
Making Waves / Sep '85.

# Brecker Brothers

## BIG IDEA.
**Tracks:** Big idea.
- 12" . . . . . . . . . . . . . . . . . . **MCST 1720**
- CD Single . . . . . . . . . . . . . . . . **MCSTD 1720**
BMG / Nov '92.

## COLLECTION: BRECKER BROTHERS.
**Tracks:** Skunk funk / Sponge / Squids / Funky sea, funky dew / Bathsheba / Dream theme / Straphangin' / East river.
- CD . . . . . . . . . . . . . . . . . . **ND 90442**
- LP . . . . . . . . . . . . . . . . . . **NL 90442**
- MC . . . . . . . . . . . . . . . . . . **NK 90442**
RCA / Apr '90 / BMG.

## COLLECTION: BRECKER BROTHERS VOL. 2.
**Tracks:** Rocks / Creature of many faces / Funky sea, funky dew (live) / Skunk funk (live) / Sponge (live) / Squids (live) / Tee'd off / Squish / Baffled / Not Ethiopia / Jacknife.

■ DELETED

■ CD . . . . . . . . . . . . . . . . . ND 83096
Novus / Jan '92.

## DON'T STOP THE MUSIC.
Tracks: Not Advised.
■ LP . . . . . . . . . . . . . . . .SPARTY 1007
Arista / Jun '77.

## EAST RIVER.
Tracks: East River / Petals.
■ 7" . . . . . . . . . . . . . . . .ARIST 211
Arista / Nov '78.

## LIVE IN NEW YORK 1992.
Tracks: Not Advised.
CD . . . . . . . . . . . . . . . . . . . JD 1248
Jazz Door / Jul '94 / Charly / Koch International /
A.D.A. Distribution.

## OUT OF THE LOOP.
Tracks: Slang / Ecovation / Scrunch / Secret heart /
African skies / When it was / Harpoon / Night crawler
/ Then she wept.
CD . . . . . . . . . . . . . . . . . . GRP 97842
GRP / Sep '94 / BMG / New Note.

## RETURN OF THE BRECKER BROTHERS.
Tracks: Above and below / That's all there is to it /
On the backside / Big idea / Bikutsi / Funk / Good
gracious / New Guinea / Roppongi / Sozinho (alone)
/ Sperical.
CD . . . . . . . . . . . . . . . . . . GRP 96842
GRP / Aug '92 / BMG / New Note.
■ DCC . . . . . . . . . . . . . . . . GRP 96845
GRP / Aug '94.

## RETURN OF THE BRECKER BROTHERS.
Tracks: Opening credits / Above & below / Spherical
/ Some skunk funk / Common ground / Song for
Barry / Inside out.
VHS . . . . . . . . . . . . . . . . . . GRP 96843
GRP / May '93 / BMG / New Note.

## SCORE.
Tracks: Not Advised.
CD . . . . . . . . . . . . . . . . . . . JD 1211
Jazz Door / Apr '91 / Charly / Koch International /
A.D.A. Distribution.

## SNEAKIN' UP BEHIND YOU.
Tracks: Sneakin' up behind you / Sponge.
■ 7" . . . . . . . . . . . . . . . . ARISTA 14
Arista / Oct '75.

# Bremers, Beverly

## DON'T SAY YOU DON'T REMEMBER.
Tracks: Don't say you don't remember / Get smart
girl.
■ 7" . . . . . . . . . . . . . . . . . . WN 18
Wand / Jun '71.

# Brenda & Tabulations

## CHILD NO ONE WANTED.
Tracks: Child no one wanted / Scuse uz y'all.
■ 7" . . . . . . . . . . . . . . . . HL 10325
London / Jan '71.

## DRY YOUR EYES.
Tracks: Dry your eyes / Wash.
■ 7" . . . . . . . . . . . . . . . . HL 10127
London / Apr '67.

## I KEEP COMING BACK FOR MORE.
Tracks: I'm a superstar / Take it or leave it / Every-
body's fool / Home to myself / Let's go all the way /
Leave me alone / I keep coming back for more.
■ LP . . . . . . . . . . . . . . . . CAL 2016
Casablanca / Sep '77.

## I'M A SUPERSTAR.
Tracks: I'm a superstar / Take it or leave it.
■ 7" . . . . . . . . . . . . . . . .CAN 105
Casablanca / Jun '77.

## LET'S GO ALL THE WAY DOWN.
Tracks: Let's go all the way down.
■ 12" . . . . . . . . . . . . . . 8269731M1
Casablanca / Sep '87.

## ONE GIRL TOO LATE.
Tracks: One girl too late / Magic of your love.
■ 7" . . . . . . . . . . . . . . . . EPC 1361
Epic / Nov '75.

## RIGHT ON THE TIP OF MY TONGUE.
Tracks: Right on the tip of my tongue / Always and
forever.
■ 7" . . . . . . . . . . . . . . . CBS 7279
CBS / Jun '71.

# Brick

## DAZZ.
Tracks: Dazz / Dazz (pt 2).
■ 7" . . . . . . . . . . . . . . . .BANG 004
Bang / Jan '77.

## DUSIC.
Tracks: Dusic / Happy.
■ 7" . . . . . . . . . . . . . . . BANG 12
Bang / Oct '77.

## GOOD HIGH.
Tracks: Brick city / Can't wait / Dazz / Good high /
Here we come / Music matic / Sister twister / South-
ern sunset / That's what it's all about.
■ LP . . . . . . . . . . . . . . . SHOT 003
Bang / Jun '77.

## MUSIC MATIC.
Tracks: Music matic / Can't wait.
■ 7" . . . . . . . . . . . . . . . . BANG 8
Bang / Apr '77.

# Brides Of Funkenstein

## FUNK OR WALK.
Tracks: Disco to go / Warship Touchante / Nappy /
Birdie / Just like you / When you're gone / Amorous.
■ LP . . . . . . . . . . . . . . . K 50545
Atlantic / Jan '79.

# Bridge

## BABY DON'T HOLD YOUR LOVE BACK.
Tracks: Baby don't hold your love back.
■ 12" . . . . . . . . . . . . . . . A 9565 T
■ 7" . . . . . . . . . . . . . . . .A 9565
Atlantic / Jul '85.

## BRIDGE IN BLUE.
Tracks: Bruno's place / I feel free / School days /
Baby what you want me to do / Glad to see you got
religion / Uptown / Hospital lady / Man in a band.
■ LP . . . . . . . . . . . . . . . .2318 069
Buddah / Nov '72.

## BURNING THE BRIDGE.
Tracks: Not Advised.
■ LP . . . . . . . . . . . . . . . . LLP 116
Legacy / Apr '88.

## INDUSTRIAL LOVE DANCE.
Tracks: Industrial love dance / Industrial love dance
(version).
■ 12" . . . . . . . . . . . . . . . SV 12003
■ 7" . . . . . . . . . . . . . . . .SV 003
Second Vision / May '84.

## SALT IN MY WOUNDS.
Tracks: Salt in my wounds.
■ 12" . . . . . . . . . . . . . . .LGYT 58
Legacy / Aug '87.

## SHAME IS A GIRL.
Tracks: Shame is a girl / Loveless.
■ 7" . . . . . . . . . . . . . . . .NCH 112
Backs / Mar '87.

# Bridges, Alicia

## ALICIA BRIDGES.
Tracks: Body heat / Breakaway / High altitudes / We
are one / City rhythm / I love the nightlife / In the
name of love / Self applause / Diamond in the rough
/ Broken woman.
■ LP . . . . . . . . . . . . . . . .239 1364
Polydor / Feb '79.

## BODY HEAT.
Tracks: Body heat / Weaker one.
■ 12" . . . . . . . . . . . . . . .POSPX 38
■ 7" . . . . . . . . . . . . . . . POSP 38
Polydor / Apr '79.

## I LOVE THE NIGHTLIFE.
Tracks: I love the nightlife / Body heat / I love the
nightlife '94 (mixes).
■ 7" . . . . . . . . . . . . . . . .2066 936
Polydor / Nov '78.
■ 12" . . . . . . . . . . . . . . .POSPX 879
■ 7" . . . . . . . . . . . . . . . POSP 879
Polydor / Aug '87.
12" . . . . . . . . . . . . . . . .12MUM 57
7" . . . . . . . . . . . . . . . . .MUM 57
CD Single . . . . . . . . . . . . MUMCD 57
MC Single . . . . . . . . . . . . MUMSC 57
Mother / Aug '94 / PolyGram.

## I LOVE THE NIGHTLIFE (OLD GOLD).
Tracks: I love the nightlife / What a difference a day
made.

12" . . . . . . . . . . . . . . . . .OG 4175
Old Gold / May '90 / Pickwick.

## PLAY IT AS IT LAYS.
Tracks: Play it as it lays / Cheap affairs.
■ 12" . . . . . . . . . . . . . . .POSPX 102
■ 7" . . . . . . . . . . . . . . . POSP 102
Polydor / Feb '80.

# Bridges, Calvin

## ROSE OF SHARON.
Tracks: Rose of Sharon / Rose of Sharon (inst).
■ 12" . . . . . . . . . . . . . . . . BRT 32
Blue Bird (2) / Apr '87.

# Bridgewater, Dee Dee

Born in 1950 in Memphis, Dee Dee Bridgewater had established herself as a fine jazz
vocalist with the Trad Jones-Mel Lewis
Band, when she was discovered by Norman
Connors. He introduced her to the R&B and
fusion scene in New York, where she recorded with Stanley Clarke on the 1973 album *Unexpected Days*, establishing her
name in soul circles. The following year she
played the part of Glinda in *The Wiz* on
Broadway, winning an ecstatic response
from critics. After recording *A Tear To A
Smile* with Pharaoh Sanders, she signed to
Atlantic in 1976; her eponymous debut album included the single *He's Gone*. Two
years later, she reunited with Stanley
Clarke, when he produced the *Just Family*
album. In the '80s, she returned to the
stage: playing Billie Holliday in the show
*Billie* and garnering superb reviews once
more.

## BAD FOR ME.
Tracks: Bad for me / Back of your mind.
■ 7" . . . . . . . . . . . . . . . . K 12370
WEA / '79.

## DEE DEE BRIDGEWATER.
Tracks: Lonely disco dancer / When love comes
knockin' / One in a million guy / Gunshots in the
night / When you're in love / That's the way love
should feel / Give in to love / Jody.
■ LP . . . . . . . . . . . . . . . . K 52263
Elektra / '88.

## JUST FAMILY.
Tracks: Just family / Thank the day.
■ 7" . . . . . . . . . . . . . . . . K 12285
Asylum / Apr '78.

## JUST FAMILY.
Tracks: Just family / Maybe today / Children are the
spirit / Sorry seems to be the hardest word / Sweet
rain / Open up your eyes / Night moves / Thank the
day / Melody maker.
■ LP . . . . . . . . . . . . . . . . K 52067
Elektra / May '78.

## LIVE IN PARIS.
Tracks: All blues / Misty / On a clear day / Dr.
Feelgood / There is no greater love / Here's that
rainy day / Medley blues / Cherokee.
■ LP . . . . . . . . . . . . . . . . AFF 172
MC. . . . . . . . . . . . . . . . . TCAFF 172
Affinity / Apr '87 / Charly / Cadillac / Swift / Jazz
Music.
CD. . . . . . . . . . . . . . . . CDCHARLY 24
Charly / Jun '87 / Charly.

## ONE IN A MILLION GUY.
Tracks: One in a million guy / Lonely disco dance.
■ 7" . . . . . . . . . . . . . . . . K 12490
Elektra / Nov '80.

## PRECIOUS THINGS (Featuring Ray
Charles).
Tracks: Not Advised.
MC. . . . . . . . . . . . . . . . CASSGP 053
Prestige / Aug '92 / Total / BMG.
CD. . . . . . . . . . . . . . . . .CDSGP 053
Prestige / Apr '93 / Total / BMG.

## TILL THE NEXT TIME SOMEWHERE
(Bridgewater, Dee Dee & Ray Charles).
Tracks: Til the next time somewhere.
■ CD Single . . . . . . . . . . . CDSSGP 1003
Prestige / Apr '93.

## WHEN LOVE COMES KNOCKIN'.
Tracks: When love comes knockin' / Gunshots in the
night.
■ 7" . . . . . . . . . . . . . . . . K 12499
Elektra / Jan '81.

## Bristol, Johnny

Prolific songwriter and producer whose early recordings included the original version of *Someday We'll Be Together* - later a hit for Diana Ross & The Supremes. With partner Harvey Fuqua, he helped develop many Motown acts including Marvin Gaye, David Ruffin, Edwin Starr and Stevie Wonder; at their height, the partnership was equal to Holland-Dozier-Holland. When Motown moved to the West Coast in '73, he signed to CBS and continued to produce hits before signing to MGM to release his own album. Featuring impressive arrangements by H.B. Barnum, *Hang On In There Baby* went gold and provided a top 5 hit single in 1974. Despite not achieving chart success again until 1980, Bristol's Ariola release *Take Me Down* was a hit on the New York disco scene, while in Britain *Love No Longer Has A Hold On Me* was well received. His 1980 duet with Amii Stewart *My Guy - My Girl* took him back into the Top 40 and he later issued two singles on the Motor City label.

### BEST OF JOHNNY BRISTOL, THE.
Tracks: You and I / I sho like groovin' with ya / Love me for a reason / Love takes years / All goodbyes aren't gone / Leave my world / Do it to my mind / Hang on in there baby / Memories don't leave like people do / She came into my life / Feeling the magic.
- ■ LP . . . . . . . . . . . . . . . . . . . . . . 2391318
Polydor / Dec '77.
- ■ MC. . . . . . . . . . . . . . . . . . . SPEMC 110
- ■ LP . . . . . . . . . . . . . . . . . . . SPELP 110
Polydor / May '88.

### FREE TO BE ME.
Tracks: Take me down / Love no longer has a hold on me / Hold onto love / Till I see you again / Loving and free / Sweet and deep / Love is on tonight / Share with me my dreams / If I can't stop you / Rosebud.
- ■ LP . . . . . . . . . . . . . . . . . . . . HANLP 2
Ariola Hansa / '82.

### HANG ON IN THERE BABY.
Tracks: Not Advised.
- ■ LP . . . . . . . . . . . . . . . . . . . . 2315 303
MGM (Polydor) / Oct '74.
- CD. . . . . . . . . . . . . . . . . . . . .550 1812
- MC. . . . . . . . . . . . . . . . . . . . .550 1814
Spectrum (1) / Sep '94 / PolyGram.

### HANG ON IN THERE BABY.
Tracks: Hang on in there baby.
- ■ 7" . . . . . . . . . . . . . . . . . . . . .2006 443
MGM (Polydor) / Aug '74.

### HANG ON IN THERE BABY (OLD GOLD).
Tracks: Hang on in there baby.
- ■ 7" . . . . . . . . . . . . . . . . . . . . .OG 9449
Old Gold / Jul '84.

### HOLD ON TO LOVE.
Tracks: Hold on to love / Loving and free.
- ■ 7" . . . . . . . . . . . . . . . . . . . .HANSA 11
Ariola / Jan '82.

### LOVE NO LONGER HAS A HOLD ON ME.
Tracks: Love no longer has a hold on me / Till I see you again.
- ■ 7" . . . . . . . . . . . . . . . . . . . .AHA 567
Ariola Hansa / Dec '80.

### STRANGERS.
Tracks: Strangers in dark corners / Waiting on love / If you ever need somebody / She's so amazing / Everyday she's around / You can't have love without complications / I'm so proud of you / When the fire is burning / Why stop it now / When he comes.
- ■ LP . . . . . . . . . . . . . . . . . . . . 2383511
Polydor / Oct '78.

### TAKE ME DOWN.
Tracks: Take me down / Rosebud.
- ■ 7" . . . . . . . . . . . . . . . . . . . .HANSA 9
Ariola Hansa / Nov '81.

## Brookins, Robert

### IN THE NIGHT.
Tracks: Our lives / If you only knew / In the beginning / You got me running / I'm holding on to U / Sensuality / Be my weakness / Are you bad enough / Come to me / In the night.
- ■ LP . . . . . . . . . . . . . . . . . . . . MCF 3373
- ■ CD. . . . . . . . . . . . . . . . . . . . DMCF 3373

- ■ MC. . . . . . . . . . . . . . . . . . . MCFC 3373
MCA / Jun '87.

### OUR LIVES.
Tracks: Our lives / Incredulous.
- ■ 12" . . . . . . . . . . . . . . . . . . . MCAT 1131
- ■ 7" . . . . . . . . . . . . . . . . . . . .MCA 1131
MCA / Jul '87.

## Brooklyn Funk Essentials

### COOL, STEADY & EASY.
Tracks: Take the L train (to Brooklyn) / Creator has a master plan / Revolution was postponed because of rain / Brooklyn recycles / Madame Zzaj / Headnaddas journey to the planet Addiskizm / Big apple boogaloo / Blow your brains out / Stickman crossing the Broklyn bridge / Dilly dally / Take the L train (to 8 ave).
- CD . . . . . . . . . . . . . . . . . . . . DOR 022CD
- LP . . . . . . . . . . . . . . . . . . . . DOR 22LP
Dorado / Jun '94 / RTM / Pinnacle.

### CREATOR HAS A MASTERPLAN.
Tracks: Creator has a masterplan.
- 12" . . . . . . . . . . . . . . . . . . . . DOR 21
- CD Single . . . . . . . . . . . . . . . . DOR 21CD
Dorado / May '94 / RTM / Pinnacle.

### WE GOT TO COME TOGETHER.
Tracks: We got to come together.
- ■ 12" . . . . . . . . . . . . . . . . . . . XLT 3
XL / Nov '89.

## Brooks, Patti

### DON'T MAKE ME WAIT.
Tracks: Don't make me wait / Popcorn / Black is black.
- ■ 7" . . . . . . . . . . . . . . . . . . . .CAN 116
Casablanca / Jan '78.

### OUR MS. BROOKS.
Tracks: After dark / This is the house where love died / Heartbreak in disguise / Come fly with me / Let's do it again / Back up singer.
- ■ LP . . . . . . . . . . . . . . . . . . . . CAL 2042
Casablanca / Mar '79.

## Broomfield

### BROOMFIELD.
Tracks: Where do I go from here / She can't get serious / Read my letter / Good times / You better get ready / Is it so hard / Through all the years / Don't cover up your feelings / Light up the world.
- ■ CD . . . . . . . . . . . . . . . . . . . . 4611642
- ■ LP . . . . . . . . . . . . . . . . . . . . 4611641
- ■ MC. . . . . . . . . . . . . . . . . . . 4611644
CBS / May '88.

### DON'T COVER UP YOUR FEELINGS.
Tracks: Don't cover up your feelings (remix) / Don't cover up your feelings (ext. remix) / Don't cover up your feelings (inst) (Available on 12" single only.) / Through all the years.
- ■ 12" . . . . . . . . . . . . . . . . . . . 6516296
- ■ 7" . . . . . . . . . . . . . . . . . . . .6516297
- ■ CD Single . . . . . . . . . . . . . . . 6516292
CBS / May '88.

### SHE CAN'T GET SERIOUS.
Tracks: She can't get serious / Light up the world.
- ■ 12" . . . . . . . . . . . . . . . . . . . 6529246
- ■ 7" . . . . . . . . . . . . . . . . . . . .6529247
CBS / Aug '88.

## Brotherhood Creed

### HELLUVA.
Tracks: Helluva.
- ■ 12" . . . . . . . . . . . . . . . . . . . MCST 1635
MCA / May '92.

## Brotherly Love

### LITTLE TOWN FLIRT.
Tracks: Little town flirt / One kiss.
- ■ 7" . . . . . . . . . . . . . . . . . . . .RCA 2528
RCA / Jan '75.

### LIVE WIRE.
Tracks: Live wire / Dead end Denise.
- ■ 7" . . . . . . . . . . . . . . . . . . . .LPBO 5032
RCA / Jun '74.

## Brothers Grimm

### DO YOU WANT ME (DO YOU NEED).
Tracks: Do you want me (do you need).
- ■ 12" . . . . . . . . . . . . . . . . . . .PNT 030
Production House / Aug '91.

### FIELD OF DREAMS.
Tracks: Field of dreams.
- ■ 12" . . . . . . . . . . . . . . . . . . .PNT 036
Production House / Apr '92.

## Brothers Johnson

Even before graduating from school, George and Louis Johnson had won supports with acts like Billy Preston and the Supremes. After stint with Billy Preston, they were recruited by Quincy Jones for his *Mellow Madness*. 'Q' also produced the first four Brothers Johnson albums, all mid-'70s million- sellers. Singles success came their way with *I'll Be Good To You*, *Get The Funk Out Of Ma Face* and *Stomp*. Their first self-produced album, *The Real Thing*, was also the first not to go platinum, but the brothers had already expanded their horizons: Louis played bass on Michael Jackson's *Thriller* while George was working with Steve Arrington. After one-off comeback with Leon Sylvers-produced *Out Of Control* in '84, they next resurfaced in '89. Renewed collaboration with Quincy Jones yielded two Johnson cuts on The Dude's *Back On The Block*; one of which was hit remake of *I'll Be Good To You*, featuring Ray Charles and Chaka Khan.

### AIN'T WE FUNKIN' NOW.
Tracks: Ain't we funkin' now / Strawberry letter 23.
- ■ 12" . . . . . . . . . . . . . . . . . . . AMSP 7379
- ■ 7" . . . . . . . . . . . . . . . . . . . .AMS 7379
A&M / Sep '78.

### BLAM.
Tracks: Ain't we funkin' now / So you won't stay / Ride-o-rocket / Mista cool / Blam / Rocket countdown/Blastoff / It's you girl / Streetwave.
- ■ LP . . . . . . . . . . . . . . . . . . . . AMLH 64714
A&M / Aug '78.

### BLAST.
Tracks: Funk it / Welcome to the club / Great awakening / I'm giving you all of my love / Real thing / Ain't we funkin' now / Strawberry letter 23 / Stomp / Get the funk out ma face / I'll be good to you.
- ■ LP . . . . . . . . . . . . . . . . . . . . AMLH 64927
A&M / Dec '82.

### CLASSICS:BROTHERS JOHNSON.
Tracks: Not Advised.
- ■ CD . . . . . . . . . . . . . . . . . . . . CDA 2509
A&M.

### DANCIN' FREE.
Tracks: Dancin' free / Do it for love / I'll be good to you.
- ■ 12" . . . . . . . . . . . . . . . . . . . AMSX 8165
- ■ 7" . . . . . . . . . . . . . . . . . . . .AMS 8165
A&M / Sep '81.

### FUNKADELIA.
Tracks: Not Advised.
- CD. . . . . . . . . . . . . . . . . . . . .550 2242
- MC. . . . . . . . . . . . . . . . . . . . .550 2244
Spectrum (1) / Aug '94 / PolyGram.

### IT'S YOU GIRL.
Tracks: It's you girl / Mista Cool / Brother man.
- ■ 7" . . . . . . . . . . . . . . . . . . . .AMS 7410
A&M / Feb '79.

### KICK IT TO THE CURB.
Tracks: Kick it to the curb / Ain't we funkin' now.
- ■ 12" . . . . . . . . . . . . . . . . . . . USAT 631
- ■ 7" . . . . . . . . . . . . . . . . . . . .USA 631
Breakout / May '88.

### KICKIN'.
Tracks: Kick it to / Kick it to the curb / Real love / I fresh / Still in love / PO Box 2000 / Ball of fire / We must be in love / I'll give it up / This is our love / Party avenue.
- ■ CD . . . . . . . . . . . . . . . . . . . . CDA 5162
- ■ LP . . . . . . . . . . . . . . . . . . . . AMA 5162
- ■ MC. . . . . . . . . . . . . . . . . . . AMC 5162
A&M / May '88.

### LIGHT UP THE NIGHT.
Tracks: Not Advised.
- ■ LP . . . . . . . . . . . . . . . . . . . . AMLK 63716
A&M / Feb '80.

44

■ DELETED

### LIGHT UP THE NIGHT.
**Tracks:** Light up the night / Streetwave / Free yourself (Only on 12″ single.).
- 12″ . . . . . . . . . . . . . . . . . . . . . AMSP 7526
- 7″ . . . . . . . . . . . . . . . . . . . . . . . AMS 7526
A&M / May '80.

### LOOK OUT FOR NUMBER ONE.
**Tracks:** Not Advised.
- LP . . . . . . . . . . . . . . . . . . . . . . . AMID 121
- MC . . . . . . . . . . . . . . . . . . . . . . CMID 121
A&M / Mar '82.

### LOVE IS.
**Tracks:** Love is / Q.
- 7″ . . . . . . . . . . . . . . . . . . . . . . . AMS 7345
A&M / Apr '78.

### OUT OF CONTROL.
**Tracks:** You keep me coming back / Lovers forever / Do you / Let's try love again / I came here to party / Out of control / Save me / Toyko / Dazed / It's all over now.
- LP . . . . . . . . . . . . . . . . . . . AMLX 649 65
A&M / Oct '84.

### REAL THING.
**Tracks:** Real thing / I want you / This had to be (Available on 12″ only).
- 12″ . . . . . . . . . . . . . . . . . . . . AMSX 8149
- 7″ . . . . . . . . . . . . . . . . . . . . . . AMS 8149
A&M / Jul '81.

### RIDE O ROCKET.
**Tracks:** Ride o rocket.
- 7″ . . . . . . . . . . . . . . . . . . . . . . . AMS 7400
A&M / Nov '78.

### RIGHT ON TIME.
**Tracks:** Runnin' for your lovin' / Free yourself, be yourself / Q / Right on time / Strawberry letter 23 / Brother man / Never leave you lonely / Love is.
- LP . . . . . . . . . . . . . . . . . . . . AMLH 64644
A&M / Jun '77.

### STOMP.
**Tracks:** Get the funk out ma face / Stomp / Let's swing.
- 12″ . . . . . . . . . . . . . . . . . . . . AMSP 7509
- 7″ . . . . . . . . . . . . . . . . . . . . . . AMS 7509
A&M / Feb '80.
- 12″ . . . . . . . . . . . . . . . . . . . . . . OG 4011
Old Gold / Jan '87.

### STOMP (THE BROTHERS JOHNSON'S GREATEST HITS).
**Tracks:** I'll be good for you / Blam / Running for your lovin' / Ain't we funkin' now / Ride 'o' rocket / Real thing / This had to be / Get the funk out ma face / Streetwave / Strawberry letter 23 / Lovers forever.
- LP . . . . . . . . . . . . . . . . . . . . . . . . . BJL 1
- MC . . . . . . . . . . . . . . . . . . . . . . . . BJC 1
Funk America / Dec '84.

### STRAWBERRY LETTER 23.
**Tracks:** Strawberry letter 23 / Brother man / I'll be good to you.
- 7″ . . . . . . . . . . . . . . . . . . . . . . . AMS 7297
A&M / Jul '77.

### WINNERS.
**Tracks:** Real thing / Dancin' free / Sunlight / Teaser / Caught up / In the way / I want you / Do it for love / Hot mama / Daydreamer dream.
- LP . . . . . . . . . . . . . . . . . . . . AMLK 63724
A&M / Jul '81.

### YOU KEEP ME COMING BACK.
**Tracks:** You keep me coming back / Deceiver / Tokyo (on 12″ only).
- 12″ . . . . . . . . . . . . . . . . . . . . . AMX 209
- 7″ . . . . . . . . . . . . . . . . . . . . . . . AM 209
A&M / Aug '84.

## Brown, Alan

### LISTEN/STRETCHING OUT.
**Tracks:** Wanted man / Crash landing / Loosen up / Pyramid / Forever / Curfew / Make us all believe / Make up your mind / Get myself straight / Messenger / Find a melody / Up above my hobby horse's head / Turning point / Build me a stage / Stretching out.
- CD . . . . . . . . . . . . . . . . . . . . . . EDCD 362
Demon / Jan '93 / Pinnacle / A.D.A. Distribution.

### LIVE AT THE MARQUEE (Brown, Alan & Jimmy James).
**Tracks:** Ain't to proud to beg / I can't turn you loose / Amen / If I had a hammer / You don't know like I know / That driving beat / Don't know what I'm gonna do / Sock it to em J.B. / It's growing / Emergency 999

/ I need you / Sunny / Headline news / Down in the valley / Boomerang.
- CD. . . . . . . . . . . . . . . . . . . . . NEBCD 652
Sequel / Jun '93 / Total / BMG.

## Brown, Bobby

### BOBBY.
**Tracks:** Humpin' around (Prelude) / Humpin' around / Two can play that game / Get away / Til the end of time / Good enough / Pretty little girl / Lovin' you down / One more night / Something in common / That's the way love is / College girl / Storm away / I'm your friend / Humpin' around (mix) (Extra track on LP only.) / Humpin' around (Epilogue).
- CD. . . . . . . . . . . . . . . . . . . . . MCD 10695
- MC. . . . . . . . . . . . . . . . . . . . . MCC 10695
- LP . . . . . . . . . . . . . . . . . . . . . MCA 10695
MCA / Aug '92 / BMG.
- DCC . . . . . . . . . . . . . . . . . . . . MCX 10417
MCA / Jan '93.

### DANCE YA KNOW IT.
**Tracks:** Not Advised.
- LP . . . . . . . . . . . . . . . . . . . . . . MCG 6074
- CD . . . . . . . . . . . . . . . . . . . . DMCG 6074
- MC . . . . . . . . . . . . . . . . . . . . MCGC 6074
MCA / Nov '89.

### DON'T BE CRUEL.
**Tracks:** Don't be cruel / My prerogative / Roni / Rock witcha / Every little step / I'll be good to you / All day, all night / Take it slow.
- LP . . . . . . . . . . . . . . . . . . . . . . MCF 3425
- CD . . . . . . . . . . . . . . . . . . . . . DMCF 3425
- MC . . . . . . . . . . . . . . . . . . . . . MCFC 3425
MCA / Sep '88.
- DCC . . . . . . . . . . . . . . . . . . . MCAD 42185
MCA / Apr '89.
- CD . . . . . . . . . . . . . . . . . . . . MCLD 19212
- MC . . . . . . . . . . . . . . . . . . . . MCLC 19212
MCA / Aug '93 / BMG.

### DON'T BE CRUEL.
**Tracks:** Don't be cruel / Don't be cruel (instrumental) / Don't be cruel (radio edit) (Available on 12″ single only) / Don't be cruel (acapella).
- 12″ . . . . . . . . . . . . . . . . . . . . MCAT 1268
- 7″ . . . . . . . . . . . . . . . . . . . . . MCA 1268
MCA / Jul '88.
- 12″ . . . . . . . . . . . . . . . . . . . . MCAT 1310
- CD Single . . . . . . . . . . . . . . CDDMCA 1310
- 7″ . . . . . . . . . . . . . . . . . . . . . MCA 1310
MCA / Jan '89.
- MC Single . . . . . . . . . . . . . . . MCAC 1310
MCA / Mar '89.

### EVERY LITTLE STEP.
**Tracks:** Every little step.
- 12″ . . . . . . . . . . . . . . . . . . . . MCAT 1338
- CD Single . . . . . . . . . . . . . . . DMCAT 1338
- 7″ . . . . . . . . . . . . . . . . . . . . . MCAR 1338
- 7″ . . . . . . . . . . . . . . . . . . . . . . MCA 1338
MCA / May '89.

### GIRL NEXT DOOR.
**Tracks:** Girl next door / Girl next door, (inst).
- 12″ . . . . . . . . . . . . . . . . . . . . MCAT 1153
- 7″ . . . . . . . . . . . . . . . . . . . . . MCA 1153
MCA / Apr '87.

### GIRLFRIEND.
**Tracks:** Girlfriend / King of stage.
- 12″ . . . . . . . . . . . . . . . . . . . . MCAT 1114
- 7″ . . . . . . . . . . . . . . . . . . . . . MCA 1114
MCA / Apr '87.

### GOOD ENOUGH.
**Tracks:** Good enough.
- 12″ . . . . . . . . . . . . . . . . . . . . MCST 1704
- 7″ . . . . . . . . . . . . . . . . . . . . . MCS 1704
- CD Single . . . . . . . . . . . . . . . MCSTD 1704
- MC Single . . . . . . . . . . . . . . . MCSC 1704
MCA / Oct '92.

### HIS PREROGATIVE.
**Tracks:** Not Advised.
- VHS . . . . . . . . . . . . . . . . . . . . . MCV 9001
MCA / Nov '89.

### HUMPIN' AROUND.
**Tracks:** Humpin' around.
- CD Single . . . . . . . . . . . . . . . MCSD 1680
- 12″ . . . . . . . . . . . . . . . . . . . . MCST 1680
- 7″ . . . . . . . . . . . . . . . . . . . . . MCS 1680
- MC Single . . . . . . . . . . . . . . . MCSC 1680
MCA / Aug '92.

### KING OF STAGE.
**Tracks:** Baby I wanna tell you something / King of stage / Spending time / You ain't been loved tonight / Love obsession / Seventeen.
- LP . . . . . . . . . . . . . . . . . . . . . MCL 1886
- CD . . . . . . . . . . . . . . . . . . . . DMCL 1886

- MC . . . . . . . . . . . . . . . . . . . . MCLC 1886
MCA / Jul '89.
- CD . . . . . . . . . . . . . . . . . . . . MCLD 19001
- MC . . . . . . . . . . . . . . . . . . . . MCLC 19001
MCA / Apr '92.

### MEGAMIX.
**Tracks:** Megamix.
- 12″ . . . . . . . . . . . . . . . . . . . . MCAT 1421
- 7″ . . . . . . . . . . . . . . . . . . . . . MCA 1421
- CD Single . . . . . . . . . . . . . . . DMCAT 1421
- MC Single . . . . . . . . . . . . . . . MCAC 1421
MCA / May '90.

### MY PREROGATIVE.
**Tracks:** My prerogative / Girl next door / Girl next door (extended version) (Only on 12″.) / My prerogative (extended remix) (Only on 12″.) / My prerogative (instrumental) (Only on 12″.).
- 12″ . . . . . . . . . . . . . . . . . . . . MCAT 1299
- 7″ . . . . . . . . . . . . . . . . . . . . . MCA 1299
- CD Single . . . . . . . . . . . . . . . DMCA 1299
MCA / Nov '88.

### ON OUR OWN.
**Tracks:** On our own / On our own (rap).
- 12″ . . . . . . . . . . . . . . . . . . . . MCAT 1350
- CD Single . . . . . . . . . . . . . . . DMCAT 1350
- MC Single . . . . . . . . . . . . . . . MCAC 1350
- 7″ . . . . . . . . . . . . . . . . . . . . . MCA 1350
MCA / Jul '89.

### RONI.
**Tracks:** Roni.
- 12″ . . . . . . . . . . . . . . . . . . . . MCAT 1384
- 7″ . . . . . . . . . . . . . . . . . . . . . MCAB 1384
- CD Single . . . . . . . . . . . . . . . DMCAT 1384
- MC Single . . . . . . . . . . . . . . . MCATC 1384
- 7″ . . . . . . . . . . . . . . . . . . . . . MCA 1384
MCA / Nov '89.

### THAT'S THE WAY LOVE IS.
**Tracks:** That's the way love is.
- 12″ . . . . . . . . . . . . . . . . . . . . MCST 1783
- 12″ Remix. . . . . . . . . . . . . . . MCSX 1783
- CD Single . . . . . . . . . . . . . . . MCSTD 1783
- MC Single . . . . . . . . . . . . . . . MCSC 1783
MCA / Jun '93.

### TWO CAN PLAY THAT GAME.
**Tracks:** Two can play that game.
- 12″ . . . . . . . . . . . . . . . . . . . . MCST 1973
- CD Single . . . . . . . . . . . . . . . MCSTD 1973
- MC Single . . . . . . . . . . . . . . . MCSC 1973
MCA / Jun '94.

### WE'VE GOT SOMETHING (Brown, Bobby & Whitney Houston).
**Tracks:** We've got something.
- 12″ . . . . . . . . . . . . . . . . . . . . MCST 1957
- 12″ . . . . . . . . . . . . . . . . . . . . MCS 1957
- CD Single . . . . . . . . . . . . . . . MCSTD 1957
- MC Single . . . . . . . . . . . . . . . MCSC 1957
MCA / Jan '94.

### WIT'CHA.
**Tracks:** Wit'cha.
- 12″ . . . . . . . . . . . . . . . . . . . . MCAT 1367
- 7″ . . . . . . . . . . . . . . . . . . . . . MCA 1367
- CD Single . . . . . . . . . . . . . . . DMCAT 1367
- 12″ . . . . . . . . . . . . . . . . . . . . MCAX 1367
MCA / Sep '89.

## Brown, Boe

### CHINATOWN.
**Tracks:** Chinatown / Dancer man.
- 12″ . . . . . . . . . . . . . . . . . . . . PT 12 547
- 7″ . . . . . . . . . . . . . . . . . . . . . PT 547
President / Aug '86.

### SOUND THAT FUNKY HORN (Brown, Boe & Uptown Horns).
**Tracks:** Sound that funky horn / Dancer man.
- 12″ . . . . . . . . . . . . . . . . . . . . PT 12 540
- 7″ . . . . . . . . . . . . . . . . . . . . . PT 540
President / Sep '85.

## Brown, Chuck

### ANY OTHER WAY TO GO.
**Tracks:** Not Advised.
- CD. . . . . . . . . . . . . . . . . . . . . RTCD 501
- LP. . . . . . . . . . . . . . . . . . . . . . RTLP 501
- MC. . . . . . . . . . . . . . . . . . . . . . RTC 501
Rhythm Attack (Germany) / Apr '90 / Charly.

### BUSTIN' LOOSE (Brown, Chuck & Soul Searchers).
**Tracks:** I gotcha now / Could it be love / Game seven / Berro e sombaro / Bustin' loose / Never gonna give you up / If it ain't funky.
- MC. . . . . . . . . . . . . . . . . . . . . EG 2605204

■ LP . . . . . . . . . . . . . . . . . . . EG 2605201
EMI / Mar '85.

## BUSTIN' LOOSE (Brown, Chuck & Soul Searchers).
Tracks: Bustin' loose / Miss fine lover / Solar funk / Bussie.
■ 12" . . . . . . . . . . . . . . . . . . 12 SRC 101
Source / Jan '80.
■ 12" . . . . . . . . . . . . . . . . . . .12 SOURCE 1
Source / Feb '85.
■ 7" . . . . . . . . . . . . . . . . . . . . SOURCE 1
Source / Mar '85.

## LIVE DC BUMPIN'Y'ALL.
Tracks: Dedication / Downright country boy / Stormy Monday / Kickin' the jams / Jazzy jam / We need some money / Loveboat / Sho' yuh right / Boogie on gogo woman / Peach and love / We need some jazz / I am somebody / Rumours / Go go swing / It don't mean a thing / Midnight sun / Moody's mood / Woody Woodpecker / Here we go again / Message.
■ LP . . . . . . . . . . . . . . . . . . . MELTLP 3
MC . . . . . . . . . . . . . . . . . . . MELTCASS 3
Rhythm King / Apr '87 / Vital Distribution / 3MV.

## WE NEED SOME MONEY (Brown, Chuck & Soul Searchers).
Tracks: We need some money.
■ 12" . . . . . . . . . . . . . . . . . . . . . . . W 6
Greyhound / Aug '84.

## Brown, Diana

## BLIND FAITH (Brown, Diana & Barrie K Sharpe).
Tracks: Blind faith / Blind faith (instrumental) / Blind faith (master jam) (Onlyon 12" single.) / Blind faith (dubwise selection) (Only on 12" single.) / Blind faith (ground beat mix) (Only on 12" single.).
■ 7" . . . . . . . . . . . . . . . . . . . . . F 114
■ 12" . . . . . . . . . . . . . . . . . . .FX 114
FFRR / Jul '89.

## EATING ME ALIVE (Brown, Diana & Barrie K Sharpe).
Tracks: Eating me alive.
■ 12" . . . . . . . . . . . . . . . . . . .FX 190
■ 7" . . . . . . . . . . . . . . . . . . . . F 190
■ CD Single . . . . . . . . . . . . . . . . FCD 190
■ MC Single . . . . . . . . . . . . . . . . FCS 190
FFRR / Jun '92.

## LOVE OR NOTHING (Brown, Diana & Barrie K Sharpe).
Tracks: Love or nothing / Don't cross the tracks / Love or nothing (Piano mix) (Available on 12" format.) / Love or nothing (Club mix) (Available on 12" format.) / Love or nothing (Grounded selection) (Available on FXR 152.) / Love or nothing (Steve Anderson remix) (Available on FXR 152.).
■ 12" . . . . . . . . . . . . . . . . . . . FX 152
■ 12" Remix . . . . . . . . . . . . . . . .FXR 152
■ 7" . . . . . . . . . . . . . . . . . . . . F 152
■ CD Single . . . . . . . . . . . . . . . . FCD 152
■ MC Single . . . . . . . . . . . . . . . . FCS 152
FFRR / Mar '91.

## MASTER PLAN (Brown, Diana & Barrie K Sharpe).
Tracks: Master plan / Yes it's you.
■ 12" . . . . . . . . . . . . . . . . . . .FX 133
■ 7" . . . . . . . . . . . . . . . . . . . . F 133
■ CD Single . . . . . . . . . . . . . . . . FCD 133
■ MC Single . . . . . . . . . . . . . . . . FCS 133
London / May '90.

## MASTERPLAN 92 (Brown, Diana & Barrie K Sharpe).
Tracks: Masterplan 92.
■ 7" . . . . . . . . . . . . . . . . . . . JAZID 056
■ CD Single . . . . . . . . . . . . . JAZID 056 CD
■ 12" . . . . . . . . . . . . . . . . . JAZID 056 T
■ MC Single . . . . . . . . . . . . . JAZID 056 MC
Acid Jazz / Sep '92.

## SUN WORSHIPPERS (Brown, Diana & Barrie K Sharpe).
Tracks: Sun worshippers (positive thinking) / Do that funky thing / Sun worshippers (positive thinking) (part 1) (Only on 12" and CD single) / Sun worshippers (positive thinking) (part 2) (Only on 12" and CD single).
■ 12" . . . . . . . . . . . . . . . . . . .FX 144
■ 7" . . . . . . . . . . . . . . . . . . . . F 144
■ CD Single . . . . . . . . . . . . . . . . FCD 144
■ MC Single . . . . . . . . . . . . . . . . FCS 144
FFRR / Aug '90.

## YOU SHOULDN'T LIE.
Tracks: You shouldn't lie.
■ 12" . . . . . . . . . . . . . . . . . . . ID 005
Indochina / May '94.

## Brown, Gloria D.

## MORE THEY KNOCK THE MORE I LOVE YOU, THE.
Tracks: More they knock, the more I love you.
■ 12" . . . . . . . . . . . . . . . . . . .TEN 52 12
■ 7" . . . . . . . . . . . . . . . . . . . . TEN 52
10 / Jul '85.

## Brown, James

James Brown's importance goes far beyond mere statistics, but his 44 U.S. Top 40 entries rank him as hitmaker eclipsed only by Elvis and the Beatles. Of his various titles - including Godfather of Soul, Hardest Working Man in Show Business, Soul Brother Number One and Minister of New New Super Heavy Funk - only Original Disco Man failed to ring true, although legend is hardly diminished by this lapse. Reviewing his debut *Please, Please, Please* in 1956, Billboard wrote, "Brown and the Famous Flames let off plenty of steam"; assessment that continued to ring true three decades later when JB samples and black consciousness fuelled hip-hop explosion. Crucial year was 1967; while rock became increasingly grandiose, JB stripped R&B's trappings to create Funk. *Cold Sweat* ushered in revolutionary sequence of anthems that boasted, among others, *Sex Machine* and *Say It Loud - I'm Black and I'm Proud.* Essential albums include hip-hop template *In the Jungle Groove* and all-time classic *Live at the Apollo* sets (third of which, 1971's *Revolution of the Mind*, was JB's thirty-second album). Legends from George Clinton to Prince and Sly Stone to Public Enemy owe debt to Brown, as do all lovers of great music.

## (GET UP I FEEL LIKE BEING A) SEX MACHINE.
Tracks: Get up I feel like a sex machine / Papa's got a brand new bag / Get on the good foot (on 12" only) / Get up offa that thing (on 12" only).
■ 7" . . . . . . . . . . . . . . . . . . .2001 071
Polydor / Sep '70.
■ 12" . . . . . . . . . . . . . . . . . POSPX 751
■ 7" . . . . . . . . . . . . . . . . . . POSP 751
Boiling Point / Jun '85.

## (GET UP I FEEL LIKE BEING A) SEX MACHINE (OLD GOLD).
Tracks: Get up, I feel like a sex machine.
■ 7" . . . . . . . . . . . . . . . . . . .OG 9438
Old Gold / Jun '88.

## (SO TIRED OF STANDING STILL WE GOT TO) MOVE ON.
Tracks: (So tired of standing still we got to) Move on.
■ 12" . . . . . . . . . . . . . . . . . . .PZ 162
■ 7" . . . . . . . . . . . . . . . . . . . PO 162
Polydor / Jul '91.

## 20 ALL TIME GREATEST HITS.
Tracks: Not Advised.
DCC . . . . . . . . . . . . . . . . . . 511 326-5
Polydor / Jan '93 / PolyGram.

## 20 GREATEST HITS: JAMES BROWN.
Tracks: Not Advised.
CD . . . . . . . . . . . . . . . . . . . .266202 2
Mainline (2) / Feb '89.

## AIN'T IT FUNKY.
Tracks: Ain't it funky (parts 1 and 2) / Fat wood (parts 1 and 2) / Cold sweat / Give it up or turnit a loose / Nose job / Use your mother / After you done it.
■ LP . . . . . . . . . . . . . . . . . . .2343 010
Polydor / Aug '70.

## AIN'T THAT A GROOVE.
Tracks: Ain't that a groove (Parts 1 & 2).
■ 7" . . . . . . . . . . . . . . . . . . 7N 25367
Pye / Mar '66.

## BEST OF JAMES BROWN (Godfather Of Soul).
Tracks: Livin' in America / Body heat / Hey America / Please, please, please / Hot pants / Think / I got you (I feel good) / Say it loud, I'm black and I'm proud / Get up, I feel like a sex machine / Make it funky / Papa's got a brand new bag / Get on the good foot / Gonna have a funky good time / Cold sweat / Honky tonk / It's a man's man's man's world / Gravity.
■ CD . . . . . . . . . . . . . . . . . . NCD 1376
■ LP . . . . . . . . . . . . . . . . . . . NE 1376
■ MC . . . . . . . . . . . . . . . . . . . CE 2376
K-Tel / Sep '87.

## BEST OF JAMES BROWN & THE FAMOUS FLAMES.
Tracks: It's a man's man's man's world / Prisoner of love / Scratch / Is it yes or is it no / Say it loud, I'm black and I'm proud / Please please please / Cold sweat - part 1 / Papa's got a brand new bag - part 1 / There was a time / I can't stand myself / Mother Popcorn - part 1 / Signed, sealed and delivered.
■ LP . . . . . . . . . . . . . . . . . . . 583 765
Polydor / Nov '69.

## BEST OF JAMES BROWN (POLYDOR).
Tracks: Say it loud, I'm black and I'm proud / Please, please, please / Try me / Lost someone / Papa's got a brand new bag / It's a man's man's man's world / Cold sweat / There was a time / Popcorn / Hot pants / Sex machine.
■ LP . . . . . . . . . . . . . . . . . . 239 152 9
MC . . . . . . . . . . . . . . . . . . . 317 752 9
Polydor / Jul '82 / PolyGram.

## BODY HEAT.
Tracks: Body heat / Woman / Kiss in 77 / I'm satisfied / What the world needs now is love / Wake up and give yourself a chance / Don't tell it.
■ LP . . . . . . . . . . . . . . . . . . .2391 258
Polydor / Feb '77.
■ LP . . . . . . . . . . . . . . . . . . PHX 1025
Polydor / Oct '82.
■ LP . . . . . . . . . . . . . . . . . . PD 6093
Polydor / Jul '88.

## BODY HEAT.
Tracks: Body heat.
■ 7" . . . . . . . . . . . . . . . . . . .2066 763
Polydor / Jan '77.

## BRING IT ON.
Tracks: Bring it on, bring it on / Today / You can't keep a good man down / Tennessee waltz / Night time is the right time / For your precious love.
■ LP . . . . . . . . . . . . . . . . . . . SNTF 906
Sonet / Sep '83.

## BRING IT ON.
Tracks: Bring it on / Night time is the right time.
■ 12" . . . . . . . . . . . . . . . . . . SONL 2258
■ 7" . . . . . . . . . . . . . . . . . . SON 2258
Sonet / Jul '83.

## BRING IT UP.
Tracks: Bring it up / Nobody knows.
■ 7" . . . . . . . . . . . . . . . . . . 7N 25411
Pye / Mar '67.

## COLD SWEAT.
Tracks: Cold sweat / Nature boy / Come rain or come shine / I loves you Porgy / Back stabbin' / Fever / Mona Lisa / I want to be around / Good rockin' tonight / Stagger Lee / Kansas City.
■ LP . . . . . . . . . . . . . . . . . . 813 492-1
Polydor / Nov '83.

## COLD SWEAT.
Tracks: Give it up turn it loose / Too funky in here / Gonna have a funky good time / Try me / Get on the good foot / Get up offa that thing / Georgia on my mind / Hot pants / I got the feeling / It's a man's man's world / Cold sweat / I can't stand it / Papa's got a brand new bag / I feel good / Please please please / Jam.
CD . . . . . . . . . . . . . . . . . . .HADCD 164
MC . . . . . . . . . . . . . . . . . . .HADMC 164
Javelin / May '94 / THE.

## COLD SWEAT (LIVE).
Tracks: Papa's got a brand new bag / Sex machine / Please please please / This is a man's world / Cold sweat.
■ LP . . . . . . . . . . . . . . . . . . PER 33 8605
Perfect / Apr '87.

## COMPACT DISC OF JAMES BROWN, THE.
Tracks: Doing it to death / Super bad / Soul power / Think / It's a man's man's world / Try me (I need you) / Bewildered / Out of sight / I got you / Prisoner of love / I got the feelin' / Maybe the last time / Lickin' stick / Mother popcorn / Papa's got a brand new bag / Sex machine / Payback mix / Please, please, please.
CD . . . . . . . . . . . . . . . . . . 825 714-2
Polydor / Sep '85 / PolyGram.

## DEAD ON THE HEAVY FUNK 1974-76.
Tracks: Superbad,superslick / Your love / Body heat / Hot (I need to be loved,loved,loved) / Get up offa that thing / Funky president / Don't tell it / Future shock of the world / Woman.
■ LP . . . . . . . . . . . . . . . . . . 827 439-1
■ MC . . . . . . . . . . . . . . . . . . 827 439-4
Polydor / Mar '86.

■ DELETED

## DUETS.
**Tracks:** Think / You've got the power / You can make it if you try / Baby, baby, baby / Let it be me / You've got to change your mind / Summertime / It's alright / Funky side of town / Gimme your love / What my baby needs now is a little more lovin' / Never get enough / You got to have a job.
- ■ **LP** . . . . . . . . . . . . . . . . . 841 516-1
- ■ **CD** . . . . . . . . . . . . . . . . . 841 516-2
- ■ **MC** . . . . . . . . . . . . . . . . . 841 516-4

Polydor / Feb '90.

## EXCITEMENT.
**Tracks:** Have mercy baby / Good good lovin' / I don't mind / Dancin' little thing / Begging, begging / Come over here / Shout and shimmy / It was you / Just won't do right / You don't have to go / Tell me what you're gonna do.
- ■ **LP** . . . . . . . . . . . . . . . . . .2489 199

Polydor / Nov '83.

## EYESIGHT.
**Tracks:** Eyesight / Never never never will forget.
- ■ **7″** . . . . . . . . . . . . . . . . . 2066915

Polydor / May '78.

## FEDERAL YEARS VOL.1.
**Tracks:** Not Advised.
- ■ **LP** . . . . . . . . . . . . . . . . . SS 8023

Solid Smoke (USA) / Jul '84.

## FEDERAL YEARS VOL.2.
**Tracks:** Not Advised.
- ■ **LP** . . . . . . . . . . . . . . . . . SS 8024

Solid Smoke (USA) / Jul '84.

## FOR GOODNESS SAKES, TAKE A LOOK AT THOSE CAKES.
**Tracks:** For goodness sakes, take a look at those cakes / Get up, I feel like a sex machine.
- ■ **7″** . . . . . . . . . . . . . . . . . POSP 24

Polydor / Feb '79.

## FROGGY MIX.
**Tracks:** Froggy mix.
- ■ **7″** . . . . . . . . . . . . . . . . . FROG 1
- ■ **12″** . . . . . . . . . . . . . . . . FROGX 1

Boiling Point / Apr '85.

## FUNKIN' IN AMERICA.
**Tracks:** Pop corn '80s / Hot / Givin' up food for funk (part 1) / Let the funk flow / I go crazy / Don't stop the funk / Super bull - super bad / Give it up or turn it loose / Unity - part 1 (The third coming).
- ■ **LP** . . . . . . . . . . . . . . . . . 831 440-1
- ■ **MC** . . . . . . . . . . . . . . . . . 831 440-4

Polydor / Mar '88 / PolyGram.

## FUNKY MEN.
**Tracks:** Funky men / Mashed potatoes.
- ■ **12″** . . . . . . . . . . . . . . . . RCAT 65
- ■ **7″** . . . . . . . . . . . . . . . . . RCA 65

RCA / May '81.

## FUNKY PRESIDENT.
**Tracks:** Not Advised.
- **CD** . . . . . . . . . . . . . . . . . . 5198542
- **LP Set** . . . . . . . . . . . . . . . . 5198541
- **MC** . . . . . . . . . . . . . . . . . . 5198544

Polydor / Jun '93 / PolyGram.

## GET ON THE GOOD FOOT.
**Tracks:** Get on the good foot / Whole world needs liberation / Your love was good for me / Cold sweat / Recitation by Hank Ballard / I got a bag of my own / Nothing beats a try but a fail / Lost someone / Funky side of town / Please, please, please / Ain't it a groove / My part / Make it funky / Dirty Harri / I know it is true.
- ■ **LP** . . . . . . . . . . . . . . . . . 2659018

Polydor / Feb '73.

## GET UP OFFA THAT THING.
**Tracks:** Get up offa that thing.
- ■ **7″** . . . . . . . . . . . . . . . . . .2066 687

Polydor / Sep '76.

## GET UP OFFA THAT THING.
**Tracks:** Get up offa that thing / Release the pleasure / You took my heart / I refuse to lose / Can't take it with you / Home again / This feeling.
- ■ **LP** . . . . . . . . . . . . . . . . . .2391228

Polydor / Nov '76.

## GET UP, GET INTO IT, GET INVOLVED.
**Tracks:** Get up, get into it, get involved (pt.I) / Get up, get into it, get involved (pt.II).
- ■ **7″** . . . . . . . . . . . . . . . . . 45-6347

King (USA) / Mar '87.

---

## GETTIN' DOWN TO IT.
**Tracks:** Sunny / That's life / Strangers in the night / Willow weep for me / Cold sweat / There was a time / Chicago / For sentimental reasons / Time after time / All the way / It had to be you / Uncle.
- ■ **LP** . . . . . . . . . . . . . . . . . .583742

Polydor / Jan '70.

## GIMME YOUR LOVE (see under Franklin, Aretha).

## GODFATHER OF SOUL.
**Tracks:** It's a man's man's man's world / Papa's got a brand new bag / Nature boy / Think / Signed, sealed and delivered / Please, please, please / How do you stop (live) / (Call me) super bad / Spinning wheel / Mona Lisa / This old heart / Good good lovin' / Bewildered / (Get up I feel like being a) sex machine.
- **CD** . . . . . . . . . . . . . . . . . . .550040-2
- **MC** . . . . . . . . . . . . . . . . . . .550040-4

Spectrum (1) / May '93 / PolyGram.

## GODFATHER RETURNS, THE.
**Tracks:** Not Advised.
- **CD** . . . . . . . . . . . . . . . . . . .550 1992
- **MC** . . . . . . . . . . . . . . . . . . .550 1994

Spectrum (1) / Sep '94 / PolyGram.

## GRAVITY.
**Tracks:** How do you stop / Livin' in America / Goliath / Repeat the beat (faith) / Return to me / Gravity / Let's get personal / Turn me loose / I'm Dr. Feelgood.
- ■ **LP** . . . . . . . . . . . . . . . . . SCT 57108
- **MC** . . . . . . . . . . . . . . . . . .40 57108

Scotti Bros (USA) / Oct '86 / PolyGram.
- **CD** . . . . . . . . . . . . . . . . . . CD 57108

Scotti Bros (USA) / Mar '87 / PolyGram.
- ■ **LP** . . . . . . . . . . . . . . . . . FZ 40380

Scotti Bros (USA) / Jul '88.

## GRAVITY.
**Tracks:** Gravity / Gravity (dub).
- ■ **12″** . . . . . . . . . . . . . . . . 6500596
- ■ **7″** . . . . . . . . . . . . . . . . . 6500597

Scotti Bros (USA) / Oct '86.

## GREAT SOUL BROTHER NO.1, THE.
**Tracks:** Not Advised.
- ■ **CD** . . . . . . . . . . . . . . . . . 01316061

Arcade / May '88.

## GREATEST HITS.
**Tracks:** Get up offa that thing / Body heat / It's a man's, man's, man's world / I got the feeling / Sex machine / Try me / Papa's got a brand new bag / Get on the good foot / Cold sweat / Please, please, please / Funky good time / It's too funky in here.
- **CD** . . . . . . . . . . . . . . . . . . YDG 4613
- **MC** . . . . . . . . . . . . . . . . . . YDG 45704

Yesterday's Gold / Aug '93 / Target / Midland Records / Target Sales & Marketing.

## GREATEST HITS.
**Tracks:** I got you / Think / Suds / Ain't that a groove / Papa's got a brand new bag / And I do just what I want / Baby you're right / Have mercy baby / It's a man's man's man's world / Cross firing.
- ■ **LP** . . . . . . . . . . . . . . . . . 623 017

Polydor / Mar '68.

## GREATEST HITS: JAMES BROWN.
**Tracks:** Please, please, please / Try me / Think / Papa's got a brand new bag / I got you (I feel good) / It's a man's man's man's world / Bring it up / Cold sweat / There was a time / I got the feelin' / Say it loud, I'm black and I'm proud / Sex machine / Hot pants / My thang / Funky President / Get up offa that thing.
- ■ **LP** . . . . . . . . . . . . . . . . . 823 352-1
- **MC** . . . . . . . . . . . . . . . . . . 823 352-4

Polydor / Feb '85 / PolyGram.

## HELL.
**Tracks:** Not Advised.
- ■ **Double LP** . . . . . . . . . . . . . PD 29001

Polydor / Jul '88.

## HEY AMERICA.
**Tracks:** Hey America.
- ■ **7″** . . . . . . . . . . . . . . . . . .2093 006

Mojo / Nov '71.

## HOT.
**Tracks:** Not Advised.
- ■ **LP** . . . . . . . . . . . . . . . . . PD 6059

Polydor / Jul '88.

## HOT (I NEED TO BE LOVED LOVED LOVED).
**Tracks:** Hot (I need to be loved, loved, loved) / Superbad, superslick (part 1).

---

- ■ **7″** . . . . . . . . . . . . . . . . . .2066 642

Polydor / Jan '76.

## HOT PANTS.
**Tracks:** Blues and pants / Can't stand it / Escape-ism / Hot pants.
- ■ **LP** . . . . . . . . . . . . . . . . . 2425086

Polydor / Nov '71.

## HOT PANTS.
**Tracks:** Hot pants.
- ■ **7″** . . . . . . . . . . . . . . . . . 2001213

Polydor / Jul '71.

## HOW DO YOU STOP.
**Tracks:** How do you stop / Repeat the beat (faith).
- ■ **12″** . . . . . . . . . . . . . . . . JAMES T1
- ■ **12″ Remix**. . . . . . . . . . . . . JAMES Q1
- ■ **7″** . . . . . . . . . . . . . . . . . JAMES 1

Scotti Bros (USA) / Apr '87.

## I CAN'T STAND MYSELF.
**Tracks:** I can't stand myself / There was a time / Get it together / Baby baby baby / Time after time / Soul of J.B. / Why did you take your love / Need your love so bad / You've gotta change your mind / Fat Eddie.
- ■ **LP** . . . . . . . . . . . . . . . . . 184 136

Polydor / Dec '68.

## I CRIED.
**Tracks:** I cried / Get up, get into it.
- ■ **7″** . . . . . . . . . . . . . . . . . 20013021

Polydor / May '71.

## I GO CRAZY.
**Tracks:** I go crazy / World Cycle Inc.
- ■ **7″** . . . . . . . . . . . . . . . . . POSP 290

Polydor / Jun '81.

## I GOT YOU (I FEEL GOOD).
**Tracks:** I got you (I feel good) / Nowhere to run.
- ■ **7″** . . . . . . . . . . . . . . . . . 7N 25350

Pye International / Feb '66.
- ■ **12″** . . . . . . . . . . . . . . . . AMY 444
- ■ **7″** . . . . . . . . . . . . . . . . . AM 444

A&M / Jul '88.

## I GOT YOU (I FEEL GOOD) (Brown, James v Dakeyne).
**Tracks:** I got you (I feel good).
- ■ **12″** . . . . . . . . . . . . . . . . 12FBI 9
- ■ **CD Single** . . . . . . . . . . . . . CDFBI 9
- ■ **MC Single** . . . . . . . . . . . . . MCFBI 9
- ■ **7″** . . . . . . . . . . . . . . . . . 7 FBI 9

FBI / Sep '92.

## I'LL GO CRAZY.
**Tracks:** I'll go crazy / I've got money / Love don't love nobody / You've got the power.
- ■ **LP** . . . . . . . . . . . . . . . . . NEP 44068

Pye / Aug '66.

## I'M REAL.
**Tracks:** Tribute / I'm real / Static / Time to get busy / She looks all types a good / Keep keepin' / Can't git enuf / It's your money / Godfather running the joint.
- **CD** . . . . . . . . . . . . . . . . . . 834 755-2
- **MC** . . . . . . . . . . . . . . . . . . POLDC 5230
- ■ **LP** . . . . . . . . . . . . . . . . . POLD 5230

Polydor / Jun '88 / PolyGram.

## I'M REAL.
**Tracks:** I'm real / Keep keepin' / Tribute (Only on 12″ and CD single.) / I'm real (FF hyped up mix) (on CD single and 12″ only.).
- ■ **12″** . . . . . . . . . . . . . . . . JSBX 1
- ■ **7″** . . . . . . . . . . . . . . . . . JSB 1
- ■ **CD Single** . . . . . . . . . . . . . JSBCD 1

Urban / May '88.
- ■ **12″** . . . . . . . . . . . . . . . . INT 127328

Intercord / Sep '88.

## IN THE JUNGLE GROOVE.
**Tracks:** It's a new day / Funky drummer / Give it up or turn it loose(remix) / I got to move (Previously unreleased) / Talking loud and saying nothing(remix) / Get up, get into it, get involved / Soul power (re-edit) / Hot pants.
- **CD** . . . . . . . . . . . . . . . . . . 829 624-2
- ■ **Double LP** . . . . . . . . . . . . . URBLP 11
- ■ **MC Set** . . . . . . . . . . . . . . URBDC 11

Urban / May '88 / PolyGram.

## IT'S A MAN'S MAN'S MAN'S WORLD.
**Tracks:** It's a man's man's man's world / Is it yes or is it no / Ain't that a groove (parts 1 & 2) / Scratch. (The) / Bewildered / Bells in the wee wee hours / Come over here / I don't mind / Just you and me / I love you, yes I do.
- ■ **LP** . . . . . . . . . . . . . . . . . .2489 197

Polydor / Nov '83.

### IT'S A MAN'S MAN'S MAN'S WORLD.
Tracks: It's a man's man's man's world.
■ 7" . . . . . . . . . . . . . . . . . . 7N 25371
Pye International / Jun '66.

### IT'S A MAN'S WORLD.
Tracks: It's a man's man's man's world / Sex machine.
■ 12" . . . . . . . . . . . . . . . PER 128 601
Konnexion / May '86.

### IT'S A MOTHER.
Tracks: Mother Popcorn - parts 1 & 2 / Mashed potato popcorn - parts 1 & 2 / I'm shook / Popcorn with a feeling / Little groove maker me - parts 1 & 2 / Any day now / If I ruled the world / You're still out of sight / Top of the stack.
■ LP . . . . . . . . . . . . . . . . . 583 768
Polydor / Nov '69.

### IT'S TOO FUNKY IN HERE.
Tracks: It's too funky in here / Are we really dancing.
■ 12" . . . . . . . . . . . . . . . . POSPX 68
■ 7" . . . . . . . . . . . . . . . . . POSP 68
Polydor / Nov '79.

### JAM/1980'S.
Tracks: Jam / Spank / Nature / Eyesight / I never never never will forget.
■ LP . . . . . . . . . . . . . . . . . 2391342
Polydor / Jun '78.

### JAMES BROWN & GUEST B.B.KING.
Tracks: Not Advised.
VHS . . . . . . . . . . . . . . . . . SVM 803
Start (Video) / Nov '92 / Sony Video Software.

### JAMES BROWN & THE NEW J.B'S.
Tracks: Mutha's nature / Give me some skin / People who criticize / Have a happy day / Bessie / If you don't give a doggone about it / Summertime / People who wake up and live / Take me higher and groove me.
■ LP . . . . . . . . . . . . . . . . . 2391300
Polydor / Sep '77.

### JAMES BROWN & THE SOUL G'S (Live at Chastain Park) (Brown, James & The Soul G's).
Tracks: It's a man's man's man's world / Get up offa that thing / Papa's got a brand new bag / I got you (I feel good) / Cold sweat.
CD . . . . . . . . . . . . . . . . CDJAM 1984
■ LP . . . . . . . . . . . . . . . . JAM 1984
MC . . . . . . . . . . . . . . . . TCJAM 1984
Charly / Aug '88 / Charly.

### JAMES BROWN AND FRIENDS (Brown, James & friends).
Tracks: Papa's got a brand new bag / How do you stop / When a man loves a woman / I'll go crazy / I got you (I feel good) / Out of sight / Livin' in America / Show interest / Cold sweat / Try me.
■ CD . . . . . . . . . . . . . . . 834 085-2
■ LP . . . . . . . . . . . . . . . 834 085-1
■ MC . . . . . . . . . . . . . . . 834 085-4
Polydor / Jan '88.

### JAMES BROWN AND FRIENDS (Brown, James & friends).
Tracks: Not Advised.
VHS . . . . . . . . . . . . . . . . . VC 4052
Video Collection / '88 / Gold & Sons / Video Collection / THE.
VHS . . . . . . . . . . . . . . . . . MC 2041
Music Club Video / Apr '90 / Video Collection / Gold & Sons / THE.

### JAMES BROWN LIVE.
Tracks: Give it up or turnit a loose / It's a man's, man's, man's world / I got the feeling / I can't stand it / Hot pants / Try me / I feel good today / Get up offa that thing / Please, please, please / Jam / Cold sweat / Georgia (on my mind) / It's too funky in here / Gonna have a funky good time / Get on the good foot / Sex machine.
CD . . . . . . . . . . . . . . . . . 15136
MC . . . . . . . . . . . . . . . . . 79010
Laserlight / Jan '93 / THE / BMG / Target.

### JAMES BROWN LIVE - HOT ON THE ONE.
Tracks: It's too funky in here / Get up offa that thing / Papa's got a brand new bag / Please, please, please / It's a man's man's world / Hot on the one.
CD . . . . . . . . . . . . . . . . 847 856-2
Polydor / May '91 / PolyGram.

### JAMES BROWN LIVE AND LOW-DOWN AT THE APOLLO VOL.1.
Tracks: I'll go crazy / Try me / Think / I don't mind / Lost someone / Please,please,please / You've got the power / I found someone / Why do you do me like

you do / I want you so bad / I love you, yes I do / Why does everything happen to me / Bewildered / Please don't go / Night train.
■ MC . . . . . . . . . . . . . . . SPEMC 46
■ LP . . . . . . . . . . . . . . . SPELP 46
Polydor / Sep '83.

### JAMES BROWN SHOW, THE.
Tracks: I'll go crazy / Try me / Think / I don't mind / Lost someone / Please please please / You've got the power / I've found someone / Why do you do me / I want you so bad / I love you yes I do / Why does everything happen to me / Bewildered / Please don't go / Night train.
■ LP . . . . . . . . . . . . . . . . 582 703
Polydor / Nov '67.

### KANSAS CITY.
Tracks: Kansas City / Stone fox.
■ 7" . . . . . . . . . . . . . . . . 7N 25418
Pye / May '67.

### LET YOURSELF GO.
Tracks: Let yourself go / Good rockin' tonight.
■ 7" . . . . . . . . . . . . . . . . 7N 25423
Pye International / Jul '67.

### LET'S GET SERIOUS.
Tracks: Let's get serious.
■ 12" . . . . . . . . . . . . . . . 12LSD 101
Lucky / Oct '88.

### LIVE.
Tracks: Not Advised.
MC Set . . . . . . . . . . . . . . TTMC 046
Tring / Jun '92 / Prism Leisure PLC / Midland Records.

### LIVE & LOWDOWN AT THE APOLLO VOL. 1.
Tracks: I'll go crazy / Try me / Think / I don't mind / Lost someone / Please please please / You've got the power / I found someone / Why do you do me like you do / I want you so bad / I love you yes I do / Why does everything happen to me / Bewildered / Please don't go / Night train.
■ LP . . . . . . . . . . . . . . . . 248 253 0
Polydor / Jul '82.

### LIVE - HOT ON THE ONE.
Tracks: It's too funky in here / Gonna have a funky good time / Get up offa that thing / Body heat / I got the feelin' / Try me / Sex machine / It's a mans mans mans world / Get on the good foot / Papa's got a brand new bag / Please please please / Jam.
■ Double LP . . . . . . . . . . . . . 2683085
Polydor / Dec '80.

### LIVE AT CHASTAIN PARK.
Tracks: Give it up or turn it loose / It's too funky in here / Try me / Get on the good foot / Get up offa that thing / Georgia on my mind / Hot pants / Cold sweat / It's a man's, man's, man's world / Cold sweat / I can't stand myself (when you touch me) / Papa's got a brand new bag / I got you / Please, please, please / Jam.
■ 12" . . . . . . . . . . . . . . . BDL 3005
President / Aug '90.
CD . . . . . . . . . . . . . . . . RTS 33001
Roots / Feb '90 / Pinnacle / Target.
CD . . . . . . . . . . . . . . . TKOCD 007
MC . . . . . . . . . . . . . . . TKOCS 007
TKO Records / '92 / TKO Records Ltd / President Records.
CD . . . . . . . . . . . . . . . CDCD 1151
Charly / Apr '94 / Charly.

### LIVE AT THE APOLLO (PART 1).
Tracks: Not Advised.
■ LP . . . . . . . . . . . . . . . RNLP 217
Rhino (USA) / Jan '86.

### LIVE AT THE APOLLO (PART 2).
Tracks: Not Advised.
■ LP . . . . . . . . . . . . . . . RNLP 218
Rhino (USA) / Jan '86.

### LIVE AT THE APOLLO VOL.1.
Tracks: Opening fanfare / Try me / I don't mind / Lost someone (part 1) / Lost someone (part 2) / Night train / I'll go crazy / Think / Medley / Closing.
CD . . . . . . . . . . . . . . . . 843 479-2
■ LP . . . . . . . . . . . . . . . 843 479-1
■ MC . . . . . . . . . . . . . . . 843 479-4
Polydor / Jul '90 / PolyGram.

### LIVE AT THE APOLLO VOL.2.
Tracks: Think / I wanna be around / Thanks / That's life / Kansas City / Let yourself go / There was a time / I feel all right / Cold sweat / It may be the last time / I got you / Prisoner of love / Out of sight / Try me / Bring it up / It's a man's man's man's world / Lost someone / Please, please, please.
■ LP Set . . . . . . . . . . . . 583 729/730

Polydor / Jun '69.
CD . . . . . . . . . . . . . . . 823 003-2
Polydor / Dec '88 / PolyGram.

### LIVE AT THE GARDEN (Brown, James & The Famous Flames).
Tracks: Out of sight / Bring it up / Try me / Let yourself go / Hip bag '67 / Prisoner of love / I got you / etc.
■ LP . . . . . . . . . . . . . . . NPL 28104
Pye / Dec '67.

### LIVE IN BERLIN.
Tracks: Not Advised.
VHS . . . . . . . . . . . . . . . CFV 08322
Channel 5 / May '89 / Channel 5 Video / P.R.O. Video / Gold & Sons.

### LIVE IN LONDON: JAMES BROWN.
Tracks: Not Advised.
VHS . . . . . . . . . . . . . . . . VVD 117
Virgin Vision / '88 / Gold & Sons / THE.

### LIVE IN NEW YORK.
Tracks: Funky good time / Get up offa that thing / Body heat / Sex machine / Try me / Brown's inferno / Papa's got a brand new bag / Good foot / This is a man's world / Got that feeling / Cold sweat / Please, please, please / Jam / Bay ridge boogy / Payback mix / Too funky in here.
■ LP . . . . . . . . . . . . . . . AFESD 1030
Audio Fidelity / Dec '81.
CD . . . . . . . . . . . . . . . ACD 150155
■ Double LP . . . . . . . . . . . . A 150155
MC . . . . . . . . . . . . . . . AC 150155
SPI Milan (France) / Jul '87 / Silva Screen / PolyGram.
CD . . . . . . . . . . . . . . . UCD 19018
MC . . . . . . . . . . . . . . . UMK 99018
Enteleky / Jul '91 / Pinnacle.

### LIVE IN NEW YORK.
Tracks: Not Advised.
VHS . . . . . . . . . . . . . . . UMV 7706
Enteleky / Jul '91 / Pinnacle.

### LIVE ON STAGE (With Special Guest B.B. King).
Tracks: Not Advised.
VHS . . . . . . . . . . . . . . . OGV 0003
Old Gold / May '90 / Pickwick.

### LIVING IN AMERICA.
Tracks: Livin' in America / Farewell.
■ 12" . . . . . . . . . . . . . . . TA 6701
■ 7" . . . . . . . . . . . . . . . A 6701
Scotti Bros (USA) / Jan '86.

### LOST YEARS, THE (Live in Santa Cruz, 1979).
Tracks: Body heat / Try me / Sex machine / Can't stand it / Jam / Papa's got a brand new bag.
■ VHS . . . . . . . . . . . . . . . 791173
BMG Video / Nov '91.

### LOVE OVERDUE.
Tracks: (So tired of standing still we got to) move / Show me - dance, dance, dance / To the funk / Teardrops on your letter / Standing on higher ground / Later for dancing / You are my everything / It's time to love (put a little love).
■ LP . . . . . . . . . . . . . . . 510079-1
MC . . . . . . . . . . . . . . . 510079-4
■ CD . . . . . . . . . . . . . . . 510079-2
Polydor / Jul '91 / PolyGram.

### MEAN ON THE SCENE.
Tracks: Too funky in here / Please please please / Good foot / Get up offa that thing / Cold sweat / Browns inferno (instrumental).
■ LP . . . . . . . . . . . . . . . PHX 1016
Phoenix (2) / Oct '82.

### MESSIN' WITH THE BLUES.
Tracks: Not Advised.
CD . . . . . . . . . . . . . . . 847 258-2
Polydor / Dec '90 / PolyGram.

### MR. DYNAMITE.
Tracks: Money won't change you / I don't mind / Doin' the limbo / I stay in the chapel every night / Scratch / Night train / I can't help it / Is it yes or is it no / Come over here / In the wee wee hours / Choo choo.
■ LP . . . . . . . . . . . . . . . 623 032
Polydor / Mar '68.

### MR. SOUL (Brown, James & The Famous Flames).
Tracks: Cold sweat / Fever / Kansas City / Stagger Lee / Good rockin' tonight / Mona Lisa / I wanna be around / Nature boy / Come rain or come shine / I loves you Porgy / Back stabbin'.

■ DELETED

■ LP . . . . . . . . . . . . . . . . 184 100
Philips / Jun '68.

## MUTHUS NATURE.
Tracks: Not Advised.
■ LP . . . . . . . . . . . . . . . PD 16111
Polydor / Jul '88.

## NATURE.
Tracks: Nature.
■ 7" . . . . . . . . . . . . . . . . 2066984
Polydor / Nov '78.

## NEW BREED, THE.
Tracks: New breed.
■ 7" . . . . . . . . . . . . . . . BF 1481
Philips / Mar '66.

## NON STOP.
Tracks: Not Advised.
■ LP . . . . . . . . . . . . . . . PD 6318
Polydor / Jul '88.

## ORIGINAL DISCO MAN.
Tracks: It's too funky in here / Let the boogie do the rest / Still / Star generation / Women are something else / Original disco man.
■ LP . . . . . . . . . . . . . . . . 2391412
Polydor / '79.

## ORIGINAL SHOWMAN LIVE.
Tracks: Give it up or turn it loose / It's too funky in here / Gonna have a funky good time / Try me / Sex machine / Get on the good foot / Get up offa that thing / Georgia on my mind.
CD . . . . . . . . . . . . . . . 26 10 382
MC . . . . . . . . . . . . . . . 26 10 384
Dillion / '92 / Sound Solutions.

## PAPA'S GOT A BRAND NEW BAG.
Tracks: Mashed potatoes / Papa's got a brand new bag / U.S.A. / This old heart of mine / Cross firing / Doin' the limbo / Baby, you're right / Love don't love nobody / Have mercy baby / And I do just what I want / I stay in the Chapel every night / You don't have to go.
■ LP . . . . . . . . . . . . . . . . 2334 009
Polydor / Nov '70.
■ LP . . . . . . . . . . . . . . . . 2489 195
Polydor / Nov '83.

## PAPA'S GOT A BRAND NEW BAG.
Tracks: Papa's got a brand new bag / Get up offa that thing.
■ 12" . . . . . . . . . . . . . . . POSPX 605
Polydor / Oct '82.
■ 12" . . . . . . . . . . . . . . . PER 12 8607
Perfect / May '87.

## PAPA'S GOT A BRAND NEW BAG (OLD GOLD).
Tracks: Papa's got a brand new bag / It's a man's man's man's world.
7" . . . . . . . . . . . . . . . . OG 9930
Old Gold / Jan '90 / Pickwick.

## PAY BACK MIX (CD VIDEO).
Tracks: Not Advised.
CD Video . . . . . . . . . . . . . 080 430 2
Polygram Music Video / Oct '88 / PolyGram.

## PAYBACK MIX PART ONE, THE.
Tracks: Payback mix / Give it up or turn it loose / Keep on doing what you're doing but make it funky (Only on 12" single.) / Stone to the bone (Only on 12" single.) / Cold sweat (Only on 12" single.).
■ 12" . . . . . . . . . . . . . . . URBX 17
■ 12" Remix . . . . . . . . . . . . URBA 17
■ 7" . . . . . . . . . . . . . . . . URB 17
Urban / Apr '88.

## PEARLS FROM THE PAST.
Tracks: Not Advised.
CD . . . . . . . . . . . . . . . KLMCD 018
Scratch / Apr '94 / Scratch Records / BMG / Grapevine Distribution.

## PEOPLE.
Tracks: Regrets / Don't stop the funk / That's sweet music / Let the funk flow / Stone cold drag / Are we really dancing / Sometimes that's all there is.
■ LP . . . . . . . . . . . . . . . . 2391 446
Polydor / Jun '80.
■ LP . . . . . . . . . . . . . . . PD 16258
Polydor / Jul '88.

## PLAYS THE REAL THING.
Tracks: Jimmy Mack / What do you like / Peewee's groove / Bernadette / Mercy mercy mercy / I never loved a man / Funky Broadway / 'D' thing.
■ LP . . . . . . . . . . . . . . . SBL 7823
Philips / Feb '68.

## PLEASE, PLEASE, PLEASE.
Tracks: Please please please / Try me / I feel that old feeling coming on / That's when I lost my heart / Chonnie on chon / Hold my baby's hand / Tell me what I did wrong / Baby cries over the ocean / Begging, begging / No, no, no, no / That dood it / I don't know / I walked alone / Love or a game / Let's make it / Just won't do right.
■ LP . . . . . . . . . . . . . . . . 2489 194
Polydor / Nov '83.
CD . . . . . . . . . . . . . . . SING 8610
■ LP . . . . . . . . . . . . . . . SING 610
MC . . . . . . . . . . . . . . . SING 4610
Sing / '88 / Charly / Cadillac.

## POPCORN.
Tracks: Popcorn / Why am I treated so bad / In the middle / Soul pride / New shift / Sudsy / Chicken / Chase.
■ LP . . . . . . . . . . . . . . . . 184 319
Polydor / Mar '70.

## PRISONER OF LOVE.
Tracks: Wait in the rain / Again / Lost someone / Bewildered / So long / Signed, sealed, delivered, I'm yours / Try me, can you (feel it part 1) / How long darling / Thing in 'G'.
■ LP . . . . . . . . . . . . . . . 813 491-1
Polydor / Nov '83.

## RAPP PLAYBACK.
Tracks: Rapp playback.
■ 12" . . . . . . . . . . . . . . . RCAT 28
■ 7" . . . . . . . . . . . . . . . . RCA 28
RCA / Jan '81.

## RAW SOUL.
Tracks: Bring it up / Don't be a dropout / Till then / Tell me that you love me / Yours and mine / Money won't change you / Only you / Let yourself go / Nearness of you / Nobody knows / Stone fox.
LP . . . . . . . . . . . . . . . NPL 28103
Pye / Nov '67.

## REGRETS.
Tracks: Regrets / Stone cold drag.
■ 7" . . . . . . . . . . . . . . . POSP 121
Polydor / Feb '80.

## REVOLUTION OF THE MIND.
Tracks: It's a new day so let a man come in and do the popcorn / Bewildered / Sex machine / Escapeism / Make it funky / Try me / I can't stand myself / Mother Popcorn / I got the feelin' / Give it up or turnit a loose / Call me super bad / Get up, get into it, get involved / Soul power / Hot pants.
■ LP . . . . . . . . . . . . . . . . 2659011
Polydor / Apr '72.

## ROOTS OF A REVOLUTION.
Tracks: I feel that old feeling coming on again / Hold my baby's hand / Chonnie on chon / Just won't do right / Let's make it / Fine old foxy self / Why does everything happen to me / Begging, begging / That dood it / There must be a reason / I want you so bad / Bewildered / Doodle bug / This old heart of mine / You've got the power / Baby you're right / I don't mind / Come over here / And I do just what I want / Tell me what you're gonna do / Hold it / Dancin' little thing / You don't have to go / Lost someone / Shout and shimmy / I found you / I don't care / I've got money / Mashed potatoes USA / Prisoner of love / Oh baby don't you weep / Maybe the last time.
■ LP . . . . . . . . . . . . . . . . REVO 1
Polydor / Jan '84.
CD Set . . . . . . . . . . . . . 817 304-2
Polydor / Nov '89 / PolyGram.

## SAY IT LOUD - I'M BLACK AND I'M PROUD.
Tracks: Say it loud - I'm black and I'm proud / I guess I'll have to cry, cry, cry / Goodbye my love / Shades of brown / Licking stick / I love you / Then you can tell me goodbye / Let them talk / Maybe I'll understand / I'll lose my mind.
■ LP . . . . . . . . . . . . . . . 583 741
Polydor / Sep '69.

## SEX MACHINE.
Tracks: Get up, I feel like a sex machine / Brother Rapp (parts 1&2) / Bewildered / I got the feelin' / Give it up or turnit a loose / Don't want nobody to give me nothing / Lickin' stick / Lowdown popcorn / Spinning wheel / If I ruled the world / There was a time / It's a man's man's man's world / Please, please, please / I can't stand myself (when you touch me) / Mother Popcorn.
■ LP Set . . . . . . . . . . . . . . 2625 004
Polydor / Jan '71.
■ Double LP . . . . . . . . . . . . 833 277-1
MC . . . . . . . . . . . . . . . 833 277-4
Polydor / Feb '88 / PolyGram.

## SEX MACHINE (The Very Best of James Brown).
Tracks: Livin' in America / Gonna have a funky good time / Try me / Get on the good foot / Prisoner of love / There's no business like show business / Get up offa that thing / I got the feeling / Papa's got a brand new bag / I got you (I feel good) / It's a man's man's man's world / (Get up I feel like being a) Sex machine.
■ VHS . . . . . . . . . . . . . . . 0839783
Polygram Music Video / '91.
VHS . . . . . . . . . . . . . . . 086 944 3
4 Front / Apr '93 / PolyGram Video.

## SEX MACHINE & OTHER SOUL CLASSICS.
Tracks: Not Advised.
MC . . . . . . . . . . . . . . . POLDC 5192
Polydor / Apr '86.

## SEX MACHINE - VERY BEST OF JAMES BROWN.
Tracks: Please please please / Think / Night train / Out of sight / Papa's got a brand new bag (part 1) / I got you (I feel good) / It's a man's man's man's world / Cold sweat / Say it loud, I'm black and I'm proud / Hey America / Make it funky / Get up (I feel like being a sex machine) / I'm a greedy man / Get on the good foot / Get up offa that thing / It's too funky in here / Livin' in America / I'm real / Hot pants (Only on CD) / Soul power (live) (Only on CD).
CD . . . . . . . . . . . . . . . 845 828-2
■ LP . . . . . . . . . . . . . . . 845 828-1
MC . . . . . . . . . . . . . . . 845 828-4
Polydor / Nov '91 / PolyGram.

## SHE'S THE ONE.
Tracks: She's the one / Funky president / Funky drummer.
■ 12" . . . . . . . . . . . . . . . URBX 13
■ 7" . . . . . . . . . . . . . . . . URB 13
Urban / Jan '88.

## SLAUGHTER'S BIG RIP OFF.
Tracks: Not Advised.
■ LP . . . . . . . . . . . . . . . . 2391 084
Polydor / '73.

## SOLID GOLD.
Tracks: Please, please, please / Try me / Good good lovin' / I'll go crazy / Think / Night train / Out of sight / Papa's got a brand new bag / I got you / It's a man's man's man's world / Cold sweat / There was a time / I got the feelin' / Say it loud, I'm black and I'm proud / Give it up or turn it loose / Mother popcorn / Get up, I feel like a sex machine / Call me superbad / Soul power / Hot pants / Make it funky / Talking loud and saying nothing / Honky tonk / Get on the good foot / Payback mix / My thang / Papa don't take no mess / Funky president / Hot / Get up offa that thing.
■ Double LP . . . . . . . . . . . . 267 904 4
Polydor / May '77.

## SOUL BROTHER - NUMBER ONE.
Tracks: Get up I feel like being a sex machine / World / It's a new day / Please, please, please / Money won't change you / Ain't it funky now / Say it loud, I'm black and I'm proud / It's a man's, man's, man's world / There was a time / Prisoner of love / I got you / Papa's got a brand new bag.
■ LP . . . . . . . . . . . . . . . . 2343 036
Polydor / May '71.

## SOUL FIRE.
Tracks: Bring it up / Is it yes or is it no / I can't stand myself / Get it together / Please, please, please let yourself go / Money won't change you / Fever / Cold sweat / That's life.
■ LP . . . . . . . . . . . . . . . . 184 148
Polydor / Aug '69.

## SOUL JUBILEE.
Tracks: Turn it loose / It's too funky in here / Gonna have a funky good time / Try me / Get on a good foot / Georgia / Hot pants / I got the feelin' / It's a man's world / Cold sweat / I can't stand it / Papa's got a brand new bag / I feel good / Please, please, please / Jam / Get up off that thing.
CD . . . . . . . . . . . . . . . CDBM 081
LP . . . . . . . . . . . . . . . BMLP 081
Blue Moon (1) / Apr '90 / Roots Records / Jazz Music / Swift / Projection / THE / Hot Shot.

## SOUL JUBILEE.
Tracks: Turn it loose / It's too funky in here / Gonna have a funky good time / Try me / Get on a good foot, get up off that thing / Georgia / Hot pants / I got the feelin' / It's a man's world / Cold sweat / I can't stand it / Papas got a brand new bag / I feel good / Please please please / Jam.

■ VHS . . . . . . . . . . . . . . . VIDJAM 1984
Charly Video / '88.
VHS . . . . . . . . . . . . . . . . MMGV 007
MMG Video / Jul '90 / THE.

## SOUL POWER.
**Tracks:** Soul power.
■ 7" . . . . . . . . . . . . . . . . . . .2001 163
Polydor / Mar '71.

## SOUL POWER (PART 1).
**Tracks:** Soul power (part 1) / It's a man's man's
man's world / King heroin (don't mess with heroin)
(Extra track on 12" only) / Don't tell it (* = Extra track
on 12" only).
■ 12" . . . . . . . . . . . . . . . . . . POSPX 783
■ 7" . . . . . . . . . . . . . . . . . . . POSP 783
Boiling Point / Apr '86.

## SOUL PRIDE.
**Tracks:** Not Advised.
CD Set . . . . . . . . . . . . . . . . . 5178452
Polydor / May '93 / PolyGram.

## SOUL SYNDROME.
**Tracks:** Rapp payback / Mashed potatoes / Funky
men / Smokin' and drinkin' / Stay with me / Honky
tonk.
■ LP . . . . . . . . . . . . . . . . . RCALP 5006
RCA / Apr '81.
■ LP . . . . . . . . . . . . . . . . . RCALP 3048
■ MC . . . . . . . . . . . . . . . . . RCAK 3048
RCA / Sep '81.

## SOUL SYNDROME PLUS (Brown, James With Bobby Byrd & The JB's).
**Tracks:** Rapp payback (where iz Moses) (long ver-
sion) / Mashed potatoes / Funky men / Smokin' and
drinkin' / Stay with me / Honky tonk / Bessie (part 1)
/ Nature (part 1) / Rock groove machine (part 1) /
Just wanna make you dance (part 1) / Back from the
dead / Way to get down / Headquarters (Augusta,
GA) / Rapp payback (where iz Moses) (part 1).
■ CD . . . . . . . . . . . . . . . . CDROUS 1043
■ Double LP . . . . . . . . . . . . . . ROUS 1043
■ MC . . . . . . . . . . . . . . . . TCROUS 1043
Roulette (EMI) / Oct '91.

## SPECIAL.
**Tracks:** Not Advised.
■ LP . . . . . . . . . . . . . . . . . . .2417 351
MC . . . . . . . . . . . . . . . . . . . .3195 270
Polydor / Sep '81 / PolyGram.

## STAR GENERATION.
**Tracks:** Star generation / Let the boogie do the rest.
■ 12" . . . . . . . . . . . . . . . . . .STEPX 2
■ 7" . . . . . . . . . . . . . . . . . . STEP 2
Polydor / Sep '79.

## STAR TIME.
**Tracks:** Please please please / Why do you do me /
Try me / Tell me what I did wrong / Bewildered /
Good good lovin' / I'll go crazy / I know it's true / (Do
the) mashed potatoes, part 1 / Think / Baby you're
right / Lost someone / Night train / I've got money /
I've got no money / I don't mind (live) / Prisoner of
love / Devil's den / Out of the blue / Out of sight /
Grits / Maybe the last time / It's a man's world / I got
you / Papa's got a brand new bag, parts 1,2 & 3 /
Papa's got a brand new bag, part 1 / I got you (I feel
good) / Ain't that a groove / It's a man's man's man's
world / Money won't change you / Don't be a dropout
/ Bring it up (Hipster's avenue) / Let yourself go /
Cold sweat / Let it together / I can't stand myself
(when you touch me) part 1 / I got the feelin' / Licking
stick-licking stick / Say it loud - I'm black and I'm
proud, part 1 / There was a time (live) / Give it up or
turnit a loose / I don't want nobody to give me
nothing (open up the door I'l / Mother popcorn /
Funky drummer / Get up (I feel like being a) sex
machine / Super bad, parts 1 & 2 / Talkin' loud &
sayin' nothing / Get up, get into it and get involved /
Soul power, parts 1 & 2 / Brother rapp/Ain't it funky
now (live) / Hot pants, part 1 / I'm a greedy man, part
1 / Make it funky, part 1 / It's a new day (live) / I got
ants in my pants, part 1 / King Heroin / There it is,
part 1 / Public enemy no. 1, part 1 / Get on the good
foot / I got a bag of my own / Doing it to death /
Payback / Papa don't take no mess, part 1 / Stoned
to the bone, part 1 / My thang / Funky president
(People it's bad) / Hot (I need to be loved, loved,
loved) / Get up offa that thing (Release the pressure)
/ Body heat, part 1 / It's too funky in here / Rapp
payback (Where iz moses) / Unity, part 1.
CD Set . . . . . . . . . . . . . . . . 849 108-2
MC Set . . . . . . . . . . . . . . . . 849 108-4
Polydor / May '91 / PolyGram.

## STATIC.
**Tracks:** Not Advised.
CD . . . . . . . . . . . . . . . . . . JSBCD 2
■ LP . . . . . . . . . . . . . . . . . . . JSB 2

MC. . . . . . . . . . . . . . . . . . . JSBC 2
Polydor / Aug '88 / PolyGram.

## STATIC.
**Tracks:** Static / I'm real (US remix) / Static (full force
def mix) (Only on 12" and CD single.).
■ 12" . . . . . . . . . . . . . . . . . .JSBX2
■ 7" . . . . . . . . . . . . . . . . . . . JSP 2
Scotti Bros (USA) / Aug '88.

## STAY WITH ME.
**Tracks:** Stay with me / Smokin' and drinkin'.
■ 7" . . . . . . . . . . . . . . . . . . . RCA 44
RCA / Feb '81.

## STRAIGHTEN UP AND FLY RIGHT.
**Tracks:** Straighten up and fly right / Flipside.
■ 7" . . . . . . . . . . . . . . . . . .SDR 003
Soldoon / Apr '76.

## SUPER BAD.
**Tracks:** Call me super bad / Let it be me / Sometime
/ Man has got to go back to the crossroads / Giving
out of juice / By the time I get to Phoenix / Soul
Brother - Number One.
■ LP . . . . . . . . . . . . . . . . . . .2310 089
Polydor / May '71.

## SUPERBAD.
**Tracks:** Superbad (Pt. I) / Superbad (Pt. II).
■ 7" . . . . . . . . . . . . . . . . . . 45-6329
King (USA) / Mar '87.

## TAKE A LOOK AT THOSE CAKES.
**Tracks:** For goodness sakes, look at those cakes /
Man understands / Someone to talk to / Spring / As
long as I love you.
■ LP . . . . . . . . . . . . . . . . . . .2391 384
Polydor / Jan '79.

## THERE IT IS.
**Tracks:** There it is / King Heroin / I'm a greedy man /
Who am I / Talkin' loud and sayin' nothing / Public
enemy No.1 / I need help / Never can say goodbye.
■ LP . . . . . . . . . . . . . . . . . . .2391033
Polydor / Nov '72.

## THIRD COMING.
**Tracks:** Popcorn 80's / Give that bass player some /
You're my only love / World cycle / Superbull /
Superbad 80's / Love 80's / I go crazy.
■ LP . . . . . . . . . . . . . . . . . POLS 1029
Polydor / May '81.

## THIS IS.
**Tracks:** Licking stick - licking stick / Good, good
lovin' / Just plain funk / Kansas City / Sunny / Money
won't change you / I got the feeling / I loves you
Porgy / That's life / Say it loud I'm black and I'm
proud.
■ LP . . . . . . . . . . . . . . . . . . . 643 317
Polydor / Nov '69.

## TIME TO GET BUSY.
**Tracks:** Time to get busy.
■ 7" . . . . . . . . . . . . . . . . 4Z9 081 30
Scotti Bros (USA) / Oct '88.

## TRY ME (Brown, James & The Famous Flames).
**Tracks:** There must be a reason / I want you so bad /
Why do you do me / I've got to cry / Strange things
happen / Fine old foxy self / Messing with the blues /
Try me / It was you / I've got to change / Can't be the
same / It hurts to tell you / I won't plead no more /
You're mine, you're mine / Gonna try / Don't let it
happen to me.
■ LP . . . . . . . . . . . . . . . . . SING 635
MC . . . . . . . . . . . . . . . . . .SING 4635
Sing / '88 / Charly / Cadillac.

## TURN IT LOOSE.
**Tracks:** Give it up or turn it loose / I'll lose my mind /
I don't want nobody to give me nothing / I'll get it
myself (parts 1 and 2).
■ 7" . . . . . . . . . . . . . . . . . . 580 701
Polydor / Jan '70.

## UNBEATABLE 16 HITS.
**Tracks:** Try me / I've got to change / Strange things
happen / I've got to cry / There must be a reason /
Why do you do me / Don't let it happen to me / Can't
be the same / It hurts to tell you / Gonna try / You're
mine / Fine old foxy self / I won't please no more /
Messing with the blues / It was you / I want you so
bad.
■ LP . . . . . . . . . . . . . . . . . . .2459 198
Polydor / Nov '83.

## UNIVERSAL JAMES.
**Tracks:** Can't get any harder / Just do it / Mine all
mine / Watch me / Georgia lina / Show me your
friends / Everybody's got a thang / How long / Make
it funky 2000 / Moments.

CD . . . . . . . . . . . . . . . . . . . 5143292
■ LP . . . . . . . . . . . . . . . . . . 5143291
■ MC . . . . . . . . . . . . . . . . . . 5143294
Polydor / Jan '93 / PolyGram.

## VIDEO BIOGRAPHY.
**Tracks:** Not Advised.
VHS . . . . . . . . . . . . . . . . . . VVD 255
Virgin Vision / Jan '88 / Gold & Sons / THE.

# Brown, Jocelyn

## ABSOLUTELY JOCELYN.
**Tracks:** Mind Buster / Freedom / Somebody else's
guy / Absolutely / Reaching out / I want to know what
love is / Turn out the lights / This love is true /
Everyday / Feel like makin' love / Many rivers to
cross / No excuse.
CD . . . . . . . . . . . . . . . . . . . JOCD 1
Capital City / Jul '92 / Grapevine Distribution.

## DAY DREAMING.
**Tracks:** Day dreaming.
■ 12" . . . . . . . . . . . . . . . . . . ARI 125
Ariwa Sounds / Sep '91.

## FREEDOM.
**Tracks:** Freedom / Somebody else's guy.
■ 7" . . . . . . . . . . . . . . . . . . . WAM 1
■ 12" . . . . . . . . . . . . . . . . . .12WAM 1
Wam / Feb '91.

## GIMME ALL YOUR LOVIN' (see under Mazelle, Kym).

## I WISH YOU WOULD.
**Tracks:** I wish you would.
■ 12" . . . . . . . . . . . . . . . . . BRWX 14
■ 7" . . . . . . . . . . . . . . . . . . BRW 14
■ 12" . . . . . . . . . . . . . . . . 12 BRW 14
4th & Broadway / Mar '84.

## JOCELYN BROWN COLLECTION.
**Tracks:** Not Advised.
CD . . . . . . . . . . . . . . . . . . CCSCD 386
■ MC . . . . . . . . . . . . . . . . . CCSMC 386
Castle / Oct '93 / BMG.

## LOVE'S GONNA GET YOU.
**Tracks:** Love's gonna get you / Love's gonna get you
(fun house mix).
■ 7" . . . . . . . . . . . . . . . . . . W 8889
■ 12" . . . . . . . . . . . . . . . . .W 8889T
WEA / Feb '86.

## NO MORE TEARS (see under Mazelle, Kym).

## ONE FROM THE HEART.
**Tracks:** Ego maniac / Love's gonna get you / Livin'
without your love / I cry real tears / Caught in the act
/ My time will come / True love / Whatever satisfies
you.
■ LP . . . . . . . . . . . . . . . . . .925445 1
■ MC . . . . . . . . . . . . . . . . . .925445 4
WEA / Apr '87.

## SOMEBODY ELSE'S GUY.
**Tracks:** Somebody else's guy.
■ 7" . . . . . . . . . . . . . . . . . . .BRW 5
■ 12" . . . . . . . . . . . . . . . . 12 BRW 5
4th & Broadway / Apr '84.

## SOMEBODY ELSE'S GUY (OLD GOLD).
**Tracks:** Somebody else's guy / Wish you would, I.
12" . . . . . . . . . . . . . . . . . .OG 4199
Old Gold / Jun '91 / Pickwick.

## TO THROUGH.
**Tracks:** To through.
■ 12" . . . . . . . . . . . . . . . . EXCL 1400
■ 7" . . . . . . . . . . . . . . . . . EXC 1400
Excaliber / Aug '85.

# Brown, Mark

## BANG BANG.
**Tracks:** Bang bang / Bang bang (instrumental).
■ 12" . . . . . . . . . . . . . . . . . ZT 43290
■ 7" . . . . . . . . . . . . . . . . . ZB 43289
■ CD Single . . . . . . . . . . . . . . ZD 43290
Motown / Nov '89.

## GOOD FEELING.
**Tracks:** Bang bang / Shall we dance / Through a
friend of mine / Good feeling / My heart misses / It's
not the way it used to be / Luv touch / Cruisin' /
Betwee you and me / Let's go all the way / Distress
signal (Only on CD.).
■ CD . . . . . . . . . . . . . . . . . ZD 72686
■ LP . . . . . . . . . . . . . . . . . ZL 72686
■ MC . . . . . . . . . . . . . . . . . ZK 72686
Motown / Nov '89.

### JUST LIKE THAT.
**Tracks:** Next time / I can't get enough of you're love / Want you back / I used to be in love / She don't care / Contagious / What do you want from me / Put a smile on your face / Why can't we be alone / Stakeout.
- **CD** . . . . . . . . . . . . . . . . . . . ZD 72623
- **LP** . . . . . . . . . . . . . . . . . . . ZL 72623
- **MC** . . . . . . . . . . . . . . . . . . . ZK 72623

Motown / Mar '88.

### NEXT TIME.
**Tracks:** Next time / Next time (inst).
- **12"** . . . . . . . . . . . . . . . . . . ZT 41774
- **7"** . . . . . . . . . . . . . . . . . . . ZB 41773

Motown / Mar '88.

## Brown, Maxine

### AM I FALLING IN LOVE.
**Tracks:** Am I falling in love / Promise me anything.
- **7"** . . . . . . . . . . . . . . . . 45POP 1102

H.M.V. / '63.

### ASK ME.
**Tracks:** Ask me.
- **7"** . . . . . . . . . . . . . . . . . . . . . . SS 188

Stateside / '63.

### I'VE GOT A LOT OF LOVE LEFT IN ME.
**Tracks:** I've got a lot of love left in me / Hold on.
- **7"** . . . . . . . . . . . . . . . . . . . . 7N 25410

Pye / Jan '67.

### IT'S TORTURE.
**Tracks:** It's torture / I got love.
- **7"** . . . . . . . . . . . . . . . . . . TOWN 110

Kent / Mar '86.

### LIKE NEVER BEFORE.
**Tracks:** It's torture / I want a guarantee / Baby cakes / Slipping through my fingers / He's the only guy I'll ever love / I've got a lot of love left in me / Do it now / When I fall in love / You're in love / Ask me / Never had it so good / Losing my touch / Misty morning eyes / Do it in the name of love / Everybody needs love / O Lord what are you doing to me.
- **LP** . . . . . . . . . . . . . . . . . . KENT 047

Kent / Nov '85.

### OH NO NOT MY BABY.
**Tracks:** Since I found you / Gotta find a way / I wonder what my baby's doing tonight / Let me give you my lovin' / It's torture / One in a million / Oh no not my baby / You're in love / Anything for a laugh / Coming back to you / Yesterday's kisses / Ask me / All in my mind / Little girl lost / I want a guarantee / Secret of livin' / Baby cakes / One step at a time / I've got a lot of love left in me / I don't need anything / Oh Lord what are you doing to me / I cry alone / Funny / Misty morning eyes / Love that man / Losing my touch / Put yourself in my place / It's gonna be alright.
- **CD** . . . . . . . . . . . . . . . . . CDKEND 949

Kent / Oct '90 / Pinnacle.

### ONE IN A MILLION.
**Tracks:** One in a million / Since I found you / Let me give you my lovin' / Little girl lost / I wonder what my baby's doing tonight / Yesterday's kisses / One step at a time / It's gonna be alright / Oh no not my baby / Anything for a laugh / Put yourself in my place / I cry alone / You're in love / I don't need anything / Funny / All in my mind.
- **LP** . . . . . . . . . . . . . . . . . . KENT 028

Kent / Oct '84.

### ONE IN A MILLION.
**Tracks:** One in a million / Let me give you my lovin'.
- **7"** . . . . . . . . . . . . . . . . . . . DDS 117

Pye Disco Demand / Jul '75.

## Brown, Miquel

### BLACK LEATHER.
**Tracks:** Black leather.
- **12"** . . . . . . . . . . . . . . . . . SOHOT 27

Record Shack / Sep '84.

### CLOSE TO PERFECTION.
**Tracks:** Close to reflection / Number one love / Come any hearts.
- **LP** . . . . . . . . . . . . . . . . . SOHO LP 8
- **MC** . . . . . . . . . . . . . . . . . SOHO TC 8

Record Shack / Oct '85.

### CLOSE TO PERFECTION.
**Tracks:** Close to perfection.
- **12"** . . . . . . . . . . . . . . . . . SOHOT 48
- **7"** . . . . . . . . . . . . . . . . . . SOHO 48

Record Shack / Aug '85.
- **12"** . . . . . . . . . . . . . . . . . SOHOB 8

Record Shack / Feb '88.

### DANCING WITH THE LIGHTS DOWN LOW.
**Tracks:** Dancing with the lights down low / Something made of love.
- **7"** . . . . . . . . . . . . . . . . . . 2059118

Polydor / May '79.

### FOOTPRINTS IN THE SAND.
**Tracks:** Footprints in the sand (Inst.) / Footprints in the sand.
- **12"** . . . . . . . . . . . . . . . . . . MARE 5
- **7"** . . . . . . . . . . . . . . . . . . MARES 5

Nightmare / Jan '87.

### HE'S A SAINT HE'S A SINNER.
**Tracks:** He's a saint, he's a sinner.
- **12"** . . . . . . . . . . . . . . . . . SOHOT 15
- **7"** . . . . . . . . . . . . . . . . . . SOHO 15

Record Shack / Feb '84.

### HE'S A SAINT, HE'S A SINNER (OLD GOLD).
**Tracks:** He's a saint, he's a sinner.
- **CD Single** . . . . . . . . . . . . . . . . OG 6511

Old Gold / '92 / Pickwick.

### MANPOWER.
**Tracks:** Not Advised.
- **LP** . . . . . . . . . . . . . . . . . SOHOLP 1

Record Shack / Nov '83.

### ON THE RADIO.
**Tracks:** On the radio.
- **12"** . . . . . . . . . . . . . . . . . SOHOT 59
- **7"** . . . . . . . . . . . . . . . . . . SOHO 59

Record Shack / Nov '85.

### SO MANY MEN SO LITTLE TIME.
**Tracks:** So many men so little time / Man power / He's a saint, he's a sinner (On LBAY 1004 only) / Black leather (On LBAY 1004 only).
- **12"** . . . . . . . . . . . . . . . . . SOHOT 6
- **7"** . . . . . . . . . . . . . . . . . . SOHO 6

Record Shack / Jun '83.
- **12"** . . . . . . . . . . . . . . . . . SOHOT 17
- **7"** . . . . . . . . . . . . . . . . . SOHO 17

Record Shack / Apr '84.
- **12"** . . . . . . . . . . . . . . . . . SOHOB 6

Record Shack / Feb '88.
- **12"** . . . . . . . . . . . . . . . . . . ERECT 6
- **7"** . . . . . . . . . . . . . . . . . . ERECT 72
- **MC Single** . . . . . . . . . . . . . ERECTMC 2

La Vie En Rose / Aug '91.
- **12"** . . . . . . . . . . . . . . . . LBAY 1004

Loading Bay / Jan '93 / Loading Bay Records.

### SO MANY MEN SO LITTLE TIME (OLD GOLD).
**Tracks:** So many men, so little time / Close to perfection.
- **12"** . . . . . . . . . . . . . . . . . . OG 4138

Old Gold / Oct '89.

### SYMPHONY OF LOVE.
**Tracks:** Symphony of love / Dancin' with the lights down low / This is something new to me / Day that they got disco in Brazil / Do it / Something made of love.
- **LP** . . . . . . . . . . . . . . . . . 238 352 5

Polydor / Mar '79.

### SYMPHONY OF LOVE.
**Tracks:** Symphony of love / When did it all begin to end.
- **7"** . . . . . . . . . . . . . . . . . . 2059036

Polydor / May '78.
- **7"** . . . . . . . . . . . . . . . . . . POSP 19

Polydor / Jan '79.

### THIRD TIME AROUND.
**Tracks:** Third time around / Where will tomorrow lead.
- **7"** . . . . . . . . . . . . . . . . . 7N 45658

Pye / Jan '77.

## Brown, Norman

### JUST BETWEEN US.
**Tracks:** Not Advised.
- **12"** . . . . . . . . . . . . . . . . . 5800911

Mojazz / Oct '92.

### JUST BETWEEN US.
**Tracks:** Not Advised.
- **CD** . . . . . . . . . . . . . . . . . 5300912

Mojazz / Feb '93 / Jetstar.
- **MC** . . . . . . . . . . . . . . . . . 5300914

Motown / Feb '93.

## Brown, O'Chi

### 100% PURE PAIN.
**Tracks:** 100% pure pain / I just want to be loved.
- **12" Remix** . . . . . . . . . . . . MAGT 296R
- **12"** . . . . . . . . . . . . . . . . . MAGT 296
- **7"** . . . . . . . . . . . . . . . . . . MAG 296

Magnet / Jul '86.

### CAN'T SAY GOODBYE TO YOU.
**Tracks:** Can't say goodbye to you.
- **12"** . . . . . . . . . . . . . . . . . CGDD 19

Carib Jems / May '82.

### I GOT A FEELING.
**Tracks:** I got a feeling / Lady / Another broken heart (Extra track available on 12" version only).
- **12"** . . . . . . . . . . . . . . . . . OCHIT 5
- **7"** . . . . . . . . . . . . . . . . . . OCHI 5

Magnet / Aug '87.

### LEARNING TO LIVE (WITHOUT YOUR LOVE) (Brown, O'Chi & Rick Astley).
**Tracks:** Learning to live (without your love) / Another broken heart.
- **12"** . . . . . . . . . . . . . . . . . MAGDT 7
- **7"** . . . . . . . . . . . . . . . . . . MAGD 7

Magnetic Dance / Oct '87.

### O'CHI.
**Tracks:** Whenever you need somebody / Fantasy / 100% pure pain / Caught in a life / Lady / Two hearts beating as one / Learning to live (without your love) / Call me up / Another broken heart.
- **CD** . . . . . . . . . . . . . . . . CD MAG 5070
- **LP** . . . . . . . . . . . . . . . . . MAGL 5070
- **MC** . . . . . . . . . . . . . . . ZCMAG 5070

Magnet / Nov '86 / WEA.

### ROCK YOUR BABY (EDIT).
**Tracks:** Rock your baby (edit) / Another broken heart.
- **12"** . . . . . . . . . . . . . . . . . OCHIT 4
- **7"** . . . . . . . . . . . . . . . . . . OCHI 4

Magnet / Feb '87.

### TWO HEARTS BEATING AS ONE.
**Tracks:** Two hearts beating as one.
- **12"** . . . . . . . . . . . . . . . . . MAGT 297
- **7"** . . . . . . . . . . . . . . . . . . MAG 297

Magnet / Oct '86.

### UNCHAINED MELODY.
**Tracks:** Unchained melody / If I'm crying.
- **7"** . . . . . . . . . . . . . . . . . . DBM 1

DBM / Jun '84.

### WHENEVER YOU NEED SOMEBODY.
**Tracks:** Whenever you need somebody (umbungo mix) / Whenever you need somebody (pull it off mix) / Whenever you need somebody.
- **12"** . . . . . . . . . . . . . . . . . MAGDT 9

Magnet / Dec '87.

### WHITER SHADE OF PALE.
**Tracks:** Whiter shade of pale / When I'm crying.
- **12"** . . . . . . . . . . . . . . . . . RR 005T
- **7"** . . . . . . . . . . . . . . . . . . RR 005

Romantic / Sep '83.

### WHY CAN'T WE BE FRIENDS.
**Tracks:** Why can't we be friends / If I'm crying.
- **12"** . . . . . . . . . . . . . . . . 12DBM 009
- **7"** . . . . . . . . . . . . . . . . . DBM 009

DBM / Jul '85.

## Brown, Peter

### BABY GETS HIGH.
**Tracks:** Baby gets high.
- **7"** . . . . . . . . . . . . . . . . . . RCA 317

RCA / Feb '83.

### CAN'T BE LOVE.
**Tracks:** Can't be love / Do it to me anyway / West of the North Star.
- **12"** . . . . . . . . . . . . . . . . TKR 13 7580
- **7"** . . . . . . . . . . . . . . . . . TKR 7580

TK / Jul '80.

### CRANK IT UP.
**Tracks:** Crank it up (pt 1) / Crank it up (pt 2).
- **12"** . . . . . . . . . . . . . . . . TKR 137545
- **7"** . . . . . . . . . . . . . . . . . TKR 7545

TK / '79.

### DANCE WITH ME.
**Tracks:** Dance with me / For your love.
- **7"** . . . . . . . . . . . . . . . . . TKR 6027

TK / Jun '78.

■ **DELETED**

51

### DO YOU WANNA GET FUNKY WITH ME.
Tracks: Do you wanna get funky with me / Burning love breakdown.
- 7".................................XB 2183
TK / Jun '77.
- 7".................................TKR 6009
TK / Jan '78.

### LOVE IN OUR HEARTS.
Tracks: Love in our hearts / Penguins.
- 7".................................TKR 7572
TK / Jan '80.

### STARGAZER.
Tracks: Crank it up / It's alright / Stargazer / Got to get the show on the road / Leadmeon / West of the North Star / Love in our hearts / Penguin.
- LP...............................KTR 83354
TK / Apr '80.

### STARGAZER.
Tracks: Stargazer / West of the north star.
- 7".................................TKR 7579
TK / May '80.

### THEY ONLY COME OUT AT NIGHT.
Tracks: They only come out at night.
- 12"................................TA 4334
- 7".................................A 4334
CBS / Jul '87.

### YOU SHOULD DO IT.
Tracks: You should do it / Without love.
- 7".................................TKR 6048
TK / Sep '78.

## Brown, Randy

### ARE YOU LONELY.
Tracks: Are you lonely.
- 12"..............................WAY 103 T
Threeway / Jul '88.

### CHECK IT OUT.
Tracks: Sweet to the bone / Heaven knows / If it's love that you want / Two fools / If I had to do it all over / Thank you for the happiness / Without you / Smoking room.
- LP................................MPS 8512
MPS (USA) / Jun '86.

### I THOUGHT OF YOU TODAY.
Tracks: I thought of you today / Use it.
- 7"................................RRS 508
Parachute (USA) / Sep '79.

### INTIMATELY.
Tracks: You say it's all / I'm here / I was blessed / Day I found you / I thought of you today / You make me happy / It scares me so / Use it / I wanna baby you / Crazy about you baby.
- LP................................RRL 2007
Parachute (USA) / Jul '79.

### MIDNIGHT DESIRE.
Tracks: Love formula 69 / We ought to be doin' it / Things that I could do to you / You're so good / With your love / Without you I can't make it through the night / Next best thing to being there / Do you love me / Love be with you.
- LP................................CCL 2010
Casablanca / Jun '80.

### WE OUGHT TO BE DOING IT.
Tracks: We ought to be doing it / Things I could do to you / You're so good (Available on 12" only.) / I wanna make love to you (Available on 12" only.) / You make me happy (Available on 12" only).
- 12"................................CANL 190
- 7".................................CAN 190
Casablanca / Mar '80.

### WELCOME TO MY ROOM.
Tracks: Not Advised.
- LP................................RRL 2005
Parachute (USA) / May '78.
- LP................................WAY LP 1
Threeway / Oct '87.

## Brown, Roy

### BLUES DELUXE.
Tracks: Cadillac baby / Hard luck blues / New Rebecca / Sweet peach / Love don't love nobody / Dreaming blues / Good man blues / Too much lovin' ain't no good / Teenage jamboree / Train time blues / Bar room blues / Long about snowdown / Beautician blues / Drum boogie / Double crossin' woman / Swingin' with Johnny / Wrong woman blues / Good rockin' man / I've got the last laugh now / Big town / Brown angel / Rock a bye baby / Lonesome lover / Answer to big town.

CD................................CDCHARLY 289
Charly / Nov '93 / Charly.

### BLUESWAY SESSIONS, THE.
Tracks: Hard times / Higher and higher / New Orleans woman / Driving me mad / Till the end of never / Soul lover / Man in trouble blues / Standing on broadway (watching the girls) / Woman trouble blues / Cryin' with the blues / Deep down in my soul.
- LP................................CRB 1199
Charly R&B / Oct '88.

### BOOGIE AT MIDNIGHT.
Tracks: Mighty mighty man / Boogie at midnight / Cadillac baby / Hard luck blues / Love don't love nobody / Too much lovin' ain't no good / Big town / Rockabye baby / Answer to big town / Ain't no rockin' no more / My gal from kokomo / Fannie Brown got married / Black diamond / Shake em up baby / Adorable one / Good looking and foxy too.
MC.................................TCCRB 1093
- LP................................CRB 1093
Charly R&B / Jul '85 / Charly.

### CHEAPEST PRICE IN TOWN.
Tracks: Not Advised.
- LP....................................91020
Faith / Feb '79.

### GOOD ROCKIN' TONIGHT.
Tracks: Travellin blues / Let the four winds blow / Love for sale / Boogie woogie blues / Good rockin' tonight / Boogie at midnight / Love don't love nobody / Losing hand / Tin pan alley.
- LP...............................MFLP 1025
Magnum Force / Jun '84.

### GOOD ROCKING TONIGHT.
Tracks: Good rockin' tonight / Long about midnight / Whose what is that / Fore day in the morning / Dreaming blues / Butcher Pete part 2 / Good man blues / Miss Fanny Brown returns / Brown angel / Grandpa stole my baby / Teenage jamboree / Black diamond / This is my last goodbye / Mighty, mighty man.
- LP....................................KIX 6
Route 66 (Sweden) / Jun '80.

### HARD LUCK BLUES.
Tracks: Not Advised.
- LP................................BID 8025
Bellaphon / Jul '88.
MC Set.............................GD 5036
Gusto (USA) / Mar '88.

### LAUGHING BUT CRYING.
Tracks: Roy Brown boogie / Special lesson No.1 / Rainy weather blues / End of my journey / Fool in love / Butcher Pete part 1 / New Rebecca / Double crossing woman / Letter from home / Hurry hurry baby / Up jumped the devil / School bell rock / Money can't buy love / Lonesome lover / Laughing but crying.
- LP....................................KIX 2
Route 66 (Sweden) / Jun '80.
CD.....................................RBD 2
Route 66 (Sweden) / Apr '91 / Swift / Wellard.

### MIGHTY, MIGHTY MAN.
Tracks: Mr. Hound Dog's in town / Bootleggin' baby / Trouble at midnight / Everything's alright / This is my last goodbye / Don't let it rain / Up jumped the devil / No love at all / Ain't it a shame / Ain't no rocking no more / Queen of diamonds / Gal from Kokomo / Fannie Brown got married / Worried life blues / Black diamond / Letter to baby / Shake 'em up baby / Rinky dinku doo / Adorable one / School bell rock / Ain't got no blues today / Good looking and foxy too.
CD...............................CDCHD 459
Ace / Sep '93 / Pinnacle / Complete Record Co. Ltd.

### SATURDAY NITE.
Tracks: Mr. Hound dog's in town / Caldonia's wedding day / Everyday / Saturday nite / I'm sticking with you / I love you I need you / I'm ready to play / Good looking and foxy too / Midnight lover man / Bootleggin' baby / Tick of the clock / We're goin' rockin' tonight / Ain't gonna do it / Slow down little Eva / Rinky dinky doo / Let the four winds blow.
- LP....................................RB 104
Mr R&B (Sweden) / Aug '87.

## Brown, Russ

### GOTTA FIND A WAY.
Tracks: Gotta find a way.
- 12"..............................TENT 122
- 7"...............................TEN 122
10 / Apr '86.
- 12"..............................JS 1001
Jump St (USA) / Sep '87.

### TAKE MY LOVE.
Tracks: Take my love / Got to find a way.
- 12"..............................TENT 182
- 7"...............................TEN 182
10 / Jun '87.

## Brown, Ruth

### BLACK IS BROWN AND BROWN IS BEAUTIFUL.
Tracks: Yesterday / Please send me someone to love / Looking back / Try me and see / Miss Browns blues / My prayer / Since I fell for you / This bitter earth.
- LP................................RHAP 10
Rhapsody / May '81.

### BLUES ON BROADWAY.
Tracks: Nobody knows you when you're down and out / Good morning heartache / If I can't sell it I'll keep sittin' on it / Tain't nobody's business if I do / St. Louis blues / Am I blue / I'm just a lucky so and so / I don't break dance / Come Sunday.
CD................................FCD 9662
Ace / Mar '94 / Pinnacle / Complete Record Co. Ltd.

### BROWN SUGAR.
Tracks: Sugar baby / Stop knocking / Old fashioned good time / I love my man / My old bed / Brown sugar / I want to sleep with you / What colour is blue / Lot more of me leaving / Life ain't no piece of cake.
- LP................................TOP 136
MC.................................KTOP 136
Topline / May '86 / Charly.

### BROWN, BLACK AND BEAUTIFUL.
Tracks: I want to sleep with you / What color is blue / Brown sugar / Lot's more of me leaving (less of me coming) / Ain't no piece of cake / Stop knocking / Old fashioned good time loving you / Sugar babe / My ol' bed / I love my man.
CD...............................SDECD 4023
LP................................SDE 4023
MC...............................SDEMC 4023
S.D.E.G. / Mar '90 / RTM / Pinnacle / ACD Trading Ltd.

### HITS, THE.
Tracks: 5-10-15 hours / Teardrops from my eyes / (Mama) he treats your daughter mean / Oh what a dream / Mambo baby / I'll wait for you / Daddy daddy / Wild wild young men / I wanna do more / So long / As long as I'm moving / It's love baby / I don't know / Lucky lips / I know / Mend your ways.
CD...............................OFF 86053
- LP..............................OFF 6053
Official / Charly / Cadillac / Jazz Music.

### I'LL WAIT FOR YOU.
Tracks: I'll wait for you / Standing on the corner / I gotta have you / Love has joined us together / I still love you / Mam oh mam / I want to be loved / New love / Look me up / I'll step aside / Mama, he treats your daughter mean / What I wouldn't give / I burned your letter / Honey boy / Sure 'nuff / Here he comes.
- LP................................OFF 6004
Official / '88.

### MISS RHYTHM (Greatest Hits & More).
Tracks: Not Advised.
CD...............................7567820612
Atlantic / Jul '93 / WEA.
CD...............................RSDCD 816
Sequel / Oct '94 / Total / BMG.

### ROCKIN' WITH RUTH.
Tracks: Teardrops from my eyes / Five, ten, fifteen hours / Daddy, daddy / Mama, he treats your daughter mean / Wild, wild young men / Love contest / Hello, little boy / Oh what a dream / Somebody touched me / Bye bye young men / I can see everybody's baby / As long as I'm moving / This little girl's gone rockin' / I can't hear a word you say / Papa daddy / Don't deceive me.
- LP................................CRB 1069
- MC...............................TCCRB 1069
Charly R&B / Mar '84.

### SUGAR BABE.
Tracks: Sugar babe / Stock knocking / Old fashioned good time / I love my man / Old bed / Brown sugar / I want to sleep with you / What colour is blue / You're gonna see a lot more of me / Leaving / Life ain't no piece of cake.
- LP...............................PTLS 1067
President / Jan '77.

### SUGAR BABE.
Tracks: Sugar babe / Stop knocking.
- 7"..................................PT 457
President / Oct '76.

■ DELETED

## SWEET BABY OF MINE.
**Tracks:** Love my baby / I'll come someday / It's all in the mind / Mend your ways / Ever since my baby's been gone / I want to do more / Am I making the same mistakes / Tears keep tumbling down / It's raining / R.B. blues / Without love / Rain is a bridgdown / Sweet baby of mine / My heart is breaking for you / I would if I could.
■ **LP** . . . . . . . . . . . . . . . . . . . . . . . . KIX 16
Route 66 (Sweden) / Aug '87.
■ **CD** . . . . . . . . . . . . . . . . . . . . . . . . RBD 16
RBD / Oct '92 / Jazz Music.

## TAKIN' CARE OF BUSINESS.
**Tracks:** Takin' care of business / 5-10-15 hours / I can see everybody's baby / On my way / God holds the power / Oh what a dream / Teardrops from my eyes / So long / Seven days.
■ **LP** . . . . . . . . . . . . . . . . . . . . . . . . RJ 202
Stockholm (Sweden) / Mar '84.
■ **CD** . . . . . . . . . . . . . . . . . . . . . . . .RBD 202
Mr.R&B (Sweden) / Dec '90 / Swift / C.M. Distribution / Wellard.

## Brown, Sharon

### I SPECIALISE IN LOVE.
**Tracks:** I specialise in love / I specialise in love (instrumental).
■ **7"** . . . . . . . . . . . . . . . . . . . . . . . . VS 494
■ **12"** . . . . . . . . . . . . . . . . . . . . . . VS 494-12
Virgin / Aug '85.
■ **CD Single** . . . . . . . . . . . . . . OILYCD 025
Deep Distraxion/Profile / Feb '94 / Vital Distribution.

### I SPECIALISE IN LOVE (OLD GOLD).
**Tracks:** I specialise in love / This beat is mine.
■ **12"** . . . . . . . . . . . . . . . . . . . . . . .OG 4100
Old Gold / Feb '89.

### LOVE DON'T HURT PEOPLE.
**Tracks:** Love don't hurt people / Unexpected.
■ **12"** . . . . . . . . . . . . . . . . . . . . . . VS 535-12
■ **7"** . . . . . . . . . . . . . . . . . . . . . . . .VS 535
Virgin / Aug '82.

## Brown, Sheree

### IT'S A PLEASURE.
**Tracks:** It's a pleasure / Straight ahead.
■ **7"** . . . . . . . . . . . . . . . . . . . . . . . .CL 232
Capitol / Jan '82.

### STRAIGHT AHEAD.
**Tracks:** You'll be dancing all night / Happiness flows / You are beautiful / Get down / I'm so bad / Passing thing / Never do you wrong / Everything you do / I wanna be by your side / It's a pleasure / Straight ahead.
■ **LP** . . . . . . . . . . . . . . . . . . . . . . EST 12153
Capitol / Apr '82.

## Brown, Shirley

Like hundreds of soul singers before her, Shirley Brown served her apprenticeship singing gospel music and had recorded two gospel albums for the Abet label before being discovered by Albert King. Signed by Stax's gospel label, Truth, her Al Jackson produced debut *Woman To Woman*(1975), was co-written by Homer Banks and sold over a million copies topping the US R&B charts. Following Stax's demise, Brown moved on to Arista, recording an eponymous album which included *I Need Somebody To Love Me*, *I'll Be Right There Lovin' You* and *A Mighty Good Feeling* which was released to great acclaim in 1977. She then all but disappeared from view until 1984 when *Intimate Storm* surfaced on the Sound Town label. Her profile was raised in the UK when the duet with Bobby Womack *Ain't Nothin' Like The Lovin' We Got* came out on Cool Tempo in 1989.

### AIN'T LIKE THE LOVE WE'VE GOT (Brown, Shirley & Bobby Womack).
**Tracks:** Ain't like the love we've got.
■ **7"** . . . . . . . . . . . . . . . . . . . . . . .COOL 197
■ **12"** . . . . . . . . . . . . . . . . . . . . . .COOLX 197
Cool Tempo / Nov '89.

### BLESSED IS THE WOMAN.
**Tracks:** Blessed is the woman / Low-down dirty lover.
■ **7"** . . . . . . . . . . . . . . . . . . . . . . .ARIST 102
Arista / Apr '77.

### BOYFRIEND.
**Tracks:** Boyfriend / Looking for the real thing.
■ **7"** . . . . . . . . . . . . . . . . . . . . . . . .BRW 31

### ■ **12"** . . . . . . . . . . . . . . . . . . . . . 12 BRW 31
4th & Broadway / Jul '85.

## FIRE AND ICE.
**Tracks:** Not Advised.
■ **LP** . . . . . . . . . . . . . . . . . . . . . .MALP 7451
**MC.** . . . . . . . . . . . . . . . . . . . . . . MALC 7451
Malaco / '89 / C.M. Distribution / Charly / Pinnacle.
**CD.** . . . . . . . . . . . . . . . . . . . . . .MALCD 7451
Malaco / Mar '93 / C.M. Distribution / Charly / Pinnacle.

## FOR THE REAL FEELING.
**Tracks:** When, where, what time / Crowding in on my mind / After a night like this / Dirty feelin' / Hang on Louie / Eyes can't see / Move me, move me / Love starved.
■ **LP** . . . . . . . . . . . . . . . . . . . . . . STX 3014
Stax / '79.
**CD.** . . . . . . . . . . . . . . . . . . . . . CDSXE 082
Stax / Nov '92 / Pinnacle.

## I AIN'T GONNA TELL NOBODY.
**Tracks:** I ain't gonna tell nobody / Love is built on a strong foundation.
■ **7"** . . . . . . . . . . . . . . . . . . . . . . CS 9025
Contempo (2) / Apr '75.

## INTIMATE STORM.
**Tracks:** Boyfriend / I don't play that / Looking for the real thing / This love / I'm up to no good / Love fever / This used to be your house / Leave the bridges standing.
■ **LP** . . . . . . . . . . . . . . . . . . . . . . BRLP 507
■ **MC.** . . . . . . . . . . . . . . . . . . . . . BRCA 507
4th & Broadway / Jun '85.

## JOY AND PAIN.
**Tracks:** Not Advised.
**CD.** . . . . . . . . . . . . . . . . . . . MALCD 7467
Ace / Jun '93 / Pinnacle / Complete Record Co. Ltd.

## LOVE FEVER.
**Tracks:** Love fever.
■ **12"** . . . . . . . . . . . . . . . . . . . . . 12 BRW 27
■ **7"** . . . . . . . . . . . . . . . . . . . . . . . BRW 27
4th & Broadway / Jun '85.

## SHIRLEY BROWN.
**Tracks:** Not Advised.
■ **LP** . . . . . . . . . . . . . . . . . . . .SPARTY 1017
Arista / '77.

## TIMELESS.
**Tracks:** Not Advised.
**CD.** . . . . . . . . . . . . . . . . . . . . MALCD 7459
Malaco / Mar '93 / C.M. Distribution / Charly / Pinnacle.

## WOMAN TO WOMAN.
**Tracks:** Woman to woman / Yes sir brother / It ain't no fun / As long as you love me / Stay with me baby / I've got to go on without you / It's worth a whipping / So glad to have you / Passion / I can't give you up / I need you tonight / Between you and me.
■ **LP** . . . . . . . . . . . . . . . . . . . . . STX 3005
Stax / Jun '78.
■ **LP** . . . . . . . . . . . . . . . . . . . .STAXL 5001
**MC.** . . . . . . . . . . . . . . . . . . . . STAXK 5001
Stax / Aug '81 / Pinnacle.
■ **LP** . . . . . . . . . . . . . . . . . . . . . SXE 002
Stax / Aug '87.
■ **LP** . . . . . . . . . . . . . . . . . . . . . . SX 002
Stax / Dec '88.
**CD.** . . . . . . . . . . . . . . . . . . . CDSXE 002
Stax / Nov '89 / Pinnacle.

## WOMAN TO WOMAN.
**Tracks:** Woman to woman.
■ **7"** . . . . . . . . . . . . . . . . . . . . STAX 2009
Stax / May '75.
■ **7"** . . . . . . . . . . . . . . . . . . . . STAX 1010
Stax / Mar '82.
■ **7"** . . . . . . . . . . . . . . . . . . . . . STAX 806
Stax / Jun '87.

## Brown, Veda

### SHORT STOPPING.
**Tracks:** Short stopping.
■ **7"** . . . . . . . . . . . . . . . . . . . . STAX 1007
Stax / Mar '82.
■ **7"** . . . . . . . . . . . . . . . . . . . . . STAX 812
Stax / Aug '87.

## Browne, Tom

### BEST OF TOM BROWNE, THE.
**Tracks:** Funkin' for Jamaica / Fungi mama / Mr. Business / Bye gones / Charisma / Thighs high (grip your hips and move) / Rockin' radio / Come for a ride / Brighter tomorrow / Secret fantasy.
■ **CD** . . . . . . . . . . . . . . . . . . . . . .260962

## ■ **MC**. . . . . . . . . . . . . . . . . . . . . . .410962
Arista / Mar '91.

## BROWNE SUGAR.
**Tracks:** Not Advised.
**CD.** . . . . . . . . . . . . . . . . . . . . . GRD 9517
GRP / Sep '88 / BMG / New Note.
■ **CD.** . . . . . . . . . . . . . . . . . . . . GRPD 9517
GRP / Aug '91.
■ **CD.** . . . . . . . . . . . . . . . . . . . GRP 95172
GRP / Sep '92.

## BYE GONES.
**Tracks:** Bye gones.
■ **12"** . . . . . . . . . . . . . . . . . . . ARIST 12462
■ **7"** . . . . . . . . . . . . . . . . . . . .ARIST 462
Arista / '82.

## FUNGI MAMA.
**Tracks:** Fungi mama / Funkin' for Jamaica / Come for a ride.
■ **7"** . . . . . . . . . . . . . . . . . . . .ARIST 450
■ **12"** . . . . . . . . . . . . . . . . . . ARIST 12450
Arista / Jan '82.

## FUNKIN' FOR JAMAICA.
**Tracks:** Funkin' for Jamaica / Her silent smile.
■ **12"** . . . . . . . . . . . . . . . . . . ARIST 12857
■ **7"** . . . . . . . . . . . . . . . . . . . .ARIST 357
Arista / '82.

## FUNKIN' FOR JAMAICA (1991 REMIX).
**Tracks:** Funkin' for Jamaica.
■ **12"** . . . . . . . . . . . . . . . . . . . . .614998
■ **7"** . . . . . . . . . . . . . . . . . . . . . .114998
Arista / Jan '92.

## FUNKIN' FOR JAMAICA (OLD GOLD).
**Tracks:** Funkin' for Jamaica / Rockin' radio.
■ **12"** . . . . . . . . . . . . . . . . . . . . .OG 4042
Old Gold / Jan '88.

## LOVE APPROACH.
**Tracks:** Funkin' for Jamaica / Her silent smile / Forever more / Dreams of lovin' you / Nocturne / Martha / Moon rise / Weak in the knees.
■ **LP** . . . . . . . . . . . . . . . . . . . . GRP 5008
Arista / Jul '80.

## MAGIC.
**Tracks:** Let's dance / Magic / I know / Midnight interlude / God bless the child / Night wind / Thighs high (grip your hips and move) / Making plans.
■ **LP** . . . . . . . . . . . . . . . . . . . . GRP 5503
Arista / '82.

## MAGIC.
**Tracks:** Magic / Midnight interlude.
■ **12"** . . . . . . . . . . . . . . . . . . . ARIST 12387
■ **7"** . . . . . . . . . . . . . . . . . . . .ARIST 387
Arista / Jan '81.

## MO'JAMAICA FUNK.
**Tracks:** Funkin' for Jamaica / Jam fo' reel / Everybody loves the sunshine / Milestones / That's what friends are for / Give me the night / Work song.
**CD.** . . . . . . . . . . . . . . . . . . . . . HIBD 8002
**LP.** . . . . . . . . . . . . . . . . . . . . . . HIB 8002
**MC.** . . . . . . . . . . . . . . . . . . . . .HIBC 8002
Hip Bop / Oct '94 / Conifer Records.

## NO LONGER.
**Tracks:** Not Advised.
**CD.** . . . . . . . . . . . . . . . . . . . . MJCD 1500
■ **LP.** . . . . . . . . . . . . . . . . . . . . MJ 1500
**MC.** . . . . . . . . . . . . . . . . . . . . MJC 1500
Malaco / '88 / C.M. Distribution / Charly / Pinnacle.
**CD.** . . . . . . . . . . . . . . . . . . . MALCD 1500
Malaco / Mar '93 / C.M. Distribution / Charly / Pinnacle.

## ROCKIN' RADIO.
**Tracks:** Rockin' radio / Never my love / Feel like makin' love / Cruisin' / Turn it up (come on y'all) / Angeline / Brighter tomorrow / Mr. Business.
■ **LP** . . . . . . . . . . . . . . . . . . . . . .205151
■ **MC** . . . . . . . . . . . . . . . . . . . . . .405151
Arista / Oct '83.

## ROCKIN' RADIO.
**Tracks:** Rockin' radio.
■ **7"** . . . . . . . . . . . . . . . . . . . .ARIST 545
Arista / Sep '83.

## THIGHS HIGH (GRIP YOUR HIPS AND MOVE).
**Tracks:** Thighs high (grip your hips and move).
■ **12"** . . . . . . . . . . . . . . . . . . . ARIST 12367
■ **7"** . . . . . . . . . . . . . . . . . . . .ARIST 367
Arista / Oct '80.

## TOMMY GUN.
**Tracks:** Not Advised.
■ **LP** . . . . . . . . . . . . . . . . . . . . . .206495

■ **DELETED**

■ MC. . . . . . . . . . . . . . . . . . . .406495
Arista / Oct '84.

## WHAT'S GOING ON.
**Tracks:** What's going on / Throw down.
■ 12" . . . . . . . . . . . . . . . . ARIST 12297
■ 7" . . . . . . . . . . . . . . . . .ARIST 297
Arista / Nov '79.

## YOURS TRULY.
**Tracks:** Fungii mama / Bygonnes / Charisma / Can't can't give it away / Lazy bird / Naima / Come for a ride / My latin sky / Message, A: pride and city.
■ LP . . . . . . . . . . . . . . . . . . GRP 5507
GRP / Dec '81.

# Brunson, Tyrone

## FRESH.
**Tracks:** Fresh / At the show / Head games / In love with you / Serve go go / Jet City / Don't wanna stop the lovin'.
■ LP . . . . . . . . . . . . . . . . . . EPC 25907
Epic / May '84.

## LOVE TRIANGLE.
**Tracks:** Love triangle / Tell me why / Free bee / Method / Lot of pop / Tender touch / Knucklehead syndrome / Space boy.
■ LP . . . . . . . . . . . . . . . . . MCF 3378
■ MC . . . . . . . . . . . . . . . . MCFC 3378
MCA / Jun '87.

## SMURF.
**Tracks:** Smurf / I need love.
■ 12" . . . . . . . . . . . . . . . EPCA 133024
■ 7" . . . . . . . . . . . . . . . . EPCA 3024
Epic / Dec '82.

## STICKY SITUATION.
**Tracks:** Sticky situation / I need love / Go for it / Don't you want it / Smurf / Hot line / New wave disco punk funk rock.
MC. . . . . . . . . . . . . . . . . . .40 25291
■ LP . . . . . . . . . . . . . . . . EPC 25291
Epic / Feb '83 / Sony.

# Bryant, Don

## COMIN' ON STRONG.
**Tracks:** Not Advised.
CD. . . . . . . . . . . . . . . . . HIUKCD 133
Demon / Aug '92 / Pinnacle / A.D.A. Distribution.

## COMING STRONG.
**Tracks:** Not Advised.
CD. . . . . . . . . . . . . . . . . HIUKCD 116
Demon / Jul '91 / Pinnacle / A.D.A. Distribution.

## DOING THE MUSTANG.
**Tracks:** Not Advised.
■ LP . . . . . . . . . . . . . . . .HIUKLP 420
Hi / Jun '88.

## PRECIOUS SOUL.
**Tracks:** She's looking good / Wonderful one / Funky Broadway / Can I change my mind / Soul man / Land of 1000 dances / Slip away / For your precious love / Expressway to your heart / Try me / When something is wrong with my baby / Cry baby.
■ LP . . . . . . . . . . . . . . . . . SHU 8409
London / Mar '70.

# Bryant, Leon

## FINDERS KEEPERS.
**Tracks:** Finders keepers / Your kind of lovin' / I'm gonna put a spell on you / Are you ready / You're my everything / Honey / I can see love loving you / Never.
■ LP . . . . . . . . . . . . . . . . . . DSR 5
De-Lite / Oct '84.

## JUST THE WAY YOU LIKE.
**Tracks:** Just the way you like / Something more.
■ 12" . . . . . . . . . . . . . . . . . DEX 3
■ 7" . . . . . . . . . . . . . . . . . .DE 3
De-Lite / May '81.

## LEON BRYANT.
**Tracks:** Mighty body / Come and get it / Just the way you like it / Something more / You can depend on / Can I / I like that rock and roll / I. promise.
■ LP . . . . . . . . . . . . . . . . . 6337174
De-Lite / Jul '81.

# Bryant, Sharon

## HERE I AM.
**Tracks:** Here I am / Body talk / Let go / Old friend / Falling / Foolish heart / In the night time / No more lonely nights.
■ CD. . . . . . . . . . . . . . . . 837 313-2

---

■ LP . . . . . . . . . . . . . . . . 837 313-1
■ MC. . . . . . . . . . . . . . . . 837 313-4
Polydor / Jul '89.

# Bryson, Peabo

Peabo Bryson has made his name with a series of duets with female vocalists; most famously Roberta Flack on *Tonight I Celebrate My Love* which reached No. 2 in the U.K. and No. 5 in the U.S. in 1983. This series of collaborations began with Natalie Cole in 1979: after a successful tour together, the pair moved into the studio and produced the album *We're The Best Of Friends*, which yielded the U.S. singles *Gimme Some Time* and *What You Won't Do For Love*. These joint ventures have overshadowed Bryson's solo career to the extent that he has only charted twice over here: the first time with Flack and more recently the title track from Disney's *Beauty And The Beast*, which reached No. 9 in 1992.

## ALL MY LOVE.
**Tracks:** Show and tell / All my love / Palm of your hand / When you're in love / One time for the lonely / Life goes on / True love / Meat to be / Like I need you.
CD. . . . . . . . . . . . . . . . . CDEST 2097
■ LP . . . . . . . . . . . . . . . . EST 2097
■ MC. . . . . . . . . . . . . . . . TCEST 2097
Capitol / May '89 / EMI.

## BORN TO LOVE (see under Flack, Roberta).

## CAN YOU STOP THE RAIN.
**Tracks:** Lost in the night / Can you stop the rain / Closer than close / Shower you with love / I can't imagine / I wish you love / You don't have to beg / I wanna be with you / I just had to fall / Soul provider / If it's really love.
■ MC. . . . . . . . . . . . . . . . . 4678574
■ CD. . . . . . . . . . . . . . . . . 4678572
■ LP . . . . . . . . . . . . . . . . . 4678571
Columbia / Jun '91 / Sony.

## CROSSWINDS.
**Tracks:** Crosswinds / I'm so into you / Smile / She's a woman / Point of view / Spread your wings / Don't touch me / Love is watching you.
■ LP . . . . . . . . . . . . . . . .EST 11875
Capitol / Feb '79.

## D.C. CAB.
**Tracks:** D.C. cab / Knock me off my feet.
■ 12" . . . . . . . . . . . . . . . .MCAT 872
■ 7" . . . . . . . . . . . . . . . . MCA 872
MCA / Mar '84.

## HEAVEN ABOVE ME (Bryson, Peabo & Roberta Flack).
**Tracks:** Heaven above me / Can we find love again.
■ 12" . . . . . . . . . . . . . . . . 12CL 310
■ 7" . . . . . . . . . . . . . . . . .CL 310
Capitol / Oct '83.

## IF YOU'RE EVER IN MY ARMS AGAIN.
**Tracks:** If you're ever in my arms again / There's no getting over you.
■ 12" . . . . . . . . . . . . . . . . E 9728T
■ 7" . . . . . . . . . . . . . . . . .E 9728
Elektra / Jun '84.

## LET THE FEELING FLOW.
**Tracks:** Let the feeling flow / Move your body.
■ 7" . . . . . . . . . . . . . . . . .CL 236
Capitol / Feb '82.

## LIVE - AND MORE (see under Flack, Roberta).

## POSITIVE.
**Tracks:** Come on over tonight / Without you / Hurt / I want to know / Tonight / Positive / When we need it bad / This time around / Still water.
■ LP . . . . . . . . . . . . . . . . . EKT 46
MC. . . . . . . . . . . . . . . . . .EKT 46C
■ CD. . . . . . . . . . . . . . . . . 9607532
Elektra / Apr '88 / WEA.

## QUIET STORM.
**Tracks:** Since I've been in love / Somebody in your life / Good combination / If you love me (let me know) / Higher you climb / Catch 22 / Only at night / After you.
■ LP . . . . . . . . . . . . . . . . . 9604841
MC. . . . . . . . . . . . . . . . . . 9604844
Elektra / Oct '86 / WEA.

---

## REACHING FOR THE SKY.
**Tracks:** Reaching for the sky / Have a good time.
■ 7" . . . . . . . . . . . . . . . .CL 15980
Capitol / Apr '78.

## REACHING FOR THE SKY.
**Tracks:** Reaching for the sky / Feel the fire / Fool already knows / Hold onto the world / Love from your heart / Love walked out on me / You haven't learned about love / Have a good time.
■ LP . . . . . . . . . . . . . . . .EST 11729
Capitol / Apr '78.

## SHOW AND TELL.
**Tracks:** Show and tell / Meat to be.
■ 12" . . . . . . . . . . . . . . . 12CL 544
■ 7" . . . . . . . . . . . . . . . .CL 544
Capitol / Sep '89.

## STRAIGHT FROM THE HEART.
**Tracks:** Slow dancing / If ever you're in my arms again / Straight from the heart / There's no getting over you / I get nervous / Learning the ways of love / Real deal / Love means forever.
CD. . . . . . . . . . . . . . . . . . 9603622
MC. . . . . . . . . . . . . . . . . . 9603624
■ LP . . . . . . . . . . . . . . . . . 9603621
Elektra / May '84 / WEA.

## TAKE NO PRISONERS.
**Tracks:** Take no prisoners / There ain't nothing out there / Let's apologise / Irresistible / Love always finds a way / Falling for you / I'm in love / Talk to me / She's over me.
CD. . . . . . . . . . . . . . . . . . 9602472
Elektra / '85 / WEA.
■ LP . . . . . . . . . . . . . . . . . EKT 7
■ MC. . . . . . . . . . . . . . . . . EKT 7C
Elektra / Jun '85.

## TAKE NO PRISONERS.
**Tracks:** Take no prisoners / Love means forever.
■ 12" . . . . . . . . . . . . . . . . EKR 14 T
■ 7" . . . . . . . . . . . . . . . . .EKR 14
Elektra / Jul '85.

## TONIGHT I CELEBRATE MY LOVE FOR YOU (see under Flack, Roberta).

## TURN THE HANDS OF TIME.
**Tracks:** I've been down / My life / Fool such as I / Man on a string / Turn the hands of time / Fiction / Why don't you make up your mind / Another love song / Piece of my heart / Dwellers of the city.
■ 12" . . . . . . . . . . . . . . . 12CL 302
■ 7" . . . . . . . . . . . . . . . .CL 302
Capitol / Sep '83.
■ 7" . . . . . . . . . . . . . . . .OG 9721
Old Gold / May '87.
■ LP . . . . . . . . . . . . . . . .EST 12138
Capitol / Apr '81.

## WITHOUT YOU (Bryson, Peabo & Regina Bell).
**Tracks:** Without you / If ever you're in my arms again (Theme for TVS's Santa Barbara) / Higher you climb (track on 12") / Again (track on 12").
■ 12" . . . . . . . . . . . . . . . .EKR 66T
■ 7" . . . . . . . . . . . . . . . . EKR 66
Elektra / Feb '88.

## YOU'RE LOOKING LIKE LOVE TO ME (Bryson, Peabo & Roberta Flack).
**Tracks:** You're looking like love to me / Let me be the one you need.
■ 7" . . . . . . . . . . . . . . . . .CL 320
Capitol / Jan '84.

# Buchanan, Courtney

## DON'T BELIEVE.
**Tracks:** Don't believe.
■ 12" . . . . . . . . . . . . . . . . CON 012
Conscious / Dec '92.

## HEAVEN.
**Tracks:** Heaven (Mixes).
12" . . . . . . . . . . . . . . . . . CON 17
Conscious / Aug '94 / Vital Distribution / Jetstar.

## R U CONSCIOUS (REMIX).
**Tracks:** R U Conscious (Remix) / R U Conscious (Album mix).
■ 12" . . . . . . . . . . . . . . . . CON 014
Conscious / Apr '93.
■ 12" . . . . . . . . . . . . . . . MCST 1792
■ CD Single . . . . . . . . . . . MCSTD 1792
■ MC Single . . . . . . . . . . . MCSC 1792
MCA / Jun '93.

■ DELETED

## Bullock, Janice

### DO YOU REALLY LOVE ME.
Tracks: Do you really love me.
- 12"............................WCST 206
- 7"............................WCS 206

Ichiban / Aug '87.

### DON'T START A FIRE.
Tracks: Don't start a fire / Do you really love me / Excited (about your love) / Turn on your radio / I'm ridin' high on your love / Right love - wrong man / We've got it right / If it turns you on.
- LP............................WIL 3003
- MC............................ZCWIL 3003

Ichiban / Aug '87 / A.D.A. Distribution / Pinnacle / ACD Trading Ltd. / Koch International / Direct Distribution.

### DON'T START A FIRE.
Tracks: Don't start a fire.
- 12"............................12 PO 3
- 7"............................87 207

Ichiban / Aug '87.

## Buoys

### GIVE UP YOUR GUNS.
Tracks: Give up your guns / Prince of thieves.
- 7"............................WN 20

Wand / Jul '71.

## Burch, Vernon

### AIN'T GONNA TELL NOBODY.
Tracks: Ain't gonna tell nobody.
- 7"............................UP 35838

United Artists / May '75.

## Burgess, Leroy

One of the original members of Black Ivory, whose Patrick Adams-produced *Don't Turn Around* was an R&B hit. Leaving to pursue a solo career in 1977, he became a writer/producer for the Salsoul label, working with a variety of artists including Inner Life. In 1983 he released the single *Heartbreaker* before joining Aleem for their New York club hit *Hooked On Your Love*. He continued to be a popular producer throughout the '80s and released a further solo single, *Running After You*, in 1991.

### SLAUGHTERHOUSE (Burgess, Leroy & Tyrone Williams).
Tracks: Slaughterhouse.
- 12"............................ZEROO 121

Zoo Experience / Aug '88.

## Burke, Keni

### ARTISTS SHOWCASE: KENI BURKE.
Tracks: Not Advised.
- LP............................MUSIC 9
- MC............................ZCMUS 9

Street Sounds / Nov '86 / BMG / Total.

### CHANGES.
Tracks: Shakin' / Hang tight / Can't get enough (do it all night) / Who do you love / Let somebody love you (On re-release only) / Changes / One minute more / Risin' to the top / All night / You're the best (On re-release only).
- LP............................PL 89551

RCA / '87.
- CD............................ND 90555
- LP............................NL 90555
- MC............................NK 90555

RCA / Jun '91.

### LET SOMEBODY LOVE YOU.
Tracks: Let somebody love you.
- 7"............................RCA 93

RCA / Jun '81.

### RISIN' TO THE TOP.
Tracks: Risin' to the top / Hang tight.
- 12"............................RCAT 252

RCA / Jun '82.

### RISIN' TO THE TOP.
Tracks: Risin' to the top.
- 12"............................PT 49104
- 7"............................PB 49103
- CD Single............................PD 49104
- MC Single............................PK 49103

RCA / Apr '92.

## RISIN' TO THE TOP (GIVE IT ALL YOU GOT).
Tracks: Rising to the top / Let somebody love you.
- 12"............................RCAT 354
- 7"............................RCA 354

RCA / '83.
- 7"............................PB 49613
- 12"............................PT 49614

RCA / Oct '87.

### RISIN' TO THE TOP (OLD GOLD).
Tracks: Risin' to the top / Let somebody love you.
- 12"............................OG 4097

Old Gold / Jan '89.

### SHAKIN'.
Tracks: Shakin' / Night riders.
- 12"............................RCAT 223
- 7"............................RCA 223

RCA / '82.

### WONDERFUL WORLD OF KENI BURKE.
Tracks: Risin' to the top / Hang tight / Gotta find a way back in your heart / Paintings of love / You are all mine / One minute more / Day / Let somebody love you / Never stop lovin' me / Something new like a sweet melody / It's the last time / Who do you love / All night / Keep on singing / Risin' to the top (remix).
- CD............................PD 90682
- LP............................PL 90682
- MC............................PK 90682

RCA / May '92.

### YOU'RE THE BEST.
Tracks: Let somebody love you / Gotta find my way back in your heart / Love is the answer / You're the best / Paintings of love / Night rides / Never stop loving me.
- LP............................RCALP 5059
- MC............................RCAK 5059

RCA / '81.

### YOU'RE THE BEST.
Tracks: You're the best / Gotta find my way back in your heart.
- 12"............................RCAT 126

RCA / Sep '81.

## Burke, Solomon

Amidst thriving church and undertaking businesses, Solomon Burke found time to cut several classics for Atlantic - although he scored few pop (rather than R&B) chart hits. *Just Out Of Reach* has been credited with kickstarting Atlantic bandwagon; accelerated by simultaneous success of Burke and Pickett's interpretations of *If You Need Me*. Ironically, Burke's best-known tune was his smallest hit; however, covers by Pickett, Rolling Stones and Blues Brothers immortalised *Everybody Needs Somebody to Love*. Quitting Atlantic for Bell in '68, Burke scored final hit with Creedence Clearwater Revival's *Proud Mary*, then spent '70s label-hopping from MGM and Dunhill to Chess. '79 found him on Infinity, for which he cut *Sidewalk, Fences & Walls*, a return-to-form produced by Jerry 'Swamp Dogg' Williams. He has since returned to church duties.

### BABY COME ON HOME.
Tracks: Baby come on home / I can't stop lovin' you.
- 7"............................AT 4073

Atlantic / Feb '66.

### BISHOP RIDES SOUTH, THE.
Tracks: Proud mary / These arms of mine / I'll be doggone / How big a fool (can a fool be) / Don't wait too long / Uptight good woman / That lucky old sun / I can't stop / Please send me someone to love / What am I living for / Generation of revelations / I'm gonna stay right here / God knows I love you / In the ghetto.
- LP............................CRB 1187
- MC............................TCCRB 1187

Charly R&B / May '88 / Charly.

### CAN'T STOP LOVIN' YOU NOW.
Tracks: Can't stop lovin' you now / Baby come on home.
- 7"............................ST 4073

Atlantic / Feb '66.

### CHANGE IS GONNA COME, A.
Tracks: Love buys love / Got to get myself some money / Let it be you and me / Love is all that matters / Don't tell me what a man won't do for a woman / Change is gonna come / Here we go again / It don't get no better than this / When a man loves a woman.
- CD............................CD 2053

Rounder / Dec '86 / Roots Records / C.M. Distribution / Topic Records / A.D.A. Distribution / Direct Distribution.
- LP............................ROUNDER 2053
- MC............................ROUNDERC 2053

Rounder / '88 / Roots Records / C.M. Distribution / Topic Records / A.D.A. Distribution / Direct Distribution.
- CD............................FIENDCD 196

Demon / Oct '90 / Pinnacle / A.D.A. Distribution.

### CRY TO ME.
Tracks: Be bop grandma / Just out of reach / Cry to me / Down in the valley / I'm hanging up my heart for you / Stupidity / Can't nobody love you / If you need me / Won't you give him one more chance) / You're good for me / Goodbye baby (baby goodbye) / Everybody needs somebody to love / Yes I do / Price / Got to get you off my mind / Maggie's farm.
- LP............................CRB 1075
- MC............................TCCRB 1075

Charly R&B / '84.

### EVERYBODY NEEDS SOMEBODY TO LOVE (Burke, Solomon & Thomas, Rufus).
Tracks: Everybody needs somebody to love / If you need me / Walking the dog / Jump Jack.
- 7"............................ATM9

Atlantic / Apr '80.

### HOME IN YOUR HEART (Best of Soloman Burke).
Tracks: Not Advised.
- CD............................8122702842

WEA / Jul '93 / WEA.

### HOMELAND.
Tracks: Not Advised.
- CD............................FIENDCD 737

Demon / Aug '93 / Pinnacle / A.D.A. Distribution.

### I FEEL A SIN COMING ON.
Tracks: I feel a sin coming on / Mountain of pride.
- 7"............................584005

Atlantic / May '66.

### I WISH I KNEW.
Tracks: I wish I knew / Get out of my life / Meet me in church / What'd I say / Save it / Why why why / Shame on me / Tell me goodbye / By the time I get to Phoenix / Since I met you.
- LP............................588 117

Atlantic / Nov '68.

### INTO MY LIFE YOU CAME.
Tracks: Not Advised.
- LP............................SL 14679

Savoy / Apr '90 / Jazz Music / Wellard / Savoy Records / Conifer Records.

### KEEP LOOKIN'.
Tracks: Keep lookin' / Suddenly.
- 7"............................584026

Atlantic / Jun '66.

### KING OF ROCK 'N' SOUL FROM THE HEART.
Tracks: Boo hoo boo / Hold on I'm coming / Sweeter than sweetness / Sidewalks / Fences and walls / Let the love flow / More / Lucky / Please come back home to me.
- LP............................CRB 1024

Charly R&B / '81.

### KING OF SOUL.
Tracks: Boo hoo boo / Hold on I'm coming / Sweeter than sweetness / Sidewalks, fences and walls / Let the love flow / More / Lucky / Please come back home to me.
- CD............................CPCD 8014

Charly / Feb '94 / Charly.

### KING SOLOMON.
Tracks: It's been a change / Take me / Time is a thief / Keep a light in the window / Baby come on home / Detroit City / Someone is watching / Party people / When she touches me / Woman how do you make love / Just a matter of time / Presents for Christmas.
- LP............................587 105

Atlantic / Apr '68.

### LORD I NEED A MIRACLE RIGHT NOW.
Tracks: Not Advised.
- LP............................SL 14660

Savoy / Apr '90 / Jazz Music / Wellard / Savoy Records / Conifer Records.

### LOVE TRAP.
Tracks: Love trap / Do you believe in the hereafter / Every breath you take / Daddy love bear / Isis / Nothing but the truth / Only God knows / Drive / Sweet spirit.
- CD............................IVCD 21336

■ **LP** . . . . . . . . . . . . . . . . . . . .IV 21336
**MC.** . . . . . . . . . . . . . . . . .IVMC 21336
Polygram T.V. / Jul '87 / PolyGram.

## MUSIC TO MAKE LOVE BY.
**Tracks:** Music to make love by (part 1) / Let me wrap my arms around you / Come rain or come shine / You and your baby blues / All the way / Thanks,I needed that / Everlasting love / Midnight and you / Music to make love by (part 2).
■ **LP** . . . . . . . . . . . . . . . . . . GCH 8098
Chess (Charly).

## ONLY LOVE.
**Tracks:** Only love / Little girl that loves me.
■ **7"** . . . . . . . . . . . . . . . . . . . . AT 4061
Atlantic / Dec '65.

## PROUD MARY.
**Tracks:** Proud Mary / These arms of mine / I'll be doggone / How big a fool / Don't wait too long / That lucky old sun / Uptight good woman / I can't stop / Please send me someone to love / What am I living for.
■ **LP** . . . . . . . . . . . . . . . . . . . SBLL 118
Bell / Sep '69.

## REST OF SOLOMON BURKE, THE.
**Tracks:** Not Advised.
■ **LP** . . . . . . . . . . . . . . . . . . . SD 8109
Atlantic / '85.

## SILENT NIGHT: A CHRISTMAS PRAYER.
**Tracks:** Not Advised.
**LP** . . . . . . . . . . . . . . . . . . SCS 0002
Savoy / Apr '90 / Jazz Music / Wellard / Savoy Records / Conifer Records.

## SOMEONE IS WATCHING.
**Tracks:** Someone is watching / Dance, dance, dance.
■ **7"** . . . . . . . . . . . . . . . . . . . AT 4044
Atlantic / Sep '65.

## SOUL ALIVE.
**Tracks:** Everybody needs somebody to love / I almost lost my mind / Just out of reach / If you need me / Tonight's the night / You're good for me / What am I living for / Monologue / Take me (just as I am) / Down in the valley / Proud Mary / Tonight's the night (reprise) / Beautiful brown eyes / Just a matter of time / Hold what you've got / He'll have to go / Cry to me / Gotta get you off my mind / Meet me in the church / Price / Words / Send me some lovin' / Having a party / Amen.
■ **Double LP** . . . . . . . . . . ROUNDER 2042/3
Rounder / '84.
■ **Double LP** . . . . . . . . . . . . DFIEND 38
Demon / '85.
**CD** . . . . . . . . . . . . . . . . . . .CD11521
Rounder / '88 / Roots Records / C.M. Distribution / Topic Records / A.D.A. Distribution / Direct Distribution.
**CD** . . . . . . . . . . . . . . . . . FIENDCD 38
Demon / Aug '90 / Pinnacle / A.D.A. Distribution.

## SOUL OF THE BLUES.
**Tracks:** Not Advised.
**CD** . . . . . . . . . . . . . . . . . BTCD 1095
Black Top (USA) / Jan '94 / C.M. Distribution Distribution / Hot Shot / Topic Records.

## TAKE ME (JUST AS I AM).
**Tracks:** Take me (just as I am) / I stayed away too long.
■ **7"** . . . . . . . . . . . . . . . . . .584122
Atlantic / Jul '67.

## TAKE ME SHAKE ME.
**Tracks:** Not Advised.
**LP** . . . . . . . . . . . . . . . . . . . SL 14717
Savoy / Apr '90 / Jazz Music / Wellard / Savoy Records / Conifer Records.

## THIS IS HIS SONG.
**Tracks:** Not Advised.
**LP** . . . . . . . . . . . . . . . . . . . SL 14738
Savoy / Apr '90 / Jazz Music / Wellard / Savoy Records / Conifer Records.

## YOU CAN RUN BUT YOU CAN'T HIDE.
**Tracks:** To thee / Why do that to me / This is it / My heart is a chapel / Picture of you / You can run but you can't hide / Friendship ring / I'm not afraid / Don't cry / Christmas presents / I'm in love / Leave my kitten alone / No man walks alone / I'm all alone / I need you tonight / Walking in a dream / You are my one love / For you and you alone.
■ **LP** . . . . . . . . . . . . . . . . . . . RB 108
Mr.R&B (Sweden) / Aug '87.
**CD** . . . . . . . . . . . . . . . . . .RBD 108
Mr.R&B (Sweden) / Apr '91 / Swift / C.M. Distribution / Wellard.

## YOU SEND ME.
**Tracks:** You send me.
■ **12"** . . . . . . . . . . . . . . . . PER 12 9606
Perfect / May '87.

# Burns, Jimmy

## I REALLY LOVE YOU.
**Tracks:** I really love you / I love you girl.
■ **7"** . . . . . . . . . . . . . . . . . .GRP 118
Grapevine (Northern Soul) / May '79.

# Burrage, Harold

## SHE KNOCKS ME OUT (1956-58).
**Tracks:** Not Advised.
■ **LP** . . . . . . . . . . . . . . . . . . FLY 579
Flyright / Jun '81.

# Burrell

## BURRELL.
**Tracks:** Trust in the music / I'll wait for you (take your time) / (On 7" only) / I really like / Gonna make you dance / Dominate me / Sunshine / Let me love you tonight / No greater love / Calling / One and only lady.
■ **LP** . . . . . . . . . . . . . . . . . . DIX 76
■ **MC** . . . . . . . . . . . . . . . . . CDIX 76
■ **CD** . . . . . . . . . . . . . . . . . DIXCD 76
10 / Aug '88.

## I REALLY LIKE.
**Tracks:** I really like (On 7" only) / I really like (LP version) (NOT on TENX 243) / Yes (ON TENX only) / I really like (12" dub) (On 12" only) / I really like (remix) (On TENR 243 only).
■ **12"** . . . . . . . . . . . . . . . . . TENR 243
■ **7"** . . . . . . . . . . . . . . . . . TEN 243
■ **12"** . . . . . . . . . . . . . . . . . TENX 243
10 / Oct '88.

## I'LL WAIT FOR YOU (TAKE YOUR TIME).
**Tracks:** Waiting / I'll wait for you (take your time) (dance mix) (On 12" only) / I'll wait for you (take your time)(acappella) (On 12" only) / I'll dub for you (take your time) (On 12" only) / I'll wait for you (take your time) (On 7" only).
■ **12"** . . . . . . . . . . . . . . . . . TENX 218
■ **7"** . . . . . . . . . . . . . . . . . TEN 218
10 / May '88.

## PUT YOUR TRUST IN THE MUSIC.
**Tracks:** Put your trust in the music / Dominate me / Put your trust in the music (version) (12" only).
■ **CD Single** . . . . . . . . . . . . TENCD 264
■ **12"** . . . . . . . . . . . . . . . . TENR 264
■ **12"** . . . . . . . . . . . . . . . . TENX 264
■ **7"** . . . . . . . . . . . . . . . . . TEN 264
10 / Feb '89.

# Burris, Warren

## WARREN BURRIS.
**Tracks:** Get up off your love / I want your love / Slow down / Dance / Secret lover / I've got it / Darling stay with me / Change my mind / You got the love / Don't let you know.
■ **CD** . . . . . . . . . . . . . . . . . TLCD 518
■ **LP** . . . . . . . . . . . . . . . . . TRPL 121
Timeless (Soul) / Jan '90.

# Burton, Jenny

## BAD HABITS.
**Tracks:** Bad habits / Let's get back to love.
■ **12"** . . . . . . . . . . . . . . . . A 9583 T
■ **7"** . . . . . . . . . . . . . . . . .A 9583
Atlantic / Jun '85.

## DO YOU WANT IT BAD ENUFF.
**Tracks:** Call me anytime / Do you want it bad enuff.
■ **12"** . . . . . . . . . . . . . . . . A 9343 T
■ **7"** . . . . . . . . . . . . . . . . .A 9343
Atlantic / Jan '87.

## JENNY BURTON.
**Tracks:** Bad habits / Dancing for my life / Let's get back to love / Love runs deeper than pride / Why can't I touch you / Load it up / Nobody can tell me (He don't love me) / Once in a lifetime love.
■ **MC** . . . . . . . . . . . . . . . . . 781 238-4
Atlantic / Apr '85.

## REMEMBER WHAT YOU LIKE.
**Tracks:** Remember what you like.
■ **12"** . . . . . . . . . . . . . . . . A 6959 T
■ **7"** . . . . . . . . . . . . . . . . .A 6959
Atlantic / Apr '84.

## SOUVENIRS.
**Tracks:** Do you want it bad enuff / Anticipation / Love me mechanically / Don't it feel good / Souvenirs / Can't forget the love / Until you come back to me / River.
■ **LP** . . . . . . . . . . . . . . . . K 781 690-1
■ **MC** . . . . . . . . . . . . . . . . K 781 690-4
Atlantic / Feb '87.

## STRANGERS IN A STRANGE WORLD
(Burton, Jenny & Patrick Jude).
**Tracks:** Strangers in a strange world.
■ **7"** . . . . . . . . . . . . . . . . . .A 9660
Atlantic / Jul '84.

# Butler, Billy

## RIGHT TRACK, THE.
**Tracks:** Right track.
■ **12"** . . . . . . . . . . . . . . . . SKM 09(12)
■ **7"** . . . . . . . . . . . . . . . . . SKM 09
Skratch (1) / Mar '85.

## RIGHT TRACK, THE (Butler, Billy & The Enchanters).
**Tracks:** Not Advised.
■ **LP** . . . . . . . . . . . . . . . . . ED 147
Edsel / Sep '85.

# Butler, Jerry

Butler's initial releases on the Vee Jay label after leaving the Impressions were not greatly successful and it was not until he reunited with Curtis Mayfield that he returned to the charts. 1960's *He Will Break Your Heart* reached No. 1 on the U.S. R&B chart and further collaborative success followed. While Mayfield pursued success with the Impressions, Butler achieved further success with *Moon River* in 1961 and *Let It Be Me* in 1964. He moved to Mercury in 1966 where he was nicknamed 'The Ice Man'; hence Gamble & Huff-produced *Ice Man Cometh* album, from which *Only The Strong Survive* reached U.S. Top Five. Duets followed with Gene Chandler and 1971's million selling *Ain't Understanding Mellow* with Brenda Lee Eager. He has since been signed to Motown and Philidelphia International and along with running his own labels also created the Butler Writers Workshop which has helped young artists including Chuck Jackson and Natalie Cole. In 1993, he contributed *Choice Of Colours* to Curtis Mayfield tribute album *People Get Ready.*

## HE WILL BREAK YOUR HEART.
**Tracks:** He will break your heart.
■ **7"** . . . . . . . . . . . . . . . . . .CTD 114
Charly / Jul '80.

## I DIG YOU BABY.
**Tracks:** I dig you baby / Some kind of magic.
■ **7"** . . . . . . . . . . . . . . . . . MF 964
Mercury / Feb '67.

## I STAND ACCUSED.
**Tracks:** I stand accused / I don't want to hear any more.
■ **7"** . . . . . . . . . . . . . . . . . W 14003
Sue / Mar '66.

## I WANNA DO IT TO YOU.
**Tracks:** I wanna do it to you / Let's go get out of town.
■ **7"** . . . . . . . . . . . . . . . . .TMG 1097
Motown / Jun '78.

## ICE MAN COMETH, THE.
**Tracks:** Not Advised.
■ **LP** . . . . . . . . . . . . . . . . . SMCL 20154
Mercury / '69.

## IT'S A LIFETIME THING (see under Houston, Thelma).

## JERRY & BETTY (see under Everett, Betty).

## MR. DREAM MERCHANT.
**Tracks:** Mr. dream merchant / Mr. D.J. / Alfie / Lost / Beside you / Yesterday / 100lbs of clay / I come to you (and 3 others).
■ **LP** . . . . . . . . . . . . . . . . . SMCL 20118
Mercury / Nov '68.

## MR. DREAM MERCHANT.
**Tracks:** Mr. Dream merchant / 'Cause I love you so.
■ **7"** . . . . . . . . . . . . . . . . . MF 1005
Mercury / Oct '67.

■ DELETED

## NOTHING SAYS I LOVE YOU LIKE I LOVE YOU.
Tracks: Cooling out / Let's make love / Sad eyes / Mighty good people / I'm glad to be back / Nothing says I love you like I love you / Dream world / Are you lonely tonight.
■ LP . . . . . . . . . . . . . . . . . . . . PIR 83180
Philadelphia Int. / Feb '79.

## ONLY THE STRONG SURVIVE.
Tracks: Send a telegram (western union man) / Only the strong survive / Lost / Don't let love hang you up / Got to see if I can get mommy (to come back home) / Just because I really love you / I could write a book / Whats the use of breaking up / Since I lost you baby / Been a long time / Moody woman / Brand new me / Can't forget about you baby / Are you happy / Go away (find yourself) / Never give up you.
■ LP . . . . . . . . . . . . . . . . . . . . JABB 6
MC. . . . . . . . . . . . . . . . . . . . . JABBC 6
Club / May '85 / PolyGram.

## SHORTY'S GOT TO.. (Butler, Jerry & The Impressions).
Tracks: Shorty's got to..
■ 7" . . . . . . . . . . . . . . . . . . . . JSP 4501
JSP / '88.

## SOUL GOES ON.
Tracks: Never give you up / Chain gang / Sittin' on the dock of the bay / Respect / You send me / Ain't that good news / Yes, my goodness, yes / These arms of mine / Change is gonna come / Guess who / Goodnight my love / I've been loving you too long.
■ LP . . . . . . . . . . . . . . . . . . . . SMCL 20144
Mercury / May '69.

## SOUL WORKSHOP - JERRY BUTLER.
Tracks: I stand accused / For your previous love / Sweet was the wine / He will break your heart / Find another girl / I'm telling you / Aware of love / Moon river / I'm the one who loves you / Make it easy on yourself / You can run (but you can't hide) / Whatever you want / Message to Martha / Where's the girl / Need to belong / Giving up on love / I've been trying / I don't want to hear it anymore / I can't stand to see you cry / Nobody needs your love / Just for you / For your precious love.
■ CD . . . . . . . . . . . . . . . . . . . . CDCHARLY 54
Charly / Jan '86.

## SPICE OF LIFE.
Tracks: I only have eyes for you / Baby I'm a-want you / Stop steppin' on my dreams / That's the way it was / So far away / One night affair / Close to you / Masquerade is over/Since I fell for you / I need you / All kinds of people.
■ LP . . . . . . . . . . . . . . . . . . . . 6338102
Mercury / '72.

## THELMA & JERRY (see under Houston, Thelma).

## TIME & FAITH.
Tracks: Not Advised.
CD. . . . . . . . . . . . . . . . . . . . . ICH 1151CD
MC. . . . . . . . . . . . . . . . . . . . . ICH 1151MC
Ichiban / Feb '94 / A.D.A. Distribution / Pinnacle / ACD Trading Ltd. / Koch International / Direct Distribution.

## TWO TO ONE (see under Houston, Thelma).

## WHATEVER YOU WANT.
Tracks: Rainbow Valley / Lonely soldier / Thanks to you / When trouble calls / Aware of love / Isle of sirens / It's too late / Moon River / Woman with soul / Let it be whatever it is / I almost lost my mind / Good times / Give it up / Believe in me / Just for you / For your precious love.
■ LP . . . . . . . . . . . . . . . . . . . . CRB 1118
Charly R&B / Mar '86.
CD. . . . . . . . . . . . . . . . . . . . . CDSGP 083
MC. . . . . . . . . . . . . . . . . . . . . CASSGP 083
Prestige / Sep '93 / Total / BMG.

## Butler, Jonathan

Moving to London from South Africa in 1985, Butler signed to Jive Records, run by fellow countrymen, Chris Calder and Ralph Simon. The following year he released his debut album *Introducing Jonathan Butler*, and soon found himself in the charts on Ruby Turner's remake of *If You're Ready (Come Go With Me)*. His second album, produced by Barry Eastmond, created great interest in the British soul scene and returned him to the charts when *Lies* climbed to [8]X18. Further albums followed and in 1988 he released *More Than Friends* which included

the Vanessa Bell Armstrong duet *True Love Never Fails*. His songs have been recorded by numerous soul artists including George Benson, Millie Jackson, Al Jarreau and Billy Ocean. Close of 1994 sees the release of latest LP *Head To Head*.

## BABY PLEASE DON'T TAKE IT.
Tracks: Baby please don't take it / Haunted by your love / Gentle love (Extra track on 12" only).
■ 12" . . . . . . . . . . . . . . . . . . . JIVET 120
■ 7" . . . . . . . . . . . . . . . . . . . . JIVE 120
Jive / May '86.

## BEST OF JONATHAN BUTLER, THE.
Tracks: Not Advised.
CD. . . . . . . . . . . . . . . . . . . . . CHIP 133
MC. . . . . . . . . . . . . . . . . . . . . HIPC 133
Jive / Mar '93 / BMG.

## HEAL OUR LAND.
Tracks: Not Advised.
■ CD . . . . . . . . . . . . . . . . . . . CHIP 102
■ LP . . . . . . . . . . . . . . . . . . . . HIP 102
■ MC . . . . . . . . . . . . . . . . . . . HIPC 102
Jive / Aug '90.

## HEAL OUR LAND.
Tracks: Heal our land.
■ 12" . . . . . . . . . . . . . . . . . . . JIVET 258
■ 7" . . . . . . . . . . . . . . . . . . . . JIVE 258
■ CD Single . . . . . . . . . . . . . . . . JIVECD 258
Jive / Jul '90.

## HOLDING ON.
Tracks: Holding on / Seventh Avenue South.
■ 12" . . . . . . . . . . . . . . . . . . . JIVET 157
Jive / Oct '87.
■ 7" . . . . . . . . . . . . . . . . . . . . JIVE 157
Jive / '88.

## INTRODUCING JONATHAN BUTLER.
Tracks: Not Advised.
■ LP . . . . . . . . . . . . . . . . . . . . HIP 31
■ CD . . . . . . . . . . . . . . . . . . . CHIP 31
■ MC . . . . . . . . . . . . . . . . . . . HIPC 31
Jive / Mar '86.

## JONATHAN BUTLER.
Tracks: Not Advised.
■ LP . . . . . . . . . . . . . . . . . . . . HIP 46
■ MC . . . . . . . . . . . . . . . . . . . HIPC 46
Jive / Oct '87.

## LIES.
Tracks: Lies / Haunted by your love.
■ 12" . . . . . . . . . . . . . . . . . . . JIVET 141
■ 7" . . . . . . . . . . . . . . . . . . . . JIVE 141
■ CD Single . . . . . . . . . . . . . . . . JIVECD 141
Jive / Jul '87.

## LIES (OLD GOLD) (see under Turner, Ruby).

## MORE THAN FRIENDS.
Tracks: There's one born every minute / Breaking away / More than friends / Take me home / True love never fails / She's a teaser / Sarah Sarah / She's hot / It's so hard to let you go / Sekona.
■ LP . . . . . . . . . . . . . . . . . . . . HIP 70
■ CD . . . . . . . . . . . . . . . . . . . CHIP 70
■ MC . . . . . . . . . . . . . . . . . . . HIPC 70
Jive / Oct '88.

## OVERFLOWING.
Tracks: Overflowing / Lies.
■ 12" . . . . . . . . . . . . . . . . . . . JIVET 172
■ 7" . . . . . . . . . . . . . . . . . . . . JIVE 172
■ CD Single . . . . . . . . . . . . . . . . JIVECD 172
Jive / Apr '88.

## SARAH SARAH.
Tracks: Sarah Sarah.
■ 12" . . . . . . . . . . . . . . . . . . . JIVET 227
■ CD Single . . . . . . . . . . . . . . . . JIVECD 227
Jive / Nov '89.

## TAKE GOOD CARE OF ME.
Tracks: Take good care of me / Song for John / Thinking of you (Extra track available on 12" only).
■ CD Single . . . . . . . . . . . . . . . . JIVECD 159
■ 12" . . . . . . . . . . . . . . . . . . . JIVET 159
■ 7" . . . . . . . . . . . . . . . . . . . . JIVE 159
Jive / Jan '88.

## THERE'S ONE BORN EVERY MINUTE.
Tracks: There's one born every minute.
■ 12" . . . . . . . . . . . . . . . . . . . JIVET 187
■ 12" Remix . . . . . . . . . . . . . . . . JIVER 187
■ 7" . . . . . . . . . . . . . . . . . . . . JIVE 187
■ CD Single . . . . . . . . . . . . . . . . JIVECD 187
Jive / Oct '88.

## TRUE LOVE NEVER FAILS (Butler, Jonathan & Vanessa Bell Armstrong).
Tracks: True love never fails / Lies / Take me home / Love songs (On 12" only) / Candlelight and you (On 12" only).
■ 7" . . . . . . . . . . . . . . . . . . . . JIVE 196
■ 12" . . . . . . . . . . . . . . . . . . . JIVET 196
Jive / Dec '88.
■ CD Single . . . . . . . . . . . . . . . . JIVECD 196
Jive / Dec '89.

## Buzz

## MARINETTI.
Tracks: Marinetti.
■ 12" . . . . . . . . . . . . . . . . . . . 12 DAN 002
Danceteria / May '88.

## SEXE.
Tracks: Sexe.
■ 12" . . . . . . . . . . . . . . . . . . . 12 DAN 008
Danceteria / May '88.

## By All Means

## BEYOND THE DREAM.
Tracks: Not Advised.
■ LP . . . . . . . . . . . . . . . . . . . . BRLP 542
MC. . . . . . . . . . . . . . . . . . . . . BRCA 542
■ CD . . . . . . . . . . . . . . . . . . . BRCD 542
4th & Broadway / Nov '89 / PolyGram.

## BY ALL MEANS.
Tracks: I surrender to your love / I'm the one who loves you / You decided to go / I believe in you / I want to thank you / Let's get started now / Slow jam (can I have this dance with you) / Somebody save me / Does it feel good to you / We're into this groove.
CD. . . . . . . . . . . . . . . . . . . . . BRCD 520
■ LP . . . . . . . . . . . . . . . . . . . . BRLP 520
■ MC . . . . . . . . . . . . . . . . . . . BRCA 520
4th & Broadway / May '88 / PolyGram.
MC. . . . . . . . . . . . . . . . . . . . . ICM 2018
MC. . . . . . . . . . . . . . . . . . . . . 842 573 4
Island / '90 / PolyGram.

## I SURRENDER TO YOUR LOVE.
Tracks: Surrender to your love / We're into this groove / Slow Jam.
■ 12" . . . . . . . . . . . . . . . . . . . 12 BRW 102
■ 7" . . . . . . . . . . . . . . . . . . . . BRW 102
■ CD Single . . . . . . . . . . . . . . . . BRCD 102
4th & Broadway / May '88.

## IT'S REAL.
Tracks: Not Advised.
CD. . . . . . . . . . . . . . . . . . . . . .530077-2
Motown / Feb '93 / PolyGram.

## LET'S GET IT ON.
Tracks: Let's get it on.
■ 12" . . . . . . . . . . . . . . . . . . . 12 BRW 154
■ 7" . . . . . . . . . . . . . . . . . . . . BRW 154
■ CD Single . . . . . . . . . . . . . . . . BRCD 154
4th & Broadway / Nov '89.

## SOMEBODY SAVE ME.
Tracks: Somebody save me.
■ 12" . . . . . . . . . . . . . . . . . . . 12 BRX 114
■ 12" . . . . . . . . . . . . . . . . . . . 12 BRW 114
■ 7" . . . . . . . . . . . . . . . . . . . . BRW 114
■ CD Single . . . . . . . . . . . . . . . . BRCD 114
4th & Broadway / Sep '88.

## Bynum, James

## TIME PASSES BY.
Tracks: Time passes by.
■ 7" . . . . . . . . . . . . . . . . . . . . GRP 117
Grapevine (Northern Soul) / Apr '79.

## Byrd, Bobby

Ex-JB player with axe to grind. Byrd first teamed with James Brown in gospel trio Three Swanees, then Flames in early '50s. Latter evolved over next decade into James Brown & the Famous Flames, for whom Byrd allegedly co-wrote such classics as *Sex Machine*. In '88, Byrd took JB's All Stars - including Fred Wesley, Maceo Parker and Lyn Collins - on tour, dubbing resultant live LP *Finally Getting Paid*. In similar vein, Byrd sued Eric B & Rakim for appropriating his early '70s classic *I Know You Got Soul* as their own.

## FINALLY GETTING PAID.
Tracks: Not Advised.
CD. . . . . . . . . . . . . . . . . . . . . RAP CD 3

LP . . . . . . . . . . . . . . . . . . . . . . RAP LP 3
Rhythm Attack (Germany) / Apr '90 / Charly.

## HEADQUARTERS, AUGUST GA.
**Tracks:** Headquarters, August Ga. (Pts 1 & 2).
■ 7" . . . . . . . . . . . . . . . . . . . . . SEV 1005
Seville / Jul '75.

## I KNOW YOU GOT SOUL.
**Tracks:** Hot pants..I'm coming, coming I'm coming / I know you got soul.
■ 7" . . . . . . . . . . . . . . . . . . . . . . . . URB 8
■ 12" . . . . . . . . . . . . . . . . . . . . . . URBX 8
Urban / Aug '87.

## I KNOW YOU GOT SOUL.
**Tracks:** I know you got soul / If you don't work, you can't eat.
■ 7" . . . . . . . . . . . . . . . . . . . . . . .2027 033
Mojo / Jul '71.

## I NEED YOUR HELP.
**Tracks:** I need your help.
■ 7" . . . . . . . . . . . . . . . . . . . . . . .2001 118
Mojo / Mar '71.

## LIVE.
**Tracks:** I need help / It's I who love you / Funky soul / I found out / You've got to change your mind / You got to have a job / I'm not to blame / I'll lose my mind / My concerto / Hang ups we don't need / You gave my heart a song to sing.
■ LP . . . . . . . . . . . . . . . . . . . . . . 2918002
Mojo / Mar '72.

## WHAT GOES AROUND COMES AROUND (Byrd, Bobby/Maceo Parker/Fred Wesley).
**Tracks:** Not Advised.
LP . . . . . . . . . . . . . . . . . . . . . . . . RAPS 3
Rhythm Attack (Germany) / Apr '90 / Charly.

## Byrd, Donald

Donald Byrd was born in 1932 in Detroit. The trumpeter came to fame with Art Blakey and Horace Silver's hard bop bands during the 1950s, and recorded extensively for the Blue Note, Savoy and Prestige labels. He also worked with John Coltrane, Jackie McLean and Sonny Rollins. Byrd moved towards a more funky sound and launched the Blackbyrds in 1973 - consisting of students who he was lecturing at the Howard University. Their aim was to experiment with Byrd's musical ideas, as a way of complementing and enhancing their studies. In 1973, Byrd recorded the *Black Byrd* album: a huge seller whose single *Walking In Rhythm* was among the first jazz-funk hits; setting the trend for their other releases. Success continued with the release of *Street Lady*, which further helped lay the foundation of contemporary dance. Consequently, Byrd's work has experienced a great resurgence in popularity during the 1990s - his work is the most sampled of all the Blue Note artists. Byrd also guested on Guru's *Jazzmatazz* album and tour in 1993, a project that took the jazz-rap genre to new heights.

### 125TH STREET NYC.
**Tracks:** Pretty baby / Gold the moon, white the sun / Giving it up / Marilyn / People suppose to be free / Veronica / Morning / I love you.
CD . . . . . . . . . . . . . . . . . . . . . . . . 71019
Discovery (USA) / Nov '94 / New Note.

### AND 125TH STREET N Y C.
**Tracks:** Pretty baby / Gold the moon, white the sun / Giving it up / Marilyn / People suppose to be free / Veronica / Morning, I love you.
■ LP . . . . . . . . . . . . . . . . . . . . . K 52199
Elektra / '88.

### AT THE HALF NOTE CAFE VOL. 1.
**Tracks:** My girl Shirl / Soulful kiddy / Portrait of Jennie / Cecile / Pure D funk (theme) / Child's play / Chant.
■ CD . . . . . . . . . . . . . . . . . . . . . . BNZ 14
Blue Note / Jun '87.
■ LP . . . . . . . . . . . . . . . . . . . BST 84060
Blue Note / Jul '89.

### AT THE HALF NOTE CAFE VOL. 2.
**Tracks:** Jeannine / Pure D funk / Between the Devil and the deep blue sea / Mr. Lucky / Kimyas / When sunny gets blue.
■ CD . . . . . . . . . . . . . . . . . . . . . BNZ 15
Blue Note / Jan '88.
■ LP . . . . . . . . . . . . . . . . . . . BLJ 84061
Blue Note / Jul '89.

## BEST OF DONALD BYRD.
**Tracks:** Change (makes you wanna hustle) / You and music / Black Byrd / Think twice / Onward 'til morning / Lanasana's priestess / Street lady / Flight time / Places and spaces / Wind parade / (Falling like) dominoes (live) / Steppin' into tomorrow / Just my imagination (running away with me) / Love's so far away / (Falling like) dominoes (2).
CD . . . . . . . . . . . . . . . . . . . . . . .BNZ 285
■ LP . . . . . . . . . . . . . . . . . . . B1 98638
Blue Note / Feb '92 / EMI.

## BLACKBYRD.
**Tracks:** Flight time / Black Byrd / Love's so far away / Mr. Thomas / Sky high / Slop jar blues / Where are we going.
CD . . . . . . . . . . . . . . . . . . . . . . .BNZ 294
■ LP . . . . . . . . . . . . . . . . . . . B1 84466
Blue Note / Aug '92 / EMI.

## BLUE NOTE COLLECTION.
**Tracks:** Lansana's priestess / Sister love / Flight time / Stepping into tomorrow / Where are we going / Think twice / Wild life / Love's so far away / Design a nation / Change / Places and spaces / Onward 'til morning / Wind parade / Just my imagination / Dominos.
■ LP . . . . . . . . . . . . . . . . . . LCSP 1867013
Liberty / Jul '83.

## BYRD IN HAND.
**Tracks:** Witchcraft / Here I am / Devil whip / Bronze dance / Clarion calls / Injuns.
■ LP . . . . . . . . . . . . . . . . . . . BST 84019
Blue Note / Jul '89.
■ CD . . . . . . . . . . . . . . . . . . . . .BNZ 165
Blue Note / May '89.

## CAT WALK, THE.
**Tracks:** Say you're mine / Duke's mixture / Each time I think of you / Cat walk / Cute / Hello bright sunflower.
■ LP . . . . . . . . . . . . . . . . . . . BST 84075
Blue Note / Nov '84.

## CHANGE MAKES YOU WANT TO HUSTLE.
**Tracks:** Change makes you want to hustle / Change makes you want to hustle (version).
■ 7" . . . . . . . . . . . . . . . . . . . . BNXW 7003
Blue Note / Jan '76.

## CITY CALLED HEAVEN, A.
**Tracks:** King Arthur / I'll always remember / City called heaven / Back down in Lu Easy Anna / Byrd song / Del Valle / Remember me / Not necessarily the blues.
CD . . . . . . . . . . . . . . . . . . . . . LCD 15302
Landmark (USA) / Aug '93 / New Note.

## DOMINOES.
**Tracks:** Dominoes / Change (makes you want to hustle).
■ 12" . . . . . . . . . . . . . . . . . . . . 12UP 622
United Artists / Apr '80.
■ 12" . . . . . . . . . . . . . . . . . . . . DOM T5
Domino (1) / Oct '88.

## DOMINOES (LIVE).
**Tracks:** Dominoes (live) / Wind parade.
■ 12" . . . . . . . . . . . . . . . . . . . . SWAVE 7
Streetwave / Mar '86.

## EARLY BYRD - THE BEST OF THE JAZZ SOUL YEARS.
**Tracks:** Slow drag / West of Pecos / Books Bossa / Jelly roll / Mustang / Blackjack / Weasil / Dude / Emperor / Little rasti (On LP only).
■ LP . . . . . . . . . . . . . . . . . . . B1 89607
Blue Note / Sep '91.
CD . . . . . . . . . . . . . . . . . . . . . .BNZ 316
LP . . . . . . . . . . . . . . . . . . . . . B 189606
Blue Note / Jun '93 / EMI.

## FANCY FREE.
**Tracks:** Fancy free / I love the girl / Uptowner / Weasil.
■ LP . . . . . . . . . . . . . . . . . . . BST 84319
Blue Note / Dec '69.
CD . . . . . . . . . . . . . . . . . . . . CDP 7897962
LP . . . . . . . . . . . . . . . . . . . . . B1 89796
Blue Note / Nov '93 / EMI.

## FIRST FLIGHT.
**Tracks:** Not Advised.
CD . . . . . . . . . . . . . . . . . . . . DELMARK 407
Delmark (USA) / Feb '87 / Cadillac / Swift / A.D.A. Distribution / Topic Records / Direct Distribution / Jazz Music / C.M. Distribution.

## FREE FORM.
**Tracks:** Pentecostal feelin' (Take 23) / Night flower (Take 15.) / Nai nai (Take 2) / French spice (Take 9) / Free form (Take 24) / Three wishes (CD only).
■ LP . . . . . . . . . . . . . . . . . . . BST 84118
Blue Note / Jul '89.
■ CD . . . . . . . . . . . . . . . . . . . .BNZ 193
Blue Note / Jun '89.

## FUEGO.
**Tracks:** Fuego / Bup a loup / Funky mama / Lament / Amen.
■ CD . . . . . . . . . . . . . . . . . . . BNZ 13
Blue Note / May '87.

## GETTING DOWN TO BUSINESS (Byrd, Donald Sextet).
**Tracks:** Theme for Malcolm / That's all there is to love / Pomponio / I got it bad (and that ain't good) (Available on CD only) / Certain attitude / Loneliest / Around the corner.
CD . . . . . . . . . . . . . . . . . . . . . LCD 15232
LP . . . . . . . . . . . . . . . . . . . . . LLP 1523
Landmark (USA) / Mar '90 / New Note.

## GROOVIN' FOR NAT.
**Tracks:** Hush / Child's play / Angel eyes / Smoothie / Suede / Friday's child / Out of this world / Groovin' for Nat.
CD . . . . . . . . . . . . . . . . . . . BLCD 760134
■ LP . . . . . . . . . . . . . . . . . BLP 60134
Black Lion / '88 / Jazz Music / Cadillac / Wellard / Koch International.

## HARLEM BLUES.
**Tracks:** Harlem blues / Fly, little Byrd / Voyage a deux / Blue monk / Alter ego / Sir Master Kool Guy.
CD . . . . . . . . . . . . . . . . . . . . . LCD 15162
■ LP . . . . . . . . . . . . . . . . . . . LLP 1516
Landmark (USA) / Jul '88 / New Note.

## HOUSE OF BYRD.
**Tracks:** Round midnight / Dig / Third / Contour / When your lover has gone / Dewey Square / Dupeltook / Once more / House of Chan / In walked George / Lover man (oh where can you be).
■ Double LP . . . . . . . . . . . . . . . PR 24066
Prestige / '79.

## I'LL ALWAYS LOVE YOU.
**Tracks:** I'll always love you / Falling.
■ 7" . . . . . . . . . . . . . . . . . . . . K 12580
Elektra / Jan '82.

## I'M TRYIN' TO GET HOME.
**Tracks:** Brother Isaac / Noah / I'm tryin' to get home / I've longed and searched for my mother / March children / Pearly gates.
■ CD . . . . . . . . . . . . . . . . . . . .BNZ 227
■ LP . . . . . . . . . . . . . . . . . . . BST 84188
Blue Note / Aug '89.

## LOVE BYRD.
**Tracks:** Love has come around / Butterfly / I feel like loving you today / I love your love / I'll always love you / Love for sale / Falling.
■ LP . . . . . . . . . . . . . . . . . . . K 52301
MC . . . . . . . . . . . . . . . . . . . K4 52301
Elektra / '88 / WEA.

## LOVE FOR SALE.
**Tracks:** Love for sale / I love your love.
■ 7" . . . . . . . . . . . . . . . . . . . . K 13172
Elektra / Apr '82.

## LOVE HAS COME AROUND.
**Tracks:** Love has come around / Loving you.
■ 12" . . . . . . . . . . . . . . . . . . . K 12559T
■ 7" . . . . . . . . . . . . . . . . . . . . K 12559
Elektra / Sep '81.

## NEW FORMULAS FROM THE JAZZ LAB (Byrd, Donald & Gigi Gryce).
**Tracks:** Not Advised.
■ LP . . . . . . . . . . . . . . . . . . . PL 43698
RCA / Jan '83.

## NEW PERSPECTIVE , A.
**Tracks:** Elijah / Beast of burden / Cristo redentor / Black discipline / Chant.
■ LP . . . . . . . . . . . . . . . . . . . BST 84124
Blue Note / Apr '85.
CD . . . . . . . . . . . . . . . . . . . . . .BNZ 157
Blue Note / Oct '90 / EMI.

## SEPTEMBER AFTERNOON (Byrd, Donald & Clare Fischer & Strings).
**Tracks:** Stardust / Indian Summer / I'm a fool to want you / Some day my prince will come / Moon mist / I get along without you very well / Touch of your lips / Lazy afternoon / Varmeland / Love is the sweetest thing / September afternoon / Dearly beloved.

         ■ DELETED

■ LP . . . . . . . . . . . . . . . . . . . DS 869
Discovery (USA) / Jun '83.

**STAR TRIPPIN.**
Tracks: Star trippin'.
■ 12" . . . . . . . . . . . . . . . . 9679620 T
Elektra / Nov '82.

**THANK YOU..FOR F.U.M.L.**
Tracks: Thank you..for F.U.M.L. / Sunning in your loveshine / Your life is ecstasy / Loving you / Have you heard the news / In love with love / Cristo Redentor / Close your eyes and look within.
■ LP . . . . . . . . . . . . . . . . . . K 52097
Elektra / Jan '79.

**THANK YOU..FOR F.U.M.L.**
Tracks: Thank you for F.U.M.L. / Loving you.
■ 7" . . . . . . . . . . . . . . . . . . K 12321
Elektra / Jan '79.

**WORDS, SOUNDS, COLOURS & SHAPES.**
Tracks: Sexy dancer / Midnight / So much in love / High energy / Star trippin' / I'm coming home / Forbidden love / Everyday.
■ LP . . . . . . . . . . . . . . . . . . K 52427
Elektra / Nov '82.

## Byrd, Gary

**CROWN, THE (2 Parts) (Byrd, Gary & The G.B.Experience).**
Tracks: Crown.
■ 7" . . . . . . . . . . . . . . . . CTMGT 1312
■ 12" . . . . . . . . . . . . . . . . TMGT 1312
Motown / Jul '83.

**RAP THE WORLD (IN YOUR LOVE) (Byrd, Gary & The G.B.Experience).**
Tracks: Rap the world (in your love) / Rap the world (in your love)(club version).
■ 12" . . . . . . . . . . . . . . . . . . INRT 1
■ 7" . . . . . . . . . . . . . . . . . . INR 1
In Recordings / Oct '86.

## Byrd, Russell

**HITCH HIKE.**
Tracks: Hitch hike.
■ 7" . . . . . . . . . . . . . . . . . . WI 305
Sue / '64.

## C.C.R. Crew

**SLAP.**
Tracks: Slap.
- 12" .................... CCYT 6
- 7" ..................... CCY 6
Circle City / Apr '88.

**STRETCHIN' THE PIECES.**
Tracks: Stretchin' the pieces.
- 12" .................... CCYT 1
- 7" ..................... CCY 1
Circle City / Nov '87.

## Cabo Frio

**JUST HAVING FUN.**
Tracks: Prism / Just having fun / Find it (hold that note) / Only time / Fast lane / San Juan sunrise / Find a way / Rachel.
- LP ................... IZEB 5710
- MC ................. IZEBC 5710
Zebra (1) / Feb '87.

## Cache

**WHERE IS MY SUNSHINE.**
Tracks: Where is my sunshine / Jazzin' and cruisin'.
- 12" .................... GP 111T
- 7" ..................... GP 111
Groove PR / Nov '81.

## Cain, Ann

**LET ME LEAD YOU TO PARADISE.**
Tracks: Let me lead you to paradise.
12" ...................... BUCKY 024
CD Single ............ BUCKY 024CD
Genesis / Jan '94 / Jetstar.

## Caine, General

**HAIRDOOZ.**
Tracks: Hairdooz / Crack killed Applejack.
- 12" .................... ZT 41034
- 7" ..................... ZB 41033
Motown / Nov '86.

**IN FULL CHILL.**
Tracks: Hairdooz / Wrassle / Buffaloes / Can't let go / All the way up / Crack killed Applejack / Ticket / Cuttin' it up / General speaks.
- LP .................... ZL 72538
- MC ................... ZK 72538
Motown / Feb '87.

## Cairo

**I LIKE BLUEBEAT.**
Tracks: I like bluebeat.
- 7" ........................ A7
Absurd / Jan '80.

**I WANT THAT GIRL.**
Tracks: I want that girl / Hold on.
- 12" .................... CBE 1235
- 7" .................... CBE 735
- CD Single ........... CBE 1235 CD
City Beat / Jan '89.

**I WANT YOU IN MY LIFE.**
Tracks: Uncle Charlie / I want you in my life.
- 7" .................... CBE 715
- 12" ................... CBE 1215
City Beat / Aug '87.

**MOVIE STARS.**
Tracks: Movie stars / Cuthberts birthday treat.
- 7" ....................... ASK 15
Absurd / Apr '81.

**ON THE REBOUND.**
Tracks: On the rebound.
- 12" ................... CHAMP 122
- 7" ................... CHAMP 2
Champion / Jul '85.

**SMOKIN'.**
Tracks: Smokin' / Smokin' (Uncle Charlie remix).
- 12" ................... CBE 1226

City Beat / May '88.
- 12" .................. CHS 123204
Chrysalis / May '88.
- 7" ..................... CBE 726
City Beat / May '88.
- CD Single ........... CHSCD 3204
Chrysalis / May '88.

**YOU ARE (Cairo/Winston Jones/Lynn Bryant).**
Tracks: You are.
- 12" .................. VSEP 601
Vista Sounds / May '83.

## Caitaine, Ria

**GIVE IT (THIS LOVE SONG).**
Tracks: Give it (this love song).
- 12" ................. DEBTX 3136
Debut (1) / Feb '92.

## Caldera

**CALDERA.**
Tracks: Guanacastle / Coastin' / Exaltation / Synesthesia / Out of the blue / El Juguete.
- LP .................. EST 11571
Capitol / Feb '77.

**DREAMER.**
Tracks: To capture the moon / Rain forest / Dream child / Celebration / Reflections on Don Quioxote / Brujerias / Himalaya.
- LP .................. EST 11952
Capitol / '79.

**TIME & CHANCE.**
Tracks: Arousing / Reviviscence / Mosaico / Magewind / Crosscountry / Passages / Dreamborne / Shanti / Horizon's end.
- LP .................. EAST 11810
Capitol / Sep '78.

## Caldwell, Bobby

**ALL OF MY LOVE.**
Tracks: All of my love / Catwalk.
- 7" ................... POSP 426
Polydor / Apr '82.

**BOBBY CALDWELL.**
Tracks: Special to me / My flame / Love won't wait / Can't say goodbye / Come to me / What you won't do for love / Kalimba song / Take me back to then / Down for the third time.
- LP .................. TKR 83362
TK / Apr '79.

**CAT IN THE HAT.**
Tracks: Coming down from love / Wrong or right / To know what you've got / You promised me / It's over / Open your eyes / Mother of creation / I don't want to lose your love.
- LP .................. TKR 83386
TK / Jun '80.

**COMING DOWN FROM LOVE.**
Tracks: Coming down from love / Open your eyes.
- 7" ................... TKR 7577
TK / Jul '80.

**DOWN FOR THE THIRD TIME.**
Tracks: Down for the third time / My flame.
- 7" ................... TKR 7515
TK / Jan '79.

**JAMAICA.**
Tracks: Jamaica / You belong to me.
- 7" ................... POSP 476
Polydor / Jul '82.

**WHAT YOU WON'T DO FOR LOVE.**
Tracks: What you won't do for love (edit) / Down for the third time (edit).
- 7" ................... TKR 7529
TK / Mar '79.
- 12" ................. MAGDT 5
- 7" .................. MAGD 5
Magnetic Dance / Jun '87.

## California Executives

**DANCING AND ROMANCING, THE.**
Tracks: I can't forget you / You know what I like / How long (do I have to wait for you) / Same for me / Let me love you tonight / Baby I love you / What are you afraid of / I can't let you go / I don't know why.
- LP .................. GMIMP 1
Groove & Move (G&M) / Dec '87.
- CD .................. TLCD 584
- LP .................. TRPL 126
Timeless (Soul) / Jan '90.

## Callier, Terry

**FIRE ON ICE.**
Tracks: Be a believer / Holdin' on (to your love) / (Everything's gonna be alright) / Disco in the sky / American violet / Love two tone / Martin St Martin.
- LP .................. K 52096
Elektra / Aug '78.

**I DON'T WANT TO SEE MYSELF.**
Tracks: I don't want to see myself.
- 12" ................. JAZID 027T
Acid Jazz / Aug '90.

**SIGN OF THE TIMES.**
Tracks: Sign of the times / Occasional rain.
- 7" ................... K 12372
WEA / '79.

**TURN YOU TO LOVE.**
Tracks: Sign of the times / Pyramids of love / Turn you to love / Do it again / Ordinary Joe / Occasional rain / Still water / You and me (will always be in love) / Mother's love.
- LP .................. K 52140
Elektra / May '85.

**VERY BEST OF TERRY CALLIER, THE.**
Tracks: Not Advised.
CD ..................... CDARC 514
LP ..................... ARC 514
Charly / Apr '94 / Charly.

## Calloway

**ALL THE WAY.**
Tracks: Sir Lancelot / I wanna be rich / Love circles / Freaks compete / You are my everything / All the way / I want you / Sugar free / You can count on me / Holiday.
- CD ..................... 4662272
- LP ..................... 4662271
- MC ..................... 4662274
Epic / Jun '90.

**I WANNA BE RICH.**
Tracks: I wanna be rich / I wanna be rich (Instrumental background vocal (Not on 7" single.) / I wanna be rich (Dance mix) (Not on 7" single.) / I wanna be rich (Dance dub) (Not on 7" single.).
- 12" ..................... 6555158
- 7" ...................... 6555157
- CD Single .............. 6555152
- MC Single ............. 6555154
Epic / Jun '90.

## Cameo

**ALLIGATOR WOMAN.**
Tracks: Not Advised.
- LP ..................... 6480 079
Casablanca / May '82.

**ATTACK ME WITH YOUR LOVE.**
Tracks: Attack me with your love / Love you anyway.
- 7" ...................... JAB 16
- 12" ..................... JABX 16
Club / Jan '85.

**BABY, NOW THAT I'VE FOUND YOU.**
Tracks: Baby, now that I've found you / Staggering.
- 7" ...................... LSE 2
Loose / Jul '83.

**BACK AND FORTH.**
Tracks: Back and forth / You can have the world.
- 12" ..................... JABX 49

■ DELETED

■ 7″ . . . . . . . . . . . . . . . . . . . . . . . JAB 49
Club / Apr '87.
■ CD Single . . . . . . . . . . . . . . . . . 8885132
Club / '88.

## BACK AND FORTH.
Tracks: Not Advised.
VHS . . . . . . . . . . . . . . . . . . VCSJAB 49
Club / Aug '87 / PolyGram.

## BEST OF CAMEO.
Tracks: Word up / Single life / Candy / Shake your pants / Rigor mortis / Attack me with your love / Talkin' out the side of your neck / Sparkle / Back and forth / Flirt / She's strange / I just want to be / Skin I'm in / It's over / She's mine.
CD . . . . . . . . . . . . . . . . . . . . . 514 929-2
MC . . . . . . . . . . . . . . . . . . . . . 514 929-4
Phonogram / Jun '93 / PolyGram.

## CAMEO: THE VIDEO SINGLES.
Tracks: Not Advised.
VHS . . . . . . . . . . . . . . . . . . . CFV 06122
Channel 5 / '87 / Channel 5 Video / P.R.O. Video / Gold & Sons.
CD Video . . . . . . . . . . . . . . . . . 080 162 9
Polygram Music Video / Oct '88 / PolyGram.

## CANDY.
Tracks: Candy.
■ 7″ Set . . . . . . . . . . . . . . . . . JABXD 43
■ 12″ . . . . . . . . . . . . . . . . . . . JABX 43
■ 7″ . . . . . . . . . . . . . . . . . . . . JAB 43
Club / Nov '86.

## CANDY (CD VIDEO).
Tracks: Not Advised.
CD Video . . . . . . . . . . . . . . . . . 080 090 2
Polygram Music Video / Sep '89 / PolyGram.

## CARDIAC ARREST.
Tracks: Still feels good / Post mortem / Smile / Funk funk / Find my way / Rigor mortis / Good times / Stay by my side.
■ LP . . . . . . . . . . . . . . . . . . . . CAL 2015
Casablanca / Sep '77.

## DON'T BE SO COOL.
Tracks: Don't be so cool / Sound table / On the one (Only on 12″ single.).
■ 12″ . . . . . . . . . . . . . . . . . . CANX 1004
■ 7″ . . . . . . . . . . . . . . . . . . . CAN 1004
Casablanca / Aug '81.

## EMOTIONAL VIOLENCE.
Tracks: Emotional violence / Money / Raw but tasty / Front street / Kid don't believe it / Another love / Don't crash / Love yourself / Nothing less than love / That kind of guy.
CD . . . . . . . . . . . . . . . . . . . 7599267342
■ LP . . . . . . . . . . . . . . . . . . 7599267341
MC . . . . . . . . . . . . . . . . . . . 7599267344
Reprise / Mar '92 / WEA.

## FEEL ME.
Tracks: Throw it down / Your love takes me out / Keep it hot / Feel me / Is this the way / Roller skates / Better days.
■ LP . . . . . . . . . . . . . . . . . . . . CCL 2016
Casablanca / Feb '81.

## FOUR FROM CAMEO (EP).
Tracks: Not Advised.
■ 12″ . . . . . . . . . . . . . . . . . . CANX 1010
■ 7″ . . . . . . . . . . . . . . . . . . . CAN 1010
Casablanca / May '82.

## FUNK FUNK.
Tracks: Funk funk / Good times.
■ 7″ . . . . . . . . . . . . . . . . . . . . CAN 112
Casablanca / Nov '77.

## GOODBYE, A.
Tracks: Goodbye / I've got your image / On the one (Extra track on 12″ only.) / Goodbye (long version) (Available on double-pack only.) / Just be yourself (Available on double-pack only.) / It's serious (Available on double-pack only.).
■ 12″ . . . . . . . . . . . . . . . . . . . JABX 28
■ 7″ . . . . . . . . . . . . . . . . . . . . JAB 28
■ 7″ Set . . . . . . . . . . . . . . . . . JABXD 28
Club / Mar '86.

## HANGIN' DOWNTOWN.
Tracks: Hangin' downtown / Talkin' out the side of your neck / You're a winner (on 12″ only).
■ 12″ . . . . . . . . . . . . . . . . . . . . JABX 4
■ 7″ . . . . . . . . . . . . . . . . . . . . . JAB 4
Club / May '84.

## I WANT IT NOW.
Tracks: I want it now.
■ 12″ . . . . . . . . . . . . . . . 12 MER 327
■ 7″ . . . . . . . . . . . . . . . . . . MER 327

## INSANE.
Tracks: Insane / I want you.
■ 7″ . . . . . . . . . . . . . . . . . . . CAN 143
Casablanca / Feb '79.

## IT'S SERIOUS.
Tracks: It's serious / Inflation.
■ 7″ . . . . . . . . . . . . . . . . . . . CAN 121
Casablanca / Mar '78.

## KNIGHTS OF THE SOUND TABLE.
Tracks: Knights by nights / Freaky dancin' / I never knew it / Use it or lose it / Sound table / Don't be so cool / I'll always stay / I like it.
■ LP . . . . . . . . . . . . . . . . . . . 6480041
Casablanca / Aug '81.

## MACHISMO.
Tracks: You make me work / Skin I'm in / I like the world / Pretty girls / Promiscuous / Soul tightened / In the night / Money / DKWIG.
■ CD . . . . . . . . . . . . . . . . . . . 836 002-2
■ LP . . . . . . . . . . . . . . . . . . . 836 002-1
■ MC . . . . . . . . . . . . . . . . . . . 836 002-4
Club / Nov '88.

## ON THE ONE.
Tracks: On the one / Cameosis.
■ 7″ . . . . . . . . . . . . . . . . . . . CAN 199
Casablanca / Jun '80.

## POST MORTEM.
Tracks: Post mortem / Rigor mortis.
■ 7″ . . . . . . . . . . . . . . . . . . . CAN 106
Casablanca / May '77.

## REAL MEN WEAR BLACK.
Tracks: Close quarters / Me / Get paid / Time, fire and space / Just a broken heart / I want it now / Attitude / Am I bad enough / Nan yea.
■ LP . . . . . . . . . . . . . . . . . . . 846 297 1
■ MC . . . . . . . . . . . . . . . . . . . 846 297 4
■ CD . . . . . . . . . . . . . . . . . . . 846 297 2
Atlanta / Jul '90.

## SECRET OMEN.
Tracks: Energy / I just want to be / Find my way / Macho / Rock / Sparkle / New York.
■ LP . . . . . . . . . . . . . . . . . . . CAL 2058
Casablanca / Oct '79.

## SHE'S MINE.
Tracks: Flirt (Only on 12″ single.) / Knights of the sound table (Only on 12″ single.) / She's mine.
■ 12″ . . . . . . . . . . . . . . . . . . . JABX 57
■ 7″ . . . . . . . . . . . . . . . . . . . . JAB 57
Club / Sep '87.

## SHE'S MINE - THE CAMEO MEGAMIX 2.
Tracks: She's mine (cameo megamix) / She's mine.
■ 12″ . . . . . . . . . . . . . . . . . JABXR 57
Club / Sep '87.

## SHE'S STRANGE.
Tracks: She's strange / Love you anyway / Talkin' out the side of your neck / Tribute to Bob Marley / Groove with you / Hangin' downtown / Leve toi.
■ LP . . . . . . . . . . . . . . . . . . . 8149 841
Casablanca / Jun '84.
■ CD . . . . . . . . . . . . . . . . . . . 814 984-2
Casablanca / Jun '87.
■ LP . . . . . . . . . . . . . . . . . . PRICE 109
■ MC . . . . . . . . . . . . . . . . . . PRIMC 109
Club / Jun '87.

## SHE'S STRANGE.
Tracks: She's strange / She's strange (Cameo megamix) / 123 (She's strange rap version) (Doublepack only.) / 123 (Club mix) (Doublepack only.)
■ 12″ . . . . . . . . . . . . . . . . . . . JABX 252
■ 12″ Remix . . . . . . . . . . . . . JABXS 25
■ 7″ . . . . . . . . . . . . . . . . . . . . JAB 25
Club / Nov '85.

## SHE'S STRANGE.
Tracks: She's strange / Groove with you.
■ 12″ . . . . . . . . . . . . . . . . . . . JABX 2
■ 7″ . . . . . . . . . . . . . . . . . . . . JAB 2
Club / Mar '84.

## SINGLE LIFE.
Tracks: Attack me with your love / Single life / I'll never look for love / Little boys - dangerous toys / I've got your image / Goodbye.
■ LP . . . . . . . . . . . . . . . . . . . JABH 11
MC . . . . . . . . . . . . . . . . . . . JABHC 11
■ LP . . . . . . . . . . . . . . . . . . 824 546-1
■ CD . . . . . . . . . . . . . . . . . . 824 546-2
Club / Aug '85 / PolyGram.

■ CD Single . . . . . . . . . . . . . . MERCD 327
Mercury / Jun '90.

## SINGLE LIFE.
Tracks: Single life / Hangin' downtown / She's strange (Old Gold release only).
■ 12″ . . . . . . . . . . . . . . . . . . . JABX 21
■ 7″ . . . . . . . . . . . . . . . . . . . . JAB 21
Club / Sep '85.
12″ . . . . . . . . . . . . . . . . . . . OG 4224
Old Gold / May '92 / Pickwick.

## SINGLE LIFE (OLD GOLD).
Tracks: Single life / She's strange.
■ 7″ . . . . . . . . . . . . . . . . . . . OG 9774
Old Gold / Feb '88.

## SKIN I'M IN.
Tracks: Skin I'm in / Honey / Cameo megamix two (Only on 12″ version.).
■ CD Single . . . . . . . . . . . . . JABCD 77
■ 12″ . . . . . . . . . . . . . . . . . . . JABX 77
■ 12″ Remix . . . . . . . . . . . . . JABXR 77
■ 7″ . . . . . . . . . . . . . . . . . . . . JAB 77
Club / Jan '89.

## SPARKLE.
Tracks: Sparkle / I just want to be / Do it with your body / Get up.
■ 12″ . . . . . . . . . . . . . . . . . . CSSL 3202
■ 7″ . . . . . . . . . . . . . . . . . . . CSS 3202
Casablanca / Jan '80.

## STYLE.
Tracks: Aphrodisiac / This life is not for me / You're a winner / Can't help falling in love / Interlude / Serenity / Cameo's dance / Let's not talk shop / Slow movin' / Heaven only knows.
■ LP . . . . . . . . . . . . . . . . . . . 811 072 1
Casablanca / Sep '83.

## THROW IT DOWN.
Tracks: Throw it down / Is this the way.
■ 12″ . . . . . . . . . . . . . . . . . . . CANL 216
Casablanca / Dec '80.

## UGLY EGO.
Tracks: I'll be with you / Insane / Give love a chance / Ugly ego / I want you / Anything you wanna do / Friend to me / Two of us.
■ LP . . . . . . . . . . . . . . . . . . . CAL 2038
Casablanca / Feb '79.

## WE ALL KNOW WHO WE ARE.
Tracks: Inflation / C on the funk / Why have I lost you / Stand by / We all know who we are / It's serious / It's over.
■ LP . . . . . . . . . . . . . . . . . . . CAL 2026
Casablanca / Apr '78.

## WE'RE GOING OUT TONIGHT.
Tracks: We're going out tonight / Sparkle.
■ 7″ . . . . . . . . . . . . . . . . . . . CAN 204
Casablanca / Apr '80.

## WORD UP.
Tracks: Word up / Urban warrior / Candy / Back and forth / Don't be lonely / She's mine / Fast, fierce and funny / You can have the world.
CD . . . . . . . . . . . . . . . . . . . 830 265 2
■ LP . . . . . . . . . . . . . . . . . . . JABH 19
MC . . . . . . . . . . . . . . . . . . . JABHC 19
Club / Sep '86 / PolyGram.

## WORD UP.
Tracks: Word up.
■ 12″ . . . . . . . . . . . . . . . . . . . JABX 38
■ 7″ . . . . . . . . . . . . . . . . . . . . JAB 38
Club / Aug '86.
■ 12″ Remix . . . . . . . . . . . . . JABXR 38
Club / Jul '87.

## WORD UP (CD VIDEO).
Tracks: Word up.
CD Video . . . . . . . . . . . . . . . . . 080 092 2
Polygram Music Video / Oct '88 / PolyGram.

## WORD UP (OLD GOLD).
Tracks: Word up / Back and forth.
12″ . . . . . . . . . . . . . . . . . . . OG 4233
Old Gold / Jun '92 / Pickwick.

## YOU MAKE ME WORK.
Tracks: You make me work / DKWIG.
■ CD Single . . . . . . . . . . . . . JABCD 70
■ 12″ . . . . . . . . . . . . . . . . . . . JABX 70
■ 12″ Remix . . . . . . . . . . . . . JABXR 70
■ 7″ . . . . . . . . . . . . . . . . . . . . JAB 70
Club / Oct '88.

■ DELETED                                             

## Cameron

**CAMERON.**
Tracks: Magic of you / Funkdown / Together / Let's get it off / Feelings / Can't live without ya.
■ LP . . . . . . . . . . . . . . . . . . . . . . . . SALP 2
Salsoul / Oct '80.

**LET'S GET IT OFF.**
Tracks: Let's get it off / Magic of you.
■ 12" . . . . . . . . . . . . . . . . . . . . . . . SAL 12 4
Salsoul / Aug '80.

**WAIT UNTIL TOMORROW.**
Tracks: Wait until tomorrow / Shadows.
■ 7" . . . . . . . . . . . . . . . . . . . . . . . ADS 9002
Ardent / Feb '89.

## Cameron, G.C.

G.C. Cameron, while not immediately recognisable by name, is perhaps best remembered as the voice on the 1970 Motown classic *It's A Shame*. After serving in Vietnam, Cameron returned to Detroit in 1967, determined to make a go of a singing career - his big break came when he replaced Chico Edwards as the lead singer in the Detroit Spinners. After leaving to pursue a solo career he met and later married Gwen Gordy, moving with her to Los Angeles where he signed with Mowest, a subsidiary of Motown, but his solo career never matched the commercial success of the Spinners. In the UK he achieved some degree of fame when the title track from his 1977 album *You're What's Missing In My Life* became a favourite of the 'rare groove' scene in the mid-80's.

**GIVE ME YOUR LOVE.**
Tracks: Let's share / Hearts & flowers / So hard to say goodbye to yesterday / Pride & joy / Give me your love / No lovin' til friday / Night like this in Georgia / Hold you to your promise / Love trap.
■ LP . . . . . . . . . . . . . . . . . . . . . . . MAL 7413
Malaco / '88.

**HEARTS AND FLOWERS.**
Tracks: Hearts and flowers / Give me your love.
■ 7" . . . . . . . . . . . . . . . . . . . . . . . MAL 006
Malaco / Apr '83.

**LIVE FOR LOVE.**
Tracks: Live for love / I love you.
■ 12" . . . . . . . . . . . . . . . . . . . . . . . FMT 11
■ 7" . . . . . . . . . . . . . . . . . . . . . . . FM 11
Flamingo / Feb '81.

**NO NEED TO EXPLAIN.**
Tracks: No need to explain.
■ 12" . . . . . . . . . . . . . . . . . . . 12 MOTC 89
Motor City / Jun '92.

**RICH LOVE, POOR LOVE (see under Syreeta).**

## Cameron, Rafael

**ALL THAT'S GOOD TO ME.**
Tracks: All that's good to me / Funtown USA.
■ 12" . . . . . . . . . . . . . . . . . . . . . . . SALT 10
■ 7" . . . . . . . . . . . . . . . . . . . . . . . SAL 10
Salsoul / Aug '81.

**CAMERONS IN LOVE.**
Tracks: Number one / All that's good to me / Let's get married / Boogie's gonna get ya' / Funtown USA / I'd go crazy / Daisy / In love.
■ LP . . . . . . . . . . . . . . . . . . . . . . . SALP 7
Salsoul / Sep '81.

## Camouflage

**BEE STING.**
Tracks: Bee sting / Take a ride.
■ 7" . . . . . . . . . . . . . . . . . . . . . . . STAT 58
State / Sep '77.

**GREAT COMMANDMENT, THE.**
Tracks: Great commandment / Pompeii.
■ 12" . . . . . . . . . . . . . . . . . . . . . . . A 9031T
■ 7" . . . . . . . . . . . . . . . . . . . . . . . A 9031
Atlantic / Mar '89.

**METHODS OF SILENCE.**
Tracks: Not Advised.
■ CD . . . . . . . . . . . . . . . . . . . . . . . K 7820022
■ LP . . . . . . . . . . . . . . . . . . . . . . . K 7820021
■ MC . . . . . . . . . . . . . . . . . . . . . . . K 7820024
Atlantic / Nov '89.

**VOICES AND IMAGES.**
Tracks: Not Advised.
■ CD . . . . . . . . . . . . . . . . . . . K 781 886 2
■ LP . . . . . . . . . . . . . . . . . . . K 781 886 1
■ MC . . . . . . . . . . . . . . . . . . . K 781 886 4
Atlantic / Apr '89.

## Campbell, Choker

**MICKEY'S MONKEY (Campbell, Choker Big Band).**
Tracks: Mickey's monkey.
■ 7" . . . . . . . . . . . . . . . . . . . . . . . TMG 517
Tamla Motown / Jun '65.

## Campbell, Tevin

**CAN WE TALK.**
Tracks: Can we talk.
■ 12" . . . . . . . . . . . . . . . . . . . . . . . W 0218T
■ 7" . . . . . . . . . . . . . . . . . . . . . . . W 0218
■ CD Single . . . . . . . . . . . . . . . . . . W 0218CD
■ MC Single . . . . . . . . . . . . . . . . . . W 0218C
Qwest / Dec '93.

**I'M READY.**
Tracks: Can we talk / Don't say goodbye girl / Interlude / Halls of desire / I'm ready / What do I say / Uncle sam / Paris 1798430 / Always in my heart / Shhh / Brown eyed girl / Infant child.
CD . . . . . . . . . . . . . . . . . . . . . . . 936245388-2
MC . . . . . . . . . . . . . . . . . . . . . . . 936245388-4
WEA / Oct '93 / WEA.

**ROUND AND ROUND.**
Tracks: round and 'round.
■ 12" . . . . . . . . . . . . . . . . . . . . . . . W 0115 T
■ 7" . . . . . . . . . . . . . . . . . . . . . . . W 0115
■ CD Single . . . . . . . . . . . . . . . . . . W 0115 CD
■ MC Single . . . . . . . . . . . . . . . . . . W 0115 C
Qwest / Jun '92.

**T.E.V.I.N.**
Tracks: Interlude/over the rainbow and on to the sun / Tell me what you want me to do / Lil' brother / Strawberry letter 23 / One song / round and 'round / Just asking me to / Perfect world / Look what we'd have (if you were mine) / She's all that.
CD . . . . . . . . . . . . . . . . . . . . . . . 7599262912
■ LP . . . . . . . . . . . . . . . . . . . . . . . 7599262911
MC . . . . . . . . . . . . . . . . . . . . . . . 7599262914
Qwest / Apr '92 / WEA.

**TELL ME WHAT YOU WANT ME TO DO.**
Tracks: Tell me what you want me to do.
■ 12" . . . . . . . . . . . . . . . . . . . . . . . W 0102T
■ 7" . . . . . . . . . . . . . . . . . . . . . . . W 0102
■ CD Single . . . . . . . . . . . . . . . . . . W 0102CD
■ MC Single . . . . . . . . . . . . . . . . . . W 0102C
WEA / Apr '92.

## Candela

**LOVE YOU MADLY.**
Tracks: Love you madly.
■ 12" . . . . . . . . . . . . . . . . . . . ARIST 12473
■ 7" . . . . . . . . . . . . . . . . . . . . . . . ARIST 473
Arista / '82.

## Candido

**BEAUTIFUL.**
Tracks: I'm on my way / Tic tac toe / Hey, Western Union man / Serenade to a savage / New World in the morning / Beautiful / I shouldn't believe / Money man / Ghana spice (part one) / Ghana spice (part two).
■ LP . . . . . . . . . . . . . . . . . . . . . . . B1 84357
Blue Note / Sep '93.

**DANCIN' AND PRANCIN'.**
Tracks: Dancin' and prancin' / Jingo / Thousand finger man / Rock and shuffle.
■ LP . . . . . . . . . . . . . . . . . . . . . . . SSLP 1517
Salsoul / Sep '79.

**DANCIN' AND PRANCIN'.**
Tracks: Dancin' and prancin' / Jingo.
■ 7" . . . . . . . . . . . . . . . . . . . . . . . SSOL 121
Salsoul / Aug '79.

**JINGO.**
Tracks: Jingo / Dancin' & prancin'.
■ 12" . . . . . . . . . . . . . . . . . . . . . . . EXCL 102
■ 7" . . . . . . . . . . . . . . . . . . . . . . . EXC 102
Excaliber / Jul '81.
■ 12" . . . . . . . . . . . . . . . . . . . MKHAN 79
Streetwave / Nov '86.

**JINGO/DANCIN' & PRANCIN'.**
Tracks: Jingo / Dancin' & prancin'.
■ 12" . . . . . . . . . . . . . . . . . . . 12SALSA 3
Salsoul / Apr '93.

## Candy & The Kisses

**LOVE GAMES FROM A-Z.**
Tracks: Love games from a-z / Love games from a-z (instrumental).
■ 7" . . . . . . . . . . . . . . . . . . . . . . . BON 3
Bonnie / '78.

**MR. CREATOR.**
Tracks: Mr. Creator / Hand it over.
■ 7" . . . . . . . . . . . . . . . . . . . . . . . TOWN 104
Kent / Apr '85.

## Cannon, Ace

**16 GREATEST HITS.**
Tracks: Not Advised.
CD . . . . . . . . . . . . . . . . . . . . . . . CD 1010
Gusto (USA) / '88.

**ACES HI & THE GREAT.**
Tracks: Not Advised.
CD . . . . . . . . . . . . . . . . . . . . . HIUKCD 125
Demon / Jun '93 / Pinnacle / A.D.A. Distribution.

**AT HIS BEST.**
Tracks: Not Advised.
■ LP . . . . . . . . . . . . . . . . . . . . . . . GT 0074
Gusto (USA) / Mar '88.

**CHRISTMAS ALBUM/CHRISTMAS CHEERS (see under Green, Al).**

**GOLDEN CLASSICS.**
Tracks: Not Advised.
■ LP . . . . . . . . . . . . . . . . . . . . . . . GT 0061
Gusto (USA) / Mar '88.

**GOLDEN SAX OF ACE.**
Tracks: Not Advised.
LP . . . . . . . . . . . . . . . . . . . . . . . WC 153
Rohit / Feb '88 / Jetstar.

**SAXY SOUNDS OF ACE.**
Tracks: Not Advised.
MC . . . . . . . . . . . . . . . . . . . . . . . WCW 17
Rohit / Feb '88 / Jetstar.

**SEA CRUISE.**
Tracks: Sea cruise / Peace in the valley.
■ 7" . . . . . . . . . . . . . . . . . . . HLU 10489
London / May '75.

**TUFF.**
Tracks: Tuff / Sittin' tight / Deep elem blues / St. Louis blues / Cannonball / Wabash blues / Blues in my heart / Heartbreak hotel / Lonesome road / Kansas City / Careless love / Searchin' / Trouble in mind.
■ LP . . . . . . . . . . . . . . . . . . . HIUKLP 412
Hi.

**TUFF SAX/MOANING SAX (2 albums on 1 CD).**
Tracks: Tuff sax / Trouble in mind / St. Louis blues / Wabash blues / Basin Street blues / Cannon ball / Blues in my heart / Blues stay away from me / Lonesome Road / Careless love / Kansas City / I've got a woman / Moanin' the blues / Trouble in mind (version 2) / Prisoner's song / Last date / Singing the blues / It's all in the game / No letter today / I left my heart in San Francisco / I can't get started with you / Prisoner of love / Moanin'.
CD . . . . . . . . . . . . . . . . . . . . . HIUKCD 121
Demon / Sep '91 / Pinnacle / A.D.A. Distribution.

## Capitols

**COOL JERK.**
Tracks: Not Advised.
■ LP . . . . . . . . . . . . . . . . . . . . . . . SS 8019
Solid Smoke (USA) / '84.

**COOL JERK.**
Tracks: Cool jerk / Under the moon of love / Pretty little angel eyes.
■ 7" . . . . . . . . . . . . . . . . . . . . . . . CR 219
Creole (Replay) / '84.
■ 12" . . . . . . . . . . . . . . . . . . . . . . . CRT 108
■ 7" . . . . . . . . . . . . . . . . . . . . . . . CR 108
Creole Classics / Aug '87.

**COOL JERK.**
Tracks: Cool jerk / Ain't that terrible.
■ 7" . . . . . . . . . . . . . . . . . . . . . . . CS 9030
Contempo (2) / Sep '75.

## COOL JERK.
**Tracks:** Cool jerk / Hello stranger.
7" . . . . . . . . . . . . . . . . . . . . . . . . . . .584004
Atlantic / Mar '66 / WEA.

## COOL JERK (OLD GOLD).
**Tracks:** Cool jerk / Cool pearl.
■ 7" . . . . . . . . . . . . . . . . . . . . . .OG 9106
Old Gold / '82.

## HONEY AND WINE.
**Tracks:** Honey and wine / Boulavogue.
7" . . . . . . . . . . . . . . . . . . . . . . . .7N 17025
Pye / Jan '66.

## Capreez

### HOW TO MAKE A SAD MAN GLAD.
**Tracks:** How to make a sad man glad.
■ 7" . . . . . . . . . . . . . . . . . . . . . . .GRP 113
Grapevine (Northern Soul) / Sep '79.

## Captain Sky

### DON'T TOUCH THAT DIAL.
**Tracks:** Not Advised.
■ 12" . . . . . . . . . . . . . . . . . . . . .PWSL 107
■ 7" . . . . . . . . . . . . . . . . . . . . . .PWS 107
Philly World (USA) / '83.

### YOU BRING ME UP.
**Tracks:** You bring me up.
■ 12" . . . . . . . . . . . . . . . . . . . . . .PRI 2003
Pana / Oct '87.

## Cargo

### DO IT.
**Tracks:** Do it.
■ 12" . . . . . . . . . . . . . . . . . . . . . .CG 1023
Cargo Gold / Jun '84.
■ 12" . . . . . . . . . . . . . . . . . . . . . .CG 1024
Cargo Gold / Jul '87.

### DON'T STOP YOUR LOVE.
**Tracks:** Don't stop your love / Cover me.
■ 12" . . . . . . . . . . . . . . . . . . . . . .YZ 66T
■ 7" . . . . . . . . . . . . . . . . . . . . . . . .YZ 66
WEA / Apr '86.
■ 12" . . . . . . . . . . . . . . . . . . . . . .CG 1026
Cargo Gold / Jun '86.

### HOLDING ON FOR LOVE.
**Tracks:** Holding on for love / It's your love.
■ 12" . . . . . . . . . . . . . . . . . . . . . .12Z 38
■ 7" . . . . . . . . . . . . . . . . . . . . . . . .Z 38
Zonophone / '82.
■ 12" . . . . . . . . . . . . . . . . . . . . . .CG 1021
Cargo Gold / Jun '82.

### JAZZ RAP.
**Tracks:** Jazz rap.
■ 12" . . . . . . . . . . . . . . . . . . . . . .CABL 205
■ 7" . . . . . . . . . . . . . . . . . . . . . . .CAB 205
Calibre / '85.
■ 12" . . . . . . . . . . . . . . . . . . . . . .CG 1025
Cargo Gold / Jun '85.

### LADY'S MAN.
**Tracks:** Lady's man.
■ LP . . . . . . . . . . . . . . . . . . . . . . .CG 1027
Cargo Gold / Mar '87.

### LOVE YOU SO (WITHOUT YOU) (Cargo & Dave Collins).
**Tracks:** Love you so (without you) / Love you so (instrumental).
■ 12" . . . . . . . . . . . . . . . . . . . . . .MKHAN 73
■ 7" . . . . . . . . . . . . . . . . . . . . . . .KHAN 73
Streetwave / Aug '86.

### LOVELY SUMMERS DAY.
**Tracks:** Lovely summers day / You bring the sunshine / Without you / Holding on for love / Ladys man / Lovely summers day (inst.) / Sunshine / Do it (inst.) / You make my world.
■ 12" . . . . . . . . . . . . . . . . . . . . . .CG 1028
Cargo Gold / Aug '87.

### SUNNY LOVE AFFAIR.
**Tracks:** Sunny love affair / Drifter.
■ 12" . . . . . . . . . . . . . . . . . . . . . .CG 1020
Cargo Gold / Jun '81.

### TENDER TOUCH.
**Tracks:** Tender touch.
■ 12" . . . . . . . . . . . . . . . . . . . . . .CG 1022
Cargo Gold / Jun '83.
■ 12" . . . . . . . . . . . . . . . . . . . . . .KOW 33T
■ 7" . . . . . . . . . . . . . . . . . . . . . . .KOW 33
Korova / '84.

## Carlton

### CALL IS STRONG, THE.
**Tracks:** Not Advised.
CD . . . . . . . . . . . . . . . . . . . . . 828 194 2
■ LP . . . . . . . . . . . . . . . . . . . . 828 194 1
MC . . . . . . . . . . . . . . . . . . . . . 828 194 4
3 Stripe / May '92 / PolyGram.

### COOL WITH NATURE.
**Tracks:** Cool with nature / Cool with nature (nature mix) / Cool with nature (Go Beat mix) / Cool with nature (drum and bass mix) (12" & CD single only.) / Cool with nature (Go Beat instrumental) (12" & CD single only.).
■ 12" . . . . . . . . . . . . . . . . . . . . .SNMXR 2
■ 12" Remix. . . . . . . . . . . . . . .SNMX 2
■ 7" . . . . . . . . . . . . . . . . . . . . . . .SNM 2
■ CD Single . . . . . . . . . . . . . . . .SNMCD 2
■ MC Single . . . . . . . . . . . . . . . .SNMC 2
3 Stripe / Jul '90.

### DO YOU DREAM.
**Tracks:** Do you dream / Come on back.
■ 12" . . . . . . . . . . . . . . . . . . . . .SNMXR 1
■ 12" . . . . . . . . . . . . . . . . . . . . . .SNMX 1
■ 7" . . . . . . . . . . . . . . . . . . . . . . .SNM 1
■ CD Single . . . . . . . . . . . . . . . .SNMCD 1
■ MC Single . . . . . . . . . . . . . . . .SNMC 1
3 Stripe / Apr '90.

### LOVE AND PAIN.
**Tracks:** Love and pain (Not on 12" single) / Love and pain (quiet storm mix) / Love and pain (radio version) (Only on 12" single) / Love and pain (drum and bass mix) (Only on 12" single) / Love and pain (original version) (Only on 12" and CD single) / Love and pain (quiet storm reprise) (Only on CD single).
■ 12" . . . . . . . . . . . . . . . . . . . . .SNMXR 4
■ 12" . . . . . . . . . . . . . . . . . . . . . .SNMX 4
■ 7" . . . . . . . . . . . . . . . . . . . . . . .SNM 4
■ CD Single . . . . . . . . . . . . . . . .SNMCD 4
■ MC Single . . . . . . . . . . . . . . . .SNMCS 4
3 Stripe / Jan '91.

## Carlton, Carl

### BAD FOR EACH OTHER.
**Tracks:** Bad for each other / Look at Mary Wonder.
■ 7" . . . . . . . . . . . . . . . . . . . . . .ACT 4537
Action / '69.

### CARL CARLTON.
**Tracks:** Sexy lady / Let me love you 'til the morning comes / Don't you wanna make love / This feeling's X-rated / She's a bad mama jama (she's built, stacked) / I've got that boogie fever / I think it's gonna be alright / Fighting in the name of love.
■ LP . . . . . . . . . . . . . . . . . . . . . . .T 628
MC . . . . . . . . . . . . . . . . . . . . . . . .C 628
20th Century / '81.

### COMPETITION AIN'T NOTHING.
**Tracks:** Competition ain't nothing / I'm not built that way.
■ 7" . . . . . . . . . . . . . . . . . . . . . .TOWN 105
Kent / '85.

### DROP BY MY PLACE.
**Tracks:** Competition ain't nothing / Three way love / Look at Mary wonder (how I got over) / Don't walk away / Drop by my place / I can feel it / I won't let that chump break your heart / You can't stop a man in love / Everlasting love / Smokin' room / Morning noon and nighttime / Ain't gonna tell anybody ('bout you) / Two timer / Sure miss loving you / You've got so much to learn about / Wild child.
■ LP . . . . . . . . . . . . . . . . . . . . . .CRB 1198
Charly R&B / Sep '88.

### EVERLASTING LOVE.
**Tracks:** Everlasting love / Smokin' room.
■ 7" . . . . . . . . . . . . . . . . . . . . . .ABC 4196
ABC Records / Feb '78.

### SHE'S A BAD MAMA JAMA (SHE'S BUILT, SHE'S STACKED) (OLD GOLD).
**Tracks:** She's a bad mama jama / Baby I need your loving.
12" . . . . . . . . . . . . . . . . . . . . . .OG 4189
Old Gold / Jul '90 / Pickwick.

### SHE'S A BAD MAMA JAMA (SHE'S BUILT, SHE'S STACKED).
**Tracks:** She's a bad mama jama (she's built, she's stacked) / This feeling rated zero.
■ 12" . . . . . . . . . . . . . . . . . . . . .TCD 2488
■ 7" . . . . . . . . . . . . . . . . . . . . . . .TC 2488
20th Century / Jul '81.

## Carlton, Larry

### ALONE BUT NEVER ALONE.
**Tracks:** Smiles and smiles to go / Perfect peace / Carrying you / Lord's prayer / High steppin' / Whatever happens / Pure delight / Alone but never alone.
■ CD . . . . . . . . . . . . . . . . . . . .MCAD 5689
■ MC . . . . . . . . . . . . . . . . . . .IMCAC 5689
■ LP . . . . . . . . . . . . . . . . . . . .IMCA 5689
MCA / Jul '87.
CD . . . . . . . . . . . . . . . . . . . . .GRP 01052
GRP / Oct '92 / BMG / New Note.

### COLLECTION: LARRY CARLTON.
**Tracks:** Small town girl / Smiles and smiles to go / Minute by minute / For heaven's sake / Nite crawler / Blues for TJ / 10 p.m. / Sleepwalk / Tequila / Bubble shuffle / Hello tomorrow / High steppin'.
■ CD . . . . . . . . . . . . . . . . . . . . .GRD 9611
■ LP . . . . . . . . . . . . . . . . . . . . . .GR 9611
■ MC . . . . . . . . . . . . . . . . . . . . .GRC 9611
GRP / Aug '90.

### DISCOVERY.
**Tracks:** Hello tomorrow / Those eyes / Knock on wood / Discovery / My home away from home / March of the jazz angels / Minute by minute / Place for skipper / Her favourite song.
■ LP . . . . . . . . . . . . . . . . . . . .XMCA 42003
■ CD . . . . . . . . . . . . . . . . . . . .MCAD 42003
■ MC . . . . . . . . . . . . . . . . . . .IMCAC 42003
MCA / Jul '87.
CD . . . . . . . . . . . . . . . . . . . . .GRP 01032
GRP / Oct '92 / BMG / New Note.

### FRIENDS.
**Tracks:** Breaking ground / South town / Tequila / Blues for TJ / Song in the 5th grade / Cruisin' / L A N Y / Friends.
■ LP . . . . . . . . . . . . . . . . . . . . .923834 1
■ MC . . . . . . . . . . . . . . . . . . . .923834 4
WEA / '83.
■ CD . . . . . . . . . . . . . . . . . . . . .GRP 01042
BMG / Aug '92.

### KID GLOVES.
**Tracks:** Kid gloves / Preacher / Michele's whistle / Oui oui si / Heart to heart / Just my imagination / Where be Mosada / Farm jazz / Terry T. / If I could I would.
CD . . . . . . . . . . . . . . . . . . . . .GRP 96832
GRP / Aug '92 / BMG / New Note.
■ DCC . . . . . . . . . . . . . . . . . . .GRP 96835
GRP / Aug '94.

### LARRY CARLTON.
**Tracks:** Room 335 / Where did you come from / Nite crawler / Point it up / Rio samba / I apologise / Don't give it up / (It was) only yesterday.
■ LP . . . . . . . . . . . . . . . . . . . . . .K 56548
WEA / '79.

### LAST NITE.
**Tracks:** So what / Don't give it up / B.P. blues / All blues / Last nite / Emotions wound us so.
■ CD . . . . . . . . . . . . . . . . . . . .MCAD 3353
■ LP . . . . . . . . . . . . . . . . . . . . .MCF 3353
■ MC . . . . . . . . . . . . . . . . . . . .MCFC 3353
MCA / Jan '87.
CD . . . . . . . . . . . . . . . . . . . . .GRP 01252
GRP / Aug '92 / BMG / New Note.

### LIVE IN JAPAN.
**Tracks:** Not Advised.
■ LP . . . . . . . . . . . . . . . . . . . . . .P 10643
Flyover / '79.

### ON SOLID GROUND.
**Tracks:** Not Advised.
CD . . . . . . . . . . . . . . . . . . . . .GRP 01062
BMG / Nov '92 / BMG.

### RENEGADE GENTLEMAN.
**Tracks:** Crazy Mama / R.C.M / Sleep medicine / Cold day in hell / Anthem / Amen A.C. / Never say naw / Farm jazz / Nothin' comes / Bogner / Red hot poker / I gotta right.
CD . . . . . . . . . . . . . . . . . . . . .GRP 97442
GRP / Aug '93 / BMG / New Note.

### SLEEPWALK.
**Tracks:** Last nite / Blues bird / Song for Katie / Frenchman's flat / Upper kern / 10.00 p.m. / You gotta get it while you can / Sleepwalk.
■ LP . . . . . . . . . . . . . . . . . . . . . .K 56974
■ MC . . . . . . . . . . . . . . . . . . . . .K4 56974
WEA / '82.
CD . . . . . . . . . . . . . . . . . . . . .GRP 01262
BMG / Aug '92 / BMG.

## Carmen, Pauli

### DIAL MY NUMBER.
**Tracks:** Dial my number / Flashback / You impress me / Big on pleasure / Lose control / High and low / Close to the bone / Dangerous.
- LP . . . . . . . . . . . . . . . . . . . . . . . CBS 26960
- MC . . . . . . . . . . . . . . . . . . . . . . .40 26960
CBS / Jul '86.

### DIAL MY NUMBER.
**Tracks:** Dial my number.
- 12" . . . . . . . . . . . . . . . . . . . . . . . TA 7096
- 7" . . . . . . . . . . . . . . . . . . . . . . . . . A 7096
CBS / May '86.

## Carne, Jean

Jean Carne started her career, with husband Doug, on the California jazz circuit, where they recorded for the Ovation label. When their marriage broke up, Jean made a living as a nightclub singer until being spotted by producer Norman Connors. She arranged for her to sing on the album *Saturday Night Special*; a subsequent tour took her to Philadelphia where she met Gamble & Huff and signed to their Philadelphia International label. Her four albums (as Jean Carn) for them failed to take off but she did record many of the tracks for which she is remembered, including *Happy To Be With You*. When the label collapsed, Kenny Gamble secured her a deal with Motown, where she was reunitd with Norman Connors and recorded *Trust Me*. In 1982 she returned to the jazz world, again as Jean Carne, and signed a new deal with Omni/ Atlantic. Her first album for them, *Closer Than Close*, was an R&B [8]X1 in the States but she has yet to make any mark on the charts over here.

### AIN'T NO WAY.
**Tracks:** Ain't no way / Flame of love / You're a part of me (Only on 12".).
- 12" . . . . . . . . . . . . . . . . . . . . . . PT 42068
- 7" . . . . . . . . . . . . . . . . . . . . . . . PB 42067
RCA / Jun '88.

### ARTISTS SHOWCASE: JEAN CARNE.
**Tracks:** We got some catching up to do / Lonely girl in a cold cold world / You love don't come easy / Trust me / I'm in love once again / No no you can't come back now / Bet your lucky star / Start the fire / When I find you love / Love don't love nobody / Free love / If you wanna go back / Sweet and wonderful / Was that all it was / You got a problem / Dindi / If you don't know me by now / Don't let it go to your head / Mystic stranger / Let's stay together / Happy to be with you.
- LP . . . . . . . . . . . . . . . . . . . . . MUSIC 7
MC . . . . . . . . . . . . . . . . . . . . . . . ZCMUS 7
Street Sounds / Sep '87 / BMG / Total.

### CLOSER THAN CLOSE.
**Tracks:** Not Advised.
- LP . . . . . . . . . . . . . . . . . . . .OMN LP 2
Omni (USA) / Sep '86.

### CLOSER THAN CLOSE.
**Tracks:** Closer than close.
- 12" . . . . . . . . . . . . . . . . . . . . 12 OMN 3
- 7" . . . . . . . . . . . . . . . . . . . . . .OMN 3
Omni (USA) / Aug '86.

### IF YOU DON'T KNOW ME BY NOW.
**Tracks:** If you don't know me by now / Completeness.
- 7" . . . . . . . . . . . . . . . . . . . . . TMG 1271
Motown / Jul '84.

### LET ME BE THE ONE.
**Tracks:** Let me be the one / Break up to make up / Closer than close (Extra track on 12".).
- 12" . . . . . . . . . . . . . . . . . . . . PT 41880
- 7" . . . . . . . . . . . . . . . . . . . . . PB 41879
RCA / Mar '88.

### TRUST ME.
**Tracks:** Steady on my mind / Don't let me slip away / Trust me / Super explosion / My baby loves me / If you don't know me by now / Completeness / Better to me.
- LP . . . . . . . . . . . . . . . . . . . . .STML 12172
Motown / Aug '82.

### WAS THAT ALL IT WAS.
**Tracks:** Was that all it was / What's on your mind.
- 7" . . . . . . . . . . . . . . . . . . . . . PIR 8840
Philadelphia Int / Aug '80.

### YOU'RE A PART OF ME.
**Tracks:** You're a part of me / Heartache / Ain't no way / Givin' up on love / Let me be the one / Closer

to you / Walkin' the line / Don't want to love any more / Early morning love / Closer than close (Extra track on CD only.) / Break up to make up (Extra track on CD only.) / Flame of love (Extra track on CD only.) / Lucky charm (Extra track on CD only.).
- CD . . . . . . . . . . . . . . . . . . . . . PD 71624
- LP . . . . . . . . . . . . . . . . . . . . . PL 71624
- MC . . . . . . . . . . . . . . . . . . . . . PK 71624
RCA / Mar '88.

## Carr, James

James Carr's story is a genuine musical tragedy. He rose to fame as part of the Goldwax stable in the early '60s, along with his friend O.V. Wright. Carr recorded the original and arguably greatest version of *Dark End Of The Street* and rose to prominence in the U.S. with his third single *You've Got My Mind Messed Up*. After a tour with Otis Redding, Wilson Pickett and James Brown, his star seemed in the ascendent, but a first attack of mental illness, which was to plague him periodically from then on, put paid to the career his magnificent voice deserved. Since that time he has recorded sporadically: 1992's *Take Me To The Limit* was his first new material in years. While not a classic LP, it shows Carr still has a wonderful voice.

### I'M A FOOL FOR YOU.
**Tracks:** I'm a fool for you / Gonna send you back to Georgia.
- 7" . . . . . . . . . . . . . . . . . . . . . SS 2052
Stateside / Oct '67.

### LET IT HAPPEN.
**Tracks:** Let it happen / Losing game.
- 7" . . . . . . . . . . . . . . . . . . . . . SS 2038
Stateside / Jul '67.

### MAN NEEDS A WOMAN.
**Tracks:** Stronger than love / Man needs a woman / More love / You didn't know it but you had me / Woman is a man's best friend / I'm a fool for you / Losing game / Message to young lovers / Life turned her that way / Send you back to Georgia / Dark end of the street / Sowed love and reaped a heartache / You got to have soul / Let it happen / You hurt so good / You got my mind messed up.
- LP . . . . . . . . . . . . . . . . . . . . . SBLL 113
Bell / Jan '69.

### SOUL SURVIVOR.
**Tracks:** Soul survivor / Man worth knowing / Put love first / I can't leave your love alone / Things a woman need / Day dreamin' / All because of your love / I'm into something / Memphis after midnight / That's how strong a woman's love is.
CD . . . . . . . . . . . . . . . . . . . . .CDCH 487
Ace / Oct '93 / Pinnacle / Complete Record Co. Ltd.

### TAKE ME TO THE LIMIT.
**Tracks:** Take me to the limit / Sugar shock / Love attack / You gotta love your woman / High on your love / She's already gone / Our garden of Eden / I can't leave your love alone / What's a little love between friends / Lack of attention.
CD . . . . . . . . . . . . . . . . . . . . .CDCH 310
- LP . . . . . . . . . . . . . . . . . . . . . CH 310
Ace / Jan '91 / Pinnacle / Complete Record Co. Ltd.

### YOU GOT MY MIND MESSED UP.
**Tracks:** You got my mind messed up / That's what I want to know.
- 7" . . . . . . . . . . . . . . . . . . . . . SS 507
Stateside / '65.

## Carr, Johnny

### COME SHARE MY LOVE.
**Tracks:** Come share my love / Come on over.
- 7" . . . . . . . . . . . . . . . . . . . . . DPR 3
Dual Purpose / Aug '84.

### IF EVER I SEE YOU AGAIN.
**Tracks:** If ever I see you again / Such feeling.
- 7" . . . . . . . . . . . . . . . . . . . . . DPR 2
Dual Purpose / Mar '84.

### PENNY ARCADE.
**Tracks:** Penny arcade / Hold on.
- 7" . . . . . . . . . . . . . . . . . . . . . DPR 1
Dual Purpose / Dec '82.

### THEN SO DO I.
**Tracks:** Then so do I / I'm just a little bit shy.
- 7" . . . . . . . . . . . . . . . . . . . . . TF 681
Fontana / Mar '66.

### THINGS GET BETTER.
**Tracks:** Things get better / You got me baby.
- 7" . . . . . . . . . . . . . . . . . . . . . TF 823
Fontana / Apr '67.

## Carr, Linda

### CHERRY PIE GUY.
**Tracks:** Cherry pie guy / Hot cakes.
- 7" . . . . . . . . . . . . . . . . . . . . .2005 059
Chelsea Collection / Feb '76.

### EVERYTIME.
**Tracks:** Everytime / Trying to be good to you.
- 7" . . . . . . . . . . . . . . . . . . . . . SS 2058
Stateside / '67.

### HIGH WIRE.
**Tracks:** Highwire.
- 7" . . . . . . . . . . . . . . . . . . . . .2005 025
Chelsea Collection / Jul '75.

### HIGH WIRE (OLD GOLD) (Carr, Linda & Dee Clark).
**Tracks:** Highwire / Ride a wild horse.
- 7" . . . . . . . . . . . . . . . . . . . . .OG 9882
Old Gold / Apr '89.

## Carroll, Diahann

### DIAHANN CARROLL.
**Tracks:** Perfect love / I can't give back the love I feel for you / I mean to shine / Somewhere between love and tomorrow / Sweet sweet candy / I've never been a fool like this before / Easy to love / Anybody else / After being your lover / I've been there before.
- LP . . . . . . . . . . . . . . . . . . . . . WL 72382
- MC . . . . . . . . . . . . . . . . . . . . . WK 72382
Motown / Aug '86.

### PEOPLE ALL AROUND THE WORLD.
**Tracks:** People all around the world.
- 12" . . . . . . . . . . . . . . . . . . . . JIVET 213
- 7" . . . . . . . . . . . . . . . . . . . . . JIVE 213
Jive / Aug '89.

### TRIBUTE TO ETHEL WATERS.
**Tracks:** Not Advised.
CD . . . . . . . . . . . . . . . . . . . . . WW 2405
West Wind / Nov '92 / Swift / Charly / Koch International / Complete Record Co. Ltd / C.M. Distribution.

### WALK ON BY.
**Tracks:** Walk on by.
- 12" . . . . . . . . . . . . . . . . . . . . JIVET 237
- 7" . . . . . . . . . . . . . . . . . . . . . JIVE 237
Jive / Nov '89.

## Carroll, Dina

U.K. singer whose early career included a disastrous association with Streetsounds' supremo Morgan Khan and equally uncelebrated solo efforts. Her breakthrough came with '91 remake of Carole King's *It's Too Late*, appropriately credited to 'Quartz Introducing Dina Carroll'. A trio of Top 20 solo hits, biggest of which was the infectious *Ain't No Man*, paved the way for her debut album: *So Close* charted at No. 2 and remained on the U.K. listing for over sixty weeks. By the close of '93, Carroll had two singles in the Top 10, and was one of the year's best-selling acts, despite her reluctant and low-key self-promotion.

### AIN'T NO MAN.
**Tracks:** Ain't no man / You'll lose a good thing.
- 12" . . . . . . . . . . . . . . . . . . . . AMY 0001
- CD Single . . . . . . . . . . . . . . . . AMCD 0001
- 7" . . . . . . . . . . . . . . . . . . . . . AM 0001
- MC Single . . . . . . . . . . . . . . . . AMMC 0001
A&M / Jun '92.

### DON'T BE A STRANGER.
**Tracks:** Don't be a stranger.
- 12" . . . . . . . . . . . . . . . . . . . . 580389-1
- 7" . . . . . . . . . . . . . . . . . . . . . 580389-7
- CD Single . . . . . . . . . . . . . . . . 580389-2
- MC Single . . . . . . . . . . . . . . . . 580389-4
A&M / Oct '93.

### EXPRESS.
**Tracks:** Express / Special kind of love (Features on 12" & CDS only.) / Ain't no man (Features on 12" & CDS only.).
- 12" . . . . . . . . . . . . . . . . . . . . 580262-1
- 7" . . . . . . . . . . . . . . . . . . . . . 580262-7
- CD Single . . . . . . . . . . . . . . . . 580262-2
- MC Single . . . . . . . . . . . . . . . . 580262-4
A&M / May '93.

■ DELETED

## PERFECT YEAR, THE.
**Tracks:** Perfect year.
■ 12" . . . . . . . . . . . . . . . . . . . .580481-1
■ 7" . . . . . . . . . . . . . . . . . . . .580480-7
■ CD Single. . . . . . . . . . . . . .580481-2
■ MC Single. . . . . . . . . . . . . .580480-4
A&M / Dec '93.

## SO CLOSE.
**Tracks:** So close / Why did I let you go.
■ 12" . . . . . . . . . . . . . . . . . . . .AMY 0101
■ 7" . . . . . . . . . . . . . . . . . . . .AM 0101
■ CD Single. . . . . . . . . . . . . .AMCD 0101
■ MC Single. . . . . . . . . . . . . .AMMC 0101
A&M / Nov '92.

## SO CLOSE.
**Tracks:** Special kind of love / Hold on / This time / Falling / So close / Ain't no man / Express / Heaven sent / You'll never know / Don't be a stranger / Why did I let you go (On CD only) / If I knew you then (On CD only).
CD . . . . . . . . . . . . . . . . . . . .540034-2
LP . . . . . . . . . . . . . . . . . . . .540034-1
MC. . . . . . . . . . . . . . . . . . . .540034-4
A&M / Jan '93 / PolyGram.
DCC . . . . . . . . . . . . . . . . . . . .540034-5
A&M / May '94 / PolyGram.

## SO CLOSE - THE VIDEOS.
**Tracks:** Ain't no man / So close / Special kind of love / I don't want to talk about it / This time / Express / Don't be a stranger.
VHS . . . . . . . . . . . . . . . . . . . .887163
VVL / Nov '93 / PolyGram.

## THIS TIME.
**Tracks:** This time / Falling / Why did I let you go (On 12"/CDs only) / Express (On 12" only).
■ 12" . . . . . . . . . . . . . . . . . . . .AMY 0184
■ 7" . . . . . . . . . . . . . . . . . . . .AM 0184
■ CD Single. . . . . . . . . . . . . .AMCD 0184
■ MC Single. . . . . . . . . . . . . .AMMC 0184
A&M / Feb '93.

# Carstairs

## IT REALLY HURTS ME GIRL.
**Tracks:** It really hurts me girl.
■ 12" . . . . . . . . . . . . . . . . . . . .HEAT 7 12
■ 7" . . . . . . . . . . . . . . . . . . . .HEAT 7
Inferno (1) / Jul '80.

# Carter, Clarence

Known as the C & C boys, Carter and partner Calvin Thomas (aka Scott) released seven singles before Carter launched his solo career in 1966 following Thomas's forced retirement. Signing to Fame he released *Tell Daddy* in 1967 scoring a R&B hit and the following year his records began crossing over to the pop charts. Now signed to Atlantic *Slip Away* reached No. 6 on the US Hot 100 and was followed by the No. 13 *Too Weak To Fight*. In 1970 he released *Patches* (previously recorded by the Chairmen Of The Board), achieving his only British hit. Subsequent singles met with more limited success and Carter went on to record a number of self-produced albums.

## BEST OF CLARENCE CARTER, THE.
**Tracks:** Not Advised.
CD . . . . . . . . . . . . . . . . . . . .RSACD 801
Sequel / Oct '94 / Total / BMG.

## BETWEEN A ROCK AND A HARD PLACE.
**Tracks:** Things ain't like they used to be / Straw that broke the camel's back / I ain't leaving, girl / Too weak to fight / Pickin' 'em down layin' 'em down / I'm between a rock and a hard place / I've got a thing for you baby / If you see my lady / Love building.
LP . . . . . . . . . . . . . . . . . . . .ICH 1068
MC. . . . . . . . . . . . . . . . . . . .ICH 1068 MC
Ichiban / Sep '90 / A.D.A. Distribution / Pinnacle / ACD Trading Ltd. / Koch International / Direct Distribution.
CD . . . . . . . . . . . . . . . . . . . .CDICH 1068
Ichiban / Oct '93 / A.D.A. Distribution / Pinnacle / ACD Trading Ltd. / Koch International / Direct Distribution.

## COURTROOM.
**Tracks:** Courtroom / Gettin' the bills.
■ 7" . . . . . . . . . . . . . . . . . . . .2091093
Atlantic / May '71.

## DOCTOR CC.
**Tracks:** Dr. CC / I stayed away too long / If you let me take you home / Left over love / You been cheatin' on me / Try me / Let's funk / Strokin'.

■ LP . . . . . . . . . . . . . . . . . . . .LPLUTE 2
Tout Ensemble / Jul '86.
MC. . . . . . . . . . . . . . . . . . . .ZCICH 1003
■ LP . . . . . . . . . . . . . . . . . . . .ICH 1003
Ichiban / Aug '87 / A.D.A. Distribution / Pinnacle / ACD Trading Ltd. / Koch International / Direct Distribution.
CD . . . . . . . . . . . . . . . . . . . .ICH 1003CD
Ichiban / Oct '93 / A.D.A. Distribution / Pinnacle / ACD Trading Ltd. / Koch International / Direct Distribution.

## DOCTOR'S GREATEST PRESCRIPTIONS, THE (The Best Of Clarence Carter).
**Tracks:** Strokin' / Trying to sleep tonight / Messin' with my mind / I was in the neighbourhood / Dr. C.C. / Love me with a feeling / I'm not just good / I'm the best / Slip away / Grandpa can't fly his kite / Kiss you all over / I've got a thing for you baby / I'm between a rock and a hard place.
■ CD . . . . . . . . . . . . . . . . . . . .CDICH 1116
■ LP . . . . . . . . . . . . . . . . . . . .ICH 1116
■ MC. . . . . . . . . . . . . . . . . . . .ICH 1116MC
Ichiban / Aug '91.
CD . . . . . . . . . . . . . . . . . . . .ICH 1116CD
Ichiban / Feb '94 / A.D.A. Distribution / Pinnacle / ACD Trading Ltd. / Koch International / Direct Distribution.

## DYNAMIC CLARENCE CARTER, THE.
**Tracks:** I'd rather go blind / Think about it / Road of love / You've been a long time comin' / Light my fire / That old time feeling / Steal away / Let me comfort you / Look what I got / Too weak to fight / Harper Valley P.T.A. / Weekend love.
■ LP . . . . . . . . . . . . . . . . . . . .588 172
Atlantic / Apr '69.

## GREATEST PRESCRIPTIONS.
**Tracks:** Not Advised.
CD . . . . . . . . . . . . . . . . . . . .ICH 116CD
LP . . . . . . . . . . . . . . . . . . . .ICH 116
MC. . . . . . . . . . . . . . . . . . . .ICH 116MC
Backs / Sep '91 / RTM / Pinnacle.

## HAVE YOU MET CLARENCE CARTER.
**Tracks:** Not Advised.
MC. . . . . . . . . . . . . . . . . . . .ICH 1141MC
■ CD . . . . . . . . . . . . . . . . . . . .ICH 1141CD
Ichiban / Nov '92 / A.D.A. Distribution / Pinnacle / ACD Trading Ltd. / Koch International / Direct Distribution.

## HOOKED ON LOVE.
**Tracks:** Not Advised.
■ LP . . . . . . . . . . . . . . . . . . . .ICH 1016
Ichiban / Nov '87.
CD . . . . . . . . . . . . . . . . . . . .CDICH 1016
MC. . . . . . . . . . . . . . . . . . . .ZCICH 1016
Ichiban / Mar '94 / A.D.A. Distribution / Pinnacle / ACD Trading Ltd. / Koch International / Direct Distribution.

## I FEEL IT.
**Tracks:** I feel it / Grandpa can't fly his kite.
■ 12" . . . . . . . . . . . . . . . . . . . .12 PO 11
■ 7" . . . . . . . . . . . . . . . . . . . .88 143
Ichiban / '88.

## I WAS IN THE NEIGHBOURHOOD.
**Tracks:** I was in the neighbourhood.
■ 12" . . . . . . . . . . . . . . . . . . . .12LUTE 2
■ 7" . . . . . . . . . . . . . . . . . . . .LUTE 2
Tout Ensemble / May '86.

## I'M NOT JUST GOOD I'M THE BEST.
**Tracks:** I'm not just good I'm the best / Kiss you all over.
■ 12" . . . . . . . . . . . . . . . . . . . .12 PO 16
Ichiban / Jan '89.

## IT'S ALL IN YOUR MIND.
**Tracks:** It's all in your mind / Willie and Laura Mae Jones.
■ 7" . . . . . . . . . . . . . . . . . . . .2091 045
Atlantic / Jan '71.

## MESSIN' WITH MY MIND.
**Tracks:** Not Advised.
■ LP . . . . . . . . . . . . . . . . . . . .ICH 001
MC. . . . . . . . . . . . . . . . . . . .ZCICH 001
Ichiban / Jan '88 / A.D.A. Distribution / Pinnacle / ACD Trading Ltd. / Koch International / Direct Distribution.
CD . . . . . . . . . . . . . . . . . . . .ICH 1001
Ichiban / Oct '93 / A.D.A. Distribution / Pinnacle / ACD Trading Ltd. / Koch International / Direct Distribution.

## MESSIN' WITH MY MIND.
**Tracks:** Messin' with my mind / It ain't what you do.
■ 12" . . . . . . . . . . . . . . . . . . . .12 ACERT 1

■ 7" . . . . . . . . . . . . . . . . . . . .ACERT 1
Certain / Oct '85.

## PATCHES.
**Tracks:** Patches / Knock on wood / Letter / I can't leave your love alone.
■ 7" . . . . . . . . . . . . . . . . . . . .2091030
Atlantic / Oct '70.
■ 7" . . . . . . . . . . . . . . . . . . . .CR 178
Blast From The Past / Aug '82.

## PATCHES.
**Tracks:** Patches / Looking for a fox.
■ 7" . . . . . . . . . . . . . . . . . . . .CS 8003
Contempo (1) / Mar '78.

## PATCHES.
**Tracks:** Willie and Laura Mae Jones / Say man / I'm just a prisoner / Let it be / I can't leave your love alone / Your love lifted me / Till I can't take it anymore / Patches / It's all in your mind / Changes / C.C. blues / Getting the bills.
■ LP . . . . . . . . . . . . . . . . . . . .2400 027
Atlantic / Jan '71.

## SNATCHING IT BACK (The Best Of Clarence Carter).
**Tracks:** Tell Daddy / Slipped, tripped and fell in love / I can't see myself / Too weak to fight / Looking for a fox / Step by step / Patches / Soul deep / Kind woman / Making love / Back door Santa.
■ CD . . . . . . . . . . . . . . . . . . . .R2 70286
Rhino (USA) / Apr '92.
CD . . . . . . . . . . . . . . . . . . . .8122702862
WEA / Jul '93 / WEA.

## SOUL DEEP.
**Tracks:** She ain't gonna do right / Road of love / Slip away / That old time feeling / Let me comfort you / Too weak to fight / I'd rather go blind / Snatching it back / Making love (at the dark end of the street) / Soul deep / I can't leave your love alone / Patches / It's all in your mind / Thread the needle / Getting the bills / I'm the one.
■ LP . . . . . . . . . . . . . . . . . . . .ED 125
Edsel / Apr '84.

## STROKIN'.
**Tracks:** Strokin' / Watch where you stroke.
■ 7" . . . . . . . . . . . . . . . . . . . .7 STROKE 1
■ 12" . . . . . . . . . . . . . . . . . . . .STROKE 1
12" . . . . . . . . . . . . . . . . . . . .MCS 86108
Ichiban / Mar '94 / A.D.A. Distribution / Pinnacle / ACD Trading Ltd. / Koch International / Direct Distribution.

## TESTIFYIN'.
**Tracks:** Bad news / Snatching it back / Soul deep / I smell a rat / Doin' our thing / You can't miss what you can't measure / Instant reaction / Making love / Feeling is right / Back door Santa / I can't do without you.
■ LP . . . . . . . . . . . . . . . . . . . .588 191
Atlantic / Sep '69.

## THIS IS.
**Tracks:** Do what you gotta do / Looking for a fox / Slippin' around / I'm qualified / I can't see myself / Wind it up / Part time love / Thread the needle / Slip away / Funky fever / She ain't gonna do right / Set me free.
■ LP . . . . . . . . . . . . . . . . . . . .588 152
Atlantic / Nov '69.

## TOUCH OF THE BLUES.
**Tracks:** I'm not just good, I'm the best / Rock me baby / Why do I stay here / It's a man down there / All night, all day / Kiss you all over / Stormy Monday blues / Dance to the blues.
LP . . . . . . . . . . . . . . . . . . . .ICH 1032
MC. . . . . . . . . . . . . . . . . . . .ZCICH 1032
Ichiban / Feb '89 / A.D.A. Distribution / Pinnacle / ACD Trading Ltd. / Koch International / Direct Distribution.
CD . . . . . . . . . . . . . . . . . . . .CDICH 1032
Ichiban / Oct '93 / A.D.A. Distribution / Pinnacle / ACD Trading Ltd. / Koch International / Direct Distribution.

## WARNING.
**Tracks:** Warning / On your way down.
■ 7" . . . . . . . . . . . . . . . . . . . .ABC 4037
Anchor (1) / Jan '75.

# Carter, Mel

## LOVE IS ALL WE NEED.
**Tracks:** Love is all we need / I wish I didn't love you so.
■ 7" . . . . . . . . . . . . . . . . . . . .LIB 66148
Liberty / Mar '66.

■ DELETED

65

**MY HEART SINGS.**
Tracks: My heart sings / When I hold the hand of the one I love.
■ 7″ . . . . . . . . . . . . . . . . . . . . . LIB 66138
Liberty / Jan '66.

## Carter, Valerie

**BLUE SIDE.**
Tracks: Blue side / What becomes of us.
■ 7″ . . . . . . . . . . . . . . . . . . . . . CBS 7327
CBS / Jun '79.

**JUST A STONE'S THROW AWAY.**
Tracks: Ooh, child / Ringing doorbells in the rain / Heartache / Face of Appalachia / So, so happy / Stone's throw away / Cowboy angel / City lights / Back to blue some more.
■ LP . . . . . . . . . . . . . . . . . . CBS 81958
CBS / Jun '77.

**OOH CHILD.**
Tracks: Ooh child / Heartache.
■ 7″ . . . . . . . . . . . . . . . . . . . . CBS 5108
CBS / May '77.

**WILD CHILD.**
Tracks: Crazy / Da doo rendezvous / What's become of us / Taking the long way home / Lady in the dark / Story of love / Blue side / Change in luck / Trying to get to you / Wild child.
■ LP . . . . . . . . . . . . . . . . . . CBS 82556
CBS / Feb '79.

## Cash, Alvin

**ALI SHUFFLE.**
Tracks: Ali shuffle / Doing the feeling.
■ 7″ . . . . . . . . . . . . . . . . . . . . CS 2110
Contempo (1) / Feb '77.
■ 7″ . . . . . . . . . . . . . . . . . . . . . BR 41
Brunswick / Mar '77.

**CHARGE.**
Tracks: Charge / Diff'rent strokes for diff'rent folks.
■ 7″ . . . . . . . . . . . . . . . . . . . . .PT 147
President / Aug '67.

**DOIN' THE ALI SHUFFLE.**
Tracks: Doin' the ali shuffle / Feel so good.
■ 7″ . . . . . . . . . . . . . . . . . . . . .PT 129
President / Mar '67.

**PHILLY FREEZE.**
Tracks: Philly freeze.
■ 7″ . . . . . . . . . . . . . . . . . . . . .SS 543
Stateside / '65.

**PHILLY FREEZE (Cash, Alvin & The Registers).**
Tracks: Philly freeze / No deposit, no return.
■ 7″ . . . . . . . . . . . . . . . . . . . . PT 115
President / Jun '66.

**TWINE TIME.**
Tracks: Twine time.
■ 7″ . . . . . . . . . . . . . . . . . . . . .SS 386
Stateside / '64.

## Cashflow

**BIG MONEY.**
Tracks: That's the ticket / Come closer / Devastation / Love education / All systems go / You know that / Big money / Love's funky.
■ CD . . . . . . . . . . . . . . . . . . 832 187-2
■ LP . . . . . . . . . . . . . . . . . . 832 187-1
■ MC . . . . . . . . . . . . . . . . . . 832 187-4
Club / Oct '88.

**CAN'T LET LOVE PASS US BY.**
Tracks: Can't let love pass us by / Can't let love pass us by (remix) (Available on 12″ remix only.) / Can't let love pass us by (remix)(dub version) (Available on 12″ remix only.) / I need your love / Spending money (Extra track available on 12″ versions only.).
■ 12″ Remix . . . . . . . . . . . . . . . .JABXR 33
■ 12″ . . . . . . . . . . . . . . . . . . JABX 33
■ 7″ . . . . . . . . . . . . . . . . . . . JAB 33
Club / Jul '86.

**CASHFLOW.**
Tracks: Party freak / Mine all mine / Can't let love pass us by / Spending money / Reach out / I need your love / Just a dream.
■ LP . . . . . . . . . . . . . . . . . . JABH 17
■ MC . . . . . . . . . . . . . . . . . . JABHC 17
Club / Jun '86.
■ CD . . . . . . . . . . . . . . . . . . 826 028-2
Club / Jan '87.

**MINE ALL MINE.**
Tracks: Mine all mine / Party freak / It's just a dream (Extra track on 12″ version only.).
■ 12″ . . . . . . . . . . . . . . . . . . .JABX 30
■ 12″ Remix . . . . . . . . . . . . . . . .JABXR 30
■ 7″ . . . . . . . . . . . . . . . . . . . JAB 30
Club / May '86.

**MINE ALL MINE (OLD GOLD).**
Tracks: Mine all mine / Party freak.
■ 12″ . . . . . . . . . . . . . . . . . . .OG 4086
Old Gold / Nov '88.

## Cashmere

**CAN I.**
Tracks: Can I / Can I (full length).
■ 7″ . . . . . . . . . . . . . . . . . . . BRW 19
■ 12″ . . . . . . . . . . . . . . . . . . 12 BRW 19
4th & Broadway / Jan '85.

**CASHMERE.**
Tracks: Not Advised.
■ LP . . . . . . . . . . . . . . . . . . BRLP 503
4th & Broadway / Feb '85.

**DO IT ANY WAY YOU WANNA.**
Tracks: Do it anyway you wanna.
■ 12″ . . . . . . . . . . . . . . . . . . PWSL 108
■ 7″ . . . . . . . . . . . . . . . . . . . PWS 108
Philly World (USA) / Mar '83.

**LET THE MUSIC TURN YOU ON.**
Tracks: Try your lovin' / Inner feelings / Contemplation / Light of love / Let the music turn you on / Tracks of my tears / Do it any way you wanna.
■ LP . . . . . . . . . . . . . . . . . . PWLP 1005
Philly World (USA) / Oct '83.

**LET THE MUSIC TURN YOU ON.**
Tracks: Let the music turn you on.
■ 12″ . . . . . . . . . . . . . . . . . . PWSL 114
■ 7″ . . . . . . . . . . . . . . . . . . . PWS 114
Philly World (USA) / Oct '83.

**TRY YOUR LOVIN'.**
Tracks: Try your lovin'.
■ 12″ . . . . . . . . . . . . . . . . . . PWSL 113
■ 7″ . . . . . . . . . . . . . . . . . . . PWS 113
Philly World (USA) / Aug '83.

**WE NEED LOVE.**
Tracks: We need love / Keep me up.
■ 7″ . . . . . . . . . . . . . . . . . . . BRW 22
■ 12″ . . . . . . . . . . . . . . . . . . 12 BRW 22
4th & Broadway / Mar '85.

## Casiopea

**CROSS POINT.**
Tracks: Not Advised.
CD . . . . . . . . . . . . . . . . . . 38XA 24
Starr / '88 / PolyGram.

**DOWN UPBEAT.**
Tracks: Not Advised.
■ LP . . . . . . . . . . . . . . . . . . SNTF 926
Sonet / Nov '84.

**FOUR BY FOUR.**
Tracks: Not Advised.
CD . . . . . . . . . . . . . . . . . . 38XA 10
Alfa / '88 / Sony.

**JIVE JIVE.**
Tracks: Not Advised.
CD . . . . . . . . . . . . . . . . . . 38XA 8
Starr / '88 / PolyGram.

**MINT JAMS.**
Tracks: Take me / Asayaka / Midnight rendezvous / Time limit / Domino line / Tears of the star / Swear.
■ LP . . . . . . . . . . . . . . . . . . SNTF 924
Sonet / '88.

**SOUNDOGRAPHY, THE.**
Tracks: Asayaka / Mid-Manhattan / Looking up / Misty lady / What can't speak a lie / Fabbydabby / Soundography / Gypsy wind / Eyes of the mind / Sunnyside feeling.
CD . . . . . . . . . . . . . . . . . . SNTCD 919
Sonet / Oct '86 / Swift / C.M. Distribution / Roots Records / Jazz Music / Sonet Records / Cadillac / Projection / Wellard / Hot Shot.
■ LP . . . . . . . . . . . . . . . . . . SNTF 919
Sonet / Jul '88.

**SOUNDOGRAPHY, THE.**
Tracks: Soundography / Looking up.
■ 7″ . . . . . . . . . . . . . . . . . . . SON 2269
Sonet / Jun '84.

## Caston & Majors

**CHILD OF LOVE.**
Tracks: Child of love / No one will know.
■ LP . . . . . . . . . . . . . . . . . . TMG 938
Tamla Motown / Feb '75.

**SING.**
Tracks: Sing / There's fear.
■ 7″ . . . . . . . . . . . . . . . . . . . TMG 951
Tamla Motown / Jun '75.

## Castor, Jimmy

**BERTHA BUTT BOOGIE (Castor, Jimmy Bunch).**
Tracks: Bertha butt boogie.
■ 7″ . . . . . . . . . . . . . . . . . . . K 10554
Atlantic / Jan '75.

**EVERYTHING IS BEAUTIFUL TO ME.**
Tracks: Everything is beautiful to me / Magic in the music.
■ 7″ . . . . . . . . . . . . . . . . . . . K 10874
WEA / '79.

**HEY LEROY.**
Tracks: Hey Leroy / Ham Locks Espanol.
■ 7″ . . . . . . . . . . . . . . . . . . . BF 1543
Philips / Jan '67.

**MAGIC SAXOPHONE.**
Tracks: Magic saxophone / Just you girl.
■ 7″ . . . . . . . . . . . . . . . . . . . BF 1590
Philips / Jun '67.

**POTENTIAL (Castor, Jimmy Bunch).**
Tracks: Potential / Daniel.
■ 7″ . . . . . . . . . . . . . . . . . . . K 10645
Atlantic / Jul '75.

**SUPER SOUND.**
Tracks: Supersound / Drifting.
■ 7″ . . . . . . . . . . . . . . . . . . . K 10728
Atlantic / Mar '76.

**SUPER SOUND (Castor, Jimmy Bunch).**
Tracks: Supersound / King Kong / Bom bom / Groove will make you move / Drifting / Magic in the music / What's best.
■ LP . . . . . . . . . . . . . . . . . . K 50190
Atlantic / '77.

## Casualeers

**DANCE DANCE DANCE.**
Tracks: Dance, dance, dance.
■ 7″ . . . . . . . . . . . . . . . . . . . .DDS 103
Pye Disco Demand / '74.

## Caswell, Johnny

**IN THIS LAND.**
Tracks: In this land / Right house wrong night.
■ 7″ . . . . . . . . . . . . . . . . . . . MCA 733
MCA / Oct '81.

**YOU DON'T LOVE ME ANYMORE.**
Tracks: You don't love me anymore / You've been leading me on.
■ 7″ . . . . . . . . . . . . . . . . . . . TOWN 106
Kent / Apr '85.

## Cayenne

**CROSS THE CHANNEL FERRY.**
Tracks: Cross the channel ferry.
■ 12″ . . . . . . . . . . . . . . . . . . .CODS 20T
■ 7″ . . . . . . . . . . . . . . . . . . . CODS 20
Coda / Aug '86.

**EVENING IN JAFFA.**
Tracks: Not Advised.
■ LP . . . . . . . . . . . . . . . . . . CODA 11
■ MC . . . . . . . . . . . . . . . . . . COCA 11
Coda / '84.
CD . . . . . . . . . . . . . . . . . . CODA 11 CD
Coda / '88 / Roots Records / Pinnacle / C.M. Distribution / Zodiac Records.

**HOT NIGHTS.**
Tracks: Not Advised.
CD . . . . . . . . . . . . . . . . . . CODA 22 CD
■ LP . . . . . . . . . . . . . . . . . . CODA 22
■ MC . . . . . . . . . . . . . . . . . . COCA 22
Coda / Sep '86 / Roots Records / Pinnacle / C.M. Distribution / Zodiac Records.
CD . . . . . . . . . . . . . . . . . . .834165-2
■ LP . . . . . . . . . . . . . . . . . . .834165-1
Landscape / Apr '88 / THE.

**ROBERTO WHO?.**
Tracks: Not Advised.
■ LP . . . . . . . . . . . . . . . . . . .GPLP 30
Groove PR / '84.

**ROBERTO WHO?.**
Tracks: Roberto who.
■ 12" . . . . . . . . . . . . . . . . . GP 3012 12
■ 7" . . . . . . . . . . . . . . . . . . .GP 3012 7
Groove PR / '81.

## Celi Bee

**ALTERNATING CURRENTS (Celi Bee & The Buzzy Bunch).**
Tracks: Macho / Together / Hold your horses / Babe / Comin' up strong / Alternating currents / Disposable love / Lost in love.
■ LP . . . . . . . . . . . . . . . . . TKR 82531
TK / Jun '78.

**BOOMERANG (Celi Bee & The Buzzy Bunch).**
Tracks: Boomerang / Can't let you go.
■ 7" . . . . . . . . . . . . . . . . . . TKR 7509
TK / Jan '79.

**CELI BEE & HER BUZZY BUNCH.**
Tracks: Superman / Smile / It's sad / Hurt me, hurt me / One love / Closer, closer.
■ LP . . . . . . . . . . . . . . . . . . XL 14060
TK / Jul '77.
■ LP . . . . . . . . . . . . . . . . . TKR 82513
TK / Apr '78.

**FLY ME ON THE WINGS OF LOVE.**
Tracks: Fly me on the wings of love / Higher and higher / Love, look what you've done to me / Midnight passion / Epilogue / Boomerang / Can't let you go / For the love of my man / You're the best thing.
■ LP . . . . . . . . . . . . . . . . . TKR 83351
TK / Mar '79.

**HOLD YOUR HORSES BABE (Celi Bee & The Buzzy Bunch).**
Tracks: Hold your horses babe / Alternating currents.
■ 7" . . . . . . . . . . . . . . . . . . TKR 6032
TK / Jun '78.

**SUPERMAN (Celi Bee & The Buzzy Bunch).**
Tracks: Superman / Hurt me, hurt me.
■ 7" . . . . . . . . . . . . . . . . . . . XB 2182
TK / May '77.

## Central Line

**BETCHA GONNA.**
Tracks: Betcha gonna / Time for some fun.
■ 12" . . . . . . . . . . . . . . . . .MERX 152
■ 7" . . . . . . . . . . . . . . . . . MER 152
Mercury / Feb '84.

**BREAKING POINT.**
Tracks: Walking into sunshine / I need your love / Breaking point / Goodbye / That's no way to treat my love / Don't tell me (you know) / You can do it / Shake it up.
■ LP . . . . . . . . . . . . . . . . . MERA 001
■ MC . . . . . . . . . . . . . . . . .MERC 001
Mercury / Jan '82.

**CHOICE.**
Tracks: Time for some fun / Betcha gonna / How about you / Lost in love / Bad floyd / Nature boy / Man at the top / Surprise surprise / You've said enough.
■ LP . . . . . . . . . . . . . . . . . MERL 33
Mercury / May '84.

**DON'T TELL ME.**
Tracks: Don't tell me / Shake it up.
■ 12" . . . . . . . . . . . . . . . . . MERX 90
■ 7" . . . . . . . . . . . . . . . . . MER 90
Mercury / Jan '82.

**LOVELY DAY.**
Tracks: Lovely day.
■ 12" . . . . . . . . . . . . . . . . .MERX 144
■ 7" . . . . . . . . . . . . . . . . . MER 144
Mercury / Jul '85.

**NATURE BOY.**
Tracks: Nature boy / Goodbye.
■ 12" . . . . . . . . . . . . . . . . .MERX 131
■ 7" . . . . . . . . . . . . . . . . . MER 131
Mercury / Dec '82.

**NATURE BOY (OLD GOLD).**
Tracks: Nature boy / Walking into sunshine.
■ 12" . . . . . . . . . . . . . . . . .OG 4053
Old Gold / Mar '88.

**STICKS AND STONES.**
Tracks: Sticks and stones / Summer romance.
■ 12" . . . . . . . . . . . . . . . . . MERX 4
■ 7" . . . . . . . . . . . . . . . . . MER 4
Mercury / Feb '80.

**SURPRISE SURPRISE.**
Tracks: Surprise surprise / Surprised / Walking into sunshine.
■ 12" . . . . . . . . . . . . . . . . .MERX 133
■ 7" . . . . . . . . . . . . . . . . . MER 133
Mercury / Mar '83.

**TIME FOR SOME FUN.**
Tracks: Time for some fun / Conviction.
■ 12" . . . . . . . . . . . . . . . . .MERX 148
■ 7" . . . . . . . . . . . . . . . . . MER 148
Mercury / Nov '83.

**WALKING INTO SUNSHINE.**
Tracks: Walking into sunshine.
■ 12" . . . . . . . . . . . . . . . . . MERX 78
■ 7" . . . . . . . . . . . . . . . . . MER 78
Mercury / Aug '81.

**WHAT WE GOT ITS HOT.**
Tracks: What we got its hot / Girl.
■ 7" . . . . . . . . . . . . . . . . . 6007225
Mercury / Nov '79.

**YOU CAN DO IT (YOU KNOW).**
Tracks: You can do it (you know) / We chose love.
■ 12" . . . . . . . . . . . . . . . . . LINE 12
■ 7" . . . . . . . . . . . . . . . . . .LINE 7
Mercury / Jan '81.

**YOU'VE SAID ENOUGH.**
Tracks: You've said enough.
■ 12" . . . . . . . . . . . . . . . . .MERX 117
■ 7" . . . . . . . . . . . . . . . . . MER 117
Mercury / Nov '82.

## Centrefold

**DICTATOR.**
Tracks: Dictator / Dictator (inst).
■ 12" . . . . . . . . . . . . . . . . .CART 412
■ 7" . . . . . . . . . . . . . . . . . .CAR 412
Carrere / May '87.

**MONEY.**
Tracks: Money / So distant / More money (CD single only.) / Money (dance mix) (CD single only.) / Money (rock mix) (CD single only.).
■ 12" . . . . . . . . . . . . . . . . . XXX T3
■ 7" . . . . . . . . . . . . . . . . . XXX 3
■ CD Single . . . . . . . . . . . . . . XXX C3
Epic / Jan '89.

## Cerrone

**CERRONE'S PARADISE.**
Tracks: Take me / Time for love / Cerrone's paradise.
■ LP . . . . . . . . . . . . . . . . . K 50377
Atlantic / Aug '77.

**CERRONE'S PARADISE.**
Tracks: Cerrone's paradise / Take me.
■ 7" . . . . . . . . . . . . . . . . . K 10961
Atlantic / Sep '77.

**CLUB UNDERWORLD.**
Tracks: Club underworld.
■ 7" . . . . . . . . . . . . . . . . . PERS 107
Personal / Aug '84.

**GOLDEN TOUCH.**
Tracks: Je suis music / Rocket in the pocket / Look for love / Music of life.
■ LP . . . . . . . . . . . . . . . . . CBS 83282
CBS / Jan '79.

**IN CONCERT.**
Tracks: Gimme some lovin' / Africanism / Love in C minor / Living it up / Cerrone's paradise / Je suis music / Supernature / Sweet drums / Rocket in my pocket / Give me love.
■ LP . . . . . . . . . . . . . . . . CBS 88459
CBS / Nov '79.

**JE SUIS MUSIC.**
Tracks: Je suis music / Rocket in the pocket.
■ 7" . . . . . . . . . . . . . . . . . CBS 6918
CBS / Jan '79.

**LOOK FOR LOVE.**
Tracks: Look for love / Music for life.
■ 7" . . . . . . . . . . . . . . . . . CBS 7174
CBS / Mar '79.

**LOVE IN 'C' MINOR.**
Tracks: Love in 'C' minor / Black is black / Midnite lady.
■ LP . . . . . . . . . . . . . . . . . K 50334
Atlantic / '79.

**LOVE IN 'C' MINOR.**
Tracks: Love in 'C' minor / Black is black.
■ 7" . . . . . . . . . . . . . . . . . K 10895
Atlantic / Feb '77.

**SUPERNATURE.**
Tracks: Supernature / Sweet drums / In the smoke / Give me love / Love is the answer.
■ LP . . . . . . . . . . . . . . . . . K 50431
Atlantic / Feb '78.

**SUPERNATURE.**
Tracks: Supernature / Give me love.
■ 7" . . . . . . . . . . . . . . . . . K 11089
Atlantic / Mar '78.
■ 12" . . . . . . . . . . . . . . . . . NWKRRT 1
Network / Sep '94 / Sony / 3MV.

**SUPERNATURE 86.**
Tracks: Supernature 86.
■ 12" . . . . . . . . . . . . . . . . .MOLIF 5
■ 7" . . . . . . . . . . . . . . . . . MOL 5
Music Of Life / Aug '86.

## Chain Reaction

**CHANGE OF ACTION.**
Tracks: Not Advised.
■ LP . . . . . . . . . . . . . . . . . CPLPS 1
Vista Sounds / '83.

**CHASE A MIRACLE.**
Tracks: Not Advised.
■ LP . . . . . . . . . . . . . . . . . CPLPS 2
Vista Sounds / '83.

**DANCE FREAK (Chain Reaction & Vanetta).**
Tracks: Dance freak.
■ 12" . . . . . . . . . . . . . . . . .BLUEC 16
Blue Chip / Jun '89.

**INDEBTED TO YOU.**
Tracks: Never lose, never win / Why can't we be lovers / Quicksand / Think I'll keep this song just like it is / Cold steel / Miss Lovely, Miss Beautiful / Hogtied / Indebted to you / Chase a miracle.
■ LP . . . . . . . . . . . . . . . . . GULP 1021
Gull / Jul '77.

**NEVER LOSE, NEVER WIN.**
Tracks: Never lose, never win / Chase a miracle.
■ 7" . . . . . . . . . . . . . . . . . GULS 60
Gull / May '78.

**WHY CAN'T WE BE LOVERS.**
Tracks: Why can't we be lovers / Hogtied.
■ 7" . . . . . . . . . . . . . . . . . GULS 53
Gull / Sep '77.

## Chairmen Of The Board

Formed by General Norman Johnson after he quit The Showmen in the late 60's, Chairmen of the Board were signed to Holland/Dozier/Holland's fledgling Invictus and their debut single *Give Me Just A Little More Time* soared into the Top 5 on both sides of the Atlantic. The follow-up *You've Got Me Dangling On A String* was their last single to reach the Top 10; of all the follow ups, only two managed to breach the Top 20 and the band split in 1973. The members pursued solo careers with varying degrees of success until they reformed in 1984 and released *Loverboy* which was immediately embraced by the U.S. 'beach music' scene. The track was released over here 3 years later where they enjoyed a brief renaissance thanks to the involvement of Style Councillor Mick Talbot.

**AGM.**
Tracks: Let me down easy / Bless you / Try on my love for size / I can't find myself / When will she tell me she needs me / Men are getting scarce / I'm on my way to a better place / Children of today / I'll come crawling / Bravo hooray / So glad you're mine.
■ LP . . . . . . . . . . . . . . . . .HDH LP 006
HDH / Jul '85.

## BITTERSWEET.
**Tracks:** Men are getting scarce / So glad you're mine / Working on a building of love / I'm a sign of changing times / Elmo James / I'm on my way to a better place / Bittersweet / Saginaw County line / Weary traveller.
■ **LP** . . . . . . . . . . . . . . . . . . . . . . . . . **SVT 1006**
Invictus / '72.

## CHAIRMAN OF THE BOARD.
**Tracks:** Chairmen of the board.
■ **7"** . . . . . . . . . . . . . . . . . . . . . . . . **INV 516**
Invictus / Sep '71.

## CHAIRMEN OF THE BOARD.
**Tracks:** Give me just a little more time / Come together / Bless you / Patches / Since the days of pigtails / I'll come crawling / You've got me dangling on a string / Bravo, hooray / Didn't we / Feelin' alright / My way / Tricked and trapped.
■ **LP** . . . . . . . . . . . . . . . . . . . . . . . . **SVT 1002**
Invictus / Nov '70.

## ELMO JAMES.
**Tracks:** Elmo James.
■ **7"** . . . . . . . . . . . . . . . . . . . . . . . . **INV 524**
Invictus / Oct '72.

## EVERYTHING'S TUESDAY.
**Tracks:** Everything's Tuesday.
■ **7"** . . . . . . . . . . . . . . . . . . . . . . . . **INV 507**
Invictus / Feb '71.

## FINDERS KEEPERS.
**Tracks:** Finders keepers.
■ **7"** . . . . . . . . . . . . . . . . . . . . . . . . **INV 530**
Invictus / Jun '73.

## GIVE ME JUST A LITTLE MORE TIME.
**Tracks:** Give me just a little more time / Working on a building of love.
■ **7"** . . . . . . . . . . . . . . . . . . . . . . . . **INV 501**
Invictus / Aug '70.
■ **7"** . . . . . . . . . . . . . . . . . . . . . . . **HDH 4511**
HDH / Oct '84.

## GIVE ME JUST A LITTLE MORE TIME (EP).
**Tracks:** Give me just a little more time / You've got me dancing on a string / Everything's Tuesday.
■ **EP** . . . . . . . . . . . . . . . . . . . . . . . **HEAT 16**
Inferno (1) / Jan '80.

## I'M ON MY WAY TO A BETTER PLACE.
**Tracks:** I'm on my way to a better place.
■ **7"** . . . . . . . . . . . . . . . . . . . . . . . . **INV 527**
Invictus / Jan '73.

## IN SESSION.
**Tracks:** Chairmen of the Board / Everything's Tuesday / Pay to the Piper / Twelfth of Never / All we need is understanding / It was almost something / Bridge over troubled water / Hanging on to a memory / I can't find myself / When will she tell me she needs me / Children of today.
■ **LP** . . . . . . . . . . . . . . . . . . . . . . . . **SVT 1003**
Invictus / Apr '71.

## LOVER BOY (MEDLEY).
**Tracks:** Loverboy.
■ **MC Single.** . . . . . . . . . . . . . . . . . **TCSYX 4**
■ **12"** . . . . . . . . . . . . . . . . . . . . . . **12SYX 4**
Syncopate / Aug '87.

## LOVERBOY (Chairmen Of The Board featuring General Johnson).
**Tracks:** Loverboy / Loverboy (instrumental) / Give me just a little more time (Extra track on double pack version only. Gatefold sleeve.) / You've got me dangling on a string (Extra track on double pack version only. Gatefold sleeve.) / Loverboy (Ian Levine remix) (Only available on 12" remix.) / Loverboy (7" version) (Only available on 12" remix.) / Loverboy (original 12" version) (Only available on 12" remix.) / Everything's Tuesday.
■ **12"** . . . . . . . . . . . . . . . . . . **12EMID 5585**
■ **12" Remix.** . . . . . . . . . . . . . . **12EMIX 5585**
■ **7"** . . . . . . . . . . . . . . . . . . . . . **EMI 5585**
■ **12"** . . . . . . . . . . . . . . . . . . . **12EMI 5585**
EMI / Aug '86.

## PAY TO THE PIPER.
**Tracks:** Pay to the piper.
■ **7"** . . . . . . . . . . . . . . . . . . . . . . . . **INV 511**
Invictus / May '71.

## SALUTE THE GENERAL.
**Tracks:** Give me just a little more time / (You've got me) Dangling on a string / Patches / Tricked and trapped (by a tricky trapper) / Since the day of pigtails / Everything's Tuesday / Pay to the piper / Chairman of the board / Hanging on (to a memory) /

---

All we need is understanding / It was almost something / Working on a building of love / Bittersweet / Elmo James.
■ **LP** . . . . . . . . . . . . . . . . . . . . . . . **HDH LP 001**
HDH / Apr '84.

## SHERO (see under Johnson, General).

## SKIN I'M IN.
**Tracks:** Not Advised.
■ **LP** . . . . . . . . . . . . . . . . . . . . . . . **INV 65868**
Invictus / Nov '74.

## SOUL AGENDA.
**Tracks:** Chairman Of The Board / Working on a building of love / Bravo, hooray / (You've got me) dangling on a string / Everything's Tuesday / I'll come crawling / Elmo James / Give me just a little more time / All we need is understanding / Men are getting scarce / Let me down easy / Pay to the piper / Patches / Tricked and trapped (by a tricky trapper) / Bless you (Available on CD only) / When will she tell me she needs me (Available on CD only) / Try on my love for size (Available on CD only) / Bittersweet (Available on CD only) / Everybody's got a song to sing (Available on CD only) / Finders keepers (Available on CD only).
**CD** . . . . . . . . . . . . . . . . . . . . . . . **HDHCD 007**
■ **LP** . . . . . . . . . . . . . . . . . . . . . . . **HDHLP 007**
HDH / Oct '89 / Pinnacle.
**MC.** . . . . . . . . . . . . . . . . . . . . . . . **HDHMC 007**
HDH / Feb '92 / Pinnacle.

## WHAT GOES AROUND COMES AROUND (see under Johnson, General).

## WORKING ON A BUILDING OF LOVE.
**Tracks:** Working on a building of love.
■ **7"** . . . . . . . . . . . . . . . . . . . . . . . . **INV 519**
Invictus / Jul '72.

## YOU'VE GOT EXTRA ADDED POWER IN YOUR LOVE.
**Tracks:** You've got extra added power in your love / Let's have fun.
■ **7"** . . . . . . . . . . . . . . . . . . . . . . . **INV 4507**
Invictus / Aug '76.

## YOU'VE GOT ME DANGLING ON A STRING.
**Tracks:** You've got me dangling on a string / Tricked and trapped.
■ **7"** . . . . . . . . . . . . . . . . . . . . . . . . **INV 504**
Invictus / Nov '70.
■ **7"** . . . . . . . . . . . . . . . . . . . . . . . **HDH 452**
HDH / Mar '84.

## Challenor, Jackie

### BACK ON MY FEET AGAIN.
**Tracks:** Back on my feet again / Never together.
■ **7"** . . . . . . . . . . . . . . . . . . . . . . . **K 18330**
WEA / Sep '80.

### GALLERY.
**Tracks:** Gallery / Lady stay.
■ **7"** . . . . . . . . . . . . . . . . . . . . . **7N 45086**
Pye / Jul '71.

### MAMA.
**Tracks:** Mama / Put me down softly.
■ **7"** . . . . . . . . . . . . . . . . . . . . . . . **K 18207**
WEA / May '80.

## Chaloner, Sue

### ANSWER MY PRAYER.
**Tracks:** Answer my Prayer.
■ **12"** . . . . . . . . . . . . . . . . . . . **12 LOSE 27**
■ **7"** . . . . . . . . . . . . . . . . . . . . . **LOSE 27**
■ **CD Single** . . . . . . . . . . . . . . . . **CD LOSE 27**
■ **MC Single.** . . . . . . . . . . . . . . . **CA LOSE 27**
Pulse 8 / Aug '92.

### I WANNA THANK YOU.
**Tracks:** I wanna thank you.
■ **12"** . . . . . . . . . . . . . . . . . . . **12LOSE 14**
Pulse 8 / Oct '91.
■ **7"** . . . . . . . . . . . . . . . . . . . . . **LOSE 14**
■ **CD Single.** . . . . . . . . . . . . . . . **CDLOSE 14**
Pulse 8 / Apr '91.

### MOVE ON UP.
**Tracks:** Move on up.
■ **12"** . . . . . . . . . . . . . . . . . . . **12LOSE 41**
■ **7"** . . . . . . . . . . . . . . . . . . . . . **LOSE 41**
■ **CD Single.** . . . . . . . . . . . . . . . **CDLOSE 41**
■ **MC Single.** . . . . . . . . . . . . . . . **CALOSE 41**
Pulse 8 / May '93.

---

### ALL STRUNG OUT OVER YOU.
**Tracks:** All strung out over you / Falling in love.
■ **7"** . . . . . . . . . . . . . . . . . . . . . . **202565**
CBS / Feb '67.

### LOVE ME LIKE THE RAIN.
**Tracks:** Love me like the rain / Pretty girls everywhere.
■ **7"** . . . . . . . . . . . . . . . . . . . . . **VL 9267**
Vocalion / Mar '66.

### NEW TIME - A NEW DAY, A.
**Tracks:** I can't turn you loose / Guess who / Do your thing / Where have all the flowers gone / Love is all I have / You got the power to turn me on / I wish it would rain / Rock me mama / No, no, no, don't say goodbye / Satisfy you / New time - a new day.
■ **LP** . . . . . . . . . . . . . . . . . . . . . . **863451**
Direction / Mar '69.

### TIME HAS COME.
**Tracks:** Time has come / All strung out / People get ready / I can't stand it / Romeo and Juliet / So tired / Uptown / Midnight hour / What the world needs now / Don't leave me.
■ **LP** . . . . . . . . . . . . . . . . . . . . . **8 63407**
Direction / Nov '68.

## Champaign

### CAN YOU FIND THE TIME.
**Tracks:** Can you find the time / Whiplash.
■ **12"** . . . . . . . . . . . . . . . . . . . **A 13 1381**
■ **7"** . . . . . . . . . . . . . . . . . . . . **A 1381**
CBS / Jul '81.

### HOW 'BOUT US.
**Tracks:** Can you find the time / Party people / Whiplash / I'm on fire / How 'bout us / Spinnin' / Dancin' together again / Lighten up / If one more morning.
■ **LP** . . . . . . . . . . . . . . . . . . . **CBS 84927**
CBS / Jun '81.
**CD.** . . . . . . . . . . . . . . . . . . . . **982990 2**
Pickwick/Sony Collector's Choice / Aug '93 / Pickwick / Pinnacle.

### HOW 'BOUT US.
**Tracks:** How 'bout us / Spinnin'.
■ **7"** . . . . . . . . . . . . . . . . . . . . . **A 1046**
CBS / May '81.

### HOW 'BOUT US (OLD GOLD).
**Tracks:** How 'bout us / Off and on love.
■ **7"** . . . . . . . . . . . . . . . . . . . . **OG 9559**
Old Gold / Sep '85.
■ **12"** . . . . . . . . . . . . . . . . . . . **OG 4033**
Old Gold / Nov '87.

### MODERN HEART.
**Tracks:** Let your body rock / Try again / Party line / Cool running / Walkin' / Keep it up / Love games / Get it again / International feel.
■ **LP** . . . . . . . . . . . . . . . . . . **CBS 25038**
**MC.** . . . . . . . . . . . . . . . . . . . **40 25038**
CBS / May '83 / Sony.

### OFF AND ON LOVE.
**Tracks:** Off and on love / Laissez le bon temps roulez.
■ **12"** . . . . . . . . . . . . . . . . . . . **TA 4768**
CBS / Oct '84.

### WOMAN IN FLAMES.
**Tracks:** Off and on love / This time / Prisoner / Intimate strangers / Woman in flames / Mardi gras / Be mine tonight / Capture the moon.
■ **LP** . . . . . . . . . . . . . . . . . . **CBS 26018**
CBS / Dec '84.

## Chandler, E.J.

### I CAN'T STAND TO LOSE YOU.
**Tracks:** I can't stand to lose you.
■ **7"** . . . . . . . . . . . . . . . . . . . . **DS 1026**
Destiny (Northern Soul) / Feb '80.

## Chandler, Gene

Born Eugene Dixon, he adopted the surname Jeff Chandler, at the behest of A&R man Carl Davis. Later signed him to Vee-Jay where his first effort, the Doo-Wop classic, *Duke Of Earl*, sold millions and began a string of hits that stretched into the '70s. Many were arranged and written by Curtis Mayfield, including *Nothing Can Stop Me* which became his first hit in Britain. When their partnership ended, so did his chart run: for over a decade his only hit was a duet with Barbara Acklin, *From The*

*Teacher To The Preacher.* Unfazed, he bought Bamboo Records and moved it to Chicago where signings Mel & Tim's *Backfield In Motion* sold over a million copies. But in 1976 he was convicted of selling heroin and served a 4 month sentence. Once released, he attempted to re-start his career but it was not until 1978, when he met up with Carl Davis again, that his fortune changed: *Get Down* sent him back into the charts, but the success of his singles never translated to album sales.

### 60'S SOUL BROTHER.
Tracks: If you can't be true (find a part time love) / Bet you never thought / Gonna be good times / Nothing can stop me / There goes the lover / I'm just a fool for you / What now / Girl don't care / There was a time / From the teacher to the preacher / Those were the good old days / Little like lovin' / Pretty little girl / My baby's gone / Tell me what I can do / Here comes the tears.
- LP .......................... KENT 049
Kent / Jan '86.

### 80.
Tracks: Does she have a friend / Lay me gently / All about the paper / Rainbow '80 / Do it baby / You've been so sweet to me / I'll be there / Let me make love to you.
- LP .......................... T 605
20th Century / Jul '80.

### DOES SHE HAVE A FRIEND.
Tracks: Does she have a friend / Let me make love to you.
- 7" .......................... TC 2451
20th Century / Jun '80.

### DUKE OF EARL.
Tracks: Duke of Earl / I fooled you this time / Nothing can stop me / You threw a lucky punch / Festival of love / You can't hurt me no more / Nite owl / Think nothing about it / Rainbow.
CD.......................... 26 42 122
MC.......................... 26 42 124
Point (2) / '92 / Sound Solutions.

### DUKE OF EARL (OLD GOLD).
Tracks: Duke of Earl / Billy's bag.
- 7" .......................... OG 9030
Old Gold / Jul '82.

### DUKE OF SOUL, THE.
Tracks: Duke of Earl / You threw a lucky punch / Night owl / Check yourself / Tear for tear / Think nothing about it / Rainbow / Rainbow '65 / What now / God bless our love / Just be true / Man's temptation.
- LP .......................... CXMB 7201
Chess (PRT) / Oct '84.

### FROM THE TEACHER TO THE PREACHER (Chandler, Gene & Barbara Acklin).
Tracks: From the teacher to the preacher / Little green apples.
- 7" .......................... BR 30
Brunswick / Jan '76.

### GENE CHANDLER.
Tracks: Duke of Earl / Stand by me / Festival of love / Daddy's home / I wake up crying / Turn on the love light / Nite owl / I'll follow you / Big lie / Kissin' in the kitchin / So many ways / Lonely island.
- LP .......................... JOYS 136
Joy / May '69.

### GET DOWN.
Tracks: Get down / Please sunrise / Tomorrow I may not feel the same / I'm the travelling kind / Greatest love ever known / Give me the cue / What now / Lovequake / Rainbow / Let me make love to you / Stay here in my heart / Does she have a friend for me / God bless our love / When you're number one / I'm attracted to you / Almost all the way to love / I'll remember you / You've been so sweet to me.
- LP .......................... BT 578
20th Century / Mar '79.
CD.......................... CDCHARLY 304
Charly R&B / Feb '92 / Charly.

### GET DOWN.
Tracks: Get down / Does she have a friend.
- 7" .......................... GOLD 511
RCA Golden Grooves / Jul '81.

### GET DOWN.
Tracks: Get down / Greatest love ever known.
- 7" .......................... BTC 1040
20th Century / Jan '79.

### GET DOWN (OLD GOLD).
Tracks: Get down / Does she have a friend for me.
- 12" .......................... OG 4128
Old Gold / '89.

### GIRL DON'T CARE.
Tracks: Girl don't care / My love.
- 7" .......................... Q 72490
Coral / Mar '67.

### I CAN TAKE CARE OF MYSELF.
Tracks: I can take care of myself / I can't save it.
- 7" .......................... ACT 4551
Action / '69.

### I FOOLED YOU THIS TIME.
Tracks: I fooled you this time / Such a pretty thing.
- 7" .......................... CRS 8047
Chess / Jan '67.

### I'LL MAKE THE LIVING ..
Tracks: I'll make the living.. / Time is a thief.
- 12" .......................... BRT 10
- 7" .......................... BR 10
Blue Bird (2) / Nov '84.

### I'M JUST A FOOL FOR YOU.
Tracks: I'm just a fool for you / Buddy ain't it a shame.
- 7" .......................... SS 500
Stateside / Mar '66.

### IT'S ALL OVER NOW.
Tracks: It's all over now / Let the music in.
- 7" .......................... PB 5092
RCA / '79.

### LIVE AT THE REGAL.
Tracks: Rainbow / If you can't be true (find a part time love) / Soul hootenanny / Monkey time / What now / Just be true / Ain't no use / Bless our love / Song called soul.
- LP .......................... CRB 1117
Charly R&B / '86.

### LIVE ON STAGE.
Tracks: Introduction / Rainbow '65 / If you can't be true / Soul Hootenanny / Monkey time / What now / Just be true / Ain't no use / Bless our love / Song called soul.
- LP .......................... ACLP 6010
Action / Jul '69.

### LOVE IS THE ANSWER.
Tracks: Love is the answer / I'm attracted to you.
- 12" .......................... TCD 2505
20th Century / Aug '81.

### NOTHING CAN STOP ME.
Tracks: Nothing can stop me.
- 7" .......................... SC 102
Soul City (60's) / Jun '68.

### SITUATION.
Tracks: Groovy situation / Simply call it love / Hallelujah I love her so / Not the marrying kind / Give me a chance / Am I blue / Bright lights and you, girl / Hey little angel / Unforgettable / It's your love I'm after.
- LP .......................... 6338 037
Mercury / Mar '71.

### STAND BY ME.
Tracks: Duke of Earl / Big lie / Nite owl / Festival of love / Stand by me / I wake up crying / Turn on your lovelight / Tear for tear / You threw a lucky punch / Rainbow / Check yourself / Baby that's love / Man's temptation / It's no good for me / Think nothing about it / Song called soul / Just be true / What now / You can't hurt me no more / Nothing can stop me / Good times (Gonna be).
- CD .......................... CDCHARLY 55
Charly / Apr '87.

### THERE WAS A TIME.
Tracks: There was a time / You can't hurt me no more / Here come the tears / Teacher teacher / Pit of loneliness / Girl don't care / Bet you never thought / Cowboys to girls / Buddy ain't it a shame / Since you've been gone / Lonely avenue.
- LP .......................... MUPS 367
MCA / May '69.

### WHEN YOU'RE NUMBER 1.
Tracks: That funky disco rhythm / When you're number one / I'll remember you / Do what comes so natural / Stay here in my heart / Dance fever.
- LP .......................... T 598
20th Century / May '80.

### WHEN YOU'RE NUMBER 1.
Tracks: When you're number 1 / I'll remember you.
- 7" .......................... TC 2411
20th Century / Sep '79.

## Chandler, George

### LITTLE GIRL.
Tracks: Little girl / Make up your mind.
- 7" .......................... PB 5020
RCA / May '77.

### ONE IN A MILLION.
Tracks: One in a million / Games are for children.
- 7" .......................... RCA 2720
RCA / Jul '76.

### THIS COULD BE THE NIGHT.
Tracks: This could be the night / Can't go back no more.
- 12" .......................... POSPX 436
- 7" .......................... POSP 436
Polydor / May '82.

## Chandler, Kenny

### BEYOND LOVE.
Tracks: Beyond love.
- 7" .......................... SS 2110
Stateside / '68.

## Chandler, Omar

### BETTER WORLD.
Tracks: Better world.
- 12" .......................... MCST 1543
- 7" .......................... MCS 1543
- CD Single .......................... MCSTD 1543
MCA / Jun '91.

### OMAR CHANDLER.
Tracks: Not Advised.
- CD .......................... MCAD 10057
- LP .......................... MCA 10057
- MC .......................... MCAC 10057
MCA / Apr '91.

### YOU CHANGED ME FOR THE BETTER.
Tracks: You changed me for the better.
- 12" .......................... MCST 1561
- 7" .......................... MCA 1561
- CD Single .......................... MCSTD 1561
MCA / Jan '92.

## Chanelle

### ONE MAN.
Tracks: One man.
- 12" Remix. .......................... COOLXR 183
- 7" .......................... COOL 183
- 12" .......................... COOLX 183
Cool Tempo / Feb '89.

## Change

### ALRIGHT LET'S GO.
Tracks: Alright let's go / Part of me.
- 12" .......................... COOLX 107
- 7" .......................... COOL 107
Cool Tempo / Mar '85.

### CHANGE OF HEART.
Tracks: Say you love me again / Change of heart / Warm / True love / You are my melody / Lovely lady / Got my eyes on you / It burns me up.
- LP .......................... WX 5
- MC .......................... WX 5C
WEA / Jun '84.

### CHANGE OF HEART.
Tracks: Change of heart / Searching / Lovers holiday (12" single only).
- 12" .......................... YZ 7T
- 7" .......................... YZ 7
WEA / Jun '84.

### CHANGE OF HEART (OLD GOLD).
Tracks: Change of heart / You are my melody.
12" .......................... OG 4204
Old Gold / Jun '91 / Pickwick.

### GLOW OF LOVE, THE.
Tracks: Lover's holiday / It's a girl's affair / Angel in my pocket / Glow of love / Searching / End.
- LP .......................... K 99107
- MC .......................... K4 99107
WEA / '80.

### GLOW OF LOVE, THE.
Tracks: Glow of love / It's a girls affair.
- 7" .......................... K 79187
WEA / Jan '81.

### LOVER'S HOLIDAY, A.
Tracks: Lover's holiday / Glow of love.
- 7" .......................... K 79141
WEA / Jun '80.

## MIRACLES.
**Tracks:** Paradise / Hold tight / Your move / Stop for love / On top / Heaven of my life / Miracles.
- **LP** . . . . . . . . . . . . . . . . . . . . . . . **K 99140**
- **MC** . . . . . . . . . . . . . . . . . . . . . . **K4 99140**

WEA / May '81.

## MUTUAL ATTRACTION.
**Tracks:** Mutual attraction.
- **7"** . . . . . . . . . . . . . . . . . . . . . **COOL 111**
- **12"** . . . . . . . . . . . . . . . . . . . **COOLX 111**

Cool Tempo / Jun '85.

## OH WHAT A FEELING.
**Tracks:** Oh what a feeling.
- **12"** . . . . . . . . . . . . . . . . . . . **COOLX 109**
- **12" Remix** . . . . . . . . . . . . . . . **COOLX 1009**
- **7"** . . . . . . . . . . . . . . . . . . . . . **COOL 109**

Cool Tempo / Apr '85.

## PARADISE.
**Tracks:** Paradise / Your move.
- **7"** . . . . . . . . . . . . . . . . . . . . . **K 79196**

WEA / Oct '81.

## SAY YOU LOVE ME AGAIN.
**Tracks:** Say you love me again / Change medley.
- **12"** . . . . . . . . . . . . . . . . . . . . . **YZ 32T**
- **7"** . . . . . . . . . . . . . . . . . . . . . . **YZ 32**

WEA / Feb '85.

## SEARCHING.
**Tracks:** Searching / Angel in my pocket.
- **7"** . . . . . . . . . . . . . . . . . . . . . **K 79156**

WEA / Sep '80.

## SEARCHING (OLD GOLD).
**Tracks:** Searching / Glow of love.
12" . . . . . . . . . . . . . . . . . . . . . . **OG 4200**
Old Gold / Jun '91 / Pickwick.

## SHARING YOUR LOVE.
**Tracks:** Not Advised.
- **LP** . . . . . . . . . . . . . . . . . . . . . **SH 8550**

MC . . . . . . . . . . . . . . . . . . . . . . **KSAC 8550**
London / Jun '82 / PolyGram.

## STOP FOR LOVE.
**Tracks:** Stop for love / Heaven of my life.
- **7"** . . . . . . . . . . . . . . . . . . . . . **K 79217**

WEA / Jul '81.

## TURN ON YOUR RADIO.
**Tracks:** Turn on the radio / Let's go together / Examination / You'll always be part of me / Oh what a feeling / Mutual attraction / Love the way you love me / If you want my love.
MC . . . . . . . . . . . . . . . . . . . . . **ZCHR 1504**
- **LP** . . . . . . . . . . . . . . . . . . . . . **CHR 1504**

Chrysalis / Apr '85 / EMI.

## VERY BEST IN YOU.
**Tracks:** Very best in you.
- **12"** . . . . . . . . . . . . . . . . . . . . **LONX 009**
- **7"** . . . . . . . . . . . . . . . . . . . . . **LON 009**

London / Jun '82.

## WILDCAT.
**Tracks:** Wildcat / Hold on.
- **7"** . . . . . . . . . . . . . . . . . . . . **EMI 2354**

EMI / Oct '75.

## YOU ARE MY MELODY.
**Tracks:** You are my melody / Glow of love.
- **12"** . . . . . . . . . . . . . . . . . . . . . **YZ 14 T**
- **7"** . . . . . . . . . . . . . . . . . . . . . **YZ 14**

WEA / Aug '84.

## Changing Faces

### CHANGING FACES.
**Tracks:** Not Advised.
CD . . . . . . . . . . . . . . . . . . . .756792369-2
LP . . . . . . . . . . . . . . . . . . . .756792369-1
MC . . . . . . . . . . . . . . . . . . . .756792369-4
Warner Bros. / Oct '94 / WEA.

### I WANT YOU.
**Tracks:** I want you / I want you (radio edit) / I want you (dance mix).
- **12"** . . . . . . . . . . . . . . . . . . . **GT 1003T**

G.T.I. Records / Nov '88.

### STROKE YOU UP.
**Tracks:** Changing faces (Mixes).
12" . . . . . . . . . . . . . . . . . . . . . **A 8251T**
CD Single . . . . . . . . . . . . . . . **A 8251CD**
MC Single . . . . . . . . . . . . . . . **A 8251C**
Atlantic / Sep '94 / WEA.

## Chanson

### CHANSON.
**Tracks:** Don't hold back / I can tell / I love you more / Why / Did you ever / All the time you need.
- **LP** . . . . . . . . . . . . . . . . . . . . **ARL 5018**

Ariola / Mar '79.

### DON'T HOLD BACK.
**Tracks:** Don't hold back / Did you ever.
- **7"** . . . . . . . . . . . . . . . . . . . . **ARO 140**

Ariola / Jan '79.

### I CAN TELL.
**Tracks:** I can tell / I can tell (version).
- **12"** . . . . . . . . . . . . . . . . . . . **AROC 168**
- **7"** . . . . . . . . . . . . . . . . . . . . **ARO 168**

Ariola / May '79.

## Chants

### BABY I DON'T NEED YOUR LOVE.
**Tracks:** Baby I don't need your love / Man without a face.
- **7"** . . . . . . . . . . . . . . . . . . . **RCA 1754**

RCA / '68.

### COME BACK AND GET THIS LOVING BABY.
**Tracks:** Come back and get this loving baby / Love-light / creation.
7" . . . . . . . . . . . . . . . . . . . . . **TF 716**
Fontana / Jun '66 / PolyGram.

### LOVE IS A PLAYGROUND.
**Tracks:** Love is a playground / Sophisticated junkyard.
- **7"** . . . . . . . . . . . . . . . . . . . . **6121109**

Fresh Air / Jun '74.

### LOVERS' STORY.
**Tracks:** Lovers' story / Wearing a smile.
7" . . . . . . . . . . . . . . . . . . . . . **F 12650**
Decca / Aug '67 / PolyGram.

## Chapter 8

Formed by two ex-Detroit Emeralds, Chapter 8's most notable contribution to soul history was Anita Baker's recording debut. Baker was group's third lead singer since 1972, although they did not release first album until 1979. Dropped by Ariola, group returned in '85 with another new line-up on Capitol; releasing two acclaimed albums before being dropped once again. Founder member Michael Powell enjoyed more success as producer of Regina Belle and Baker's solo releases. Another former member, Carolyn Crawford, recorded for Philadelphia International and with Bohannon.

### FOREVER.
**Tracks:** Stronger love / Give me a chance / So in love / Understanding / I can't wait / One and only / Real love / Forever / Last time / Long time to love.
- **CD** . . . . . . . . . . . . . . . . . . **CDEST 2073**
- **MC** . . . . . . . . . . . . . . . . . . **TCEST 2073**
- **LP** . . . . . . . . . . . . . . . . . . . **EST 2073**

Capitol / Aug '88.

### WE NEED LOVE.
**Tracks:** We need love / I just wanna be your girl.
- **12"** . . . . . . . . . . . . . . . . . . . **OG 4508**

Old Gold / Apr '89.

## Chapter Five

### ONE IN A MILLION.
**Tracks:** One in a million / Hey hey.
- **7"** . . . . . . . . . . . . . . . . . . . **CBS 2696**

CBS / '67.

### YOU CAN'T MEAN IT.
**Tracks:** Anything that you do / You can't mean it.
- **7"** . . . . . . . . . . . . . . . . . . **CBS 202395**

CBS / Nov '66.

## Charlene

### HIT AND RUN LOVER.
**Tracks:** Not Advised.
- **LP** . . . . . . . . . . . . . . . . . . . . **ZL 72176**
- **MC** . . . . . . . . . . . . . . . . . . . . **ZK 72176**

Motown / Oct '84.

### I'VE NEVER BEEN TO ME.
**Tracks:** I've never been to me / It ain't easy comin' down / Can't we try / Hungry / Hey mama / I won't remember ever loving you / Johnny doesn't live here

anymore / After the ball / I need a man / If I could see myself.
- **LP** . . . . . . . . . . . . . . . . . . **STML 12171**

MC . . . . . . . . . . . . . . . . . . **CSTML 12171**
Motown / Jul '82 / PolyGram.

### I'VE NEVER BEEN TO ME.
**Tracks:** I've never been to me / Somewhere in my life.
- **7"** . . . . . . . . . . . . . . . . . . **TMG 1260**

Motown / Mar '82.

### I'VE NEVER BEEN TO ME (ORIGINAL).
**Tracks:** I've never been to me / Freddie.
- **7"** . . . . . . . . . . . . . . . . . . . **PROD 4**

Prodigal / Aug '77.

### IF YOU TAKE AWAY THE PAIN UNTIL THE..
**Tracks:** If you take away the pain until the morning / Rick's song.
- **7"** . . . . . . . . . . . . . . . . . . **TMG 1310**

Motown / Aug '83.

### IT AIN'T EASY COMIN' DOWN.
**Tracks:** It ain't easy comin' down / On my way to you.
- **7"** . . . . . . . . . . . . . . . . . . . **PROD 2**

Prodigal / Feb '77.

### IT AIN'T EASY COMIN' DOWN.
**Tracks:** It ain't easy comin' down / Ninca te ido ar mi / If I could see myself.
- **7"** . . . . . . . . . . . . . . . . . . **TMG 1272**

Motown / Aug '82.

### SKY IS THE LIMIT.
**Tracks:** Sky is the limit / Living still goes on / Rise up / I want the world to know he's mine / There was nothing to believe in / Jesus is love / Prayer / You knew just what I needed / Cover me.
- **LP** . . . . . . . . . . . . . . . . . . . **CLS 8011**

MC . . . . . . . . . . . . . . . . . . **TC CLS 8011**
Chapel Lane / Dec '83.

### USED TO BE.
**Tracks:** If you take away the pain until the morning / Used to be / Heaven help us all / I want to go back there again / Rainbows / Last song / Some things never change / Richie's song / You're home.
- **LP** . . . . . . . . . . . . . . . . . . **STML 12179**
- **MC** . . . . . . . . . . . . . . . . . . **CSTML 12179**

Motown / Dec '82.

### USED TO BE (see under Wonder, Stevie).

### WE'RE BOTH IN LOVE WITH YOU.
**Tracks:** We're both in love with you / Richie's song.
- **12"** . . . . . . . . . . . . . . . . . . **TMGT 1352**
- **7"** . . . . . . . . . . . . . . . . . . . **TMG 1352**

Motown / Oct '84.

## Charles & Eddie

Black New Yorker Charles Pettigrew and Hispanic Californian Eddie Chacon scored platinum U.K. No. 1 with *Would I Lie to You?* in 1992. Gaye/Green-cloning debut *Duophonic* - for which Stateside label was specially revived - sold well on back of single. However, Buffalo Springfield sample on follow-up failed to work same alchemy that helped Oui 3 into charts, and pair sunk from sight.

### DUOPHONIC.
**Tracks:** House is not a home / N.Y.C. / Would I lie to you / Hurt no more / I understand / Unconditional / Love is a beautiful thing / Where do we go from here / Father to son / December 2 / Be a little easy on me / Vowel song / Shine / Bonus cut.
CD . . . . . . . . . . . . . . . . . . **CDESTU 2186**
MC . . . . . . . . . . . . . . . . . **TCESTU 2186**
- **LP** . . . . . . . . . . . . . . . . . . **ESTU 2186**

Capitol / Nov '92 / EMI.

### HOUSE IS NOT A HOME.
**Tracks:** House is not a home / I understand / Would I lie to you (Features on 7" & MCS only.) / House is not a home (mix).
- **7"** . . . . . . . . . . . . . . . . . . . **CD 688**
- **CD Single** . . . . . . . . . . . . . **CDCLS 688**
- **CD Single** . . . . . . . . . . . . . . **CDCL 688**
- **MC Single** . . . . . . . . . . . . . **TCCL 688**

EMI / May '93.

### N.Y.C. (CAN YOU BELIEVE THIS CITY).
**Tracks:** N.Y.C. (Can you believe this city) / Would I lie to you / N.Y.C. (Can you believe this city)(mix) / Would I lie to you (mix) / Where do we go from here / December 2.
- **12"** . . . . . . . . . . . . . . . . . . **12CL 681**
- **7"** . . . . . . . . . . . . . . . . . . . **CL 681**
- **CD Single** . . . . . . . . . . . . . **CDCL 681**

■ MC Single. . . . . . . . . . . . . . . . . TCCL 681
EMI / Feb '93.

## WOULD I LIE TO YOU.

Tracks: Would I lie to you / Unconditional / Would I lie to you (mix).
■ 12". . . . . . . . . . . . . . . . . . . . . . 12 CL 673
■ 7". . . . . . . . . . . . . . . . . . . . . . .CL 673
■ CD Single. . . . . . . . . . . . . . . . CDCL 673
■ MC Single. . . . . . . . . . . . . . . . TCCL 673
Capitol / Sep '92.

# Charles, Colin

## FORNICATION.

Tracks: Fornication.
12". . . . . . . . . . . . . . . . . . . . . . . .SPG 001
SPG Shake / Jan '94 / Jetstar.

# Charles, Ray

One of the most important artists in black music, Ray Charles Robinson was born in Georgia, 1932 (surname was later dropped to avoid confusion with boxer Sugar Ray). After moving to Seattle, he spent early '50s in Nat King Cole-influenced trio, devoting remainder of decade to development of own style - his fusion of R&B, gospel and jazz was instrumental in creation of soul music. Big breakthrough was 1959's self-penned classic *What'd I Say?*. Ray Charles left Atlantic for ABC later that year scoring further hits such as *Georgia On My Mind* and *Hit The Road, Jack*. Charles' subsequent move into country music, although damaging to his credibility, was a huge success, the 1962 cut *I Can't Stop Loving You* topped both U.S. and U.K. charts - giving Ray Charles his biggest ever hit. He continued to score hits throughout the '60s in the UK, on the HMV and Stateside labels. Charles signed to his own label, Tangerine in 1968 which was renamed Crossover in 1973 but his choice of material from this period onward would often leave much to be desired - his work veering alarmingly towards MOR. However, Ray Charles' influence is undeniable: he was instrumental in the birth of soul itself and has played a major role in the popularisation of black music. In 1990, he returned to the charts on top 10 hit single, *I'll Be Good To You*, with Chaka Khan and Quincy Jones.

## 14 ORIGINAL GREATEST HITS:RAY CHARLES.

Tracks: Not Advised.
■ LP . . . . . . . . . . . . . . . . . . . . . . .K 5011
King (USA) / Mar '88.

## 16 GREATEST HITS.

Tracks: What'd I say / Busted / Here we go again / I can't stop loving you / That lucky old sun / Let's go get stoned / Hide nor hair / Georgia on my mind / Unchain my heart / I got a woman / Hit the road Jack / Eleanor Rigby / Don't set me free / America the beautiful.
CD. . . . . . . . . . . . . . . . . . . . . . .264823 2
MC. . . . . . . . . . . . . . . . . . . . . . .264823 4
Mainline (2) / Jan '90.

## 16 ORIGINAL HITS: RAY CHARLES.

Tracks: Not Advised.
MC. . . . . . . . . . . . . . . . . . . . . . .MC 1631
Timeless Treasures / Sep '87 / THE.

## 1950.

Tracks: Not Advised.
■ LP . . . . . . . . . . . . . . . . . . . . . . 522 011
Vogue / '84.

## 20 GOLDEN GREATS.

Tracks: Georgia on my mind / What'd I say / Sitting on top of the world / Ain't that fine / Can't you see darling / Sentimental blues / If I give you my love / She's on the ball / Ray Charles blues / How long / Come rain or come shine / Alone in the city / Someday / This love of mine / I'm going down to the river / You always miss the water (when the well runs dry) / Baby won't you please come home / Don't put all your dreams in one basket / I've had my fun / Let's have a ball.
■ LP . . . . . . . . . . . . . . . . . . . . . DVLP 2005
MC. . . . . . . . . . . . . . . . . . . . . . DVMC 2005
Deja Vu / Aug '85 / Jazz Music / Music Collection International.
CD . . . . . . . . . . . . . . . . . . . . . . DVCD 2005
Deja Vu / Sep '87 / Jazz Music / Music Collection International.

## 20 GOLDEN PIECES: RAY CHARLES.

Tracks: Alone in the city / Can anyone ask for more / Rockin' chair blues / Let's have a ball / How long how long blues / Sentimental blues / You always miss the water (when the well runs dry) / I've had my fun / Sitting on top of the world / Ain't that fine / Don't put all your dreams in one basket / Ray Charles blues / Honey honey / She's on the ball / Baby won't you please come home / If I give you my love / This love of mine / Can't you see me, darling / Someday / I'm going down to the river.
■ LP . . . . . . . . . . . . . . . . . . . . . BDL 2012
Bulldog Records / Jul '82.

## 20 GREATEST HITS: RAY CHARLES.

Tracks: Not Advised.
■ LP . . . . . . . . . . . . . . . . . . . . . B 90108
MC. . . . . . . . . . . . . . . . . . . . MB 990108
Masters (Holland) / Jan '87.

## 25TH ANNIVERSARY IN SHOW BUSINESS.

Tracks: Not Advised.
■ LP . . . . . . . . . . . . . . . . . . . . . K 60014
Atlantic / '87.

## AIN'T IT SO.

Tracks: Some enchanted evening / Blues in the night / Just because / What'll I do / One of these days / Love me or set me free / Drift away / Love me tonight.
■ LP . . . . . . . . . . . . . . . . . . . . . SHL 8537
London / '79.

## ALONE IN THE CITY.

Tracks: Not Advised.
MC. . . . . . . . . . . . . . . . . . . . RMB 45009
Remember / Jan '92 / Midland Records / BMG.
CD. . . . . . . . . . . . . . . . . . . . RMB 75009
Remember / Nov '93 / Midland Records / BMG.

## AT NEWPORT.

Tracks: Right time / In a little Spanish town / I got a woman / Blues waltz / Hot rod / Talkin' 'bout you / Sherry / Fool for you.
■ LP . . . . . . . . . . . . . . . . . . . . . 588 132
Atlantic / Feb '69.
■ LP . . . . . . . . . . . . . . . . . . . . . K 30032
Atlantic / Apr '73.

## AUDIO ARCHIVE.

Tracks: I wonder who's kissing her now / Let's have a ball / Goin' down slow / Sitting on top of the world / Alone in the city / Blues is my middle name / This love of mine / Now she's gone / Can anyone ask for more / c.c. rider / Rockin' chair blues / Hey now / Sentimental blues / Can't you see darling / Tell me baby / Baby let me hold your hand / I won't let you go / I'm gonna drown myself / Snow is fallin' / If I give you my love.
CD. . . . . . . . . . . . . . . . . . . . . CDAA 003
MC. . . . . . . . . . . . . . . . . . . . . MCAA 003
Tring / Jan '92 / Prism Leisure PLC / Midland Records.

## AUTHENTIC RAY CHARLES, THE.

Tracks: Don't put all your dreams / Before sunrise / St. Pete Florida blues / How long blues / You always miss your water / I've had my fun.
■ EP . . . . . . . . . . . . . . . . . . . . . EPC 701
Concert Hall/Pop Parade / Jul '62.

## BACK HOME.

Tracks: Not Advised.
CD. . . . . . . . . . . . . . . . . . . . . CDCD 1128
Charly / Mar '93 / Charly.

## BEST OF RAY CHARLES - THE ATLANTIC YEARS.

Tracks: Not Advised.
CD. . . . . . . . . . . . . . . . . . . .812271722-2
Atlantic / Aug '94 / WEA.

## BEST OF RAY CHARLES, THE.

Tracks: Not Advised.
CD. . . . . . . . . . . . . . . . . . .756781368-2
WEA / Mar '93 / WEA.

## BLUES.

Tracks: What have I done / Goin' down slow / Now she's gone / Rocking chair blues / Sentimental blues / Can anyone ask for more / Honey honey / Baby won't you let me please come home / You always miss the water (When the well runs dry) / How long / Alone in the city / Let's have a ball / This love of mine / Can't you see darling / If I give you my love / Some day (Blues is my middle name) / Don't put all your dreams in one basket / I found my baby there / She's on the ball.
CD. . . . . . . . . . . . . . . . . . . . .16223CD
Success (3) / Oct '94 / Pickwick.

## BLUES + JAZZ.

Tracks: Not Advised.
CD. . . . . . . . . . . . . . . . . . . . . .271607-2
Atlantic / Jun '94 / WEA.

## BLUES IS MY MIDDLE NAME.

Tracks: Not Advised.
CD. . . . . . . . . . . . . . . . . . . . . . ONN 37
Object Enterprises / May '89 / Gold & Sons / THE / Midland Records.

## BLUES IS MY MIDDLE NAME.

Tracks: Goin' down slow / Alone in the city / Now she's gone / Rockin' chair blues / Sentimental blues / Can anyone ask for more / Let's have a ball / This love of mine / Can't you see darling / If I give you my love / Sitting on top of the world / Now she's gone / I'm gonna drown myself / Snow is fallin' / Blues is my middle name / I wonder who's kissing her now / c.c. rider / Hey now / Tell me baby / All to myself alone / Baby let me hold your hand / I won't let you go / I'm glad for you sake / Walkin' and talkin' / I'm wonderin' and wonderin' / I found my baby there.
CD. . . . . . . . . . . . . . . . . . . . CDGRF 033
MC. . . . . . . . . . . . . . . . . . . . MCGRF 033
Tring / '93 / Prism Leisure PLC / Midland Records.

## BOODY BUTT.

Tracks: Boody butt / Zig zag.
■ 7" . . . . . . . . . . . . . . . . . . . .6121-001
Tangerine / May '71.

## BROTHER RAY.

Tracks: Compared to what / Anyway you want to / Don't you love me anymore / Poor man's song / Now that we've found each other / Ophelia / I can't change it / Questions.
■ LP . . . . . . . . . . . . . . . . . . . . . SH 8546
London / Jan '81.

## BUSTED.

Tracks: Busted.
■ 7" . . . . . . . . . . . . . . . . . . . . POP 1221
H.M.V. / Oct '63.

## BUSTED.

Tracks: Not Advised.
CD. . . . . . . . . . . . . . . . . . . . . TL 1325
Traditional Line / Sep '92 / Charly / A.D.A. Distribution / Koch International.

## C.C. RIDER.

Tracks: C.C. rider / I wonder who's kissing her now / Going down slow / Lovin' the girls / Kiss me baby / All alone again / Sitting on top of the world / Tell me baby / Baby let me hold your hand / Hey now / All to myself alone / Walkin' and talkin'.
■ LP . . . . . . . . . . . . . . . . . . . . . CBR 1018
MC. . . . . . . . . . . . . . . . . . . . . KCBR 1018
Premier (Sony) / Jun '85 / Sony / Pinnacle.

## CAN'T STOP LOVING YOU.

Tracks: Not Advised.
■ LP . . . . . . . . . . . . . . . . . . . . . PLP 22
MC. . . . . . . . . . . . . . . . . . . . . PMC 22
Platinum (W.Germany) / Oct '85.

## CLASSIC YEARS, THE.

Tracks: Sticks and stones / Georgia on my mind / Ruby / Hard hearted Hannah / Theme that got / One mint julep / I've got news for you / Hit the road Jack / Unchain my heart / Hide nor hair / At the club / I can't stop loving you / Born to lose / You don't know me / You are my sunshine / Your cheatin' heart / Don't set me free / Take these chains from my heart / No one / Without love (there is nothing) / Busted / That lucky old sun / Baby don't you cry / My heart cries for you / My baby don't dig me / No one to cry to / Smack dab in the middle / Makin' whoopee / Cry / Crying time / Together again / Let's go get stoned / Please say you're fooling / I don't need no doctor / In the heat of the night / Yesterday / Eleanor Rigby / Understanding and nine more.
CD. . . . . . . . . . . . . . . . . . . . ESBCD 144
Essential / Jul '91 / Total / BMG.
CD. . . . . . . . . . . . . . . . . . . CDSGP 0121
MC. . . . . . . . . . . . . . . . . . CASSGP 0121
Prestige / Jun '94 / Total / BMG.

## COLLECTABLES, THE.

Tracks: Not Advised.
■ CD . . . . . . . . . . . . . . . . . . . . NCD 5149
K-Tel / '89.

## COLLECTION VOL.1.

Tracks: Your cheatin' heart / Hit the road Jack / Georgia on my mind / Unchain my heart / One mint julep / Take these chains from my heart / I can't stop loving you / Busted / You are my sunshine / Making whoopee / Let's go get stoned / My heart cries for you / Feel so bad / Lucky old sun / Smack dab in the middle / Crying time / If it wasn't for bad luck / In the heat of the night / Eleanor Rigby / Born to lose / No one / Hard hearted Hannah / Yesterday.

CD . . . . . . . . . . . . . . . . . . . . . CCSCD 241
■ Double LP . . . . . . . . . . . . . . . . . CCSLP 241
MC . . . . . . . . . . . . . . . . . . . . . . CCSMC 241
Castle Collector Series / Mar '90 / BMG / Pinnacle /
Castle Communications.

## COLLECTION VOL.2.
**Tracks:** Not Advised.
CD . . . . . . . . . . . . . . . . . . . . . . CCSCD 328
Castle Collector Series / Apr '92 / BMG / Pinnacle /
Castle Communications.
■ MC . . . . . . . . . . . . . . . . . . . . CCSMC 328
Castle / Apr '92.

## COLLECTION: RAY CHARLES.
**Tracks:** Yesterday / Your cheatin' heart / Georgia on
my mind / I can't stop loving you / Busted / Together
again / Take these chains from my heart / Crying
time / Half as much / Here we go again / Born to lose
/ Eleanor Rigby / You don't know me / Hit the road
Jack / I gotta woman (live) / What'd I say (live).
CD . . . . . . . . . . . . . . . . . . . . . . RCLD 101
■ LP . . . . . . . . . . . . . . . . . . . . . RCLP 101
MC . . . . . . . . . . . . . . . . . . . . . . RCLC 101
Arcade / Mar '90 / Sony / Grapevine Distribution.

## COME LIVE WITH ME.
**Tracks:** Not Advised.
■ LP . . . . . . . . . . . . . . . . . . . . . SHU 8467
London-American / '74.

## COMPARED TO WHAT.
**Tracks:** Compared to what / Now that found each
other.
■ 7" . . . . . . . . . . . . . . . . . . . . . HL 10579
London-American / Feb '81.

## COUNTRY SIDE OF RAY CHARLES.
**Tracks:** Not Advised.
■ LP . . . . . . . . . . . . . . . . . . . . . ADAH 447
MC . . . . . . . . . . . . . . . . . . . . . . ADAHC 447
Arcade Music Gala / Apr '86.

## CRYIN' TIME.
**Tracks:** Cryin' time.
■ 7" . . . . . . . . . . . . . . . . . . . . . POP 1502
H.M.V. / Feb '66.

## DO I EVER CROSS YOUR MIND?.
**Tracks:** I had it all / Do I ever cross your mind /
Woman sensuous woman / Then I'll be over you /
Lay around and love on you / Love of my life / They
call it love / If I were you / Workin' man's woman / I
was on Georgia time.
■ LP . . . . . . . . . . . . . . . . . . . . . CBS 25764
■ MC . . . . . . . . . . . . . . . . . . . . . 40 25764
CBS / Jul '84.

## DOING HIS THING.
**Tracks:** Same thing that can make you laugh /
Finders keepers, losers weepers / You ought to
change your ways / Baby please / Come and get it /
We can make it / I'm ready / That thing called love / If
it wasn't for bad luck / I told you so.
■ LP . . . . . . . . . . . . . . . . . . . . . SSL 10293
Stateside / Feb '70.

## DON'T CHANGE ON ME.
**Tracks:** Don't change on me / Sweet memories.
■ 7" . . . . . . . . . . . . . . . . . . . . . PRO 524
Probe / Apr '71.

## DON'T SET ME FREE.
**Tracks:** Don't set me free.
■ 7" . . . . . . . . . . . . . . . . . . . . . POP 1133
H.M.V. / Mar '63.

## EARLY YEARS.
**Tracks:** Not Advised.
■ LP . . . . . . . . . . . . . . . . . . . . . ZET 707
Zeta / '88.

## ELEANOR RIGBY.
**Tracks:** Eleanor Rigby.
■ 7" . . . . . . . . . . . . . . . . . . . . . SS 2120
Stateside / Jul '68.

## EVERYTHING.
**Tracks:** Kiss me baby / Sitting on top of the world /
I'm gonna drown myself / All alone again / Lovin' the
girls / I will not let you go / I'm glad for your sake /
Walkin' and talkin'.
■ LP . . . . . . . . . . . . . . . . . . . . . MAN 5029
Manhattan Records / Sep '80.

## FANTASTIC RAY CHARLES, THE.
**Tracks:** Going down slow / Blues is my middle name
/ If I give you my love / Can't you see, darling / Goin'
away blues / Sitting on top of the world / Late in the
evening blues / Here am I / Ray's blues / I'm just a
lonely boy / St. Pete blues / Easy ridin' gal / c.c. rider
/ I wonder who's kissing her now / I'm going down to
the river / I'm glad for your sake / Ego song / I used
to be so happy / Hey now / What have I done / All

night long / All to myself alone / Oh baby / I live only
for you.
■ Double LP . . . . . . . . . . . . . . . . . ALB 103
Musidisc / Mar '85.

## FRIENDSHIP.
**Tracks:** Two old cats like us / This old heart of mine /
We didn't see a thing / Who cares / Rock 'n' roll
shoes / Friendship / It ain't gonna worry my mind /
Little hotel room / Crazy old soldier / Seven Spanish
angels.
■ LP . . . . . . . . . . . . . . . . . . . . . CBS 26060
■ MC . . . . . . . . . . . . . . . . . . . . . 40 26060
CBS / Oct '84.
CD . . . . . . . . . . . . . . . . . . . . . . 9825942
Pickwick/Sony Collector's Choice / Oct '91 / Pickwick
/ Pinnacle.

## GENIUS + SOUL = JAZZ.
**Tracks:** From the heart / I've got news for you /
Moanin' / Let's go / One mint julep / I'm gonna move
to the outskirts of town / Stompin' room / Mr. C /
Strike up the band / Birth of the blues / Alabamy
bound / Basin Street blues / New York's my home.
■ LP . . . . . . . . . . . . . . . . . . . . . ESSLP 009
■ CD . . . . . . . . . . . . . . . . . . . . . ESSCD 009
■ MC . . . . . . . . . . . . . . . . . . . . . ESSMC 009
Essential / Aug '89.
■ CD . . . . . . . . . . . . . . . . . . . . . JZ-CD310
Suisa / Feb '91.
CD . . . . . . . . . . . . . . . . . . . . . . CLACD 339
Castle / Aug '93 / BMG.

## GENIUS OF RAY CHARLES, THE.
**Tracks:** Not Advised.
CD . . . . . . . . . . . . . . . . . . . . . . 756781338-2
Atlantic / Jun '93 / WEA.

## GENIUS, THE.
**Tracks:** Sitting on top of the world / Kiss my baby /
I'm gonna drown myself / All alone again / I had my
fun / Snow is falling / Blues is my middle name / Oh
baby / C.C. rider / Hey now / Tell me baby / Going
down slowly / Walkin' and talkin' / I'm glad for your
sake / Baby let me hold your hand / All to myself
alone.
CD . . . . . . . . . . . . . . . . . . . . . . XELCD 106
■ LP . . . . . . . . . . . . . . . . . . . . . XELLP 106
MC . . . . . . . . . . . . . . . . . . . . . . XELMC 106
Exel / Mar '88 / Henry Hadaway Organisation / EMI.

## GEORGIA ON MY MIND.
**Tracks:** Not Advised.
■ LP . . . . . . . . . . . . . . . . . . . . . SM 3926
Joker (USA) / '88.

## GEORGIA ON MY MIND.
**Tracks:** Georgia on my mind.
■ 7" . . . . . . . . . . . . . . . . . . . . . POP 792
H.M.V. / Dec '60.

## GEORGIA TIME.
**Tracks:** I had it all / Do I ever cross your mind /
Workin' man's woman / I was on Georgia time / Two
old cats like us / This ole heart / Friendship / This
page on my mind / Slip away / Love is worth the pain
/ Rock 'n' roll shoes / Stranger in my hometown /
Let's call the whole thing off / Save the bones for
Henry Jones / Nothing like a hundred miles / I wish
I'd never loved you at all.
CD . . . . . . . . . . . . . . . . . . . . . . PWKS 4169
MC . . . . . . . . . . . . . . . . . . . . . . PWKMC 4169
Pickwick / Sep '93 / Pickwick.

## GOIN' DOWN SLOW.
**Tracks:** Going down slow / Alone in the city / Now
she's gone / Rockin' chair blues / Can anyone ask
for more / Let's have a ball / This love of mine / Can't
see you darling / If I give you my love.
■ LP . . . . . . . . . . . . . . . . . . . . . MTM 002
Meteor / Jun '84.

## GOLD COLLECTION, THE.
**Tracks:** Not Advised.
CD . . . . . . . . . . . . . . . . . . . . . . D2CD05
MC . . . . . . . . . . . . . . . . . . . . . . D2MC05
Recording Arts / Dec '92 / THE.

## GREAT HITS.
**Tracks:** Going down slow / All night long / I'm givin'
up / Guitar blues / Talkin' 'bout you / I found my baby
there / I'm wonderin' and wonderin' / By myself /
Snowfall.
■ LP . . . . . . . . . . . . . . . . . . . . . PHX 1013
Phoenix (2) / '82.

## GREAT RAY CHARLES, THE.
**Tracks:** Ray / Melancholy baby / Black coffee /
There's no you / Doodlin' / Sweet sixteen bars / I
surrender dear / Undecided.
■ LP . . . . . . . . . . . . . . . . . . . . . 588 124
Atlantic / Nov '68.
CD . . . . . . . . . . . . . . . . . . . . . . 756781731-2
Atlantic / Jun '93 / WEA.

## GREATEST COUNTRY AND WESTERN HITS.
**Tracks:** Your cheating heart / Hey good lookin' /
Take these chains from my heart / Don't tell me your
troubles / I can't stop loving you / Just a little lovin' /
It makes no difference now / You don't know me /
You are my sunshine / Someday (you'll want me to
want you) / I love you so much it hurts / Careless
love / Oh, lonesome me / Midnight / No letter today /
Crying time / Together again / Don't let her know /
I'll never stand in your way (Only on CD) / Hang
your head in shame (Only on CD).
CD . . . . . . . . . . . . . . . . . . . . . . NEXCD 100
■ LP . . . . . . . . . . . . . . . . . . . . . NEXLP 100
■ MC . . . . . . . . . . . . . . . . . . . . . NEXMC 100
Sequel / Dec '89 / Total / BMG.

## GREATEST HITS: RAY CHARLES.
**Tracks:** Not Advised.
■ LP . . . . . . . . . . . . . . . . . . . . . CLP 1626
H.M.V. / Jul '63.

## GREATEST HITS: RAY CHARLES, VOL. 2.
**Tracks:** I can't stop loving you / Makin' whoopee /
Don't set me free / You don't know me / Cincinatti kid
/ Let's go get stoned / Yesterday / Together again /
Take these chains from my heart / Busted / Cryin'
time / In the heat of the night / I chose to sing the
blues / Here we go again / Your cheatin' heart / That
lucky old sun.
■ LP . . . . . . . . . . . . . . . . . . . . . SSL 10241
Stateside / Oct '68.

## HEART TO HEART - 20 HOT HITS.
**Tracks:** Not Advised.
■ LP . . . . . . . . . . . . . . . . . . . . . RAY TV 1
London / Jul '80.

## HERE AM I.
**Tracks:** Easy riding gal / Tapeworld / Ray's blues /
Here am I / Blow my baby back home / Blues is my
middle name.
■ LP . . . . . . . . . . . . . . . . . . . . . B 10106
MC . . . . . . . . . . . . . . . . . . . . . . MB9 10106
Barclay (France) / Apr '83 / PolyGram.

## HERE WE GO AGAIN.
**Tracks:** Here we go again / Someone ought to write a
book about it.
■ 7" . . . . . . . . . . . . . . . . . . . . . POP 1595
H.M.V. / Jul '67.

## HIS GREATEST HITS.
**Tracks:** Not Advised.
CD . . . . . . . . . . . . . . . . . . . . . . PRS 23005
MC . . . . . . . . . . . . . . . . . . . . . . PRS 843005
Personality / '93 / BMG.

## HIS GREATEST HITS.
**Tracks:** Not Advised.
■ CD Set . . . . . . . . . . . . . . . . . . . 6200 2
MMS Records / Apr '94.

## HIT THE ROAD JACK.
**Tracks:** Not Advised.
■ LP . . . . . . . . . . . . . . . . . . . . . PLP 21
MC . . . . . . . . . . . . . . . . . . . . . . PMC 21
Platinum (W.Germany) / Oct '85.

## HIT THE ROAD JACK.
**Tracks:** Hit the road Jack / Georgia on my mind.
■ 7" . . . . . . . . . . . . . . . . . . . . . RACH 1
Arcade / May '90.

## HIT THE ROAD JACK.
**Tracks:** Hit the road Jack.
■ 7" . . . . . . . . . . . . . . . . . . . . . POP 935
H.M.V. / Oct '61.

## HITS OF A GENIUS.
**Tracks:** Not Advised.
CD . . . . . . . . . . . . . . . . . . . . . . 99009
■ LP . . . . . . . . . . . . . . . . . . . . . 39009
MC . . . . . . . . . . . . . . . . . . . . . . 69009
Commander / May '88.

## HOPELESSLY.
**Tracks:** Hopelessly / I chose to sing the blues.
■ 7" . . . . . . . . . . . . . . . . . . . . . POP 1551
H.M.V. / '66.

## I CAN SEE CLEARLY NOW.
**Tracks:** I can see clearly now / Let it be.
■ 7" . . . . . . . . . . . . . . . . . . . . . HL 10554
London / Aug '80.

## I CAN'T STOP LOVING YOU.
**Tracks:** Hit the road Jack / Hallelujah I love her so /
Mess around / Let's go get stoned / Don't let the sun
catch you cryin' / What'd I say / Georgia on my mind
/ I got a woman / Drown in my own tears / Night time

■ DELETED

is the right time / Eleanor Rigby / I can't stop loving you.
■ LP . . . . . . . . . . . . . . . . . . . . . . . . SSP 3075
Pickwick / Sep '80.
■ 7" . . . . . . . . . . . . . . . . . . . . . . . . . . 24004
Colorado / '88.

### I CAN'T STOP LOVING YOU.
Tracks: I can't stop loving you.
■ 7" . . . . . . . . . . . . . . . . . . . . . . . . POP 1034
H.M.V. / Jun '62.

### I DON'T NEED NO DOCTOR.
Tracks: I don't need no doctor / Please say you're fooling.
■ 7" . . . . . . . . . . . . . . . . . . . . . . . . POP 1566
H.M.V. / Dec '66.

### I WISH YOU WERE HERE TONIGHT.
Tracks: 3/4 time / I wish you were here tonight / Ain't your memory got no pride at all / Born to love me / I don't want no stranger sleepin' in my bed / Let your love flow / You feel good all over / String bean / You've got the longest leaving act in town / Shakin' your head.
■ LP . . . . . . . . . . . . . . . . . . . . . . CBS 25065
■ MC . . . . . . . . . . . . . . . . . . . . . .40 25065
CBS / Mar '83.
CD. . . . . . . . . . . . . . . . . . . . . . . . . 9022892
Pickwick/Sony Collector's Choice / Apr '90 / Pickwick / Pinnacle.

### I WISH YOU WERE HERE TONIGHT.
Tracks: I wish you were here tonight / You feel good all over.
■ 7" . . . . . . . . . . . . . . . . . . . . . . . . . A 3407
CBS / May '83.

### I WONDER WHO'S KISSING HER NOW?.
Tracks: I wonder who's kissing her now / She's on the ball / Baby won't you please come home.
■ 12" . . . . . . . . . . . . . . . . . . . . . . .CYZ 119
■ 7" . . . . . . . . . . . . . . . . . . . . . .CYZ 7 119
Charly / Feb '87.

### I'M ALL YOURS - BABY.
Tracks: Yours / I didn't know what time it was / Love is here to stay / Memories of you / Till the end of time / I had the craziest dream / Someday / Indian love call / I dream of you / Gloomy Sunday.
■ LP . . . . . . . . . . . . . . . . . . . . . .SSL 10281
Stateside / Jul '69.

### IF I GIVE YOU MY LOVE.
Tracks: Alone in the city / Can anyone ask for more / Rockin' chair blues / Let's have a ball / If I give you my love / Can't see you darling / This love of mine / Sentimental blues / Now she's gone / Going down slow.
■ LP . . . . . . . . . . . . . . . . . . . . . . . F 50014
MC. . . . . . . . . . . . . . . . . . . . . . MF 950014
IMS / Oct '82 / PolyGram.
CD. . . . . . . . . . . . . . . . . . . . . . . PD 50014
IMS / May '88 / PolyGram.

### IN PERSON.
Tracks: Right time / What'd say / Yes indeed / Spirit-feel / Frenesi / Drown in my own tears / Tell the truth.
■ LP . . . . . . . . . . . . . . . . . . . . . . . 587 164
Atlantic / Apr '69.

### INGREDIENTS IN A RECIPE FOR SOUL.
Tracks: Not Advised.
CD. . . . . . . . . . . . . . . . . . . . . . . . TL 1332
Traditional Line / Mar '94 / Charly / A.D.A. Distribution / Koch International.

### JAMMIN' THE BLUES.
Tracks: Not Advised.
■ LP . . . . . . . . . . . . . . . . . . . . . . . . 20078
MC. . . . . . . . . . . . . . . . . . . . . . . . . 40078
Astan / Nov '84.

### JUST BETWEEN US.
Tracks: Nothing like a hundred miles / I wish I'd never loved you at all / Too hard to love you / Now I don't believe that anymore / Let's call the whole thing off / Stranger in my own hometown / Over the top / I'd walk a little more for you / If that's what'cha want / Save the bones for Henry Jones.
CD. . . . . . . . . . . . . . . . . . . . . . . . 4611832
■ LP . . . . . . . . . . . . . . . . . . . . . . 4611831
MC. . . . . . . . . . . . . . . . . . . . . . . 4611834
CBS / Sep '88 / Sony.

### KING OF THE BLUES.
Tracks: Not Advised.
MC. . . . . . . . . . . . . . . . . . . . . . . AMP 011
Ampro / Sep '81.

### LEGEND LIVES.
Tracks: Not Advised.
■ CD . . . . . . . . . . . . . . . . . . . ADEHCD 780
Arcade / May '88.

### LET'S GO GET STONED.
Tracks: Let's go get stoned / Train.
■ 7" . . . . . . . . . . . . . . . . . . . . . . POP 1537
H.M.V. / Jun '66.

### LIVE.
Tracks: Not Advised.
CD. . . . . . . . . . . . . . . . . . . . . .756781732-2
Atlantic / Jun '93 / WEA.

### LIVE : RAY CHARLES.
Tracks: Not Advised.
■ Double LP . . . . . . . . . . . . . . . . . . . 2-503
Atlantic / Nov '87.

### LIVING LEGEND.
Tracks: Not Advised.
CD. . . . . . . . . . . . . . . . . . . . . . ARC 94642
MC. . . . . . . . . . . . . . . . . . . . . . ARC 94644
Arcade / Mar '93 / Sony / Grapevine Distribution.

### LOVE AND PEACE.
Tracks: You 20th century fox / Take off that dress / She knows / Riding thumb / We had it all / No achievement showing / Peace that we never before could enjoy / Is there anybody out there / Give the poor man a break.
■ LP . . . . . . . . . . . . . . . . . . . . . . SHU 8519
London / Oct '78.

### LOVE COUNTRY STYLE.
Tracks: If you were mine / Ring of fire / Your love is so doggone good / Don't change on me / Till I can't take it anymore / You still got a place in my heart / I keep it hid / Sweet memories / Good morning dear / Show me the sunshine.
■ LP . . . . . . . . . . . . . . . . . . . . . . SPB 1015
Probe / Nov '70.

### LOVE SONGS COLLECTION, THE.
Tracks: I wonder who's kissing her now / Here am I / Oh baby / I used to be so happy / Honey honey / Ego song / Hey now / Late in the evening blues / I live only for you / St. Pete's blues / I'm glad for your sake / I'm just a lonely boy / All night long / c.c. rider / All to myself alone / Blues is my middle name.
CD. . . . . . . . . . . . . . . . . . . . . . DVCD 2123
Deja Vu / Jul '88 / Jazz Music / Music Collection International.
■ LP . . . . . . . . . . . . . . . . . . . . . DVLP 2123
MC. . . . . . . . . . . . . . . . . . . . . . DVMC 2123
Deja Vu / Jun '88 / Jazz Music / Music Collection International.

### MAKIN' WHOOPEE.
Tracks: Makin' whoopee.
■ 7" . . . . . . . . . . . . . . . . . . . . . . POP 1383
H.M.V. / Jan '65.

### MESSAGE FROM THE PEOPLE.
Tracks: Lift every voice & sing / Seems like I gotta do wrong / Heaven help us all / There'll be no peace without all men as one / Hey mister / What have they done to my song Na / Abraham, Martin & John / Take me home, country roads / Every Saturday night / America the beautiful.
■ LP . . . . . . . . . . . . . . . . . . . . . . SPB 1060
Probe / Sep '72.

### MODERN SOUNDS IN COUNTRY AND WESTERN MUSIC VOL.1.
Tracks: Not Advised.
■ LP . . . . . . . . . . . . . . . . . . . . . . CLP 1580
H.M.V. / Jul '62.

### MODERN SOUNDS IN COUNTRY AND WESTERN MUSIC VOL.2.
Tracks: Not Advised.
■ LP . . . . . . . . . . . . . . . . . . . . . . CLP 1613
H.M.V. / Feb '63.

### MY KIND OF JAZZ.
Tracks: Golden boy / Boody butt / This here / I remember Clifford / Sidewinder / Bluesette / Pas-se-o-ne blues / Zig zag / Angel city / Senor blues.
■ LP . . . . . . . . . . . . . . . . . . . . . . 6495001
Tangerine / Jul '71.

### MY WORLD.
Tracks: My world / Song for you / None of us are free / So help me God / Let me take over / One drop of love / If I could / Love has a mind of its own / I'll be there / Still crazy after all these years.
CD. . . . . . . . . . . . . . . . . . . . .759926735-2
MC. . . . . . . . . . . . . . . . . . . . .759926735-4
WEA / Mar '93 / WEA.

### NO ONE TO CRY TO.
Tracks: No one to cry to.
■ 7" . . . . . . . . . . . . . . . . . . . . . . POP 1333
H.M.V. / Sep '64.

### OH LORD I'M ON MY WAY.
Tracks: Oh Lord I'm on my way / Oh Bess, oh where's my Bess.
■ 7" . . . . . . . . . . . . . . . . . . . . . HLU 10541
London-American / Oct '76.

### PAGES OF MY MIND, THE.
Tracks: Pages of my mind / Slip away / Anybody with the blues / Class reunion / Caught a touch of your love / Little bit of heaven / Dixie moon / Over and over (again) / Beaucoup love / Love is worth the pain.
■ LP . . . . . . . . . . . . . . . . . . . . . CBS 26856
MC. . . . . . . . . . . . . . . . . . . . . . .40 26856
CBS / Aug '86 / Sony.

### PORTRAIT OF RAY.
Tracks: Never say naw / Sun died / Am I blue / Yesterdays / When I stop dreaming / That's a lie / I can't leave / Sweet young thing like you / Bright lights and you / Understanding / Eleanor Rigby / Go on home.
■ LP . . . . . . . . . . . . . . . . . . . . . .SSL 10269
Stateside / Feb '69.

### RAY CHARLES.
Tracks: Not Advised.
MC. . . . . . . . . . . . . . . . . . . . . . SSC 3075
Pickwick / Sep '80 / Pickwick.
MC. . . . . . . . . . . . . . . . . . . . . ZCGAS 729
Audio Fidelity / Oct '84 / Telstar/Ronco.
CD. . . . . . . . . . . . . . . . . . . . . .ENT CD 203
■ LP . . . . . . . . . . . . . . . . . . . . . ENT 13005
MC. . . . . . . . . . . . . . . . . . . . . . ENT MC 13005
Entertainers / Sep '87 / BMG.
■ LP . . . . . . . . . . . . . . . . . . . . . . BID 8011
Bellaphon / Jul '88.
CD. . . . . . . . . . . . . . . . . . . . . . .LECD 049
Dynamite (2) / May '94 / THE.

### RAY CHARLES.
Tracks: Confession blues / Can anyone ask for anymore / This love of mine / How long blues / Blues before sunrise / I've had my fun / c.c. rider / Late in the evening blues / Th'ego song / I wonder who's kissing her now / Baby won't you please come home / I'm glad for your sake / Kissa me baby / Hey now / Snow is falling / Misery in my heart / Let me hear you call my name / Why did you go / Walkin' and talkin'.
CD. . . . . . . . . . . . . . . . . . . . . . CDCD 1069
Charly / Mar '93 / Charly.

### RAY CHARLES (DOUBLE CASSETTE).
Tracks: Not Advised.
MC Set . . . . . . . . . . . . . . . . . . DTO 10202
Ditto / '88 / Pickwick.

### RAY CHARLES (JOKER (USA)).
Tracks: Not Advised.
■ LP . . . . . . . . . . . . . . . . . . . . . .SM 3712
Joker (USA) / '88.

### RAY CHARLES AND BETTY CARTER (Charles, Ray & Betty Carter).
Tracks: Every time we say goodbye / You and I / Goodbye, we'll be together again / People will say we're in love / Cocktails for two / Side by side / Baby it's cold outside / Together / For all we know / It takes two to tango / Alone together / Just you and me / But on the other hand baby / I never see Maggie alone / I like to hear it sometimes.
■ LP . . . . . . . . . . . . . . . . . . . . . ESSLP 012
■ CD . . . . . . . . . . . . . . . . . . . . . ESSCD 012
■ MC . . . . . . . . . . . . . . . . . . . . . ESSMC 012
Essential / Nov '89.

### RAY CHARLES AND BETTY CARTER (Charles, Ray & Betty Carter).
Tracks: Not Advised.
CD. . . . . . . . . . . . . . . . . . . . . . PRS 23003
MC. . . . . . . . . . . . . . . . . . . . . . PRS 843003
Personality / '93 / BMG.

### RAY CHARLES BLUES.
Tracks: Not Advised.
■ LP . . . . . . . . . . . . . . . . . . . . . . 20079
MC. . . . . . . . . . . . . . . . . . . . . . . 40079
Astan / Nov '84.

### RAY CHARLES COLLECTION.
Tracks: Yesterday / Your cheatin' heart / I can't stop loving you / Eleanor Rigby / Hit the road Jack.
CD. . . . . . . . . . . . . . . . . . . . . . RCLD 101

MC. . . . . . . . . . . . . . . . . . . . . RLCL 101
Westmoor / Aug '92 / BMG.

## RAY CHARLES IN L.A.
**Tracks:** Not Advised.
CD. . . . . . . . . . . . . . . . . . . . . . TL 1313
Traditional Line / Sep '92 / Charly / A.D.A. Distribution / Koch International.

## RAY CHARLES LIVE '93.
**Tracks:** Not Advised.
CD. . . . . . . . . . . . . . . . . . . . . . JD 1263
Jazz Door / Mar '94 / Charly / Koch International / A.D.A. Distribution.

## RAY CHARLES LIVE 1991.
**Tracks:** If you go away / It hurts to be in love / It's not easy being green / Good life / All I ever need is you / Your cheating heart / Georgia on my mind.
VHS . . . . . . . . . . . . . . . . . .853650231-3
Warner Music Video / Oct '92 / WEA.

## RAY CHARLES LIVE EP.
**Tracks:** Makin' whooppee / I gotta woman.
■ EP . . . . . . . . . . . . . . . . . . . 7EG 8932
H.M.V. / Feb '66.

## RAY CHARLES STORY, THE.
**Tracks:** Baby won't you please come home / Ego song / You always miss the water (when the well runs dry) / St. Pete's blues / I live only for you / What have I done / C.C. rider / I've had my fun / Honey honey / Here am I / I wonder who's kissing her now / Ray Charles blues / She's on the ball / If I give you my love / I'm going down to the river / Let's have a ball / Hey now / Sitting on top of the world / Sentimental blues / I used to be so happy / Ain't that fine / All to myself alone / Georgia on my mind / What'd I say / Come rain or come shine.
CD Set . . . . . . . . . . . . . . . .DVRECD 02
MC Set . . . . . . . . . . . . . . . .DVREMC 02
Deja Vu / May '89 / Jazz Music / Music Collection International.

## RAY CHARLES VOL.2.
**Tracks:** Alone in the city / Can anyone ask for more / Rockin' chair blues / Let's have a ball / If I give you my love / Can't see you darling / This love of mine / Sentimental blues / Now she's gone / Going down slow.
■ LP . . . . . . . . . . . . . . . . . . .SM 3729
Joker (USA) / Apr '81.

## RAY OF HOPE.
**Tracks:** c.c. rider / I wonder who's kissing her now / Hey now / Tell me baby / Kiss me baby / I'm gonna drown myself / Winter scene / Lovin' the girls.
■ LP . . . . . . . . . . . . . . . . . . .MAN 5020
Manhattan Records / Aug '80.

## RIGHT TIME, THE.
**Tracks:** Leave my woman alone / My Bonnie / That's enough / Drown in my own tears / Fool for you / Hallelujah I love her so / This little girl of mine / Mary Ann / I got a woman / Yes indeed / Swanee River rock / Lonely avenue / I had a dream / Early in the morning / Right time / I'm movin' on / What kind of man are you (Extra track on CD only) / I want to know (Extra track on CD only) / What'd I say (part 1) (Extra track on the CD only) / What'd I say (part 2) (Extra track on the CD only) / Jumpin' in the mornin'.
■ CD . . . . . . . . . . . . . . . . . . 241 119-2
■ LP . . . . . . . . . . . . . . . . . . 241 119-1
■ MC . . . . . . . . . . . . . . . . . . 241 119-4
Atlantic / Jul '87.

## ROCK + SOUL = GENIUS.
**Tracks:** Not Advised.
CD. . . . . . . . . . . . . . . . . . .JMY 1009-2
JMY / Aug '91 / Harmonia Mundi (UK).

## ROCKIN' WITH RAY.
**Tracks:** Not Advised.
■ LP . . . . . . . . . . . . . . . . . . .SM 3871
Joker (USA) / '88.

## SALUTE TO RAY CHARLES, A.
**Tracks:** Hallelujah I love her so / Georgia on my mind / Sticks and stones / Right time / This little girl of mine / Crying time / Ruby / Unchain my heart / Born to lose / Your cheating heart / Come rain or come shine / Hit the road Jack / I can't stop loving you / You are my sunshine / Busted / What'd I say / Let the good times roll / One mint julep.
■ LP Set . . . . . . . . . . . . . . . .2659 009
Atlantic / Nov '71.

## SEVEN SPANISH ANGELS.
**Tracks:** Seven spanish angels / Who cares.
■ 7" . . . . . . . . . . . . . . . . . . .A 4991
CBS / May '85.

## SHAKE YOUR TAIL FEATHER.
**Tracks:** Shake your tail feather / Minnie the moocher.
■ 7" . . . . . . . . . . . . . . . . . . K 11615
Atlantic / Oct '80.

## SIMPLY RAY.
**Tracks:** All to myself alone / Going down slow / Baby let me hold your hand / I won't let you go / Sitting on top of the world / By myself / Winter scene / Lovin' the girls.
■ LP . . . . . . . . . . . . . . . . . . MAN 5019
Manhattan Records / May '80.

## SOUL MEETING (Charles, Ray & Milt Jackson).
**Tracks:** Hallelujah I love her so / Blue genius / X-ray blues / Soul meeting / Love on my mind / Bags of blues.
■ LP . . . . . . . . . . . . . . . . . K 50234
Atlantic / Jul '76.
CD. . . . . . . . . . . . . . . .756781951-2
Atlantic / Mar '93 / WEA.

## SPIRIT OF CHRISTMAS, THE.
**Tracks:** What child is this / Little drummer boy / Santa Claus is coming to town / This time of the year / Rudolph the red nosed reindeer / That spirit of Christmas / All I want for Christmas / Christmas in my heart / Winter wonderland / Christmas time.
■ LP . . . . . . . . . . . . . . . . . CBS 26562
■ MC . . . . . . . . . . . . . . . . . .40 26562
CBS / Dec '85.

## STAR COLLECTION.
**Tracks:** I got a woman / Let the good times roll / Ray / Loosing hand / Mess around / Mary Ann / This little girl of mine / Talkin' bout you / Undecided / Alexanders ragtime band / Don't let the sun catch you crying.
■ LP . . . . . . . . . . . . . . . . . K 20015
■ MC . . . . . . . . . . . . . . . . . K4 20015
Atlantic / '88.

## TAKE THESE CHAINS FROM MY HEART.
**Tracks:** Take these chains from my heart.
■ 7" . . . . . . . . . . . . . . . . . POP 1161
H.M.V. / May '63.

## TELL THE TRUTH.
**Tracks:** Mess around / It should've been me / Losing hand / Greenbacks / I got a woman / This little girl of mine / Hallelujah / I love her so / Drown in my own tears / Leave my woman alone / Lonely Avenue / That's enough / Talkin' 'bout you / You be my baby / Right time / Tell the truth / What'd I say.
■ LP . . . . . . . . . . . . . . . . . CRB 1071
■ MC . . . . . . . . . . . . . . . . . TCCRB 1071
Charly R&B / Mar '84.

## THIS LOVE OF MINE.
**Tracks:** Kiss me baby / Baby let me hold your hand / C.C. rider / I wonder who's kissing her now / I'm going down to the river / They're crazy about me / Going down slow / Sentimental blues / Can anyone ask for more / Rockin' chair blues / If I give you my love / This love of mine.
■ LP . . . . . . . . . . . . . . . . . TOP 126
MC . . . . . . . . . . . . . . . . . . KTOP 126
Topline / '86 / Charly.
CD. . . . . . . . . . . . . . . . . . TOP CD 512
Topline / Apr '87 / Charly.

## THROUGH THE EYES OF LOVE.
**Tracks:** My first night alone without you / I can make it thru the days / Someone to watch over me / Perfect love / If you wouldn't be my lady / You leave me breathless / Never ending song of love / Rainy night in Georgia.
■ LP . . . . . . . . . . . . . . . . . SPB 1066
Probe / Feb '73.

## TOGETHER AGAIN.
**Tracks:** Together again / You're just about to lose your clown.
■ 7" . . . . . . . . . . . . . . . . . POP 1519
H.M.V. / Apr '66.

## TRUE TO LIFE.
**Tracks:** Not Advised.
■ LP . . . . . . . . . . . . . . . . . SHU 8509
London-American / Jan '78.

## TWO ON ONE: RAY CHARLES & NAT KING COLE (Charles, Ray & Nat King Cole).
**Tracks:** Not Advised.
CD. . . . . . . . . . . . . . . . . . CDTT 8
Charly / Apr '94 / Charly.

## VOLCANIC ACTION OF MY SOUL.
**Tracks:** See you then / What am I living for / Feel so bad / Long and winding road / Three bells / All I ever

need is you / Wichita lineman / Something / I may be wrong / Down in the valley.
■ LP . . . . . . . . . . . . . . . . . SPB 1039
Probe / Jul '71.

## WHAT HAVE I DONE TO THEIR SONGS.
**Tracks:** What have they done to my song Ma / Long and winding road / I keep it hid / Perfect love / Eleanor Rigby / Wichita lineman / Never ending song of love / Something / Take me home country roads / See you then / Yesterday / Sweet memories.
■ LP . . . . . . . . . . . . . . . . . .ZGU 139
London / Jun '77.

## WHAT IS LIFE?.
**Tracks:** Going to the river / Steppin' out baby / Dear heart / Glow worm / Take some and leave some / All alone / I'll do anything but work / My mama told me / I'm yours for the asking / Blow my baby back home / Too late to change / What is life.
■ LP . . . . . . . . . . . . . . . . . B 90112
■ MC . . . . . . . . . . . . . . . . . MB9 90112
Barclay (France) / Apr '83 / PolyGram.

## WHAT'D I SAY.
**Tracks:** What'd I say / Jumpin' in the mornin' / You be my baby / Tell me how do you feel / What kind of man are you / Rockhouse / Rollin' with my baby / Tell all the world about you / My bonnie / That's enough.
■ LP . . . . . . . . . . . . . . . . . 588 161
Atlantic / Sep '69.
■ CD . . . . . . . . . . . . . . . . . .15 091
■ MC . . . . . . . . . . . . . . . . . .79 540
Laserlight / Aug '91.

## WHAT'D I SAY.
**Tracks:** What'd I say / I got a woman.
7" . . . . . . . . . . . . . . . . . . .584093
Atlantic / Mar '67 / WEA.

## YES INDEED.
**Tracks:** It's alright / I want to know / Yes indeed / Swanee River Rock / Blackjack / Heartbreaker / etc.
■ LP . . . . . . . . . . . . . . . . . .590014
Atlantic / Dec '67.

## YESTERDAY.
**Tracks:** Yesterday.
■ 7" . . . . . . . . . . . . . . . . . SS 2071
Stateside / Dec '67.

## YOU DON'T KNOW ME.
**Tracks:** You don't know me.
■ 7" . . . . . . . . . . . . . . . . . POP 1064
H.M.V. / Sep '62.

## YOU WIN AGAIN.
**Tracks:** You win again / Bye bye love.
■ 7" . . . . . . . . . . . . . . . . . POP 1589
H.M.V. / Apr '67.

## YOUR CHEATIN' HEART.
**Tracks:** Your cheatin' heart.
■ 7" . . . . . . . . . . . . . . . . . POP 1099
H.M.V. / Dec '62.

# Charles, Tina

## BABY DON'T YOU KNOW ANYMORE.
**Tracks:** Baby don't you know anymore / Joe.
■ 7" . . . . . . . . . . . . . . . . . MAM 35
Mam / Jul '71.

## BOOGIE ROUND THE CLOCK.
**Tracks:** Boogie round the clock / Boogie round the clock (version).
■ 7" . . . . . . . . . . . . . . . . . CBS 7024
CBS / Feb '79.

## DANCE LITTLE LADY.
**Tracks:** Not Advised.
■ LP . . . . . . . . . . . . . . . . . CBS 81617
CBS / Nov '76.
MC. . . . . . . . . . . . . . . . . . HSC 3047
■ LP . . . . . . . . . . . . . . . . . SHM 3047
Hallmark / Apr '81 / Pickwick.

## DANCE LITTLE LADY.
**Tracks:** Dance little lady.
■ 7" . . . . . . . . . . . . . . . . . CBS 4480
CBS / Aug '76.

## DOCTOR LOVE.
**Tracks:** Dr. Love.
■ 7" . . . . . . . . . . . . . . . . . CBS 4779
CBS / Dec '76.

## FALLING IN LOVE IN SUMMERTIME.
**Tracks:** Falling in love in summertime / I'll be your light.
■ 7" . . . . . . . . . . . . . . . . . CBS 5415
CBS / Jun '77.

■ DELETED

## GO TO WORK ON MY LOVE.
Tracks: Go to work on my love / Learn by your mistakes.
■ 12"................................. MTR 12001
■ 7".................................. MTR 7001
MTR / May '90.

## HEART 'N' SOUL.
Tracks: Love bug / Sweets for my sweet / I'll go where your music takes me / Stop what you're doing to me / Rendezvous / Fallin' in love in the summertime / I gotta dance with you / I'll be your light / Ain't gonna hide my love / Go.
■ LP..................................... 82180
CBS / Oct '77.

## HEART'N'SOUL.
Tracks: Not Advised.
■ LP.............................. CBS 82180
CBS / Sep '77.

## I CAN'T DANCE TO THAT MUSIC THAT YOU'RE PLAYIN'.
Tracks: I can't dance to that music that you're playing / Joe.
■ 7"................................. MAM 142
M.A.M. / Apr '76.

## I LOVE TO LOVE.
Tracks: I love to love (teenage mix) / I love to love.
■ 7".............................. CBS 3937
CBS / Feb '76.
■ 7".............................. CBS 5966
CBS / Apr '82.
■ 12"............................. DECKS 121
■ 12"............................. DECK 121
■ 7"............................... DECK 1
Disco Mix / Aug '86.
■ 12"............................. DECK 126
■ 7"............................... DECK 6
DMC / Aug '87.

## I LOVE TO LOVE.
Tracks: I love to love (but my baby just loves to dance) / You set my heart on fire (part 1) / Hey boy / Take all of me / Love me like a lover / Why / Hold me / Disco fever / Disco love.
■ LP.............................. CBS 81290
CBS / Mar '76.
CD......................................983277 2
Pickwick/Sony Collector's Choice / Sep '93 / Pickwick / Pinnacle.

## I LOVE TO LOVE (OLD GOLD).
Tracks: I love to love / You set my heart on fire.
■ 7"................................OG 9198
Old Gold / Feb '89.

## I'LL GO WHERE YOUR MUSIC TAKES ME.
Tracks: I'll go where your music takes me / Stop what you're doing to me.
■ 7".............................. CBS 6062
CBS / Mar '78.

## JUST ONE SMILE.
Tracks: Just one smile / I'm just as bad as you / Lover boy / Dance with me / Makin' all the right moves / Somewhere / Love is a many splendoured thing / Secret love / Fire down below / Boogie round the clock.
■ LP.............................. CBS 84240
CBS / Jun '80.

## JUST ONE SMILE.
Tracks: Just one smile / Fire down below.
■ 7".............................. CBS 8301
CBS / Mar '80.

## LOVE BUG-SWEETS FOR MY SWEET.
Tracks: Love bug-sweets for my sweet (medley).
■ 7".............................. CBS 5680
CBS / Oct '77.

## LOVE HUNGER.
Tracks: Love hunger / Played for a fool.
■ 12"............................. SONL 2276
■ 7".............................. SON 2276
Sonet / Feb '85.

## LOVE ME LIKE A LOVER.
Tracks: Love me like a lover.
■ 7".............................. CBS 4237
CBS / May '76.

## MAKIN' ALL THE RIGHT MOVES.
Tracks: Makin' all the right moves / Love me now.
■ 7".............................. CBS 6594
CBS / Sep '78.

## RENDEZVOUS.
Tracks: Rendezvous.
■ 7".............................. CBS 5174
CBS / May '77.

## ROLLIN'.
Tracks: Rollin' / Don't throw your love.
■ 7".............................. POSP 218
Polydor / Jan '81.

## RUNNING INTO DANGER.
Tracks: Running into danger / Running track.
■ 12"............................. SONL 2287
■ 7".............................. SON 2287
Sonet / Sep '85.

## SECOND TIME AROUND.
Tracks: Second time around / Played for a fool.
■ 7".............................. SON 2300
Sonet / Sep '86.

## TINA CHARLES: GREATEST HITS.
Tracks: I love to love / Dance little lady dance / Rendezvous / It's the time for a change of heart / Hold me / You set my heart on fire / Dr. Love / I'll go where your music takes me / Love bug / Sweets for my sweet / Disco fever / Love me like a lover / Makin' all the right moves.
■ LP.............................. CBS 83201
CBS / Dec '78.

## TINA SINGS.
Tracks: Not Advised.
■ LP..............................MAME 3001
M.A.M. / Apr '77.

## TURN BACK THE HANDS OF TIME.
Tracks: Turn back the hands of time / Night follows day.
■ 7".............................. POSP 162
Polydor / Aug '80.

## YOU SET MY HEART ON FIRE.
Tracks: You set my heart on fire / Can't stop my feet from dancing.
■ 7".............................. CBS 3415
CBS / Jul '75.
■ 7".............................. CBS 7784
CBS / Sep '78.

# Charme

## DO IT FOR LOVE.
Tracks: Do it for love / Georgie porgie.
■ 12"............................. PC 1727
RCA / Jan '80.

## GEORGIE PORGIE.
Tracks: Georgie Porgie / Rock the boat.
■ 7"................................RCA 464
■ 12"............................RCAT 464
RCA / Nov '84.

# Charo & The Salsoul..

## CUCHI CUCHI (Charo & The Salsoul Orchestra).
Tracks: Cuchi cuchi / Dance a little bit closer / Let's spend the night together / Borriquito / More of you / El reloj / Speedy gonzalez / Cookie jar / You're the right size / Only you.
■ LP.............................. SSLP 1501
Salsoul / May '78.

## DANCE A LITTLE BIT CLOSER (Charo & The Salsoul Orchestra).
Tracks: Dance a little bit closer / Cuchi-cuchi.
■ 7".............................. SSOL 101
Salsoul / Apr '78.

# Cheatham, Oliver

## BE THANKFUL FOR WHAT YOU'VE GOT.
Tracks: Be thankful for what you've got / Show me.
■ 12"............................. CHAMP 1254
■ 7".............................. CHAMP 54
Champion / Oct '87.

## BLESS THE LADIES.
Tracks: Bless the ladies / Just to be with you.
■ 12"............................MCAT 846
■ 7".............................. MCA 846
MCA / Oct '83.

## CELEBRATE.
Tracks: Celebrate.
■ 12"............................. CHAMP 1225
■ 7".............................. CHAMP 25
Champion / Nov '86.

## GET DOWN SATURDAY NIGHT.
Tracks: Get down saturday night / Something about you.
■ 12"............................MCAT 828
■ 7".............................. MCA 828
MCA / Jul '83.

## GET DOWN SATURDAY NIGHT (OLD GOLD).
Tracks: Get down saturday night / You can do it.
■ 12".............................OG 4063
Old Gold / May '88.

## GO FOR IT.
Tracks: Go for it / Wish on a star / Celebrate / S.O.S. / Show me / Can't wait for Saturday night / All for me / Good times.
■ CD.............................. CHAMPCD 1006
■ LP.............................. CHAMP 1006
■ MC.............................. CHAMPK 1006
Champion / Jul '87.

## GO FOR IT.
Tracks: Go for it / Go for it (version).
■ 12"............................. CHAMP 1224
■ 7".............................. CHAMP 24
■ 12"............................. CHAMP 1263
■ 7".............................. CHAMP 63
Champion / Feb '88.

## JUST TO BE WITH YOU.
Tracks: Just to be with you / Make your mind up.
■ 12"............................MCAT 831
■ 7".............................. MCA 831
MCA / Sep '83.

## MAMA SAID.
Tracks: Mama said / Look of love.
■ 12"............................. MS 312
■ 7".............................. MSS 3
Move / Aug '85.

## S.O.S.
Tracks: S.O.S. (Dub mix).
■ 7".............................. CHAMP 11
■ 12"............................. CHAMP 1211
Champion / May '86.

## SATURDAY NIGHT.
Tracks: Get down Saturday night / Make your mind up / Something about you / Bless the ladies / Do me right / Never gonna give you up / Through it all / Just to be with you.
■ LP.............................. MCF 3179
MCA / Nov '83.

## TURNING POINT.
Tracks: Turning point / Play me trade me.
■ 12"............................. MS 6
■ 7".............................. MSS 6
PRT / Nov '85.

## WISH ON A STAR.
Tracks: Wish on a star / Wish on a star (acca dub).
■ 7".............................. CHAMP 40
■ 12"............................. CHAMP 1240
Champion / Jun '87.

# Checker, Chubby

When Hank Ballard failed to turn up at Dick Clark's American Bandstand TV show, recent Cameo Parkway signing Chubby Checker stepped in with a hastily prepared cover of Ballard's *The Twist*. The response was so positive that it was quickly released as a single and shot to No. 1, selling over three million in its 15 weeks on the chart. Checker then achieved a U.S. chart first when the single was re-promoted the following year, and again topped the chart as the associated dance craze took hold. By 1964, Checker had achieved 20 Top 40 hits and sold 15 million records before public interest waned.

## 16 GREATEST HITS: CHUBBY CHECKER.
Tracks: Twist / Limbo rock / Slow twistin' / Fly / Let's twist again / Popeye the hitchiker / Loddy lo / Dancin' party / Birdland / Hucklebuck / Twenty miles / Hooka tooka / Let's limbo some more / Hey bobba needle / Dance the mess around.
■ CD.............................. CD 33
Bescol / May '87.

## 20 GREATEST HITS: CHUBBY CHECKER.
Tracks: Let's twist again / Twist / Hucklebuck / Hooka tooka / Twist it up / Pony time.
CD.............................. FUNCD 9038
■ LP.............................. FUN 9038

MC. . . . . . . . . . . . . . . . . . . . . . FUNC 9038
Fun (Holland) / Oct '88 / Pinnacle.

### 20 TWISTIN' HITS.
**Tracks:** Twist / Limbo rock / Pony time / Let's twist again / Slow twistin' / Fly / Huckleback / Loady lo / Popeye / Dancin' party / Twenty miles / Let's limbo some more.
CD. . . . . . . . . . . . . . . . . . . . . 26 42 062
MC. . . . . . . . . . . . . . . . . . . . . 26 42 064
Point (2) / '92 / Sound Solutions.

### 20 TWISTIN' HITS.
**Tracks:** Not Advised.
CD. . . . . . . . . . . . . . . . . . . . . . 2636032
MC. . . . . . . . . . . . . . . . . . . . . . 2636034
Black Tulip / Oct '89.

### BEST OF CHUBBY CHECKER.
**Tracks:** Not Advised.
MC. . . . . . . . . . . . . . . . . . . . . . . . 16-7
Creole / Jul '84 / THE / BMG.

### BEST OF CHUBBY CHECKER.
**Tracks:** Not Advised.
■ MC. . . . . . . . . . . . . . . . . . . . GM 0201
K-Tel / Aug '84.

### DANCIN' PARTY.
**Tracks:** Dancin' party.
■ 7". . . . . . . . . . . . . . . . . . . . . DB 4876
Columbia / Aug '62.
■ 7". . . . . . . . . . . . . . . . . . . . HLU 10524
London-American / Mar '76.

### FOR TWISTERS ONLY.
**Tracks:** Not Advised.
■ LP. . . . . . . . . . . . . . . . . . . . .33SX 1341
Columbia / Mar '62.

### GARY US BONDS MEETS CHUBBY CHECKER (see under Bonds, Gary U.S.).

### GREATEST HITS: CHUBBY CHECKER.
**Tracks:** Twist / Limbo rock / Dancin' party / Hey bobba needle / Loddy lo / Slow twistin' / Fly / Pony time / Let's twist again / Let's limbo some more / Birdland / Dance the mess around / Popeye (the hitchiker) / Twenty miles / Twist it up / Huckleback.
■ CD. . . . . . . . . . . . . . . . . . . ONCD 5130
■ LP. . . . . . . . . . . . . . . . . . . . NE 1361
K-Tel / May '87.

### JINGLE BELL ROCK (Checker, Chubby & Bobby Rydell).
**Tracks:** Jingle bell rock.
■ 7". . . . . . . . . . . . . . . . . . . . . . C 205
Cameo Parkway / Dec '62.

### LEGENDS IN MUSIC - CHUBBY CHECKER.
**Tracks:** Not Advised.
CD. . . . . . . . . . . . . . . . . . . . . LECD 062
Wisepack / Jul '94 / THE / Conifer Records.

### LET'S GO DOWN.
**Tracks:** Let's go down / Goodbye Victoria.
■ 7". . . . . . . . . . . . . . . . . . . . HL 10331
London / May '71.

### LET'S TWIST AGAIN.
**Tracks:** Not Advised.
■ LP. . . . . . . . . . . . . . . . . . . . NE 1209
■ MC. . . . . . . . . . . . . . . . . . . . CE 2209
K-Tel / Jun '83.

### LET'S TWIST AGAIN.
**Tracks:** Not Advised.
CD. . . . . . . . . . . . . . . . . . . RMB 75058
MC. . . . . . . . . . . . . . . . . . RMB 45058
Remember / Nov '93 / Midland Records / BMG.

### LETS TWIST AGAIN.
**Tracks:** Twist / Lets twist again / Dancin' party / Pony Time.
■ 7". . . . . . . . . . . . . . . . . . . . . DB 4691
Columbia / Aug '61.
■ 7". . . . . . . . . . . . . . . . . . . . HL 10512
London-American / Nov '75.
■ 7". . . . . . . . . . . . . . . . . . . . CR 189
Blast From The Past / Aug '82.
■ 12". . . . . . . . . . . . . . . . . . . . CRT 100
■ 7". . . . . . . . . . . . . . . . . . . . CR 100
Creole Classics / Apr '87.

### LIMBO ROCK.
**Tracks:** Limbo rock.
■ 7". . . . . . . . . . . . . . . . . . . . . P 849
Cameo Parkway / Nov '62.

### MR. TWISTER.
**Tracks:** Not Advised.
CD. . . . . . . . . . . . . . . . . . . CDCD 1043
Charly / Mar '93 / Charly.

### PEARLS FROM THE PAST VOL. 2 - CHUBBY CHECKER.
**Tracks:** Not Advised.
CD. . . . . . . . . . . . . . . . . . . KLMCD 014
Scratch / Apr '94 / Scratch Records / BMG / Grapevine Distribution.

### PONY TIME.
**Tracks:** Pony time.
■ 7". . . . . . . . . . . . . . . . . . . . . DB 4591
Columbia / Mar '61.

### SLOW TWISTIN'.
**Tracks:** Slow twistin'.
■ 7". . . . . . . . . . . . . . . . . . . . . DB 4808
Columbia / Apr '62.

### STILL TWISTIN'.
**Tracks:** Let's twist again / Twist / Slow twistin / Pony time / Fly / Birdland / Limbo rock / Let's limbo some more / Dancin' party / Huckleback / Dance the mess around / Twist it up.
■ LP. . . . . . . . . . . . . . . . . . . .TOP 155
MC. . . . . . . . . . . . . . . . . . . .KTOP 155
Topline / Oct '86 / Charly.

### TEACH ME TO TWIST (Checker, Chubby & Bobby Rydell).
**Tracks:** Teach me to twist.
■ 7". . . . . . . . . . . . . . . . . . . . . DB 4802
Columbia / Apr '62.

### TWIST DOCH MAL MIT MIR.
**Tracks:** Baby kiss kiss kiss / Twist doch mal mit mir / Holla hi, holla ho / Der twist beginnt / Troola trolla trolla / Autobahn baby / Twist mit mir.
■ LP. . . . . . . . . . . . . . . . . . . BF 15339
Bear Family / Aug '88.

### TWIST WITH CHUBBY CHECKER.
**Tracks:** Not Advised.
■ LP. . . . . . . . . . . . . . . . . . . .33SX 1315
Columbia / Jan '62.

### TWIST, THE.
**Tracks:** Twist.
■ 7". . . . . . . . . . . . . . . . . . . . . DB 4503
Columbia / Sep '60.

### WHAT DO YA SAY.
**Tracks:** What do ya say.
■ 7". . . . . . . . . . . . . . . . . . . . . P 806
Cameo Parkway / Oct '63.

### YOU JUST DON'T KNOW.
**Tracks:** You just don't know / Two hearts make one love.
■ 7". . . . . . . . . . . . . . . . . . . . HLU 10557
London-American / Apr '78.

## Checkmates Unlimited

### PROUD MARY.
**Tracks:** Proud Mary.
■ 7". . . . . . . . . . . . . . . . . . . . AMS 769
A&M / Nov '69.

## Cheeks, Judy

### I STILL LOVE YOU.
**Tracks:** I still love you / I still love you (12" mix) (on 12" version only) / Believe.
■ 12". . . . . . . . . . . . . . . . . . . POSPX 914
■ 7". . . . . . . . . . . . . . . . . . . . POSP 914
Polydor / Apr '88.

### JUST ANOTHER LIE.
**Tracks:** Just another lie / I'll be waiting.
■ 12". . . . . . . . . . . . . . . . . . . . PZ 11
■ 7". . . . . . . . . . . . . . . . . . . . PO 11
■ CD Single. . . . . . . . . . . . . . . PZCD 11
Polydor / Jul '88.

### LITTLE GIRL IN ME.
**Tracks:** Little girl in me / Why don't you kiss me baby.
■ 7". . . . . . . . . . . . . . . . . . . . ARO 14
Ariola / '79.

### MELLOW LOVIN'.
**Tracks:** Mellow lovin' / Darling that's me.
■ 7". . . . . . . . . . . . . . . . . . . . ARO 121
Ariola / '78.

### NO OUTSIDERS.
**Tracks:** Gonna wait on love / No outsiders / Just another lie / Step too far / I still love you / I'm in love with you baby / Other woman / Tell him / Love me like you used to / Believe / One way.
CD. . . . . . . . . . . . . . . . . . . 833 526-2
■ LP. . . . . . . . . . . . . . . . . . . POLD 5231
MC. . . . . . . . . . . . . . . . . . . POLDC 5231
Polydor / Sep '88 / PolyGram.

### REACH.
**Tracks:** Reach / Can't get enough / Reach (mixes).
12". . . . . . . . . . . . . . . . . . . .12TIV 12
■ 7". . . . . . . . . . . . . . . . . . . . TIV 12
CD Single. . . . . . . . . . . . . . . CDTIV 12
■ MC Single. . . . . . . . . . . . . . TCTIV 12
Chrysalis / Jun '94 / EMI.

### SO IN LOVE (THE REAL DEAL).
**Tracks:** So in love (The real deal).
■ 7". . . . . . . . . . . . . . . . . . . . .TIV 6
■ MC Single. . . . . . . . . . . . . . TCTIV 6
Positiva / Oct '93.
. . . . . . . . . . . . . . . . . . . . . . 12TIV 6
CD Single. . . . . . . . . . . . . . . CDTIV 6
Positiva / Jun '94 / EMI.

## Chequers

### CHECK US OUT.
**Tracks:** Not Advised.
■ LP. . . . . . . . . . . . . . . . . . . CRLP 504
Creole / '79.

### HARD TIMES.
**Tracks:** Hard times.
■ 7". . . . . . . . . . . . . . . . . . . . MT 102
Mathias / Mar '83.

### HEY MISS PAYNE.
**Tracks:** Hey Miss Payne.
■ 7". . . . . . . . . . . . . . . . . . . . CR 116
Creole / Feb '76.

### ROCK ON BROTHER.
**Tracks:** Not Advised.
■ 7". . . . . . . . . . . . . . . . . . . . CR 111
Creole / Oct '75.

### UNDECIDED LOVE.
**Tracks:** Undecided love / East and West side.
■ 7". . . . . . . . . . . . . . . . . . . . CR 101
Creole / Jan '75.

## Cherrelle

### AFFAIR.
**Tracks:** Looks aren't everything / Pick me up / Discreet / Affair / What more can I do for you / Everything I miss at home / Keep it inside / My friend / Crazy / Lucky / Home / Happy that you're with me / Saturday love.
■ LP. . . . . . . . . . . . . . . . . . . OZ 441 48
■ LP. . . . . . . . . . . . . . . . . . . .460734 1
■ MC. . . . . . . . . . . . . . . . . . .460734 4
Tabu / Nov '88.
CD. . . . . . . . . . . . . . . . . . . .466790 2
■ LP. . . . . . . . . . . . . . . . . . . .466790 1
MC. . . . . . . . . . . . . . . . . . .466790 4
Tabu / Apr '90 / Sony.

### AFFAIR.
**Tracks:** Affair / I didn't mean to turn you on / Affair (Storm mix) (Not on 7" single.) / Affair (Liason dangereuse dub) (12" single only.) / Saturday love (Steve Anderson remix) (Not on 7" single.) / Affair (Remix) (Only on cassette single.)
■ 12". . . . . . . . . . . . . . . . . . .656202 6
■ 7". . . . . . . . . . . . . . . . . . . .656202 4
■ 7". . . . . . . . . . . . . . . . . . . .656202 7
■ CD Single. . . . . . . . . . . . . . .656202 2
Tabu / Aug '90.

### AFFAIR.
**Tracks:** Affair / New love / Affair (steamy affair mix) / Affair (street dub hip hop mix).
■ 12". . . . . . . . . . . . . . . . . . . 654 673 1
■ 12". . . . . . . . . . . . . . . . . . . 654 673 8
■ 7". . . . . . . . . . . . . . . . . . . . 654 673 7
■ CD Single. . . . . . . . . . . . . . . 654 673 2
Tabu / Apr '89.

### ARTIFICIAL HEART.
**Tracks:** Oh no it's u again / Artificial heart.
■ 7". . . . . . . . . . . . . . . . . . . . .A 7185
Tabu / May '86.

### EVERYTHING I MISS AT HOME.
**Tracks:** Everything I miss at home / Where do I run to / I didn't mean to turn you on (Only on 12" version and CD single.).
■ 12". . . . . . . . . . . . . . . . . . .653066 8
■ 12". . . . . . . . . . . . . . . . . . .653066 6
■ 7". . . . . . . . . . . . . . . . . . . .653066 7
■ CD Single. . . . . . . . . . . . . . .653066 2
Tabu / Nov '88.

### FRAGILE - HANDLE WITH CARE.
**Tracks:** Fragile handle with care / I didn't mean to turn you on / Like I will / I will wait for you / Who's it gonna be / Stay with me / When you look in my eyes / I need you now.
■ LP. . . . . . . . . . . . . . . . . . . TBU 26064

■ DELETED

■ MC. . . . . . . . . . . . . . . . . . .40 26064
Tabu / Sep '84.

## FRAGILE..HANDLE WITH CARE.
Tracks: Fragile..handle with care / Stay with me.
■ 12" . . . . . . . . . . . . . . . . . . . . TA 4825
■ 7" . . . . . . . . . . . . . . . . . . . . . A 4825
CBS / Oct '84.

## HIGH PRIORITY.
Tracks: Opening / You look so good to me / Artifical
heart / New love / Oh no it's u again / Saturday love /
Will you satisfy / Where do I run to / High priority /
New love (reprise).
■ LP . . . . . . . . . . . . . . . . . . . TBU 26699
■ MC. . . . . . . . . . . . . . . . . . .40 26699
Tabu / Jan '86.

## I DIDN'T MEAN TO TURN YOU ON.
Tracks: I didn't mean to turn you on / I need you.
■ 12" . . . . . . . . . . . . . . . . . . . . TA 4656
■ 7" . . . . . . . . . . . . . . . . . . . . . A 4656
Tabu / Aug '84.

## SATURDAY LOVE (Cherrelle & Alexander O'Neal).
Tracks: Saturday love / I didn't mean to turn you on /
Saturday love (remix).
■ 12" . . . . . . . . . . . . . . . . . . QTA 6829
■ 12" . . . . . . . . . . . . . . . . . . . TA 6829
■ 7" . . . . . . . . . . . . . . . . . . . . . A 6829
Tabu / Jan '86.

## SATURDAY LOVE (REMIX).
Tracks: Saturday love (feelin' luv mix) / Happy that
you're with me / Saturday love (feelin' luv ext. mix) /
Foolin' around / Will you satisfy.
■ 12" . . . . . . . . . . . . . . . . . . .655800 6
■ 12" Remix. . . . . . . . . . . . . .655800 8
■ 7" . . . . . . . . . . . . . . . . . . . .655800 7
■ CD Single . . . . . . . . . . . . .655800 2
■ MC Single . . . . . . . . . . . . .655800 4
Tabu / Mar '90.

## TEARS OF JOY.
Tracks: Tears of joy.
■ 12" . . . . . . . . . . . . . . . . . . . . AMY 861
■ 7" . . . . . . . . . . . . . . . . . . . . . AM 861
Tabu / Mar '92.

## WILL YOU SATISFY?.
Tracks: When you look in my eyes / Will you satisfy* /
Saturday love / Saturday love (remix).
■ 12" . . . . . . . . . . . . . . . . . . DTA 6927
■ 7" . . . . . . . . . . . . . . . . . . . . . A 6927
■ 7" Set . . . . . . . . . . . . . . . . DA 6927
■ 12" . . . . . . . . . . . . . . . . . . . TA 6927
Tabu / Feb '86.

## WOMAN I AM, THE.
Tracks: Not Advised.
CD. . . . . . . . . . . . . . . . . . . . .364005 2
■ LP . . . . . . . . . . . . . . . . . . . .364005 1
MC. . . . . . . . . . . . . . . . . . . .364005 4
A&M / Oct '91 / PolyGram.

## Cherry People

## AND SUDDENLY.
Tracks: And suddenly / Imagination.
■ 7" . . . . . . . . . . . . . . . . . . . . BM 112
Black Magic (2) / Jan '76.

## Cheyenne

## I'VE WAITED TOO LONG (FOR YOUR LOVE).
Tracks: I've waited too long (for your love).
■ 12" . . . . . . . . . . . . . . . . . . .12SY 21
■ 7" . . . . . . . . . . . . . . . . . . . . . SY 21
Syncopate / Nov '88.

## Chi-Lites

Having struggled through 1960s, Chicago
quartet Chi-Lites suddenly became stars at
turn of decade. Led by former cab driver
Eugene Record and produced by soul veteran Carl Davis, group first scored with (For
God's Sake) Give More Power To The People. Using Temptations template, they followed protest song with ballad, namely
classic Have You Seen Her?. Oh Girl - No. 1
in '73 - was their last major domestic success; however, they continued to chart in
U.K.: Homely Girl, reissue of Have You
Seen Her/Oh Girl, It's Time For Love, Too
Good To Be Forgotten and You Don't Have
To Go all made Top 10. Temporary departure of Record in '76 for solo career coincided with slump in group's fortunes from
which they have never recovered, despite

minor comeback with 1983's Changing For
You. Now fronted by Anthony Watson, Record having quit again in mid-'80s, group's
memory is kept alive by host of covers and
frequent appearances on love song
compilations.

## 19 GREATEST HITS.
Tracks: Not Advised.
CD. . . . . . . . . . . . . . . . . . . 26 20 252
MC. . . . . . . . . . . . . . . . . . . 26 20 254
Point (2) / '92 / Sound Solutions.

## 20 GOLDEN PIECES: CHI-LITES.
Tracks: I'm ready (if I don't get to go) / Love uprising
/ Coldest day of my life / Oh girl / I wanna pay you
back / I like your loving / Have you seen her / For
God's sake give more power to the people / Are you
my woman (tell me so) / We are neighbours / Letter
to myself / Homely girl / Too good to be forgotten / I
found sunshine / Stoned out of my mind / Toby / Give
it away / Lonely man / Living in the footsteps of
another man / Devil's doing his work.
■ LP . . . . . . . . . . . . . . . . . . . BDL 2040
Bulldog Records / Aug '84.

## ALL I WANNA DO IS MAKE LOVE TO YOU.
Tracks: All I wanna do is make love to you / Love
shock.
■ 7" . . . . . . . . . . . . . . . . . . . . TC 2479
20th Century / Jan '81.

## BEST OF THE CHI-LITES.
Tracks: Give it away / Let me be the man my daddy
was / 24 hours of sadness / I like your lovin' (do you
like mine) / Are you my woman (tell me so) / For
God's sake) give more power to the people / Have
you seen her / Oh girl / Coldest days of my life (part
1) / We need order / Letter to myself / Stoned out of
my mind / I found sunshine / Homely girl / Too good
to be forgotten / There will never be any peace (until
God is seated at the.. / Toby / It's time for love / You
don't have to go.
CD. . . . . . . . . . . . . . . . . . CDKEN 911
Kent / Jun '87 / Pinnacle.

## CHANGING FOR YOU.
Tracks: Bad motor scooter / Changing for you /
Touch me / Making love / Bottoms up / I just wanna
hold you / You take the cake / I love.
■ LP . . . . . . . . . . . . . . . . . . RBLP 1003
MC. . . . . . . . . . . . . . . . . . . ZCRB 1003
R & B / Aug '83.

## CHANGING FOR YOU.
Tracks: Changing for you / Bottoms up.
■ 12" . . . . . . . . . . . . . . . . . . RBSL 215
■ 7" . . . . . . . . . . . . . . . . . . . .RBS 215
R & B / Jul '83.

## CHI-LITES CLASSICS.
Tracks: Have you seen her / Give it away / I want to
pay you back / Love uprising / I never had it so good
/ Too good to be forgotten / Toby / Coldest day of my
life / Homely girl / Lonely man / I found sunshine /
Stoned out of my mind / Oh girl / For God's sake give
more power to the people.
■ LP . . . . . . . . . . . . . . . . . . . LIT 101
MC. . . . . . . . . . . . . . . . . . . ZC LIT 101
SMP / Sep '83 / Jetstar.

## CHI-LITETIME.
Tracks: You don't have to go / There will never be
any peace / Here I am / Devil is doing his work / Half
a love / Too good to be forgotten / Homely girl / Have
you seen her / Coldest days of my life / You got to be
the one / I found sunshine / Stoned out of my mind / I
forget to say I love you till I'm gone / I nevr had it so
good / Oh girl.
■ LP . . . . . . . . . . . . . . . . . . SHU 8520
London / Dec '78.

## DEVIL IS DOING HIS WORK, THE.
Tracks: Devil is doing his work / I'm not a gambler.
■ 7" . . . . . . . . . . . . . . . . . . . . BR 32
Brunswick / Feb '76.

## ETERNITY.
Tracks: Eternity / Eternity (versions).
■ 12" . . . . . . . . . . . . . . . . . . 12 PO 55
Ichiban / Oct '90.

## FANTASIC.
Tracks: Bubbling, babbling fool / If I had a girl / I've
got love on my mind / Let's touch / Love at it's best /
My first at it's best / Coldest day of my life / Stop still /
Suddenly / Who's in love with me.
■ LP . . . . . . . . . . . . . . . . . . . 9100041
Mercury / Oct '77.

## GIVE IT AWAY.
Tracks: Give it away / Let me be the man my daddy
was / My whole world ended / I heard it through the

grapevine / What do I wish for you / That's my baby
for you / I'm gonna make you love me / You're no
longer part of my heart / 24 hours of sadness / To
change my love / Twelfth of never.
■ LP . . . . . . . . . . . . . . . . . . .MUPS 397
MCA / Jan '70.

## GIVE MORE POWER TO THE PEOPLE.
Tracks: Give more power to the people.
■ 7" . . . . . . . . . . . . . . . . . . .MU 1138
MCA / Aug '71.

## GIVE MORE POWER TO THE PEOPLE.
Tracks: Yes I'm ready / Love uprising / Have you
seen her / Twelfth of never / Give more power to the
people / I want to pay you back / We are neighbours
/ Troubles a'comin' / You got me walkin' / What do I
wish for.
■ LP . . . . . . . . . . . . . . . . . . .MUPS 437
MCA / Nov '71.

## GREATEST HITS.
Tracks: Not Advised.
CD. . . . . . . . . . . . . . . . . . KWEST 5402
Disky / Mar '93 / THE.

## GREATEST HITS: CHILITES.
Tracks: Not Advised.
CD. . . . . . . . . . . . . . . . . . . .246 2535
■ LP . . . . . . . . . . . . . . . . . . .226 2535
MC. . . . . . . . . . . . . . . . . . . .216 2535
Street Life / May '88.

## HALF A LOVE.
Tracks: Half a love / Here I am / I never had it so
good / Living in the footsteps of another man / When
temptation comes / That's my baby for you / It's time
for love / Take a trip to the islands / Go away dream
/ I'm not a gambler / Ain't too much of nothing / I'm
gonna make you love me.
■ LP . . . . . . . . . . . . . . . . . . SHU 8521
London / Dec '78.

## HARD ACT TO FOLLOW.
Tracks: Hard act to follow / Hard act to follow (inst.).
■ 12" . . . . . . . . . . . . . . . . . .12 ACERT 3
■ 7" . . . . . . . . . . . . . . . . . . . ACERT 3
Certain / Oct '85.

## HAVE YOU SEEN HER.
Tracks: Have you see her / Homely girl / I found
sunshine / Too good to be forgotten / (For God's
sake) give more power to the people.
■ 7" . . . . . . . . . . . . . . . . . . .MU 1146
MCA / Jan '72.
■ 7" . . . . . . . . . . . . . . . . . . . TC 2481
20th Century / Apr '81.
■ 12" . . . . . . . . . . . . . . . . SKM 02(12)
■ 7" . . . . . . . . . . . . . . . . . . . SKM 02
Skratch (1) / Jun '84.

## HAVE YOU SEEN HER?.
Tracks: Have you seen her / Oh girl.
■ 7" . . . . . . . . . . . . . . . . . . . BR 20
Brunswick / Jun '75.

## HEART AND SOUL OF THE CHI-LITES.
Tracks: Have you seen her / Vanishing love / My first
mistake / If I had a girl / Heavenly body / Me and you
/ All I wanna do is make love to you / Oh girl / Happy
being lonely / Hot on a thing called love / Whole lotta
good loving / Never speak to a stranger / Tell me
where it hurts / Love shock.
■ CD . . . . . . . . . . . . . . . . KNCD 12059
■ MC. . . . . . . . . . . . . . . . KNMC 12059
Knight / Jul '91.

## HEAVENLY BODY.
Tracks: Heavenly body / Strung out / round and
'round / Love shock / Have you seen her / All I
wanna do is make love to you / Give me a dream /
Super mad (about you, baby).
■ LP . . . . . . . . . . . . . . . . . . . . T 619
20th Century / Dec '80.

## HOMELY GIRL.
Tracks: Homely girl.
■ 7" . . . . . . . . . . . . . . . . . . . .BR 9
Brunswick / Mar '74.

## HOMELY GIRL (OLD GOLD CD SINGLE).
Tracks: Homely girl / Have you seen her / Oh girl.
■ CD Single . . . . . . . . . . . . . . .OG 6108
Old Gold / Nov '88.

## I FOUND SUNSHINE.
Tracks: I found sunshine / My heart just keeps on
breakin'.
■ 7" . . . . . . . . . . . . . . . . . . . BR 12
Brunswick / Jul '74.

## I NEVER HAD IT SO GOOD.
Tracks: I never had it so good / Here I am.
■ 7" ............................................. BR 29
Brunswick / Nov '75.

## IT'S CHI-LITE TIME.
Tracks: You don't have to go / There will never be
any peace / Here I am / Devil is doing his work / Half
a love / Too good to be forgotten / It's time for love /
Homely girl / Have you seen her / Coldest days of my
life / You got to be the one / I found sunshine /
Stoned out of my mind / I forgot to say I love you till
I'm gone / I never had it so good / Oh girl.
■ LP ......................................... BRLS 3023
Brunswick / Nov '76.

## IT'S TIME FOR LOVE.
Tracks: It's time for love.
■ 7" ............................................. BR 25
Brunswick / Sep '75.

## JUST SAY YOU LOVE ME.
Tracks: Happy music / Solid love affair / Just you and
I tonite / Just say you love me / Inner city blues /
There's a change / Eternity / Only you.
LP ........................................... ICH 1057
Ichiban / Jun '90 / A.D.A. Distribution / Pinnacle /
ACD Trading Ltd. / Koch International / Direct
Distribution.
CD .......................................... CDICH 1057
MC ......................................... ICH 1057C
Ichiban / Mar '94 / A.D.A. Distribution / Pinnacle /
ACD Trading Ltd. / Koch International / Direct
Distribution.

## LONELY MAN.
Tracks: Oh girl / Living in the footsteps of another
man / Love is / Being in love / Lonely man / Man &
the woman / Ain't to much of nothin' / Inner city
blues / Coldest days of my life.
■ LP ......................................... MUPS 457
MCA / Jul '72.

## LOVE ALBUM, THE.
Tracks: Have you seen her / Homely girl / Toby / It's
time for love / Lonely man / Yes I'm ready (if I don't
get to go) / Letter to myself / Coldest days of my life /
Oh girl / Marriage licence / I want to pay you back
(for loving me) / Stoned out of my mind / Too good to
be forgotten / I found sunshine / You don't have to go
/ Give more power to the people.
MC ............................................... 411855
■ LP ........................................... 211855
■ CD ........................................... 261855
Ariola / Jan '92 / BMG.

## MAKING LOVE.
Tracks: Making love / Bad motor scooter.
■ 12" ........................................ RBL 217
■ 7" .......................................... RBS 217
R & B / Sep '83.

## ME AND YOU.
Tracks: Me and you / Tell me where it hurts / Whole
lot of good good lovin' / Oh girl / Get down with me /
Try my side (of love) / Hot on a thing (called love) /
Never speak to a stranger.
■ LP ............................................ T 635
20th Century / Dec '81.

## ME AND YOU.
Tracks: Me and you / Tell me where it hurts.
■ 12" ........................................ TCD 132
■ 7" .......................................... TC 2503
20th Century / Oct '81.

## OH GIRL.
Tracks: Oh girl.
■ 7" .......................................... MU 1156
MCA / May '72.

## SOLID LOVE AFFAIR.
Tracks: Solid love affair / Happy music.
■ 12" ........................................ 12 PO 61
Ichiban / Mar '91.

## STAY A LITTLE LONGER.
Tracks: Stay a little longer / Hi'ya.
■ 12" ........................................ 12P5005
■ 7" .......................................... 7P5005
PRT / Jan '80.

## SWEET SOUL MUSIC.
Tracks: Have you seen her / Heavenly body / Strung
out / Round and round / Give me a dream / Super
mad / All I wanna do is make love to you / Love
shock / Me and you / Tell me where it hurts / Oh girl
/ Get down with me / Hot on a thing (called love) /
Never speak to a stranger / Whole lot of good loving
/ Try my side (of love).
CD ........................................... CPCD 8019
Charly / Feb '94 / Charly.

## THERE'S A CHANGE.
Tracks: There's a change / Happy music.
■ 12" ........................................ ICHT 708
■ 7" .......................................... ICHS 708
Ichiban / Jun '90.

## TOO GOOD TO BE FORGOTTEN.
Tracks: Too good to be forgotten.
■ 7" .......................................... BR 13
Brunswick / Nov '74.

## VANISHING LOVE.
Tracks: Vanishing love / I turn away.
■ 7" .......................................... 6167485
Mercury / Feb '77.

## VERY BEST OF THE CHI-LITES, THE.
Tracks: Have you seen her / For god's sake give
more power to the people / Oh girl / Coldest day of
my life, The (part 1) / Homely girl / Are you my
woman? (tell me so) / Let me be the man my daddy
was / There will never be any peace (until god is se /
I found sunshine / Too good to be forgotten / It's time
for love / You don't have to go / I like your lovin' /
Stoned out of my mind / Give it away / Letter to
myself.
CD ........................................... MCCD 029
MC ........................................... MCTC 029
Music Club / May '91 / Gold & Sons / THE / Video
Collection / C.M. Distribution.

## VERY BEST OF: CHI-LITES.
Tracks: Not Advised.
CD ........................................... BRCD 47
■ LP .......................................... BRLP 47
MC ........................................... BRMC 47
BR Music/BR Music (Holland) / Oct '88 / BMG.

## YOU DON'T HAVE TO GO.
Tracks: You don't have to go.
■ 7" .......................................... BR 34
Brunswick / Jul '76.

## YOU DON'T HAVE TO GO (OLD GOLD).
Tracks: You don't have to go / Too good to be
forgotten / I found sunshine.
■ 12" ........................................ OG 4119
Old Gold / May '89.

# Chic

Bernard Edwards and Nile Rodgers had
years of small-time band experience before
forming Chic in 1977. Dance Dance Dance
(Yowsah Yowsah Yowsah) reached No. 6 on
both sides of Atlantic, initiating string of
successes that rank among most elegant
fruits of disco; including two U.S. chart-
toppers, Le Freak and Good Times (their
biggest British hit, I Want Your Love,
reached No. 4). In 1980, Edwards and
Rodgers turned attentions to outside production, building on success with Sister
Sledge and rejuvenating Diana Ross' career. Over-exposure of Chic sound and high-
profile failure of underrated collaboration
with Debbie Harry prompted split in early
'80s. Rodgers bounced back in '83, producing David Bowie's best-selling Let's Dance;
renewed reputation was confirmed in January '85, when he took over Billboard's Top
3, with hits by Madonna, Duran Duran and
Honeydrippers. Reunion with Bernard Edwards' for '92's Chic-Ism was formulaic and
under-bought, but Chic's place in hearts
and history of soul is assured.

## 26.
Tracks: 26 / Chip off the old block.
■ 7" .......................................... K 11617
Atlantic / Oct '82.

## BELIEVER.
Tracks: Believer / You are beautiful / Party every-
body / Give me the lovin' / In love with music / You
got some love for me / Take a closer look / Show me
your light.
■ LP .......................................... 780 107-1
■ MC .......................................... 780 107-4
Atlantic / '84.

## BEST OF CHIC VOL.2, THE.
Tracks: Not Advised.
CD ........................................... 812271086-2
WEA / Mar '93 / WEA.

## C'EST CHIC.
Tracks: Le freak / Chic cheer / I want your love /
Happy man / Dance, dance, dance / Savoir faire / At
last I am free / Sometimes you win / Funny bone /
Everybody dance.
■ LP .......................................... K 50565

■ MC .......................................... K4 50565
Atlantic / Jan '79.

## CHIC.
Tracks: Dance, dance, dance / Sao Paulo / You can
get by / Everybody dance / Est-ce que c'est chic /
Falling in love with you / Strike up the band.
■ LP .......................................... K 50441
Atlantic / Mar '78.

## CHIC CHEER.
Tracks: Chic cheer / Savoire faire.
■ 12" ........................................ A 9604 T
■ 7" .......................................... A 9604
Atlantic / Nov '84.

## CHIC MYSTIQUE.
Tracks: Chic mystique.
■ 12" ........................................ W 0083T
WEA / Feb '92.

## CHIC'S GREATEST HITS.
Tracks: Le freak / I want your love / Dance, dance,
dance / Everybody dance / My forbidden lover /
Good times / My feet keep dancing.
■ LP .......................................... K 50686
MC ........................................... K4 50686
Atlantic / Jan '80 / WEA.

## CHIC-ISM.
Tracks: Chic mystique / Your love / Jusagroove /
Something you can feel / One and only one / Doin'
that thing to me / Chicism / In it to win it / My love's
for real / Take my love / High / M.M.F.T.C.F. / Chic
mystique (reprise).
CD ........................................... 7599263942
MC ........................................... WX 463C
Warner Bros. / Mar '92 / WEA.

## DANCE DANCE DANCE (Yowsah Yow-
sah Yowsah).
Tracks: Dance, dance, dance / Sao Paulo.
■ 7" .......................................... K 11038
Atlantic / Nov '77.

## EVERYBODY DANCE.
Tracks: Everybody dance / You can get by.
■ 7" .......................................... K 11097
Atlantic / Apr '78.

## FREAK OUT (Chic & Sister Sledge).
Tracks: Le freak / I want your love / He's the greatest
dancer / Everybody dance / We are family (Remix) /
Thinking of you / My forbidden lover / All American
girls / Lost in music (remix) / Frankie / Good times /
Mama never told me / Dance, dance, dance / My feet
keep dancing / Got to love somebody / Jack le freak
(edit).
■ CD .......................................... TCD 2319
■ LP .......................................... STAR 2319
■ MC .......................................... STAC 2319
Telstar/Ronco / Nov '87.

## GOOD TIMES.
Tracks: Good times / Warm summer night.
■ 7" .......................................... K 11310
Atlantic / Jun '79.
■ 7" .......................................... A 9107
■ 12" ........................................ A 9107 T
Atlantic / Mar '88.

## GOOD TIMES (OLD GOLD).
Tracks: Good times / Everybody dance.
12" .......................................... OG 4178
Old Gold / Jul '90 / Pickwick.

## HANGIN'.
Tracks: Hangin'.
■ 12" ........................................ A 9898 T
■ 7" .......................................... A 9898
Atlantic / Jan '83.

## I WANT YOUR LOVE.
Tracks: I want your love / Funny bone.
■ 7" .......................................... K 11245
Atlantic / Mar '79.

## I WANT YOUR LOVE (OLD GOLD).
Tracks: I want your love / My forbidden lover.
12" .......................................... OG 4190
Old Gold / Sep '90 / Pickwick.

## JACK THE FREAK.
Tracks: Jack the freak / Savoir faire.
■ 12" ........................................ ROOF T3
Raise The Roof / Sep '87.
■ 12" ........................................ A 9198 T
Atlantic / Sep '87.
■ 7" .......................................... ROOF 3
Raise The Roof / Sep '87.
■ 7" .......................................... A 9198
Atlantic / Sep '87.

## LE FREAK.
Tracks: Savoir faire / Chic / Le freak.
- ■ 7" . . . . . . . . . . . . . . . . . . . . . . K 11209
Atlantic / '78.
- ■ 12" . . . . . . . . . . . . . . . . . . . K 11209 T
Atlantic / Aug '86.

## LE FREAK (OLD GOLD).
Tracks: Le freak / Dance, dance, dance.
12" . . . . . . . . . . . . . . . . . . . . OG 4184
Old Gold / Jul '90 / Pickwick.

## MEGA CHIC.
Tracks: Mega Chic.
- ■ 12" . . . . . . . . . . . . . . . . . . . . A 7949 T
- ■ 7" . . . . . . . . . . . . . . . . . . . . . A 7949
- ■ CD Single . . . . . . . . . . . . . . A 7949 CD
East West / Jul '90.

## MEGACHIC (The Best of Chic).
Tracks: Megachic (medley) / Chic cheer / My feet keep dancing / Good times / I want your love / Everybody dance / Le freak / Dance, dance, dance.
CD . . . . . . . . . . . . . . . . . . . . . 2292417502
- ■ LP . . . . . . . . . . . . . . . . . . . 2292417501
- ■ MC . . . . . . . . . . . . . . . . . . . 2292417504
WEA / Aug '90 / WEA.

## MY FEET KEEP DANCIN'.
Tracks: My feet keep dancing / Will you cry when you hear this song.
- ■ 7" . . . . . . . . . . . . . . . . . . . . K 11415
Atlantic / Dec '79.

## MY FORBIDDEN LOVER.
Tracks: My forbidden lover.
- ■ 7" . . . . . . . . . . . . . . . . . . . . K 11385
Atlantic / Oct '79.

## REAL PEOPLE.
Tracks: Real people / Rebels are we / You can't do it alone / Chip off the old block / I got protection / Open up / I loved you more / 26.
- ■ LP . . . . . . . . . . . . . . . . . . . . K 50711
- ■ MC . . . . . . . . . . . . . . . . . . K4 50711
Atlantic / '88.

## REBEL WE ARE.
Tracks: Rebel we are / Open up.
- ■ 7" . . . . . . . . . . . . . . . . . . . . K 11539
Atlantic / Jul '80.

## RISQUE.
Tracks: Good times / Warm summer night / My feet keep dancing / My forbidden lover / Can't stand to love you / Will you cry (when you hear this song) / What about me.
- ■ LP . . . . . . . . . . . . . . . . . . . . K 50634
- ■ MC . . . . . . . . . . . . . . . . . . K4 50634
Atlantic / '88.

## TAKE IT OFF.
Tracks: Flashback / Take it off / Just out of reach / Telling lies / Stage fright / So fine / Baby doll / Your love is cancelled / Play Ray / Would you be my baby.
- ■ LP . . . . . . . . . . . . . . . . . . . . K 50845
Atlantic / Feb '82.

## THEIR GREATEST HITS (see under Rose Royce).

## TONGUE IN CHIC.
Tracks: Hangin' / I feel your love comin' on / When you love someone / Chic / Hey fool / Sharing love / City lights.
- ■ LP . . . . . . . . . . . . . . . . . . . 780 031-1
Atlantic / Dec '82.

## YOUR LOVE.
Tracks: Your love.
- ■ 12" . . . . . . . . . . . . . . . . . . . . W 0107T
WEA / May '92.

# Chiffons

## 20 GREATEST HITS: CHIFFONS.
Tracks: Not Advised.
- ■ LP . . . . . . . . . . . . . . . . . . . . BRLP 18
- ■ MC . . . . . . . . . . . . . . . . . . . BRMC 18
BR Music/BR Music (Holland) / Oct '88 / BMG.

## DOO-LANG DOO-LANG DOO-LANG.
Tracks: He's so fine / My boyfriend's back / Stop look and listen / Tonight I met an angel / Oh my lover / Love so fine / Why am I so shy / I have a boyfriend / Nobody knows what's going on / One fine day / When the boy's happy (the girl's happy too) / Sweet talking guy / My block / I'm gonna dry my eyes / Did you ever go steady / Out of this world.
- ■ LP . . . . . . . . . . . . . . . . . . . . ACT 002
Impact (Ace) / Mar '85.

## EVERYTHING YOU EVER WANTED TO HEAR .. BUT COULDN'T.
Tracks: One fine day / Tonight I'm gonna dream / Out of this world / He's so fine / I have a boyfriend / Nobody knows what's going on / When the boy's happy (the girl's happy too) / Tonight I met an angel / Sweet talking guy / Love so fine / Open your eyes / Sailor boy / Stop look and listen / My block / Oh my lover / Just for tonight.
- ■ LP . . . . . . . . . . . . . . . . . . LRSLP 1001
Laurie / Oct '81.
- ■ LP . . . . . . . . . . . . . . . . . . . NL 89022
- ■ MC . . . . . . . . . . . . . . . . . . NK 89022
Laurie / '84 / Pinnacle.

## FABULOUS CHIFFONS, THE.
Tracks: He's so fine / One fine day / Sweet talkin' guy / My block / When the boy's happy (the girl's happy too) / Love so fine / I have a boyfriend / Sailor boy / Nobody knows what's going on in my mind but me / Out of this world / Stop, look and listen / Keep the boy happy.
CD . . . . . . . . . . . . . . . . . . . CDFAB 010
MC . . . . . . . . . . . . . . . . . . . FABC 010
Ace Fabulous / Oct '91 / Pinnacle.

## FLIPS, FLOPS AND RARITIES.
Tracks: He's a bad one / Lucky me / What am I gonna do with you / Dream dream dream / Heavenly place / March / Tonight I'm gonna dream / Just for tonight / Up on the bridge / Real thing / Love me like you're gonna lose me / Easy to love / Teach me how / When I go to sleep at night / Open your eyes / If I knew then.
- ■ LP . . . . . . . . . . . . . . . . . . . . ACT 007
Impact (Ace) / Jan '86.

## GREATEST RECORDINGS.
Tracks: He's so fine / My boyfriend's back / Stop, look and listen / Oh my lover / One fine day / Love so fine / Nobody knows what's going on (in my mind but me) / Out of this world / Mystic voice / Up on the bridge / Dream, dream, dream / My block / Did you ever go steady / March / Keep the boy happy / When the boy's happy (the girl's happy too) / Real thing / Sweet talking guy / I have a boyfriend / Sailor boy / I'm gonna dry my eyes (Available on CD format only.) / Open your eyes (I will be there) (Available on CD format only.) / Heavenly place (Available on CD format only.) / Teach me how (Available on CD format only.) / He's a bad one (Available on CD format only.) / If I knew then (what I know now) (Available on CD format only.) / Lucky me (Available on CD format only.) / Why am I so shy (Available on CD format only.) / Tonight I met an angel (Available on CD format only.) / When I go to sleep at night (Available on CD format only.) / Tonight I'm gonna dream (Available on CD format only.) / Down down down (Available on CD format only.) / My sweet lord (Available on CD format only.).
CD . . . . . . . . . . . . . . . . . . . CDCH 293
MC . . . . . . . . . . . . . . . . . . . CHC 293
- ■ LP . . . . . . . . . . . . . . . . . . . CH 293
Ace / Apr '90 / Pinnacle / Complete Record Co. Ltd.

## HE'S SO FINE.
Tracks: He's so fine / Sweet talking guy / One fine day.
- ■ 7" . . . . . . . . . . . . . . . . . . . . SS 172
Stateside / Apr '63.
- ■ 7" . . . . . . . . . . . . . . . . . . . . CR 183
Blast From The Past / Aug '82.
- ■ 7" . . . . . . . . . . . . . . . . . . . . GOLD 545
RCA Golden Grooves / May '82.
- ■ 7" . . . . . . . . . . . . . . . . . . . . CUT 115
Classic Cuts / Oct '82.

## MY BOY FRIEND'S BACK.
Tracks: My boy friend's back / I got plenty o' nuttin'.
- ■ 7" . . . . . . . . . . . . . . . . . . . . SS 578
Stateside / Jan '67.

## ONE FINE DAY.
Tracks: One fine day / Love so fine.
- ■ 7" . . . . . . . . . . . . . . . . . . . . SS 202
Stateside / Jul '63.
- ■ 7" . . . . . . . . . . . . . . . . . . HLP 10330
London / Apr '71.
- ■ 7" . . . . . . . . . . . . . . . . . . . GOLD 536
RCA Golden Grooves / Aug '81.

## ONE FINE DAY.
Tracks: Not Advised.
CD . . . . . . . . . . . . . . . . . . . RMB 75071
Remember / Apr '94 / Midland Records / BMG.

## PICK HITS OF THE RADIO GOOD GUYS.
Tracks: Easy to love / He's so fine / I have a boyfriend / It's my party / Just for tonight / Locomotion / Love so fine / Nobody knows what's going on / Oh my lover / One fine day / Out of this world / Sailor boy / Stop, look and listen / Sweet talking guy / Tonight I met an angel / Tonight I'm gonna dream.

- ■ LP . . . . . . . . . . . . . . . . . . . . SON 005
Philips.

## SWEET TALKIN' GUY.
Tracks: Sweet talkin' guy / He's so fine / Up on the bridge / Nobody knows what's goin' on / Thumbs down / Just a boy / Down, down, down / Out of this world / My boyfriend's back / Open your eyes / Keep the boy happy / See you in September.
- ■ LP . . . . . . . . . . . . . . . . . . . . ZGP 125
H.M.V. / Nov '72.

## SWEET TALKIN' GUY.
Tracks: Sweet talkin' guy / Did you ever go steady.
- ■ 7" . . . . . . . . . . . . . . . . . . . . SS 512
Stateside / May '66.
- ■ 7" . . . . . . . . . . . . . . . . . . HL 10271
London-American / Mar '72.
- ■ 7" . . . . . . . . . . . . . . . . . . . HR 183
Creole / Aug '82.

## SWEET TALKIN' GUY (OLD GOLD).
Tracks: Sweet talkin' guy / He's so fine.
- ■ 7" . . . . . . . . . . . . . . . . . . . . OG 9406
Old Gold / Jun '84.

# Childe, Sonny

## GIVING UP ON LOVE.
Tracks: Giving up on love / Mighty nice.
- ■ 7" . . . . . . . . . . . . . . . . . . . . F 12218
Decca / Sep '65.

## HEARTBREAK.
Tracks: Heartbreak / I still love you.
- ■ 7" . . . . . . . . . . . . . . . . . . . . 56141
Polydor / Jan '67.

# Chill Fac-torr

## CHILL FAC-TORR.
Tracks: Shout / Fox hunting / Twist (round 'n' round) / I'll satisfy your desire / Burning desires / It's been a long time / Let's get closer.
- ■ LP . . . . . . . . . . . . . . . . . . . PWLP 1006
- ■ MC . . . . . . . . . . . . . . . . . ZCPW 1006
Philly World (USA) / Nov '83 / PolyGram.

## SHOUT (THE EXOTIC).
Tracks: Shout (the exotic) / Burning desires.
- ■ 12" . . . . . . . . . . . . . . . . . . . PWSL 115
- ■ 7" . . . . . . . . . . . . . . . . . . . PWS 115
Philly World (USA) / Oct '83.

## TWIST.
Tracks: Twist / round and 'round.
- ■ 12" . . . . . . . . . . . . . . . . . . . PWSL 109
- ■ 7" . . . . . . . . . . . . . . . . . . . PWS 109
Philly World (USA) / Mar '83.

# Chimes

## 1-2-3.
Tracks: 1-2-3 (Only on 7" and CD single.) / Underestimate (Only on 7" single.) / 1-2-3 (UK raw mix) (Only on 12" and CD single.) / Underestimate (special extended version) (Only on 12" and CD single.) / Body rock (demo version) (Only on 12" single.) / 1-2-3 (silent club dub) (On 655166 8 only) / 1-2-3 (gospel mix) (On 655166 8 only) / 1-2-3 (Philly mix) (On 655166 8 only).
- ■ 12" . . . . . . . . . . . . . . . . . . . 6551666
- ■ 12" . . . . . . . . . . . . . . . . . . . 6551668
- ■ 7" . . . . . . . . . . . . . . . . . . . 6551667
- ■ CD Single . . . . . . . . . . . . . . 6551662
- ■ MC Single . . . . . . . . . . . . . . 6551664
CBS / Aug '89.

## CHIMES.
Tracks: Love so tender / Heaven / True love / 1-2-3 / Underestimate / Love comes to mind / I still haven't found what I'm looking for (street mix) / Don't make me wait / Stronger together / Stay / I still haven't found what I'm looking for.
CD . . . . . . . . . . . . . . . . . . . 4664812
- ■ LP . . . . . . . . . . . . . . . . . . . 4664811
MC . . . . . . . . . . . . . . . . . . . 4664814
CBS / Jun '90 / Sony.

## HEAVEN.
Tracks: Heaven / So much in love (demo version) (Only on 7" single.) / Heaven (mixes) / So much in love (extended demo version) (Only on 12" and CD single.) / Heaven (heavy club) (Only on 12" and CD single.).
- ■ 12" . . . . . . . . . . . . . . . . . . . 6554326
- ■ 12" . . . . . . . . . . . . . . . . . . . 6554325
- ■ 12" Remix . . . . . . . . . . . . . . 6554328
- ■ 7" . . . . . . . . . . . . . . . . . . . 6554327
- ■ CD Single . . . . . . . . . . . . . . 6554322
- ■ MC Single . . . . . . . . . . . . . . 6554324
CBS / Nov '89.

## HEAVEN.
Tracks: Heaven.
| 12" Remix. | CHIMQT 3 |
| 12". | CHIMT 3 |
| 7". | CHIM 3 |
| CD Single. | CHIMCD 3 |
| MC Single. | CHIMMC 3 |
CBS / Sep '90 / Sony.

## I STILL HAVEN'T FOUND WHAT I'M LOOKING FOR.
Tracks: I still haven't found what I'm looking for / No need to pretend / I still haven't found what.(Manasseh mix) (Only on 12" single.) / I still haven't found what.(boom dub mix) (Only on 12" single.) / I still haven't found.(Streetmix).
| 12". | CHIM QT1 |
| 12". | CHIMT 1 |
| 7". | CHIM 1 |
| CD Single. | CHIM C1 |
| MC Single. | CHIM M1 |
CBS / May '90.

## LOVE COMES TO MIND.
Tracks: Love comes to mind / Love comes to mind (extended remix) (Available on CHIM T4 and CHIM QT4 formats only.) / Love comes to mind (Manasseh 12") (Available on 12" and CD single format only.) / Stay (extended remix) (Available on 12" and CD single format only.) / Stronger together (remix) (7", cassette and CHIM QT4 format only.) / Body rock (demo version) (Available on CHIM QT4 only.)
| 12". | CHIM T4 |
| 12". | CHIM QT4 |
| 7". | CHIM 4 |
| CD Single. | CHIM C4 |
| MC Single. | CHIM M4 |
CBS / Nov '90.

## STRONGER TOGETHER.
Tracks: Stronger together / Underestimate.
| 12". | 6558516 |
| 7". | 6558517 |
CBS / Apr '90.

## TRUE LOVE.
Tracks: True love / True love (Louie Louie remix) (12" & CD single only.) / True love (Louie Louie instrumental) (CD single only.) / Stronger together (Red zone mix) / Ready for love.
| 12". | CHIM T2 |
| 7". | CHIM 2 |
| CD Single. | CHIM C2 |
| MC Single. | CHIM M2 |
CBS / Jul '90.

## Chocolate Milk

## BLUE JEANS.
Tracks: Blue jeans / Like my lady's love / Running on empty / Honey bun / Let's go all the way / I've been loving you too long / Video queen.
| LP | RCALP 3070 |
RCA / Mar '82.

## COMIN'.
Tracks: Comin' / Something new / Do unto others / Feel the need / With all our love / Starbright / I refuse / Island love.
| LP | PL 11830 |
RCA / Jan '77.

## GIRL CALLIN'.
Tracks: Girl callin' / Thinking of you.
| 7". | PB 1222 |
RCA / '78.

## HIPNOTISM.
Tracks: I'm your radio / Forever and a day / Hey lover / Body rhythm / I can't believe you said it's over / Hipnotism / Would it be alright / Dawn / Showdown.
| LP | PL 13569 |
RCA / Jan '81.

## I'M YOUR RADIO.
Tracks: I'm your radio / Would it be alright / Action speaks louder than words (Only on 12" format.).
| 12". | PC 2030 |
| 7". | PB 2030 |
RCA / Aug '80.

## LET'S GO ALL THE WAY.
Tracks: Let's go all the way / Blue Jeans.
| 12". | RCAT 200 |
RCA / Mar '82.

## Christopher, Gavin

## GAVIN CHRISTOPHER.
Tracks: Feeling the love / Talkin' your love away / What can I say what can I do / Dancin' up a storm / We're in love / This side of heaven / Lady mysterious / We'll always be together / Be your own best friend.
| LP | RSS 8 |
RSO / Aug '79.

## ONE STEP CLOSER TO YOU.
Tracks: Once you get started / Love is knocking at your door / Sparks turn into fire / Could this be the night / That's the kind of guy I am / One step closer to you / Are we running from love / In the heat of passion / Back in your arms.
| LP | MTL 1002 |
| MC | TCMTL 1002 |
EMI-Manhattan / May '86.

## ONE STEP CLOSER TO YOU.
Tracks: One step closer to you (inst) / One step closer to you (club mix) / Accapella plus / Short version / One step closer to you.
| 12". | 12MT 10 |
| 7". | MT 10 |
EMI-Manhattan / May '86.

## Cinderellas

## BABY, BABY (I STILL LOVE YOU).
Tracks: Baby, baby (I still love you) / Please don't wake me.
| 7". | PX 11026 |
Colpix / '64.

## Circle City

## MOMENTS OF INERTIA.
Tracks: Moments of inertia.
| 12". | WAP 40 |
| CD Single. | WAP 40CD |
Warp / Jan '94 / RTM / Pinnacle.

## Circle In The Round

## CIRCLE OF CRUELTY.
Tracks: Circle of cruelty.
| 12". | DOR 004 |
Dorado / Jul '92.

## Cissel, Chuck

## IF I HAD THE CHANCE.
Tracks: Not Advised.
| LP | AL 9581 |
Arista (USA) / Oct '94 / Arista (Imports).

## Ciyo

## COME OUT TO PLAY.
Tracks: Come out to play.
| 7". | CIYO 3 |
Ciyo / Dec '88.

## DON'T LET HIM GET TO YOU (Ciyo & Claudia Fontaine).
Tracks: Don't let him get to you.
| 12". | DIV 001P |
ARP / Dec '93.

## URBAN ATMOSPHERE.
Tracks: Groove / Don't diss me / Don't let him get to you / If love's a gift of life / Home deh yah / We know we are / Get out the way..beep beep / Love is around..love is found / Days of feelings / Just give me a break / Give me the night / Urban atmosphere.
| CD | DIVCD 01 |
Diverse Records / May '94 / New Note.

## CJ & Co.

## DEADEYE DICK.
Tracks: Burning drums of fire / Deadeye Dick / Beware the stranger / Big city sidewalk / Hear say / You're still the sweetest thing in my life.
| LP | K 50491 |
Westbound / Aug '78.

## DEVIL'S GUN.
Tracks: Devil's gun / We got our own thang / Free to be me / Get a groove in order to move / Sure can't go to the Moon.
| LP | K 50380 |
Westbound / Jul '77.

## DEVIL'S GUN.
Tracks: Devil's gun / Free to be me.
| 7". | K 10956 |
Atlantic / Jun '77.

## Clark, Chris

## FROM HEAD TO TOE.
Tracks: From head to toe / Beginning of the end.
| 7". | TMG 624 |
Tamla Motown / Oct '67.

## LOVE'S GONE BAD.
Tracks: Love's gone bad / Put yourself in my place.
| 7". | TMG 591 |
Tamla Motown / Jan '67.

## SOUL SOUNDS.
Tracks: I want to go back there again / Love's gone bad / Born to love you baby / If you should walk away / Whisper you love me / Got to get you into my life / Day by day or never / From head to toe / Do right baby / Until you love someone / Put yourself in my place / Sweeter as the days go by.
| LP | STML 11069 |
Tamla Motown / Feb '68.

## Clark, Dee

## DELECTABLE SOUND OF DEE CLARK.
Tracks: Seven nights / Just like a fool / 24 boyfriends / Why don't you come home / Blues get off my shoulder / Just can't help myself / Because I love you / Money (that's what I want) / Dance on little girl / Drums in my heart / You are like the wind / Fever / Ol' man river / Little boy blue / How is he treating you / I'm going back to school.
| LP | CRB 1113 |
Charly R&B / Apr '86.

## HEARTBREAK.
Tracks: Heartbreak.
| 7". | SS 355 |
Stateside / '64.

## I'M YOUR SOLDIER BOY.
Tracks: I'm your soldier boy.
| 7". | SS 180 |
Stateside / '63.

## JUST KEEP IT UP.
Tracks: Just keep it up.
| 7". | HL 8915 |
London-American / Oct '59.

## KEEP IT UP.
Tracks: Not Advised.
| LP | CRB 1010 |
Charly R&B / Jul '88.

## RAINDROPS.
Tracks: I'm a soldier boy / Shook up over you / I just can't help myself / When I call on you / Just like a fool / Seven nights / Why don't you come home / 24 boyfriends / Oh little girl / Wondering / Nobody but you / Blues get off my shoulder / Just keep it up / Hey little girl / Your friends / Raindrops / You're telling our secrets / (Don't) walk away from me / You are like the wind / Drums in my heart / Bring back my heart / Fever.
| CD | CDCHARLY 69 |
Charly / Apr '87.

## RIDE A WILD HORSE.
Tracks: Ride a wild horse.
| 7". | 2005 037 |
Chelsea Collection / Oct '75.

## T.C.B.
Tracks: T.C.B.
| 7". | SS 400 |
Stateside / '65.

## Clark Sisters

## BEAUTY SHOP BEAT.
Tracks: Not Advised.
| LP | CRL 57290 |
Coral / Jun '60.

## BRINGING IT BACK HOME.
Tracks: Not Advised.
| CD | WSTCD 9113 |
Word (UK) / '92 / Word Records (UK) / Sony.

## CHANNEL FOLK.
Tracks: Devoted to you / You've got a friend / Pack up your sorrows / Be bye love / This will be our last song together / Streets of London / Jet plane.
| MC | ERON 010 CA |
Eron / Sep '85.

## CHICAGO.
Tracks: Chicago.
| 7". | HLD 8791 |
London / Mar '59.

■ DELETED

## HEART AND SOUL.
Tracks: Not Advised.
■ LP . . . . . . . . . . . . . . . . . . . REJ R 5010
■ MC. . . . . . . . . . . . . . . . . . . REJ C 5010
Rejoice / Mar '87 / Word Records (UK) / Sony.
■ CD . . . . . . . . . . . . . . . . . . . REJ D 5010
Rejoice / '88 / Word Records (UK) / Sony.

## IS MY LIVING IN VAIN (Clark Sisters With Mattie Moss Clark).
Tracks: Is my living in vain / Ha ya / Salvation means more to me / Now is the time / Pure gold / They were overcome / Speak Lord / Expect you miracle.
CD . . . . . . . . . . . . . . . . . . . 26 20 382
MC . . . . . . . . . . . . . . . . . . . 26 20 384
Point (2) / '92 / Sound Solutions.

## MORE THAN CONQUERORS.
Tracks: Not Advised.
CD . . . . . . . . . . . . . . . . . . . REJ R 5022
■ LP . . . . . . . . . . . . . . . . . . REJ R 5022
MC . . . . . . . . . . . . . . . . . . . REJ C 5022
Rejoice / '88 / Word Records (UK) / Sony.

## SALUTE TO THE GREAT SINGING GROUPS, A.
Tracks: My blue Heaven / Until the real thing comes along / Bei mir bist du schon / Paper doll / I'll get by / I've got a gal in Kalamazoo / Dream / Sugartime / Getting sentimental over you / Undecided / I'm forever blowing bubbles / When I take my sugar to tea.
■ LP . . . . . . . . . . . . . . . . . . JASM 1501
Jasmine / May '83.

## SING SING SING.
Tracks: Not Advised.
■ LP . . . . . . . . . . . . . . . . . . JASM 1038
Jasmine / Mar '84.

## SWING AGAIN.
Tracks: Not Advised.
■ LP . . . . . . . . . . . . . . . . . . JASM 1518
Jasmine / '88.

## YOU BROUGHT THE SUNSHINE INTO MY LIFE.
Tracks: You brought the sunshine into my life / Overdose of the Holy Ghost.
■ 12″ . . . . . . . . . . . . . . . . . . E 9810T
■ 7″ . . . . . . . . . . . . . . . . . . . E 9810
Westbound / Aug '83.

# Clarke, Rhonda

## BETWEEN FRIENDS.
Tracks: Not Advised.
CD . . . . . . . . . . . . . . . . . . . 40882
■ LP . . . . . . . . . . . . . . . . . . FZ 40882
Tabu / Oct '89 / Sony.

## STATE OF ATTRACTION.
Tracks: State of attraction.
■ 12″ . . . . . . . . . . . . . . . . . 4Z9 68842
Tabu / Oct '89.

# Clarke, Rick

## GET BUSY.
Tracks: Get busy.
■ 12″ . . . . . . . . . . . . . . . . . . WAT 2
■ 12″ Remix. . . . . . . . . . . . . . WATR 2
■ 7″ . . . . . . . . . . . . . . . . . . . WA 2
W.A. / Aug '88.

## GROOVIN' ON A BASSLINE.
Tracks: Groovin' on a bassline.
■ 12″ . . . . . . . . . . . . . . . . . . WAT 4
W.A. / Sep '89.

## I REALLY WANT TO BE WITH YOU (Clarke, Rick & Emma).
Tracks: I really want to be with you / I've been watching you.
■ 7″ . . . . . . . . . . . . . . . . . PB 41331
■ 12″ . . . . . . . . . . . . . . . . PT 41332
RCA / Jun '87.

## I'LL SEE YOU ALONG.
Tracks: I'll see you along.
■ 12″ . . . . . . . . . . . . . . . . . . WAT 1
W.A. / Apr '88.

## IF YOU THINK YOU'RE IN LOVE.
Tracks: If you think you're in love.
■ 12″ . . . . . . . . . . . . . . . . . . WAT 3
■ 7″ . . . . . . . . . . . . . . . . . . . WA 3
W.A. / Dec '88.

## LOVE WITH A STRANGER.
Tracks: Love with a stranger.
■ 12″ . . . . . . . . . . . . . . . . . . LR 11
Local / Oct '85.

## PERFECT LADY.
Tracks: Perfect lady / Looking out for you.
■ 12″ . . . . . . . . . . . . . . . . PT 41498R
■ 7″ . . . . . . . . . . . . . . . . . PB 41497R
RCA / Oct '87.

## TIME KEEPS MOVING ON.
Tracks: Not Advised.
CD . . . . . . . . . . . . . . . . . . . WALCD 1
■ LP . . . . . . . . . . . . . . . . . . WALP 1
MC. . . . . . . . . . . . . . . . . . . WALMC 1
Groove & Move (G&M) / Nov '89 / Groove & Move Records.

# Clarke, Sharon Dee

## DANCE YOUR WAY OUT OF THE DOOR.
Tracks: Dance your way out of the door (dub mix) / Dance your way out of the door.
■ 12″ . . . . . . . . . . . . . . . . ARIST 12682
■ 7″ . . . . . . . . . . . . . . . . . .ARIST 682
Arista / Oct '86.

## HE'S COMING BACK.
Tracks: He's coming back (inst. mix) / He's coming back (7″ mix).
■ 12″ . . . . . . . . . . . . . . . . DEBTX 3017
Debut (1) / Mar '87.

## MR RIGHT.
Tracks: Mr. Right.
■ 12″ . . . . . . . . . . . . . . . . . RUMAT 15
■ 7″ . . . . . . . . . . . . . . . . . . RUMA 15
Rumour / Jun '90.

## RUNAWAY LOVE.
Tracks: Runaway love / Runaway love (mixes).
■ 12″ . . . . . . . . . . . . . . . . . RUMAT 68
■ 7″ . . . . . . . . . . . . . . . . . . RUMA 68
■ CD Single. . . . . . . . . . . . . RUMACD 68
■ MC Single. . . . . . . . . . . . . RUMAMC 68
Rumour / Feb '94.

## SOMETHING SPECIAL.
Tracks: Something special / Something special (version).
■ 12″ . . . . . . . . . . . . . . . . . . URBA 31
■ 12″ . . . . . . . . . . . . . . . . . URBX 31
■ 7″ . . . . . . . . . . . . . . . . . . . URB 31
Urban / Mar '89.

# Clarke, Stanley

Highly influential bass player who began playing in rock bands in the late sixties before moving into jazz and fusion. Developed funky style with Chick Corea's Return To Forever in early seventies. Launched solo career during this time and 1975 album *Journey To Love* produced the extremely funky single *Silly Putty*. Continued to make albums combining jazz and funk and helped to expose the bass as a versatile instrument capable of taking both lead and rhythm roles. Achieved chart success in 1981 with George Duke collaboration *Sweet Baby* from their *Duke Clarke Project* album. Since 1978 has produced records for a variety of artists including Roy Ayres and Dee Dee Bridgewater and has contributed to sessions for McCoy Tyner, Aretha Franklin and Donna Summer.

## 3 (Clarke, Stanley & George Duke).
Tracks: Pit bulls (An endangered species) / Oh Oh / No place to hide / Somebody else / Mothership connection / Right by my side / From the deepest corner of my heart / Lady / Find out who you are / Quiet time / Fingerprints / Always.
■ CD . . . . . . . . . . . . . . . . . . 4670112
■ LP . . . . . . . . . . . . . . . . . . 4670111
■ MC. . . . . . . . . . . . . . . . . . 4670114
Epic / Jul '90.

## BORN IN THE U.S.A.
Tracks: Born in the U.S.A. / Campo Americano.
■ 12″ . . . . . . . . . . . . . . . . . . TA 6372
■ 7″ . . . . . . . . . . . . . . . . . . . A 6372
Epic / Jul '85.

## CLARKE/DUKE PROJECT II (Clarke, Stanley & George Duke).
Tracks: Put it on the line / Heroes / Try me, baby / Every reason to smile / Great danes / Good times / You're gonna love it / Trip you in love / Atlanta.
■ LP . . . . . . . . . . . . . . . . . . EPC 25685
■ MC. . . . . . . . . . . . . . . . . . .40 25685
Epic / Dec '83.

## COLLECTION: STANLEY CLARKE.
Tracks: Not Advised.
CD . . . . . . . . . . . . . . . . . . . CCSCD 242
■ Double LP. . . . . . . . . . . . . CCSLP 242

## MC. . . . . . . . . . . . . . . . . . .CCSMC 242
Castle Collector Series / Jun '90 / BMG / Pinnacle / Castle Communications.

## FIND OUT (Clarke, Stanley Band).
Tracks: Find out / What if I should fall in love / Born in the USA / Sky's the limit / Don't turn the lights out / Campo Americano / Stero typica / Psychedelic / My life.
■ LP . . . . . . . . . . . . . . . . . . EPC 26521
■ MC. . . . . . . . . . . . . . . . . . .40 26521
Epic / Jul '85.
■ CD . . . . . . . . . . . . . . . . . . CD 26521
CBS / May '87.

## FUSE ONE (Clarke, Stanley/Larry Coryell/John McLaughlin).
Tracks: Not Advised.
■ LP . . . . . . . . . . . . . . . . . . . . 1063
IMS / Mar '81.

## HEAVEN SENT YOU.
Tracks: Heaven sent you / Speedball.
■ 7″ . . . . . . . . . . . . . . . . . . . .A 4493
Epic / Jun '84.

## HEROES (Clarke, Stanley & George Duke).
Tracks: Heroes / Atlanta.
■ 12″ . . . . . . . . . . . . . . . . . . TA 3860
■ 7″ . . . . . . . . . . . . . . . . . . . A 3860
Epic / Nov '83.

## HIDEAWAY.
Tracks: Overjoyed / My love, her inspiration / Where do we go / Boys of Johnson street / Old friends / When it's cold outside / Listen to the beat of your heart / Basketball / I'm here to stay.
■ MC. . . . . . . . . . . . . . . . . . .40 26964
■ CD . . . . . . . . . . . . . . . . . . CD 26964
Epic / Nov '86.

## HOT FUN.
Tracks: Hot fun / Life is just a game.
■ 7″ . . . . . . . . . . . . . . . . . . . K 10889
Atlantic / Feb '77.

## I WANNA PLAY FOR YOU.
Tracks: Rock'n'roll jelly / All about / Jamaican boy / Christopher Ivanhoe / My greatest hits / Strange weather / I wanna play for you / Just a feeling / Streets of Philadelphia / School days / Quiet afternoon / Together again / Blues for Mingus / Off the planet / Hot fun.
■ MC Set . . . . . . . . . . . . . . . .40 88331
Epic / Aug '79.
■ Double LP. . . . . . . . . . . . . EPC 22133
Epic / May '82.

## IF THIS BASS COULD ONLY TALK.
Tracks: If this bass could talk / I wanna play for you / Funny how time flies / Bassically taps / Working man / Come take my hand / Stories to tell / Tradition.
■ MC. . . . . . . . . . . . . . . . . . . 4608834
■ CD . . . . . . . . . . . . . . . . . . 4608832
■ LP . . . . . . . . . . . . . . . . . . 4608831
Epic / Aug '88.

## JOURNEY TO LOVE.
Tracks: Silly putty / Journey to love / Hello, Jeff / Song to John / Concerto for jazz-rock orchestra.
MC. . . . . . . . . . . . . . . . . . .40 32093
■ LP . . . . . . . . . . . . . . . . . . EPC 32093
Epic / Nov '81 / Sony.

## LET ME KNOW YOU.
Tracks: Straight to the top / Let me know you / You are the one for me / I just want to be your brother / Force of love / Play the bass / Secret to my heart / New York City.
■ LP . . . . . . . . . . . . . . . . . . EPC 85846
Epic / Sep '82.

## LIVE IN MONTREUX (Clarke, Stanley & George Duke).
Tracks: Not Advised.
CD . . . . . . . . . . . . . . . . . . . JD 1234
Jazz Door / Feb '94 / Charly / Koch International / A.D.A. Distribution.

## MODERN MAN.
Tracks: Opening (statement) / He lives on / More hot fun / Slow dance / Interlude / Serious occasion / Got to find my own place / Dayride / It's what she didn't say / Modern man / Relaxed occasion / Rock 'n' roll jelly / Closing (statement).
MC. . . . . . . . . . . . . . . . . . .40 32108
■ LP . . . . . . . . . . . . . . . . . . CBS 32108
CBS / Feb '84 / Sony.
■ CD . . . . . . . . . . . . . . . . . . CD 82674
CBS / May '87.

## MORE HOT FUN.
**Tracks:** More hot fun / Slow dance.
■ 7"....................................... EPC 6353
Epic / May '78.

## PROJECT (Clarke, Stanley & George Duke).
**Tracks:** Wild dog / Louie Louie / Sweet baby / I just want to love you / Never judge a cover by it's book / Let's get started / Winners / Touch & go / Finding my way.
■ LP...................................... EPC 84848
Epic / May '81.

## ROCKS, PEBBLES AND SAND.
**Tracks:** Danger street / All hell broke loose / Rocks, pebbles & sand / You / Me together / Underestimation / We supply / Story of a man and a woman / She thought I was Stanley Clarke / Fool again / I nearly went crazy (until I realised what had occurred).
■ LP...................................... EPC 84342
Epic / Jul '80.
MC........................................ .40 32300
■ LP...................................... EPC 32300
Epic / Mar '83 / Sony.

## SCHOOL DAYS.
**Tracks:** School days / Quiet afternoon / Danger / Desert song / Hot fun / Life is just a game / Dancer.
■ LP...................................... EPC 32094
■ MC....................................... .40 32094
Epic / Mar '82.
■ CD....................................... 4504022
Epic / May '87.

## SHIELDSTONE (Clarke, Stanley & Bill Shields).
**Tracks:** Not Advised.
CD........................................ RSVCD 9001
■ LP...................................... RSVP 9001
Optimism / Oct '87.

## STANLEY CLARKE.
**Tracks:** Vulcan princess / Yesterday Princess / Lopsy lu / Power / Spanish phases for strings and bass / Life suite (part 1) / Life suite (part 2) / Life suite (part 3) / Life suite (part 4).
■ LP...................................... EPC 32042
Epic / Jul '81.

## STRAIGHT TO THE TOP.
**Tracks:** Straight to the top / Forces of love.
■ 7"....................................... EPCA 2697
Epic / Aug '82.

## SWEET BABY (Clarke, Stanley & George Duke).
**Tracks:** Sweet baby / Never judge a cover by it's book.
■ 7"....................................... EPC A 1123
Epic / Apr '81.

## TIME EXPOSURE.
**Tracks:** Play the bass 103 / Are you ready / Speedball / heaven sent you / Time exposure / Future shock / Future / Spacerunner / I know just how you feel.
■ LP...................................... EPC 25486
■ MC....................................... .40 25486
Epic / May '84.

## YOU/ME TOGETHER.
**Tracks:** You/me together / Rocks, pebbles and sand.
■ 7"....................................... EPC 8945
Epic / Aug '80.

# Class Action

## WEEKEND.
**Tracks:** Weekend.
■ 12"...................................... JIVET 35
■ 7"....................................... JIVE 35
Jive / Aug '85.

# Clay, Judy

## PRIVATE NUMBER (Clay, Judy & William Bell).
**Tracks:** Private number / Such a fever.
■ 7"....................................... STXS 2042
Stax / Jul '76.

## PRIVATE NUMBER (Clay, Judy & William Bell).
**Tracks:** Private number / Love-eye-tis.
■ 7"....................................... STAX 101
Stax / Nov '68.
■ 7"....................................... STAX 801
Stax / Jun '87.

## STORYBOOK CHILDREN (Clay, Judy & Billy Vera).
**Tracks:** Storybook children / Country girl and city man / Let it be me / Soul man / Good morning blues / We're in love / When do we go / Bring it on home to me / Do right woman - do right man / Really together / Ever since / So good.
■ LP...................................... 588 158
Atlantic / Nov '69.

## YOU CAN'T RUN AWAY FROM YOUR HEART.
**Tracks:** You can't run away from your heart / It takes a lotta good love.
7"........................................ .601022
Stax / Oct '67 / Pinnacle.

# Clay, Otis

Clay first hit R&B charts in 1967 with *That's How It Is (When You're In Love)*. Mississippi-born gospel graduate had been touring with various groups since '50s and begun recording in '64. Unsettled career continued until Clay was signed by producer Willie Mitchell to Hi Records in early '70s, yielding R&B successes like *If I Could Reach Out* and *Trying To Live My Life Without You*. Latter was later covered by rock star Bob Seger. Dropped from Hi in '74, Clay resumed pattern of label-hopping and largely overlooked recordings, although '80s saw him working with George Jackson and, in '89, reunited with Mitchell.

## ALL I NEED IS YOU.
**Tracks:** All I need is you.
■ 7"....................................... .PT 456
President / Nov '76.

## CALL ME.
**Tracks:** Not Advised.
CD........................................ WAY 269510-2
LP........................................ WAY 269510-1
MC........................................ WAY 269510-4
Waylo / Apr '90 / Charly.

## GOSPEL TRUTH, THE.
**Tracks:** Not Advised.
CD........................................ BP 5005CD
Blind Pig (USA) / May '94 / Topic Records / Projection / Swift / C.M. Distribution / Roots Records / Direct Distribution / Impetus Records / Hot Shot.

## I'LL TREAT YOU RIGHT.
**Tracks:** Not Advised.
■ CD...................................... CDBB 9520
Bullseye Blues / Jul '92.

## I'M SATISFIED.
**Tracks:** I'm satisfied / I testify.
■ 7"....................................... .PT 132
President / May '67.

## IT'S EASIER SAID THAN DONE.
**Tracks:** It's easier said than done / Flame in your heart.
■ 7"....................................... .PT 121
President / Jan '67.

## LIVE IN JAPAN.
**Tracks:** Not Advised.
■ Double LP............................... STING 004/5
Blue Sting / Nov '86.

## LIVE IN TOKYO.
**Tracks:** Not Advised.
CD........................................ WAY 269503-2
MC........................................ WAY 269503-4
Waylo / Apr '90 / Charly.
CD........................................ 269 503 2
MMS Records / Apr '94 / BMG.

## LOVE BANDIT.
**Tracks:** Love bandit.
■ 12"...................................... PIN 105T
Pinnacle / Jul '84.

## ON MY WAY HOME.
**Tracks:** Not Advised.
CD........................................ BBCD 9536
MC........................................ BBC 9536
Bullseye Blues / Jun '93 / New Note / Topic Records / Direct Distribution.

## ONLY WAY IS UP, THE.
**Tracks:** Not Advised.
CD........................................ WAY 269504-2
MC........................................ WAY 269504-4
Waylo / Apr '90 / Charly.

## OTIS CLAY 45'S.
**Tracks:** Not Advised.
CD........................................ HILOCD 1
Hi / Dec '93 / Pinnacle.

## SOUL MAN LIVE IN JAPAN.
**Tracks:** Not Advised.
■ Double LP............................... .R 7609
Rooster (USA) / Oct '88.

## THAT'S HOW IT IS.
**Tracks:** Not Advised.
CD........................................ HIUKCD 110
Demon / Jul '91 / Pinnacle / A.D.A. Distribution.

## THAT'S HOW IT IS.
**Tracks:** That's how it is / Show place.
■ 7"....................................... .PT 148
President / Sep '67.

## TRYING TO LIVE MY LIFE WITHOUT YOU.
**Tracks:** Trying to live my life without you / I die a little each day / Holding on to a dying love / I can't make it alone / You can't keep running from my love / Let me be the one / Brand new thing / Precious, precious / I don't know the meaning of pain / That's how it is / Too many hands / I love you, I need you / Home is where the heart is.
■ LP...................................... HIUKLP 406
Hi / May '87.

# Clay, Tom

## WHAT THE WORLD NEEDS NOW.
**Tracks:** What the world needs now is love.
■ 7"....................................... MW 3013
Mowest / Oct '81.

# Clayton, Merry

## GIMME SHELTER ODE '70.
**Tracks:** Country road / Tell all the people / Bridge over troubled water / Gimme shelter / I've got life / Here come those heartaches again / Forget it I got it / You've been acting strange / I ain't gonna worry my life away / Good girls.
■ LP...................................... .AMLS 995
A&M / Nov '70.

## MERRY CLAYTON.
**Tracks:** Southern man / Walk on in / After all this time / Love me or let me be lonely / Song for you / Sho' nuff / Steamroller / Same old story / Light on the hill / Grandma's hands / Whatever.
■ LP...................................... AMLS 67012
A&M / May '72.

## WHEN THE WORLD TURNS BLUE.
**Tracks:** When the world turns blue / Let me make you cry a little longer.
■ 7"....................................... MCA 571
MCA / Mar '80.

## YES.
**Tracks:** Yes / Five satins / In the still of the night.
■ 12"...................................... PT 49564
■ 7"....................................... PB 49563
RCA / Apr '88.

# Clayton, Michael

## FRIENDS AND LOVERS.
**Tracks:** Friends and lovers / Friends and lovers (versions).
■ 12"...................................... 12 PO 54
Ichiban / Oct '90.

## MICHAEL CLAYTON.
**Tracks:** Friends and lovers / All of my heart / Driftin' on a dream / Call my name / You're the one for me / Serious / Friends and lover theme (instrumental).
LP........................................ .GEM 4027
MC........................................ GEM 4027MC
Gemc / Jul '90 / Backs Distribution / Ichiban Records (UK).

# Clayton, Willie

**BOBBY MCCLURE & WILLIE CLAYTON**
(see under McClure, Bobby).

## FEELS LIKE LOVE.
**Tracks:** Not Advised.
CD........................................ .ICH 1155CD
MC........................................ ICH 1155MC
Ichiban / Feb '94 / A.D.A. Distribution / Pinnacle / ACD Trading Ltd. / Koch International / Direct Distribution.

■ DELETED

## FOREVER.
Tracks: Not Advised.
CD . . . . . . . . . . . . . . . . . . . . . . TLCD 627
■ LP . . . . . . . . . . . . . . . . . . . . . . TRPL 127
Timeless (Soul) / Nov '88 / RTM / Pinnacle.

## OPEN THE DOOR.
Tracks: Open the door / What a way to put it / Show me / Where has the love gone / Love pairs / In the mood / Dear Lover / Tell me / Woman needs to be loved / Best years of my life / Show and tell / Do to you / Leavin' me / So tied up.
CD . . . . . . . . . . . . . . . . . . . . . . ATCD 020
■ LP . . . . . . . . . . . . . . . . . . . . . . ATLP 020
About Time / Nov '92 / BMG.

## TELL ME.
Tracks: Not Advised.
■ LP . . . . . . . . . . . . . . . . . . . . . . 889 659-1
Polydor / Sep '89.

# Clements, Soul Joe

## EVER, EVER.
Tracks: Ever, ever / Smoke and ashes.
■ 7" . . . . . . . . . . . . . . . . . . . . . . PXM 10
Plexium / '69.

# Clifford, Linda

## BRIDGE OVER TROUBLED WATER.
Tracks: Bridge over troubled water.
■ 12" . . . . . . . . . . . . . . . . . . . . . RSOX 30
■ 7" . . . . . . . . . . . . . . . . . . . . . . RSO 30
RSO / May '79.

## DON'T GIVE IT UP.
Tracks: Don't give it up / Another bad dream / Sweet melodies (Only on 12" single.).
■ 12" . . . . . . . . . . . . . . . . . . . . . RSOX 37
■ 7" . . . . . . . . . . . . . . . . . . . . . . RSO 37
RSO / Jul '79.

## FROM NOW ON.
Tracks: From now on / You can do it.
■ 7" . . . . . . . . . . . . . . . . . . . . . . K 17078
Curtom / Jan '78.

## GREATEST HITS: LINDA CLIFFORD.
Tracks: If my friends could see me now / Don't give it up / Runaway love / Red light / Shoot your best shot / From now on.
■ LP . . . . . . . . . . . . . . . . . . . . . . CUR 2007
■ MC . . . . . . . . . . . . . . . . . . . . . . CUR 2007MC
Curtom / Nov '89.
CD . . . . . . . . . . . . . . . . . . . . . . CUR 2007CD
Curtom / Oct '94 / ACD Trading Ltd. / Pinnacle / Koch International.

## I'M YOURS.
Tracks: Shoot your best shot / I had a talk with my man / It don't hurt no more / Red light / I want to get away with you / If you let me / I'm yours.
MC . . . . . . . . . . . . . . . . . . . . . . 3216 281
RSO / Nov '80 / PolyGram.
■ LP . . . . . . . . . . . . . . . . . . . . . . 239 428 1
RSO / Jan '81.

## IF MY FRIENDS COULD SEE ME NOW.
Tracks: If my friends could see me now / Runaway love.
■ 7" . . . . . . . . . . . . . . . . . . . . . . K 17163
Curtom / Jun '78.

## IF MY FRIENDS COULD SEE ME NOW.
Tracks: If my friends could see me now / You are you are / Runaway love / Broadway gypsy lady / I feel like falling in love / Please darling, don't say goodbye / Gypsy lady.
■ LP . . . . . . . . . . . . . . . . . . . . . . K 56498
Curtom / '75.

## LET ME BE YOUR WOMAN.
Tracks: Let me be your woman / Bridge over troubled water / Don't give it up / Hold me close / One of those songs / Don't let me have another bad dream / I can't let this good thing get away / Sweet melodies.
■ LP . . . . . . . . . . . . . . . . . . . . . . RSD 5005
RSO / May '79.

## RED LIGHT.
Tracks: Red light / Ralph and Monty / Hot lunch jam.
■ 12" . . . . . . . . . . . . . . . . . . . . . RSOX 64
■ 7" . . . . . . . . . . . . . . . . . . . . . . RSO 64
RSO / Jul '82.

## RIGHT COMBINATION (Clifford, Linda & Curtis Mayfield).
Tracks: Rock you to your socks / Right combination / I'm so proud / Ain't no love lost / It's lovin' time / Love's sweet sensation / Between you baby and me.
■ LP . . . . . . . . . . . . . . . . . . . . . . 2394269
RSO / Aug '80.

---

## RUNAWAY LOVE.
Tracks: Runaway love / If my friends could see me now.
■ 12" . . . . . . . . . . . . . . . . . . . . . CRCT 002
■ 7" . . . . . . . . . . . . . . . . . . . . . . CRC 002
Cambra / Oct '84.
■ 12" . . . . . . . . . . . . . . . . . . . . . 12 CUR 104
Curtom / Feb '90.

## SHOOT YOUR BEST SHOT.
Tracks: Shoot your best shot / If you let me.
■ 7" . . . . . . . . . . . . . . . . . . . . . . RSO 69
RSO / Nov '80.

# Clinton, George

Although dates are probably irrelevant for a man who, according to Public Enemy's Chuck D, "celebrates birthdays in reverse", George Clinton was born in 1940. He formed the Parliaments in 1955, scoring first hit with '67's I Wanna Testify. The self-proclaimed Dr Funkenstein then delivered the P-Funk empire, which enjoyed major success with Parliament and Funkadelic before its ignominious collapse in the early '80s. Clinton bounced back with '82's Computer Games, featuring the monster hit Atomic Dog, but subsequent albums and collaborations marked artistic decline which even Prince (who bailed Clinton out of financial ruin by signing him to Paisley Park) could not halt. Renaissance came when hip-hop community tired of James Brown samples and began raiding P-Funk archives. Initiated by De La Soul and Digital Underground, trend prompted wholesale looting by Dr Dre and peaked with Ice Cube's remodelling of Funkadelic's One Nation Under A Groove (confusingly renamed Bop Gun, an old Parliament hit), featuring Clinton himself. Hey Man.. Smell My Finger, Clinton's first solo album since '89, featured all-star cast of admirers and former henchmen and was reportedly Paisley Park's biggest non-Prince release. Clinton has also overseen series of archive releases and plans a Parliafunkadeliment revival, Dope Dogs, for the end of '94.

## ATOMIC DOG.
Tracks: Atomic dog / Man's best friend.
■ 12" . . . . . . . . . . . . . . . . . . . . . 12CL 280
■ 7" . . . . . . . . . . . . . . . . . . . . . . CL 280
Capitol / Jan '83.

## CINDERELLA THEORY.
Tracks: Airbound / Tweakin' / Cinderella theory / Why should I dog U out / Serious slammin' / There I go again / (She got it) Goin' on / Banana boat song / French kiss / Rita bewitched / Kredit kard / Airbound (reprise).
CD . . . . . . . . . . . . . . . . . . . . . . K 925 994 2
■ LP . . . . . . . . . . . . . . . . . . . . . . K 925 994 1
MC . . . . . . . . . . . . . . . . . . . . . . K 925 994 4
Paisley Park / Aug '89 / WEA.

## COMPUTER GAMES.
Tracks: Get dressed / Man's best friend / Loopzilla / Pot sharing totts / Computer games / Atomic dog / Free alterations / One fun at a time.
■ MC . . . . . . . . . . . . . . . . . . . . . . TCEST 12246
■ LP . . . . . . . . . . . . . . . . . . . . . . EST 12246
Capitol / Nov '82.

## DO FRIES GO WITH THAT SHAKE.
Tracks: Do fries go with that shake / Pleasures of exhaustion (do it till you drop) / Scratch medley (Extra track on 12" version).
■ 7" . . . . . . . . . . . . . . . . . . . . . . CL 402
Capitol / Apr '86.

## DOUBLE OH-OH.
Tracks: Double oh oh / Bangla Desh.
■ 12" . . . . . . . . . . . . . . . . . . . . . 12CL 363
■ 7" . . . . . . . . . . . . . . . . . . . . . . CL 363
Capitol / Jul '85.

## HEY MAN, SMELL MY FINGER.
Tracks: Martial law / Paint the white house black / Way up / Dis beat disrupts / Get satisfied / Hollywood / Rhythm and rhyme / Big pump / If true love / High in my hello / Maximumnimess / Kickback / Flag was still there / Martial law (hey man..small my finger).
CD . . . . . . . . . . . . . . . . . . . . . . 759925518-2
MC . . . . . . . . . . . . . . . . . . . . . . 759925518-4
WEA / Oct '93 / WEA.

## LOOPZILLA.
Tracks: Loopzilla / Pot sharing tots.
■ 12" . . . . . . . . . . . . . . . . . . . . . 12CL 271
■ 7" . . . . . . . . . . . . . . . . . . . . . . CL 271
Capitol / Dec '82.

---

## MOTHERSHIP CONNECTION.
Tracks: Not Advised.
VHS . . . . . . . . . . . . . . . . . . . . . . VVC 187
Virgin Vision / '87 / Gold & Sons / THE.

## R & B SKELETONS (IN THE CLOSET).
Tracks: Hey good lookin' / Do fries go with that shake / Mixmaster suite: Startin' from scratch / Counter irritant / Nothin' left to burn / Electric pygmies / Intense / Cool Joe / R & B skeletons (in the closet).
■ CD . . . . . . . . . . . . . . . . . . . . . . CZ 470
EMI / Aug '91.

## SAMPLE SOME OF DISC, SAMPLE SOME OF DAT.
Tracks: Not Advised.
CD . . . . . . . . . . . . . . . . . . . . . . MOLCD 026
LP . . . . . . . . . . . . . . . . . . . . . . MOLLP 026
Music Of Life / Jan '93 / Grapevine Distribution.
CD . . . . . . . . . . . . . . . . . . . . . . MOLCD 36
LP . . . . . . . . . . . . . . . . . . . . . . MOLLP 36
Music Of Life / Nov '94 / Grapevine Distribution.

## SAMPLE SOME OF DISC, SAMPLE SOME OF DAT VOL. 2.
Tracks: Not Advised.
CD . . . . . . . . . . . . . . . . . . . . . . MOLCD 33
LP . . . . . . . . . . . . . . . . . . . . . . MOLLP 33
Music Of Life / Sep '93 / Grapevine Distribution.

## SOME OF MY BEST JOKES ARE FRIENDS.
Tracks: Some of my best jokes are friends / Double oh / Bullet proof / Pleasures of exhaustion (do it till I drop) / Bodyguard / Bangla Desh / Thrashin'.
■ LP . . . . . . . . . . . . . . . . . . . . . . CLINT 1
MC . . . . . . . . . . . . . . . . . . . . . . TC CLINT 1
Capitol / Sep '85 / EMI.

## WHY SHOULD I DOG U OUT.
Tracks: Why should I dog U out / Why should I dog U out (part 2).
■ 12" . . . . . . . . . . . . . . . . . . . . . W 7557T
■ 7" . . . . . . . . . . . . . . . . . . . . . . W 7557
■ CD Single . . . . . . . . . . . . . . . . . . 922557 7
Paisley Park / Jul '89.

## YOU SHOULDN'T NUF BIT FISH.
Tracks: Nusbian nut / Quickie / Last dance / Silly millameter / Stingy / You shouldn't nuf bit fish.
MC . . . . . . . . . . . . . . . . . . . . . . TCEST 712308
■ LP . . . . . . . . . . . . . . . . . . . . . . EST 712308
Capitol / Jan '84 / EMI.
■ CD . . . . . . . . . . . . . . . . . . . . . . CZ 469
Capitol / Oct '91.

# Clinton, Larry

## SHE'S WANTED IN THREE STATES.
Tracks: She's wanted in three states / If I knew.
■ 7" . . . . . . . . . . . . . . . . . . . . . . GRP 120
Grapevine (Northern Soul) / Sep '79.

# Clovers

## ALL RIGHTY OH SWEETIE.
Tracks: Wonder where my baby's gone / I confess / Needless / Hey doll baby / Comin' on good / Good golly Miss Molly.
■ LP . . . . . . . . . . . . . . . . . . . . . . H 807
Dr. Horse (Sweden) / Sep '89.

## DOWN IN THE ALLEY.
Tracks: Not Advised.
CD . . . . . . . . . . . . . . . . . . . . . . 756782312-2
WEA / Mar '93 / WEA.

## FIVE COOL CATS.
Tracks: One mint julep / Good lovin' / Lovey dovey / I got my eyes on you / Down in the alley / Your cash ain't nothin' but trash / In the morning time / Don't you know I love you / Blue velvet / Love bug / I could be loved by you / Nip sip / Devil or angel / Your tender lips / So young / All about you.
■ LP . . . . . . . . . . . . . . . . . . . . . . ED 126
MC . . . . . . . . . . . . . . . . . . . . . . CED 126
Edsel / Mar '86 / Pinnacle.

## LOVE BUG.
Tracks: All about you / Love bug / If I could be loved by you / So young / Down in the alley / Nip sip / If I love you / In the morning time / Your tender lips / Fool fool fool / Wishing for your love / There's no tomorrow.
■ LP . . . . . . . . . . . . . . . . . . . . . . 587 162
Atlantic / Mar '69.

## Club Nouveau

### IT'S A COLD COLD WORLD.
Tracks: It's a cold cold world / Better way.
- 12" . . . . . . . . . . . . . . . . . . W 8101T
- 7" . . . . . . . . . . . . . . . . . . W 8101
WEA / May '88.

### JEALOUSY.
Tracks: Lust / Jealousy (instrumental).
- 12" . . . . . . . . . . . . . . . . . W 8551T
- 7" . . . . . . . . . . . . . . . . . W 8551
WEA / Nov '86.

### LEAN ON ME.
Tracks: Lean on me / Pump it up.
- 12" . . . . . . . . . . . . . . . . . W 8430 T
- 7" . . . . . . . . . . . . . . . . . W 8430
WEA / Feb '87.

### LIFE LOVE AND PAIN.
Tracks: Jealousy / Why you treat me so bad / Lean on me / Promises promises / Situation number / Heavy on my mind / Let me go.
- CD . . . . . . . . . . . . . . . . . . 9255312
- LP . . . . . . . . . . . . . . . . . . 9255311
- LP . . . . . . . . . . . . . . . . . . WX 100
- MC . . . . . . . . . . . . . . . . . . WX 100C
WEA / Nov '86.

### LISTEN TO THE MESSAGE.
Tracks: It's a cold cold world / Listen to the message / Dancin' to be free / Why is it that / For the love of Francis / Envious / What's going 'round / Only the strong survive / Better way.
- CD . . . . . . . . . . . . . . . . K 925687 2
WEA / Jul '88.
- LP . . . . . . . . . . . . . . . . . . WX 159
- MC . . . . . . . . . . . . . . . . . . WX 159C
WEA / May '88.

### NO FRIEND OF MINE.
Tracks: No friend of mine / No friend of mine (version).
- 12" . . . . . . . . . . . . . . . . . . W 2769T
- 7" . . . . . . . . . . . . . . . . . . W 2769
WEA / Jan '90.

### UNDER A NEW NOUVEAU GROOVE.
Tracks: Not Advised.
- CD . . . . . . . . . . . . . . . . . 7599259912
- LP . . . . . . . . . . . . . . . . . 7599259911
- MC . . . . . . . . . . . . . . . . . 7599259914
WEA / Feb '90.

## Coasters

### 16 GREATEST HITS.
Tracks: Not Advised.
- CD . . . . . . . . . . . . . . . . . . CD 1006
Gusto (USA) / '88.

### 20 GREAT ORIGINALS.
Tracks: Riot in cell block 9 / Smokey Joe's cafe / Framed / Turtle dovin' / Down in Mexico / Young blood / Searchin' / Idol with the golden head / Yakety yak / Zing went the strings of my heart / Shadow knows Charlie Brown / Along came Jones / Poison ivy / What about us / I'm a hog for you baby / Run red run / Shoppin' for clothes / Little Egypt / Bad blood.
- LP . . . . . . . . . . . . . . . . . K 30057
Atlantic / May '78.

### ALL TIME GREAT HITS.
Tracks: Poison Ivy / Along came Jones / Down in Mexico / Shadow knows / I'm a hog for you / Charlie Brown / Yakety yak / etc.
- LP . . . . . . . . . . . . . . . . . 590015
Atlantic / Dec '67.

### CHARLIE BROWN.
Tracks: Charlie Brown / Three cool cats.
- 7" . . . . . . . . . . . . . . . . . HLE 8819
London-American / Mar '59.

### CHARLIE BROWN (OLD GOLD).
Tracks: Charlie Brown / Poison Ivy.
- 7" . . . . . . . . . . . . . . . . . OG 9056
Old Gold / Nov '80.

### COASTIN' ALONG.
Tracks: Just like me / Keep on rollin' / Wait a minute / Stewball / Snake and the bookworm / What about us / Little Egypt / Wake me shake me / Run red run / My babe / Bad blood / Girls girls girls.
- LP . . . . . . . . . . . . . . . . . 588 134
Atlantic / Feb '69.

### EARLY YEARS.
Tracks: That is rock & roll / Poison ivy / Along came Jones / Searchin' / Shoppin' for clothes / Yakety yak / Little Egypt / Charlie Brown / Down in Mexico / Smokey Joe's cafe / Riot in cell block number nine /

Young blood / Turtle dovin' / Idol with the golden head.
- LP . . . . . . . . . . . . . . . . . K 30031
Atlantic / Apr '73.

### GREATEST HITS.
Tracks: Not Advised.
- CD . . . . . . . . . . . . . . . . . 7567903862
Atlantic / Jul '93 / WEA.

### HUNGRY.
Tracks: Hungry / Oh rocking my soul / Humdinger / T.V. fanatic / Prophet / Deodorant song / It don't take much / It ain't sanitary / Prison break / Here I am / As quiet as it's kept / Whip it on me baby.
- LP . . . . . . . . . . . . . . . . . JOYS 189
Joy / Apr '71.

### JUKE BOX GIANTS.
Tracks: Run red run / Yakety yak / As quiet as it's kept / Young blood / Whip it on me, baby / Poison ivy / It don't take much / Along came Jones / Down in Mexico / It ain't sanitary / Little Egypt / Searchin' / Deodorant song / Charlie Brown / T.V. fanatic / Love potion no. 9.
- LP . . . . . . . . . . . . . . . . . AFEMP 1019
Audio Fidelity / May '82.

### JUST COASTIN'.
Tracks: I got to boogie / If I had a hammer / Poison ivy / Young blood / Along came Jones / Searchin' / Charlie Brown / Yakety-yak / Benjamin & Loretta / Chick is guilty.
- CD . . . . . . . . . . . . . . . . . C5CD 579
C5 / Feb '92 / Pinnacle.

### LEGENDS IN MUSIC - THE COASTERS.
Tracks: Not Advised.
- CD . . . . . . . . . . . . . . . . . LECD 076
Wisepack / Jul '94 / THE / Conifer Records.

### LET'S GO TO THE DANCE (Rare Early Rock 'n' Roll Sides).
Tracks: Not Advised.
- LP . . . . . . . . . . . . . . . . . LS 13
Harmony / Jul '88.

### POISON IVY.
Tracks: Poison ivy / I'm a hog for you.
- 7" . . . . . . . . . . . . . . . . . HLE 8938
London-American / Oct '59.

### SEARCHIN'.
Tracks: Searchin'.
- 7" . . . . . . . . . . . . . . . . . HLE 8450
London-American / Sep '57.

### SORRY BUT I'M GONNA HAVE TO PASS.
Tracks: Sorry but I'm gonna have to pass.
- 7" . . . . . . . . . . . . . . . . . A 4519
- CD Single . . . . . . . . . . . . . A 4519CD
- MC Single . . . . . . . . . . . . . A 4519C
Atlantic / Mar '94.

### THUMBIN' A RIDE.
Tracks: That is rock'n'roll / Three cool cats / (Ain't that) just like me / Keep on rolling / Wait a minute / Stewball / Snake and the bookworm / Wake me, shake me / Girls, girls, girls (part 1) / Gee golly / Sorry but I'm gonna have to pass / What is the secret of your success / Lady like / Besame mucho (part 2) / Thumbin' a ride / Ridin' hood.
- LP . . . . . . . . . . . . . . . . . ED 156
- MC . . . . . . . . . . . . . . . . . CED 156
Edsel / Sep '85 / Pinnacle.

### VERY BEST OF THE COASTERS, THE.
Tracks: Not Advised.
- CD . . . . . . . . . . . . . . . . . 954832656-2
- MC . . . . . . . . . . . . . . . . . 954832656-4
Atlantic / Mar '94 / WEA.

### WHAT IS THE SECRET TO YOUR SUCCESS, 1957-64.
Tracks: My baby comes to me / Gee Golly / Sorry but I'm gonna have to pass / Teach me how to shimmy / The P.T.A.
- CD . . . . . . . . . . . . . . . . . RBD 102
- LP . . . . . . . . . . . . . . . . . RB 102
Mr.R&B (Sweden) / Jan '91 / Swift / C.M. Distribution / Wellard.

### YAKETY YAK.
Tracks: Yakety yak / Charlie Brown.
- 7" . . . . . . . . . . . . . . . . . HLE 8665
London-American / Aug '58.

### YAKETY YAK.
Tracks: Yakety yak / Searchin'.
- 7" . . . . . . . . . . . . . . . . . 584087
Atlantic / '67.

### YAKETY YAK.
Tracks: Not Advised.
- CD . . . . . . . . . . . . . . . . . 8122714282
Pickwick / Oct '94 / Pickwick.

### YAKETY YAK (OLD GOLD).
Tracks: Yakety yak / Along came Jones.
- 7" . . . . . . . . . . . . . . . . . OG 9089
Old Gold / Jul '82.

## Coffee

### CASANOVA.
Tracks: Casanova.
- 12" . . . . . . . . . . . . . . . . . MERX 38
- 7" . . . . . . . . . . . . . . . . . MER 38
De-Lite / Sep '80.

### CASANOVA (OLD GOLD).
Tracks: Casanova / I wanna be with you.
- 12" . . . . . . . . . . . . . . . . . OG 4173
Old Gold / May '90 / Pickwick.

### SHARON.
Tracks: Sharon / Day O.
- 12" . . . . . . . . . . . . . . . . . DIS 1004
M & R / May '86.

### SLIP AND DIP.
Tracks: Slip and dip / I wanna be with you.
- 12" . . . . . . . . . . . . . . . . . DEX 1
- 7" . . . . . . . . . . . . . . . . . DE 1
De-Lite / Dec '80.

### SLIPPIN' AND DIPPIN'.
Tracks: Slip and dip / Mom and Dad 1980 / I wanna be with you / Casanova / Promise / Can you get to this.
- LP . . . . . . . . . . . . . . . . . 6359 028
De-Lite / Dec '80.

## Coffey, Dennis

### BACK HOME.
Tracks: Funk connection / Back home / Free spirit / Our love goes on / Forever / High on love / Boogie magic / Wings of fire.
- LP . . . . . . . . . . . . . . . . . K 50371
Westbound / Jun '77.

### GETTING IT ON '75.
Tracks: Getting it on '75 / Chicano.
- 7" . . . . . . . . . . . . . . . . . SXX 6
Sussex / Jan '75.

### GIVE ME THAT FUNK.
Tracks: Give me that funk / Calling Planet Earth.
- 7" . . . . . . . . . . . . . . . . . LV 6
Atlantic / Feb '79.

### INSTANT COFFEY.
Tracks: Not Advised.
- LP . . . . . . . . . . . . . . . . . LPSX 9
Not Advised / '87.

## Cognac

### DON'T BOTHER TO KNOCK.
Tracks: Don't bother to knock.
- 12" . . . . . . . . . . . . . . . . . RISET 1
- 7" . . . . . . . . . . . . . . . . . RISE 1
Rise / Apr '86.

### HOW HIGH (Cognac & Salsoul Orchestra).
Tracks: How high / Nothing can change this love.
- 7" . . . . . . . . . . . . . . . . . WOT 41
Electric / Oct '79.

## Cold Blood

### COLD BLOOD.
Tracks: I wish how I knew / If you will / You got me hummin' / I just want to make love to you / I'm a good woman / Let me down easy / Watch your step.
- LP . . . . . . . . . . . . . . . . . 588 218
Atlantic / May '70.

## Cole, Natalie

Studying to become child psychologist, Natalie Cole became distracted by music, and toured world after graduating in 1972. Introduced to producers Chuck Jackson and (future husband) Marvin Yancey, she recorded demos which secured her contract with Capitol. 1975 debut *Inseperable* began four-year run of success, which peaked with '77 U.S. hit *I've Got Love on My Mind*. At turn of decade she began personal and musical

■ DELETED

decline, recovering commercially in late '80s with Top 5 U.K. hits *Pink Cadillac* and *Miss You Like Crazy*. By this time she had largely left soul behind and destroyed any vestiges of credibility with tasteless revival of late father Nat King Cole for studio-created duet.

## BE THANKFUL.
Tracks: Be thankful / La costa.
■ 7″ . . . . . . . . . . . . . . . . . . . . CL 15961
Capitol / Jan '78.

## CHRISTMAS SONG (CHESTNUTS ROASTING ON AN OPEN FIRE).
Tracks: Christmas song / We three kings of Orient are.
■ 7″ . . . . . . . . . . . . . . . . . . . . AM 487
A&M / Dec '88.

## EVERLASTING.
Tracks: Everlasting / Jump start / Urge to merge / Split decision / When I fall in love / Pink cadillac / I live for your love / In my reality / I'm the one / More than the stars / What I must do (Track on cassette only.).
■ LP . . . . . . . . . . . . . . . . . . MTL 1012
EMI-Manhattan / Aug '87.
■ MC . . . . . . . . . . . . . . . . TCMTL 1012
EMI / Aug '87.
■ CD . . . . . . . . . . . . . . . . . . CZ 365
■ MC . . . . . . . . . . . . . . . TCATAK 161
■ LP . . . . . . . . . . . . . . . . . ATAK 161
EMI / Oct '90.
CD . . . . . . . . . . . . . . . . . . . 7559611142
MC . . . . . . . . . . . . . . . . . . . 7559611144
Elektra / Jul '91 / WEA.

## EVERLASTING.
Tracks: Not Advised.
■ CD . . . . . . . . . . . . . . . . CDP 7909822
■ LP . . . . . . . . . . . . . . . . MTLX 1012
■ MC . . . . . . . . . . . . . . TC-MTLX 1012
EMI-Manhattan / '88.

## EVERLASTING.
Tracks: Everlasting / Everlasting (12″ mix) (on 12″ only.) / Everlasting (dub) (on 12″ only.) / Pink cadillac (12″ turbo mix) (on 12″ only.) / When I fall in love.
■ 12″ . . . . . . . . . . . . . . . . 12MT 46
■ 12″ . . . . . . . . . . . . . . . 12MTX 46
■ 7″ . . . . . . . . . . . . . . . . . MTX 46
■ 7″ . . . . . . . . . . . . . . . . . MT 46
■ CD Single . . . . . . . . . . . . CDMT 46
EMI-Manhattan / Jun '88.

## GOOD TO BE BACK.
Tracks: Safe / As a matter of fact / Rest of the night / Miss you like crazy / Good to be back / Gonna make you mine / Starting over again / Don't mention my heartache / I can't cry / Someone's rocking my dreamboat / Wild women do (power mix with rap) (Reissue only.).
CD . . . . . . . . . . . . . . . . . CDMTL 1042
MC . . . . . . . . . . . . . . . . . TCMTL 1042
■ LP . . . . . . . . . . . . . . . . MTL 1042
EMI-Manhattan / May '89 / EMI.
■ CD . . . . . . . . . . . . . . . CDMTLX 1042
■ LP . . . . . . . . . . . . . . . MTLX 1042
■ MC . . . . . . . . . . . . . TCMTLX 1042
EMI-Manhattan / May '90.
CD . . . . . . . . . . . . . . . . . . . 7559611152
MC . . . . . . . . . . . . . . . . . . . 7559611154
Elektra / Jul '91 / WEA.

## HAPPY LOVE.
Tracks: You were right girl / Only love / Nothin' but a fool / Joke is on you / These eyes / When a man loves a woman / I can't let go / Love and kisses / Across the nation.
■ LP . . . . . . . . . . . . . . . . . EST 12165
Capitol / Dec '81.

## HEART AND SOUL OF NATALIE COLE.
Tracks: This will be / Inseparable / Mr. Melody / Gimme some time / Sophisticated lady / Lucy in the sky with diamonds (live).
■ CD . . . . . . . . . . . . . . . KNCD 12055
■ MC . . . . . . . . . . . . . . KNMC 12055
Knight / Jul '91.

## HOLLY & IVY.
Tracks: Not Advised.
CD . . . . . . . . . . . . . . . . . .755961704-2
MC . . . . . . . . . . . . . . . . . .755961704-4
Warner Bros. / Nov '94 / WEA.

## I LIVE FOR YOUR LOVE.
Tracks: I live for your love / I'm the one / In my reality / Jump start (deluxe dub mix).
■ 12″ . . . . . . . . . . . . . . . . 12MT 31
■ 7″ . . . . . . . . . . . . . . . . . MT 31
EMI-Manhattan / Nov '87.

## I LIVE FOR YOUR LOVE.
Tracks: I live for your love / Urge to merge / When I fall in love (12″ & CD single only.) / Pink cadillac (turbo mix) (12MTX only.) / I wanna be that woman (12″ mix) (12MTX only.).
■ 12″ . . . . . . . . . . . . . . . . 12MTX 57
EMI-Manhattan / Dec '88.
■ 12″ . . . . . . . . . . . . . . . . 12MT 57
■ 7″ . . . . . . . . . . . . . . . . . MT 57
■ CD Single . . . . . . . . . . . . CDMT 57
EMI-Manhattan / Oct '88.

## I LOVE YOU SO.
Tracks: I love you so / You're so good / It's been you / Your lonely heart / Winner / Oh, daddy / Sorry / Stand by / Who will carry on.
■ LP . . . . . . . . . . . . . . . . EST 11928
Capitol / May '79.

## I LOVE YOU SO.
Tracks: I love you so / Oh Daddy.
■ 7″ . . . . . . . . . . . . . . . . . CL 16084
Capitol / May '79.

## I'M READY.
Tracks: Too much mister / I won't deny you / I'm ready / Keep it on the outside / Time / Straight from the heart / Where's your angel / I'm your mirror.
■ LP . . . . . . . . . . . . . . . . EPC 25039
MC . . . . . . . . . . . . . . . . . .40 25039
Epic / Sep '83 / Sony.

## I'VE GOT LOVE ON MY MIND.
Tracks: I've got love on my mind / Unpredictable you.
■ 7″ . . . . . . . . . . . . . . . . . CL 15912
Capitol / Apr '77.

## I'VE GOT LOVE ON MY MIND.
Tracks: Not Advised.
CD . . . . . . . . . . . . . . . . . . . JD 1236
Jazz Door / Feb '94 / Charly / Koch International / A.D.A. Distribution.

## JUMP START.
Tracks: Jump start (deluxe dub mix) (Only on 12 MTX 50.) / Jump start (car mix) (Only on 12 MTX 50.) / More than the stars (Only on 12 MTX 50.) / Jump start (radio edit) (Only on MT 50, MT 22 & 12 MT 22.) / I wanna be that woman (12″ version) (Only on CD single.) / This will be (Only on Cd single.) / Jump start (dance mix) (Only on CD single & 12 MT 50.) / I wanna be that woman (Not on CD single and 12 MTX 22.) / Pink cadillac (Only on 12 MT 50.).
■ 12″ . . . . . . . . . . . . . . . . 12MT 22
■ 12″ . . . . . . . . . . . . . . . 12MTX 22
■ 7″ . . . . . . . . . . . . . . . . . MT 22
EMI-Manhattan / Jul '87.
■ 12″ . . . . . . . . . . . . . . . . 12MT 50
■ 7″ . . . . . . . . . . . . . . . . . MT 50
■ CD Single . . . . . . . . . . . . CDMT 50
EMI-Manhattan / Aug '88.

## MISS YOU LIKE CRAZY.
Tracks: Miss you like crazy / Good to be back / Urge to merge (12″ vocal mix) (12″ & CD single only.) / I live for your love (CD single only.).
■ 12″ . . . . . . . . . . . . . . . . 12MT 63
■ 7″ . . . . . . . . . . . . . . . . . MT 63
■ CD Single . . . . . . . . . . . . CDMT 63
EMI-Manhattan / Apr '89.

## NATALIE COLE COLLECTION.
Tracks: Not Advised.
■ CD . . . . . . . . . . . . . . CDP 746 619 2
Capitol / '88.
■ LP . . . . . . . . . . . . . . . . . SN 16310
Capitol / Jul '88.

## NATALIE LIVE.
Tracks: Sophisticated lady / Que sera sera / Lovers / I'm catching hell living here alone / Mr. Melody / This will be / Party lights / I've got love on my mind / Lucy in the sky with diamonds / Inseparable / Cry baby / Can we get together again / I can't say no if you ask me / Something's got a hold on me / Be thankful / Our love.
■ Double LP . . . . . . . . . . . . E-STSP 18
Capitol / Jul '78.

## NOTHIN' BUT A FOOL.
Tracks: Nothin' but a fool / Joke is on you.
■ 7″ . . . . . . . . . . . . . . . . . CL 227
Capitol / Jul '81.

## OUR LOVE.
Tracks: Our love / Annie Mae.
■ 7″ . . . . . . . . . . . . . . . . . CL 15987
Capitol / May '78.

## OVER YOU (see under Parker, Ray Jnr.).

## PARTY LIGHTS.
Tracks: Party lights / Inseparable / This will be / Sophisticated lady.
■ 7″ . . . . . . . . . . . . . . . . . CLX 101
Capitol / Jul '77.

## PINK CADILLAC.
Tracks: Pink cadillac / I wanna be that woman / Pink cadillac (club vocal) (club vocal 12″ version.) / Pink cadillac (7″ version) (on club vocal 12″ version.) / Pink cadillac (turbo mix) / Jump start (radio edit) (Track on C.D. Single only.).
■ 12″ . . . . . . . . . . . . . . . . 12MT 35
■ 12″ . . . . . . . . . . . . . . . 12MTX 35
■ 12″ P.Disc. . . . . . . . . . . 12MTP 35
■ 7″ . . . . . . . . . . . . . . . . . MT 35
■ 7″ . . . . . . . . . . . . . . . . . MTX 35
■ CD Single . . . . . . . . . . . . CDMT 35
EMI-Manhattan / Feb '88.

## REST OF THE NIGHT.
Tracks: Rest of the night (12″ & CD single only.) / As a matter of fact (12″ only.) / Someone's rocking my dreamboat / Rest of the night (edit) (Not on 12″.) / Miss you like crazy (CD single only.).
■ 12″ . . . . . . . . . . . . . . . . 12MT 69
■ 7″ . . . . . . . . . . . . . . . . MTLH 69
■ 7″ . . . . . . . . . . . . . . . . . MT 69
■ CD Single . . . . . . . . . . . . CDMT 69
■ MC Single . . . . . . . . . . . TCMT 69
EMI-Manhattan / Jul '89.

## SOMEONE THAT I USED TO LOVE.
Tracks: Someone that I used to love / Don't look back.
■ 7″ . . . . . . . . . . . . . . . . . CL 16166
Capitol / Sep '80.

## SOPHISTICATED LADY.
Tracks: Sophisticated lady / Good morning heartache.
■ 7″ . . . . . . . . . . . . . . . . . CL 15840
Capitol / May '76.

## SOPHISTICATED LADY.
Tracks: This will be / Good morning heartache / Touch me / Unpredictable you / Sophisticated lady / Joey / I've got love on my mind / Needing you / Your face stays in my mind / Can we get together again / Heaven is with you / Our love / I love you so / Keep smiling / Not like mine / Be thankful / Who will carry on You / Oh daddy / Stand by.
CD . . . . . . . . . . . . . . . . . CDMFP 5984
■ MC . . . . . . . . . . . . . . . TCMFP 5984
MFP / Jun '93 / EMI.

## SOUL OF NATALIE COLE, THE (1975-1980).
Tracks: This will be / Lovers / Mr. Melody / Annie Mae / I can't break away / La costa / Peaceful living / (I've seen) Paradise / Stairway to the stars / Inseparable / I love him so much / Be mine tonight / What you won't do for love / Still I love / Love will find you / Party lights / This will be (remix).
CD . . . . . . . . . . . . . . . . . CDEST 2157
■ MC . . . . . . . . . . . . . . . TCEST 2157
Capitol / Oct '91 / EMI.

## STAND BY.
Tracks: Stand by / Who will carry on.
■ 7″ . . . . . . . . . . . . . . . . . CL 16072
Capitol / Mar '79.

## STARTING OVER AGAIN.
Tracks: Starting over again / I do / Annie Mae (12″ & CD single only.) / Miss you like crazy (CD single only.).
■ 12″ . . . . . . . . . . . . . . . . 12MT 77
■ 7″ . . . . . . . . . . . . . . . . . MT 77
■ CD Single . . . . . . . . . . . . CDMT 77
■ MC Single . . . . . . . . . . . TCMT 77
EMI-Manhattan / Nov '89.

## TAKE A LOOK.
Tracks: I wish love you / I'm beginning to see the light / Swingin' shepherd blues / Crazy he calls me / Cry me a river / Undecided / Fiesta in blue / I'm gonna laugh you right out of my life / Let there be love / It's sand man / Don't explain / As time goes by / Too close for comfort / Calypso blues / This will make you laugh / Lovers / All about love / Take a look.
CD . . . . . . . . . . . . . . . . . .755961496-2
MC . . . . . . . . . . . . . . . . . .755961496-4
East West / Jun '93 / WEA.

## TAKE A LOOK.
Tracks: Take a look.
■ 7″ . . . . . . . . . . . . . . . . . EKR 170
■ CD Single . . . . . . . . . . . EKR 170CDX
■ CD Single . . . . . . . . . . . EKR 170CD
■ MC Single . . . . . . . . . . . EKR 170C
Elektra / Jun '93.

### THANKFUL.
**Tracks:** Lovers / Our love / La costa / Nothing stronger than love / Be thankful / I can't stay away / Annie Mae / Keeping a light.
■ LP . . . . . . . . . . . . . . . . . . . . . . . . . . EST 11708
Capitol / Feb '78.

### THIS WILL BE.
**Tracks:** This will be.
■ 7" . . . . . . . . . . . . . . . . . . . . . . . . . . CL 15834
Capitol / Oct '75.

### THIS WILL BE.
**Tracks:** This will be.
■ 12" . . . . . . . . . . . . . . . . . . . . . . . . . . 12CL 629
■ 7" . . . . . . . . . . . . . . . . . . . . . . . . . . .CL 629
■ CD Single . . . . . . . . . . . . . . . . . . CDCL 629
■ MC Single . . . . . . . . . . . . . . . . . . TCCL 629
Capitol / Oct '91.

### TOO MUCH MISTER.
**Tracks:** Too much mister / Where's your angel.
■ 7" . . . . . . . . . . . . . . . . . . . . . . . . . . .A 3617
Epic / Aug '83.

### UNFORGETTABLE.
**Tracks:** Very thought of you / It's only a paper moon / Route 66 / Mona lisa / L.O.V.E / This can't be love / Smile / Lush life / That Sunday / That summer / Orange coloured sky / For sentimental reasons/ Tenderly/Autumn leaves / Straighten up and fly right / Avalon / Don't get around much anymore / Too young / Nature boy / Darling / Je vous aime beaucoup / Almost like being in love / Thou swell / Non dimenticar / Our love is here to stay.
CD . . . . . . . . . . . . . . . . . . . . . . . . . . 7559610492
■ LP . . . . . . . . . . . . . . . . . . . . . . . . . . EKT 91
MC . . . . . . . . . . . . . . . . . . . . . . . . . .EKT 91C
Elektra / Jun '91 / WEA.
MiniDisc . . . . . . . . . . . . . . . . . . . .755961049-8
Elektra / Aug '93 / WEA.
DCC . . . . . . . . . . . . . . . . . . . . . . . .7559 610495
WEA / Jan '93 / WEA.

### UNFORGETTABLE CONCERT, THE.
**Tracks:** Not Advised.
VHS . . . . . . . . . . . . . . . . . . . . . . . 8536 40139 3
Warner Music Video / May '92 / WEA.

### VERY THOUGHT OF YOU, THE.
**Tracks:** Very thought of you.
■ 7" . . . . . . . . . . . . . . . . . . . . . . . . . .EKR 147
■ CD Single . . . . . . . . . . . . . . . . . . EKR 147CD
■ MC Single . . . . . . . . . . . . . . . . . . EKR 147C
Elektra / May '92.

### VIDEO HITS.
**Tracks:** Pink cadillac / Miss you like crazy / Jump start / Everlasting / I live for your love / Rest of the night.
■ VHS . . . . . . . . . . . . . . . . . . MVR 99 0083 3
PMI / Sep '89.
VHS . . . . . . . . . . . . . . . . . . . . . . . 8536 40137 3
Warner Music Video / Nov '91 / WEA.

### WE'RE THE BEST OF FRIENDS (Cole, Natalie & Peabo Bryson).
**Tracks:** Gimme sometime / This love affair / I want to be where you are / Your lonely heart / What you won't do for love / We're the best of friends / Let's fall in love / You send me / Love will find you.
■ LP . . . . . . . . . . . . . . . . . . . . . . . . . . EST 12019
Capitol / Dec '79.

### WILD WOMEN DO.
**Tracks:** Wild women do (Power mix with rap) (Not on 12"'s.) / Wild women do (U.S. single version) (Not on 12MTX 81.) / Wild women do (Power mix with rap Ext.) (12" only.) / Wild women do (Get wild wit me dub mix) (12" only.) / Wild women do (Underground wacko mix) (12" only.) / Wild women do (Get wild with me club mix) (12MTX 81 only.) / Wild women do (Get wild with me mix) (12MTX 81 & CD single only.)
■ 7" . . . . . . . . . . . . . . . . . . . . . . . . . . MT 81
■ 12" . . . . . . . . . . . . . . . . . . . . . . . . .12MTX 81
■ 12" . . . . . . . . . . . . . . . . . . . . . . . . .12MT 81
■ 7" . . . . . . . . . . . . . . . . . . . . . . . . . . MTX 81
■ CD Single . . . . . . . . . . . . . . . . . . CDMT 81
■ MC Single . . . . . . . . . . . . . . . . . . TCMT 81
EMI-Manhattan / Apr '90.

## Coleman, Bobby

### PLEASURE GIRL.
**Tracks:** Pleasure girl / You don't have to tell me.
■ 7" . . . . . . . . . . . . . . . . . . . . . . . . . . 7N 25365
Pye International / '65.

## Coleman, Durrell

### SOMEBODY TOOK MY LOVE.
**Tracks:** Somebody took my love / When a man loves a woman.
■ 12" . . . . . . . . . . . . . . . . . . . . . . . . . . 12 BRW 46
■ 7" . . . . . . . . . . . . . . . . . . . . . . . . . . BRW 46
4th & Broadway / Apr '86.

## Collage

### GET IN TOUCH WITH ME.
**Tracks:** Get in touch with me / Winners and losers / Love is for everyone (Extra track on 12") / Romeo where's Juliet.
■ 12" . . . . . . . . . . . . . . . . . . . . . . . . . . MCAT 1128
■ 7" . . . . . . . . . . . . . . . . . . . . . . . . . . MCA 1128
MCA / Jun '87.

### ROMEO WHERE'S JULIET.
**Tracks:** Romeo where's Juliet / Let's rock 'n' roll.
■ 12" . . . . . . . . . . . . . . . . . . . . . . . . . . MCAT 1006
■ 7" . . . . . . . . . . . . . . . . . . . . . . . . . . MCA 1006
MCA / Oct '86.

### ROMEO WHERE'S JULIET (OLD GOLD).
**Tracks:** Romeo where's Juliet / You get the best from me.
■ 12" . . . . . . . . . . . . . . . . . . . . . . . . . . OG 4116
Old Gold / May '89.

### SHINE THE LIGHT.
**Tracks:** Not Advised.
■ LP . . . . . . . . . . . . . . . . . . . . . . . . . . CF 3297
MCA / Nov '85.

## Collier, Mitty

### SHADES OF GENIUS.
**Tracks:** Come back baby / I had a talk with my man / Would you have listened / I gotta get away from it all / My babe / Hallelujah (I love him so) / Drown in my own tears / No faith,no love / Together / Let them talk / Little Miss Loneliness / Ain't that love.
■ LP . . . . . . . . . . . . . . . . . . . . . . . . . . GCH 8049
MC . . . . . . . . . . . . . . . . . . . . . . . . . . GCHK 78049
Chess (Charly) / Jun '88 / Charly.

## Collins, Bootsy

Spaced bassist who defected from James Brown's band to George Clinton's P-Funk (dis)organisation. Played starring role in success of Parliament and Funkadelic, and was rewarded with own outlet Bootsy's Rubber Band; biggest hit was U.S. R&B [8]X1 *Bootzilla*. In wake of P-Funk dissolution, Collins became sought-after sessioneer, working with acts ranging from Trouble Funk to Keith Richard. Renewed interest in P-Funk in early '90s prompted reunion with Clinton and formation of Bootsy's New Rubber Band for 1994 *Blasters Of The Universe* album.

### BACK IN THE DAY - THE BEST OF BOOTSY COLLINS.
**Tracks:** Not Advised.
CD . . . . . . . . . . . . . . . . . . . . . .759926581-2
Warner Bros. / Aug '94 / WEA.

### BLASTERS OF THE UNIVERSE (Bootsy's New Rubber Band).
**Tracks:** Blasters of the universe / J.R. (Just right) / Funk express card / Bad girls / Back n the day / Where r the children / Female troubles (The national anthem) / Wide track / Funk me dirty / Blasters of the universe 2 (The sequel) / Good night Eddie / Sacred place / Half pass midnight / It's a silly serious world.
CD Set . . . . . . . . . . . . . . . . . . .RCD 90307-08
MC Set . . . . . . . . . . . . . . . . . . .RAC 90307-08
Rykodisc / Aug '94 / Vital Distribution / Topic Records / Direct Distribution / C.M. Distribution / A.D.A. Distribution.

### BODY SLAM.
**Tracks:** Body slam.
■ 12" . . . . . . . . . . . . . . . . . . . . . . . . . . 9299190
Blue Bird (2) / Aug '86.

### ONE GIVETH, THE COUNT TAKETH AWAY, THE.
**Tracks:** Shine o'Myte (rap popping) / Landshark / Count Dracula / Funkateer, I / Lexicon (of love) / So nice you name him twice / What's wrong radio / Music to smile by / Play on playboy / Take a lickin' and keep on kickin' / Funky funkateer.
■ LP . . . . . . . . . . . . . . . . . . . . . . . . . . K 56998
WEA / Apr '82.

### PARTY ON PLASTIC.
**Tracks:** Party on plastic.
■ 12" . . . . . . . . . . . . . . . . . . . . . . . . . . 6530036
■ 7" . . . . . . . . . . . . . . . . . . . . . . . . . . 6530037
CBS / Sep '88.

### PLAYER OF THE YEAR.
**Tracks:** As in 'I love you' / Bootsy / Bootzilla Hollywood squares / Funk attack / May the force be with you / Roto Tooter / Very yes 'player of the year'.
■ LP . . . . . . . . . . . . . . . . . . . . . . . . . . K 56424
WEA / Mar '78.

### WHAT'S BOOTSY DOIN'.
**Tracks:** Party on plastic / Subliminal seduction (funk me dirty) / Leakin' / Electro-cutie (shock it to me) / First one to the egg wins (the human race) / Love song / (I wannabee) kissin' the luv gun / Yo moma loves ya / Save what's mine for me.
■ CD . . . . . . . . . . . . . . . . . . . . . . . . . . 4629182
■ LP . . . . . . . . . . . . . . . . . . . . . . . . . . 4629181
■ MC. . . . . . . . . . . . . . . . . . . . . . . . . . 4629184
CBS / Nov '88.

## Collins, Keanya

### BARNABUS COLLINS - LOVE BANDIT.
**Tracks:** Barnabus Collins - love bandit / I call you Daddy.
■ 7" . . . . . . . . . . . . . . . . . . . . . . . . . . GRP 105
Grapevine (Northern Soul) / '78.

## Collins, Lyn

### LYN COLLINS (THE FEMALE PREACHER).
**Tracks:** Not Advised.
■ LP . . . . . . . . . . . . . . . . . . . . . . . . . . URBLP 7
■ MC. . . . . . . . . . . . . . . . . . . . . . . . . . URBMC 7
Urban / Apr '88.

## Collins, Rodger

### SHE'S LOOKING GOOD.
**Tracks:** She's looking good / I'm serving time.
■ 7" . . . . . . . . . . . . . . . . . . . . . . . . . . VF 9288
Vocalion / Mar '67.

### YOU SEXY SUGAR PLUM (BUT I LIKE IT).
**Tracks:** You sexy sugar plum (but I like it) / I'll be here (when the morning comes).
■ 7" . . . . . . . . . . . . . . . . . . . . . . . . . . FTC 132
Fantasy / Apr '76.

## Collins, Willie

### WHERE YOU GONNA BE TONIGHT.
**Tracks:** Ain't no woman / Determination (Featuring McFadden & Whitehead.) / First time making love / Let's get started / Girl in the corner / Where you gonna be tonight / Restless / Sticky situation.
■ LP . . . . . . . . . . . . . . . . . . . . . . . . . . EST 2012
■ MC. . . . . . . . . . . . . . . . . . . . . . . . . . TCEST 2012
Capitol / May '86.

### WHERE YOU GONNA BE TONIGHT - (EDIT).
**Tracks:** Where you gonna be tonight (edit) / Sticky situation.
■ 12" . . . . . . . . . . . . . . . . . . . . . . . . . . 12CL 410
■ 7" . . . . . . . . . . . . . . . . . . . . . . . . . . .CL 410
Capitol / Jun '86.

## Colon, Willie

### AMERICAN COLOR (Colon, Willie & Legal Alien).
**Tracks:** Aerolinea desamor / Color Americano / Me voy / Estoy por ti rezando / Carmelina / Vida nocturna / Colgaditos / Hasta que te conoci.
LP . . . . . . . . . . . . . . . . . . . . . . . . . . 158031
MC. . . . . . . . . . . . . . . . . . . . . . . . . . 158034
■ CD . . . . . . . . . . . . . . . . . . . . . . . . . . 158032
Messidor / Aug '90 / Koch International / Cadillac.

### CONTRABANDO.
**Tracks:** Bailando asi / Manana amor / Contrabando / Che che cole / Barrunto / Te conozco / Calle luna calle sol / Lo que es de juan / Pregunta por ahi / Especial no.5 / Soltera / Quien eres.
■ LP . . . . . . . . . . . . . . . . . . . . . . . . . . 1015958
Messidor / Apr '87.
CD. . . . . . . . . . . . . . . . . . . . . . . . . . MES 159592
MC. . . . . . . . . . . . . . . . . . . . . . . . . . MES 159594
Messidor / Apr '93 / Koch International / Cadillac.

### CORAZON GUERRERO.
**Tracks:** Not Advised.
■ LP . . . . . . . . . . . . . . . . . . . . . . . . . . SLP 619
Syllaphone / Mar '89.

■ DELETED

## HONRA Y CULTURA.

**Tracks:** No / Quinientos anos (five hundred years) / Cuando vuelva a verte (if you were mine) / Fragilidad (fragility) / Honra y cultura (honour and culture) / Scandal / Mi gran amor (my great love) / Divino maestro (divine teacher) / Si fuera mia (when I return).

CD . . . . . . . . . . . . . . . . . . . . .158092
MC. . . . . . . . . . . . . . . . . . . . . .158094
Messidor / Aug '91 / Koch International / Cadillac.

## SALSA'S BAD BOY.

**Tracks:** Sangrigorda / Zambullete / De que / Americano latino / Gitana / Ya llego / Dos jueyes / Guaracha / La banda / La murga / Ah ah o no / Usted abuso / ue bien te vez / No me digan que es muy tarde / Segun un color / Todos somos iguales.
■ CD . . . . . . . . . . . . . . . . . CDCHARLY 238
Charly / Aug '90.

## SET FIRE TO ME - (LATIN JAZZBO VERSION).

**Tracks:** Set fire to me - latin jazzbo version / Inferno dub.
■ 12" . . . . . . . . . . . . . . . . . . . AMY 330
■ 7" . . . . . . . . . . . . . . . . . . . . AM 330
A&M / Jun '86.

## SHE DON'T KNOW I'M ALIVE.

**Tracks:** She don't know I'm alive / She don't know I'm alive (dub) / Set fire to me.
■ 12" . . . . . . . . . . . . . . . . . . . AMY 380
■ 7" . . . . . . . . . . . . . . . . . . . . AM 380
A&M / Feb '87.

## SIEMBRA (Colon, Willie & Reuben Blades).

**Tracks:** Not Advised.
■ LP . . . . . . . . . . . . . . . . . . . . SLP 537
Syllaphone / Mar '89.

## TIEMPO PA'MATAR.

**Tracks:** El diablo / Tiempo pa'matar / Noche de lose enmascarados / Callejon sin salido / Volo / Falta de consideracion / Gitana / Serenata.
■ LP . . . . . . . . . . . . . . . . . . . . 1115927
Messidor / Jan '87.
■ LP . . . . . . . . . . . . . . . . . . . . SLP 631
Syllaphone / Mar '89.
CD. . . . . . . . . . . . . . . . . . . . . .159272
Messidor / Dec '90 / Koch International / Cadillac.
CD. . . . . . . . . . . . . . . . . . . .MES 159272
MC. . . . . . . . . . . . . . . . . . . .MES 159274
Messidor / Feb '93 / Koch International / Cadillac.

## TOP SECRETS (Colon, Willie & Legal Alien).

**Tracks:** Not Advised.
CD. . . . . . . . . . . . . . . . . . . . . . 15980
■ LP . . . . . . . . . . . . . . . . . . . . 15979
MC. . . . . . . . . . . . . . . . . . . . . . 15978
Messidor / Jun '89 / Koch International / Cadillac.
CD. . . . . . . . . . . . . . . . . . . .MES 159802
Messidor / Jun '93 / Koch International / Cadillac.

# Color Me Badd

## ALL 4 LOVE.

**Tracks:** All 4 love.
■ 12" . . . . . . . . . . . . . . . . . . .W 0053T
■ CD Single . . . . . . . . . . . . . .W 0053CD
■ MC Single . . . . . . . . . . . . . . .W 0053C
■ 7" . . . . . . . . . . . . . . . . . . . W 0053
Giant / Aug '91.

## CHOOSE.

**Tracks:** Choose / Choose (mixes).
■ 12" . . . . . . . . . . . . . . . .74321 19943-1
■ 7" . . . . . . . . . . . . . . . . .74321 19943-7
■ CD Single . . . . . . . . . . . .74321 19943-2
■ MC Single . . . . . . . . . . . .74321 19943-4
Giant / Apr '94.

## COLOR ME BADD.

**Tracks:** I wanna sex you up / All 4 love / Heartbreaker / I adore mi amor / Groove my mind / Roll the dice / Slow motion / Thinkin' back / Color me badd / Your da one I onena love.
CD. . . . . . . . . . . . . . . . . . . . WX 425CD
MC. . . . . . . . . . . . . . . . . . . . WX 425C
■ LP . . . . . . . . . . . . . . . . . . . WX 425
GRP/Impulse / Jul '91 / Pinnacle.

## ◄ ADORE MI AMOR.

**Tracks:** I adore mi amor.
■ 12" . . . . . . . . . . . . . . . . . . .W 0067T
■ 7" . . . . . . . . . . . . . . . . . . . W 0067
■ CD Single . . . . . . . . . . . . . .W 0067CD
■ MC Single . . . . . . . . . . . . . . .W 0067C
Giant / Oct '91.

## I WANNA SEX YOU UP.

**Tracks:** I wanna sex you up.
■ 7" . . . . . . . . . . . . . . . . . . . W 0036
■ 12" . . . . . . . . . . . . . . . . . .W 0036T
■ CD Single . . . . . . . . . . . . . .W 0036CD
■ MC Single . . . . . . . . . . . . . .W 0036C
Giant / May '91.

## TIME & CHANCE.

**Tracks:** Intro / Time & chance / Groovy now / Let me have it all / Roseanna's little sister / How deep / La tremenda (Intro) / In thee / Sunshine choose / Bells / Wildflower / Living without her / Close to heaven / Trust me / Let's start with forever / God is love / God is loove (Outro) / C'est la vie / I remember.
CD. . . . . . . . . . . . . . . . .74321 16674-25
MC. . . . . . . . . . . . . . . . .74321 16674-49
RCA / Nov '93 / BMG.

## TIME & CHANCE.

**Tracks:** Time & chance / How deep / Time & chance (mixes) (On CD & 12" only).
■ CD Single . . . . . . . . . . . .74321 16899-2
■ 12" . . . . . . . . . . . . . . . .74321 16899-1
■ 7" . . . . . . . . . . . . . . . . .74321 16899-7
■ MC Single . . . . . . . . . . . .74321 16899-4
Giant / Nov '93.

# Colour Club

## COLOUR CLUB.

**Tracks:** Welcome to the Colour Club / Scene / Freedom words / Great issue: Freedom / Trust in me / Consumption / Scene II / On & on / Scene III / Chicago / Cultures of jazz / Scene IV / Howbotsuntinkikdis / Scene V / State of mind / Don't wait too long.
CD. . . . . . . . . . . . . . . . . . . .JVC 20342
JVC / Aug '94 / New Note.

# Colourblind

## NOTHING BETTER.

**Tracks:** Nothing better / Nothing better (mixes).
■ 12" . . . . . . . . . . . . . . . . . . . .AG 3
■ CD Single . . . . . . . . . . . . . . .AG 3CD
WEA / Oct '93.

## YOU'RE GONNA MAKE ME.

**Tracks:** You're gonna make me (Mixes).
12" . . . . . . . . . . . . . . . . . . . .AG 7
CD Single . . . . . . . . . . . . . . .AG 7CD
Ore / Oct '94 / WEA.

# Commodores

Having met at school, four original Commodores formed band in '60s and signed to Motown in '72. Band logged numerous hits in U.S. charts between '74 and '81, of which biggest were *Easy, Three Times A Lady* and *Still*. As writer of their greatest successes, Lionel Richie was destined for solo career, for which he split in '81. Commodores struggled without him, although they scored one-off smash in '85 with tribute to Marvin Gaye and Jackie Wilson, *Nightshift* (new line-up including ex-Heatwave vocalist J.D. Nicholas). Band quit Motown in '86 and by '94 were reduced to remaking greatest hits for compilation albums.

## 13.

**Tracks:** I'm in love / Turn off the lights / Nothing like a woman / Captured / Touchdown / Welcome home / Do woman you / Only you.
■ LP . . . . . . . . . . . . . . . . . . STMA 8039
MC. . . . . . . . . . . . . . . . . . CSTMA 8039
Motown / Sep '83 / PolyGram.
■ CD . . . . . . . . . . . . . . . . . CSTCD 8039
Motown / Nov '92.

## 14 GREATEST HITS.

**Tracks:** Machine gun / Slippery when wet / Sweet love / Fancy dancer / Easy / Brick house / Too hot ta trot / Three times a lady / X-rated movie / Sail on / Still / Wonderland / Old-fashioned love / Lady (you bring me up).
■ CD . . . . . . . . . . . . . . . .MCD 06068 MD
Motown / May '84.
■ CD . . . . . . . . . . . . . . . . . . ZD 72421
Motown / Feb '87.
CD. . . . . . . . . . . . . . . . . . . . .530096-2
Motown / Jan '93 / PolyGram.

## ALL THE GREAT HITS.

**Tracks:** Still / Easy / Flying high / Three times a lady / Lady (you bring me up) / Brick house / Lucy / Painted picture / Sail on / Reach high / Wonderland / Oh no / Why you wanna try me / Machine gun / Zoo. The (the human zoo) / Heroes.
■ LP . . . . . . . . . . . . . . . . . . . ZL 72051

## ■ MC. . . . . . . . . . . . . . . . . . . ZK 72051
Motown / '85.

## ALL THE GREAT LOVE SONGS.

**Tracks:** Sweet love / Just to be close to you / Easy / Three times a lady / Say yeah / Still / Loving you / Sail on / Old fashioned love / Jesus is love / Lady (you bring me up) / Oh no / This love / Lucy.
■ CD . . . . . . . . . . . . . . . . . . ZD 72222
Motown / Oct '84.
CD. . . . . . . . . . . . . . . . . . . . .530151-2
MC. . . . . . . . . . . . . . . . . . . . .530151-4
Motown / Jan '93 / PolyGram.

## ANIMAL INSTINCT.

**Tracks:** Animal instinct / Lightin' up the night.
■ 12" . . . . . . . . . . . . . . . . . . ZT 40098
■ 7" . . . . . . . . . . . . . . . . . . . ZB 40097
Motown / Apr '86.

## BEST OF THE COMMODORES, THE.

**Tracks:** Three times a lady / Still / Sail on / Lady (you bring me up) / Wonderland / Oh no / Too hot ta trot / Zoom / Nightshift / Easy / Janet / Flying high / Lucy / Just to be close to you / Machine gun / Brick house.
■ LP . . . . . . . . . . . . . . . . . . STAR 2249
■ MC . . . . . . . . . . . . . . . . . STAC 2249
Telstar/Ronco / Nov '85.

## BRICK HOUSE.

**Tracks:** Brick house / Sweet love.
■ 7" . . . . . . . . . . . . . . . . . . .TMG 1086
Motown / Oct '81.

## CAUGHT IN THE ACT.

**Tracks:** Wide open / Slippery when wet / Bump / I'm ready / This is your life / Let's do it right / Better never than forever / Look what you've done to me / You don't know that I know.
■ LP . . . . . . . . . . . . . . . . . . STMS 5032
■ MC . . . . . . . . . . . . . . . . . CSTMS 5032
Motown / Apr '82.

## COMPACT COMMAND PERFORMANCES (14 Greatest Hits).

**Tracks:** Machine gun / Slippery when wet / Sweet love / Fancy dancer / Easy / Brick house / Too hot ta trot / Three times a lady / X-rated movie / Sail on / Still / Wonderland / Old-fashioned love / Lady (you bring me up).
■ CD . . . . . . . . . . . . . . . . . . WD 72421
Motown / '88.

## COVER STORY.

**Tracks:** Not Advised.
VHS . . . . . . . . . . . . . . . . . . . SV 1810
Stylus Video / Apr '90 / EMI / Pinnacle / THE / Gold & Sons.

## EASY.

**Tracks:** Easy / Machine gun / I feel sanctified / Brick house (Only on 12" version).
■ 7" . . . . . . . . . . . . . . . . . . .TMG 1073
Motown / Oct '81.
■ 12" . . . . . . . . . . . . . . . . . . ZT 41794
■ 7" . . . . . . . . . . . . . . . . . . . ZB 41793
Motown / Aug '88.

## FANCY DANCER.

**Tracks:** Fancy dancer / Cebu.
■ 7" . . . . . . . . . . . . . . . . . . .TMG 1062
Motown / Jan '77.

## FLIPHITS.

**Tracks:** Three times a lady / Sail on / Still / Easy.
■ MC Single . . . . . . . . . . . . . .CTME 2031
Motown / Jul '83.

## FLYING HIGH.

**Tracks:** Flying high / Funky situation.
■ 7" . . . . . . . . . . . . . . . . . . .TMG 1111
Motown / Jun '78.

## GOIN' TO THE BANK.

**Tracks:** Going to the bank / Serious love.
■ 12" . . . . . . . . . . . . . . . . . POSPX 826
■ 7" . . . . . . . . . . . . . . . . . . POSP 826
Polydor / Oct '86.

## GREAT LOVE SONGS BY LIONEL RICHIE.

**Tracks:** Just to be close to you / Sweet love / Easy / Three times a lady / Still / Endless love / Sail on / Oh no / Lucy / Girl I think the world about you.
■ CD . . . . . . . . . . . . . . . . . . ZD 72388
■ MC . . . . . . . . . . . . . . . . . WK 72437
■ LP . . . . . . . . . . . . . . . . . . WL 72437
Motown / Jun '86.

## GREATEST HITS: COMMODORES.

**Tracks:** Three times a lady / Zoom / Brick house / Sweet love / Too hot ta trot / I feel sanctified / Easy / Flying high / Just to be close to you / Slippery when wet / Machine gun / Zoo.

■ **LP** . . . . . . . . . . . . . . . . . . . .STML 12100
■ **MC** . . . . . . . . . . . . . . . . . . .CSTML 12100
Motown / Oct '81.
■ **LP** . . . . . . . . . . . . . . . . . . . . . . ZL 72030
■ **MC** . . . . . . . . . . . . . . . . . . . . . ZK 72030
Motown / '85.

### GRIPP.
Tracks: Gripp.
■ **12"** . . . . . . . . . . . . . . . . . . . 871 691-1
■ **7"** . . . . . . . . . . . . . . . . . . . 871 370-7
Polydor / Apr '89.

### HEROES.
Tracks: Got to be together / Celebrate / Old fashioned love / Heroes / All the way down / Sorry to say / Wake up children / Mighty spirit / Jesus is love.
■ **LP** . . . . . . . . . . . . . . . . . . STMA 8034
■ **MC** . . . . . . . . . . . . . . . . . CSTMA 8034
Motown / Oct '81.

### HEROES.
Tracks: Heroes / Don't you be worried.
■ **7"** . . . . . . . . . . . . . . . . . . .TMG 1206
Motown / Oct '86.

### HITS VOL. 1 & 2.
Tracks: Not Advised.
**CD** . . . . . . . . . . . . . . . . . . . . . AR 9902121
**MC** . . . . . . . . . . . . . . . . . . . . . AR 9904121
Arcade / Feb '94 / Sony / Grapevine Distribution.

### HOT ON THE TRACKS.
Tracks: Lets get started / Girl I think the world about you / High on sunshine / Just to be close to you / Fancy dancer / Come inside / Thumpin music / Quick draw / Can't let you tease me.
■ **LP** . . . . . . . . . . . . . . . . . . STMS 5076
■ **MC** . . . . . . . . . . . . . . . . . CSTMS 5076
Motown / Oct '82.

### HOT ON THE TRACKS/IN THE POCKET (2 Classic Albums).
Tracks: Let's get started / Girl I think the world about you / High on sunshine / Just to be close to you / Fancy dancer / Come inside / Thumpin' music / Captain Quickdraw / Can't let you tease me / Lady (you bring me up) / Saturday night / Keep on taking me higher / Oh no / Why you wanna try me / This love / Been lovin' you / Lucy.
■ **CD** . . . . . . . . . . . . . . . . . . . ZD 72551
Motown / Jul '87.

### I FEEL SATISFIED.
Tracks: I feel satisfied / It is as good as you make it.
■ **7"** . . . . . . . . . . . . . . . . . . . TMG 935
Tamla Motown / Jan '75.

### IN THE POCKET.
Tracks: Lady (you bring me up) / Saturday night / Keep on taking me higher / Oh no / Why you wanna try me / This love / Been lovin' you / Lucy.
■ **LP** . . . . . . . . . . . . . . . . . . .STML 12156
■ **MC** . . . . . . . . . . . . . . . . . .CSTML 12156
Motown / Oct '81.

### JANET.
Tracks: Janet / I'm in love.
■ **12"** . . . . . . . . . . . . . . . . . . . ZT 40312
■ **7"** . . . . . . . . . . . . . . . . . . . ZB 40311
Motown / Aug '85.

### JESUS IS LOVE.
Tracks: Jesus is love / Mighty spirit.
■ **7"** . . . . . . . . . . . . . . . . . . .TMG 1218
Motown / Oct '81.

### JUST TO BE CLOSE TO YOU.
Tracks: Just to be close to you / X-rated movie.
■ **7"** . . . . . . . . . . . . . . . . . . .TMG 1058
Motown / Oct '76.
■ **7"** . . . . . . . . . . . . . . . . . . .TMG 1127
Motown / Nov '78.

### LADY (YOU BRING ME UP).
Tracks: Lady (you bring me up) / Gettin' it.
■ **12"** . . . . . . . . . . . . . . . . . TMGT 1238
■ **7"** . . . . . . . . . . . . . . . . . . .TMG 1238
Motown / Oct '81.

### LET'S DO IT RIGHT.
Tracks: Let's do it right / This is your life.
■ **7"** . . . . . . . . . . . . . . . . . . .TMG 1007
Tamla Motown / Oct '75.

### LIVE: COMMODORES.
Tracks: Won't you come dance with me / Slippery when wet / Come inside / Just to be close to you / Zoom / Easy / Funny feelings / Fancy dancer / Sweet love / I feel sanctified / Brick house / Too hot ta trot.
■ **Double LP** . . . . . . . . . . . . . . TMSP 6007
■ **MC Set** . . . . . . . . . . . . . . CTMSP 6007
Motown / Oct '81.
■ **Double LP** . . . . . . . . . . . . . . . WL 72439

■ **MC** . . . . . . . . . . . . . . . . . . . WK 72439
Motown / Jun '86.

### LOVE SONGS: COMMODORES.
Tracks: Three times a lady / Old-fashioned love / Easy / This love / Sail on / Wonderland / Zoom / Still / Sweet love / Saturday night / Lucy / Just to be close to you / Heaven knows / Oh no.
■ **LP** . . . . . . . . . . . . . . . . . . . NE 1171
■ **MC** . . . . . . . . . . . . . . . . . . . CE 2171
K-Tel / Jul '82.

### LUCY.
Tracks: Lucy / Heaven knows.
■ **12"** . . . . . . . . . . . . . . . . . TMGT 1282
■ **7"** . . . . . . . . . . . . . . . . . . .TMG 1282
Motown / Oct '82.

### MACHINE GUN.
Tracks: Machine gun / Young girls are my weakness / I feel sanctified / Bump rapid fire / Assembly line / Zoo (human zoo) / Gonna blow your mind / There's a song in my heart / Superman.
■ **LP** . . . . . . . . . . . . . . . . . . STMS 5002
■ **MC** . . . . . . . . . . . . . . . . . CSTMS 5002
Motown / Oct '81.

### MACHINE GUN.
Tracks: Machine gun / There's a song in my heart.
■ **7"** . . . . . . . . . . . . . . . . . . . TMG 902
Tamla Motown / Aug '74.

### MIDNIGHT MAGIC.
Tracks: Midnight magic / Gettin' it / You're special / Still / Wonderland / Loving you / Sexy lady / Sail on / 12.01 am.
■ **LP** . . . . . . . . . . . . . . . . . . STMA 8032
■ **MC** . . . . . . . . . . . . . . . . . CSTMA 8032
Motown / Oct '81.
■ **LP** . . . . . . . . . . . . . . . . . . . WL 72249
■ **MC** . . . . . . . . . . . . . . . . . . . WK 72249
Motown / May '85.

### MOVIN' ON.
Tracks: Hold on / Free / Mary, Mary / Sweet love / Can't get a witness / Gimme my mule / Time / Cebu.
■ **LP** . . . . . . . . . . . . . . . . . . STMS 5003
■ **MC** . . . . . . . . . . . . . . . . . CSTMS 5003
Motown / Oct '81.

### NATURAL HIGH.
Tracks: Fire girl / X-rated movie / Flying high / Three times a lady / I like what you do / Such a woman / Say yeah / Visions.
■ **LP** . . . . . . . . . . . . . . . . . . .STML 12087
Motown / Jun '78.

### NATURAL HIGH/ MIDNIGHT MAGIC.
Tracks: Fire girl / X-rated movie / Flying high / Three times a lady / Such a woman / Say yeah / I like what you do / Visions / Gettin' it / Midnight magic / You're special / Still / Wonderland / Sexy lady / Loving you / Sail on / 12.01 a.m. - reprise.
■ **CD** . . . . . . . . . . . . . . . . . . . ZD 72455
Motown / Oct '86.

### NIGHTSHIFT.
Tracks: Nightshift / Animal instinct / I keep running / Lay back / Slip up the tongue / Play this record twice / Janet / Woman in my life / Lightin' up the night.
■ **LP** . . . . . . . . . . . . . . . . . . . ZL 72343
■ **MC** . . . . . . . . . . . . . . . . . . . ZK 72343
■ **CD** . . . . . . . . . . . . . . . . . . . ZD 72343
Motown / '85.
■ **LP** . . . . . . . . . . . . . . . . . . . WL 72652
■ **MC** . . . . . . . . . . . . . . . . . . . WK 72652
■ **CD** . . . . . . . . . . . . . . . . . . . WD 72652
Motown / Mar '90.

### NIGHTSHIFT.
Tracks: Nightshift / I keep running.
■ **12"** . . . . . . . . . . . . . . . . . TMGT 1371
■ **7"** . . . . . . . . . . . . . . . . . . .TMG 1371
Motown / Jan '85.

### OH NO.
Tracks: Oh no / Are you happy.
■ **7"** . . . . . . . . . . . . . . . . . . .TMG 1245
Motown / Oct '81.

### OLD FASHIONED LOVE.
Tracks: Old fashioned love.
■ **7"** . . . . . . . . . . . . . . . . . . .TMG 1193
Motown / Oct '81.

### ONLY YOU.
Tracks: Only you / Cebu.
■ **7"** . . . . . . . . . . . . . . . . . . .TMG 1317
Motown / Sep '83.

### REACH HIGH.
Tracks: Reach high.
■ **12"** . . . . . . . . . . . . . . . . . TMGT 1292

■ **7"** . . . . . . . . . . . . . . . . . . .TMG 1292
Motown / Feb '83.

### RISE UP.
Tracks: Cowboys to girls / Rise up / Losing you / Who's making love / Sing a simple song / Baby this is forever / Love canoe / Come by here / Keep on dancing.
**CD** . . . . . . . . . . . . . . . . . . . CDBM 035
**LP** . . . . . . . . . . . . . . . . . . .BMLP 035
**MC** . . . . . . . . . . . . . . . . . . . BMC 035
Blue Moon (1) / Apr '87 / Roots Records / Jazz Music / Swift / Projection / THE / Hot Shot.
**LP** . . . . . . . . . . . . . . . . . . PER 33 8602
**MC** . . . . . . . . . . . . . . . . . PER 733 8602
Perfect / Aug '87 / Pinnacle.

### ROCK SOLID.
Tracks: Grrip / Bump the la la / Solitaire / Miracle man / Strechhh / So nice / Thank you / I'm gonna need your loving / Homeless / Right here 'n now / Ain't givin' up.
■ **CD** . . . . . . . . . . . . . . . . . 835 369-2
■ **LP** . . . . . . . . . . . . . . . . . 835 369-1
■ **MC** . . . . . . . . . . . . . . . . . 835 369-4
Polydor / Apr '89.

### SAIL ON.
Tracks: Sail on / Captain Quickdraw.
■ **7"** . . . . . . . . . . . . . . . . . . .TMG 1155
Motown / Oct '81.

### STAR PORTRAITS: THE COMMODORES.
Tracks: Not Advised.
**VHS** . . . . . . . . . . . . . . . . . GEMV 5009
Gemini Vision / Sep '94 / Sony / THE.

### STILL.
Tracks: Still / Such a woman.
■ **7"** . . . . . . . . . . . . . . . . . . .TMG 1166
Motown / Oct '79.

### STILL.
Tracks: Still / Sail on.
■ **7"** . . . . . . . . . . . . . . . . . . . ZB 41901
Motown / Apr '88.

### SUPERMAN.
Tracks: Superman / It is as good as you make it.
■ **7"** . . . . . . . . . . . . . . . . . . . TMG 930
Tamla Motown / Feb '75.

### THREE TIMES A LADY.
Tracks: Three times a lady / Can't let you tease me.
■ **7"** . . . . . . . . . . . . . . . . . . .TMG 1113
Motown / Apr '83.

### TURN OFF THE LIGHTS.
Tracks: Turn off the lights / Painted picture.
■ **12"** . . . . . . . . . . . . . . . . . TMGT 1322
■ **7"** . . . . . . . . . . . . . . . . . . .TMG 1322
Motown / Nov '83.

### UNITED.
Tracks: Going to the bank / Take it from me / United in love / Can't dance all night / You're the only woman I need / Land of the dreamer / Talk to me / wanna rock you / Let's apologise / Serious love.
■ **CD** . . . . . . . . . . . . . . . . . 831 194-2
■ **LP** . . . . . . . . . . . . . . . . . POLH 31
■ **MC** . . . . . . . . . . . . . . . . . .POLHC 31
Polydor / Nov '86.

### UNITED IN LOVE.
Tracks: United in love / Talk to me / Going to the bank (credit card mix) (On 12" only).
■ **12"** . . . . . . . . . . . . . . . . . POSPX 866
■ **7"** . . . . . . . . . . . . . . . . . . . POSP 866
Polydor / May '87.

### WHY YOU WANNA TRY ME.
Tracks: Why you wanna try me.
■ **12"** . . . . . . . . . . . . . . . . . TMGT 1256
■ **7"** . . . . . . . . . . . . . . . . . . .TMG 1256
Motown / Apr '82.

### WONDERLAND.
Tracks: Wonderland / Loving you.
■ **7"** . . . . . . . . . . . . . . . . . . .TMG 1173
Motown / Oct '81.

### XX NO TRICKS.
Tracks: Not Advised.
**CD** . . . . . . . . . . . . . . . . . . . FG 2-801
Freestyle (2) / Mar '94 / BMG.

### ZOO, THE (Human zoo, The).
Tracks: Zoo, The (Human zoo, The).
■ **7"** . . . . . . . . . . . . . . . . . . . TMG 924
Tamla Motown / Nov '74.

## ZOOM.

Tracks: Squeeze the fruit / Funny feelings / Heaven knows / Zoom / Won't you come dance with me / Brick house / Funky situation / Patch it up / Easy.

■ LP . . . . . . . . . . . . . . . . . . . .STML 12057
Tamla Motown / May '77.
■ LP . . . . . . . . . . . . . . . . . . . . STMS 5061
Motown / Sep '82.
■ LP . . . . . . . . . . . . . . . . . . . . WL 72101
■ MC . . . . . . . . . . . . . . . . . . . . WK 72101
Motown / May '84.
■ CD . . . . . . . . . . . . . . . . . . . . WD 72101
Motown / Apr '91.
CD . . . . . . . . . . . . . . . . . . . .530095-2
MC . . . . . . . . . . . . . . . . . . . .530095-4
Motown / Jan '93 / PolyGram.

## ZOOM.

Tracks: Zoom / Too hot ta trot.
■ 7" . . . . . . . . . . . . . . . . . . . .TMG 1096
Motown / Jan '78.

# Con Funk Shun

## BURNIN' LOVE.

Tracks: Do ya / Burnin' love / How long / Jo Jo / She's sweet / She's a star / It's time girl / You make me wanna love again / Burnin' love (single) / Burnin' love (dub edit).

■ LP . . . . . . . . . . . . . . . . . . . . 826 963-1
■ MC . . . . . . . . . . . . . . . . . . . . 826 963-4
Club / Aug '86.

## BURNIN' LOVE.

Tracks: Burnin' love (single).
■ 12" . . . . . . . . . . . . . . . . . . . .JABX 32
■ 7" . . . . . . . . . . . . . . . . . . . . JAB 32
Club / Jun '86.

## CHASE ME.

Tracks: Chase me / I think I found the answer.
■ 7" . . . . . . . . . . . . . . . . . . . .6167815
Mercury / Aug '79.

## ELECTRIC LADY.

Tracks: Turn the music up / Rock it all night / I'm leaving baby / Tell me what you're gonna do / Electric lady / Don't go / Circle of love / Pretty lady.
■ LP . . . . . . . . . . . . . . . . . . . . 824 345-1
Polydor / Aug '85.
CD . . . . . . . . . . . . . . . . . . . . 824 345-2
Polydor / '88 / PolyGram.

## FEVER.

Tracks: Can you feel the groove tonight / Indiscreet sweet / Baby, I'm hooked (right into your love) / Thinking about you, baby / Don't let your love grow cold / Lovin' fever / Hard lovin' / If I'm your lover.
■ LP . . . . . . . . . . . . . . . . . . . . 814 447 1
Polydor / Feb '84.

## IT'S GOT TO BE ENOUGH.

Tracks: It's got to be enough / Early morning sunshine.
■ 7" . . . . . . . . . . . . . . . . . . . . MER 14
Mercury / May '80.

## LOVESHINE.

Tracks: Can't go away / I think I found the answer / Loveshine / Magic woman / Make it last / Shake & dance with me / So easy / Wanna be there / When the feelin's right.
■ LP . . . . . . . . . . . . . . . . . . . . 9100055
Mercury / Jul '78.

## SECRETS.

Tracks: Confunshunizeya / Doowhachavannadoo / Fun / I'll set you out O.K. / Indian summer love / Secrets / Tears in my eyes / Who has the time.
■ LP . . . . . . . . . . . . . . . . . . . . 9100043
Mercury / Dec '77.

## SPIRIT OF LOVE.

Tracks: Got to be enough / By your side / Curtain call / Early morning sunshine / Spirit of love / Happy face / All up to you / Juicy / Honey wild / Lovestruck.
■ LP . . . . . . . . . . . . . . . . . . . .6337 102
Mercury / Aug '80.

## TOO TIGHT.

Tracks: Too tight / Play wid it.
■ 12" . . . . . . . . . . . . . . . . . . . . MERX 57
■ 7" . . . . . . . . . . . . . . . . . . . . MER 57
Mercury / Jan '81.

## TOUCH.

Tracks: Too tight / Lady's wild / Give your love to me / Play wid it / Pride and glory / Kidnapped / Welcome back to love / Touch / Can't say goodbye.
■ LP . . . . . . . . . . . . . . . . . . . .6337 154
Mercury / Feb '81.

# Conley, Arthur

Having taken Conley under his wing in 1965, fellow Georgian Otis Redding finally steered his charge to success in 1967. Pair reworked Sam Cooke's Yeah Man as Sweet Soul Music, which made Top 10 on both sides of Atlantic. After Redding's death, Conley failed to capitalise on success and, after one more U.S. hit with Funky Street, sunk into obscurity.

## ARTHUR CONLEY.

Tracks: Funky Street / Aunt Dora's love soul shack / Burning fire / Ha ha ha / I've been loving you too long / Sweet soul music / Shake, rattle & roll / Baby what you want me to do / Let nothing separate us / People sure act funny / Wholesale love / Ob la di ob la da.

■ LP . . . . . . . . . . . . . . . . . . . . K 20062
■ MC . . . . . . . . . . . . . . . . . . . . K4 20062
Atlantic / '88.

## FUNKY STREET.

Tracks: Funky street.
■ 7" . . . . . . . . . . . . . . . . . . . . 584 175
Atlantic / Apr '68.

## I'M LIVIN' GOOD.

Tracks: I'm livin' good / I'm so glad you're here.
■ 7" . . . . . . . . . . . . . . . . . . . .2091120
Atlantic / Jun '71.

## MORE SWEET SOUL.

Tracks: Ob-la-di, ob-la-da / Shing-a-ling / One night is all I need / I got a feeling / Aunt Dora's love soul shack / Stuff you gotta watch / Something you got / Is that you love / Speak her name / Run on / That can't be my baby / Take a step.
■ LP . . . . . . . . . . . . . . . . . . . . 228 019
Atco / Apr '69.

## SHAKE RATTLE AND ROLL.

Tracks: Not Advised.

## SHAKE, RATTLE AND ROLL.

Tracks: Shake, rattle & roll.
■ 7" . . . . . . . . . . . . . . . . . . . .584121
Atlantic / Jul '67.

## SHAKE, RATTLE AND ROLL.

Tracks: I've been loving you too long / Love got me / Change is gonna come / Hand and glove / Ha ha ha / Shake, rattle and roll / You don't have to see me / Baby what you want me to do / I'll take the blame / Keep on talking.
■ LP . . . . . . . . . . . . . . . . . . . . 587 084
Atlantic / Nov '68.

## SOUL DIRECTIONS.

Tracks: Funky St. / Burning fire / Otis sleep on / Hearsay / This love of mine / Love comes and goes / People sure act funny / How to hurt a guy / Get another fool / Put our love together.
■ LP . . . . . . . . . . . . . . . . . . . . 588 128
Atlantic / Nov '68.

## SWEET SOUL MUSIC.

Tracks: Sweet soul music / Down on Funky Street / Shake, rattle and roll (Extra track on 12").
■ 7" . . . . . . . . . . . . . . . . . . . . 584 083
Atlantic / Apr '67.
■ 7" . . . . . . . . . . . . . . . . . . . .2091106
Atlantic / Jul '71.
■ 7" . . . . . . . . . . . . . . . . . . . . K 10108
Atlantic / Jul '81.
■ 12" . . . . . . . . . . . . . . . . . . . . YZ 120T
■ 7" . . . . . . . . . . . . . . . . . . . .YZ 120
WEA / May '87.

## SWEET SOUL MUSIC.

Tracks: Gee whiz / B.A.B.Y / Sweet soul music / Funky street.
■ 7" . . . . . . . . . . . . . . . . . . . .ATM 8
Atlantic / Apr '80.

## SWEET SOUL MUSIC (OLD GOLD).

Tracks: Sweet soul music / Funky street.
■ 7" . . . . . . . . . . . . . . . . . . . .OG 9501
Old Gold / Jan '85.

# Connors, Norman

After stints with likes of John Coltrane and Pharoah Saunders, Connors launched his solo career in 1972 with Dance Of Magic on Buddah. Escalating jazz-funk profile peaked with You Are My Starship in '76, title track of which was U.S. hit; album also included reworking of Stylistics' Betcha By Golly Wow, featuring Phyllis Hyman. Latter was just one of many vocalists featured on Connors' work; others including Michael Henderson, Jean Carne, Glenn Jones, Prince Phillip Mitchell and, most recently, Angela Bofill (Intuition). In late '70s, he assembled Starship Orchestra, and began augmenting own career with outside production. He recorded for Capitol in late '80s and was last spotted on Motown.

## BEST OF NORMAN CONNORS (The Buddah Collection).

Tracks: Once I've been there / You are my starship / Mother of the future / Captain Connors / Be there in the morning / Kwasi / This is your life / Betcha by golly wow / Valentine love / Stella / Butterfly / Kingston / We both need each other / Romantic journey.
CD . . . . . . . . . . . . . . . . . . . . NEXCD 118
■ LP . . . . . . . . . . . . . . . . . . . . NEXLP 118
■ MC . . . . . . . . . . . . . . . . . . . .NEXMC 118
Sequel / Aug '90 / Total / BMG.

## BEST OF NORMAN CONNORS AND FRIENDS, THE.

Tracks: You are my starship / We both need each other / Betcha by golly wow / Dindi / Romantic journey / Once I've been there / This is your life / Wouldn't you like to see / Valentine love.
■ LP . . . . . . . . . . . . . . . . . . . . BDLP 4057
Buddah / May '79.

## INVITATION.

Tracks: Your love / Handle me gently / Be there in the morning / Invitation / Together / Disco land / I have a dream / Beijo partido / Kingston.
■ LP . . . . . . . . . . . . . . . . . . . . DISC 06
■ MC . . . . . . . . . . . . . . . . . . . . ZCDX 06
Buddah / Dec '79.

## LOVIN' YOU (Connors, Norman featuring Gabrielle Goodman).

Tracks: Loving you / I am your melody.
■ 7" . . . . . . . . . . . . . . . . . . . .CL 485
Capitol / '88.
■ 12" . . . . . . . . . . . . . . . . . . . . 12CL 485
Capitol / May '88.

## PASSION.

Tracks: I am my melody / You're my one and only love / Heaven in your eyes / Private stock / Loving you / Shabba / That's the way of the world / Welcome to my life / Samba for Maria / Passion.
■ CD . . . . . . . . . . . . . . . . . . . . CDEST 2056
■ LP . . . . . . . . . . . . . . . . . . . . EST 2056
■ MC . . . . . . . . . . . . . . . . . . . .TCEST 2056
Capitol / Mar '88.

## REMEMBER WHO YOU ARE.

Tracks: Not Advised.
CD . . . . . . . . . . . . . . . . . . . .530202-2
■ MC . . . . . . . . . . . . . . . . . . . .530202-4
Motown / Jan '93 / PolyGram.

## ROMANTIC JOURNEY.

Tracks: You are everything / Once I've been there / Destination moon / Romantic journey / Last tango in Paris / For you are everything / Thembi.
■ LP . . . . . . . . . . . . . . . . . . . . BDLP 4045
Buddah / May '77.

## SATURDAY NIGHT SPECIAL/YOU ARE MY STARSHIP (2 albums on one CD).

Tracks: Saturday night special / Dindi / Maiden voyage / Valentine love / Akia / Skin diver / Kwasi / We both need each other / Betcha by golly wow / Bubbles / You are my starship / Just imagination / So much love / Creator has a master plan.
CD . . . . . . . . . . . . . . . . . . . . NEXCD 186
Sequel / May '92 / Total / BMG.

## SAY YOU LOVE ME.

Tracks: Say you love me / Captain Connors.
■ 7" . . . . . . . . . . . . . . . . . . . .BDS 476
Buddah / Jun '78.

## TAKE IT TO THE LIMIT.

Tracks: Take it to the limit / Melancholy fire / You've been on my mind / I don't need nobody else / Justify / Black cow / You bring me joy / Everywhere inside of me.
■ LP . . . . . . . . . . . . . . . . . . . . AL 9534
Arista / Nov '80.

## TAKE IT TO THE LIMIT.

Tracks: Take it to the limit / Black cow.
■ 7" . . . . . . . . . . . . . . . . . . . .ARIST 363
Arista / Sep '80.

## THIS IS YOUR LIFE (Connors, Norman & Starship Orchestra).

Tracks: Stella / This is your life / Wouldn't you like to see / Listen / Say you love me / Captain Connors /

You make me feel brand new / Butterfly / Creator / Captain Connors (12" Version).
■ **LP** . . . . . . . . . . . . . . . . . . . . . . . **BDLP 4053**
Buddah / Jul '78.
**CD** . . . . . . . . . . . . . . . . . . . . . . . **NEMCD 637**
Sequel / Mar '93 / Total / BMG.

## YOU ARE MY STARSHIP.
**Tracks:** We both need each other / Betcha by golly wow / Bubbles / Just imagination / You are my starship / So much love / Creater has a master plan (peace).
■ **LP** . . . . . . . . . . . . . . . . . . . . . . . **BDLP 4043**
Buddah / Jan '77.

## Conquest, Leena

### BOUNDARIES.
**Tracks:** Boundaries (mixes).
12" . . . . . . . . . . . . . . . . . . . . . . . 7432120852-1
CD Single . . . . . . . . . . . . . . . . . 7432120852-2
MC Single . . . . . . . . . . . . . . . . . 7432120852-4
Natural Response / Jun '94 / BMG.

## Conscious People

### ATTITUDE.
**Tracks:** Attitude.
12" . . . . . . . . . . . . . . . . . . . . . . . . **TTC 010**
Tom Tom Club / Jul '94 / Jetstar.

## Consuelo, Ann

### SEE THE DAY.
**Tracks:** See the day.
■ **12"** . . . . . . . . . . . . . . . . . . . **CHAMP 12293**
Champion / Apr '92.

## Contours

### BABY HIT AND RUN.
**Tracks:** Baby hit and run.
■ **7"** . . . . . . . . . . . . . . . . . . . . . . **TMG 886**
Tamla Motown / Feb '74.

### CAN YOU DO IT.
**Tracks:** Can you do it.
■ **7"** . . . . . . . . . . . . . . . . . . . . . . . **SS 299**
Stateside / '64.

### CAN YOU JERK LIKE ME.
**Tracks:** Can you jerk like me.
■ **7"** . . . . . . . . . . . . . . . . . . . . . . . **SS 381**
Stateside / '64.

### DETERMINATION.
**Tracks:** Determination / Just a little misunderstanding.
■ **7"** . . . . . . . . . . . . . . . . . . . . . . **TMG 564**
Tamla Motown / Jun '66.

### DO YOU LOVE ME?.
**Tracks:** Do you love me / Money.
■ **12"** . . . . . . . . . . . . . . . . . . . . . **ZT 41904**
■ **7"** . . . . . . . . . . . . . . . . . . . . . **ZB 41903**
Motown / May '88.

### DO YOU LOVE ME? (NOW THAT I CAN DANCE).
**Tracks:** Do you love me / Just a little misunderstanding / Shake Sherrie / Can you do it / Don't let her be your baby / First I look at the purse / Whole lotta woman / Can you jerk like me / It's so hard being a loser / You get ugly.
■ **CD** . . . . . . . . . . . . . . . . . . . . . . **WD 72731**
■ **MC** . . . . . . . . . . . . . . . . . . . . . . **WK 72731**
Motown / Feb '91.

### FIRST I LOOK AT THE PURSE.
**Tracks:** First I look at the purse.
■ **7"** . . . . . . . . . . . . . . . . . . . . . . **TMG 531**
Tamla Motown / Sep '65.

### IT'S SO HARD BEING A LOSER.
**Tracks:** It's so hard being a loser / Your love grows more precious every day.
■ **7"** . . . . . . . . . . . . . . . . . . . . . . **TMG 605**
Tamla Motown / May '67.

### JUST A LITTLE MISUNDERSTANDING.
**Tracks:** Just a little misunderstanding.
■ **7"** . . . . . . . . . . . . . . . . . . . . . . **TMG 723**
Tamla Motown / Jan '70.

### RUNNING IN CIRCLES.
**Tracks:** Running in circles.
■ **12"** . . . . . . . . . . . . . . . . . . **12 MOTC 45**
Motor City / Nov '91.

## Controllers

Vocal quartet Soul Controllers had to wait best part of decade between convening at high school and winning acclaim with Frederick Knight-produced 1977 debut *Somebody's Gotta Win, Somebody's Gotta Lose*. After handful of albums on TK subsidiary Juana, they made one-off independent single (cover of Marvin Gaye's *Distant Lovers*), then signed to MCA in '84. Within four years, group had moved again, to Capitol. Controllers have never been major players on soul scene, but talent has sustained them through lack of commercial smashes.

### CONTROLLERS, THE.
**Tracks:** Love's in need / I'll miss you always / Hello / If somebody cares / You ain't fooling me / Somebody's gotta win / Reaper / Sho nuff a blessin' / Listen to the children.
■ **LP** . . . . . . . . . . . . . . . . . . . . . . **MCF 3241**
■ **MC** . . . . . . . . . . . . . . . . . . . . . **MCFC 3241**
MCA / Nov '84.
■ **LP** . . . . . . . . . . . . . . . . . . . . . . **TRLP 106**
Timeless (Soul) / Jun '87.

### CRUSHED.
**Tracks:** Crushed / Nothing can stop this feeling.
■ **12"** . . . . . . . . . . . . . . . . . . . . **MCAT 923**
■ **7"** . . . . . . . . . . . . . . . . . . . . . **MCA 923**
MCA / Oct '84.

### FOR THE LOVE OF MY WOMAN.
**Tracks:** Sleeping alone / Play time / Knocking at your door / For the love of my woman / Keep in touch / Love is on our side / My secret fantasy.
■ **LP** . . . . . . . . . . . . . . . . . . . . . . **MCF 3404**
■ **MC** . . . . . . . . . . . . . . . . . . . . . **MCFC 3404**
MCA / Nov '87.

### IS THAT LONG ENOUGH FOR YOU.
**Tracks:** Is that long enough for you / Pictures and memories.
■ **7"** . . . . . . . . . . . . . . . . . . . . . . **PT 448**
President / Feb '76.

### MY LOVE IS REAL.
**Tracks:** People want music / Heaven I only one step away / This train / My love is real / Fill your life with love (love's in) / Just for love / Gettin' over you / Castles in the sky / If tomorrow never comes.
■ **LP** . . . . . . . . . . . . . . . . . . . . . **TRPL 112**
Timeless (Soul) / Jan '90.

### NEXT IN LINE.
**Tracks:** I can't turn the boogie loose / If tears were pennies / Let me entertain you / We don't / Gunning for your love / Ankle chain / I just don't know / Hurt again by love.
■ **LP** . . . . . . . . . . . . . . . . . . . . . **TRLP 102**
Timeless (Soul) / Dec '87.
■ **LP** . . . . . . . . . . . . . . . . . . . . . **TRPL 102**
Timeless (Soul) / Jan '90.

### SOMEBODY'S GOTTA WIN, SOMEBODY'S GOTTA LOSE.
**Tracks:** Somebody's gotta win, somebody's gotta lose / Feeling a feeling.
■ **7"** . . . . . . . . . . . . . . . . . . . . . **TKR 6016**
TK / Aug '78.

### STAY.
**Tracks:** Distant lover / Stay / So glad / Bad bad jama / My secret fantasy / Breakout the love / Deep in love / Got a thang.
■ **LP** . . . . . . . . . . . . . . . . . . . . . **MCF 3324**
■ **MC** . . . . . . . . . . . . . . . . . . . . . **MCFC 3324**
MCA / Jun '86.

### STAY.
**Tracks:** Stay / Undercover lover.
■ **12"** . . . . . . . . . . . . . . . . . . . . **MCAT 1052**
■ **7"** . . . . . . . . . . . . . . . . . . . . . **MCA 1052**
MCA / '86.

### TIMELESS SOUL COLLECTION.
**Tracks:** Not Advised.
■ **CD** . . . . . . . . . . . . . . . . . . . . . . **CDTR 1**
Timeless (Soul) / Dec '87.

## Conway & Temple

### YOU CAN LAY YOUR HEAD ON MY SHOULDER.
**Tracks:** You can lay your head on my shoulder.
■ **12"** . . . . . . . . . . . . . . . . . . . . **JIVET 27**
■ **7"** . . . . . . . . . . . . . . . . . . . . . **JIVE 27**
Jive / Jul '85.

## Conway Brothers

### LADY IN RED.
**Tracks:** Por-sha / Why you wanna do me like you do / What love will do / B.O.C / I can't fight it / Lady in red / If you love me / Oio jamova me / Medley fire / Skin tight / O-H-I-O.
■ **LP** . . . . . . . . . . . . . . . . . . . . . **ICH 1006**
**MC** . . . . . . . . . . . . . . . . . . . . . **ZCICH 1006**
Ichiban / Feb '88 / A.D.A. Distribution / Pinnacle / ACD Trading Ltd. / Koch International / Direct Distribution.

### RAISE THE ROOF.
**Tracks:** Raise the roof.
■ **12"** . . . . . . . . . . . . . . . . . . . . **TEN 83-12**
■ **7"** . . . . . . . . . . . . . . . . . . . . . **TEN 83**
10 / Dec '85.

### TURN IT UP.
**Tracks:** Raise the roof / Set it out / Over and over / Get live / Gonna refuse your love / Turn it up / Call me / Together.
**MC** . . . . . . . . . . . . . . . . . . . . . . **CXID 9**
■ **LP** . . . . . . . . . . . . . . . . . . . . . . **XID 9**
10 / Jun '88 / EMI.

### TURN IT UP.
**Tracks:** Turn it up.
■ **12"** . . . . . . . . . . . . . . . . . . . . **TEN 57-12**
■ **7"** . . . . . . . . . . . . . . . . . . . . . **TEN 57**
10 / Jun '85.

## Cooke, Sam

One of secular soul and pop's golden voices, Sam Cooke began in gospel. Son of Baptist minister, he first sang in church aged nine and, in his early teens, was member of Highway QCs. Latter were taught by R.B. Robinson, member of Soul Stirrers, one of America's most proficient gospel acts. Cooke joined Stirrers in early '50s, enhanced their already high reputation and establishing himself as teen idol. Having left in '57, he switched to secular music and came up with first - and biggest U.S. hit chart-topping *You Send Me*. Biggest U.K. hit proved to be *Twistin' The Night Away*. Cooke was still scoring regular U.S. hits when he died in December 1964, aged 33. Immortality was cemented by posthumous Top 10 success of *Shake*, whose classic b-side, *A Change Is Gonna Come*, became anthem of escalating civil rights movement. Cooke's work influenced host of other acts, most notably Otis Redding.

### 20 GREATEST HITS: SAM COOKE.
**Tracks:** Not Advised.
**CD** . . . . . . . . . . . . . . . . . . . . . . . . **94042**
Compact Collection / Sep '87.

### 3 GREAT GUYS (Paul Anka/Sam Cooke/ Neil Sedaka).
**Tracks:** Laugh laugh laugh / I remember / I ain't gonna cheat on you no more / Talkin' trash / Without your love / Another day, another heartache / I can't say a word / No, no / I'm gonna forget about you / Tenderness / This endless night / Too late.
■ **LP** . . . . . . . . . . . . . . . . . . . . . **NL 89456**
■ **MC** . . . . . . . . . . . . . . . . . . . . . **NK 89456**
RCA / Nov '84.

### ANOTHER SATURDAY NIGHT.
**Tracks:** You send me / Little red rooster (available on 12" only) / Frankie and Johnny (available on 12" only) / Another Saturday night.
■ **7"** . . . . . . . . . . . . . . . . . . . . . **RCA 1341**
RCA / May '63.
■ **12"** . . . . . . . . . . . . . . . . . . . . **PT 49850**
■ **7"** . . . . . . . . . . . . . . . . . . . . . **PB 49849**
RCA / Apr '86.

### ANOTHER SATURDAY NIGHT (EP).
**Tracks:** Another Saturday night / Soothe me / Chain gang / It's got the whole world shakin'.
■ **EP** . . . . . . . . . . . . . . . . . . . . . **PE 9511**
RCA / Jul '80.

### BEST OF SAM COOKE.
**Tracks:** You send me / Only sixteen / Everybody loves to cha cha / For sentimental reasons / Wonderful world / Summertime / Chain gang / Cupid / Twistin' the night away / Sad mood / Having a party / Bring it on home to me.
■ **LP** . . . . . . . . . . . . . . . . . . . . . **PMP 1010**
**MC** . . . . . . . . . . . . . . . . . . . . . **PMPK 1010**
Premier (Sony) / Feb '88 / Sony / Pinnacle.

### CHAIN GANG.
**Tracks:** Chain gang.
■ **7"** . . . . . . . . . . . . . . . . . . . . . **RCA 1202**

■ DELETED

RCA / Sep '60.
■ **CD Single** . . . . . . . . . . . . . . . PD 49455
RCA / Jun '89.

## CUPID.
**Tracks:** Cupid.
■ **7"** . . . . . . . . . . . . . . . . . . RCA 1242
RCA / Jul '61.

## DIAMOND SERIES: SAM COOKE.
**Tracks:** Ain't that good news / Good times / Another Saturday night / Change is gonna come / Falling in love / Smoke rings / For sentimental reasons / These foolish things / Cry me a river / Little girl / Try a little love / Bridge of tears / When a boy falls in love / Shake / Yeah man / Win your love for me.
■ **CD** . . . . . . . . . . . . . . . . . . CD 90122
Diamond Series / Apr '88.

## FABULOUS SAM COOKE, THE.
**Tracks:** Having a party / Sad mood / Twistin' the night away / Try a little tenderness / Good times / For sentimental reasons / Another Saturday night / Summertime / Shake / Only sixteen / Everybody loves to cha cha / Send me some lovin' / Wonderful world / Nothing can change this love / Ain't that good news / Little red rooster / Cupid / Chain gang / Frankie and Johnny / Bring it on home to me / Tennessee waltz / Win your love for me / You send me.
■ **Double LP** . . . . . . . . . . . . . . CR 050
■ **MC Set** . . . . . . . . . . . . . . . . CRT 050
Cambra / '85.

## FEEL IT.
**Tracks:** Feel it / Chain gang / Cupid / It's all right / I love you for sentimental reasons / Twistin' the night away / Somebody have mercy / Bring it on home to me / Nothing can change this love / Having a party.
■ **MC** . . . . . . . . . . . . . . . . . . PK 85181
■ **LP** . . . . . . . . . . . . . . . . . . PL 85181
RCA / '87.

## FRANKIE AND JOHNNY.
**Tracks:** Frankie and Johnny.
■ **7"** . . . . . . . . . . . . . . . . . . RCA 1361
RCA / Sep '63.

## GOLDEN AGE OF SAM COOKE.
**Tracks:** You send me / Win your love / Love you most of all / Only sixteen / Wonderful world / Chain gang / Sad mood / Cupid / Frankie and Johnny / Twistin' the night away / Having a party / Bring it on home to me / Nothing can change this love / Another Saturday night / Little red rooster / Ain't that good news / Good times / Tennessee waltz / Shake / Change is gonna come.
■ **LP** . . . . . . . . . . . . . . . . . . RS 1054
RCA / '76.
■ **LP** . . . . . . . . . . . . . . . . . . PL 89021
RCA / '87.

## GRAFFITI COLLECTION.
**Tracks:** Not Advised.
CD . . . . . . . . . . . . . . . . . . . GRCD 04
MC . . . . . . . . . . . . . . . . . . . GRMC 04
Graffiti Collection / Aug '90 / THE.

## HEAVEN IS MY HOME (Cooke, Sam & The Soul Stirrers).
**Tracks:** That's heaven to me / Deep river / I thank God / Heaven is my home / God is standing by / Pass me not / Steal away / Must Jesus bear his cross alone / Lead me Jesus / Trouble in mind / Sometimes / Somebody.
CD . . . . . . . . . . . . . . . . . . C5CD-523
■ **LP** . . . . . . . . . . . . . . . . . . C5-523
C5 / Jul '88 / Pinnacle.

## IN THE BEGINNING (Cooke, Sam & The Soul Stirrers).
**Tracks:** He's my friend 'til the end / I'm gonna build on that shore / Jesus, wash away my troubles / Must Jesus bear his cross alone / Jesus, I'll never forget / Nearer to thee / Any day now / Touch the hem of his garment / I don't want to cry / Lovable / Forever alternative take) (Available on CD only) / I'll come running back to you / Happy in love / I need you now That's all I need to know / One more river (Available on CD only) / He's so wonderful (Available on CD only) / Jesus gave me water (Available on CD only) / That's all I need to know (alternative take) (Available on CD only) / I don't want to cry (alternative take) (Available on CD only) / Forever / Lovable alternative take) (Available on CD only).
CD . . . . . . . . . . . . . . . . . CDCHD 280
■ **LP** . . . . . . . . . . . . . . . . . . CHD 280
Ace / Nov '89 / Pinnacle / Complete Record Co. Ltd.

## MAGIC OF SAM COOKE, THE.
**Tracks:** You send me / Only sixteen / Stealing kisses Talk of the town / Love you most of all / Comes ove / Lover come back to me / Everybody loves to cha cha cha / Little things you do / Good morning

heartache / Win your love for me / Moonlight in Vermont / There I've said it again / Stealaway / All of my life / That lucky old sun / God bless this child / When I fall in love.
CD . . . . . . . . . . . . . . . . . . MCCD 021
MC . . . . . . . . . . . . . . . . . . MCTC 021
Music Club / May '91 / Gold & Sons / THE / Video Collection / C.M. Distribution.

## MAN AND HIS MUSIC, THE.
**Tracks:** Meet me at Mary's place / Good times / Shake / Sad mood / Bring it on home to me / That's where it's at / That's heaven to me / Touch the hem of his garment / You send me / I'll come running back to you / Win your love for me / Wonderful world / Cupid / Just for you / Chain gang / Only sixteen / When a boy falls in love / Rome wasn't built in a day / Everybody loves to cha cha / Nothing can change this love / Love will find a way / Another Saturday night / Having a party / Somebody have mercy / Ain't that good news / Soothe me / Change is gonna come.
CD Set . . . . . . . . . . . . . . . . PD 87127
■ **Double LP** . . . . . . . . . . . . . PL 87127
MC Set . . . . . . . . . . . . . . . . PK 87127
RCA / Apr '86 / BMG.

## MR. SOUL.
**Tracks:** I wish you love / Willow weep for me / Smoke rings / All the way / Send me some lovin' / Cry me a river / Driftin' blues / I love you for sentimental reasons / Nothing can change this love / Little girl / These foolish things.
■ **LP** . . . . . . . . . . . . . . . . . INTS 5024
■ **MC** . . . . . . . . . . . . . . . . . INTK 5024
RCA / '80.

## ONE AND ONLY.
**Tracks:** Jamaica farewell / Don't get around much anymore / Faraway places / Little girl blue / Song is ended / Bali Ha'i / Trouble in mind / They call the wind Maria / Swing low, sweet chariot / Since I met you baby.
■ **LP** . . . . . . . . . . . . . . . . . INTS 1005
RCA Victor / Jul '69.

## ONLY SIXTEEN.
**Tracks:** Only sixteen.
■ **7"** . . . . . . . . . . . . . . . . . . POP 642
H.M.V. / Aug '59.

## SAM COOKE.
**Tracks:** Only sixteen / Let's go steady again / When I fall in love / Crazy in love with you / Desire me / Little things you do / You send me / Steal away / Tammy / Darling, I need you now / You were made for me / What a wonderful world.
■ **LP** . . . . . . . . . . . . . . . . . COUNT 2
■ **MC** . . . . . . . . . . . . . . . . . ZC CNT 2
Dakota (Countdown Series) / '82.

## SAM COOKE.
**Tracks:** Not Advised.
CD . . . . . . . . . . . . . . . . . . DVCD 2095
■ **LP** . . . . . . . . . . . . . . . . . DVLP 2095
MC . . . . . . . . . . . . . . . . . . DVMC 2095
Deja Vu / Jan '87 / Jazz Music / Music Collection International.

## SAM COOKE.
**Tracks:** Not Advised.
MC . . . . . . . . . . . . . . . . . . ZCGAS 721
Audio Fidelity / '84 / Telstar/Ronco.

## SAM COOKE.
**Tracks:** Not Advised.
CD . . . . . . . . . . . . . . . . . . . .295039
Ariola / Oct '94 / BMG.
MC . . . . . . . . . . . . . . . . . . . .495039
Ariola / Oct '94 / BMG.

## SAM COOKE LIVE AT HARLEM SQUARE 1963.
**Tracks:** Feel it / Chain gang / Cupid / It's alright / For sentimental reasons / Twistin' the night away / Somebody have mercy / Bring it home to me / Nothing can change this love / Having a party.
■ **CD** . . . . . . . . . . . . . . . . PCD 15181
RCA / '88.
■ **MC** . . . . . . . . . . . . . . . . NK 90454
■ **CD** . . . . . . . . . . . . . . . . ND 90454
RCA / Feb '90.

## SAM COOKE WITH THE SOUL STIR-RERS (Cooke, Sam & The Soul Stirrers).
**Tracks:** Peace in the valley / It won't be very long / How far am I from Canaan / Just another day / Come and go to that land / Any day now / He'll make a way / Nearer to thee / Be with me Jesus / One more river / I'm so glad (trouble don't last always) / Wonderful / Farther along / Touch the hem of his garment / Jesus, wash away my troubles / Must Jesus bear the cross alone / That's heaven to me / Were you there / Mean old world / Lord remember me / Lovable /

Forever / I'll come running back to you / That's all I need to know / I don't want to cry.
CD . . . . . . . . . . . . . . . . . CDCHD 359
Ace / Nov '91 / Pinnacle / Complete Record Co. Ltd.

## SOLITUDE.
**Tracks:** All of my life / You send me / Danny boy / Ol' man river / Ain't misbehavin' / When I fall in love / God bless the child / That lucky old sun / Only sixteen / Solitude / Summertime / Tammy / Almost in your arms.
■ **Double LP** . . . . . . . . . . . . . . CR 117
■ **MC Set** . . . . . . . . . . . . . . . CRT 117
Cambra / '85.

## SWING OUT BROTHER.
**Tracks:** Solitude / Talk of the town / Crazy in love with you / I've got a right to sing the blues / Good morning heartache / Ain't nobody's business / Lover come back to me / That lucky old sun / They can't take that away from me / Moonlight in Vermont / When I fall in love.
■ **LP** . . . . . . . . . . . . . . . . . .TOP 171
MC . . . . . . . . . . . . . . . . . . KTOP 171
Topline / Apr '87 / Charly.

## THIS IS SAM COOKE.
**Tracks:** Frankie and Johnny / You send me / Sad mood / Summertime / Chain gang / Feel it / For sentimental reasons / Another Saturday night / Wonderful world / Having a party / Baby, baby, baby / Only sixteen / Love will find a way / Bring it on home to me / Twistin' the night away / Little red rooster / Cupid / Sugar dumpling / Send me some lovin' / Everybody loves to cha cha.
■ **Double LP** . . . . . . . . . . . . . DPS 2007
RCA Red Seal / '79.

## TWISTIN' THE NIGHT AWAY.
**Tracks:** You send me / Only sixteen / Everybody loves to cha cha / For sentimental reasons / Wonderful world / Summertime (end s1) / Chain gang / Cupid / Twistin' the night away / Sad mood / Having a party / Bring it on home to me.
■ **LP** . . . . . . . . . . . . . . . . . CBR 1012
MC . . . . . . . . . . . . . . . . . KCBR 1012
Premier (Sony) / '84 / Sony / Pinnacle.

## TWISTIN' THE NIGHT AWAY.
**Tracks:** Twistin' the night away.
■ **7"** . . . . . . . . . . . . . . . . . . RCA 1277
RCA / Mar '62.

## TWISTING THE NIGHT AWAY.
**Tracks:** Twisting the night away / Cupid / Only sixteen.
■ **7"** . . . . . . . . . . . . . . . . . . RCA 2093
RCA / Jun '71.

## TWO ON ONE: SAM COOKE & JACKIE WILSON (Cooke, Sam & Jackie Wilson).
**Tracks:** Not Advised.
CD . . . . . . . . . . . . . . . . . . CDTT 1
Charly / Apr '94 / Charly.

## WHEN I FALL IN LOVE.
**Tracks:** There, I've said it again / Let's go steady again / When I fall in love / Little things you do / You send me / Ol' man river / Moonlight in Vermont / Around the world / Everybody loves to cha cha / Along the Navajo trail / Someday / I cover the waterfront / Mary Mary-Lou / Love most of all / Only sixteen / Win your love for me.
■ **LP** . . . . . . . . . . . . . . . . . NUTM 23
■ **MC** . . . . . . . . . . . . . . . TC NUTM 23
EMI / '79.
■ **LP** . . . . . . . . . . . . . . . . . ARA 1007
MC . . . . . . . . . . . . . . . . . ARAC 1007
Arena / Feb '87.

## WONDERFUL WORLD.
**Tracks:** Chain gang / Cupid (available on 12" version only) / Change is gonna come (available on 12" version only) / Wonderful world.
■ **7"** . . . . . . . . . . . . . . . . . .POP 754
H.M.V. / Jul '60.
■ **12"** . . . . . . . . . . . . . . . . . PT 49872
■ **7"** . . . . . . . . . . . . . . . . . PB 49871
RCA / Mar '86.

## WONDERFUL WORLD (1) (Best of Sam Cooke).
**Tracks:** You send me / Only sixteen / Everybody loves to cha cha / For sentimental reasons / Wonderful world / Summertime / Chain gang / Cupid / Twistin' the night away / Sad mood / Having a party / Bring it on home to me.
CD . . . . . . . . . . . . . . . . . . ND 89903
RCA / Apr '88 / BMG.

## WONDERFUL WORLD (1).
**Tracks:** Not Advised.
CD . . . . . . . . . . . . . . . . . . CD 180001
Card/Grand Prix / Apr '87.

## WONDERFUL WORLD (2).
**Tracks:** There, I've said it again / Let's go steady again / When I fall in love / Little things you do / You send me / Ol' man river / Moonlight in Vermont / Around the world / Danny boy / Ain't misbehavin' / Summertime / Wonderful world / Everybody loves to cha cha / Along the Navajo trail / Someday you'll want me to want you / I cover the waterfront / Mary, Mary Lou / Love you most of all / Only sixteen / Win your love for me.
| | |
|---|---|
| CD | CDFA 3195 |
| MC | TCFA 3195 |
| ■ LP | FA 3195 |
Fame / May '88 / EMI.
| | |
|---|---|
| ■ LP | PFP 1008 |
| MC | PFC 1008 |
Performance / May '89.

## WORLD OF SAM COOKE, THE.
**Tracks:** Only sixteen / Everybody loves to cha cha / There, I've said it again / Steal away / Lover come back to me / You send me / Win your love for me / I love you most of all / Good morning heartache / Talk of the town / Little things you do / Stealing kisses.
| | |
|---|---|
| CD | CDINS 5001 |
| ■ LP | INS 5001 |
| MC | TCINS 5001 |
Instant (2) / Jul '89 / Charly.

## YOU SEND ME.
**Tracks:** You send me / Stealing kisses / There, I've said it again / Ol' man river / All of my life / Steal away / Little things you do / Everybody loves to cha cha / Only sixteen / Win your love for me / I love you most of all / God bless the child / When I fall in love / Good morning heartache / Almost in your arms / Bells of St. Mary's / Danny boy / I cover the waterfront / Solitude / That lucky old sun / Ain't misbehavin'.
| | |
|---|---|
| ■ LP | TOP 125 |
| MC | KTOP 125 |
Topline / '86 / Charly.

## YOU SEND ME.
**Tracks:** You send me.
| | |
|---|---|
| ■ 7" | HLU 8506 |
London-American / Jan '58.
| | |
|---|---|
| ■ 7" | G45 44 |
EMI Golden 45's / Feb '85.
| | |
|---|---|
| ■ CD Single | TOP CD 507 |
Topline / Apr '87.
| | |
|---|---|
| ■ 12" | PER 12 8605 |
Perfect / May '87.

## YOU SEND ME.
**Tracks:** Not Advised.
| | |
|---|---|
| CD | CDCD 1093 |
| MC | CDMC 1093 |
Charly / Apr '93 / Charly.

## YOU SEND ME.
**Tracks:** Not Advised.
| | |
|---|---|
| CD | OR 0017 |
Music Collection International / Aug '87 / THE / Jazz Music.

## YOU SEND ME (2).
**Tracks:** Not Advised.
| | |
|---|---|
| ■ LP | RMB 5615 |
Crusader / Feb '89.

## Cookies

## CHAINS.
**Tracks:** Chains.
| | |
|---|---|
| ■ 7" | HLU 9634 |
London-American / Jan '63.

## COMPLETE COOKIES.
**Tracks:** Chains / Don't say nothin' bad about my baby / Girls grow up faster than boys / Will power / Old crowd / Stranger in my arms / Softly in the night / Foolish little girl / I want a boy for my birthday / On Broadway / Only to other people / I never dreamed / I'm into something good / We love & learn / Randy / They're jealous of me.
| | |
|---|---|
| CD | NEMCD 649 |
Sequel / Jun '94 / Total / BMG.

## TO SEE SUCH FUN.
**Tracks:** To see such fun / You're the one.
| | |
|---|---|
| ■ 7" | 7N 45065 |
Pye / May '71.

## Cool Notes

## BILLY THE KID.
**Tracks:** Billy the kid / Kidnap my baby.
| | |
|---|---|
| ■ 12" | JADC 008 |
Jama / '80.

## DOWN TO EARTH.
**Tracks:** Not Advised.
| | |
|---|---|
| ■ LP | MMM 1001 |
Mass Media / '82.

## HAVE A GOOD FOREVER.
**Tracks:** Look what you've done to me / My love is hot / Why not / Come on back to me / Have a good forever / Spend the night / You're never too young / I don't wanna stop / All I wanna do / I love you / In your car.
| | |
|---|---|
| MC | ADCAS 1 |
| ■ LP | ADLP 1 |
Abstract Dance / '85.

## HAVE A GOOD FOREVER.
**Tracks:** Have a good forever / Natural energy.
| | |
|---|---|
| ■ 12" | ADT 5 |
| ■ 7" | AD 5 |
Abstract Dance / '85.

## I FORGOT.
**Tracks:** I forgot / I just want it.
| | |
|---|---|
| ■ 12" | 12 AD 002 |
| ■ 7" | AD 002 |
Abstract Dance / '84.

## I FORGOT HOW TO LOVE YOU.
**Tracks:** I forgot / Why can't we be friend.
| | |
|---|---|
| ■ 12" | MMM 12 1008 |
| ■ 7" | MMM 7 1008 |
Mass Media / '82.

## I WANNA DANCE.
**Tracks:** I wanna dance / Blown it / In your car.
| | |
|---|---|
| ■ 12" | SGR 116 |
| ■ 7" | SG 116 |
Sour Grape / '84.

## IN YOUR CAR.
**Tracks:** In your car / Secrets of the night.
| | |
|---|---|
| ■ 12" Remix | ADTR 4 |
| ■ 7" | AD 4 |
| ■ 12" | ADT 4 |
Abstract Dance / '85.

## INTO THE MOTION.
**Tracks:** Into the motion / Come on back / Look what you've done to me (Remix) (Available on 12" only).
| | |
|---|---|
| ■ 12" | ADT 8 |
| ■ 7" | AD 8 |
Abstract Dance / May '86.

## JUST GIRLS.
**Tracks:** Just girls / Sweet vibes.
| | |
|---|---|
| ■ 12" | JADC 017 |
| ■ 7" | JA 017 |
Jama / Nov '81.

## LIKE A FOOL.
**Tracks:** Like a fool / Like a fool (version).
| | |
|---|---|
| ■ 7" | VOY 004 |
Voyage International / Sep '79.

## MAGIC LOVER.
**Tracks:** Magic lover.
| | |
|---|---|
| ■ 12" | RHA T102 |
| ■ 7" | RHA 102 |
HHO (Henry Hadaway Organisation) / Oct '88.

## MAKE THIS A SPECIAL NIGHT.
**Tracks:** Make this a special night.
| | |
|---|---|
| ■ 12" | PWLT 200 |
| ■ 7" | PWL 200 |
| ■ CD Single | PWLCD 200 |
| ■ MC Single | PWLMC 200 |
PWL / Oct '91.

## MOMENTARY VISION.
**Tracks:** Momentary vision / Girls night out / Your love is taking over (Extra track available on 12" version only).
| | |
|---|---|
| ■ 12" | ADT 10 |
| ■ 7" | AD 10 |
Abstract Dance / Oct '86.

## MORNING CHILD.
**Tracks:** Morning child.
| | |
|---|---|
| ■ 12" | MMM 12 1011 |
Mass Media / '82.

## MY TUNE.
**Tracks:** My tune.
| | |
|---|---|
| ■ 12" | JABC 0024 |
Jama / '84.

## MY TUNE.
**Tracks:** My tune / Cause we don't.
| | |
|---|---|
| ■ 7" | SC 3 |
Scope / '79.

## SPEND THE NIGHT.
**Tracks:** Spend the night / Halu (spring) / I forgot (on 12" only).
| | |
|---|---|
| ■ 12" | ADT 3 |
| ■ 12" Remix | ADTR 3 |
| ■ 7" | AD 3 |
Abstract Dance / '85.

## SPEND THE NIGHT.
**Tracks:** Not Advised.
| | |
|---|---|
| CD | ST 5003 |
Star Collection / Nov '93 / BMG.

## SPEND THE NIGHT (1990 REMIX).
**Tracks:** Spend the night (remix).
| | |
|---|---|
| ■ 12" | SYDT 5 |
| ■ CD Single | CDSYD 5 |
| ■ 7" | SYD 5 |
Swanyard / Sep '90.

## SPEND THE NIGHT (OLD GOLD).
**Tracks:** Spend the night / In your car.
| | |
|---|---|
| 12" | OG 4182 |
Old Gold / Jul '90 / Pickwick.

## SUGAR SUGAR.
**Tracks:** Sugar sugar.
| | |
|---|---|
| ■ 7" | GEMS 32 |
Gem (2) / May '80.

## TELL ME.
**Tracks:** Tell me.
| | |
|---|---|
| ■ 12" | SDT 15 |
White / Oct '89.

## YOU'RE NEVER TOO YOUNG.
**Tracks:** You're never to young / Sound of summer.
| | |
|---|---|
| ■ 12" | 12 AD 001 |
| ■ 7" | AD 001 |
Abstract Dance / Aug '84.

## YOU'RE NEVER TOO YOUNG.
**Tracks:** You're never too young.
| | |
|---|---|
| ■ 12" | MTR 12007 |
MTR / Jul '90.

## YOU'RE NEVER TOO YOUNG (1990).
**Tracks:** You're never too young (1990).
| | |
|---|---|
| ■ 12" | MTR 12009 |
| ■ 7" | MTR 7009 |
MTR / May '90.

## Cool Runners

## I SHOULD HAVE LOVED YOU.
**Tracks:** I should have loved you / Satellite music.
| | |
|---|---|
| ■ 12" | MKHAN 65 |
| ■ 7" | KHAN 65 |
Streetwave / Mar '86.

## PLAY THE GAME.
**Tracks:** Play the game / Hawaiian dream.
| | |
|---|---|
| ■ 7" | MCA 760 |
| ■ 12" | MCAT 760 |
MCA / Feb '82.

## Cooper, Craig T.

## COOPER PROJECT.
**Tracks:** Not Advised.
| | |
|---|---|
| LP | D 172947 |
Valley Vue / Jul '89 / Jetstar.

## GET THAT THANG.
**Tracks:** Not Advised.
| | |
|---|---|
| LP | D 172992 |
Valley Vue / May '90 / Jetstar.

## Cooper, Michael

## JUST WHAT I LIKE.
**Tracks:** Just what I like / Turn the lights out / Girl's got it goin' on / Best / Should have been you / Do you love me baby / My baby's house / Over and over / Wild side.
| | |
|---|---|
| ■ LP | K 9259231 |
| ■ CD | K 9259232 |
| ■ MC | K 9259234 |
WEA / Aug '89.

## LOVE IS SUCH A FUNNY GAME.
**Tracks:** To prove my love / You've got a friend / Dinner for two / Just thinkin' 'bout cha / No other lover / Oceans wide / Love is such a funny game / Quickness / Look before you leave.
| | |
|---|---|
| ■ LP | 925653 1 |

■ DELETED

■ MC. . . . . . . . . . . . . . . . . . . . .925653 4
WEA / Dec '87.

## TO PROVE MY LOVE.
Tracks: To prove my love / To prove my love (version).
■ 12". . . . . . . . . . . . . . . . . . . . . W 200T
■ 7". . . . . . . . . . . . . . . . . . . . . W 200
WEA / Feb '88.
■ 12". . . . . . . . . . . . . . . . . . . .W 8200T
■ 7". . . . . . . . . . . . . . . . . . . . . W 8200
WEA / Sep '88.

## Copeland, Johnny

### AIN'T NOTHIN' BUT A PARTY (Live in Houston, Texas).
Tracks: Not Advised.
CD. . . . . . . . . . . . . . . . . . . . . .CD 2055
■ LP . . . . . . . . . . . . . . . . ROUNDER 2055
MC. . . . . . . . . . . . . . . . . .ROUNDER 2055C
Rounder / '88 / Roots Records / C.M. Distribution / Topic Records / A.D.A. Distribution / Direct Distribution.

### BRINGIN' IT ALL BACK HOME.
Tracks: Kasavubu / Jungle / Ngote / Djeli, djeli blues / Abidjan / Bozalimalamu / Same thing / Conakry.
■ LP . . . . . . . . . . . . . . . . . . . . FIEND 47
Demon / Feb '86.
■ LP . . . . . . . . . . . . . . . . ROUNDER 2050
MC. . . . . . . . . . . . . . . . . .ROUNDER 2050C
Rounder / '88 / Roots Records / C.M. Distribution / Topic Records / A.D.A. Distribution / Direct Distribution.

### COPELAND COLLECTION, VOL 1.
Tracks: Not Advised.
■ LP . . . . . . . . . . . . . . . . . . . . .HCS 107
MC. . . . . . . . . . . . . . . . . . . . .HCS 107 TC
Home Cooking (USA) / Jul '88 / Swift.

### COPELAND SPECIAL.
Tracks: Claim jumper / I wish I was single / Everybody wants a piece of me / Copeland special / It's my own tears that's being wasted / Third party / Big me / Down on bended knee / Done got over it / St. Louis blues.
■ LP . . . . . . . . . . . . . . . . . . . . FIEND 3
Demon / May '82.
■ LP . . . . . . . . . . . . . . . . ROUNDER 2025
MC. . . . . . . . . . . . . . . . . .ROUNDER 2025C
Rounder / '88 / Roots Records / C.M. Distribution / Topic Records / A.D.A. Distribution / Direct Distribution.

### DEDICATED TO THE GREATEST.
Tracks: It's me / Love attack / I waited too long / Stealing / Mother Nature / Invitation / Wizard of oz / Old man blues / Dear mother / Johnny Ace medley / No puppy love / Oh how I miss you.
■ LP . . . . . . . . . . . . . . . . . . . . KENT 067
Kent / Apr '87.

### DOWN ON BENDED KNEES.
Tracks: Down on bended knees / There's a blessing / May the best man win / I got to go home / Coming to see about you / It's my own tears that's being wasted / I wish I was single / It's me / I'm going to make my home where.... / If love is your friend / You're gonna reap what you sow / Suffering city / Hurt hurt hurt / Old man blues / Love prayer.
■ LP . . . . . . . . . . . . . . . . . . . . RB 1002
Mr.R&B (Sweden) / Feb '85.

### FURTHER ON UP THE ROAD.
Tracks: Not Advised.
CD. . . . . . . . . . . . . . . . . . . AIM 1032CD
MC. . . . . . . . . . . . . . . . . . . . AIM 1032C
Aim (2) / Oct '93 / Topic Records / Direct Distribution / A.D.A. Distribution.

### HOUSTON ROOTS.
Tracks: Rock me baby take 1 / Late hours / I wish I was single / Hear what I said / Please let me know / Baby please don't go / I don't want nobody / Night time is the right time (part 1) / Night time is the right time (part 2) / I need you now / Heebie jeebies / All these things / Rock me baby take 2.
■ CD . . . . . . . . . . . . . . . . . . . . .CHD 238
? / Mar '88.

### I'LL BE AROUND.
Tracks: Rock and roll Lilly / Year round blues / It don't bother you / Mama told me / Heebie jeebies / Just one more time / Working man's blues / Funny feeling / I'll be around / Ain't nobody's business / What's alright mama / Trying to reach my goal / Hear what I said / Ghetto child / Do better somewhere else / You must believe in yourself.
■ LP . . . . . . . . . . . . . . . . . . . . RB 1001
Mr.R&B (Sweden) / Oct '84.

## MAKE MY HOME WHERE I HANG MY HAT.
Tracks: Natural born believer / Make my home where I hang my hat / Devil's hand / Cold outside / Love Utopia / Boogie woogie nighthawk / Honky tonkin' / Well well baby-la / Old man blues / Rock 'n' roll Lilly.
■ LP . . . . . . . . . . . . . . . . . . . . FIEND 4
Demon / Nov '82.
■ LP . . . . . . . . . . . . . . . . . . ROUNDER 2030
Rounder / Jan '87.
MC. . . . . . . . . . . . . . . . . . .ROUNDER 2030C
Rounder / '88 / Roots Records / C.M. Distribution / Topic Records / A.D.A. Distribution / Direct Distribution.

## TEXAS TWISTER.
Tracks: Midnight fantasy / North Caroline / Don't stop by the creek son / Excuses / Jessanne / Houston / When the rain starts fallin' / I de go now / Early in the morning / Twister / Idiom / Easy to love / Media / Morning coffee / Jelly roll / Where or when.
■ LP . . . . . . . . . . . . . . . . . . . . FIEND 15
Demon / '84.
CD. . . . . . . . . . . . . . . . . . . . . CD 11504
■ LP . . . . . . . . . . . . . . . . ROUNDER 2040
MC. . . . . . . . . . . . . . . . . .ROUNDER 2040C
Rounder / '88 / Roots Records / C.M. Distribution / Topic Records / A.D.A. Distribution / Direct Distribution.

## THREE SIDES OF JOHNNY COPELAND, THE.
Tracks: Remus trach him down / Shuffle in C / Cut off my right arm / You've got me singing a love song / Texas party / Down on bending knees / Johnny gone / Nobody but you / Daily bread / My woman has a black cat bone / Railroad Bill / Learned my lesson.
VHS . . . . . . . . . . . . . . . . . . . MMGV 018
MMG Video / Jan '91 / THE.

## WHEN THE RAIN STARTS FALLIN'.
Tracks: Not Advised.
CD. . . . . . . . . . . . . . . . . . . . . CD 11515
Rounder / '88 / Roots Records / C.M. Distribution / Topic Records / A.D.A. Distribution / Direct Distribution.

## Cordell, Phil

### DOIN' THE BEST I CAN.
Tracks: Doin' the best I can / Cheatin' in the dark.
■ 7". . . . . . . . . . . . . . . . . . . . . PROD 6
Prodigal / Oct '77.

### HEARTS ON FIRE.
Tracks: Hearts on fire / Ginny was a rock rock 'n' roller.
■ 7". . . . . . . . . . . . . . . . . . . . .VS 246
Virgin / '79.

## Coryell, Larry

### ASPECTS.
Tracks: Kowloon jag / Titus / Pyramids / Rodrigo reflections / Yin-yang / Woman of truth and future.
■ LP . . . . . . . . . . . . . . . . . . . . ARTY 133
Arista / Jul '76.

### AT VILLAGE GATE.
Tracks: Not Advised.
■ LP . . . . . . . . . . . . . . . . . . . . VSD 6573
Vanguard (1) / '77.

### BACK TOGETHER (Coryell, Larry & Alphonse Mouzon).
Tracks: Beneath the earth / Express / Back together again / Phonse / Transvested express / Crystallization / Rock 'n' roll lovers / Get on up / Reconciliation / Mr. C / High love.
■ LP . . . . . . . . . . . . . . . . . . . . K 50382
WEA / Aug '77.

### BOLERO (Coryell, Larry & Brian Keane).
Tracks: Improvisation on "Bolero" / Nothing is forever / Something for Wolfgang Amadeus / Tombeau de couperin (Prelude from) / Elegancia del sol / Fancy frogs / 6 Watch hill road / Blues in Madrid / Motel time / At the airport / Brazilia / Piece for Larry / La pluie / Patty's song.
CD. . . . . . . . . . . . . . . . . . . . . ECD 22046
Evidence / Mar '93 / Harmonia Mundi (UK).

### BOLERO AND SCHEHERAZADE.
Tracks: Not Advised.
CD. . . . . . . . . . . . . . . . . . . . . 810 024-2
Philips / May '93 / PolyGram.

### COMING HOME.
Tracks: Good citizen swallow / Glorielle / Twelve and twelve / Confirmation / It never entered my mind.

CD. . . . . . . . . . . . . . . . . . . . . MCD 5303
■ LP . . . . . . . . . . . . . . . . . . . . .MR 5303
Muse / Jan '86 / New Note / Jazz Horizons / C.M. Distribution.

### DRAGON GATE.
Tracks: Not Advised.
LP . . . . . . . . . . . . . . . . . . . SHAN 97005
Shanachie / Jun '90 / A.D.A. Distribution / Jazz Music / C.M. Distribution / Koch International.

### EQUIPOISE.
Tracks: Unemployed Floyd / Tender tears / Equipoise / Christina / Joy Spring / First things first.
CD. . . . . . . . . . . . . . . . . . . . . .MCD 5319
■ LP . . . . . . . . . . . . . . . . . . . . .MR 5319
Muse / Feb '87 / New Note / Jazz Horizons / C.M. Distribution.

### FALLEN ANGEL.
Tracks: Inner city blues / Pieta / Fallen / Thus spoke z / Never never / Stella by starlight / Angel in sunset / Monk's corner / Stardust / Westerly winds / Misty / Moors / I remember bill.
■ CD . . . . . . . . . . . . . . . . . . . CTI 10142
CTI (1) / Nov '93.
CD. . . . . . . . . . . . . . . . . . . . . ESJCD 237
Essential Jazz / Oct '94 / BMG.

### FUSE ONE (see under Clarke, Stanley).

### INTRODUCING 11TH HOUSE.
Tracks: Not Advised.
■ LP . . . . . . . . . . . . . . . . . . . VSD 79342
Vanguard (1) / Jun '74.

### JUST LIKE BEING BORN (Coryell, Larry & Brian Keane).
Tracks: Not Advised.
■ LP . . . . . . . . . . . . . . . . . . . . FF 337
Flying Fish / Mar '89.

### L'OISEAU DE FEU (THE FIREBIRD)/PETROUCHKA.
Tracks: Not Advised.
CD. . . . . . . . . . . . . . . . . . . . . .8128 642
■ LP . . . . . . . . . . . . . . . . . . . . .8128 641
Philips / '84 / PolyGram.

### LE SACRE DU PRINTEMPS.
Tracks: Not Advised.
CD. . . . . . . . . . . . . . . . . . . . . 814 750 2
Philips / PolyGram.

### LEVEL ONE.
Tracks: Other side / Level one / Diedra / Some greasy stuff / Nyctaphobia / Suite.
■ LP . . . . . . . . . . . . . . . . . . . . ARTY 113
Arista / '76.

### LIVE FROM BAHIA.
Tracks: Harbour / Old city, new city / Crab peddler / Oshum, goddess of love / Bloco loco / Panama / Bahian night walk / Gabriela's song / Vera cruz.
CD. . . . . . . . . . . . . . . . . . . . . CTI 10052
CTI (1) / Sep '92 / New Note.

### PLANET END.
Tracks: Not Advised.
■ LP . . . . . . . . . . . . . . . . . . . VSD 79367
Vanguard (1) / '77.

### QUIET DAY IN SPRING, A (Coryell, Larry & Urbaniak, Michal).
Tracks: Not Advised.
CD. . . . . . . . . . . . . . . . . . . SCCD 311 87
Steeplechase (USA) / '88 / Cadillac.

### RESTFUL MIND, THE.
Tracks: Improvisation on Robert De Visee's Minuet II / Ann Arbor / Pavane for a dead princess / Improvisation on Robert De Visee's Sarabande / Song for Jim Webb / Julie La Belle / Restful mind.
■ LP . . . . . . . . . . . . . . . . . . . VSD 79353
Vanguard (1) / '75.

### RETURN.
Tracks: Cisco at the disco / Rue Gregoire du Tour / Three mile island / Return / Sweet shuffle / Mediterranean sundance / Entre dos Aguas.
■ LP . . . . . . . . . . . . . . . . . . . VSD 79426
Vanguard (1) / Jan '80.

### SHINING HOUR.
Tracks: Not Advised.
LP . . . . . . . . . . . . . . . . . . VG 651600632
Muse / Apr '91 / New Note / Jazz Horizons / C.M. Distribution.
CD. . . . . . . . . . . . . . . . . . . . . MCD 5360
LP . . . . . . . . . . . . . . . . . . . . . MR 5360
Muse / Sep '92 / New Note / Jazz Horizons / C.M. Distribution.

■ DELETED

## SPACES.
**Tracks:** Spaces / Rene's theme / Gloria's step / Wrong is right / Chris / New year's day in Los Angeles-1968.
■ LP . . . . . . . . . . . . . . . . . . . . . . . .6359 005
Vanguard (1) / Mar '71.
■ LP . . . . . . . . . . . . . . . . . . . . VSD 79345
Vanguard (1) / '74.
CD . . . . . . . . . . . . . . . . . . . . . VMCD 7305
■ LP . . . . . . . . . . . . . . . . . . . . VMLP 5305
MC . . . . . . . . . . . . . . . . . . . . . VMTC 6305
Start / Aug '89 / THE / Koch International.

## STANDING OVATION.
**Tracks:** Not Advised.
■ LP . . . . . . . . . . . . . . . . . . . . . . AN 3024
Arista / May '81.

## TOGETHER (Coryell, Larry & Emily Remler).
**Tracks:** Arabian nights / Joy Spring / Ill wind / How my heart sings / Six beats, six strings / Gerri's blues / First things first.
CD . . . . . . . . . . . . . . . . . . . . . . . CCD 4289
Concord Jazz / Nov '86 / New Note.

## TOKUDO.
**Tracks:** Not Advised.
CD . . . . . . . . . . . . . . . . . . . . . . .MCD 5350
LP . . . . . . . . . . . . . . . . . . . . . . . MR 5350
Muse / Sep '92 / New Note / Jazz Horizons / C.M. Distribution.

## TRIBUTARIES.
**Tracks:** File / Mother's day / Little B's poem / Zimbabwe / Solo on Wednesday / Thurman Munson / Equinox / Alster fields.
■ CD . . . . . . . . . . . . . . . . . . . . . ND 83072
■ LP . . . . . . . . . . . . . . . . . . . . . NL 83072
■ MC . . . . . . . . . . . . . . . . . . . . . NK 83072
RCA / Apr '90.

# Cosmetic

## SO TRANQUILIZIN.
**Tracks:** All things must change / Be my girl / Take it to the top / All my love / N-er-gize me / About the money / So tranquilizin / Jet set.
CD . . . . . . . . . . . . . . . . . . . . . . . 1883102
■ LP . . . . . . . . . . . . . . . . . . . . . . 1883101
MC . . . . . . . . . . . . . . . . . . . . . . . 1883104
Gramavision / '85 / New Note.

## SO TRANQUILIZIN.
**Tracks:** So tranquilizin.
■ 12" . . . . . . . . . . . . . . . . . . . . . .GR 1210
Gramavision / Dec '85.

# Counts

## WHAT'S UP THE FRONT THAT - COUNTS.
**Tracks:** What's up front that - counts / Rhythm changes / Thinking single / Why not start all over again / Pack of lies / Bills / Motor city / What's it all about.
CD . . . . . . . . . . . . . . . . . . . . .CDSEWM 063
LP . . . . . . . . . . . . . . . . . . . . . . SEWD 063
South Bound / Nov '94 / Pinnacle.

# Covay, Don

South Carolina-born Little Richard protege who endured string of failures in early '60s. Eventual success with 1964 single *Mercy Mercy* brought him to attention of Atlantic, for whom he wrote Aretha Franklin classic *Chain Of Fools*; Franklin also took his *See Saw*, co-written with Steve Cropper, into charts. Covay's solo career boasted no such smashes, although he did make no. 29 in UK with 1974's *It's Better To Have (and Don't Need)*.

## 40 DAYS 40 NIGHTS.
**Tracks:** 40 days 40 nights / Usual place.
■ 7" . . . . . . . . . . . . . . . . . . . . . .584114
Atlantic / Jun '67.

## DIFFERENT STROKES FOR DIFFERENT FOLKS.
**Tracks:** Sweet thank / Daddy, please don't go out tonight / Stop by / Bad luck / Hitchin' a ride / Standing in the grits line / In the sweet bye & bye / Ain't noghtin a yourng gril can do / If there's a will there's a way / What's in the headlines.
CD . . . . . . . . . . . . . . . . . . . . . .SR 652329
Sky Ranch (WMD) / Nov '92 / New Note.

## HOUSE OF.. (Covay, Don & Lemon Jefferson Blues Band).
**Tracks:** Not Advised.
■ LP . . . . . . . . . . . . . . . . . . . . . K 550255
Atlantic / Mar '76.

## IT'S BETTER TO HAVE (AND DON'T NEED).
**Tracks:** It's better to have (and don't need).
■ 7" . . . . . . . . . . . . . . . . . . . . . .6052 634
Mercury / Sep '74.

## MERCY (Covay, Don & The Goodtimers).
**Tracks:** See-saw / I never get enough of your love / Iron out the rough spots / Sookie sookie / Woman's love / Watching the late late show / Somebody's got to love you / Temptation was too strong / Mercy, mercy / Boomerang / Can't stay away / Come see about me / Take this hurt off me / You're good for me / Precious you / Daddy loves baby.
■ LP . . . . . . . . . . . . . . . . . . . . . . ED 127
Edsel / May '84.

## MERCY MERCY (Covay, Don & The Goodtimers).
**Tracks:** Not Advised.
■ 7" . . . . . . . . . . . . . . . . . . . . . AT 4006
Atlantic / '64.

## SEESAW.
**Tracks:** Seesaw / Mercy mercy / Last night / Soul finger.
■ EP . . . . . . . . . . . . . . . . . . . . . .ATM 1
Atlantic / Apr '80.

## SEESAW (Covay, Don & The Goodtimers).
**Tracks:** Seesaw / I never get enough of your love.
■ 7" . . . . . . . . . . . . . . . . . . . . . AT 4056
Atlantic / Dec '65.

## SEESAW.
**Tracks:** Seesaw / Mercy, mercy.
■ 7" . . . . . . . . . . . . . . . . . . . . . 2091104
Atlantic / Jul '71.

## SHINGALING '67.
**Tracks:** Shingaling '67 / I was there.
■ 7" . . . . . . . . . . . . . . . . . . . . . .584062
Atlantic / Feb '67.

## SOOKIE SOOKIE.
**Tracks:** Sookie sookie / Watching the late late show.
■ 7" . . . . . . . . . . . . . . . . . . . . . AT 4078
Atlantic / Mar '66.

## SWEET THANG.
**Tracks:** Sweet thang / Daddy please don't go tonight / Why did you put your shoes under my bed / Stop by / Bad luck / Hitchin' a ride / Standing in the grits line / In the sweet bye and bye / Ain't nothing a young girl can do / If there's a will there's a way / What's in the headlines.
■ LP . . . . . . . . . . . . . . . . . . . . . .TOP 137
MC . . . . . . . . . . . . . . . . . . . . . KTOP 137
Topline / May '87 / Charly.

# Covington, Matt

## WE GOT ONE.
**Tracks:** Not Advised.
■ 12" . . . . . . . . . . . . . . . . . . . .EXPAND 29
Expansion / Jun '92.

# Cox, Margie

## STANDING AT THE ALTAR.
**Tracks:** Standing at the altar.
7" . . . . . . . . . . . . . . . . . . . . . NPG 60667
CD Single . . . . . . . . . . . . . . . . . . NPG 60665
MC Single . . . . . . . . . . . . . . . . . . NPG 60669
New Power Generation / Aug '94 / Grapevine Distribution / THE.

# Crawford, Carolyn

## COMING ON STRONG.
**Tracks:** Coming on strong / Nice feeling.
■ 7" . . . . . . . . . . . . . . . . . . . . . 6167753
Mercury / Feb '79.

## HEARTACHE.
**Tracks:** Not Advised.
■ LP . . . . . . . . . . . . . . . . . . . . .MOTCLP 42
■ CD . . . . . . . . . . . . . . . . . . . CDMOTCLP 42
Motor City / Dec '90.

## WHEN SOMEONE'S GOOD TO YOU.
**Tracks:** When someone's good to you.
■ 7" . . . . . . . . . . . . . . . . . . . . . .SS 384
Stateside / Feb '65.

# Crawford, Hank

## CAJUN SUNRISE.
**Tracks:** What a difference you've made in my life / don't want no happy songs / New York's one soulfu city / Take this job & shove it / Just the way you are Daytime friends / Evergreen / Cajun sunrise.
■ LP . . . . . . . . . . . . . . . . . . . . . .KU 39
Polydor / '79.

## HANK CRAWFORD'S BACK.
**Tracks:** Funky pigeon / I can't stop loving you / You'l never find another love like mine / Canadian sunset Midnight over Memphis.
■ LP . . . . . . . . . . . . . . . . . . . . . .KU 33
Kudu / Apr '77.

## ROADHOUSE SYMPHONY (Crawford Hank & Dr. John).
**Tracks:** Roadhouse symphony / Track magick / Jubi lee / Say it isn't so / Time is on our side / Precious Lord / Sugar ditch.
■ LP . . . . . . . . . . . . . . . . . . . . . M 914
Milestone / Feb '86.

## SOUL BROTHERS (Crawford, Hank & Jimmy McGriff).
**Tracks:** Not Advised.
■ LP . . . . . . . . . . . . . . . . . . . . .MX 917
Milestone / May '89.

## SOUL SURVIVORS (see under McGriff Jimmy).

## SOUTH CENTRAL.
**Tracks:** Falling in love with love / I should care South Central / I want to talk about you / In a mellow tone / Conjunction Mars / Fool that I am / Splanky / C holy night.
CD . . . . . . . . . . . . . . . . . . . . . .MCD 920
Milestone / Oct '93 / Jazz Music / Pinnacle / Cadillac

## TICO RICO.
**Tracks:** Tico Rico / Teach me tonight / Lady Soul Lullaby of love / I've just seen a face / Lament Funky rooster.
■ LP . . . . . . . . . . . . . . . . . . . . . .KU 3
Kudu / Sep '77.

## WILDFLOWER.
**Tracks:** Not Advised.
■ CD . . . . . . . . . . . . . . . . . . . . . 450566
CBS / '88.

# Crawford, Randy

Georgia-born singer who followed well trodden path from gospel to pop in search of success. Mid-'70s albums were largely overlooked but she cracked charts in '79 a voice of Crusaders' transatlantic hit *Stree Life*. Her solo career blossomed in U.K rather than home-land; appropriately-title *Now We May Begin* hit U.K. Top 10 in 198 and yielded biggest success, *One Day I'. Fly Away*. Smaller but equally fine hits *You Might Need Somebody* and *Rainy Night I. Georgia* kept parent album *Secret Com bination* on charts for 60 weeks. Subsequen successes were inevitably on smaller scale although she returned to Top 5 in '86 with *Almaz*. Crawford is now regarded as MO rather than soul, although interpretation o *Knockin' On Heaven's Door* from *Letha Weapon 2* soundtrack confirmed her endu ing talent.

## ABSTRACT EMOTIONS.
**Tracks:** Can't stand the pain / Actual emotional love World of fools / Betcha / Higher than anyone ca count / Desire / Getting away with murder / Over night / Almaz / Don't wanna be normal.
CD . . . . . . . . . . . . . . . . . . . . . .925423
MC . . . . . . . . . . . . . . . . . . . . . WX 46
■ LP . . . . . . . . . . . . . . . . . . . . . WX 4
WEA / Jul '86 / WEA.

## ALMAZ.
**Tracks:** Almaz / Desire.
■ 12" . . . . . . . . . . . . . . . . . . . . . W 8583
■ 7" . . . . . . . . . . . . . . . . . . . . . . W 858
WEA / Oct '86.

## DON'T SAY IT'S OVER.
**Tracks:** I'm glad there is you / Love's mystery / Ca we bring it back / Keep me loving you / In my life Elusive boogie / Mad over you / Why can't we take chance / Year after year / Don't say it's over.
CD . . . . . . . . . . . . . . . . . . . . . .936245381-
MC . . . . . . . . . . . . . . . . . . . . . .936245381-
Warner Bros. / Nov '93 / WEA.

■ DELETE

## ENDLESSLY.
Tracks: Endlessly / Endlessly (version).
■ 7″ . . . . . . . . . . . . . . . . . . . . . . K 17457
WEA / Sep '79.

## EVERYTHING MUST CHANGE.
Tracks: Everything must change / I let you walk away / I'm easy / I had to see you one more time / I've never been to me / Don't let me down / Something so right / Soon as I touched him / Only your love song lasts / Gonna give lovin a try.
■ LP . . . . . . . . . . . . . . . . . . . . . . K 56328
■ MC. . . . . . . . . . . . . . . . . . . . K4 56328
WEA / Nov '80.

## GETTING AWAY WITH MURDER.
Tracks: Getting away with murder / Overnight / Don't wanna be normal (Extra track available on 12″ version only).
■ 12″. . . . . . . . . . . . . . . . . . . . W 8641T
■ 7″ . . . . . . . . . . . . . . . . . . . . . W 8641
WEA / Jul '86.

## GREATEST HITS: RANDY CRAWFORD.
Tracks: Streetlife / Secret combination / One hello / Rainy night in Georgia / You bring the Sun out / Imagine / Tender falls the rain / Windsong / One day I'll fly away / He reminds me / You might need somebody / Endlessly / Take it away from her (put it on me) / Happy feet / Nightline / Last night at danceland.
■ LP . . . . . . . . . . . . . . . . . . . . . NE 1281
■ MC. . . . . . . . . . . . . . . . . . . . . CE 2281
K-Tel / Sep '84.

## HE REMINDS ME.
Tracks: He reminds me / Declaration of love / One day I'll fly away (Available on 12″ only.)
■ 12″. . . . . . . . . . . . . . . . . . . . K 17970 T
■ 7″ . . . . . . . . . . . . . . . . . . . . . K 17970
WEA / Jan '83.

## HIGHER THAN ANYONE CAN COUNT.
Tracks: Higher than anyone can count / Tender falls the rain.
■ 12″. . . . . . . . . . . . . . . . . . . . . W 8423T
■ 7″ . . . . . . . . . . . . . . . . . . . . . W 8423
WEA / Mar '87.

## IMAGINE.
Tracks: Imagine / Tender falls the rain.
■ 7″ . . . . . . . . . . . . . . . . . . . . . K 17906
WEA / Jan '82.

## KNOCKIN' ON HEAVEN'S DOOR.
Tracks: Knockin' on heaven's door.
■ 12″. . . . . . . . . . . . . . . . . . . . W 2865 T
■ 7″ . . . . . . . . . . . . . . . . . . . . . W 2865
■ CD Single. . . . . . . . . . . . . . . W 2865 CD
WEA / Sep '89.

## LAST NIGHT AT DANCELAND.
Tracks: Last night at Danceland.
■ 7″ . . . . . . . . . . . . . . . . . . . . . K 17631
WEA / Jun '80.

## LOVE SONGS: RANDY CRAWFORD.
Tracks: One day I'll fly away / You might need somebody / Rainy night in Georgia / Trade winds / He reminds me / Nightline / Windsong / Secret combination / Almaz / Imagine / In real life / Everything must change / I don't want to lose him / Someone to believe in / One Hello.
■ CD . . . . . . . . . . . . . . . . . . . . TCD 2299
■ LP . . . . . . . . . . . . . . . . . . . . STAR 2299
■ MC. . . . . . . . . . . . . . . . . . . . STAC 2299
Telstar/Ronco / Sep '87.

## LOVE THEME-THE COMPETITION.
Tracks: Love theme - the competition.
■ 7″ . . . . . . . . . . . . . . . . . . . . . MCA 676
MCA / Mar '81.

## MISS RANDY CRAWFORD.
Tracks: Hallelujah glory hallelujah / I can't get you off my mind / I'm under the influence of you / Over my head / Desperado / Take it away from her (put it on me) / Single woman, married man / Half steppin' / This man / At last.
■ LP . . . . . . . . . . . . . . . . . . . . K 56882
■ MC. . . . . . . . . . . . . . . . . . . . K4 56882
WEA / WEA.

## NIGHTLINE.
Tracks: Happy feet / This old heart of mine / Lift me up / Ain't no foolin' / Go on and live it up / Nightline / Living on the outside / Why / Bottom line / In real life.
■ MC. . . . . . . . . . . . . . . . . . . . .923976 4
■ LP . . . . . . . . . . . . . . . . . . . . .923976 1
WEA / Nov '83.
CD. . . . . . . . . . . . . . . . . . . . . .923976 2
WEA / May '87 / WEA.

## NIGHTLINE.
Tracks: Nightline / Night won't last forever / Last night at danceland.
■ 12″. . . . . . . . . . . . . . . . . . . . . W 9530 T
■ 7″ . . . . . . . . . . . . . . . . . . . . . W 9530
WEA / Oct '83.

## NOW WE MAY BEGIN.
Tracks: Now we may begin / Blue flame / When your life was low / My heart is not as young as it used to be / Last night at danceland / Tender falls the rain / One day I'll fly away / Same old story, same old song.
MC. . . . . . . . . . . . . . . . . . . . . K4 56791
■ LP . . . . . . . . . . . . . . . . . . . . K 56791
WEA / May '80 / WEA.

## ONE DAY I'LL FLY AWAY.
Tracks: One day I'll fly away / Blue flame.
■ 12″. . . . . . . . . . . . . . . . . . . . .K 17680 T
■ 7″ . . . . . . . . . . . . . . . . . . . . . K 17680
WEA / Aug '80.

## ONE DAY I'LL FLY AWAY (OLD GOLD).
Tracks: One day I'll fly away / You might need somebody.
■ 7″ . . . . . . . . . . . . . . . . . . . . .OG 9571
Old Gold / Mar '86.

## ONE HELLO.
Tracks: One hello / That's how heartaches are made.
■ 7″ . . . . . . . . . . . . . . . . . . . . . K 17948
WEA / Jun '82.

## RAINY NIGHT IN GEORGIA.
Tracks: Rainy night in Georgia.
■ 7″ . . . . . . . . . . . . . . . . . . . . . K 17840
WEA / Aug '81.

## RAW SILK.
Tracks: I stand accused / Declaration of love / Someone to believe in / Endlessly / Love is like a newborn child / Where there was darkness / Nobody / I hope you'll be very unhappy without me / I got myself a happy song / Just to keep you satisfied / Blue mood.
■ LP . . . . . . . . . . . . . . . . . . . . K 56592
■ MC. . . . . . . . . . . . . . . . . . . . K4 56592
■ MC. . . . . . . . . . . . . . . . . . . . K4 66114
WEA / Oct '82.

## RICH AND THE POOR, THE.
Tracks: Knockin' on heaven's door / Every kinda people / Wrap-u-up / This is the love / Seperate lives / I believe that love can change the world / Rich and poor / Cigarette in the rain / Love is / I don't feel much like crying / All it takes is love.
■ CD . . . . . . . . . . . . . . . . . . . .K 9260022
■ LP . . . . . . . . . . . . . . . . . . . . WX 308
■ MC. . . . . . . . . . . . . . . . . . . . WX 308 C
WEA / Sep '89.

## SECRET COMBINATION.
Tracks: You might need somebody / Rainy night in Georgia / That's how heartaches are made / Two lives / You bring the Sun out / Rio De Janeiro blue / Secret combination / When I lose my way / Time for love / Trade winds.
■ LP . . . . . . . . . . . . . . . . . . . . K 56904
MC. . . . . . . . . . . . . . . . . . . . . K4 56904
WEA / May '81 / WEA.
CD. . . . . . . . . . . . . . . . . . . . . K2 56904
WEA / Mar '87 / WEA.

## SECRET COMBINATION.
Tracks: Secret combination / Streetlife.
■ 7″ . . . . . . . . . . . . . . . . . . . . . K 17872
WEA / Oct '81.

## TENDER FALLS THE RAIN.
Tracks: Tender falls the rain / I stand accused.
■ 7″ . . . . . . . . . . . . . . . . . . . . . LV 42
WEA / Nov '80.

## VERY BEST OF RANDY CRAWFORD.
Tracks: Not Advised.
CD. . . . . . . . . . . . . . . . . . . . . DINCD 58
MC. . . . . . . . . . . . . . . . . . . . . DINMC 58
Dino / Feb '93 / Pinnacle.

## WHY.
Tracks: Why / Lift / Everything must change.
■ 12″. . . . . . . . . . . . . . . . . . . . W 9438T
■ 7″ . . . . . . . . . . . . . . . . . . . . . W 9438
WEA / Jan '84.

## WINDSONG.
Tracks: Look who's lonely now / I have ev'rything but you / He reminds me / Letter full of tears / This night won't last forever / One hello / Windsong / When I'm gone / Don't come knockin' / I don't want to lose him / We had a love so strong.
■ LP . . . . . . . . . . . . . . . . . . . . .K 5701 1

## NIGHTLINE.
■ MC. . . . . . . . . . . . . . . . . . . . K4 57011
WEA / Jun '82.

## WRAP U UP.
Tracks: Wrap u up / All it takes is love / Tender falls the rain.
■ 12″. . . . . . . . . . . . . . . . . . . .W 9969T
■ 7″ . . . . . . . . . . . . . . . . . . . . . W 9969
■ CD Single. . . . . . . . . . . . . . . W 9969CD
WEA / Feb '90.

## YOU MIGHT NEED SOMEBODY.
Tracks: You might need somebody / You bring the sun out.
■ 7″ . . . . . . . . . . . . . . . . . . . . . K 17803
WEA / May '81.

## I GOT THE FEVER.
Tracks: I got the fever.
■ 7″ . . . . . . . . . . . . . . . . . . . . . SS 2205
Stateside / Jun '72.
■ 7″ . . . . . . . . . . . . . . . . . . . . . BM 109
Black Magic (2) / Jan '76.

## DON'T BE AFRAID.
Tracks: Don't be afraid.
■ 7″ . . . . . . . . . . . . . . . . . . . . . 2066680
Polydor / Apr '76.

## MIGRATION.
Tracks: Migration.
■ 7″ . . . . . . . . . . . . . . . . . . . . . SXX 5
Sussex / Jul '75.

## WHO IS HE AND WHAT IS HE TO YOU.
Tracks: Who is he and what is he to you.
■ 7″ . . . . . . . . . . . . . . . . . . . . . SXX 1
Sussex / Aug '74.

In addition to being guitarist, producer and A&R director for Stax, Steve Cropper's CV boasts co-writing credits on *Knock On Wood*, *(Sittin' On The) Dock Of The Bay* and *Green Onions*. As pivotal member of Stax house band, Cropper was with label from its genesis in 1961 to collapse in early '70s. Ensuing decade included work with RCO All-Stars, featuring Dr John, Paul Butterfield and fellow Stax veteran Donald Dunn. Latter played with Cropper in Mar-Keys and MG's, although they achieved highest profile with spoof/tribute band Blues Brothers, who continue to tour regularly.

## FUNKY BROADWAY.
Tracks: Funky broadway / Crop dustin'.
■ 7″ . . . . . . . . . . . . . . . . . . . . . STAX 147
Stax / Jul '70.

## JAMMED TOGETHER (Cropper, Steve/ Pop Staples / Albert King).
Tracks: What'd I say / Opus de soul / Big bird / Trashy dog / Water / Tupelo / Baby what you want me to do / Homer's theme / Don't turn your heater down / Knock on wood.
■ LP . . . . . . . . . . . . . . . . . . . .SXATS 1020
Stax / Nov '69.
CD. . . . . . . . . . . . . . . . . . . . CDSXE 028
LP . . . . . . . . . . . . . . . . . . . . . SXE 028
Stax / Jul '90 / Pinnacle.

## WITH A LITTLE HELP FROM MY FRIENDS.
Tracks: Crop dustin' / Land of 1000 dances / ninety nine and a half (won't do) / Boogaloo down Broadway / Funky Broadway / With a little help from my friends / Oh pretty woman / I'd rather drink muddy water / Way I feel tonight / In the midnight hour / Rattlesnake.
■ LP . . . . . . . . . . . . . . . . . . . .SXATS 1008
Stax / Nov '69.
CD. . . . . . . . . . . . . . . . . . . . .MFCD 837
Mobile Fidelity Sound Lab(USA) / '88.
■ LP . . . . . . . . . . . . . . . . . . . . SXE 008
■ LP . . . . . . . . . . . . . . . . . . . . SX 008
Stax / Feb '88.
CD. . . . . . . . . . . . . . . . . . . . CDSXE 008
Ace / Aug '92 / Pinnacle / Complete Record Co. Ltd.

## YOUR AUTUMN OF TOMORROW.
Tracks: Your autumn of tomorrow / Uncle Funk.
■ 7″ . . . . . . . . . . . . . . . . . . . . .HEAT 13
Inferno (1) / Jul '80.

## Crown Heights Affair

**DANCE LADY DANCE.**
Tracks: Come fly with me / Dance lady dance /
Empty soul of mine / Number one woman / Rock is
hit / You don't have to say you love me.
■ LP . . . . . . . . . . . . . . . . . . . . . 637 276 2
Mercury / Apr '79.

**DANCE LADY DANCE.**
Tracks: Dance lady dance / Empty soul of mine.
■ 12" . . . . . . . . . . . . . . . . . . . . . .9198 161
■ 7" . . . . . . . . . . . . . . . . . . . . . .6168 804
Mercury / Apr '79.

**DREAM WORLD.**
Tracks: Galaxy of love / I love you / Say a prayer for
two / Dream world / Things are going to get better /
I'm gonna love you forever / Cherry.
■ LP . . . . . . . . . . . . . . . . . . . . . .6372 754
Philips / Sep '78.

**ESSENTIAL    DANCEFLOOR    ARTISTS
VOL. 1 - CROWN HEIGHTS AFFAIR.**
Tracks: Dreaming a dream / Foxy lady / Dancin' / Far
out / I'm gonna love you forever / Galaxy of love /
You gave me love / Use your body and soul / Say a
prayer for two.
CD . . . . . . . . . . . . . . . . . . . . . DGPCD 665
Deep Beats / Mar '94 / BMG.

**GALAXY OF LOVE.**
Tracks: Galaxy of love.
■ 7" . . . . . . . . . . . . . . . . . . . . . .6168 801
Philips / Aug '78.

**HEAVY LOVING.**
Tracks: Heavy loving / Rock the world.
■ 12" . . . . . . . . . . . . . . . . . . . . . . DEX 13
■ 7" . . . . . . . . . . . . . . . . . . . . . . . DE 13
De-Lite / Sep '83.

**I'LL DO ANYTHING.**
Tracks: I'll do anything / I'll do anything (accapella) /
I'll do anything (dub) (12" only.) / I'll do anything
(club) (CD single only.) / I'll do anything (disco
version 1) (12SBKX only.) / I'll do anything (disco
version 2) (12SBKX only.)
■ 12" . . . . . . . . . . . . . . . . . . .12SBK 7003
■ 12" . . . . . . . . . . . . . . . . . . 12SBKX 7003
■ CD Single . . . . . . . . . . . . . . . CDSBK 7003
■ MC Single . . . . . . . . . . . . . . . TCSBK 7003
SBK / Dec '89.
■ 7" . . . . . . . . . . . . . . . . . . . . . . SBK 7003
SBK / Nov '89.

**I'M GONNA LOVE YOU FOREVER.**
Tracks: I'm gonna love you forever.
■ 7" . . . . . . . . . . . . . . . . . . . . . .6188 808
Mercury / Nov '78.

**LOVE RIP OFF.**
Tracks: Love rip off / Your love makes me hot.
■ 12" . . . . . . . . . . . . . . . . . . . . . . DEX 10
■ 7" . . . . . . . . . . . . . . . . . . . . . . . DE 10
De-Lite / Oct '82.

**MAKE ME THE ONE.**
Tracks: Make me the one / Make me the one
(instrumental).
■ 7" . . . . . . . . . . . . . . . . . . . . . . CBE 704
City Beat / May '86.

**SOMEBODY TELL ME WHAT TO DO.**
Tracks: Somebody tell me what to do / Heart upside
down.
■ 12" . . . . . . . . . . . . . . . . . . . . . . . DEX 8
■ 7" . . . . . . . . . . . . . . . . . . . . . . . . DE 8
De-Lite / Aug '82.

**SURE SHOT.**
Tracks: You gave me love / I don't want to change
you / Sure shot / You've been gone / I see the light /
Use your body and soul / Tell me you love me.
■ LP . . . . . . . . . . . . . . . . . . . . . 637 276 7
De-Lite / May '80.

**THINK POSITIVE.**
Tracks: Somebody tell me what to do / Love rip off /
Heart upside down / Think positive / I got somethin'
for ya / Wine and dine you / Your love makes me hot
/ Let me ride on the wave of your love.
■ LP . . . . . . . . . . . . . . . . . . . . . . . DSR 2
De-Lite / Sep '82.

**YOU GAVE ME LOVE.**
Tracks: You gave me love / Use your body and soul.
■ 12" . . . . . . . . . . . . . . . . . . . . . MERX 9
■ 7" . . . . . . . . . . . . . . . . . . . . . . MER 9
De-Lite / May '80.

**YOU GAVE ME LOVE (OLD GOLD).**
Tracks: You gave me love / Galaxy of love.
12" . . . . . . . . . . . . . . . . . . . . . . OG 4172
Old Gold / May '90 / Pickwick.

**YOU'VE BEEN GONE.**
Tracks: You've been gone / Far out.
■ 12" . . . . . . . . . . . . . . . . . . . . . MERX 28
■ 7" . . . . . . . . . . . . . . . . . . . . . . MER 28
De-Lite / Jul '80.

## Cruise, Erin

**EAT YOUR HEART OUT.**
Tracks: Follow your heart / Eat your heart out.
12" . . . . . . . . . . . . . . . . . . . . . .LBAY 16
Loading Bay / Jan '93 / Loading Bay Records.

## Cruize

**HEY BOY.**
Tracks: Hey boy.
■ 12" . . . . . . . . . . . . . . . . . . . BOSS 12005
Boss / Jan '91.

## Crusaders

Texan jazz-funk pioneers, who formed in
early '50s as Swingsters. With line-up
boasting Wilton Felder, Wayne Henderson,
Joe Sample and Nesbert Hooper, they recorded throughout '60s as Jazz Crusaders;
streamlining name at turn of decade.
Change reflected shift to more commercial
style which yielded gold albums and sold-
out tours in late '70s. They also had successful subsidiary careers as session
players. Henderson left in '75; remaining
trio augmented line-up with noted musicians like guitarist Larry Carlton. In '79,
band dropped instrumental format, and began featuring guest vocalists. First and
most successful collaboration was transatlantic hit *Street Life* with Randy Crawford;
others included Bill Withers and Joe
Cocker, while Bobby Womack appeared on
two acclaimed singles by Felder. Drummer
Hooper quit in '83 and group split in '86,
although inevitable reformation was mere
years away.

**BEST OF THE CRUSADERS.**
Tracks: Put it where you want it / Stomp and buck
dance / Greasy spoon / Scratch / So far away / Hard
times / So far away (live) / Don't let it get you down /
Keep that same old feeling / That's how I feel / Soul
caravan / Chain reaction / Ballad for Joe / Do you
remember when / Way back home.
■ MC Set . . . . . . . . . . . . . . . . CABD 612
ABC Records / Dec '76.
■ Double LP . . . . . . . . . . . . . . . ABCD 612
ABC Records / Jan '77.

**BEST OF THE CRUSADERS, THE.**
Tracks: Put it where you want it / Stomp and buck
dance / Greasy spoon / Keep that same old feeling /
So far away / Hard times / So far away (live) / Don't
let it get you down / Scratch / That's how I feel / Soul
caravan / Chain reaction / Ballad for Joe (Louis) / Do
you remember when / Way back home.
■ MC . . . . . . . . . . . . . . . . . . MCLDC 602
MCA / Jul '78.

**CHAIN REACTION.**
Tracks: Not Advised.
■ LP . . . . . . . . . . . . . . . . . . . . CAB 5144
ABC Records / Apr '77.
■ LP . . . . . . . . . . . . . . . . . MFSL 1-010
Mobile Fidelity Sound Lab(USA) / Jun '79.

**CRUSADERS AND BEYOND, THE.**
Tracks: Street life / Inherit the wind / Stomp and buck
dance / Burnin' up the carnival / (No matter how high
I get) I'll be lookin' up to you / Keep that same old
feeling / Snowflakes / Brazos river / Breakdown /
Soul shadows / Let's dance together / Time bomb /
Voices in the rain.
CD . . . . . . . . . . . . . . . . . . . MCCD 163
MC . . . . . . . . . . . . . . . . . . .MCTC 163
Music Collection International / Jul '94 / THE / Jazz
Music.

**CRUSADERS EP.**
Tracks: Put it where you want it / Stomp and buck
dance / Keep that same old feeling / Chain reaction.
■ EP . . . . . . . . . . . . . . . . . . ABE 12013
ABC Records / Dec '77.

**CRUSADERS, THE.**
Tracks: Not Advised.
MC . . . . . . . . . . . . . . . . . . . . GTDC 083
GTD / '89 / A.D.A. Distribution.

**FEEL IT.**
Tracks: Feel it / Way we was.
■ 7" . . . . . . . . . . . . . . . . . . . . . ABC 4183
ABC Records / Jul '77.

**FREE AS THE WIND.**
Tracks: Free as the wind / I felt the love / Way we
was / Nite crawler / Feel it / Sweet n sour / River rat /
It happens every day.
■ LP . . . . . . . . . . . . . . . . . . . . ABCL 5226
ABC Records / Jul '77.
■ LP . . . . . . . . . . . . . . . . . . . . MCL 1764
■ MC . . . . . . . . . . . . . . . . . . . MCLC 1764
ABC Records / '83.

**FREEDOM SOUND (Jazz Crusaders).**
Tracks: Greek / MJS funk (alternate version) / Coon
(alternate version) / Freedom sound / Exodus
(Theme from) / That's it / MJS Funk / Coon.
■ CD . . . . . . . . . . . . . . . . . CDP 796 864 2
Pacific Jazz / Feb '92.

**GOLDEN YEARS, THE.**
Tracks: Young rabbits / Blues up tight / Fancy dance
/ Eleanor Rigby / Way back home / Hard times /
Thank you / Stomp and buck dance / Greasy spoon /
Ballad for Joe / Chain reaction / Rainbow visions /
Spiral / Keep that same old feeling / Free as the
wind / I felt the love / Way we was / Night crawler /
Sweet 'n' sour / It happens everyday / So far away /
Put it where you want it / Marcella's dream / Fairy
tales / Street life / Huster / Carnival of the night /
Elegant evening / Last call / Search for soul / Don't
let it get you down.
CD Set . . . . . . . . . . . . . . . . . GRP 50072
GRP / Aug '92 / BMG / New Note.

**GOOD AND BAD TIMES, THE.**
Tracks: Good times / Way it goes / Sweet dreams /
Mischievious ways / Sometimes you can take it or
leave it / Three wishes.
■ LP . . . . . . . . . . . . . . . . . . . . MCF 6022
■ MC . . . . . . . . . . . . . . . . . . . MCFC 6022
MCA / Dec '86.
■ CD . . . . . . . . . . . . . . . . . . . MCAD 5781
MCA / Jun '89.

**HEALING THE WOUNDS.**
Tracks: Pessimisticism / Mercy, mercy, mercy / Little
things mean a lot / Cause we've ended as lovers /
Shake dance / Maputo / Running man / Healing the
wounds.
CD . . . . . . . . . . . . . . . . . . . GRD 9638
■ LP . . . . . . . . . . . . . . . . . . . . GR 9638
■ MC . . . . . . . . . . . . . . . . . . . GRC 9638
GRP / May '91 / BMG / New Note.
■ CD . . . . . . . . . . . . . . . . . . . MCD 9638
MCA / Jan '93.

**I'M SO GLAD I'M STANDING HERE
TODAY.**
Tracks: I'm so glad I'm standing here today.
■ 12" . . . . . . . . . . . . . . . . . . .MCAT 741
■ 7" . . . . . . . . . . . . . . . . . . . . MCA 741
MCA / Sep '81.

**IMAGES.**
Tracks: Fair tales / Marcella's dream / Bayou bot-
toms / Merry go round / Cosmic reign / Covert action
/ Snow flake / Fairy tales.
■ LP . . . . . . . . . . . . . . . . . . . . MCL 1625
■ MC . . . . . . . . . . . . . . . . . . . MCLC 1625
ABC Records / Aug '81.
■ CD . . . . . . . . . . . . . . . . . . GRP 01162
GRP / Oct '92.

**LAST CALL.**
Tracks: Last call / Honky tonk struttin'.
■ 12" . . . . . . . . . . . . . . . . . . .MCAT 657
■ 7" . . . . . . . . . . . . . . . . . . . . MCA 657
MCA / Jan '81.

**LIFE IN THE MODERN WORLD.**
Tracks: Passion fruit / A C / Life in the modern world
/ Samplin' / Mulholland nights / Let me prove myself
tonight / Destiny / D C / Some people just never
learn / Coulda', woulda, shoulda'.
■ LP . . . . . . . . . . . . . . . . . . . . MCF 3420
■ CD . . . . . . . . . . . . . . . . . . . DMCF 3420
■ MC . . . . . . . . . . . . . . . . . . . MCFC 3420
MCA / Jun '88.

**LIVE IN JAPAN.**
Tracks: Rainbow seeker / Hustler / Sweet gentle love
/ Spiral / Melodies of love / Carmel / So far away /
Brazos river breakdown / In all my wildest dreams /
Put it where you want.
CD . . . . . . . . . . . . . . . . . . . GRP 97462
GRP / Nov '93 / BMG / New Note.

**NEW MOVES.**
Tracks: New moves / Dead end / Street life (on 12"
only).

■ DELETED

■ 7″ . . . . . . . . . . . . . . . . . . . . . MCA 894
■ 12″ . . . . . . . . . . . . . . . . . . . MCAT 894
MCA / Jul '84.

## NIGHT LADIES.
**Tracks:** Night ladies.
■ 7″ . . . . . . . . . . . . . . . . . . . . . MCA 853
■ 12″ . . . . . . . . . . . . . . . . . . . MCAT 853
MCA / Apr '84.

## ONGAKU DAI-LIVE IN JAPAN.
**Tracks:** Introduction / Rainbow seeker / Hustler / Sweet gentle love / Drum introduction / Spiral / Carmel / In all my wildest dreams / Put it where you want it.
■ LP . . . . . . . . . . . . . . . . . . . CRP 16002
Crusaders (Audiophile series) / Apr '82.

## PASS THE PLATE.
**Tracks:** Not Advised.
CD . . . . . . . . . . . . . . . . . . . . .530308-2
Polygram / Nov '94 / PolyGram.

## RHAPSODY AND BLUES.
**Tracks:** Soul shadows / Honky tonk struttin' / Elegant evening / Rhapsody and blues / Last call / Sweet gentle love.
■ LP . . . . . . . . . . . . . . . . . . . . .MCG 4010
MCA / Jul '80.
■ LP . . . . . . . . . . . . . . . . . . . . . MCL 1771
■ MC. . . . . . . . . . . . . . . . . . . . MCLC 1771
MCA / Sep '86.

## RHAPSODY AND BLUES/STREET LIFE.
**Tracks:** Street life / My lady / Rodeo drive (high steppin') / Carnival of the night / Hustler / Night faces / Soul shadows / Honky tonk struttin' / Elegant evening / Rhapsody and blue / Last call / Sweet gentle love.
■ MC Set . . . . . . . . . . . . . . . MCA 2 102
MCA (Twinpax Cassettes) / Sep '84.

## ROYAL JAM.
**Tracks:** I'm so glad I'm standing here today / One day I'll fly away / Fly with wings of love / Burnin' up the carnival / Last call / Thrill is gone / Better not look down / Hold on (I feel your love is changing) / Street life / I just can't leave your love alone / Never make a move too soon.
■ LP . . . . . . . . . . . . . . . . . . . MCDW 455
■ MC . . . . . . . . . . . . . . . . . . . MCDC 455
MCA / Jun '82.
■ CD . . . . . . . . . . . . . . . . . . . MCAD 8017
MCA / Jul '87.
CD . . . . . . . . . . . . . . . . . . . . GRP 01352
GRP / Feb '93 / BMG / New Note.

## SAMPLE A DECADE (1).
**Tracks:** So far away / Bayou bottoms / Soul shadows / Don't let it get you down / My mama told me so / I'm so glad I'm standing here today / Soul caravan / Nite crawler / Fairytales / Honky tonk struttin' / Chain reaction / And then there was the blues / Street life / Hold on / Snow flake / Rhapsody and blues / Sweet'n'sour / Night ladies / Rodeo drive (high steppin') / Free as the wind.
CD . . . . . . . . . . . . . . . . . . . . VSOPCD 131
■ Double LP. . . . . . . . . . . . . . VSOPLP 131
MC. . . . . . . . . . . . . . . . . . . . VSOPMC 131
Connoisseur Collection / Jan '89 / Pinnacle.

## SCRATCH.
**Tracks:** Scratch / Eleanor Rigby / Hard times / So far away / Way back home.
■ LP . . . . . . . . . . . . . . . . . . . . MCL 1709
■ MC . . . . . . . . . . . . . . . . . . . MCLC 1709
MCA / Sep '82.
■ CD . . . . . . . . . . . . . . . . . . . GRP 01152
GRP / Nov '92.

## SCRATCH.
**Tracks:** Scratch / Street life.
■ 12″ . . . . . . . . . . . . . . . . . . . .MCAT 513
■ 7″ . . . . . . . . . . . . . . . . . . . . MCA 513
MCA / Jul '82.

## SOUTHERN COMFORT.
**Tracks:** Not Advised.
CD . . . . . . . . . . . . . . . . . . . . GRP 01362
GRP / Nov '92 / BMG / New Note.

## STANDING TALL.
**Tracks:** Not Advised.
■ LP . . . . . . . . . . . . . . . . . . . . MCF 3122
MCA / Sep '81.

## STOMP AND BUCK DANCE.
**Tracks:** Stomp and buck dance / Ballad for Joe Louis.
■ 7″ . . . . . . . . . . . . . . . . . . . . ABC 4051
Anchor (1) / Apr '75.

■ DELETED

## STREET LIFE.
**Tracks:** Street life / My lady / Rodeo drive (high steppin') / Carnival of the night / Hustler / Night faces / Inherit the wind.
■ CD . . . . . . . . . . . . . . . . . . . DIDX 153
MCA.
■ LP . . . . . . . . . . . . . . . . . . . MCF 3008
MCA / Jul '79.
■ LP . . . . . . . . . . . . . . . . . . . MCL 1815
■ MC . . . . . . . . . . . . . . . . . . . MCLC 1815
MCA / Sep '86.
■ CD . . . . . . . . . . . . . . . CMCAD 31024
MCA / Jul '87.
■ CD . . . . . . . . . . . . . . . . . DMCA 107
MCA / '88.
CD. . . . . . . . . . . . . . . . . . MCLD 19004
■ MC . . . . . . . . . . . . . . . . . MCLC 19004
MCA / Apr '92 / BMG.

## STREET LIFE (OLD GOLD).
**Tracks:** Street life / Inherit the wind.
■ 12″ . . . . . . . . . . . . . . . . . . .OG 4065
Old Gold / May '88.

## THIS OLD WORLD'S TOO FUNKY FOR ME.
**Tracks:** This old world's too funky for me / I'm so glad / Luckenbach, Texas (Available on 12″ only).
■ 12″ . . . . . . . . . . . . . . . . . .MCAT 754
■ 7″ . . . . . . . . . . . . . . . . . . MCA 754
MCA / Nov '81.

## THOSE SOUTHERN NIGHTS.
**Tracks:** Spiral / Keep that same old feeling / My Mama told me so / Till the sun shines / And then there was the blues / Serenity / Feeling funky.
■ LP . . . . . . . . . . . . . . . . . . . MCL 1645
■ MC . . . . . . . . . . . . . . . . . . MCLC 1645
MCA / Feb '82.

## VOCAL ALBUM, THE.
**Tracks:** Street life / This old world's too funky for me / Better not look down / Inherit the wind / Hold on (I feel our love is changing) / Help / Soul shadows / Way it goes / I'm so glad I'm standing here today / I'll still be lookin' up to you, (no matter how high I get) / Burnin' up the carnival.
■ CD . . . . . . . . . . . . . . . . . DMCF 3395
■ LP . . . . . . . . . . . . . . . . . . MCF 3395
■ MC. . . . . . . . . . . . . . . . . MCFC 3395
MCA / Jul '87.

## VOCAL TAPE, THE.
**Tracks:** Not Advised.
■ LP . . . . . . . . . . . . . . . . . . MCF 3171
■ MC . . . . . . . . . . . . . . . . MCFC 3171
MCA / Aug '83.

## YOUNG RABBITS (Jazz Crusaders).
**Tracks:** Not Advised.
■ Double LP. . . . . . . . . . . . . . BND 4028
Blue Note / '79.

# Crysis

## I WILL SURVIVE.
**Tracks:** I will survive.
■ 12″ . . . . . . . . . . . . . . . . . DEBTX 3118
Debut (2) / Jul '93.

# Crystals

## ALL GROWN UP.
**Tracks:** All grown up / Twist.
■ 7″ . . . . . . . . . . . . . . . . . . .2010 020
Phil Spector Int. / Apr '77.

## BEST OF THE CRYSTALS.
**Tracks:** There's no other (like my baby) / Oh yeah, maybe baby / Uptown / What a nice way to turn 17 / He hit me (and it felt like a kiss) / No one ever tells you / He's a rebel / I love you, Eddie / Another country - another world / Please hurt me / He's sure the boy I love / Look in my eyes / Do doo ron ron / Heartbreaker / Then he kissed me / I wonder / Little boy / Girls can tell / All grown up.
CD . . . . . . . . . . . . . . . . . . PSCD 1007
■ MC . . . . . . . . . . . . . . . . PSTC 1007
Phil Spector Int. / Sep '92 / EMI.

## CRYSTALS MEET THE SHANGRI-LAS, THE (Crystals & the Shangri-las).
**Tracks:** Not Advised.
CD . . . . . . . . . . . . . . . . . . K3015-2
MC. . . . . . . . . . . . . . . . . . U3015-2
Spectrum (CD) / Jun '89 / M.S.D.

## DA DOO RON RON.
**Tracks:** And then he kissed me / Da doo ron ron / He's a rebel.
■ 7″ . . . . . . . . . . . . . . . . . . HLU 9732
London-American / Jun '63.
■ 7″ . . . . . . . . . . . . . . . . . . K 19010
WEA / Oct '74.
■ 7″ . . . . . . . . . . . . . . . . . . CR 182
Creole (Replay) / Aug '82.
■ 7″ . . . . . . . . . . . . . . . . . . CR 109
Creole Classics / Aug '87.
■ 12″ . . . . . . . . . . . . . . . . . .CRT 109
Creole Classics / Oct '87.
■ 12″ . . . . . . . . . . . . . . . . . BANG 3
Explosion / May '88.

## HE'S A REBEL.
**Tracks:** He's a rebel / I love you Eddie
■ 7″ . . . . . . . . . . . . . . . . . HLU 9611
London-American / Nov '62.
■ 7″ . . . . . . . . . . . . . . . . . 2010002
Phil Spector Int. / Jun '75.

## I WONDER.
**Tracks:** I wonder.
■ 7″ . . . . . . . . . . . . . . . . . HLU 9852
London-American / Mar '64.

## PHIL SPECTOR WALL OF SOUND, VOL.3.
**Tracks:** He's a rebel / Uptown / There's no other / Oh yeah / Maybe baby / Please hurt me / No one ever tells you / Da doo ron ron / Mashed potato time / Another country / Another world / He's sure the boy I love / Then he kissed me / On Broadway / What a nice way to turn seventeen / He hit me (and it felt like a kiss) / I love you, Eddie / Look in my eyes.
■ LP . . . . . . . . . . . . . . . . . .2307 006
Phil Spector Int. / Oct '75.

## THEN HE KISSED ME.
**Tracks:** Then he kissed me.
■ 7″ . . . . . . . . . . . . . . . . . HLU 9773
London-American / Sep '63.

## UPTOWN.
**Tracks:** Not Advised.
CD . . . . . . . . . . . . . . . . . . .U 4062
Spectrum (1) / Jun '88 / PolyGram.

# Cummings, Burton

## MY OWN WAY TO ROCK.
**Tracks:** My own way to rock / Song for him.
■ 7″ . . . . . . . . . . . . . . . . PRT 5567
Portrait / Sep '77.

## WHEN A MAN LOVES A WOMAN.
**Tracks:** When a man loves a woman / Roll with the punches.
■ 7″ . . . . . . . . . . . . . . . . PRT 6655
Portrait / Sep '78.

# Curry, Mini

## 100 PER CENT.
**Tracks:** 100 per cent / If they only knew / I think I'm over you / I like it / Have we lost / Serious / Doll in the window / First time.
■ CD . . . . . . . . . . . . . . . . . CDTR 6
Timeless (Soul) / Dec '87.
■ LP . . . . . . . . . . . . . . . . . TRLP 118
Timeless (Soul) / Jan '88.
■ LP . . . . . . . . . . . . . . . . . TRPL 118
Timeless (Soul) / Jan '90.

# Curry, Tyrone

## TYRONE CURRY.
**Tracks:** I'm so in love / Take this love / Overload / Joy ride / Have we lost / Let's have some fun tonight / Play it cool / Need your lovin' / Give it up.
■ LP . . . . . . . . . . . . . . . . . TRLP 120
Timeless (Soul) / Dec '87.
■ CD . . . . . . . . . . . . . . . . . CDTR 5
Timeless (Soul) / Jan '90.

# Curtis, Chantal

## GET ANOTHER LOVE.
**Tracks:** Get another love.
■ 7″ . . . . . . . . . . . . . . . . . 7P 5003
PRT / Jul '79.

## GET ANOTHER LOVE.
**Tracks:** Get another love / Hey taxi driver / I'm burnin' / Hit man / Bet your bottom dollar / I gotta know.
■ LP . . . . . . . . . . . . . . . . . DISC 02
Pye / '79.

## Curtis, King

Curtis Ousley emerged from early '50s be-bop scene to put his stamp on records like Coasters' *Yakety Yak*. Fruitful relationship with Atlantic label yielded appearances with Aretha Franklin and others, placing Curtis at forefront of sax-playing. He also scored hits with his bands Noble Knights and Kingpins, notably *Soul Twist* in '62 and *Memphis Soul Stew* in '67. Appearances with John Lennon, Duane Allman and Billy Preston hinted at rockier direction his career might have taken, had he not been tragically murdered in 1971.

### 20 GOLDEN PIECES: KING CURTIS (Curtis, King & The Noble Knights).
Tracks: Tequila / Night train / Java / Harlem nocturne / Honky tonk / Soul twist / Memphis / Watermelon man / Soul serenade / Swingin' shepherd blues / My last date (with you) / Wiggle wobble / Tanya / Tennessee waltz / Bill Bailey won't you please come home / Misty / Sister Sadie / Ain't that good news / Peter Gunn / One mint julep.
■ LP . . . . . . . . . . . . . . . . . BDL 2009
Bulldog Records / Jul '82.

### AT SMALL'S PARADISE.
Tracks: Tough talk / Philly dog / Preach / Blowin' in the wind / Peter Gunn / Get along Cindy / Pots & pans / Shadow of your smile / Road runner / Something on your mind / Soul theme.
■ LP . . . . . . . . . . . . . . . . . K 30029
Atlantic / Apr '73.

### BEST OF KING CURTIS.
Tracks: Harper Valley P.T.A. / Ode to Billy Joe / Soul serenade / I heard it through the grapevine / Dock of the bay / Memphis soul stew / Spanish Harlem / Jump back / Something on your mind / You've lost that lovin' feelin' / Makin' hey / I was made to love her.
■ LP . . . . . . . . . . . . . . . . . 228 002
Atco / Aug '69.

### BLUES AT MONTREUX (Curtis, King & Champion Jack Dupree).
Tracks: Junker's blues / Sneaky Pete / Everything's gonna be alright / Get with it / Poor boy blues / I'm having fun.
■ LP . . . . . . . . . . . . . . . . . SD 1637
Atlantic / Nov '87.
■ MC . . . . . . . . . . . . . . . . . CS 1673
Atlantic / '88.

### CAPITOL YEARS: KING CURTIS (1962-1965).
Tracks: Turn 'em on / Beach party / Beautiful brown eyes / Your cheatin' heart / Tennessee waltz / Wagon wheels / High noon / Anytime / Home on the range / Night train to Memphis / I'm movin' on / Raunchy / Tumbling tumbleweeds / Walking the floor over you / Slow drag / New dance / Frisky / Alexander's ragtime band / Amorosa (Bossa Nova) / Strollin' home / Mess around / Sukiyaki / Summer dream / Do the monkey / Feel all right / Turn 'em on (Mono) / Theme from 'Lillies of the field'(Amen), Part 2 / Theme from 'Lillies of the field'(Amen), Part 1 / More soul / Soul serenade / Honky tonk / Watermelon man / Memphis / Soul twist / Night train / Tequila / Wiggle wobble / One mint julep / Last last year / Swingin' shepherd blues / My last date / Hide away / Harlem Nocturne / Java / Stranger on the shore / Melancholy serenade / Summer dream (2) / Tanya / Hung over / Soul twine (Stereo) / Soul twine (Mono) / Moon river / Girl from Ipanema / Sister Sadie / Something you've got / Take these chains from my heart / Let it be me / Hung over (Remake) / Misty (Re-make) / Bill Bailey / Peter Gunn / Shake / Ain't that good news / Twistin' the night away / Good times / Send me some lovin' / Bring it on home to me / Change is gonna come / You send me / Cupid / Having a party / Chain gang / Prance / Something you've got (Overdub).
CD Set . . . . . . . . . . . . . . . BCD 15670
Bear Family / Mar '93 / Rollercoaster Records / Swift / Direct Distribution / Topic Records.

### DIDN'T HE PLAY.
Tracks: Home cooking / Soul groove part 1 / Soul groove part 2 / Pickin' chicken / Clementine / Blowin' off steam / Didn't he play / Blue nocturne / Hello sunshine / Count your blessings / Write me a love letter / Jealous fool / Don't put me down like this.
■ LP . . . . . . . . . . . . . . . . . RL 074
Red Lightnin' / Jun '88.

### ETERNALLY SOUL (Curtis, King & the Shirelles).
Tracks: Mama, here comes the bride / Take the last train home / Welcome home baby / I got a woman / I still want you / Love is a swingin' thing / Ooh poop

pah doo / New Orleans / Mister Twister / Potato chips.
■ LP . . . . . . . . . . . . . . . . . WNS 4
Wand / Sep '70.

### EVERYBODY'S TALKIN'.
Tracks: Groove me / You're the one / Honky tonk / Love the one you're with / If I were a carpenter / Everybody's talkin' / Ridin' thumb / Alexander's ragtime band / Central Park / Wet funk.
■ LP . . . . . . . . . . . . . . . . . K 40360
Atlantic / May '72.

### GET READY.
Tracks: Get ready / Sugar foot / Floatin' / Bridge over troubled water / Soulin' / Teasin' / Something / Promenade / Let it be / Someday we'll be together.
■ LP . . . . . . . . . . . . . . . . . 2400 019
Atco / Nov '70.

### GIVE A TWIST PARTY (see under Shirelles).

### GOOD TO ME.
Tracks: Good to me / Hold on I'm comin'.
■ 7" . . . . . . . . . . . . . . . . . 584109
Atlantic / May '67.

### INSTANT GROOVE.
Tracks: Castle rock / Chili / Restless guitar / Honey dripper / Birth of the blues / Peter Gunn / Boss / Rocky roll / This is soul / Quicksand / Memphissoul stew / Cookout / There is something on your mind / Instant groove / Patty cake / Pop corn Willy.
LP . . . . . . . . . . . . . . . . . ED 315
Edsel / Feb '90 / Pinnacle.
■ CD . . . . . . . . . . . . . . . . . EDCD 315
Demon / Feb '90.

### INSTANT GROOVE.
Tracks: Instant groove / Hey Joe / Foot pattin' / Wichita lineman / Games people play / Sing a simple song / Weight / La Jeanne / Little green apples / Somewhere / Hold me tight / Hey Jude.
■ LP . . . . . . . . . . . . . . . . . 228 027
Atco / Nov '69.

### IT'S GREAT TO BE RICH (EP).
Tracks: It's great to be rich / Lester's comet / La Cucaracha / Don't know where I've been / Sweet home Chicago.
■ 12" . . . . . . . . . . . . . . . . . RLEP 0045
Red Lightnin' / Jun '83.

### IT'S PARTY TIME.
Tracks: Free for all / Easy like / Hot saxes / I'll wait for you / Party time twist / Low down / Keep movin' / (Let's do) the hully gully twist / Slow motion / Firefly / Something frantic.
CD . . . . . . . . . . . . . . . . . CDCH 262
LP . . . . . . . . . . . . . . . . . CDCH 262LP
Ace / Nov '93 / Pinnacle / Complete Record Co. Ltd.

### IT'S PARTY TIME WITH KING CURTIS.
Tracks: Free for all / Easy like / Hot saxes / I'll wait for you / Party time twist / Low down / Keep movin' / (Let's do) the hully gully twist / Slow motion / Firefly / Something frantic.
■ LP . . . . . . . . . . . . . . . . . CH 262
Ace / Aug '89.

### JAZZ GROOVE.
Tracks: Da duh dah / Have you heard / Willow weep for me / Little brother soul / In a funky groove / Soul meeting / Lazy soul / All the way / Jeep's blues / What is this thing called love / Do you have soul now.
■ Double LP . . . . . . . . . . . . . . . PR 24033
Prestige / Sep '80.

### KING SIZE SOUL (Curtis, King & the Kingpins).
Tracks: Ode to Billie Joe / Whiter shade of pale / For what it's worth / To Sir with love / Memphis soul stew / When a man loves a woman / I never loved a man / Live for life / I was made to love her / C.C. rider.
■ LP . . . . . . . . . . . . . . . . . 587 093
Atlantic / Mar '68.

### LIVE IN NEW YORK.
Tracks: Jaywalk / Trouble in mind / African waltz / What'd I say / I have to worry / Twist / Canadian sunset / How high the moon / K.C. special.
■ LP . . . . . . . . . . . . . . . . . JSP 1091
JSP / Aug '85.

### MEMPHIS SOUL STEW.
Tracks: Memphis soul stew / Blue nocturne.
7" . . . . . . . . . . . . . . . . . 584134
Atlantic / Sep '67 / WEA.

### MISTER SOUL (Curtis, King & The Noble Knights).
Tracks: Tanya / Tennessee waltz / Bill Bailey won't you please come home / Misty soul twist / Sister Sadie / Night train / Ain't that good news / Soul serenade / Peter Gunn / One mint julep.
■ LP . . . . . . . . . . . . . . . . . SPE 6607
Ember / Jul '70.

### SINGS THE BLUES / TROUBLE IN MIND.
Tracks: Not Advised.
■ LP . . . . . . . . . . . . . . . . . OBC 512
Original Blues Classics / Jan '88.

### SOUL GROOVE.
Tracks: Blowin' off steam / Dark eyes / Who's sorry now / Sweet Georgia Brown / Sometimes I'm happy / Pickin' chicken / Soul groove part 1 / Soul groove part 2 / Clementine / Take me out to the ball game.
■ LP . . . . . . . . . . . . . . . . . BMLP 1036
Blue Moon (1) / Jul '87.

### SOUL SERENADE (Curtis, King & The Noble Knights).
Tracks: Tequila / Night train / Java Jones / Harlem nocturne / Honky tonk / Soul twist / Memphis Tennessee / Watermelon man / Soul serenade / Swingin' shepherd blues / My last date / Wiggle wobble.
■ LP . . . . . . . . . . . . . . . . . SPE 6600
Ember / Dec '67.

### SOUL TWIST (Curtis, King & Others).
Tracks: Not Advised.
■ LP . . . . . . . . . . . . . . . . . COL 5119
Collectables (USA) / Jul '88.

### SWEET SOUL.
Tracks: Valley of the dolls / Soul serenade / I heard it through the grapevine / Sweet inspiration / By the time I get to Phoenix / Spooky / Honey / Up, up and away / Look of love / Dock of the bay.
■ LP . . . . . . . . . . . . . . . . . 588 115
Atlantic / Oct '68.

### THAT'S ALRIGHT.
Tracks: Not Advised.
■ LP . . . . . . . . . . . . . . . . . RL 042
Red Lightnin' / May '83.

### TROUBLE IN MIND.
Tracks: Trouble in mind / Jivin' time / Nobody wants you when you're down and out / Bad bad whiskey / I have to worry / Woke up this morning / But that's alright / Ain't nobody's business / Don't deceive me / Deep fry.
CD . . . . . . . . . . . . . . . . . OBCCD 512
Original Blues Classics / Nov '92 / Pinnacle.
CD . . . . . . . . . . . . . . . . . CDCHD 545
Ace / Jul '94 / Pinnacle / Complete Record Co. Ltd.

### WIGGLE WOBBLE.
Tracks: Wiggle wobble / Night train.
7" . . . . . . . . . . . . . . . . . SPE 1000
Specialty / Oct '67 / Pinnacle.

## Curtis, T.C.

### BODYSHAKE.
Tracks: Body shake / Body shake (part 2).
■ 12" . . . . . . . . . . . . . . . . . GP 112T
Groove PR / Dec '81.

### DANCE TO THE BEAT.
Tracks: Dance to the beat.
■ 12" . . . . . . . . . . . . . . . . . TC 002
Hot Melt / Mar '84.

### GET OUT OF MY LIFE.
Tracks: Get out of my life.
■ 12" . . . . . . . . . . . . . . . . . 12 TCT 15
Hot Melt / Feb '88.

### JACKO (Curtis, T.C. & T.Jam).
Tracks: Jacko.
■ 12" . . . . . . . . . . . . . . . . . 12 TCT 14
■ 12" . . . . . . . . . . . . . . . . . 12 TCT 14
■ 7" . . . . . . . . . . . . . . . . . 7 TCT 14
Hot Melt / Aug '87.

### LET'S MAKE LOVE.
Tracks: Step by step / Dance to the beat (remix).
■ 12" . . . . . . . . . . . . . . . . . 12 TC 005
■ 7" . . . . . . . . . . . . . . . . . TC 005
Hot Melt / Apr '86.
■ 12" . . . . . . . . . . . . . . . . . 12 TC 006
■ 7" . . . . . . . . . . . . . . . . . 7 TC 006
Hot Melt / Jul '86.

### LOVE GOT ME ON A MERRY GO ROUND.
Tracks: Love got me on a merry go round / What's your problem / Reunited.

■ DELETED

■ 12″. . . . . . . . . . . . . . . . . . . . . . 12 TC 011
Hot Melt / May '87.

## PARTY DOWN.
Tracks: Party down.
■ 7″. . . . . . . . . . . . . . . . . . . . . . . . RR 001
Romantic / Nov '82.

## SLAVE OF LOVE.
Tracks: Slave of love / Slave of love (dub mix) / Slave of love (remix) / Let's make love (remix) / Body shake.
■ 12″ Remix. . . . . . . . . . . . . . . 12 TC 007R
Hot Melt / Nov '86.
■ 12″. . . . . . . . . . . . . . . . . . . . . 12 TC 007
■ 7″. . . . . . . . . . . . . . . . . . . . . . 7 TC 007
Hot Melt / Sep '86.

## SLAVE OF LOVE (1990).
Tracks: Slave of love (1990).
■ 12″. . . . . . . . . . . . . . . . . . . . . 12 TCT 25
Hot Melt / Dec '90.

## SLAVE OF LOVE - FINAL COUNTDOWN MIX.
Tracks: Let's make love.
■ 12″. . . . . . . . . . . . . . . . . . . . . 15 TC 007
Hot Melt / Jan '87.

## STEP BY STEP.
Tracks: Not Advised.
■ LP. . . . . . . . . . . . . . . . . . . . . . CURTIS 1
MC. . . . . . . . . . . . . . . . . . . . . CURTIS 14
Hot Melt / Apr '87 / Pinnacle / Black Marketing.

## STRANGER.
Tracks: Stranger.
■ 12″. . . . . . . . . . . . . . . . . . . . . 12 TCT 18
■ 7″. . . . . . . . . . . . . . . . . . . . . . 7 TC 18
Hot Melt / Dec '88.

## TAKE IT EASY.
Tracks: Take it easy.
■ 12″. . . . . . . . . . . . . . . . . . . VS 775-12
■ 7″. . . . . . . . . . . . . . . . . . . . . . VS 775
Virgin / Jun '85.

## YOU CAN'T TOUCH MY LADY.
Tracks: You can't touch my lady.
■ 12″. . . . . . . . . . . . . . . . . . . . . 12 TCT 23
■ 7″. . . . . . . . . . . . . . . . . . . . . . 7 TC 23
Hot Melt / Jul '89.

## YOU SHOULD HAVE KNOWN BETTER.
Tracks: You should have known better / You should have known better (dub mix).
■ 12″. . . . . . . . . . . . . . . . . . . . VS 754-12
■ 7″. . . . . . . . . . . . . . . . . . . . . . VS 754
Virgin / Feb '85.

## Cymande

## BRA.
Tracks: Bra.
■ 12″. . . . . . . . . . . . . . . . . . . . . . JD 777
J.D. (USA) / Nov '87.

## BROTHERS ON THE SLIDE.
Tracks: Brothers on the slide / Pon de Dungle.
■ 7″. . . . . . . . . . . . . . . . . . . . . CS 2019
Contempo (2) / Jun '74.

## CYMANDE.
Tracks: Message / Brothers on the slide / Dove / Bra / Fug / For baby woh / Rickshaw / Equitorial forest / Listen / Getting it back / Anthracite / Willy's headache / Genevieve / Pon de dungle / Rastafarian folk song / One more / Zion I.
CD. . . . . . . . . . . . . . . . . . . NEX CD 202
Sequel / Jul '92 / Total / BMG.

## MESSAGE.
Tracks: Message / Zion 1.
■ 7″. . . . . . . . . . . . . . . . . . . . . . ALA 4
Alaska / Jan '75.

## Cymone, Andre

## A.C.
Tracks: Dance electric / Lipstick lover / Pretty wild girl / Book of love / Satisfaction / Sweet sensuality / Vacation / Neon pussycat.
■ LP. . . . . . . . . . . . . . . . . . . . CBS 26597
MC. . . . . . . . . . . . . . . . . . . . .40 26597
CBS / '85 / Sony.

## DANCE ELECTRIC.
Tracks: Dance electric / Red light.
■ 12″. . . . . . . . . . . . . . . . . . . . . TX 6435
■ 7″. . . . . . . . . . . . . . . . . . . . . .A 6435
CBS / Sep '85.

## MAKE ME WANNA DANCE.
Tracks: Make me wanna dance.
■ 12″. . . . . . . . . . . . . . . . . . . . . TA 3818
■ 7″. . . . . . . . . . . . . . . . . . . . . .A 3818
CBS / Oct '83.

## SURVIVIN' IN THE 80'S.
Tracks: M.O.T.F / Survivin' in the 80's / Make me wanna dance / Lovedog / Body thanu / Filay / What are we doing here / Don't let the furniture (come down on you).
■ LP. . . . . . . . . . . . . . . . . . . . CBS 25767
MC. . . . . . . . . . . . . . . . . . . . .40 25767
CBS / '83 / Sony.

## SURVIVIN' IN THE 80'S.
Tracks: Survivin' in the 80's / What are we doin'.
■ 12″. . . . . . . . . . . . . . . . . . . . . TA 4328
CBS.
■ 7″. . . . . . . . . . . . . . . . . . . . . .A 4328
CBS / Jul '87.

# D

## D Note

### BABEL.
Tracks: Judgement / Babel / Now's the time / Aria / Bronx bull / Rain / Pharoah / More I see / Message / Lychia / Scheme of things / D votion.
CD . . . . . . . . . . . . . . . . . . . . . . . . DOR 012CD
LP . . . . . . . . . . . . . . . . . . . . . . . . . DOR 012LP
Dorado / Apr '93 / RTM / Pinnacle.

### HORROR.
Tracks: Horror.
12" . . . . . . . . . . . . . . . . . . . . . . . . . . DOR 27
CD Single . . . . . . . . . . . . . . . . . . . . DOR 27CD
Dorado / Oct '94 / RTM / Pinnacle.

### INIQUITY WORKER.
Tracks: Iniquity worker.
12" . . . . . . . . . . . . . . . . . . . . . . . . . DOR 028
Dorado / Nov '94 / RTM / Pinnacle.

### MORE I SEE, THE.
Tracks: More I see / Devotion / More I see (Devotion).
■ 12" . . . . . . . . . . . . . . . . . . . . . . . . DOR 011
Dorado / Apr '93.

### NOW IS THE TIME.
Tracks: Now is the time.
■ 12" . . . . . . . . . . . . . . . . . . . . . . . . DOR 015
■ CD Single . . . . . . . . . . . . . . . . . . DOR 015CD
Dorado / Sep '93.

### RAIN.
Tracks: Rain.
■ 12" . . . . . . . . . . . . . . . . . . . . . . . . DOR 006
Dorado / Aug '92.

### SCHEME OF THINGS.
Tracks: Scheme of things.
■ 12" . . . . . . . . . . . . . . . . . . . . . . . . DOR 002
Dorado / Apr '92.

## D-Mob

### C'MON AND GET MY LOVE.
Tracks: C'mon and get my love / C'mon and get my love (Version).
■ 12" . . . . . . . . . . . . . . . . . . . . . . . . .FX 117
■ 7" . . . . . . . . . . . . . . . . . . . . . . . . . . F 117
■ CD Single . . . . . . . . . . . . . . . . . . . .FCD 117
■ MC Single . . . . . . . . . . . . . . . . . . . .FCS 117
FFRR / Sep '89.

### IT IS TIME TO GET FUNKY.
Tracks: It is time to get funky / Trance dance / C'mon and get my love.
■ 12" . . . . . . . . . . . . . . . . . . . . . . . . .FX 107
■ 7" . . . . . . . . . . . . . . . . . . . . . . . . . . F 107
■ CD Single . . . . . . . . . . . . . . . . . . . .FCD 107
■ MC Single . . . . . . . . . . . . . . . . . . . .FCS 107
FFRR / May '89.

### IT IS TIME TO GET FUNKY (OLD GOLD).
Tracks: Not Advised.
■ 12" . . . . . . . . . . . . . . . . . . . . . . . . .OG 4240
Pickwick / Oct '92.

### LITTLE BIT OF THIS, A.
Tracks: C'mon and get my love / All I do / It really don't matter / That's the way of the world / It is time to get funky / Put your hands together / Rhythm from within / Trance dance / We call it acieed.
■ LP . . . . . . . . . . . . . . . . . . . . . . . 828 195 1
London / Oct '89.
CD . . . . . . . . . . . . . . . . . . . . . . . . 828 195 2
MC . . . . . . . . . . . . . . . . . . . . . . . . 828 195 4
London / May '92 / PolyGram.

### LITTLE BIT OF THIS, A LITTLE BIT OF THAT.
Tracks: That's the way of the world / Put your hands together / C'mon and get my love / It is time to get funky / We call it acieed.
■ VHS . . . . . . . . . . . . . . . . . . . . . . .081944 3
Channel 5 / Apr '90.

### ONE DAY.
Tracks: One day (mixes).
12" . . . . . . . . . . . . . . . . . . . . . . . . . .FX 239
CD Single . . . . . . . . . . . . . . . . . . . .FCD 239
MC Single . . . . . . . . . . . . . . . . . . . .FCS 239
FFRR / Oct '94 / PolyGram.

### PUT YOUR HANDS TOGETHER.
Tracks: Put your hands together / Rhythm from within.
■ 12" . . . . . . . . . . . . . . . . . . . . . . . .FXR 124
■ 12" . . . . . . . . . . . . . . . . . . . . . . . . .FX 124
■ 7" . . . . . . . . . . . . . . . . . . . . . . . . . . F 124
■ CD Single . . . . . . . . . . . . . . . . . . . .FCD 124
■ MC Single . . . . . . . . . . . . . . . . . . . .FCS 124
London / Dec '89.

### THAT'S THE WAY OF THE WORLD (D Mob featuring Cathy Dennis).
Tracks: That's the way of the world / That's the way of the world (version).
■ 12" . . . . . . . . . . . . . . . . . . . . . . . . .FX 132
■ CD Single . . . . . . . . . . . . . . . . . . . .FCD 132
■ MC Single . . . . . . . . . . . . . . . . . . . .FCS 132
■ 7" . . . . . . . . . . . . . . . . . . . . . . . . . . F 132
FFRR / Mar '90.

### WE CALL IT ACIEED.
Tracks: We call it acieed / We call it acieed (matey instrumental) / Matey beat (Only on the 12" version.) / We call it acieed (matey mix).
■ 12" . . . . . . . . . . . . . . . . . . . . . . . FFRXR 13
■ 12" . . . . . . . . . . . . . . . . . . . . . . . .FFRX 13
■ 7" . . . . . . . . . . . . . . . . . . . . . . . . . FFR 13
FFRR / Sep '88.

### WHY (D-Mob & Cathy Dennis).
Tracks: Wait (mixes).
■ 12" . . . . . . . . . . . . . . . . . . . . . . . . .FX 227
■ 7" . . . . . . . . . . . . . . . . . . . . . . . . . . F 227
■ CD Single . . . . . . . . . . . . . . . . . . . .FCD 227
■ MC Single . . . . . . . . . . . . . . . . . . . .FCS 227
FFRR / Dec '93.

## D-Train

### D-TRAIN.
Tracks: You're the one for me / Walk on by / Trying to get over / Lucky day / D train (theme) / Keep on / Love vibration / You're the one for me (reprise).
■ LP . . . . . . . . . . . . . . . . . . . . . . . EPC 85683
■ MC . . . . . . . . . . . . . . . . . . . . . . . .40 85683
Prelude / Apr '82.

### D-TRAIN (EP).
Tracks: You're the one for me / Walk on by / Keep on / D Train (theme).
■ MC Single . . . . . . . . . . . . . . . . EPC A 40 2626
Epic / Aug '82.

### D-TRAIN - THE COLLECTION.
Tracks: Not Advised.
CD . . . . . . . . . . . . . . . . . . . . . . . . CCSCD 387
MC . . . . . . . . . . . . . . . . . . . . . . . .CCSMC 387
Castle / Oct '93 / BMG.

### ESSENTIAL DANCEFLOOR ARTISTS VOL. 2 - D-TRAIN.
Tracks: You're the one for me / Keep on / Don't you wanna ride (the D-Train) / Walk on by / Keep giving me love / Something's on your mind / Music / Thank you / You're the reason.
CD . . . . . . . . . . . . . . . . . . . . . . . DGPCD 666
Deep Beats / Mar '94 / BMG.

### GO FOR IT BABY.
Tracks: Not Advised.
CD . . . . . . . . . . . . . . . . . . . . . . . . TRCD 9916
Tramp / Nov '93 / Direct Distribution / A.D.A. Distribution / C.M. Distribution / Topic Records.

### KEEP GIVING ME LOVE.
Tracks: Keep giving me love / Don't you wanna ride.
■ 12" . . . . . . . . . . . . . . . . . . . . . . . . TA 3497
■ 7" . . . . . . . . . . . . . . . . . . . . . . . . . A 3497
Prelude / Jul '83.

### KEEP ON.
Tracks: Keep on / Love vibrations / You're the one for me (on 12" only).
■ 12" . . . . . . . . . . . . . . . . . . . . . EPCA 132543
■ 7" . . . . . . . . . . . . . . . . . . . . . . . EPCA 2543
Epic / Jul '82.

### MUSIC.
Tracks: Keep giving me love / Shadow of your smile / Are you ready for me / Music / Children of the world / Let me show you / Don't you wanna ride.

### LP . . . . . . . . . . . . . . . . . . . . . . . PRL 25295
Prelude / Jun '83.

### MUSIC.
Tracks: Music / Are you ready for me.
■ 7" . . . . . . . . . . . . . . . . . . . . . . . ZB 40431
■ 12" . . . . . . . . . . . . . . . . . . . . . . . ZT 40432
Prelude / Sep '85.

### MUSIC (PART 1).
Tracks: Music (part 1).
■ 12" . . . . . . . . . . . . . . . . . . . . . . . .TA 3332
■ 7" . . . . . . . . . . . . . . . . . . . . . . . . .A 3332
Prelude / Apr '83.

### SHADOW OF YOUR SMILE.
Tracks: Shadow of your smile / Are you ready for me.
■ 7" . . . . . . . . . . . . . . . . . . . . . . . . .A 3694
Prelude / Sep '83.

### SOMETHING'S ON YOUR MIND.
Tracks: I treasure your pleasure / Something's on your mind / You're the reason / Hustle and bustle of the city / Thank you / I'll do anything / So far away.
■ LP . . . . . . . . . . . . . . . . . . . . . . .PRSLP 6001
■ MC . . . . . . . . . . . . . . . . . . . . . . .PRSK 6001
Prelude / Apr '84.

### THANK YOU.
Tracks: Thank you.
■ 12" . . . . . . . . . . . . . . . . . . . . . . .MHST 102
Prelude / Jul '84.

### WALK ON BY.
Tracks: Walk on by / Lucky day.
■ 12" . . . . . . . . . . . . . . . . . . . . . . . A 132298
■ 7" . . . . . . . . . . . . . . . . . . . . . . . . A 2298
Epic / May '82.

### YOU'RE THE ONE FOR ME.
Tracks: You're the one for me / Keep on / Walk on by / I treasure your pleasure / Music / Keep giving me love / Shadow of your smile / Something's on your mind.
■ LP . . . . . . . . . . . . . . . . . . . . . . . ZL 70885
■ MC . . . . . . . . . . . . . . . . . . . . . . . ZK 70885
Prelude / Sep '85.

### YOU'RE THE ONE FOR ME.
Tracks: You're the one for me.
■ 12" . . . . . . . . . . . . . . . . . . . . . . . A 132016
■ 7" . . . . . . . . . . . . . . . . . . . . . . . .A 2016
Epic / Feb '82.
■ 7" . . . . . . . . . . . . . . . . . . . . . . . ZB 40302
■ 12" . . . . . . . . . . . . . . . . . . . . . . . ZT 40302
Prelude / Jul '85.
■ CD Single . . . . . . . . . . . . . . . . . . CDWGAF 105
■ MC Single . . . . . . . . . . . . . . . . . .WGAFCA 105
■ 12" . . . . . . . . . . . . . . . . . . . . 12 WGAF 105
WGAF / Feb '94.

## D.B. Crew

### DISCOVERING THE REAL U.
Tracks: Discovering the real u.
■ 12" . . . . . . . . . . . . . . . . . . . . . . . .FD 001
F.D.R. Records / Jan '93.

## Da Costa, Paulino

### AGORA.
Tracks: Simbora / Terra / Toledo bagel / Berimbau variations / Belisco / Ritmo number one.
■ LP . . . . . . . . . . . . . . . . . . . . . . .2335 747
Pablo Jazz (USA) / Jan '77.
■ LP . . . . . . . . . . . . . . . . . . . . . . .2310 785
MC . . . . . . . . . . . . . . . . . . . . . . . K10 785
Pablo Jazz (USA) / '82 / Wellard / Complete Record Co. Ltd.

### HAPPY PEOPLE.
Tracks: Deja vu / Put your mind on vacation / Take it on up / Love till the end of time / Seeing is believing / Dreamflow / Carnival of colours / Let's get together / Happy people.
■ LP . . . . . . . . . . . . . . . . . . . . . . .231 2102
MC . . . . . . . . . . . . . . . . . . . . . . . .K 12 102
Pablo Jazz (USA) / '82 / Wellard / Complete Record Co. Ltd.

■ DELETED

## SUNRISE.
Tracks: Taj Mahal / I'm going to Rio / African sunrise / Walkman / O mar e meu chao / You came into my life / My love / You've got a special kind of love / Carioca / Groove.
- ■ LP . . . . . . . . . . . . . . . . . . . . . . . .2312 143
- MC. . . . . . . . . . . . . . . . . . . . . . . .K 12 143
Verve / Sep '84 / PolyGram.
CD . . . . . . . . . . . . . . . . . . . . . CD 231 2143
Pablo Jazz (USA) / Apr '94 / Wellard / Complete Record Co. Ltd.

## TAJ MAHAL.
Tracks: Taj Mahal.
- ■ 12". . . . . . . . . . . . . . . . . . . . . . . . .5155
Pablo Jazz (USA) / Sep '84.

## TUDO BEM (Da Costa, Paulino & Joe Pass).
Tracks: Corcovado / Tears / Wave / Voice / If you went away / Que que ha / Gentle rain / Barquinho / Luciana / I live to love.
- ■ LP . . . . . . . . . . . . . . . . . . . . . .231 0824
- MC. . . . . . . . . . . . . . . . . . . . . . .K10 824
Pablo Jazz (USA) / '82 / Wellard / Complete Record Co. Ltd.

### Dallon, Miki

## CHEAT AND LIE.
Tracks: Cheat and lie / (I'm gonna) find a cave.
- ■ 7". . . . . . . . . . . . . . . . . . . . . . . . .JH 306
Strike (60's) / '66.

## WHAT WILL YOUR MAMA SAY NOW.
Tracks: What will your mama say now.
- ■ 7". . . . . . . . . . . . . . . . . . . . . . . . .JH 318
Strike (60's) / '66.

### Damaris

## WHAT ABOUT MY LOVE?.
Tracks: What about my love / Hooray for love.
- ■ 12". . . . . . . . . . . . . . . . . . . . . . . TA 4172
- ■ 7". . . . . . . . . . . . . . . . . . . . . . . .A 4172
CBS / Mar '84.

### Damier, Chez

## CAN YOU FEEL IT.
Tracks: Can you feel it.
- ■ 12". . . . . . . . . . . . . . . . . . . . . KMSUK 3
KMS / Jun '92.

## I NEVER KNEW LOVE.
Tracks: I never knew love / I never knew love (mixes).
- ■ 12". . . . . . . . . . . . . . . . . . . . . NWKT 64
Network (Kool Kat) / Nov '92.

## UNITED STATES EP.
Tracks: Not Advised.
- ■ 12". . . . . . . . . . . . . . . . . . . . TIME 0793
Time / Aug '93.

### Dan-Elle

## TAKE CARE OF YOURSELF.
Tracks: Take care of yourself / Fire and desire.
12". . . . . . . . . . . . . . . . . . . . . . . SCGT 104
SCG Records / May '94 / Jetstar.

## YOU TOLD ME.
Tracks: You told me.
12". . . . . . . . . . . . . . . . . . . . . . SCGDJ 104
SCG Records / Mar '94 / Jetstar.

### Daniels, Eddie

## BENNY RIDES AGAIN (Daniels, Eddie & Gary Burton).
Tracks: Sing, sing, sing / Stompin' at the Savoy / Moonglow / Airmail special / Let's dance / Slipped disc / Memories of you / Avalon / In a mist / Grand slam / After you've gone / Goodbye / Knockin' on wood.
- CD. . . . . . . . . . . . . . . . . . . . . GRP 96652
- ■ MC. . . . . . . . . . . . . . . . . . . . GRP 96654
GRP / May '92 / BMG / New Note.

## BLACKWOOD.
Tracks: Not Advised.
- ■ LP . . . . . . . . . . . . . . . . . . . . GRP 95841
- ■ CD . . . . . . . . . . . . . . . . . . . . GRP 95842
- ■ MC. . . . . . . . . . . . . . . . . . . . GRP 95844
GRP / Apr '89.

## BREAK THROUGH.
Tracks: Not Advised.
- ■ CD . . . . . . . . . . . . . . . . . . . . GRP 95332
GRP / Jan '93.

## BREAKTHROUGH.
Tracks: Solfeggietto / Metamorphosis / Circle dance / Aja's theme / Divertimento / Concerto for jazz concerto / Allegro / Adagio / Presto.
- ■ LP . . . . . . . . . . . . . . . . . . . GRP 91024
- ■ MC . . . . . . . . . . . . . . . . . . . . .C 1024
- ■ CD . . . . . . . . . . . . . . . . . . . GRPD 9533
GRP / Apr '86.
CD . . . . . . . . . . . . . . . . . . . . GRP 95322
GRP / Jul '92 / BMG / New Note.

## BRIEF ENCOUNTER.
Tracks: Brief encounter / Child is born / Path / Sway / There is no greater love / Ligia.
- ■ LP . . . . . . . . . . . . . . . . . . . . . MR 5154
Muse / Apr '81.
CD. . . . . . . . . . . . . . . . . . . . . MCD 5154
Muse / Sep '92 / New Note / Jazz Horizons / C.M. Distribution.

## MEMO FROM PARADISE.
Tracks: Not Advised.
- ■ CD. . . . . . . . . . . . . . . . . . . . GRPD 9561
GRP / Jul '91.
- ■ CD. . . . . . . . . . . . . . . . . . . . GRP 95612
GRP / Jan '93.

## MEMO'S FROM PARADISE.
Tracks: Spectralight / Dreaming / Heartline / Love of my life / Homecoming / Memo's from Paradise / Seventh Heaven / Capriccio twilight / Impressions from ancient dreams / Flight of the dove / Eight-pointed star (Bonus track on CD only.)
- CD. . . . . . . . . . . . . . . . . . . . GRPD 9651
- ■ LP . . . . . . . . . . . . . . . . . . . GRP 91050
- ■ MC. . . . . . . . . . . . . . . . . . GRPM 91050
GRP / May '88 / BMG / New Note.

## NEPENTHE (NO SORROW).
Tracks: Sun dance / Equinox / Nepenthe / Waltz of another colour / Suenos (dreams) / Chaser / Only one / Chant / Quiet space / Reverie for a rainy day (Available on CD only) / Soul eyes (Available on CD only).
- ■ LP . . . . . . . . . . . . . . . . . . . GRP 96071
- ■ MC. . . . . . . . . . . . . . . . . . . GRP 96074
- ■ CD . . . . . . . . . . . . . . . . . . . GRP 96072
GRP / Mar '90.

## REAL TIME.
Tracks: Rainbow shadows / Man I love / Love walked in / Blue bolero / Sweet Lorraine / Thad's lament / Falling in love with love / My foolish heart / You stepped out of a dream / Tricotism / Farrell.
CD. . . . . . . . . . . . . . . . . . . . . . JD 118
Chesky Records / Oct '94 / New Note.

## THIS IS NOW.
Tracks: 34 skidoo / It was always you / How my heart sings / New thing / Soft shoe for Thad / Double image / Cry / 3 and 1 / All the stars are out / In a sentimental mood / That was then.. This is now / Body & soul.
- ■ LP . . . . . . . . . . . . . . . . . . . GRP 96351
- ■ MC. . . . . . . . . . . . . . . . . . . GRP 96354
- ■ CD . . . . . . . . . . . . . . . . . . . GRP 96352
GRP / May '91.

## TO BIRD WITH LOVE.
Tracks: She rote / East of the sun / Just friends / Old folks / Little suede shoes / Passport / Repitition / This is the time.
- ■ LP . . . . . . . . . . . . . . . . . . . GRP 91034
- ■ CD . . . . . . . . . . . . . . . . . . . GRD 9544
- ■ MC. . . . . . . . . . . . . . . . . . GRPM 91034
GRP / May '87.
- ■ CD . . . . . . . . . . . . . . . . . . . GRP 95442
GRP / Jan '93.

## UNDER THE INFLUENCE.
Tracks: Slam dunk / Mr. Cool (for Stan) / Waltz for Bill (Evans) / Meus melhores momentos / Heartland / I hear a rhapsody / Weaver of dreams / Coyote waits / Rio grande / I fall in love too easily / Five / Blue mood.
CD. . . . . . . . . . . . . . . . . . . . . GRP 97172
GRP / Apr '93 / BMG / New Note.

### Dante

## FREAK IN ME.
Tracks: Freak in me / Freak in me (version) / One more time.
- ■ 12". . . . . . . . . . . . . . . . . . . . . . BR 47
Blue Bird (2) / Feb '88.

### Dante, Steven

## FIND OUT.
Tracks: I'm too scared / Ready to love / Imagination / Candy / Real thing (With Jellybean.) / Love follows / Find out / Taking love to the limit / It's only love / Ghosts.

- ■ CD . . . . . . . . . . . . . . . . . . . . CCD 1632
- ■ LP . . . . . . . . . . . . . . . . . . . . . CTLP 6
- ■ MC. . . . . . . . . . . . . . . . . . . . ZCTLP 6
Chrysalis / Aug '88.

## GIVE IT UP FOR LOVE.
Tracks: Give it up for love.
- ■ 12". . . . . . . . . . . . . . . . . . . . COOLX 118
- ■ 7". . . . . . . . . . . . . . . . . . . . COOL 118
Cool Tempo / '86.

## I'M TOO SCARED.
Tracks: I'm too scared.
- ■ 12". . . . . . . . . . . . . . . . . . . .DANTEX 1
- ■ 7". . . . . . . . . . . . . . . . . . . . . DANTE 1
- ■ CD Single. . . . . . . . . . . . . . . . SDCD 1
Cool Tempo / Jun '88.

## JUST MY IMAGINATION.
Tracks: Just my imagination / If it makes you feel good / Just my imagination (dancin' Danny D remix).
- ■ CD Single . . . . . . . . . . . . . . . . SDCD 2
- ■ 12". . . . . . . . . . . . . . . . . . . .DANTEX 2
- ■ 7". . . . . . . . . . . . . . . . . . . . . DANTE 2
Cool Tempo / Sep '88.

## LOVE FOLLOWS.
Tracks: Love follows / Taking love to the limit.
- ■ 12". . . . . . . . . . . . . . . . . . . .DANTEX 3
- ■ 7". . . . . . . . . . . . . . . . . . . . . DANTE 3
Cool Tempo / Jan '89.

## SO LONG.
Tracks: So long / Lovin' eyes.
- ■ 12". . . . . . . . . . . . . . . . . . . .CHS 122897
- ■ 7". . . . . . . . . . . . . . . . . . . . CHS 2897
Cool Tempo / Jul '85.

### D'Arby, Terence Trent

## DANCE LITTLE SISTER.
Tracks: Dance little sister (part 1) / Dance little sister (part 2).
- ■ 7". . . . . . . . . . . . . . . . . . . . . TRENT 3
- ■ MC Single. . . . . . . . . . . . . . . TRENTC 3
- ■ 12". . . . . . . . . . . . . . . . . . . . TRENTT 3
- ■ 7". . . . . . . . . . . . . . . . . . . . TRENT Q3
CBS / Sep '87.

## DELICATE (D'Arby, Terence Trent & Des'ree).
Tracks: Delicate (featuring Des'ree) / She's my baby / Dance little sister / Survivor (Only on CD single).
- ■ 7". . . . . . . . . . . . . . . . . . . . . 6593317
- ■ CD Single. . . . . . . . . . . . . . . . 6593312
- ■ MC Single. . . . . . . . . . . . . . . . 6593314
Columbia / Jun '93.

## DO YOU LOVE ME LIKE YOU SAY.
Tracks: Do you love me like you say / Do you love me like you say (mix) / Read my lips (I dig your scene) / Perfumed pavillion (The motion of my memories) (Features on MCS & CDS only.)
- ■ 12". . . . . . . . . . . . . . . . . . . .659073 6
- ■ CD Single. . . . . . . . . . . . . . . .659073 2
- ■ CD Single. . . . . . . . . . . . . . . .659073 5
- ■ MC Single. . . . . . . . . . . . . . . .659073 8
Columbia / Apr '93.

## IF YOU LET ME STAY.
Tracks: If you let me stay / Loving you is another word for lonely.
- ■ 12". . . . . . . . . . . . . . . . . . . . TRENT T1
- ■ 7". . . . . . . . . . . . . . . . . . . . . TRENT 1
CBS / Feb '87.

## INTRODUCING THE HARDLINE (LIVE).
Tracks: Not Advised.
VHS . . . . . . . . . . . . . . . . . . . . . 5426 50
CBS-Fox / Mar '88 / Sony / THE.
VHS . . . . . . . . . . . . . . . . . . . . . 49001-2
CMV Enterprises (Video) / Jul '89 / Sony.

## INTRODUCING THE HARDLINE ACCORDING TO TERENCE TRENT D'ARBY.
Tracks: If you all get to Heaven / If you let me stay / Wishing well / I'll never turn my back on you (fathers words) / Dance little sister / Seven more days / Let's go forward / Rain / Sign your name / As yet untitled / Who's loving you.
CD. . . . . . . . . . . . . . . . . . . . . . 4509112
MC. . . . . . . . . . . . . . . . . . . . . . 4509114
- ■ CD P.Disc. . . . . . . . . . . . . . . . 4509119
- ■ LP . . . . . . . . . . . . . . . . . . . . 4509111
CBS / Jul '87 / Sony.
- ■ LP P.Disc . . . . . . . . . . . . . . . . 4509110
CBS / Nov '87.
MiniDisc. . . . . . . . . . . . . . . . . . .450911-3
Columbia / Feb '93 / Sony.

## LET HER DOWN EASY.
Tracks: Let her down easy / Turn the page / Do you love me like you say (On 12" only) / Sign your name (On CD single only) / Delicate (On CD single only).
- 12".............................6598646
- 7"..............................6598647
- CD Single........................6598642
- MC Single........................6598644

Columbia / Nov '93.

## NEITHER FISH NOR FLESH.
Tracks: Declaration / Neither fish nor flesh / I have faith in these desolate times / It feels so good to love someone like you / I'll be alright / Billy don't fall / This side of love / Attracted to you / Roly poly / You will pay tomorrow / I don't want to bring your Gods down / And I need to be with someone tonight.
- LP..............................4658091
- CD..............................4658092
- MC..............................4658094

CBS / Oct '89.

## SHE KISSED ME.
Tracks: She kissed me / Do you love me like you say.
- 12"............................659592 6
- CD Single......................659592 2
- MC Single......................659592 4

Columbia / Sep '93.

## SIGN YOUR NAME.
Tracks: Sign your name / Greasy chicken / Under my thumb (12" only.) / Jumpin' Jack Flash (On 12" only) / If you all get to heaven (On 10" only) / Dance little sister (On CD picture single only).
- 12"............................TRENT T4
- 7".............................TRENT Q4
- 7".............................TRENT 4
- 7" P.Disc......................TRENT P4

CBS / Dec '87.
- CD P.Disc......................TRENT C4
- 10"............................TRENT G4

CBS / Jan '88.

## TERENCE TRENT D'ARBY'S SYMPHONY OR DAMN (Exploring The Tension Inside The Sweetness).
Tracks: Welcome to the Monasteryo / She kissed me / Do you love me like you say / Baby let me share my love / Delicate / Neon messiah / Penelope please / Wet your lips / Turn the page / Castilian blues / T.I.T.S./F&J / Are you happy / Succumb to me / I still love you (Extra track included with LP version.) / Seasons (Extra track included in LP version.) / Let her down easy (Extra track included in LP version.).
- CD..............................473561 2
- LP..............................473561 1
- MC..............................473561 4
- MiniDisc........................473561 8

Columbia / May '93 / Sony.

## TERENCE TRENT D'ARBY: INTERVIEW PICTURE DISC.
Tracks: Not Advised.
- LP P.Disc.......................BAK 2145

Baktabak / Oct '89.

## THIS SIDE OF LOVE.
Tracks: This side of love / Sad song for sister Sarah serenade / Sign your name (live).
- 12"............................TRENT T5
- 12"............................TRENT Q5
- 7".............................TRENT 5
- CD Single......................TRENT P5
- CD Single......................TRENT C5
- MC Single......................TRENT M5

CBS / Nov '89.

## TO KNOW SOMEONE DEEPLY IS TO KNOW SOMEONE SOFTLY.
Tracks: To know someone / Loose variations on a dead man's vibe in Cm (Only on 7" single.) / To know someone deeply (upsetter mix) (Only on 12" and CD single.) / Rain (live) (Only on 12" and CD single.).
- 12"............................TRENT T6
- 7".............................TRENT 6
- 7" P.Disc......................TRENT E6
- CD Single......................TRENT C6
- MC Single......................TRENT M6

CBS / Jan '90.

## TOUCH WITH TERENCE TRENT D'ARBY, THE.
Tracks: Not Advised.
- CD..............................839 308-2
- LP..............................839 308-1
- MC..............................839 308-4

Polydor / Aug '89 / PolyGram.

## WISHING WELL.
Tracks: Wishing well / Elevators and hearts.
- 12"............................TRENT T2
- 12" Remix.....................TRENTR 2
- 7"............................TRENTG 2

---

- 7".............................TRENT 2
- 7".............................TRENTQ 2

CBS / Jun '87.

# Darien

## HE SENT ME AN ANGEL.
Tracks: He sent me an angel / Catch me.
- 12".............................12 PO 60

Wilbe / Jan '91.

# Dash, Sarah

## SINNER MAN.
Tracks: Sinner man / Look, but don't touch.
- 7".............................KIR 6973

Kirshner (USA) / Feb '79.

# David Disco Dance..

## DON'T WALK GO (Go to a disco) (David Disco Dance Orchestra).
Tracks: Not Advised.
- LP.............................KM 12826

David Disco / Jan '86.

# Davies, Carol

## BUNNY AND THE BUBBLE.
Tracks: Bunny and the bubble.
- 7"...............................EKL 79

EKL / Oct '84.

## HEART OF GOLD.
Tracks: It's in my genes / When my money's gone / Sexual favours / Sticky situation / Serious money / Dissin' Jerome / Thigh's the limit / Mirror mirror on the wall / Frown is just a smile upside down.
- CD............................K 9259032
- LP............................K 9259031
- MC............................K 9259034

WEA / Jul '89.

# Davis, Betty

## BETTY DAVIS.
Tracks: Not Advised.
- CD...........................UFOXY 1CD
- LP.............................UFOXY 1

UFO / Oct '93 / Pinnacle.

## THEY SAY I'M DIFFERENT.
Tracks: Not Advised.
- CD...........................UFOXY 3CD
- LP.............................UFOXY 3

Vexfilms / Mar '94 / Pinnacle.

# Davis, Darlene

## I FOUND LOVE (The Belated '87 Valentine).
Tracks: I found love.
- 7".............................OUSX 1

Serious / Mar '87.

## I FOUND LOVE (RADIO MIX).
Tracks: I found love / Dare to dance (Available on 12" version only).
- 12"...........................12OUS 1
- 7".............................7OUS 1

Serious / Feb '87.

# Davis, Geater

## SAD SHADES OF BLUE.
Tracks: I ain't worried about Jody / Your heart is so cold / I know my baby loves me / I'll meet you / Why does it hurt so bad / Whole lot of woman / Sad shade of blue / Will be him or me / Long cold winter / I've got to pay the price / I'm gonna change / Two that sticks together / I'm so in love with you.
- LP.............................CRB 1132

Charly R&B / '87.

# Davis, John

## AIN'T THAT ENOUGH FOR YOU? (Davis, John & The Monster Orchestra).
Tracks: Ain't that enough for you / Disco fever / I've got the hots for you / Bite of the apple / I'll be the music / Whatever happened to me and you.
- LP.............................MLP 3002

Miracle / '87.

## AIN'T THAT ENOUGH FOR YOU? (Davis, John & The Monster Orchestra).
Tracks: Ain't that enough for you / Disco fever.
- 7"...............................M 2

Miracle / Feb '79.

---

## LOVE MAGIC.
Tracks: Love magic / Holler.
- 12"...........................CBS 137479
- 7".............................CBS 7479

CBS / Nov '79.

## MAGIC IS YOU (Davis, John & The Monster Orchestra).
Tracks: Magic is you / You are the one.
- 7"............................2058 923

Polydor / Sep '77.

## UP JUMPED THE DEVIL (Davis, John & The Monster Orchestra).
Tracks: Up jumped the devil / You've got to give it up.
- 7"............................2058 870

Polydor / May '77.

## WHO DO YOU LOVE.
Tracks: Who do you love / You satisfy me.
- CD Single.......................873 455-2
- 12".............................PZ 72
- 7".............................PO 72

Polydor / Feb '90.

# Davis, Mary

## DON'T WEAR IT OUT.
Tracks: Don't wear it out / Steppin' out / Just be good to me.
- 12"...........................655 296 6
- 7"............................655 296 7
- CD Single......................655 296 2

Tabu / Mar '90.

## SEPARATE WAYS.
Tracks: Don't wear it out / Baby, baby (you ain't treating me right) / Separate ways / I'm gonna love you better / I get nervous / I wanna be sure / Some kind of lover / Have you been loved / Sweet obsession.
- CD..............................465 877 2
- LP..............................465 877 1
- MC..............................465 877 4

Tabu / Apr '90 / Sony.

## STEPPING OUT.
Tracks: Stepping out / I'm gonna love you better.
- 12"...........................651256 6
- 7"............................651256 7

Tabu / Nov '87.

# Davis, Miles

American trumpeter who ranks among most innovative and influential figures in jazz, despite farcical U.K. chart history - solitary week at No 71 in July 1970 with *Bitches Brew* LP. Born in Illinois in 1926, Davis served apprenticeship with legendary saxophonist Charlie Parker, before crucial union with orchestral arranger Gil Evans in 1940s. Popularity grew further with assembling of classic quintet in mid-'50s, including saxophonist John Coltrane. By close of decade, however, Davis had tired of conventional formats. Subsequent eclectism yielded 'rock' album *Miles In the Sky* and funky *On the Corner* (featuring, among others, James M'tume and Herbie Hancock); while posthumous *Doo-Bop* set touched on hip-hop. Ill-health slowed his activities in '80s, and he died in September '91. His last work included occasional jamming with Prince, results of which are regrettably available on bootleg only. Nonetheless, legitimate releases are more-than-adequate legacy.

## '58 SESSIONS.
Tracks: On Green Dolphin Street / Fran dance / Stella by starlight / Love for sale / Straight, no chaser / My funny valentine / Oleo.
- CD..............................4679182
- MC..............................4679184

Columbia / Apr '92 / Sony.

## 1955-61 (Davis, Miles Quintet).
Tracks: S'posin' / There is no greater love / Stablemates / Budo / Just squeeze me / Vierd blues / So what / 'Round midnight.
- LP.............................LPJT 57

Giants Of Jazz / '86.
- MC.............................MCJT 57

Giants Of Jazz / Mar '92 / Wellard / Swift / Target / Jazz Music / BMG.

## 1958 MILES.
Tracks: Not Advised.
- LP...........................20 AP 1401

Japanese Import / May '79.

## AGHARTA.
**Tracks:** Prelude / Maiysha / Interlude / Theme from Jack Johnson.
■ **Double LP** . . . . . . . . . . . . . . **CBS 88159**
CBS / Jan '87.
**CD** . . . . . . . . . . . . . . . . . . . .467897 2
Columbia / Sep '93 / Sony.

## AMANDLA.
**Tracks:** Catembe / Big time / Jo Jo / Jilli / Cobra / Hannibal / Amandla / Mr. Pastorius.
**CD** . . . . . . . . . . . . . . . . . . K 925873-2
■ **LP** . . . . . . . . . . . . . . . . . . **WX 250**
■ **MC** . . . . . . . . . . . . . . . . . **WX 250C**
WEA / May '89 / WEA.

## AND MODERN JAZZ GIANTS.
**Tracks:** Not Advised.
**CD** . . . . . . . . . . . . . . . . . OJCCD 347-2
Original Jazz Classics / Feb '92 / Ace Records / Complete Record Co. Ltd / Jazz Music / BMG.

## ARTISTRY IN JAZZ (Greatest hits).
**Tracks:** Not Advised.
**CD** . . . . . . . . . . . . . . . . . . . VDJ 1586
JVC/Fantasy / May '87 / Target.

## ASCENSEUR POUR L'ECHAFAUD (Davis, Miles & Art Blakey Jazz Messengers).
**Tracks:** Generique / L'assassinat de carala / Sur l'autoroute / Julien dans l'ascenseur / Florence sur les Champs Elysees / Diner au motel / Evasion de Julien / Visite du vigile / Au bar du petit bac / Chez le photographe du motel.
**CD** . . . . . . . . . . . . . . . . . . 822 566-2
Philips / '88 / PolyGram.

## AT BIRDLAND, 1951.
**Tracks:** Not Advised.
■ **LP** . . . . . . . . . . . . . . . . . . . .BEP 501
Beppo / Jun '76.

## AT BIRDLAND: MILES DAVIS (Davis, Miles Sextet).
**Tracks:** Hot house / Embraceable you / Ouverturia / 52nd Street theme / Wee Chubb's blues.
■ **LP** . . . . . . . . . . . . . . . . . . . BLJ 8023
Jazz Live (Italy) / Apr '81.

## AT FILLMORE.
**Tracks:** Not Advised.
**CD** . . . . . . . . . . . . . . . . . . .476909 2
Columbia / Oct '94 / Sony.

## AT HIS RAREST OF ALL RARE PERFORMANCES: VOL 1.
**Tracks:** Not Advised.
■ **LP** . . . . . . . . . . . . . . . . . .KLJ 20025
Kings Of Jazz.

## AT LAST (Davis, Miles & The Lighthouse All Stars).
**Tracks:** Infinity promenade / Round midnight / Night in Tunisia / Drum conversation / At last.
■ **LP** . . . . . . . . . . . . . . . . . . .COP 001
Boplicity / May '85.
**CD** . . . . . . . . . . . . . . . . . OJCCD 480-2
Original Jazz Classics / Feb '92 / Ace Records / Complete Record Co. Ltd / Jazz Music / BMG.

## AUDIO ARCHIVE.
**Tracks:** Out of nowhere / Night in Tunisia / Yardbird suite / Scrapple the apple / Ornithology / Don't blame me / Moose the mooche / Bird of paradise / Embraceable you / My old flame / Birdnest / Tweet bop / Slam blam blues / Cool head blues / Riff raff.
**CD** . . . . . . . . . . . . . . . . . . CDAA 027
**MC** . . . . . . . . . . . . . . . . . . MCAA 027
IMD / Jun '92 / BMG.

## AURA.
**Tracks:** Intro / White / Yellow / Orange / Red / Green / Blue / Electric red / Indigo / Violet.
**CD** . . . . . . . . . . . . . . . . . . .4633512
■ **LP** . . . . . . . . . . . . . . . . . .4633511
■ **MC** . . . . . . . . . . . . . . . . . .4633514
CBS / Oct '89 / Sony.

## BAGS GROOVE.
**Tracks:** Not Advised.
**CD** . . . . . . . . . . . . . . . . . . JW 77005
Jazz World / May '93 / New Note / Target Sales & Marketing.

## BAGS' GROOVE.
**Tracks:** Bag's groove / Airegin / Oleo / But not for me (take 2) / But not for me (take 1).
■ **CD** . . . . . . . . . . . . . . . . . . VDJ 1531
JVC/Fantasy / Nov '86.
■ **LP** . . . . . . . . . . . . . . . . . . . OJC 245
Original Jazz Classics / Jan '87.
■ **LP** . . . . . . . . . . . . . . . . . . . PR 7109

## MC.
**MC** . . . . . . . . . . . . . . . . . . . PRC 7109
Prestige / Mar '88 / Total / BMG.
**CD** . . . . . . . . . . . . . . . . . OJCCD 245-2
Original Jazz Classics / Feb '92 / Ace Records / Complete Record Co. Ltd / Jazz Music / BMG.

## BALLADS.
**Tracks:** Baby won't you please come home / I fall in love too easily / Bye bye blackbird / Basin Street blues / Once upon a summertime / Song no.2 / Wait till you see her / Corcovado.
**CD** . . . . . . . . . . . . . . . . . . .4610992
■ **LP** . . . . . . . . . . . . . . . . . .4610991
■ **MC** . . . . . . . . . . . . . . . . . .4610994
Sony Music / Apr '89 / Sony.

## BEST OF MILES DAVIS, THE.
**Tracks:** Move / Godchild / Budo / Dear old Stockholm / Donna / Yesterdays / Tempus fugit / Enigma / C.T.A. / Well you needn't / It never entered my mind / Weirdo / Somethin' else / Autumn leaves.
**CD** . . . . . . . . . . . . . . . . . . .BNZ 286
Blue Note / Feb '92 / EMI.

## BIRDLAND DAYS.
**Tracks:** Not Advised.
**CD** . . . . . . . . . . . . . . . . . . FSCD 124
Fresh Sounds / Jan '91 / Charly / Cadillac / Jazz Music.

## BIRDLAND SESSIONS.
**Tracks:** Not Advised.
**CD** . . . . . . . . . . . . . . . . LEJAZZCD 23
Le Jazz / Feb '94 / Jazz Music / Charly.

## BIRTH OF THE COOL.
**Tracks:** Move / Jeru / Moon dreams / Venus De Milo / Budo / Deception / Darn that dream (CD only.) / Godchild / Boplicity / Rocker / Israel / Rouge.
■ **LP** . . . . . . . . . . . . . . . . . CAPS 1024
Capitol / Jul '78.
**CD** . . . . . . . . . . . . . . . . . . . CZ 274
Pacific Jazz / Apr '90 / EMI.
**CD** . . . . . . . . . . . . . . . CDP 792 862 2
EMI / Sep '92 / EMI.

## BITCHES BREW.
**Tracks:** Pharaoh's dance / Bitches brew / Spanish key / John McLaughlin / Miles runs down the voodoo down / Sanctuary.
■ **Double LP** . . . . . . . . . . . . . CBS 66236
CBS / Jul '87.
**CD Set** . . . . . . . . . . . . . . . . 4606022
■ **MC Set** . . . . . . . . . . . . . . . 4606024
Columbia / Oct '91 / Sony.

## BITCHES BREW LIVE.
**Tracks:** Not Advised.
**CD** . . . . . . . . . . . . . . . . . . JZCD 373
Recording Arts / Nov '92 / THE.

## BLUE CHRISTMAS.
**Tracks:** Little Melonae / Budo / Sweet Sue / On Green Dolphin Street / Fran dance / Stella by starlight / Blue Christmas.
■ **LP** . . . . . . . . . . . . . . . . . CBS 21070
■ **MC** . . . . . . . . . . . . . . . . .40 21070
CBS / May '83.

## BLUE HAZE.
**Tracks:** Not Advised.
■ **LP** . . . . . . . . . . . . . . . . . . .OJC 093
Original Jazz Classics / Jun '86.
**CD** . . . . . . . . . . . . . . . . . OJCCD 093-2
Original Jazz Classics / Feb '92 / Ace Records / Complete Record Co. Ltd / Jazz Music / BMG.
**CD** . . . . . . . . . . . . . . . . . CDSGP 042
Prestige (USA) / Mar '93 / Jazz Music / Cadillac / Complete Record Co. Ltd.

## BOPPING THE BLUES.
**Tracks:** Don't sing me the blues (Take 1) / Don't sing me the blues (Take 2) / I've always got the blues (Take 1, incomplete) / I've always got the blues (Take 2) / I've always got the blues (Take 3) / Don't explain to me, baby (Take 1) / Don't explain to me, baby (Take 2) / Don't explain to me, baby (Take 3) / Don't explain to me, baby (Take 4) / Baby, won't you make up your mind (Take 1).
**CD** . . . . . . . . . . . . . . . . . BLCD 760102
■ **LP** . . . . . . . . . . . . . . . . . BLP 60102
Black Lion / Jun '88 / Jazz Music / Cadillac / Wellard / Koch International.

## CBS YEARS 1955-85.
**Tracks:** Generique / All blues / Eighty-one / Blues for Pablo / Summertime / Straight, no chaser / Footprints / Florence sur les Champs Elysees / I thought about you / Some day my prince will come / Bye bye blackbird / My funny valentine / Love for sale / Budo / Miles / Files de Kilimanjaro / Fran dance / Seven steps to heaven / Flamenco sketches / So what / Water babies / Saeta / Masqualero / Pinocchio / Summer night / Fall / It's about that time / Sivad /

What it is / Ms. Morrisine / Shout / Honky Tonk / Star on Cicely / Thinkin' one thing and doin' another / Miles runs the voodoo down.
**CD** . . . . . . . . . . . . . . . . . . 463 246 2
■ **LP** . . . . . . . . . . . . . . . . . 463 246 1
■ **MC** . . . . . . . . . . . . . . . . . 463 246 4
Jam Today / Feb '89 / Jetstar.

## CHRONICLE.
**Tracks:** Not Advised.
**CD Set** . . . . . . . . . . . . . . . . 8PCD 012
Prestige / Apr '92 / Total / BMG.

## CHRONICLE: THE COMPLETE PRESTIGE RECORDINGS.
**Tracks:** Ahmad's blues / Airegin / Bag's groove / Bemsha swing / Bitty ditty / Blue haze / Blue 'n' boogie / Blue room / Blues by five / Bluing / But not for me / Changes / Compulsion / Conception / Denial / Diane / Dig / Dr. Jackle / Down / Doxy / Ezz-thetic / Floppy / For adults only / Four / Gal in Calico / Green haze / Half nelson / Hibeck / How am I to know / I could write a book / I know / I didn't / I see your face before me / I'll remember April / If I were a bell / In your own sweet way / It could happen to you / It never entered my mind / It's only a paper moon / Just squeeze me / Love me or leave me / Man I love / Miles ahead / Minor march / Morpheus / My funny valentine / Night in Tunisia / No line / Odjenar / Old devil moon / Oleo / Out of the blue / Round about midnight / Salt peanuts / Serpent's tooth / Smooch / Solar / Something I dreamed last night / S'posin' / Stablemates / Surrey with the fringe on top / Swing spring / Tasty pudding / Theme / There is no greater love / 'Trane's blues / Tune up / Vierd blues / Walkin' / Well you needn't / When I fall in love / When lights are low / Whispering / Will you still be mine / Willie the wailer / Wouldn't you / Yesterdays / You don't know what love is / You're my everything.
■ **LP Set** . . . . . . . . . . . . . . . . P 012
Prestige / Dec '80.

## CIRCLE IN THE ROUND.
**Tracks:** Circle in the round / Two bass hit / Love for sale / Blues No. 2 / Teo's bag / Side car / Splash sanctuary / Guinevere.
■ **Double LP** . . . . . . . . . . . . . CBS 88471
CBS / Feb '80.
■ **Double LP** . . . . . . . . . . . . . CBS 22132
CBS / '88.
**CD Set** . . . . . . . . . . . . . . . . .467989 2
Columbia / Sep '93 / Sony.

## COLLECTION: MILES DAVIS.
**Tracks:** Milestones / Gone / So what / I thought about you / Walkin' / Frelon brun / Miles runs the voodoo down / Medley gemini/Double image / Fat time / What it is / Human nature.
**CD** . . . . . . . . . . . . . . . . . CCSCD 243
**MC.** . . . . . . . . . . . . . . . . . CCSMC 243
■ **Double LP** . . . . . . . . . . . . CCSLP 243
Castle Collector Series / Jun '90 / BMG / Pinnacle / Castle Communications.

## COLLECTION: MILES DAVIS.
**Tracks:** My funny Valentine / So what / Straight, no chaser / Milestones / Some day my Prince will come / Autumn leaves / Oleo / Fran dance / Oh-leu-cha / Walkin' / Theme.
**MC.** . . . . . . . . . . . . . . . . . DVMC 2039
Deja Vu / Aug '85 / Jazz Music / Music Collection International.
**CD** . . . . . . . . . . . . . . . . . DVCD 2039
Deja Vu / Sep '87 / Jazz Music / Music Collection International.

## COLLECTOR'S ITEM.
**Tracks:** Compulsion / Serpent's tooth / Round about midnight / In your own sweet way / Vierd blues / No line / My old flame / Nature boy / There's no cry / Easy living / Alone together.
■ **Double LP** . . . . . . . . . . . . . PR 24022
Prestige / '79.
■ **Double LP** . . . . . . . . . . . . . . OJC 071
Prestige (USA) / Feb '84.
**CD** . . . . . . . . . . . . . . . . . . . 98406
Carrere (France) / Apr '87.

## COLLECTORS ITEMS.
**Tracks:** Not Advised.
**CD** . . . . . . . . . . . . . . . . . OJCCD 071-2
Original Jazz Classics / Feb '92 / Ace Records / Complete Record Co. Ltd / Jazz Music / BMG.

## COLUMBIA YEARS 1955-1985.
**Tracks:** Generique / All blues / Eighty-one / Blues for Pablo / Summertime / Straight, no chaser / Footprints / Florence sur les Champs Eleysees / I thought about you / Someday my Prince will come / Bye bye blackbird / My funny valentine / Love for sale / Budo / Miles / Filles de Kilimanjaro / Fran dance (put your little foot right out) / Seven steps to heaven / Flamenco sketches / So what / Water babies / Saeta /

Masqalero / Pinocchio / Summernight / Fall / It's all about that time / Sivad / What it is / Ms. Morrisine / Shout / Honky tonk / Star on Cicely / Thinkin' one thing and doin' another / Miles runs the voodoo down.
■ CD Set . . . . . . . . . . . . . . . . . . . 4632462
Columbia / Feb '92.

**COMPACT JAZZ: MILES DAVIS.**
Tracks: Jitterbug waltz / Django / Wild man blues / Round midnight / Generique / L'assassinat de Carala / Sur l'autoroute / Julien dans l'asceseur / Florence sur les Champs Elysees / Diner au motel / Evasion de Julien / Visite du vigile / Au bar du petit bac / Chez le photographe du motel / Au privave / She rote / K.C. blues / Star eyes.
CD . . . . . . . . . . . . . . . . . . . . . 838 254-2
MC . . . . . . . . . . . . . . . . . . . . . 838 254-4
Verve / Jan '90 / PolyGram.

**COMPLETE AMSTERDAM CONCERT, THE.**
Tracks: Not Advised.
■ LP . . . . . . . . . . . . . . . . . . . CEL 6745
MC . . . . . . . . . . . . . . . . . . . . CEL 6746
Celluloid (France) / Jul '85 / C.M. Distribution.

**COMPLETE CONCERT 1964, THE (My Funny Valentine & Four More).**
Tracks: Introduction by Mort Fega / My funny valentine / All of you / Go-go (Theme and re-introduction) / Stella by starlight / All blues / I thought about you / So what / Walkin' / Joshua / Go-go (Theme and announcement) / Four / Seven steps to heaven / There is no greater love / Do-go (Theme and announcement )(2).
CD Set . . . . . . . . . . . . . . . . . .471246 2
Columbia / May '93 / Sony.

**CONCERTO DE ARANJUEZ (Davis, Miles & Gil Evans).**
Tracks: Not Advised.
CD . . . . . . . . . . . . . . . . . . .GOJCD 53023
Giants Of Jazz / Aug '88 / Wellard / Swift / Target / Jazz Music / BMG.

**CONCIERTO DE ARANJUEZ.**
Tracks: Not Advised.
CD . . . . . . . . . . . . . . . . . . . . .CD 14543
Jazz Portraits / Jan '94 / Complete Record Co. Ltd.

**COOKIN' AND RELAXIN' (Davis, Miles Quintet).**
Tracks: Cookin' - My funny valentine / Blues by five / Airegin / Tune up / When the lights are low / Relaxin' - If I were a bell / You're my everything / I could write a book / Oleo / It could happen to you / Woody 'n' you.
CD . . . . . . . . . . . . . . . . . . . . CDJZD 003
Prestige / Jan '91 / Total / BMG.

**COOKIN' WITH THE MILES DAVIS QUINTET.**
Tracks: Not Advised.
CD . . . . . . . . . . . . . . . . . . . . VDJ 1512
JVC/Fantasy / '87 / Target.
CD . . . . . . . . . . . . . . . . . . OJCCD 128-2
Original Jazz Classics / Aug '94 / Ace Records / Complete Record Co. Ltd / Jazz Music / BMG.

**COPENHAGEN 1960 (Davis, Miles & John Coltrane).**
Tracks: So what / On green dolphin street / All blues theme.
LP . . . . . . . . . . . . . . . . . . . . . .RJ 501
Magnum Music / Nov '92 / Magnum Music Group / THE.

**COTE BLUES.**
Tracks: Not Advised.
CD . . . . . . . . . . . . . . . . . . . JMY 1010-2
JMY / Aug '93 / Harmonia Mundi (UK).

**DAVISIANA (Davis, Miles Quintet).**
Tracks: Not Advised.
CD . . . . . . . . . . . . . . . . . . . .MCD 0332
Moon / Jan '92 / Harmonia Mundi (UK) / New Note.

**DECOY.**
Tracks: Decoy / Robot 415 / Code MD / Freaky deaky / What is it / That's right / That's what happened.
■ LP . . . . . . . . . . . . . . . . . . CBS 25951
MC . . . . . . . . . . . . . . . . . . .40 25951
CBS / Jun '84 / Sony.
CD . . . . . . . . . . . . . . . . . . . CD 25951
Columbia / Sep '93 / Sony.

**DIG (Davis, Miles featuring Sonny Rollins).**
Tracks: Not Advised.
CD . . . . . . . . . . . . . . . . . . OJCCD 005-2
Original Jazz Classics / Feb '92 / Ace Records / Complete Record Co. Ltd / Jazz Music / BMG.

**DIRECTIONS.**
Tracks: Song of our country / Round midnight / So near, so far / Limbo / Water on the pond / Fun / Directions / Ascent / Duran / Londa / Willie Nelson.
■ Double LP . . . . . . . . . . . . . . . . 88514
CBS / May '81.

**DOO BOP.**
Tracks: Mystery / Doo bop song / Chocolate chip / High speed chase / Blow / Sonya / Fantasy / Duke booty / Mystery (reprise).
■ LP . . . . . . . . . . . . . . . . . 7599269381
WEA / Jun '92.
CD . . . . . . . . . . . . . . . . . . 7599269382
MC . . . . . . . . . . . . . . . . . . 7599269384
WEA / Mar '94 / WEA.

**DOWN.**
Tracks: Not Advised.
CD . . . . . . . . . . . . . . . . . . . .CDJJ 620
Jazz & Jazz / Jan '92.

**E.S.P.**
Tracks: E.S.P. / Eighty one / Little one / R.J. / Agitation / Iris / Mood.
CD . . . . . . . . . . . . . . . . . . . . 4678992
■ MC . . . . . . . . . . . . . . . . . . 4678994
Columbia / Oct '91 / Sony.

**ESSENTIAL MILES DAVIS, THE.**
Tracks: Round Midnight / My funny valentine / Cencierto De aranjuez / Summertime / All blues / Milestones / Wallkin.
CD . . . . . . . . . . . . . . . . . . . . 4671442
MC . . . . . . . . . . . . . . . . . . . 4671444
Columbia / Aug '92 / Sony.

**EVOLUTION OF A GENIUS 1945-1954.**
Tracks: Now's the time / Donna Lee / Milestones / Jeru / Boplicity / Rocker / Ezz-thetic / Yesterdays / Compulsion / Tempus fugit / Tune up / It never entered my mind / Old devil moon / I'll remember April / Walkin' / But not for me.
CD . . . . . . . . . . . . . . . . . . . .GOJCD 0221
Giants Of Jazz / '88 / Wellard / Swift / Target / Jazz Music / BMG.
CD . . . . . . . . . . . . . . . . . . . . .ENTCD 221
Entertainers / '89 / BMG.
CD . . . . . . . . . . . . . . . . . .GOJCD 53009
Giants Of Jazz / Mar '92 / Wellard / Swift / Target / Jazz Music / BMG.

**EVOLUTION OF A GENIUS 1945-1958.**
Tracks: Not Advised.
CD Set . . . . . . . . . . . . . . . . . .CDB 1203
Giants Of Jazz / Apr '92 / Wellard / Swift / Target / Jazz Music / BMG.

**EVOLUTION OF A GENIUS 1954-1958 (Davis, Miles & Friends).**
Tracks: Not Advised.
CD . . . . . . . . . . . . . . . . . . .GOJCD 53063
Giants Of Jazz / Mar '92 / Wellard / Swift / Target / Jazz Music / BMG.

**EVOLUTION OF A GENIUS 1957-1958.**
Tracks: Not Advised.
CD . . . . . . . . . . . . . . . . . . . .CD 53071
Giants Of Jazz / May '93 / Wellard / Swift / Target / Jazz Music / BMG.

**EZZ-THETIC (Davis, Miles & Lee Konitz).**
Tracks: Not Advised.
■ LP . . . . . . . . . . . . . . . . . . . 1902119
Fantasy Inc (USA) / Feb '86.

**FILLES DE KILIMANJARO.**
Tracks: Frelon brun (brown hornet) / Tout de suit / Petits machins (little stuff) / Filles de Kilimanjaro (girls of Kilimanjaro) / Mademoiselle Mabry.
CD . . . . . . . . . . . . . . . . . . . . 4670882
■ MC . . . . . . . . . . . . . . . . . . 4670884
Columbia / Oct '91 / Sony.

**FIRST MILES.**
Tracks: Not Advised.
CD . . . . . . . . . . . . . . . . . . . . SV 0159
Savoy Jazz / Apr '92 / Conifer Records.

**GEMINI.**
Tracks: Not Advised.
CD . . . . . . . . . . . . . . . . . . . . .JD 1201
Jazz Door / Mar '92 / Charly / Koch International / A.D.A. Distribution.

**GET UP WITH IT.**
Tracks: He loved him madly / Maiysha / Honky tonk / Rated X / Calypso frelimo / Red China blues / Mtume / Billy Preston.
■ LP . . . . . . . . . . . . . . . . . . . 88092
CBS / '87.
CD . . . . . . . . . . . . . . . . . . CLCD 9211552
Line / Jun '94 / C.M. Distribution / Grapevine Distribution / A.D.A. Distribution / Conifer Records.

**GREATEST HITS: MILES DAVIS.**
Tracks: Seven steps to Heaven / All blues / Some day my prince will come / Walkin' / My funny valentine / E.S.P. / Round midnight / So what.
■ LP . . . . . . . . . . . . . . . . . . CBS 63620
CBS / Jul '87.

**GREEN DOLPHIN STREET (Davis, Miles Quintet).**
Tracks: Not Advised.
CD . . . . . . . . . . . . . . . . . . . . NI 4002
Natasha / Jun '93 / Jazz Music / A.D.A. Distribution / Topic Records / Direct Distribution / Cadillac / C.M. Distribution.

**GREEN HAZE.**
Tracks: Will you still be mine / I see your face before me / I didn't / Gal in Calico / Night in Tunisia / Green haze / Just squeeze me (but don't tease me) / No greater love / How am I to know / S'posin' / Theme / Stablemates.
■ Double LP . . . . . . . . . . . . . . . PR 24064
Prestige / '79.

**HEARD 'ROUND THE WORLD.**
Tracks: If I were a bell / My funny valentine / So what / Walkin' / All of you / Milestones / Autumn leaves.
■ LP . . . . . . . . . . . . . . . . . . CBS 88626
CBS / Apr '84.

**IMMORTAL CONCERTS (Konserthuset, Stockholm, March 22, 1960) (Davis, Miles & John Coltrane).**
Tracks: So what / Fran dance / All blues / Theme / On green Dolphin street / Walkin'.
CD . . . . . . . . . . . . . . . . . . . AVI 2004
AVI (USA) / Jan '86.
■ Double LP . . . . . . . . . . . . . DRLP 90/91
Dragon / Jun '86.
■ Double LP . . . . . . . . . . . . .DRLP 129/130
Dragon / Feb '87.

**IN A SILENT WAY.**
Tracks: Ssh peaceful / In a silent way / It's about that time.
■ LP . . . . . . . . . . . . . . . . . . CBS 63630
CBS / Jul '87.
CD . . . . . . . . . . . . . . . . . . . . 4509822
■ MC . . . . . . . . . . . . . . . . . . 4509824
Columbia / Oct '93 / Sony.

**IN CONCERT.**
Tracks: Not Advised.
CD . . . . . . . . . . . . . . . . . . . .476910 2
Columbia / Oct '94 / Sony.

**JAZZ PORTRAITS.**
Tracks: Now's the time / Night in Tunisia / Donna Lee / Cheryl / Milestones / Half nelson / Marmaduke / Jeru / Boplicity / Rocker / Ezz-thetic / Yesterdays / Compulsion / Tempus fugit / Tune up / It never entered my mind / Old devil moon / I'll remember April.
CD . . . . . . . . . . . . . . . . . . . . CD 14503
Jazz Portraits / May '94 / Complete Record Co. Ltd.

**KIND OF BLUE.**
Tracks: So what / Freddie Freeloader / Blue in green / Al blues / Flamenco sketches.
■ LP . . . . . . . . . . . . . . . . . . CBS 62066
CBS / '83.
■ CD . . . . . . . . . . . . . . . . . . CD 62066
CBS / Mar '87.
MiniDisc. . . . . . . . . . . . . . . . . 62066-3
Columbia / Feb '93 / Sony.
CD . . . . . . . . . . . . . . . . . . . . 4606032
LP . . . . . . . . . . . . . . . . . . . 4606031
MC . . . . . . . . . . . . . . . . . . . 4606034
Columbia / Sep '93 / Sony.

**KIND OF BLUE/MILESTONES/STELLA BY STARLIGHT.**
Tracks: Not Advised.
CD Set . . . . . . . . . . . . . . . . . . 4722742
Columbia / Oct '92 / Sony.

**KONSERTHUSET, STOCKHOLM (March 22, 1960) (Davis, Miles & John Coltrane).**
Tracks: Not Advised.
CD . . . . . . . . . . . . . . . . . . .GOJCD 0233
Giants Of Jazz / Jan '88 / Wellard / Swift / Target / Jazz Music / BMG.

**LEGENDARY MASTERS, THE (1948-1952).**
Tracks: Godchild / Moon dreams / Hallucinations / Darn that dream / Move (mood) / Conceptions / Opmet (out of the blue) / Chase / Why do I love you / S'il vous plait / Move / Max is making wax / Tune up / Bye bye blackbird / Rollin' blowin' walkin' / But not for me / Night in Tunisia / Fran dance / Walkin' / It never entered my mind / Round about midnight /

What's new / Blues for pablo / On Green Dolphin
Street.
CD.........................RARECD 08
■ LP.........................RARELP 08
Recording Arts Ref. Edition / '88 / Music Collection
International.

### LEGENDARY MASTERS, THE (1956-1959).
Tracks: Tune up / Walkin' / Bye bye blackbird / It
never entered my mind / Rollin' blowin' walkin' /
Round about midnight / But not for me / What's new /
Night in Tunisia / Blues for Pablo.
CD.........................RARECD 09
■ LP.........................RARELP 09
Recording Arts Ref. Edition / '88 / Music Collection
International.

### LEGENDARY MASTERS, THE (1960).
Tracks: Walkin' (theme) / Fran dance / On Green
Dolphin Street / So what.
CD.........................RARECD 10
■ LP.........................RARELP 10
Recording Arts Ref. Edition / '88 / Music Collection
International.

### LEGENDARY MASTERS, THE (BOX SET) (Unissued or rare 1948-60).
Tracks: Not Advised.
CD Set ................ RARECD 08/10
■ LP Set ................ RARELP 08/10
Recording Arts Ref. Edition / Apr '88 / Music Collec-
tion International.

### LEGENDARY STOCKHOLM CONCERT (Davis, Miles & John Coltrane).
Tracks: Not Advised.
CD.........................NI 4011
Natasha / Jan '93 / Jazz Music / A.D.A. Distribution /
Topic Records / Direct Distribution / Cadillac / C.M.
Distribution.

### LIVE - NONET 1948/ JAM 1949.
Tracks: Not Advised.
CD.........................RJD 514
Royal Jazz / Dec '90 / Jazz Music.

### LIVE AT CARNEGIE HALL:MILES DAVIS.
Tracks: Concierto de Aranjuez / Concierto de Aran-
juez (part 2) / Teo / Walkin' / I thought about you.
■ LP.........................4600641
■ MC.........................4600644
CBS / Feb '88.

### LIVE AT MONTREUX (Davis, Miles & Quincy Jones).
Tracks: Introduction by Claude Nobs and Quincy
Jones / Boplicity / Introduction to Miles ahead med-
ley / Springsville / Maids of cadiz / Duke / My ship /
Miles ahead / Blues for pablo / Introduction to Porgy
and Bess medley / Orgone / Gone, gone, gone /
Summertime / Here come de honey man / Pan piper
/ Solea.
CD.........................9362452214-2
Warner Bros. / Sep '93 / WEA.

### LIVE AT MONTREUX (VIDEO) (Davis, Miles & Quincy Jones).
Tracks: Time after time / Round midnight / Miles
ahead / Maids of Cadiz / My ship / Sketches of Spain
/ Tutu / Boplicity / Duke / Summertime / Here comes
the honeymoon / Pan piper / Solea.
VHS.........................7599 38342 3
Warner Music Video / Jul '93 / WEA.

### LIVE AT NEWPORT 1958 & 1963 (Davis, Miles & Thelonious Monk).
Tracks: Introduction (1) / Ah-leu-cha / Straight, no
chaser / Fran dance / Two bass hit / Bye bye
blackbird / Theme / Introduction (2) / Criss cross /
Light blue / Nutty / Blue monk / Epistrophy.
CD Set .........................C2K 53585
Columbia / Oct '94 / Sony.

### LIVE AT THE HIGH HAT 1953.
Tracks: Not Advised.
CD.........................JD 1216
Jazz Door / Apr '91 / Charly / Koch International /
A.D.A. Distribution.

### LIVE AT THE PLUGGED NICKEL.
Tracks: Walkin' / Agitation / On Green Dolphin Street
/ So what / Theme / 'Round about midnight / Stella
by starlight / All blues / Yesterdays.
■ Double LP.........................88606
CBS / '83.

### LIVE IN 1958.
LP.........................EB 418
Flyright / Dec '90 / Hot Shot / Roots Records /
Wellard / Charly / Swift / Projection / Jazz Music.

### LIVE IN 1958-59 (Davis, Miles All Stars).
Tracks: Not Advised.
CD.........................EBCD 21012
Flyright / Dec '90 / Hot Shot / Roots Records /
Wellard / Charly / Swift / Projection / Jazz Music.

### LIVE IN COPENHAGEN, 1960 (Davis, Miles Quintet).
Tracks: Not Advised.
CD.........................CDRJ 501
■ LP.........................RJ 501
Royal Jazz / '89 / Jazz Music.

### LIVE IN EUROPE 1960 & 1967 (Davis, Miles Quintet).
Tracks: Not Advised.
CD.........................JU 320
Jazz-Up / Mar '90 / Pinnacle.

### LIVE IN NEW YORK 1957-59 (Davis, Miles & John Coltrane).
Tracks: Not Advised.
CD.........................JD 1242
Jazz Door / Jul '94 / Charly / Koch International /
A.D.A. Distribution.

### LIVE IN SINDELFINGEN 1964 (Davis, Miles Quintet).
Tracks: Not Advised.
CD.........................JZCD 372
Recording Arts / Nov '92 / THE.

### LIVE IN St LOUIS & PARIS 1963 (Davis, Miles Quintet).
Tracks: Not Advised.
CD.........................JZCD 371
Recording Arts / Nov '92 / THE.

### LIVE IN STOCKHOLM (1960) (Davis, Miles & John Coltrane).
Tracks: Not Advised.
CD.........................GOJCD 53014
Giants Of Jazz / Mar '92 / Wellard / Swift / Target /
Jazz Music / BMG.

### LIVE IN STOCKHOLM 1960 (Davis, Miles & John Coltrane).
Tracks: Not Advised.
■ LP Set .........................DRAGON 90-91
Dragon / Aug '89.

### LIVE IN STOCKHOLM 1960.
Tracks: Not Advised.
■ LP.........................DRAGON 129-30
Dragon / Jun '89.

### LIVE IN STOCKHOLM 1960 COMPLETE (Davis, Miles & Coltrane & Stitt).
Tracks: Not Advised.
CD.........................DRCD 228
Dragon / Sep '89 / Roots Records / Cadillac / Wellard
/ Projection / C.M. Distribution.

### LIVE MILES (More Music From The Le- gendary Carnegie Hall Concert).
Tracks: Not Advised.
■ CD.........................4600642
Columbia / '91.

### LIVE TUTU (Davis, Miles Band).
Tracks: Not Advised.
CD.........................JZCD 375
Recording Arts / Nov '92 / THE.

### LIVE-EVIL.
Tracks: Sivad / Little church / Gemini/Double image /
What I say / Nem um talev / Selim / Funky tonk /
Inamorata.
■ LP.........................CBS 67219
CBS / Jan '77.

### LIVE: MILES DAVIS & JOHN COLTRANE (Davis, Miles & John Coltrane).
Tracks: Green Dolphin Street / Walkin' / Theme / So
what / Round midnight.
■ LP.........................UJ 19
Unique Jazz / Nov '86.

### MAN WITH THE HORN (Davis, Miles & John Coltrane).
Tracks: Fat time / Backseat Betty / Shout Aida / Man
with the horn / Ursula.
■ LP.........................CBS 84708
CBS / Aug '81.
■ CD.........................CD 84708
CBS / '83.
MC.........................40 84708
Prix D'Ami (France) / Sep '86.
CD.........................4687012
Columbia / Sep '93 / Sony.

### MASTERPIECES, THE (1954).
Tracks: Not Advised.
■ LP.........................LPJT 55
Giants Of Jazz / Sep '87.
MC.........................MCJT 55
Giants Of Jazz / Mar '92 / Wellard / Swift / Target /
Jazz Music / BMG.

### MELLOW MILES.
Tracks: Miles / Summertime / So what / Time after
time / Miles ahead / Freddie freeloader / Bye bye
blackbird / Pfrancing / Round midnight / If ain't
necessarily / Human nature.
CD.........................4694402
MC.........................4694404
Columbia / Dec '91 / Sony.

### MILES & TRANE (Davis, Miles & John Coltrane).
Tracks: So what / Duke / Blues for Pablo / Impres-
sions / My favourite things.
VHS.........................VIDJAZZ 5
Jazz On Jazz / Jan '92.

### MILES AHEAD.
Tracks: Springsville / Maids of Cadiz / Duke / My
ship / Miles ahead / Blues for Pablo / New rhumba /
Meaning of the blues / Lament / I don't wanna be
kissed.
CD.........................4606002
■ MC.........................4606064
CBS / '91 / Sony.
CD.........................CD 14540
Jazz Portraits / Jan '94 / Complete Record Co. Ltd.

### MILES AHEAD (PRESTIGE).
Tracks: Compulsion / Maids of Cadiz / My ship /
Meaning of the blues / I don't wanna be kissed /
Round midnight / Duke / Miles ahead / New rhumba /
Lament.
■ LP.........................PR 7822
■ MC.........................PRC 7822
Prestige / May '88.

### MILES AND COLTRANE (Davis, Miles & John Coltrane).
Tracks: Not Advised.
CD.........................4608242
■ MC.........................4608244
Columbia / Oct '93 / Sony.

### MILES AND HORNS.
Tracks: Not Advised.
CD.........................OJCCD 053-2
Original Jazz Classics / Feb '92 / Ace Records /
Complete Record Co. Ltd / Jazz Music / BMG.

### MILES DAVIS.
Tracks: My funny Valentine / Blues by five / Airegin /
Tune up / When lights are low / If I were a bell /
You're my everything / I could write a book / Oleo / It
could happen to you / Woodyn' you.
■ LP Set.........................PR 24001
Prestige / '72.

### MILES DAVIS & KEITH JARRETT LIVE (Davis, Miles Band).
Tracks: Not Advised.
CD.........................JZCD 374
Recording Arts / Nov '92 / THE.

### MILES DAVIS & LENNIE TRISTANO (Da- vis, Miles & Lennie Tristano).
Tracks: Not Advised.
CD.........................NI 4015
Natasha / Aug '93 / Jazz Music / A.D.A. Distribution /
Topic Records / Direct Distribution / Cadillac / C.M.
Distribution.

### MILES DAVIS & MILT JACKSON (Davis, Miles & Milt Jackson).
Tracks: Not Advised.
CD.........................OJCCD 012-2
Original Jazz Classics / Feb '92 / Ace Records /
Complete Record Co. Ltd / Jazz Music / BMG.

### MILES DAVIS & THE HI-HAT ALL STARS.
Tracks: Not Advised.
■ LP.........................FS 280
Fresh Sounds / Feb '88.

### MILES DAVIS & THE JAZZ GIANTS.
Tracks: Not Advised.
CD.........................FCD 60015
Fantasy / Oct '93 / Pinnacle / Jazz Music.

### MILES DAVIS & THE LIGHTHOUSE ALL- STARS (Davis, Miles & Lighthouse Allstars).
Tracks: Not Advised.
CD.........................98610
Carrere (France) / Apr '87.

**MILES DAVIS & THE MODERN JAZZ GIANT (Davis, Miles & the Modern Jazz Giants).**
Tracks: Not Advised.
CD . . . . . . . . . . . . . . . . . . . . . . . VDJ 1605
JVC/Fantasy / Jan '89 / Target.

**MILES DAVIS - 1957-58.**
Tracks: Not Advised.
MC. . . . . . . . . . . . . . . . . . . . . . . MCJT 84
Giants Of Jazz / Mar '92 / Wellard / Swift / Target / Jazz Music / BMG.

**MILES DAVIS - LIVE IN EUROPE 1988.**
Tracks: Not Advised.
CD . . . . . . . . . . . . . . . . . . . . . . .OMDCD 101
OMD / Mar '93 / Koch International.

**MILES DAVIS 1945-51 VOL 1 (Early days, The).**
Tracks: Not Advised.
■ LP . . . . . . . . . . . . . . . . . . . . . . LPJT 24
MC. . . . . . . . . . . . . . . . . . . . . . . MCJT 24
Giants Of Jazz / Sep '87 / Wellard / Swift / Target / Jazz Music / BMG.

**MILES DAVIS ALL STARS AND GIL EVANS (Davis, Miles & Gil Evans).**
Tracks: Not Advised.
■ LP . . . . . . . . . . . . . . . . . . . . . . .BEP 502
Beppo / Jun '76.

**MILES DAVIS ALLSTARS (Feat.John Coltrane/Cannonball Adderley).**
Tracks: Not Advised.
■ LP . . . . . . . . . . . . . . . . . . . . . . . EB 409
MC. . . . . . . . . . . . . . . . . . . . . . . .EBC 409
Jazz Band / Nov '88 / Charly / Swift / Jazz Music / Cadillac.

**MILES DAVIS AND JAZZ HOOFER (Davis, Miles & Jazz Hoofer).**
Tracks: Not Advised.
VHS . . . . . . . . . . . . . . . . . . . . . . .KJ 021
Kay Jazz (Video) / '88 / Gold & Sons / Cadillac / Jazz Music.

**MILES DAVIS AT CARNEGIE HALL, 1961.**
Tracks: Not Advised.
■ CD . . . . . . . . . . . . . . . . . . . . . CD 85554
CBS.

**MILES DAVIS CHRONICLE.**
Tracks: Not Advised.
CD Set . . . . . . . . . . . . . . . . . . .PCD 012-2
Passport Jazz (USA) / '91.

**MILES DAVIS IN L.A., 1946.**
Tracks: Not Advised.
■ LP . . . . . . . . . . . . . . . . . . . . . .SM 3717
Joker (USA) / '79.

**MILES DAVIS QUINTET (Lincoln Centre 1964) (Davis, Miles Quintet).**
Tracks: Not Advised.
CD . . . . . . . . . . . . . . . . . . . .GOJCD 53047
Giants Of Jazz / Mar '92 / Wellard / Swift / Jazz Music / BMG.

**MILES DAVIS VOL. 1.**
Tracks: Dear old Stockholm / Chance it (Alternative take) / Chance it (alt. take) / Donna (alt. take) / Donna / Woody 'n' you / Yesterdays / How deep is the ocean / Take off / Lazy Susan / Leap / Well you needn't / Weirdo / It never entered my mind.
■ CD . . . . . . . . . . . . . . . . . . . . . .BNZ 111
Blue Note / Nov '88.

**MILES DAVIS VOL. 2.**
Tracks: Kelo (alt.) / Kelo / Enigma (alt.) / Enigma / Ray's idea (alt.) / Ray's idea / Tempus fugit / Tempus fugit (alt.) / C.T.A. (alt.) / C.T.A. / I waited for you.
■ CD . . . . . . . . . . . . . . . . . . . . .BNZ 240
Blue Note / Apr '90.

**MILES DAVIS, DIZZY GILLESPIE & CHARLIE PARKER (Davis, Miles/Dizzy Gillespie/Charlie Parker).**
Tracks: Not Advised.
■ Double LP . . . . . . . . . . . . . . . . . VJD 529
Vogue Jazz (France) / Nov '76.

**MILES DAVIS, VOL 1.**
Tracks: Tempus fugit / Kelo / Enigma / Ray's idea / How deep is the ocean / C.T.A. / Dear old Stockholm / Chance it / Yesterdays / Donna / Woody 'n' you / Woody 'n' you (alt take).
■ LP . . . . . . . . . . . . . . . . . . . . . BLP 1501
Blue Note / Aug '82.
■ MC. . . . . . . . . . . . . . . . . . .TCBST 81501
Blue Note / Mar '86.

■ LP . . . . . . . . . . . . . . . . . . . . . BST 81501
Blue Note / Jul '89.

**MILES DAVIS, VOL 2.**
Tracks: Take off / Weirdo / Woody 'n' you / I waited for you / Ray's idea / Donna / Well you needn't / Lazy Susan / Tempus fugit / It never entered my mind.
■ LP . . . . . . . . . . . . . . . . . . . . . BLP 1502
Blue Note / Aug '82.
■ MC. . . . . . . . . . . . . . . . . . . . 4BN 81502
Blue Note / Aug '85.
■ LP . . . . . . . . . . . . . . . . . . . . . BST 81502
Blue Note / Jul '89.

**MILES IN BERLIN.**
Tracks: Not Advised.
■ CD . . . . . . . . . . . . . . . . . . . . . CD 62976
CBS / May '87.

**MILES IN MONTREUX - LIVE 1989.**
Tracks: Not Advised.
CD . . . . . . . . . . . . . . . . . . . . .JD 001235
Jazz Door / Sep '93 / Charly / Koch International / A.D.A. Distribution.

**MILES IN PARIS.**
Tracks: Not Advised.
CD Video . . . . . . . . . . . . . . . . 9031 71550 6
VHS . . . . . . . . . . . . . . . . . . . 9031 71550 3
Warner Music Video / Dec '90 / WEA.

**MILES IN PARIS (Davis, Miles Orchestra).**
Tracks: Not Advised.
LP . . . . . . . . . . . . . . . . . . .JAZZDOOR 1201
I.T.M. / Dec '90 / C.M. Distribution / Charly / Koch International / Complete Record Co. Ltd.

**MILES IN THE SKY.**
Tracks: Stuff / Paraphernalia / Black comedy / Country son.
CD . . . . . . . . . . . . . . . . . . . . . .477209 2
Columbia / Sep '93 / Sony.

**MILES OF FUN.**
Tracks: Moose the mooche / Yardbird suite / Ornithology / Night in Tunisia / Bird's nest / Bird of paradise.
■ LP . . . . . . . . . . . . . . . . . . . . . MAN 5028
Manhattan Records / Jul '80.

**MILES OF JAZZ (Davis, Miles & Charlie Parker).**
Tracks: Not Advised.
■ LP . . . . . . . . . . . . . . . . . . . . .SJAZZ 7
MC. . . . . . . . . . . . . . . . . . . . . .SJAZZC 7
Star Jazz (USA) / '88 / Charly.

**MILES SMILES.**
Tracks: Orbits / Circle / Footprints / Dolores / Freedom jazz dance / Ginger bread boy.
CD . . . . . . . . . . . . . . . . . . . . . .4710042
■ MC. . . . . . . . . . . . . . . . . . . . .4710044
Columbia / Apr '92 / Sony.

**MILESTONES.**
Tracks: Not Advised.
CD . . . . . . . . . . . . . . . . . . . . . .4608272
MC. . . . . . . . . . . . . . . . . . . . . .4608274
Columbia / Oct '93 / Sony.

**MILESTONES 1945-54.**
Tracks: Not Advised.
CD . . . . . . . . . . . . . . . . . . . . . CD 56009
Jazz Roots / Aug '94 / Target / BMG.

**MUSINGS OF MILES, THE.**
Tracks: I didn't / Will you still be mine / Green haze / I see your face before me / Night in Tunisia / Gal in Calico.
■ LP . . . . . . . . . . . . . . . . . . . . . OJC 004
Original Jazz Classics / Jun '84.
CD . . . . . . . . . . . . . . . . . . . OJCCD 004-2
Original Jazz Classics / Feb '92 / Ace Records / Complete Record Co. Ltd / Jazz Music / BMG.

**MY FUNNY VALENTINE.**
Tracks: Not Advised.
■ CD . . . . . . . . . . . . . . . . . . . . CD 85558
CBS / May '87.

**NEFERTITI.**
Tracks: Nefertiti / Fall / Hand jive / Madness / Riot / Pinocchio.
CD . . . . . . . . . . . . . . . . . . . . . .4670842
■ MC. . . . . . . . . . . . . . . . . . . . .4670894
Columbia / Oct '91 / Sony.

**NEW MILES DAVIS QUINTET.**
Tracks: Not Advised.
CD . . . . . . . . . . . . . . . . . . . OJCCD 006-2
Original Jazz Classics / Feb '92 / Ace Records / Complete Record Co. Ltd / Jazz Music / BMG.

**NIGHT IN TUNISIA, A.**
Tracks: Embraceable you / Bird of paradise / Out of nowhere / My old flame / Don't blame me / Scrapple from the apple.
■ LP . . . . . . . . . . . . . . . . . . . . .SJAZZ 2
MC. . . . . . . . . . . . . . . . . . . . . .SJAZZC 2
Star Jazz (USA) / Apr '86 / Charly.

**ON THE CORNER.**
Tracks: On the corner / New York girl / Thinkin' one thing & doin' another / Vote for Miles / Black satin / One & one / Helen Butte / Mr. Freedom X.
■ LP . . . . . . . . . . . . . . . . . . . . CBS 85549
CBS / Jan '87.
■ LP . . . . . . . . . . . . . . . . . . . .BGOLP 30
Beat Goes On / Dec '88.
CD . . . . . . . . . . . . . . . . . . . . . BGOCD 30
Beat Goes On / Jul '91 / Pinnacle.
CD . . . . . . . . . . . . . . . . . . . . . .474371 2
Columbia / Feb '94 / Sony.

**PANGAEA.**
Tracks: Zimbabwe / Gondwana.
CD . . . . . . . . . . . . . . . . . . . . . .467087 2
Columbia / Sep '93 / Sony.

**PARAPHERNALIA.**
Tracks: Not Advised.
CD . . . . . . . . . . . . . . . . . . . . JMY 1013-2
JMY / Aug '92 / Harmonia Mundi (UK).

**PARIS CONCERT.**
Tracks: Not Advised.
CD . . . . . . . . . . . . . . . . . . . . . JZCD 341
Suisa / Jan '93 / Jazz Music / THE.

**PORGY & BESS (Davis, Miles & Gil Evans Orchestra).**
Tracks: Buzzard song / Bess, you is my woman now / Gone gone gone / Summertime / Bess, oh where's my Bess / Prayer / O Doctor Jesus / Fisherman / Strawberry and devil crab / My man's gone now / It ain't necessarily so / Here comes de honey man / I loves you Porgy / There's a boat that's leaving shortly for New York.
■ LP . . . . . . . . . . . . . . . . . . . CBS 32188
■ MC. . . . . . . . . . . . . . . . . . . .40 32188
CBS / Sep '82.
CD . . . . . . . . . . . . . . . . . . . . . .4509852
■ MC. . . . . . . . . . . . . . . . . . . . .4509854
Columbia / Oct '93 / Sony.

**PORTRAIT OF MILES DAVIS, A.**
Tracks: Bye bye blackbird / On Green Dolphin Street / Oleo / Autumn leaves / Sanctuary / Spanish key / Konda / Come get it / Jean Pierre / Decoy / Time after time / Something's on your mind.
■ LP . . . . . . . . . . . . . . . . . . . . .4505931
MC. . . . . . . . . . . . . . . . . . . . . .4505934
CBS / Feb '88 / Sony.

**PRE-BIRTH OF THE COOL (Davis, Miles & His Tuba Band).**
Tracks: Why do I love you / Godchild / S'il vous plait / Moon dreams / Hallucinations / Darn that dream / Move.
■ LP . . . . . . . . . . . . . . . . . . . . BLJ 8003
Jazz Live (Italy) / Apr '81.

**QUIET NIGHTS.**
Tracks: Not Advised.
■ CD . . . . . . . . . . . . . . . . . . . . CD 85556
CBS / Jun '87.

**RARITIES AND PRIVATE COLLECTIONS 1956-59.**
Tracks: Not Advised.
CD . . . . . . . . . . . . . . . . . . . . . JZ-CD314
Suisa / Feb '91 / Jazz Music / THE.

**REAL BIRTH OF THE COOL - RARE AND LIVE.**
Tracks: Not Advised.
CD . . . . . . . . . . . . . . . . . . . . . JZ-CD313
Suisa / Feb '91 / Jazz Music / THE.

**RELAXIN' (Davis, Miles Quintet).**
Tracks: Not Advised.
CD . . . . . . . . . . . . . . . . . . . OJCCD 190-2
Original Jazz Classics / Aug '94 / Ace Records / Complete Record Co. Ltd / Jazz Music / BMG.

**RELAXIN' WITH MILES (Davis, Miles Quintet).**
Tracks: Not Advised.
CD . . . . . . . . . . . . . . . . . . . . . VDJ 1503
JVC/Fantasy / Apr '86 / Target.
CD . . . . . . . . . . . . . . . . . . . . OJCCD 190
Original Jazz Classics / Oct '92 / Ace Records / Complete Record Co. Ltd / Jazz Music / BMG.

■ DELETED

## RELAXIN' WITH THE MILES DAVIS QUINTET.
**Tracks:** Not Advised.
CD . . . . . . . . . . . . . . . . . . . JW 77009
Jazz World / May '93 / New Note / Target Sales & Marketing.

## ROUND ABOUT MIDNIGHT.
**Tracks:** Round about midnight / Ah leu cha / All of you / Bye bye blackbird / Tadd's delight / Dear old Stockholm.
CD . . . . . . . . . . . . . . . . . . . CD 62323
CBS / May '87 / Sony.
CD . . . . . . . . . . . . . . . . . . . 4606052
■ MC . . . . . . . . . . . . . . . . . 4606054
Columbia / Oct '91 / Sony.

## ROUND MIDNIGHT.
**Tracks:** Not Advised.
CD . . . . . . . . . . . . . . . . . . . ORO 128
Music Collection International / Oct '91 / THE / Jazz Music.
CD . . . . . . . . . . . . . . . . . . GOJCD 53045
Giants Of Jazz / Mar '92 / Wellard / Swift / Target / Jazz Music / BMG.

## SATURDAY NIGHT AT THE BLACK HAWK.
**Tracks:** Not Advised.
CD . . . . . . . . . . . . . . . . . . . 4651912
■ LP . . . . . . . . . . . . . . . . . . 4651911
MC . . . . . . . . . . . . . . . . . . . 4651914
CBS / '88 / Sony.

## SEVEN STEPS TO HEAVEN.
**Tracks:** Basin Street blues / Seven steps to heaven / I fall in love too easily / So near, so far / Baby won't you please come home / Joshua.
CD . . . . . . . . . . . . . . . . . . . 4669702
■ MC . . . . . . . . . . . . . . . . . 4669704
Columbia / Apr '92 / Sony.

## SKETCHES OF SPAIN.
**Tracks:** Concierto de Aranjuez / Amor brujo / Pan piper / Saeta / Solea.
■ LP . . . . . . . . . . . . . . . . . CBS 32023
■ MC . . . . . . . . . . . . . . . . . .40 32023
CBS / Mar '81.
■ MC . . . . . . . . . . . . . . . . . .40 22146
CBS / Feb '83.
■ CD . . . . . . . . . . . . . . . . . CD 62327
CBS / Dec '85.
■ LP . . . . . . . . . . . . . . . . . . 4606041
CBS / Apr '88.
CD . . . . . . . . . . . . . . . . . . . 4606042
MC . . . . . . . . . . . . . . . . . . . 4606044
Columbia / Oct '91 / Sony.

## SOME DAY MY PRINCE WILL COME.
**Tracks:** Someday my prince will come / Old folks / Drad-dog / Teo / I thought about you / Pfancing.
CD . . . . . . . . . . . . . . . . . MFCD 828
Mobile Fidelity Sound Lab(USA) / Jan '86.
■ CD . . . . . . . . . . . . . . . . . 4663122
■ MC . . . . . . . . . . . . . . . . . 4663124
Columbia / Oct '91.

## SORCERER.
**Tracks:** Prince of Darkness / Vonetta / Limbo / Masqualero / Pee Wee / Sorcerer.
■ LP . . . . . . . . . . . . . . . . . CBS 21143
■ MC . . . . . . . . . . . . . . . . . .40 21143
CBS / Jul '87.
CD . . . . . . . . . . . . . . . . . . . 4743692
Columbia / Sep '93 / Sony.

## STAR PEOPLE.
**Tracks:** Come get it / It gets better / Speak / Star people / U'un I / Star on Cicely.
■ LP . . . . . . . . . . . . . . . . . . 25395
CBS / Jun '83.
CD . . . . . . . . . . . . . . . . . . CD 25395
Columbia / Sep '93 / Sony.

## STEAMIN' WITH THE MILES DAVIS QUINTET.
**Tracks:** Not Advised.
CD . . . . . . . . . . . . . . . . . . . VDJ 1522
JVC/Fantasy / '88 / Target.
CD . . . . . . . . . . . . . . . . . OJCCD 391-2
Original Jazz Classics / Feb '92 / Ace Records / Complete Record Co. Ltd / Jazz Music / BMG.

## STOCKHOLM 1960.
**Tracks:** Not Advised.
CD . . . . . . . . . . . . . . . . . . . RJD 509
Royal Jazz / Oct '92 / Jazz Music.

## SUPER HORNS (Davis, Miles & Freddie Hubbard).
**Tracks:** Not Advised.
CD . . . . . . . . . . . . . . . . . . . RC 83144
MC . . . . . . . . . . . . . . . . . . . 82144
Royal Collection / Mar '93 / BMG.

## TALLEST TREES.
**Tracks:** Bag's groove / Smooch / Miles ahead / Airegin / Oleo / But not for me / Doxy / Man I love / Swing spring / Blue haze / Round midnight / Bemsha swing.
■ Double LP . . . . . . . . . . . . . . PR 24012
Prestige / '73.

## THEIR GREATEST CONCERT (Davis, Miles & John Coltrane).
**Tracks:** Not Advised.
CD . . . . . . . . . . . . . . . . . . JZ-CD315
Jazz Music / Feb '91 / Jazz Music / THE.

## TIME AFTER TIME.
**Tracks:** Time after time / Katia (prelude).
■ 12" . . . . . . . . . . . . . . . . . . TA 4871
■ 7" . . . . . . . . . . . . . . . . . . .A 4871
CBS / May '85.

## TRANSITION.
**Tracks:** Not Advised.
CD . . . . . . . . . . . . . . . . . . MRCD 125
Magnetic / Sep '91 / Charly.

## TRIBUTE TO JACK JOHNSON.
**Tracks:** Right off / Yesternow.
CD . . . . . . . . . . . . . . . . . . .471003 2
Columbia / Sep '93 / Sony.

## TUNE UP.
**Tracks:** When lights are low / Tune up / Four / That old devil moon / Solar / You don't know what love is / Love me or leave me / I'll remember April / Walkin' / Blue 'n' boogie / But not for me / Bags' groove / Man I love.
■ Double LP . . . . . . . . . . . . . . PR 24077
Prestige / '79.

## TUNE UP (Davis, Miles & Stan Getz).
**Tracks:** Not Advised.
CD . . . . . . . . . . . . . . . . . . . NI 4008
Natasha / Jun '93 / Jazz Music / A.D.A. Distribution / Topic Records / Direct Distribution / Cadillac / C.M. Distribution.

## TUTU.
**Tracks:** Tutu / Tomaas / Portia / Splatch / Backyard ritual / Perfect way / Don't lose your mind / Full nelson.
CD . . . . . . . . . . . . . . . . . . .925490 2
■ LP . . . . . . . . . . . . . . . . . .925490 1
MC . . . . . . . . . . . . . . . . . . .925490 4
WEA / Oct '86 / WEA.

## UNIQUE VOL 2, THE (1951-54).
**Tracks:** Not Advised.
■ LP . . . . . . . . . . . . . . . . . . LPJT 43
Giants Of Jazz / Sep '87.
MC . . . . . . . . . . . . . . . . . . . MCJT 43
Giants Of Jazz / Mar '92 / Wellard / Swift / Target / Jazz Music / BMG.

## WALKIN'.
**Tracks:** Not Advised.
■ LP . . . . . . . . . . . . . . . . . . OJC 213
Original Jazz Classics / Apr '86.
CD . . . . . . . . . . . . . . . . . . . 98437
Carrere (France) / Apr '87.
CD . . . . . . . . . . . . . . . . . . . VDJ 1541
JVC/Fantasy / May '87 / Target.
CD . . . . . . . . . . . . . . . . . OJCCD 213-2
Original Jazz Classics / Feb '92 / Ace Records / Complete Record Co. Ltd / Jazz Music / BMG.
CD . . . . . . . . . . . . . . . . . . . JW 77017
Jazz World / Jul '93 / New Note / Target Sales & Marketing.
CD . . . . . . . . . . . . . . . . . . . JHR 73568
Jazz Hour / Nov '93 / Target / Jazz Music.
CD . . . . . . . . . . . . . . . . . . . CD 14537
Jazz Portraits / Jan '94 / Complete Record Co. Ltd.

## WALKIN' (2) (Davis, Miles All Stars).
**Tracks:** Walkin' / Blue'n'boogie / Solar / You don't know what love is / Love me or leave me.
CD . . . . . . . . . . . . . . . . . . CDRIVM 004
Riverside (USA) / Sep '89 / Jazz Music / Pinnacle / Cadillac.

## WATER BABIES.
**Tracks:** Water babies / Sweet pea / Duel Mr.Tillman Anthony / Two faced / Capricorn.
■ MC . . . . . . . . . . . . . . . . . .40 21136
■ LP . . . . . . . . . . . . . . . . . CBS 21136
CBS / Jul '86.

## WE WANT MILES.
**Tracks:** Jean Pierre / Backseat Betty / Fast track / My man's gone now / Kix.
■ Double LP . . . . . . . . . . . . . . 88579
CBS / May '82.
CD . . . . . . . . . . . . . . . . . . .469902 2
Columbia / Sep '93 / Sony.

## WHAT I SAY VOL.1.
**Tracks:** Not Advised.
CD . . . . . . . . . . . . . . . . . . JMY 1015-2
JMY / Apr '94 / Harmonia Mundi (UK).

## WHAT I SAY VOL.2.
**Tracks:** Not Advised.
CD . . . . . . . . . . . . . . . . . . JMY 1016-2
JMY / Apr '94 / Harmonia Mundi (UK).

## WORKIN' (Davis, Miles Quintet).
**Tracks:** Not Advised.
CD . . . . . . . . . . . . . . . . . . OJCCD 296-2
Original Jazz Classics / Feb '92 / Ace Records / Complete Record Co. Ltd / Jazz Music / BMG.

## WORKIN' AND STEAMIN'.
**Tracks:** It never entered my mind / Four / In your own sweet way / Theme, The (take 1) / Trane's blues / Ahmad's blues / Half Nelson / Theme, The (take 2) / Surrey with the fringe on top / Salt peanuts / Something I dreamed last night / Diane / Well you needn't / When I fall in love.
■ Double LP . . . . . . . . . . . . . . PR 24034
Prestige / '79.
CD Set . . . . . . . . . . . . . . . . 4PRCD 8805
Prestige (USA) / Oct '93 / Jazz Music / Cadillac / Complete Record Co. Ltd.

## WORKIN' WITH THE MILES DAVIS QUINTET.
**Tracks:** Not Advised.
CD . . . . . . . . . . . . . . . . . . . VDJ 1521
JVC/Fantasy / Apr '86 / Target.

## WORLD OF JAZZ.
**Tracks:** Yardbird suite / Cool blues / Lover's theme / Hot lips / Mr. Lucky.
■ LP . . . . . . . . . . . . . . . . . MAN 5022
Manhattan Records / Jul '80.

## YOU'RE UNDER ARREST.
**Tracks:** One phone call / Street scenes / Human nature / Ms. Morrisine / Katia (prelude) / Time after time / You're under arrest / Then there were none / Something's on your mind.
MC . . . . . . . . . . . . . . . . . . .40 26447
■ LP . . . . . . . . . . . . . . . . . CBS 26447
CBS / Jun '85 / Sony.
CD . . . . . . . . . . . . . . . . . . . CD 26447
CBS / May '87 / Sony.
MiniDisc. . . . . . . . . . . . . . . . MD 26447
Columbia / Aug '93 / Sony.
CD . . . . . . . . . . . . . . . . . . .468703 2
Columbia / Sep '93 / Sony.

## Davis, Richard Anthony

### BRING ME BACK.
**Tracks:** Bring me back (Mix).
12" . . . . . . . . . . . . . . . . . . 12EMH 7
Intimate / Feb '94 / Jetstar.

### LOVERS FOR LIFE.
**Tracks:** Lovers for life.
12" . . . . . . . . . . . . . . . . . 12 EMH 7R
Intimate / Sep '94 / Jetstar.

## Davis, Ruth

### YOU'RE GONNA GET NEXT TO ME (see under Kirkland, Bo).

## Davis, Tyrone

Began his career recording on Ray Charles' Tangerine label but without success. Moving to Dakar, he scored his first chart hit when *Can I Change My Mind* made No. 5 in 1969; further hits included 1970's *Turn Back The Hands Of Time*. Moving to CBS, he worked with producer Leo Graham and released *Give It Up (Turn It Loose)* in 1976. Success continued with R&B hits *In The Mood* and *Are You Serious*. He also put out consistently good albums, including the Future label releases *Sexy Thing* ('85) and *Man Of Stone* ('87).

### BEST OF THE FUTURE YEARS, THE.
**Tracks:** Not Advised.
CD . . . . . . . . . . . . . . . . . . . ICH 1153CD
MC . . . . . . . . . . . . . . . . . . . ICH 1153MC

Ichiban / Feb '94 / A.D.A. Distribution / Pinnacle / ACD Trading Ltd. / Koch International / Direct Distribution.

### CAN I CHANGE MY MIND.
**Tracks:** She's lookin' good / Knock on wood / Have you ever wondered why / Slip away / Let the good times roll / Can I change my mind / Open the door to your heart / Call on me / Just the one I've been looking for / You can't keep a good man down / Woman needs to be loved.
■ LP . . . . . . . . . . . . . . . . . . . . . . 588 209
Atlantic / Mar '70.

### CAN I CHANGE MY MIND?.
**Tracks:** If you wanna keep him / Where have you been / I gotta tell somebody / After loving you / Happiness / Your love is doggone good / You've become a part of me / I'll take you all the way there / Home / Seems like I gotta do wrong.
■ LP . . . . . . . . . . . . . . . . . . . . MAN 5034
Manhattan Records / Sep '80.

### COULDN'T FORGET YOU.
**Tracks:** Couldn't forget you / Just my way of loving you.
■ 7" . . . . . . . . . . . . . . . . . . . . . . 2090078
Atlantic / May '71.

### FLASHIN' BACK.
**Tracks:** Not Advised.
■ LP . . . . . . . . . . . . . . . . . . . . . . FR 1003
Future / Jul '88.

### I'LL ALWAYS LOVE YOU.
**Tracks:** I'll always love you / Prove my love / Talk to you / Let me love you / Do U still love me / Can I change your mind / Woman needs to be loved / Mom's apple pie.
■ LP . . . . . . . . . . . . . . . . . . . . ICH 1103
■ MC . . . . . . . . . . . . . . . . . . ICH 1103 MC
Ichiban / Apr '91.
CD . . . . . . . . . . . . . . . . . . . . . CDICH 1103
Ichiban / Oct '93 / A.D.A. Distribution / Pinnacle / ACD Trading Ltd. / Koch International / Direct Distribution.

### IN THE MOOD AGAIN.
**Tracks:** Give it up (turn it loose) / Close to you / All you got / This I swear / I got carried away / In the mood / Ain't nothing I can do / How sweet it is (to be loved by you).
■ LP . . . . . . . . . . . . . . . . . . . . CRB 1214
Charly R&B / Aug '89.

### MAN OF STONE.
**Tracks:** I'm in love again / You are the one / You make me feel so good / All of me / You're everything (I want in a woman) / I wanna talk love / I've got you (you've got me) / Serious love.
■ LP . . . . . . . . . . . . . . . . . . . . TRPL 116
Timeless (Soul) / Jan '90.

### PACIFIER.
**Tracks:** Turning point / Are you serious / Overdue / You can win if you want / Be honest with me / Let me be your pacifier / You stay on my mind / Where did we lose / One in a million / Sexy thing / More and more.
■ LP . . . . . . . . . . . . . . . . . . . . TRLP 104
Timeless (Soul) / Jan '90.

### SOMETHING'S MIGHTY WRONG.
**Tracks:** Not Advised.
CD . . . . . . . . . . . . . . . . . . . . . ICH 1135CD
MC . . . . . . . . . . . . . . . . . . . . ICH 1135MC
Ichiban / Apr '94 / A.D.A. Distribution / Pinnacle / ACD Trading Ltd. / Koch International / Direct Distribution.

### TIMELESS SOUL COLLECTION.
**Tracks:** Not Advised.
■ CD . . . . . . . . . . . . . . . . . . . . . CDTR 2
Timeless (Soul) / Dec '87.

### TURN BACK THE HANDS OF TIME.
**Tracks:** Turn back the hands of time / Waiting was not in vain / Let me back in / Love bones / I'll be right here / Something you got / Undying love / Just because of you / If it's love that you're after / I keep coming back.
■ LP . . . . . . . . . . . . . . . . . . . . . .2465 021
Atlantic / Apr '71.

### TURNING POINT.
**Tracks:** Turning point / Don't let it be too late.
■ 7" . . . . . . . . . . . . . . . . . . . . . . BR 31
Brunswick / Feb '76.

### TYRONE DAVIS STORY, THE.
**Tracks:** Can I change my mind / (One way ticket) to nowhere / Turning point / I wish it was me / After all this time / So good to be home with you / I had it all the time / Woman needs to be loved / Turn back the

hands of time / Is it something you've got / Without you in my life / Have you ever wondered why / There's got to be a answer / You keep me holding on / I keep coming back.
■ LP . . . . . . . . . . . . . . . . . . . . KENT 037
Kent / Mar '85.

### WHAT IF A MAN.
**Tracks:** What if a man.
■ 7" . . . . . . . . . . . . . . . . . . . . . . SS 2092
Stateside / '69.

### YOU STAY ON MY MIND.
**Tracks:** You stay on my mind / Let me be your pacifier / I found myself when I lost you / All because of your love / You can win if you want / I won't let go / Something good about a woman / You're my heart / You're my soul.
CD . . . . . . . . . . . . . . . . . . . .ICH 1170CD
MC . . . . . . . . . . . . . . . . . . . . ICH 1170MC
Ichiban / May '94 / A.D.A. Distribution / Pinnacle / ACD Trading Ltd. / Koch International / Direct Distribution.

## Dawson, Cliff

### SOMEHOW.
**Tracks:** Somehow / Somehow (part 2).
■ 12" . . . . . . . . . . . . . . . . . .12ROUND 2003
■ 7" . . . . . . . . . . . . . . . . . . . ROUND 2003
Half Moon / Sep '82.

## Day, Morris

### COLOR OF SUCCESS.
**Tracks:** Color of success / Character / Oak tree / Love sign / Don't wait for me / Love addiction.
■ MC . . . . . . . . . . . . . . . . . . .925320 4
■ LP . . . . . . . . . . . . . . . . . . .925320 1
WEA / Nov '85.

### COLOR OF SUCCESS.
**Tracks:** Color of success.
■ 7" . . . . . . . . . . . . . . . . . . . . W 8809
■ 12" . . . . . . . . . . . . . . . . . . . W 8809 T
WEA / Feb '86.

### DAY DREAMING.
**Tracks:** Daydreaming / Yo luv / Fishnet / Man's pride,A / Are you ready / Love is a game / Moonlite / Sally.
■ LP . . . . . . . . . . . . . . . . . . . K 925651 1
■ MC . . . . . . . . . . . . . . . . . . K 925651 4
WEA / Feb '88.

### FISH NET.
**Tracks:** Fish net / Maybe.
■ 12" . . . . . . . . . . . . . . . . . . . .W 8201T
■ 7" . . . . . . . . . . . . . . . . . . . . W 8201
WEA / Feb '88.

### OAK TREE, THE.
**Tracks:** Oak tree, The (dance inst) / Oak tree (acapella).
■ 12" . . . . . . . . . . . . . . . . . . . W 8899 T
■ 7" . . . . . . . . . . . . . . . . . . . . W 8899
WEA / Jan '86.

## Day, Patti

### DRIVE ME.
**Tracks:** Drive me.
■ 12" . . . . . . . . . . . . . . . . . . . . SWRT 1
■ 7" . . . . . . . . . . . . . . . . . . . . .SWR 1
Starway / Mar '91.

### HOT STUFF.
**Tracks:** Hot stuff.
■ 12" . . . . . . . . . . . . . . . . . . . . SWRT 5
■ 7" . . . . . . . . . . . . . . . . . . . . SWR 5
■ CD Single . . . . . . . . . . . . . . . . SWRCD 5
Starway / Oct '91.

### NO ONE.
**Tracks:** No one.
■ 12" . . . . . . . . . . . . . . . . . . . .HALT 2T
■ 7" . . . . . . . . . . . . . . . . . . . . HALT 2
Hal / Jul '90.

### RIGHT BEFORE MY EYES.
**Tracks:** Right before my eyes / Right before my eyes (version).
■ 12" . . . . . . . . . . . . . . . . . . DEBTX 3088
■ 7" . . . . . . . . . . . . . . . . . . . DEBT 3088
Debut (1) / Nov '89.
■ 12" . . . . . . . . . . . . . . . . . . . . SWRT 3
■ 7" . . . . . . . . . . . . . . . . . . . . SWR 3
■ CD Single . . . . . . . . . . . . . . . . SWRCD 3
Starway / Jun '91.

## Daye, Eddie

### GUESS WHO LOVES YOU (Daye, Eddie & Four Bars).
**Tracks:** Guess who loves you.
■ 7" . . . . . . . . . . . . . . . . . . . .HRH 004
Horaces / Jun '90.

## Dayeene

### AROUND THE WORLD.
**Tracks:** Around the world.
■ 7" . . . . . . . . . . . . . . . . . . . . . FAZE 8
■ CD Single . . . . . . . . . . . . . . . .CDFAZE 8
■ MC Single . . . . . . . . . . . . . . . .CAFAZE 8
Faze 2 / Sep '92.

## Dayton

### FEEL THE MUSIC.
**Tracks:** Sound of music / It must be love / Out tonight / So what / Love you anyway / Caught in the middle / Eyes / Promise me / Looking up.
■ LP . . . . . . . . . . . . . . . . . . EST 7122971
MC . . . . . . . . . . . . . . . . . TCEST 712297 4
Capitol / Nov '83 / EMI.

### HOT FUN IN THE SUMMERTIME.
**Tracks:** Hot fun in the summertime / Eyes on you.
■ 12" . . . . . . . . . . . . . . . . . . . 12UP 655
■ 7" . . . . . . . . . . . . . . . . . . . . UP 655
United Artists / Aug '82.

### SOUND OF MUSIC, THE.
**Tracks:** Sound of music / Promise me / Love you anyway.
■ 7" . . . . . . . . . . . . . . . . . . . .CL 318
Capitol / Dec '83.
■ 12" . . . . . . . . . . . . . . . . . . . 12CLX 318
Capitol / '84.

## Dazz Band

### GREATEST HITS: DAZZ BAND.
**Tracks:** Let it whip / Joystick / Invitation to love / Party right here / Swoop (I'm your's) / Keep it live / Cheek to cheek / Knock knock / On the one for fun / Let it all blow.
■ LP . . . . . . . . . . . . . . . . . . . WL 72433
■ MC . . . . . . . . . . . . . . . . . . WK 72433
Motown / Jul '86.

### HEARTBEAT.
**Tracks:** Heartbeat.
■ 12" . . . . . . . . . . . . . . . . . . TMGT 1368
■ 7" . . . . . . . . . . . . . . . . . . . TMG 1368
Motown / Jan '85.

### HOT SPOT.
**Tracks:** If only you were in my shoes / Hot spot / Paranoid / All the way / S.C.L. & P. / She used to be my girl / When you needed roses / Slow rap.
■ LP . . . . . . . . . . . . . . . . . . . .ZL72391
Motown / Sep '85.

### HOT SPOT.
**Tracks:** Hot spot / I've been waiting.
■ 12" . . . . . . . . . . . . . . . . . . . ZT 40308
■ 7" . . . . . . . . . . . . . . . . . . . ZB 40307
Motown / Jul '85.

### INVITATION TO LOVE.
**Tracks:** Shake it up / Invitation to love / Magnetized / Hello girl / Skate lovers / Carry on / Do it again / Sooner or later / Beyond the horizon.
■ LP . . . . . . . . . . . . . . . . . .STML 12146
Motown / Oct '81.

### JOYSTICK.
**Tracks:** To the roof / Joystick / Swoop (I'm yours) / Until you / Rock with me / Straight out of school / Now that I have you / Laughing at you / T.Mata (instrumental).
■ LP . . . . . . . . . . . . . . . . . . .STML 12201
■ MC . . . . . . . . . . . . . . . . . .CSTML 12201
Motown / Apr '84.

### JOYSTICK.
**Tracks:** Joystick / Don't get caught in the middle.
■ 12" . . . . . . . . . . . . . . . . . . TMGT 1328
Motown / Jan '84.

### JUKEBOX.
**Tracks:** Let it all blow / Keep you comin' back for more / She's the one / Dream girl / Heartbeat / Undercover lover / I've been waiting / Main attractions / So much love.
■ LP . . . . . . . . . . . . . . . . . . . ZL 72335
■ MC . . . . . . . . . . . . . . . . . . ZK 72335
Motown / Nov '84.

■ DELETED

## KEEP IT LIVE.
**Tracks:** Let it whip / Gamble with my love / I'll keep on lovin' you / Just can't wait till the night / Shake what you got / Keep it live / Just believe in love / Can we dance / Let me love you until.
■ **LP** . . . . . . . . . . . . . . . . . . . . .STML 12173
Motown / Aug '82.

## KEEP IT LIVE.
**Tracks:** Keep it live.
■ **12"** . . . . . . . . . . . . . . . . . . . . TMGT 1279
■ **7"** . . . . . . . . . . . . . . . . . . . . . TMG 1279
Motown / Aug '82.

## LET IT ALL BLOW.
**Tracks:** Let it all blow.
■ **7"** . . . . . . . . . . . . . . . . . . . . . TMG 1361
■ **12"** . . . . . . . . . . . . . . . . . . . . TMGT 1361
Motown / Oct '84.

## LET IT WHIP.
**Tracks:** Let it whip / Everyday love.
■ **7"** . . . . . . . . . . . . . . . . . . . . . TMG 1270
■ **12"** . . . . . . . . . . . . . . . . . . . . TMGT 1270
Motown / Jun '82.

## LOVE M.I.A.
**Tracks:** Love M.I.A. / Place in my heart.
■ **12"** . . . . . . . . . . . . . . . . . . .GEF 12T
■ **7"** . . . . . . . . . . . . . . . . . . . . GEF 12
Geffen / Sep '86.

## ON THE ONE.
**Tracks:** Party right here / Cheek to cheek / On the one for fun / Don't get caught in the middle / Love song / Bad girl / Nice girls / Stay a while with me / We have more than love.
■ **12"** . . . . . . . . . . . . . . . . . . . TMGT 1299
■ **7"** . . . . . . . . . . . . . . . . . . . . TMG 1299
■ **LP** . . . . . . . . . . . . . . . . . . . .STML 12181
Motown / Mar '83.

## ROCK THE ROOM.
**Tracks:** Anticipation / Single girl / Open sesame / One time lover / Body drum / Huff and puff / All the way / Rock the room / Once in a lifetime love.
■ **CD** . . . . . . . . . . . . . . . . . . . PD 86928
■ **LP** . . . . . . . . . . . . . . . . . . . PL 86928
■ **MC** . . . . . . . . . . . . . . . . . . . PK 86928
RCA / Jun '88.

## SHAKE IT UP.
**Tracks:** Shake it up / Only love.
■ **12"** . . . . . . . . . . . . . . . . . . . . TMGT 1213
■ **7"** . . . . . . . . . . . . . . . . . . . . . TMG 1213
Motown / Oct '81.

## SWOOP I'M YOURS.
**Tracks:** Swoop (I'm yours) / Bad girl.
■ **7"** . . . . . . . . . . . . . . . . . . . . . TMG 1338
■ **12"** . . . . . . . . . . . . . . . . . . . . TMGT 1338
Motown / '84.

## WILD AND FREE.
**Tracks:** Wild and free / Body and mind / Time / Beat that's right / All I need / Love M.I.A. / Hooks in me / Sunglasses / It's alright / Something you said.
■ **LP** . . . . . . . . . . . . . . . . . . . . 9241101
■ **MC** . . . . . . . . . . . . . . . . . . . . 9241104
Geffen / Aug '86.
■ **CD** . . . . . . . . . . . . . . . . . . . . 9241102
Geffen / Mar '87.

## WILD AND FREE.
**Tracks:** Not Advised.
■ **12"** . . . . . . . . . . . . . . . . . . . . GEF 6T
Geffen.

# D'Bora

## DREAM ABOUT YOU.
**Tracks:** Not Advised.
■ **LP** . . . . . . . . . . . . . . . . . . . . 8672791
Smash (USA) / Jul '91.

## DREAM ABOUT YOU.
**Tracks:** Dream about you.
■ **12"** . . . . . . . . . . . . . . . . . . . . PZ 161
■ **7"** . . . . . . . . . . . . . . . . . . . . PO 161
■ **MC Single.** . . . . . . . . . . . . . . . POCS 161
Polydor / Sep '91.

## E.S.P.
**Tracks:** Not Advised.
**CD.** . . . . . . . . . . . . . . . . . . . . 5114272
■ **LP** . . . . . . . . . . . . . . . . . . . . 5114271
■ **MC** . . . . . . . . . . . . . . . . . . . . 5114274
Polydor / Oct '91 / PolyGram.

# DD Sound

## CAFE.
**Tracks:** She's not a disco lady / Backstreet baby / Show me your love.
■ **LP** . . . . . . . . . . . . . . . . . . . SKLR 5306
Decca / Mar '79.

## DISCO DELIVERY.
**Tracks:** Burning love / Shopping baby / Disco bass / Let's share love / Slow motion.
■ **LP** . . . . . . . . . . . . . . . . . . . . 9100606
Mercury / Dec '77.

# De Sario, Teri

## AIN'T NOTHING GONNA KEEP ME FROM YOU.
**Tracks:** Ain't nothing gonna keep me from you / Sometime kind of thing.
■ **7"** . . . . . . . . . . . . . . . . . . . .CAN 128
Casablanca / Jul '78.

## BACK IN YOUR ARMS AGAIN.
**Tracks:** Back in your arms again / Sometime kind of thing.
■ **7"** . . . . . . . . . . . . . . . . . . . .CAN 137
Casablanca / Jan '79.

## CAUGHT.
**Tracks:** Caught / By myself / In trouble again / Feel like letting go / Where will they run / I found love / There's nothing better / Words / You better run / My life.
■ **LP** . . . . . . . . . . . . . . . . . . . 6302065
Mercury / Dec '80.

## CAUGHT.
**Tracks:** Caught / I've got a secret.
■ **7"** . . . . . . . . . . . . . . . . . . . .CAN 213
Casablanca / Nov '80.

## DANCING IN THE STREETS (De Sario, Teri & KC).
**Tracks:** Dancing in the streets / Moonlight madness.
■ **7"** . . . . . . . . . . . . . . . . . . . .CAN 203
Casablanca / Aug '80.

## PLEASURE TRAIN.
**Tracks:** Stuff dreams are made of / Back in your arms again / Pleasure train / It takes a man and a woman / Ain't nothing gonna keep me from you / Song & dance man / Sometime kind of thing / Baby I don't want your love / Loving you the first time.
■ **LP** . . . . . . . . . . . . . . . . . . . CAL 2040
Casablanca / Dec '78.

## VOICES IN THE WIND.
**Tracks:** Not Advised.
■ **LP** . . . . . . . . . . . . . . . . . . .DAY R 4036
Dayspring / May '86.

## YES I'M READY.
**Tracks:** Yes i'm ready / With your love.
■ **7"** . . . . . . . . . . . . . . . . . . . . NB 2225
Casablanca / Jan '80.

# Deal, Bill

## BEST OF BILL DEAL AND THE RHONDELLS (Deal, Bill & The Rhondells).
**Tracks:** I've been hurt / Whay kind of fool do you think I am / May I / Are you ready for this / Can I change my mind / Words / Touch me / I've gotta be me / Soulful strut / It's too late / Everybody's got something to hide / Nothing succeeds like success / Swinging tight / I'm gonna make you love me / I've got my needs / Harlem shuffle / River deep, mountain high / Hooked on a feeling / Hey bulldog / Tuck's theme / So what if it rains / I live in the night.
**CD** . . . . . . . . . . . . . . . . . . . .NEMCD 644
Sequel / Apr '94 / Total / BMG.

## BILL DEAL & THE RHONDELLS (Deal, Bill & The Rhondells).
**Tracks:** I've been hurt / Nothing succeeds like success / What kind of fool do you think I am / Swinging tight / May I / I'm gonna make you love me / Are you ready for this / I've got my needs / Can I change my mind / Harlem shuffle / Words / River deep mountain high / Touch me / Hooked on a feeling / I've got to be me / Hey bulldog / Soulful strut / Tuck's theme / It's too late / So what if it rains / Everybody's got something to hide / I live in the night.
■ **LP** . . . . . . . . . . . . . . . . . . .RNLP 70129
Rhino (USA) / May '86.

# Dealers

## MIDNIGHT DOG.
**Tracks:** Midnight dog / Higher than God's hat.
■ **7"** . . . . . . . . . . . . . . . . . . . . PVT 73
Private Stock / Oct '76.

# Dean, Johnny

## SITTING AROUND MY TABLE.
**Tracks:** Sitting around my table.
■ **12"** . . . . . . . . . . . . . . . . . . . .MS 7
Move / Oct '85.

# DeBarge

Having served apprenticeship with Switch (biggest hit *There'll Never Be* in 1978), Bobby and Tommy DeBarge recruited four brothers for family group. Signed to Motown, they enjoyed greatest success with transatlantic 1985 hit *Rhythm Of The Night*. Group began slow disintegration in '86 when lead singer El quit for sporadically successful solo career; latest product of which is Babyface-produced *Heart, Mind & Soul*. His songs have also been covered by Patti LaBelle, Blackstreet and Jomanda. Less salubrious aspects of the DeBarge story include Chico and Bobby being busted for drug trafficking, and James's stormy marriage to Janet Jackson (immortalised in *Control*'s more vitriolic moments). Appropriately, group's final album was titled *Bad Boys*.

## ALL THIS LOVE.
**Tracks:** All this love / I'm in love with you.
■ **7"** . . . . . . . . . . . . . . . . . . . . TMG 1308
■ **12"** . . . . . . . . . . . . . . . . . . . TMGT 1308
Motown / Jul '83.

## BAD BOYS.
**Tracks:** Not Advised.
■ **CD** . . . . . . . . . . . . . . . . . . . SHCD 5004
■ **LP** . . . . . . . . . . . . . . . . . . . SHL 2004
Panarecord Int / '88.

## DANCE ALL NIGHT.
**Tracks:** Dance all night / Dance all night (inst).
■ **12"** . . . . . . . . . . . . . . . . . . . SHR 21010
■ **7"** . . . . . . . . . . . . . . . . . . . . SHR 1010
Striped Horse / Jun '87.

## GREATEST HITS: DEBARGE.
**Tracks:** Rhythm of the night / Who's holding Donna now / You wear it well / Stop don't tease me / I like it / All this love / Time will reveal / Love me in a special way / Share my world / Single heart / Heart is not so smart.
■ **CD** . . . . . . . . . . . . . . . . . . . ZD 72449
Motown / Dec '86.
■ **CD** . . . . . . . . . . . . . . . . . . . WD 72449
Motown / Feb '88.

## I LIKE IT.
**Tracks:** I like it / Hesitated.
■ **12"** . . . . . . . . . . . . . . . . . . . TMGT 1296
■ **7"** . . . . . . . . . . . . . . . . . . . . TMG 1296
Motown / Mar '83.

## IN A SPECIAL WAY.
**Tracks:** Be my lady / Stay with me / Time will reveal / Need somebody / Love me in a special way / Queen of my heart / Baby won'cha come quick / I give up on you / Dream.
■ **LP** . . . . . . . . . . . . . . . . . . . STML 12200
**MC.** . . . . . . . . . . . . . . . . . . .CSTML 12200
Motown / Apr '84 / PolyGram.

## LOVE ALWAYS.
**Tracks:** Love always / Walls come tumbling down / You wear it well (Extra track on 12" version only).
■ **12"** . . . . . . . . . . . . . . . . . . . ELDT 2
■ **7"** . . . . . . . . . . . . . . . . . . . . ELD 2
Motown / Aug '86.

## RHYTHM OF THE NIGHT.
**Tracks:** Prime time / Heart is not so smart / Who's holding Donna now / Give it up / Single heart / You wear it well / Walls come tumbling down / Share my world / Rhythm of the night.
■ **LP** . . . . . . . . . . . . . . . . . . . ZL 72340
■ **MC** . . . . . . . . . . . . . . . . . . . ZK 72340
■ **CD** . . . . . . . . . . . . . . . . . . . ZD 72340
Motown / May '85.
■ **CD** . . . . . . . . . . . . . . . . . . . WD 72653
Motown / Nov '90.

## RHYTHM OF THE NIGHT.
**Tracks:** Rhythm of the night / Queen of my heart.
■ **12"** . . . . . . . . . . . . . . . . . . . TMGT 1376

■ 7" . . . . . . . . . . . . . . . . . . . TMG 1376
Motown / Mar '85.

### STOP DON'T TEASE ME.
Tracks: Stop don't tease me / Hesitated.
■ 12" . . . . . . . . . . . . . . . . . . . GF 1635
Motown / Sep '82.

### TIME WILL REVEAL.
Tracks: Time will reveal / I'll never fall in love again.
■ 12" . . . . . . . . . . . . . . . . . TMGT 1329
■ 7" . . . . . . . . . . . . . . . . . . TMG 1329
Motown / Mar '84.

### WHO'S HOLDING DONNA NOW?.
Tracks: Who's holding Donna now / Be my lady.
■ 12" . . . . . . . . . . . . . . . . . . ZT 40214
■ 7" . . . . . . . . . . . . . . . . . . ZB 40213
Motown / Jun '85.

### WHO'S JOHNNY?.
Tracks: Who's Johnny / Love me in a special way / Rhythm.
■ 12" . . . . . . . . . . . . . . . . . . . ELDT 1
■ 7" . . . . . . . . . . . . . . . . . . . . ELD 1
Motown / May '86.

## DeBarge, Bunny

### IN LOVE.
Tracks: Not Advised.
■ LP . . . . . . . . . . . . . . . . . . ZL 72570
■ MC . . . . . . . . . . . . . . . . . . ZK 72570
Motown / '86.

## DeBarge, Chico

### CHICO DEBARGE.
Tracks: Talk to me / Who are you kidding / You can make it better / I'll love you for now / I like my body / Girl next door / Cross that line / You're much too fast / If it takes all night.
■ LP . . . . . . . . . . . . . . . . . . ZL 72524
■ MC . . . . . . . . . . . . . . . . . . ZK 72524
Motown / Nov '86.

### GIRL NEXT DOOR, THE.
Tracks: Girl next door / You're much too fast.
■ 7" . . . . . . . . . . . . . . . . . . ZB 41123
Motown / Mar '87.

### TALK TO ME.
Tracks: Talk to me / If it takes all night.
■ 12" . . . . . . . . . . . . . . . . . . ZT 40888
■ 7" . . . . . . . . . . . . . . . . . . ZB 40887
Motown / Oct '86.

## DeBarge, El

### EL DEBARGE.
Tracks: Who's Johnny / Secrets of the night / I wanna hear it from my heart / Someone / When love has gone / Private line / Love always / Lost without her love / Thrill of the chase / Don't say it's over.
■ LP . . . . . . . . . . . . . . . . . . ZL 72441
■ MC . . . . . . . . . . . . . . . . . . ZK 72441
Motown / Jul '86.
■ CD . . . . . . . . . . . . . . . . . . ZD 72441
Motown / Mar '87.

### GEMINI.
Tracks: Real love / Cross my heart / Somebody loves you / Broken dreams (think about it) / Broken dreams (think about it) (reprise) / Turn the page / After you / Love life / Make you mine.
■ CD . . . . . . . . . . . . . . . . . . ZD 72621
■ LP . . . . . . . . . . . . . . . . . . ZL 72621
■ MC . . . . . . . . . . . . . . . . . . ZK 72621
Motown / May '89.

### HEART IS NOT SO SMART, THE.
Tracks: Heart is not so smart / Share my world.
■ 12" . . . . . . . . . . . . . . . . . . ZT 40498
■ 7" . . . . . . . . . . . . . . . . . . ZB 40497
Motown / Nov '85.

### HEART, MIND & SOUL.
Tracks: Where you are / Can't get enough / Where is my love / You got the love I want / It's got to be real / Slide / I'll be there / Special lady / Starlight, moonlight, candlight / You are my dream / Heart, mind and soul.
CD . . . . . . . . . . . . . . . . . .936245375-2
MC . . . . . . . . . . . . . . . . . .936245375-4
Warner Bros. / Jun '94 / WEA.

### IN THE STORM.
Tracks: Elmo funk / Fast lane / After the dance / My heart belongs to you / Cry (interlude) / Love me tonight / Poco tonight / Since I fell in love with you / And then I wrote (interlude) / Thick / Another

chance / Leggs / Elmo funk (interlude) / You to turn me on / Prelude to midnight / Special.
CD . . . . . . . . . . . . . . . . . .7599262602
■ LP . . . . . . . . . . . . . . . . . .7599262601
MC. . . . . . . . . . . . . . . . . .7599262604
WEA / Apr '92 / WEA.

### REAL LOVE.
Tracks: Real love / Real love (House mix) / Real love (Extended house mix).
■ 12" . . . . . . . . . . . . . . . . . . ZT 42686
■ 7" . . . . . . . . . . . . . . . . . . ZB 42685
■ CD Single . . . . . . . . . . . . . . ZD 42686
Motown / Mar '89.

### YOU WEAR IT WELL (El DeBarge with DeBarge).
Tracks: You wear it well / Baby won'cha come quick.
■ 7" . . . . . . . . . . . . . . . . . . ZB 40345
■ 12" . . . . . . . . . . . . . . . . . . ZT 40346
Motown / Aug '85.

## Dee Dee

### DEE DEE.
Tracks: Not Advised.
MC. . . . . . . . . . . . . . . . . . .JZC 36370
Not Advised / Sep '89.

## Dee, Jay

### SIMPLE SOLUTION.
Tracks: Simple solution.
■ 12" . . . . . . . . . . . . . . . . . . EZY 1202
Debut (1) / Aug '92.

## Dee, Sonny

### CHICAGO - THAT'S JAZZ (Dee, Sonny Allstars).
Tracks: Please don't talk about me / Mama's gone goodbye / Everybody loves my baby / I cried for you / Blue and brokenhearted / I can't believe that you're in love with me / I want a little girl / Spain / Glad rag doll / Roses of Picardy / At sundown / If I could be with you / Ain't she sweet / Blues my naughty sweetie gives to me.
MC. . . . . . . . . . . . . . . . . . LA 5017C
Lake / Oct '90 / Target / BMG / Direct Distribution.

### CHICAGO - THAT'S JAZZ VOL.2 (Dee, Sonny Allstars).
Tracks: Who's sorry now / My cutie's due at two to two / You're in kentucky sure as you're born / Trouble in mind / Mandy make up you're mind / Is it true what they say about Dixie / When / Mama's gone / Goodbye / Do you know what it means to miss New Orleans / Moonglow / Who cares / It's been so long / Lady's in love with you / Blue & broken hearted / Miss Annabelle Lee / Since my best girl turned me down.
CD. . . . . . . . . . . . . . . . . . LACD 26
MC. . . . . . . . . . . . . . . . . . LA 5026C
Lake / Mar '93 / Target / BMG / Direct Distribution.

## Deep Joy

### FALL.
Tracks: Fall / Fall (version).
■ 12" . . . . . . . . . . . . . . . . . BRAINK 05
Brainiak / Dec '90.

### MAKE SOME SENSE OF THIS.
Tracks: Make sense of this (mixes) / Take.
12" . . . . . . . . . . . . . . . . . . MW 021
Mo Wax / Jul '94 / Vital Distribution.

### SOMETHING INSIDE.
Tracks: Something inside.
■ 12" . . . . . . . . . . . . . . . . . . KINT 5
Kinetix / Jul '92.

## Dees, Sam

Principally known in the U.K. as a songwriter, Alabama-born Dees is also an acclaimed solo artist. He cut several, independently-released sides in the '60s, before joining Chess in '71; by which time he had penned songs for acts including Clarence Carter, Ben E King, Tyrone Davis and the Persuaders. Dees' own I'm So Very Good, released on the Clintone label in '72, proved one of his most popular tracks, and led to a deal with Atlantic (although he continued label-hopping throughout his career). Although he still records under his own name, he has made more of a commercial mark with hits for Larry Graham, Aretha Franklin, Whitney Houston, Regina Belle and Atlantic Starr.

### AFTER ALL.
Tracks: After all / True believer in love.
■ 12" . . . . . . . . . . . . . . . . . PT 43140
■ 7" . . . . . . . . . . . . . . . . . PB 43139
■ CD Single . . . . . . . . . . . . . . PD 43140
RCA / Oct '89.

### SHOW MUST GO ON, THE.
Tracks: Child of the streets / Show must go on / Come back strong / Just out of my reach / Claim jumpin / Troubled child / What's it gonna be / Worn out broken heart / Good guys / So tied up.
■ LP . . . . . . . . . . . . . . . . . SD 18134
Atlantic / '73.

### STORYBOOK CHILDREN.
Tracks: Storybook children / Just as sure.
■ 7" . . . . . . . . . . . . . . . . . K 10719
Atlantic / Apr '76.

### SURVIVE.
Tracks: Survive / Fly angel fly / Survive /long version.
■ 12" . . . . . . . . . . . . . . . . . MS 11
Move / Sep '86.

## Defunkt

### AVOID THE FUNK (Defunkt Anthology).
Tracks: Not Advised.
■ LP . . . . . . . . . . . . . . . . . HNBL 1320
Hannibal / May '88.
CD. . . . . . . . . . . . . . . . . . HNCD 1320
MC. . . . . . . . . . . . . . . . . . HNBC 1320
Hannibal / May '89 / Vital Distribution / A.D.A. Distribution / Topic Records / Direct Distribution.

### CRISIS.
Tracks: Not Advised.
CD. . . . . . . . . . . . . . . . . . EMY 1352
Enemy / Mar '92 / Grapevine Distribution.

### DEFUNKT.
Tracks: Make them dance / Strangling me with your love / In the good times / Blues / Defunkt / Thermonuclear sweat / Melvin's tune / We all dance together.
MC. . . . . . . . . . . . . . . . . . HNBC 1301
■ LP . . . . . . . . . . . . . . . . . HNBL 1301
Hannibal / Nov '88 / Vital Distribution / A.D.A. Distribution / Topic Records / Direct Distribution.

### LIVE AT THE KNITTING FACTORY, NYC.
Tracks: Not Advised.
CD Set . . . . . . . . . . . . . . . EMY 122
Enemy / Sep '91 / Grapevine Distribution.

### MADE IN AMERICA.
Tracks: Smooth love / Eraserhead / Peace of mind / In America / Change / Love you from afar / Tell me / Spiritual sponsor / Self-disclosure.
CD. . . . . . . . . . . . . . . . . . ANCD 8730
MC. . . . . . . . . . . . . . . . . . ANC 8730
■ LP . . . . . . . . . . . . . . . . . AN 8730
Antilles/New Directions / Jun '88 / Grapevine Distribution.

### RAZORS EDGE.
Tracks: Razor's edge / Strangling me with your love.
■ 12" . . . . . . . . . . . . . . . . . HNS 1201
■ 7" . . . . . . . . . . . . . . . . . HNS 01
Hannibal / Oct '81.

### THERMONUCLEAR SWEAT.
Tracks: Not Advised.
■ LP . . . . . . . . . . . . . . . . . HNBL 1311
Hannibal / Jan '84.

## Deja

### MADE TO BE TOGETHER.
Tracks: Made to be together / Sexy dancer.
■ CD Single . . . . . . . . . . . . . TENCD 268
■ 12" . . . . . . . . . . . . . . . . . TENX 268
■ 7" . . . . . . . . . . . . . . . . . TEN 268
10 / Feb '89.

### SERIOUS.
Tracks: You and me tonight / Serious / Somethings turn around / That's where you'll find me / Heart beat / Premonition / Life / What to do now / Summer love / Straight to the point.
■ CD . . . . . . . . . . . . . . . . . DIXCD 58
■ LP . . . . . . . . . . . . . . . . . DIX 58
■ MC . . . . . . . . . . . . . . . . . CDIX 58
10 / Feb '88.

### SERIOUS.
Tracks: Serious (7" only) / You and me tonight (On all versions) / Serious (extended version) (On TENT 132 only) / Serious (dub version) (On 12" only) / Serious (extra beat boys mix) (On TENR 132 only).
■ 7" . . . . . . . . . . . . . . . . . TEN 132

■ 12".................... TENT 132
■ 12".................... TENR 132
10 / Oct '87.

### THAT'S WHERE YOU'LL FIND ME.
Tracks: That's where you'll find me / You and me tonight (12" only) / That's where you'll find me (album version).
■ 7".................... TEN 208
■ 12".................... TENT 208
10 / Feb '88.

## Del Capris

### HEY LITTLE WAY OUT GIRL.
Tracks: Hey little way out girl.
■ 7"....................GRP 112
Grapevine (Northern Soul) / Mar '79.

## Delaney & Bonnie

### ACCEPT NO SUBSTITUTE.
Tracks: Get ourselves together / Someday / Ghetto / When the battle is over / Dirty old man / Love me a little bit longer / I can't take it much longer / Do right woman, do right man / Soldiers of the cross / Gift of love.
CD....................CDTB 050
■ LP....................THBL 050
Thunderbolt / Feb '88 / THE / Jazz Music.

### BEST OF DELANEY & BONNIE.
Tracks: Not Advised.
■ LP.................... K 40429
Atlantic / Jan '73.

### COMIN' HOME.
Tracks: Comin' home.
■ 7".................... 584 308
Atlantic / Dec '69.

### HOME.
Tracks: It's been a long time coming / We can love / Everybody loves a winner / Just plain beautiful / Pour your love on me / Right now love / My baby specializes / Things get better / Hard to say goodbye / Piece of my heart.
■ LP....................SXATS 1029
Stax / Mar '70.
CD....................CDSXE 029
Stax / May '90 / Pinnacle.

### MISS ANN.
Tracks: Miss Ann / Let me be your man.
■ 7"....................2091 065
Atlantic / '71.

### ON TOUR (Delaney & Bonnie & Eric Clapton).
Tracks: Not Advised.
■ LP....................2400 013
Atlantic / Jun '70.
■ LP.................... K 30030
Atlantic / Jul '87.

### ORIGINAL.
Tracks: Get ourselves together / Someday / Ghetto / When the battle is over / Dirty old man / Love me a little bit longer / I can't take it much longer / Do right woman - do right man / Soldiers of the cross / Gift of love.
■ LP....................EKS 74039
Elektra / Jul '69.

### TOGETHER.
Tracks: Only you know & I know / Wade in the river jordan / Sound of the city / Well, well / I know how it feels to be lonely / Comin' home / Move em' out / Big change comin' / Good thing / Groupie / I know something about you / Country life.
■ LP.................... 64959
CBS / Jul '72.

## Delano, Rohan

### INTIMATE CONNECTIONS (Delano, Rohan & The Code).
Tracks: Intimate connections.
■ 12"....................VIST 008
V4 Visions / Jun '92.

## Delegation

### DARLIN'.
Tracks: Darlin'.
■ 12"....................613491
Arista / Aug '90.

### DARLIN' I THINK ABOUT YOU.
Tracks: Darlin' I think about you.
■ 12"....................613178

■ 7"....................113178
■ CD Single.....................663178
Arista / May '90.

### DELEGATION.
Tracks: Feels so good / Dance prance boogie / In love's time / Singing / Twelfth house / In the night / Turn on to city life / Free to be me / I wantcha' back / Gonna keep my eyes on you.
■ LP....................ARL 5062
Arista / Mar '81.

### DEUCES HIGH.
Tracks: What took you so long / I figure I'm out of your life / If you were a song / Gonna bring the house down / Tell her / Dance like Fred Astaire / No words to say / Would you like to start a thang with me / Dance-time USA.
■ LP....................ARL 5070
Arista / Apr '82.

### EAU DE VIE.
Tracks: Heartache no.9 / Sho'nuff sold on you / One more step to take / Blue girl / Darlin' / You and I / Stand up / Welcome to my world / Put a little love on me.
■ MC....................ZCARL 5035
■ LP....................ARL 5035
Arista / Dec '79.

### FREE TO BE ME.
Tracks: Free to be me / I want you back.
■ 7"....................ARO 261
Arista / May '81.

### HEARTACHE.
Tracks: Heartache / Stand up and reach for the sky.
■ 7"....................ARO 246
Arista / Oct '80.

### HONEY I'M RICH.
Tracks: Honey I'm rich / Let me take you to the stone.
■ 7"....................STAT 75
State / Apr '78.

### IF YOU WERE A SONG.
Tracks: If you were a song.
■ 7"....................DU 001
Dude / '82.

### IT'S YOUR TURN.
Tracks: It's your turn / Can we get it back.
■ 12"....................TA 3832
■ 7"....................A 3832
CBS / Nov '83.

### OH HONEY.
Tracks: Oh honey / Love is like a fire.
■ 7"....................STAT 82
State / '77.

### PROMISE OF LOVE, THE.
Tracks: Promise of love / You've been doing me wrong / We can make it / Heaven is by your side / Back door love / Where is the love / We used to know / Soul trippin' / You and your love / Someone oughta write a song (about you baby) / Steppin' out of line.
■ LP....................ETAT 14
State / '77.

### PROMISE OF LOVE, THE.
Tracks: Promise of love / It only happens.
■ 7"....................STAT 25
State / Aug '76.

### PUT A LITTLE LOVE ON ME.
Tracks: Put a little love on me / Welcome to my world.
■ 7"....................ARO 188
Arista / Jun '80.

### TWELFTH HOUSE.
Tracks: Twelfth house / Singing / Dance prance boogie (12" only).
■ 12"....................AROD 252
■ 7"....................ARO 252
Arista / Feb '81.

### WHAT TOOK YOU SO LONG.
Tracks: What took you so long / Bring the house down.
■ 12"....................AROD 277
■ 7"....................ARO 277
Arista / Mar '82.

### WHERE IS THE LOVE (WE USED TO KNOW).
Tracks: Where is the love (we used to know) / Back door love.
■ 7"....................STAT 40
■ 7"....................2088 050
State / Apr '77.

### YOU AND I.
Tracks: You and I / Stand up.
■ 7"....................ARO 214
Ariola / Mar '80.

### YOU'VE BEEN DOING ME WRONG.
Tracks: You've been doing me wrong / Baby you're my mystery.
■ 7"....................STAT 55
State / Aug '77.

## Delfonics

Philadelphia quartet who specialised in elegant harmonies. Originally Four Gents, group formed in 1964, changing name on being signed to Philly Groove in '68. Immediate success with *La La Means I Love You* set pattern for subsequent hits, peaking with million-selling *Didn't I (Blow Your Mind This Time)*. Delfonics were then supplanted by Stylistics on pop chart, though they made occasional return to R&B listing; latterly augmented by R&B singer Major Harris. Group's U.K. chart record began and finished in '71, comprising three reissues of U.S. hits.

### ALIVE AND KICKING.
Tracks: Lying to myself / I told you so / First thing on my mind / Hey baby / Think it over / Pardon me girl / Seventeen (and in love) / I don't want to make you wait / Love is / Can't go on living / Start all over again.
■ LP....................BELLS 245
■ MC....................ZCBEL 245
Bell / '74.

### DELFONICS.
Tracks: Didn't I / Funny feeling / When you get right down to it / Baby I love you / Delfonics theme / Trying to make a fool of me / Down is up, up is down / Over is over / Think about me / I gave to you.
■ LP....................SBLL 137
Bell / Jan '71.

### DIDN'T I (BLOW YOUR MIND THIS TIME).
Tracks: Didn't I (blow your mind this time).
■ 7"....................BELL 1099
Bell / Apr '71.

### ECHOES - THE BEST OF THE DELFONICS.
Tracks: La la means I love you / When you get right down to it / Somebody loves you / Tell me this is a dream / I'm sorry / Face it girl it's over / Ready or not here I come / Didn't I (blow your mind this time) / Trying to make a fool of me / Break your promise / I don't want to make you wait / Hey love / I told you so / Over and over / You got yours and I'll get mine.
■ LP....................210627
■ CD....................260627
■ MC....................410627
Arista / Apr '90.

### HE DON'T REALLY LOVE YOU.
Tracks: He didn't really love you / Without you.
■ 7"....................209 2007
Mojo / Jul '71.

### LA LA MEANS I LOVE YOU.
Tracks: La la means I love you.
■ 7"....................BELL 1165
Bell / Jul '71.

### LA LA MEANS I LOVE YOU.
Tracks: I'm sorry / Break your promise / Shadow of your smile / Hurt so bad / Losing you / Alfie / La la means I love you / You're gone / Look of love / Can you remember / Lover's concerto.
■ LP....................SBLL 106
Bell / Sep '68.

### LA LA MEANS I LOVE YOU (OLD GOLD).
Tracks: La la means I love you.
■ 7"....................OG 9124
Old Gold / '82.

### READY OR NOT HERE I COME.
Tracks: Ready or not here I come.
■ 7"....................BELL 1175
Bell / Oct '71.

### SOUND OF SEXY SOUL.
Tracks: Ready or not here I come / Let it be me / Hot dog / You can't be loving him / Ain't that peculiar / With these hands / Face it girl, it's over / Goin' out of my head / My new love / Somebody loves you / Scarborough Fair Canticle / Every time I see my baby.

■ LP . . . . . . . . . . . . . . . . . . SBLL 121
Bell / Sep '69.

**SUPER HITS.**
**Tracks:** La la means I love you / Didn't I (blow your mind this time) / When you get right down to it / Ready or not here I come / Trying to make a fool of me / With these hands / Over and over / Let it be me / Loving him / Walk right up to the sun / Scarborough Fair/Canticle.
■ LP . . . . . . . . . . . . . . . . . . BELLS 204
Bell / Mar '72.

**SYMPHONIC SOUL: GREATEST HITS.**
**Tracks:** La la means I love you / I'm sorry / Break your promise / Ready or not here I come / Somebody loves you / Funny feeling / You get yours and I'll get mine / Trying to make a fool of me / Didn't I (blow your mind this time) / When you get right down to it / Hey love / Over and over / Walk right up to the sun / With these hands / Loving him / Face it girl it's over.
■ LP . . . . . . . . . . . . . . . . . . CRB 1184
MC. . . . . . . . . . . . . . . . . . TCCRB 1184
Charly R&B / Jun '88 / Charly.

**TELL ME THIS IS A DREAM.**
**Tracks:** Not Advised.
■ LP . . . . . . . . . . . . . . . . . . BELLS 217
Bell / Feb '73.

## Dells

**ALL ABOUT THE PAPER.**
**Tracks:** All about the paper / I touched a dream.
■ 12" . . . . . . . . . . . . . . . . . . TCD 2463
■ 7" . . . . . . . . . . . . . . . . . . TC 2463
20th Century / Oct '80.

**BREEZY BALLADS & TENDER TUNES.**
**Tracks:** Not Advised.
■ LP . . . . . . . . . . . . . . . . . . SS 8029
Solid Smoke (USA) / Feb '85.

**BRING BACK THE LOVE.**
**Tracks:** Bring back the love / Learning to love you was easy.
■ 7" . . . . . . . . . . . . . . . . . . 6145037
Chess / Feb '75.

**DELLS VS. THE DRAMATICS, THE (Dells & The Dramatics).**
**Tracks:** Love is missing from our lives / I'm in love / Choosing up on you / Strung out over you / Playin' the love game / Door to your heart / Don't make me no promises / Tune up / I wish it was me you loved.
■ LP . . . . . . . . . . . . . . . . . . CA 60027
Cadet / '74.

**FREEDOM MEANS..**
**Tracks:** Freedom means / Rather be with you / Love we had / One less bell to answer / It's all up to you / If you go away/Love story / Make it with you / Free and easy / Melody man / Freedom theme.
■ LP . . . . . . . . . . . . . . . . . . 6310102
Chess / Oct '71.

**FROM STREETCORNER TO SOUL.**
**Tracks:** She's just an angel / Now I pray / Why do you have to go / You're still in my heart / Q-bop she bop / My best girl / I'm calling / Rain don't tell nobody / Hold on to what you've got / Wait until tomorrow / Stay in my corner / Let's do it over / Hey sugar (don't get serious) / Poor little boy / It looks like it's over.
■ LP . . . . . . . . . . . . . . . . . . CRB 1055
Charly R&B / Dec '84.

**GREATEST HITS.**
**Tracks:** Stay in my corner / Always together / There is / Love is so simple / Please don't change me now / Wear it on our face / Make sure / O-O, I love you / Does anybody know I'm here / Hallways of my mind / Change we go thru / I can't do enough.
■ LP . . . . . . . . . . . . . . . . . . CRLS 4554
Chess / Sep '69.

**GREATEST HITS: ALWAYS TOGETHER.**
**Tracks:** Not Advised.
LP . . . . . . . . . . . . . . . . . . DET 203
Chess (Charly) / '91 / Charly.

**HAPPY SONG.**
**Tracks:** Happy song / Look at us now.
■ 12" . . . . . . . . . . . . . . . . . . TCT 133
RCA / Nov '81.

**I CAN SING A RAINBOW.**
**Tracks:** I can sing a rainbow.
■ 7" . . . . . . . . . . . . . . . . . . CRS 8099
Chess / Jul '69.

**I TOUCHED A DREAM.**
**Tracks:** So you are love / All about the paper / Passionate breezes / I touched a dream / Just a little love / Look at us now / Your song.

---

■ LP . . . . . . . . . . . . . . . . . . T 618
20th Century / Oct '80.

**LOVE IS BLUE/OH WHAT A NIGHT.**
**Tracks:** Sing a rainbow / Love is blue / Oh, what a night / Dock of the bay / Little understanding / One mint Julep / Whiter shade of pale / Summer place / Glory of love / Honey / Wichita lineman / By the time I get to Phoenix.
■ LP . . . . . . . . . . . . . . . . . . CRLS 4555
Chess / Nov '69.

**MY LADY, SO PERFECT FOR ME.**
**Tracks:** My lady, so perfect for me / Sweetness.
■ 12" . . . . . . . . . . . . . . . . . . 12 PO 70
Urgent / Sep '91.

**OH WHAT A NIGHT.**
**Tracks:** There is / Oh, what a night / Stay in my corner / Love is blue / Always togther / Wear it on our face / When I'm in your arms / Higher and higher.
CD. . . . . . . . . . . . . . . . . . RTS 33009
Roots / Nov '90 / Pinnacle / Target.
CD. . . . . . . . . . . . . . . . . . 26 42 132
MC. . . . . . . . . . . . . . . . . . 26 42 134
Point (2) / '92 / Sound Solutions.

**OH WHAT A NIGHT.**
**Tracks:** Oh what a night / It's not unusual / My baby just cares for me / Every day I have the blues / I got a woman / Jeepers creepers / Stay in my corner / Let's do it over / What do we prove / Witchcraft / Don't dream of anybody but me.
■ LP . . . . . . . . . . . . . . . . . . JOYS 186
Joy / Apr '71.

**OH WHAT A NIGHT.**
**Tracks:** Not Advised.
CD. . . . . . . . . . . . . . . . . . 2636507
MC. . . . . . . . . . . . . . . . . . 2636504
Black Tulip / Oct '89.

**ROCKIN' ON BANDSTAND.**
**Tracks:** Jo jo / Zing zing zing / I can't help myself / Dance, dance, dance / Baby do / Time makes you change / Wedding day / Oh what a night / Come on baby / At the bandstand / Cherry Bea / Swinging teens / Baby open up your heart / Restless days, sleepless nights / I can't dream / I wanna go home.
■ LP . . . . . . . . . . . . . . . . . . CRB 1056
Charly R&B / Aug '83.

**SECOND TIME.**
**Tracks:** Can we skip that part / You can depend on me / My lady, so perfect for me / No win situation / Hott / That's how heartaches are made / Thought of you just a little too much / Sweetness.
CD. . . . . . . . . . . . . . . . . . URG 4108CD
LP . . . . . . . . . . . . . . . . . . URG 4108
MC. . . . . . . . . . . . . . . . . . URG 4108MC
Backs / Sep '91 / RTM / Pinnacle.

**STAY IN MY CORNER.**
**Tracks:** Stay in my corner / Always together / Sing a rainbow / Love is blue / Oh what a night.
■ 7" . . . . . . . . . . . . . . . . . . CTD 110
Charly / Jul '80.
■ 7" . . . . . . . . . . . . . . . . . . CHES 4004
Chess (PRT) / Jul '85.

**TOGETHER AGAIN (Greatest hits vol.1).**
**Tracks:** Not Advised.
■ LP . . . . . . . . . . . . . . . . . . CHESS 203
Chess (Charly) / '87.

**WHATEVER TURNS YOU ON.**
**Tracks:** Happy song / It took a woman like you to make a man out of me / Whatever turns you on / How can we find the love we lost / When we don't know how it got away / Ain't it a shame (every time I hold you ) / Heavens just a step away / Is it it / Stay in my corner.
■ LP . . . . . . . . . . . . . . . . . . T 633
20th Century / Dec '81.

**YOUR SONG.**
**Tracks:** Your song / Look at us now.
■ 7" . . . . . . . . . . . . . . . . . . TC 2478
20th Century / Jan '81.

## Delory, Al

**RIGHT ON (Delory, Al & Mandango).**
**Tracks:** Right on / Jesus Cristo.
■ 7" . . . . . . . . . . . . . . . . . . CL 15911
Capitol / Feb '77.

**YESTERDAY.**
**Tracks:** Yesterday / Traffic jam.
■ 7" . . . . . . . . . . . . . . . . . . HLU 9999
London-American / Nov '65.

---

## Delray, Leon

**I'M STILL WAITIN'.**
**Tracks:** All the lonely girls / Please don't ask me why / Macho man / I'm not in love / My love for you / Day by day / Good mornin' / I wanna be free (creepin') / Unfree / I'm still waiting (for your call) / I wonder will we ever learn / I wanna be free (reprise-dance).
CD. . . . . . . . . . . . . . . . . . 101S 8770572
101 South / Nov '93 / New Note.

## Delroy

**WALK AWAY FROM LOVE.**
**Tracks:** Walk away from love.
■ 12" . . . . . . . . . . . . . . . . . . DR 01
Thomas & Sons / Sep '89.

## Deluxe

**DELUXE E.P.**
**Tracks:** Not Advised.
■ 12" . . . . . . . . . . . . . . . . . . ABS 11
Absolute 2 / Mar '93.

**I'VE GOT A FEELING.**
**Tracks:** I've got a feeling / My momma and papa.
■ 12" . . . . . . . . . . . . . . . . . . UNQ 3T
■ 7" . . . . . . . . . . . . . . . . . . UNQ 3
Unique / Jul '88.

**JUST A LITTLE MORE.**
**Tracks:** Not Advised.
CD. . . . . . . . . . . . . . . . . . UNQCD 1
■ LP . . . . . . . . . . . . . . . . . . UNQLP 1
MC. . . . . . . . . . . . . . . . . . UNQC 1
Danceyard / May '89.

**JUST A LITTLE MORE.**
**Tracks:** Just a little more.
■ 12" . . . . . . . . . . . . . . . . . . UNQ 5 T
■ 7" . . . . . . . . . . . . . . . . . . UNQ 5
Danceyard / Mar '89.

**SO GOOD (REMIX).**
**Tracks:** So good.
■ 12" . . . . . . . . . . . . . . . . . . UNQ 106T
Unyuce Artists / Aug '89.

**YOUR LOVING DRIVES ME CRAZY.**
**Tracks:** Your loving drives me crazy.
■ 12" . . . . . . . . . . . . . . . . . . UNQ 2
Unique / May '88.

## Demps, Louvain

**BETTER TIMES.**
**Tracks:** Not Advised.
■ CD . . . . . . . . . . . . . . . . . . MOTCCD 82
Motor City / Oct '92.

## Deodato, Eumir

**ALSO SPRACH ZARATHUSTRA.**
**Tracks:** Also sprach Zarathustra.
■ 7" . . . . . . . . . . . . . . . . . . CTI 4000
Creed / May '73.
■ 7" . . . . . . . . . . . . . . . . . . CTI SP 004
CTI (1) / Feb '76.

**BEST OF DEODATO.**
**Tracks:** Also sprach Zarathustra / Prelude to the afternoon of a faun / Nights in white satin / Rhapsody in blue / Pavane for a dead princess / Do it again.
CD. . . . . . . . . . . . . . . . . . 813 660-2
Mercury / Jan '88 / PolyGram.

**CARAVAN/WATSUI STRUT.**
**Tracks:** Caravan / Watsui strut.
■ 7" . . . . . . . . . . . . . . . . . . MCA 215
MCA / Nov '75.

**DEODATO.**
**Tracks:** Not Advised.
■ LP . . . . . . . . . . . . . . . . . . ENALP 7
MC. . . . . . . . . . . . . . . . . . ZCENA 7
Proto / '84 / Proto Records.

**HAPPY HOUR.**
**Tracks:** Keep on moving / Happy hour / Just this one night / Tears of a clown / Sweet magic / Keep it in the family / I never get enough.
■ LP . . . . . . . . . . . . . . . . . . K 56983
WEA / '82.

**HAPPY HOUR.**
**Tracks:** Happy hour / Sweet magic (7" only) / Night cruiser (12"only) / Whistle bump (12" only).
■ 12" . . . . . . . . . . . . . . . . . . K 17960T
■ 7" . . . . . . . . . . . . . . . . . . K 17960
WEA / '82.

■ DELETED

## JOAO DONATO.
Tracks: Not Advised.
■ LP . . . . . . . . . . . . . . . . . . . . . . . . . . .MR 5017
Muse / '77.

## KEEP ON MOVING.
Tracks: Keep on moving / Whistle bump.
■ 12″ . . . . . . . . . . . . . . . . . . . . . . . K 17996T
■ 7″ . . . . . . . . . . . . . . . . . . . . . . . . . K 17996
WEA / '82.

## LOVE ISLAND.
Tracks: Not Advised.
■ LP . . . . . . . . . . . . . . . . . . . . . . . . K 56416
WEA / '78.

## MOONLIGHT SERENADE.
Tracks: Moonlight serenade / Havana strut.
■ 7″ . . . . . . . . . . . . . . . . . . . . . . . . MCA 141
MCA / Jun '74.

## MOTION.
Tracks: Not Advised.
■ LP . . . . . . . . . . . . . . . . . . . . . . . . 9251751
WEA / Jan '85.

## NIGHT CRUISER.
Tracks: Night cruiser / East side strut / Skatin' /
Uncle funk / Love magic / Groovitation.
■ LP . . . . . . . . . . . . . . . . . . . . . . . K 56848
WEA.

## NIGHT CRUISER.
Tracks: Night cruiser / Love magic.
■ 7″ . . . . . . . . . . . . . . . . . . . . . . . . K 17696
WEA / Oct '80.

## PRELUDE.
Tracks: Also sprach Zarathustra / Spirit of summer /
Carly and Carole / Baubles, bangles & beads /
Prelude to the afternoon of a faun / September 13 /
Area code 808 / Pina Colada / Love Island / Whistle
bump / San Juan sunset / Take the 'A' train / Tahiti
hut (Ta Pa E) / Chariot of the Gods.
■ LP . . . . . . . . . . . . . . . . . . . . . . .CTI 6021
CTI (1) / '76.

## PRELUDE AND DEODATO 2.
Tracks: Not Advised.
■ CD . . . . . . . . . . . . . . . . . . . . . . . 4505582
CBS / Jan '88.

## VERY TOGETHER.
Tracks: Peter Gunn / Spanish boogie / Amani / Black
widow / Juanita / I shot the sheriff / Star trek / Univac
loves you.
■ LP . . . . . . . . . . . . . . . . . . . . . . . MCF 2774
MCA / '76.

## WHIRLWINDS.
Tracks: Moonlight serenade / Ava Maria / Do it again
/ West 42nd Street / Havana strut / Whirlwinds.
■ LP . . . . . . . . . . . . . . . . . . . . . . . .MCG 3518
MCA / '74.

## WHISTLE BUMP.
Tracks: Whistle bump.
■ 7″ . . . . . . . . . . . . . . . . . . . . . . . . K 17190
WEA / Jun '78.
■ 7″ . . . . . . . . . . . . . . . . . . . . . . . . LV 39
WEA / Jun '80.

# Desanto, Sugar Pie

## DOWN IN THE BASEMENT (THE CHESS YEARS).
Tracks: In the basement (part1) / I want to know /
Mama didn't raise no fools / There's gonna be trou-
ble / I don't feel sorry / Maybe you'll be there / Do I
make myself clear / Use what you got / Can't let you
go / Soulful dress / I don't wanna fuss / Going back
to where I belong / It won't be long / She's got
everything / Wish you were mine / Slip-in mules.
■ LP . . . . . . . . . . . . . . . . . . . . . . . LPM 7001
Chess (Charly) / '89.
■ CD . . . . . . . . . . . . . . . . . . . . . . .CHD 9275
■ LP . . . . . . . . . . . . . . . . . . . . . . . CH 9275
Chess (MCA) / Jul '90.
■ CD . . . . . . . . . . . . . . . . . . . . .CHLD 19162
Chess (MCA) / Mar '93.

## LOVIN' TOUCH.
Tracks: Not Advised.
■ LP . . . . . . . . . . . . . . . . . . . . . . . DD 4310
Diving Duck (Holland) / Jul '87.

## SISTERS OF SOUL (see under Bass, Fontella).

## USE WHAT YOU GOT.
Tracks: In the basement Part 1 / I want to know /
Mama didn't raise no fools / There's gonna be trouble / I don't feel sorry / Maybe you'll be there / Do I
make myself clear / Slip-in mules / Ask me / Use
what you got / Can't let you go / Soulful dress / I
don't wanna fuss / Going back to where I belong / It
won't be long / She's got everything / Wish you were
mine / It's done and forgotten / Tell me what's the
matter / I still care / Slip-in mules (alternative take).
■ CD . . . . . . . . . . . . . . . . . . . . . . .CDRED 33
Charly / '91 / Charly.

# Design

## DAY OF THE FOX.
Tracks: Nature's children / Day of the fox / I feel the
earth move / Can this be love / Pisces hymn / Meet
my friends / If you think about me / Fallen angel /
You better believe it / Yellow bird / When morning
comes.
■ LP . . . . . . . . . . . . . . . . . . . . . . . SLRZ 1037
Regal Zonophone / Feb '73.

# Des'ree

Market-leader in (admittedly-underpopu-
lated) 'folk-funk' genre. Young South Londoner's 1991 debut featured production by
Ashley Ingram (ex-Imagination) and Young
Disciples' Femi, and spawned U.K. hit Feels
So High. Second album, I Ain't Movin', added Family Stand (of Ghetto Heaven fame)
to production cast and spent fleeting period
in U.K. Top 20.

## FEEL SO HIGH.
Tracks: Feel so high / Stand on my own ground (Only
on 12″ and CD Single.) / Got to be strong.
■ 12″ . . . . . . . . . . . . . . . . . . . . . . . 6573666
■ 7″ . . . . . . . . . . . . . . . . . . . . . . . . 6573667
CD . . . . . . . . . . . . . . . . . . . . . . . . . 6573662
■ MC Single . . . . . . . . . . . . . . . . . . 6573664
Sony Soho2 / Aug '91 / Sony.

## FEEL SO HIGH.
Tracks: Feel so high.
■ 12″ . . . . . . . . . . . . . . . . . . . . . . . 6576896
■ 7″ . . . . . . . . . . . . . . . . . . . . . . . . 6576897
■ CD Single . . . . . . . . . . . . . . . . . . 6576892
■ MC Single . . . . . . . . . . . . . . . . . . 6576894
Sony Soho2 / Jan '92.

## I AIN'T MOVIN.
Tracks: I ain't movin / I ain't movin (Mixes).
12″ . . . . . . . . . . . . . . . . . . . . . . . .660467 6
CD Single . . . . . . . . . . . . . . . . . . .660467 5
CD Single . . . . . . . . . . . . . . . . . . .660467 2
MC Single . . . . . . . . . . . . . . . . . . .660467 4
Sony Soho2 / Jun '94 / Sony.

## I AIN'T MOVIN'.
Tracks: Herald the day / Crazy maze / You gotta be /
Little child / Strong enough / Trip on love / I ain't
movin' / Living in the city / In my dreams / Love is
here / I ain't movin' (Percussion reprise).
MiniDisc. . . . . . . . . . . . . . . . . . . . .475843 8
Sony Soho2 / Jul '94 / Sony.
CD . . . . . . . . . . . . . . . . . . . . . . . . . 475843 2
LP . . . . . . . . . . . . . . . . . . . . . . . . . 475843 1
MC. . . . . . . . . . . . . . . . . . . . . . . . .475843 4
Sony Soho2 / May '94 / Sony.

## LITTLE CHILD.
Tracks: Little child / Looking philosophical (Not on
660451-5.) / Caring world (On 660451-2 only.) / Com-
petitive world (On 660451-2 only.) / Deep inside your
mind (On 660451-5 only.) / You gotta be (On 660451-5
only.) / Take a chance (On 660451-5 only.).
CD Single . . . . . . . . . . . . . . . . . . .660451-2
CD Single . . . . . . . . . . . . . . . . . . .660451-5
MC Single . . . . . . . . . . . . . . . . . . .660451-4
Sony Soho2 / Aug '94 / Sony.

## MIND ADVENTURES.
Tracks: Average man / Feel so high / Sun of '79 /
Why should I love you / Stand on my own ground /
Competitive world / Mind adventures / Laughter /
Save me / Momma, please don't cry.
CD . . . . . . . . . . . . . . . . . . . . . . . . . 4712632
MC. . . . . . . . . . . . . . . . . . . . . . . . .4712634
■ LP . . . . . . . . . . . . . . . . . . . . . . . 4712631
Sony Soho2 / Feb '92 / Sony.
MiniDisc. . . . . . . . . . . . . . . . . . . . .471263-3
Sony Soho2 / Feb '93 / Sony.

## MIND ADVENTURES.
Tracks: Mind adventures.
■ 12″ . . . . . . . . . . . . . . . . . . . . . . . 6578636
■ 7″ . . . . . . . . . . . . . . . . . . . . . . . . 6578637
■ CD Single . . . . . . . . . . . . . . . . . . 6578632
■ MC Single . . . . . . . . . . . . . . . . . . 6578634
Sony Soho2 / Mar '92.

## WHY SHOULD I LOVE YOU.
Tracks: Why should I love you / Competitive world /
Mind adventures (Only available on CD Single.) /

(You make me feel like) a natural woman (Only
available on CD Single.).
■ 7″ . . . . . . . . . . . . . . . . . . . . . . . . 6580917
■ CD Single . . . . . . . . . . . . . . . . . . 6580912
■ MC Single . . . . . . . . . . . . . . . . . . 6580914
Sony Soho2 / May '92.

## YOU GOTTA BE.
Tracks: You gotta be / You gotta be (mixes) / Sun of
'79 (Not available on 12) / Feel so high (Available on
CDS 2 only).
■ CD Single . . . . . . . . . . . . . . . . . .660134 5
■ CD Single . . . . . . . . . . . . . . . . . .660134 2
■ 12″ . . . . . . . . . . . . . . . . . . . . . . .660134 6
■ MC Single . . . . . . . . . . . . . . . . . .660134 4
Sony Soho2 / Apr '94.

# Detroit Emeralds

Detroit Emeralds - brothers Abe and Ivory
Tilmon plus James Mitchell - regularly hit
U.S. soul charts in early '70s with singles
like Do Me Right. 1972 brought the trio a
pair of pop hits: You Want It You Got It and
dancefloor favourite Baby Let Me Take You
(In My Arms). They never returned to U.S.
listing but enjoyed three UK Top 40 hits in
1973: You Want It You Got It, I Think Of You
and their biggest and best-known song Feel
the Need In Me. Latter enjoyed two revivals
in U.K.: Emeralds' discofied remake made
no. 12 in '77; six years later, cover by Forrest hit Top 20. Brightest Emerald was Abe
Tilmon, who wrote and co-produced bulk of
their material. He died in 1982, by which
time group had effectively sunk; Mitchell
and Marvin Willis (another Emeralds
associate) having formed Floaters in 1977.

## DANCE SCHOOL.
Tracks: Dance school.
■ 12″ . . . . . . . . . . . . . . . . . . . . . . . TRIP1 3
■ 7″ . . . . . . . . . . . . . . . . . . . . . . . .TRIP 3
Orbit / Nov '83.

## DO ME RIGHT NOW.
Tracks: Do me right / Just now and then.
■ 7″ . . . . . . . . . . . . . . . . . . . . . . . . 7N 25544
Pye / Mar '71.

## DO ME RIGHT/YOU WANT IT YOU GOT IT.
Tracks: Do me right / Wear this ring (With love) /
Long live the king / What you gonna do about me /
You can't take this love for you, from me / Just now
and then / Lee / If I lose your love / And I love her / I
can't see myself (Doing without you) / Holding on /
Admit your love is gone / You want it you got it /
There's love for me somewhere / I'll never sail the
sea again / Take my love / Feel the need / I've got to
move / Baby let me take you (in my arms) / I bet you
get the one you love / Till you decide to come home /
Radio promo medley: (You want it you got it, Do me
right, Wear this ring, Feel the need in me, Baby let
me take you in my arms).
CD . . . . . . . . . . . . . . . . . . . . . . CDSEWD 067
Westbound / Apr '93 / Pinnacle.

## FEEL THE NEED.
Tracks: Feel the need / J.A.'s rap groove UK.
■ 7″ . . . . . . . . . . . . . . . . . . . . . . . .6146 020
Janus / Feb '73.
■ 12″ . . . . . . . . . . . . . . . . . . . . . .MIDASX 1
■ 7″ . . . . . . . . . . . . . . . . . . . . . . . MIDAS 1
Midas (2) / Jun '89.

## FEEL THE NEED.
Tracks: Set it out / Take it or leave me / Feel the
need / Wednesday / Love for you / Look what's
happened to our love / Sexy ways / Love has come
to me.
■ LP . . . . . . . . . . . . . . . . . . . . . . . K 50372
Atlantic / Aug '77.

## FEEL THE NEED.
Tracks: Feel the need / Love has come to me.
■ 7″ . . . . . . . . . . . . . . . . . . . . . . . . K 10945
WEA / '77.

## I THINK OF YOU.
Tracks: I think of you.
■ 7″ . . . . . . . . . . . . . . . . . . . . . . . .6146 104
Westbound / Aug '73.

## I'M IN LOVE WITH YOU.
Tracks: Shake your head / You're getting a little too
smart / Whatcha gonna wear tomorrow / My dreams
have got the best of me / So long / I think of you (you
control me) / Heaven couldn't be like this/Without
you baby/I'm in love..
CD . . . . . . . . . . . . . . . . . . . . . . .CDSEW 006
■ LP . . . . . . . . . . . . . . . . . . . . . . . SEW 006
MC. . . . . . . . . . . . . . . . . . . . . . . .SEWC 006
Westbound / Jun '89 / Pinnacle.

## I'M IN LOVE WITH YOU/FEEL THE NEED IN ME.
**Tracks:** Shake your head / So long / You're getting too smart / I think of you/you control me / Whatcha gonna wear tomorrow / Heaven couldn't be like this/ without you baby / My dreams have got the best of you / Set it out / Take it or leave it / Feel the need in me / Wednesday / Love for you / Look what has happened to our love / Sexy ways / Love has come to me.
CD. . . . . . . . . . . . . . . . . . . . . . . . CDSEWD 068
Stax / Nov '93 / Pinnacle.

## LET'S GET TOGETHER.
**Tracks:** Let's get together / Turn on lady / (Call me) Travelling man / I can't seem to forget / What's the deal / Treat her like a lady / I just don't know about this girl / Have a good day.
■ LP . . . . . . . . . . . . . . . . . . . . . . . K 50452
Atlantic / May '78.

## TURN ON LADY.
**Tracks:** Turn on lady / I just don't know about this girl of mine.
■ 7" . . . . . . . . . . . . . . . . . . . . . . . K 11155
Atlantic / Jun '78.

## YOU WANT IT YOU GOT IT.
**Tracks:** You want it you got it.
■ 7" . . . . . . . . . . . . . . . . . . . . . .6146 103
Westbound / May '73.

## YOU WANT IT, YOU GOT IT.
**Tracks:** You want it, you got it / There's a love for me somewhere / I'll never sail the sea again / Take my love / Feel the need in me / I've got to move / Baby let me take you (in my arms) / I bet you get the one you love / Till you decide to come home.
■ LP . . . . . . . . . . . . . . . . . . . . . . . 6310207
Janus / Jun '72.
CD. . . . . . . . . . . . . . . . . . . . . CDSEW 011
MC. . . . . . . . . . . . . . . . . . . . . . SEWC 011
■ LP . . . . . . . . . . . . . . . . . . . . . SEW 011
Westbound / Oct '89 / Pinnacle.

## Detroit Spinners

Variously known as Motown Spinners, Detroit Spinners and simply Spinners, core members originally convened as high-school band. At close of '50s, they met Berry Gordy's brother-in-law Harvey Fuqua, who - after one hit on Tri-Phi label - took them to Motown in '65. Largely fruitless period ended with transatlantic Top 20 hit *It's A Shame*, produced and co-written by Stevie Wonder. Greatest success came when group - now featuring vocalist Philippe Wynne - hooked up with Atlantic and producer Thom Bell. String of smashes ensued, including classic *Could It Be I'm Falling In Love*, *Ghetto Child*, and U.S. No 1 *Then Came You* with Dionne Warwick. Wynne quit in '77 to pursue solo career (highlight of which was stint with Funkadelic) and group lost Bell's services too. With new producer Michael Zager, they made brief comeback in 1980, topping U.K. charts for first time with remake of Four Seasons' *Working My Way Back To You*. Another cover, Sam Cooke's *Cupid*, kept them near top of charts, but band could not consolidate success and '80s recordings were only minor sellers. Wynne died in July '84.

## 20 GOLDEN CLASSICS: DETROIT SPINNERS.
**Tracks:** It's a shame / Together we can make such sweet music / I'll always love you / Tomorrow may never come / We'll have it made / Where is that girl / Truly yours / At sundown / Sing a rainbow / Love is blue weather / That's what girls are for / It hurts to be in love / For all we know / O-o-oh child / I've got to find myself a brand new baby / My lady love / Message from a blackman / My whole world ended.
■ LP . . . . . . . . . . . . . . . . . . . . STMR 9011
■ MC. . . . . . . . . . . . . . . . . . . . CSTMR 9011
Motown / Jun '80.

## 2ND TIME AROUND (Motown Spinners).
**Tracks:** It's a shame / I've got to find myself a brand new baby / Together we can make such sweet music / Bad, bad weather / Pay them no mind / My lady love / Souly ghost / Ooh child / In my dairy / My whole world ended / At sundown / Sing a rainbow / Love is blue.
■ LP . . . . . . . . . . . . . . . . . . . . .STML 11182
Tamla Motown / Apr '71.

## ARE YOU READY FOR LOVE?.
**Tracks:** Are you ready for love / Once you fall in love.

## BODY LANGUAGE.
**Tracks:** Body language / With my eyes.
■ 7" . . . . . . . . . . . . . . . . . . . . . . . K 11392
Atlantic / May '80.

## CAN'T SHAKE THIS FEELING.
**Tracks:** Can't shake this feeling / Knack for me / You go your way and I'll go mine / Love connection (raise the window down) / Never thought I'd fall in love / Didn't I (blow your mind this time) / Send a little love / Love is such a crazy feeling.
■ LP . . . . . . . . . . . . . . . . . . . . . . . K 50838
Atlantic / Nov '81.

## COULD IT BE I'M FALLING IN LOVE.
**Tracks:** Could it be I'm falling in love.
■ 7" . . . . . . . . . . . . . . . . . . . . . . . K 10283
Atlantic / Apr '73.

## COULD IT BE I'M FALLING IN LOVE (EP).
**Tracks:** You're throwing a good love away / Could it be I'm falling in love / Games people play / Lazy Susan.
■ EP . . . . . . . . . . . . . . . . . . . . . . . K 10935
Atlantic / Apr '77.

## COULD IT BE I'M FALLING IN LOVE (OLD GOLD).
**Tracks:** Could it be I'm falling in love / Working my way back to you.
■ 7" . . . . . . . . . . . . . . . . . . . . . .OG 9916
Old Gold / '89.

## COULD IT BE I'M FALLING IN LOVE (OLD GOLD) (2).
**Tracks:** Could it be I'm falling in love / Ghetto child.
12" . . . . . . . . . . . . . . . . . . . . . .OG 4187
Old Gold / Jul '90 / Pickwick.

## CROSSFIRE.
**Tracks:** Two of a kind / Right or wrong / Our time for love / Crossfire / Keep on keepin' on / Not just another lover / Love is in season / All your love / Secrets.
■ LP . . . . . . . . . . . . . . . . . . . . 780 165-1
Atlantic / May '84.

## CUPID - I'VE LOVED YOU FOR A LONG TIME.
**Tracks:** Cupid - I've loved you for a long time.
■ 7" . . . . . . . . . . . . . . . . . . . . . . . K 11498
Atlantic / Jun '80.

## DANCIN' AND LOVIN'.
**Tracks:** Disco ride / Body language / Let's boogie, let's dance / Medley: Working my way back to you / Forgive me girl / With my eyes / One one two two boogie woogie avenue (home of the boogie).
■ LP . . . . . . . . . . . . . . . . . . . . . . K 50667
■ MC. . . . . . . . . . . . . . . . . . . . . K4 50667
Atlantic / Mar '80.

## DETROIT SPINNERS.
**Tracks:** That's what girls are made for / I'll always love you / Truly yours / For all we know / It hurts to be in love / Tomorrow may never come / Sweet thing / I cross my heart / Where is that girl / Like a good man should / How can I / I just can't help but feel the pain.
■ LP . . . . . . . . . . . . . . . . . . . . .STML 11060
Tamla Motown / Jan '68.

## DETROIT SPINNERS/8.
**Tracks:** I'm gonna getcha / I'm tired of giving / Painted magic / You got the love that I need / Heaven on Earth / Back in the arms of love / Love is one step away / Easy come, easy go / Baby I need your love.
■ LP . . . . . . . . . . . . . . . . . . . . . . K 50418
Atlantic / Feb '78.

## FROM HERE TO ETERNALLY.
**Tracks:** It's a natural affair / Don't let the man get you / Plain and simple love song / Are you ready for love / I love the music / One man wonderful band / If you wanna do a dance / Once you fall in love.
■ LP . . . . . . . . . . . . . . . . . . . . . . K 50544
Atlantic / '79.

## GHETTO CHILD.
**Tracks:** Ghetto child.
■ 7" . . . . . . . . . . . . . . . . . . . . . . . K 10359
Atlantic / Sep '73.

## GHETTO CHILD (1990 BOILERHOUSE MIX).
**Tracks:** Ghetto child (1990 boilerhouse mix) / Ghetto child (Original mix).
■ 12" . . . . . . . . . . . . . . . . . . . . A 7814 T
■ 7" . . . . . . . . . . . . . . . . . . . . . .A 7814
Atlantic / Sep '90.

## GOLDEN GREATS: DETROIT SPINNERS.
**Tracks:** Could it be I'm falling in love / Ghetto child / We belong together / Rubber band man / Right or wrong / I'll be around / Mighty love / Just can't get you out of my mind / One of a kind (love affair) / Love is in season.
■ LP . . . . . . . . . . . . . . . . . . . . 781 627-1
■ MC. . . . . . . . . . . . . . . . . . . . 781 627-4
Atlantic / Aug '85.

## GRAND SLAM.
**Tracks:** City full of memories / Magic in the moonlight / If I knew / I'm calling you now / So far away / Just let love in / Funny how time slips away / Loverboy / No other love.
■ LP . . . . . . . . . . . . . . . . . . . . 780 020-1
■ MC. . . . . . . . . . . . . . . . . . . . 790 020-4
Atlantic / Nov '82.

## I JUST WANT TO FALL IN LOVE.
**Tracks:** I just want to fall in love / Love trippin'.
■ 7" . . . . . . . . . . . . . . . . . . . . . . . K 11624
Atlantic / Oct '80.

## I LOVE THE MUSIC.
**Tracks:** I love the music / Don't let the man get you.
■ 7" . . . . . . . . . . . . . . . . . . . . . . . K 11347
Atlantic / '77.

## I'LL ALWAYS LOVE YOU.
**Tracks:** I'll always love you.
■ 7" . . . . . . . . . . . . . . . . . . . . . . TMG 523
Tamla Motown / '65.

## I'LL BE AROUND.
**Tracks:** I'll be around / City full of memories.
■ 12" . . . . . . . . . . . . . . . . . . . . A 9891 T
■ 7" . . . . . . . . . . . . . . . . . . . . . .A 9891
Atlantic / Jan '83.

## IF YOU WANNA DO A DANCE ALL NIGHT.
**Tracks:** If you wanna do a dance all night / Once in a life proposal.
■ 7" . . . . . . . . . . . . . . . . . . . . . . . K 11175
Atlantic / Jul '78.

## IT'S A SHAME.
**Tracks:** It's a shame.
■ 7" . . . . . . . . . . . . . . . . . . . . . . TMG 755
Tamla Motown / Jun '77.
■ 7" . . . . . . . . . . . . . . . . . . . . TMG 1189
Motown / Oct '80.
■ 7" . . . . . . . . . . . . . . . . . . . . ZB 41929
Motown / Apr '88.

## KNACK FOR ME.
**Tracks:** Knack for me / Can't shake this feeling.
■ 7" . . . . . . . . . . . . . . . . . . . . . . . K 11707
Atlantic / May '82.

## LABOUR OF LOVE.
**Tracks:** Long live soul music / Standing on the rock / Yesterday once more / Nothing remains the same / Almost all the way to love / Winter of our love / Be my love / Give your lady what she wants / Man just don't know what a woman goes through / Deacon.
■ LP . . . . . . . . . . . . . . . . . . . . . . K 50777
Atlantic / May '81.

## LIVING A LITTLE LAUGHING A LITTLE.
**Tracks:** Living a little laughing a little / I've got to make it on my own.
■ 7" . . . . . . . . . . . . . . . . . . . . . . . K 10571
Atlantic / Jun '75.

## LOVE IS IN SEASON.
**Tracks:** Love is in season / Living a little, laughing a little / Could it be I'm falling in love.
■ 12" . . . . . . . . . . . . . . . . . . . . A 9649 T
■ 7" . . . . . . . . . . . . . . . . . . . . . .A 9649
Atlantic / Aug '85.

## LOVE TRIPPIN'.
**Tracks:** Love trippin' / Heavy on the sunshine / Medley - Cupid / I've loved you for a long time / I just want to be with you / Streetwise / Working my way back to you / I just want to fall in love / Now that you're mine again / Split decision / I'm takin' you back / Pipedream / Body language.
■ LP . . . . . . . . . . . . . . . . . . . . . . K 50731
■ MC. . . . . . . . . . . . . . . . . . . . . K4 50731
Atlantic / '88.

## LOVIN' FEELING.
**Tracks:** Put us together again / I found an angel / You're number one / She does / That's what girls are made for / More today than yesterday / Witness / Two can be one / Show me your magic.
■ LP . . . . . . . . . . . . . . . . . . . . 790 456-1
■ MC. . . . . . . . . . . . . . . . . . . . 790 456-4
Atco / Oct '85.

Atlantic / '77.
■ 7" . . . . . . . . . . . . . . . . . . . . . . . K 11286
WEA / '77.

                                         ■ DELETED

## MAGIC IN THE MOONLIGHT.
**Tracks:** Magic in the moonlight / So far away.
- 12"................................A 9962 T
- 7".................................A 9962
Atlantic / Nov '82.

## PUT US TOGETHER AGAIN.
**Tracks:** Put us together again / Show me your magic / Right or wrong.
- 12"................................B 9604 T
- 7".................................B 9604
Atlantic / Jan '86.

## RIGHT OR WRONG I'LL BE AROUND.
**Tracks:** Right or wrong I'll be around.
- 12"................................A 9666T
- 7".................................A 9666
Atlantic / May '84.

## RUBBERBAND MAN, THE.
**Tracks:** Rubber band man.
- 7".................................K 10807
Atlantic / Sep '76.

## SMASH HITS.
**Tracks:** Rubber band man / One of a kind (love affair) / Ghetto child / Games people play / Could it be I'm falling in love / Sadie / Mighty love / Then came you / I'll around / Clown / Just can't get you out of my mind / How could I let you get away / Living a little, laughing a little / Wake up Susan.
- MC................................K4 50363
- LP................................K 50363
Atlantic / Apr '77.

## SPLIT DECISION.
**Tracks:** Split decision / Now that you're mine again.
- 7".................................K 11558
Atlantic / Sep '80.

## SWEET SOUL MUSIC.
**Tracks:** Not Advised.
- CD................................550 4082
- MC................................550 4084
Spectrum (1) / Aug '94 / PolyGram.

## SWEET THING.
**Tracks:** Sweet thing.
- 7".................................TMG 514
Tamla Motown / '65.

## TOGETHER WE CAN MAKE SUCH SWEET MUSIC (Motown Spinners).
**Tracks:** Together we can make such sweet music / Truly yours.
- 7".................................TMG 766
Tamla Motown / Mar '71.

## WAKE UP SUSAN.
**Tracks:** Wake up Susan / If you can't be in love.
- 7".................................K 10799
Atlantic / Jan '77.

## WORKING MY WAY BACK TO YOU.
**Tracks:** Working my way back to you / I'll be around / Disco ride.
- 7".................................K 11432
Atlantic / Feb '80.
- 7".................................A 9071
- 12"................................A 9071 T
Atlantic / May '88.

## WORKING MY WAY BACK TO YOU (OLD GOLD).
**Tracks:** Working my way back to you / Forgive me girl / Cupid / I've loved you for a long time.
- 12"................................OG 4180
Old Gold / Jul '90 / Pickwick.

## YESTERDAY ONCE MORE.
**Tracks:** Yesterday once more / Nothing remains the same / Be my love.
- 12"................................K 11564 T
- 7".................................K 11564
Atlantic / Mar '81.

## DeVaughan, William

## BE THANKFUL FOR WHAT YOU'VE GOT.
**Tracks:** Not Advised.
- CD................................CHELD 1002
- LP................................CHELV 1002
- MC................................CHELC 1002
Start / Jun '89 / THE / Koch International.

## BE THANKFUL FOR WHAT YOU'VE GOT.
**Tracks:** Be thankful for what you've got.
- 7".................................2005 002
Chelsea Collection / Jul '74.
- 7".................................EMI 5101
EMI / Sep '80.

## CREME DE CREME.
**Tracks:** Creme de creme.
- 12"................................EXCL 527
- 7".................................EXC 527
Excaliber / Dec '82.

## FIGURES CAN'T CALCULATE.
**Tracks:** Figures can't calculate / Love comes so easy with you / Boogie Dan / You send me / Be thankful for what you've got / I've never found a girl / Hold on to love.
- LP................................EMC 3347
EMI / Oct '80.

## Di Franco, Linda

## MY BOXX.
**Tracks:** My box / Dance it up.
- 12"................................YZ 68T
- 7".................................YZ 68
WEA / May '86.

## RISE OF THE HEART, THE.
**Tracks:** T.V. Scene / Look of love / Yankee / Stay / Dance it up / My boss / Bless my soul / Fran / Blame it on Rio / Rise of the heart.
- LP................................WX 50
- MC................................WX 50C
WEA / May '86.

## TV SCENE.
**Tracks:** TV scene / Incredible close.
- 12"................................YZ 43 T
- 7".................................YZ 43
WEA / Sep '85.

## Diamond, Greg

## CHAINS (Diamond, Greg & Bionic Boogie).
**Tracks:** Chains / Hot butterfly.
- 7".................................POSP 50
Polydor / May '79.

## CREAM.
**Tracks:** Cream (always rises to the top) / Paradise.
- 7".................................POSP 18
Polydor / Jan '79.

## DOING THAT (FANCY DANCER).
**Tracks:** Doing that (fancy dancer) / Holdin' back.
- 7".................................TKR 7534
TK / Mar '79.

## HOT BUTTERFLY (Diamond, Greg & Bionic Boogie).
**Tracks:** Hot butterfly / Hot butterfly (exit) / Fess up to the boogie / When the shit hits the fan (rocket pocket).
- 12"................................URBX 16
- 7".................................URB 16
Urban / Mar '88.

## STARCRUISER.
**Tracks:** Fancy dancer / Island boogie / Starcruiser / Bring back your love / Holding back / This side of midnight / Too hot to reggae / Arista vista.
- LP................................TKR 82549
TK / Feb '79.

## THIS SIDE OF MIDNIGHT.
**Tracks:** This side of midnight / Sea cruiser.
- 7".................................TKR 7511
TK / Oct '78.

## Diamond, Keith

## DIP (Diamond, Keith Band).
**Tracks:** Dip / You'll always be there.
- 12"................................PD 11812
RCA / Oct '81.

## Dibango, Manu

## ABELE DANCE.
**Tracks:** Abele dance.
- CD Single................................CELD 1711
Celluloid (USA) / Dec '93.

## ADELE DANCE.
**Tracks:** Adele dance.
- 12"................................CART 339
Carrere / Jul '84.

## AFRI JAZZY.
**Tracks:** Masa lemba / Bushman promenade / Gombo sauce / Soir au village / Makossa '87 (Big blow) / Kango / Doula serenade / Abelley sphere.
- CD................................URBCD 1
- LP................................URBLP 1
- MC................................URBMC 1

Urban / Jun '87.
- CD................................EMY 1372
Enemy / Oct '92 / Grapevine Distribution.

## AMBASSADOR.
**Tracks:** Happy feeling / Cava chouia / Bona sango / Choci / Mumbele style / Night jet.
- LP................................ILPS 9658
Island / Mar '81.

## BAO BAO.
**Tracks:** Not Advised.
- CD................................MAUCD 632
Demon / Nov '92 / Pinnacle / A.D.A. Distribution.

## BIG BLOW.
**Tracks:** Big blow / Aloko party.
- 7".................................FR 13755
Decca / Feb '78.

## DELIVERANCE.
**Tracks:** Not Advised.
- LP................................AF 1984
Afro-Rhythmes / Mar '89.

## ELECTRIC AFRICA.
**Tracks:** Not Advised.
- CD................................827 014-2
Polydor / '88 / PolyGram.
- CD................................CELD 6114
Celluloid (USA) / Dec '93 / Charly / Cadillac.

## GONE CLEAR.
**Tracks:** Full up / Goro city / Dr. Bird / Tek time / Reggae makossa / Frozen soul.
- LP................................ILPS 9539
Island / Jan '80.

## GORO CITY.
**Tracks:** Goro city / Reggae makossa.
- 12"................................12 WIP 6556
Island / Jan '80.

## HAPPY FEELING.
**Tracks:** Not Advised.
- MC................................C 1003
Sterns / Mar '89 / Sterns Records / C.M. Distribution / Projection / Cadillac.

## HAPPY FEELING.
**Tracks:** Happy feeling / Goro city.
- 12"................................12WIP 6672
- 7".................................WIP 6672
Island / Feb '81.

## HOMEMADE.
**Tracks:** Not Advised.
- LP................................362018
Sterns.

## MAKOSSA.
**Tracks:** Makossa / Gombo sauce.
- 12"................................URBX 2
- 7".................................URB 2
Urban / May '87.

## MANU DIBANGO.
**Tracks:** Andy / Matumba / Motapo / Sun explosion.
- LP................................SKLR 5303
Decca / Feb '79.
- LP................................ALB 364
Musidisc / Aug '90 / Vital Distribution / Discovery / A.D.A. Distribution / Harmonia Mundi (UK).

## MINCALOR (Dibango, Manu & MC Mello).
**Tracks:** Mincalor.
- 12"................................EXPR 126
Expression / Sep '91.

## NEGROPOLITAINES.
**Tracks:** Not Advised.
- CD................................859052
- MC................................859054
Melodie / Nov '92 / Triple Earth / Discovery.

## PATA PIYA.
**Tracks:** Pata piya / Abele.
- 12"................................CEL 705
- 7".................................SCEL 705
Celluloid (France) / Jul '85.

## POLYSONIK.
**Tracks:** Not Advised.
- CD................................EXPALCD 7
- LP................................EXPAL 7
- MC................................EXPALMC 7
Expression / May '91 / Pinnacle.

## RASTA SOUVENIR.
**Tracks:** Not Advised.
- Double LP................................ESP 7512/3
- MC................................C 1002
Disques Esperance / Mar '89.

■ DELETED

## SOUL MAKOSSA.
**Tracks:** Soul makossa / Rencontre / Taoumba / Moni / New bell 'hard pulsation' / O Boso / Kata kata / Soukouss / Pepe soup / Essimo / Nights in Zeralda.
CD..........................................139 215
Musidisc / Dec '86 / Vital Distribution / Discovery / A.D.A. Distribution / Harmonia Mundi (UK).
CD........................................FC 065CD
LP..........................................403651
MC.........................................FC 065C
Musidisc / Aug '90 / Vital Distribution / Discovery / A.D.A. Distribution / Harmonia Mundi (UK).

## SOUL MAKOSSA.
**Tracks:** Soul makossa / Big blow.
■ 12".....................................LONX 19
■ 7".......................................LON 19
London / Aug '83.

## SUN EXPLOSION.
**Tracks:** Not Advised.
MC..........................................C 1001
Sterns / Mar '89 / Sterns Records / C.M. Distribution / Projection / Cadillac.

## WAKA JUJU.
**Tracks:** Not Advised.
■ LP......................................2933 130
Polygram (Import) / Oct '82.
■ LP......................................ESP 7515
Disques Esperance / Mar '89.

## WAKAFRIKA.
**Tracks:** Soul makossa / Biko / Wakafrika / Emma / Homeless / Lady / Hi-life / Wimoweh / Am oh / Jingo / Pata pata / Diarabi / Ca va chouia.
CD.......................................BLM 001CD
MC.......................................BLM 001MC
Blue Music / Jun '94 / Pinnacle.

# Dickey, Gwen

## CAR WASH.
**Tracks:** Car wash / Wishing on a star.
■ 12".......................................SYRT 7
■ 7".........................................SYR 7
■ CD Single...............................CD SYR 7
■ MC Single................................CA SYR 7
Swanyard / Nov '89.

## DON'T STOP.
**Tracks:** Don't stop.
■ 12"......................................SYDT 21
■ 7"........................................SYD 21
■ CD Single................................CDSYD 21
Swanyard / Oct '92.

# Diggs, David

## REAL WORLD.
**Tracks:** Not Advised.
■ LP.......................................PA 8037
Palo Alto / Jan '84.
MC.......................................PAC 8037
Palo Alto / Jul '86.

# Dillard, Moses

## MY ELUSIVE DREAMS (Dillard, Moses & Joshua).
**Tracks:** My elusive dreams.
■ 7".......................................SS 2059
Stateside / '67.

# Diplomats

## I'LL KEEP HOLDING ON.
**Tracks:** I'll keep holding on.
■ 7"..........................................EX 1
Exchange / Nov '82.

# Diplomats

## DIPLOMATS.
**Tracks:** Not Advised.
CD.....................................RIPEXD 197
LP.....................................RIPELP 197
Ripe / May '94 / Jetstar.

## LAST CHANCE.
**Tracks:** Last chance.
12".....................................12RIPE 201
Ripe / Mar '94 / Jetstar.

# Direct Drive

## ABC (FALLING IN LOVE'S NOT EASY).
**Tracks:** ABC (falling in love's not easy) / Anything.
■ 12"....................................POSPX 742
■ 7".....................................POSP 742
Boiling Point / Apr '85.

## ANYTHING.
**Tracks:** Anything / I won't be back tonight.
■ 7"........................................7 DRD 2
Direct Drive / Nov '84.
■ 12"....................................POSPX 728
■ 7".....................................POSP 728
Polydor / Jan '85.

## DON'T DEPEND ON ME.
**Tracks:** Don't depend on me / Time machine.
■ 12"...................................DRIVE 20/20
Oval / Jan '82.

## I'M THE ONE.
**Tracks:** I'm the one / Time's running out.
■ 12"...................................DRIVE 21/12
■ 7".....................................DRIVE 21
Oval / Apr '82.

## IN THE MIDDLE OF SPRING.
**Tracks:** In the middle of Spring / Can I say sorry.
■ 12"...................................PASH 01(12)
■ 7"......................................PASH 01
Passion (1) / Jul '83.

## NEED SOME SUNSHINE.
**Tracks:** Need some sunshine / Pass the paper.
■ 12"......................................12 DRD 3
■ 7".......................................7 DRD 3
Direct Drive / Nov '85.

## OH YEAH.
**Tracks:** Oh yeah.
■ 12".......................................GOT 1
Direct Drive / Mar '86.

## PASS THE PAPER.
**Tracks:** Pass the paper / Don't stop the carnival / Overdrive.
■ 7".......................................7 DRD 1
Direct Drive / Aug '84.

# Dixon, Jessy

## AIN'T GOT TIME TO DIE.
**Tracks:** Not Advised.
■ LP.....................................RMLP 030
MC.....................................RMC 030
Word (UK) / '88 / Word Records (UK) / Sony.

## IT'S ALL RIGHT NOW.
**Tracks:** I expect to see him / He'll be right there / Father me / I'm satisfied / Hold on / It's all right / Come to me / Lord, You've been so good to me / Born again / He has done great things.
■ LP......................................LS 7045
MC......................................LC 7045
Light / May '82 / Word Records (UK) / Sony.

## SANCTUARY.
**Tracks:** Not Advised.
■ LP....................................PWRO 1072
MC....................................PWCO 1072
Word (UK) / Jan '89 / Word Records (UK) / Sony.

## SATISFIED (LIVE).
**Tracks:** Satisfied / It's so good / Through the blood / I want to get to know you / Heavenly dove / He really didn't have to die / What do you call Him / I choose to follow you / Jesus is alive and well / Operator.
■ LP......................................LS 7065
MC......................................LC 7065
Light / May '82 / Word Records (UK) / Sony.

## SILENT PARTNER.
**Tracks:** Not Advised.
■ LP....................................PWRO 1078
MC....................................PWCO 1078
Word (UK) / Jan '89 / Word Records (UK) / Sony.

## WINNING SIDE, THE.
**Tracks:** Not Advised.
■ LP....................................PWRO 1091
MC....................................PWCO 1091
Word (UK) / Jan '89 / Word Records (UK) / Sony.

## YOU BRING THE SUN OUT.
**Tracks:** Not Advised.
■ LP......................................LS 7051
Light / '91.

# Doheny, Ned

## TO PROVE MY LOVE.
**Tracks:** To prove my love / On the swingshift.
■ 7".....................................CBS 9481
CBS / Jan '81.

## TO PROVE MY LOVE (OLD GOLD).
**Tracks:** To prove my love / Nite life.
■ 12".....................................OG 4503
Old Gold / Sep '88.

# Don-E

## CRAZY.
**Tracks:** Crazy / Unbreakable / Crazy (mixes) (Available on 12 and CDS only).
■ 12"....................................12 BRW 272
■ 7"......................................BRW 272
■ CD Single...............................BRCD 272
■ MC Single................................BRCA 272
4th & Broadway / Aug '93.

## LOVE MAKES THE WORLD GO ROUND.
**Tracks:** Love makes the world go round / Mystery.
■ 12"...................................12BRW 242
■ 7"......................................BRW 242
■ MC Single................................BRCA 242
■ CD Single...............................BRCD 242
4th & Broadway / Mar '92.

## OH MY GOSH.
**Tracks:** Oh my gosh (mixes).
■ CD Single..............................864829-2
■ 12"....................................12 BRW 260
■ 7"......................................BRW 260
■ MC Single................................BRCA 260
4th & Broadway / Jan '93.

## PEACE IN THE WORLD.
**Tracks:** Peace in the world / Love makes the world go round (12" only) / Skip to my lou (12" & CD single only).
■ 12"....................................12 BRW 256
■ 7"......................................BRW 256
■ CD Single...............................BRCD 256
■ MC Single................................BRCA 256
4th & Broadway / Jun '92.

## UNBREAKABLE.
**Tracks:** Intro / Welcome to my world / Oh my gosh / Love makes the world go round / Unbreakable / Someday somehow / Interlude / Undercover lover / Stop what you're doing / Me oh my / Emancipate our love / Peace in the world / Never ever / So fine / U don't have 2 cry.
CD.......................................BRCD 586
■ LP......................................BRLP 586
MC......................................BRCA 586
4th & Broadway / Jul '92 / PolyGram.

# Do'reen

## AIN'T GONNA WALK IN YOUR SHADOW NO MORE.
**Tracks:** Ain't gonna walk in your shadow.
■ 12"....................................STONED 1
Rumour / Jul '93.

# Dorsey, Gail Ann

## CORPORATE WORLD, THE.
**Tracks:** Wasted country / If only you / Just another dream / So hard to let you go / Corporate world / No time / S.W.4 / Wishing I was someone else / Carry me off to heaven / Missiles of midnight (On CD and Cassette only).
■ CD......................................244046 2
■ LP......................................WX 220
■ MC......................................WX 220C
WEA / Oct '88.

## JUST ANOTHER DREAM.
**Tracks:** Just another dream / Look what love's got me doing again / Meet you tonight.
■ 12"......................................YZ 369T
■ 7".......................................YZ 369
■ CD Single...............................YZ 369CD
WEA / Mar '89.

## RUDE BLUE.
**Tracks:** Not Advised.
CD.......................................CID 9999
MC.......................................ICT 9999
Island / Feb '93 / PolyGram.

## WASTED COUNTRY.
**Tracks:** Wasted country / Happy ending.
■ 12"......................................YZ 194T
■ 7".......................................YZ 194
■ CD Single...............................YZ 194CD
WEA / Jul '88.

## WHERE IS THE LOVE.
**Tracks:** Where is your love / Try it out on me / Base in your faith (12" only) / Meet you tonight.
■ CD Single..............................YZ 324 CD
■ 12"......................................YZ 324T
■ 7".......................................YZ 324
WEA / Nov '88.

## Dorsey, Lee

Former sailor, boxer and car salesman, Dorsey decided to try his luck at singing. Propelled to fame in 1961 by infectious *Ya Ya*, Dorsey (produced by Allen Toussaint) continued to hit U.S. R&B and pop charts throughout first half of '60s, cracking U.K. charts in '66. After transatlantic No. 8 *Working In A Coalmine*, his final success was *Holy Cow*, whereupon Dorsey retreated from international stardom to more modest New Orleans fame. After brief comebacks in '70s, Dorsey became unlikely inspiration for punk/new wave acts including Fleshtones, Devo and The Clash, but died in '86.

### ALL WAYS FUNKY.
**Tracks:** Hello mama / Hoodlum Joe / Confusion / People sure act funny / Messed around (and fell in love) / Lonely Avenue / What am I living for / When am I living for / Here comes the hurt again / Ay la ay / Li'l Liza Jane / People gonna talk / My old car / Hello good looking / My babe / Drainin'.
■ **LP** . . . . . . . . . . . . . . . . . . . . . . **CRB 1036**
Charly R&B / Feb '82.

### AM I THAT EASY TO FORGET?.
**Tracks:** Lottie mo / Lover of love / Oo-na-nay / You better tell her / Great googa mooga / As quiet as it's kept / Lonelyology (for your love) / Ride your pony (live) / Coca cola commercial (my old car) / Coca cola commercial (little babe) / Occapella / Sneaking Sally thru the alley / Tears, tears and more tears / Riverboat / Yes we can / Soul mine / If I were a carpenter / Honest I do / Place where we can / Can I be the one / Night people / Am I that easy to forget / Before the next teardrop falls / Ya ya (live) / Working in a coalmine / Lottie mo (live).
■ **Double LP** . . . . . . . . . . . . . . . . . . **CDX 21**
Charly / Dec '87.

### CAN YOU HEAR ME?.
**Tracks:** Mellow good time / Working in a coalmine / Can you hear me / Greatest love / Mexico / Get out of my life woman / Ride your pony / Confusion / Holy cow / Don't you ever leave me / Neighbours daughter / Little dab a doya / Kitty cat song / Shortnin' bread / So long / People I wish you could see me / Work work work / Here comes the hurt again / Hello mama / Feeling / My old car / Everything I do gonh be funky.
■ **CD** . . . . . . . . . . . . . . . . . . **CDCHARLY 39**
Charly / Jan '87.

### CONFUSION.
**Tracks:** Confusion / Neighbour's daughter.
■ **7"** . . . . . . . . . . . . . . . . . . . . . . **SS 506**
Stateside / May '66.

### FREEDOM FOR THE FUNK.
**Tracks:** Not Advised.
**CD** . . . . . . . . . . . . . . . . . . . . **CPCD 8068**
Charly / Nov '94 / Charly.

### GET OUT OF MY LIFE WOMAN.
**Tracks:** Get out of my life woman.
■ **7"** . . . . . . . . . . . . . . . . . . . . . . **SS 485**
Stateside / Feb '66.
■ **7"** . . . . . . . . . . . . . . . . . . . . . **CTD 129**
Charly / Mar '81.

### GO-GO GIRL.
**Tracks:** Go-go girl / I can hear you callin'.
**7"** . . . . . . . . . . . . . . . . . . . . . **SS 2055**
Stateside / Oct '67 / EMI.

### GONH BE FUNKY.
**Tracks:** Working in a coalmine / Holy cow / Do-re-mi / Lover was born / Give it up / Can you hear me / Freedom for the stallion / Ride your pony / Get out of my life woman / Ya, ya / Love lots of lovin' (With Betty Harris.) / Candy yam / Go go girl / You're breaking me up / On your way down / Everything I do gonh be funky.
■ **LP** . . . . . . . . . . . . . . . . . . . . . **CRB 1001**
Charly R&B / '85.

### GREAT GOOGA MOOGA.
**Tracks:** Lottie mo / Do-re-me / Hoodlum Joe / You're breaking me up / Ay-la-ay / Great googa mogga / People sure act funny / Ride your pony / Can you hear me / Get out of my life woman / Confusion / Working in a coalmine / Holy cow / My old car / Go go girl / Love lots of lovin / Four corners (part 1) / Lover was born.
**CD** . . . . . . . . . . . . . . . . . . . . . . **CDNEV 3**
Charly / Sep '91 / Charly.

### HOLY COW.
**Tracks:** Holy cow / Operation heartache.
■ **7"** . . . . . . . . . . . . . . . . . . . . . . **SS 552**
Stateside / Oct '66.

### MY OLD CAR.
**Tracks:** My old car / Why wait until tomorrow.
■ **7"** . . . . . . . . . . . . . . . . . . . . **SS 2017**
Stateside / May '67.

### NEW LEE DORSEY.
**Tracks:** Not Advised.
■ **LP** . . . . . . . . . . . . . . . . . . . **SSL 10192**
Stateside / Dec '66.

### OCCOPELLA.
**Tracks:** Occopella / Yes we can one.
■ **7"** . . . . . . . . . . . . . . . . . . . . **2066063**
Mojo / Jan '71.

### RAIN RAIN GO AWAY.
**Tracks:** Rain rain go away / Gotta find a job.
■ **7"** . . . . . . . . . . . . . . . . . . . . . . **SS 593**
Stateside / Feb '67.

### RIDE YOUR PONY.
**Tracks:** Ride your pony / Kitty cat song.
■ **7"** . . . . . . . . . . . . . . . . . . . . . . **SS 441**
Stateside / '65.

### RIDE YOUR PONY.
**Tracks:** Ride your pony / Kitty cat song / Work, work, work / Can you hear me.
■ **EP** . . . . . . . . . . . . . . . . . . . . **SE 1038**
Stateside / Feb '66.

### SOUL MINE.
**Tracks:** Not Advised.
**CD** . . . . . . . . . . . . . . . . . . . **CDCD 1115**
Charly / Jul '93 / Charly.

### WORK WORK WORK.
**Tracks:** Work work work.
■ **7"** . . . . . . . . . . . . . . . . . . . . . . **SS 465**
Stateside / '65.

### WORKING IN A COALMINE.
**Tracks:** Working in a coalmine / Ya, ya / Why wait until tomorrow / Do-re-mi / Ride your pony / Gotta find a job / Holy cow / Get out of my life woman / My old car / Go go girl / Cynthia / Everything I do gonh be funky.
■ **LP** . . . . . . . . . . . . . . . . . . . **TOP 102**
Topline / Nov '84.

### WORKING IN A COALMINE.
**Tracks:** Working in a coalmine / Holy cow / Get out of my life woman / Ride your pony.
■ **CD Single** . . . . . . . . . . . . . . . . . **CDS 5**
Charly R&B / Feb '89.

### WORKING IN A COALMINE.
**Tracks:** Working in a coalmine / Ya, ya / Holy cow.
■ **7"** . . . . . . . . . . . . . . . . . . . . **SS 528**
Stateside / Aug '66.
■ **7"** . . . . . . . . . . . . . . . . . . . **CTD 101**
Charly / Jul '80.
■ **7"** . . . . . . . . . . . . . . . . . . . **CR 212**
Creole (Replay) / Aug '84.
■ **7"** . . . . . . . . . . . . . . . . . . . **SKM 07**
SMP / Jun '84.

### WORKING IN A COALMINE.
**Tracks:** Not Advised.
**CD** . . . . . . . . . . . . . . . . . . **REP 4169-WZ**
Repertoire (Germany) / Aug '91 / Pinnacle.

### WORKING IN A COALMINE.
**Tracks:** Not Advised.
**CD** . . . . . . . . . . . . . . . . . . **RMB 75055**
**MC** . . . . . . . . . . . . . . . . . . **RMB 45055**
Remember / Nov '93 / Midland Records / BMG.

### WORKING IN A COALMINE (OLD GOLD).
**Tracks:** Working in a coalmine / Ride your pony.
■ **7"** . . . . . . . . . . . . . . . . . . **OG 9108**
Old Gold / '82.

### YES WE CAN.
**Tracks:** Yes we can / Riverboat / Tears, tears and more tears / O me-o, my-o / Sneakin' Sally through the alley / Who's gonna help Brother get further / Games people play / When the bill's paid / Occapella / Gator tail / Would you.
■ **LP** . . . . . . . . . . . . . . . . . . . . **2489 006**
Polydor / Apr '71.

## Double Exposure

### TEN PERCENT.
**Tracks:** Ten percent / Gonna give my love away / Everyman / Baby I need your loving / Just can't say hello / My love is free / Pick me.
■ **LP** . . . . . . . . . . . . . . . . . . . . **SZS 5503**
Salsoul / Jan '77.
**CD** . . . . . . . . . . . . . . . . . . . . **CPCD 8062**
**LP** . . . . . . . . . . . . . . . . . . . . **CPLP 8062**
Charly / Nov '94 / Charly.

### TEN PERCENT/MY LOVE IS FREE.
**Tracks:** Ten percent/My love is free.
■ **12"** . . . . . . . . . . . . . . . . . **12 SALSA 2**
Salsoul / Apr '93.

## Douglas, Carl

### CHOOSE BETWEEN TWO LOVERS.
**Tracks:** Choose between two lovers / Shame.
■ **7"** . . . . . . . . . . . . . . . . . . **7N 46155**
Pye / '79.

### DANCE THE KUNG FU.
**Tracks:** Dance the kung fu.
■ **7"** . . . . . . . . . . . . . . . . . . **7N 45418**
Pye / Nov '74.

### DO YOU NEED MY LOVE.
**Tracks:** Do you need my love / Lean on me.
■ **7"** . . . . . . . . . . . . . . . . . . **CBS 7101**
CBS / Mar '71.

### GIRL, YOU'RE SO FINE.
**Tracks:** Girl, you're so fine / Too hot to handle.
■ **7"** . . . . . . . . . . . . . . . . . . **7N 45660**
Pye / Jan '77.

### GOLDEN HOUR OF CARL DOUGLAS.
**Tracks:** Kung Fu fighting / Witchfinder general / When you got love / Changing times / I want to give you my everything / Dance the Kung Fu / Never had this dream before / I don't care what people say / Blue eyed soul / Girl you're so fine / Run back / Love peace and happiness / I'll be your light / Too hot to handle / What's good for the goose / M.O.R.F. / Green tangerines and wild evergreens / Mistakes of mine / I'll keep lovin' you / Stand up for love.
■ **LP** . . . . . . . . . . . . . . . . . . **GH 678**
■ **MC** . . . . . . . . . . . . . . . . . **ZCGH 67881**
Golden Hour / Jun '79.

### I WANT TO GIVE YOU MY EVERYTHING.
**Tracks:** I want to give you my everything / Witchfinder general.
■ **7"** . . . . . . . . . . . . . . . . . . **7N 45551**
Pye / Nov '75.

### KEEP ON PLEASING ME.
**Tracks:** Keep on pleasing me / Stop.
■ **7"** . . . . . . . . . . . . . . . . . . **7N 46053**
Pye / Mar '78.

### KUNG FU FIGHTING.
**Tracks:** Kung fu fighting / Gambling man.
■ **7"** . . . . . . . . . . . . . . . . . . **7N 45377**
Pye / Jun '74.

### KUNG FU FIGHTING.
**Tracks:** Kung fu fighting.
■ **7"** . . . . . . . . . . . . . . . . . . . . **FBS 9**
Flashback / May '79.

### KUNG FU FIGHTING (OLD GOLD).
**Tracks:** Kung fu fighting / Run back.
■ **7"** . . . . . . . . . . . . . . . . . . **OG 9135**
Old Gold / Jul '82.

### KUNG FU FIGHTING (RE-RELEASE).
**Tracks:** Kung fu fighting.
■ **12"** . . . . . . . . . . . . . . . . . . **PYT 23**
■ **7"** . . . . . . . . . . . . . . . . . . **PYS 23**
PRT / May '89.

### RUN BACK.
**Tracks:** Run back.
■ **7"** . . . . . . . . . . . . . . . . . . **7N 46018**
Pye / Dec '77.

### SHANGHAI'D.
**Tracks:** Shanghai'd / Girl you're so fine.
■ **7"** . . . . . . . . . . . . . . . . . . **7N 45556**
Pye / Jan '76.

### STIR A LITTLE SWEETNESS IN ME.
**Tracks:** Stir a little sweetness in me / Hi de ho.
■ **12"** . . . . . . . . . . . . . . . . . . **LS 001**
Landslide / Dec '82.

## Douglas, Carol

### 20 GOLDEN PIECES: CAROL DOUGLAS.
**Tracks:** Doctor's orders / Midnight love affair / Light my fire / Burnin' / Night fever / Baby don't let this good love die / We're gonna make it / Dancing queen / All night long / I fell in love with love / Take me (make me lose control) / Hurricane is coming tonight / We do it / I want to stay with you / I'll take a chance on love / Who, what, when, where and why / I've got you on my mind / Boy you know just what I'm after / Friend in need / Will we make it tonight.
■ **LP** . . . . . . . . . . . . . . . . . . **BDL 2022**
Bulldog Records / '81.

## BURNIN'.
**Tracks:** Burnin' / Let's get down to doin' it tonight.
■ 12"................................ **BURN 12 7**
Midsong / Sep '78.

## HURRICANE IS COMING TONITE.
**Tracks:** Hurricane is coming tonite / I fell in love with you.
■ 7"................................ **RCA 2543**
RCA / Apr '75.

## I'VE GOT THE ANSWER.
**Tracks:** I've got the answer / We're gonna make it.
■ 7"................................ **2001904**
Midsong / Nov '79.

## NIGHT FEVER.
**Tracks:** Night fever.
■ 7"................................ **GULS 61**
Gull / Jul '78.

# Downing, Big Al

## BIG AL DOWNING & THE POE KATS (Downing, Big Al & The Poe Kats).
**Tracks:** Not Advised.
■ LP................................ **JLP 1111**
Jumble / Nov '87.

## DOWN ON THE FARM.
**Tracks:** Down on the farm / Miss Lucy / Georgia slop / Yes, I'm loving you.
■ EP................................ **RCEP 105**
Rollercoaster / Feb '88.

## I'LL BE HOLDING ON.
**Tracks:** I'll be holding on (2 pts).
■ 7"................................ **6145036**
Chess / Feb '75.

## ROCKIN' 'N' ROLLIN'.
**Tracks:** Down on the farm / Oh babe / Miss Lucy / Just around the corner / Yes, I'm loving you / Rock 'n' roll boogie / Rock 'n' roll record girl / Piano Nellie / Georgia slop / When my blue moon turns to gold again / It must be love / If I had our love to live over / Please come home / Words of love / Heartbreak Hill / I found someone to love / Story of my life / Saints.
■ LP................................ **ROLL 2015**
Rollercoaster / May '88.

# Downing, Don

## LONELY DAYS, LONELY NIGHTS.
**Tracks:** Lonely days, lonely nights.
■ 7"................................ **PEO 102**
People / Nov '73.

# Downing, Will

As sought-after session singer, Downing appeared on late '70s work by - among others - Rose Royce, Billy Ocean and Jennifer Holliday. After spell with Arthur Baker, he produced Wally Jump Jnr & The Criminal Element, and graduated to solo status. Retaining Baker's services, Downing scored immediate hit with debut album and *A Love Supreme* single in '88. Latter, reworking John Coltrane's classic, hinted at direction he pursued in early '90s. Although these acclaimed recordings sold far better than many other jazz acts, he returned to upper echelons of pop chart only with Mica Paris duet *Where Is the Love* in '89.

## COME TOGETHER AS ONE.
**Tracks:** Come together as one / Sake of love / Sometimes I cry / Love call / Love we share / Too soon / I'll wait / Rules of love / Test of time / Closer to you / Wishing on a star.
CD................................ **BRCD 538**
■ LP................................ **BRLP 538**
■ MC................................ **BRCA 538**
4th & Broadway / Oct '89 / PolyGram.

## COME TOGETHER AS ONE.
**Tracks:** Come together as one / Dream together mix / Love supreme / In my dreams / Free.
■ 12"................................ **12 BRW 159**
■ 12"................................ **12 BRX 159**
■ 12" Remix................................ **12 BRZ 159**
■ 7"................................ **BRW 159**
■ CD Single................................ **BRCDX 159**
■ CD Single................................ **BRCD 159**
■ MC Single................................ **BRCA 159**
4th & Broadway / Jan '90.

## COME TOGETHER AS ONE.
**Tracks:** Love supreme / Test of time / In my dreams / Free / Where is the love / Come together as one.
VHS................................ **IVA 048**

## DREAM FULFILLED, A.
**Tracks:** She / I'll wait / Giving my all to you / I try / For all we know / Something's going on / Don't make me wait / I go crazy / No love intended / World is a ghetto.
CD................................ **BRCD 565**
■ LP................................ **BRLP 565**
■ MC................................ **BRCA 565**
4th & Broadway / Apr '91 / PolyGram.

## FREE.
**Tracks:** Free / Dancing in the moonlight / Free (Percappella) (Only on the 12" version.).
■ 12"................................ **12 BRW 112**
■ 7"................................ **BRW 112**
■ CD Single................................ **BRCDP 112**
4th & Broadway / Sep '88.

## I GO CRAZY.
**Tracks:** I go crazy (radio version) / I go crazy (long version) (12 & CD single only) / I'll wait.
■ 12"................................ **12BRW 220**
■ 7"................................ **BRW 220**
■ CD Single................................ **BRCD 220**
■ MC Single................................ **BRCA 220**
4th & Broadway / May '91.

## IN MY DREAMS.
**Tracks:** In my dreams.
■ 12"................................ **12 BRW 104**
■ 7"................................ **BRW 104**
■ CD Single................................ **BRCDP 104**
4th & Broadway / May '88.

## LOVE SUPREME, A.
**Tracks:** Love supreme, A (jazz in the house mix) / Love supreme, A (album mix) / Love supreme, A (dub in the house remix).
■ 7"................................ **BRW 90**
■ 12"................................ **12 BRW 90**
■ 12"................................ **BRWX 90**
■ CD Single................................ **BRCDX 90**
4th & Broadway / Mar '88.

## LOVE'S THE PLACE TO BE.
**Tracks:** Not Advised.
CD................................ **BRCD 597**
LP................................ **BRLP 597**
MC................................ **BRCA 597**
4th & Broadway / Jul '93 / PolyGram.

## LOVE'S THE PLACE TO BE.
**Tracks:** Love's the place to be / I'll wait / Everything to me (Available on CDS only) / Dancing in the moonlight (Available on CDS only).
■ 7"................................ **BRW 292**
■ CD Single................................ **BRCD 292**
■ MC Single................................ **BRCA 292**
4th & Broadway / Dec '93.

## SOMETHING'S GOING ON.
**Tracks:** Something's going on / Something's going on (instrumental).
■ 12"................................ **12BRW 235**
■ MC Single................................ **BRCA 235**
■ 7"................................ **BRW 235**
■ CD Single................................ **BRCD 235**
4th & Broadway / Sep '91.

## TEST OF TIME.
**Tracks:** Test of time.
■ 12"................................ **12 BRW 146**
■ 7"................................ **BRW 146**
■ CD Single................................ **BRCD 146**
4th & Broadway / Aug '89.

## THERE'S NO LIVING WITHOUT YOU.
**Tracks:** There's no living without you / Deeper meaning.
■ 12"................................ **12 BRW 278**
■ 7"................................ **BRW 278**
■ CD Single................................ **BRCD 278**
■ MC Single................................ **BRCA 278**
4th & Broadway / Sep '93.

## WHERE IS THE LOVE (Downing, Will & Mica Paris).
**Tracks:** Where is the love / Same feeling / My one temptation (12" & CD single only) / Love supreme.
■ 12"................................ **12 BRW 122**
■ 7"................................ **BRW 122**
■ CD Single................................ **BRCD 122**
4th & Broadway / Jan '89.

## WILL DOWNING.
**Tracks:** In my dreams / Do you / Free / Love supreme (12" & CD single only) / Security / Set me free / Sending out an S.O.S. / Dancing in the moonlight / Do you remember love.
■ CD................................ **BRCD 518**
■ LP................................ **BRLP 518**

VHS................................ **0832563**
Island Visual Arts / Mar '90 / PolyGram / THE.

■ MC................................ **BRCA 518**
4th & Broadway / Mar '88.
CD................................ **IMCD 190**
Island / Mar '94 / PolyGram.

# Dozier, Lamont

The middle part of the legendary Holland-Dozier-Holland Motown songwriting team, Lamont actually joined Berry Gordy's label as an artist, but quickly found his metier on the other side of the studio glass. Many of the biggest hits by The Supremes, Four Tops, Temptations, Marvin Gaye, Martha Reeves & The Vandellas and Gladys Knight & The Pips were supplied by H-D-H. Their love affair with the chart's peaks lasted throughout the 60's until, disenchanted with their financial agreement with Motown, the trio split to form Hot Wax/Invictus Records. Freda Payne's *Band Of Gold* and several hits by Chairman Of The Board, not to mention the Holland-Dozier ballad *Why Can't We Be Lovers*, kept the company afloat until '73, when Dozier signed a solo deal with ABC Records. The albums *Out Here On My Own* ('73) and *Black Bach* ('74) are regarded as soul classics, as is *Peddlin' Music On The Side*, cut for Warners in '77 and featuring the original version of *Going Back To My Roots* (an international hit for Odyssey). Thereafter Dozier resorted largely to indie label releases; an album simply entitled *Lamont* in '81 being of particular note, though he did manage one further LP for Atlantic in the late '80's. As a songwriter and producer, Dozier oversaw albums for Margie Joseph, Ben E King and Zingara (which group launched the career of James Ingram). During the '80s, he switched to the pop world, supplying hits for Simply Red (*Infidelity*) and Alison Moyet (*Invisible*).

## ALL CRIED OUT.
**Tracks:** All cried out.
■ 7"................................ **ABC 4056**
ABC Records / May '75.

## BIGGER THAN LIFE.
**Tracks:** Bigger than life / Right where I wanna be / On the one / Round trip ticket / Love wars / Scarlett O'Hara / Call the wagon / Nowhere to go but up / Second wind / Hero of my heart.
■ LP................................ **FIEND 12**
Demon / Nov '83.

## BITTERSWEET.
**Tracks:** Boogie business / Love me to the max / True love is bittersweet / Tough act to follow / I got it all with you / We're just here to feel good / Let your love run free / Fly away little birdsong.
■ LP................................ **K 56594**
WEA / '79.

## BLACK BACH.
**Tracks:** Shine / Put out my fire / Let me start tonite / All cried out / Intermission / Prelude / Rose / Thank you for the dream / I wanna be with you / Blue sky and silver bird.
■ LP................................ **ABCD 839**
ABC Records / '74.

## BOOGIE BUSINESS.
**Tracks:** Boogie business / Going back to my roots.
■ 12"................................ **LV 24**
WEA / '79.

## COOL ME OUT.
**Tracks:** Cool me out / Starting over.
■ 7"................................ **A 1235**
CBS / Aug '81.

## GOING BACK TO MY ROOTS.
**Tracks:** Going back to my roots / Going back to my roots (part 2).
■ 7"................................ **K 16942**
Atlantic / '79.

## INSIDE SEDUCTION.
**Tracks:** Not Advised.
CD................................ **7567822282**
MC................................ **7567822284**
East West / Dec '91 / WEA.

## MOTOR CITY (PARTS 1 & 2).
**Tracks:** Motor city.
■ 12"................................ **D 1020 T**
■ 7"................................ **D 1020**
Demon / Feb '84.

## OUT HERE ON MY OWN.
**Tracks:** Not Advised.
■ LP................................ **ABCL 5042**
ABC Records / '74.

■ DELETED

### EDDLIN' MUSIC ON THE SIDE.
acks: (Hello) Sight for sore eyes / What am I gonna
bout you (girl) (The coke song) / Break the ice /
ar down the walls / Going back to my roots /
mily / Peddlin' music on the side.
■ LP . . . . . . . . . . . . . . . . . . . . . . . BS 3039
arner Bros. / '77.

### CH IN PARADISE.
acks: Rich in paradise.
7" . . . . . . . . . . . . . . . . . . . . . . . MIX 001
I / Nov '89.

### GHT THERE.
acks: It's the same old song / Right there / Jump
ht on in / Groovin' on a natural high / Can't get off
til the feeling stops / Good eye / With a little bit of
ending / In a wild frame of mind / Ain't never loved
body (like I love you) / Joy.
LP . . . . . . . . . . . . . . . . . . . . . . K 56225
EA / Nov '83.

### CARLETT O'HARA.
acks: Scarlett O'Hara.
12" . . . . . . . . . . . . . . . . . . . . . . D 1018 T
7" . . . . . . . . . . . . . . . . . . . . . .D 1018
emon / Oct '83.

### GHT FOR SORE EYES.
acks: Sight for sore eyes / Tear down your wall.
7" . . . . . . . . . . . . . . . . . . . . . K 17070
EA / Jan '78.

## Dr. Strut

### OCTOR STRUT.
acks: Look in your eyes / Granit palace / Canadian
ar / More stuff / Blowtop / Soul sermonette /
icken strut / Eddieisms / Who cares / No you came
re for an argument.
LP . . . . . . . . . . . . . . . . . . . .STML 12120
otown / Oct '81.

### TRUTTIN.
acks: Struttin / Acufukture / Blue lodge / CMS /
m city / Commuter rabbit / After / For folon / Nitwit
Nice 'n' sleazy / No, you came here for an
gument.
LP . . . . . . . . . . . . . . . . . . . .STML 12132
otown / Oct '81.

### TRUTTIN.
acks: Struttin.
7" . . . . . . . . . . . . . . . . . . . . . TMG 1190
otown / Oct '81.

## Dr. York

### EW.
acks: Not Advised.
LP . . . . . . . . . . . . . . . . . . . . . SPLP 004
C. . . . . . . . . . . . . . . . . . . . . . SPLC 004
artan / Nov '85.

### E-NEW.
acks: Not Advised.
C . . . . . . . . . . . . . . . . . . . . . CYRC 78636
LP . . . . . . . . . . . . . . . . . . . . YRC 78636
eset / Jul '87 / Pinnacle.

### HAKE 'N' SKATE.
acks: Shake and skate / Roll a rock.
12" . . . . . . . . . . . . . . . . . . . . .GP 110T
7" . . . . . . . . . . . . . . . . . . . . . GP 110
oove PR / Sep '81.

## Drama

### OVE'S ABOUT TO CHANGE MY MIND.
acks: Love's about to change my mind.
" . . . . . . . . . . . . . . . . . . . . .ALMY 032
mighty / Jan '93 / Total / BMG.

## Dramatics

fter succession of minor hits and misses
n various labels, vocal quartet Dramatics
gned to Stax and hit with 1971's *Whatcha*
*ee Is Whatcha Get*, a US top 10 hit. Al-
ough group never charted in U.K., song
ecame classic on both sides of Atlantic.
lbum of same name went gold, spawning
econd crossover hit, *In The Rain*. Despite
rther soul successes, Dramatics jumped
hip from collapsing Stax empire and
amed with Dells for one-off album *The*
*ells Vs The Dramatics*, on Chess subsidi-
ry Cadet. Group continued to sell well for
mainder of '70s on ABC and MCA, but
eclining fortunes in aftermath of disco
ompted split in '82. Singer L.J. Reynolds

went solo on Capitol, but reunited with
band-mates when group reformed in mid-'
80s. No longer big-sellers but with talent
undiminished, group enjoyed highest profile
in recent years backing on Snoop Doggy
Dogg's *Doggy Dogg World*.

### BEST OF THE DRAMATICS.
Tracks: Not Advised.
CD. . . . . . . . . . . . . . . . . . . FCD 60003
London / Apr '87 / PolyGram.

### DELLS VS. THE DRAMATICS, THE (see under Dells).

### DRAMATICS LIVE, THE.
Tracks: Get up and get down / This guy's in love with
you / That's the way I feel about cha / In the rain /
Thank you for your love / Respect yourself / Toast to
the fool / Whatcha see is watcha get.
■ LP . . . . . . . . . . . . . . . . . . . .SX 018
Stax / Nov '88.

### I CAN'T STAND IT.
Tracks: I can't stand it / It's dramatic music.
■ 12" . . . . . . . . . . . . . . . . . . .12CL 252
■ 7" . . . . . . . . . . . . . . . . . . . .CL 252
Capitol / Jul '82.

### IN THE RAIN.
Tracks: In the rain.
■ 7" . . . . . . . . . . . . . . . . . . . STAX 809
Stax / Aug '87.

### NEW DIMENSIONS.
Tracks: Live it up / Treat me right / I can't stand /
She's my kind of girl / It's a dramatic music / I didn't
want to loose your love / I believe in you / Night life.
■ LP . . . . . . . . . . . . . . . . . . .EST 12205
Capitol / Jul '82.

### POSITIVE STATE OF MIND.
Tracks: Not Advised.
■ LP . . . . . . . . . . . . . . . . . . . .V 3402
Volt (USA) / May '89.

### SHAKE IT WELL.
Tracks: Shake it well / Spaced out over you.
■ 7" . . . . . . . . . . . . . . . . . . . ABC 4210
ABC Records / Jun '78.

### SOMEWHERE IN TIME.
Tracks: Dream lady / Razor blade / One love ago /
Show me what you got / When love is over / Some-
where in time / In the rain / I fell for you / Hey you
get off my mountain / Girl stop your weeping / Be my
girl / Days of yea and nea / Luv's callin' / She's wild.
■ LP . . . . . . . . . . . . . . . . . . . .F 9642
Fantasy / Jun '86.

### WATCHA SEE IS WATCHA GET/ A DRA-MATIC EXPERIENCE (Two LPs on one CD).
Tracks: Get up and get down / Thank you for your
love / Hot pants in the Summertime / Whatcha see is
whatcha get / In the rain / (Gimme some) Good soul
music / Fall in love, lady love / Mary don't cha
wanna / Devil is dope / You could become the very
heart of me / Now you got me loving you / Fell for
you / Jim, what's wrong with him / Hey you get off
my mountain / Beautiful people / Beware of the man
(with the candy in his hand).

### WHATCHA SEE IS WHATCHA GET.
Tracks: Whatcha see is whatcha get / Devil is dope /
In the rain / And I panicked.
■ 12" . . . . . . . . . . . . . . . . . . STAT 809
Stax / Nov '87.

### WHATCHA SEE IS WHATCHA GET.
Tracks: Get up get down / Thank you for your love /
Hot pants in the summer time / Whatcha see is
whatcha get / In the rain / Good soul music / Fall in
love, lady love / Mary don't cha wanna.
■ LP . . . . . . . . . . . . . . . . . . . 2362025
Stax / Jul '72.

### WHATCHA SEE IS WHATCHA GET/DRA-MATIC EXPERIENCE, A.
Tracks: Get up and get down / Thank you for your
love / Hot pants in the summertime / Whatcha see is
whatcha get / In the rain / (Gimme some) Good soul
music / Fall in love, lady love / Mary don't cha
wanna / Devil is dope / You could become the very
heart of me / Now you got me loving you / Fell for
you / Jim, what's wrong with him / Hey you - Get off
my mountain / Beautiful people / Beware of the man
(with the candy in his hand).
CD. . . . . . . . . . . . . . . . . . . CDSXD 963
Stax / Jan '91 / Pinnacle.

## Drennon, Eddie

### LET'S DO THE LATIN HUSTLE (Drennon, Eddie & BBS Unlimited).
Tracks: Let's do the latin hustle.
■ 7" . . . . . . . . . . . . . . . . . . . 7N 25702
Pye International / Feb '76.

### WOULD YOU LIKE TO DANCE TO MY MUSIC.
Tracks: Would you like to dance to my music / Just
too bad.
■ 7" . . . . . . . . . . . . . . . . . . . 7N 25758
Pye International / Nov '77.

## Drifters

Aptly-named Drifters have seen over 50
men pass through ranks. Of their dozen
lead singers, most celebrated are Clyde
McPhatter and Ben E. King, although Johnnie Moore sang on more hits than any
other. Debut *Money Honey* topped U.S. R&B
chart for 11 weeks but, after four further
smashes, McPhatter left for army, then solo
career. Revised line-up, with King, hit pop
chart in '59 with *There Goes My Baby* and
climaxed with *Save The Last Dance For Me*.
Third great vocalist, Rudy Lewis, enjoyed
three hitmaking years, scoring with *Up On*
*The Roof* and *On Broadway*, but died in '64.
His replacement was Moore, who - having
first sung lead in mid-'50s - took them into
charts with *Under The Boardwalk*. After *Sa-*
*turday Night At the Movies*, Drifters were
ignored at home, but suddenly became Top
10 regulars in U.K. with likes of *Kissin' In*
*The Back Row Of The Movies*. '76 hit *You're*
*More Than A Number In My Little Red Book*
was their last before shift into cabaret circuit; enlivened only by return of Ben E. King
in '80s. Group are celebrated not only for
hits and illustrious personnel, but also their
influence on soul, evident in Motown's
1960's output.

### 16 GREATEST HITS.
Tracks: Not Advised.
■ CD. . . . . . . . . . . . . . . . . . . .CD 1009
Gusto (USA) / '88.

### 20 GREATEST HITS: DRIFTERS.
Tracks: Not Advised.
CD . . . . . . . . . . . . . . . . . . . .SPEC 85006
Spectrum (CD) / Dec '88 / M.S.D.
■ LP . . . . . . . . . . . . . . . . . . . MA 17983
MC . . . . . . . . . . . . . . . . . MAMC 917983
Masters (Holland) / Dec '88.

### 24 ORIGINAL HITS.
Tracks: Saturday night at the movies / Dance with
me / Some kind of wonderful / When my little girl is
smiling / Come on over to my place / Save the last
dance for me / At the club / Up on the roof / On
Broadway / There goes my baby / I'll take you where
the music's playing / Under the boardwalk / Sweet
Caroline / I'm free (for the rest of your life) / Kissin'
in the back row of the movies / Every night / Like
sister and brother / Songs we used to sing / There
goes my first love / Love games / Love me love the
life I lead / If it feels good do it / Blessing in disguise
/ Down on the beach tonight.
■ LP . . . . . . . . . . . . . . . . . . . K 60106
■ MC . . . . . . . . . . . . . . . . . . . K4 60106
Atlantic / Nov '75.

### 6 TRACK HITS.
Tracks: Can I take you home little girl / Something
tells me / Love games / Down on the beach tonight /
Say goodbye to Angelina / Like sister and brother.
■ EP . . . . . . . . . . . . . . . . . . . 7SR 5013
Scoop 33 / Sep '83.

### 70'S CLASSICS.
Tracks: Kissin' in the back row of the movies / You're
more than a number in my little black book / Hello
happiness / Like sister and brother / There goes my
first love / Sweet Caroline / Harlem child / Like a
movie I've seen before / Songs we used to sing /
Love games / Down on the beach tonight / Every
nite's a saturday night with you / Can I take you
home tonight little girl / Anothe lonely weekend /
Summer in the city / Midnight cowboy.
CD. . . . . . . . . . . . . . . . . . . MCCD 100
MC. . . . . . . . . . . . . . . . . . .MCTC 100
Music Club / Mar '93 / Gold & Sons / THE / Video
Collection / C.M. Distribution.

### AT THE CLUB.
Tracks: At the club / Saturday night at the movies.
■ 7" . . . . . . . . . . . . . . . . . . . .AT 4019
Atlantic / Apr '65.

■ 7″ . . . . . . . . . . . . . . . . . . K 10148
Atlantic / Mar '72.

## BABY WHAT I MEAN.
Tracks: Baby what I mean / Aretha.
■ 7″ . . . . . . . . . . . . . . . . . . .584065
Atlantic / Feb '67.

## BEN E KING & THE DRIFTERS (see under King, Ben E.).

## BEST OF THE DRIFTERS.
Tracks: Save the last dance for me / Up on the roof / When my little girl is smiling / Dance with me / I've got sand in my shoes / There goes my baby / I'll take you home / Come on over to my place / Under the boardwalk / At the club / This magic moment / (If you cry) true love, true love / I count the tears / Saturday night at the movies / Some kind of wonderful / On Broadwalk.
CD . . . . . . . . . . . . . . . . . . . .PWKS 589
MC . . . . . . . . . . . . . . . . . . . HSC 3310
Pickwick / Jul '90 / Pickwick.

## BOOGIE WOOGIE ROLL (Greatest Hits 1953-58).
Tracks: Not Advised.
CD . . . . . . . . . . . . . . . . . . 7567819272
Atlantic / Jul '93 / WEA.

## CAN I TAKE YOU HOME LITTLE GIRL.
Tracks: Can I take you home little girl.
■ 7″ . . . . . . . . . . . . . . . . . . BELL 1462
Bell / Nov '75.

## COLLECTION: DRIFTERS.
Tracks: Up on the roof / Saturday night at the movies / Save the last dance for me / There goes my baby / This magic moment / Dance with me / On Broadway / Sweets for my sweet / Please stay / Under the boardwalk.
CD . . . . . . . . . . . . . . . . . . . . .OR 0007
Music Collection International / Apr '87 / THE / Jazz Music.

## COLLECTION: DRIFTERS (2).
Tracks: Like sister and brother / Every night / You're more than a number in my little red book / Down on the beach tonight / Sweet Caroline / Hello happiness / There goes my first love / You've got your troubles / Another lovely weekend / Say goodbye to Angelina / Please help me down / Can I take you home little girl / Kissin' in the back row of the movies / If it feels good do it / Summer in the city / I'm feelin' sad (oh so lonely) / Do you have to go now / Love games / Midnight cowboy / Songs we used to sing / I'll get to know your name along the way / Every night is a Saturday night with you / Harlem child / Like a movie I've seen before.
■ Double LP . . . . . . . . . . . . . . . .CCSLP 204
■ CD . . . . . . . . . . . . . . . . . . .CCSCD 204
■ MC . . . . . . . . . . . . . . . . . . .CCSMC 204
Castle Collector Series / Nov '88.

## COME ON OVER TO MY PLACE.
Tracks: Come on over to my place / Up on the roof / I don't want to go on without you.
■ 7″ . . . . . . . . . . . . . . . . . . . AT 4023
Atlantic / Apr '65.
■ 7″ . . . . . . . . . . . . . . . . . . . K 10216
Atlantic / Sep '86.

## DANCE WITH ME.
Tracks: Dance with me.
■ 7″ . . . . . . . . . . . . . . . . . . . HLE 8988
London-American / Jan '60.

## DIAMOND SERIES: DRIFTERS.
Tracks: Kissin' in the back row of the movies / Down on the beach tonight / Love games / Like sister and brother / Can I take you home, little girl / There goes my first love / Hello, happiness / Harlem child / You're more than a number in my little red book / Another lonely weekend / Summer in the city / Every night is a Saturday night with you / Do you have to go now / Like a movie I've seen before / Twice a week / Midnight cowboy.
■ CD . . . . . . . . . . . . . . . . . . CD 258812
Diamond Series / Apr '88.

## DOWN ON THE BEACH TONIGHT.
Tracks: Down on the beach tonight.
■ 7″ . . . . . . . . . . . . . . . . . . BELL 1381
Bell / Oct '74.

## DRIFTERS.
Tracks: Not Advised.
CD . . . . . . . . . . . . . . . . . . .LECD 039
Dynamite (2) / May '94 / THE.

## DRIFTERS WITH BEN E KING (see under King, Ben E.).

## DRIFTERS, THE.
Tracks: Spanish Harlem / This magic moment / Save the last dance for me / Under the boardwalk / Caribbean queen (no more love on the run) / Penny lover / Wonderful world / Reet petite / Stand by me / Ain't too proud to beg / It's the same old song / Since I lost my baby / I can't help myself / On Broadway / Nothing's gonna change my love for you / (Sittin' on) the dock of the bay.
■ LP . . . . . . . . . . . . . . . ENT LP 13032
MC . . . . . . . . . . . . . . . ENT MC 13032
Entertainers / Nov '87 / BMG.
CD . . . . . . . . . . . . . . . . . .100421-2
■ LP . . . . . . . . . . . . . . . . . .510456-4
Europa / Jul '88.

## DRIFTERS, THE.
Tracks: Not Advised.
CD . . . . . . . . . . . . . . . . . . .295034
MC . . . . . . . . . . . . . . . . . . .495034
Ariola / Oct '94 / BMG.

## DRIFTERS, THE (TELSTAR).
Tracks: Not Advised.
■ LP . . . . . . . . . . . . . . . . STAR 2373
■ CD . . . . . . . . . . . . . . . . . TCD 2373
■ MC . . . . . . . . . . . . . . . . STAC 2373
Telstar/Ronco / Oct '90.

## EVERY NIGHT'S A SATURDAY NIGHT WITH YOU.
Tracks: Every night's a Saturday nite with you.
■ 7″ . . . . . . . . . . . . . . . . . . BELL 1491
Bell / Sep '76.

## GOLDEN HITS: DRIFTERS.
Tracks: There goes my baby / True love, true love (If you cry) / Dance with me / This magic moment / Save the last dance for me / I count the tears / Some kind of wonderful / Up on the roof / On Broadway / Under the boardwalk / I've got sand in my shoes / Saturday night at the movies.
■ LP . . . . . . . . . . . . . . . . . . 588 103
Atlantic / May '68.
■ LP . . . . . . . . . . . . . . . . . K 40018
■ MC . . . . . . . . . . . . . . . . . K4 40018
Atlantic / '74.
CD . . . . . . . . . . . . . . . . . K 240 018
Atlantic / Jan '87 / WEA.
CD . . . . . . . . . . . . . . . . . 9781440 2
Atlantic / Jul '88 / WEA.

## GOOD GRAVY (see under McPhatter, Clyde).

## GREATEST.
Tracks: Hello happiness / Kissin' in the back row of the movies / Always something there to remind me / Every night / Sweet Caroline / If it feels good do it / Save the last dance for me / There goes my first love / Like sister and brother / I can't live without you / Harlem child / You've got your troubles / Love games / Down on the beach tonight.
■ LP . . . . . . . . . . . . . . . . . MFP 5734
MC . . . . . . . . . . . . . . . . TC MFP 5734
MFP / Oct '85 / EMI.
CD . . . . . . . . . . . . . . . . CDMFP 5734
MFP / Oct '91 / EMI.

## GREATEST HITS.
Tracks: Not Advised.
MC Set . . . . . . . . . . . . . . . .TTMC 043
Tring / Jun '92 / Prism Leisure PLC / Midland Records.

## GREATEST HITS & MORE 1959-65.
Tracks: Not Advised.
CD . . . . . . . . . . . . . . . . . 7567819312
Atlantic / Jul '93 / WEA.

## GREATEST HITS LIVE: DRIFTERS.
Tracks: Not Advised.
■ LP . . . . . . . . . . . . . . . . . . 20091
MC . . . . . . . . . . . . . . . . . . 40091
Astan / Nov '84.

## GREATEST HITS: BEN E KING AND THE DRIFTERS (see under King, Ben E.).

## GREATEST HITS: DRIFTERS WITH BEN E.KING (Drifters & Ben E. King).
Tracks: Not Advised.
CD . . . . . . . . . . . . . . . . . FUNCD 9031
■ LP . . . . . . . . . . . . . . . . . FUN 9031
MC . . . . . . . . . . . . . . . . . FUNC 9031
Fun (Holland) / Oct '88 / Pinnacle.

## HELLO HAPPINESS.
Tracks: Hello happiness.
■ 7″ . . . . . . . . . . . . . . . . . BELL 146?
Bell / Mar '76.

## HONEY YOU'RE HEAVEN TO ME.
Tracks: Honey you're heaven to me / When ya com in' home.
■ 7″ . . . . . . . . . . . . . . . . . .ARIST 19?
Arista / May '78.

## I COUNT THE TEARS.
Tracks: I count the tears.
■ 7″ . . . . . . . . . . . . . . . . . HLK 928?
London-American / Mar '61.

## I'LL TAKE YOU HOME.
Tracks: I'll take you home.
■ 7″ . . . . . . . . . . . . . . . . . HLK 978?
London-American / Oct '63.

## I'LL TAKE YOU WHERE THE MUSIC'S PLAYING.
Tracks: I'll take you where the music's playing / Fa from the maddening crowd.
■ 7″ . . . . . . . . . . . . . . . . . AT 404?
Atlantic / Sep '65.

## I'LL TAKE YOU WHERE THE MUSIC'S PLAYING.
Tracks: I'll take you where the music's playing / I've got sand in my shoes / At the club / I don't want to g? on without you / Answer the phone / He's just ? playboy / Follow me / Spanish lace / Chains of life Far from the maddening crowd / Outside world Come over to my place.
■ LP . . . . . . . . . . . . . . . . . ATL 503?
Atlantic / Feb '66.

## I'M NOT THAT KIND OF GUY.
Tracks: I'm not that kind of guy / What am I doing falling in love with you.
■ 7″ . . . . . . . . . . . . . . . . . EPC 855?
Epic / May '80.

## JUKE BOX GIANTS.
Tracks: There goes my baby / This magic moment Some kind of wonderful / Dance with me / Save the last dance for me / Sweets for my sweet / Saturda night at the movies / I'll take you home / Under th? boardwalk / I count the tears / Up on the roof Please stay / On Broadway / When my little girl is smiling / White Christmas / If you cry-true love.
■ LP . . . . . . . . . . . . . . . . . AFEMP 102?
Audio Fidelity / May '82.

## KISSIN' IN THE BACK ROW OF THE MO VIES (OLD GOLD).
Tracks: Kissin' in the back row of the movies / Like sister like brother / There goes my first love.
■ CD Single . . . . . . . . . . . . . . . .OG 615?
Old Gold / Feb '92.

## KISSING IN THE BACK ROW.
Tracks: Not Advised.
CD . . . . . . . . . . . . . . . . . . PWKS 411?
MC . . . . . . . . . . . . . . . . . PWKMC 411?
Pickwick / Sep '92 / Pickwick.

## KISSING IN THE BACK ROW OF THE MOVIES.
Tracks: Kissin' in the back row of the movies / You're more than a number in my little red book.
■ 7″ . . . . . . . . . . . . . . . . . BELL 135?
Bell / Jun '74.

## KISSING IN THE BACK ROW OF THE MOVIES (OLD GOLD).
Tracks: Kissing in the back row of the movies You're more than a number..
■ 7″ . . . . . . . . . . . . . . . . . .OG 945?
Old Gold / Jun '88.

## LIKE SISTER AND BROTHER.
Tracks: Like sister and brother.
■ 7″ . . . . . . . . . . . . . . . . . BELL 131?
Bell / Aug '73.

## LIKE SISTER AND BROTHER (OLD GOLD).
Tracks: Like sister and brother / There goes my firs love / Kissing in the back row / You're more than a number in my little red book.
■ 7″ . . . . . . . . . . . . . . . . . .OG 912?
Old Gold / Jul '82.

## LIVE AT HARVARD UNIVERSITY.
Tracks: White Christmas / Lonely winds / Bells of S Mary's / True love / This magic moment / Up on th roof / Honey love / Under the boardwalk / Ther goes my baby / Saturday night at the movies / Whe my little girl is smiling / On Broadway / Save the las dance for me / Money honey.

■ DELETE?

■ LP . . . . . . . . . . . . . . . . . . SHLP 124
MC. . . . . . . . . . . . . . . . . . . SHTC 124
Castle Showcase / Apr '86 / Arabesque Ltd.

**LOVE GAMES.**
Tracks: Not Advised.
■ LP . . . . . . . . . . . . . . . . . . BELLS 246
Bell / Dec '75.

**LOVE GAMES.**
Tracks: Love games.
■ 7" . . . . . . . . . . . . . . . . . . BELL 1396
Bell / Feb '75.

**MEMORIES ARE MADE OF THIS.**
Tracks: Memories are made of this / My island in the sun.
■ 7" . . . . . . . . . . . . . . . . . . AT 4084
Atlantic / Mar '66.

**NOW.**
Tracks: Not Advised.
■ LP . . . . . . . . . . . . . . . . . . BELLS 219
Bell / Feb '73.

**ON BROADWAY.**
Tracks: Not Advised.
CD. . . . . . . . . . . . . . . . . . . 15 074
MC. . . . . . . . . . . . . . . . . . . 79 524
Laserlight / Aug '92 / THE / BMG / Target.

**ON BROADWAY.**
Tracks: Not Advised.
CD. . . . . . . . . . . . . . . . . . . U 4037
Spectrum (1) / Jun '88 / PolyGram.

**OUTSIDE WORLD, THE.**
Tracks: Outside world / Follow me.
■ 7" . . . . . . . . . . . . . . . . . . AT 4034
Atlantic / '65.

**PEARLS FROM THE PAST - THE DRIFTERS.**
Tracks: Not Advised.
CD. . . . . . . . . . . . . . . . . . . KLMCD 008
Scratch / Nov '93 / Scratch Records / BMG / Grapevine Distribution.

**ROCKIN' AND DRIFTIN'.**
Tracks: Moonlight bay / Ruby baby / Drip-drop / I got to get myself a woman / Fools fall in love / Hypnotized / Yodee Yakee / I know / Soldier of fortune / Drifting away from you / Your promise to be mine / It was a tear / Adorable / Steamboat.
■ LP . . . . . . . . . . . . . . . . . . 587 123
Atlantic / Oct '68.

**ROSE BY ANY OTHER NAME.**
Tracks: Rose by any other name / Be my lady.
■ 7" . . . . . . . . . . . . . . . . . . 2091 064
Atlantic / Mar '71.

**SATURDAY NIGHT AT THE CLUB.**
Tracks: Saturday night at the movies / Up in the streets of Harlem / Country to the city / She never talked to me that way / Only in America / Still burning in my heart / Please stay / Up jumped the devil / Be my lady / Rose by any other name / Aretha Baby what I mean / Beautiful music.
■ LP . . . . . . . . . . . . . . . . . . SHM 3029
Pickwick / Jun '80.

**SATURDAY NIGHT AT THE MOVIES.**
Tracks: Saturday night at the movies / I'll take you where the music's playing.
■ 7" . . . . . . . . . . . . . . . . . . K 10493
Atlantic / '74.

**SATURDAY NIGHT AT THE MOVIES.**
Tracks: Saturday night at the movies / Under the boardwalk / Up on the roof (12" only) / Save the last dance for me (12" only) / At the club.
■ 12" . . . . . . . . . . . . . . . . . . CRT 98
■ 7" . . . . . . . . . . . . . . . . . . CR 98
Creole Classics / Mar '87.

**SATURDAY NIGHT AT THE MOVIES (OLD GOLD).**
Tracks: Saturday night at the movies / At the club.
■ 7" . . . . . . . . . . . . . . . . . . OG 9103
Old Gold / May '81.

**SAVE THE LAST DANCE FOR ME.**
Tracks: Saturday night at the movies / Come on over to my place / Save the last dance for me / At the club / I count the tears / When my little girl is smiling / Up on the roof / Dance with me / Under the boardwalk / I've got sand in my shoes / There goes my baby / On Broadway / I'll take you home / This magic moment / Some kind of wonderful / I'll take you where the music's playing / If you cry-true love (Extra track on the CD only) / True love (Extra track on the CD only) / Sweets for my sweet (Extra track on the CD only) /

Please stay (Extra track on the CD only) / Drip drop (Extra track on the CD only).
■ MC. . . . . . . . . . . . . . . . . . . ORC 007
Orchid Music / Feb '82.
■ CD. . . . . . . . . . . . . . . . . . . 241 122 2
■ MC. . . . . . . . . . . . . . . . . . . 241 121 4
■ LP . . . . . . . . . . . . . . . . . . 241 121 1
Atlantic / May '87.

**SAVE THE LAST DANCE FOR ME.**
Tracks: Save the last dance for me / When my little girl is smiling.
■ 7" . . . . . . . . . . . . . . . . . . LIG 9014
Lightning / Apr '79.

**SAVE THE LAST DANCE FOR ME.**
Tracks: Save the last dance for me.
■ 7" . . . . . . . . . . . . . . . . . . HLK 9201
London-American / Nov '60.

**SAVE THE LAST DANCE FOR ME.**
Tracks: On Broadway / Save the last dance for me / Dance with me / There goes my baby / Up on the roof / Under the boardwalk / (Sittin' on) The dock of the bay / Another Saturday night / Stand by me / Cupid / Wonderful world / You send me / Unchained melody / Summertime / Bring it on home to me / Tie a yellow ribbon (Round the ole oak tree).
CD. . . . . . . . . . . . . . . . . . . PWK 007
Pickwick / '88 / Pickwick.

**SAVE THE LAST DANCE FOR ME.**
Tracks: Not Advised.
CD. . . . . . . . . . . . . . . . . . . AVC 511
MC. . . . . . . . . . . . . . . . . . . AVM 511
Avid / Dec '92 / ACD Trading Ltd. / BMG.

**SAVE THE LAST DANCE FOR ME.**
Tracks: I count the tears / Somebody new dancin' with you / Jackpot / Sweets for my sweet / No sweet lovin' / Mexican divorce / Save the last dance for me / When my little girl is smiling / Some kind of wonderful / Please stay / Nobody but me / Roomful of tears.
■ LP . . . . . . . . . . . . . . . . . . 587 063
Atlantic / Nov '67.

**SAVE THE LAST DANCE FOR ME (2ND REISSUE).**
Tracks: Save the last dance for me / Stand by me.
■ 7" . . . . . . . . . . . . . . . . . . K 10110
Atlantic / '74.

**SAVE THE LAST DANCE FOR ME (OLD GOLD).**
Tracks: Save the last dance for me.
■ 7" . . . . . . . . . . . . . . . . . . OG 9014
Old Gold / Jul '82.

**SOME KIND OF WONDERFUL.**
Tracks: This magic moment / I count the tears / Save the last dance for me / Under the boardwalk / Please don't go / Money money / Some kind of wonderful.
■ LP . . . . . . . . . . . . . . . . . . MFM 026
Magnum Force / Apr '87.

**SPOTLIGHT ON DRIFTERS.**
Tracks: Under the boardwalk / I count the tears / Up on the roof / Please stay / On Broadway / When my little girl is smiling / True love, true love / There goes my baby / This magic moment / Some kind of wonderful / Dance with me / Save the last dance for me / Sweets for my sweet / Saturday night at the movies.
CD. . . . . . . . . . . . . . . . . . . HADCD 122
MC. . . . . . . . . . . . . . . . . . . HADMC 122
Javelin / Feb '94 / THE.

**STAND BY ME: ULTIMATE COLLECTION, THE (see under King, Ben E.).**

**THEIR GOES MY BABY.**
Tracks: Not Advised.
■ LP . . . . . . . . . . . . . . . . . . RMB 5636
Crusader / Mar '89.

**THEIR TOP HITS.**
Tracks: Not Advised.
MC. . . . . . . . . . . . . . . . . . . 816
Timeless Treasures / Jul '86 / THE.

**THERE GOES MY FIRST LOVE.**
Tracks: There goes my first love.
■ 7" . . . . . . . . . . . . . . . . . . BELL 1433
Bell / Sep '75.

**THERE GOES MY FIRST LOVE.**
Tracks: There goes my first love / Harlem child / Cut is deep / Love games.
■ LP . . . . . . . . . . . . . . . . . . MFP 50352
MFP / Nov '77.

**THIS MAGIC MOMENT.**
Tracks: Not Advised.
■ LP . . . . . . . . . . . . . . . . . . 20094
■ . . . . . . . . . . . . . . . . . . . 40094
Astan / Nov '84.

**UNDER THE BOARDWALK.**
Tracks: Under the boardwalk / At the club / Cool jerk / Some kind of wonderful.
■ 7" . . . . . . . . . . . . . . . . . . ATM 6
Atlantic / Apr '80.

**UNDER THE BOARDWALK.**
Tracks: Under the boardwalk / On Broadway.
■ 7" . . . . . . . . . . . . . . . . . . K 10691
Atlantic / Nov '75.

**UNDER THE BOARDWALK.**
Tracks: Under the boardwalk.
■ 7" . . . . . . . . . . . . . . . . . . AT 4001
Atlantic / Sep '64.

**UP IN THE STREETS OF HARLEM.**
Tracks: Up in the streets of Harlem / You can't love 'em all.
■ 7" . . . . . . . . . . . . . . . . . . 584020
Atlantic / Jun '66.

**UP ON THE ROOF.**
Tracks: Not Advised.
CD. . . . . . . . . . . . . . . . . . . RMB 75639
MC. . . . . . . . . . . . . . . . . . . YDG 45838
Remember / Nov '93 / Midland Records / BMG.
CD. . . . . . . . . . . . . . . . . . . 8122712302
Pickwick / Oct '94 / Pickwick.

**UP ON THE ROOF.**
Tracks: There goes my baby / Sweets for my sweet / This magic moment / Up on the roof / Mexican divorce / Stranger on the shore / What to do / Save the last dance for me / Loneliness or happiness / Another night with the boys / Room full of tears / When my little girl is smiling / Ruby baby.
■ LP . . . . . . . . . . . . . . . . . . 588 160
Atlantic / Mar '69.

**VERY BEST OF THE DRIFTERS.**
Tracks: Not Advised.
■ CD . . . . . . . . . . . . . . . . . . TCD 2280
■ LP . . . . . . . . . . . . . . . . . . STAR 2280
■ MC . . . . . . . . . . . . . . . . . . STAC 2280
Telstar/Ronco / Oct '86.

**VERY BEST OF THE DRIFTERS.**
Tracks: Not Advised.
CD. . . . . . . . . . . . . . . . . . . 812271211-2
Atlantic / Jun '93 / WEA.

**WE GOTTA SING.**
Tracks: We gotta sing / Nylon stockings.
■ 7" . . . . . . . . . . . . . . . . . . AT 4062
Atlantic / Jan '66.

**WHEN MY LITTLE GIRL IS SMILING.**
Tracks: When my little girl is smiling.
■ 7" . . . . . . . . . . . . . . . . . . HLK 9522
London-American / Apr '62.

**YOU BETTER MOVE ON.**
Tracks: You better move on / Save the last dance for me.
■ 7" . . . . . . . . . . . . . . . . . . K 11743
Atlantic / Aug '82.

**YOU'RE MORE THAN A NUMBER IN MY LITTLE RED BOOK.**
Tracks: You're more than a number in my little red book / Do you have to go now.
■ 7" . . . . . . . . . . . . . . . . . . ARIST 78
Arista / Dec '76.

## Driza Bone

**BRIGHTEST STAR.**
Tracks: Brightest star (Mixes).
CD Single. . . . . . . . . . . . . . . . BRCDX 293
4th & Broadway / Sep '94 / PolyGram.
12" . . . . . . . . . . . . . . . . . . 12 BRW 293
CD Single . . . . . . . . . . . . . . . . BRCD 293
MC Single . . . . . . . . . . . . . . . . BRCA 293
4th & Broadway / Sep '94 / PolyGram.

**CATCH THE FIRE.**
Tracks: Catch the fire / Real love.
■ 12" . . . . . . . . . . . . . . . . . . 12BRW 232
■ 7" . . . . . . . . . . . . . . . . . . BRW 232
■ MC Single. . . . . . . . . . . . . . . BRCA 232
■ CD Single . . . . . . . . . . . . . . . BRCD 232
4th & Broadway / Sep '91.

**CONSPIRACY.**
Tracks: Last time / Real love / Hit / Gonna happen / Neighbourhood / Pressure / Woman and a man / Brightest star / Don't U want me / Conspiracy.
CD . . . . . . . . . . . . . . . . . . . . . . . . . . .BRCD 593
LP . . . . . . . . . . . . . . . . . . . . . . . . . . . .BRLP 593
MC . . . . . . . . . . . . . . . . . . . . . . . . . . . .BRCA 593
4th & Broadway / Aug '94 / PolyGram.

**PRESSURE.**
Tracks: Pressure / Pressure (mixes).
■ 12" . . . . . . . . . . . . . . . . . . . . . .12 BRW 264
■ 7" . . . . . . . . . . . . . . . . . . . . . . . . . BRW 264
■ CD Single . . . . . . . . . . . . . . . . . .BRCD 264
■ MC Single . . . . . . . . . . . . . . . . . .BRCA 264
4th & Broadway / Mar '94.

**REAL LOVE.**
Tracks: Real love / Real jazzy (Only on 12" and CD single) / Real dub (Only on 12" and CD single).
■ 7" . . . . . . . . . . . . . . . . . . . . . . . . . BRW 223
■ MC Single . . . . . . . . . . . . . . . . . .BRCA 223
■ 12" . . . . . . . . . . . . . . . . . . . . . . .12BRW 223
■ CD Single . . . . . . . . . . . . . . . . . .BRCD 223
4th & Broadway / Jun '91.

## Duke

**NEW BEGINNING.**
Tracks: New beginning (Mixes).
12" . . . . . . . . . . . . . . . . . . . . . . . . VST 1497
CD Single . . . . . . . . . . . . . . . . . . VSCDG 1497
MC Single . . . . . . . . . . . . . . . . . . . VSC 1497
Virgin / Jun '94 / EMI.

**SO IN LOVE WITH YOU.**
Tracks: So in love with you / So in love with you (mixes) / Revolution of the soul (On VSC 1504/ VSCDG 1504 only) / Rise above (On VSC 1504/ VSCDG 1504 only) / From Alaska to Mombassa (On VSCDX 1504 only) / Destiny (On VSCDX 1504 only).
12" . . . . . . . . . . . . . . . . . . . . . . . . VST 1504
CD Single . . . . . . . . . . . . . . . . . . VSCDG 1504
CD Single . . . . . . . . . . . . . . . . . . VSCDX 1504
MC Single . . . . . . . . . . . . . . . . . . . VSC 1504
Virgin / Sep '94 / EMI.

## Duke, Doris

**FULL TIME WOMAN.**
Tracks: Full time woman.
■ 7" . . . . . . . . . . . . . . . . . . . . . . . . CS 2064
Contempo (1) / Sep '75.

**GRASSHOPPER.**
Tracks: Grasshopper.
■ 7" . . . . . . . . . . . . . . . . . . . . . . . . CS 2037
Contempo (1) / Nov '74.

**IF SHE'S YOUR WIFE, WHO AM I.**
Tracks: If she's your wife, who am I.
■ 7" . . . . . . . . . . . . . . . . . . . . . . .2092 017
Mojo / Oct '71.

**LITTLE BIT OF LOVIN'.**
Tracks: Little bit of lovin'.
■ 7" . . . . . . . . . . . . . . . . . . . . . . . . CS 2047
Contempo (1) / Feb '75.

**TO THE OTHER WOMAN.**
Tracks: To the other woman / I don't care anymore.
■ 7" . . . . . . . . . . . . . . . . . . . . . . . 2092005
Mojo / Jul '71.

## Duke, George

Keyboard player who developed his style serving jazz apprenticeship, followed by four years with Frank Zappa's legendary Mothers Of Invention. Jazz-funk-soul style emerged in partnership with Billy Cobham and was consolidated on solo albums on Epic, including *From Me To You* ('77) and *Brazilian Love Affair* ('80). Collaboration with Stanley Clarke yielded U.S. No. 19 *Sweet Baby* from the acclaimed 1981 album *Duke Clarke Project*. Has worked extensively as a producer: credits include Taste Of Honey's 1981 No. 3 *Sukiyaki* and Deniece Williams' 1984 hit *Let's Hear It For The Boy*, which reached No. 1 in the U.S. and No. 2 in the U.K. Duke has also been a busy session musician, appearing on recordings by Aretha Franklin, Quincy Jones and the Whispers.

**1976 SOLO KEYBOARD ALBUM.**
Tracks: Mr. McFreeze / Love reborn / Excerpts from the opera Tzina / Spock gets funky / Pathways / Vulcan mind probe / Dream that ended.
■ LP . . . . . . . . . . . . . . . . . . . . . . . .EPC 25021
Epic / '83.

**3 (see under Clarke, Stanley).**

**BORN TO LOVE YOU.**
Tracks: Born to love you / You are the light.
■ 7" . . . . . . . . . . . . . . . . . . . . . . . . .A 3612
Epic / Aug '83.

**BRAZILIAN LOVE AFFAIR.**
Tracks: Brazilian love affair / Summer breezin' / Cravo E Canela / Alone / 6 a.m. / Brazilian sugar / Sugar loaf mountain / Love reborn / Up from the sea it arose and ate Rio in one / I need you now / Ao que vai Nascer.
■ LP . . . . . . . . . . . . . . . . . . . . . .EPC 84311
Epic / Jul '80.

**BRAZILIAN LOVE AFFAIR.**
Tracks: Brazilian love affair.
■ LP . . . . . . . . . . . . . . . . . . . . . . .EPC 8751
Epic / Jul '80.
■ MC Single. . . . . . . . . . . . . . . . .A 40 2630
CBS / Aug '82.

**BRAZILIAN LOVE AFFAIR (OLD GOLD).**
Tracks: Brazilian love affair / Heaven sent.
12" . . . . . . . . . . . . . . . . . . . . . . . .OG 4194
Old Gold / Oct '90 / Pickwick.

**CLARKE/DUKE PROJECT II (see under Clarke, Stanley).**

**COLLECTION: GEORGE DUKE.**
Tracks: Reach for it / Dukey stick / Party down / Say that you will / Festival / I want you for myself / Brazilian love affair / Up from the sea it arose & ate Rio in one swift bite / Sweet baby / Shine on / Son of reach for it (the funky dream) / Born to love you / Heroes / Better ways / Mothership connection / Finger prints.
CD . . . . . . . . . . . . . . . . . . . . . . .CCSCD 298
■ MC. . . . . . . . . . . . . . . . . . . . . .CCSMC 298
Castle Collector Series / Oct '91 / BMG / Pinnacle / Castle Communications.

**FOLLOW THE RAINBOW.**
Tracks: Party down / Say that you will / Funkin' for the thrill / Sunrise / Festival / I'm for real / Straight from the heart / Corina, Corina / Pluck / Follow the rainbow.
■ LP . . . . . . . . . . . . . . . . . . . . . .EPC 83336
Epic / Apr '79.

**FROM ME TO YOU.**
Tracks: From me to you / Carry on / What do they really fear / 'Scuse me miss / You and me / Broken dreams / Up on it / Seasons / Down in it / Sing it.
■ LP . . . . . . . . . . . . . . . . . . . . . .EPC 81850
Epic / Jul '77.

**GEORGE DUKE.**
Tracks: Broken glass / I just want to be in your life / Good friends / So mean to me / Stand with your man / Island girl / King for a day / Morning, you and love / I can make it better / African violet.
■ LP . . . . . . . . . . . . . . . . . . . . . .EPC 32348
Epic / Sep '83.
■ LP . . . . . . . . . . . . . . . . . . . . . . .9604801
MC. . . . . . . . . . . . . . . . . . . . . . . . . .9604804
Elektra / Oct '86 / WEA.

**GUARDIAN OF THE LIGHT.**
Tracks: Overture / Light / Shane / Born to love you / Silly fightin' / You / War fugue interlude / Reach out / Give me your love / Stand / Soon / Celebrate / Fly away.
MC. . . . . . . . . . . . . . . . . . . . . . . . .40 25262
■ LP . . . . . . . . . . . . . . . . . . . . . .EPC 25262
Epic / May '83 / Sony.

**I LOVE THE BLUES, SHE HEARD MY CRY.**
Tracks: Chariot / Look into her eyes / Sister serene / That's what she said / Mashavu / Rokkinrowl / Prepare yourself / Giant child within us / Someday / I love the blues she heard my cry.
■ LP . . . . . . . . . . . . . . . . . . . . . . 817 488-1
MPS Jazz (Germany) / Sep '84.
■ CD . . . . . . . . . . . . . . . . . . . . . 817 488-2
Polydor / Sep '84.

**I SURRENDER.**
Tracks: I surrender / Jam.
■ 12" . . . . . . . . . . . . . . . . . . . . . . .EKR 15T
■ 7" . . . . . . . . . . . . . . . . . . . . . . . . EKR 15
Elektra / Jul '85.

**I WANT YOU FOR MYSELF.**
Tracks: I want you for myself / Dog man.
■ 7" . . . . . . . . . . . . . . . . . . . . . . .CBS 8137
CBS / Jan '80.

**I WILL ALWAYS BE YOUR FRIEND.**
Tracks: I will always be your friend / Framed.
■ 7" . . . . . . . . . . . . . . . . . . . . . . EPCA 266
Epic / Aug '82.

**LIVE IN MONTREUX (see under Clarke, Stanley).**

**MASTER OF THE GAME.**
Tracks: Look what you find / Every step I take / Games / I want you for myself / In the distance / love you more / Dog man / Everybody's talkin'.
■ LP . . . . . . . . . . . . . . . . . . . . . .EPC 8395
Epic / Jan '80.

**NIGHT AFTER NIGHT.**
Tracks: Miss wriggle / Children of the night / Love ballad / Guilty / Same ole love / Say hello / You are the only one in my life / Brazilian coffee / This lovin / Mystery eyes.
■ CD . . . . . . . . . . . . . . . . . . . . . .EKT 52CD
■ LP . . . . . . . . . . . . . . . . . . . . . . .EKT 52
■ MC. . . . . . . . . . . . . . . . . . . . . .EKT 52 C
Elektra / Feb '89.

**PARTY DOWN.**
Tracks: Party down / Reach for it.
■ 12" . . . . . . . . . . . . . . . . . . . . .EPC 12714
■ 7" . . . . . . . . . . . . . . . . . . . . . . EPC 714
Epic / '79.

**PRIMAL.**
Tracks: Second time around / Night has a thousand eyes / Days of wine and roses / Jeannine / Little girl blue / Secret love.
■ LP . . . . . . . . . . . . . . . . . . . . .5C 064 61170
MPS Jazz (France) / '79.

**PROJECT (see under Clarke, Stanley).**

**REACH FOR IT.**
Tracks: Beginning / Lemme at it / Hot fire / Reach for it / Just for you / OMI (Fresh water) / Searchin' my mind / Watch out baby / Diamonds / End / Bring it on home.
MC. . . . . . . . . . . . . . . . . . . . . . . . .4679664
Epic / Jun '91 / Sony.
■ CD . . . . . . . . . . . . . . . . . . . . . .4679662
Epic / Jan '92.

**REACH FOR IT.**
Tracks: Reach for it / Just for you.
■ 7" . . . . . . . . . . . . . . . . . . . . . .EPC 6170
Epic / Mar '78.

**REACH OUT.**
Tracks: Reach out.
■ 12" . . . . . . . . . . . . . . . . . . . . . . .TA 3267
■ 7" . . . . . . . . . . . . . . . . . . . . . . . .A 3267
Epic / Apr '83.

**RIDE ON LOVE.**
Tracks: Ride on love / Son of reach for it.
■ 12" . . . . . . . . . . . . . . . . . . . .EPCA 132372
■ 7" . . . . . . . . . . . . . . . . . . . . .EPCA 2372
Epic / May '82.

**SAY THAT YOU WILL.**
Tracks: Say that you will / I'm for real.
■ 7" . . . . . . . . . . . . . . . . . . . . . .EPC 7095
Epic / May '79.

**SECRET RENDEZVOUS.**
Tracks: Got to get back to love / Stay awhile / Thinking of you / Secret rendezvous / Take it on / She can wait forever / Better ways / Your life / Ipanema lady.
■ LP . . . . . . . . . . . . . . . . . . . . . .EPC 26059
Epic / Sep '89.

**SHINE ON.**
Tracks: Shine on / Positive energy.
■ 12" . . . . . . . . . . . . . . . . . . . . . . .132072
■ 7" . . . . . . . . . . . . . . . . . . . . . .EPCA 2072
Epic / May '80.

**SNAPSHOT.**
Tracks: From the void (intro) / History (I remember) / Snapshot / No rhyme, no reason / 6 O'clock / Ooh baby / Fame / Geneva / Speak low / Keeping love alive / Until sunrise / Bus tours / In the meantime (interlude) / Morning after.
CD . . . . . . . . . . . . . . . . . . . . . .9362450262
Warner Bros. / Oct '92 / WEA.

**SWEET BABY (see under Clarke, Stanley).**

**THIEF IN THE NIGHT.**
Tracks: Not Advised.
MC. . . . . . . . . . . . . . . . . . . . . . . . . .EKT 3C
■ LP . . . . . . . . . . . . . . . . . . . . . . . .EKT 3
Elektra / May '85 / WEA.

CD . . . . . . . . . . . . . . . . . . . . 9603982
Elektra / '88 / WEA.

**THIEF IN THE NIGHT.**
Tracks: Thief in the night / La la.
■ 12" . . . . . . . . . . . . . . . . . . . EKR 5T
■ 7" . . . . . . . . . . . . . . . . . . . . . EKR 5
Elektra / Apr '85.

## Dukes

**AIN'T NO SMOKE WITHOUT FIRE.**
Tracks: Ain't no smoke without fire / Dogs in the yard.
■ 7" . . . . . . . . . . . . . . . . . . . EPC 4755
Epic / Nov '76.

**DUKES.**
Tracks: Hearts in trouble / Leaving it all behind / All in a game / Billy Niles / Crazy fools / Who's gonna tell you / Time on your side / I'll try to help / Heartbreaker.
■ LP . . . . . . . . . . . . . . . . . . . K 56710
WEA / Oct '79.

**DUKES.**
Tracks: Mystery girl / I'm a survivor / Thank you for the party / Memories / Excitement of the new / Love dance / Soul mates / So much in love / Fate / Nite music.
■ LP . . . . . . . . . . . . . . . . . . . K 58497
WEA / Oct '82.

**HEARTS IN TROUBLE.**
Tracks: Hearts in trouble / Who's gonna tell you.
■ 7" . . . . . . . . . . . . . . . . . . . K 17453
WEA / Jul '79.

**I'M A SURVIVOR.**
Tracks: I'm a survivor / Every woman in the world.
■ 7" . . . . . . . . . . . . . . . . . . . K 19252
WEA / Aug '82.

**LEAVIN' IT ALL BEHIND.**
Tracks: Leaving it all behind / I'll try to help.
■ 7" . . . . . . . . . . . . . . . . . . . K 17551
WEA / Feb '80.

**MYSTERY GIRL.**
Tracks: Mystery girl / My simple heart.
■ 7" . . . . . . . . . . . . . . . . . . . K 18867
WEA / Oct '81.

**STARRY NIGHT.**
Tracks: Starry night / When your woman cries.
■ 7" . . . . . . . . . . . . . . . . . . . EPC 5930
Epic / Jan '78.

**TELEPHONES NEVER SLEEP.**
Tracks: Telephones never sleep / I told you.
■ 7" . . . . . . . . . . . . . . . . . . . EPC 3385
Epic / Sep '75.

**THANK YOU FOR THE PARTY.**
Tracks: Thank you for the party / Love's fool.
■ 7" . . . . . . . . . . . . . . . . . . . K 19136
WEA / May '82.

## Dunbar, Ernesta

**CHECKING OUT.**
Tracks: Checking out / Checking out (remix).
■ 12" . . . . . . . . . . . . . . . . . . . HAKT 6
Hardcore / Sep '87.

## Duncan, Celena

**DO IT.**
Tracks: Do it / Feels so good to be in love again.
■ 12" . . . . . . . . . . . . . . . . . . . RCAT 235
■ 7" . . . . . . . . . . . . . . . . . . . .RCA 235
RCA / Jun '82.

**FASTER THAN THE EYE CAN SEE.**
Tracks: Faster than the eye can see (instrumental) / Faster than the eye can see.
■ 12" . . . . . . . . . . . . . . . . . . . MARE 12
■ 7" . . . . . . . . . . . . . . . . . . . MARES 12
Nightmare / Mar '87.

**SHINE ON.**
Tracks: Shine on / You've got the love I need.
■ 12" . . . . . . . . . . . . . . . . . . . RCAT 156
■ 7" . . . . . . . . . . . . . . . . . . . .RCA 156
RCA / Nov '81.

**WANT YOUR LOVE BACK, I (Part 1 and Part 2).**
Tracks: I want your love back.
■ 12" . . . . . . . . . . . . . . . . . . . RCAT 307
■ 7" . . . . . . . . . . . . . . . . . . . .RCA 307
RCA / Feb '83.

■ DELETED

## Duncan, Daryll

**HEAVEN.**
Tracks: Boomerang / Phone / James Brown / Best friend / My dream / One touch / Heaven / Girlfriend.
■ LP . . . . . . . . . . . . . . . . . . . ZL 72624
■ MC . . . . . . . . . . . . . . . . . . . ZK 72624
Motown / Mar '88.

**JAMES BROWN.**
Tracks: James Brown (part 1) / James Brown (part 2).
■ 12" . . . . . . . . . . . . . . . . . . . ZT 41740
■ 7" . . . . . . . . . . . . . . . . . . . ZB 41739
Motown / Feb '88.

**ROCK THE HOUSE.**
Tracks: Rock the house / Rock the house (inst).
■ 12" . . . . . . . . . . . . . . . . . . . ZT 41278
■ 7" . . . . . . . . . . . . . . . . . . . ZB 41277
Motown / May '87.

## Dunlap, Gene

**IT'S JUST THE WAY I FEEL.**
Tracks: Rock dancin' / Before you break my heart / I got you / Love dancin' / Title track / Should I take her back, should I let her go / Surest things can change.
■ LP . . . . . . . . . . . . . . . . . . . .EST 12130
Capitol / '81.

**IT'S JUST THE WAY I FEEL.**
Tracks: It's just the way I feel / Love dancin' / Surest things can change.
■ 12" . . . . . . . . . . . . . . . . . . . 12CL 16183
■ 7" . . . . . . . . . . . . . . . . . . . CL 16183
Capitol / Feb '81.

**PARTY IN ME.**
Tracks: Party in me / Jam city / Something special / This one's on me / Take my love / Our moments together / Something inside my head / Corner pocket / There will never be another.
■ LP . . . . . . . . . . . . . . . . . . . .EST 12190
Capitol / Jan '82.

**ROCK RADIO.**
Tracks: Rock radio / Surest things can change.
■ 12" . . . . . . . . . . . . . . . . . . . 12CL 16186
■ 7" . . . . . . . . . . . . . . . . . . . CL 16186
Capitol / Apr '81.

## Dunn, Larry

**LOVER'S SILHOUETTE (Dunn, Larry Orchestra).**
Tracks: Lover's silhouette / 2000 SKY-5 / Don't it make you wanna cry / Italian lady (A song for Mama) / Heaven sent (Michael's song) / Where's the love / Between 7 and earth / Pure faith (guitar interlude) / Maybe in my dreams / Jahap / Enchanted.
CD . . . . . . . . . . . . . . . . . . . 101S 870712
101 South / Nov '93 / New Note.

## Dunnery, Francis

**AMERICAN LIFE IN THE SUMMERTIME.**
Tracks: American life in the summertime / New vibration.
CD Single . . . . . . . . . . . . . . . . . A 7254CD
MC Single . . . . . . . . . . . . . . . . . A 7254C
Atlantic / Jul '94 / WEA.

**FEARLESS.**
Tracks: Not Advised.
CD . . . . . . . . . . . . . . . . . . .756782582-2
MC . . . . . . . . . . . . . . . . . . .756782582-4
Warner Bros. / Aug '94 / WEA.

**WHAT'S HE GONNA SAY.**
Tracks: What's he gonna say / Let's end it now / American life in the summertime.
7" . . . . . . . . . . . . . . . . . . . . .A 7218
CD Single . . . . . . . . . . . . . . . . A 7218CD2
CD Single . . . . . . . . . . . . . . . . A 7218CD
MC Single . . . . . . . . . . . . . . . . A 7218C
Atlantic / Oct '94 / WEA.

## Dupars

**LOVE COOKIN'.**
Tracks: Love cookin' / We rockin'.
■ 7" . . . . . . . . . . . . . . . . . . . CS 2104
Contempo (1) / Jan '77.

## Dupree, Cornell

**CAN'T GET THROUGH.**
Tracks: Not Advised.
CD . . . . . . . . . . . . . . . . . . . .CDMT 020
Magnum Music / Mar '93 / Magnum Music Group / THE.

**CHILD'S PLAY.**
Tracks: Not Advised.
CD . . . . . . . . . . . . . . . . . . . .CDMT 024
MMG / Jan '94 / THE.

**GUITAR GROOVE.**
Tracks: Staying alive I & 2 / Boogie nights / Shake it well / How deep is your love / Lovely day / Slip slidin' away / It's so easy.
■ LP . . . . . . . . . . . . . . . . . . . .TOP 167
MC . . . . . . . . . . . . . . . . . . . .KTOP 167
Topline / Apr '87 / Charly.

**TEASIN'.**
Tracks: Teasin' / Blue nocturne / Jamaican lady / Feel all right / How long will it last / What would I do without you / Okie Dokie stomp / Plain Ol'blues.
■ LP . . . . . . . . . . . . . . . . . . . K 50071
Atlantic / Feb '87.

## Duprees

**BEST OF THE DUPREES.**
Tracks: You belong to me / Why don't you believe me / Check yourself / Save your heart for me / Carousel / Two different worlds / Hope / Goodnight my love / Sky's the limit / People / My own true love / Have you heard / Delicious / Groovin' is easy / My love, my love / Ring of love / One in a million / Beautiful / My special angel / Delicious (Disco version).
CD . . . . . . . . . . . . . . . . . . . NEMCD 674
Sequel / Apr '94 / Total / BMG.

**DELICIOUS.**
Tracks: Delicious / Sky's the limit.
■ 7" . . . . . . . . . . . . . . . . . . . .STAT 22
State / May '76.

## Duverney, Ondrea

**OBSESSION.**
Tracks: Obsession.
12" . . . . . . . . . . . . . . . . . . . EZY 1209
Passion (2) / Jun '94.

**YOU KNOW WHAT IT'S LIKE.**
Tracks: You know what it's like / Obsession.
■ 12" . . . . . . . . . . . . . . . . . . . EZY 1209
E-Zee / Jul '93.

## Dyke & The Blazers

**FUNKY BROADWAY.**
Tracks: Funky Broadway part 1 / Funky Broadway part 2.
■ 7" . . . . . . . . . . . . . . . . . . . 7N 25413
Pye International / Feb '67.

**SO SHARP.**
Tracks: Funky Broadway (part 1) / Funky Broadway (part 2) / Uhh (part 1) / Runaway people / We got more soul / It's your thing / Shot gun Slim / So sharp / Let a woman be a woman - let a man be a man / You are my sunshine / Funky walk (part 2) / Wrong house / Don't bug me (On CD only) / City dump (On CD only) / My sisters and my brothers (On CD only) / Funky Walk part 1 (On CD only) / Uhh part 2 (On CD only) / Broadway combination (On CD only) / Stuff (On CD only) / Funky bull part 1 (On CD only) / Funky bull part 2 (On CD only) / Wobble (On CD only) / Uhh (edit) (On CD only) / I'm so all alone (On CD only).
CD . . . . . . . . . . . . . . . . . . . CDKEND 004
Kent / Aug '91 / Pinnacle.
LP . . . . . . . . . . . . . . . . . . . .KEND 004
Kent / Sep '91 / Pinnacle.

## Dynamic Superiors

**DECEPTION.**
Tracks: Deception / One-nighter.
■ 7" . . . . . . . . . . . . . . . . . . . .TMG 1016
Tamla Motown / Dec '75.

**NOWHERE TO RUN.**
Tracks: Nowhere to run / Nowhere to run (version).
■ 7" . . . . . . . . . . . . . . . . . . . .TMG 1077
Motown / Jul '77.

**SHOO-SHOE SHINE.**
Tracks: Shoo-shoe shine / Release me.
■ 7" . . . . . . . . . . . . . . . . . . . . TMG 929
Tamla Motown / Jan '75.

123

## STAY AWAY.

**Tracks:** Stay away / Supersensuousensation.
■ 7" . . . . . . . . . . . . . . . . . . . . . TMG 1071
Motown / May '77.

## YOU NAME IT.

**Tracks:** Stay away / Looking away / Many, many changes / Before the street lights come on / I can't stay away / If I could meet you / I can't afford to be poor.
■ LP . . . . . . . . . . . . . . . . . . . . . STML 12051
Motown / Feb '77.

# Dynasty

## ADVENTURES IN THE LAND OF MUSIC.

**Tracks:** Adventures in the land of music / I've just begun to love you / Groove control / Take another look at love / Day and night / Do me right / Something to remember / Ice breaker.
■ LP . . . . . . . . . . . . . . . . . . . . . SOLA 3
Solar / Aug '80.

## BEST OF DYNASTY, THE.

**Tracks:** I don' want to be a freak (but I can't help myself) / I've just begun to love you / Do me right / Adventures in the land of music / Love in the fast lane / Check it out / Satisfied / Something to remember / Groove control / Here I am / Strokin' / Does that ring a bell (12" mix) / Only one.
CD . . . . . . . . . . . . . . . . . . . . . NEMCD 679
Sequel / Oct '94 / Total / BMG.

## DO ME RIGHT.

**Tracks:** Do me right / I've just begun to love you.
■ 12" . . . . . . . . . . . . . . . . . . . . . SOT 14
■ 7" . . . . . . . . . . . . . . . . . . . . . SO 14
Solar / Nov '80.

## DOES THAT RING A BELL?.

**Tracks:** Does that ring a bell / Love in the fast lane.
■ 12" . . . . . . . . . . . . . . . . . . . . . E 9911T
■ 7" . . . . . . . . . . . . . . . . . . . . . E 9911
Elektra / Apr '83.

## FOUR PIECE OF THE ROCK.

**Tracks:** Four piece of the rock.
■ 12" . . . . . . . . . . . . . . . . . . . . . FC 1539
■ 7" . . . . . . . . . . . . . . . . . . . . . PB 1539
RCA / Jun '79.

## GROOVE CONTROL.

**Tracks:** Groove control / Something to remember.
■ 12" . . . . . . . . . . . . . . . . . . . . . SOT 18
■ 7" . . . . . . . . . . . . . . . . . . . . . SO 18
Solar / Mar '81.

## HERE I AM.

**Tracks:** Here I am / Give it up to love.
■ 7" . . . . . . . . . . . . . . . . . . . . . K 12550
WEA / Jul '81.

## I DON'T WANNA BE A FREAK (OLD GOLD).

**Tracks:** I don't wanna be a freak / Music.
■ 12" . . . . . . . . . . . . . . . . . . . . . OG 4064
Old Gold / May '88.

## I DON'T WANT TO BE A FREAK.

**Tracks:** I don't want to be a freak.
■ 7" . . . . . . . . . . . . . . . . . . . . . FB 1694
Solar / Oct '79.

## I'VE JUST BEGUN TO LOVE YOU.

**Tracks:** I've just begun to love you / When you feel like giving.
■ 12" . . . . . . . . . . . . . . . . . . . . . SO12-10
Solar / Jul '80.

## LOVE IN THE FAST LANE.

**Tracks:** Love in the fast lane / High time.
■ 7" . . . . . . . . . . . . . . . . . . . . . K 12577
Solar / Nov '81.

## ONLY ONE.

**Tracks:** Only one / Check it out.
■ 12" . . . . . . . . . . . . . . . . . . . . . E 9814 T
■ 7" . . . . . . . . . . . . . . . . . . . . . E 9814
Solar / Jul '83.

## RIGHT BACK AT CHA.

**Tracks:** Right back at cha / Check it out / Strokin' / Only one / Questions / Does that ring a bell / Straight out / That's the way I feel about you / I can't stop loving you / All's fair in love and war.
■ LP . . . . . . . . . . . . . . . . . . . . . K 52419
Solar / Nov '82.

## SATISFIED.

**Tracks:** Satisfied / It's still a thrill.
■ 12" . . . . . . . . . . . . . . . . . . . . . SO 12-3
■ 7" . . . . . . . . . . . . . . . . . . . . . SO 3
Solar / Mar '80.

## SECOND ADVENTURE, THE.

**Tracks:** Right back at cha / Pain, got a hold on me / Man in love / Give your love to me / You're my angel / Love in the fast lane / Revenge / Give it up for love / High time / That loving feeling.
■ LP . . . . . . . . . . . . . . . . . . . . . K 52306
Solar.

## YOUR PIECE OF THE ROCK.

**Tracks:** You piece of the rock / I don't want to be a freak / Satisfied / When you feel like giving / It's still a thrill.
■ Mini LP . . . . . . . . . . . . . . . . . . . . . FL 13398
Grunt / Feb '80.

# Dyson, Ronnie

A leading role in the hit musical Hair led t a contract with CBS but his debut singl actually came from another less successf musical, Salvation. *(If You Let Me Mak Love To You Then) Why Can't I Touch Yo* reached No. 8 on the U.S. chart in 1970; th following year he had his only UK cha entry, *When You Get Right Down To I* Further R&B hits followed in the U.S. and i 1974 he supported The Supremes on a U.K tour. Produced by Chuck Jackson and Mar vin Yancy, 1976's *The More You Do It (Th More I Like It To Be Done To Me)* was we received and followed by a number of al bums. Dyson achieved his last chart hit i 1983 with *All Over Your Face*, produced b Butch Ingram, before his untimely death i 1990.

## ALL OVER YOUR FACE.

**Tracks:** All over your face / Don't need you now.
■ 12" . . . . . . . . . . . . . . . . . . . . . B 9841
■ 7" . . . . . . . . . . . . . . . . . . . . . B 984
Cotillion / Sep '83.

## MORE YOU DO IT, THE.

**Tracks:** Song for you / Close to you / More you do it / You set my spirits free / You and me / Love won't le me wait / Lovin' feeling / Won't you come stay wit me / Jive talkin'.
■ LP . . . . . . . . . . . . . . . . . . . . . CBS 8167
CBS / Feb '77.

## ONE MORE CHANCE FOR THE FOOL.

**Tracks:** One more chance for the fool / Foreplay.
■ 7" . . . . . . . . . . . . . . . . . . . . . K 1913
Cotillion / Apr '82.

## SEE THE CLOWN.

**Tracks:** See the clown / Shine (come towards the light).
■ 7" . . . . . . . . . . . . . . . . . . . . . ADS 900
Ardent / Jul '90.

## WE CAN MAKE IT LAST FOREVER.

**Tracks:** We can make it last forever / Just a little love from me.
■ 7" . . . . . . . . . . . . . . . . . . . . . CBS 2430
CBS / Jun '74.

## WHEN YOU GET RIGHT DOWN TO IT.

**Tracks:** When you get right down to it.
■ 7" . . . . . . . . . . . . . . . . . . . . . CBS 7449
CBS / Dec '71.

# E

## E.U.

**DA'BUTT.**
Tracks: Da'butt / Da'butt (B Boy dub) / Da'butt (radio mix) (Track on 12" version only) / Da'butt (Ext.soundtrack version/Marcus Miller mix) (Track on 12" version only).
| | |
|---|---|
| 12"............................12MT 43 | |
| 7"..............................MT 43 | |
EMI-Manhattan / Jul '88.

**E.U.FREEZE.**
Tracks: E.U. freeze / E.U. freeze (instr.).
| | |
|---|---|
| 7"..............................GOGO 3 | |
| 12".............................12 GOGO 3 | |
4th & Broadway / Apr '85.

**FUTURE FUNK.**
Tracks: Not Advised.
| | |
|---|---|
| LP.............................LP DANCE 1 | |
4aad / Jun '83.

## E.V.E.

**GROOVE OF LOVE.**
Tracks: Groove of love (Mixes).
| | |
|---|---|
| 12"...........................MCST 2007 | |
| 12"...........................MCSX 2007 | |
| CD Single....................MCSTD 2007 | |
| MC Single....................MCSC 2007 | |
Gasoline Alley / Sep '94.

## Eager, Brenda Lee

**WATCH MY BODY TALK.**
Tracks: Watch my body talk.
| | |
|---|---|
| 12"...............................TA 4850 | |
Epic / Oct '84.

## Ealey, Theodis

**IF YOU LEAVE ME, I'M GOING WHI CHA.**
Tracks: Not Advised.
| | |
|---|---|
| CD............................ICH 1164CD | |
Ichiban / Jan '94 / A.D.A. Distribution / Pinnacle / CD Trading Ltd. / Koch International / Direct Distribution.

## Earland, Charles

**COMING TO YOU LIVE.**
Tracks: Cornbread / Take me to heaven / Good question / I will never tell / Zee funkin' space / It's the woman in you / Coming to you live / Spend the night with me.
| | |
|---|---|
| LP.............................CBS 84815 | |
CBS / Feb '81.

**DOGGIE BOOGIE BABY.**
Tracks: Doggie boogie baby.
| | |
|---|---|
| 12"...........................MCAT 880 | |
| 7"............................MCA 880 | |
MCA / Sep '83.

**I AIN'T JIVIN I'M JAMMIN'.**
Tracks: I ain't jivin' I'm jammin' / Thinking of you / City lights / One for Andre / World of competition / Sweety pie / Tell it like it is / Cease the bombing.
| | |
|---|---|
| CD.............................MCD 5481 | |
Muse / Jul '94 / New Note / Jazz Horizons / C.M. Distribution.

**IN THE POCKET.**
Tracks: Tackhead / In the alley / Grant's groove / Ballad for Mom / Good date.
| | |
|---|---|
| LP..............................MR 5240 | |
Muse / Aug '82.

**INFANT EYES.**
Tracks: We are not alone / Blues for Rudy / Thang / Infant eyes / Is it necessary.
| | |
|---|---|
| LP..............................MR 5181 | |
Muse / Apr '81.

**LEAVING THIS PLANET.**
Tracks: Leaving this planet / Red clay / Warp factor 8 / Brown eyes / Asteroid / Mason's galaxy / No me esqueca (Don't forget me) / Tyner / Van jay / Never ending melody.
| | |
|---|---|
| CD............................PRCD 66002-2 | |
Prestige / Jan '94 / Pinnacle / Complete Record Co. Ltd.

## LET THE MUSIC PLAY.
Tracks: Let the music play.
| | |
|---|---|
| 7"...............................6167 703 | |
Mercury / Aug '78.

**LET THE MUSIC PLAY (OLD GOLD).**
Tracks: Let the music play / Can't live without your love.
| | |
|---|---|
| 12"...............................OG 4188 | |
Old Gold / Jul '90 / Pickwick.

**PLEASANT AFTERNOON.**
Tracks: Not Advised.
| | |
|---|---|
| LP...............................MR 5201 | |
Muse / '81.

**WE ALL LIVE IN THE JUNGLE.**
Tracks: We all live in the jungle / Intergalactic love song.
| | |
|---|---|
| 7"...............................6167 414 | |
Mercury / Aug '76.

**WHIP APPEAL.**
Tracks: Not Advised.
| | |
|---|---|
| CD...............................MCD 5409 | |
| MC...............................MC 5409 | |
Muse / Nov '91 / New Note / Jazz Horizons / C.M. Distribution.

## Earth, Wind & Fire

Variously dubbed "the Creator's Band" (by themselves) and "Earth, Hot Air and No Fire" (by George Clinton), EWF epitomised grandiose '70s funk. Leader (and ex-Chess house drummer) Maurice White added jazz and African elements to usual JB/Sly influences; formula which gave them six hits between 1970 and '74. Major breakthrough came with 1975 single *Shining Star* and album *That's The Way Of The World*, both U.S. chart-toppers. 1979 was stunning year for EWF: *September, Boogie Wonderland* (featuring the Emotions) and *After the Love Has Gone* were consecutive transatlantic Top 10 hits, while *I Am* LP made them first act to lift five UK chart singles from one studio album (Michael Jackson matched feat four months later). However, after U.S./ U.K. no. 3 *Let's Groove*, band began to disintegrate. Philip Bailey forged highest-profile solo career, including hit duet with Phil Collins, *Easy Lover* (Collins also borrowed EWF brass section Phoenix Horns). Band reformed in '87 to scant acclaim and sales, but were still together in '93, when *Millenium* album boasted input of Gerald Albright, Ronnie Laws and Prince.

**AFTER THE LOVE HAS GONE.**
Tracks: After the love has gone / Rock that.
| | |
|---|---|
| 7".............................CBS 7721 | |
CBS / Jul '79.

**ALL 'N' ALL.**
Tracks: Serpentine fire / Fantasy / In the marketplace (interlude) / Jupiter / Love's holiday / Brazilian rhyme / I'll write a song for you / Master mind / Runnin' / Brazilian rhyme (interlude) / Be ever wonderful.
| | |
|---|---|
| LP.............................CBS 86051 | |
CBS / Jan '78.
| | |
|---|---|
| LP.............................CBS 32266 | |
| MC.............................40 32266 | |
CBS / Mar '83 / Sony.
| | |
|---|---|
| CD.............................CD 82238 | |
CBS / May '87.
| | |
|---|---|
| CD.............................32DP 366 | |
CBS / '88 / Sony.
| | |
|---|---|
| CD.............................982842 2 | |
| MC.............................982842 4 | |
Pickwick/Sony Collector's Choice / Apr '94 / Pickwick / Pinnacle.

**BACK ON THE ROAD.**
Tracks: Back on the road / Take it to the sky.
| | |
|---|---|
| 7".............................CBS 9377 | |
CBS / Dec '80.

**BEST OF EARTH, WIND & FIRE, THE.**
Tracks: Not Advised.
| | |
|---|---|
| CD.............................TCD 2631 | |
Telstar/Ronco / Nov '92.

## BEST OF EARTH, WIND AND FIRE VOL 1, THE.
Tracks: Got to get you into my life / Fantasy / Saturday night / Love music / Getaway / That's the way of the world / September / Shining star / Reasons / Sing a song.
| | |
|---|---|
| LP.............................CBS 83284 | |
CBS / Dec '78.
| | |
|---|---|
| MC.............................40 32536 | |
| LP.............................CBS 32536 | |
CBS / Nov '84 / Sony.
| | |
|---|---|
| CD.............................CD 83284 | |
CBS / Mar '87 / Sony.
| | |
|---|---|
| CD.............................CD 32536 | |
CBS / Jun '89 / Sony.
| | |
|---|---|
| CD.............................477508 2 | |
Columbia / Oct '94 / Sony.

**BEST OF EARTH, WIND AND FIRE VOL. 2, THE.**
Tracks: Turn on (the beat box) / Let's groove / After the love has gone / Fantasy / Devotion / Serpentine fire / Love's holiday / Boogie wonderland / Saturday nite / Mighty mighty.
| | |
|---|---|
| CD.............................4632002 | |
| MC.............................4632004 | |
Columbia / May '91 / Sony.

**BOOGIE WONDERLAND.**
Tracks: Boogie wonderland / Boogie wonderland (version).
| | |
|---|---|
| 12".............................CBS 127292 | |
| 7".............................CBS 7292 | |
CBS / May '79.

**BOOGIE WONDERLAND.**
Tracks: Boogie wonderland.
| | |
|---|---|
| 7"...............................A 7253 | |
| 12".............................TA 7253 | |
CBS / Jun '86.

**BOOGIE WONDERLAND (OLD GOLD).**
Tracks: Boogie wonderland / Let's groove / Star.
| | |
|---|---|
| 7"...............................OG 9558 | |
Old Gold / '88.
| | |
|---|---|
| CD...............................OG 6501 | |
Old Gold / Jul '90 / Pickwick.

**CAN'T LET GO.**
Tracks: Can't let go / Love music.
| | |
|---|---|
| 7".............................CBS 8077 | |
CBS / Dec '79.

**COLLECTION: EARTH, WIND & FIRE.**
Tracks: Not Advised.
| | |
|---|---|
| CD.............................NCD 3322 | |
| LP..............................NE 1322 | |
| MC..............................CE 2322 | |
K-Tel / May '86.

**EARTH WIND AND FIRE: VERY BEST OF VOL.1.**
Tracks: Not Advised.
| | |
|---|---|
| CD.............................ADEHCD 821/0 | |
Arcade / May '88.

**EARTH WIND AND FIRE: VERY BEST OF VOL.2.**
Tracks: Not Advised.
| | |
|---|---|
| CD.............................ADEHCD 821/1 | |
Arcade / May '88.

**EARTH, WIND & FIRE.**
Tracks: Help somebody / Moment of truth / Love is life / Fan the fire / C'mon children / World today / Bad tune.
| | |
|---|---|
| LP.............................WS 1905 | |
Warner Bros. / Jun '71.

**EARTH, WIND AND FIRE (CBS).**
Tracks: Not Advised.
| | |
|---|---|
| LP Set.............................CBS 66350 | |
CBS / Oct '79.

**EARTH, WIND AND FIRE (PICKWICK).**
Tracks: Not Advised.
| | |
|---|---|
| LP.............................SSP 3078 | |
Pickwick / Oct '80.

**ELECTRIC UNIVERSE.**
Tracks: Not Advised.
| | |
|---|---|
| CD.............................CD CBS 257 72 | |
CBS / '88 / Sony.

## ETERNAL DANCE, THE.
Tracks: Fan the fire / Love is life / I think about lovin' you / Interlude / Time is on your side / Where have all the flowers gone / Power / Keep your head to the sky / Mighty mighty / Feelin' blue / Hey girl / Open our eyes / Shining star / That's the way of the world / Kalimba story/Sing a message to you (live) / Head to the sky/Devotion (live) / Sun goddess (live) / Mighty mighty (live) / Can't hide love / Sing a song / Sunshine / Getaway / Saturday nite spirit / Ponta de areia / Fantasy / Saturday night spirit / Ponta de Ariea 'Brazilian rhyme' / Serpentine fire / I'll write a song for you / Be ever wonderful / Beijo / Got to get you into my life / September / Boogie wonderland / After the love has gone / In the stone / Dirty / Let me talk / And love goes on / Pride demo / Let's groove / Wanna be with you / Little girl / Night dreamin' / Fall in love with me / Magnetic / System of survival / Thinking of you / Gotta find out.

| | | |
|---|---|---|
| CD Set | | 472614-2 |
| MC Set | | 472614-4 |

Columbia / Jan '93 / Sony.

## ETERNAL VISION, THE.
Tracks: Not Advised.

| | | |
|---|---|---|
| VHS | | 491502 |

Sony Music Video / Jan '93 / Sony.

## FACES.
Tracks: Let me talk / Turn it into something good / Pride / You / Sparkle / Back on the road / Song in my heart / You went away / Love goes on / Sailaway / Take it to the sky / Win or lose / Share your love / In time / Faces.

| | | |
|---|---|---|
| ■ Double LP | | CBS 88498 |
| ■ MC | | 40 88498 |

CBS / Oct '80.

| | | |
|---|---|---|
| CD | | 983316 2 |

Pickwick/Sony Collector's Choice / Mar '94 / Pickwick / Pinnacle.

## FALL IN LOVE WITH ME.
Tracks: Fall in love with me / Lady sun.

| | | |
|---|---|---|
| ■ 12″ | | A 12 2927 |
| ■ 7″ | | A 2927 |

CBS / Jan '83.

## FANTASY.
Tracks: Fantasy / Be ever wonderful.

| | | |
|---|---|---|
| ■ 7″ | | CBS 6056 |

CBS / Feb '78.

## FANTASY (OLD GOLD).
Tracks: Fantasy / September.

| | | |
|---|---|---|
| ■ 7″ | | OG 9556 |

Old Gold / Sep '85.

## GET AWAY.
Tracks: Get away / Get away (version).

| | | |
|---|---|---|
| ■ 7″ | | CBS 4532 |

CBS / Aug '76.

## GRATITUDE.
Tracks: Introduction medley / Africano/Power / Yearnin' learnin' / Devotion / Sun goddess / Reasons / Sing a message to you / Shining star / New world symphony / Sunshine / Sing a song / Gratitude / Celebrate / You can't hide love.

| | | |
|---|---|---|
| ■ Double LP | | CBS 22129 |

CBS / Jun '82.

| | | |
|---|---|---|
| ■ CD | | CD 88160 |

CBS / May '87.

## HEAD TO THE SKY.
Tracks: Evil / Jeep your head to the sky / Build your nest / World's a masquerade / Clover / Zanzibar / Turn it into something good / You / Sparkle / Back on the road / Song in my heart / You went away / And love goes on / Sailaway / Take it to the sky / Win or lose / Share your love / In time / Faces / Got to get you into my life.

| | | |
|---|---|---|
| MC | | 40 32017 |
| ■ LP | | CBS 32017 |

CBS / Mar '81 / Sony.

| | | |
|---|---|---|
| CD | | 982997 2 |

Pickwick/Sony Collector's Choice / Aug '93 / Pickwick / Pinnacle.

## HELP SOMEBODY.
Tracks: Help somebody / Love is life.

| | | |
|---|---|---|
| ■ 7″ | | WB 6125 |

Warner / May '71.

## HERITAGE.
Tracks: Interlude / Soweto / Takin' chances / Heritage / Good time / Body wrap / Anything you want / Bird / Wanna be the man / Close to home / Daydreamin' / King of the groove / I'm in love / For the love of you / Gotta find out / Motor / Faith / Welcome / Soweto (reprise).

| | | |
|---|---|---|
| ■ CD | | 4662422 |
| ■ LP | | 4662421 |
| ■ MC | | 4662424 |

CBS / Mar '90.

## HERITAGE.
Tracks: Heritage / Gotta find out (7″ only.) / Heritage (percussapella mix) (12″ only.) / Heritage (ext. version) (12″ only.) / Fantasy (CD single only.) / September (CD single only.) / Heritage (ext. version) (CD single only.) / Brazilian rhyme (interlude) / Got to get you into my life / I've had enough.

| | | |
|---|---|---|
| ■ 12″ | | EWF T3 |
| ■ 12″ | | EWF QT3 |
| ■ 7″ | | EWF 3 |
| ■ CD Single | | CDEWF 3 |
| ■ MC Single | | EWF M3 |

CBS / Feb '90.

## I AM.
Tracks: In the stone / Can't let go / After the love is gone / Let your feelings show / Boogie wonderland / Star / Wait / Rock that / You and I.

| | | |
|---|---|---|
| ■ LP | | CBS 86084 |

CBS / Jun '79.

| | | |
|---|---|---|
| ■ LP | | CBS 32656 |
| ■ MC | | 40 32656 |

CBS / Jun '85.

| | | |
|---|---|---|
| ■ CD | | CD 86084 |

CBS / May '87.

## I AM/ALL N' ALL/RAISE.
Tracks: Not Advised.

| | | |
|---|---|---|
| CD Set | | 4673882 |

CBS / Dec '90 / Sony.

## I'VE HAD ENOUGH.
Tracks: I've had enough.

| | | |
|---|---|---|
| ■ 7″ | | A 1959 |

CBS / Feb '82.

## IN THE STONE.
Tracks: In the stone / Africano.

| | | |
|---|---|---|
| ■ 12″ | | 138252 |
| ■ 7″ | | CBS 8252 |

CBS / Mar '80.

## JUPITER.
Tracks: Jupiter / Runnin'.

| | | |
|---|---|---|
| ■ 7″ | | CBS 6267 |

CBS / May '78.

## LAST DAYS AND TIME.
Tracks: Time is on your side / They don't see / Make it with you / Power / Remember the children / Where have all the flowers gone / I'd rather have you / Mom.

| | | |
|---|---|---|
| ■ LP | | CBS 31761 |
| ■ MC | | 40 31761 |

CBS / Oct '79.

| | | |
|---|---|---|
| CD | | 9827362 |

CBS / Feb '92 / Sony.

## LET ME TALK.
Tracks: Let me talk.

| | | |
|---|---|---|
| ■ 7″ | | CBS 8982 |

CBS / Oct '80.

## LET'S GROOVE.
Tracks: Let's groove / Let's groove (Instrumental).

| | | |
|---|---|---|
| ■ 7″ | | A 1679 |

CBS / Nov '81.

## LET'S GROOVE (OLD GOLD).
Tracks: Let's groove / Boogie wonderland.

| | | |
|---|---|---|
| ■ 12″ | | OG 4019 |

Old Gold / Sep '87.

## LIVE IN CONCERT.
Tracks: Not Advised.

| | | |
|---|---|---|
| VHS | | VFM 007 |

Videoform / '84 / Gold & Sons.

## LIVE IN JAPAN 1990.
Tracks: System of survival / Get away / That's the way of the world / September / After the love is gone / Fantasy / Let's groove / Reasons / Shining star / Kalimba tree / For the love of you / Brazilian rhyme.

| | | |
|---|---|---|
| Laser Disc | | PLMJB 00431 |

Pioneer LDCE / Jul '92 / Video Collection / THE.

## LOVE GOES ON.
Tracks: Love goes on / Faces.

| | | |
|---|---|---|
| ■ 7″ | | CBS 9521 |

CBS / Feb '81.

## MAGIC MIND.
Tracks: Magic mind.

| | | |
|---|---|---|
| ■ 7″ | | CBS 6490 |

CBS / Jul '78.

## MAGNETIC.
Tracks: Magnetic / Speed of love.

| | | |
|---|---|---|
| ■ 12″ | | TA 3887 |
| ■ 7″ | | A 3887 |

CBS / Nov '83.

## MILLENIUM, YESTERDAY, TODAY.
Tracks: Even if you wonder / Sunday morning / Blood brothers / Kalimba interlude / Spend the night / Divine / Two hearts / Honor the magic / Love is the greatest story / "L" word / Just another lonely night / Super hero / Wouldn't change a thing about you / Love across the wire / Chicago (Chi-town) blues / Kalimba blues.

| | | |
|---|---|---|
| CD Set | | 9362452742 |
| MC Set | | 9362452744 |

WEA / Sep '93 / WEA.

## OPEN OUR EYES.
Tracks: Not Advised.

| | | |
|---|---|---|
| ■ LP | | CBS 32033 |

CBS / '81.

## POWER LIGHT.
Tracks: Fall in love with me / Spread your love / Side by side / Straight from the heart / Speed of love / Freedom of choice / Something special / Hearts to heart / Miracles.

| | | |
|---|---|---|
| ■ LP | | CBS 25120 |

CBS / Feb '83.

| | | |
|---|---|---|
| CD | | CD CBS 251 20 |

CBS / '88 / Sony.

## RAISE.
Tracks: Let's groove / Lady sun / You are a winner / My love / Evolution orange / Kalimba tree / I've had enough / Wanna be with you / Changing times.

| | | |
|---|---|---|
| ■ LP | | CBS 85272 |
| ■ CD | | CD 85272 |

CBS / Nov '81.

| | | |
|---|---|---|
| ■ LP | | CBS 32809 |
| ■ MC | | 40 32809 |

CBS / Aug '86.

## REASONS.
Tracks: Reasons / Gratitude.

| | | |
|---|---|---|
| ■ 7″ | | CBS 4240 |

CBS / May '76.

## SATURDAY NITE.
Tracks: Saturday nite / Departure.

| | | |
|---|---|---|
| ■ 7″ | | CBS 4835 |

CBS / Jan '77.

## SEPTEMBER.
Tracks: September / Can't have love.

| | | |
|---|---|---|
| ■ 7″ | | CBS 6922 |

CBS / Dec '78.

## SERPENTINE FIRE.
Tracks: Serpentine fire / Serpentine fire (version).

| | | |
|---|---|---|
| ■ 7″ | | CBS 5778 |

CBS / Nov '77.

## SHINING STAR.
Tracks: Shining star / Yearning learning.

| | | |
|---|---|---|
| ■ 7″ | | CBS 3137 |

CBS / Nov '75.

## SPIRIT.
Tracks: Getaway / On your face / Imagination / Spirit / Saturday nite / Earth, wind and fire / Departure / Biyo / Burnin' bush.

| | | |
|---|---|---|
| ■ LP | | CBS 81451 |

CBS / Nov '76.

| | | |
|---|---|---|
| ■ LP | | SHM 3133 |

Hallmark / Apr '84.

## SPREAD YOUR LOVE.
Tracks: Spread your love / Heart to heart.

| | | |
|---|---|---|
| ■ 7″ | | A 3211 |

CBS / Mar '83.

## STAR.
Tracks: Star.

| | | |
|---|---|---|
| ■ 7″ | | CBS 7092 |

CBS / Oct '79.

## STAR (OLD GOLD).
Tracks: Star (Only available on CD Single.) / Saturday nite / After the love is gone / I've had enough.

| | | |
|---|---|---|
| ■ 12″ | | OG 4008 |

Old Gold / Feb '86.

## SUNDAY MORNING.
Tracks: Sunday morning.

| | | |
|---|---|---|
| ■ 7″ | | W 0205 |
| ■ CD Single | | W 0205CD |
| ■ MC Single | | W 0205C |

Warner Bros. / Oct '93.

## SYSTEM OF SURVIVAL.
Tracks: System of survival / System of survival (Percapella mix) (On 12″ version only.) / Writing on the wall (On 12″ version.) / System of survival (dub 1 mix) (On 12″ version.) / System of survival (7″ mix) (On 12″ picture bag version.) / System of survival (7″ mix) (On 12″ picture bad version.).

| | | |
|---|---|---|
| ■ 7″ | | EWF 1 |

CBS / Oct '87.

| | | |
|---|---|---|
| ■ 12″ | | EWF QT1 |

■ DELETED

■ 12".............................. EWF T1
■ CD Single................... CDGEWF 1
■ CD Single....................CD EWF 1
CBS / Oct '88.

## THAT'S THE WAY OF THE WORLD.
Tracks: Shining star / That's the way of the world / Happy feelin' / All about love / Yearnin' learnin' / Reasons / Africano / See the light.
■ LP ................................. 80575
CBS / '75.
■ LP ........................... CBS 32054
CBS / Dec '81.
■ CD ............................. CD 80575
CBS / May '87.

## THINKING OF YOU.
Tracks: Thinking of you / Thinking of you (house mix) / Thinking of you (12" version) / Thinking of you (house mix with vocals) / Money tight.
■ 12".............................. EWF QT2
■ 12".............................. EWF T2
■ 7" ................................ EWF 2
■ CD Single................... CDEWF 2
CBS / Feb '88.

## TOUCH.
Tracks: Touch / September / After the love has gone (12" only.) / Boogie wonderland (12" only.)
■ 12".............................. TA 4164
■ 7" ................................ A 4164
CBS / Jan '84.

## TOUCH THE WORLD.
Tracks: System of survival / Evil Roy / Thinking of you / You and I / Musical interlude new horizons / Money tight / Every now and then / Touch the world / Here today and gone tomorrow / Victim of the modern heart.
CD.................................. 4604092
■ LP ................................. 4604091
■ MC ................................ 4604094
CBS / Nov '87 / Sony.

## VERY BEST OF EARTH,WIND & FIRE.
Tracks: Not Advised.
■ CD ............................. TCD 2531
■ MC ............................ STAC 2531
Telstar/Ronco / Nov '92.

## WANNA BE THE MAN.
Tracks: Wanna be the man / Wanna be the man (dub mix) / Wanna be the man (extended mix) (Available on 12" & CD single only.) / Wanna be the man (remix edit) (Available on 12" and CD single only.)
■ 12".............................. EWF T4
■ 7" ................................ EWF 4
■ CD Single................... CD EWF 4
■ MC Single....................EWF M4
CBS / Sep '90.

## WANNA BE WITH YOU.
Tracks: Wanna be with you / My love.
■ 7" ................................ A 2074
CBS / Mar '82.

## YOU.
Tracks: You / Pride.
■ 7" ................................ A 1204
CBS / May '81.

# Eastbound Expressway

## CLOUDBURST.
Tracks: Cloudburst / Cloudburst (version).
■ 7" ................................ CS 2122
Contempo (1) / Aug '77.

## FRANTIC LOVE.
Tracks: Frantic love.
■ 12"............................ SOHOT 19
■ 7" ............................... SOHO 19
Record Shack / May '84.

## KNOCK ME SENSELESS.
Tracks: Knock me senseless / Knock me senseless (Inst).
■ 12".......................... PASH 61(12)
■ 7" ............................... PASH 61
Passion (1) / Oct '86.

## PRIMITIVE DESIRE.
Tracks: Primitive desire / Primitive desire (version).
■ 12"............................... SOHOT 9
Record Shack / Nov '83.

## RAINSTORM.
Tracks: Rainstorm / Rainstorm (Nightmare dub mix).
■ 12".......................... PASH 70(12)
Passion (1) / Apr '87.

## YOU'RE A BEAT.
Tracks: You've a beat / You're a beat(Dub version).
■ 12".......................... PASH 53(12)

---

■ 7" ................................ PASH 53
Passion (1) / Mar '86.

# Eastside Connection

## YOU'RE SO RIGHT FOR ME.
Tracks: You're so right for me / Over please.
■ 7" ................................. CR 149
Creole / Apr '78.

# Eaton, Cleveland

## BAMA BOOGIE WOOGIE.
Tracks: Bama boogie woogie / West coast disco / Funky funky music / Pure love / Whammy omy / Flying high / Chi-town theme / Funky cello.
■ LP ............................... MLP 3001
Miracle / Jan '79.

## BAMA BOOGIE WOOGIE.
Tracks: Bama boogie woogie / Funky cello.
■ 7" ................................. GULS 63
Gull / Sep '78.

## IT'S A SHAME (Eaton, Cleveland & Cinnamon).
Tracks: It's a shame / Cryin' tears for you.
■ 7" ................................... M 14
Miracle / Jan '80.

## KEEP LOVE ALIVE.
Tracks: Birmingham train / I'm lonely tonight / Burnin' / I don't know / Get off / Flyin' high / Free at last / Keep love alive.
■ LP ............................... MLP 3008
Miracle / Mar '80.

# Ebony Brothers

## BRIGHTEN UP YOUR NIGHT.
Tracks: Brighten up your night / Touch is hot.
■ 7" ................................. RCA 376
RCA / Nov '83.

# Ebonys

## YOUR THE REASON WHY.
Tracks: Your the reason why / Sexy ways.
■ 7" ............................... CBS 7384
CBS / Aug '71.

# Eckstine, Billy

## BASIN STREET EAST (Eckstine, Billy & Quincy Jones).
Tracks: Alright Ok you win / Caravan / Don't get around much anymore / I'm just a lucky so and so / Sophisticated lady / In the still of the night / Ma, she's making eyes at me / Everything I have is yours / Fool that I am / I'm falling for you / Work song.
■ LP ................................. SONO 28
Philips / Nov '76.

## BE-BOP BIG BANDS (Eckstine, Billy & Dizzy Gillespie).
Tracks: Not Advised.
VHS ................................. VJC 2006
Vintage Jazz Classics / Feb '93 / Direct Distribution / Topic Records / A.D.A. Distribution / C.M. Distribution / Jazz Music.

## BILLY ECKSTINE AND QUINCY JONES (Eckstine, Billy & Quincy Jones).
Tracks: Not Advised.
■ CD ............................... 8325922
■ MC ............................... 8325924
Emarcy / Feb '91.

## BLOWING THE BLUES AWAY (Eckstine, Billy & His Orchestra).
Tracks: Not Advised.
■ LP ................................. ST 1015
Swingtime / Jan '87.

## ET BASIN STREET EAST (Eckstine, Billy & Quincy Jones).
Tracks: Alright, okay, you win / I'm falling for you / Fool that I am / Everything I have is yours / In the still of the night / Duke Ellington medley / Work song / Ma he's making eyes at me.
■ LP ............................... MVL 310
Mercury / Dec '67.
■ LP ............................... SFL 13039
Fontana / Sep '68.

## GENTLE ON MY MIND.
Tracks: For love of Ivy / Time after time / Gentle on my mind / Together 'til the end of time / I'll be here with you / Nothing but trouble / Woman / I need a

---

dream / I did it all for you / More I see you / Good morning heartache / You better believe it.
■ LP .............................. STML 11101
Tamla Motown / Jul '69.

## GIGI.
Tracks: Gigi.
■ 7" .............................. AMT 1018
Mercury (EMI) / Feb '59.

## GLOOMY SUNDAY.
Tracks: My deep blue dream / Penny for your thoughts / I've got to pass your home / Gloomy Sunday / I love the loveliness of you / All of me / Where are you / What's new / Surrender dear, I / Memoires of you / Our love / There are such times / Say it isn't so / I do, do you / Blues.
CD................................... 650145
Savoy / May '91 / Jazz Music / Wellard / Savoy Records / Conifer Records.

## GOLDEN HITS.
Tracks: Caravan / I apologise / Somehow / Blue moon / Prisoner of love / My foolish heart / Everything I have is yours / My destiny / I'm falling for you / Coquette / No orchids for my lady / Bewildered.
■ LP ................................ MVL 312
Mercury / Feb '68.

## GOLDEN HOUR: BILLY ECKSTINE.
Tracks: Just a little lovin' / What the world needs now is love / My Cherie amour / Taste of my tears / Remembering / I am yours / Maybe this time / Sophisticated lady / We've only just begun / Make it with you / If she walked into my life / Very thought of you / Loving arms / All in love is fair / Walk a mile in my shoes / Feel the warm / Mixed-up girl.
■ LP ................................. GH 842
Golden Hour / Oct '75.

## GREATEST HITS: BILLY ECKSTINE.
Tracks: I apologise / Love me or leave me / St. Louis blues / Here comes the blues / Life is just a bowl of cherries / Tenderly / Taking a chance on love / Everything I have is yours / How high the moon / Laura / You're driving me crazy / No one but you / I left my hat in Haiti / As long as I love.
■ MC ............................... SPEMC 64
■ LP ............................... SPELP 64
Polydor / Mar '84 / PolyGram.

## HAD YOU BEEN AROUND.
Tracks: Had you been around.
■ 7" ............................... TMG 533
Tamla Motown / '65.

## I AM A SINGER.
Tracks: Not Advised.
■ LP .................................. KIM 1
Kim / Mar '87.

## IMAGINATION.
Tracks: It was so beautiful / I gotta right to sing the blues / Love is just around the corner / I don't stand a ghost of a chance / Faded summer love / What a little moonlight can do / Imagination / Lullaby of the leaves / I cover the waterfront / I wished on the moon / That's all.
■ LP ............................... MOIR 129
Memoir / Jun '88.
■ MC ............................. CMOIR 129
Memoir / Nov '89.

## MR. B AND THE BAND - SAVOY SESSIONS.
Tracks: Lonesome lover blues / Last night / Cottage for sale / I love the rhythm in a riff / Prisoner of love / It ain't like that / I'm in the mood for love / You call it madness / All I sing is the blues / Long long journey / I only have eyes for you / You're my everything / Jitney man / Blue / Second balcony jump / Tell me pretty baby / Love is the thing / Without a song / Cool breeze / Don't take you love from me / Oop bop sh'bam, the things you are / Jelly jelly / My silent love / Time on my hands / All the things you are / In a sentimental mood / Blues for sale / Serenade in blue / Solitude / Sophisticated lady.
■ Double LP ...................... WL 70552
Savoy (France) / Feb '86.

## NO COVER, NO MINIMUM.
Tracks: Have a song on me / I've grown accustomed to her face / Lady luck / Lush life / Without a song / Moonlight in vermont / I want a little girl / I'm beginning to see the light / Fools rush in / In the still of the night / Prisoner of love / Little mama / I apologise / Til there was you / I let a song go out of my heart / Alright, okay, you win / 'Deed I do / It might as well be Spring / That's for me / You'll never walk alone / Misty.
CD............................... CDROU 1050
Roulette Jazz / Sep '92 / EMI.

---

■ DELETED                                                                                                    127

## NO ONE BUT YOU.
**Tracks:** No one but you.
■ 7" ................................. MGM 164
MGM (EMI) / Sep '57.

## ONCE MORE WITH FEELING.
**Tracks:** Not Advised.
■ LP ...................................FS 134
Fresh Sounds / Feb '88.

## PASSING STRANGERS (Eckstine, Billy & Sarah Vaughan).
**Tracks:** Passing strangers.
■ 78 rpm. .............................. MT 164
Mercury (Pye) / '57.
■ 7" ................................. MF 1082
Mercury / Mar '69.

## PRIME OF MY LIFE.
**Tracks:** Prime of my life / Maybe today / Who can I turn to / As long as she needs me / Down to Earth / Feeling good / Had you been around / Love is gone / Just loving you / Climb every mountain / Fantasy / This is all I ask.
■ LP ................................. TML 11025
Tamla Motown / Feb '66.

## SENIOR SOUL.
**Tracks:** I'll always have faith in you / Man who sings / Song for you / Thank you for the moment / Please send me someone to love / Today was tomorrow yesterday / Don't lose faith in me Lord / I believe in music / Living like a gypsy / When something is wrong with my baby.
■ LP ................................. 2325084
Stax / Nov '72.

## SINGING IN 10 GREAT MOVIES.
**Tracks:** More / Moon river / Never on Sunday / Tender is the night / Manha de carnaval / A felicidade / Three coins in the fountain / Tonight / On Green Dolphin Street / Good life.
■ LP ................................. WL 1130
Wing / Dec '67.

## SOMETHING MORE.
**Tracks:** Something more / All in love is fair / Mixed-up girl / Song for you / Remembering / Sophisticated lady / Feel the warm / Think about things / Very thought of you / Thank you for the moment / Maybe this time, Mister / You've gone and got the blues.
■ LP ................................. STAXL 5007
MC. ................................. STAXK 5007
Stax / Oct '81 / Pinnacle.

## TOGETHER (Eckstine, Billy Big Band).
**Tracks:** Blowin' the blues away (Instrumental number.) / Deed I do (Vocal number.) / I wanna talk about you (Vocal number.) / Together (Vocal number.) / Mean to me (Vocal number.) / Without a song (Vocal number.) / Mr. Chips (Instrumental number.) / Airmail special (Instrumental number.) / Don't blame me (Vocal number.) / If that's the way you feel (Vocal number.) / Opus X (Instrumental number.) / Love me or leave me (Instrumental number.).
■ LP ................................. SPJ 100
Spotlite / May '83.

# Ecstasy, Passion & Pain

## ASK ME.
**Tracks:** Ask me.
■ 7" ................................. 7N 25669
Pye / Nov '74.

## DON'T BURN YOUR BRIDGES.
**Tracks:** Don't burn your bridges.
■ 7" ................................. 7N 25641
Pye / Mar '74.

## GOOD THINGS DON'T LAST FOREVER.
**Tracks:** Good things don't last forever.
■ 7" ................................. 7N 25660
Pye / May '74.

## ONE BEAUTIFUL DAY.
**Tracks:** One beautiful day.
■ 7" ................................. 7N 25675
Pye / Mar '75.

# Eddie & Ernie

## I CAN'T DO IT (I JUST CAN'T LEAVE YOU).
**Tracks:** I can't do it (I just can't leave you) / Lost friends.
■ 7" ................................. UP 35782
United Artists / Feb '75.

# Edwards, Alton

## EVERYBODY'S WATCHING.
**Tracks:** Everybody's watching.
■ 12" ................................. MKHAN 5
■ 7" ................................. KHAN 5
Streetwave / Mar '84.

## I JUST WANNA (SPEND SOME TIME WITH YOU).
**Tracks:** I just wanna (spend some time with you).
■ 7" ................................. STRA 1897
Streetwave / Jan '82.

## SHINING LIGHT.
**Tracks:** Shining light / To have a friend.
■ 7" ................................. A 2767
CBS / Sep '82.

## STRANGE WOMAN.
**Tracks:** Strange woman / What love.
■ 12" ................................. A 13 2275
■ 7" ................................. A 2275
CBS / Nov '82.

## TAKE ME.
**Tracks:** Take me / Girl girl.
■ 12" ................................. A 13 3146
■ 7" ................................. A 3146
CBS / Feb '83.

# Edwards, Dennis

## COOLIN' OUT.
**Tracks:** Try a little tenderness / State of limbo / No such thing / Amanda / Why do people fall in love / Givin' so much / Coolin' out / Breakin' loose / Wrap you.
■ LP ................................. ZL 72390
MC. ................................. ZK 72390
Motown / Aug '85 / PolyGram.

## DON'T LOOK ANY FURTHER.
**Tracks:** I'm up for you / Don't look any further / (You're my) aphrodisiac / Can't fight it / Another place in time / Shake hands (come out dancin') / I though I could handle it / Just like you / Let's go up.
■ CD ................................. WD 72625
■ LP ................................. WL 72625
■ MC. ................................. WK 72625
Motown / Apr '84.

## DON'T LOOK ANY FURTHER.
**Tracks:** Don't look any further / I thought I could handle it.
■ 12" ................................. TMGT 1334
■ 7" ................................. TMG 1334
Motown / Jun '87.

## YOU'RE MY APHRODISIAC.
**Tracks:** You're my aphrodisiac / Shake hands (come out dancin').
■ 12" ................................. TMGT 1340
■ 7" ................................. TMG 1340
Motown / May '84.

# Edwards, John

## BABY HOLD ONTO ME.
**Tracks:** Not Advised.
■ 7" ................................. K 10817
Atlantic / '76.

# Edwards, Sandra

## GIVE ME SOME EMOTION.
**Tracks:** Give me some emotion / I love you.
■ 12" ................................. SAND 12-001
Soultown / Jul '86.

## WINNER TAKES IT ALL.
**Tracks:** Winner takes it all / Jump start.
■ 12" ................................. BOLTS 11/12
Bolts / Jan '88.

# El Chicano

## CELEBRATION.
**Tracks:** Viva tirado / Mas zacate / Brown eyed girl / El grito / Satisfy me woman / La cucaracha / Juntos / Senor blues / In a silent way / I feel free.
■ LP ................................. MUPS 456
MCA / Sep '72.

## DO YOU WANT ME.
**Tracks:** Do you want me.
■ 12" ................................. TA 3722
■ 7" ................................. A 3722
CBS / Sep '83.

## LET ME DANCE WITH YOU.
**Tracks:** Let me dance with you / Do you want me (on 12" only).
■ 12" ................................. MKHAN 24
■ 7" ................................. KHAN 24
Streetwave / Aug '84.

# El Coco

## COCOMOTION.
**Tracks:** Cocomotion / Let's get it together.
■ 7" ................................. 7N 25761
Pye International / Jan '78.

## DANCE MAN.
**Tracks:** Dance man / Love exciter / Cocomotion / Love in your life.
■ 12" ................................. AVISL 104
■ 7" ................................. AVIS 104
AVI (USA) / Jun '79.

## DANCING IN PARADISE.
**Tracks:** Dancing in paradise / Love in your life.
■ 7" ................................. 7N 25792
Pye International / Sep '78.

## I'M AS MAD AS HELL.
**Tracks:** I'm as mad as hell / Love vaccine.
■ 7" ................................. 7N 25772
Pye International / Mar '78.

## LET'S GET IT TOGETHER.
**Tracks:** Let's get it together / Cocomotion '79 / Sait le chat.
■ 12" ................................. AVISL 109
AVI (USA) / May '80.

## LET'S GET IT TOGETHER (1977).
**Tracks:** Let's get it together (1977).
■ 7" ................................. 7N 25732
Pye International / Jan '77.

## ONE STEP BACK FOR LOVE.
**Tracks:** Not Advised.
■ 12" ................................. EXPAND 37
Expansion / Mar '93.

## UNDER CONSTRUCTION.
**Tracks:** Under construction / Masquerade.
■ 7" ................................. 7N 25782
Pye International / Jun '78.

# Elbert, Donnie

## GET READY.
**Tracks:** Get ready / Along came pride.
■ 7" ................................. CBS 2807
CBS / Jun '67.

## I CAN'T HELP MYSELF.
**Tracks:** I can't help myself.
■ 7" ................................. 6105 009
Avco-Embassy / Feb '72.

## LITTLE PIECE OF LEATHER.
**Tracks:** Little piece of leather.
■ 7" ................................. HL 10370
London-American / Apr '72.

## LITTLE PIECE OF LEATHER, A.
**Tracks:** Run little girl / Who's it gonna be / Little piece of leather / Memphis / Do what cha wanna / Your red wagon / Down home blues / Never again / That funky ol' feeling / Lilly Lou.
CD ................................. TKOCD 021
MC. ................................. TKOCS 021
TKO Records / Apr '92 / TKO Records Ltd / President Records.

## WHERE DID OUR LOVE GO.
**Tracks:** Where did our love go.
■ 7" ................................. HL 10352
London-American / Jun '72.

## YOU CAN PUSH IT (OR PULL IT).
**Tracks:** You can push it (or pull it).
■ 7" ................................. WI 396
Sue / '65.

## YOU DON'T HAVE TO BE A STAR.
**Tracks:** You don't have to be a star / At the club / Free.
■ 12" ................................. SHL 107
■ 7" ................................. SH 107
Sugarhill / Jul '81.

## YOU'RE GONNA CRY WHEN I'M GONE.
**Tracks:** You're gonna cry when I'm gone / Another tear will take its place.
■ 7" ................................. BRAD 7501
Bradley's / Jan '75.

■ DELETED

## Electric Funk

### ON A JOURNEY.
Tracks: On a journey.
- ■ 12" . . . . . . . . . . . . . . . . . . . . EPCA 132299
- ■ 7" . . . . . . . . . . . . . . . . . . . . . EPCA 2299

Epic / Nov '82.

## Elgins

### DARLING BABY.
Tracks: In the midnight hour / Heaven must have sent you / I understand my man / Good lovin' / It's gonna be hard times / Put yourself in my place / 6845-789 / No time for tears / How sweet it is / Stay in my lonely arms / When a man loves a woman.
- ■ LP . . . . . . . . . . . . . . . . . . . .STML 11081

Tamla Motown / Sep '68.

### HEAVEN MUST HAVE SENT YOU.
Tracks: Heaven must have sent you.
- ■ 7" . . . . . . . . . . . . . . . . . . . TMG 583

Tamla Motown / '66.

### HEAVEN MUST HAVE SENT YOU.
Tracks: Heaven must have sent you / Stay in my lonely arms.
- ■ 7" . . . . . . . . . . . . . . . . . . . TMG 771

Tamla Motown / Apr '71.

### IT'S BEEN A LONG LONG TIME.
Tracks: It's been a long long time / I understand my man.
- ■ 7" . . . . . . . . . . . . . . . . . . . TMG 615

Tamla Motown / Jul '67.

### PUT YOURSELF IN MY PLACE.
Tracks: Put yourself in my place / Darling baby.
- ■ 7" . . . . . . . . . . . . . . . . . . . TMG 551

Tamla Motown / '65.

### PUT YOURSELF IN MY PLACE.
Tracks: Put yourself in my place.
- ■ 7" . . . . . . . . . . . . . . . . . . . TMG 787

Tamla Motown / Oct '71.

### SENSATIONAL.
Tracks: Not Advised.
- ■ CD . . . . . . . . . . . . . . . . . . . MOTCCD 75

Motor City / Oct '92.

## Ellington, Denise

### ONE IN A MILLION.
Tracks: One in a million.
- 12" . . . . . . . . . . . . . . . . . . . . . DR 001

Disco Beat / Mar '94 / Jetstar.

## Ellington, Lance

### DON'T YOU EVER LEAVE ME AGAIN.
Tracks: Don't you ever leave me again.
- ■ 12" . . . . . . . . . . . . . . . . . . . AMY 702
- ■ 7" . . . . . . . . . . . . . . . . . . . . AM 702

A&M / Sep '90.

### GIVE ME LOVE.
Tracks: Give me love (Mixes).
- CD Single . . . . . . . . . . . . . . . MCSTD 2006
- ■ 12" . . . . . . . . . . . . . . . . . . . MCST 2006
- ■ 12" Remix . . . . . . . . . . . . . . . MCSX 2006
- ■ MC Single . . . . . . . . . . . . . . . MCSC 2006

MCA / Oct '94 / BMG.

### LONELY.
Tracks: Lonely.
- ■ 12" . . . . . . . . . . . . . . . . 7432115833-1

Warner Bros. / Aug '93.
- ■ 7" . . . . . . . . . . . . . . . . . 7432115833-7
- ■ CD Single . . . . . . . . . . . . 7432115833-2
- ■ MC Single . . . . . . . . . . . . 7432115833-4

RCA / Aug '93.

### LOVE ME MORE.
Tracks: Love me more / Don't you ever leave me again.
- ■ 7" . . . . . . . . . . . . . . . . . . . UNKNOWN

A&M / Jan '91.

### LOVE SCARED.
Tracks: Love scared.
- ■ 12" . . . . . . . . . . . . . . . . . . . AMY 585
- ■ 7" . . . . . . . . . . . . . . . . . . . . AM 585
- ■ CD Single . . . . . . . . . . . . . . . AMCD 585
- ■ MC Single . . . . . . . . . . . . . . AMMC 585

A&M / Jul '90.

### PLEASURE AND PAIN.
Tracks: Not Advised.
- ■ CD . . . . . . . . . . . . . . . . . . . CDA 7049
- ■ LP . . . . . . . . . . . . . . . . . . . AMA 7049

- ■ MC . . . . . . . . . . . . . . . . . . . AMC 7049

A&M / May '90.

### TREAT ME RIGHT.
Tracks: Treat me right / It's up to you.
- ■ 12" . . . . . . . . . . . . . . . . . . . USAT 683
- ■ 7" . . . . . . . . . . . . . . . . . . . . USA 683

Breakout / Apr '90.

## Ellingtons

### DESTINED TO BECOME A LOSER.
Tracks: Destined to become a loser / You've got to love your baby.
- ■ 7" . . . . . . . . . . . . . . . . . . . GRP 114

Grapevine (Northern Soul) / Mar '79.

## Ellis, Shirley

### CLAPPING SONG (OLD GOLD).
Tracks: Clapping song.
- ■ 7" . . . . . . . . . . . . . . . . . . . . OG 9161

Old Gold / Jul '82.

### CLAPPING SONG, THE.
Tracks: Clapping song / This is beautiful.
- ■ 7" . . . . . . . . . . . . . . . . . . . HLR 9961

London-American / May '65.

### CLAPPING SONG, THE (EP).
Tracks: Clapping song / Ever see a diver kiss his wife while the bubbles.. (..bounce about above the water) / Name game / Nitty gritty.
- ■ EP . . . . . . . . . . . . . . . . . . . MCEP 1

MCA / Jun '78.

### EVER SEE A DIVER KISS HIS WIFE.
Tracks: Ever see a diver kiss his wife / Stardust.
- ■ 7" . . . . . . . . . . . . . . . . . . . HLR 10021

London-American / Feb '66.

### SUGAR LET'S SHING-A-LING.
Tracks: Sugar let's shing-a-ling / How lonely is lonely.
- ■ 7" . . . . . . . . . . . . . . . . . . . CBS 2817

CBS / Jun '67.

## Ellison, John

### WELCOME BACK.
Tracks: Not Advised.
- CD . . . . . . . . . . . . . . . . . . AFT 6113CD
- MC . . . . . . . . . . . . . . . . . . AFT 6113MC

Ichiban / Jun '94 / A.D.A. Distribution / Pinnacle / ACD Trading Ltd. / Koch International / Direct Distribution.

## Ellison, Lorraine

Philadelphia soulstress who sang gospel with her sisters in high school. Subsequent group Ellison Singers faded into history when Lorraine signed solo to Mercury. 1965's I Dig You baby was R&B hit; next year, on Warner Brothers, Stay With Me cracked pop chart and became definitive deep soul classic. Unable to top it, she never became major star, although her compositions were successfully revived by Janis Joplin, Garnet Mimms and Howard Tate.

### CALL ME ANY TIME YOU NEED SOME LOVIN'.
Tracks: Call me any time you need some lovin' / Please don't teach me to love you.
- ■ 7" . . . . . . . . . . . . . . . . . . . 6052073

Mercury / May '71.

### LORRAINE ELLISON.
Tracks: Walk around heaven / Country woman's prayer / Do better than you're doin' / If only I could see him / No relief / I'll fly away / Road I took to you / Stormy weather / Many rivers to cross.
- ■ LP . . . . . . . . . . . . . . . . . . . K 46296

WEA / Sep '74.

### PHILADELPHIA'S QUEEN OF SOUL.
Tracks: Stay with me baby / Good love / No matter how it all turns out / Heart and soul / Heart be still / When love flies away / Try (just a little bit harder) / I want to be loved / You really got a hold on me / He's my guy / He ain't heavy he's my brother / Many rivers to cross.
- ■ LP . . . . . . . . . . . . . . . . . . . K 52630

WEA / Apr '76.

### STAY WITH ME.
Tracks: Only your love / Try (just a little bit harder) / I'm gonna cry 'till my tears run dry / I want to be loved / Hurt came back again / Stay with me / You

don't know nothing about love / You're easy on my mind / No matter how it all turns out / Good love / Heart be still.
- ■ LP . . . . . . . . . . . . . . . . . . . BMLP 025

Blue Moon (1) / Aug '85.

### STAY WITH ME.
Tracks: Stay with me / I got my baby back.
- ■ 7" . . . . . . . . . . . . . . . . . . .WB 5850

Warner / Nov '66.

### STAY WITH ME BABY.
Tracks: Stay with me baby / I've got my baby back.
- ■ 7" . . . . . . . . . . . . . . . . . . . K 16001

WEA / Jul '81.

### STAY WITH ME BABY (OLD GOLD).
Tracks: Stay with me baby / Watcha gonna do about it.
- ■ 7" . . . . . . . . . . . . . . . . . . .OG 9912

Old Gold / '89.

## Ellison, Willie

### I DON'T JUST WANT YOUR BODY.
Tracks: I don't just want your body / I don't just want your body (instrumental).
- ■ 7" . . . . . . . . . . . . . . . . . . . ADS 9005

Ardent / Apr '90.

### LOVE'S GOT A HOLD ON YOU.
Tracks: Love's got a hold on you / Love out of reach.
- ■ 12" . . . . . . . . . . . . . . . . . .RBUSL 57
- ■ 7" . . . . . . . . . . . . . . . . . . . RBUS 57

Red Bus / Sep '80.

### WIDE WORLD.
Tracks: Wide world / Chained lover.
- ■ 7" . . . . . . . . . . . . . . . . . . . RBUS 50

Red Bus / Mar '80.

## Emotions

Chicago trio who started as modestly-monickered Heavenly Sunbeams in mid-'50s. By 1969, Jeanette, Wanda and Sheila Hutchinson were signed to Stax as Emotions, scoring biggest hit with Isaac Hayes/David Porter-penned So I Can Love You. Minor hits continued into early '70s, but career ground to halt with collapse of label. Encouraged by Earth Wind & Fire's Maurice White, Emotions returned to limelight in '77, singing on international smashes Best of My Love and EWF's Boogie Wonderland. Although they never returned to charts, group remained active in '80s and early '90s, recording for CBS and Motown. Their Blind Alley gained second wind as star sample on Wreckx-N-Effex new jack anthem Rump Shaker, while Emotions were cited as influence by likes of Blackgirl.

### BABY I'M THROUGH.
Tracks: Baby i'm through / i wanna come back.
- ■ 7" . . . . . . . . . . . . . . . . . STXS 2020

Stax / Jan '75.

### BEST OF MY LOVE.
Tracks: Best of my love.
- ■ 7" . . . . . . . . . . . . . . . . . . . CBS 5555

CBS / Sep '77.

### COME INTO OUR WORLD.
Tracks: What's the name of you love / 'Cause I love you / On and on / I should be dancing / Come into my world / Where is your love / Movie / Yes I am / Layed back.
- ■ LP . . . . . . . . . . . . . . . . . . . 83483

CBS / Feb '80.

### FLOWERS.
Tracks: Flowers (wizdum 7" remix) / Flowers (original version) / Flowers (wizdum 12" remix) (Available on 12" format only.) / Flowers (sun mix) (Available on 12" format only.).
- ■ 12" . . . . . . . . . . . . . . . . . . . 6563606
- ■ 7" . . . . . . . . . . . . . . . . . . . 6563607
- ■ MC Single . . . . . . . . . . . . . . . 6563604

CBS / Oct '90.

### FLOWERS.
Tracks: I don't wanna lose your love / Me for you / You've got the right to know / We go through the changes / You're a special part of my life / No plans for tomorrow / How can you stop loving someone / Flowers / God will take care of you.
- CD . . . . . . . . . . . . . . . . . . .982996 2

Pickwick/Sony Collector's Choice / Aug '93 / Pickwick / Pinnacle.

## HEART ASSOCIATION (Best Of The Emotions).
**Tracks:** So I can love you / Best part of a love affair / Stealing love / When tomorrow comes / Heart association / You make me want to love you / Show me how / I could never be happy / My honey and me / From toys to boys / Shouting out love / I like it / Tricks were made for kids / Boss love maker / Take me back / Somebody wants what I got.
■ LP . . . . . . . . . . . . . . . . . . . STX 3008
Stax / Feb '79 / Pinnacle.

## I DON'T WANNA LOSE YOUR LOVE.
**Tracks:** I don't wanna lose your love / How can you stop loving someone.
■ 7" . . . . . . . . . . . . . . . . . . . CBS 5819
CBS / Dec '77.

## IF I ONLY KNEW.
**Tracks:** Supernatural / Good times / Miss your love / If I only knew then / Just a girl in town / Shine your love on me / Giving you all I got / Closer to you / Eternally.
■ LP . . . . . . . . . . . . . . . . . . . ZL 72371
■ MC. . . . . . . . . . . . . . . . . . . ZK 72371
Motown / Jun '85.

## MISS YOUR LOVE.
**Tracks:** Miss your love / I can't wait to make you mine.
■ 12" . . . . . . . . . . . . . . . . . . ZT 40114
■ 7" . . . . . . . . . . . . . . . . . . ZB 40113
Motown / May '85.

## REJOICE.
**Tracks:** Best of my love / Feeling is / Long way to go / Key to my heart / Love's what's happening / How'd I know that love would slip away / Don't ask my neighbours / Blessed / Rejoice.
■ LP . . . . . . . . . . . . . . . . . . CBS 82065
CBS / Nov '77.

## SMILE.
**Tracks:** Smile / Changes.
■ 7" . . . . . . . . . . . . . . . . . . . CBS 6537
CBS / Aug '78.

## SO I CAN LOVE YOU.
**Tracks:** So I can love you / Somebody wants what I got / Going on strike / I found my man / Got to be the man / Best part of a love affair / I like it / My letter / Day dreams / It's not fair / Two lovers.
■ LP . . . . . . . . . . . . . . . . . .SXATS 1030
Stax / Jun '70.

## SO I CAN LOVE YOU/ UNTOUCHED.
**Tracks:** So I can love you / Somebody wants what I got / Going on strike / I found my man / Got to be the man / Best part of a love affair / I like it / My letter / Day dreams / It's not fair / Two lovers / Take me back / Nothing seems impossible / Boss love maker / It's been fun / Love ain't easy onesided / Blind Alley / Show me how / If you think it / Love is the hardest thing to find / Tricks were for kids / Boy, I need you.
CD . . . . . . . . . . . . . . . . . . CDSXD 947
Stax / Oct '89 / Pinnacle.

## SUNBEAM.
**Tracks:** Smile / Love is right on / Time is passing by / Walking the line / Ain't no doubt about it / Love vibes / I wouldn't lie / My everything / Spirit of summer / Whole lot of shakin' / Music box.
■ LP . . . . . . . . . . . . . . . . . . CBS 82864
CBS / Oct '78.

## SUNSHINE.
**Tracks:** Shouting out love / Gee whiz / I really miss you / Ain't no sunshine / Runnin' back / Anyway you look at it / Baby I'm through / Innocent / Put a little love away.
■ LP . . . . . . . . . . . . . . . . . . STX 3003
Stax / Mar '78.

## WHOLE LOT OF SHAKIN'.
**Tracks:** Whole lot of shakin' / Time is passing by.
■ 7" . . . . . . . . . . . . . . . . . . . CBS 6757
CBS / Oct '78.

## Emperors

## KARATE.
**Tracks:** Karate / I've got to have her.
■ 7" . . . . . . . . . . . . . . . . . . . .SS 565
Stateside / Nov '66.

## En Vogue

Premier 'New Jill Swing' quartet, distinguished by vintage (*Hold On* was international smash in 1990), humour, versatility and sheer talent. Band were formed in October '88 by Denzil Foster and Thomas McElroy, formerly of Timex Social Club and Club Nouveau, and producers of Tony Toni Tone's debut. En Vogue share Oakland origins with TTT; reinforcing city's soul pedigree, which stretches from Sly Stone to Digital Underground. Promise of debut *Born To Sing* was more than realised by 1992 follow-up *Funky Divas*; album spawned clutch of hits (including another Top Fiver, *My Lovin'*) and acclaimed tour. Associated projects include Cindy Herron's impressive turn in '92 film *Juice* and collaboration with Salt-N-Pepa on brilliant *Whatta Man* in '93. En Vogue were rumoured to have split in '94 but are, apparently, merely pursuing solo projects.

## BORN TO SING.
**Tracks:** Party / Strange / Lies / Hip hop bugle boy / Hold on / Part of me / You don't have to worry / Time goes on / Just can't stay away / Don't go / Luv lines / Waitin' on you.
CD . . . . . . . . . . . . . . . . . . 7567820842
■ LP . . . . . . . . . . . . . . . . . . 7567820841
MC. . . . . . . . . . . . . . . . . . . 7567820844
Atlantic / Jun '90 / WEA.

## BORN TO SING.
**Tracks:** Not Advised.
VHS . . . . . . . . . . . . . . . . . . UNKNOWN
Warner Music Video / Feb '91 / WEA.

## DON'T GO.
**Tracks:** Don't go / Part me / Hold on (Not available on 7" format.)
■ 12" . . . . . . . . . . . . . . . . . . A 7753T
■ 7" . . . . . . . . . . . . . . . . . . A 7753
■ CD Single . . . . . . . . . . . . . . A 7753CD
■ MC Single. . . . . . . . . . . . . . A 7753C
Atlantic / Jan '91.

## FREE YOUR MIND.
**Tracks:** Free your mind.
■ 12" . . . . . . . . . . . . . . . . . . A 8468T
■ 7" . . . . . . . . . . . . . . . . . . A 8468
■ CD Single . . . . . . . . . . . . . . A 8468CD
■ MC Single. . . . . . . . . . . . . . A 8468C
Atlantic / Oct '92.

## FUNKY DIVAS.
**Tracks:** This is your life / My lovin' / Hip hop lover / Free your mind / Desire / Give him something he can feel / It ain't over till the fat lady sings / Give it up, turn it loose / Yesterday / Hooked on your love / Love don't love you / What is love / Runaway love (On Oct '93 reissues only) / Whatta man (On Oct '93 reissues only).
CD . . . . . . . . . . . . . . . . . . 7567921212
■ LP . . . . . . . . . . . . . . . . . . 7567921211
MC. . . . . . . . . . . . . . . . . . . 7567921214
East West / Apr '92 / WEA.
MiniDisc. . . . . . . . . . . . . .756792121-8
East West / Apr '93 / WEA.
CD . . . . . . . . . . . . . . . . . .756792310-2
LP . . . . . . . . . . . . . . . . . .756792310-1
MC. . . . . . . . . . . . . . . . . .756792310-4
East West / Oct '93 / WEA.

## FUNKY DIVAS.
**Tracks:** You don't have to worry / Don't go / Lies / Hold on / My lovin' / Giving him something he can feel / Free your mind / Give it up, turn it loose.
VHS . . . . . . . . . . . . . . . . . . 8536503933
Warner Music Video / Feb '93 / WEA.

## GIVE IT UP, TURN IT LOOSE.
**Tracks:** Give it up, turn it loose.
■ 12" . . . . . . . . . . . . . . . . . . A 8445T
■ 7" . . . . . . . . . . . . . . . . . . A 8445
■ CD Single . . . . . . . . . . . . . . A 8445CD
■ MC Single. . . . . . . . . . . . . . A 8445C
East West / Dec '92.

## GIVING HIM SOMETHING HE CAN FEEL.
**Tracks:** Giving him something he can feel / Hold on / My lovin' (Only on 12" and CD single) / You don't have to worry (Only on CD and 12" single).
■ 12" . . . . . . . . . . . . . . . . . . A 8524 T
■ 7" . . . . . . . . . . . . . . . . . . A 8524
■ CD Single . . . . . . . . . . . . . . A 8524 CD
■ MC Single. . . . . . . . . . . . . . A 8524 C
East West / Jul '92.

## HOLD ON.
**Tracks:** Hold on.
■ 12" . . . . . . . . . . . . . . . . . .A 7908 TX
■ 7" . . . . . . . . . . . . . . . . . . 086 234
■ 7" . . . . . . . . . . . . . . . . . . A 7908
■ MC Single. . . . . . . . . . . . . . A 7908 C
■ 12" . . . . . . . . . . . . . . . . . . A 7908 T
■ CD Single . . . . . . . . . . . . . . A 7908 CD
Atlantic / Apr '90.

## LA VIE.
**Tracks:** Not Advised.
VHS . . . . . . . . . . . . . . . . . . IVA 060
Island Visual Arts / Dec '90 / PolyGram / THE.

## LIES.
**Tracks:** Lies.
■ 7" . . . . . . . . . . . . . . . . . . .A 7893
■ CD Single . . . . . . . . . . . . . . A 7893CD
■ MC Single. . . . . . . . . . . . . . A 7893C
■ 12" . . . . . . . . . . . . . . . . . . A 7893T
WEA / Jul '90.

## LOVE DON'T LOVE YOU.
**Tracks:** Love don't love you.
■ 12" . . . . . . . . . . . . . . . . . . A 8424T
■ 7" . . . . . . . . . . . . . . . . . . .A 8424
■ CD Single . . . . . . . . . . . . . . A 8424CD
■ MC Single. . . . . . . . . . . . . . A 8424C
East West / Apr '93.

## MY LOVIN'.
**Tracks:** My lovin'.
■ 12" . . . . . . . . . . . . . . . . . . A 8578T
■ 7" . . . . . . . . . . . . . . . . . . .A 8578
■ CD Single . . . . . . . . . . . . . . A 8578CD
■ MC Single. . . . . . . . . . . . . . A 8578C
East West / Mar '92.

## RUNAWAY LOVE.
**Tracks:** Runaway love / Runaway love (Mixes) / What is love (Available on CDS & 12" only.) / Hip hop lover (Available on 12" only.) / Desire (Available on CDS only.).
■ 12" . . . . . . . . . . . . . . . . . . AB 359T
■ 7" . . . . . . . . . . . . . . . . . . AB 359
■ CD Single . . . . . . . . . . . . . . AB 359CD
■ MC Single. . . . . . . . . . . . . . AB 359C
East West / Oct '93.

## SILENT NITE (Happy holiday mix).
**Tracks:** Silent nite (happy holiday mix).
■ 12" . . . . . . . . . . . . . . . . . . A8644 T
Atlantic / Dec '91.

## YOU DON'T HAVE TO WORRY.
**Tracks:** You don't have to worry / Luv lines.
■ 12" . . . . . . . . . . . . . . . . . . A 7812T
■ 7" . . . . . . . . . . . . . . . . . . .A 7812
■ CD Single . . . . . . . . . . . . . . A 7812CD
■ MC Single. . . . . . . . . . . . . . A 7812C
East West / Sep '90.

## Enchanters

## WE GOT LOVE.
**Tracks:** We got love / I've lost all communications.
■ 7" . . . . . . . . . . . . . . . . . . .WB 2054
WEA / Jan '66.

## Enchantment

## ANYWAY YOU WANT IT.
**Tracks:** Anyway you want it / Oasis of love.
■ 7" . . . . . . . . . . . . . . . . . . . PB 1481
RCA / May '79.

## DANCE TO THE MUSIC.
**Tracks:** Dance to the music / Gloria.
■ 7" . . . . . . . . . . . . . . . . . . UP 36204
United Artists / Feb '77.

## FEEL LIKE DANCING.
**Tracks:** Feel like dancing.
■ 7" . . . . . . . . . . . . . . . . . . MHS 104
■ 12" . . . . . . . . . . . . . . . . . .MHST 104
Prelude / Apr '85.

## JOURNEY TO THE LAND OF ENCHANTMENT.
**Tracks:** Future gonna get you / Magnetic feel / Anyway you want it / Love melodies / Oasis of love / I wanna boogie / Fun / Let me entertain you / Forever more / Where do we go from here / Journey.
■ LP . . . . . . . . . . . . . . . . . . FL 13269
RCA / '79.

## SETTIN' IT OUT.
**Tracks:** Settin' it out / Are you ready for love.
■ 12" . . . . . . . . . . . . . . . . . . RCAT 32
■ 7" . . . . . . . . . . . . . . . . . . RCA 32
RCA / Jan '81.

## English, Barbara Jean

## BETTER IF YOU DON'T GET TO KNOW ME.
**Tracks:** Better if you don't get to know me.
■ 12" . . . . . . . . . . . . . . . BLUE CHIP 17 T
■ 7" . . . . . . . . . . . . . . . BLUE CHIP 17
Blue Chip / May '89.

■ DELETED

### EXPERIENCE.
Tracks: Not Advised.
CD . . . . . . . . . . . . . . . . . . . . BLUEBJCD 1
Blue Chip / Apr '89 / Backs Distribution.
■ LP . . . . . . . . . . . . . . . . . . . BLUEBJLP 1
Blue Chip / Mar '89.

### EXPERIENCE.
Tracks: Experience.
■ 12" . . . . . . . . . . . . . . . . . . . . . BLUEC 21
Blue Chip / Aug '89.

### I'M LIVING A LIE.
Tracks: I'm living a lie / Key in the mailbox.
■ 7" . . . . . . . . . . . . . . . . . . . . . . CS 2062
Contempo (1) / Jul '75.

## Equals

### 20 GREATEST HITS: EQUALS.
Tracks: Not Advised.
■ LP . . . . . . . . . . . . . . . . . . . . . . 20050
MC. . . . . . . . . . . . . . . . . . . . . . . 40050
Astan / Nov '84.

### 20 GREATEST HITS: EQUALS (2).
Tracks: Baby come back / Black skinned blue eyed boys / Police on my back / Viva Bobby Joe / Good times / Butterfly red white and blue / Give love a try / You've got too many boyfriends / Michael and the slipper tree / Hold me closer / I get so excited / Softly softly / Soul groovin' / Happy Birthday girl / I won't be there / Rub a dub / Giddy up.
CD . . . . . . . . . . . . . . . . . . . 266 201 2
LP . . . . . . . . . . . . . . . . . . . . 226 201 5
MC. . . . . . . . . . . . . . . . . . . . 216 201 5
Mainline (2) / Jan '90.

### 6 TRACK HITS.
Tracks: Baby come back / Softly softly / Viva Bobby Joe / I won't be there / Black skinned blue eyed boys / Michael and his slipper tree.
■ EP . . . . . . . . . . . . . . . . . . . . . 7SR 5007
MC. . . . . . . . . . . . . . . . . . . . . . 7SC 5007
Scoop 33 / Sep '83.

### ALL THE HITS PLUS MORE.
Tracks: Not Advised.
■ LP . . . . . . . . . . . . . . . . . . . . . PRST 001
Prestige / Mar '90.
CD. . . . . . . . . . . . . . . . . . . . . . CDPT 001
MC. . . . . . . . . . . . . . . . . . . . . ZPRST 001
Prestige / Jun '92 / Total / BMG.

### BABY COME BACK.
Tracks: Not Advised.
■ LP . . . . . . . . . . . . . . . . . . . . . . PLP 27
MC. . . . . . . . . . . . . . . . . . . . . . . PMC 27
Platinum (W.Germany) / Oct '85.

### BABY COME BACK.
Tracks: Baby come back / Hold me closer.
■ 7" . . . . . . . . . . . . . . . . . . . . . LIG 9021
Lightning / '79.

### BABY COME BACK.
Tracks: Baby come back.
■ 7" . . . . . . . . . . . . . . . . . . . . . . PT 135
President / May '68.

### BABY COME BACK (OLD GOLD).
Tracks: Baby come back / Hold me closer.
■ 7" . . . . . . . . . . . . . . . . . . . . . OG 9021
Old Gold / Jul '82.

### BEAUTIFUL CLOWN.
Tracks: Beautiful clown / Daily love.
■ 7" . . . . . . . . . . . . . . . . . . . . . . PT 464
President / Jun '77.

### BEST OF THE EQUALS.
Tracks: Baby come back / Giddy up a ding dong / Soul groovin' / Give love a try / I get so excited / You got too many boyfriends / I won't be there / Laurel and Hardy / Police on my back / Good times are gone forever / Butterfly red white and blue / Hold me closer.
■ LP . . . . . . . . . . . . . . . . . . . . . JOYS 137
Joy / '73.
■ LP . . . . . . . . . . . . . . . . . . . . . . 20048
MC. . . . . . . . . . . . . . . . . . . . . . . 40048
Astan / Nov '84.

### BLACK SKINNED BLUE-EYED BOYS.
Tracks: Black skinned blue eyed boys.
■ 7" . . . . . . . . . . . . . . . . . . . . . . PT 325
President / Dec '70.

### BLACK SKINNED BLUE-EYED BOYS (OLD GOLD).
Tracks: Black skinned blue eyed boys.
■ 7" . . . . . . . . . . . . . . . . . . . . . OG 9033
Old Gold / Jul '82.

### DOIN THE 45S.
Tracks: Baby come back / Gigolo Sam / Rub-a-dub-dub / Soul brother Clifford / Blue skinned blue eyed boys / Viva Bobby Joe / Michael and his slipper tree / I can see but you don't know / Happy birthday girl / Softly softly.
■ LP . . . . . . . . . . . . . . . . . . . . RHAS 9017
Rhapsody / '74.
■ LP . . . . . . . . . . . . . . . . . . . . . . 20047
MC. . . . . . . . . . . . . . . . . . . . . . . 40047
Astan / Nov '84.

### EQUALS EXPLOSION.
Tracks: Not Advised.
■ LP . . . . . . . . . . . . . . . . . . . . . PTLS 1015
President / Nov '68.

### FIRST AMONG EQUALS.
Tracks: Baby come back / Michael and his slipper tree / Black skinned blue eyed boy / I get so excited / Viva Bobby Joe / Laurel and Hardy / Hold me closer / Soul brother Clifford / I won't be there / I'm a poor man / Softly softly / Teardrops / Rub a dub dub / Police on my back / I can see, but you don't know / Butterfly red white & blue / Cinderella / Christine / No love could be sweeter / I'm gonna dance all night / Diversion / Honey gum / Leaving you is hard to do / Ain't got knowthing to give to you / You'd better tell her / Put some rock & roll in your soul / Look what you've done to my daughter / Sould groovin / Good times are gone forever / You lied just to save your name / My life aint easy / Fire / Ding dong / You got too many boyfriends / Green light / Reincarnation / Let's go to the moon / Hey baby it's time you got going.
CD Set . . . . . . . . . . . . . . . . . 94190-2
MC Set . . . . . . . . . . . . . . . . . 94190-4
Ice / Sep '94 / Pinnacle.

### FUNKY LIKE A TRAIN.
Tracks: Funky like a train / Born ya / Funky like a train (extended version).
■ 12" . . . . . . . . . . . . . . . . . . . JABX 58
■ 7" . . . . . . . . . . . . . . . . . . . . JAB 58
Club / Sep '87.

### GREATEST HITS: EQUALS.
Tracks: Not Advised.
■ MC . . . . . . . . . . . . . . . . . . . DSK 122
Design / Feb '88.

### I GET SO EXCITED.
Tracks: I get so excited.
■ 7" . . . . . . . . . . . . . . . . . . . . . . PT 180
President / Feb '68.

### LAUREL AND HARDY.
Tracks: Laurel and Hardy.
■ 7" . . . . . . . . . . . . . . . . . . . . . . PT 200
President / Aug '68.

### MICHAEL AND THE SLIPPER TREE.
Tracks: Michael and the slipper tree.
■ 7" . . . . . . . . . . . . . . . . . . . . . . PT 240
President / Apr '69.

### NO PLACE TO GO.
Tracks: No place to go.
■ 12" . . . . . . . . . . . . . . . . . . . 12MOG 1
■ 7" . . . . . . . . . . . . . . . . . . . . MOG 1
Moggie / Jul '83.

### PROFILE: EQUALS.
Tracks: Baby come back / Giddy up a ding dong / Viva Bobby Joe / I get so excited / Police on my back / I won't be there / Hold me closer / Michael and his slipper tree / Soul brother Clifford / Another sad and lonely night / My life ain't easy.
■ LP . . . . . . . . . . . . . . . . . . . . 6.24605
MC. . . . . . . . . . . . . . . . . . . . CL4 24605
Teldec (1) / Mar '83 / Pinnacle / C.M. Distribution / Swift.

### RED DOG.
Tracks: Red dog / Something beautiful.
■ 7" . . . . . . . . . . . . . . . . . . . . . . GUY 5
Ice / Feb '78.

### RUB-A DUB-DUB.
Tracks: Rub-a dub-dub.
■ 7" . . . . . . . . . . . . . . . . . . . . . . PT 275
President / Dec '69.

### SOFTLY SOFTLY.
Tracks: Softly softly.
■ 7" . . . . . . . . . . . . . . . . . . . . . . PT 222
President / Nov '68.

### ULTIMATE HIT COLLECTION, THE.
Tracks: Not Advised.
CD . . . . . . . . . . . . . . . . . . . REP 4214-WZ
Repertoire (Germany) / Aug '91 / Pinnacle.

### UNEQUALLED EQUALS.
Tracks: Not Advised.
■ LP . . . . . . . . . . . . . . . . . . . . . PTL 1006
President / Nov '67.

### VERY BEST OF THE EQUALS, THE.
Tracks: Baby come back / Hold me closer / Viva Bobby Joe / Laurel & Hardy / Another sad & lonely night / Rub a dub dub / Softly softly / Soul brother Clifford / I get so excited / Teardrops / You'd better tell her / I can see, but you don't know / Black skinned blue eyed boy / I won't there / I'm a poor man / Michael & his slipper tree / Cinderella / Christine / Friday night / Honey gum / No love can be sweeter / Ain't got nothing to give you / Leaving you is hard to do / Put some rock'n'roll in your soul / Diversion.
CD . . . . . . . . . . . . . . . . . . . SEECD 374
See For Miles / Jul '93 / Pinnacle.

### VIVA BOBBY JOE.
Tracks: Viva Bobby Joe.
■ 7" . . . . . . . . . . . . . . . . . . . . . . PT 260
President / Jul '69.

### VIVA BOBBY JOE (OLD GOLD).
Tracks: Viva Bobby Joe / I can't let you go.
■ 7" . . . . . . . . . . . . . . . . . . . . . OG 9025
Old Gold / Jul '82.

## Eruption

### ERUPTION.
Tracks: I can't stand the rain / Movin' / I'll take you there / Computer love / Way we were / Do you know what it feels like / Be yourself / I can't carry on / Wayward love / Party party.
■ LP . . . . . . . . . . . . . . . . . . . . . K 50454
Atlantic / Apr '78.

### I CAN'T STAND THE RAIN.
Tracks: I can't stand the rain / Be yourself.
■ 7" . . . . . . . . . . . . . . . . . . . . . K 11068
Atlantic / Feb '78.

### JOY TO THE WORLD.
Tracks: Joy to the world / Time.
■ 7" . . . . . . . . . . . . . . . . . . . . . RBUS 75
Red Bus / Dec '82.

### LEAVE A LIGHT.
Tracks: Leave a light / Sweet side / Up and away / Left me in the rain / Valley of the dolls / One way ticket / Hey there lonely girl / No good searchin' / Fire is gone / I can't stand the rain.
■ LP . . . . . . . . . . . . . . . . . . . . . K 50632
Atlantic / '79.

### LEAVE A LIGHT.
Tracks: Leave a light / Give me a little piece of your sweet side.
■ 7" . . . . . . . . . . . . . . . . . . . . . K 11213
Atlantic / Jan '79.

### LET ME TAKE YOU BACK IN TIME.
Tracks: Let me take you back in time / Funky lover.
■ 7" . . . . . . . . . . . . . . . . . . . . RCA 2581
RCA / '79.

### LOVE IS A FEELIN'.
Tracks: Love is a feelin' / Let me take you back in time / Funky lover.
■ 12" . . . . . . . . . . . . . . . . . . . . PE 5080
RCA / '79.

### ONE WAY TICKET.
Tracks: One way ticket / Left me in the rain.
■ 7" . . . . . . . . . . . . . . . . . . . . . K 11266
Atlantic / Apr '79.

## Escoffreys

### LOOK WHO'S LOVING ME.
Tracks: Look who's loving me.
■ 12" . . . . . . . . . . . . . . . . . . . . A 5928T
East West / Dec '91.

## Escovedo, Pete

### MISTER E.
Tracks: Whatcha gonna do / Tassajara / Un poquito / Let's wait awhile / Gingerbread girl / Caribe / Take some time / Dr. Macumba / Mister E / Dawn - the beginning.
CD. . . . . . . . . . . . . . . . . . . . . CCD 45005
■ LP . . . . . . . . . . . . . . . . . . . . . CR 5005
MC. . . . . . . . . . . . . . . . . . . . . . CRC 5005
Crossover / May '88.

## YESTERDAY'S MEMORIES - TOMORROW'S DREAMS.
Tracks: Charanga sunrise / Moving pictures / Azteca Mozambique / Ah ah / Cueros / Modern dance / Zina's Zamba / Yesterday's memories, tomorrow's dreams / Revolt.

| | |
|---|---|
| CD | CCD 45002 |
| ■ LP | CR 5002 |
| MC | CRC 5002 |

Concord Jazz / Jul '87 / New Note.

## Esquires

### AND GET AWAY.
Tracks: And get away.

| | |
|---|---|
| ■ 7" | SS 2077 |

Stateside / '67.

### GET ON UP.
Tracks: Get on up.

| | |
|---|---|
| ■ 7" | SS 2048 |

Stateside / '67.

## Essex

### EASIER SAID THAN DONE.
Tracks: Easier said than done.

| | |
|---|---|
| ■ 7" | DB 7077 |

Columbia / Aug '63.

## Eternal

### ALWAYS AND FOREVER.
Tracks: Stay / Crazy / Save our love / Oh baby, I.. / I'll be there / Sweet funky thing / Never gonna give you up / Just a step from heaven / Let's stay together / This love's for real / So good / If you need me tonight / Don't say goodbye / Amazing grace.

| | |
|---|---|
| CD | CDEMD 1053 |
| LP | EMD 1053 |
| MC | TCEMD 1053 |

EMI / Nov '93 / EMI.

### JUST A STEP FROM HEAVEN.
Tracks: Just a step from heaven (Mixes) / Stay (Features on CDS and MCS only.) / I've got to be with you (Features on CDS and MCS only.).

| | |
|---|---|
| ■ 12" | 12 EM 311 |
| ■ CD Single | CDEM 311 |
| ■ 7" | EM 311 |
| ■ MC Single | TCEM 311 |

EMI / Apr '94.

### MIND ODYSSEY.
Tracks: Mind odyssey.

| | |
|---|---|
| ■ 12" | WAP 27 |
| ■ CD Single | WAP 27CD |
| ■ MC Single | WAP 27MC |

Warp / Dec '92.

### OH BABY, I.
Tracks: Oh Baby, I (mixes) / Sweet funky thing / Decisions (Features on CD only.).

| | |
|---|---|
| 12" | 12 EM 353 |
| 7" | EM 353 |
| CD Single | CDEM 353 |
| MC Single | TCEM 353 |

EMI / Oct '94 / EMI.

### SAVE OUR LOVE.
Tracks: Save our love / If you need me (Not on 12") / Hey baby (On 7" & cassette only) / Save our love (mixes) (On CD & 12" only).

| | |
|---|---|
| ■ 12" | 12EM 296 |
| ■ 7" | EM 296 |
| ■ CD Single | CDEM 296 |
| ■ MC Single | TCEM 296 |

EMI / Jan '94.

### SO GOOD.
Tracks: So good (mixes) / Ain't no how I'm steppin'/ Loving you (On 2nd CD only).

| | |
|---|---|
| 7" | EM 339 |
| CD Single | CDEM 339 |
| CD Single | CDEMS 339 |
| MC Single | TCEM 339 |

EMI / Aug '94 / EMI.

### STAY.
Tracks: Stay / Stay (mixes).

| | |
|---|---|
| ■ 12" | 12 EM 283 |
| ■ 7" | EM 283 |
| ■ CD Single | CDEM 283 |
| ■ MC Single | TCEM 283 |

EMI / Sep '93.

## Etoria, Tony

### I CAN PROVE IT.
Tracks: I can prove it / Angel for lovers to be.

| | |
|---|---|
| ■ 7" | GT 89 |

GTO / Jun '77.

### SO FAR SO GOOD.
Tracks: So far, so good / Move it out.

| | |
|---|---|
| ■ 7" | COB 6 |

Cobra / Jan '80.

## Evans, Margie

### ANOTHER BLUES DAY.
Tracks: Not Advised.

| | |
|---|---|
| ■ LP | LR 42.060 |

L&R / Dec '88.

### MISTREATED WOMAN.
Tracks: Not Advised.

| | |
|---|---|
| ■ LP | LR 42.050 |

L&R.

## Evans, Richard

### DO RE MI FOR SOUL.
Tracks: Do re mi for soul / Burning spear.

| | |
|---|---|
| ■ 7" | AMS 7438 |

A&M / Jun '79.

## Everett, Betty

Born in Mississippi, Everett moved to Chicago and came to public attention in 1963 with *You're No Good*. Song was returned to chart by Swinging Blue Jeans and became U.S. No. 1 for Linda Ronstadt in 1975; same year that Linda Lewis scored U.K. No 6 with Everett's '64 biggie *It's In His Kiss (The Shoop Shoop Song)* (hit again in '91, for Cher). Everett also scored with two other '64 singles: *Getting Mighty Crowded* and *Let It Be Me*; latter a duet with Jerry Butler. Further R&B hits ensued, but she did not return to pop chart until '69, with *There'll Come A Time*. After couple of well-received albums on Fantasy in early '70s, she gradually faded from view.

### 1957 - 1961 (Everett, Betty & Lillian Offitt).
Tracks: Tell me darling / I'll weep no more / Killer diller / My life depends on you / My love / Ain't gonna cry / Oh mama / Will my man be home tonight / Man don't work / My man is a lover / Troubles / Shine on.

| | |
|---|---|
| ■ LP | FLY 589 |

Flyright / Oct '86.

### DELICIOUS TOGETHER (Everett, Betty & Jerry Butler).
Tracks: Let it be me / Love is strange / Just be true / Since I don't have you / It's alright / Our day will come / Ain't that lovin' you baby / I can't stand it / Way you do things you do / Let the good times roll / Fever.

| | |
|---|---|
| ■ LP | JOY 123 |

Joy / Oct '68.

### GETTING MIGHTY CROWDED.
Tracks: Getting mighty crowded / Shoop shoop song.

| | |
|---|---|
| ■ 7" | TF 520 |

Fontana / Jan '65.

| | |
|---|---|
| ■ 7" | CTD 104 |

Charly / Jul '80.

### I CAN'T HEAR YOU.
Tracks: I can't hear you no more.

| | |
|---|---|
| ■ 7" | SS 321 |

Stateside / '64.

### I GOT TO TELL SOMEBODY.
Tracks: I got to tell somebody / Why are you leaving you.

| | |
|---|---|
| ■ 7" | LBF 15428 |

Liberty / Jan '71.

### IT'S IN HIS KISS.
Tracks: Not Advised.

| | |
|---|---|
| ■ LP | JOY 106 |

Joy / Aug '68.

### IT'S IN HIS KISS (SHOOP SHOOP SONG).
Tracks: It's in his kiss (shoop shoop song).

| | |
|---|---|
| ■ 7" | SS 280 |

Stateside / '63.

### IT'S IN HIS KISS (SHOOP SHOOP SONG).
Tracks: It's in his kiss.

| | |
|---|---|
| ■ 7" | PT 215 |

President / Oct '68.

### JERRY AND BETTY (Everett, Betty & Jerry Butler).
Tracks: Not Advised.

| | |
|---|---|
| ■ LP | CRM 2022 |

Charly / Nov '81.

### LOVE RHYMES/HAPPY ENDINGS.
Tracks: Sweet Dan / I gotta tell somebody / I wanna be there / Be anything (but mine) / Wondering / Who will your next fool be / I'm your friend / Just a matter of time / I'm afraid of losing you / La-la-la / Try it you'll like it / Here's the gift / God only knows / Things I say to his shoulder / Bedroom eyes / Keep it up / Just a little piece of you / Don't let it end ('til you let it begin) / As far as we can go / Happy endings.

| | |
|---|---|
| CD | CDSEWD 085 |

South Bound / Jul '93 / Pinnacle.

### REAL THING, THE.
Tracks: Real thing (Original Vee Jay recording. Composers: Valerie Simpson, Nicholas Ashford) / Shoe won't fit (Composers: Valerie Simpson, Nicholas Ashford, Josie Armstead.) / It's in his kiss (Composer: Rudy Clarke.) / Way you do the things you do (With Jerry Butler. Composers: Bobby Rogers, William 'Smokey' Robinson.) / You're no good / Chained to your love / Hands off / It hurts to be in love / Hound dog / Until you were done / I need you so / I can't hear you no more / Let it be me / Love is strange / I can't stand it / Just be true / Getting mighty crowded / Chained to a memory / I'm gonna be ready / No place to hide / Too hot to hold / Trouble over the weekend.

| | |
|---|---|
| ■ CD | CDCHARLY 56 |

Charly / Jan '87.

### THERE'LL COME A TIME.
Tracks: You're falling in love / Better tomorrow than today / Maybe / 1900 yesterday / Sugar I need a change / I can't say no to you / Hold on / There'll come a time / Take me / Is there a chance for me / Same old me.

| | |
|---|---|
| ■ LP | SAK 101 |

Soul Bag / Jul '69.

### TRUE LOVE.
Tracks: True love / You can do it.

| | |
|---|---|
| ■ 7" | UP 36400 |

United Artists / May '78.

### YOU'RE NO GOOD.
Tracks: You're no good.

| | |
|---|---|
| ■ 7" | SS 259 |

Stateside / '63.

## Everis

### I LIKE THE WAY.
Tracks: I like the way.

| | |
|---|---|
| ■ 12" | 12 JUJA 1 |

Juice Jams / Jul '93.

### SUMMERTIME.
Tracks: Summertime.

| | |
|---|---|
| ■ 7" | SOUL 014 |

Soultown / Aug '91.

## Everyday People

### HEADLINE NEWS.
Tracks: Headline news (Not on 12".) / Keep away from love / Headline news (12" version) (12" & CD single only.) / Headline news (Accapella) (12" only.) / Headline news (dub) (CD single only.).

| | |
|---|---|
| ■ 7" | SBK 5 |
| ■ 12" | 12SBK 5 |
| ■ CD Single | CDSBK 5 |
| ■ MC Single | TCSBK 5 |

SBK / Mar '90.

### I GUESS IT DOESN'T MATTER.
Tracks: I guess it doesn't matter (Not on 12".) / Inside your love.

| | |
|---|---|
| ■ 12" Remix | 12SBKX 8 |
| ■ 12" | 12SBK 8 |
| ■ CD Single | CDSBK 8 |

SBK / Jun '90.

| | |
|---|---|
| ■ 7" | SBK 8 |
| ■ MC Single | TCSBK 8 |

SBK / May '90.

### THIS KIND OF WOMAN.
Tracks: This kind of woman (Not on CD single.) / All I see / This kind of woman (edit) (CD single only.) / This kind of woman (album version) (CD single only.) / I guess it doesn't matter (CD single only.).

■ DELETED

■ 7″ . . . . . . . . . . . . . . . . . . . . SBK 14
■ MC Single. . . . . . . . . . . . . . .TCSBK 14
■ 12″. . . . . . . . . . . . . . . . . . 12SBK 14
■ CD Single. . . . . . . . . . . . . . .CDSBK 14
SBK / Sep '90.

## YOU WASH, I'LL DRY.
**Tracks:** Make him wait / Headline news / I guess it doesn't matter / More than a friend / Good as gold / This kind of woman / Second nature / Place in the sun / I've been there / All I see / Let somebody love you.
■ CD. . . . . . . . . . . . . . . . . . . . SBKCD 4
■ LP. . . . . . . . . . . . . . . . . . . . SBKLP 4
■ MC. . . . . . . . . . . . . . . . . . . . SBKTC 4
SBK / Jun '90 / EMI.

## Exciters

## BLOWING UP MY MIND.
**Tracks:** Blowing up my mind.
■ 7″ . . . . . . . . . . . . . . . . . . . . CS 2033
Contempo (1) / Jan '76.

## LITTLE BIT OF SOAP, A.
**Tracks:** Little bit of soap / I'm gonna get him someday.
■ 7″ . . . . . . . . . . . . . . . . . . HLZ 10018
London-American / Jan '66.

## REACHING FOR THE BEST.
**Tracks:** Reaching for the best.
■ 7″ . . . . . . . . . . . . . . . . . . . BTC 1005
20th Century / Oct '75.

## TELL HIM.
**Tracks:** Tell him / Hard way to go / Drama of love / I dreamed / It's love that really counts / Are you keeping score / Say it with love / He's got the power / Remember me / So long, goodnight / Handful of memories / Get him / It's so exciting / If love came your way / Do wah diddy / We were lovers / Having my fun / All grown up / Tell him (unedited version) / He's got the power (unedited version).
■ CD. . . . . . . . . . . . . . . . . . . . CZ 433
EMI / Jun '91.

## TELL HIM.
**Tracks:** Tell him.
■ 7″ . . . . . . . . . . . . . . . . . . . . UP 1011
United Artists / Feb '63.

## YOU BETTER COME HOME.
**Tracks:** You better come home / Weddings make me cry.
■ 7″ . . . . . . . . . . . . . . . . . . HLZ 10038
London / Mar '66.

## Executive Suite

## WHEN THE FUEL RUNS OUT.
**Tracks:** When the fuel runs out.
■ 7″ . . . . . . . . . . . . . . . . . . . 2001597
Polydor / Aug '75.

# F

## Fair, Yvonne

Fair's most notable success was 1976 U.K. No. 5 *It Should've Been Me* - a raucous rendition produced by Motown's Norman Whitfield. Previously she had sung in the Chantels before spells in James Brown's revue and Chuck Jackson's band. Unfortunately, solo success came too late as she had already left the Motown organisation after her 1975 album *The Bitch Is Black*.

### FUNKY MUSIC SHO NUFF TURNS ME ON.
**Tracks:** Funky music sho nuff turns me on / Let your hair down.
■ 7" . . . . . . . . . . . . . . . . . . . . . . TMG 913
Tamla Motown / Aug '74.

### IT SHOULD HAVE BEEN ME.
**Tracks:** It should have been me.
■ 7" . . . . . . . . . . . . . . . . . . . . . TMG 1013
Tamla Motown / Nov '75.

### IT'S BAD FOR ME TO SEE YOU.
**Tracks:** It's bad for me to see you / Walk out the door if you wanna.
■ 7" . . . . . . . . . . . . . . . . . . . . . TMG 1025
Tamla Motown / May '76.

## Faith, Hope & Charity

### BATTLE OF THE SEXES.
**Tracks:** Battle of the sexes.
■ 12" . . . . . . . . . . . . . . . . . . . . . YZ 480T
■ 7" . . . . . . . . . . . . . . . . . . . . . . . YZ 480
■ CD Single . . . . . . . . . . . . . . . . . YZ 480 CD
East West / Jun '90.

### GROWING PAINS.
**Tracks:** Growing pains.
■ 12" . . . . . . . . . . . . . . . . . . . . . . YZ 523 T
■ 7" . . . . . . . . . . . . . . . . . . . . . . . YZ 523
■ CD Single . . . . . . . . . . . . . . . . . YZ 523 CD
■ MC Single . . . . . . . . . . . . . . . . . YZ 523 MC
East West / Sep '90.

### JUST ONE LOOK.
**Tracks:** Just one look / Disco Dan.
■ 7" . . . . . . . . . . . . . . . . . . . . . . RCA 2632
RCA / Jan '76.

### LIFE GOES ON.
**Tracks:** Life goes on / You gotta tell her.
■ 7" . . . . . . . . . . . . . . . . . . . . . . PB 0865
RCA / Mar '77.

### TO EACH HIS OWN.
**Tracks:** To each his own / Find a way.
■ 7" . . . . . . . . . . . . . . . . . . . . . . RCA 2599
RCA / Aug '75.

## Falcons

### FALCONS' STORY, PART 3.
**Tracks:** Not Advised.
■ LP . . . . . . . . . . . . . . . . . . . . . RELIC 8010
Relic (USA) / Sep '87.

### I FOUND A LOVE.
**Tracks:** Not Advised.
■ LP . . . . . . . . . . . . . . . . . . . . . RELIC 8006
Relic (USA) / '85.

### YOU'RE SO FINE.
**Tracks:** Not Advised.
■ LP . . . . . . . . . . . . . . . . . . . . . RELIC 8005
Relic (USA) / '85.

## Family

### FAMILY, THE.
**Tracks:** High fashion / Mutiny / Screams of passion / Yes / Rivers run dry / Nothing compares 2 U / Susannah's clothes / Desire.
■ LP . . . . . . . . . . . . . . . . . . . . . .925322 1
WEA / Aug '85.

## Family Brown

### I'M GONNA GETCHA.
**Tracks:** I'm gonna getcha.
■ 12" . . . . . . . . . . . . . . . . . . . . . . . VIBE 4T
Buzz Int. / Apr '84.

## Fantasia

### EVERGREEN.
**Tracks:** Evergreen / Evergreen (version).
■ 12" . . . . . . . . . . . . . . . . . . . . PASH 16(12)
Passion (1) / Jan '84.

### GO BACK TO THE START.
**Tracks:** Go back to the start.
■ 12" . . . . . . . . . . . . . . . . . . . .CHS 123343
■ 7" . . . . . . . . . . . . . . . . . . . . . CHS 3343
Chrysalis / Jun '89.

### GOTTA GET AWAY.
**Tracks:** Gotta get away / She needs my love.
7" . . . . . . . . . . . . . . . . . . . . . . . SS 2031
Stateside / Jun '67 / EMI.

### TONIGHT'S THE PARTY.
**Tracks:** Tonight's the party / Emily's party.
■ 12" . . . . . . . . . . . . . . . . . . . .CHS 123300
■ 7" . . . . . . . . . . . . . . . . . . . . . CHS 3300
Chrysalis / Oct '88.

## Fantastic Four

From '60s soulsters to '70s funkateers to '80s obscurities: does this sound familiar? Fantastic Four were Detroit vocal quartet who recorded series of singles for Ric-Tic label (later bought out by Motown) in late '60s; finding second wind decade later in heyday of dance. They advised *Bring Your Own Funk* but thoughtfully came armed with two LPs on Westbound (home of Funkadelic). Other hits were *Got to Have Your Love* and *Sexy Lady*, demonstrating quantum lyrical leap from '60s singles *I've Got To Have You* and *Goddess of Love*.

### ALVIN STONE (BIRTH AND DEATH OF A GANGSTER)/NIGHT PEOPLE.
**Tracks:** Alvin Stone (birth and death of a gangster) / Have a little mercy / This moment last forever / Words / My love won't stop at nothing / Medley: Night people / Lies divided by jive / If I lose my job / Hideaway / By the river under the tree / Don't risk your happiness on foolishness / They took the show on the road.
CD . . . . . . . . . . . . . . . . . . . . . CDSEWD 057
Westbound / Jan '93 / Pinnacle.

### B.Y.O.F. (BRING YOUR OWN FUNK).
**Tracks:** B.Y.O.F. (Bring your own funk) / Sexy lady.
■ 7" . . . . . . . . . . . . . . . . . . . . . . . LV 14
Atlantic / Feb '79.

### BACK IN CIRCULATION.
**Tracks:** Not Advised.
■ CD . . . . . . . . . . . . . . . . . . . MOTCCD 76
Motor City / Oct '92.

### FANTASTIC FOUR.
**Tracks:** I love you madly / Whole world is a stage / You gave me something / I've got to have you / Share your love with me / Goddess of love / Can't stop looking for my baby / As long as I live / Man in love / Romeo and Juliet / I don't wanna live without you / Just the lonely.
■ LP . . . . . . . . . . . . . . . . . . . . .STML 11105
Tamla Motown / Jul '69.

### GOT TO HAVE YOUR LOVE.
**Tracks:** She'll be right for me / Mixed up moods and attitudes / There's no fire down below / Ain't been good to you / Cash money / I got to have all the love you got.
■ LP . . . . . . . . . . . . . . . . . . . . . . K 50415
Atlantic.
CD . . . . . . . . . . . . . . . . . . . .CDSEWD 92
Ace / Jun '94 / Pinnacle / Complete Record Co. Ltd.

## Fantastics

### BABY, MAKE YOUR OWN SWEET MUSIC.
**Tracks:** Baby, make your own sweet music / Who could be lovin' you.
■ 7" . . . . . . . . . . . . . . . . . . . . . .2027 004
Mojo / Jul '71.

### FOR OLD TIME'S SAKE.
**Tracks:** For old time's sake / Exodus main theme.
■ 7" . . . . . . . . . . . . . . . . . . . . . . DM 334
Deram / Jun '71.

### IS THERE A DOCTOR IN THE HOUSE?.
**Tracks:** Is there a doctor in the house / Tear down Saturday night.
■ 7" . . . . . . . . . . . . . . . . . . . . BELL 1402
Bell / Feb '75.

### SOMETHING OLD SOMETHING NEW.
**Tracks:** Something old something new / High and dry.
■ 7" . . . . . . . . . . . . . . . . . . . . BLL 1141
Bell / Feb '71.

### SOMETHING OLD, SOMETHING NEW.
**Tracks:** Something old, something new / I fell in love last night at the disco / What I did for love / All in love is fair.
■ 7" . . . . . . . . . . . . . . . . . . . . BELL 1141
Bell / Mar '71.
■ EP . . . . . . . . . . . . . . . . . . . . . BANG 2
Stagecoach / Jan '83.

### SOMETHING OLD, SOMETHING NEW (CREOLE (REPLAY)).
**Tracks:** Something old, something new / You always hurt the one you love / Jesamine.
■ 7" . . . . . . . . . . . . . . . . . . . . . CR 197
Creole (Replay) / Nov '80.

### SOMETHING OLD, SOMETHING NEW (OLD GOLD).
**Tracks:** Something old, something new / Blame it on the Pony Express.
■ 7" . . . . . . . . . . . . . . . . . . . . .OG 9876
Old Gold / Apr '89.

### SOMETHING WONDERFUL.
**Tracks:** Something wonderful / Man made world.
■ 7" . . . . . . . . . . . . . . . . . . . . BLL 1162
Bell / Jun '71.

## Fantasy

### I WANT WHAT I WANT.
**Tracks:** I want what I want.
■ 12" . . . . . . . . . . . . . . . . . . . . . TART 2
Affair / Sep '86.

## Farrell, Joe

### JOE FARRELL WITH PAUL HORN (Farrell, Joe & Paul Horn).
**Tracks:** Not Advised.
CD . . . . . . . . . . . . . . . . . . . . . CLCD 5018
Cleo / Jul '89 / Jazz Music.

### NIGHT DANCING.
**Tracks:** Night dancing / Silver lace.
■ 7" . . . . . . . . . . . . . . . . . . . . . . . LV 2
Atlantic / Dec '78.

### QUINTET/COREN/HANCOCK.
**Tracks:** Not Advised.
■ CD . . . . . . . . . . . . . . . . . . . . . 4505592
CBS / '88.

### VIM 'N' VIGOR (Farrell, Joe & Louis Hayes Quartet).
**Tracks:** Arab arab / Besame mucho / Three little words / Miles mode / Vim 'n' vigor.
■ CD . . . . . . . . . . . . . . . . . . . CDSJP 197
Timeless (Jazz) / Jun '91.

■ DELETED

## Farrow, Gene

### DANCE WITH ME.
Tracks: Dance with me / Do it again.
- 7"..................................... MAG 133
Magnet / Oct '78.

### DON'T STOP NOW (Farrow, Gene & GF Band).
Tracks: Don't stop now.
- 7"..................................... MAG 125
Magnet / Aug '78.

### MOVE YOUR BODY.
Tracks: Not Advised.
- MC.............................. TCMAGL 5024
Magnet / Dec '78.

### MOVE YOUR BODY.
Tracks: Move your body / Can you keep it up all night.
- 7"..................................... MAG 109
Magnet / Jan '78.

### ONE NIGHT IN NEW YORK.
Tracks: One night in New York / Danger zone.
- 7"..................................... MAG 145
Magnet / Apr '79.

### UNIQUE MYSTIQUE.
Tracks: Unique mystique / I go to pieces.
- 12................................. 12 RIA 4
Rialto (1) / Nov '81.
- 7"..................................... RIA 4
Rialto (1) / Jan '82.

## Fascinations

### GIRLS ARE OUT TO GET YOU.
Tracks: Girls are out to get you / You'll be sorry.
- 7"..................................... SS 594
Stateside / Feb '67.
- 7"..................................... WI 4049
Sue / Jun '68.
- 7"..................................... 2092 004
Mojo / Jul '71.

## Fashions

### I.O.U. (A LIFETIME OF LOVE).
Tracks: I.O.U. (a lifetime of love) / He gives me love (la la la).
- 7"..................................... E 2444
Evolution / '69.

## Fat Larry's Band

Led by drummer Larry James, FLB rose from Philadelphia and enjoyed trio of minor dance hits in late '70s, of which biggest was Center City. They survived death of disco to score huge hit with uncharacteristally sappy Zoom in '82, but promptly returned to obscurity. Chances of revival were blighted by James' fatal heart attack in 1984.

### ACT LIKE YOU KNOW.
Tracks: Act like you know.
- 12"..................................... VS 491 12
- 7"..................................... VS 491
Virgin / Apr '82.

### BEST OF FAT LARRY'S BAND - BRIGHT CITY LIGHTS.
Tracks: Centre city / Fascination / We just can't get it together / Boogie town / Looking for love / Close encounters of a funky kind / Last chance to dance / Hey Pancho, it's disco.
- LP..................................... FT 564
Fantasy / Jan '80.

### BOOGIE TOWN.
Tracks: Boogie town / Space lady.
- 7"..................................... FTC 168
Fantasy / Mar '79.

### BREAKIN' OUT.
Tracks: Act like you know / Traffic stoppers / Zoom / House party / Breakin' out / Be my lady / Golden moment / Video.
- LP..................................... V 2229
Virgin / Oct '82.
- MC..................................... OVEDC 64
Virgin / '87.
- LP..................................... OVED 64
Virgin / Aug '88.

### CENTER CITY.
Tracks: Center city / Night time boogie.
- 7"..................................... K 10951
W.M.O.T.(USA) / Jul '77.

### DON'T LET IT GO TO YOUR HEAD.
Tracks: Don't let it go to your head.
- 12"..................................... VS 632-12
- 7"..................................... VS 632
Virgin / Oct '83.

### FASCINATION.
Tracks: Fascination / We just want to play for you.
- 7"..................................... K 11002
WEA / Sep '77.

### FEEL IT.
Tracks: Feel it / Nightime boogie / Down on the avenue / Music makers / Center city / Fascination / Life of an entertainer / We just want to play for you.
- LP..................................... K 50330
Atlantic / Oct '77.

### GOLDEN MOMENT.
Tracks: Golden moment / Video.
- 12"..................................... VS 51412
- 7"..................................... VS 514
Virgin / Nov '82.

### HERE COMES THE SUN.
Tracks: Here comes the sun / Love alive.
- 12"..................................... 12FTC 185
- 7"..................................... FTC 185
Fantasy / Jan '80.

### LOOKING FOR LOVE TONIGHT.
Tracks: Looking for love tonight.
- 7"..................................... FTC 179
Fantasy / Aug '79.

### NICE.
Tracks: Not Advised.
- LP..................................... OMN LP 1
Omni (USA) / Jul '86.

### NICE.
Tracks: Which one should I choose / Nice.
- 12"..................................... 12 OMN 2
- 7"..................................... OMN 2
Omni (USA) / May '86.

### OFF THE WALL.
Tracks: Sparkle / Peaceful journey / Castle of joy / Passing time / Easy / Don't you worry about tomorrow / Time / I love you so / In the pocket.
- LP..................................... STX 3004
Stax / Mar '78.
- CD..................................... CDSXE 069
Stax / Nov '92 / Pinnacle.

### STAND UP.
Tracks: Party after midnight / Can't keep my hands to myself / Play with me / Stand up / You've waited too long / Dirty words / You gotta help yourself.
- LP..................................... F 9699
Fantasy / Nov '80.

### STRAIGHT FROM THE HEART.
Tracks: Straight from the heart / Imagination / Stubborn kind of fellow / Always / Kilowatt / Tune me up / In my song / Don't let it go to your head / Hitman.
- LP..................................... V 2289
- MC..................................... TCV 2289
Virgin / Nov '83.

### STRAIGHT FROM THE HEART.
Tracks: Straight from the heart.
- 12"..................................... VS 652T
- 7"..................................... VS 652
Virgin / Jan '84.

### STUBBORN KIND OF FELLOW.
Tracks: Stubborn kind of fellow / Changes.
- 12"..................................... VS 589 12
- 7"..................................... VS 589
Virgin / Apr '83.

### ZOOM.
Tracks: Zoom / House party / Traffic stoppers (On 12" only) / Don't let it go to your head / Act like you know / Straight from the heart.
- 12"..................................... VS 546-12
- 7"..................................... VS 546
Virgin / '82.
- CD Single..................................... CDT 31
Virgin / '88.

## Fatback Band

Funky New Yorkers who made splash in early 70's, peaking commercially with dance classics Are You Ready Do the Bus Stop and (Do The) Spanish Hustle. Having 'sold out' fusion roots, group's fortunes mirrored those of disco; although they returned to U.K. charts in '84, with I Found Lovin'. Same tune, remixed and reissued,

became band's biggest U.K. hit in '87, reaching no. 7.

### (ARE YOU READY) DO THE BUS STOP.
Tracks: (Are you ready) do the bus stop / Wicky wacky.
- 7"..................................... 2066 637
Polydor / Dec '75.
- 12"..................................... POSOX 601
Polydor / Nov '82.

### (ARE YOU READY) DO THE BUS STOP (2).
Tracks: (Are you ready) do the bus stop / Yum yum (gimme sum).
- 12"..................................... SEWT 704
- 12" Remix..................................... SEWTR 704
- 7"..................................... SEWS 704
South Bound / Sep '90.

### 14 KARAT.
Tracks: Lets do it again / Angel / Backstrokin' / Concrete jungle / Without your love / Gotta get my hands on some (money) / Your love is strange / Lady groove / Chillin' out.
- LP..................................... 2391 493
Polydor / Nov '80.
- CD..................................... CDSEWM 060
Ace / Jun '93 / Pinnacle / Complete Record Co. Ltd.

### ALL NITE PARTY.
Tracks: All nite party / Party pella.
- 12"..................................... STSX 2
- 7"..................................... STS 2
Start / Apr '88.

### BACK STROKIN'.
Tracks: Back strokin' / I've gotta get my hands on some more money.
- 12"..................................... POSPX 149
- 7"..................................... POSP 149
Polydor / Aug '80.

### BEST OF THE FATBACK BAND.
Tracks: Spanish hustle / Yum, yum / Wicky wacky / Party time / Put your love / Trompin' / (Are you ready) do the bus stop / Keep on stepping / Disco crazy / Boogie with Fatback / Night fever.
- LP..................................... 2391 246
Spring / Dec '76.

### BRIGHT LIGHTS, BIG CITY.
Tracks: Freak the freak the funk / Let me do it to you / Big city / Boogie woogie / Hesitation / Wild dreams.
- LP..................................... 239 138 7
Polydor / Mar '79.

### BRITE LITES/ BIG CITY.
Tracks: Freak the freak the funk (rock) / Let me do it to you / Big city / (Do the) boogie woogie / Hesitation / Wild dreams.
- CD..................................... CDSEWM 045
South Bound / Jan '92 / Pinnacle.

### DO THE BOOGIE WOOGIE.
Tracks: Do the boogie woogie / Freak the freak the funk.
- 7"..................................... POSP 46
Polydor / May '79.

### DO THE SPANISH HUSTLE.
Tracks: Do the Spanish hustle.
- 7"..................................... 2066 656
Polydor / Feb '76.

### DOUBLE DUTCH.
Tracks: Double dutch / Spank the baby.
- 7"..................................... 2066 777
Spring / Mar '77.

### FATBACK BAND "LIVE".
Tracks: Not Advised.
- CD..................................... SCD 12
- LP..................................... STL 12
- MC..................................... STC 12
Start / Jun '87 / THE / Koch International.

### FIRED UP 'N' KICKIN'.
Tracks: I'm fired up / Boogie freak / Get out on the dance floor / At last / I like girls / Snake / Can't you see.
- LP..................................... 2391351
Spring / Aug '78.
- CD..................................... CDSEW 041
South Bound / Jul '91 / Pinnacle.

### GIGOLO.
Tracks: Rockin' to the beat / Rub down / I'm so in love / Higher / Do it / Gigolo / Oh girl / Na na, hey hey, kiss her goodbye.
- CD..................................... CDSEWM 081
South Bound / Nov '93 / Pinnacle.

## GIRL IS FINE (SO FINE).
Tracks: Girl is fine.
■ 12"................POSPX 590
■ 7".................POSP 590
Spring / Apr '83.

## GIRLS ON MY MIND.
Tracks: Girls on my mind / Just be my love.
■ 12"................FBACK 1T
■ 7".................FBACK 1
Atlantic / May '85.

## GREATEST HITS: FATBACK.
Tracks: Wicky wacky / Bus stop / Is this the future / I found lovin' / Backstrokin'.
■ LP.................TANLP 4
MC..................ZCTAN 4
Important / Sep '85.

## GREATEST, THE.
Tracks: Wicky wacky / Yum yum / Bus stop / Spanish hustle / Gotta get my hands on some (money) / She's my shining star / Sunshine lady / Is this the future / Girl is fine (so fine) / I found lovin'.
CD..................CDCHE 1
■ LP.................CHELP 1
MC..................ZCHE 1
Master Mix / Dec '87 / Wellard / Jazz Music / Grapevine Distribution.

## HOT BOX.
Tracks: Hot box / Come and get the love / Love spell / Gotta get my hands on some (money) / Backstrokin' / Street band.
CD..................CDSEWM 056
South Bound / Sep '92 / Pinnacle.

## I FOUND LOVIN'.
Tracks: I found lovin' / Is this the future.
■ 12"................12 CHE 8401
■ 7".................CHE 8401
Master Mix / Jun '84.
■ 12"................TANT 10
■ 12" Remix.........TANRT 10
■ 7".................TAN 10
Important / Sep '86.

## I FOUND LOVIN' (LIVE) (Fatback with Steve Walsh).
Tracks: I found lovin' (live) / I found lovin'.
■ 12"................OG 4141
Old Gold / Oct '89.

## I LIKE GIRLS.
Tracks: I like girls / Get out on the dance floor.
■ 7".................2066923
Polydor / Jun '78.

## IS THIS THE FUTURE.
Tracks: Is this the future / Wicky wacky.
■ 12"................TANT 7
■ 7".................TAN 7
Important / Oct '85.

## IS THIS THE FUTURE.
Tracks: Is this the future / Double love affair / Spread love / Funky aerobics (Body movement) / Up against the wall / Finger lickin' good / Sunshine lady / Girl is fine.
■ LP.................POLD 5108
Polydor / Jul '83.
CD..................CDSEWM 058
South Bound / Apr '94 / Pinnacle.

## KEEP ON STEPPIN'.
Tracks: Mr. Bass man / Stuff / New York style / Love / Can't stop the flame / Wicky wacky / Feeling / Keep on stepping / Breaking up with someone you love is hard to do.
CD..................CDSEW 001
■ LP.................SEW 001
■ MC.................SEWC 001
South Bound / Jun '89 / Pinnacle.

## KOOL WHIP.
Tracks: Kool whip / Concrete jungle.
■ 12"................POSPX 321
■ 7".................POSP 321
Polydor / Sep '81.

## LET'S DO IT AGAIN.
Tracks: Let's do it again / Chillin' out / Hot box (on 12" only).
■ 12"................POSPX 196
■ 7".................POSP 196
Spring / Jan '81.

## LOVER UNDER COVER.
Tracks: Lover under cover / You've got that magic.
■ 12"................A 9638 T
■ 7".................A 9638
■ 12"................FBACK 2T
■ 7".................FBACK 2
Atlantic / Jun '85.

## MAN WITH THE BAND.
Tracks: Man with the band / Master Booty / Funk backin' / Mile high / I gotta thing for you / Midnight freak / Zodiac man.
■ LP.................2391314
Polydor / Dec '77.
CD..................CDSEW 036
■ LP.................SEW 036
South Bound / Jan '91 / Pinnacle.

## MILE HIGH.
Tracks: Mile high / Midnight freak.
■ 7".................2066900
Spring / Mar '78.

## NIGHT FEVER.
Tracks: Night fever / Little funky dance / If that's the way you want it / Joint (you and me) / Disco crazy / Booty / No more room on the dancefloor / December 1963 (oh what a night).
CD..................CDSEW 008
■ LP.................SEW 008
■ MC.................SEWC 008
South Bound / Aug '89 / Pinnacle.

## NIGHT FEVER.
Tracks: Night fever.
■ 7".................2066 706
Spring / Aug '76.

## NYCNYUSA.
Tracks: Double Dutch / Soul finger (gonna put on you) / Spank the baby / Duke walk / NYCNYUSA / Love street / Changed man / Cosmic woman.
■ LP.................2391265
Polydor / May '77.
CD..................CDSEW 030
■ LP.................SEW 030
■ MC.................SEWC 030
South Bound / Jul '90 / Pinnacle.

## ON THE FLOOR.
Tracks: On the floor / U.F.O. (Unidentified funk object) / Burn baby burn / She's my shining star / Hip so slick / Do it to me now.
■ LP.................SP 16736
Spring / Jul '82.
CD..................CDSEWM 091
South Bound / Mar '94 / Pinnacle.

## PARTY TIME.
Tracks: Party time.
■ 7".................2066 682
Polydor / May '76.

## PHOENIX.
Tracks: Drum song / I love you so / Jump up baby jump up / Big brother / You've got that magic / Call out my name / Lover man / Just be my love.
■ LP.................7901681
Cotillion / Jul '84.

## RAISING HELL.
Tracks: (Are you ready) to do the bus stop / All day / Put your love (in my tender care) / Groovy kind of day / Spanish hustle / I can't help myself / Party time.
■ LP.................2391203
South Bound / Mar '76.
CD..................CDSEW 028
■ LP.................SEW 028
■ MC.................SEWC 028
South Bound / Apr '90 / Pinnacle.

## RHYTHM OF THE NIGHT.
Tracks: Rhythm of the night / Naughty dancer.
■ 12"................GMT 12002
■ 7".................GMT 002
Groove & Move (G&M) / Jun '87.

## SHE'S A GO-GETTER.
Tracks: She's a go-getter / Evil.
■ 12"................A 9506T
■ 7".................A 9506
Atlantic / Sep '85.

## SHE'S MY SHINING STAR.
Tracks: She's my shining star / Hip so slick.
■ 12"................POSPX 494
■ 7".................POSP 494
Polydor / Jan '82.

## SO DELICIOUS.
Tracks: Girls on my mind / Go out with a bang / Lover under cover / Sequence 96 / Let's play tonight / She's a go-getter / So delicious / Evil.
■ LP.................790253 1
MC..................790253 4
Cotillion / Apr '85 / WEA.

## SUNSHINE LADY.
Tracks: Sunshine lady / Gotta get my hands on some (money).
■ 12"................12 CHE 8415

■ 7".................CHE 8415
Master Mix / Jul '87.

## TAKE IT ANY WAY YOU WANT IT.
Tracks: Take it any way you want it / Lady groove.
■ 12"................POSPX 283
■ 7".................POSP 283
Polydor / Jun '81.

## TASTY JAM.
Tracks: Take it any way you want it / Wanna dance / Keep your fingers out of the jam / Kool whip / High steppin' lady / Get ready for the night.
■ LP.................2391 512
Spring / Jun '81.
CD..................CDSEWM 088
South Bound / Feb '94 / Pinnacle.

## TONITE'S ALL NIGHT PARTY.
Tracks: Not Advised.
CD..................SCD 16
■ LP.................STL 16
MC..................STC 16
Start / Jun '88 / THE / Koch International.

## WITH LOVE.
Tracks: He's a freak undercover / Rastajam / I love your body language / I found lovin' / I wanna be your lover / Please stay / Wide glide.
CD..................CDSEW 024
■ LP.................SEW 024
South Bound / Feb '90 / Pinnacle.
■ MC.................SEWC 024
South Bound / Mar '90.

## XII.
Tracks: You're my candy sweet / Disco bass / Gimme that sweet, sweet lovin' / King Tim III (personality jock) / Disco queen / Love in perfect harmony.
CD..................CDSEW 049
South Bound / Apr '92 / Pinnacle.

## YUM YUM.
Tracks: Yum yum (gimme some) / Trompin' / Let the drums speak / Put the funk on you / Feed me your love / (When you wanna boogie) boogie with Fatback / Got to learn how to dance / If you could turn into me / (Hey) I feel real good.
CD..................CDSEW 016
■ LP.................SEW 016
■ MC.................SEWC 016
South Bound / Nov '89 / Pinnacle.

## YUM YUM.
Tracks: Yum yum.
■ 12" Remix.........DEBTX 3122
Debut (2) / Jul '91.

## YUM YUM GIMME SOME.
Tracks: Yum yum gimme some.
■ 7".................2066 590
Polydor / Sep '75.

# Father

## FATHER'S DAY.
Tracks: Not Advised.
■ CD.................MCAD 10061
■ LP.................MCA 10061
■ MC.................MCAC 10061
MCA / Aug '91.

## I'LL DO 4 U.
Tracks: I'll do 4 U.
■ 12"................MCST 1525
■ 7".................MCS 1525
■ CD Single.........MCSTD 1525
MCA / Apr '91.

## IT'S GONNA BE ALRIGHT.
Tracks: It's gonna be alright.
■ 12"................MCST 1786
■ CD Single.........MCSTD 1786
MCA / Jul '93.

## LISA BABY.
Tracks: Lisa baby.
■ 12"................MCST 1557
■ 12" Remix.........MCSX 1557
■ 7".................MCS 1557
■ CD Single.........MCSTD 1557
MCA / Aug '91.

## SEX IS LAW.
Tracks: 69 / R & B swinger / Sex is law / Once she gets pumpin' / On and on / I beeped you / Ain't nuttin' but a party / Now is the time / For the brothers who ain't here / Wiggle / Something from the radio.
CD..................MCD 10937
■ LP.................MCA 10937
MCA / Feb '94 / BMG.

## Father's Angels

### BOK TO BACH.
Tracks: Bok to Bach / Don't knock it.
■ 7" . . . . . . . . . . . . . . . . . . . . . . . MGM 1459
MGM (EMI) / '68.

## Faure, Mike

### VOICE OF THE WIND.
Tracks: Not Advised.
CD . . . . . . . . . . . . . . . . . . . . . . CDPC 794
MC . . . . . . . . . . . . . . . . . . . . . ZPREC 794
Prestige / Sep '90 / Total / BMG.

## Fearon, Phil

In keeping with Thatcherite times, largely unlamented Britfunkers Galaxy were enterprise initiative formed by London muso Phil Fearon. Fearon had played with late '70s acts Hi-Tension and Kandidate, enjoying biggest hit in '79 with latter's I Don't Wanna Lose You. Galaxy were launched with 1982's Head Over Heels; cracking U.K. charts following year with Dancing Tight. Handful of poppy hits followed before Fearon dropped group billing for final Top 10 entry I Can Prove It. He also founded independent label 20/20.

### AIN'T NOTHING BUT A HOUSE PARTY.
Tracks: Burning all my bridges / Ain't nothing but a house party.
■ 7" . . . . . . . . . . . . . . . . . . . . . . . PF 2
■ 12" . . . . . . . . . . . . . . . . . . . . . . PFX 2
Ensign / Nov '86.

### BEST OF PHIL FEARON & GALAXY, THE (Fearon, Phil & Galaxy).
Tracks: Dancing tight / Head over heels / What do I do / Nothing is too good for you / I can prove it / Everybody's laughing / Burning my bridges / Wait until tonight (my love) / All I give to you / You don't need a reason / This kind of love / Ain't nothing but a house party / If you're gonna fall in love / Fantasy real.
CD . . . . . . . . . . . . . . . . . . . . . MCCD 150
MC . . . . . . . . . . . . . . . . . . . . . MCTC 150
Music Club / Feb '94 / Gold & Sons / THE / Video Collection / C.M. Distribution.

### DANCING TIGHT - THE BEST OF GALAXY (Fearon, Phil & Galaxy).
Tracks: What do I do / Dancing tight / This kind of love / Head over heels / You don't need a reason / Wait until tonight (my love) / If you're gonna fall in love / Everybody's laughing / I can prove it / All I give to you / Fantasy real / Ain't nothing but a house party / Nothing is too good for you / Anything you want.
CD . . . . . . . . . . . . . . . . . . . . CDCHEN 31
■ LP . . . . . . . . . . . . . . . . . . . . . CHEN 31
■ MC . . . . . . . . . . . . . . . . . . . TCCHEN 31
Ensign / Oct '92 / EMI.

### EVERYBODY'S LAUGHING (Fearon, Phil & Galaxy).
Tracks: Everybody's laughing.
■ 7" P.Disc . . . . . . . . . . . . . . . . . PENY 514
■ 12" . . . . . . . . . . . . . . . . . . . . 12ENY 514
■ 7" . . . . . . . . . . . . . . . . . . . . . ENY 514
Ensign / Jun '84.

### FANTASY REAL (Fearon, Phil & Galaxy).
Tracks: Fantasy real / Anything you want.
■ 12" . . . . . . . . . . . . . . . . . . . 12ENY 507
■ 7" . . . . . . . . . . . . . . . . . . . . . ENY 507
Ensign / Oct '83.

### I CAN PROVE IT.
Tracks: Il gurnata / I can prove it.
■ 7" . . . . . . . . . . . . . . . . . . . . . . . PF 1
■ 12" . . . . . . . . . . . . . . . . . . . . . PFX 1
Chrysalis / Jul '86.

### NOTHING IS TOO GOOD FOR YOU.
Tracks: Nothing is too good for you / You've still got my love.
■ 12" . . . . . . . . . . . . . . . . . . . . . PF 312
■ 7" . . . . . . . . . . . . . . . . . . . . . . PF 3
Ensign / Jul '87.

### PHIL FEARON & GALAXY (Fearon, Phil & Galaxy).
Tracks: Not Advised.
■ LP . . . . . . . . . . . . . . . . . . . . . ENCL 2
Ensign / Aug '84.

### THIS KIND OF LOVE (Fearon, Phil & Galaxy).
Tracks: Not Advised.
■ LP . . . . . . . . . . . . . . . . . . . . . ENCL 4
Ensign / Feb '85.

### THIS KIND OF LOVE (Fearon, Phil & Galaxy, featuring Dee Galdes).
Tracks: This kind of love / Sharing love.
■ 7" . . . . . . . . . . . . . . . . . . . . . ENY 521
■ 12" . . . . . . . . . . . . . . . . . . . 12ENY 521
■ 12" . . . . . . . . . . . . . . . . . . 12XENY 521
Ensign / Jul '85.

### WHAT DO I DO (OLD GOLD) (Fearon, Phil & Galaxy).
Tracks: What do I do / I can prove it.
■ 12" . . . . . . . . . . . . . . . . . . . . OG 4133
Old Gold / Aug '89.

### WHAT DO I DO? (Fearon, Phil & Galaxy).
Tracks: What do I do / Pina colada.
■ 12" . . . . . . . . . . . . . . . . . . . 12ENY 510
■ 7" . . . . . . . . . . . . . . . . . . . . . ENY 510
Ensign / Mar '84.

## Feel

### I'D LIKE TO.
Tracks: I'd like to.
■ 12" . . . . . . . . . . . . . . . . . . . . BDSL 499
■ 7" . . . . . . . . . . . . . . . . . . . . . BDS 499
Buddah / Jan '83.

## Felder, Wilton

### FOREVER ALWAYS.
Tracks: Lillies of the nile / For lovers only / My way / My one and only love / Rainbow visions / Forever / Goin' crazy / Asian flower / African queen / Mr. Felder.
CD . . . . . . . . . . . . . . . . . . . . . PAR 20182
Par / Jun '93 / New Note.

### GENTLE FIRE.
Tracks: Gentle fire / Driftin' on a dream / Only for those who care / I got to feel like you do / Summer nights in Rio / Somewhere in my past.
■ LP . . . . . . . . . . . . . . . . . . . . MCF 3167
■ MC . . . . . . . . . . . . . . . . . . . MCFC 3167
MCA / Apr '83.

### I WILL STILL BE LOOKING UP TO YOU.
Tracks: I will still be looking up to you / La luz.
■ 12" . . . . . . . . . . . . . . . . . . . MCAT 919
■ 7" . . . . . . . . . . . . . . . . . . . . MCA 919
MCA / Jan '85.

### INHERIT THE WIND.
Tracks: Not Advised.
■ LP . . . . . . . . . . . . . . . . . . . MCG 4013
MCA / Nov '80.

### INHERIT THE WIND.
Tracks: Inherit the wind / Until the morning comes.
■ 12" . . . . . . . . . . . . . . . . . . . MCAT 646
■ 7" . . . . . . . . . . . . . . . . . . . . MCA 646
MCA / Nov '80.

### INSIGHT.
Tracks: Insight / You know who I am.
■ 12" . . . . . . . . . . . . . . . . . . . MCAT 665
■ 7" . . . . . . . . . . . . . . . . . . . . MCA 665
MCA / Jan '81.

### NOCTURNAL MOODS.
Tracks: Feel so much better / Night moves / Southern pearl / If I knew then what I know now / Sugar loaf / Love steps / Out of sight not out of mind / Since I fell for you / Music of the night.
CD . . . . . . . . . . . . . . . . . . . PAR 2010CD
Par / Aug '93 / New Note.

### SECRETS (featuring Bobby Womack/All-trinna Grayson).
Tracks: Secrets / (No matter how high I get) I'll still be looking / La luz / Truth song / I found you.
■ LP . . . . . . . . . . . . . . . . . . . . MCF 3237
■ MC . . . . . . . . . . . . . . . . . . . MCFC 3237
MCA / Feb '85.

### WE ALL HAVE A STAR.
Tracks: We all have a star / I know who I am / Why believe / Cycles of time / Let's dance together / My name is love / You and me and ecstasy.
■ LP . . . . . . . . . . . . . . . . . . . . MCL 1652
■ MC . . . . . . . . . . . . . . . . . . . MCLC 1652
ABC Records / Feb '82.

## Ferguson, Sheila

### WHEN WILL I SEE YOU AGAIN.
Tracks: When will I see you again.
■ 12" . . . . . . . . . . . . . . . . . . 12STAS 2711
■ CD Single . . . . . . . . . . . . . . CDSTAS 2711
■ MC Single . . . . . . . . . . . . . . CASTAS 2711
XS Rhythm / Jan '94.

## Ferrell, Rachelle

### RACHELLE FERRELL.
Tracks: I'm special / Welcome to my love / Waiting / It only took a minute / With open arms / 'til you come back to me / You can't get (until you learn to start giving) / Nothing has ever felt like this / I know you love me / Sentimental.
CD . . . . . . . . . . . . . . . . . . . . CDEST 2177
■ MC . . . . . . . . . . . . . . . . . . . TCEST 2177
Capitol / Sep '92 / EMI.

## Ferrier, Robert

### KISS YOU ALL OVER.
Tracks: Kiss you all over.
■ CD Single . . . . . . . . . . . . . CONTRCD 005
■ 12" . . . . . . . . . . . . . . . . . CONTRT 005
Contribution / Nov '93.

### LOVE GUARANTEED.
Tracks: Love guaranteed (mixes) / Is this the last time / Together forever.
■ 12" . . . . . . . . . . . . . . . . . . CNTRT 003
Contribution / Jan '93.

## Fest, Manfredo

### JUNGLE CAT.
Tracks: Not Advised.
■ CD . . . . . . . . . . . . . . . . . . . . . CD 470
DMP / Mar '90.

### SEND IN THE CLOWNS.
Tracks: Send in the clowns.
■ 12" . . . . . . . . . . . . . . . . . . . . . BRT 1
■ 7" . . . . . . . . . . . . . . . . . . . . . . BR 1
Blue Bird (2) / May '83.

## Fever

### DO YOU WANT ME.
Tracks: Do you want me / One tonight.
■ 12" . . . . . . . . . . . . . . . . . . . . FTCT 190
Fantasy / Oct '80.

### UP TO MY EYES IN LOVE.
Tracks: Up to my eyes in love / Like a bolt from the blue.
■ 7" . . . . . . . . . . . . . . . . . . . . . MAG 99
Magnet / Aug '77.

## Fiagbe, Lena

### GOTTA GET IT RIGHT.
Tracks: Gotta get it right.
■ 12" . . . . . . . . . . . . . . . . . . . 12MUM 44
■ CD Single . . . . . . . . . . . . . . MUMCD 44
■ MC Single . . . . . . . . . . . . . . MUMSC 44
Mother / Oct '93.

### IS IT BECAUSE.
Tracks: Is it because / What we need is love / Here & now (On CD only).
7" . . . . . . . . . . . . . . . . . . . . . MUM 60
CD Single . . . . . . . . . . . . . . . MUMCD 60
MC Single . . . . . . . . . . . . . . . MUMSC 60
Mother / Oct '94 / PolyGram.

### VISIONS.
Tracks: Jus wanna be me / What's it like to be beautiful / Is it because / Here we go again / Visions / If you know / Everybody needs some luck / It is / You come from Earth / Gotta get it right / People people (CDST only) / I like the light (CDST only) / You are my world (CDST only) / Clock (CDST only) / It's a family affair (CDST only) / Warm love (CDST only) / Waiting in vain (CDST only).
CD . . . . . . . . . . . . . . . . . . . MUMCD 9413
CD Set . . . . . . . . . . . . . . . . MUM 9413-0
MC . . . . . . . . . . . . . . . . . . . MUMC 9413
Mother / May '94 / PolyGram.

### WHAT'S IT LIKE TO BE BEAUTIFUL.
Tracks: What's it like to be beautiful / Another season (Not on MUMDD 49) / Got to get it right (On MUMDD 49 only) / What's it like to be beautiful (Mix) (On MUMDD 49 only) / You come from Earth (On MUMCD 49 only) / Go the way you feel (On MUMCD 49 only) / London town (On MUMCD 49 only).
■ 7" . . . . . . . . . . . . . . . . . . . . MUM 49

■ MC Single. . . . . . . . . . . . . MUMSC 49
■ CD Single. . . . . . . . . . . . . MUMDD 49
■ CD Single. . . . . . . . . . . . . MUMCD 49
Mother / Mar '94.

## YOU COME FROM EARTH.
**Tracks:** You come from earth.
■ 7". . . . . . . . . . . . . . . . . . . . . MUM 42
■ CD Single. . . . . . . . . . . . . MUMCD 42
■ MC Single. . . . . . . . . . . . . MUMSC 42
■ CD Single. . . . . . . . . . . . . MUMDD 42
Mother / Jul '93.

## Fidels

### TRY A LITTLE HARDER.
**Tracks:** Try a little harder / Try a little harder (instrumental).
■ 7". . . . . . . . . . . . . . . . . . . DJS 10689
DJM / Jul '76.

## Fields, Alvin

### SPECIAL DELIVERY.
**Tracks:** Special delivery / Anyway you like it / All in the name of love / All that I am / Lucky number seven / Share my dream / Fire of life / Punk funk.
■ LP . . . . . . . . . . . . . . . . . . . AMLH 64890
A&M / Jul '82.

## Fields, Richard 'Dimples'

Although his U.K. chart record comprises solitary No. 56 placing for *I've Got To Learn To Say No* in 1982, Fields achieved slightly greater recognition at home in U.S. Debut album spawned singles *Like Your Loving* and *She's Got Papers On Me*, latter featuring Betty Wright. After second, gold album *Mr, Look So Good*, he collaborated with Ohio Players and later wrote and produced 9.9's hit *All Of Me For All Of You*. Fields subsequently slipped from fame's glare but is still up and about, 'Dimples' presumably intact.

### DARK GABLE.
**Tracks:** Shake em down / Make my dreams come true / I'd really love to see you tonight / Star I've always wanted to be / She's a bad lil lady / Don't give up too soon / One special one / You sure know how to give a party / I won't rush you.
■ LP . . . . . . . . . . . . . . . . . . . PL 85582
MC. . . . . . . . . . . . . . . . . . . . . PK 85582
RCA / Sep '85 / BMG.

### DIMPLES.
**Tracks:** I like your loving / Let me take you in my arms tonight / Let the lady dance / Lovely lady / In the still of the night / She's got papers on me / I've got to learn to say no / Earth angel / Don't ever take your love.
■ LP . . . . . . . . . . . . . . . . . . . EPC 85345
Epic / Dec '81.

### GIVE EVERYBODY SOME.
**Tracks:** People treat you funky / Butter / Wish somebody loved me / Don't ever stop chasing your dreams / You shouldn't have made it so good / Let it all hang out / You send me / Moody's mood for love / Goodbye son, hello her.
■ LP . . . . . . . . . . . . . . . . . . . EPC 252 26
Epic / Jan '83.

### I LIKE YOUR LOVIN'.
**Tracks:** I like your lovin' / Lovely lady.
■ 7". . . . . . . . . . . . . . . . . . . . EPCA 1554
Epic / Aug '81.

### I'VE GOT TO LEARN TO SAY NO.
**Tracks:** I've got to learn to say no / She's got papers on me.
■ 7". . . . . . . . . . . . . . . . . . . . EPCA 1918
Epic / Feb '82.

### IF IT AIN'T ONE THING IT'S ANOTHER.
**Tracks:** Mr. Look so good / If it ain't one thing it's another.
■ 7". . . . . . . . . . . . . . . . . . . . EPCA 2425
Epic / May '82.

### MMM..
**Tracks:** Jazzy lady / Your wife is cheatin' on us / Dear Mr God / Woman let me into your life / Dog or a hog / We've gotta stop meeting like this / Don't turn your back on my love / I need you so.
■ LP . . . . . . . . . . . . . . . . . . . PL 85169
■ MC. . . . . . . . . . . . . . . . . . . PK 85169
■ CD. . . . . . . . . . . . . . . . . . . PD 85169
RCA / Aug '84.

### MR. LOOK SO GOOD.
**Tracks:** If it ain't one thing ..it's another / After I put my lovin' on you / Baby work out / Mr. Look so good / Taking applications / Freak on the side / Sincerely / Lady is bad.
■ LP . . . . . . . . . . . . . . . . . . . EPC 85693
Epic / May '82.

### TELLIN IT LIKE IT IS.
**Tracks:** Tell it like it is / You're everything I want in a woman / Hooked on your lovin' / Stand up on it / Never gonna let the sweet get away / Dor or hog / I won't rush you / I can't live with or without you / Do you belong to the dope man.
■ LP . . . . . . . . . . . . . . . . . . . 4600021
MC. . . . . . . . . . . . . . . . . . . . . 4600024
CBS / Sep '87 / Sony.

### YOUR WIFE IS CHEATIN ON US.
**Tracks:** Your wife is cheatin' on us / Woman let me into your life.
■ 7". . . . . . . . . . . . . . . . . . . . . RCA 433
■ 12". . . . . . . . . . . . . . . . . . . RCAT 433
RCA / Jun '84.

## Fifth Of Heaven

### (WITHOUT YOU) BABY I'M LOST.
**Tracks:** (Without you) baby I'm lost / Just a little more.
■ 12". . . . . . . . . . . . . . . . . . . .12FOH 2
Mixout / Dec '89.

### I NEED YOUR LOVE.
**Tracks:** I need your love / I need your love (Lurve and passion mix) / Song for Burt.
■ 12". . . . . . . . . . . . . . . . . . . 12 FOH 3
Mixout / Jul '90.

### JUST A LITTLE MORE.
**Tracks:** Just a little more / Just a little more (surrender mix) (Only available on 12".) / Song for Bert.
■ 12". . . . . . . . . . . . . . . . . . . 12 FOH 1
■ 7". . . . . . . . . . . . . . . . . . . . 7FOH 1
Mixout / May '89.

## Films

### ABOVE THE RIM (Original Soundtrack) (Various Artists).
**Tracks:** Anything / Old time's sake / Part-time lover / Big pimpin' / Didn't mean to turn you on / Doggie style / Regulate / Pour out a little liquor / Gonna give it to ya / Afro puffs / Jus so ya no / Hoochies need love too / I'm still in love with you / Crack 'em / U bring da dog out / Blowed away / It's not deep enough / Dogg pound 4 life.
CD. . . . . . . . . . . . . . . . . .654492359-2
LP. . . . . . . . . . . . . . . . . . .654492359-1
MC. . . . . . . . . . . . . . . . . .654492359-4
Death Row / Apr '94 / WEA.

### ACROSS 110TH STREET (Film Soundtrack) (Womack, Bobby & Peace).
**Tracks:** Across 110th street / If you don't want my love / Quicksand / Do it right / Hang on in there / Across 110th street (pt 2) / Harlem clavinette / Harlem love theme.
■ LP . . . . . . . . . . . . . . . . . . . UAS 29451
United Artists / '73.

### ADDAMS FAMILY VALUES (Various Artists).
**Tracks:** It's your thing / Be thankful for what you've got / Express yourself / Whatcha see is what you get / Family affair / Night people / Supernatural thing / Do your thing (love on) / Do it any way you wanna / May you always drink bizarre / Addams family.
CD. . . . . . . . . . . . . . . . . . . 521 502-2
MC. . . . . . . . . . . . . . . . . . . 521 502-4
Polydor / Dec '93 / PolyGram.

### BATMAN (Film soundtrack) (Prince).
**Tracks:** Future / Electric chair / Arms of orion / Partyman / Vicking waiting / Trust / Lemon crush / Scandalous / Batdance.
CD. . . . . . . . . . . . . . . . . . . . 9259782
WEA / '89 / WEA.
CD. . . . . . . . . . . . . . . . . . . . 9259362
CD P.Disc. . . . . . . . . . . . . . . 9254892
■ LP . . . . . . . . . . . . . . . . . . . WX 281
MC. . . . . . . . . . . . . . . . . . . . WX 281C
WEA / Jun '89 / WEA.

### BEAT STREET (Film soundtrack) (Various Artists).
**Tracks:** Beat street / Baptize the beat / Strangers in a strange world / Frantic situation / Beat street strut / Us girls / This could be the night / Breaker's revenge / Tu carino - Carmen's theme.
■ MC. . . . . . . . . . . . . . . . . . . 780 154-4
■ CD . . . . . . . . . . . . . . . . . . 780 154-2

■ LP . . . . . . . . . . . . . . . . . . . 780 154-1
Atlantic / Jul '84.

### BEAT STREET VOLUME 2 (Original soundtrack) (Various Artists).
**Tracks:** Son of beat street / Give me all / Nothin's gonna come easy / Santa's rap / It's alright by me / Battle cry / Phony four MC's-wappin' / Into the night.
■ LP . . . . . . . . . . . . . . . . . . . 780 158-1
■ MC. . . . . . . . . . . . . . . . . . . 780 158-4
Atlantic / Oct '84.

### BEST OF CAR WASH (Rose Royce).
**Tracks:** Car wash / Zig zag / Water / Doin' what comes naturally / I'm going down / Put your money where your mouth is / I wanna get next to you / Daddy rich / Yo yo / Sunrise.
■ LP . . . . . . . . . . . . . . . . . . . MCF 2799
MCA / Jul '77.
■ LP . . . . . . . . . . . . . . . . . . . MCL 1609
■ MC. . . . . . . . . . . . . . . . . . . MCLC 1609
MCA / '81.
■ CD. . . . . . . . . . . . . . . . . . . DMCF 3424
MCA / '88.

### BEVERLY HILLS COP (Film Soundtrack) (Various Artists).
**Tracks:** New attitude / Don't get stopped in Beverly Hills / Do you really (want my love) / Emergency / Neutron dance / Heat is on / Gratitude / Stir it up / Rock 'n' roll me again / Axel F.
CD. . . . . . . . . . . . . . . . . . . DMCF 3253
■ LP . . . . . . . . . . . . . . . . . . . MCF 3253
■ MC. . . . . . . . . . . . . . . . . . MCFC 3253
MCA / '85 / BMG.
■ LP . . . . . . . . . . . . . . . . . . . MCL 1870
■ MC. . . . . . . . . . . . . . . . . . MCLC 1870
MCA / '88 / BMG.
■ CD. . . . . . . . . . . . . . . . . . . DMCL 1870
MCA / Jul '88.
CD. . . . . . . . . . . . . . . . . . . MCLD 19087
MCA / Sep '92 / BMG.

### BIG CHILL, THE (Film soundtrack) (Various Artists).
**Tracks:** I heard it through the grapevine / My girl / Good lovin' / Tracks of my tears / Joy to the world / Ain't too proud to beg / (You make me feel like) a natural woman / I second that emotion / Whiter shade of pale.
■ LP . . . . . . . . . . . . . . . . . . . STMR 9021
■ MC. . . . . . . . . . . . . . . . . . CSTMR 9021
■ CD . . . . . . . . . . . . . . . . . . ZD 72347
Motown / Jul '84.
■ LP . . . . . . . . . . . . . . . . . . . ZL 72138
■ MC. . . . . . . . . . . . . . . . . . ZK 72138
Motown / '88.
CD. . . . . . . . . . . . . . . . . . . .530017-2
MC. . . . . . . . . . . . . . . . . . . .530017-4
Motown / Jan '93 / PolyGram.

### BLANKMAN (Various Artists).
**Tracks:** Super hero / Do you wanna get down / Dig deep / Cry on / Do you like it baby / Here he comes / Could it be I'm falling in love / Anyone can be a hero / Live into the future / Never say never / Talk of the town.
CD. . . . . . . . . . . . . . . . . . . . 4768212
MC. . . . . . . . . . . . . . . . . . . . 4768214
Epic / Oct '94 / Sony.

### BLUES BROTHERS (Film soundtrack) (Various Artists).
**Tracks:** Shake a tailfeather / Think / Minnie the moocher / Rawhide / Night people / She caught the Katy / Gimme some lovin' / Old landmark / Sweet home Chicago / Peter Gunn / Everybody needs somebody to love.
MC. . . . . . . . . . . . . . . . . . . K4 50715
■ LP . . . . . . . . . . . . . . . . . . . K 50715
Atlantic / Oct '80 / WEA.
CD. . . . . . . . . . . . . . . . . . . K250 715
Atlantic / Feb '87 / WEA.
■ LP . . . . . . . . . . . . . . . . . . . DINTV 56
Dino Entertainment / Dec '92.
DCC. . . . . . . . . . . . . . . . . . .7567 814715
WEA / Jan '93 / WEA.

### BODYGUARD, THE (Various Artists).
**Tracks:** I will always love you / I have nothing / I'm every woman / Run to you / Queen of the night / Jesus loves me / Even if my heart would break / Someday (I'm coming back) / It's gonna be a lovely day / (What's so funny 'bout) peace, love and understanding / Waiting for you / Trust in me.
CD. . . . . . . . . . . . . . . . . . .782218699-2
MC. . . . . . . . . . . . . . . . . . .782218699-4
Arista / Mar '93 / BMG.

### BOOMERANG (Original Soundtrack) (Various Artists).
**Tracks:** Give U my heart / It's gonna be alright / Tonight is right / I'd die without you / 7 day weekend

■ DELETED

/ End of the road / Reversal of a dog / Love shoulda brought you home / There you go / Don't wanna love you / Feels like heaven / Hot sex.
MC. ... 73008 26006-44
■ CD ... 73008 26006-20
Arista / Aug '92 / BMG.

## BOYZ N THE HOOD (Film soundtrack) (Various Artists).
Tracks: How to survive in South Central / Just ask me to / Mama don't take no mess / Growin' up in the hood / Just a friendly game of baseball / Me and you / Work it out / Every single weekend / Too young / Hangin out / It's your life / Spirit / Setembro / Black on black crime.
CD. ... 7599266432
■ LP. ... 7599266431
MC. ... 7599266434
WEA / Aug '91 / WEA.

## BREAKDANCE (1984 Film Soundtrack) (Various Artists).
Tracks: Breakin' There's no stopping us / When I.C.U / Radiotron / Stylin'.profilin' / Din.daa daa / Gotta have the money / Believe in the beat / Set it out / I don't wanna come down / Oye mamacita.
■ CD. ... 821 919-2
■ LP. ... POLD 5147
■ MC. ... POLDC 5147
Polydor / Jun '87.

## BREAKDANCE 2 - ELECTRIC BOOGA-LOO (Film Soundtrack) (Various Artists).
Tracks: Electric boogaloo / Radiotron / Din daa daa / When I.C.U. / Gotta have the money / Believe in the beat / Set it out / I don't wanna come down / Stylin' profilin' / Oye Mamacita.
■ LP. ... POLD 5168
■ CD. ... 823 696-2
■ MC. ... POLDC 5168
Polydor / Dec '84.

## CAN'T STOP THE MUSIC (Original Soundtrack) (Various Artists).
Tracks: Not Advised.
■ MC. ... 7199 051
Mercury / '80.
■ LP. ... 6399 051
Mercury / Aug '80.

## CAR WASH (Rose Royce).
Tracks: Not Advised.
■ LP. ... FA 3043
Fame / Nov '82.

## CARLITO'S WAY (Various Artists).
Tracks: I love music / Rock the boat / Rock your baby / Perece mentira / Backstabbers / Sound of Philadelphia / Got to be real / Lady Marmalade / Pillow talk / El watusi / Oye como va / You are so beautiful.
CD. ... 474994 2
LP. ... 474994 1
MC. ... 474994 4
Columbia / Jan '94 / Sony.

## CLAUDINE (Knight, Gladys & The Pips).
Tracks: Not Advised.
■ LP. ... BDLP 4010
Buddah / '74.

## COLOR PURPLE, THE (Film Soundtrack) (Various Artists).
Tracks: Overture / Main title / Celie leaves with Mr Corrine and Olivia / Nettie teaches Celie / Separation / Celie and Harpo grow up / Mr. dresses to see Shug / Sophia leaves Harpo / Celie cooks Shug breakfast / Three on the road / Bus pulls out / First letter / Letter search / Nellie's letters / High life / Heaven belongs to you / Katutoka Corrine / Celie shaves Mr / Scarification ceremony / I'm here / Champagne train / Reunion / Finale / Careless love / Dirty dozens / Miss Celie's blues / Junk bucket blues / Don't make me, no never mind / My heart will always lead me back to you / Body & soul / Maybe God is tryin' to tell you somethin'.
■ Double LP. ... 925389 1
MC Set ... 925389 4
Qwest / Aug '86 / WEA.
CD Set ... 925389 2
Silva Screen / Jan '89 / Silva Screen / Conifer Records / Total / BMG.

## COMING TO AMERICA (1988 film soundtrack) (Various Artists).
Tracks: Coming to America / Better late than never / All dressed up / I like it like that / That's the way it is (acid house remix) / Addicted to you / Comin' correct / Living the good life / Transparent / Come into my life.
■ CD. ... 790 958-2
■ LP. ... 790 958-1
■ MC. ... 790 958-4
Atlantic / Jul '88.

## COOLEY HIGH (Various Artists).
Tracks: Not Advised.
■ LP. ... STML 12045
Motown / Jan '77.

## CROOKLYN (Various Artists).
Tracks: Crooklyn / Respect yourself / Everyday people / Pusher man / Thin line between love & hate / El pito (I'll never go back to Georgia) / ABC / Oh girl / Mighty love / Mr. Bigg Stuff / Ooh child / Pass the peas / Time has come today / People make the world go round.
CD. ... MCD 11036
MCA / Jun '94 / BMG.

## DEEP COVER (Various Artists).
Tracks: Deep cover / Love or lust / Down with my nigga / Sex is on / Way (is in the house) / Minute you fall in love / John & Betty's theme / Mr. Loverman / I see ya Jay / Nickel slick nigga / Typical relationship / Digits / Sound of one hand clapping / Why you frontin' on me.
CD. ... 471669 2
MC. ... 471669 4
Epic / Feb '93 / Sony.

## DO THE RIGHT THING (1989 Film Soundtrack) (Various Artists).
Tracks: Fight the power / My fantasy / Party hearty / Can't stand it / Prove to me / We love (jingle) / Feel so good / Don't shoot me / Hard to say / Why don't we try / Never explain love / Tu y yo.
■ LP. ... MOT 6272
Motown / Jul '89.
■ CD. ... ZD 72665
■ LP. ... ZL 72665
■ MC. ... ZK 72665
Motown / Jun '89.

## ENDLESS LOVE (Original soundtrack) (Various Artists).
Tracks: Endless love / Dreaming of you / I was made for lovin' you / Dreamin'.
■ LP. ... 6337 182
MC. ... 7141 182
Mercury / PolyGram.

## ENDLESS LOVE (Various Artists).
Tracks: Not Advised.
CD Set ... OXO 13
Object Enterprises / Oct '88 / Gold & Sons / THE / Midland Records.

## FAST BREAK (Film soundtrack) (Preston, Billy & Syreeta).
Tracks: More than just a friend / He didn't say / Go for it / Welcome to Cadwallader / With you I'm born again / Books and basketball half time / Big game.
■ LP. ... STML 12107
Motown / Oct '81.

## FREEDOM TO PARTY (Various Artists).
Tracks: Not Advised.
CD. ... MODCD 1048
■ LP. ... MODEM 1048
MC. ... MODEMC 1048
Filmtrax / May '90 / BMG.

## FRIED GREEN TOMATOES (Various Artists).
Tracks: Not Advised.
CD. ... MCAD 10461
■ MC. ... MCAC 10461
MCA / Mar '92 / BMG.

## GIRL GROUPS: THE STORY OF A SOUND (Film Soundtrack) (Various Artists).
Tracks: Leader of the pack / Stop in the name of love / Give him a great big kiss / My guy / You should have seen the way he looked at me / Come see about me / Will you love me tomorrow / Needle in a haystack / Dancing in the street / My boyfriend's back / Baby love / Remember (walkin' in the sand) / Please Mr. Postman / Someday we'll be together / Back in my arms again / Chapel of love.
■ LP. ... STMR 9020
■ MC. ... CSTMR 9020
Motown / Mar '84.
■ LP. ... WL 72140
■ CD. ... WD 72140
Motown / Apr '88.

## GOONIES (Film Soundtrack) (Various Artists).
Tracks: Goonies 'r' good enough / Eight arms to hold you / Love is always / I got nothing / 14K / Wherever you're goin' (it's alright) / She's so good to me / What a thrill / Save the night / Goonies.
MC. ... 40 70264
■ LP. ... EPC 70264
Epic / Nov '85 / Sony.

■ CD. ... CD 70264
Epic / '88.

## HOUSE PARTY (Original Soundtrack) (Various Artists).
Tracks: Why you get funky on me / What a feeling / Jive time sucker / House party / U.T.F.O. / Dr Ice / I can't do nothing for you man / Fun house / To da break of dawn / Kid vs Play (the battle) / Surely / This is love.
■ LP. ... ZL 72699
■ CD. ... ZD 72699
■ MC. ... ZK 72699
Motown / Apr '90.

## HOUSE PARTY 2 (Various Artists).
Tracks: Announcement of pajama jammi jam / House party (Don't know what you come to do) / Christopher Robinson scholarship fund / Ready or not (House party II new jack theme) / Kid n' play wreck shop / Ain't gonna hurt nobody (House party II theme) / I like your style (House party II swing theme) / Kid & Sydney break up candelight & you (House party II love / I lust 4 U (House party II passion theme) / Bilal gets off / Let me know something (House party II Harris U theme) / Yo baby yo (House party II mental theme) / F.F.F. Rap what's on your mind (House party II rap theme) / Big ol' jazz (House party II memorial) / You gotta pay what you owe / It's so hard to say goodbye to yesterday (House party film t / Confidence / It's so hard to say goodbye to yesterday (Acapella reprise) / Kid's goobye thanks to pope.
LP. ... MCA 10397
MCA (USA) / Nov '91 / MCA (Imports).
CD. ... MCLD 19246
MC. ... MCLC 19246
MCA / Apr '94 / BMG.

## I'M GONNA GIT YOU SUCKA (Various Artists).
Tracks: I'm gonna git you sucka / Clean up your act / He's a fly guy / If ever a love there was / Magic man.
■ LP. ... 209622
■ CD. ... 259622
■ MC. ... 409622
Arista / Feb '89.

## JUNGLE FEVER (Original Soundtrack Recording) (Wonder, Stevie).
Tracks: Fun day / Queen in the black / These three words / Each other's throat / If she breaks your hearts / Gotta have you / Make sure you're sure / Jungle fever / I go sailing / Chemical love / Lighting up the candles.
■ CD. ... ZD 72750
■ LP. ... ZL 72750
■ MC. ... ZK 72750
Motown / Jun '91.

## JUS' JEEPIN' (Various Artists).
Tracks: Deep cover / I made love (4 da very 1st time) / Live at the barbeque / How I could just kill a man / You can't see what I can see / Fudge pudge / True fu-schnick / Blue cheese / Lisa baby / Scenario / Half time / Horny lil devil / Dwyck / Daddy.
CD. ... CDELV 09
LP. ... LPELV 09
MC. ... MCELV 09
Passion/Debut/Scratch Music / Jun '94 / Pinnacle / 3MV.

## KISS OF THE SPIDERWOMAN (Film soundtrack) (Badarou, Wally).
Tracks: Overture / Most ravishing woman / Visions of the ultra-rhine / Kabaret / Je me moque de l'amour / Molina's fantasies / Lunapark / Novel das nove / Spider Island / Pavihao IV / Avocado scene / Theme / Call / Valentin's message / Blue for you / Goodbye mama / Finale.
■ MC. ... ICT 12
■ LP. ... ISTA 12
Island / Jan '86.

## KRUSH GROOVE (Film soundtrack) (Various Artists).
Tracks: Can't stop the street / I can't live without my radio / If I ruled the world / All you can eat / Feel the spin / Holly rock / She's on it / Love triangle / Tender love / Krush groovin'.
■ LP. ... 925295 1
■ MC. ... 925295 4
WEA / Mar '86.

## LEAN ON ME (Film soundtrack) (Various Artists).
Tracks: Not Advised.
■ CD. ... 925843 2
WEA / '88.

## MACK, THE (Hutch, Willie).
**Tracks:** Not Advised.
■ LP . . . . . . . . . . . . . . . . . . . . . STMA 8003
Tamla Motown / . '73.

## MACKENNA'S GOLD (Jones, Quincy).
**Tracks:** Not Advised.
■ LP . . . . . . . . . . . . . . . . . . . . . . . . SF 8017
RCA Victor / Jul '69.

## MADE IN AMERICA (Original Soundtrack Recording) (Various Artists).
**Tracks:** Go Away / Does he do it good / Made in America / Colours of love / What is this / Made in Love / I know I don't walk on water / Dance or die / Smoke on the water / If you need a miracle / Stand.
CD . . . . . . . . . . . . . . . . . . . .755961498-2
MC . . . . . . . . . . . . . . . . . . . .755961498-4
WEA / Jun '93 / WEA.

## MAHOGANY (Original Soundtrack) (Various Artists).
**Tracks:** Do you know where you're going to / Feeling again / You don't ever have to be alone / Can you hear it in my music / Christian's theme / After you / My hero is a gun / Cat fight / Erucu / Let's go back to day one / Tracy / She's the ideal girl / Sweets (and other things) / Mahogany suite.
■ LP . . . . . . . . . . . . . . . . . . . STMS 5082
MC . . . . . . . . . . . . . . . . . . . CSTMS 5082
Motown / Nov '82 / PolyGram.
■ LP . . . . . . . . . . . . . . . . . . . . WL 72355
Motown / '90.

## MO' MONEY (Film soundtrack) (Various Artists).
**Tracks:** Mo' money groove / Best things in life are free / Ice cream dream / Let's just run away ([8]X) / I adore you / Get off my back / Forever love / Money can't buy you love / Let's get together (so groovy now) / Joy / New style / Job ain't nuthin' but work / My dear / Brother Will.
CD . . . . . . . . . . . . . . . . . . . . . 3610042
MC . . . . . . . . . . . . . . . . . . . . . 3610044
A&M / Jun '92 / PolyGram.

## MY GIRL (Film Soundtrack) (Various Artists).
**Tracks:** My girl / More today than yesterday / Hot fun in the summertime / Wedding bell blues / Do wah diddy diddy / Good lovin' / Bad moon rising / If you don't know me by now / I only have eyes for you / Saturday in the park / My girl (Theme from).
■ LP . . . . . . . . . . . . . . . . . . . . 4692131
CD . . . . . . . . . . . . . . . . . . . . . 4692132
MC . . . . . . . . . . . . . . . . . . . . . 4692134
Epic / Sep '94 / Sony.

## NEW JACK CITY (Original Soundtrack) (Various Artists).
**Tracks:** New jack hustler / I'm dreamin' / I wanna sex you up / I'm still waiting / (There you go) tellin' me no again / Facts of life / For the love of money/Living for the city (medley) / Lyrics 2 the rhythm / Get it together (black is a force) / In the dust / New jack city (Available on CD only).
CD . . . . . . . . . . . . . . . . . . . 7599244092
■ LP . . . . . . . . . . . . . . . . . . 7599244091
MC . . . . . . . . . . . . . . . . . . . 7599244094
Giant / Apr '91 / BMG.

## PARADE (Original Soundtrack - Under The Cherry Moon) (Prince & The Revolution).
**Tracks:** Christopher Tracey's parade / New position / I wonder u / Under the cherry moon / Girls and boys / Life can be so nice / Venus de Milo / Mountains / Do u lie / Kiss / Anotherloverholenyohead / Sometimes it snows in April.
CD . . . . . . . . . . . . . . . . . . . .925395 2
■ LP . . . . . . . . . . . . . . . . . . . . . WX 39
MC . . . . . . . . . . . . . . . . . . . . . WX 39C
WEA / Apr '86 / WEA.

## POSSEE, THE (Various Artists).
**Tracks:** Posse (Shoot 'em up) / Posse love / One night of love / Cruel Jim Crow (Please don't play that) / I think to myself / Jesse / Tell me / Free at last / If I knew at all / Freemansville (Homecoming) / Ride of your life / Let the hammer fall.
CD . . . . . . . . . . . . . . . . . . . .540081-2
LP . . . . . . . . . . . . . . . . . . . .540081-1
MC . . . . . . . . . . . . . . . . . . . .540081-4
A&M / May '93 / PolyGram.

## PURPLE RAIN (Film Soundtrack) (Prince & The Revolution).
**Tracks:** Let's go crazy / Take me with u / Beautiful ones / Computer blue / Darling Nikki / When doves cry / I would die 4 u / Baby I'm a star / Purple rain.
CD . . . . . . . . . . . . . . . . . . . .925110 2

WEA / Aug '84 / WEA.
■ LP . . . . . . . . . . . . . . . . . . . .925110 1
MC . . . . . . . . . . . . . . . . . . . .925110 4
WEA / Jul '84 / WEA.
DCC . . . . . . . . . . . . . . . . . . .7599 251105
WEA / Jan '93 / WEA.

## RAGE IN HARLEM, A (Film Soundtrack) (Various Artists).
**Tracks:** Brown eyed handsome man / Walking along / Elevator operation / We belong together / Juke / Boll weevil song / Adios / Ain't got no home / Please please please / Church bells may ring / Pledging my love / Honest I do / Heaven is in your heart / Sugar daddy blues / Just because / Luckiest girl in the world / Dust my broom / I asked for water / I'm in love again / Bo diddley / Why oh why / Let the good times roll / Rage in Harlem.
CD . . . . . . . . . . . . . . . . . . . 7599266172
MC . . . . . . . . . . . . . . . . . . . 7599266174
WEA / Sep '91 / WEA.

## RAGE IN HARLEM, A (Bernstein, Elmer).
**Tracks:** Rage in Harlem / Imabelle / Seduction / Jackson / New of love / Easy money / Morning at Jackson's / Jackson and Goldie / Tender words / Major chase / Gus / Big Kathy killed / Fight / Pop slim / Aftermath / Happy train.
■ CD . . . . . . . . . . . . . . . . . . . VSD 5325
■ LP . . . . . . . . . . . . . . . . . . . . VS 5325
■ MC . . . . . . . . . . . . . . . . . . . VSC 5325
Varese Sarabande Records / Jul '91.

## RETURN OF SUPERFLY (Film Soundtrack) (Various Artists).
**Tracks:** Superfly 1990 / Eazy Street / Cheeba cheeba / Funky in the club / On the real tip / Showdown / Forbidden / Superfly 1990 (Hip hop instrumental) / For the love of you / Take you home / There's a riot jumpin' off / Somethin' like dis.
■ CD . . . . . . . . . . . . . . . . . . . CDEST 2129
■ LP . . . . . . . . . . . . . . . . . . . . EST 2129
■ MC . . . . . . . . . . . . . . . . . . . TCEST 2129
Capitol / Aug '90.

## RUNNING SCARED (Original Soundtrack) (Various Artists).
**Tracks:** Sweet freedom / Man size love / I just wanna be loved / Running scared / Once in a lifetime / I know what I want / Say you really want me / El Chase / Never too late to start.
■ LP . . . . . . . . . . . . . . . . . . . MCG 6012
■ CD . . . . . . . . . . . . . . . . . . . DMCG 6012
■ MC . . . . . . . . . . . . . . . . . . . MCGC 6012
MCA / '86.
■ CD . . . . . . . . . . . . . . . . . . CMCAD 31053
MCA / Sep '87.

## RUTHLESS PEOPLE (Original Soundtrack) (Various Artists).
**Tracks:** Ruthless people / Give me the reason / Modern woman / Wherever I lay my hat / No say in it / Waiting to see you / Dance champion / Neighbourhood watch / Stand on it / Don't you want my love.
■ LP . . . . . . . . . . . . . . . . . . . EPC 70299
MC . . . . . . . . . . . . . . . . . . . .40 70299
■ CD . . . . . . . . . . . . . . . . . . . CD 70299
Epic / Nov '86 / Sony.

## SATURDAY NIGHT FEVER (Film Soundtrack) (Various Artists).
**Tracks:** Stayin' alive / How deep is your love / Night fever / More than a woman / Jive talkin' / You should be dancing / Calypso breakdown / If I can't have you / Fifth of Beethoven / Open sesame / Boogie shoes / M.F.S.B. / K. Jee / Disco inferno / Manhattan skyline / Night on disco mountain / Salsation.
■ Double LP . . . . . . . . . . . . . . . .2658 123
RSO / Mar '78.
CD Set . . . . . . . . . . . . . . . . . . 800 068-2
RSO / '83 / PolyGram.
■ Double LP . . . . . . . . . . . . . . . . SPDLP 5
MC Set . . . . . . . . . . . . . . . . . . 351 701-4
RSO / Jan '84 / PolyGram.

## SECRET LIFE OF PLANTS (Wonder, Stevie).
**Tracks:** Earth's creation / First garden / Voyage to India / Same old story / Venus flytrap and the bug / Ai no sono / Seed's a star and tree medley / Power flower / Secret life of plants / Tree / Finale / Send one your love / Race babbling (instrumental) / Outside my window / Black orchid / Ecclesiastes / Kesse ye lolo de ye / Come back as a flower.
■ Double LP . . . . . . . . . . . . . . . TMSP 6009
■ MC Set . . . . . . . . . . . . . . . . CTMSP 6009
■ CD Set . . . . . . . . . . . . . . . . . ZD 72145
Motown / Oct '81.
CD . . . . . . . . . . . . . . . . . . . .530106-2
MC . . . . . . . . . . . . . . . . . . . .530106-4
Motown / Jan '93 / PolyGram.

## SHAFT (Hayes, Isaac).
**Tracks:** Shaft, Theme from / Bumpy's lament / Walk from Regio's / Ellie's love theme / Shaft's cab ride / Cafe Regio's / Early Sunday morning / Be yourself / Friend's place / Soulsville / No name bar / Bumpy's blues / Shaft strikes again / Do your thing / End theme.
■ LP . . . . . . . . . . . . . . . . . . . .2659 007
Polydor / Dec '71.
CD . . . . . . . . . . . . . . . . . . . CDSXD 021
■ LP Set . . . . . . . . . . . . . . . . . . SX2 021
MC . . . . . . . . . . . . . . . . . . . SXC2 021
Stax / Oct '89 / Pinnacle.

## SHAFT IN AFRICA (Bar-Kays).
**Tracks:** Not Advised.
■ LP . . . . . . . . . . . . . . . . . . . . SPB 1077
Probe / '73.
■ LP . . . . . . . . . . . . . . . . . . . ABCL 5035
ABC Records / '74.

## SHAFT'S BIG SCORE (Various Artists).
**Tracks:** Blowin' your mind / Other side / Smart money / First meeting / Ashby - Kelly man / Don't misunderstand / Move on in / Symphony for shafted souls (big chase) / Take off / Dance of the cars water ballet part 1 / Dance of the cars water ballet part 2 / Call and response / Last amen.
■ LP . . . . . . . . . . . . . . . . . . . . 2315115
■ MC . . . . . . . . . . . . . . . . . . . .3110 073
Polydor / '73.

## SHE'S GOTTA HAVE IT (Film Soundtrack) (Various Artists).
**Tracks:** She's gotta have it (Opening credits) / Brooklyn Bridge / He's on it / Thought / Nola / Ferrybank restaurant / Work montage / Who will be the one / Nola- instrumental / Thought, A (reprise) / Nola cleans up / Opal / Final confession / Ind Line / She's walkin' / Opal (reprise) / Hawk / Nola - piano / End credits.
■ LP . . . . . . . . . . . . . . . . . . . . AN 8713
■ MC . . . . . . . . . . . . . . . . . . . ANC 8713
Antilles/New Directions / Mar '87.

## SHORT EYES (Mayfield, Curtis).
**Tracks:** Do do wap is strong here / Back against the wall / Need someone to love / Heavy dude / Short eyes / Break it down / Another fool in love / Father confessor.
■ LP . . . . . . . . . . . . . . . . . . . . K 564444
Warner Bros. / Mar '78.

## SISTER ACT 2: BACK IN THE HABIT (Various Artists).
**Tracks:** Greatest medley ever told / Never should've let you go / Get up offa that thing / Dancing in the street / Oh happy day / Ball of confusion (that's what the world is today) / His eye is on the sparrow / Deeper love / Wandering eyes / Pay attention / Ode to joy / Joyful, joyful / Ain't no mountain high enough.
CD . . . . . . . . . . . . . . . . . . .74321 18455-2
MC . . . . . . . . . . . . . . . . . . .74321 18455-4
Arista / Jan '94 / BMG.

## SOUL MAN (Film Soundtrack) (Various Artists).
**Tracks:** Soul man / Outside / Bang, bang, bang (who's on the phone) / Totally academic / Suddenly it's magic / Sweet Sarah / Black girls / Models / Love and affection / Eek-ah-bo-static automatic.
MC . . . . . . . . . . . . . . . . . . . AMC 3903
■ LP . . . . . . . . . . . . . . . . . . . AMA 3903
A&M / Jan '87 / PolyGram.

## SOUL TO SOUL (Various Artists).
**Tracks:** Not Advised.
■ LP . . . . . . . . . . . . . . . . . . . . 2400201
Atlantic / Jan '72.

## STAYIN' ALIVE (Film Soundtrack) (Various Artists).
**Tracks:** Woman in you / Love you too much / Breakout / Someone belonging to someone / Life goes on / Stayin' alive / Far from over / Look out for number one / Finding out the hard way / Moody girl / (We dance) so close to the fire / I'm never gonna give you up.
CD . . . . . . . . . . . . . . . . . . . . 813 269-2
■ LP . . . . . . . . . . . . . . . . . . . . RSBG 3
MC . . . . . . . . . . . . . . . . . . . TRSBG 3
RSO / Jul '83 / PolyGram.

## SUPERFLY (Film soundtrack) (Mayfield, Curtis).
**Tracks:** Little child runnin' wild / Freddie's dead / Give me your love (Love song) / No thing on me (cocaine song) / Superfly / Pusherman / Junkie chase (Instrumental) / Eddie you should know better / Think (Instrumental).
■ LP . . . . . . . . . . . . . . . . . . . . 2318065
Buddah / Nov '72.

■ DELETED

■ LP . . . . . . . . . . . . . . . . . . . RSS 5
RSO / Sep '79.
LP . . . . . . . . . . . . . . . . . . CUR 2002
MC. . . . . . . . . . . . . . . . . . ZZCUR 2002
Ichiban / Jun '88 / A.D.A. Distribution / Pinnacle /
ACD Trading Ltd. / Koch International / Direct
Distribution.
CD . . . . . . . . . . . . . . . . . . MPG 74028
Movieplay Gold / Nov '93 / Target / BMG.
MC. . . . . . . . . . . . . . . . . MPG 474028
Movieplay Gold / Jan '94 / Target / BMG.
CD . . . . . . . . . . . . . . . . . CDCUR 2002
Ichiban / Oct '94 / A.D.A. Distribution / Pinnacle /
ACD Trading Ltd. / Koch International / Direct
Distribution.
CD . . . . . . . . . . . . . . . . . CURCD 2002
Curtom / Sep '94 / ACD Trading Ltd. / Pinnacle /
Koch International.

## T.C.B. - THE ORIGINAL SOUNDTRACK (Ross, Diana & The Supremes With The Temptations).
Tracks: T.C.B. / Stop, in the name of love / You keep
me hangin' on / Get ready / Way you do the things
you do / Taste of honey / Eleanor Rigby / Do you
know the way to San Jose / Mrs. Robinson / Respect
/ Somewhere / Ain't too proud to beg / Hello, young
lovers / For once in my life / I know I'm losing you /
With a song in my heart / Without a song / Come see
about me / My world is empty without you / Baby
love / I hear a symphony / Impossible dream.
■ LP . . . . . . . . . . . . . . . . . STML 11110
Tamla Motown / Jul '69.

## THANK GOD IT'S FRIDAY (Film Soundtrack) (Various Artists).
Tracks: Not Advised.
■ LP . . . . . . . . . . . . . . . . . . K 66076
Casablanca / May '78.

## TOUGH GUYS/TRUCK TURNER (Hayes, Isaac).
Tracks: Title theme / Randolph & Dearborn / Red
rooster / Joe Bell / Hung up on my baby / Kidnapped
/ Run Fay run / Buns o'plenty / End theme / Main
title: Truck Turner / House of beauty / Blue's crib /
Driving in the sun / Breakthrough / Now we're one /
Duke / Dorinda's party / Persuit of the pimpmobile /
We need each other girl / House full of girls /
Hospital shootout / You're in my arms again / Give it
to me / Drinking / Insurance company.
CD . . . . . . . . . . . . . . . . CDSXE 2095
Stax / Jul '93 / Pinnacle.

## TROUBLE MAN (Film soundtrack) (Gaye, Marvin).
Tracks: Trouble man main theme (2) / 'T' plays it
cool / Poor Abbey Walsh / Break in (police shoot big)
/ Cleo's apartment / Trouble man / Trouble man,
Theme from / 'T' stands for trouble / Trouble man
main theme (1) / Life is a gamble / Deep in it / Don't
mess with Mr. T / There goes mister 'T'.
■ LP . . . . . . . . . . . . . . . . . STML 11225
Tamla Motown / Feb '73.
■ LP . . . . . . . . . . . . . . . . . STMS 5065
■ MC . . . . . . . . . . . . . . . . . CSTMS 5065
Motown / Jul '82.
■ LP . . . . . . . . . . . . . . . . . . WL 72215
■ MC . . . . . . . . . . . . . . . . . . WK 72215
Motown / '86.
■ CD . . . . . . . . . . . . . . . . . . WD 72215
Motown / Sep '91.
CD . . . . . . . . . . . . . . . . . . .530097-2
Motown / Jan '92 / PolyGram.

## UPTIGHT (Booker T & The MG's).
Tracks: Johnny, I love you / Cleveland now / Chil-
dren don't get weary / Tank's lament / Blues in the
gutter / We've got Johnny Wells / Down at Ralph's
joint / Deadwood Dick / Run tank run / Time is tight.
■ LP . . . . . . . . . . . . . . . . SXATS 1005
Stax / Jun '69.
CD . . . . . . . . . . . . . . . . . CDSXE 024
■ LP . . . . . . . . . . . . . . . . . SXE 024
Stax / Jan '90 / Pinnacle.

## WATTSTAX (Various Artists).
Tracks: Oh la de da / I like the things about you /
Respect yourself / I'll take you there / Knock on
wood / Lay your loving on me / I like what you're
doing (to me) / Gee Whiz / I have a God who loves /
Do the breakdown / Do the funky chicken / Do the
Funky Penguin / Son of shaft / Feel it / I can't turn
you loose / Killing floor / I'll play the blues for you /
Angel of mercy / I don't know what this world is
coming to / Hearsay / Ain't no sunshine.
CD Set . . . . . . . . . . . . . . CDSXE2 079
Stax / Nov '92 / Pinnacle.

## WHAT'S LOVE GOT TO DO WITH IT (Turner, Tina).
Tracks: I don't wanna fight / Rock me baby / Disco
inferno / Why must we wait until tonight / Stay awhile

/ Nutbush City Limits / You know I love you / Proud
Mary / Fool in love / It's gonna work out fine / Shake
a tailfeather / I might have been Queen / What's love
got to do with it (live) / Tina's wish.
CD . . . . . . . . . . . . . . . . CDPSCD 128
MC. . . . . . . . . . . . . . . . . TCPCSD 128
MiniDisc. . . . . . . . . . . . . . MDPCSD 128
■ LP . . . . . . . . . . . . . . . . . PCSD 128
EMI / Jun '93 / EMI.

## WHITE MEN CAN'T JUMP (Film Sound-track) (Various Artists).
Tracks: White men can't jump / Sympin ain't easy /
Hook / Let me make it up to you tonight / Don't ever
let 'em see you sweat / I'm going up / Can you come
out and play / Watch me do my thang / If I lose /
Jump for it / Just a closer walk with thee.
CD . . . . . . . . . . . . . . . . CDMTL 1067
■ LP . . . . . . . . . . . . . . . . . MTL 1067
MC. . . . . . . . . . . . . . . . . TCMTL 1067
EMI-Manhattan / Jul '92 / EMI.

## WHO'S THE MAN (Various Artists).
Tracks: Not Advised.
CD . . . . . . . . . . . . . . . . . MCD 10794
■ LP . . . . . . . . . . . . . . . . MCA 10794
■ MC . . . . . . . . . . . . . . . . MCC 10794
MCA / May '93 / BMG.

## WIRED (Film Soundtrack) (Various Artists).
Tracks: I'm a king bee / Soul man / Raven's theme /
Two thousand pounds / Still looking for a way / You
are so beautiful / I can't turn you loose / You don't
know like I know / Choice / Bee / Angel of death.
CD . . . . . . . . . . . . . . . . . VSD 5237
■ LP . . . . . . . . . . . . . . . . . VS 5237
MC. . . . . . . . . . . . . . . . . VSC 5237
Varese Sarabande Records / Oct '89 / Silva Screen /
Pinnacle.

## WOMAN IN RED (Film soundtrack) (Wonder, Stevie).
Tracks: Woman in red / It's you / It's more than you /
I just called to say I love you / Love light in flight /
Moments aren't moments / Weakness / Don't drive
drunk.
■ LP . . . . . . . . . . . . . . . . . ZL 72285
■ MC . . . . . . . . . . . . . . . . . ZK 72285
Motown / Sep '84.
■ CD . . . . . . . . . . . . . . . . . WD 72609
Motown / Oct '87.
CD . . . . . . . . . . . . . . . . . .530030-2
MC. . . . . . . . . . . . . . . . . .530030-4
Motown / Jan '93 / PolyGram.

## Fine Quality

### AAH DANCE.
Tracks: Aah dance.
■ 12" . . . . . . . . . . . . . . . . . SHL 110
■ 7" . . . . . . . . . . . . . . . . . . SH 110
Sugarhill / Feb '82.

## Finished Touch

### DOWN SOUND.
Tracks: Down sound / Down sound (part 2).
■ 7" . . . . . . . . . . . . . . . . . TMG 1151
Motown / Jul '79.

### NEED TO KNOW YOU BETTER.
Tracks: Need to know you better / I love to see you
dance / Trying to kick the habit / Dancin' on / New
frontiers / Sunshine love / You dance into my life /
Mighty good friends / Strokin'.
■ LP . . . . . . . . . . . . . . . . STML 12095
Motown / Oct '78.

## First Choice

Singing as the Debronettes in the late sixties this all girl band were introduced to
writer/producer Alan Felder and Norman
Harris, guitarist with MFSB, who produced
their first single *This Is The House Where
Love Died*. Although it sold poorly it led to a
deal with Philly Groove and *Armed And
Extremely Dangerous* became a Top 30 hit
on both sides of the Atlantic in 1973. Later
singles also sold well particularly *Smarty
Pants* which became a U.K. Top 10. They
moved to the Salsoul label in 1977 and issued two
singles but split in 1984. Reformed in 1987
by Rochelle Fleming to release a single, a
consequent reissue of 1977's *Let No Man
Put Asunder* became a dance hit in the UK.

### ARMED AND EXTREMELY DANGEROUS.
Tracks: Armed and extremely dangerous.
■ . . . . . . . . . . . . . . . . . BELL 1297
Bell / May '73.

### BEST OF FIRST CHOICE.
Tracks: Armed & extremely dangerous / Smarty
pants / One step away / Newsy neighbours / This
little woman / This is the house (where love is) /
Love & happiness / Runnin' out of fools / Wake up to
me / Player / Guilty / Love freeze / Boy named
Junior / All I need is time / Guess what Mary Jones
did / Hustler Bill / You took the words right out of my
mouth / You've been doing wrong (for so long) /
Don't fake it / Why can't I touch you (if you let me
make love to you) / This is the house.
CD . . . . . . . . . . . . . . . . CDSEWD 096
South Bound / Aug '94 / Pinnacle.

### DELUSIONS.
Tracks: Not Advised.
CD . . . . . . . . . . . . . . . . . CPCD 8060
LP . . . . . . . . . . . . . . . . . CPLP 8060
Charly / Nov '94 / Charly.

### DOCTOR LOVE.
Tracks: Dr. Love / I love you more than before.
■ 7" . . . . . . . . . . . . . . . . . SSOL 104
Salsoul / Aug '78.

### DR. LOVE.
Tracks: Dr. Love / Let no man put asunder / Let no
man put asunder (mixes).
■ 12" . . . . . . . . . . . . . . . . 12 SALSA 7
■ 12" Remix. . . . . . . . . . . . . 12 SALSA 7
■ CD Single. . . . . . . . . . . . . CDSALSAR 7
■ MC Single. . . . . . . . . . . . CSSALSAR 7
Salsoul / Jul '93.

### HOLD YOUR HORSES.
Tracks: Let me down easy / Good morning midnight /
Great expectations / Hold your horses / Love thang /
Double cross.
■ LP . . . . . . . . . . . . . . . . . SSLP 1514
Salsoul / '79.

### HOLD YOUR HORSES.
Tracks: Hold your horses / Now that you've thrown it
all away.
■ 7" . . . . . . . . . . . . . . . . . SSOL 115
Salsoul / Jan '79.

### LET NO MAN PUT ASUNDER.
Tracks: Let no man put asunder.
■ 12" . . . . . . . . . . . . . . . . . OUS 3
■ 7" . . . . . . . . . . . . . . . . . 7OUS 3
Serious / Jun '87.

### SMARTY PANTS.
Tracks: Smarty pants.
■ 7" . . . . . . . . . . . . . . . . . BELL 1324
Bell / Aug '73.

## First Circle

### BOYS NIGHT OUT.
Tracks: Working up a sweat / Miracle worker / In the
name of love / Dream you came back / Get off it /
Can't find a love / You're on my mind / Boy's night
out.
■ MC . . . . . . . . . . . . . . . . TCAML 3118
■ LP . . . . . . . . . . . . . . . . . AML 3118
EMI-America / Apr '87.

### CAN'T FIND A LOVE.
Tracks: Can't find a love.
■ 12" . . . . . . . . . . . . . . . . . V 19264
EMI-America / Sep '87.

### MIRACLE WORKER.
Tracks: Miracle worker (radio edit) / Miracle worker
(dub version) / Can't find a love (On 12" only).
■ 7" . . . . . . . . . . . . . . . . . EA 232
■ 12" . . . . . . . . . . . . . . . . 12 EA 232
■ 12" Remix. . . . . . . . . . . . . 12EAX 232
EMI-America / May '87.

## First Light

### A.M.
Tracks: A.M.
■ 12" . . . . . . . . . . . . . . . FLIGHT 23/12
■ 7" . . . . . . . . . . . . . . . . FLIGHT 23
Oval / Nov '82.

### DON'T BE MISTAKEN.
Tracks: Don't be mistaken / Horse with no name.
■ 7" . . . . . . . . . . . . . . . FLIGHT 22-12
Oval / May '82.

## EXPLAIN THE REASON.
Tracks: Explain the reason.
- 12" . . . . . . . . . . . . . . . . . . . . . . LONX 26
- 7" . . . . . . . . . . . . . . . . . . . . . . . LON 26
London / May '83.

## FIRST LIGHT.
Tracks: Don't be mistaken / Explain the reason / Daybreak / I don't care / Horse with no name / AM / She's a mystery / Time machine.
- LP . . . . . . . . . . . . . . . . . . . . . . .8132 241
Metronome / Aug '83.

## HORSE WITH NO NAME.
Tracks: Horse with no name / Don't be mistaken.
- 12" . . . . . . . . . . . . . . . . . . . .FLIGHT 12 22
- 7" . . . . . . . . . . . . . . . . . . . . . FLIGHT 22
Oval / Jun '84.

## LOVING YOU.
Tracks: Loving you / No way out.
- 12" . . . . . . . . . . . . . . . . . . . . . .SGT 121
- 7" . . . . . . . . . . . . . . . . . . . . . . . SGT 1
- CD Single . . . . . . . . . . . . . . . . . CDSGT 1
Sgt.Pepper / May '89.

## RIGHT OR WRONG.
Tracks: Right or wrong.
- 12" . . . . . . . . . . . . . . . . . . . . . .SGT 123
- 7" . . . . . . . . . . . . . . . . . . . . . . . SGT 3
- CD Single . . . . . . . . . . . . . . . . . . SGD 3
Sgt.Pepper / May '90.

## SO EASY.
Tracks: So easy / No way out.
- 12" . . . . . . . . . . . . . . . . . . . . . .SGT 128
Sgt.Pepper / Nov '90.

## WISH YOU WERE HERE.
Tracks: Wish you were here / Stop the clock.
- 12" . . . . . . . . . . . . . . . . . . . . . .LONX 43
- 7" . . . . . . . . . . . . . . . . . . . . . . LON 43
London / Jan '84.

## YOU HAD IT ALL.
Tracks: Right or wrong / Illusion / You had it all / Winner / You and me / Loving you / So easy / No way out / I'll write again / Don't push me.
- CD . . . . . . . . . . . . . . . . . . . . . . SGTCD 1
- LP . . . . . . . . . . . . . . . . . . . . . . SGTLP 1
- MC . . . . . . . . . . . . . . . . . . . . . . SGTMC 1
Sgt.Pepper / Mar '90 / BMG.

## First Love

### THINGS ARE NOT THE SAME.
Tracks: Things are not the same / Without you (extended version) / Can I be with you tonight.
- 12" . . . . . . . . . . . . . . . . . . . . . TEN 43-12
- 7" . . . . . . . . . . . . . . . . . . . . . . TEN 43
10 / Feb '85.

## Fischer, Lisa

### HOW CAN I EASE THE PAIN.
Tracks: How can I ease the pain.
- 12" . . . . . . . . . . . . . . . . . . . . . EKR 127T
Elektra / Jun '91.

### SAVE ME.
Tracks: Save me.
- 12" . . . . . . . . . . . . . . . . . . . . . EKR 134T
- 7" . . . . . . . . . . . . . . . . . . . . . .EKR 134
- CD Single . . . . . . . . . . . . . . . . . EKR 134CD
- MC Single . . . . . . . . . . . . . . . . . EKR 134C
Elektra / Oct '91.

### SO INTENSE.
Tracks: Save me / Get back to love / How can I ease the pain / So intense / Wildflower / Some girls / So tender / Send the message of love / Chain of broken hearts / Last goodbye.
- CD . . . . . . . . . . . . . . . . . . . . . 7559608892
- LP . . . . . . . . . . . . . . . . . . . . . 7559608891
- MC . . . . . . . . . . . . . . . . . . . . . 7559608894
Elektra / May '91 / WEA.

### SO INTENSE.
Tracks: So intense.
- 12" . . . . . . . . . . . . . . . . . . . . . .EKT 87C
- 7" . . . . . . . . . . . . . . . . . . . . . . EKT 87
Elektra / May '91.

## Fishbelly Black

### FISHBELLY BLACK.
Tracks: Not Advised.
- CD . . . . . . . . . . . . . . . . . . . . . . BBCD 72107
Backbeat / Dec '93 / Jetstar.

### GET UP, GET DOWN (Fishbelly Black & Roy Ayers).
Tracks: Not Advised.
- CD . . . . . . . . . . . . . . . . . . . . . . BBCD 72112
Backbeat / Feb '94.

## Five Special

### JUST A FEELING.
Tracks: Just a feeling.
- 12" . . . . . . . . . . . . . . . . . . . . K 12588T
- 7" . . . . . . . . . . . . . . . . . . . . . K 12588
Elektra / Jan '82.

### WHY LEAVE US ALONE.
Tracks: Why leave us alone / Why leave us alone (instrumental).
- 7" . . . . . . . . . . . . . . . . . . . . . K 12368
WEA / '79.

### YOU'RE SOMETHING SPECIAL.
Tracks: You're something special / It's such a groove / Watcha got for music.
- 7" . . . . . . . . . . . . . . . . . . . . . K 12388
Asylum / Nov '79.

## Five Stairsteps

### BEST OF THE FIVE STAIRSTEPS
Tracks: You waited too long / Comeback / Behind curtains / Under the spell of your love / Baby make me feel so good / Love's happening / Little young lover / Ooh child / Because I love you / I love you stop / I feel a song in my heart / Hush child / Look out / World of fantasy / Danger, she's a stranger / Ooo baby baby / Don't change your love / We must be in love / Stay close to me / I'm the one who loves you / Dear Prudence / Didn't it look so easy / Peace is gonna come / Easy way / Snow.
- CD . . . . . . . . . . . . . . . . . . . . . NEXCD 114
Sequel / May '90.

### OOH CHILD.
Tracks: Ooh child / Because I love you.
- 7" . . . . . . . . . . . . . . . . . . . . . .BDS 429
Buddah / Apr '75.

## Five Star

### ALL FALL DOWN.
Tracks: All fall down / First Avenue.
- 12" . . . . . . . . . . . . . . . . . . . . . PT 40040
- 7" . . . . . . . . . . . . . . . . . . . . . PB 40039
RCA / Apr '85.

### ANOTHER WEEKEND.
Tracks: Another weekend / Mews / Another weekend (extended remix) / Another weekend (dub mix).
- 12" . . . . . . . . . . . . . . . . . . . . . PT 42082
- 7" . . . . . . . . . . . . . . . . . . . . . PB 42081
RCA / May '88.

### BETWEEN THE LINES.
Tracks: Somewhere somebody / Whenever you're ready / Strong as steel / Read between the lines / Live giving love / Ain't watcha do / Made out of love / You should have waited / Knock twice / Hard race.
- MC . . . . . . . . . . . . . . . . . . . . . PK 71505
- CD . . . . . . . . . . . . . . . . . . . . . PD 71505
- LP . . . . . . . . . . . . . . . . . . . . . PL 71505
RCA / Sep '87.

### BETWEEN THE LINES.
Tracks: Find the time / Ain't watcha do / Rain or shine / All fall down / Let me be the one / Love take over / R.S.V.P. / System addict / If I say yes / Whenever you're ready / System addict (instrumental) / Stay out of my life / Somewhere somebody / Slightest touch / Strong as steel.
- VHS . . . . . . . . . . . . . . . MVP 99 1160 2

### CAN'T WAIT ANOTHER MINUTE.
Tracks: Can't wait another minute.
- 7" . . . . . . . . . . . . . . . . . . . . . PB 40697
Tent / Apr '86.

### CRAZY.
Tracks: Crazy / I like the way you dance.
- 12" . . . . . . . . . . . . . . . . . . . . . RCAT 451
- 7" . . . . . . . . . . . . . . . . . . . . . .RCA 451
RCA / Oct '84.

### FIND THE TIME.
Tracks: Find the time / Sky.
- 12" . . . . . . . . . . . . . . . . . . . . . PT 40800
- 7" . . . . . . . . . . . . . . . . . . . . . PB 40799
Tent / Jul '86.

### FIVE STAR.
Tracks: Slightest touch / System addict / Can't wait another minute / Another weekend / With every heartbeat / Stay out of my life / Rain or shine / Find the time / R.S.V.P. / Love take over / If I say yes / Let me be the one / Strong as steel / There's a brand new world / Rock my world / All fall down.
- CD . . . . . . . . . . . . . . . . . . . . . .4667042
- LP . . . . . . . . . . . . . . . . . . . . . .4667041
- MC . . . . . . . . . . . . . . . . . . . . . .4667044
Epic / Apr '90 / Sony.
- CD . . . . . . . . . . . . . . . . . .74321 18325-2
- MC . . . . . . . . . . . . . . . . . .74321 18325-4
Ariola Express / Feb '94 / BMG.

### GREATEST HITS: FIVE STAR.
Tracks: Can't wait another minute / Whenever you're ready / Rain or shine / Find the time / System addict / Stay out of my life / Let me be the one / Rock my world / With every heartbeat (CD only.) / Slightest touch / All fall down / If I say yes / Somewhere somebody / R.S.V.P. / Strong as steel / Love take over / Another weekend / Something about my baby (CD only.).
- LP . . . . . . . . . . . . . . . . . . . . . PL 74080
- CD . . . . . . . . . . . . . . . . . . . . . PD 74080
- MC . . . . . . . . . . . . . . . . . . . . . PK 74080
RCA / Oct '89.

### GREATEST HITS: FIVE STAR.
Tracks: Can't wait another minute / Whenever you're ready / Rain or shine / Find the time / System addict / Stay out of my life / Let me be the one / Rock my world / Slightest touch / All fall down / If I say yes / R.S.V.P. / Strong as steel / Love take over / Another weekend.
- VHS . . . . . . . . . . . . . . . . . . . . . 790 327
BMG Video / Nov '89.

### GREATEST HITS: FIVE STAR.
Tracks: Rain or shine / R.S.V.P. / Can't wait another minute / System addict / Hide and seek / All fall down.
- MC . . . . . . . . . . . . . . . . . . . . . THPA 1231
Telstar/Ronco / Nov '87 / BMG.

### HIDE AND SEEK.
Tracks: Hide and seek / I'm gonna make this a night . .
- 12" . . . . . . . . . . . . . . . . . . . . . .RCAT 399
- 7" . . . . . . . . . . . . . . . . . . . . . .RCA 399
RCA / May '84.

### HOT LOVE.
Tracks: Hot love / Act one / Hot love (extended version) (Only on 12" and CD single.).
- MC Single . . . . . . . . . . . . . . . . . .FIVE M2
Epic / Jul '90.
- 12" . . . . . . . . . . . . . . . . . . . . .FIVE T 2
- 7" . . . . . . . . . . . . . . . . . . . . . .FIVE P 2
- CD Single . . . . . . . . . . . . . . . . . CDFIVE 2
Epic / Jun '90.

### IF I SAY YES.
Tracks: If I say yes / Let me down easy / Can't wait another minute / Say goodbye / Crazy / Winning.
- 12" . . . . . . . . . . . . . . . . . . . . . PT 40982
- 7" . . . . . . . . . . . . . . . . . . . . . PB 40981
RCA / Nov '86.

### LAST TAKEOVER.
Tracks: Last takeover / Keep in touch / Let me be the one (Only on 12" single.).
- 12" . . . . . . . . . . . . . . . . . . . . . PT 40354
- 7" . . . . . . . . . . . . . . . . . . . . . PB 40353
RCA / Aug '85.

### LET ME BE THE ONE.
Tracks: Let me be the one / Beat 47 / Love games (on 12" only).
- 12" . . . . . . . . . . . . . . . . . . . . . PT 40194
- 7" . . . . . . . . . . . . . . . . . . . . . PB 40193
RCA / Jul '85.

PMI / Dec '87.
- VHS . . . . . . . . . . . . . . . . . . . . . MVA 011
PMI / Jun '90.

142

■ DELETED

## LET ME BE YOURS.
Tracks: Let me be yours / Let me be yours (remix) (Track on 12" version.) / Someone's in love (dub) (On 12" only.) / Can't wait another minute (Track on CD single only.).
- ■ 12" ............................ PT 42344
- ■ 7" ............................. PB 42343
- ■ CD Single ...................... PD 42344

RCA / Nov '88.

## LUXURY OF LIFE.
Tracks: Love take over / All fall down / Let me be the one / System addict / Hide and seek / R.S.V.P. / Now I'm in control.
- ■ LP .............................. PL 70735
- ■ MC .............................. PK 70735
- ■ CD .............................. PD 70735

Tent / Aug '86.
- CD ................................ ND 74515
- MC ................................ NK 74515

RCA / Feb '90 / BMG.

## LUXURY OF LIFE VIDEO SELECTION.
Tracks: Not Advised.
- VHS .............................. RVT 10930

RCA / May '86 / BMG.

## MUSIC AND MEDIA INTERVIEW PICTURE DISC.
Tracks: Not Advised.
- LP P.Disc ........................ MM 1203

Music & Media / Feb '88.

## PROBLEMATIC.
Tracks: Problematic / Big funk.
- ■ 12" ........................... TENTT 4
- ■ 7" ............................ TENT 4

Tent / Oct '83.

## R.S.V.P.
Tracks: R.S.V.P.
- ■ 7" ............................. PB 40445
- ■ 12" ............................ PT 40446

Tent / Nov '85.

## RAIN OR SHINE.
Tracks: Rain or shine.
- ■ 12" ............................ PT 40902
- ■ 7" ............................. PB 40901

Tent / Aug '86.

## ROCK MY WORLD.
Tracks: Rock my world.
- ■ 12" ............................ PT 42146
- ■ 7" ............................. PB 42145

RCA / Jul '88.

## ROCK THE WORLD.
Tracks: Free time / Physical attraction / Someone's in love / If I say yes / Please don't say goodnight / Stay out of my life / Are you man enough / Show me what you've got for me / Slightest touch / Don't you know I love you.
- ■ CD ............................. PD 71747
- ■ LP ............................. PL 71747
- ■ MC ............................. PK 71747

Tent / Aug '88.

## SHINE.
Tracks: Shine / Feelings.
- ■ 12" ............................ 6574806
- ■ 7" ............................. 6574807
- ■ CD Single ...................... 6574802
- ■ MC Single ...................... 6574804

Epic / Oct '91.

## SILK AND STEEL.
Tracks: Can't wait another minute / Find the time / Rain or shine / If I say yes / Please don't say goodnight / Stay out of my life / Are you man enough / Show me what you've got for me / Slightest touch / Don't you know I love you.
- ■ CD ............................. PD 71100
- ■ LP ............................. PL 71100
- ■ MC ............................. PK 71100

Tent / Aug '86.

## SILK AND STEEL.
Tracks: Not Advised.
- VHS .............................. RVT 11268

RCA/Columbia (Video) / '87 / Gold & Sons / THE / Sony.

## SLIGHTEST TOUCH.
Tracks: Slightest touch.
- ■ 12" ............................ PT 41266

RCA / Apr '87.

## SLIGHTEST TOUCH, THE (OLD GOLD).
Tracks: Slightest touch / Love takeover.
- 12" .............................. OG 4201

Old Gold / Jun '91 / Pickwick.

## SOMEWHERE SOMEBODY.
Tracks: Somewhere somebody / Have a good time.
- ■ 12" ............................ PT 41662
- ■ 7" ............................. PB 41661

RCA / Nov '87.

## STRONG AS STEEL.
Tracks: Strong as steel / Man / Can't wait another minute.
- ■ MC Single ...................... PB 41565C

RCA / Nov '78.
- ■ 12" ............................ PT 41566
- ■ 7" ............................. PB 41565

RCA / Sep '87.

## SYSTEM ADDICT.
Tracks: System addict / Pure energy / Winning.
- ■ 12" ............................ PT 40516
- ■ 7" ............................. PB 40515

Tent / Jan '86.
- ■ CD Single ...................... PD 42647

Tent / Jun '89.

## THERE'S A BRAND NEW WORLD.
Tracks: There's a brand new world / U / Rescue me (Only on 12".).
- ■ 12" ............................ PT 42236
- ■ 7" ............................. PB 42235

RCA / Sep '88.
- ■ CD Single ...................... PD 42236

RCA / Jun '89.

## TREAT ME LIKE A LADY.
Tracks: Treat me like a lady (7" only) / Don't stop / Treat me like a lady (ext. version) (Not on 7".) / Treat me like a lady (tough mix) (Not on 7".) / Treat me like a lady (tough mix) (FIVE QT1 only.) / Treat me like a lady (tough dub) (FIVE QT1 only.).
- ■ 12" ............................ FIVE T1
- ■ 7" ............................. FIVE 1
- ■ 7" ............................. FIVE Q1
- ■ CD Single ...................... CDFIVE 1

Epic / Feb '90.
- ■ 12" ............................ FIVE QT1
- ■ MC Single ...................... FIVE M1

Epic / Mar '90.

## WHENEVER YOU'RE READY.
Tracks: Whenever you're ready.
- ■ 12" ............................ PT 41478
- ■ 7" ............................. PB 41477

Tent / Aug '87.

## WITH EVERY HEARTBEAT.
Tracks: With every heartbeat / Sound sweet / Let me be yours / With every heartbeat (dub).
- ■ MC Single ...................... PK 42693

RCA / Apr '89.
- ■ 7" ............................. PB 42693 G
- ■ 12" ............................ PT 42694
- ■ 7" ............................. PB 42693
- ■ CD Single ...................... PD 42694

RCA / Mar '89.

# Flack, Roberta

Unlikely soul guru Clint Eastwood secured Flack's reputation by featuring her version of *First Time Ever I Saw Your Face* in 1972 movie *Play Misty For Me*. Originally released on her 1969 *First Take* debut, song topped U.S. charts and made No. 14 in U.K. '72 also marked beginning of collaboration with fellow Atlantic star Donny Hathaway that lasted until his suicide in '79 (one of their final recordings, *Back Together Again*, became Flack's biggest U.K. hit, reaching No. 3 in 1980). Moderately successful solo releases were again eclipsed in 1981 by collaboration with Peabo Bryson, which peaked with '83 smash *Tonight I Celebrate My Love*. Subsequent decade was less eventful chart-wise, although hits collection *Softly With These Songs* was silver-selling Top 10 success in '94.

## BACK TOGETHER AGAIN (Flack, Roberta & Donny Hathaway).
Tracks: Back together again / First time I ever saw your face.
- ■ 12" ............................ K 11481 T
- ■ 7" ............................. K 11481

Atlantic / '80.
- ■ CD Single ...................... A 5681CD

Atlantic / Feb '94.

## BEST OF ROBERTA FLACK.
Tracks: Killing me softly with his song / Closer I get to you / You've got a friend / Feel like makin' love / Will you love me tomorrow / Where is the love / First time ever I saw your face / Back together again / If I ever see you again / You are my heaven / Jesse.
- ■ LP ............................. K 50840

MC ................................ K4 50840

Atlantic / '81 / WEA.
- CD ................................ 250840 2

Atlantic / Feb '87 / WEA.
- CD ................................ 250840

Atlantic / '89 / WEA.

## BEST OF ROBERTA FLACK - SOFTLY WITH THESE SONGS.
Tracks: First time ever I saw your face / Will you still love me tomorrow / Where is the love / Killing me softly with his song / Feel like makin' love / Closer I get to you / More than everything / Only heaven can wait (for love) / Back together again / Making love / Tonight, I celebrate my love / Oasis / And so it goes / You know what it's like / Set the night to music / My foolish heart / Uh-uh ooh-ooh look out (here it comes).
- CD ................................ 756782498-2
- MC ................................ 756782498-4

East West / Feb '94 / WEA.

## BLUE LIGHTS IN THE BASEMENT.
Tracks: Why don't you move in with me / Closer I get to you / Fine fine day / This time I'll be sweeter / 25th of last December / After you / I'd like to be baby to you / Soul deep / Love is the healing / Where I'll find you.
- ■ LP ............................. K 50440
- ■ MC ............................. K4 50440

Atlantic / Mar '78.

## BORN TO LOVE (Flack, Roberta & Peabo Bryson).
Tracks: Tonight, I celebrate my love / Blame it on me / Heaven above / Born to love / Maybe / I just came here to dance / Comin' alive / You're lookin' like love to me / Can we find love again.
- ■ LP ............................. ATAK 2
- ■ MC ............................. TCATAK 2
- ■ LP ............................. EST 7122841

Capitol / Sep '83.
- CD ................................ MUSCD 508
- MC ................................ MUSMC 508

Music Collection International / Nov '94 / THE / Jazz Music.

## CHAPTER TWO.
Tracks: Reverend Lee / Do what you gotta do / Just like a woman / Let it be me / Gone away / Until it's time for you to go / Impossible dream / Business goes on as usual.
- ■ LP ............................. K 40097

Atlantic.
- ■ LP ............................. 2400 023

Atlantic / Dec '70.

## CLOSER I GET TO YOU, THE (Flack, Roberta & Donny Hathaway).
Tracks: Closer I get to you / Love is the healing.
- ■ 7" ............................. K 11099

Atlantic / May '78.

## COME SHARE MY LOVE.
Tracks: Come share my love / When it's over.
- ■ 7" ............................. K 11211

Atlantic / Nov '78.

## DON'T MAKE ME WAIT TOO LONG.
Tracks: Don't make me wait too long.
- ■ 7" ............................. K 11555

Atlantic / Aug '80.

## EVENING WITH ROBERTA FLACK, AN.
Tracks: Not Advised.
- VHS .............................. V 9050

MSD / Sep '87 / Multiple Sound Distributors / Gold & Sons.

## FEEL LIKE MAKIN' LOVE.
Tracks: Feeling that glow / I wanted it too / I can see the sun in late December / Some gospel according to Mathew / Feel like makin' love / Mr. Magic / Early every midnight / Old heart break top ten / She's not blind.
- ■ LP ............................. K 50049

Atlantic.

## FEEL LIKE MAKIN' LOVE.
Tracks: Feel like makin' love.
- ■ 7" ............................. K 10467

Atlantic / Aug '74.

## FIRST TAKE.
Tracks: Compared to what / Angelitos negros / Our ages or our hearts / I told Jesus / Hey, that's no way to say goodbye / First time ever I saw your face / Tryin' times / Ballad of the sad young man.
- ■ LP ............................. 588 204

Atlantic / Nov '69.
- ■ LP ............................. K 40040
- ■ MC ............................. K4 40040

Atlantic / '88.

## FIRST TAKE / CHAPTER TWO.
**Tracks:** Compared to what / Angelitos negros / Our ages or your hearts / First time ever I saw your face / Trying times / Ballad of the sad young man / Do what you gotta do / Just like a woman / Let it be me / Gone away until it's time / Impossible dream / Business goes on as usual.
■ Double LP . . . . . . . . . . . . . . . . . . K 60062
Atlantic / '75.

## FIRST TIME I EVER SAW YOUR FACE.
**Tracks:** Killing me softly / First time ever I saw your face / Will you still love me tomorrow / Bridge over troubled water / To love somebody / Sunday & sister Jones / Sweet bitter love / Let them talk / See you then / Go up Moses.
■ LP . . . . . . . . . . . . . . . . . . . SHM 3022
Pickwick / Jun '80.

## FIRST TIME I EVER SAW YOUR FACE.
**Tracks:** First time ever I saw your face / Will you still love me tomorrow.
■ 7" . . . . . . . . . . . . . . . . . . . K 10161
Atlantic / '79.

## FIRST TIME I EVER SAW YOUR FACE.
**Tracks:** First time ever I saw your face / Killing me softly with his song.
■ 7" . . . . . . . . . . . . . . . . . . . K 10845
Atlantic / '84.

## GREATEST HITS: ROBERTA FLACK.
**Tracks:** Tonight, I celebrate my love / Feel like makin' love / Killing me softly with his song / You've got a friend / Closer I get to you / Will you love me tomorrow / Maybe / Where is the love / First time ever I saw your face / Jessie / If ever I see you again / You're lookin' like love to me / Don't make me wait too long / You are my Heaven / Heaven above me / Back together again.
■ LP . . . . . . . . . . . . . . . . . . . NE 1269
■ MC . . . . . . . . . . . . . . . . . . . CE 2269
K-Tel / '84.

## HEAVEN ABOVE ME (see under Bryson, Peabo).

## I'M THE ONE.
**Tracks:** I'm the one / Til the morning comes / Love and let love / Never loved before / In the name of love / Ordinary man / Making love / Happiness / My love for you.
■ LP . . . . . . . . . . . . . . . . . . . K 50890
Atlantic / '84.

## IN CONCERT.
**Tracks:** Not Advised.
VHS . . . . . . . . . . . . . . . . . . . OGV 0009
Old Gold / Jul '91 / Pickwick.

## INDEPENDENT MAN.
**Tracks:** Independent man / Feeling's good.
■ 7" . . . . . . . . . . . . . . . . . . . K 11238
Atlantic / Feb '79.

## KILLING ME SOFTLY.
**Tracks:** Killing me softly with his song / Jesse / No tears (In the end) / I'm the girl / River / Conversation love / When you smile / Suzanne.
■ MC . . . . . . . . . . . . . . . . . . . K4 50021
■ LP . . . . . . . . . . . . . . . . . . . K 50021
Atlantic / '74.

## KILLING ME SOFTLY WITH HIS SONG.
**Tracks:** Killing me softly with his song.
■ 7" . . . . . . . . . . . . . . . . . . . K 10282
Atlantic / Feb '73.

## KILLING ME SOFTLY WITH HIS SONG (OLD GOLD).
**Tracks:** Killing me softly with his song / First time ever I saw your face.
■ 7" . . . . . . . . . . . . . . . . . . . OG 9524
Old Gold / Jun '88.

## LET THE NIGHT TO MUSIC (Flack, Roberta with Maxi Priest).
**Tracks:** Let the night to music / First time ever I saw your face / Killing me softly with his song.
■ CD Single . . . . . . . . . . . . . . . A 7607CD
■ 12" . . . . . . . . . . . . . . . . . . A 7607T
■ 7" . . . . . . . . . . . . . . . . . . . A 7607
■ MC Single . . . . . . . . . . . . . . A 7607C
East West / Oct '91.

## LIVE - AND MORE (Flack, Roberta & Peabo Bryson).
**Tracks:** Only Heaven can wait / You are my Heaven / Make the world stand still / Feel the fire / Killing me softly with his song / More than everything / Feel like makin' love / When will I learn / Back together again / Love in every season / I believe in you / God don't like ugly / If only for one night / Love is a waiting

game / Reachin' for the sky / Don't make me wait too long.
■ Double LP . . . . . . . . . . . . . . K 60155
MC . . . . . . . . . . . . . . . . . . . K4 60155
Atlantic / '81 / WEA.

## LOVE IS A WAITING GAME (Flack, Roberta & Peabo Bryson).
**Tracks:** Love is a waiting game / Back together again.
■ 12" . . . . . . . . . . . . . . . . . . LV 45
■ 7" . . . . . . . . . . . . . . . . . . . K 11586
Atlantic / '81.

## MAKING LOVE.
**Tracks:** Making love / Jesse.
■ 12" . . . . . . . . . . . . . . . . . . K 11715 T
■ 7" . . . . . . . . . . . . . . . . . . . K 11715
Atlantic / '82.

## MAYBE.
**Tracks:** Maybe / I just came here to dance / Move your body (On 12" only).
■ 12" . . . . . . . . . . . . . . . . . . 12CL 327
■ 7" . . . . . . . . . . . . . . . . . . . CL 327
Capitol / '84.

## NO ONE EMOTION (see under Benson, George).

## OASIS.
**Tracks:** Oasis / Something magic / Uh uh ooh ooh look out (here it comes) / And so it goes / Shock to my system / You know what it's like / You who brought me love / And so it goes (reprise) / My someone to love / (His name) Brazil.
■ CD . . . . . . . . . . . . . . . . . . 781 916-2
■ LP . . . . . . . . . . . . . . . . . . . WX 229
■ MC . . . . . . . . . . . . . . . . . . . WX 229C
Atlantic / Oct '88.

## QUIET FIRE.
**Tracks:** Go up Moses / Bridge over troubled water / Sunday & Sister Jones / See you then / Will you still love me tomorrow / To love somebody / Let them talk / Sweet bitter love.
■ LP . . . . . . . . . . . . . . . . . . . K 40297
Atlantic / Apr '72.

## ROBERTA FLACK.
**Tracks:** What a woman really means / You are everything / Independent man / If ever I see you again / And the feeling's good / Knowing that we're made for each other / Come share my love / Baby I love you so / When it's over.
■ LP . . . . . . . . . . . . . . . . . . . K 50495
■ MC . . . . . . . . . . . . . . . . . . . K4 50495
Atlantic / Dec '78.

## ROBERTA FLACK IN CONCERT.
**Tracks:** Not Advised.
VHS . . . . . . . . . . . . . . . . . . . SVM 809
Start (Video) / Nov '92 / Sony Video Software.

## ROBERTA FLACK, FEATURING DONNY HATHAWAY (Flack, Roberta & Donny Hathaway).
**Tracks:** Only heaven can wait / God don't like ugly / You are my heaven / Disguises / Don't make me wait too long / Back together again / Stay with me.
■ MC . . . . . . . . . . . . . . . . . . . K4 50696
■ LP . . . . . . . . . . . . . . . . . . . K 50696
Atlantic / '80.

## SET THE NIGHT TO MUSIC.
**Tracks:** Waiting game / Set the night to music / When someone tears your heart in two / Something your heart has been telling me / You make me feel brand new / Unforgettable / Summertime / Natural thing / My foolish heart / Friend / Always.
CD . . . . . . . . . . . . . . . . . . . 7567823212
MC . . . . . . . . . . . . . . . . . . . 7567823214
LP . . . . . . . . . . . . . . . . . . . 7567823211
East West / Nov '91 / WEA.

## STAR PORTRAITS: ROBERTA FLACK.
**Tracks:** Not Advised.
VHS . . . . . . . . . . . . . . . . . . . GEMV 5011
Gemini Vision / Sep '94 / Sony / THE.

## TONIGHT I CELEBRATE MY LOVE FOR YOU (see under Bryson, Peabo).

## TONIGHT I CELEBRATE MY LOVE FOR YOU (DOUBLE A) (see under Bryson, Peabo).

## UH-UH OOH-OOH LOOK OUT(HERE IT COMES).
**Tracks:** Uh uh ooh ooh look out (here it comes).
■ 12" . . . . . . . . . . . . . . . . . . A 8941T
■ 7" . . . . . . . . . . . . . . . . . . . A 8941

■ MC Single . . . . . . . . . . . . . . A 8941C
Atlantic / Jun '89.

## WHERE IS THE LOVE (Flack, Roberta & Donny Hathaway).
**Tracks:** Where is the love.
■ 7" . . . . . . . . . . . . . . . . . . . K 10202
Atlantic / Aug '72.

## WHERE IS THE LOVE (OLD GOLD) (Flack, Roberta & Donny Hathaway).
**Tracks:** Where is the love / Back together again.
■ 7" . . . . . . . . . . . . . . . . . . . OG 9502
Old Gold / Jan '85.

## YOU ARE MY HEAVEN (Flack, Roberta & Donny Hathaway).
**Tracks:** You are my heaven / I'll love you forever.
■ 7" . . . . . . . . . . . . . . . . . . . K 11414
Atlantic / Jan '80.

## YOU'VE GOT A FRIEND (Flack, Roberta & Donny Hathaway).
**Tracks:** You've got a friend / Gone away.
■ 7" . . . . . . . . . . . . . . . . . . . 2091116
Atlantic / Jun '71.

# Flaming Ember

## WESTBOUND NO.9.
**Tracks:** Spinning wheel / Westbound no.9 / Mind, body and soul / Shades of green / Going in circles / Why don't you stay / Flashbacks and re-runs / This girl is a woman now / Stop the world (and let me off) / Heart on (loving you) / Where's all the joy / Empty crowded room / I'm not my brother's keeper.
■ LP . . . . . . . . . . . . . . . . . . . SHW 5001
Hot Wax / Jan '71.
■ LP . . . . . . . . . . . . . . . . . . . HDH LP 009
HDH / Oct '88.
CD . . . . . . . . . . . . . . . . . . . HDHCD 503
HDH / Apr '92 / Pinnacle.

## WESTBOUND NO.9.
**Tracks:** Westbound no.9 / Mind, body and soul.
■ 12" . . . . . . . . . . . . . . . . . . HDH 4512
HDH / Jan '85.

# Flaming Emeralds

## HAVE SOME EVERYBODY.
**Tracks:** Have some everybody / Have some everybody (instrumental).
■ . . . . . . . . . . . . . . . . . . . . GRP 104
Grapevine (Northern Soul) / Feb '78.

# Flamingos

## BOOGALOO PARTY.
**Tracks:** Boogaloo party / Jenny take a ride.
■ 7" . . . . . . . . . . . . . . . . . . . BF 1786
Philips / Jun '69.
■ 7" . . . . . . . . . . . . . . . . . . . CUT 114
Classic Cuts / Oct '80.

## CHESS SESSIONS, THE.
**Tracks:** Not Advised.
■ LP . . . . . . . . . . . . . . . . . . . DET 201
Chess (Charly) / Jul '87.

## I ONLY HAVE EYES FOR YOU.
**Tracks:** Not Advised.
CD . . . . . . . . . . . . . . . . . . . NEMCD 609
Sequel / Apr '91 / Total / BMG.

## I'LL BE HOME.
**Tracks:** Someday someway / Golden teardrops / Cross over the bridge / Carried away / You ain't ready / Hurry home baby / Blues in the letter / On my merry way / Dream of a lifetime / If I could love you / I really don't want to know / I found a new baby / Ko ko mo / That's my baby (chicka boom) / Whispering stars / Chickie-um-bah / I'll be home / Kiss from your lips / Get with it / Nobody's love / Would I be crying / Shilly dilly / Stolen love.
CD . . . . . . . . . . . . . . . . . . . CDINS 5072
Charly / Jun '93 / Charly.

## IT'S GOTTA BE BAD.
**Tracks:** It's gotta be bad / Sometimes.
■ 7" . . . . . . . . . . . . . . . . . . . ULT 1001
Cambridge / May '82.

## REQUESTFULLY YOURS.
**Tracks:** Not Advised.
■ LP . . . . . . . . . . . . . . . . . . . END LP 308
End / Apr '79.

## SERENADE.
**Tracks:** Not Advised.
■ LP . . . . . . . . . . . . . . . . . . . END LP 304
End / Apr '79.

## Flemming, Rochelle

**LOVE ITCH.**
Tracks: Love itch.
- 12" . . . . . . . . . . . . . . . . . . . . . .12SLN 1
- 7" . . . . . . . . . . . . . . . . . . . . . . . 7SLN 1
Streetnoise / Mar '86.

## Fletcher, Darrow

**PAIN GETS A LITTLE DEEPER.**
Tracks: Pain gets a little deeper / My judgement day.
- 7" . . . . . . . . . . . . . . . . . . . . HLU 10024
London-American / Feb '66.

## Fletcher, Don

**TWO WRONGS DON'T MAKE A RIGHT.**
Tracks: Two wrongs don't make a right / I'm so glad.
- 7" . . . . . . . . . . . . . . . . . . . . . . VP 9271
Vocalion / May '66.

## Flirtations

**DIRTY WORK.**
Tracks: Dirty work / No such thing as a miracle.
- 7" . . . . . . . . . . . . . . . . . . . . . . . 2058495
Polydor / Jun '74.

**EARTHQUAKE.**
Tracks: Earthquake.
- 12" . . . . . . . . . . . . . . . . . . . . . IANT 101
- 7" . . . . . . . . . . . . . . . . . . . . . . IAN 101
Siam / Oct '83.
- 12" . . . . . . . . . . . . . . . . . . . . . RUMAT 3
Rumour / Aug '89.

**MR. UNIVERSE.**
Tracks: Mr. Universe / Somebody cared for me.
- 7" . . . . . . . . . . . . . . . . . . . . . RCA 2554
RCA / Jun '75.

**READ ALL ABOUT IT.**
Tracks: Read all about it / Nightmare dub mix.
- 12" . . . . . . . . . . . . . . . . . . PASH 67(12)
Passion (1) / Nov '86.

## Flirts

**(DON'T PUT ANOTHER DIME IN THE) JUKEBOX.**
Tracks: Jukebox.
- 12" . . . . . . . . . . . . . . . . . . . . . QUEL 3
- 7" . . . . . . . . . . . . . . . . . . . . . . QUE 3
O / Nov '82.

**FLIRTS.**
Tracks: Jukebox / Boy crazy / On the beach / Passion / We just want to dance / Calling all boys / Jungle rock / I only want to ride my life / Surf's up.
- LP . . . . . . . . . . . . . . . . . . . . . QUELP 1
Vanguard (1) / Mar '83.

**MISS YOU.**
Tracks: Miss you / Voulez vous.
- 12" . . . . . . . . . . . . . . . . . . . . .650069 6
- 7" . . . . . . . . . . . . . . . . . . . . . .650069 7
Epic / Aug '86.

**PASSION.**
Tracks: Passion / Calling all boys.
- 7" . . . . . . . . . . . . . . . . . . . . . . QUEL 6
- 7" . . . . . . . . . . . . . . . . . . . . . . QUE 6
O / Apr '83.

**QUESTIONS OF THE HEART.**
Tracks: All you ever think about is sex / Daddy I'm not a baby / Boys on the beach / My boyfriend is a marine / Just another kiss / Special angel / Motorama(turn up the radio) / Forgive / Like a thief in the night / After midnight.
- LP . . . . . . . . . . . . . . . . . . . . . 4502791
- MC. . . . . . . . . . . . . . . . . . . . . 4502794
Epic / Feb '87 / Sony.

**YOU AND ME.**
Tracks: You and me.
- 12" . . . . . . . . . . . . . . . . . . . . . TA 6760
- 7" . . . . . . . . . . . . . . . . . . . . . .A 6760
Epic / May '86.

## Floaters

**FLOAT ON.**
Tracks: Float on.
- 7" . . . . . . . . . . . . . . . . . . . . . ABC 4187
ABC Records / Jul '77.

**FLOAT ON (RE-RELEASE).**
Tracks: Float on.
- 12" . . . . . . . . . . . . . . . . . . . . MCAT 1403

---

- 7" . . . . . . . . . . . . . . . . . . . . . MCA 1403
- MC Single. . . . . . . . . . . . . . . . . MCAC 1403
MCA / Mar '90.

**FLOATERS.**
Tracks: Not Advised.
- LP . . . . . . . . . . . . . . . . . . . . ABCL 5229
ABC Records / Aug '77.

**MAGIC.**
Tracks: Magic / I just want to be with you.
- 7" . . . . . . . . . . . . . . . . . . . . . ABC 4216
ABC Records / May '78.

**MAGIC.**
Tracks: Magic / I dedicate my love to you / Time is now / Whatever your sign / Let's try love / Anything that keeps you satisfied / I just want to be with you.
- LP . . . . . . . . . . . . . . . . . . . . ABCL 5243
ABC Records / May '78.

## Floyd, Eddie

Floyd first found fame with Falcons, singing on Detroit band's 1959 U.S. hit *You're So Fine*. He quit for solo career in early '60s, signing to Stax in '65, for whom he wrote and recorded *Knock On Wood* with guitarist Steve Cropper. Label boss Jim Stewart felt song was too close to *In the Midnight Hour* and shelved it for nine months; finally released in late '66, it became chart hit and enduring classic (being successful revived by David Bowie in '74 and Amii Stewart in '79). Other Floyd-penned classics include Wilson Pickett's 1966 hit *634-5789* and his own *Raise Your Hand*. After final hit with cover of Sam Cooke's *Bring It On Home To Me*, Floyd faded into obscurity.

**BEAT SONG.**
Tracks: Beat song / London.
- 7" . . . . . . . . . . . . . . . . . . . . . . SEE 9
I-Spy / Aug '80.

**BYE BYE BABY.**
Tracks: Bye bye baby.
- 7" . . . . . . . . . . . . . . . . . . . . SPE 1001
Speciality / '67.

**CHI TOWN HUSSLER.**
Tracks: Chi town hussler / Never too old.
- 7" . . . . . . . . . . . . . . . . . . . . . CS 2101
Contempo (1) / Dec '76.

**CHRONICLE.**
Tracks: Knock on wood / Raise your hand / Things get better / Love is a doggone thing / On a Saturday night / Big bird / I've never found a girl / Bring it on home / I've got to have your love / Consider me / Don't tell your Mama / Why is the wine sweeter / California girl / My girl / Best years of my life / Blood is thicker than water / Soul street / I've got a reason to smile.
- LP . . . . . . . . . . . . . . . . . . . . STM 7005
Stax / Oct '78.

**FLASHBACK.**
Tracks: Flashback / Love's gonna get to you / From your head to your toes / Soul is back again / She likes the soaps / You don't say no / Pretty girls / Gonna satisfy you / Daddy's coming home.
- LP . . . . . . . . . . . . . . . . . . . . . WIL 3005
- MC. . . . . . . . . . . . . . . . . . . . .ZCWIL 3005
Ichiban / Apr '88 / A.D.A. Distribution / Pinnacle / ACD Trading Ltd. / Koch International / Direct Distribution.

**FROM YOUR HEAD TO YOUR TOES.**
Tracks: From your head to your toes / She likes the soaps / Soul is back again.
- 12" . . . . . . . . . . . . . . . . . . . . 12 PO 10
Ichiban / May '88.

**I'VE NEVER FOUND A GIRL.**
Tracks: Bring it on home to me / Never gonna give you up / Girl I love you / Hobo / I need you woman / I've never found a girl (to love me like you do) / I'll take her / Slip away / I'm just the kind of fool / Water / Sweet things you do.
- LP . . . . . . . . . . . . . . . . . . . . SXATS 1003
Stax / Feb '69.
- CD . . . . . . . . . . . . . . . . . . . CDSXE 059
Stax / Jul '92 / Pinnacle.

**KNOCK ON WOOD.**
Tracks: Knock on wood / Something you got / But it's alright / I stand accused / If you gotta make a fool of somebody / I don't want to cry / Raise your hand / Got to make a comeback / 634 5789 / Love me feeling bad / High heel sneakers / Warm and tender love.
- LP . . . . . . . . . . . . . . . . . . . . . 589-006
Stax / Apr '67.

---

- LP . . . . . . . . . . . . . . . . . . . . . 228 014
Atco / Sep '69.
- MC. . . . . . . . . . . . . . . . . . . . 7567802834
East West / Jul '91 / WEA.
- CD . . . . . . . . . . . . . . . . . . . . 7567802832
Pickwick / Oct '94 / Pickwick.

**KNOCK ON WOOD.**
Tracks: Knock on wood.
- 7" . . . . . . . . . . . . . . . . . . . . . STAX 807
Stax / Aug '87.
- 12" . . . . . . . . . . . . . . . . . . . . . STAT 807
Stax / Nov '87.

**KNOCK ON WOOD.**
Tracks: Knock on wood / Got to make a comeback.
- 7" . . . . . . . . . . . . . . . . . . . . . .584041
Atlantic / Feb '67.

**KNOCK ON WOOD (EP).**
Tracks: Knock on wood / Bring it on home to me / Girl I love you.
- EP . . . . . . . . . . . . . . . . . . . . STAX 2010
Stax / Aug '78.

**KNOCK ON WOOD (OLD GOLD).**
Tracks: Knock on wood / Hold on I'm coming.
- 7" . . . . . . . . . . . . . . . . . . . . .OG 9498
Old Gold / Jan '85.

**KNOCK ON WOOD - THE BEST OF EDDIE FLOYD.**
Tracks: Knock on wood / Raise your hand / Big bird / On a Saturday night / Things get better / Love is a doggone good thing / I've never found a girl / Consider me / Bring it on home to me / I've got to have your love / Blood is thicker than water / Baby lay your head down / Too weak to fight / Oh how it rained / Why is the wine sweeter (on the other side) / Soul Street / Don't tell your mama (On CD only) / Girl, I love you (On CD only) / People, get it together (On CD only) / Something to write home about (On CD only) / Check me out (On CD only) / Stealing love (On CD only).
- CD . . . . . . . . . . . . . . . . . . . CDSX 010
- LP . . . . . . . . . . . . . . . . . . . . SX 010
- MC. . . . . . . . . . . . . . . . . . . . SXC 010
Stax / Mar '88 / Pinnacle.

**RAISE YOUR HAND.**
Tracks: Raise your hand / I've just been feeling bad.
- 7" . . . . . . . . . . . . . . . . . . . . .601001
Stax / Mar '67.

**RARE STAMPS/I'VE NEVER FOUND A GIRL.**
Tracks: Bring it on home to me / Never give you up / Girl I love you / Hobo / I need you woman / I've never found a girl / I'll take her / Slip away / I'm just the kind of fool / Water / Sweet things you do / Knock on wood / Raise your hand / Love's a doggone good thing / On a Saturday night / Thing's get better / Big bird / Got to make a comeback / I've just been feeling bad / This house / I've got to have your love / Consider me / Never let you go / Ain't that good / Laurie.
- CD . . . . . . . . . . . . . . . . . . . CDSXD 096
Stax / Jul '93 / Pinnacle.

**SET MY SOUL ON FIRE.**
Tracks: Set my soul on fire / Will I be the one.
- 7" . . . . . . . . . . . . . . . . . . . . HL 10129
London / Apr '67 / PolyGram.

**THINGS GET BETTER.**
Tracks: Things get better / Good love bad love.
- 7" . . . . . . . . . . . . . . . . . . . . .601016
Stax / Aug '67.

**THINGS GET BETTER.**
Tracks: Things get better / Raise your hand.
- 7" . . . . . . . . . . . . . . . . . . . . K 10595
Atlantic / Aug '75.

**YOU'VE GOT TO HAVE EDDIE.**
Tracks: That's all / It's not unusual / Can I change my mind / Proud Mary / Long line rider / Satisfy my hunger / Sea gull / Too weak to fight / I sowed love / Non-stop to midnight / Don't tell your mama / If you're gonna do it.
- LP . . . . . . . . . . . . . . . . . . . . .SXATS 1023
Stax / Nov '69.
- LP . . . . . . . . . . . . . . . . . . . . . 2363010
Stax / Aug '71.

---

■ DELETED

145

## Floyd, King

**BABY LET ME KISS YOU.**
Tracks: Baby let me kiss you / Please don't leave me lonely.
■ 7" . . . . . . . . . . . . . . . . . . . . . . . . . . 2091079
Atlantic / May '71.

**BODY ENGLISH.**
Tracks: Body English / I really love you.
■ 7" . . . . . . . . . . . . . . . . . . . . . . . . . CS 2103
Contempo (1) / Jan '77.

**GROOVE ME.**
Tracks: Groove me / Let us be / Woman don't go astray / Baby let me kiss you / Messing up my mind / It's wonderful / So glad I found you / Don't leave me lonely / Day in the life of a fool / What our love needs.
■ LP . . . . . . . . . . . . . . . . . . . . . . . . 2466014
Atlantic / Oct '71.

**GROOVE ME.**
Tracks: Groove me / What our love needs.
■ 7" . . . . . . . . . . . . . . . . . . . . . . . 2091 051
Atlantic / Mar '71.

## FM Inc

**CALL ME ANYTIME.**
Tracks: Not Advised.
■ 12" . . . . . . . . . . . . . . . . . . . . . . . . NTD 002
Nuff Tuff / Oct '92.

## Fontaine, Claudia

**DON'T LET HIM GET TO YOU (see under Ciyo).**

**NATURAL HIGH.**
Tracks: Natural high / Let's love.
■ 12" . . . . . . . . . . . . . . . . . . . . . . FX 13905
■ 7" . . . . . . . . . . . . . . . . . . . . . . . . F 13905
Decca / Jun '81.

## Force

**DIRTY DOG.**
Tracks: Dirty dog / Rock your baby.
■ 7" . . . . . . . . . . . . . . . . . . . . . . . PIR 7928
Philadelphia Int. / Nov '79.

**EYE TO EYE.**
Tracks: Tomorrow may never come (This extra track on 12" version only) / Amigo (This extra track on 12" version only).
■ 12" . . . . . . . . . . . . . . . . . . . . . . . B 9478 T
■ 7" . . . . . . . . . . . . . . . . . . . . . . . . . B 9478
Valentino / Jan '87.

**FAMINE ETHIOPIA.**
Tracks: Famine Ethiopia / S.O.S.
■ 12" . . . . . . . . . . . . . . . . . . . . . . MAB 001
Mab / Dec '84.

**FORCE.**
Tracks: New frontiers / Eye to eye / No fixed emotion / Amigo / Change your heart / Tomorrow may never come / All too much / Turn to love / All alone / I hear the sound / Shout.
■ LP . . . . . . . . . . . . . . . . . . . . . . .790555 1
MC. . . . . . . . . . . . . . . . . . . . . . . . .790555 4
Valentino / Jan '87 / WEA.

**MISSION IMPOSSIBLE.**
Tracks: Mission Impossible / Microphone mania.
■ 12" . . . . . . . . . . . . . . . . . . . . . . . . VL 004
Vinyl Lab / Feb '89.

**MUSIC.**
Tracks: Music.
■ 12" . . . . . . . . . . . . . . . . . . . . . . . . . . DS 2
Destiny / Mar '80.

**PURE POWER.**
Tracks: Pure power.
■ 12" . . . . . . . . . . . . . . . . . . . . . . . RONIN 3
Ronin / Dec '90.

**SHOUT.**
Tracks: Shout / Change your heart.
■ 7" . . . . . . . . . . . . . . . . . . . . . . . . . B 2423
Atlantic / Sep '87.

**STAR WARS DISCO.**
Tracks: Star wars disco / Funky hat.
■ 7" . . . . . . . . . . . . . . . . . . . . . . . . . CP 15
Splash / Oct '77.

**TOMORROW MAY NEVER COME.**
Tracks: Tomorrow may never come / I heard the sound.

■ 7" . . . . . . . . . . . . . . . . . . . . . . . . B 9452
Valentino / Apr '87.

## Force MD's

**FORGIVE ME GIRL.**
Tracks: Forgive me girl.
■ 7" . . . . . . . . . . . . . . . . . . . . . . . . IS 207
■ 12" . . . . . . . . . . . . . . . . . . . . . . .12IS 207
Tommy Boy / Oct '84.

**HERE I GO AGAIN.**
Tracks: Here I go again / Itchin' for a scratch.
■ 7" . . . . . . . . . . . . . . . . . . . . . . . . IS 286
■ 12" . . . . . . . . . . . . . . . . . . . . . . .12IS 286
Island / Jun '86.

**LOVE IS A HOUSE.**
Tracks: Love is a house / Love is a house (inst).
■ 12" . . . . . . . . . . . . . . . . . . . . . . . U 8252 T
■ 7" . . . . . . . . . . . . . . . . . . . . . . . . U 8252
WEA / Jul '87.

**LOVE LETTERS.**
Tracks: Tears / Forgive me girl / Itchin' for a scratch.
■ LP . . . . . . . . . . . . . . . . . . . . . . . ILPS 9820
Tommy Boy / Apr '85.

**TEARS.**
Tracks: Tears / Forgive me girl.
■ 7" . . . . . . . . . . . . . . . . . . . . . . . . IS 195
■ 12" . . . . . . . . . . . . . . . . . . . . . . .12IS 195
Tommy Boy / Feb '85.

**TENDER LOVE.**
Tracks: One plus one / Tears / Uh oh / Here I go again / Chillin' / Tender love / Will you be my girlfriend / Walking on air / Force MD's meet The Fat Boys / Smoke on the water / Shine it on me.
■ LP . . . . . . . . . . . . . . . . . . . . . . . ILPS 9837
■ MC. . . . . . . . . . . . . . . . . . . . . . . .ICT 9837
Tommy Boy / May '86.

**TENDER LOVE.**
Tracks: Tender love.
■ 7" . . . . . . . . . . . . . . . . . . . . . . . . PT 551
President / Jan '86.
■ 12" . . . . . . . . . . . . . . . . . . . . . 12 ISX 269
Tommy Boy / Mar '86.

**TOUCH AND GO.**
Tracks: Love is a house / Would you love me / Touch & go / Couldn't care less / Your love drives me crazy / Midnite lover / Take your love back / Sweet dreams.
CD . . . . . . . . . . . . . . . . . . . . . . . 254 889 2
■ LP . . . . . . . . . . . . . . . . . . . . . . . 254 889 1
MC. . . . . . . . . . . . . . . . . . . . . . . . 254 889 4
Tommy Boy / Sep '87 / Pinnacle / RTM.

## Ford, Pennye

**CHANGE YOUR WICKED WAYS.**
Tracks: Change your wicked ways.
■ 7" . . . . . . . . . . . . . . . . . . . . . . .RCA 503
■ 12" . . . . . . . . . . . . . . . . . . . . . . . XET 503
Total Experience / Oct '84.

**DANGEROUS.**
Tracks: Dangerous / Change your wicked ways.
■ 7" . . . . . . . . . . . . . . . . . . . . . . . FB 49975
■ 12" . . . . . . . . . . . . . . . . . . . . . . FT 49976
Total Experience / Apr '85.

**PENNYE.**
Tracks: I feel the music / Uh, oh I made a mistake / Change your wicked ways / Serious love / Don't you know I love you / Ready for love / Dangerous / Never let you go.
■ LP . . . . . . . . . . . . . . . . . . . . . . . PL 89449
MC. . . . . . . . . . . . . . . . . . . . . . . . PK 89449
Total Experience / Jun '85 / PolyGram.

## Formations

**AT THE TOP OF THE STAIRS.**
Tracks: At the top of the stairs.
■ 7" . . . . . . . . . . . . . . . . . . . . . . . .2027 001
Mojo / Jul '71.

## Forrest

**DANCING WITH MY SHADOW.**
Tracks: Dancing with my shadow / Could this be love.
■ 12" . . . . . . . . . . . . . . . . . . . . . . TA 3913
■ 7" . . . . . . . . . . . . . . . . . . . . . . . A 3913
CBS / Nov '83.

**FEEL THE NEED IN ME.**
Tracks: Feel the need.
■ 12" . . . . . . . . . . . . . . . . . . . . . . TA 3411

■ 7" . . . . . . . . . . . . . . . . . . . . . . . A 3411
CBS / May '83.

**FORREST.**
Tracks: One lover / Feel the need / Could this be love / Just let it happen / Hand it over / Dancing with my shadow / Comin' up / I want you / Rock the boat / I just want to love you.
MC. . . . . . . . . . . . . . . . . . . . . . . .40 25579
■ LP . . . . . . . . . . . . . . . . . . . . . . CBS 25579
CBS / Oct '83 / Sony.

**ONE LOVER (DON'T STOP THE SHOW).**
Tracks: One lover (don't stop the show) / Comin'.
■ 12" . . . . . . . . . . . . . . . . . . . . . . TA 3734
■ 7" . . . . . . . . . . . . . . . . . . . . . . . A 3734
CBS / Sep '83.

**ROCK THE BOAT.**
Tracks: Rock the boat / Loving you.
■ 12" . . . . . . . . . . . . . . . . . . . . . A 13 3163
■ 7" . . . . . . . . . . . . . . . . . . . . . . A 13 3163
CBS / Feb '83.

**SHE'S SO DIVINE.**
Tracks: She's so divine.
■ 12" . . . . . . . . . . . . . . . . . . . . . . TA 4629
■ 7" . . . . . . . . . . . . . . . . . . . . . . . A 4629
CBS / Aug '84.

## Fortune, Sonny

**FOUR-IN-ONE.**
Tracks: Four in one / Criss cross / Reflections / Monk's dream / Hornin' in / Coming on the Hudson / Trinkle tinkle / Pannonica / Hackensack / Ask me now.
CD. . . . . . . . . . . . . . . . . . . . . . CDP 8282432
Blue Note / Sep '94 / EMI.

**IT AIN'T WHAT IT WAS.**
Tracks: It ain't what it was / Gentle rain / Wayne-ish / Lush life / Straight street / With sound reason / Swing touch.
■ CD . . . . . . . . . . . . . . . . . . . . . KCD 5033
Konnexion / Nov '92.

**MONK'S MOOD.**
Tracks: Little rootie tootie / Mysterioso / Nutty / I mean you / Monk's wood / Ruby my dear / In walked bud / Off minor.
CD. . . . . . . . . . . . . . . . . . . . . . KCD 5048
Konnex / Nov '93 / New Note.

## Foster, Diana

**I'M GONNA SHARE IT WITH YOU.**
Tracks: I'm gonna share it with you / Time out.
■ 7" . . . . . . . . . . . . . . . . . . . . . . . . CC 7
Casino Classics / '79.

## Foster, Gina

**BLACK ANGEL.**
Tracks: Black angel.
■ 12" . . . . . . . . . . . . . . . . . . . . . . .TAXIE 101
Taxi (1) / Jul '93.

**CRY IN VAIN.**
Tracks: Cry in vain / Take me away / One kiss.
■ 12" . . . . . . . . . . . . . . . . . . . . . . PT 43483
■ 7" . . . . . . . . . . . . . . . . . . . . . . PB 43483
■ CD Single . . . . . . . . . . . . . . . . . PD 43484
RCA / May '90.

**EVERYTHING I WANT.**
Tracks: Everything I want / Here I am / So in love / Cry in vain / Love is a house / Love is in my system / One kiss / Contact / Take me away.
■ CD . . . . . . . . . . . . . . . . . . . . . . PD 74192
■ LP . . . . . . . . . . . . . . . . . . . . . . PL 74192
■ MC. . . . . . . . . . . . . . . . . . . . . . PK 74192
RCA / Jul '90.

**LOVE IS A HOUSE.**
Tracks: Take me away / One kiss (Available on 12" and CD only) / Love is a house.
■ 12" . . . . . . . . . . . . . . . . . . . . . . PT 42748
■ 7" . . . . . . . . . . . . . . . . . . . . . . PB 42748
■ CD Single . . . . . . . . . . . . . . . . . PD 42748
RCA / Jun '89.
■ 7" . . . . . . . . . . . . . . . . . . . . . . PB 43073
■ CD Single . . . . . . . . . . . . . . . . . PD 43074
■ 12" . . . . . . . . . . . . . . . . . . . . . . PT 43074
RCA / Sep '89.

■ DELETED

## Foster, Ian

### IAN FOSTER.
Tracks: Out for the count / Heaven (sent your love to me) / This time / We've lost this feeling / Tell me it's true / You make all the right moves / Ooh wee baby.
| | |
|---|---|
| CD. | DMCF 3399 |
| ■ LP. | MCF 3399 |
| ■ MC. | MCFC 3399 |
MCA / Nov '87 / BMG.

### OUT FOR THE COUNT.
Tracks: Out for the count.
| | |
|---|---|
| ■ 12". | MCAT 1183 |
| ■ 7". | MCA 1183 |
MCA / Aug '87.

### TELL ME IT'S TRUE.
Tracks: Tell me it's true / Tell me it's true (instrumental).
| | |
|---|---|
| ■ 12". | MCAT 1025 |
| ■ 7". | MCA 1025 |
MCA / May '86.

## Foster, Ronnie

### DELIGHT.
Tracks: Argentina / You're the one / We as love / Let me in your life / Feet / When will I write you a song / Delight / I've got your love.
| | |
|---|---|
| ■ LP. | CBS 83776 |
CBS / '79.

### LOVE SATELLITE.
Tracks: Why don't you look inside / Soft heart / Happy song / Shooting star / Midnight plane / I want to bring my love home / Easier said than done / Nassau day / Love satellite.
| | |
|---|---|
| ■ LP. | CBS 83037 |
CBS / Apr '79.

## Foundations

### BABY, NOW THAT I'VE FOUND YOU.
Tracks: Baby now that I've found you.
| | |
|---|---|
| ■ 7". | 7N 17366 |
Pye / Jul '67.

### BABY, NOW THAT I'VE FOUND YOU.
Tracks: Baby, now that I found you / Build me up buttercup.
| | |
|---|---|
| ■ 7". | FBS 6 |
Flashback / Apr '79.
| | |
|---|---|
| ■ 12". | 12P 372 |
| ■ 7". | 7P 372 |
PRT / Apr '87.
| | |
|---|---|
| ■ 12". | PYT 24 |
| ■ 7". | PYS 24 |
PRT / Apr '89.

### BABY, NOW THAT I'VE FOUND YOU (OLD GOLD).
Tracks: Baby now that I've found you / Build me up buttercup.
| | |
|---|---|
| ■ 7". | OG 9407 |
Old Gold / Jun '84.

### BACK ON MY FEET AGAIN.
Tracks: Back on my feet again.
| | |
|---|---|
| ■ 7". | 7N 17417 |
Pye / Jan '68.

### BACK TO THE BEAT.
Tracks: Baby now that I've found you / Build me up buttercup / Back on my feet again / Any old time (you're lonely and sad) / In the bad bad old days (before you loved me) / Born to live and born to die / I can take or leave your loving / Stop her on sight (S.O.S).
| | |
|---|---|
| ■ LP. | DOW 7 |
| ■ MC. | ZCDOW 7 |
PRT / Apr '83.

### BEST OF THE FOUNDATIONS.
Tracks: Baby now that I've found you / Back on my feet again / Tomorrow / Harlem shuffle / Mr. Personality man / I can take or leave your loving / Let the heartaches begin / Am I groovin' you / That same old feeling / Any old time (you're lonely and sad) / Build me up buttercup / In the bad bad old days (before you loved me) / Born to live and born to die / Waiting on the shores of nowhere / Come on back to me / Jerkin' the dog / Take away the emptiness too / My little chickadee / Love is alright / We are happy people.
| | |
|---|---|
| ■ CD. | PYC 4003 |
| ■ LP. | PYL 4003 |
| ■ MC. | PYM 4003 |
PRT / Oct '87.

### BORN TO LIVE AND BORN TO DIE.
Tracks: Born to live and born to die.
| | |
|---|---|
| ■ 7". | 7N 17809 |
Pye / Sep '69.

### BUILD ME UP.
Tracks: Not Advised.
| | |
|---|---|
| CD. | 550 7492 |
| MC. | 550 7494 |
Spectrum (1) / Sep '94 / PolyGram.

### BUILD ME UP BUTTERCUP.
Tracks: Build me up buttercup.
| | |
|---|---|
| ■ 7". | 7N 17638 |
Pye / Nov '68.

### CLOSER TO LOVING YOU.
Tracks: Closer to loving you / Change my life.
| | |
|---|---|
| ■ 7". | P 2603 |
Psycho (2) / Apr '78.

### DIGGIN' THE FOUNDATIONS.
Tracks: Not Advised.
| | |
|---|---|
| CD. | REP 4183-WZ |
Repertoire (Germany) / Aug '91 / Pinnacle.

### FROM THE FOUNDATIONS.
Tracks: Baby now that I've found you / Take or leave your loving / Just a little while longer / Come on back to me / Call me / etc.
| | |
|---|---|
| ■ LP. | NPL 18206 |
Pye / Dec '67.
| | |
|---|---|
| CD. | REP 4182-WZ |
Repertoire (Germany) / Aug '91 / Pinnacle.

### GOLDEN HOUR OF THE FOUNDATIONS GREATEST HITS.
Tracks: Baby now that I've found you / Back on my feet again / Tomorrow / Harlem shuffle / Mr. Personality man / I can take or leave your loving / Let the heartaches begin / Am I groovin' you / That same old feeling / Any old time (you're lonely and sad) / Build me up buttercup / In the bad bad old days (Before you loved me) / Born to live and born to die / Waiting on the shores of nowhere / Come on back to me / Jerkin' the dog / Take away the emptiness too / My little chickadee / Love is alright / We are happy people.
| | |
|---|---|
| ■ CD. | KGHCD 104 |
| ■ MC. | KGHMC 104 |
Knight / Apr '90.

### IN THE BAD BAD OLD DAYS.
Tracks: In the bad bad old days (before you loved me).
| | |
|---|---|
| ■ 7". | 7N 17702 |
Pye / Mar '69.

### IT'S ALL RIGHT.
Tracks: Back on my feet again / I can take or leave your lovin' / It's all right / Baby now that I've found you.
| | |
|---|---|
| ■ 7". | NEP 24297 |
Pye / Mar '68.

### ROCKING THE FOUNDATIONS.
Tracks: Horse / People are funny / Harlem shuffle / Comin' home baby / Tomorrow / Am I groovin' you / Any old time / Look of love / Stop her on sight / Happy people.
| | |
|---|---|
| ■ LP. | NSPL 18227 |
Pye / Oct '68.

## Four Kents

### MOVING FINGER WRITES, THE.
Tracks: Moving finger writes.
| | |
|---|---|
| ■ 7". | RCA 1705 |
RCA / Jun '68.

## Four Tops

Jazz singers Four Aims realised potential when they signed to Motown, amended name and teamed with songwriters Holland-Dozier-Holland. String of hits - including *Bernadette* and *Standing in the Shadows of Love* - fronted by Levi Stubbs' soaring vocals, peaked with transatlantic 1966 No. 1 *Reach Out (I'll Be There)*. Band were rarely out of charts in ensuing years; other classics including *Walk Away Renee* and 1970 Supremes collaboration *River Deep Mountain High*. Recording fortunes slumped in 1974, by which time group had left Motown. Relentless touring paid off when Tops returned to charts with singles *When She Was My Girl* and *Don't Walk Away* in 1981 and '82, respectively; incredibly, line-up was unchanged after two decades plus. Contemporary successes include 1988 Top 10 hit *Loco in Acapulco* and *Singles Collection* album in '92; latter being most recent

example of Four Tops' Greatest Hits that grace U.K. Top 20 every ten years or so. 1989's *Indestructible* album featured contributions from Aretha Franklin, Smokey Robinson and Kenny G.

### 20 GOLDEN GREATS: FOUR TOPS.
Tracks: Reach out I'll be there / Walk away Renee / Standing in the shadows of love / Seven rooms of gloom / I can't help myself / It's the same old song / Bernadette / Baby, I need your loving / What is a man / Do what you gotta do / It's all in the game / River deep, mountain high / Still water / If I were a carpenter / Loving you is sweeter than ever / You keep running away / Yesterday's dreams / I'm in a different world / You gotta have love in your heart / Simple game.
| | |
|---|---|
| ■ LP. | EMTV 26 |
| MC. | CMTV 26 |
Motown / Oct '81 / PolyGram.

### 7 ROOMS OF GLOOM.
Tracks: Seven rooms of gloom / I'll turn to stone.
| | |
|---|---|
| ■ 7". | TMG 612 |
Tamla Motown / Jun '67.

### 7 ROOMS OF GLOOM.
Tracks: 7 rooms of gloom / Loving you is sweeter than ever.
| | |
|---|---|
| ■ 7". | ZB 41905 |
Motown / Apr '88.

### AIN'T NO WOMAN.
Tracks: Ain't no woman.
| | |
|---|---|
| ■ 7". | PRO 586 |
Probe / Mar '73.

### ANTHOLOGY - FOUR TOPS.
Tracks: Baby I need your loving / Without the one you love / Ask the lonely / I can't help myself / It's the same old song / Something about you / Shake me wake me / Loving you is sweeter than ever / Reach out I'll be there / Standing in the shadows of love / I got a feeling / Bernadette / Seven rooms of gloom / (You keep) running away / Walk away Renee / If I were a carpenter / Yesterdays dreams / I'm in a different world / Can't seem to get you out of my mind / It's all in the game / Still water (Pre-computerised listing shows two tracks: Still water(love) and Still w) / River deep, mountain high / Just seven numbers / In these changing times / I can't quit your love / (It's the way) nature planned it / You gotta have love in your heart / What is a man / Do what you gotta do / MacArthur Park part 2 / Simple game / So deep within you / Hey man (medley) / We gotta get you a woman.
| | |
|---|---|
| ■ Double LP. | TMSP 6013 |
| ■ MC Set. | CTMSP 6013 |
| ■ Double LP. | ZL 72352 |
Motown / Sep '82.
| | |
|---|---|
| CD. | 530 190-2 |
Motown / Jan '92 / PolyGram.

### ANTHOLOGY - FOUR TOPS (CD).
Tracks: Sad souvenirs / Ask the lonely / Then / Helpless / Reach out and touch / MacArthur Park / Place in the sun / Hey man / You a woman / For once in my life / Reflections / Still water / Just seven numbers / I got a feeling / Everybody's talkin' / Walk away Renee / Yesterday's dreams.
| | |
|---|---|
| ■ CD Set. | ZD 72528 |
Motown / Oct '86.
| | |
|---|---|
| ■ CD Set. | WD 72528 |
Motown / Apr '89.

### ASK THE LONELY.
Tracks: Ask the lonely.
| | |
|---|---|
| ■ 7". | TMG 507 |
Tamla Motown / '65.

### AT THE TOP.
Tracks: H.E.L.P. / Bits and pieces / Seclusion / Put it on the news / This house / Just in time / Inside a brokenhearted man / When your dreams take wings and fly.
| | |
|---|---|
| ■ LP. | ABCL 5262 |
ABC Records / Jan '79.

### BABY I NEED YOUR LOVING.
Tracks: Baby I need your loving / Yesterday's dreams.
| | |
|---|---|
| ■ 7". | TMG 978 |
Tamla Motown / Jun '75.
| | |
|---|---|
| ■ CD Single. | ZD 41947 |
Motown / Jun '89.

### BACK TO SCHOOL AGAIN.
Tracks: Back to school again / Rock-a-hula-lula.
| | |
|---|---|
| ■ 7". | RSO 89 |
RSO / Jun '82.

### BACK WHERE I BELONG.
Tracks: Not Advised.
| | |
|---|---|
| ■ LP. | STML 12197 |

■ DELETED

■ MC. . . . . . . . . . . . . . . . . . . . . .CSTML 12197
Motown / Nov '83.

## BERNADETTE.
Tracks: Bernadette / If I were a carpenter.
■ 7" . . . . . . . . . . . . . . . . . . . TMG 803
Tamla Motown / Mar '72.
■ 7" . . . . . . . . . . . . . . . . . . . TMG 995
Tamla Motown / Oct '75.

## BERNADETTE.
Tracks: Bernadette / I got a feeling.
■ 7" . . . . . . . . . . . . . . . . . . . TMG 601
Tamla Motown / Mar '67.

## BEST OF THE FOUR TOPS.
Tracks: Reach out I'll be there / Walk away Renee / Standing in the shadows of love / Seven rooms of gloom / I can't help myself / It's the same old song / Bernadette / Baby, I need your loving / What is a man / Do what you gotta do / It's all in the game / River deep, mountain high / Still water / If I were a carpenter / Loving you is sweeter than ever / You keep running away / Yesterday's dreams / I'm in a different world / You gotta have love in your heart / Simple game.
■ LP . . . . . . . . . . . . . . . . . . . . NE 1160
■ MC. . . . . . . . . . . . . . . . . . . . CE 2160
K-Tel / Jan '82.

## BEST OF THE SUPREMES & FOUR TOPS.
(see under Supremes).

## CHANGING TIMES.
Tracks: In these changing times / Just seven numbers / Raindrops keep fallin' on my head / Right before my eyes / I almost had her / Try to remember / Something's tearing at the edges of time / Sing a song of yesterday / Long and winding road.
■ LP . . . . . . . . . . . . . . . . . . . .STML 11173
Tamla Motown / Mar '71.

## COLLECTION: FOUR TOPS.
Tracks: Not Advised.
■ CD . . . . . . . . . . . . . . . . . . . CCSCD 344
■ MC. . . . . . . . . . . . . . . . . . . CCSMC 344
Castle Collector Series / Jun '92.

## DO WHAT YOU GOTTA DO.
Tracks: Do what you gotta do.
■ 7" . . . . . . . . . . . . . . . . . . . TMG 710
Tamla Motown / Sep '69.

## DON'T WALK AWAY.
Tracks: Don't walk away / I'll never ever leave again.
■ 12" . . . . . . . . . . . . . . . . . . . CANX 1006
■ 7" . . . . . . . . . . . . . . . . . . . CAN 1006
Casablanca / Oct '81.

## FABULOUS FOUR TOPS, THE.
Tracks: I can't help a feeling / I got a feeling / Your love is amazing / Yesterday's dreams / I'm grateful / Little green apples.
■ LP . . . . . . . . . . . . . . . . . . . . TMS 3502
■ MC. . . . . . . . . . . . . . . . . . . . TMC 3502
Motown / '82.

## FLIPHITS(4 TRACK CASSETTE EP).
Tracks: It's all in the game / Bernadette / Standing in the shadows of love / If I were a carpenter.
■ MC Single. . . . . . . . . . . . . . . CTME 2032
Motown / Jul '83.

## FOR YOUR LOVE.
Tracks: For your love / You'll never find a better man.
■ 7" . . . . . . . . . . . . . . . . . . . ABC 4199
ABC Records / Jan '78.

## FOUR TOPS.
Tracks: Baby I need your loving / Without the one you love / Where did you go / Ask the lonely / Your love is amazing / Sad souvenirs / Don't turn away / Tea house in China Town / Left with a broken heart / Love has gone / Call on me.
■ LP . . . . . . . . . . . . . . . . . . . STMS 5033
■ MC. . . . . . . . . . . . . . . . . . . CSTMS 5033
Motown / Mar '82.

## FOUR TOPS (Four Tops & The Supremes).
Tracks: Reach out I'll be there / I can't help myself / Do what you gotta do / Yesterday's dreams.
■ MC Single. . . . . . . . . . . . . . . CTME 2023
Motown / May '83.

## FOUR TOPS.
Tracks: I can't help myself / Ask the lonely / Something about you / It's the same old song.
■ EP . . . . . . . . . . . . . . . . . . . TME 2012
Tamla Motown / Feb '66.

## FOUR TOPS LIVE!.
Tracks: Not Advised.
■ LP . . . . . . . . . . . . . . . . . . . .STML 11041
Tamla Motown / Feb '67.

## FOUR TOPS ON TOP.
Tracks: Not Advised.
■ LP . . . . . . . . . . . . . . . . . . . TML 11037
Tamla Motown / Nov '66.

## FOUR TOPS SECOND ALBUM.
Tracks: Baby I need your loving / Without the one you love / Where did you go / Ask the lonely / Your love is amazing / Sad souvenirs / Tea house in China / Left with a broken heart / Love has gone / Call on me / I can't help myself / Love feels like fire / Is there anything that I can do / Something about you / It's the same old song.
■ CD . . . . . . . . . . . . . . . . . . . ZD 72491
Motown / Nov '86.

## FOUR TOPS SINGLES COLLECTION.
Tracks: Reach out I'll be there / Standing in the shadows of love / Bernadette / Walk away Renee / If I were a carpenter / Simple game / 7 rooms of gloom / Loving you is sweeter than ever / You keep running away / What is a man / Loco in Acapulco / Indestructible / When she was my girl / It's all in the game / Still water (love) / I can't help myself / Do what you gotta do / Keeper of the castle / Don't walk away.
CD . . . . . . . . . . . . . . . . . . . 5157102
■ LP . . . . . . . . . . . . . . . . . . . 5157101
MC. . . . . . . . . . . . . . . . . . . 5157104
Polydor / Sep '92 / PolyGram.

## FOUR TOPS STORY 1964-72.
Tracks: Baby I need your loving / Without the one you love / Ask the lonely / I can't help myself / It's the same old song / Something about you / Shake me wake me / Loving you is sweeter than ever / Yesterday's dream / I'm in a different world / What is a man / Do what you gotta do / It's all in the game / Still water / Just seven numbers / Reach out I'll be there / Standing in the shadows of love / Bernadette / 7 rooms of gloom / I'll turn to stone / You keep running away / Walk away Renee / If I were a carpenter / In these changing times / I can't quit your love / Nature planned it / River deep, mountain high / You gotta have love in your heart.
■ Double LP . . . . . . . . . . . . TMSP 11241/2
Tamla Motown / Nov '73.
■ Double LP . . . . . . . . . . . . TMSP 1124
Motown / Oct '81.

## FOUR TOPS: 19 GREATEST HITS (Compact command performances).
Tracks: Baby I need your loving / Ask the lonely / I can't help myself / It's the same old song / Something about you / Shake me, wake me / Reach out I'll be there / Standing in the shadows of love / Bernadette / Loving you is sweeter than ever / Walk away Renee / You keep running away / If I were a carpenter / Yesterday's dreams / It's all in the game / Still water / Just seven numbers / MacArthur Park / (It's the way) nature planned it.
■ CD . . . . . . . . . . . . . . . . . . . WD 72220
Motown / Oct '87.

## GREATEST HITS: FOUR TOPS.
Tracks: Baby I need your loving / It's the same old song / Reach out I'll be there / Ask the lonely / Standing in the shadows of love / Loving you is sweeter than ever / I can't help myself / Without the one you love / Seven rooms of gloom / Something about you / Bernadette / Shake me, wake me (when it's over) / I'll keep running away / Where did you go / I'll turn to stone / Darling I hum our song.
■ LP . . . . . . . . . . . . . . . . . . .STML 11061
Tamla Motown / Jan '68.
■ LP . . . . . . . . . . . . . . . . . . . WL 72280
■ MC. . . . . . . . . . . . . . . . . . . WK 72280
Motown / Apr '85.
■ CD . . . . . . . . . . . . . . . . . . . WD 72280
Motown / Feb '88.

## GREATEST HITS: FOUR TOPS VOL.2.
Tracks: Walk away Renee / It's all in the game / If I were a carpenter / Still water (love) / Just seven numbers / What is a man / I can't help myself / Simple game / Do what you gotta do / I'm in a different world / In these changing times / Don't let him take your love from me / Yesterday's dreams / MacArthur Park.
■ LP . . . . . . . . . . . . . . . . . . .STML 11195
Tamla Motown / Nov '71.

## HEART 'N' SOUL.
Tracks: Not Advised.
CD . . . . . . . . . . . . . . . . . . . KNCD 12065
MC. . . . . . . . . . . . . . . . . . . KNMC 12065
Knight / Jul '91 / Castle Communications / BMG.

## HITS OF GOLD.
Tracks: Standing in the shadows of love / Key / Seven rooms of gloom / Where did you go / Look of love / Honey / Loving you is sweeter than ever / I'm grateful / Sunny / This guy's in love with you / Daydream believer / Light my fire.
■ LP . . . . . . . . . . . . . . . . . . . TMS 3514
■ MC. . . . . . . . . . . . . . . . . . . TMC 3514
Motown / Oct '82.

## HOT NIGHTS.
Tracks: Hot nights / Red hot love / I believe in you and me / Let's jam / We got bus'ness / This is love / So up for you / Livin it up too much / Four of us.
■ CD . . . . . . . . . . . . . . . . . . . ZD 72480
■ LP . . . . . . . . . . . . . . . . . . . ZL 72480
Motown / Oct '86.

## I CAN'T HELP MYSELF.
Tracks: I can't help myself / It's the same old song.
■ 7" . . . . . . . . . . . . . . . . . . . TMG 515
Tamla Motown / Jul '65.
■ 7" . . . . . . . . . . . . . . . . . . . TMG 732
Tamla Motown / Mar '70.
■ 7" . . . . . . . . . . . . . . . . . . .TMG 1120
Motown / Mar '83.

## I JUST CAN'T WALK AWAY.
Tracks: I just can't walk away / Hang.
■ 12" . . . . . . . . . . . . . . . . . . . TMGT 1321
■ 7" . . . . . . . . . . . . . . . . . . . TMG 1321
Motown / Oct '83.

## I'LL TURN TO STONE.
Tracks: I'll turn to stone.
■ 7" . . . . . . . . . . . . . . . . . . . TMG 829
Tamla Motown / Sep '72.

## I'M IN A DIFFERENT WORLD.
Tracks: I'm in a different world.
■ 7" . . . . . . . . . . . . . . . . . . . TMG 675
Tamla Motown / Nov '68.

## IF I WERE A CARPENTER.
Tracks: If I were a carpenter.
■ 7" . . . . . . . . . . . . . . . . . . . TMG 647
Tamla Motown / Mar '68.

## INDESTRUCTIBLE.
Tracks: Indestructible / Loco in Acapulco / Sun ain't gonna shine / Let's jam / Change of heart / When you dance / If ever a love there was / Next time / Are you with me / I'm only wounded.
■ CD . . . . . . . . . . . . . . . . . . .258840
■ LP . . . . . . . . . . . . . . . . . . .208840
■ MC. . . . . . . . . . . . . . . . . . .408840
Arista / Oct '88.
■ CD . . . . . . . . . . . . . . . . . . .261567
■ LP . . . . . . . . . . . . . . . . . . .211567
■ MC. . . . . . . . . . . . . . . . . . .411567
Arista / Jun '91.

## INDESTRUCTIBLE (Four Tops & Smokey Robinson).
Tracks: Indestructible / Are you with me / Indestructible (versions) / Next time (Only on 7" picture disc.)
■ 7" . . . . . . . . . . . . . . . . . . .111510
■ CD Single . . . . . . . . . . . . . . .661717
■ 12" . . . . . . . . . . . . . . . . . . .611510
■ 12" . . . . . . . . . . . . . . . . . . .611717
Arista / Aug '88.
■ 7" . . . . . . . . . . . . . . . . . . .111717
Arista / Sep '88.
■ 12" . . . . . . . . . . . . . . . . . . .612160
■ 12" . . . . . . . . . . . . . . . . . . .612074
■ 7" . . . . . . . . . . . . . . . . . . .112074
■ 7" P.Disc . . . . . . . . . . . . . . .112151
■ CD Single . . . . . . . . . . . . . . .162074
Arista / Feb '89.

## IT'S ALL IN THE GAME.
Tracks: Not Advised.
■ LP . . . . . . . . . . . . . . . . . . . MFP 50416
■ MC. . . . . . . . . . . . . . . . . . .TCMFP 50416
MFP / Jan '79.

## IT'S ALL IN THE GAME.
Tracks: Simple game / It's all in the game.
■ 7" . . . . . . . . . . . . . . . . . . . TMG 736
Tamla Motown / May '70.
■ 7" . . . . . . . . . . . . . . . . . . . TMG 965
Tamla Motown / Apr '75.
■ 7" . . . . . . . . . . . . . . . . . . . ZB 41907
Motown / Apr '88.

## IT'S THE SAME OLD SONG.
Tracks: It's the same old song.
■ 7" . . . . . . . . . . . . . . . . . . . TMG 528
Tamla Motown / Sep '65.

## JUST SEVEN NUMBERS (CAN STRAIGHTEN OUT MY LIFE).
**Tracks:** Just seven numbers.
■ **7"** .................................... TMG 770
Tamla Motown / May '71.

## KEEPER OF THE CASTLE.
**Tracks:** Keeper of the castle.
■ **7"** .................................... PRO 575
Probe / Nov '72.

## KEEPER OF THE CASTLE.
**Tracks:** Keeper of the castle / Ain't no woman / Put a little love away / Turn on the light of your love / When tonight meets tomorrow / Love music / Remember what I told you to forget / Dreaming / Good Lord knows / Jubilee with soul / Love makes you human / Kee.
■ **LP** .................................... SPB 1064
Probe / Jan '73.
■ **LP** .................................... ABCL 5023
ABC Records / '75.

## LEGEND.
**Tracks:** Not Advised.
**CD** ........................................ 295 704
EMS / Jul '90.

## LIVE AND IN CONCERT.
**Tracks:** Not Advised.
■ **CD** .................................... DMCL 1890
MCA / Aug '89.

## LIVE: FOUR TOPS.
**Tracks:** Introduction / It's the same old song / It's not unusual / Baby, I need your loving / Reach out I'll be there / I'll turn to stone / I left my heart in San Francisco / You can't hurry love / Ask the lonely / Climb every mountain / Girl from Ipanema / If I had a hammer / I can't help myself / I like everything about you.
■ **LP** .................................... STMS 5087
**MC** .................................... CSTMS 5087
Motown / Feb '83 / PolyGram.

## LOCO IN ACAPULCO.
**Tracks:** Loco in Acapulco / Four of us / Loco in Acapulco (body mix) (Only on 12" version.).
■ **12"** .................................... 611916
■ **12"** .................................... 611850
■ **7"** .................................... 111850X
■ **7" P.Disc** .................................... 11197
■ **CD Single** .................................... 661850
Arista / Jan '89.

## LOOK OF LOVE, THE.
**Tracks:** Standing in the shadows of love / Look of love / Seven rooms of gloom / Where did you go / Sunny / Honey / Loving you is sweeter than ever / Daydream believer / I'm grateful / This guy's in love with you / Key / Light my fire.
**CD** .................................... 550077-2
**MC** .................................... 550077-4
Spectrum (1) / May '93 / PolyGram.

## LOVING YOU IS SWEETER THAN EVER.
**Tracks:** Loving you is sweeter than ever.
■ **7"** .................................... TMG 568
Tamla Motown / Jul '66.

## MAGIC.
**Tracks:** I can feel the magic / Don't tell me that it's over / Sexy ways / Easier said than done / Don't turn away / I'm ready for love / Again / Remember me / Maybe tomorrow.
■ **LP** .................................... ZL 72301
■ **MC** .................................... ZK 72301
Motown / Jul '85.

## MAGNIFICENT 7, THE (see under Supremes).

## MAIN STREET PEOPLE.
**Tracks:** I just can't get you out of my mind / It won't be the first time / Sweet understanding love / Am I not my brothers keeper / Are you man enough / Whenever there's blue / Too little, too late / Peace of mind / One woman man / Main street people.
■ **LP** .................................... CRB 1129
Charly R&B / Jun '86.

## MOTOWN SPECIAL.
**Tracks:** Reach out, I'll be there / If I were a carpenter / Standing in the shadows of love / Can't seem to get you out of my mind / Remember when / We've got a strong love / Bernadette / I'll turn to stone / I like everything about you / Since you've been gone / Stay in my lonely arms / Place in the sun.
■ **LP** .................................... STMX 6004
Motown / Mar '77.

## MOTOWN'S GREATEST HITS: FOUR TOPS.
**Tracks:** Not Advised.
**CD** .................................... 530016-2
**MC** .................................... 530016-4
■ **LP** .................................... 530016-1
Motown / Jan '92 / PolyGram.

## NATURE PLANNED IT.
**Tracks:** I am your man / Nature planned it / I'll never change / She's an understanding woman / I can't quit your love / Walk with me, talk with me, darling / Hey man, we got to get you a woman / You got to forget him darling / If you let me / Happy / How will I forget you.
■ **LP** .................................... STML 11206
Tamla Motown / Jun '72.

## NOW.
**Tracks:** Key / What is a man / My past just crossed my future / Don't let him take your love from me / Eleanor Rigby / Little green apples / Do what you gotta do / MacArthur Park / Don't bring back memories / Wish I didn't love you so / Opportunity knock / Fool on the hill.
■ **LP** .................................... STML 11113
Tamla Motown / Sep '69.

## ONE MORE MOUNTAIN.
**Tracks:** Sad hearts / One more mountain to climb / Givin' it up / I believe in you and me / I'm the one / Keep on lightin' my fire / Nobody's gonna love you like I do / Dream on / Whatever it is.
■ **LP** .................................... CANS 3
**MC.** .................................... CANSC 3
Casablanca / Aug '82.

## REACH OUT.
**Tracks:** Reach out I'll be there / Walk away Renee / Seven rooms of gloom / If I were a carpenter / Last train to Clarksville / I'll turn to stone / I'm a believer / Standing in the shadows of love / Bernadette / Cherish / Wonderful baby / What else is there to do (but think about you).
■ **LP** .................................... STML 11056
Tamla Motown / Jan '68.
■ **LP** .................................... STMS 5004
■ **MC** .................................... CSTMS 5004
Motown / Oct '81.
■ **LP** .................................... WL 72067
■ **MC** .................................... WK 72067
Motown / '85.
■ **CD** .................................... WD 72067
Motown / Jun '89.

## REACH OUT, I'LL BE THERE.
**Tracks:** Reach out I'll be there.
■ **7"** .................................... TMG 579
Tamla Motown / Oct '66.

## REACH OUT, I'LL BE THERE.
**Tracks:** Reach out I'll be there / Standing in the shadows of love.
■ **7"** .................................... TMG 1049
Tamla Motown / Sep '76.
■ **7"** .................................... ZB 41943
■ **12"** .................................... ZT 41944
Motown / May '88.

## REACH OUT/STILL WATERS RUN DEEP.
**Tracks:** What else is there to do but think about you / If I were a carpenter / Reach out I'll be there / Walk away Renee / Seven nights of gloom / Last train to Clarksville / I'll turn to stone / Still water / Reflections / It's all in the game / Everybody's talkin' / Love is the answer / I wish I were your mirror / Elusive butterfly / Bring me together / L.A. (my town) / I'm a believer / Standing in the shadows of love / Cherish / Bernadette / Wonderful baby.
■ **CD** .................................... ZD 72472
Motown / Feb '87.

## RIVER DEEP MOUNTAIN HIGH (see under Supremes).

## SAD HEARTS.
**Tracks:** Sad hearts / I believe in you and me.
■ **12"** .................................... CANX 1012
■ **7"** .................................... CAN 1012
Casablanca / Jul '82.

## SECOND ALBUM.
**Tracks:** I can't help myself / Love feels like fire / Is there anything that I can do / Something about you / It's the same old song / Helpless / Just as long as you need me / Darlin' / I hum our song / I like everything about you / Since you've been gone / Stay in my lonely arms / I'm grateful.
■ **LP** .................................... STMS 5077
■ **MC** .................................... CSTMS 5077
Motown / Oct '82.

## SEVEN LONELY NIGHTS.
**Tracks:** Seven lonely nights / I can't hold on much longer.
■ **7"** .................................... ABC 4057
Anchor (1) / Jun '75.

## SEVEN ROOMS OF GLOOM.
**Tracks:** Seven rooms of gloom / If I were a carpenter.
■ **7"** .................................... TMG 958
Tamla Motown / Feb '75.

## SHAKE ME WAKE ME.
**Tracks:** Shake me wake me / Just as long as you need me.
■ **7"** .................................... TMG 553
Tamla Motown / Mar '66.

## SHOW MUST GO ON, THE.
**Tracks:** Show must go on / Can't live without you / Save it for a rainy day / Running from your love / See the real me / Love is a joy / You'll never find a better man / Candy.
■ **LP** .................................... ABCL 5223
ABC Records / Dec '77.

## SIMPLE GAME.
**Tracks:** Simple game / Still water.
■ **7"** .................................... TMG 785
Tamla Motown / Sep '71.
■ **7"** .................................... TMG 972
Tamla Motown / May '75.

## SINGLES COLLECTION: FOUR TOPS.
**Tracks:** Not Advised.
**CD** .................................... 515710-2
**MC** .................................... 515710-4
Motown / Jan '92 / PolyGram.

## SOMETHING ABOUT YOU.
**Tracks:** Something about you.
■ **7"** .................................... TMG 542
Tamla Motown / '66.

## SOUL SPIN.
**Tracks:** Look out your window / Barbara's boy / Lost in a pool of red / Got to get you into my life / Stop the world / Nothing / This guy's in love with you / Light my fire / Honey / Look of love / California dreamin'.
■ **LP** .................................... STML 11138
Tamla Motown / Feb '70.

## STANDING IN THE SHADOWS OF LOVE.
**Tracks:** Standing in the shadows of love / Since you've been gone.
■ **7"** .................................... TMG 589
Tamla Motown / Jan '67.

## STILL WATER (LOVE).
**Tracks:** Still water.
■ **7"** .................................... TMG 752
Tamla Motown / Oct '70.

## STILL WATERS RUN DEEP.
**Tracks:** Still water / Reflection / It's all in the game / Everybody's talkin' / Love is the answer / I wish I were your mirror / Elusive butterfly / Bring me together / L.A. (my town).
■ **LP** .................................... STML 11149
Tamla Motown / Jun '70.
■ **LP** .................................... STMS 5063
■ **MC** .................................... CSTMS 5063
Motown / Jun '82.
■ **CD** .................................... WD 72734
■ **MC** .................................... WK 72734
Motown / Mar '91.

## SUN AIN'T GONNA SHINE, THE.
**Tracks:** Sun ain't gonna shine / Loco in Acapulco.
■ **12"** .................................... 612252
■ **MC Single** .................................... 409995
■ **7"** .................................... 112378
■ **7"** .................................... 112252
■ **CD Single** .................................... 662252
Arista / Jul '89.

## SUPER HITS.
**Tracks:** Reach out I'll be there / I can't help myself / Walk away Renee / Standing in the shadows of love / Seven rooms of gloom / It's the same old song / What is a man / Bernadette / If I were a carpenter / It's all in the game / Do what you gotta do / Still water / Loving you is sweeter than ever / Yesterday's dreams / You keep running away / I'm in a different world / Simple game.
■ **LP** .................................... STMA 8024
■ **MC** .................................... CSTMA 8024
Motown / Oct '81.

## SWEET UNDERSTANDING LOVE.
**Tracks:** Sweet understanding love.
■ **7"** .................................... PRO 604
Probe / Nov '73.

## TEMPTATIONS AND THE FOUR TOPS (see under Temptations).

## THEIR GREATEST HITS.
**Tracks:** Not Advised.
- CD . . . . . . . . . . . . . . . . . . . . . . TCD 2437
- LP . . . . . . . . . . . . . . . . . . . . . STAR 2437
- MC . . . . . . . . . . . . . . . . . . . . . STAC 2437

Telstar/Ronco / Nov '90.

## TONIGHT.
**Tracks:** When she was my girl / Don't walk away / Tonight / I'm gonna love you / Who's right, who's wrong / Let me set you free / Something to remember / From a distance / All I do / I'll never ever leave again.
- LP . . . . . . . . . . . . . . . . . . . . . . .6480 059
- MC . . . . . . . . . . . . . . . . . . . . . .7190 058

Casablanca / Nov '81.
- CD . . . . . . . . . . . . . . . . . . . . . 800 049-2

Casablanca / Jan '83.
- LP . . . . . . . . . . . . . . . . . . . . . 836 967 1
- MC . . . . . . . . . . . . . . . . . . . . . 836 967 4

Casablanca / Feb '89.

## TONIGHT I'M GONNA LOVE YOU ALL OVER.
**Tracks:** Tonight I'm gonna love you all over / From a distance.
- 12" . . . . . . . . . . . . . . . . . . . . . CANX 1008
- 7" . . . . . . . . . . . . . . . . . . . . . CAN 1008

Casablanca / Feb '82.

## UNTIL YOU LOVE SOMEONE - MORE BEST OF THE FOUR TOPS (1965-1970).
**Tracks:** Teahouse in your kitchen / Your love is amazing / Since you've been gone / Helpless / Love feels like fire / I like everything about you / Stay in my lonely arms / Brenda / Until you love someone / You can't hurry love / Wonderful baby / What else is there to do (but think about you) / What is a man / Nothing / L.A. (My town) / Reflections.
- CD . . . . . . . . . . . . . . . . . . . .812271183-2
- MC . . . . . . . . . . . . . . . . . . . .812271183-4

WEA / Jun '93 / WEA.

## WALK AWAY RENEE.
**Tracks:** Walk away Renee.
- 7" . . . . . . . . . . . . . . . . . . . . . TMG 634

Tamla Motown / Dec '67.
- 7" . . . . . . . . . . . . . . . . . . . . . TMG 1011

Tamla Motown / Oct '75.

## WALK WITH ME TALK WITH ME DARLING.
**Tracks:** Walk with me talk with me darling.
- 7" . . . . . . . . . . . . . . . . . . . . . TMG 823

Tamla Motown / Aug '72.

## WHAT IS A MAN.
**Tracks:** What is a man.
- 7" . . . . . . . . . . . . . . . . . . . . . TMG 698

Tamla Motown / May '69.

## WHEN SHE WAS MY GIRL.
**Tracks:** When she was my girl / Something to remember.
- 12" . . . . . . . . . . . . . . . . . . . . . CANX 1005
- 7" . . . . . . . . . . . . . . . . . . . . . CAN 1005

Casablanca / Dec '81.

## WITH LOVE.
**Tracks:** Don't walk away / Sweet understanding love / When she was my girl / I believe in you and me / Tonight I'm gonna love you all over / Ain't no woman (Like the one I got) / One more mountain to climb / Keeper of the castle / Let me set you free / Sad hearts / Are you man enough / Seven lonely nights / Catfish / We all gotta stick together.
- CD . . . . . . . . . . . . . . . . . . . . . . 5501352
- MC . . . . . . . . . . . . . . . . . . . . . . 5501354

Spectrum (1) / Oct '93 / PolyGram.

## WITHOUT THE ONE YOU LOVE.
**Tracks:** Without the one you love / There's no love left.
- 7" . . . . . . . . . . . . . . . . . . . . . SS 371

Stateside / '64.

## YESTERDAY'S DREAMS.
**Tracks:** Can't seem to get you out of my mind / I'm in a different world / We've got a strong love / By the time I get to Phoenix / Remember when / Sunny / Never my love / Daydream believer / Once upon a dream / Sweetheart tree / Place in the sun.
- LP . . . . . . . . . . . . . . . . . . . . .STML 11087

Tamla Motown / Jan '68.

## YESTERDAY'S DREAMS.
**Tracks:** Yesterday's dreams.
- 7" . . . . . . . . . . . . . . . . . . . . . TMG 665

Tamla Motown / Aug '68.

## YOU GOTTA HAVE LOVE IN YOUR HEART (see under Supremes).

## YOU KEEP RUNNING AWAY.
**Tracks:** You keep running away.
- 7" . . . . . . . . . . . . . . . . . . . . . TMG 623

Tamla Motown / Oct '67.

## YOUR SONG.
**Tracks:** Your song / I'm here again.
- 12" . . . . . . . . . . . . . . . . . . . . . CABL 124
- 7" . . . . . . . . . . . . . . . . . . . . . .CAB 124

Calibre / Jun '84.

# Fourth Generation

## AIN'T NOBODY.
**Tracks:** Ain't nobody.
- 12" . . . . . . . . . . . . . . . . . . . . . JDPD 014

White / Feb '89.

## LET'S GET IT RIGHT.
**Tracks:** Let's get it right.
- 12" . . . . . . . . . . . . . . . . . . . . . .STDI 5

Soul Train / Jul '89.

# Fowler, Barbara

## COME AND GET MY LOVIN'.
**Tracks:** Come and get my lovin'.
- 12" . . . . . . . . . . . . . . . . . . . . . CHE 8405

Master Mix / Sep '84.

# Foxx, Inez

## AT MEMPHIS AND MORE.
**Tracks:** There's a hand that's reaching out / Let me down easy / Crossing over the bridge / I had a talk with my man / You're saving me for a rainy day / You don't want my love / Lady, the doctor and the prescription / Time / Mousa muse / Circuits overloaded / I just want to know (before you go) / He ain't all good but he ain't all bad / One woman's man / Watch the dog / You hurt me for the last time.
- CD . . . . . . . . . . . . . . . . . . . . CDSXD 034

Stax / Oct '90 / Pinnacle.

## YOU SHOULDN'T HAVE SET MY SOUL ON FIRE.
**Tracks:** You shouldn't have set my soul on fire / Live for today.
- 7" . . . . . . . . . . . . . . . . . . . . . 7N 25546

Pye / Mar '71.

# Foxx, Inez & Charlie

## COME BY HERE.
**Tracks:** Come by here / No stranger to love.
- 7" . . . . . . . . . . . . . . . . . . . . . .SS 556

Stateside / Nov '66.

## COME BY HERE.
**Tracks:** My special prayer / Tightrope / No stranger to love / Baby take it all / Guilty / I stand accused / Undecided / Never love a robin / Stranger I don't know / I love you 1000 times.
- LP . . . . . . . . . . . . . . . . . . . . . 8 63085

Direction / Sep '68.

## HUMMINGBIRD.
**Tracks:** Hummingbird / If I need anyone.
- 7" . . . . . . . . . . . . . . . . . . . . . HLC 10009

London-American / Dec '65.

## HURT BY LOVE.
**Tracks:** Hurt by love.
- 7" . . . . . . . . . . . . . . . . . . . . . .WI 323

Sue / Jul '64.

## INEZ AND CHARLIE FOXX.
**Tracks:** Mockin' bird / I ain't goin' for that / You are the man / Hard to get / You fixed my heartache / Count the days / Vaya con dios / Fellows in Vietnam / Like little children / I got it.
- LP . . . . . . . . . . . . . . . . . . . . . 8 63281

Direction / May '68.

## MOCKINGBIRD (Best of Inez & Charlie Foxx).
**Tracks:** Mockingbird / Searching for my C.C. / Broken-hearted fool / My momma told me / Don't do it no more / I wanna see my baby / If I need anyone / Here we go round the mulberry bush / Hurt by love / Sitting hero / La dee dah I love you / I fancy you / Down by the seashore / Ask me / Confusion / Jaybirds.
- MC . . . . . . . . . . . . . . . . . . . .TCSSL 6000
- LP . . . . . . . . . . . . . . . . . . . . . SSL 6000

Stateside / Mar '86.

## MOCKINGBIRD.
**Tracks:** Mockingbird / Hurt by love.
- 7" . . . . . . . . . . . . . . . . . . . . . .G 4536

EMI Golden 45's / Feb '85.

## MOCKINGBIRD.
**Tracks:** Mockingbird.
- 7" . . . . . . . . . . . . . . . . . . . . . UP 2269

United Artists / '68.

## MOCKINGBIRD (RE-RELEASE).
**Tracks:** Mockingbird / La dee dah I love you.
- 7" . . . . . . . . . . . . . . . . . . . . . ENS 3

Virgin / Oct '83.

## TIGHTROPE.
**Tracks:** Tightrope / My special prayer.
- 7" . . . . . . . . . . . . . . . . . . . . . .SS 586

Stateside / Jan '67.

## TIGHTROPE.
**Tracks:** Tightrope / Baby take it all.
- 7" . . . . . . . . . . . . . . . . . . . . . 7N 25561

Pye / Jul '71.

# Foxy

## GET OFF.
**Tracks:** Get off / You make me hot.
- 7" . . . . . . . . . . . . . . . . . . . . . TKR 6040

TK / Jul '78.

## GET OFF.
**Tracks:** Tena's song / Ready for love / Mademoiselle / You / Get off / Lucky me / Goin' back to you / It's happening.
- LP . . . . . . . . . . . . . . . . . . . . . TKR 82544

TK / Nov '78.

## HEADHUNTER.
**Tracks:** Headhunter / Lady of the street.
- 7" . . . . . . . . . . . . . . . . . . . . . TKR 7550

TK / Aug '79.

## HOT NUMBER.
**Tracks:** Hot number / Call it love.
- 7" . . . . . . . . . . . . . . . . . . . . . TKR 7532

TK / '79.

## HOT NUMBERS.
**Tracks:** Headhunter / Devil boogie / Give me a break / Nobody will ever take me away from you / Chicapbon chicapbon / Hot numbers / Lady / Give me that groove / Lady of the streets.
- LP . . . . . . . . . . . . . . . . . . . . . TKR 83353

TK / '79.

## PARTY BOYS.
**Tracks:** Girls / Let's be bad tonight / Sambambe Rio / I belong to you / She's so cool / Rrrrock / Fantasy / Pensando en ti / Party boys.
- LP . . . . . . . . . . . . . . . . . . . . . TKR 83384

TK / May '80.

# Fran, Carol

## SEE THERE (Fran, Carol & Clarence Holliman).
**Tracks:** Not Advised.
- CD . . . . . . . . . . . . . . . . . . . . . BT 1100CD
- MC . . . . . . . . . . . . . . . . . . . . . BT 1100C

Black Top (USA) / Apr '94 / C.M. Distribution / Direct Distribution / Hot Shot / Topic Records.

## SOUL SENSATION (Fran, Carol & Clarence Holliman).
**Tracks:** Not Advised.
- MC . . . . . . . . . . . . . . . . . . . . . BT 1071C

Black Top (USA) / '92 / C.M. Distribution / Direct Distribution / Hot Shot / Topic Records.
- CD . . . . . . . . . . . . . . . . . . . . . BT 1071CD

Black Top (USA) / Feb '92 / C.M. Distribution / Direct Distribution / Hot Shot / Topic Records.

# Frankie & Classicals

## I ONLY HAVE EYES FOR YOU.
**Tracks:** I only have eyes for you / What shall I do.
- 7" . . . . . . . . . . . . . . . . . . . . . BF 1586

Philips / '67.

## WHAT SHALL I DO?.
**Tracks:** What shall I do / I only have eyes for you.
- 7" . . . . . . . . . . . . . . . . . . . . . DDS 101

Pye Disco Demand / '74.

■ DELETED

## Frankie & Johnny

**CLIMB EVERY MOUNTAIN.**
**Tracks:** Climb every mountain / I wanna make you understand.
■ 7" . . . . . . . . . . . . . . . . . . . . . . R 5518
Parlophone / Jun '66.

**I'LL HOLD YOU.**
**Tracks:** I'll hold you / Never gonna leave you.
■ 7" . . . . . . . . . . . . . . . . . . . . . HEAT 8
Inferno (1) / Mar '83.

**NEVER GONNA LEAVE YOU.**
**Tracks:** Never gonna leave you / I'll hold you.
■ 7" . . . . . . . . . . . . . . . . . . . . . F 22376
Decca / Apr '66.

## Franklin, Aretha

'Queen of Soul' whose reign spans 25 years plus. After six fruitless years with CBS, Aretha moved to Atlantic, where vice president Jerry Wexler teamed her with might of Muscle Shoals studio. Result was debut hit / Never Loved A Man (the Way I Love You), followed by definitive version of Otis Redding's Respect. Latter was U.S. no. 1 and first U.K. hit. Best of highly-acclaimed albums from this period was 1968's million-selling Lady Soul, whose attractions included (You Make Me Feel Like) A Natural Woman and Chain Of Fools; latter being one of several hits penned by Aretha's sister Carolyn. Mid to late '70s did Aretha no favours, as she flirted with styles ranging from gospel to disco with equally uncommercial results. Appearance in Blues Brothers and signing to Arista in 1980 paved way for major upswing in fortunes; although some '60s soul stars have managed comebacks, few were as spectacular as Aretha's. Who's Zoomin' Who, produced by then-infallible Narada Michael Walden, returned her to international album and single charts; duets with Eurythmics, George Michael, Elton John, James Brown and Whitney Houston raised profile even further. Later studio albums were regularly overshadowed by repackagings of illustrious past; although '94 smash Deeper Love proved Aretha can still cut it; becoming her biggest U.K. hit since I Say A Little Prayer in 1968.

**(YOU MAKE ME FEEL) A NATURAL WOMAN.**
**Tracks:** (You make me feel) a natural woman / Never loved a man (the way I love you) / Do right woman, do right man (Extra track on 12" version only.)
■ 12" . . . . . . . . . . . . . . . . . . . . A 9409 T
■ 7" . . . . . . . . . . . . . . . . . . . . . A 9409
Atlantic / May '86.

**20 GREATEST HITS: ARETHA FRANKLIN.**
**Tracks:** Not Advised.
CD . . . . . . . . . . . . . . . . . . . . .241135 2
■ LP . . . . . . . . . . . . . . . . . .K 2411352
WEA / Oct '87 / WEA.

**30 GREATEST HITS.**
**Tracks:** I never loved a man / Respect / Do right woman, do right man / Dr. Feelgood / Save me / Baby I love you / (You make me feel like) a natural woman / Chain of fools / Since you've been gone / Ain't no way / Think / I say a little prayer / House that Jack built / See saw / Weight / Share your love with me / Eleanor Rigby / Call me / Spirit in the dark / Don't play that song / You're all I need to get by / Bridge over troubled water / Spanish harlem / Rock steady / Oh me oh my (I'm a fool for you baby) / Day dreaming / Wholly holy / Angel / Until you come back to me / I'm in love.
CD . . . . . . . . . . . . . . . . . .756781668-2
WEA / Mar '93 / WEA.

**AFTER HOURS.**
**Tracks:** Bitter earth / Once in a lifetime / Misty / There is no greater love / Unforgettable / If I should lose you / Don't cry, baby / Just for a thrill / I'm wandering / Don't say you're sorry again / Look for the silver lining.
CD . . . . . . . . . . . . . . . . . . . . .983303 2
Pickwick/Sony Collector's Choice / Oct '93 / Pickwick / Pinnacle.

**AIN'T NOBODY EVER LOVED YOU.**
**Tracks:** Ain't nobody ever loved you / Integrity / Ain't nobody ever loved you (dub mix) / (Percappella) Integrity.
■ 12" . . . . . . . . . . . . . . . . . . ARIST 12667

■ 7" . . . . . . . . . . . . . . . . . . . .ARIST 667
Arista / Jul '86.

**ALMIGHTY FIRE.**
**Tracks:** Almighty fire (woman of the future) / Lady lady / More than just a joy / Keep on loving you / I needed you baby / Close to you / No matter who you love / This you can believe / I'm your speed.
■ LP . . . . . . . . . . . . . . . . . . . . K 50445
Atlantic / Jun '78.

**AMAZING GRACE.**
**Tracks:** Not Advised.
■ Double LP . . . . . . . . . . . . . . . . 2-906
Atlantic / Nov '87.
CD . . . . . . . . . . . . . . . . . .756781324-2
Atlantic / Jun '93 / WEA.

**ANGEL.**
**Tracks:** Angel.
■ 7" . . . . . . . . . . . . . . . . . . . . K 10346
Atlantic / Sep '73.

**ANOTHER NIGHT.**
**Tracks:** Love me forever / School days / Together again.
■ 12" . . . . . . . . . . . . . . . . . ARIST 12657
■ 12" Remix . . . . . . . . . . . . . ARIST 22657
■ 7" . . . . . . . . . . . . . . . . . . .ARIST 657
Arista / Feb '86.

**ARETHA.**
**Tracks:** Jimmy Lee / I knew you were waiting (for me) (duet with George Michael) / Do you still remember / Jumpin' Jack Flash / Rockalott / Angel cries, An / He'll come along / If you need my love tonight (duet with Larry Graham.) / Look to the rainbow.
■ LP . . . . . . . . . . . . . . . . . . SPART 1147
■ MC . . . . . . . . . . . . . . . . . . TCART 1147
Arista / Oct '80.
■ LP . . . . . . . . . . . . . . . . . . . .208020
■ CD . . . . . . . . . . . . . . . . . . . .258020
■ MC . . . . . . . . . . . . . . . . . . . .408020
Arista / Oct '86.
■ LP . . . . . . . . . . . . . . . . . . . .208883
■ CD . . . . . . . . . . . . . . . . . . . .258883
■ MC . . . . . . . . . . . . . . . . . . . .408883
Arista / May '88.

**ARETHA (CBS).**
**Tracks:** Won't be long / Over the rainbow / Love is the only thing / Sweet lover / All night long / Who needs you / Right now / Are you sure / Maybe I'm a fool / It ain't necessarily so / Blue by myself / Today I sing the blues.
■ LP . . . . . . . . . . . . . . . . . . CBS 32408
MC . . . . . . . . . . . . . . . . . . . .40-32408
CBS Cameo / Jan '84 / Sony.

**ARETHA ARRIVES.**
**Tracks:** Satisfaction / You are my sunshine / Never let me go / 96 tears / Prove it / Night life / That's life / I wonder / Ain't nobody / Going down slow / Baby I love you.
■ LP . . . . . . . . . . . . . . . . . . . 588 085
Atlantic / Nov '67.

**ARETHA FRANKLIN BOX SET.**
**Tracks:** Not Advised.
CD Set . . . . . . . . . . . . . . . 8122710632
Atlantic / Nov '92 / WEA.

**ARETHA IN PARIS.**
**Tracks:** Satisfaction / Don't let me lose this dream / Soul serenade / Night life / Baby I love you / Groovin' / Natural woman / Come back baby / Dr Feelgood / Respect / Since you've been gone / I never loved a man / Chain of fools.
■ LP . . . . . . . . . . . . . . . . . . . 588 149
Atlantic / Dec '68.
■ LP . . . . . . . . . . . . . . . . . . . SD8207
Atlantic / Jun '88.

**ARETHA NOW.**
**Tracks:** Think / I say a little prayer / See-saw / Night time is the right time / You send me / You're a sweet sweet man / I take what I want / Hello sunshine / Change / I can't see myself leaving you.
■ LP . . . . . . . . . . . . . . . . . . . 588 114
Atlantic / Sep '68.

**ARETHA SINGS THE BLUES.**
**Tracks:** Drinking again / Today I sing the blues / What a difference a day made / Without the one you love / Trouble in mind / Muddy Water / Only the lonely / I wonder (where are you tonight?) / Laughing on the outside (crying on the inside) / Take a look / Nobody knows the way I feel this morning / Evil gal blues / This bitter earth / Maybe I'm a fool.
■ CD . . . . . . . . . . . . . . . . . CD 26676
CBS / '91.

**ARETHA'S GOLD.**
**Tracks:** I never loved a man (the way I love you) / Do right woman, do right man / Respect / Dr. Feelgood / Baby, I love you / (You make me feel like) a natural woman / Chain of fools / Since you've been gone (sweet sweet baby) / Ain't no way / Think / You send me / House that Jack built / I say a little prayer / See-saw.
■ LP . . . . . . . . . . . . . . . . . . . K 40036
Atlantic.
■ LP . . . . . . . . . . . . . . . . . . . 588 192
Atlantic / Sep '69.
CD . . . . . . . . . . . . . . . . . .756781445-2
Atlantic / Jun '93 / WEA.

**ARETHA'S GREATEST HITS.**
**Tracks:** Spanish Harlem / Chain of fools / Don't play that song / I say a little prayer / Dr. Feelgood / Let it be / Do right woman, do right man / Bridge over troubled water / Respect / Baby I love you / (You make me feel like) a natural woman / I never loved a man (the way I love you) / You're all I need to get by / Call me.
■ LP . . . . . . . . . . . . . . . . . . . . ZFB 61
Argo / Nov '67.
■ LP . . . . . . . . . . . . . . . . . . . 2400188
Atlantic / Dec '71.
■ LP . . . . . . . . . . . . . . . . . . . K 40279
■ MC . . . . . . . . . . . . . . . . . . K4 40279
Atlantic / '87.
CD . . . . . . . . . . . . . . . . . .756781451-2
Atlantic / Jun '93 / WEA.

**ARETHA'S JAZZ.**
**Tracks:** Not Advised.
CD . . . . . . . . . . . . . . . . . .756781230-2
WEA / Mar '93 / WEA.

**BABY I LOVE YOU.**
**Tracks:** Baby I love you / Going down slow
■ 7" . . . . . . . . . . . . . . . . . . . 584 127
Atlantic / Aug '67.

**BEST OF ARETHA FRANKLIN.**
**Tracks:** Chain of fools / I say a little prayer / You make me feel like a natural woman / Think / Rock steady / Until you come back to me / Respect / Spanish Harlem / Dr. Feelgood / Do right woman, do right man / I never loved a man (the way I love you) / Save me.
■ LP . . . . . . . . . . . . . . . . . . 780 169-1
MC . . . . . . . . . . . . . . . . . . 780 169-4
Atlantic / Jul '84 / WEA.
■ CD . . . . . . . . . . . . . . . . 7567 81280-2
Atlantic / '86.

**BRAND NEW ME.**
**Tracks:** Brand new me / Spirit in the dark.
■ 7" . . . . . . . . . . . . . . . . . . . 2091169
Atlantic / Jul '71.

**BREAK IT TO ME GENTLY.**
**Tracks:** Break it to me gently / Meadows of springtime.
■ 7" . . . . . . . . . . . . . . . . . . . K 10938
Atlantic / May '77.

**BRIDGE OVER TROUBLED WATER.**
**Tracks:** Bridge over troubled water / Brand new me.
■ 7" . . . . . . . . . . . . . . . . . . . 2091090
Atlantic / May '71.

**CAN'T RUN YOU LOOSE.**
**Tracks:** Can't run you loose / United together.
■ 12" . . . . . . . . . . . . . . . . . ARIST 12395
Arista / Apr '81.

**CHAIN OF FOOLS.**
**Tracks:** Chain of fools / Satisfaction.
■ 7" . . . . . . . . . . . . . . . . . . . 584 157
Atlantic / Dec '67.

**CHICAGO GOLDEN YEARS.**
**Tracks:** Not Advised.
■ LP . . . . . . . . . . . . . . . . . . . .515007
Vogue / Oct '88.

**COLLECTION: ARETHA FRANKLIN.**
**Tracks:** Walk on by / It ain't necessarily so / What a difference a day made / Once in a lifetime (live) / Over the rainbow / You made me love you / Say it isn't so / Unforgettable / My guy / Exactly like you / Try a little tenderness / I'm sitting on top of the world / Skylark / Solitude / Where are you / Love for sale (live) / Swanee / I surrender dear / Look for the silver lining / Lover come back to me / Make someone happy / Ol' man river / I apologise.
CD . . . . . . . . . . . . . . . . . . CCSCD 152
■ Double LP . . . . . . . . . . . . . CCSLP 152
MC . . . . . . . . . . . . . . . . . .CCSMC 152
Castle Collector Series / Jul '87 / BMG / Pinnacle / Castle Communications.

## DEEPER LOVE, A.
**Tracks:** Deeper love / Deeper love (mixes).
- 12" ............................7432118702-1
- CD Single ......................7432118975-2
- CD Single ......................7432118702-2
- MC Single ......................7432118702-4

Arista / Jan '94.

## DON'T PLAY THAT SONG.
**Tracks:** Don't play that song.
- 7" ...............................2091 027

Atlantic / Aug '70.

## DON'T PLAY THAT SONG.
**Tracks:** Don't play that song / Thrill is gone / Pullin' / You and me / Honest I do / Spirit in the dark / When the battle is over / One way ticket / Try Matty's / That's all I want from you / Oh no not my baby / Why I sing the blues.
- LP ..............................2400 021

Atlantic / Dec '70.

## ELECTRIFYING/SOUL SISTER.
**Tracks:** Not Advised.
- Double LP ..................CBS 22188

CBS / Aug '85.

## EVERYDAY PEOPLE.
**Tracks:** Everyday people / You can't take me for granted (Only available on 7" & CD single).
- 12" ...............................614420
- 7" ................................114420
- CD Single .........................664420

Arista / Jul '91.

## FIRST LADY OF SOUL.
**Tracks:** Not Advised.
- Double LP ....................SMR 8506
- MC Set ......................SMC 8506

Stylus / Nov '85.

## FREEWAY OF LOVE.
**Tracks:** Freeway of love / Until you say you love me / Jump to it (Extra track on 12" version only.) / Freeway of love (Pink Cadillac Mix) / Freeway of love (rock Mix) / Freeway of love (7" Version).
- 12" .........................ARIST 12624
- 7" ...........................ARIST 624
- 7" ..........................ARIST 22624

Arista / Apr '86.
- CD Single .........................162052

Arista / Jun '89.

## GET IT RIGHT.
**Tracks:** Get it right / Pretender / Every girl (Wants my guy) / When you love me like that / I wish it would rain / Better friends than lovers / I've got your love / Giving in.
- LP ...............................205544
- MC ..............................405544

Arista / Jul '83.

## GET IT RIGHT.
**Tracks:** Get it right / Giving in.
- 12" .........................ARIST 12537
- 7" ...........................ARIST 537

Arista / Jul '85.

## GIMME YOUR LOVE (Franklin, Aretha & James Brown).
**Tracks:** Gimme your love / Gimme your love (Parts one & two, purple mix) (12" only.) / He's the boy / Gimme your love (album version) (12" only.)
- 12" ..............................612727
- 7" ...............................112728
- CD Single .........................662727

Arista / Nov '89.

## GOSPEL ROOTS.
**Tracks:** Not Advised.
CD ...............................CDCD 1164
Charly / Apr '94 / Charly.

## GREAT ARETHA FRANKLIN, THE.
**Tracks:** Won't be long / Over the rainbow / Love is the only thing / Sweet lover / All night long / Who needs you / Right now / Are you sure / Maybe I'm a fool / It ain't necessarily so / Blue my breath / Today I sing the blues.
CD ...............................9022912
Pickwick/Sony Collector's Choice / Mar '94 / Pickwick / Pinnacle.

## GREATEST HITS.
**Tracks:** Mockingbird / Soulville / Lee cross / Skylark / Take it like you give it / Try a little tenderness / Take a look / Runnin' out of fools / Sweet bitter love / Rock-a-bye your baby with a Dixie melody / Cry like a baby / God bless the child.
- LP ................................65436

CBS / Nov '71.

## GREATEST HITS 1980-1994.
**Tracks:** Not Advised.
- CD ..........................74321 16202-2
- MC ..........................74321 16202-4

Arista / Jan '94 / BMG.

## GREATEST HITS: ARETHA FRANKLIN (1960-1965).
**Tracks:** Soulville / Lee Cross / Skylark / Take it like you give it / Try a little tenderness / Take a look / Runnin' out of fools / Sweet bitter love / Rock-a-bye your baby with a Dixie melody / Cry like a baby / God bless the child.
- LP ...............................4506261
- MC ...............................4506264

CBS / Apr '87.
CD ................................9825842
Pickwick/Sony Collector's Choice / Oct '91 / Pickwick / Pinnacle.

## HOLD ON I'M COMING.
**Tracks:** Hold on I'm coming / Kind of man / I can't turn you loose.
- 12" .........................ARIST 12442
- 7" ...........................ARIST 442

Arista / '82.

## I KNEW YOU WERE WAITING (FOR ME) (Franklin, Aretha & George Michael).
**Tracks:** I knew you were waiting (for me).
- 12" ...............................DUET 2T
- 7" ................................DUET 2

Epic / Jan '87.

## I NEVER LOVED A MAN.
**Tracks:** I never loved a man / Do right woman.
- 7" ...............................584084

Atlantic / Apr '67.

## I NEVER LOVED A MAN THE WAY I LOVE YOU.
**Tracks:** Not Advised.
- LP ..............................587-006

Atlantic / Aug '67.
- LP ..............................SD8139

Atlantic / Jun '88.
CD ............................756781439-2

Atlantic / Mar '93 / WEA.

## I SAY A LITTLE PRAYER.
**Tracks:** I say a little prayer.
- 7" ...............................584 206

Atlantic / May '68.
- 7" ...............................209 1111

Atlantic / Jul '71.

## I SAY A LITTLE PRAYER.
**Tracks:** Save me / Baby I love you / Think / Groovin' / You are my sunshine / Come back baby / Chain of fools / Dr Feelgood / Money won't change you / Going down slow / I say a little prayer / I can't get no satisfaction.
- LP ...............................2464 007

Atlantic / Jun '70.

## I SAY A LITTLE PRAYER (OLD GOLD).
**Tracks:** I say a little prayer / Respect.
- 7" ...............................OG 9102

Old Gold / Jul '82.

## IT ISN'T, IT WASN'T, IT AIN'T NEVER GONNA BE (Franklin, Aretha & Whitney Houston).
**Tracks:** It isn't, it wasn't, it ain't never gonna be.
- 12" ...............................612545
- 12" Remix ........................612683
- 7" ................................112545
- CD Single .........................662545
- MC Single .........................410093

Arista / Sep '89.

## IT'S JUST YOUR LOVE (OLD GOLD).
**Tracks:** It's just your love / Love me right.
- 12" ...............................OG 4511

Old Gold / Apr '89.

## JAZZ TO SOUL.
**Tracks:** Today I sing the blues / (Blue) by myself / Maybe I'm a fool / All night long / Blue holiday / Nobody likes you / Sweet lover / Just for a thrill / If ever I would leave you / Once in a while / This bitter earth / God bless the child / Skylark / Muddy water / Drinking again / What a difference a day makes / Unforgettable / Love for sale / Misty / Impossible / This could be the start of something / Won't be long / Operation heartbreak / Soulville / Runnin' out of fools / Trouble in mind / Walk on by / Every little bit hurts / Mockingbird / You'll lose a good thing / Cry like a baby / Take it like you give it / Land of dreams / Can't you just see me / (No no) I'm losing you / Bit of soul / Why was I born / Until you were gone / Lee cross.

## CD Set ............................CD 485
Legacy / Nov '93 / Sony.

## JIMMY LEE.
**Tracks:** Jimmy Lee / You need my love tonight Aretha megamix (Only available on 12" version.) Angel cries, An / Jimmy Lee (dub).
- 12" ...............................RIST
- 7" ................................RIS
- CD Single .........................RICD

Arista / Feb '87.

## JUMP TO IT.
**Tracks:** Jump to it / Love me right / If she don't war your lovin' / This is for real / It's just for love / wanna make it up to you / It's your thing / Just m day dream / Get it right.
- LP ...............................20474
- MC ...............................40474
- CD ...............................25474

Arista / Mar '84.
- LP ...............................20906
- CD ...............................25906
- MC ...............................40906

Arista / May '88.

## JUMP TO IT.
**Tracks:** Jump to it / Just my daydream.
- 12" .........................ARIST 124
- 7" ...........................ARIST 4

Arista / '82.

## JUMP TO IT (OLD GOLD).
**Tracks:** Jump to it / Get it right.
- 12" ...............................OG 405

Old Gold / '88.
CD Single ..........................OG 650
Old Gold / Jun '90 / Pickwick.

## JUMPIN' JACK FLASH.
**Tracks:** Jumpin' Jack Flash / Integrity.
- 12" .........................ARIST 1267
- 7" ...........................ARIST 67

Arista / Oct '86.

## LA DIVA.
**Tracks:** Ladies only / It's gonna get a bit better What if I should ever need you / Honey I need you love / I was made for you / Only star / Reasons why You brought me back to life / Half a love / Feeling
- LP ................................K 5063

Atlantic / Oct '79.

## LADY SOUL.
**Tracks:** Chain of fools / Money won't change you People get ready / Niki Hoeky / Natural woman Since you've been gone / Good to me as I am to yo / Come back baby / Groovin' / Ain't no way.
- LP ...............................588-09
Atlantic / Apr '68.
- CD ..............................K 781818
WEA / Sep '89.
CD ............................756781818-
Atlantic / Mar '93 / WEA.

## LEGENDARY QUEEN OF SOUL.
**Tracks:** Mockingbird / How glad i am / Walk on by You'll lose a good thing / Every little bit hurts / I can wait until i see my baby's face / You made me lov you / Nobody likes you / Rough lover / Lee cross Runnin' out of fools / Won't be long / Until you wer gone / Blue holiday / One room paradise / Cry like baby / Can't you just see me / Two sides of love / won't cry anymore / I'll keep on smiling.
- Double LP ...................CBS 221
CBS / May '83.

## LET ME IN YOUR LIFE.
**Tracks:** Let me into your life / Every natural thing Ain't nothing like the real thing / I'm in love / Unt you come back to me / Masquerade is over / Wit pen in hand / Oh baby / Eight days on the road / you don't think / Song for you.
- LP ................................K 5003
Atlantic / May '78.

## LIVE AT FILLMORE WEST.
**Tracks:** Respect / Love the one you're with / Bridg over troubled water / Eleanor Rigby / Make it wit you / Don't play that song / Dr. Feelgood / Spirit i the dark / Reach out and touch.
- LP ...............................2400 13
Atlantic / Aug '71.
CD ............................812271526-
Atlantic / Feb '94 / WEA.

## LOVE ALL THE HURT AWAY.
**Tracks:** You can't always get what you want / Hold o I'm coming / It's my turn / Living in the streets / Lov all the hurt away / There's a star for everyone / Tru and honesty / Search on / Whole lot of me / Kind c man.
- LP ...............................SPART 117
- MC ..............................TCART 117

■ DELETE

Arista / Sep '81.
■ CD . . . . . . . . . . . . . . . . . . . . . . . .253913
Arista / Nov '85.

## OVE ME RIGHT.
racks: Love me right / It's just your love.
■ 12" . . . . . . . . . . . . . . . . . . . . ARIST 12500
■ 7" . . . . . . . . . . . . . . . . . . . .ARIST 500
Arista / Jan '83.

## NATURAL WOMAN.
racks: Natural woman / Never let me go.
■ 7" . . . . . . . . . . . . . . . . . . . .584141
atlantic / Oct '67.

## NATURAL WOMAN, A.
racks: Not Advised.
■ CD . . . . . . . . . . . . . . . . . . . .291014
riola Express / Nov '92.

## NEVER GROW OLD (Franklin, Aretha & Reverend Franklin).
racks: Mother loves her children / I will trust in the ord / Old ship of Zion (parts 1 & 2) / Never grow old I'm going through (parts 1 & 2) / Precious Lord (part & 2) / You grow closer.
■ LP . . . . . . . . . . . . . . . . . . . .GCH 8014
MC. . . . . . . . . . . . . . . . . . . . GCHK 78014
hess (Charly) / Jan '87 / Charly.

## OH HAPPY DAY.
racks: Oh happy day / Lords' prayer.
■ 12" . . . . . . . . . . . . . . . . . . . .609780
■ 7" . . . . . . . . . . . . . . . . . . . .109780
rista / Feb '88.

## ONE LORD, ONE FAITH, ONE BAPTISM.
racks: Walk in the light / Prayer invitation by Rev ecil Franklin / Introduction by Rev Jesse Jackson / esus hears every prayer / Surely God is able / ord's prayer / Oh happy day / We need power / peech by Rev Jesse Jackson / Ava Maria / Intro-uction by Rev Jaspar Williams / Higher ground / rayer invitation by Rev Donald Parsons / I've been the storm too long / Packing up, getting ready to o.
■ LP . . . . . . . . . . . . . . . . . . . .208715
■ CD . . . . . . . . . . . . . . . . . . . .258715
■ MC. . . . . . . . . . . . . . . . . . . . 408715
rista / Nov '87.

## QUEEN OF SOUL.
racks: Respect / Think / Jumpin' Jack Flash / Natur-woman / I knew you were waiting / Freeway of ve / Chain of fools.
HS . . . . . . . . . . . . . . . . . . . . VC 4046
ideo Collection / Aug '88 / Gold & Sons / Video ollection / THE.
HS . . . . . . . . . . . . . . . . . . . .MC 2001
usic Club Video / Sep '89 / Video Collection / Gold Sons / THE.

## QUEEN OF SOUL.
racks: I never loved a man (the way I love you) / Do ght woman, do right man / Dr Feelgood (love is a erious business) / Baby, I love you / (You make me el like) A natural woman / Chain of fools / Since ou've been gone (sweet sweet baby) / Ain't no way Save me / House that Jack built / Think / I say a tle prayer / See saw / Day dreaming / Call me / on't play that song (you lied) / Border song (Holy oses) / You're all I need to get by / I'm in love / panish Harlem / Rock steady / Angel / Until you ome back to me (that's what I'm gonna do).
D . . . . . . . . . . . . . . . . . . . .756780606-2
C. . . . . . . . . . . . . . . . . . . . 756780606-4
EA / Oct '94 / WEA.

## E-THINK.
racks: Re-think.
. . . . . . . . . . . . . . . . . . . . A 7635 T
tlantic / Jul '91.

## ESPECT.
racks: Respect / Do right woman, do right man / ck steady" (*Extra track on 12").
7" . . . . . . . . . . . . . . . . . . . 584 115
lantic / Jun '67.
12" . . . . . . . . . . . . . . . . . . . YZ 121 T
7" . . . . . . . . . . . . . . . . . . . .YZ 121
lantic / Jun '87.

## ESPECT.
acks: Not Advised.
. . . . . . . . . . . . . . . . . . . .TS 009
at's Soul / Mar '94 / BMG.

## OCKALOTT.
acks: Rockalott / Look at the rainbow.
12" . . . . . . . . . . . . . . . . . . . RIST 20
7" . . . . . . . . . . . . . . . . . . . RIS 20
ista / Jun '87.

## SO SWELL.
Tracks: Not Advised.
CD . . . . . . . . . . . . . . . . . . . .246 2525
■ LP . . . . . . . . . . . . . . . . . . . .226 2525
MC. . . . . . . . . . . . . . . . . . . . 216 2525
Street Life / May '88.

## SONGS OF FAITH.
Tracks: Not Advised.
CD . . . . . . . . . . . . . . . . . . . . VGCD 600 168
Vogue / Oct '88 / BMG.

## SOUL '69.
Tracks: Ramblin' / Today I sing the blues / River's invitation / Pitiful / Crazy he calls me / Bring it on home to me / Tracks of my tears / If you gotta make a fool of somebody / Gentle on my mind / So long / I'll never be free / Elusive butterfly.
■ LP . . . . . . . . . . . . . . . . . . . . 588 169
Atlantic / Apr '69.
CD . . . . . . . . . . . . . . . . . . . .812271523-2
Atlantic / Feb '94 / WEA.

## SOUL QUEENS VOL.1.
Tracks: Power / He's alright / Day is past / White as snow / Yield not to temptation / Jesus on the main line / This little girl of mine / There is a fountain / Precious lord / You grow closer.
CD . . . . . . . . . . . . . . . . . . . . SMS 059
Pickwick / Oct '92 / Pickwick.

## SOUL SENSATION (Franklin, Aretha & Percy Sledge).
Tracks: Day is passed and gone / He will wash you as white as snow / While the blood runs warm / Yield not to temptation / He's alright / Jesus on the main-line / This little light of mine / Make it last / When a man loves a woman / Walkin' in the sun / Warm and tender love / Good love / Out of left field / Behind closed doors / Just out of reach / I believe you / Take time to know her.
CD . . . . . . . . . . . . . . . . . . . .CDBMD 001
MC. . . . . . . . . . . . . . . . . . . . BMDC 001
Blue Moon (1) / Dec '87 / Roots Records / Jazz Music / Swift / Projection / THE / Hot Shot.

## SOUL SURVIVOR.
Tracks: Day is passed and gone / He will wash you as white as snow / While the blood runs warm / Yield not to temptation / He's alright / Jesus on the main-line / This little light of mine.
■ LP . . . . . . . . . . . . . . . . . . . . BMM 004
Blue Moon (1) / Jun '86.

## SPANISH HARLEM.
Tracks: Spanish harlem.
■ 7" . . . . . . . . . . . . . . . . . . . .2091 138
Atlantic / Oct '71.

## SPARKLE.
Tracks: Sparkle / Giving him something he can feel / Hooked on your love / Look into your heart / I get high / Jump / Loving you baby / Rock with me.
■ LP . . . . . . . . . . . . . . . . . . . . K 56248
Atlantic / Apr '77.

## SPIRIT IN THE DARK.
Tracks: Not Advised.
CD . . . . . . . . . . . . . . . . . . . .812271524-2
Atlantic / Feb '94 / WEA.

## SWEET PASSION.
Tracks: Break it to me gently / When I think about you / What I did for love / No one could ever love you more / Tender touch / Touch me up / Sunshine will never be the same / Meadows of a springtime / Mumbles / I've got the music in me / Passion.
■ LP . . . . . . . . . . . . . . . . . . . . K 50368
Atlantic / Jul '77.

## TAKE A LOOK.
Tracks: Running out of fools / Won't be long / Today I sing the blues / Walk on by / Soulville / Without the one you love / I can't wait until I see my baby's face / One step ahead / Mocking bird / If ever I would leave you / How glad I am / Every little bit hurts / My guy / Try a little tenderness.
■ LP . . . . . . . . . . . . . . . . . . . . SBPG 63269
CBS / Jun '68.

## TEN YEARS OF GOLD.
Tracks: I never loved a man (the way I love you) / Respect / Baby, I love you / (You make me feel like) A natural woman / Think / See-saw / Spanish harlem / Rock steady / Daydreaming / Angel / Until you come back to me / Something he can feel.
■ LP . . . . . . . . . . . . . . . . . . . . K 50328
■ MC. . . . . . . . . . . . . . . . . . . . K4 50328
Atlantic / Dec '76.

## THINK.
Tracks: Think.
■ 7" . . . . . . . . . . . . . . . . . . . . 584 186
Atlantic / May '68.

## THINK.
Tracks: Think / Respect.
■ 7" . . . . . . . . . . . . . . . . . . . . K 11614
Atlantic / Oct '82.

## THIS GIRL'S IN LOVE WITH YOU.
Tracks: Son of a preacher man / Share your love with me / Dark end of the street / Let it be / Eleanor Rigby / This girl's in love with you / It ain't fair / Weight / Call me / Sit down and cry.
■ LP . . . . . . . . . . . . . . . . . . . .2400 004
Atlantic / May '70.

## THROUGH THE STORM.
Tracks: Gimme your love / He's the boy / It ain't never gonna be / Think / Mercy / It isn't, it wasn't, it ain't never gonna be / Through the storm / If ever a love there was.
■ LP . . . . . . . . . . . . . . . . . . . . AL 8572
■ LP . . . . . . . . . . . . . . . . . . . .209842
■ CD . . . . . . . . . . . . . . . . . . . .259842
■ MC. . . . . . . . . . . . . . . . . . . . 409842
Arista / May '89.

## THROUGH THE STORM (Franklin, Aretha & Elton John).
Tracks: Through the storm / Come to me / Oh happy day.
■ 12" . . . . . . . . . . . . . . . . . . . .612185
■ 7" . . . . . . . . . . . . . . . . . . . .112185
■ 7" P.Disc . . . . . . . . . . . . . . . . . .112377
■ CD Single . . . . . . . . . . . . . . . . . .162185
■ MC Single . . . . . . . . . . . . . . . . . .409957
Arista / Apr '89.

## TOUCH ME UP.
Tracks: Touch me up / When I think about you.
■ 7" . . . . . . . . . . . . . . . . . . . . K 11007
Atlantic / Nov '77.

## UNITED TOGETHER.
Tracks: United together / Can't turn you loose.
■ 7" . . . . . . . . . . . . . . . . . . . .ARIST 395
Arista / Feb '81.

## UNTIL YOU COME BACK TO ME.
Tracks: Until you come back to me / If you don't think.
■ 7" . . . . . . . . . . . . . . . . . . . . K 10399
Atlantic / Feb '74.

## WHAT A FOOL BELIEVES.
Tracks: What a fool believes / School days.
■ 12" . . . . . . . . . . . . . . . . . . . . ARIST 12377
■ 7" . . . . . . . . . . . . . . . . . . . .ARIST 377
Arista / Dec '80.

## WHAT YOU SEE IS WHAT YOU SWEAT.
Tracks: Everyday people / Everchanging time / What you see is what you sweat / Mary goes round / I dreamed a dream / Someone else's eyes / Doctor's orders / You can't take me for granted / What did you give / Everyday people (remix).
■ LP . . . . . . . . . . . . . . . . . . . .211724
■ MC. . . . . . . . . . . . . . . . . . . . 411724
Arista / Jul '91.
CD . . . . . . . . . . . . . . . . . . . .261724
Arista / Feb '94 / BMG.

## WHO'S ZOOMIN' WHO.
Tracks: Who's zoomin' who / Sweet bitter love.
■ 12" . . . . . . . . . . . . . . . . . . . . ARIST 12633
■ 7" . . . . . . . . . . . . . . . . . . . .ARIST 633
Arista / Nov '85.

## WHO'S ZOOMIN' WHO?.
Tracks: Freeway of love / Another night / Sweet bitter love / Who's zoomin' who / Sisters are doin' it for themselves / Until you say you love me / Push / Ain't nobody ever loved you / Integrity.
■ CD . . . . . . . . . . . . . . . . . . . .610456
■ LP . . . . . . . . . . . . . . . . . . . .207202
■ MC. . . . . . . . . . . . . . . . . . . . 407202
Arista / Dec '85.
CD . . . . . . . . . . . . . . . . . . . .259053
■ LP . . . . . . . . . . . . . . . . . . . .209053
MC. . . . . . . . . . . . . . . . . . . . 409053
Arista / Aug '88 / BMG.

## WILLING TO FORGIVE.
Tracks: Willing to forgive / Jump to it (mixes).
■ 7" . . . . . . . . . . . . . . . . . . . .74321 21334-1
■ CD Single . . . . . . . . . . . . . . . . . .74321 21334-2
■ MC Single. . . . . . . . . . . . . . . . . .74321 21334-4
Arista / Jun '94.

## WITHOUT LOVE.
Tracks: Without love / Don't go breaking.
■ 7" . . . . . . . . . . . . . . . . . . . . K 10543
Atlantic / Jan '75.

## YEAH.
Tracks: This could be the start of something / Once in a lifetime / Misty / More / There is no greater love

/ Muddy water / If I had a hammer / Impossible / Today / Today I love everybody / Without the one you love / Trouble in mind / Love for sale.
■ LP . . . . . . . . . . . . . . . . . . . . . . . CBS 21066
■ MC. . . . . . . . . . . . . . . . . . . . . .40 21066
CBS / Jul '86.

### YOU'RE ALL I NEED TO GET BY.
Tracks: You're all I need to get by / Border song.
■ 7" . . . . . . . . . . . . . . . . . . . . . . .2091 063
Atlantic / Mar '71.

### YOUNG, GIFTED AND BLACK.
Tracks: Oh me oh my / Day dreaming / Rock steady / Young, gifted and black / All the King's horses / Brand new me / April fools / I've been loving you too long / First snow in Kokomo / Long and winding road / Didn't I / Border song.
■ LP . . . . . . . . . . . . . . . . . . . . . K 40323
Atlantic / Apr '72.
CD. . . . . . . . . . . . . . . . . . . . . .812271527-2
Atlantic / Feb '94 / WEA.

## Franklin, Carolyn

### BABY DYNAMITE.
Tracks: Reality / It's true I'm gonna miss you / What cha' gonna do / I don't want to lose you / Boxer / I can't love without you / What now my love / Alone / There I go / On a back street / More than ever before.
■ LP . . . . . . . . . . . . . . . . . . . . . RD/SF 8035
RCA Victor / Oct '69.

## Franklin, Erma

### (TAKE A LITTLE) PIECE OF MY HEART.
Tracks: (Take a little) Piece of my heart.
■ 7" . . . . . . . . . . . . . . . . . . . . . .658384-7
■ CD Single . . . . . . . . . . . . . . . . . .658384-2
■ MC Single . . . . . . . . . . . . . . . . . .658384-4
Epic / Sep '92.

### I'M JUST NOT READY FOR LOVE.
Tracks: I'm just not ready for love / Right to cry.
■ 7" . . . . . . . . . . . . . . . . . . . . . . BOY 36
Jay Boy / Aug '71.

### PIECE OF MY HEART.
Tracks: Piece of my heart / Big boss man.
■ 7" . . . . . . . . . . . . . . . . . . . . . . BOY 41
Jay Boy / Jul '71.
■ 7" . . . . . . . . . . . . . . . . . . . . . HLM 10501
London / Jul '75.

### PIECE OF MY HEART - THE BEST OF ERMA FRANKLIN.
Tracks: (Take a little) Piece of my heart / Hello again / Ev'rytime we say goodbye / What kind of girl (do you think I am) / Don't blame me / Detour ahead / Time after time / It's over / Never let me go / Each night I cry / Saving my love for you / Pledging my love / Man I love / Abracadabra / Love is blind.
CD . . . . . . . . . . . . . . . . . . . . . .472413-2
■ MC . . . . . . . . . . . . . . . . . . . . .472413-4
Epic / Nov '92 / Sony.

### SOUL SISTER.
Tracks: By the time I get to Phoenix / Change my thoughts from you / Light my fire / You've been cancelled / For once in my life / Can't see my way / Hold on, I'm comin' / Saving my love for you / Son of a preacher man / Gotta find me a lover / Baby I love you.
■ LP . . . . . . . . . . . . . . . . . . . . .MUPS 394
MCA / Jan '70.

## Franklin, Rodney

### DIAMOND INSIDE OF YOU.
Tracks: Malibu shuffle / Gotta give it up / Stop to love / Woman of the world / Shasta wind / Woogie / Turn to love / Mediterranean shore / Interlude / Diamond inside of you.
■ LP . . . . . . . . . . . . . . . . . . . . . PL 83038
■ CD . . . . . . . . . . . . . . . . . . . . . PD 83038
■ MC. . . . . . . . . . . . . . . . . . . . . PK 83038
Novus / Feb '89.

### ENDLESS FLIGHT.
Tracks: Dance tonight / Cancion para mi mama / Vibrations / Benetta / Morning light / Endless flight / Mansaje de Dios / Return to the source / Hill Street blues.
■ LP . . . . . . . . . . . . . . . . . . . . . CBS 84945
CBS / Dec '81.

### GROOVE, THE.
Tracks: Groove / God bless the blues.
■ 7" . . . . . . . . . . . . . . . . . . . . . CBS 8529
CBS / Apr '80.

### GROOVE, THE (OLD GOLD).
Tracks: Groove / In the bush / Check out the groove / Strut your funky stuff.
■ 7" . . . . . . . . . . . . . . . . . . . . . .OG 9562
Old Gold / Sep '85.
■ 12" . . . . . . . . . . . . . . . . . . . . . .OG 4004
Old Gold / Feb '86.

### GROOVE, THE (OLD GOLD) (2).
Tracks: Groove / Birdland.
12" . . . . . . . . . . . . . . . . . . . . . .OG 4197
Old Gold / Nov '90 / Pickwick.

### HILL STREET BLUES.
Tracks: Hill Street blues / Mensaje de dios.
■ 7" . . . . . . . . . . . . . . . . . . . . . .A 1827
CBS / Dec '81.

### IT TAKES TWO.
Tracks: Motion / Look what's showing through / Broken wings / Eagle and the Condor / It takes two / Rollin' in our love / My wish / Let there be piece.
■ LP . . . . . . . . . . . . . . . . . . . . . CBS 26992
■ MC. . . . . . . . . . . . . . . . . . . . . .40 26992
CBS / Aug '86.

### LEARNING TO LOVE.
Tracks: Enuff is enuff / That's the way I feel about love / Sunshine / Don't wanna let you go / Sailing / Genesis / New day / Nature's way / Early morning / Let there be light / Learning to love.
■ LP . . . . . . . . . . . . . . . . . . . . . CBS 85978
CBS / Jan '83.

### RODNEY FRANKLIN.
Tracks: Windy City / Life moves on / In the centre / I like the music / Awakening / Make it hot / Theme for Jackie / On the oath / Creation.
■ LP . . . . . . . . . . . . . . . . . . . . . CBS 84528
CBS / Sep '80.

### SKYDANCE.
Tracks: Fiesta / Destiny / Song for you / Children / One from the heart / Skydance.
■ LP . . . . . . . . . . . . . . . . . . . . . CBS 26399
CBS / Jun '85.

### STREET LANGUAGE.
Tracks: Let freedom ring / Ballad of fat Eddie / When I'm free again / She loves the jerk / When the blue hour comes / Oh King Richard / Looking for you / Stay (don't be cruel) / Best I can / Past like a mast.
■ LP . . . . . . . . . . . . . . . . . . . . . CBS 57021
■ MC. . . . . . . . . . . . . . . . . . . . . .40 57021
CBS / Sep '86.

### YOU'LL NEVER KNOW.
Tracks: Felix Leo / God bless the blues / Watcher / Journey / Groove / You'll never know / Return / Parkay man.
■ LP . . . . . . . . . . . . . . . . . . . . . CBS 83812
CBS / May '80.

## Frantique

### FRANTIQUE.
Tracks: Disco dancer / Getting serious / Night people / These days / Strut your funky stuff.
■ LP . . . . . . . . . . . . . . . . . . . . . PIR 83784
Philadelphia Int. / Oct '79.

### STRUT YOUR FUNKY STUFF.
Tracks: Strut your funky stuff.
■ 7" . . . . . . . . . . . . . . . . . . . . . PIR 7728
Philadelphia Int. / Aug '79.

### STRUT YOUR FUNKY STUFF (OLD GOLD) (see under Franklin, Rodney).

## Frazier, Billy

### BILLY WHO? (Frazier, Billy & Friends).
Tracks: Billy who / Billy who? (part 2).
■ 12" . . . . . . . . . . . . . . . . . . . . . FIZY 5003
■ 7" . . . . . . . . . . . . . . . . . . . . . FIZZ 503
Champagne / Nov '80.

## Fredrix, Dee

### AND SO I WILL WAIT FOR YOU.
Tracks: And so I will wait for you / Love your brother.
■ 7" . . . . . . . . . . . . . . . . . . . . . .YZ 725
■ CD Single . . . . . . . . . . . . . . . . . .YZ 725CD
■ MC Single . . . . . . . . . . . . . . . . . .YZ 725C
East West / Feb '93.

### DIRTY MONEY.
Tracks: Dirty money.
■ 12" . . . . . . . . . . . . . . . . . . . . . YZ 750T
■ 7" . . . . . . . . . . . . . . . . . . . . . .YZ 750
■ CD Single . . . . . . . . . . . . . . . . . . YZ 750CD

■ MC Single. . . . . . . . . . . . . . . .YZ 750C
East West / Jun '93.

### GRACE.
Tracks: Dirty money / And so I will wait for you / Whatever it takes / Hold on to what we've got / How can this be wrong / There but for the grace / If I could relive your love / Don't get in my way / Buried treasure / Look my way.
CD . . . . . . . . . . . . . . . . . . . . .450991788-2
MC. . . . . . . . . . . . . . . . . . . . .450991788-4
East West / Mar '93 / WEA.

### LIVE MY LIFE.
Tracks: Live my life (Mixes).
MC. . . . . . . . . . . . . . . . . . . . .YZ 854C
East West / Oct '94 / WEA.
12" . . . . . . . . . . . . . . . . . . . . .YZ 854T
7" . . . . . . . . . . . . . . . . . . . . .YZ 854
CD Single . . . . . . . . . . . . . . . . .YZ 854CD
East West / Oct '94 / WEA.

## Free

### SOUL PARTY.
Tracks: Soul party / Taking it away (would be break ing my heart).
■ 7" . . . . . . . . . . . . . . . . . . . . . BF 1754
Philips / '69.

## Freeez

### ALONE.
Tracks: Alone.
■ 7" . . . . . . . . . . . . . . . . . . . . . BEG 58
Beggars Banquet / Jan '82.

### ANTI-FREEZ.
Tracks: Flying high / Alone / Southern Freeez / One to one / Fly by night / Roller chase / Caribbean winter.
■ LP . . . . . . . . . . . . . . . . . . . . . BEGA 53
MC. . . . . . . . . . . . . . . . . . . . . BEGC 53
Beggars Banquet / Jul '84 / WEA / RTM / Pinnacle.

### ANTI-FREEEZ.
Tracks: Anti-freeez.
■ 12" . . . . . . . . . . . . . . . . . . . . . BEG 66T
■ 7" . . . . . . . . . . . . . . . . . . . . . BEG 66
Beggars Banquet / Oct '81.

### FLYING HIGH.
Tracks: Flying high.
■ 12" . . . . . . . . . . . . . . . . . . . . . BEG 55T
■ 7" . . . . . . . . . . . . . . . . . . . . . BEG 55
Beggars Banquet / Apr '81.

### FREEEZ FRAME (The Best Of Freeez).
Tracks: Not Advised.
CD. . . . . . . . . . . . . . . . . . . . . MCCD 131
MC. . . . . . . . . . . . . . . . . . . . .MCTC 131
Music Club / Sep '93 / Gold & Sons / THE / Video Collection / C.M. Distribution.

### GONNA GET YOU.
Tracks: We've got the juice / Can't keep my love Love's gonna get you / Pop goes my love / I.O.U. Freezin' / Can you / Watch me.
■ LP . . . . . . . . . . . . . . . . . . . . . BEGA 48
■ MC . . . . . . . . . . . . . . . . . . . . . BEGC 48
Beggars Banquet / Nov '83.

### I.O.U.
Tracks: I.O.U. / I dub you / We got the jazz.
■ 12" . . . . . . . . . . . . . . . . . . . . . BEG 96T
■ 7" . . . . . . . . . . . . . . . . . . . . . BEG 96
Beggars Banquet / Jun '83.
■ 12" . . . . . . . . . . . . . . . . . . . . . CBE 1209
■ 7" . . . . . . . . . . . . . . . . . . . . . CBE 709
City Beat / Dec '86.

### I.O.U. (OLD GOLD).
Tracks: I.O.U.
12" . . . . . . . . . . . . . . . . . . . . . .OG 4169
Old Gold / May '90 / Pickwick.

### IDLE VICE.
Tracks: VIPs / Other side / Within these walls Volunteers / Train of thoughts / Naked as a razor That beats my patience / One second chance / Spy o Baghdad.
MC. . . . . . . . . . . . . . . . . . . . . BEGC 62
■ LP . . . . . . . . . . . . . . . . . . . . . BEGA 62
Beggars Banquet / Oct '85 / WEA / RTM / Pinnacle

### KEEP IN TOUCH.
Tracks: Keep in touch / Keep in touch (part 2).
■ 12" . . . . . . . . . . . . . . . . . . . . . CABL 103
■ 7" . . . . . . . . . . . . . . . . . . . . . .CAB 103
Calibre / Jun '80.

■ DELETED

## LOVE'S GONNA GET YOU.
Tracks: Love's gonna get you / Love's gonna get you (version).
■ 12" . . . . . . . . . . . . . . . . . . . . . BEG 103 T
■ 7" . . . . . . . . . . . . . . . . . . . . . . .BEG 103
Beggars Banquet / Nov '83.

## ONE TO ONE.
Tracks: One to one.
■ 12" . . . . . . . . . . . . . . . . . . . . . BEG 78T
■ 7" . . . . . . . . . . . . . . . . . . . . . . BEG 78
Beggars Banquet / Jun '82.

## POP GOES MY LOVE.
Tracks: Pop goes my love / Scratch goes my dub / No need for greed.
■ 12" . . . . . . . . . . . . . . . . . . . . . BEG 98T
■ 7" . . . . . . . . . . . . . . . . . . . . . . BEG 98
Beggars Banquet / Oct '83.

## SOUTHERN FREEEZ.
Tracks: Marpose / Caribbean winter / Easy on the onions / Sunset / Flying high / Southern Freeez / Rollerchase / First love / Finale.
■ LP . . . . . . . . . . . . . . . . . . . . . . BEGA 22
■ MC . . . . . . . . . . . . . . . . . . . . . . BEGC 22
Beggars Banquet / Feb '81.

## SOUTHERN FREEEZ.
Tracks: Southern freeez.
■ 12" . . . . . . . . . . . . . . . . . . . . . BEG 51T
■ 7" . . . . . . . . . . . . . . . . . . . . . . BEG 51
Beggars Banquet / Feb '81.

## SOUTHERN FREEEZ (RADIO MIX).
Tracks: Southern Freeez (inst) / Southern freeez.
■ 12" . . . . . . . . . . . . . . . . . . . 12 TOCO 14
■ 7" . . . . . . . . . . . . . . . . . . . . . TOCO 14
Total Control / May '87.

## THAT BEATS MY PATIENCE.
Tracks: That beats my patience / All the way.
■ 12" . . . . . . . . . . . . . . . . . . . . . BEG 129T
■ 7" . . . . . . . . . . . . . . . . . . . . . .BEG 129
Beggars Banquet / Apr '85.

## TRAIN OF THOUGHT.
Tracks: Train of thought.
■ 7" . . . . . . . . . . . . . . . . . . . . . .BEG 141
■ 12" . . . . . . . . . . . . . . . . . . . . . BEG 141T
Beggars Banquet / Jul '85.

# Freeman, Bobby

## DO YOU WANNA DANCE?.
Tracks: Not Advised.
■ LP . . . . . . . . . . . . . . . . . . . . . JGM 1086
Jubilee / Sep '87.

## DO YOU WANNA DANCE?.
Tracks: Do you wanna dance / Big fat woman.
■ 7" . . . . . . . . . . . . . . . . . . . . . REV 6003
Revival / Jul '82.

# Freeman, George

## BIRTH SIGN.
Tracks: Not Advised.
■ LP . . . . . . . . . . . . . . . . . . . . . . DS 424
Delmark (USA) / '86.
■ D . . . . . . . . . . . . . . . . . . . . . . DD 424
Delmark (USA) / Aug '94 / Cadillac / Swift / A.D.A. Distribution / Topic Records / Direct Distribution / Jazz Music / C.M. Distribution.

## NEW IMPROVED FUNK.
Tracks: Not Advised.
■ LP . . . . . . . . . . . . . . . . . . . . . .PLEO 22
Not Advised / '87.

# Freeman, Louise

## LISTEN TO MY HEART.
Tracks: When push comes to shove / Save your love / Nothin's gonna win me (but love) / Love is gone / Back in stride / I don't want to talk about it / Fever / Unchained melody.
■ C . . . . . . . . . . . . . . . . . . . . . . ICH 1111
■ C . . . . . . . . . . . . . . . . . . . . ICH 1111MC
Chiban / Jun '91 / A.D.A. Distribution / Pinnacle / CD Trading Ltd. / Koch International / Direct Distribution.
■ D . . . . . . . . . . . . . . . . . . . . . .CDICH 1111
Chiban / Oct '93 / A.D.A. Distribution / Pinnacle / CD Trading Ltd. / Koch International / Direct Distribution.

# Fresh

## SUMMER IN THE CITY.
Tracks: Love life / Summer in the city.
■ 12" . . . . . . . . . . . . . . . . . . . . JIVET 154
■ 7" . . . . . . . . . . . . . . . . . . . . . JIVE 154
Jive / Aug '87.

# Fresh Air

## MISS YOU.
Tracks: Miss you.
■ 12" . . . . . . . . . . . . . . . . . . . . EXPAND 34
Expansion / Jan '93.

# Friends Of Distinction

## GRAZING IN THE GRASS.
Tracks: Grazing in the grass / I need you.
■ 7" . . . . . . . . . . . . . . . . . . . . . RCA 1838
RCA / Jan '71.

## LOVE ME OR LET ME BE LONELY.
Tracks: Not Advised.
■ 7" . . . . . . . . . . . . . . . . . . . . . RCA 2336
RCA / Jan '73.

## THIS GENERATION.
Tracks: This generation.
■ 7" . . . . . . . . . . . . . . . . . . . . . RCA 1952
RCA / '70.

# Funk Deluxe

## I SURRENDER.
Tracks: I surrender.
■ 12" . . . . . . . . . . . . . . . . . . . . . TTT 007
Tam Tam / Jun '89.

## THIS TIME.
Tracks: This time / This time (dub version).
■ 12" . . . . . . . . . . . . . . . . . . . MKHAN 14
Streetwave / Jun '86.

# Funk Inc.

## ACID INC - THE BEST OF FUNK INC.
Tracks: Chicken lickin' / Sister Jane / Jung bongo / Where are we going / Smokin' at Tiffany's / Kool's back again / Give me your love / Let's make love and stop the war / Better half (On CD only) / Bowlegs (On CD only).
■ LP . . . . . . . . . . . . . . . . . . . . BGP 1011
MC . . . . . . . . . . . . . . . . . . . . BGPC 1011
BGP / Jun '88 / Pinnacle.
CD . . . . . . . . . . . . . . . . . . . . CDBGP 1011
BGP / Oct '91 / Pinnacle.

## CHICKEN LICKIN'.
Tracks: Chickin lickin' / Running away / They trying to get me / Better half / Let's make peace and stop the war / Jung bongo.
LP . . . . . . . . . . . . . . . . . . . . . BGPD 1042
BGP / Sep '92 / Pinnacle.

## FUNK INC.
Tracks: Kool is back / Bowlegs / Sister Jane / Thrill is gone / Whipper.
LP . . . . . . . . . . . . . . . . . . . . . BGPD 1041
BGP / Sep '92 / Pinnacle.

## FUNK INC./CHICKEN' LICKIN'.
Tracks: Kool is back / Bowlegs / Sister Janie / Thrill is gone / Whipper / Chicken' lickin' / Running away / They trying to get me / Better half / Let's make peace and stop the war / Jung bongo.
CD . . . . . . . . . . . . . . . . . . . . CDBGPD 040
Fantasy / Sep '92 / Pinnacle / Jazz Music.

## HANGIN' OUT.
Tracks: Smokin' at Tiffany's / Give me your love / We can be friends / Dirty red / I can see clearly now / I'll be around.
LP . . . . . . . . . . . . . . . . . . . . . BGPD 1059
Ace / Feb '93 / Pinnacle / Complete Record Co. Ltd.

## HANGIN' OUT/SUPERFUNK.
Tracks: Smokin at tiffany's / Give me your love / We can be friends / Dirty red / I can see clearly now / I'll be around / Message from the Meters / Goodbye, so long / Hill where the lord hides / Honey, I love you / Just don't mean a thing / I'm gonna love you just a little bit more baby.
CD . . . . . . . . . . . . . . . . . . . . CDBGPD 058
BGP / Feb '93 / Pinnacle.

## PRICED TO SELL.
Tracks: It's not the spotlight / Priced to sell / God only knows / Where are we going / Gimme some lovin' / Somewhere in my mind / Girl of my dreams.
CD . . . . . . . . . . . . . . . . . . . . CDBGPM 075

## LP . . . . . . . . . . . . . . . . . . . . BGPD 1075
BGP / Jun '93 / Pinnacle.

## SUPERFUNK.
Tracks: Message from the Meters / Goodbye, so long / Hill where the Lord hides / Honey, I love you / Just don't mean a thing / I'm gonna love you just a little bit more baby.
LP . . . . . . . . . . . . . . . . . . . . BPGD 1060
BGP / Feb '93 / Pinnacle.

# Funk Masters

## BOUWKOOL.
Tracks: Bouwkool.
■ 12" . . . . . . . . . . . . . . . . . . . . MF 003
Master Funk / Nov '82.

## HAVE YOU GOT THE TIME.
Tracks: Have you got the time / Have you got the time (version).
■ 12" . . . . . . . . . . . . . . . . . . . . MF 008
■ 7" . . . . . . . . . . . . . . . . . . . .7MF 008
Master Funk / Nov '84.
■ 12" . . . . . . . . . . . . . . . . . . . . MS 008
■ 7" . . . . . . . . . . . . . . . . . . . .7MS 008
Master Funk / Jul '87.

## IT'S OVER.
Tracks: It's over.
■ 12" . . . . . . . . . . . . . . . . . . . . MF 004
■ 7" . . . . . . . . . . . . . . . . . . . .7MF 004
Master Funk / Oct '84.

## LOVE MONEY.
Tracks: Love money / Money we love.
■ 12" . . . . . . . . . . . . . . . . . . . .TAN 001
Tania Music / Oct '81.

## MERRY CHRISTMAS (Funk Masters & Bouw Kool).
Tracks: Merry Christmas.
■ 12" . . . . . . . . . . . . . . . . . . . . MF 006
■ 7" . . . . . . . . . . . . . . . . . . . .7MF 006
Master Funk / Nov '84.

## SHAKE YOUR BODY DOWN.
Tracks: Shake your body down.
■ 12" . . . . . . . . . . . . . . . . . . . .TWD 1955
Master Funk / Feb '88.

# Funkadelic

Having launched Parliament in 1970, George Clinton turned his attention to funk-rock fusion initiated by Hendrix and Sly Stone. Funkadelic's early albums were druggy affairs, showcasing guitarist Eddie Hazel; epitomised by sprawling double *America Eats Its Young*. Bid for commercial success heralded by excellent *Cosmic Slop*, although Funkadelic albums continued to chart lower than Parliament. Breakthrough came with dance-orientated *One Nation Under A Groove*, whose title track was transatlantic hit. U.S. success continued before group fell victim to collapse of P-Funk empire. Attempt by associates to hijack Funkadelic yielded one Clinton-free album, before court-case proved his ownership of name. Highlights of group's career can be found on two collections: 1992's *Music For Your Mother*, covering Westbound label releases, and '94's *Best of Funkadelic 1976-1981*, featuring later Warner Bros hits.

## AMERICA EATS ITS YOUNG.
Tracks: You hit the nail on the head / If you don't like the effects, don't produce the cause / Everybody is going to make it this time / Joyful process / We hurt too / Loose booty / Philmore / I call my baby pussy-cat / America eats its young / Biological speculation / That was my girl / Balance / Miss Lucifer's love / Wake up.
CD . . . . . . . . . . . . . . . . . . . . CDSEWD 029
MC . . . . . . . . . . . . . . . . . . . . SEWC 2 029
■ LP . . . . . . . . . . . . . . . . . . . . SEW2 029
Westbound / Jul '90 / Pinnacle.

## BEST OF FUNKADELIC 1976-1981, THE.
Tracks: One nation under a groove / Cholly (funk getting ready to roll) / Who says a funk band can't play rock / Comin' round the mountain / Smokey / Cosmic slop (live) / Electric spanking of war babies / Funk gets stronger (part one) / Uncle Jam (edited version) / Icka prick.
LP . . . . . . . . . . . . . . . . . . . . LPGR 104
Charly / Jun '93 / Charly.
CD . . . . . . . . . . . . . . . . . . . . .CDGR 104
Charly / Feb '94 / Charly.

## CHOLLY FUNK GETTING READY TO ROLL.
**Tracks:** Cholly funk getting ready to roll / Into you.
■ 7" . . . . . . . . . . . . . . . . . . . . . . . . . K 17321
WEA / Mar '79.

## COSMIC SLOP.
**Tracks:** Nappy dugout / You can't miss what you can't measure / March to the witch's castle / Let's make it last / Cosmic slop / No compute / This broken heart / Trash a go go / Can't stand the strain.
LP . . . . . . . . . . . . . . . . . . . . . . . . SEWA 035
LP . . . . . . . . . . . . . . . . . . . . . . . SEW 035
■ MC . . . . . . . . . . . . . . . . . . . . . . SEWC 035
Westbound / Jan '91 / Pinnacle.
CD . . . . . . . . . . . . . . . . . . . . . . . . CDSEW 035
Westbound / Feb '94 / Pinnacle.

## ELECTRIC SPANKING OF WAR BABIES.
**Tracks:** Electric spanking of war babies / Electrocuties / Funk gets stronger / Brettino's bounce / She loves you / Shockwaves / Oh, I / Icka-prick.
■ LP . . . . . . . . . . . . . . . . . . . . . . . K 56874
WEA / Oct '81.
CD . . . . . . . . . . . . . . . . . . . . . . . . CDGR 102
LP . . . . . . . . . . . . . . . . . . . . . . . LPGR 102
Charly / Jun '93 / Charly.

## ELECTRIC SPANKING OF WAR BABIES.
**Tracks:** Electric spanking of war babies.
■ 12" . . . . . . . . . . . . . . . . . . . . . . K 17786T
■ 7" . . . . . . . . . . . . . . . . . . . . . . . K 17786
WEA / Apr '81.

## FREE YOUR MIND AND YOUR ASS WILL FOLLOW.
**Tracks:** Free your mind and your ass will follow / Friday night, August 14th / Funky dollar bill / I wanna know if it's good to you / Some more / Eulogy and light.
■ LP . . . . . . . . . . . . . . . . . . . . . . NSPL 28184
Pye / May '71.
CD . . . . . . . . . . . . . . . . . . . . . . . . CDSEW 012
■ LP . . . . . . . . . . . . . . . . . . . . . . . SEW 012
■ MC . . . . . . . . . . . . . . . . . . . . . . SEWC 012
Westbound / Jan '90 / Pinnacle.

## FUNKADELIC.
**Tracks:** Mommy, what's a Funkadelic / I bet you / Music for my mother / I got a thing, you got a thing, everybody's got a thing / Good old music / Qualify and satisfy / What is soul.
■ LP . . . . . . . . . . . . . . . . . . . . . . NSPL 28137
Pye / Oct '70.
CD . . . . . . . . . . . . . . . . . . . . . . . . CDSEW 010
■ MC . . . . . . . . . . . . . . . . . . . . . . SEWC 010
■ LP . . . . . . . . . . . . . . . . . . . . . . . SEW 010
Westbound / Aug '89 / Pinnacle.

## FUNKADELIC LIVE.
**Tracks:** Funkentelechy / Cosmic slop / Maggot brain / Bop gun / Funk gettin' ready to roll / It ain't legal / Flash light / Mothership connection / Give up the funk / Let's take it to the stage / Do that stuff / Undisco kidd / Children of production / Atomic dog / Maceo, not Charlie / Red hot Mama / Into you / Standing on the verge / One nation under a groove / Comin' round the mountain / Won't you dance / Quickie / Aquaboogie / I wanna know it it's good to you baby / Up for the down stroke / Hit it or quit it / Gamin' on ya / Put your hands together / Dog you out / P-funk / You do me / Nickel bag o'solos / Dope dog / I call my baby pussy / Lampin / Microphone fiend / underground angel / Yank my doodle sum'else / I got a thing / All your goodies are gone / Lifted.
CD Set . . . . . . . . . . . . . . . . . . . . . NEFCD 273
Sequel / Oct '94 / Total / BMG.

## FUNKADELIC PICTURE DISC BOX SET.
**Tracks:** Not Advised.
CD Set . . . . . . . . . . . . . . . . . . . WBOXPD 4
Westbound / Aug '90 / Pinnacle.

## HARDCORE FUNK JAM.
**Tracks:** Not Advised.
CD . . . . . . . . . . . . . . . . . . . . . . . CPCD 8064
Charly / Nov '94 / Charly.

## HARDCORE JOLLIES.
**Tracks:** Osmosis phase one / Comin' round the mountain / Smokey / If you got funk, you got style / Hardcore jollies / Territubis phase two / Soul mate /

Cosmic slop / You scared the lovin outta me / Adolescent funk.
■ LP . . . . . . . . . . . . . . . . . . . . . . . K 56299
WEA / Feb '78.
CD . . . . . . . . . . . . . . . . . . . . . . . . CDGR 101
LP . . . . . . . . . . . . . . . . . . . . . . . LPGR 101
Charly / Jun '93 / Charly.

## KNEE DEEP.
**Tracks:** Knee deep.
■ 7" . . . . . . . . . . . . . . . . . . . . . . . K 17494
WEA / Jan '80.

## LET'S TAKE IT TO THE STAGE.
**Tracks:** Good to your earhole / Better by the pound / Be my beach / No head no backstage pass / Let's take it to the stage / Get off your ass and jam / I owe you something good / Stuff and things / Song is familiar / Atmosphere.
LP . . . . . . . . . . . . . . . . . . . . . . . SEWA 044
■ MC . . . . . . . . . . . . . . . . . . . . . . SEWC 044
Westbound / Feb '92 / Pinnacle.
CD . . . . . . . . . . . . . . . . . . . . . . . . CDSEW 044
Westbound / Feb '94 / Pinnacle.

## MAGGOT BRAIN.
**Tracks:** Maggot brain / Can you get to that / Hit it and quit it / You and your folks, me and my folks / Super stupid / Back in our minds / Wars of Armageddon.
■ LP . . . . . . . . . . . . . . . . . . . . . . . 6310201
Janus / Nov '71.
CD . . . . . . . . . . . . . . . . . . . . . . . . CDSEW 002
MC . . . . . . . . . . . . . . . . . . . . . . . SEWC 002
■ LP . . . . . . . . . . . . . . . . . . . . . . . SEW 002
■ LP . . . . . . . . . . . . . . . . . . . . . . SEWA 002
Westbound / Jun '89 / Pinnacle.

## MUSIC FOR YOUR MOTHER.
**Tracks:** Music for my mother / Music for my mother (instrumental) / Can't shake it loose / As good as I can feel / I'll bet you / Qualify and satisfy / Open our eyes / I got a thing, you got a thing, everybody got a thing / Fish, chips and sweat / I wanna know if it's good to you (instrumental) / You and your folks, me and my folks / Funky dollar bill / Can you get to that / Back in our minds / I miss my baby / Baby I owe you something good / Hit it and quit it / Whole lot of BS / Loose booty / Joyful process / Cosmic slop / If you don't like the effects, don't produce the cause / Standing on the verge of getting it on / Jimmy's got a little bit of bitch in him / Red hot mamma / Vital juices / Better by the pound / Stuffs and things / Let's take it to the stage / How do yeaw view you.
CD Set . . . . . . . . . . . . . . . . . . . . CDSEW2 055
■ Double LP . . . . . . . . . . . . . . . . . SEW2 055
■ MC . . . . . . . . . . . . . . . . . . . . . . SEWC2 055
Ace / Oct '92 / Pinnacle / Complete Record Co. Ltd.

## ONE NATION UNDER A GROOVE.
**Tracks:** One nation under a groove / One nation under a groove (part 2).
■ 7" . . . . . . . . . . . . . . . . . . . . . . . K 17246
WEA / '78.

## ONE NATION UNDER A GROOVE.
**Tracks:** One nation under a groove / Groovallegiance / Who says a funk band can't play rock / Promentalshitbackwashpsychosisenema squad / Into you / Cholly / Lunchmeataphobia / P.E. squad / Doodoo chasers / Maggot brain.
■ LP . . . . . . . . . . . . . . . . . . . . . . . K 56539
WEA / Dec '78.
CD . . . . . . . . . . . . . . . . . . . . . . . . CDGR 100
Charly / Jul '93 / Charly.
LP . . . . . . . . . . . . . . . . . . . . . . . LPGR 100
Charly / Jun '93 / Charly.

## PICTURE COMPACT DISC BOX SET VOL.2.
**Tracks:** Not Advised.
CD Set . . . . . . . . . . . . . . . . . . . WBOXPD 5
Westbound / Feb '94 / Pinnacle.

## STANDING ON THE VERGE OF GETTING IT ON.
**Tracks:** Red hot mama / Alice in my fantasies / I'll stay / Sexy ways / Standing on the verge of getting it on / Jimmy's got a little bit of bitch in him / Good thoughts, bad thoughts.
LP . . . . . . . . . . . . . . . . . . . . . . . SEWA 040
■ MC . . . . . . . . . . . . . . . . . . . . . . SEWC 040
Westbound / Aug '91 / Pinnacle.

CD . . . . . . . . . . . . . . . . . . . . . . . CDSEW 040
Westbound / Feb '94 / Pinnacle.

## TALES OF KIDD FUNKADELIC.
**Tracks:** Butt to buttresuscitation / Let's take it to the people / Undisco kidd / Take your dead ass home / I'm never gonna tell it / Tales of kidd funkadelic / How do yeaw view you.
LP . . . . . . . . . . . . . . . . . . . . . . . SEWA 054
Westbound / Mar '93 / Pinnacle.
CD . . . . . . . . . . . . . . . . . . . . . . . . CDSEW 054
Westbound / Feb '94 / Pinnacle.

## UNCLE JAM WANTS YOU.
**Tracks:** Freak of the week / (Not just) knee deep / Uncle Jam / Field manoeuvers / Holly wants to go to California / Foot soldiers.
■ LP . . . . . . . . . . . . . . . . . . . . . . . K 56712
WEA / Oct '79.
CD . . . . . . . . . . . . . . . . . . . . . . . . CDGR 103
LP . . . . . . . . . . . . . . . . . . . . . . . LPGR 103
Charly / Jun '93 / Charly.

## YOU AND YOUR FOLKS, ME AND MINE.
**Tracks:** You and your folks, me and mine / Funky dollar bill.
■ 7" . . . . . . . . . . . . . . . . . . . . . . . 7N 25548
Pye / Apr '71.

# Funkapolitan

## AS THE TIME GOES BY.
**Tracks:** As the time goes by / As the time goes by (rap).
■ 7" . . . . . . . . . . . . . . . . . . . . . . . LON 001
London / Aug '81.

## FUNKAPOLITAN.
**Tracks:** Run, run, run / Illusions / War / If only / In the crime of life / Behold the super ace / There it is again / As time goes by.
■ LP . . . . . . . . . . . . . . . . . . . . . . . SH 8548
London / May '82.

## IN THE CRIME OF LIFE.
**Tracks:** In the crime of life / War.
■ 12" . . . . . . . . . . . . . . . . . . . . . . LONX 002
■ 7" . . . . . . . . . . . . . . . . . . . . . . . LON 002
London / Apr '82.

## RUN, RUN, RUN.
**Tracks:** Run, run, run / Time and space.
■ 12" . . . . . . . . . . . . . . . . . . . . . . LONX 006
■ 7" . . . . . . . . . . . . . . . . . . . . . . . LON 006
London / Jun '82.

# Futures

## AIN'T NO TIME FA NOTHING.
**Tracks:** Ain't no time for nothing / Easy money.
■ 12" . . . . . . . . . . . . . . . . . . . . . . OG 4502
Old Gold / Sep '88.

# Fuzz

## FUZZ.
**Tracks:** I think I got the making of a true love affair / I'm so glad / All about love / It's all over / Like an open door / Search your mind / Leave it all behind me / Ooo baby baby / I love you for all seasons.
■ LP . . . . . . . . . . . . . . . . . . . . . . 2916010
Mojo / Dec '71.

## I'M SO GLAD.
**Tracks:** I'm so glad / All about love.
■ 7" . . . . . . . . . . . . . . . . . . . . . . . DDS 104
Pye Disco Demand / Jun '74.

# Fyza

## AIN'T NO SUNSHINE.
**Tracks:** Ain't no sunshine.
■ 12" . . . . . . . . . . . . . . . . . . . . . STONED 2
Rumour / Aug '93.

■ DELETED

# G

## G.Q.

**BEST OF GQ, THE.**
Tracks: Disco nights (Rock freak) / Boogie oogie oogie / This happy feeling / Shake / Is it cool / Standing ovation (CD only) / GQ down / Make my dream a reality / I love (the skin you're in) / Someday (in your life) / Sad girl / Sitting the park / Don't stop this feeling / I do love you.
CD . . . . . . . . . . . . . . . . . . . . . . .263016
LP . . . . . . . . . . . . . . . . . . . . . . .213016
MC . . . . . . . . . . . . . . . . . . . . . . .413016
Arista / Jun '92.

**DISCO NIGHTS.**
Tracks: Not Advised.
LP . . . . . . . . . . . . . . . . . . . . . . . ARTY 169
Arista / Sep '79.

**DISCO NIGHTS (ROCK FREAK).**
Tracks: Disco nights (rock freak).
12" . . . . . . . . . . . . . . . . . . . ARIST 12245
7" . . . . . . . . . . . . . . . . . . . . . .ARIST 245
Arista / Feb '79.

**DISCO NIGHTS (ROCK FREAK) (OLD GOLD).**
Tracks: Disco nights (rock freak) / Unlock the funk / Make my dream a reality (Only on CD single.).
12" . . . . . . . . . . . . . . . . . . . . . . .OG 4043
CD Single . . . . . . . . . . . . . . . . . . .OG 6509
Old Gold / Jan '88.
Old Gold / Jul '90 / Pickwick.

**FACE TO FACE.**
Tracks: Shake / You put some love in my life / Shy baby / Sad girl / I love the skin (you are in) / Boogie oogie feelin' / Dark side of the sun / Face to face / You've got the floor.
LP . . . . . . . . . . . . . . . . . . . . . SPART 1163
Arista / Oct '81.

**GO DOWN.**
Tracks: Go down / It's like that / Lies.
12" . . . . . . . . . . . . . . . . . . . ARIST 12353
Arista / May '80.

**I DO LOVE YOU.**
Tracks: I do love you / Spirit.
7" . . . . . . . . . . . . . . . . . . . . . .ARIST 303
Arista / Oct '79.

**MAKE MY DREAM A REALITY.**
Tracks: Make my dream a reality.
12" . . . . . . . . . . . . . . . . . . . ARIST 12263
7" . . . . . . . . . . . . . . . . . . . . . .ARIST 263
Arista / May '79.

**SHAKE.**
Tracks: Shake / Skin you're in.
12" . . . . . . . . . . . . . . . . . . . ARIST 12427
7" . . . . . . . . . . . . . . . . . . . . . .ARIST 427
Arista / Nov '81.

**SITTING IN THE PARK.**
Tracks: Sitting in the park / I do love you / Someday your life.
12" . . . . . . . . . . . . . . . . . . . ARIST 12358
7" . . . . . . . . . . . . . . . . . . . . . .ARIST 358
Arista / Jul '80.

**TWO.**
Tracks: Not Advised.
LP . . . . . . . . . . . . . . . . . . . . . SPART 1116
Arista / Feb '80.

## Gable, Eric

**CAUGHT IN THE ACT.**
Tracks: Not Advised.
LP . . . . . . . . . . . . . . . . . . . . . . D1 75603
Orpheus / Sep '89.

**PROCESS OF ELIMINATION.**
Tracks: Process of elimination / Process of elimination (mixes).
CD Single . . . . . . . . . . . . . . . . .660228 2
12" . . . . . . . . . . . . . . . . . . . . . .660228 6
MC Single . . . . . . . . . . . . . . . . . .660228 4
Epic / Mar '94.

---

## PROCESS OF ELIMINATION.
Tracks: Process of elimination / Don't wanna hurt nobody / Driving me crazy / Call me / I'll be around / I'm not the one / Try again / Let me rock / Don't stop / This time.
CD . . . . . . . . . . . . . . . . . . . . . .474266 2
LP . . . . . . . . . . . . . . . . . . . . . .474266 1
MC . . . . . . . . . . . . . . . . . . . . . .474266 4
Epic / Apr '94 / Sony.

## Gabrielle

**BECAUSE OF YOU.**
Tracks: Beacuse of you (Mixes).
■ 12" . . . . . . . . . . . . . . . . . . .GODX 109
■ 7" . . . . . . . . . . . . . . . . . . . GOD 109
■ CD Single . . . . . . . . . . . . . .GODCD 109
■ MC Single . . . . . . . . . . . . . GODMC 109
Go Discs / Feb '94.

**DREAMS.**
Tracks: Dreams.
■ 12" . . . . . . . . . . . . . . . . . . . . . VIC 33
Victim / Feb '92.
■ 12" . . . . . . . . . . . . . . . . . . . .GODX 99
■ 7" . . . . . . . . . . . . . . . . . . . . GOD 99
■ CD Single . . . . . . . . . . . . . . GODCD 99
■ MC Single . . . . . . . . . . . . . .GODMC 99
Go Beat / Jun '93.

**FIND YOUR WAY.**
Tracks: Going nowhere / Who could love you / Find your way / I wanna know / Dreams / I wish / We don't talk / Second chance / Say what you gotta say / Because of you / Inside your head.
CD . . . . . . . . . . . . . . . . . . . . . . 8284412
LP . . . . . . . . . . . . . . . . . . . . . . 8284411
MC . . . . . . . . . . . . . . . . . . . . . . 8284414
Go Beat / Oct '93 / PolyGram.

**I WISH.**
Tracks: I wish.
■ 12" . . . . . . . . . . . . . . . . . . .GODX 108
■ 7" . . . . . . . . . . . . . . . . . . . GOD 108
■ CD Single . . . . . . . . . . . . . .GODCD 108
■ MC Single . . . . . . . . . . . . . GODMC 108
Go Discs / Dec '93.

## Gage, Yvonne

**DOIN' IT IN A HAUNTED HOUSE.**
Tracks: Doin' it in a haunted house.
■ 12" . . . . . . . . . . . . . . . . . . . . TA 4519
■ 7" . . . . . . . . . . . . . . . . . . . . .A 4519
Epic / Jun '84.

**GARDEN OF EVE.**
Tracks: Garden of Eve / Tonight I wanna love you.
■ 12" . . . . . . . . . . . . . . . . . . . K 11708T
■ 7" . . . . . . . . . . . . . . . . . . . . K 11708
Atlantic / Jan '82.

**LOVER OF MY DREAMS.**
Tracks: Lover of my dreams.
■ 12" . . . . . . . . . . . . . . . . . . . PIN 102T
■ 7" . . . . . . . . . . . . . . . . . . . . PIN 102
Pinnacle / Apr '84.

**WINTER DAYS AND SUMMER NIGHTS (Gage, Yvonne featuring Me).**
Tracks: Winter days and summer nights.
■ 12" . . . . . . . . . . . . . . . . . . .WDRX 8
■ 7" . . . . . . . . . . . . . . . . . . . .WDR 8
World Dance / Jan '91.

## Gaines, Billy

**I FOUND SOMEONE (Gaines, Billy & Sarah).**
Tracks: I found someone / No one loves me like you.
■ 12" . . . . . . . . . . . . . . . . . . .EXPAND 27
Expansion / Jun '89.

**LOVE'S THE KEY (Gaines, Billy & Sarah).**
Tracks: Loves the key.
■ 12" . . . . . . . . . . . . . . . . . . .EXPAND 39
Passion/Debut/Scratch Music / Jul '93.

---

## NO ONE LOVES ME LIKE YOU (Gaines, Billy & Sarah).
Tracks: No one loves me like you / One within / I've found someone / We must believe / Keep on giving / If I had known / We forget / That's the life / Walking in the spirit / His purpose will prevail.
CD . . . . . . . . . . . . . . . . . . . . . CD 02832
MC . . . . . . . . . . . . . . . . . . . . . CO 02832
Benson (USA) / Jan '92 / Word Records (UK).

## Gaines, Rosie

**AFTER THE RAIN (Gaines, Rosie & The Loveman).**
Tracks: After the rain / After the rain (mix) / One more night.
■ 12" . . . . . . . . . . . . . . . . . . .AT 12-018
About Time / Nov '93.

**ONLY WANNA BE IN YOUR ARMS.**
Tracks: Only wanna be in your arms / Heart like stone / Be strong.
■ 12" . . . . . . . . . . . . . . . . . . . . AT 04
About Time / Feb '92.

## Gale, Eric

**BEST OF ERIC GALE.**
Tracks: Ginseng woman / Let me slip it to you / Multiplication / Trio / De rabbit / Lookin' good / Red ground / Oh Mary don't you weep.
■ LP . . . . . . . . . . . . . . . . . . . CBS 84201
CBS / May '80.

**BLUE HORIZON.**
Tracks: Blue horizon / Wait until the city sleeps / When Tokyo / Mako d'amour / Clock a pa / Call me at the same number / 97th and Columbus.
■ LP . . . . . . . . . . . . . . . . . . . . K 52349
Elektra / '82.

**BLUE HORIZON.**
Tracks: Blue horizon / Wait until the city sleeps / When Tokyo / Mako D'Amour / Clock-a-pa / Call me at the same number / 97th & Columbus.
CD . . . . . . . . . . . . . . . . . . . . . . 71008
Discovery (USA) / Jun '93 / New Note.

**ISLAND BREEZE.**
Tracks: Boardwalk / We'll make it / My momma told me so / Island breeze / I know that's right.
■ LP . . . . . . . . . . . . . . . . . . . . 9601981
Elektra / '84.

**PART OF YOU.**
Tracks: Lookin' good / Nesumi / Holding on to love / Let me slip it to you / Trio.
■ MC . . . . . . . . . . . . . . . . . . . .40 83464
■ LP . . . . . . . . . . . . . . . . . . . CBS 83464
CBS / Jul '79.

**TOUCH OF SILK.**
Tracks: You got your life in my hands / Touch of silk / War paint / Once in a smile / With you I'm born again / Au privave / Lie to love.
■ LP . . . . . . . . . . . . . . . . . . . CBS 84509
MC . . . . . . . . . . . . . . . . . . . . .40 84509
CBS / Dec '80 / Sony.

## Gap Band

**ALL OF MY LOVE.**
Tracks: All of my love (7" mix) (7" & CD single only.) / All of my love (instrumental) (7" only.) / All of my love (ext. mix) (Not on 7".) / All of my love (Just coolin' mix) (Not on 7".) / All of my love (bonus beats) (12" only.)
■ 12" . . . . . . . . . . . . . . . . . . . 203 650 6
■ 12" . . . . . . . . . . . . . . . . . . . 12CL 558
■ 7" . . . . . . . . . . . . . . . . . . . 203 650 7
■ 7" . . . . . . . . . . . . . . . . . . . .CL 558
■ CD Single . . . . . . . . . . . . . . 203 650 2
■ CD Single . . . . . . . . . . . . . . CDCL 558
Capitol / Dec '89.

**BABY BABA BOOGIE.**
Tracks: Baby baba boogie / Shake.
■ 12" . . . . . . . . . . . . . . . . . . . 9198316
■ 7" . . . . . . . . . . . . . . . . . . . 6167824
Mercury / Aug '79.

## BEST OF THE GAP BAND.
**Tracks:** Oops upside your head / Early in the morning / Yearning for your love / Outstanding / Burn rubber on me / Can't get over you / You dropped a bomb on me / Someday / Party train.
- ■ LP . . . . . . . . . . . . . . . . . . . . . . JABH 15
- MC . . . . . . . . . . . . . . . . . . . . . . JABHC 15
Club / Jan '87 / PolyGram.

## BEST OF THE GAP BAND, THE.
**Tracks:** Early in the morning / Shake / Outstanding / Why you wann hurt me / Yearning / Open your mind / You dropped a bomb on me / You can always count on me / I don't believe you want to get up and dance / Steppin' out / Humping around / Boys are back in town / Party train.
- CD . . . . . . . . . . . . . . . . . . . . . 522 457-2
Mercury / Jun '94 / PolyGram.

## BIG FUN.
**Tracks:** Big fun / Big fun (serious dub mix).
- ■ 12" . . . . . . . . . . . . . . . . . . . . . FT 49780
- ■ 7" . . . . . . . . . . . . . . . . . . . . . FB 49779
Total Experience / Nov '86.

## BOYS ARE BACK IN TOWN.
**Tracks:** Boys are back in town / Steppin' / I don't believe you want to get up / Oops upside your head.
- ■ 7" . . . . . . . . . . . . . . . . . . . . . . MER 2
- ■ 12" . . . . . . . . . . . . . . . . . . . . . MERX 2
Mercury / Feb '80.

## BURN RUBBER ON ME (WHY YOU WAN-NA MAKE ME BLUE).
**Tracks:** Burn rubber on me / Nothing comes to sleepers.
- ■ 12" . . . . . . . . . . . . . . . . . . . . . MERX 52
- ■ 7" . . . . . . . . . . . . . . . . . . . . . . MER 52
Mercury / Dec '80.

## EARLY IN THE MORNING.
**Tracks:** Early in the morning / I'm in love.
- ■ 12" . . . . . . . . . . . . . . . . . . . . . MERX 97
- ■ 7" . . . . . . . . . . . . . . . . . . . . . . MER 97
Mercury / Jun '82.

## GAP BAND.
**Tracks:** Out of the blue / Stand up and dance with me / Not guilty / God is watching you / Little bit of love / Hang on / Knuckle head funkin' / Thinking of you / Silly grin.
- LP . . . . . . . . . . . . . . . . . . . . . . FL 12168
Tattoo / Jul '77 / Grapevine Distribution.

## GAP BAND 2.
**Tracks:** Steppin' out / No hiding place / I don't believe you want to get up and dance / Who do you call / You are my high / Party lights / Boys are back in town.
- ■ LP . . . . . . . . . . . . . . . . . . . . . . 9111062
Mercury / Oct '80.

## GAP BAND 3.
**Tracks:** When I look in your eyes / Yearning for your love / Burn rubber on me / Nothin' comes to sleepers / Are you living / Sweet Caroline / Humpin' / Way / Gash gash gash.
- ■ LP . . . . . . . . . . . . . . . . . . . . . . 6337110
Mercury / Jan '88.

## GAP BAND 4.
**Tracks:** Early in the morning / Seasons no reason to change / Lonely like me / Outstanding / Stay with me / You dropped a bomb on me / I can't get over you / Talkin' back.
- ■ LP . . . . . . . . . . . . . . . . . . . . . . MERS 6
- MC . . . . . . . . . . . . . . . . . . . . . . MERSC 6
Mercury / Jun '82 / PolyGram.
- ■ LP . . . . . . . . . . . . . . . . . . . . . . FL 89476
- ■ MC . . . . . . . . . . . . . . . . . . . . . . FK 89476
RCA / Nov '84.

## GAP BAND 6.
**Tracks:** Beep a freak / Don't you leave me / Disrespect / Sun don't shine everyday / Video junkie / Weak spot / I believe / I found my baby.
- ■ LP . . . . . . . . . . . . . . . . . . . . . . FL 89476
Total Experience / Jan '85.

## GAP BAND 7.
**Tracks:** Not Advised.
- ■ LP . . . . . . . . . . . . . . . . . . . . . . FL 85714
- ■ MC . . . . . . . . . . . . . . . . . . . . . . FK 85714
Total Experience / Jan '86.

## GAP BAND 8.
**Tracks:** Big fun / I can't live without your love / Get loose, get funky / Don't take it away / Going in circles / Keep holding on / I'll always love you / Bop-b-da-da-da (that's how music came about) / I owe it to myself.
- ■ LP . . . . . . . . . . . . . . . . . . . . . . FL 89992
- ■ MC . . . . . . . . . . . . . . . . . . . . . . FK 89992
RCA / Jan '87.

## GOING IN CIRCLES.
**Tracks:** Going in circles / Keep holding on / Disrespect.
- ■ 12" . . . . . . . . . . . . . . . . . . . . . FT 49716
- ■ 7" . . . . . . . . . . . . . . . . . . . . . FB 49715
Total Experience / Apr '87.

## HUNTING.
**Tracks:** Hunting.
- ■ 12" . . . . . . . . . . . . . . . . . . . . . MERX 63
- ■ 7" . . . . . . . . . . . . . . . . . . . . . . MER 63
Mercury / Apr '81.

## I'M GONNA GIT YOU SUCKA.
**Tracks:** I'm gonna git you sucka / I'm gonna git you sucka (ext) / Tripped out (dub) (Available on 12" only) / Tripped out (ext) (Available on 12" only) / I'm gonna git you (sugar shack) (Only on 12" (612095)).
- ■ 12" . . . . . . . . . . . . . . . . . . . . . .612062
- ■ 12" . . . . . . . . . . . . . . . . . . . . . .612016
- ■ 12" . . . . . . . . . . . . . . . . . . . . . .612095
- ■ 7" . . . . . . . . . . . . . . . . . . . . . . .112016
- ■ CD Single . . . . . . . . . . . . . . . . . .662016
- ■ CD Single . . . . . . . . . . . . . . . . . .162016
Arista / Feb '89.

## I'M READY (IF YOU'RE READY).
**Tracks:** I'm ready (if you're ready) / Party train.
- ■ 12" . . . . . . . . . . . . . . . . . . . . . . X 004
- ■ 7" . . . . . . . . . . . . . . . . . . . . . . .TE 004
Total Experience / Oct '83.

## JAMMIN' IN AMERICA.
**Tracks:** Jammin' in America / Burn rubber on me / Oops upside your head (Only on 12" single.).
- ■ 12" . . . . . . . . . . . . . . . . . . . . . . TEX 6
- ■ 7" . . . . . . . . . . . . . . . . . . . . . . . TE 6
Total Experience / Jun '84.

## OOPS UPSIDE YOUR HEAD.
**Tracks:** Oops upside your head.
- ■ 12" . . . . . . . . . . . . . . . . . . . . . MERX 22
- ■ 7" . . . . . . . . . . . . . . . . . . . . . . MER 22
Mercury / Jul '80.

## OOPS UPSIDE YOUR HEAD ('87 MIX).
**Tracks:** Oops upside your head / Oops uppercut.
- ■ 12" . . . . . . . . . . . . . . . . . . . . . JABX 54
- ■ 7" . . . . . . . . . . . . . . . . . . . . . . JAB 54
- ■ MC Single . . . . . . . . . . . . . . . . . . JABM 54
Club / Jun '87.

## OOPS UPSIDE YOUR HEAD (OLD GOLD).
**Tracks:** Oops upside your head / Burn rubber on me / Outstanding.
- ■ 12" . . . . . . . . . . . . . . . . . . . . . OG 4132
Old Gold / Aug '89.
- CD Single . . . . . . . . . . . . . . . . . . OG 6516
Old Gold / '92 / Pickwick.

## OUTSTANDING.
**Tracks:** Outstanding.
- ■ 7" . . . . . . . . . . . . . . . . . . . . . . TE 001
- ■ 12" . . . . . . . . . . . . . . . . . . . . . TEX 001
Total Experience / Jan '83.

## PARTY LIGHTS.
**Tracks:** Party lights / Baba baba boogie.
- ■ 12" . . . . . . . . . . . . . . . . . . . . . MERX 37
- ■ 7" . . . . . . . . . . . . . . . . . . . . . . MER 37
Mercury / Sep '80.

## PARTY TRAIN.
**Tracks:** Party train / Outstanding club.
- ■ 12" . . . . . . . . . . . . . . . . . . . . . JABX 62
- ■ 7" . . . . . . . . . . . . . . . . . . . . . . JAB 62
Club / Oct '87.

## ROUND TRIPP.
**Tracks:** All of my love / Addicted to your love / We can make it alright / It's our duty / Wednesday lover / I like it / I'm dreaming / Antidote (to love) / No easy out / Jam / Let's talk about love.
- ■ CD . . . . . . . . . . . . . . . . . . . . . CDEST 2116
- ■ LP . . . . . . . . . . . . . . . . . . . . . . EST 2116
- ■ MC . . . . . . . . . . . . . . . . . . . . . .TCEST 2116
Capitol / Nov '89.

## SOMEDAY.
**Tracks:** Someday / Shake a leg / Outstanding (On 12" only).
- ■ 7" . . . . . . . . . . . . . . . . . . . . . . TE 5
- ■ 12" . . . . . . . . . . . . . . . . . . . . . TEX 5
Total Experience / Feb '83.

## THAT'S HOW MUSIC CAME ABOUT.
**Tracks:** That's how music came about / I owe it to myself / Bop-b-da-b-da-da (that's how music came about) (Available on 12" only).
- ■ 12" . . . . . . . . . . . . . . . . . . . . . FT 49756
- ■ 7" . . . . . . . . . . . . . . . . . . . . . FB 49755
Total Experience / Feb '87.

## V-JAMMIN'.
**Tracks:** Where are we goin / Shake a leg / I'm read if you're ready / Jammin' in America / Smile / Part train / Jam the motha' / I expect more / You're something special / Someday.
- ■ LP . . . . . . . . . . . . . . . . . . . . . . TEL
Total Experience / Oct '83.

## YEARNING FOR YOUR LOVE.
**Tracks:** Yearning for your love / Ooops upside you head.
- ■ 12" . . . . . . . . . . . . . . . . . . . . . MERX 7
- ■ 7" . . . . . . . . . . . . . . . . . . . . . . MER 7
Mercury / Jun '81.

## YOU DROPPED A BOMB ON ME.
**Tracks:** You dropped a bomb on me / Lonely like me
- ■ 12" . . . . . . . . . . . . . . . . . . . . . MERX 11
- ■ 7" . . . . . . . . . . . . . . . . . . . . . . MER 11
Mercury / Sep '82.

# Gardier, Donna

## GOOD THING.
**Tracks:** Good thing.
- ■ 7" . . . . . . . . . . . . . . . . . . . . . . VS 134
- ■ 12" . . . . . . . . . . . . . . . . . . . . . VST 134
- ■ 12" Remix . . . . . . . . . . . . . . . . . . VSTX 134
- ■ CD Single . . . . . . . . . . . . . . . . . . VSCDT 134
Virgin / Jun '91.

## I'LL BE THERE.
**Tracks:** I'll be there.
- ■ 7" . . . . . . . . . . . . . . . . . . . . . . VS 130
- ■ 12" . . . . . . . . . . . . . . . . . . . . . VST 130
- ■ 12" Remix . . . . . . . . . . . . . . . . . . VSTX 130
Virgin / Oct '90.

## REACH OUT.
**Tracks:** Reach out.
- ■ CD Single . . . . . . . . . . . . . . . . . . CSCDT 132
- ■ 12" . . . . . . . . . . . . . . . . . . . . . VST 132
- ■ 12" Remix . . . . . . . . . . . . . . . . . . VSTX 132
- ■ 7" . . . . . . . . . . . . . . . . . . . . . . VS 132
Virgin / Feb '91.

## REACH OUT.
**Tracks:** Reach out / What could be sweeter / Light o love / Make me believe / I'll be there / When will yo be mine / Put your love in the right place / Slov motion emotion / Good thing / Let me be the one Reach out (Reprise).
- ■ CD . . . . . . . . . . . . . . . . . . . . . CDV 265
- ■ LP . . . . . . . . . . . . . . . . . . . . . . V 265
- ■ MC . . . . . . . . . . . . . . . . . . . . . . TCV 265
Virgin / Jun '91.

# Gardner, Joanna

## JOANNA GARDNER.
**Tracks:** I never thought / We can make it / Specia feelings / Friday night / Watching you / I could neve love another like you / Pick up the pieces / Spooky
- ■ LP . . . . . . . . . . . . . . . . . . . . . . POLD 517
Polydor / Aug '85.

## WATCHING YOU.
**Tracks:** Watching you / Pick up the pieces.
- ■ 12" . . . . . . . . . . . . . . . . . . . . . POSPX 74
- ■ 7" . . . . . . . . . . . . . . . . . . . . . . POSP 74
Polydor / May '85.

# Gardner, Taana

## YOU CAN'T KEEP COMING IN AND OU OF MY LIFE.
**Tracks:** You can't keep coming in and out of my life
- ■ 12" . . . . . . . . . . . . . . . . . . . . . NP 5007
Next Plateau / Jun '88.

# Garrett, Lee

## YOU'RE MY EVERYTHING.
**Tracks:** You're my everything.
- ■ 7" . . . . . . . . . . . . . . . . . . . . . . CHS 208
Chrysalis / May '76.

# Garrett, Siedah

## K.I.S.S.I.N.G.
**Tracks:** K.I.S.S.I.N.G. / Taboo.
- ■ 12" . . . . . . . . . . . . . . . . . . . . . W 7928
- ■ 7" . . . . . . . . . . . . . . . . . . . . . . W 7928
- ■ CD Single . . . . . . . . . . . . . . . . . . W 7928 C
WEA / May '88.

## KISS OF LIFE.
**Tracks:** K.I.S.S.I.N.G. / Refuse to be loose / Innocer side / Night of no return / Kiss of life / Groove

midnight / Ruby diamond / Baby's got it bad / Nobody does me.
■ CD . . . . . . . . . . . . . . . . . . . 925 689 2
■ LP . . . . . . . . . . . . . . . . . . . WX 175
■ MC. . . . . . . . . . . . . . . . . . . WX 175C
Reprise/Slash (USA) / Jun '88.

## Garrett, Vernon

### CAUGHT IN THE CROSSFIRE.
Tracks: Lonely, lonely nights / Bottom line / Drifting apart / Love me right / If you can't help me baby / Somebody done messed up / Don't make me pay for his mistakes / Walkin' the back streets and crying / Caught in the crossfire.
LP . . . . . . . . . . . . . . . . . . . . ICH 1128
MC. . . . . . . . . . . . . . . . . . . MCICH 1128
Ichiban / Jan '92 / A.D.A. Distribution / Pinnacle / ACD Trading Ltd. / Koch International / Direct Distribution.
CD. . . . . . . . . . . . . . . . . . CDICH 1128
Ichiban / Oct '93 / A.D.A. Distribution / Pinnacle / ACD Trading Ltd. / Koch International / Direct Distribution.

### IF I COULD TURN BACK THE HANDS OF TIME.
Tracks: If I could turn back the hands of time / You and me together.
■ 7" . . . . . . . . . . . . . . . . . . . SS 2006
Stateside / Mar '67.

### SHINE IT ON.
Tracks: Shine it on / Things are lookin' better.
■ 7" . . . . . . . . . . . . . . . . . . . SS 2026
Stateside / Jun '67.

### TOO HIP TO BE HAPPY.
Tracks: Are you the one / You just call me / You don't know nothin' about love / Too hip to be happy / Doors of my heart / Special kind of lady / She's a burglar / I'll be doggone / Gonna have to use my head / Lil' black woman.
CD. . . . . . . . . . . . . . . . . . . ICH 1169CD
MC. . . . . . . . . . . . . . . . . . . ICH 1169MC
Ichiban / May '94 / A.D.A. Distribution / Pinnacle / ACD Trading Ltd. / Koch International / Direct Distribution.

## Garvin, Rex

### I GOTTA GO NOW.
Tracks: I gotta go now / Believe it or not.
■ 7" . . . . . . . . . . . . . . . . . . . .584097
Atlantic / Feb '67.

### SOCK IT TO 'EM J.B.
Tracks: Sock it to 'em J.B.
■ 7" . . . . . . . . . . . . . . . . . . . K 10105
Atlantic / Jan '75.

## Gary's Gang

### KEEP ON DANCING.
Tracks: Keep on dancing / Let's love dance tonight.
■ 7" . . . . . . . . . . . . . . . . . . CBS 7109
CBS / Feb '79.

### KEEP ON DANCING.
Tracks: Showtime / Party tonight / Do it at the disco / Let's lovedance tonight / Keep on dancing / You'll always be my everything.
■ LP . . . . . . . . . . . . . . . . . . CBS 83583
CBS / Apr '79.

### KEEP ON DANCING (1990).
Tracks: Keep on dancing (1990).
■ 12" . . . . . . . . . . . . . . . . . .BCM 470X
■ 7" . . . . . . . . . . . . . . . . . . BCM 470
■ CD Single . . . . . . . . . . . .BCM 470CD
BCM / Jul '90.

### KEEP ON DANCING (OLD GOLD).
Tracks: Keep on dancing / Let's love dance tonight.
■ 12" . . . . . . . . . . . . . . . . . OG 4025
Old Gold / Nov '87.

### KNOCK ME OUT.
Tracks: Knock me out / Knock me out (instrumental).
■ 12" . . . . . . . . . . . . . . . . ARIST 12499
■ 7" . . . . . . . . . . . . . . . . . .ARIST 499
Arista / Oct '82.

### LET'S LOVE DANCE TONIGHT.
Tracks: Let's love dance tonight / Showtime.
■ 12" . . . . . . . . . . . . . . . . CBS 127328
■ 7" . . . . . . . . . . . . . . . . . CBS 7328
CBS / Feb '79.

### MAKING MUSIC.
Tracks: Making music.
■ 12" . . . . . . . . . . . . . . . . . . TA 3788

■ 7" . . . . . . . . . . . . . . . . . . .A 3788
CBS / Sep '83.

## Gaye, Frankie

### IT TAKES TWO (Gaye, Frankie & Kim Weston).
Tracks: It takes two.
■ 7" . . . . . . . . . . . . . . . . . .MARE 110
Nightmare / Aug '89.

### MY BROTHER.
Tracks: Not Advised.
■ CD . . . . . . . . . . . . . . . . . MOTCCD 56
Motor City / Oct '92.

## Gaye, Marvin

Born in Washington in 1938, Marvin Pentz Gay - he later added the 'e' to emphasise his hetrosexuality - gravitated from local vocal groups The Rainbows, Marquees and Moonglows to become Motown's premier male singer of the sixties. Joining Detroit label as a session drummer, he both married company boss Berry Gordy's sister Anna and hit with *Stubborn Kind Of Fellow* in '62. Gaye spent most of 1960's around the chart tops, either solo *How Sweet It Is, I Heard It Through The Grapevine, Ain't That Peculiar* and *Abraham, Martin & John* or dueting with an array of the company's top female vocalists, including Mary Wells, Kim Weston and Tammy Terrell. The latter's death in 1970 of a brain tumour provoked Marvin into a long period of creative abstinence, ended in '71 by the release of his masterwork *What's Going On*. A soundtrack to the movie *Trouble Man* and duet project with Diana Ross and another solo album, *Let's Get It On* established him as America's number one soulman before, under pressure from the collapse of his marriage and his increasing substance abuse, Marvin's interest in his recording career wained *I Want You* (1976) was largely the work of producer/writer Leon Ware, while *Here My Dear* (1979) chronicled his bitter divorce from Anna Gordy. A final Motown album *In Our Lifetime* was followed by the retreat to Europe, where CBS Records executive, Larkin Arnold inked him to the deal from which sprang his last number one single, *Sexual Healing*. He was shot dead in Los Angeles by his father on April 1, 1984 after a violent family argument.

### 15 GREATEST HITS.
Tracks: How sweet it is (to be loved by you) / Ain't that peculiar / I heard it through the grapevine / You're all I need to get by / Your precious love / Too busy thinking about my baby / That's the way love is / What's going on / Mercy mercy me / Inner city blues / Trouble man / My mistake / Let's get it on / I want you / Got to give it up.
■ CD . . . . . . . . . . . . . . . TCD 06069 TD
Motown / May '84.

### 18 GREATEST HITS: MARVIN GAYE.
Tracks: I heard it through the grapevine / Let's get it on / Too busy thinking about my baby / How sweet it is (to be loved by you) / You're all I need to get by / Got to give it up / You are everything / Can I get a witness / I'll be doggone / What's going on / Abraham, Martin and John / It takes two / You ain't livin' till you're lovin' / Onion song / Wherever I lay my hat (that's my home).
■ LP . . . . . . . . . . . . . . . . . . WL 72645
■ MC . . . . . . . . . . . . . . . . . WK 72645
Motown / Sep '88.
■ CD . . . . . . . . . . . . . . . . . WD 72645
Motown / Jan '89.

### ABRAHAM, MARTIN AND JOHN.
Tracks: Abraham, Martin and John / Ben.
■ 7" . . . . . . . . . . . . . . . . . TMG 734
Tamla Motown / May '70.
■ 7" . . . . . . . . . . . . . . . . . .TMG 1165
Motown / Oct '81.

### AIN'T NO MOUNTAIN HIGH ENOUGH (Gaye, Marvin & Tammi Terrell).
Tracks: Ain't no mountain high enough / Give a little love.
■ 7" . . . . . . . . . . . . . . . . . TMG 611
Tamla Motown / Jun '67.

### AIN'T NOTHING LIKE THE REAL THING (Gaye, Marvin & Tammi Terrell).
Tracks: Ain't nothing like the real thing.
■ 7" . . . . . . . . . . . . . . . . . TMG 655
Tamla Motown / Jun '68.

### AIN'T THAT PECULIAR.
Tracks: Ain't that peculiar.
■ 7" . . . . . . . . . . . . . . . . . TMG 539
Tamla Motown / '65.

### AIN'T THAT PECULIAR.
Tracks: Ain't that peculiar / I'll be doggone.
■ 7" . . . . . . . . . . . . . . . . . ZB 41909
Motown / Apr '88.

### ANTHOLOGY - MARVIN GAYE (Volumes 1 & 2).
Tracks: Chained / End of our road / Mercy me / Inner city blues / Trouble man / Distant lover / After the dance / Once upon a time / Forever / It takes two / If this world were mine / Stubborn kind of fellow / Hitch hike / Pride and joy / Can I get a witness / What's the matter with you baby (with Mary Wells.) / You're a wonderful one / Try it baby / Baby don't you do it / What good am I without you (with Kim Weston.) / How sweet it is (to be loved by you) / Pretty little baby / Ain't that peculiar / Ain't no mountain high enough (with Tammi Terrell.) / One more heartache / Take this heart of mine / Your precious love (with Tammi Terrell.) / Your unchanging love / You / If I could build my whole world around you (with Tammi Terrell.) / Ain't nothing like the real thing (with Tammi Terrell.) / How can I forget / Heaven sent you, I know (with Kim Weston.) / I heard it through the grapevine / Good lovin' ain't easy to come by / Too busy thinking about my baby / That's the way love is / You're all I need to get by (with Tammi Terrell.) / What's going on / Mercy, mercy me / Save the children / You're the man (part 1) / Let's get it on / Come get to this / I want you / Got to give it up.
■ Double LP . . . . . . . . . . . . TMSP 1128
Motown / Oct '81.
■ Double LP . . . . . . . . . . . . ZL 72156
Motown / '85.
■ CD Set. . . . . . . . . . . . . . . ZD 72534
Motown / Oct '86.
■ CD Set. . . . . . . . . . . . . . . WD 72534
Motown / Mar '89.

### ANTHOLOGY: MARVIN GAYE.
Tracks: Not Advised.
CD . . . . . . . . . . . . . . . . . .530181-2
Motown / Jan '92 / PolyGram.

### BEST OF MARVIN GAYE.
Tracks: I heard it through the grapevine / Too busy thinking about my baby / That's the way love is / Abraham, Martin and John / What's going on / Inner city blues / Mercy mercy me / Let's get it on / Come get to this / You sure love to ball / I want you / After the dance / Come live with me angel / Save the children.
■ LP . . . . . . . . . . . . . . . . .STML 12042
Motown / Nov '76.
MC. . . . . . . . . . . . . . . . .CSTML 12042
Motown / Oct '81 / PolyGram.
■ LP . . . . . . . . . . . . . . . . . ZL 72029
■ MC . . . . . . . . . . . . . . . . . ZK 72029
Motown / '85.
■ CD . . . . . . . . . . . . . . . . . WD 72612
■ LP . . . . . . . . . . . . . . . . . WL 72612
■ MC . . . . . . . . . . . . . . . . . WK 72612
Motown / Jun '90.

### BEST OF MARVIN GAYE.
Tracks: Not Advised.
CD . . . . . . . . . . . . . . . . . .530292-2
MC. . . . . . . . . . . . . . . . . .530292-4
Motown / Mar '94 / PolyGram.

### BEST OF MARVIN GAYE.
Tracks: Not Advised.
VHS . . . . . . . . . . . . . . . . .WNR 2042
Wienerworld Video / Apr '94 / VCI Distribution / THE.

### CAN I GET A WITNESS.
Tracks: Can I get a witness.
■ 7" . . . . . . . . . . . . . . . . . .SS 243
Stateside / '63.

### COMPACT COMMAND PERFORMANCES - VOL. 2.
Tracks: Stubborn kind of fellow / Hitch hike / Pride and joy / Can I get a witness / You're a wonderful one / Try it baby / Baby don't you do it / I'll be doggone / Pretty little baby / One more heartache / Take this heart of mine / Little darlin' / Your unchanging love / You / Chained / How can I forget / End of our road / Come get to this / After the dance / Distant lover.
■ CD . . . . . . . . . . . . . . . . . ZD 72508
Motown / Mar '87.
■ CD . . . . . . . . . . . . . . . . . WD 72508
Motown / Sep '89.

**COMPACT COMMAND PERFORM-ANCES - VOL.1.**
Tracks: How sweet it is (to be loved by you) / I heard it through the grapevine / Your precious love / That's the way round is / Mercy mercy me / Trouble man / Let's get it on / Got to give it up / Ain't that peculiar / You're all I need to get by / Too busy thinking about my baby / What's going on / Inner city blues / My mistake (was to love you) / I want you.
■ CD.................... ZD 72422
Motown / '87.
■ CD.................... WD 72422
Motown / Apr '89.

**DIANA & MARVIN (Gaye, Marvin & Diana Ross).**
Tracks: You are everything / Love twins / Don't knock my love / You're a special part of me / Pledging my love / Just say just / Stop, look, listen (to your heart) / I'm falling in love with you / My mistake (was to love you) / Include me in your life.
■ LP.................... STMA 8015
Tamla Motown / Jan '74.
■ LP.................... STMS 5001
■ MC.................... CSTMS 5001
Motown / Oct '81.
■ CD.................... WD 72066
■ LP.................... WL 72066
■ MC.................... WK 72066
Motown / Aug '88.
CD.....................530048-2
MC.....................540048-4
Motown / Jan '93 / PolyGram.

**DISTANT LOVER.**
Tracks: Not Advised.
CD.................... ST 5001
Star Collection / Nov '93 / BMG.

**DISTANT LOVER.**
Tracks: Third World girl / I heard it through the grapevine / Come get to this / Let's get it on / God is my friend / What's going on / Inner city blues / Joy / Ain't nothing like the real thing / Heaven must have sent you / If this world were mine / Rockin' after midnight / Distant lover / Sexual healing.
CD....................HADCD 165
MC....................HADMC 165
Javelin / May '94 / THE.

**DON'T KNOCK MY LOVE (see under Ross, Diana).**

**DREAM OF A LIFETIME.**
Tracks: Sanctified lady / Savage in the sack / Masochistic beauty / It's madness / Ain't it funny / Symphony / Life's opera / Dream of a lifetime.
■ LP.................... CBS 26239
■ MC.....................40 26239
CBS / Jun '85.
CD....................9825912
Pickwick/Sony Collector's Choice / Jun '94 / Pickwick / Pinnacle.

**DREAM OF A LIFETIME/ROMANTICALLY YOURS/MIDNIGHT LOVE.**
Tracks: Sanctified lady / Savage in the sack / Masochistic baby / It's madness / Ain't it funny (how things turn around) / Symphony / Life's opera / Dream of a lifetime / More / Why did I choose you / Maria / Shadow of your smile / Fly me to the moon (in other words) / I won't cry anymore / Just like / Walkin' in the rain / I live for you / Stranger in my life / Happy go lucky / Midnight lady / Sexual healing / Rockin' after midnight / Til tomorrow / Turn on some music / Third world girl / Joy / My love is waiting.
CD Set ....................477525 2
Columbia / Oct '94 / Sony.

**EARLY YEARS 1961-1964.**
Tracks: Can I get a witness / I'm crazy 'bout my baby / Pride and joy / Got to get my hands on some lovin' / One of these days / You're a wonderful one / Hitch hike / Try it, baby / Stubborn kind of fellow / I'm yours, you're mine / Never let you go / Taking my time / Wherever I lay my hat / Let your conscience be your guide / Mr. Sandman / It hurt me too.
■ LP.................... STMR 9004
■ MC.................... CSTMR 9004
Motown / Oct '81.

**EASY (Gaye, Marvin & Tammi Terrell).**
Tracks: Good lovin' ain't easy to come by / California soul / Love woke me up this morning / This poor heart of mine / I ain't my puppet / Onion song / What you gave me / Baby I need your loving / I can't believe you love me / How you gonna keep it / More, more, more / Satisfied feelin'.
■ LP....................STML 11132
Tamla Motown / Feb '70.
■ LP.................... WL 72507

■ MC.................... WK 72507
Motown / Sep '86.

**EGO TRIPPING OUT.**
Tracks: Ego tripping out.
■ 7"....................TMG 1168
Motown / Oct '81.

**FOR THE VERY LAST TIME.**
Tracks: Not Advised.
CD....................MDCD 1
MMG / Jan '94 / THE.

**FUNKY SPACE.**
Tracks: Funky space / Reincarnation.
■ 7"....................TMG 1138
Motown / Feb '79.

**GOOD LOVIN' AIN'T EASY TO COME BY (Gaye, Marvin & Tammi Terrell).**
Tracks: Good lovin' ain't easy to come by.
■ 7"....................TMG 697
Tamla Motown / Jun '69.

**GOT TO GIVE IT UP.**
Tracks: Got to give it up / How sweet is is.
■ 7"....................TMG 1069
Tamla Motown / May '77.
■ 7"....................TMG 1381
■ 12"....................TMGT 1381
Motown / Apr '85.

**GREATEST HITS.**
Tracks: Your unchanging love / Take this heart / Try it baby / Pride and joy / Stubborn kind of fellow / One more heartache / You're a wonderful one / Forever / Can I get a witness / Now you've won me / Baby don't you do it / Little darling / Ain't that peculiar / Pretty little baby / I'll be doggone / How sweet it is.
■ LP....................STML 11065
Tamla Motown / Mar '68.

**GREATEST HITS (Gaye, Marvin & Tammi Terrell) (Gaye, Marvin & Tammi Terrell).**
Tracks: You're all I need to get by / Ain't no mountain high enough / Ain't nothing like the real thing / Good lovin' ain't easy to come by / What you gave me / Keep on lovin' me honey / Two can have a party / Onion song / If I could build my whole world around you / You ain't livin' till you're lovin' / Your precious love / If this world were mine / California soul / Hold me oh my darling.
■ LP....................STML 11153
Tamla Motown / Aug '70.
■ MC....................CSTML 11153
Tamla Motown / Oct '81.

**GREATEST HITS LIVE: MARVIN GAYE.**
Tracks: All the way round / Since I had you / Come get to this / Let's get it on / Ain't that peculiar / You're a wonderful one / Stubborn kind of fellow / Pride and joy / Little darlin' / I heard it through the grapevine / Hitch hike / You / Too busy thinking 'bout my baby / How sweet it is (to be loved by you) / Inner City blues / God is love / What's going on / Save the children / It takes two / Distant lover / You're all I need to get by / Ain't nothing like the real thing / Ain't no mountain high enough / Your precious love.
VHS....................VMF 008
Videoform / Sep '84 / Gold & Sons.
VHS....................WNR 1068
Wienerworld Video / Apr '90 / VCI Distribution / THE.
■ VHS.................... 790 479
BMG Video / Oct '90.

**GREATEST HITS: DIANA & MARVIN (see under Ross, Diana).**

**GREATEST HITS: MARVIN GAYE.**
Tracks: I heard it through the grapevine / Let's get it on / Too busy thinking about my baby / How sweet it is (to be loved by you) / You're all I need to get by / Got to give it up / You are everything / Midnight lady / Sexual healing / What's going on / Abraham, Martin and John / It takes two / Stop, look, listen (to your heart) / My love is waiting / Onion song / Wherever I lay my hat.
■ LP.................... STAR 2234
■ MC.................... STAC 2234
Telstar/Ronco / Nov '83.

**GREATEST HITS: MARVIN GAYE.**
Tracks: All the way round / Since I had you / Come get to this / Let's get it on / Ain't that peculiar / You're a wonderful one / Stubborn kind of fellow / Pride and joy / Little darlin' / I heard it through the grapevine / Hitch hike / You / Too busy thinking about my baby / How sweet it is (to be loved by you) / Inner city blues / God is love / What's going on / Save the children / It takes two / Distant lover / You're all I need to get by / Ain't nothing like the real

thing / Ain't no mountain high enough / Your precious love.
VHS....................CFV 02472
Channel 5 / '87 / Channel 5 Video / P.R.O. Video / Gold & Sons.

**GREATEST HITS: MARVIN GAYE & TAMMI TERRELL (Gaye, Marvin & Tammi Terrell).**
Tracks: Your precious love / Ain't no mountain high enough / You're all I need to get by / Ain't nothing like the real thing / Good livin' ain't easy to come by / If this world were mine / Onion song / I could build my whole world around you / Keep on lovin' me, honey / What you gave me / You ain't livin' till you're lovin' / Hold me, oh my darling.
■ LP.................... STMS 5066
■ MC.................... CSTMS 5066
Motown / Jul '82 / PolyGram.
■ CD.................... WD 72103
■ LP.................... WL 72103
■ MC.................... WK 72103
Motown / '86.

**HEAVY LOVE AFFAIR.**
Tracks: Heavy love affair / Far cry.
■ 12"....................TMGT 1232
■ 7"....................TMG 1232
Motown / Oct '81.

**HERE, MY DEAR.**
Tracks: Here my dear / I met a little girl / When did you stop loving me, when did I stop loving you / Anger / Funky space reincarnation / You can leave but it's goin' to cost you / Falling in love again / Is that enough / Everybody needs love / Time to get it together / Sparrow / Anna's song.
■ Double LP.................... TMSP 6008
■ MC Set.................... CTMSP 6008
Motown / Oct '81.
CD....................530253-2
Motown / Feb '94 / PolyGram.

**HITS OF MARVIN GAYE.**
Tracks: I heard it through the grapevine / Abraham, Martin and John / What's going on / Inner city blues / That's the way is / How sweet it is (to be loved by you) / Mercy mercy me / Too busy thinking about my baby / You / Your unchanging love / Chained / How can I forget / End of our road / Little darlin'.
■ LP....................STML 11201
Motown / Feb '72.
■ LP.................... ZL 72216
Motown / '85.

**HOW SWEET IT IS (TO BE LOVED BY YOU).**
Tracks: You're a wonderful one / How sweet it is (to be loved by you) / Try it baby / Baby don't you do it / Need your lovin' (want you back) / One of these days / No good without you / Stepping closer to your heart / Need somebody / Me and my lonely room / Now that you've won me / Forever.
■ LP.................... MFP 50423
MFP / Feb '79.
■ CD.................... WD 72732
Motown / Mar '91.

**HOW SWEET IT IS (TO BE LOVED BY YOU).**
Tracks: How sweet it is (To be loved by you).
■ 7"....................SS 360
Stateside / Dec '64.

**I HEARD IT THROUGH THE GRAPEVINE.**
Tracks: You / Tear it down / Chained / I heard it through the grapevine / At last / Some kind of wonderful / Loving you is sweeter ever / Change what you can / It's love I need / Every now and then / There goes my baby / Tear it on down.
■ LP.................... WL 72374
■ MC.................... WK 72374
Motown / Apr '85.
■ CD.................... WD 72374
Motown / Jun '89.

**I HEARD IT THROUGH THE GRAPEVINE.**
Tracks: I heard it through the grapevine.
■ 7"....................TMG 686
Tamla Motown / Feb '69.
■ 7"....................TMG 923
Tamla Motown / Nov '74.
■ MC Single.................... ZV 40702
■ 12"....................ZT 40702
■ 7"....................ZB 40701
Motown / Apr '86.

**I HEARD IT THROUGH THE GRAPEVINE/ I WANT YOU.**
Tracks: You / Tear it on down / Chained / I heard it through the grapevine / At last / Some kind of wonderful / Loving you is sweeter than ever /

Change what you can / It's love I need / Every now and then / You're what's happening in the world today / There goes my baby / I want you / Come live with me angel / After the dance (instrumental) / Feel all my love inside / I wanna be where you are / I want you (intro jam) / All the way 'round / Since I had you / Soon I'll be loving you / After the dance.
■ CD . . . . . . . . . . . . . . . . . . . ZD 72457
Motown / Nov '86.

## I WANT YOU.
Tracks: I want you / Come live with me angel / Angel / After the dance (Instrumental.) / Feel all my love inside / I wanna be where you are / All the way round / Since I had you / Soon I'll be loving you again / I want you (intro jam) / After the dance (plus instrumental.)
■ LP . . . . . . . . . . . . . . . . . . .STML 12025
Motown / Oct '81.
■ LP . . . . . . . . . . . . . . . . . . . WL 72027
Motown / '86.
■ CD . . . . . . . . . . . . . . . . . . . WD 72027
Motown / Mar '90.

## I'LL BE DOGGONE.
Tracks: I'll be doggone.
■ 7" . . . . . . . . . . . . . . . . . . . TMG 510
Tamla Motown / '65.

## IF I COULD BUILD MY WHOLE WORLD AROUND YOU (Gaye, Marvin & Tammi Terrell).
Tracks: If I could build my whole world around you.
■ 7" . . . . . . . . . . . . . . . . . . . TMG 635
Tamla Motown / Jan '68.

## IN OUR LIFETIME.
Tracks: Praise / Life is for learning / Love party / Funk me / Far cry / Love me now or love me later / Heavy love affair / In our lifetime.
■ LP . . . . . . . . . . . . . . . . .STML 12149
■ MC . . . . . . . . . . . . . . . . .CSTML 12149
Motown / Oct '81.

## IT TAKES TWO (Gaye, Marvin & Kim Weston).
Tracks: It takes two / It's got to be a miracle.
■ 7" . . . . . . . . . . . . . . . . . . . TMG 590
Tamla Motown / Jan '67.

## IT'S MADNESS.
Tracks: It's madness / Ain't it funny.
■ 12" . . . . . . . . . . . . . . . . . . TA 6462
■ 7" . . . . . . . . . . . . . . . . . . . A 6462
CBS / Jul '85.

## JOY (PART 1).
Tracks: Joy (part 1) / Turn on some music.
■ 12" . . . . . . . . . . . . . . . . . A 13 3242
■ 7" . . . . . . . . . . . . . . . . . . A 3242
CBS / Mar '83.

## LAST CONCERT TOUR, THE.
Tracks: Introduction / Third world girl / I heard it through the grapevine / Come get to this / God is my friend / What's going on / Ain't nothing like the real thing / Your precious love / Love twins / If this world were mine / Joy / Percussion interlude / Inner city blues / Let's get it on / Distant lover / Rockin' after midnight / Sexual healing / Final chapter.
CD . . . . . . . . . . . . . . . . . 7599244362
MC . . . . . . . . . . . . . . . . . 7599244364
WEA / Nov '91 / WEA.

## LEGEND.
Tracks: Not Advised.
■ CD . . . . . . . . . . . . . . . . . . 295 705
EMS / Jul '90.

## LET'S GET IT ON.
Tracks: Let's get it on / Please don't stay (once you go away) / If I should die tonight / Keep gettin' it on / Distant lover / You sure love to ball / Just to keep you satisfied / Come get to this.
■ LP . . . . . . . . . . . . . . . . . . STMA 8013
Tamla Motown / Nov '73.
■ LP . . . . . . . . . . . . . . . . . STMS 5034
■ MC . . . . . . . . . . . . . . . . . CSTMS 5034
Motown / Mar '82.
■ LP . . . . . . . . . . . . . . . . . . WL 72085
■ MC . . . . . . . . . . . . . . . . . WK 72085
Motown / Apr '84.
■ CD . . . . . . . . . . . . . . . . . . WD 72085
Motown / Apr '88.
CD . . . . . . . . . . . . . . . . . . .530055-2
MC . . . . . . . . . . . . . . . . . . .530055-4
Motown / May '90 / PolyGram.

## LET'S GET IT ON.
Tracks: Let's get it on.
■ 7" . . . . . . . . . . . . . . . . . . . TMG 868
Tamla Motown / Aug '73.

## LITTLE DARLING (I NEED YOU).
Tracks: Little darlin'.
■ 7" . . . . . . . . . . . . . . . . . . . TMG 574
Tamla Motown / Sep '66.

## LIVE.
Tracks: Not Advised.
CD . . . . . . . . . . . . . . . . . STACD 082
MC . . . . . . . . . . . . . . . . . STAMC 082
Wisepack / Jul '93 / THE / Conifer Records.

## LIVE.
Tracks: Not Advised.
CD . . . . . . . . . . . . . . . . . .112007-2
MC . . . . . . . . . . . . . . . . . .112007-4
Scratch / Oct '94 / Scratch Records / BMG / Grapevine Distribution.

## LIVE AT THE LONDON PALLADIUM.
Tracks: You're all I need to get by (with Florence Lyles.) / Ain't nothing like the real thing (with Florence Lyles.) / Your precious love (with Florence Lyles.) / It takes two (with Florence Lyles.) / Ain't no mountain high enough (with Florence Lyles.) / Intro theme / All the way round / Since I had you / Come get to this / Let's get it on / Closing theme / Got to give it up / Ain't that peculiar / You're a wonderful one / Stubborn kind of fellow / Pride and joy / Little darlin' / I heard it through the grapevine / Hitch hike / You / Too busy thinking about my baby / How sweet it is (to be loved by you) / Inner city blues / God is love / What's going on / Save the children.
■ LP . . . . . . . . . . . . . . . . . TMSP 6006
Tamla Motown / May '77.
■ LP . . . . . . . . . . . . . . . . . WL 72213
■ MC . . . . . . . . . . . . . . . . . WK 72213
Motown / Aug '86.
■ CD . . . . . . . . . . . . . . . . . . ZD 72218
Motown / Mar '87.
■ CD . . . . . . . . . . . . . . . . . . WD 72213
Motown / May '89.

## LOVE MAN.
Tracks: Ego tripping out / Life's a game of give and take / Life is now in session / I offer you nothing but love / Just because you're so pretty / Dance 'n' be happy / Funk me, funk me, funk me / Love's plea.
■ LP . . . . . . . . . . . . . . . . .STML 12126
Motown / Dec '79.

## LOVE SONGS: MARVIN GAYE & SMOKEY ROBINSON (Gaye, Marvin & Smokey Robinson).
Tracks: Sexual healing / Abraham, Martin and John / Just to see her / You are everything / How sweet it is (To be loved by you) / (Come 'round here) I'm the one you need / It takes two / Tears of a clown / Being with you / let's get it on / I second that emotion / Tracks of my tears / Too busy thinking about my baby / Ooo baby baby / My love is waiting / I heard it through the grapevine.
■ CD . . . . . . . . . . . . . . . . . TCD 2331
■ LP . . . . . . . . . . . . . . . . . STAR 2331
■ MC . . . . . . . . . . . . . . . . . STAC 2331
Telstar/Ronco Nov '88.

## LUCKY LUCKY ME.
Tracks: Lucky, lucky me.
■ 12" . . . . . . . . . . . . . . . . . TMGX 1426
■ 7" . . . . . . . . . . . . . . . . . TMG 1426
■ MC Single . . . . . . . . . . . . . TMGCS 1426
■ CD Single . . . . . . . . . . . . . TMGCD 1426
Motown / May '94.

## M.P.G.
Tracks: Too busy thinking about my baby / This magic moment / That's the way love is / End of our road / Seek and you shall find / Memories / Only a lonely man would know / It's a bitter pill to swallow / More than a heart can stand / Try my true love / I got to get to California / It don't take much to keep me.
■ LP . . . . . . . . . . . . . . . . .STML 11119
Tamla Motown / Sep '69.
■ LP . . . . . . . . . . . . . . . . . STMS 5064
■ MC . . . . . . . . . . . . . . . . . CSTMS 5064
Motown / Aug '82.
CD . . . . . . . . . . . . . . . . . . 5302102
Motown / Aug '93 / PolyGram.

## MAGIC OF MARVIN GAYE, THE.
Tracks: How sweet it is (to be loved by you) / Little darlin' / Take this heart of mine / One more heartache / Night life / One for my baby.
■ LP . . . . . . . . . . . . . . . . . TMS 3508
■ MC . . . . . . . . . . . . . . . . . TMC 3508
Motown / '82.

## MARVIN GAYE.
Tracks: Let's get it on / You are everything / It takes two / Too busy thinking 'bout my baby / What's going on / Ain't I all need to get by / That's the way love is / Midnight lady / I heard it through the grapevine / Sexual healing / Abraham, Martin and John / Onion song / How sweet it is (to be loved by you) / Got to give it up / Sanctified lady / My love is waiting / Stop, look, listen / Wherever I lay my hat.
■ LP . . . . . . . . . . . . . . . . . STAR 2427
■ MC . . . . . . . . . . . . . . . . . STAC 2427
■ CD . . . . . . . . . . . . . . . . . TCD 2427
Telstar/Ronco / Oct '90.

## MARVIN GAYE (Hosted by Smokey Robinson).
Tracks: I heard it through the grapevine / Sexual healing / How sweet it is (to be loved by you) / Your precious love.
■ VHS . . . . . . . . . . . . . . . . . VC 4048
Video Collection / Aug '88 / Gold & Sons / Video Collection / THE.

## MARVIN GAYE - LIVE.
Tracks: Not Advised.
CD Set . . . . . . . . . . . . . . . . STADD 536
MC Set . . . . . . . . . . . . . . . STAMCD 536
Stardust / Apr '93 / Pickwick / Conifer Records.

## MARVIN GAYE AND HIS GIRLS.
Tracks: Once upon a time / What's the matter with you, baby / It's got to be a miracle (this thing called love) / It takes two / Your precious love / Good lovin' ain't easy to come by / You're all I need to get by / You ain't livin' till you're lovin' / What good am I without you / I want you around / Deed I do / Together.
■ LP . . . . . . . . . . . . . . . . .STML 11123
Motown / Nov '69.
■ LP . . . . . . . . . . . . . . . . . STMS 5088
■ MC . . . . . . . . . . . . . . . . . CSTMS 5088
Motown / Feb '83.
■ LP . . . . . . . . . . . . . . . . . WL 72115
Motown / '86.

## MARVIN GAYE AND HIS WOMEN.
Tracks: You're a special part of me / My mistake (was to love you) / Once upon a time / What's the matter with you, baby / What good am I without you / It takes two / It's got to be a miracle (this thing called love) / I want you around / Ain't no mountain high enough / Your precious love / If I could build my whole world around you / Ain't nothing like the real thing / You're all I need to get by / Keep on lovin' me, honey / Good lovin' ain't easy to come by / What you gave me / If this world were mine / California soul / Onion song / Two can have a party / Little ole boy, little ole girl.
■ CD . . . . . . . . . . . . . . . . . . WD 72397
Motown / Oct '87.

## MARVIN GAYE IN THE GROOVE.
Tracks: You / Tear it on down / Chained / Some kind of wonderful / I heard it through the grapevine / At last I found a love / Loving you is sweeter than ever / Change what you can / It's love I need / Every now and then / You're what's happening / There goes my baby.
■ LP . . . . . . . . . . . . . . . . .STML 11091
Tamla Motown / Jan '69.

## MARVIN GAYE: LIVE.
Tracks: Beginning / Introduction / Overture / Trouble man / Inner city blues / Distant lover / Jan / Fossil medley (I'll be doggone) / Try it baby / Can I get a witness / You're a wonderful one / Stubborn kind of fellow / How sweet it is (to be loved by you) / Let's get it on / What's going on.
■ LP . . . . . . . . . . . . . . . . . STMS 5035
■ MC . . . . . . . . . . . . . . . . . CSTMS 5035
Motown / Mar '82 / PolyGram.
■ LP . . . . . . . . . . . . . . . . . WL 72086
■ MC . . . . . . . . . . . . . . . . . WK 72086
Motown / '86.
■ LP . . . . . . . . . . . . . . . . . SHM 3209
■ MC . . . . . . . . . . . . . . . . . HSC 3209
Hallmark / Mar '87 / Pickwick.
■ CD . . . . . . . . . . . . . . . . . . WD 72086
Motown / Feb '88.

## MIDNIGHT LOVE.
Tracks: Joy / My love is waiting / Midnight lady / Sexual healing / Rockin' after midnight / Til tomorrow / Turn on some music / Third world girl.
■ LP . . . . . . . . . . . . . . . . . CBS 85977
CBS / Nov '82.
■ LP . . . . . . . . . . . . . . . . . CBS 32776
■ MC . . . . . . . . . . . . . . . . . .40 32776
CBS / Apr '86.

## MIDNIGHT LOVE/DREAM OF A LIFETIME.
Tracks: Midnight lady / Sexual healing / Rockin' after midnight / 'Til tomorrow / Turn on some music / Third world girl / Joy / My love is waiting / Sanctified lady / Savage in the sake / Masochistic beauty / It's madness / Ain't it funny (how things turn out) / Symphony / Life's opera / Dream of a lifetime.
CD Set . . . . . . . . . . . . . . . . 4610172
Columbia / Jul '92 / Sony.

**MOTOWN REMEMBERS MARVIN GAYE.**
**Tracks:** I heard it through the grapevine / World is rated X / Lonely lover / Just like a man / I'm going home / No greater love / Dark side of the world / Loving and affection / I'm in love with you / That's the way it goes / Baby I'm glad that things worked out so well / Baby don't you leave me.
■ LP . . . . . . . . . . . . ZL 72463
■ MC. . . . . . . . . . . . ZK 72463
Motown / Jun '86.

**MOTOWN'S GREATEST HITS - MARVIN GAYE.**
**Tracks:** Not Advised.
CD. . . . . . . . . . . . .530012-2
MC. . . . . . . . . . . . .530012-4
Motown / Jan '92 / PolyGram.

**MUSICAL TESTAMENT 1964/1984.**
**Tracks:** Crossroads / Right on / After the dance / Try it baby / I heard it through the grapevine / Loving and affection / Parting of the ways / Just to keep you satisfied / When did you stop loving me, when did I stop loving you / Distant lover / Anger / Witness to love / Baby don't you do it / Little darling I need you / Lonely lover / That's the way love is / Dark side of the world / End of our road / Introspection / Star spangled banner / Save the children / Wholy, holy / His eye is on the sparrow / Life is a gamble / If I should die tonight.
■ MC. . . . . . . . . . . . ZK 72639
■ CD . . . . . . . . . . . . ZD 72639
■ Double LP. . . . . . . . . ZL 72639
Motown / Jul '88.

**MY LOVE IS WAITING.**
**Tracks:** My love is waiting / Rockin' after midnight.
■ 12". . . . . . . . . . . . A 13 3048
■ 7" . . . . . . . . . . . . .A 3048
CBS / Dec '83.

**NIGHTLIFE.**
**Tracks:** Nightlife / I'll be doggone / Little darling (I need you) / Take this heart of mine / Hey diddle diddle / One more heartache / Too busy thinking about my baby / How sweet it is (to be loved by you) / You've been a long time coming / Your unchanging love / You're the one for me / I worry 'bout you / One for my baby (and one more for the road).
CD. . . . . . . . . . . . .550072-2
MC. . . . . . . . . . . . .550072-4
Spectrum (1) / May '93 / PolyGram.

**ONCE UPON A TIME (Gaye, Marvin & Mary Wells).**
**Tracks:** Once upon a time.
■ 7" . . . . . . . . . . . . .SS 316
Stateside / Jul '64.

**ONE MORE HEARTACHE.**
**Tracks:** One more heartache / When I had your love.
■ 7" . . . . . . . . . . . . TMG 552
Tamla Motown / '66.

**ONION SONG (Gaye, Marvin & Tammi Terrell).**
**Tracks:** Onion song / You are everything.
■ 7" . . . . . . . . . . . . TMG 715
Tamla Motown / Nov '69.
■ 7" . . . . . . . . . . . . TMG 993
Tamla Motown / Oct '75.
■ 7" . . . . . . . . . . . .TMG 1047
Tamla Motown / Sep '76.

**POPS, WE LOVE YOU (see under Ross, Diana).**

**PRAISE.**
**Tracks:** Praise / Funk me.
■ 12". . . . . . . . . . . .TMGT 1225
■ 7" . . . . . . . . . . . .TMG 1225
Motown / Oct '81.

**PRETTY LITTLE BABY.**
**Tracks:** Pretty little baby.
■ 7" . . . . . . . . . . . . TMG 524
Tamla Motown / '65.

**ROMANTICALLY YOURS.**
**Tracks:** More / Why did I choose you / Maria / Shadow of your smile / Fly me to the moon / I won't cry anymore / Just like / Walking in the rain / I live for you / Stranger in my life / Happy go lucky.
■ LP . . . . . . . . . . . . CBS 26783
■ MC. . . . . . . . . . . . .40 26783
CBS / Dec '85.
■ LP . . . . . . . . . . . . CBS MG 241
CBS / Aug '87.
MC. . . . . . . . . . . . .902121-4
Pickwick / Oct '92 / Pickwick.
CD. . . . . . . . . . . . .902121-2
Pickwick/Sony Collector's Choice / Jun '94 / Pickwick / Pinnacle.

**SANCTIFIED LADY.**
**Tracks:** Sanctified lady.
■ 12". . . . . . . . . . . . TA 4894
■ 7" . . . . . . . . . . . . .A 4894
CBS / May '85.

**SAVE THE CHILDREN.**
**Tracks:** Save the children.
■ 7" . . . . . . . . . . . . TMG 796
Tamla Motown / Dec '71.

**SEEK AND YOU SHALL FIND - MORE BEST OF MARVIN GAYE (1963-81).**
**Tracks:** Wherever I lay my hat / Get my hands on some lovin' / No good without you / You've been a long time coming / When I had your love / You're what's happening (in the world today) / Loving you is sweeter than ever / It's a bitter pill to swallow / Seek and you shall find / Gonna keep on tryin' 'till I win your love / Gonna give her all the love I've got / I wish it would rain / Abraham, Martin and John / Save the children / You sure love to ball / Ego tripping out / Praise / Heavy love affair.
CD. . . . . . . . . . . . .812271182-2
MC. . . . . . . . . . . . .812271182-4
WEA / Jun '93 / WEA.

**SEXUAL HEALING.**
**Tracks:** Sexual healing / My love is waiting / Sexual healing (instrumental).
■ 12". . . . . . . . . . . . TA 2855
■ 7" . . . . . . . . . . . . .A 2855
CBS / Oct '82.

**SEXUAL HEALING (OLD GOLD).**
**Tracks:** Sexual healing / My love is waiting.
■ 12". . . . . . . . . . . .OG 4075
Old Gold / Aug '88.
■ 7" . . . . . . . . . . . .OG 9749
Old Gold / Jan '88.
■ CD Single. . . . . . . . .OG 6158
Old Gold / Feb '92.

**TAKE THIS HEART OF MINE.**
**Tracks:** Take this heart of mine.
■ 7" . . . . . . . . . . . . TMG 563
Tamla Motown / '66.

**THAT STUBBORN KINDA FELLOW/HOW SWEET IT IS (2 Classic albums).**
**Tracks:** Stubborn kind of fellow / Pride and joy / Hitch hike / Get my hands on some lovin' / Wherever I lay my hat / Soldier's plea / It hurt me too / Taking my time / Hello there angel / I'm yours, you're mine / You're a wonderful one / How sweet it is (to be loved by you) / Try it baby / Baby don't you do it / Need your lovin' (want you back) / One of these days / No good without you / Stepping closer to your heart / Need somebody / Me and my lonely room / Now that you've won me / Forever.
■ CD . . . . . . . . . . . . ZD 72562
Motown / Jul '87.

**THAT'S THE WAY LOVE IS.**
**Tracks:** Gonna give her all the love I've got / Yesterday / Groovin' / I wish it would rain / That's the way love is / How can I forget / Abraham, Martin and John / Gonna keep on tryin' till I win your love / No time for tears / Cloud 9 / Don't you miss me a little bit baby / So long.
■ LP . . . . . . . . . . . .STML 11136
Tamla Motown / Apr '70.
■ CD . . . . . . . . . . . . WD 72736
Motown / Apr '91.
CD. . . . . . . . . . . . . 5302142
Motown / Aug '93 / PolyGram.

**TOO BUSY THINKING 'BOUT MY BABY.**
**Tracks:** Too busy thinking 'bout my baby / Wherever I lay my hat.
■ 7" . . . . . . . . . . . . TMG 705
Tamla Motown / Jul '69.

**TRIBUTE TO THE GREAT NAT KING COLE, A.**
**Tracks:** Nature boy / Ramblin' rose / Too young / Pretend / Straighten up and fly right / Mona Lisa / Unforgettable / To the ends of the earth / Sweet Lorraine / It's only a paper moon / Send for me / Calypso blues.
■ LP . . . . . . . . . . . . TML 11022
Motown / Feb '66.
■ CD . . . . . . . . . . . . WD 72210
■ MC. . . . . . . . . . . . WK 72210
Motown / Sep '91.
CD. . . . . . . . . . . . .530054-2
MC. . . . . . . . . . . . .530054-4
Motown / Jan '92 / PolyGram.

**TROUBLE MAN/M.P.G. (2 Classic Albums).**
**Tracks:** Too busy thinking about my baby / This magic moment / That's the way love is / End of our road / Seek and you shall find / Memories / Only a lonely man would know / It's a bitter pill to swallow / More than a heart can stand / Try my true love / It don't take much to keep me / I got to get to California / Trouble man / 'T' plays it cool / Poor Abbey Walsh / 'T' stands for trouble / Cleo's apartment / Life is a gamble / Don't mess with Mr. T / Deep in it / Trouble man main theme / Break in (police shoot big) / Trouble man, Theme from / There goes mister 'T' / M.P.G.
■ CD . . . . . . . . . . . . ZD 72500
Motown / Feb '87.

**UNITED (Gaye, Marvin & Tammi Terrell).**
**Tracks:** Ain't no mountain high enough / You got what it takes / If I could build my whole world around you / Something stupid / Your precious love / Hold me oh my darling / Two can have a party / Little ole boy, little ole girl / If this world were mine / Sad wedding / Give a little love / Oh how I'd miss you.
■ LP . . . . . . . . . . . .STML 11062
Tamla Motown / Jan '68.
■ LP . . . . . . . . . . . . STMS 5036
MC. . . . . . . . . . . . . CSTMS 5036
Motown / Mar '82 / PolyGram.
■ LP . . . . . . . . . . . . WL 72211
MC. . . . . . . . . . . . . WK 72211
■ CD . . . . . . . . . . . . WD 72211
Motown / Feb '88 / PolyGram.

**VERY BEST OF MARVIN GAYE,THE.**
**Tracks:** I heard it through the grapevine / Let's get it on / Too busy thinking about my baby / How sweet it is (to be loved by you) / Your all I need to get by / Got to give it up / You are everything / Midnight lady / Sexual healing / Whats going on / Abraham, Martin and John / It takes two / Stop, look, listen (to your heart) / My love is waiting / Onion song / Wherever I lay my hat.
■ CD . . . . . . . . . . . . TCD 2234
Telstar/Ronco / Jul '86.

**WHAT'S GOING ON.**
**Tracks:** What's going on / God is love.
■ 7" . . . . . . . . . . . . TMG 775
Tamla Motown / May '71.

**WHAT'S GOING ON/LET'S GET IT ON.**
**Tracks:** What's going on / What's happening brother / Flying high / Save the children / God is love / Mercy mercy me / Right on / Wholly holy / Inner city blues / Let's get it on / Please don't stay (once you go away) / If I should die tonight / Keep gettin' it on / Come get to this / Distant lover / Sure love to ball / Just to keep you satisfied.
■ CD . . . . . . . . . . . . ZD 72456
Motown / Nov '86.

**WHAT'S GOING ON?.**
**Tracks:** What's going on / What's happening brother / Flyin' high / Save the children / God is love / Mercy mercy me / Right on / Wholly holy / Inner city blues.
■ LP . . . . . . . . . . . .STML 11190
Tamla Motown / Oct '71.
■ LP . . . . . . . . . . . . WL 72611
■ CD . . . . . . . . . . . . WD 72611
■ MC. . . . . . . . . . . . WK 72611
Motown / Apr '88.

**WHAT'S GOING ON?.**
**Tracks:** What's going on / I heard it through the grapevine / Wherever I lay my hat (on 12" only).
■ 7" . . . . . . . . . . . . TMG 987
Tamla Motown / Sep '75.

**WORLD IS X-RATED.**
**Tracks:** World is rated X / Lonely lover / World is rated X (instrumental) (On 12"version only.).
■ 12". . . . . . . . . . . . ZT 40758
■ 7" . . . . . . . . . . . . ZB 40758
Motown / Jun '86.

**YOU AIN'T LIVIN' UNTIL YOU'RE LOVIN' (Gaye, Marvin & Tammi Terrell).**
**Tracks:** You ain't livin' till you're lovin' / Easiest way to fall.
■ 7" . . . . . . . . . . . . TMG 681
Tamla Motown / Dec '69.

**YOU ARE EVERYTHING (see under Ross, Diana).**

**YOU'RE ALL I NEED (Gaye, Marvin & Tammi Terrell).**
**Tracks:** Ain't nothing like the real thing / Keep on lovin' me, honey / You're all I need to get by / Baby dontcha worry / You ain't livin' till you're lovin' / Give in, you just can't win / When love comes knocking at my heart / I can't help but love you / That's how it is (since you've been gone) / I'll never stop loving you, baby / Memory chest.
■ LP . . . . . . . . . . . .STML 11084
Tamla Motown / Nov '68.
■ LP . . . . . . . . . . . . STMS 5005

162 ■ DELETED

■ MC. . . . . . . . . . . . . . . . . . **CSTMS 5005**
Motown / Oct '81.
■ **CD** . . . . . . . . . . . . . . . . . . . **WD 72208**
■ MC. . . . . . . . . . . . . . . . . . . **WK 72208**
Motown / May '91.
**CD** . . . . . . . . . . . . . . . . . . . **530 216-2**
Polydor / Sep '93 / PolyGram.

### YOU'RE ALL I NEED TO GET BY (Gaye, Marvin & Tammi Terrell).
**Tracks:** You're all I need to get by / Two can have a party.
■ **7"** . . . . . . . . . . . . . . . . . . . **TMG 668**
Tamla Motown / Oct '81.

### YOUR UNCHANGING LOVE.
**Tracks:** Your unchanging love / I'll take good care of you.
■ **7"** . . . . . . . . . . . . . . . . . . . **TMG 618**
Tamla Motown / Aug '67.

## Gayle, Michelle

### LOOKING UP.
**Tracks:** Looking up.
■ **12"** . . . . . . . . . . . . . . . .74321 15453-1
■ **7"** . . . . . . . . . . . . . . . . .74321 15453-7
■ **CD Single** . . . . . . . . . . . .74321 15453-2
■ **MC Single**. . . . . . . . . . . .74321 15454-4
RCA / Jul '93.

### SWEETNESS.
**Tracks:** Sweetness (Mixes).
**12"** . . . . . . . . . . . . . . . 7432123019-1
**7"** . . . . . . . . . . . . . . . . 7432123019-7
**CD Single** . . . . . . . . . . . 7432123019-2
**MC Single** . . . . . . . . . . . 7432123019-4
RCA / Sep '94 / BMG.

### WALK WITH PRIDE.
**Tracks:** Get off my back / Happy just to be with you / Walk with pride / Looking up / Girlfriend / Freedom / Personality / It doesn't matter / Your love / Sweetness / One day / Say what's on your mind / Rise up / Baby don't go / All night long.
**CD** . . . . . . . . . . . . . . . . .74321 23412-2
**MC** . . . . . . . . . . . . . . . . .74321 23412-4
RCA / Oct '94 / BMG.

## Gaynor, Gloria

### AIN'T NO BIGGER FOOL.
**Tracks:** Ain't no bigger fool / Don't read me wrong.
■ **12"** . . . . . . . . . . . . . . . . . 214 125 9
■ **7"** . . . . . . . . . . . . . . . . . 209 524 1
Polydor / Jun '80.

### BE SOFT WITH ME TONIGHT.
**Tracks:** Be soft with me tonight / Be soft with me tonight (club mix) / If only you'd believe it / If only you'd believe it (inst).
■ **CD Single** . . . . . . . . . . . . . . .CDFAN 11
Fanfare / Apr '87.

### BE SOFT WITH ME TONIGHT.
**Tracks:** Be soft with me tonight.
■ **12"** . . . . . . . . . . . . . . . . . BCM 12554
■ **7"** . . . . . . . . . . . . . . . . . . BCM 7554
■ **CD Single** . . . . . . . . . . . . BCM 720554
BCM / Jun '92.

### BEST OF GLORIA GAYNOR.
**Tracks:** Never can say goodbye / Reach out / Casanova Brown / We can start all over again / I've got you under my skin / Do it yourself / Honey bee / All I need is your sweet lovin' / Be mine / Most of all / Walk on by / How high the moon.
■ **LP** . . . . . . . . . . . . . . . . . . 2391312
Spring / Nov '77.

### COLLECTION: GLORIA GAYNOR.
**Tracks:** Not Advised.
■ **CD** . . . . . . . . . . . . . . . . . .CCSCD 340
■ **MC** . . . . . . . . . . . . . . . . . .CCSMC 340
Castle Collector Series / Jun '92.

### EVERY BREATH YOU TAKE.
**Tracks:** Every breath you take / Don't dare call it love.
■ **12"** . . . . . . . . . . . . . . . . . HONEY 1 12
■ **7"** . . . . . . . . . . . . . . . . . . HONEY 1
Stylus / Jun '86.

### GLORIA GAYNOR (ECSTASY).
**Tracks:** Runaround love / Mack side / Stop in the name of love / Tease me / America / For you my love / Love me real / Even a fool would let go.
■ **LP** . . . . . . . . . . . . . . . . . . . XTLP 1
**MC**. . . . . . . . . . . . . . . . . . . XTCC 1
Ecstasy / Nov '83.

### GLORIA GAYNOR (POLYDOR).
**Tracks:** Let me know (I have a right) / Say somethin' / You took me in again / Don't stop us / Tonight / Can't fight the feelin' / Midnight rocker / One number one.
■ **LP** . . . . . . . . . . . . . . . . . . 2391426
Polydor / Nov '79.

### GLORIA GAYNOR - THE HITS.
**Tracks:** Not Advised.
**CD** . . . . . . . . . . . . . . . . .OVCCD 003
**MC** . . . . . . . . . . . . . . . . .OVCC 003
Satellite Music / Mar '94 / THE.

### GLORIOUS.
**Tracks:** Why should I pay / As time goes by / Hands of time / Most of all / We can start all over again / Sweet sweet melody / Life ain't worth living / This side of the pain / So much love.
■ **LP** . . . . . . . . . . . . . . . . . . 2391264
Polydor / May '77.

### GREATEST HITS: GLORIA GAYNOR.
**Tracks:** I will survive / Never can say goodbye / Reach out I'll be there / Casanova Brown / We can start all over again / I've got you under my skin / If you want it / Do it yourself / Let me know (I have a right) / Honeybee / All I need is your sweet lovin' / Be mine / Most of all / Walk on by / How high the moon.
■ **LP** . . . . . . . . . . . . . . . . . 248 257 3
**MC**. . . . . . . . . . . . . . . . . 319 257 3
Polydor / Jun '82 / PolyGram.

### HEART AND SOUL OF GLORIA GAYNOR.
**Tracks:** Never can say goodbye / All I need is your sweet lovin' / Anybody wanna party / Let's mend what's been broken / Ain't no bigger fool / Substitute / Reach out (I'll be there) / How the moon / Honey bee / Walk on by / Let's make a deal / (If you want it) do it yourself / Let me know (I have a right) / I will survive.
■ **CD** . . . . . . . . . . . . . . . . KNCD 12058
■ **MC** . . . . . . . . . . . . . . . KNMC 12058
Knight / Jul '91.

### HIT COLLECTION.
**Tracks:** Not Advised.
**CD** . . . . . . . . . . . . . . . . . . . 30824
Scratch / Oct '94 / Scratch Records / BMG / Grapevine Distribution.

### HONEY BEE.
**Tracks:** Honey bee / Come tonight.
■ **7"** . . . . . . . . . . . . . . . . . . . 2006419
MGM (Polydor) / Jun '74.

### HOW HIGH THE MOON.
**Tracks:** How high the moon / My man's gone.
■ **7"** . . . . . . . . . . . . . . . . . .2006 558
MGM (Polydor) / Jan '76.

### I AM GLORIA GAYNOR.
**Tracks:** I am what I am / Chain of whispers / Strive eeny meeny macker rack / Bullseye / Only in a love song / I've been watching you / More than enough.
■ **LP** . . . . . . . . . . . . . . . . . CHR 1466
■ **MC** . . . . . . . . . . . . . . . . ZCHR 1466
Chrysalis / Mar '84.

### I AM WHAT I AM.
**Tracks:** I am what I am / More than enough.
■ **12"** . . . . . . . . . . . . . . . CHS 122765
■ **7"** . . . . . . . . . . . . . . . . . CHS 2765
Chrysalis / Dec '83.

### I KINDA LIKE ME.
**Tracks:** I kinda like me / Fingers in the fire / Let's mend what's been broken / Yesterday we were like buddies / I can stand the pain / I love you 'cause / When you get around to it / Chasin' me into somebody else's arms / Story of the Jones.
■ **LP** . . . . . . . . . . . . . . . . .2391 514
Polydor / Jun '81.

### I WILL SURVIVE.
**Tracks:** I will survive.
■ **7"** . . . . . . . . . . . . . . . . . . 2059017
Polydor / Jan '79.
■ **7"** . . . . . . . . . . . . . . . . . .A 1772
CBS / Nov '81.
■ **12"** . . . . . . . . . . . . . . . . .PZ 270
■ **7"** . . . . . . . . . . . . . . . . . .PO 270
■ **CD Single** . . . . . . . . . . . .PZCD 270
■ **MC Single**. . . . . . . . . . . .POCS 270
Polydor / Jun '93.

### I WILL SURVIVE.
**Tracks:** I will survive / Honey Bee.
■ **12"** . . . . . . . . . . . . . . . POSPX 600
Polydor / Oct '82.
■ **12"** . . . . . . . . . . . . . . . .887036 1
Polydor (Holland) / Sep '87.

### I WILL SURVIVE.
**Tracks:** Not Advised.
**CD** . . . . . . . . . . . . . . . . . . . LECD 441
Stardust / Aug '93 / Pickwick / Conifer Records.

### I WILL SURVIVE.
**Tracks:** Not Advised.
**CD** . . . . . . . . . . . . . . . . . . .LMCD 001
Wisepack / Sep '93 / THE / Conifer Records.

### I WILL SURVIVE (2ND RE-ISSUE).
**Tracks:** I will survive / Never can say goodbye / Honey Bee (Only on 12" single.) / Reach out (I'll be there) (Only on 12" single.)
■ **12"** . . . . . . . . . . . . . . . POSPX 766
■ **7"** . . . . . . . . . . . . . . . . POSP 766
Polydor / Sep '84.

### I WILL SURVIVE (OLD GOLD).
**Tracks:** I will survive / Never can say goodbye.
■ **7"** . . . . . . . . . . . . . . . . .OG 9436
Old Gold / Jun '88.
**12"** . . . . . . . . . . . . . . . . .OG 4166
Old Gold / May '90 / Pickwick.
■ **CD Single** . . . . . . . . . . . .OG 6162
Old Gold / Feb '92.

### I WILL SURVIVE - THE BEST OF GLORIA GAYNOR.
**Tracks:** I will survive (Original version) / Honey bee / Never can say goodbye / Reach out (I'll be there) / Let me know (I have a right) / How high the moon / Casanova Brown / (If you want it) Do it yourself / I am what I am / All I need is your sweet lovin' / Walk on by / We can start all over again / Let's mend what's been broken / I will survive (Classic 12" mix).
**CD** . . . . . . . . . . . . . . . . . . 5196652
**MC** . . . . . . . . . . . . . . . . . . 5196654
Polydor / Jul '93 / PolyGram.

### LET ME KNOW (I HAVE THE RIGHT).
**Tracks:** Let me know (I have the right) / One number one.
■ **7"** . . . . . . . . . . . . . . . . . . STEP 5
Polydor / Oct '79.

### LET'S MEND WHAT'S BEEN BROKEN.
**Tracks:** Let's mend what's been broken / I love you cause.
■ **7"** . . . . . . . . . . . . . . . . . . POSP 34
Polydor / Jul '81.

### LOVE ME REAL.
**Tracks:** Love me real / America.
■ **12"** . . . . . . . . . . . . . . . . . XTCT 4
■ **7"** . . . . . . . . . . . . . . . . . . XTC 4
Ecstasy / Sep '83.

### LOVE TRACKS.
**Tracks:** Stoplight / Anybody wanna party / Please, be there / Goin' out of my head / I will survive / You can exit / I said yes / Substitute.
■ **LP** . . . . . . . . . . . . . . . . .2391 385
Polydor / Mar '79.

### MOST OF ALL.
**Tracks:** Most of all / So much love.
■ **7"** . . . . . . . . . . . . . . . . .2066 804
Polydor / May '77.

### MY LOVE IS MUSIC.
**Tracks:** My love is music / If I need you.
■ **12"** . . . . . . . . . . . . . . . . .CART 357
■ **7"** . . . . . . . . . . . . . . . . . .CAR 357
Carrere / Mar '85.

### NEVER CAN SAY GOODBYE.
**Tracks:** Honey bee / Never can say goodbye / Reach out and touch / I'll be there / All I need is your sweet lovin' / Searchin' / We belong together / False alarm / Real good people.
■ **LP** . . . . . . . . . . . . . . . . .2315 321
MGM (Polydor) / Mar '75.
■ **LP** . . . . . . . . . . . . . . . . .2482 476
Polydor / Oct '80.

### NEVER CAN SAY GOODBYE.
**Tracks:** Never can say goodbye.
■ **7"** . . . . . . . . . . . . . . . . .2006 463
MGM (Polydor) / '74.

### POWER OF,THE.
**Tracks:** Don't you dare call it love / Eye of the tiger / Heat is on / Every breath you take / Feel so real / Broken wings / Power of love.
■ **CD** . . . . . . . . . . . . . . . . . SMD 618
■ **Double LP** . . . . . . . . . . . . SMR 618
■ **MC Set** . . . . . . . . . . . . . . SMC 618
Stylus / Jan '86.

### REACH OUT.
**Tracks:** Reach out. I'll be there / Can't fight the feelin' / How high the moon / Tonight / Don't stop us / One number one / This love affair / I've got you

under my skin / Substitute / Anybody wanna party /
Let me know (I have a right) / Honey bee / Goin' out
of my head.
CD . . . . . . . . . . . . . . . . . . . . . . . . . . . .550201-2
MC . . . . . . . . . . . . . . . . . . . . . . . . . . . .550201-2
Spectrum (1) / Mar '94 / PolyGram.

### REACH OUT I'LL BE THERE.
Tracks: Reach out I'll be there.
■ 7" . . . . . . . . . . . . . . . . . . . . . . . . . . .2006 531
MGM (Polydor) / Mar '75.

### STORIES.
Tracks: Ain't no bigger fool / I let love slip right
through my hands / On a diet of you / Lock me up /
All my life / Don't read me wrong / Luckiest girl in
the world / Make me yours.
■ LP . . . . . . . . . . . . . . . . . . . . . . . . . . .2391 457
Polydor / Aug '80.

### STRIVE.
Tracks: Strive / I've been waiting for you.
■ 12" . . . . . . . . . . . . . . . . . . . . . . . . . . . GAYX 1
■ 7" . . . . . . . . . . . . . . . . . . . . . . . . . . . . GAY 1
Chrysalis / Mar '84.

### THIS LOVE AFFAIR.
Tracks: This love affair / For the first time.
■ 7" . . . . . . . . . . . . . . . . . . . . . . . . . . . 2066922
Polydor / Jun '78.

### TONIGHT.
Tracks: Tonight / Say something.
■ 12" . . . . . . . . . . . . . . . . . . . . . . . . . . STEPX 8
■ 7" . . . . . . . . . . . . . . . . . . . . . . . . . . . STEP 8
Polydor / Nov '79.

## Gaz

### SING SING.
Tracks: Sing sing / Good, the bad and the ugly.
■ 7" . . . . . . . . . . . . . . . . . . . . . . . . . . SSOL 116
Salsoul / Feb '79.

## Gemini

### ANOTHER YOU ANOTHER ME.
Tracks: Another you another me / Falling / Copy love
(On 12" version only.).
■ 12" . . . . . . . . . . . . . . . . . . . . . . . . POSPX 795
■ 7" . . . . . . . . . . . . . . . . . . . . . . . . . POSP 795
Polydor / Oct '86.

### GEMINI.
Tracks: Not Advised.
■ LP . . . . . . . . . . . . . . . . . . . . . . . . . POLD 5189
■ MC . . . . . . . . . . . . . . . . . . . . . . . . POLDC 5189
■ CD . . . . . . . . . . . . . . . . . . . . . . . . 829 064-2
Polydor / Oct '86.

### JUST LIKE THAT.
Tracks: Just like that / Live on the love.
■ 12" . . . . . . . . . . . . . . . . . . . . . . . . POSPX 782
■ 7" . . . . . . . . . . . . . . . . . . . . . . . . . POSP 782
Polydor / Mar '86.

### SOMETHING BEAUTIFUL.
Tracks: Something beautiful / Very last time.
■ 7" . . . . . . . . . . . . . . . . . . . . . . . . . 7N 45087
Pye / Aug '71.

## Gems For Jem

### GROOVE ME.
Tracks: Groove me.
■ 12" . . . . . . . . . . . . . . . . . . . . . . . . DEBTX 3129
Debut (2) / Oct '91.

### INSPIRATION.
Tracks: Not Advised.
■ 12" . . . . . . . . . . . . . . . . . . . . . . . . DEBTX 3144
Debut (1).

### LIFTING ME HIGHER.
Tracks: Lifting me higher.
12" . . . . . . . . . . . . . . . . . . . . . . . . 12 BOKS 3
CD Single . . . . . . . . . . . . . . . . . . . . CDSBOK 3
Box 21 / May '94 / 3MV.

### TIME FOR LOVE.
Tracks: Time for love.
■ 12" . . . . . . . . . . . . . . . . . . . . . . . . . EZY 1204
E-Zee / May '93.

### WE'RE ON THE MOVE.
Tracks: We're on the move.
■ 12" . . . . . . . . . . . . . . . . . . . . . . . . DEBTX 3114
Debut (2) / Jun '91.

## General Assembly

### SENSITIVE MIND (Varner, Don & General Assembly).
Tracks: Sensitive mind / Lovin' time.
■ 7" . . . . . . . . . . . . . . . . . . . . . . . . . . DES 202
Destiny (Northern Soul) / Mar '83.

## George, Leslie

### ARE YOU LISTENING.
Tracks: Are you listening.
■ 7" . . . . . . . . . . . . . . . . . . . . . . . . . . PO 263
■ CD Single . . . . . . . . . . . . . . . . . . . . PZCD 263
■ MC Single . . . . . . . . . . . . . . . . . . . POCS 263
Polydor / Aug '93.

## Georgio

### LOVER'S LANE.
Tracks: Lovers Lane / Lovers Lane (after hours mix)
/ Lovers Lane (new after hours mix) (track on 12") /
Lovers Lane (club mix) / Lovers Lane (Georgio's
love dance mix) (track on 12").
■ 12" . . . . . . . . . . . . . . . . . . . . . . . . ZT 41612
■ 7" . . . . . . . . . . . . . . . . . . . . . . . . . ZB 41611
Motown / Nov '88.

### SEXAPPEAL.
Tracks: Sexappeal / Lovers Lane / 1/4 2 9 / Menage a
trois / Tina Cherry / Hey u / I won't change.
■ MC . . . . . . . . . . . . . . . . . . . . . . . . ZK 72583
■ LP . . . . . . . . . . . . . . . . . . . . . . . . ZL 72583
Motown / Nov '87.

### SEXAPPEAL.
Tracks: Sexappeal / Sexappeal (instrumental).
■ 7" . . . . . . . . . . . . . . . . . . . . . . . . ZB 41209
■ 12" . . . . . . . . . . . . . . . . . . . . . . . ZT 41210
Motown / Mar '87.

### TINA CHERRY.
Tracks: Tina Cherry.
■ 12" . . . . . . . . . . . . . . . . . . . . . . . . ZT 41556
■ 7" . . . . . . . . . . . . . . . . . . . . . . . . . ZB 41555
Motown / Oct '87.

## Germaine, Nikita

### SWEET AS IT COMES.
Tracks: Not Advised.
■ CD . . . . . . . . . . . . . . . . . . . . . . . . .530177-2
■ MC . . . . . . . . . . . . . . . . . . . . . . . . .530177-4
Motown / Jan '92.

## Geyer, Renee

### HEADING IN THE RIGHT DIRECTION.
Tracks: Heading in the right direction / Moving
along.
■ 7" . . . . . . . . . . . . . . . . . . . . . . . . .206 6802
Polydor / Aug '77.

### SAY I LOVE YOU.
Tracks: Say I love you / Good lovin'.
■ 12" . . . . . . . . . . . . . . . . . . . . . . . A 13 2056
■ 7" . . . . . . . . . . . . . . . . . . . . . . . . . A 2056
CBS / Apr '82.

### SING TO ME.
Tracks: Without love / All my love / Woman in love /
Everyday of the week / Sing to me / Telling it like this
/ Fever / Guess who I saw today / Faithful love /
Memory.
■ LP . . . . . . . . . . . . . . . . . . . . . . . .252139 1
WEA / '85.

## Gibson, Anthony T.

### COMPLETE ANTHONY T. GIBSON, THE.
Tracks: Aint no way / Say it isn't so / Special kinda
woman / My heart is in your hands / Sitting in the
park / I want a lover / Is it for real / Girl on
the sidelines / Is it for real / Take the money and run
/ At this moment / Searching for romance.
CD . . . . . . . . . . . . . . . . . . . . . . . . AT CD-016
About Time / Apr '93 / BMG.

## Gibson Brothers

### CUBA.
Tracks: Cuba / Oh what a life / West Indies / Better
do it Salsa / You / Que sera mi vida.
■ LP . . . . . . . . . . . . . . . . . . . . . . . . ILPS 9579
Island / Jul '79.
■ MC . . . . . . . . . . . . . . . . . . . . . . . . ICT 9579
Island / May '81.

### CUBA.
Tracks: Cuba / Better do it salsa.
■ 12" . . . . . . . . . . . . . . . . . . . . . . 12WIP 6483

Island / '79.
■ 7" . . . . . . . . . . . . . . . . . . . . . . . . WIP 6483
Island / Mar '79.
■ 7" . . . . . . . . . . . . . . . . . . . . . . . . WIP 6561
Island / Feb '80.

### CUBA (88 REMIX).
Tracks: Cuba (88 remix) / Cuba (88 remix) (versions).
■ 12" . . . . . . . . . . . . . . . . . . . . . . DEBTX 3055
■ 7" . . . . . . . . . . . . . . . . . . . . . . . DEBT 3055
Debut (1) / Sep '88.

### DEDICATED FOOL.
Tracks: Not Advised.
■ LP . . . . . . . . . . . . . . . . . . . . . . . HMS 141 1
MC . . . . . . . . . . . . . . . . . . . . . . . . HMS 141 4
Homestead / Apr '89 / SRD.

### HITS.
Tracks: Not Advised.
CD . . . . . . . . . . . . . . . . . . . . . . . . KWEST 5408
MC . . . . . . . . . . . . . . . . . . . . . . . . KWEST 4408
Disky / Feb '93 / THE.

### I LEFT MY HEART IN JAMAICA.
Tracks: I left my heart in Jamaica / Limbo.
■ 12" . . . . . . . . . . . . . . . . . . . . . . . A 132084
■ 7" . . . . . . . . . . . . . . . . . . . . . . . . .A 2084
Epic / Apr '82.

### KEEPERS.
Tracks: Keepers.
■ 7" . . . . . . . . . . . . . . . . . . . . . . . . SR 0488
Shadowline / Feb '88.

### LATIN AMERICA.
Tracks: Latin America / West Indies.
■ 12" . . . . . . . . . . . . . . . . . . . . . . 12WIP 6659
■ 7" . . . . . . . . . . . . . . . . . . . . . . . WIP 6659
Island / Oct '80.

### MARIANA.
Tracks: Mariana.
■ 7" . . . . . . . . . . . . . . . . . . . . . . . WIP 6617
Island / Jul '80.

### MEAN MISTREATER.
Tracks: Mean Mistreater.
■ 7" . . . . . . . . . . . . . . . . . . . . . . HMSJ 7047
Homestead / Nov '92.

### METROPOLIS.
Tracks: Metropolis / Because I love you.
■ 12" . . . . . . . . . . . . . . . . . . . . . . 12WIP 6640
■ 7" . . . . . . . . . . . . . . . . . . . . . . . WIP 6640
Island / Sep '80.

### MY HEART'S BEATING (TIC TAC).
Tracks: My heart's beating / Come alive and dance.
■ 12" . . . . . . . . . . . . . . . . . . . . . . .BUYIT 184
■ 7" . . . . . . . . . . . . . . . . . . . . . . . .BUY 184
Stiff / Jun '83.

### NON-STOP DANCE.
Tracks: Non-stop dance / Never said goodbye.
■ 7" . . . . . . . . . . . . . . . . . . . . . . . .2058 890
Polydor / Jun '77.

### ON THE RIVIERA.
Tracks: Metropolis / Mariana / All I ever want is you /
Good girl bad boy / Latin America / Dancin' the
mambo / Fly away.
MC . . . . . . . . . . . . . . . . . . . . . . . . ZCI 9620
■ LP . . . . . . . . . . . . . . . . . . . . . . . ILPS 9620
Island / Aug '80 / PolyGram.

### OOH WHAT A LIFE.
Tracks: Ooh What a life / You.
■ 12" . . . . . . . . . . . . . . . . . . . . . 12XWIP 6503
■ 7" . . . . . . . . . . . . . . . . . . . . . . . WIP 6503
Island / Jul '79.

### PARTY TONIGHT.
Tracks: Party tonight / B'Lola.
■ 12" . . . . . . . . . . . . . . . . . . . . . . MKHAN 68
■ 7" . . . . . . . . . . . . . . . . . . . . . . . KHAN 68
Streetwave / Jul '86.

### QUARTIER LATIN.
Tracks: Quartier latin / Limbo / I left my heart in
Jamaica / Sheela / 'A' train to Bombay / Caribbean
concerto / Paranoi / I, I, I love you / Baisers sales.
■ LP . . . . . . . . . . . . . . . . . . . . . . . EPC 85468
Epic / Mar '82.

### QUARTIER LATIN.
Tracks: Quartier latin / I-I-I-love you.
■ 7" . . . . . . . . . . . . . . . . . . . . . . . EPCA 1843
Epic / Dec '81.

### QUE SERA MI VIDA '89'.
Tracks: Que sera mi vida '89'.
■ 12" . . . . . . . . . . . . . . . . . . . . . . DEBTX 3070

■ DELETED

■ **7"** . . . . . . . . . . . . . . . . . . . . **DEBT 3070**
Debut (1) / May '89.

## QUE SERA MI VIDA (IF YOU SHOULD GO).
**Tracks:** Que sera mi vida.
■ **7"** . . . . . . . . . . . . . . . . . . . . **WIP 6525**
Island / Nov '79.

# Gil, Gilberto

## ACOUSTIC.
**Tracks:** Not Advised.
**CD** . . . . . . . . . . . . . . . . . . .**450995324-2**
Warner Bros. / May '94 / WEA.

## MINHA IDEOLOGIA NOITE NEON.
**Tracks:** Minha ideologia, minha religiao / Nos barracos da cidade (barracos) / Roque santeiro, o rock / Seu Olhar / Febril / Touches pas mon pote / Logos versus logo / Oracao pela libertacao da Africa do sul / Cliche do cliche / Casinha feliz / Duas luas.
■ **LP** . . . . . . . . . . . . . . . . . . .**253045 1**
WEA / Jul '86.

## NIGHTINGALE.
**Tracks:** Sarara / Goodbye my girl / Ella / Here and now / Balaforn / Alapala / Maracatus Atomico / Move along with me / Nightingale / Samba de Los Angeles.
■ **LP** . . . . . . . . . . . . . . . . . . . **K 52120**
Elektra / '79.

## O ETERNO DEUS MU DANCA.
**Tracks:** Not Advised.
■ **LP** . . . . . . . . . . . . . . . . . . . **2566201**
■ **MC** . . . . . . . . . . . . . . . . . . . **2566204**
WEA / Sep '89.

## ORIENTE - LIVE IN TOKYO.
**Tracks:** Not Advised.
**CD** . . . . . . . . . . . . . . . . . . . **WW 2211**
West Wind / Feb '93 / Swift / Charly / Koch International / Complete Record Co. Ltd / C.M. Distribution.

## PALCO.
**Tracks:** Palco / Samba de Los Angeles.
■ **7"** . . . . . . . . . . . . . . . . . . . **K 79285**
WEA / Mar '82.

## PARABOLICAMARA.
**Tracks:** Madalena / Parabolicamara / Un sonho / Buda nago / Serafim / Quero seu funk / Neve na bahia / Ya olokum / O fim da historia / De onde vem o baiao / Falso toureiro / Sina.
**CD** . . . . . . . . . . . . **9031762922**
WEA / Mar '92 / WEA.

## RACA HUMANA.
**Tracks:** Extra II / Felix por um triz / Pessoa nefasta / Tempo rei / Vamos fugir / A mao da limpeza / Indigo blue / Vem morena / A raca humana.
■ **LP** . . . . . . . . . . . . . . . . . . .**252112 1**
WEA / Sep '85.

## SOUNDS OF BRAZIL.
**Tracks:** Not Advised.
**CD** . . . . . . . . . . . . . . . . . . . **SOW 90121**
Sounds Of The World / Jun '94 / BMG.

## SOY LOCO POR.
**Tracks:** Not Advised.
■ **LP** . . . . . . . . . . . . . . . . . . . **BR 4000**
Braziloid / May '88.

## TODA MENINA BAINA.
**Tracks:** Toda menina baina / Dono do pedaco.
■ **12"** . . . . . . . . . . . . . . . . . . . **U 9451 T**
■ **7"** . . . . . . . . . . . . . . . . . . .**U 9451**
WEA / Jul '85.

## TOUCHES PAS MON POTE.
**Tracks:** Toda menina baina / Polco (Extra track on 12" version only) / Touches pas mon pote.
■ **7"** . . . . . . . . . . . . . . . . . . .**U 8623**
■ **12"** . . . . . . . . . . . . . . . . . . . **U 8623T**
WEA / Jun '86.

# Giles, Donna

## AND I'M TELLING YOU I'M NOT GOING.
**Tracks:** And I'm telling you I'm not going (mixes).
**12"** . . . . . . . . . . . . . . . . . . . **CLUBA 011**
Club Vision / Apr '94 / Vital Distribution.
**12"** . . . . . . . . . . . . . . . . . . . **AG 4**
**CD Single** . . . . . . . . . . . . . . . . . **AG 4CD**
**MC Single** . . . . . . . . . . . . . . . . . **AG 4C**
Ore / Aug '94 / WEA.

# Giles, Eddie

## THAT'S HOW STRONG MY LOVE IS.
**Tracks:** That's how strong my love is / Nothing takes the place of you.
■ **7"** . . . . . . . . . . . . . . . . . . .**CTD 124**
Charly / Jul '80.

# Gill, Johnny

Bobby Brown's replacement in New Edition, Gill went on to establish successful solo career. Signed to Motown, he supported Janet Jackson on her international *Rhythm Nation* tour, appeared on *New Jack City* soundtrack and was able to call on superstar producers such as Jam & Lewis for 1993's *Provocative*. Collaboration with Shabba Ranks, *Slow And Sexy*, yielded U.K. Top 20 hit in '92.

## CUTE SWEET LOVE ADDICTION.
**Tracks:** Cute sweet love addiction.
■ **CD Single** . . . . . . . . . . **TMGCD 1420**
■ **MC Single** . . . . . . . . . . **TMGCS 1420**
■ **12"** . . . . . . . . . . . . . . . **TMGX 1420**
■ **7"** . . . . . . . . . . . . . . . .**TMG 1420**
Motown / Dec '93.

## JOHNNY GILL.
**Tracks:** Rub you the right way / Wrap my body tight / Never know love / Lady Dujour / Giving my all to you / My my my (reprise) / Fairweather friend / Feels so much better / My my my / Just another lonely night / Let's spend the night / Wrap my body tight (Jazzie B 12" remake version) (Only on CD and cassette.) / My my my (live) (Only on CD and cassette).
■ **MC** . . . . . . . . . . . . . . . . **ZK 72698**
■ **CD** . . . . . . . . . . . . . . . . **ZD 72698**
■ **LP** . . . . . . . . . . . . . . . . **ZL 72698**
Motown / May '90.
■ **CD** . . . . . . . . . . . . . . . . **ZD 72747**
■ **MC** . . . . . . . . . . . . . . . . **ZK 72747**
Motown / May '91.
**CD** . . . . . . . . . . . . . . . . . **530025-2**
**MC** . . . . . . . . . . . . . . . . . **530025-4**
Motown / Jan '92 / PolyGram.

## PERFECT COMBINATION (see under Lattisaw, Stacy).

## PROVOCATIVE.
**Tracks:** Not Advised.
**CD** . . . . . . . . . . . . . . . . . . . **530206-2**
**MC** . . . . . . . . . . . . . . . . . . . **530206-4**
■ **LP** . . . . . . . . . . . . . . . . . . . **530206-1**
Motown / Jan '93 / PolyGram.

## VIDEO HITS.
**Tracks:** Rub you the right way / My, my, my / Fairweather friend / Wrap my body tight / Floor.
**VHS** . . . . . . . . . . . . . . . . . **087 740 3**
Polygram Music Video / Aug '93 / PolyGram.

## WHERE DO WE GO FROM HERE (see under Lattisaw, Stacy).

# Gilliam, Roberta

## ALL I WANT IS MY BABY.
**Tracks:** All I want is my baby.
■ **7"** . . . . . . . . . . . . . . . . . . .**U 8828**
■ **12"** . . . . . . . . . . . . . . . . . . . **U 8828T**
WEA / Jan '86.

# Gilstrap, Jim

## SWING YOUR DADDY.
**Tracks:** Not Advised.
**CD** . . . . . . . . . . . . . . . . **CHELD 1005**
■ **LP** . . . . . . . . . . . . . . . **CHELV 1005**
**MC** . . . . . . . . . . . . . . . **CHELC 1005**
Start / May '89 / THE / Koch International.

## SWING YOUR DADDY.
**Tracks:** Swing your daddy (2 pts).
■ **7"** . . . . . . . . . . . . . . . . . .**2005 021**
Chelsea Collection / Mar '75.

## SWING YOUR DADDY (OLD GOLD).
**Tracks:** Swing your daddy / I'm doin' fine now.
■ **7"** . . . . . . . . . . . . . . . . . . .**OG 9886**
Old Gold / Apr '89.

# Girault, Martine

## REVIVAL.
**Tracks:** Revival / Revival (mixes).
■ **12"** . . . . . . . . . . . . . . . . . .**FX 195**
■ **CD Single** . . . . . . . . . . . . . . . . **FCD 195**
FFRR / Aug '92.

■ **12"** . . . . . . . . . . . . . . . . . . .**FX 205**
■ **7"** . . . . . . . . . . . . . . . . . . .**F 205**
■ **CD Single** . . . . . . . . . . . . . . . **FCD 205**
■ **MC Single** . . . . . . . . . . . . . . . **FCS 205**
FFRR / Jan '93.

# Giscombe, Junior

Norman Giscombe came to fame in 1982, known simply as Junior, with *Mama Used To Say*. Having initially flopped in '81, it hit U.S./U.K. charts following year. *Ji* album was another U.K. success, but he did not return to upper reaches of chart until '87 duet with Kim Wilde, *Another Step*. Stateside success was also low-key, although he did collaborate with obvious influence Stevie Wonder. Having moved into production, Junior is best-remembered for Grammy-winning debut, latterly sampled by Jungle Brothers and Warren G.

## ACQUIRED TASTE.
**Tracks:** Stone lover / Somebody / Not tonight / Oh Louise / Thing called love / Do you really want my love / Look what you've done to me / Come on over / Together.
■ **LP** . . . . . . . . . . . . . . . . . .**LONLP 14**
**MC.** . . . . . . . . . . . . . . . . . .**LONC 14**
■ **CD** . . . . . . . . . . . . . . . . . . .**LONCD 14**
London / Mar '86 / PolyGram.

## ALL OVER THE WORLD.
**Tracks:** All over the world.
■ **12"** . . . . . . . . . . . . . . . . . **MCST 1691**
■ **7"** . . . . . . . . . . . . . . . . **MCS 1691**
■ **CD Single** . . . . . . . . . . . **MCSTD 1691**
■ **MC Single** . . . . . . . . . . . . **MCSC 1691**
MCA / Oct '92.

## COME ON OVER.
**Tracks:** Mama used To Say / Come on over.
■ **12"** . . . . . . . . . . . . . . . . . **LONX 84**
■ **7"** . . . . . . . . . . . . . . . . . **LON 84**
London / Jan '86.

## COMMUNICATION BREAKDOWN.
**Tracks:** Communication breakdown.
■ **12"** . . . . . . . . . . . . . . . . .**MERX 134**
■ **7"** . . . . . . . . . . . . . . . . . **MER 134**
Mercury / Apr '83.

## DO YOU REALLY WANT MY LOVE.
**Tracks:** Do you really want my love.
■ **12"** . . . . . . . . . . . . . . . . . **LONX 60**
■ **7"** . . . . . . . . . . . . . . . . . **LON 60**
London / Jan '85.

## EXCUSE ME.
**Tracks:** Excuse me / Was that love.
■ **7"** . . . . . . . . . . . . . . . . . **RCA 2545**
RCA / Jun '75.

## HIGH LIFE.
**Tracks:** High life / Right back at the start / High life (full length version) (12" version only).
■ **12"** . . . . . . . . . . . . . . . . . **LONX 194**
■ **7"** . . . . . . . . . . . . . . . . .**LON 194**
London / Aug '88.

## INSIDE LOOKIN' OUT.
**Tracks:** Communication breakdown / Woman say it / Sayin' something / Baby I want you back / You're the one / Storyteller / F.B. eye / Runnin' / Tell me.
■ **LP** . . . . . . . . . . . . . . . . . . . **MERS 20**
**MC.** . . . . . . . . . . . . . . . . . . **MERSC 20**
Mercury / Jun '83 / PolyGram.

## JI.
**Tracks:** Mama used to say / Love dies / Too late / Is this love / Let me know / Down down / I can't help it / Darling you.
■ **LP** . . . . . . . . . . . . . . . . . . . **MERS 3**
Mercury / Jun '82.

## LET ME KNOW.
**Tracks:** Let me know / I can't help it.
■ **12"** . . . . . . . . . . . . . . . . . .**MERX 116**
■ **7"** . . . . . . . . . . . . . . . . . **MER 116**
Mercury / Sep '82.

## MAMA USED TO SAY.
**Tracks:** Too late.
■ **12"** . . . . . . . . . . . . . . . . . **MERX 80**
■ **7"** . . . . . . . . . . . . . . . . . **MER 80**
Mercury / Sep '81.

## MAMA USED TO SAY.
**Tracks:** Mama used to say (re-issue).
■ **12"** . . . . . . . . . . . . . . . . . **MERX 98**
■ **7"** . . . . . . . . . . . . . . . . . **MER 98**
Mercury / Oct '84.

## MAMA USED TO SAY (OLD GOLD).
Tracks: Mama used to say / Mama used to say (part 2) / Too late.
■ 12" .................................. OG 4241
■ CD Single .......................... OG 4241
Pickwick / Oct '92.

## MORNING WILL COME.
Tracks: Morning will come.
■ 12" Remix ................... MCSX 1504
■ 12" ............................... MCST 1504
■ 7" ................................... MCS 1504
■ CD Single ...................... MCSTD 1504
MCA / Jan '91.

## OH LOUISE.
Tracks: Oh Louise.
■ 12" ............................... LONX 75
■ 7" ................................... LON 75
London / Nov '85.

## RENEWAL.
Tracks: Then came you / Never gonna let you walk away / Morning will come / Stop fanning the fire / Why / You can't have what you can't get / All over the world / Step off / Stand strong / You don't have to look / Now that we're here / Morning will come (reprise).
■ LP ................................. MCA 10688
■ MC ............................... MCC 10688
■ CD ............................... MCD 10688
MCA / Nov '92.

## RUNNIN'.
Tracks: Runnin' / Women say it.
■ 7" ................................... MER 145
■ 12" ............................... MERX 145
Mercury / Aug '83.

## SOMEBODY.
Tracks: Somebody.
■ 12" ............................... LONX 50
■ 7" ................................... LON 50
London / Jul '84.

## SOPHISTICATED STREET.
Tracks: Whodunnit / Right back at the start / Yes (if you want me) / It's true what some say / That's love / Living in the right way / Say that you care / High life / I'll get over you / If ever.
■ CD ............................... 828 093 2
■ LP ............................... LONLP 53
■ MC ............................... LONC 53
London / Jun '88.

## STAND STRONG.
Tracks: Not Advised.
■ CD ............................... DMCG 6105
■ LP ............................... MCG 6105
■ MC ............................... MCGC 6105
MCA / Sep '90.

## STAND STRONG.
Tracks: Stand strong / Stand strong (version).
■ 12" Remix ................... MCAX 1454
■ 12" ............................... MCAT 1454
■ 7" ................................... MCA 1454
■ CD Single ...................... DMCAT 1454
■ MC Single ...................... MCAC 1454
MCA / Oct '90.

## STEP OFF.
Tracks: Step off.
■ 12" ............................... MCAT 1432
■ 12" Remix ................... MCAX 1432
■ 7" ................................... MCA 1432
■ CD Single ...................... DMCAT 1432
■ MC Single ...................... MCAC 1432
MCA / Jul '90.

## THEN CAME YOU.
Tracks: Then came you.
■ 12" ............................... MCST 1676
■ 7" ................................... MCS 1676
■ CD Single ...................... MCSTD 1676
■ MC Single ...................... MCSC 1676
MCA / Aug '92.

## TOO LATE.
Tracks: Too late / In words.
■ 12" ............................... MERX 112
■ 7" ................................... MER 112
Mercury / Jun '82.

## YES (IF YOU WANT ME).
Tracks: Yes (if you want me) / Not tonight.
■ 12" ............................... LONX 149
■ 7" ................................... LON 149
London / Jul '87.

## Glass House

### CRUMBS OFF THE TABLE.
Tracks: Crumbs off the table / Bad bill of goods.
■ 7" ............................... HDH 458
HDH / Dec '84.

### CRUMBS OFF THE TABLE.
Tracks: Crumbs off the table / If it ain't love (it don't matter) / Touch me Jesus / I surrendered / You ain't livin' (unless you're lovin') / Stealing moments (from another woman's life) / Let it flow / Giving up the flow / Thanks I needed that / I don't see me in your eyes anymore / Hotel / I can't be you, you can't be me / He's in my life / V.I.P. / Look what we've done to love / Heaven is there to guide us / Don't go looking for something (you don't want to see).
■ CD ............................... HDHCD 505
HDH / Apr '92 / Pinnacle.

### DEATH IN A ROLLS ROYCE.
Tracks: Death in a Rolls Royce / Russian roulette.
■ 7" ............................... ESSAR 007
Coach House / Aug '82.

## Glen, Marla

### THIS IS MARLA GLEN.
Tracks: Cost of freedom / Believer / Destiny (to get up again) / Enough / Personal / Control / Travel / Feet on the ground / You hurt me.
■ CD ............................... 7432117875-2
■ MC ............................... 7432117875-3
Arista / Feb '94 / BMG.

## Glenn, Garry

### FEELS GOOD TO FEEL GOOD.
Tracks: Do you have to go / Torch for you / Running away / Out of a dream / I'm still waiting / Feels good to feel good / Lonely nights / Can't get enough of love / Love makes it right.
■ LP ............................... ZL 72617
■ MC ............................... ZK 72617
Motown / Oct '87.

### G.G.
Tracks: Not Advised.
■ LP ............................... PPO 2012
PPL (USA) / Nov '87.

## Glories

### I STAND ACCUSED.
Tracks: I stand accused / Wish they could write a song.
■ 7" ............................... 2786
CBS / May '67.

### I STAND ACCUSED (OF LOVING YOU).
Tracks: I stand accused (of loving you) / Wish they could write a song.
■ 7" ............................... CBS 2786
CBS / Jun '67.

## Glover, Bobby

### YOUR SPELL.
Tracks: Your spell / Bright skies, sunny days / It's my turn / Happy.
■ 12" ............................... OG 4507
Old Gold / Sep '88.

## Godfrey, Ray

### COME AND GET THESE MEMORIES.
Tracks: Come and get these memories / I'm the other half you.
■ 7" ............................... GRP 111
Grapevine (Northern Soul) / Sep '78.

## Goins, Herbie

### NO.1 IN YOUR HEART (Goins, Herbie & The Nightimers).
Tracks: No. 1 in your heart.
■ 7" ............................... R 5478
Parlophone / '66.

### SOULTIME (Goins, Herbie & The Nightimers).
Tracks: Outside of heaven / Look at Granny run run / I don't mind / Pucker up buttercup / Coming home to you / No. 1 in your heart / (I can't get no) Satisfaction / Good good lovin' / Cruisin' / Knock on wood / Thirty six-twenty Two-thirty six / Turn on your lovelight / Coming home to you (Live).
■ CD ............................... SEECD 362
See For Miles / Oct '92 / Pinnacle.

## Golden Eagles

### LIGHTNING AND THUNDER (Live at the H & R Bar, New Orleans).
Tracks: Shotgun Joe / Little Liza Jane / Two way e way / Shallow water, oh mama / Sew-sew-sew / Indian red / Hold 'em Joe.
■ LP ............................... FIEND 118
Demon / May '88.

### LIGHTNING AND THUNDER (ROUNDER) (Golden Eagles & Monk Boudreaux).
Tracks: Not Advised.
■ CD ............................... CD 2073
■ LP ............................... ROUNDER 2073
■ MC ............................... ROUNDER 2073C
Rounder / '88 / Roots Records / C.M. Distribution / Topic Records / A.D.A. Distribution / Direct Distribution.

## Goldsmith, Glen

### DREAMING.
Tracks: Dreaming / Dreaming (inst) / I won't cry (Extra track on 12").
■ 12" ............................... PT 41712
■ 7" ................................... PB 41711
RCA / Feb '88.

### I WON'T CRY.
Tracks: I won't cry (remix) / I won't cry (instrumental) / I won't cry (dub).
■ 12" ............................... PT 41494
■ 7" ................................... PB 41493
RCA / Aug '87.

### LEARN 2 LIVE.
Tracks: Learn 2 live.
■ 12" ............................... 12 SCR005
■ 7" ................................... 7SCR 005
■ CD Single ...................... C7SCR 005
■ MC Single ...................... CASCR 005
Scratch / Mar '93.

### ONE LIFE.
Tracks: One life.
■ 12" ............................... PT 43182
■ 7" ................................... PB 43179
■ CD Single ...................... PD 43180
RCA / Nov '89.

### SAVE A LITTLE BIT.
Tracks: Save a little bit / Give your word.
■ 12" ............................... PT 42148
■ 7" ................................... PB 42147
■ CD Single ...................... PD 42148
RCA / Aug '88.

### WHAT YOU SEE IS WHAT YOU GET.
Tracks: What you see is what you get / What you see is what you get (corrosive) / I won't cry / Save a little bit / Dreaming / Undercover / Gone too far / Shame / Keep in touch / Rhythm of romance / Shadow of doubt.
■ CD ............................... PD 71750
■ MC ............................... PK 71750
■ LP ............................... PL 71750
RCA / Aug '88.

### WHAT YOU SEE IS WHAT YOU GET.
Tracks: What you see is what you get.
■ 12" ............................... PT 42076
■ 7" ................................... PB 42075
■ CD Single ...................... PD 42077
RCA / May '88.

### WHAT YOU SEE IS WHAT YOU GET.
Tracks: Not Advised.
VHS ............................... V 9137
MSD / Sep '88 / Multiple Sound Distributors / Gold & Sons.

### YOU GOT ME DANCIN' (Goldsmith, Glen & MC Hammer).
Tracks: You got me dancin' / On the one.
■ 12" Remix ................... PT 43268
■ 7" ................................... PB 43313
■ CD Single ...................... PD 43314
■ 12" ............................... PT 43314
RCA / Aug '90.

## Gonzalez

### AIN'T NO WAY TO TREAT A LADY.
Tracks: Ain't no way to treat a lady.
■ 12" ............................... 12SID 111
■ 7" ................................... SID 111
Sidewalk / Jun '79.

### CLOSER TO YOU.
Tracks: Closer to you / Get it.
■ 12" ............................... 12P 283
PRT / Aug '83.

**DIGITAL LOVE AFFAIR.**
Tracks: Digital love affair / Disco can't go on forever.
■ 12"............................12EMI 5097
■ 7"................................EMI 5097
EMI / Aug '80.

**GONZALEZ.**
Tracks: Not Advised.
■ LP...............................SWK 2001
Sidewalk / Mar '79.

**I HAVEN'T STOPPED DANCING YET.**
Tracks: I haven't stopped dancing yet / Carnival.
■ 7"................................EMI 2706
EMI / Sep '77.

**I HAVEN'T STOPPED DANCING YET.**
Tracks: I haven't stopped dancing yet / You're all I need.
■ 12"...........................12SID 102
■ 7"..............................SID 102
Sidewalk / Feb '79.

**I HAVEN'T STOPPED DANCING YET (2ND RE-ISSUE).**
Tracks: I haven't stopped dancing yet / Ain't no way to treat a lady.
■ 12"............................DANCE 112
Dance On Wax / Jun '87.
■ 7"...............................DANCE 1
Dance On Wax / Mar '89.

**I WANT TO GET CLOSER TO YOU.**
Tracks: I want to get closer to you / Cuidado.
■ 12"............................TOOTL 121
■ 7"..............................TOOT 121
Tooti Frooti / Mar '82.

**JUST LET IT LAY.**
Tracks: Just let it lay.
■ 7"................................EMI 2868
EMI / Nov '78.

**JUST MY IMAGINATION.**
Tracks: Just my imagination / Lets get it on.
■ 12"..............................12P 304
■ 7"................................7P 304
PRT.

**MOVE IT TO THE MUSIC.**
Tracks: Love it / People's party / Livin' in the light of your love / Take me the way / Ain't no way to treat a lady / Love is like a slave / Dance machine / Move it to the music.
■ LP...............................SWK 2003
Sidewalk / Dec '79.

**PIRATES.**
Tracks: Pirates.
■ 12"..............................12P 314
■ 7"...............................7 P 314
Tooti Frooti / Jun '84.

## Gooding, Cuba

After death of leader Don McPherson, Gooding was recruited into Main Ingredient in 1969 and sang on million-sellers *Everybody Plays the Fool* ('72) and *Just Don't Want To Be Lonely* ('74). As they declined in late '70s, Gooding launched solo career on Motown with creatively-monickered *The First Cuba Gooding Album*. Microscopic sales led him to be dropped in '83; after which he scored minor dance hit with reworking of Ingredient's *Happiness Is Just Around the Bend*, then rejoined group.

**CUBA GOODING.**
Tracks: Mind pleaser / All I can give you is love / Where would I be without you / Hold on to what you got / Fool of the year / We're in love / Ain't nothin' to it / Someone to go home to / As long as there's you.
■ LP.............................STML 12083
Motown / Jun '78.

**HAPPINESS IS JUST AROUND THE BEND.**
Tracks: Happiness is just around the bend.
■ 12"..............................LONX 41
■ 7"................................LON 41
London / Nov '83.

**LOVE DANCER.**
Tracks: Disco royale / Trust me / I'm yours now / Hey, the party's in here / Dance floor lover / Tell me how long it's been / Running man.
■ LP.............................STML 12113
Motown / '79.

**MEANT TO BE IN LOVE.**
Tracks: Not Advised.
CD...............................TRI 4162CD

MC................................TRI 4162MC
Ichiban / Feb '94 / A.D.A. Distribution / Pinnacle / ACD Trading Ltd. / Koch International / Direct Distribution.

## Goody Goody

**NUMBER ONE DEE JAY.**
Tracks: Number one dee jay.
■ 7"...................................LV 3
Atlantic / Dec '78.

## Gordon, Denise

**I NEVER KNEW LOVE LIKE THIS BEFORE.**
Tracks: I never knew love like this before / Give it up.
■ 12"............................12ZAM 003
■ 7"..............................7ZAM 003
RMO / Jan '91.

## Gota

**SOMEDAY.**
Tracks: Someday.
12"...............................12 RPL 001
7".................................7 RPL 001
CD Single..........................CDRPL 001
MC Single..........................CARPL 001
Respect / Jun '94 / Total.

**SOMETHING TO TALK ABOUT.**
Tracks: Move / It's so different here / European comfort / Someday / Changes / Play fair / Someday reprise / Take you anywhere / All alone / Chillin' chil'ren / Groove ride / Easy when you want it.
CD................................RPLCD 1
MC................................RPLMC 1
Respect / Jul '94 / Total.

## Graham Central Station

**AIN'T NO BOUT A DOUBT IT.**
Tracks: Jam / Your love / It's alright / I can't stand the rain / Ain't nothing but a Warner Brothers party / Ole Smokey / Easy rider / Water luckiest people.
■ LP................................K 56147
WEA / Jun '75.

**FEEL THE NEED.**
Tracks: Feel the need / We be's getting down.
■ 7"................................K 16506
WEA / Apr '75.

**GRAHAM CENTRAL STATION.**
Tracks: We've been waiting / It ain't no fun to me / Hair / We be's getting down / Tell me what it is / Can you handle it / People / Why / Ghetto.
■ LP................................K 56062
WEA / Mar '73.

**IT'S ALRIGHT.**
Tracks: It's alright / I ain't nothing but a Warner Bros. party.
■ 7"................................K 16593
Warner / Jul '75.

**NOW DO U WANTA DANCE.**
Tracks: Happ-e 2 c u a-ginn / Now do u wanta dance / Last train / Love and happiness / Earthquake / Crazy chicken / Stomped beat up and whooped / Lead me on / Saving my love for you / Have faith in me.
■ LP................................K 56359
WEA / Jun '77.

## Graham, Jaki

**AIN'T NOBODY.**
Tracks: Ain't nobody.
12"...............................12 LOSE 64
7".................................LOSE 64
CD Single..........................CDLOSE 64
MC Single..........................CALOSE 64
Pulse 8 / Jul '94 / Sony / 3MV.

**BAND OF GOLD.**
Tracks: Band of gold.
■ 12"............................ESST 2015
■ 7"..............................ESS 2015
■ CD Single.......................ESSX 2015
■ MC Single.......................ESSM 2015
Essential / Apr '92.

**BETTER PART OF ME, THE.**
Tracks: Better part of me / From now own (7" remix) (12" only.) / No mercy.
■ 12"............................12JAKI 16
■ 7"..............................JAKI 16
■ CD Single.......................CDJAKI 16

■ MC Single.......................TCJAKI 16
EMI / Aug '89.

**BREAKING AWAY.**
Tracks: Set me free / Breaking away / Still in love / Love under moonlight / Lets get blue (Duet with Derek Bramble.) / Stop the world (and let me off) / Luv 2 much / Love of your life / Closest one (Duet with Derek Bramble.) / Step right up / Mated (Duet with David Grant.) / Love me tonight.
■ CD.............................CDP 746 367 2
■ LP..............................EMC 3514
■ MC.............................TCEMC 3514
EMI / Sep '86.

**BREAKING AWAY.**
Tracks: Breaking away.
■ 12".............................12JAKI 8
■ 7"...............................JAKI 8
EMI / Jul '86.

**EVERY LITTLE BIT HURTS.**
Tracks: Every little bit hurts (LP version) / Faking the feeling (LP version) / Shy guy (12" version).
■ 12"............................12JAKI 17
■ 7"..............................JAKI 17
■ CD Single.......................CDJAKI 17
EMI / Nov '89.

**FROM NOW ON.**
Tracks: From now on / Provocative / Better part of me / Faking the feeling / I still run to you / Baby don't you want me / I want to thank you (Heavenly Father) / First in line / Every little bit hurts / Nobody's fool (CD only.).
■ LP..............................EMC 3560
■ MC.............................TCEMC 3560
■ CD.............................CDEMC 3560
EMI / Sep '89.

**FROM NOW ON.**
Tracks: From now on / Nobody's fool / From now on (ext. version) (12" only.) / From now on (here and now mix) (CD single & 12JAKIX only.) / From now on (doomsday dub) (12JAKIX only.) / From now on (Accadub) (12JAKIX only.
■ 12"............................12JAKI 15
■ 12" Remix......................12JAKIX 15
■ 7"..............................JAKI 15
■ CD Single.......................CDJAKI 15
■ MC Single.......................TCJAKI 15
EMI / Jun '89.

**HEAVEN KNOWS.**
Tracks: round and 'round / Heaven knows / Could it be I'm falling in love / I fell for you / Hold on / Facts of love / You're mine / Loving you / What's the name of your game / Stay the way you are.
■ LP.................................JK 1
■ MC...............................TC JK 1
EMI / Jul '85.
■ LP................................FA 3181
■ MC.............................TCFA 3181
Fame / Jun '87.
■ CD.............................CDFA 3181
Fame / Jul '88.

**HEAVEN KNOWS (FEELS SO GOOD).**
Tracks: Heaven knows / You're mine.
■ 7"...............................JAKI 5
EMI / Jun '84.
■ 12"............................12 JAKI 5
EMI / Aug '85.

**LET'S GET BLUE.**
Tracks: Let's get blue (Duet with Derek Bramble) / Still in love / Love under moonlight / Love 2 much (too much)(12" mix) / Still in (dub).
■ 12"............................12 JAKIX 10
EMI / Mar '87.

**LIVING FOR YOU (see under Hardcastle, Paul).**

**MATED (see under Grant, David).**

**MEGAMIX.**
Tracks: Set me free / Closest one / Step right up.
■ 12"............................12 JAKIX 9
EMI / Nov '86.

**NO MORE TEARS.**
Tracks: No more tears / Have you seen him / No more tears (Fon Force re-mix) (Only on 12".) / No more tears (Home-Bass mix) (Only on 12".) / Set me free (Only on CD single.).
■ 12"............................12JAKI 12
■ 7"..............................JAKI 12
■ CD Single.......................CDJAKI 12
EMI / Jun '88.

**ONCE MORE WITH THE FEELING.**
Tracks: Once more with the feeling / Hold on.
■ 12"............................12JAKI 13

■ 7" . . . . . . . . . . . . . . . . . . . . JAKI 13
EMI / Nov '84.

## ROUND AND ROUND.
Tracks: round and 'round / Victim of emotion.
■ 12" . . . . . . . . . . . . . . . . . . 12 JAKI 4
■ 7" . . . . . . . . . . . . . . . . . . . . JAKI 4
EMI / Jun '85.

## SET FREE.
Tracks: Could it be I'm falling in love / Step right up / Set me free / Mated.
■ VHS . . . . . . . . . . . . . . . . MVR 99 0061 2
PMI / Nov '86.
VHS . . . . . . . . . . . . . . . . . . . . . MC 2027
Music Club Video / Jun '89 / Video Collection / Gold & Sons / THE.

## SET ME FREE.
Tracks: Set me free / Stop the world (and let me off).
■ 12" . . . . . . . . . . . . . . . . . . 12 JAKI 7
■ 7" . . . . . . . . . . . . . . . . . . . . JAKI 7
EMI / Apr '86.

## SET ME FREE (OLD GOLD).
Tracks: Set me free / Mated.
12" . . . . . . . . . . . . . . . . . . . OG 4222
Old Gold / '92 / Pickwick.

## STEP RIGHT UP.
Tracks: Step right up / Closest one (Duet with Derek Bramble.).
■ 12" . . . . . . . . . . . . . . . . . . 12 JAKI 9
■ 7" . . . . . . . . . . . . . . . . . . . . JAKI 9
EMI / Nov '86.

## STILL IN LOVE (LIGHTS DOWN MIX).
Tracks: Still in love (lights down mix) / Love too much (too much mix).
■ 12" . . . . . . . . . . . . . . . . . . 12JAKI 10
■ 7" . . . . . . . . . . . . . . . . . . . JAKI 10
EMI / Feb '87.

## WHAT'S THE NAME OF YOUR GAME.
Tracks: What's the name of your game / Hold on.
■ 12" . . . . . . . . . . . . . . . . . . 12JAKI 1
EMI / Apr '84.

# Graham, Larry

A pivotal member of Sly & the Family Stone, Graham was clearly in tune with Sly's cosmic vision; prompting curtailment of 1968 U.K. tour when he was busted in London. Ironically, Mr Stone's erratic behaviour was one factor in Graham's decision to quit in '72, when he formed Graham Central Station. Equally funky outfit won loyal soul following, crossing over to pop charts in '75 with Your Love single and Ain't No Dout-A-Boubt It album. After final LP in '78, Graham launched solo career with Star Walk album. 1980 brought him million-seller with One In A Million You; new fame as ballad singer continued with soul hit Just Be My Lady and sole U.K. chart entry, Sooner Or Later in '82. However, Graham is best-remembered for revolutionary bass-playing; "thumb-thwack" style clearly influenced, among others, Bootsy Collins.

## FIRED UP.
Tracks: What we all need is more love / For your love / Nobody's gonna steal you away / That's why I love you / How does it feel / Let's go / Cruisin' / Tearing out my heart / Fired up / Love all the hurt away.
■ LP . . . . . . . . . . . . . . . . . . . 925307 1
■ MC . . . . . . . . . . . . . . . . . . . 925307 4
WEA / Jun '85.

## I'M SICK AND TIRED.
Tracks: I'm sick and tired / Victory.
■ 12" . . . . . . . . . . . . . . . . . . W 9510T
■ 7" . . . . . . . . . . . . . . . . . . . W 9510
WEA / Aug '83.

## JUST BE MY LADY.
Tracks: Just be my lady / Loving you is beautiful / Guess who / Our love keeps growing strong / Can't nobody take your place / No place like home / Baby you are my sunshine / I just love you / Feels like love / Remember when.
■ LP . . . . . . . . . . . . . . . . . . . K 56909
WEA / Jun '81.

## JUST BE MY LADY.
Tracks: Just be my lady / Feels like love.
■ 7" . . . . . . . . . . . . . . . . . . K 17839
WEA / Aug '81.

## ONE IN A MILLION YOU.
Tracks: One in a million you / Stand up and shout about love / Sweetheart / There's something about

you / Forever yours / I'm so glad it's summer again / When we get married / Time for you and me / I just can't stop dancing / Sunshine love and music.
■ LP . . . . . . . . . . . . . . . . . . . K 56843
WEA / Mar '81.

## ONE IN A MILLION YOU.
Tracks: One in a million you / Entertainer.
■ 7" . . . . . . . . . . . . . . . . . . K 17985
WEA / Sep '80.

## SOONER OR LATER.
Tracks: Sooner or later / Still thinkin' of you / Don't stop when you're hot / You're my girl / I feel good / Walk baby walk / Let me come into your life / Hold up your hand / Easy love.
■ LP . . . . . . . . . . . . . . . . . . . K56992
WEA / Aug '82.

## SOONER OR LATER.
Tracks: Sooner or later / One in a million.
■ 7" . . . . . . . . . . . . . . . . . . K 17925
WEA / Jul '82.

## STARWALK.
Tracks: Starwalk / Boogie baby.
■ 7" . . . . . . . . . . . . . . . . . . K 17451
WEA / Aug '79.

# Granger, Gerri

## I GO TO PIECES.
Tracks: I go to pieces / Panic / Shake a tailfeather.
■ 7" . . . . . . . . . . . . . . . . . . . CC 3
Casino Classics / Sep '78.

# Grant, David

After Brit-funk duo Linx split in 1982, David Grant chalked up four U.K. hits from eponymous solo LP; biggest of which was Watching You Watching Me. Career subsequently stalled and Grant took year off before returning to charts in 1985 via two duets with Jaki Graham: Could It Be I'm Falling In Love? made No. 5, higher than Detroit Spinners' original, and Mated just cracked Top 20. Grant then hurtled back into obscurity, although recent releases on 4th & Broadway have scraped lower reaches of chart.

## ANXIOUS EDGE.
Tracks: Not Advised.
■ LP . . . . . . . . . . . . . . . . . 846 843 1
■ LP . . . . . . . . . . . . . . . . . . . BRLP 552
MC. . . . . . . . . . . . . . . . . . . BRCA 552
■ MC. . . . . . . . . . . . . . . . . . 846 843 4
■ CD . . . . . . . . . . . . . . . . . . BRCD 552
4th & Broadway / Oct '90 / PolyGram.

## BEFORE TOO LONG.
Tracks: Before too long / Before too long (Soomcone mix) / Tonight.
■ 12" . . . . . . . . . . . . . . . . . . POSPX 889
■ 7" . . . . . . . . . . . . . . . . . . . POSP 889
Polydor / Oct '87.

## BEST OF DAVID GRANT & LYNX.
Tracks: Mated / So this is romance / Watching you, watching me / Rock the midnight / Where our love begins / Organize (remix) / Love will find a way / Intuition / Could it be I'm falling in love / Stop and go / Plaything / Can't help myself / Throw away the key / You're lying.
CD . . . . . . . . . . . . . . . . . . CDCHR 6051
MC. . . . . . . . . . . . . . . . . . TCCHR 6051
Chrysalis / Oct '93 / EMI.

## CHANGE.
Tracks: Before too long / Change / Touch / Take us back / Ultimate love / Emblems / Thank you / Under one flag.
■ CD . . . . . . . . . . . . . . . . . . 833 482-2
■ LP . . . . . . . . . . . . . . . . . . . POLH 37
■ MC. . . . . . . . . . . . . . . . . . POLHC 37
Polydor / Sep '87.

## CHANGE.
Tracks: Change / Change (Alternate Mix) (On 12" version only.) / Change (Dub version) (On 12" version only.) / Fire me up.
■ 12" . . . . . . . . . . . . . . . . . . POSPX 871
■ 7" . . . . . . . . . . . . . . . . . . . POSP 871
Polydor / Jul '87.

## CLOSE TO YOU.
Tracks: Goodbye love / Close to you.
■ 12" . . . . . . . . . . . . . . . . . . GRANX 8
■ 7" . . . . . . . . . . . . . . . . . . . GRAN 8
Chrysalis / Mar '86.

## COULD IT BE I'M FALLING IN LOVE
(Grant, David & Jaki Graham).
Tracks: Could it be I'm falling in love / Turn around.
■ 12" . . . . . . . . . . . . . . . . . . GRANX 6
■ 7" . . . . . . . . . . . . . . . . . . . GRAN 6
Chrysalis / Mar '85.
■ CD Single . . . . . . . . . . . . . CDCHS 5003
Chrysalis / Jan '94.

## DAVID GRANT.
Tracks: Rock the midnight / Love will find a way / Wrap yourself around me / Stop and go / Organise / In the flow of love / Holding on / Watching me, watching you / You are all.
■ LP . . . . . . . . . . . . . . . . . . . CHR 1448
■ MC . . . . . . . . . . . . . . . . . ZCHR 1448
Chrysalis / Oct '83.

## HAVE YOURSELF A MERRY LITTLE CHRISTMAS.
Tracks: Have yourself a merry little Christmas / It's my life.
■ 7" . . . . . . . . . . . . . . . . . . CHS 2659
Chrysalis / Dec '82.

## HOPES AND DREAMS.
Tracks: Where our love begins / Turn around / Hopes and dreams / Take my heart / So excited / Could it be I'm falling in love / Crime of passion / Cool September / Love is alive / How many times.
■ LP . . . . . . . . . . . . . . . . . . . CHR 1483
MC. . . . . . . . . . . . . . . . . . ZCHR 1483
Chrysalis / May '85 / EMI.

## HURT.
Tracks: Hurt.
■ 12" . . . . . . . . . . . . . . . . . . INTOX 104
In Disc / Jul '92.

## INTUITION '88'.
Tracks: Intuition '88' / Intuition '88' (version).
■ 12" . . . . . . . . . . . . . . . . . . FRES T1
■ 7" . . . . . . . . . . . . . . . . . . FRESTR 001
■ 7" . . . . . . . . . . . . . . . . . . . FRES 1
■ 7" . . . . . . . . . . . . . . . . . . FRES TX1
Fresher / Nov '88.

## KEEP IT TOGETHER.
Tracks: Keep it together.
■ 12" . . . . . . . . . . . . . . . . . 12 BRW 169
■ 7" . . . . . . . . . . . . . . . . . . . BRW 169
■ 12" Remix . . . . . . . . . . . . . 12 BRX 169
■ CD Single . . . . . . . . . . . . . . BRCD 169
4th & Broadway / Mar '90.

## LIFE.
Tracks: Life / Life (instrumental).
■ 12" . . . . . . . . . . . . . . . . . 12 BRW 145
■ 7" . . . . . . . . . . . . . . . . . . . BRW 145
■ CD Single . . . . . . . . . . . . . . BRCD 145
4th & Broadway / Sep '89.

## LIFE (RE-RELEASE).
Tracks: Life (instrumental) (On 7" and CD only.) / Life.
■ 12" . . . . . . . . . . . . . . . . . 12 BRW 184
■ 7" . . . . . . . . . . . . . . . . . . . BRW 184
■ CD Single . . . . . . . . . . . . . . BRCD 184
4th & Broadway / Jul '90.

## LOVE WILL FIND A WAY.
Tracks: Love will find a way / Klix trax.
■ 12" . . . . . . . . . . . . . . . . . . GRANX 3
■ 7" . . . . . . . . . . . . . . . . . . . GRAN 3
Chrysalis / Oct '83.

## MATED (Grant, David & Jaki Graham).
Tracks: Mated / Facts of love / Have yourself a merry little Christmas.
■ 12" . . . . . . . . . . . . . . . . . . 12 JAKI 6
■ 7" . . . . . . . . . . . . . . . . . . . JAKI 6
EMI / Nov '85.

## ORGANISE.
Tracks: Organise / Wrap yourself around me / Kiss away the blues (on 12" only).
■ 12" . . . . . . . . . . . . . . . . . . GRANX 5
■ 7" . . . . . . . . . . . . . . . . . . . GRAN 5
Chrysalis / Feb '84.

## ROCK THE MIDNIGHT.
Tracks: Rock the midnight.
■ 7" . . . . . . . . . . . . . . . . . . . GRAN 4
Chrysalis / Nov '83.

## STOP AND GO.
Tracks: Stop and go / Stop and go (instrumental).
■ 7" . . . . . . . . . . . . . . . . . . . GRAN 1
■ 12" . . . . . . . . . . . . . . . . . . GRANX 1
Chrysalis / Apr '83.

■ DELETED

## TAKE US BACK.
Tracks: Take us back / Tell me.
- 12" .................. POSPX 854
- 7" .................... POSP 854
Polydor / Mar '87.

## WATCHING YOU WATCHING ME.
Tracks: Watching you watching me / In the flow of love.
- 12" ................. GRANX 2
- 7" .................. GRAN 2
Chrysalis / '83.

## WATCHING YOU WATCHING ME (OLD GOLD).
Tracks: Watching you watching me / Could it be I'm falling in love.
- 12" ..................OG 4135
Old Gold / Aug '89.

## WHERE OUR LOVE BEGINS.
Tracks: Where our love begins / Loving you / Love is alive.
- 12" ................. GRANX 7
- 7" .................. GRAN 7
Chrysalis / May '85.

# Grant, Earl

## HOUSE OF BAMBOO.
Tracks: House of Bamboo / Fever / Mission impossible / Crickets sing for Anna Maria.
- 12" ..................LONX 111
London / Sep '86.

## STAND BY ME.
Tracks: Stand by me / After hours.
- 7" ....................... 05945
Brunswick / Nov '65.

# Grant, Tom

## EDGE OF THE WORLD.
Tracks: Bernie S groove / Land of love / Night on the town / Awakening / Don't wait for night / Be with you / Angles crossing / Street vendor / Edge of the world / Need to hear you say I love you.
- CD ..................... 843 011-2
- MC ..................... 843 011-4
Polydor / May '91 / PolyGram.

# Gray, Dobie

## DRIFT AWAY.
Tracks: Drift away.
- 7" ...................... MCA 146
MCA / Jul '74.
- 7" .....................MCA 1154
MCA / Jun '87.

## DRIFT AWAY.
Tracks: Not Advised.
- CD ..................CDCOT 106
Target Sales & Marketing / Jan '94 / BMG.

## DRIFT AWAY (OLD GOLD).
Tracks: Drift away / Why can't we live together.
- 7" ....................OG 9428
Old Gold / Jul '84.

## IN CROWD, THE.
Tracks: In crowd / Be a man.
- 7" ...................... HL 9953
London-American / Feb '65.
- 7" ..................... F 13918
Decca / Mar '82.

## OUT ON THE FLOOR.
Tracks: Out on the floor / Funky funky feeling.
- 7" ...................... BM 107
Black Magic (2) / Sep '75.
- 7" P.Disc ........... UKBURN 2 P
Inferno (1) / Feb '83.
- 12" ............... 12 UKBURN 2
- 7" ............... UKBURN 2
Inferno (1) / Oct '83.

## SINGS FOR 'IN' CROWDERS THAT GO 'GO-GO'.
Tracks: The 'in' crowd / Blue ribbons (for her curls) / Monkey jerk / Walk with love / Look at me / Be a man / No room to cry / Out on the floor / See you at the 'go-go' / Mr. Engineer / In Hollywood / Broken in two / That's how you treat a cheater / Feeling in my heart.
- LP ...................... KENT 071
Kent / Aug '87.

## SPENDING TIME MAKING LOVE AND GOING CRAZY.
Tracks: Spending time making love and going crazy / In crowd.

---

- 7" ...................... INF 115
Infinity / Aug '79.

## WATCH OUT FOR LUCY.
Tracks: Watch out for Lucy / Turning on you.
- 7" ...................... MCA 171
MCA / Jan '75.

## WHAT A LADY.
Tracks: What a lady / If love must go.
- 7" .................... 2089 017
Capricorn / Apr '76.

## WHO'S LOVIN' YOU.
Tracks: Who's lovin' you / I can see clearly now.
- 7" ...................... INF 105
Infinity / '79.

# Greaves, R.B.

## FIRE AND RAIN.
Tracks: Fire and rain.
- 7" .................... 2091013
Atlantic / '70.

## PAPERBACK WRITER.
Tracks: Paperback writer.
- 7" .................... 2091170
Atlantic / '71.

# Green, Al

Born in Forest City, Arkansas, though musically regarded as Memphis through-and-through, Al Green toured the South and Mid-West gospel circuits as part of his family group before, in '63, converting to the devil's music. He'd enjoyed only one hit of note, Back Up Train on the tiny Hotline label when he came to the attention of Memphis band leader/producer, Willie Mitchell, who signed him to Hi Records. Over the next half dozen years the Green-Mitchell partnership produced 10 albums of high quality and even had saleability; their first two, Green Is Blues and Gets Next To You (both '70) spawning a hit cover of the Temptations I Can't Get Next To You as well as a top five UK single, Tired Of Being Alone. The third and fourth albums, Let's Stay Together ('71) and I'm Still In Love With You ('72), however, honed to perfection the Hi sound. Mitchell's steel-hand-in-velvet-glove productions an apt accompaniment to Green's elastic, caressing vocal style. The run maintained by Call Me, Livin' For You, Explores Your Mind and Al Green Is Love before in '76, prompted by a girlfriend's suicide, Green returned to the church and gospel music. If Belle (77) and Truth In Time ('78) bridged the divide, by '80 Green was recording only straight gospel, his The Lord Will Make A Way winning a Grammy for Myrrh Records. Further similar albums Higher Plane, Precious Lord and Trust In God followed in the first half of the 80s, and Green was ordained as a minister, purchasing his own church in Memphis. A reunion with Willie Mitchell on 85's Going Away (A & M) saw first signs of a move back towards an inspirational approach, and since then the Reverand Al has cut several more albums in the style, clearly enjoying his flirtations with soul and pop. His live shows these days often include selections from his 70's soul repertoire and occasionally see him throwing his shirt in very un-reverandlike manner into the audience. His most recent album for RCA, Don't Look Back, was produced by a mixture of Fine Young Cannibals and Arthur Baker and has been his highest commercial success since the '70s - perhaps because it ought to recreate that punching, Memphis backdrop.

## AL.
Tracks: Tired of being alone / Call me (come back home) / I'm still in love with you / Here I am (come and take me) / Let's stay together / Sha la la (make me happy) / L.O.V.E. (Love) / Look what you done for me / Love and happiness / Take me to the river / I can't get next to you / How can you mend a broken heart / I tried to tell myself / I've never found a girl / Oh me, oh my (Dreams in my arms) / You ought to be with me.
- CD ................... AGREECD 1
- LP ................... AGREENLP 1
- MC ................... AGREEMC 1
Beechwood / Oct '92 / Pinnacle.

## AL GREEN E.P.
Tracks: I tried to tell myself / Something / What am I gonna do with myself / Summertime.

---

- EP .................. STOU 8685
Decca / Jun '77.

## AL GREEN GETS NEXT TO YOU.
Tracks: I can't get next to you / Are you lonely for me baby / God is standing by / Tired of being alone / I'm a ram / Drivin' wheel / Light my fire / You say it / Right now right now / All because / My girl / Get back / Driving wheel / Letter / One woman.
- LP .................. SHU 8424
London / Dec '71.
- LP .................HIUKLP 403
Hi / Mar '86.

## AS LONG AS WE'RE TOGETHER.
Tracks: As long as we're together / As long as we're together (version).
- 12" ................. USAT 658
- 7" ..................USA 658
Breakout / Jun '89.

## BACK UP TRAIN (Green, Al & The Soulmates).
Tracks: Back up train / Don't leave me.
- 7" .................. SS 2079
Stateside / '68.

## BACK UP TRAIN.
Tracks: Back up train / Hot wire / Stop and check myself / Let me help you / I'm reachin' out / Don't hurt me no more / Lovers hideaway / Don't leave me / What's it all about / I'll be good to you / Guilty / That's all it takes / Get yourself together.
- LP .................. ACLS 6008
Action / Jul '69.

## BELLE ALBUM, THE.
Tracks: Belle / Loving you / Feels like summer / Georgia boy / I feel good / All in all / Chariots of fire / Dream.
- LP .................. HLP 6004
Hi-Cream / Sep '79.
- LP .................HIUKLP 421
Hi / Feb '86.

## CALL ME.
Tracks: Call me / Have you been making out OK / Stand up / I'm so lonesome I could cry / Your love is like the morning sun / Here I am / Funny how time slips away / You ought to be with me / Jesus is waiting.
- LP .................. SHU 8457
London-American / '73.
- LP .................HIUKLP 409
Hi / Jun '85.

## CALL ME/I'M STILL IN LOVE WITH YOU.
Tracks: Not Advised.
- CD ..................HIUKCD 111
Hi / Mar '91 / Pinnacle.

## CHRISTMAS ALBUM/CHRISTMAS CHEERS (Green, Al & Ace Cannon).
Tracks: White Christmas / Christmas song / Winter wonderland / I'll be home for Christmas / Jingle bells / What Christmas means to me / Oh holy night / Silent night / Feels like Christmas / Santa Claus is coming to town / Rudolph the red nosed reindeer / Here comes Santa Claus / Frosty the snowman / Blue Christmas / I saw Mommy kissing Santa Claus / Let it snow, let is snow / Jingle bell rock / Rockin' around the Christmas tree.
- CD ..................HIUKCD 126
Hi / Nov '91 / Pinnacle.

## COVER ME GREEN.
Tracks: I want to hold your hand / My girl / The letter / Light my fire / I say a little prayer / Summertime / Get back / For the good times / Oh pretty woman / I'm so lonesome I could cry / Lean on me / Unchained melody / Ain't no mountain high enough / People get ready / Amazing grace.
- CD ..................HIUKCD 107
- LP .................. HIUK 107
- MC ................HIUKCASS 107
Hi / Apr '91 / Pinnacle.

## CREAM OF AL GREEN.
Tracks: Tired of being alone / Love and happiness / Here I am / I feel good / Call me / Unchained melody / I stand accused / I can't get next to you / Let's stay together / How can you mend a broken heart / You ought to be with me / Belle / Let's get married / Look what you done for me / I'm still in love with you.
- LP .................. HLPC 101
- MC ................... ZCHLP 101
Hi-Cream / Jan '80 / Pinnacle.

## DON'T LOOK BACK.
Tracks: Best love / Love is a beautiful thing / Waiting on you / What does it take / Keep on pushing love / You are my everything / One love / People in the world / Give it everything / Your love / Fountain of love / Don't look back / Love in motion.

CD. . . . . . . . . . . . . . . . . .74321 16310-2
LP. . . . . . . . . . . . . . . . . .74321 16310-1
MC. . . . . . . . . . . . . . . . . .74321 16310-4
RCA / Oct '93 / BMG.

## EXPLORES YOUR MIND.
Tracks: Sha-la-la / Take me to the river / God blessed our love / City / One night stand / I'm hooked on you / Stay with me forever / Hangin' on / School days.
■ LP . . . . . . . . . . . . . . . . . SHU 8479
London-American / Dec '74.
CD. . . . . . . . . . . . . . . . . HIUKCD 413
■ LP . . . . . . . . . . . . . . . .HIUKLP 413
Hi / Sep '86 / Pinnacle.

## FLIPSIDE OF AL GREEN, THE.
Tracks: Not Advised.
CD. . . . . . . . . . . . . . . . . HIUKCD 141
Hi / May '93 / Pinnacle.

## FULL OF FIRE.
Tracks: There's no way / I'd fly away / Full of fire / Together again / Soon as I get home / Let it shine / Glory, glory / That's the way it is / Always.
■ LP . . . . . . . . . . . . . . . .HIUKLP 417
Hi / May '86.

## GOING AWAY.
Tracks: Going away / True love / He is the Light / I feel like going on / Be with me, Jesus / You brought the sunshine / Power / Building / Nearer my God to thee.
■ LP . . . . . . . . . . . . . . . . . AMA 5102
■ MC. . . . . . . . . . . . . . . . . AMC 5102
A&M / Nov '85.

## GOING AWAY.
Tracks: Going away / Building up.
■ 12". . . . . . . . . . . . . . . . . AMY 288
■ 7". . . . . . . . . . . . . . . . . AM 288
A&M / Nov '85.

## GOOD TIME AND BELLE ALBUM.
Tracks: Not Advised.
CD. . . . . . . . . . . . . . . . . HIUKCD 119
Demon / Sep '91 / Pinnacle / A.D.A. Distribution.

## GOSPEL ACCORDING TO AL GREEN.
Tracks: Let's stay together / People get ready / Hallelujah.
■ VHS . . . . . . . . . . . . . . . . HEN 2267
Hendring Video / Nov '90.

## GREATEST HITS.
Tracks: Let's stay together / I can't get next to you / You ought to be with me / Look what you done for me / Let's get married / Tired of being alone / Call me / I'm still in love with you / Here I am (come and take me) / How can you mend a broken heart.
■ LP . . . . . . . . . . . . . . . . . SHU 8481
London-American / Apr '75.
CD. . . . . . . . . . . . . . . . . HIUKCD 425
■ LP . . . . . . . . . . . . . . . .HIUKLP 425
■ MC. . . . . . . . . . . . . . . .HIUKCASS 425
Hi / Feb '87 / Pinnacle.

## GREEN IS BLUES.
Tracks: One woman / Talk to me / My girl / Letter / I stand accused / Gotta find a new world / What am I gonna do with myself / Tomorrow's dream / Get back baby / Summertime.
■ LP . . . . . . . . . . . . . . . .HIUKLP 401
Hi / Mar '86.

## GREEN IS BLUES/AL GREEN GETS NEXT TO YOU.
Tracks: One woman / Talk to me / My girl / Letter / I stand accused / Gotta find a new world / What am I gonna do with myself / Tomorrow's dream / Get back baby / Get back / Summertime / I can't get next to you / Are you lonely for me baby / God is standing by / Tired of being alone / I'm a ram / Drivin' wheel / Light my fire / You say it / Right now right now / All because.
CD. . . . . . . . . . . . . . . . . HIUKCD 106
Hi / Aug '90 / Pinnacle.

## HAVE A GOOD TIME.
Tracks: Keep me cryin' / Smile a little bit more / I tried to tell myself / Something / Truth marches on / Have a good time / Nothing takes the place of you / Hold on forever.
■ LP . . . . . . . . . . . . . . . .HIUKLP 419
Hi / Jul '86.

## HI-LIFE - THE BEST OF AL GREEN.
Tracks: Let's stay together / Tired of being alone / Sha-la-la / Look what you done for me / How can you mend a broken heart / Living for you / Take me to the

river / I can't get next to you / I'm still in love with you / Let's get married / Belle / L-O-V-E.
■ CD. . . . . . . . . . . . . . . . . NCD 3420
■ LP . . . . . . . . . . . . . . . . . NE 1420
■ MC. . . . . . . . . . . . . . . . . CE 2420
K-Tel / Sep '88.

## HIGHER PLANE.
Tracks: Higher plane / People get ready / By my side / Spirit might come - on and on / Where love rules / Amazing grace / His name is Jesus / Battle hymn of the Republic.
■ LP . . . . . . . . . . . . . . . . . HLP 6006
MC. . . . . . . . . . . . . . . . . ZCHLP 6006
Hi-Cream / Feb '82 / Pinnacle.
■ LP . . . . . . . . . . . . . . . .HIUKLP 431
Hi / Nov '85.

## I CAN'T GET NEXT TO YOU.
Tracks: I can't get next to you / Ride Sally ride.
■ 7". . . . . . . . . . . . . . . . . HLU 10324
London / Jan '71.

## I GET JOY.
Tracks: Not Advised.
■ CD. . . . . . . . . . . . . . . . 395 228-2
■ LP . . . . . . . . . . . . . . . . 395 228-1
■ MC. . . . . . . . . . . . . . . . 395 228-4
A&M / Jun '89.

## I'M STILL IN LOVE WITH YOU.
Tracks: I'm still in love with you / I'm glad you're mine / Love and happiness / What a wonderful thing love is / Simply beautiful / Oh pretty woman / For the good times / Look what you done for me / One of these good old days.
■ LP . . . . . . . . . . . . . . . . . SHU 8443
London-American / '72.
■ LP . . . . . . . . . . . . . . . .HIUKLP 407
Hi / Jun '85.

## I'M STILL IN LOVE WITH YOU.
Tracks: I'm still in love with you.
■ 7". . . . . . . . . . . . . . . . . HL 10382
London-American / Aug '72.

## IS LOVE.
Tracks: L-O-V-E (love) / Rhymes / Love sermon / There is love / Could I be the one / Love ritual / I didn't know / Oh me, oh my (dreams in my arms) / I gotta be more (take me higher) / I wish you were here.
■ LP . . . . . . . . . . . . . . . .HIUKLP 415
Hi / Jul '86.

## IS LOVE / FULL OF FIRE.
Tracks: L-O-V-E (Love) / Rhymes / Love sermon / There is love / Could I be the one / Love ritual / I didn't know / Oh me, oh my (dreams in my arms) / I gotta be more (take me higher) / I wish you were here / Glory, glory / That's the way it is / Always / There's no way / I'd fly away / Full of fire / Together again / Soon as I get home / Let it shine.
CD. . . . . . . . . . . . . . . . . HIUKCD 114
Demon / May '91 / Pinnacle / A.D.A. Distribution.

## L.O.V.E. (LOVE).
Tracks: L.O.V.E. (love).
■ 7". . . . . . . . . . . . . . . . . HL 10482
London-American / Mar '75.

## LET'S STAY TOGETHER.
Tracks: Let's stay together / I've never found a girl / So you're leaving / It ain't no fun to me / Talk to me, talk to me / Old time lovin' / Judy / What is this feelin' / Tomorrow's dream / How can you mend a broken heart / La la for you.
■ LP . . . . . . . . . . . . . . . . . SHU 8430
London-American / Apr '72.
■ LP . . . . . . . . . . . . . . . .HIUKLP 405
Hi / Feb '85.
CD. . . . . . . . . . . . . . . . . HIUKCD 405
Hi / Jul '86 / Pinnacle.

## LET'S STAY TOGETHER.
Tracks: Let's stay together / I'm still in love with you / You ought to be with me.
■ 12". . . . . . . . . . . . . . . . HIUK 45 7001T
■ 7". . . . . . . . . . . . . . . . HIUK 45 7001
Hi / Sep '85.

## LIVIN' FOR YOU.
Tracks: Living for you / Home again / Free at last / Let's get married / So good to be here / Sweet sixteen / Unchained melody / My God is real / Beware.
■ LP . . . . . . . . . . . . . . . .HIUKLP 411
Hi / Nov '85.

## LIVIN' FOR YOU / EXPLORES YOUR MIND.
Tracks: Livin' for you / Home again / Free at last / Let's get married / So good to be here / Sweet sixteen / Unchanged malady / My God is real /

Beware / Sha-la-la / Take me to the river / God blessed our love / City / One nite stand / I'm hooked on you / Stay with me forever / Hangin' on / School days.
CD. . . . . . . . . . . . . . . . . HIUKCD 113
Demon / May '91 / Pinnacle / A.D.A. Distribution.

## LOOK WHAT YOU DONE FOR ME.
Tracks: Look what you done for me.
■ 7". . . . . . . . . . . . . . . . . HL 10369
London-American / May '72.

## LORD WILL MAKE A WAY, THE.
Tracks: Lord will make a way / Pass me not / Too close / Highway to Heaven / Saved / None by the righteous / In the holy name of Jesus / I have a friend above all others.
■ LP . . . . . . . . . . . . . . . . . MYR 1109
MC. . . . . . . . . . . . . . . . . MC 1109
Myrrh / May '82 / Word Records (UK) / Sony.
■ LP . . . . . . . . . . . . . . . .HIUKLP 433
Hi / Jul '86.

## LOVE IS A BEAUTIFUL THING.
Tracks: Love is a beautiful thing / Love in motion / Love is a beautiful thing (mixes) (On CD single & 12" only).
■ 12". . . . . . . . . . . . . . . 7432116269-1
■ 7". . . . . . . . . . . . . . . 7432116269-7
■ CD Single. . . . . . . . . . . 7432116269-2
■ MC Single. . . . . . . . . . . 7432116269-4
RCA / Sep '93.

## LOVE IS REALITY.
Tracks: Just can't let you go / I can feel it / Love is reality / Positive attitude / Again / Sure feels good / I like it / You don't know me / Long time / Why.
CD. . . . . . . . . . . . . . . . . 701927160X
MC. . . . . . . . . . . . . . . . . 7019271502
Word (UK) / Apr '92 / Word Records (UK) / Sony.

## LOVE RITUAL.
Tracks: Love ritual / So good to be here / Ride Sally ride / Surprise attack / Love is real / I think it's for the feeling / Up above my head / Strong as death / Mimi / I want to hold your hand.
CD. . . . . . . . . . . . . . . . . HIUKCD 443
■ LP . . . . . . . . . . . . . . . .HIUKLP 443
MC. . . . . . . . . . . . . . . . .HIUKCASS 443
Hi / '89 / Pinnacle.

## NEVER MET NOBODY LIKE YOU.
Tracks: Never met nobody like you / Higher plane.
■ 7". . . . . . . . . . . . . . . . . HIUK 45 7003
Hi / Feb '85.

## OH ME, OH MY (DREAMS IN MY ARMS).
Tracks: Oh me, oh my (dreams in my arms) / Strong as death.
■ 7". . . . . . . . . . . . . . . . . HLU 10493
London / Jul '75.

## PRECIOUS LORD.
Tracks: Precious Lord / What a friend we have in Jesus / Old rugged cross / Morning star / How great Thou art / Glory to His name / Rock of ages / In the garden / Hallelujah.
■ LP . . . . . . . . . . . . . . . . . HLP 6007
Hi-Cream / Nov '82.
■ LP . . . . . . . . . . . . . . . .HIUKLP 429
Hi / Jun '85.

## SHA-LA-LA (MAKE ME HAPPY).
Tracks: Sha-la-la.
■ 7". . . . . . . . . . . . . . . . . HL 10470
London-American / Nov '74.

## SOUL SURVIVOR.
Tracks: Everything's gonna be alright / Jesus will fix it / You know and I know / So real to me / Introduction - soul survivor / Soul survivor / You've got a friend / He ain't heavy, he's my brother / 23rd Psalm.
■ LP . . . . . . . . . . . . . . . . . AMA 5150
■ MC. . . . . . . . . . . . . . . . . AMC 5150
A&M / Mar '87.

## SPOTLIGHT ON AL GREEN.
Tracks: Tired of being alone / Take me to the river / Living for you / Let's get married / Love ritual / School days / Let's stay together / How can you mend a broken heart / Call me (come back home) / You ought to be with me / Here I am (come and take me) / Oh me, oh my (dreams in my arms) / Sha-la-la / Oh pretty woman / Love and happiness / I can't get next to you / For the good times / L.O.V.E. / I'm still in love with you / Look what you done for me / I stand accused / Unchained melody / Belle / To sir with love.
■ MC Set . . . . . . . . . . . . . .ZCSPT 1016
■ Double LP. . . . . . . . . . . . . SPOT 1016
PRT / Oct '81.

■ DELETED

## SUPREME AL GREEN, THE.
Tracks: Tired of being alone / I can't get next to you / Let's stay together / How can you mend a broken heart / Love and happiness / I'm still in love with you / Simply beautiful / What a wonderful thing love is / Call me (come back home) / My God is real / Let's get married / Sha la la (make me happy) / Take me to the river / Love ritual / L-O-V-E (love) / I didn't know / Full of fire / Belle.

- CD. . . . . . . . . . . . . . . . . . . HIUKCD 130
- MC. . . . . . . . . . . . . . . . . HIUKCASS 130
Hi / Apr '92 / Pinnacle.

## TAKE ME TO THE RIVER (Greatest Hits Vol. 2).
Tracks: Drivin' wheel / I've never found a girl / Love and happiness / Living for you / Sha-la-la / L-O-V-E / One woman / Take me to the river / Rhymes / Oh me, oh my (dreams in my arms) / Glory, glory / Full of fire / Keep me cryin' / Belle.

- CD. . . . . . . . . . . . . . . . . . HIUKCD 438
- LP. . . . . . . . . . . . . . . . . . . HIUKLP 438
- MC. . . . . . . . . . . . . . . . . HIUKCASS 438
Hi / Oct '87 / Pinnacle.

## TIRED OF BEING ALONE.
Tracks: Tired of being alone / How can you mend a broken heart.
- 12". . . . . . . . . . . . . . . . . . 12 HCS 107
- 7". . . . . . . . . . . . . . . . . . . HCS 107
Hi-Cream / Jan '80.
- 7". . . . . . . . . . . . . . . . . . . . FBS 14
Flashback / Jan '83.

## TIRED OF BEING ALONE.
Tracks: Tired of being alone / Right now, right now.
- 7". . . . . . . . . . . . . . . . . . . HL 10337
London-American / Oct '71.

## TOKYO - LIVE.
Tracks: Love / Tired of being alone / Let's stay together / How can you mend a broken heart / All 'n' all / God blessed our love / You ought to be with me / For the good times / Belle / Sha-la-la / Let's get married / Dream / I feel good / Love and happiness.
- MC Set . . . . . . . . . . . . . . . . ZHCD 5001
- Double LP. . . . . . . . . . . . . . . HCD 5001
Hi-Cream / Jul '81 / Pinnacle.
- Double LP. . . . . . . . . . . . . . . . 8302ML2
Motown / Aug '87.
- CD. . . . . . . . . . . . . . . . . . . HIUKCD 104
Hi / Apr '90 / Pinnacle.

## TRUE LOVE.
Tracks: True love / You brought the sunshine / Going away (On 12"version only).
- 12". . . . . . . . . . . . . . . . . . . AMY 302
- 7". . . . . . . . . . . . . . . . . . . . AM 302
A&M / Jan '86.

## TRUST IN GOD.
Tracks: Don't it make you wanna go home / No not one / Trust in God / Lean on me / Ain't no mountain high enough / Up the ladder to the roof / Never met nobody like you / Holy spirit / All we need is a little more love.
- LP. . . . . . . . . . . . . . . . . . . HIUKLP 423
Hi / Feb '85.
- CD. . . . . . . . . . . . . . . . . . . HIUKCD 423
Hi / Jul '86 / Pinnacle.

## WAITING ON YOU.
Tracks: Waiting on you.
- 12". . . . . . . . . . . . . . . . . 7432119349-1
- CD Single. . . . . . . . . . . . . 7432119349-2
- MC Single. . . . . . . . . . . . . 7432119349-4
RCA / Aug '94.

## WHITE CHRISTMAS.
Tracks: White Christmas / Christmas song / Winter wonderland / I'll be home for Christmas / Jingle bells / What Christmas means to me / Oh holy night / Silent night / It feels like Christmas.
- LP. . . . . . . . . . . . . . . . . XHIUKLP 437
Hi / Nov '87.

## YOU SAY IT.
Tracks: You say it / I'll be standing by / True love / Right now, right now / Memphis, Tennessee / I'm a ram / Listen / Baby what's wrong with you / Ride Sally ride / Eli's game / Sweet song / Everything to me / Starting all over again.
- CD. . . . . . . . . . . . . . . . . . HIUKCD 444
- LP. . . . . . . . . . . . . . . . . . . HIUKLP 444
Hi / Jun '90 / Pinnacle.

## Green, Garland

### JUST WHAT THE DOCTOR ORDERED.
Tracks: Not Advised.
- LP . . . . . . . . . . . . . . . . . . . KENT 097
Kent / Mar '90 / Pinnacle.

### SPRING SIDES, THE.
Tracks: Please come home / Sweet loving woman / Nothing can take you from me / Come through me / Sending my best wishes / Let the good times roll / Just loving you / You and I go good together / Bumpin' and stompin' / Since you've been gone / He didn't know (he kept on talking) / Just what the doctor ordered.
- LP . . . . . . . . . . . . . . . . . . . KEND 097
Kent / '92.

## Green, Jesse

### COME WITH ME.
Tracks: Come with me / Come with me (version).
- 7" . . . . . . . . . . . . . . . . . . . EMI 2615
EMI / Jun '77.

### DISCO CRAZY.
Tracks: Disco crazy / Life can be beautiful.
- 7" . . . . . . . . . . . . . . . . . . . EMI 2810
EMI / Jun '78.

### FLIP.
Tracks: Flip.
- 7" . . . . . . . . . . . . . . . . . . . EMI 2564
EMI / Dec '76.

### GO AWAY DREAM.
Tracks: Go away dream / Dream dub.
- 7" . . . . . . . . . . . . . . . . . . . 6121600
Sunbeam / Feb '75.

### HURRICANE WOMAN.
Tracks: Hurricane woman / Summer days.
- 7" . . . . . . . . . . . . . . . . . . EMBS 349
Ember / '77.

### I BELIEVE IN YOU.
Tracks: I believe in you / I have won you baby.
- 7" . . . . . . . . . . . . . . . . . . . EMI 2718
EMI / Nov '77.

### NICE AND SLOW.
Tracks: Nice and slow / You came you saw you conquered / Greatest love / Don't knock my love / You're a miracle / Highways of the sea / Flip / You are the star / Let's get it on / Easy / Don't let me down.
- LP . . . . . . . . . . . . . . . . . . . EMC 3164
EMI / Feb '77.

### NICE AND SLOW.
Tracks: Nice and slow / Come with me.
- 7" . . . . . . . . . . . . . . . . . . . EMI 2492
EMI / Aug '76.

### NICE AND SLOW (REISSUES).
Tracks: Nice and slow / Gimmi gimmi your loving.
- 12". . . . . . . . . . . . . . . . . . . EXCL 520
Excalibur / Jun '82.
- 12". . . . . . . . . . . . . . . . . . . . RBL 01
Red Bus / Aug '87.
- 12". . . . . . . . . . . . . . . . . . . JESSE T2
- 12". . . . . . . . . . . . . . . . . . . JESSE 2
Atlas / Jul '87.

### WILL YOU, WON'T YOU.
Tracks: Will you, won't you / I have won you baby.
- 7" . . . . . . . . . . . . . . . . . . . EMI 2603
EMI / Mar '77.

### YOUR LOVE.
Tracks: Your love / Your love(Instrumental).
- 12". . . . . . . . . . . . . . . . . . . JESSET 1
- 7" . . . . . . . . . . . . . . . . . . . JESSE 1
BMW / Oct '86.

## Green, Tee

### SOMEDAY WE'LL ALL BE FREE.
Tracks: Someday we'll all be free.
- 12". . . . . . . . . . . . . . . . . . . EZY 1201
Debut (1) / Jul '92.

## Greene, Laura

### CAN'T HELP LOVIN' THAT MAN.
Tracks: Can't help lovin' dat man / It's a good day for a parade.
- 7" . . . . . . . . . . . . . . . . . . . GRP 135
Grapevine (Northern Soul) / Dec '79.

## Gregory, Dennis

### LOVE'S GONNA LOVE.
Tracks: Love's gonna love / Lost in this love affair.
- 12". . . . . . . . . . . . . . . . . . . SCD 016
Sound City / Nov '85.

### OH YOUNG LADY.
Tracks: Oh young lady / Young lady (Dub).
- 12". . . . . . . . . . . . . . . . . . . SCD 017
Sound City / Jul '86.

### TONIGHT I'M STAYING HERE WITH YOU.
Tracks: Tonight I'm staying here with you / After the party.
- 7" . . . . . . . . . . . . . . . . . . . SCD 014
Sound City / Apr '85.

## Grey & Hanks

### DANCIN'.
Tracks: Dancin' / How can y ou live without love.
- 12". . . . . . . . . . . . . . . . . . . PC 1458
- 7" . . . . . . . . . . . . . . . . . . . PB 1458
RCA / Feb '79.

### NOW I'M FINE.
Tracks: Now I'm fine / Love's in command.
- 12". . . . . . . . . . . . . . . . . . . PC 1922
RCA / Mar '80.

### YOU FOOLED ME.
Tracks: You fooled me / Dancin'.
- 7" . . . . . . . . . . . . . . . . . . . DDC 007
RCA / Jun '79.

## Grier, Roosevelt

### IN MY TENEMENT.
Tracks: In my tenement / Wrapped tied and tangled.
- 7" . . . . . . . . . . . . . . . . . . . HRH 002
Horaces / '88.

## Griffin, Angee

### GENTLE.
Tracks: Not Advised.
- LP . . . . . . . . . . . . . . . . . . . SL 7000
Skyline / Sep '89.

## Griffin, Billy

Given unenviable task of replacing Smokey Robinson in Miracles, Griffin proved himself up to task when City Of Angels album became one of Motown's biggest sellers. Attendant single Love Machine topped U.S. chart in '76 and made U.K. Top Five. Ironically, group then left for CBS and split within two years. Meanwhile, Griffin embarked on solo career which eventually netted him U.K. hit with Hold Me Tighter In the Rain in '83. Held back by contractual disputes with CBS, he became backing singer until resuming career in '89, going on to join reunited Miracles.

### BE WITH ME.
Tracks: Be with me / Stone's throw from heaven / Hold me tighter in the rain / Love is not a word / Beat is getting stronger / 2nd day love story / Breaking out / Understand.
- LP . . . . . . . . . . . . . . . . . . . CBS 85591
CBS / Feb '83.

### BE WITH ME.
Tracks: Be with me / Stones throw from heaven.
- 12". . . . . . . . . . . . . . . . . . . A 13 3209
- 7" . . . . . . . . . . . . . . . . . . . A 3209
CBS / Mar '83.

### BELIEVE IT OR NOT.
Tracks: Believe it or not / E.S.P.
- 7" . . . . . . . . . . . . . . . . . . . A 9374
- 12". . . . . . . . . . . . . . . . . . . A 9374 T
Atlantic / Nov '86.

### GIRL IS FINE, THE.
Tracks: Girl is fine / E.S.P.
- 12". . . . . . . . . . . . . . . . . . . A 9275 T
- 7" . . . . . . . . . . . . . . . . . . . A 9275
Atlantic / Apr '87.

### HOLD ME TIGHTER IN THE RAIN.
Tracks: Hold me tighter in the rain / Understand.
- 12". . . . . . . . . . . . . . . . . . . A 132935
- 7" . . . . . . . . . . . . . . . . . . . A 2935
CBS / Jan '83.

## HOLD ME TIGHTER IN THE RAIN (OLD GOLD).
**Tracks:** Hold me tighter in the rain / Serious.
■ **7"** . . . . . . . . . . . . . . . . . . . . . . . .OG 9563
Old Gold / Sep '85.
■ **12"** . . . . . . . . . . . . . . . . . . . . . . .OG 4077
Old Gold / Aug '88.

## IF I EVER LOSE THIS HEAVEN.
**Tracks:** If i ever lose this heaven / This ain't puppy love.
■ **12"** . . . . . . . . . . . . . . . . . . . . . TX 6415
■ **7"** . . . . . . . . . . . . . . . . . . . . . . .A 6415
CBS / Jul '85.

## RESPECT.
**Tracks:** Respect / Don't stop lovin' me / Serious / Save your love for me / Don't ask me to be friends / So many ways / Hit me with the beat / Dreaming.
■ **LP** . . . . . . . . . . . . . . . . . . . . CBS 25697
CBS / Apr '84.

## SERIOUS.
**Tracks:** Serious / Hit me with the beat.
■ **7"** . . . . . . . . . . . . . . . . . . . . . . .A 4053
CBS / Jan '84.

## SYSTEMATIC.
**Tracks:** Systematic / If i ever lose this heaven / Waiting to touch / This ain't puppy love / Electrified / Everybody needs somebody / Easy thing to say / Can't keep running away.
■ **LP** . . . . . . . . . . . . . . . . . . . . CBS 26449
CBS / Jul '85.

## Grusin, Dave

### COLLECTION: DAVE GRUSIN.
**Tracks:** Not Advised.
CD . . . . . . . . . . . . . . . . . . . . . . . GR 95792
■ **LP** . . . . . . . . . . . . . . . . . . . . . GR 95793
■ **MC** . . . . . . . . . . . . . . . . . . . . . GR 95794
GRP / Jan '89 / BMG / New Note.

### DAVE GRUSIN AND NY-LA DREAM BAND (Grusin, Dave & NY-LA Dream Band).
**Tracks:** Shuffle city / Count down / Serengeti walk / Champ, The (theme from) / What matters most / Three days of the condor.
■ **CD** . . . . . . . . . . . . . . . . . . . GRPD 9501
GRP / Jun '84.
■ **LP** . . . . . . . . . . . . . . . . . . . . GRP 91001
■ **MC** . . . . . . . . . . . . . . . . . . . GRPM 91001
GRP / Sep '88.

### DAVE GRUSIN AND NY-LA DREAM BAND (Grusin, Dave & NY-LA Dream Band).
**Tracks:** Number 8 / Morning glory / Count down / Mountain dance / Heart is a lonely hunter / Heaven can wait / Three days of the condor / What matters most / Summer sketches / Anthem internationale.
■ **VHS** . . . . . . . . . . . . . . . . . . . GRV 9501
GRP Video / Jul '92.

### DISCOVERED AGAIN.
**Tracks:** Not Advised.
■ **LP** . . . . . . . . . . . . . . . . . . . . . . .ST 500
Sheffield Treasury / Oct '82.

### FLIP OF THE COIN (Grusin, Dave & Stanley Turrentine).
**Tracks:** Don't touch / It's gotta be me / Same old me / Flip of the coin / Love's finally found me / Brown eyed woman / Ma cherie amour / Yesterme yesteryou yesterday / Wedding bell blues.
■ **LP** . . . . . . . . . . . . . . . . . . . . MAN 5008
Manhattan Records / Jun '80.

### GERSHWIN CONNECTION,THE.
**Tracks:** Not Advised.
CD . . . . . . . . . . . . . . . . . . . . . GRP 20052
■ **LP** . . . . . . . . . . . . . . . . . . . . GRP 20051
■ **MC** . . . . . . . . . . . . . . . . . . . GRP 20054
GRP / Oct '91 / BMG / New Note.
DCC . . . . . . . . . . . . . . . . . . . . . GRX 20055
GRP / Jan '93 / BMG / New Note.

### GRUSIN COLLECTION, THE.
**Tracks:** Not Advised.
CD . . . . . . . . . . . . . . . . . . . . . GRP 95792
■ **LP** . . . . . . . . . . . . . . . . . . . . GRP 95791
■ **MC** . . . . . . . . . . . . . . . . . . . GRP 95794
GRP / Aug '91 / BMG / New Note.

### HARLEQUIN (Grusin, Dave & Lee Ritenour).
**Tracks:** Harlequin / Early a.m. attitude / San Y Sidro / Before it's too late / Cats of Rio / Grid lock / Silent message / Bird.
■ **LP** . . . . . . . . . . . . . . . . . . . . GRPA 1015

---

GRP / Aug '85.
■ **LP** . . . . . . . . . . . . . . . . . . . GRP 91015
■ **MC** . . . . . . . . . . . . . . . . . . GRPM 91015
GRP / Sep '88.
■ **DCC** . . . . . . . . . . . . . . . . . GRX 95225
GRP / Jan '93.

### HOMAGE TO DUKE.
**Tracks:** Cotton tail / Things ain't what they used to be / Satin doll / Mood indigo / Just squeeze me (But don't tease me) / Caravan / East St. Louis toodle-oo / C jam blues / Duke / Sophisticated lady / Take the 'A' train.
CD . . . . . . . . . . . . . . . . . . . . . GRP 97222
GRP / May '93 / BMG / New Note.

### LIVE IN JAPAN.
**Tracks:** Modaji / Trade winds / Shamballa / Friends and strangers / Band introduction / Uh oh / Don and Dave / Captain caribe.
■ **MC** . . . . . . . . . . . . . . . . . . . . .409339
■ **CD** . . . . . . . . . . . . . . . . . . . . .259339
■ **LP** . . . . . . . . . . . . . . . . . . . . .209339
Arista / Oct '88.

### MIGRATION.
**Tracks:** Not Advised.
CD . . . . . . . . . . . . . . . . . . . . GRP 95922
■ **LP** . . . . . . . . . . . . . . . . . . . GRP 95921
■ **MC** . . . . . . . . . . . . . . . . . . GRP 95924
GRP / Sep '89 / BMG / New Note.

### MOUNTAIN DANCE.
**Tracks:** Rag bag / Friends and strangers / City lights / Rondo-"if you hold out your hand" / Thanksong / Capitain Caribe / Either way / Mountain dance.
■ **LP** . . . . . . . . . . . . . . . . . . . . GRP 5010
GRP / '83.
■ **LP** . . . . . . . . . . . . . . . . . . . GRP 91018
■ **MC** . . . . . . . . . . . . . . . . . . . . .C 1018
■ **CD** . . . . . . . . . . . . . . . . . . GRPD 9507
GRP / Sep '85.

### NIGHT LINES.
**Tracks:** Secret place / Night-lines / Kitchen dance / Somewhere between old and New York / Bossa barbeque / Power Wave / Thankful 'n' thoughtful / St. Elsewhere / Haunting me.
■ **Double LP** . . . . . . . . . . . . . . GRP 91006
■ **MC** . . . . . . . . . . . . . . . . . . . GRPC 1006
■ **CD Set** . . . . . . . . . . . . . . . . GRPD 9504
GRP / Sep '84.

### ONE OF A KIND.
**Tracks:** Modaji / Heart of the lonely hunter / Catavento / Montage / Playera.
■ **LP** . . . . . . . . . . . . . . . . . . . GRP 91011
■ **MC** . . . . . . . . . . . . . . . . . . GRPM 90101
GRP / Sep '88.
CD . . . . . . . . . . . . . . . . . . . . . GRP 95142
GRP / Dec '93 / BMG / New Note.

### ORCHESTRAL ALBUM, THE.
**Tracks:** Cuba libre (Se fue) / Santa Clara suite (Four movements) / Three cowboy songs (Three movements) / Medley (Bess you is my woman/I loves you Porgy) / Suite from the Milagro Beanfield War (Five movements) / Heart is a lonely hunter / Summer sketches / Condor / On Golden Pond.
CD . . . . . . . . . . . . . . . . . . . . . GRP 97972
GRP / Oct '94 / BMG / New Note.

### OUT OF THE SHADOWS.
**Tracks:** Last train to Paradiso / She could be mine / Crystal morning / Five brothers / Athem internationale / Serengeti walk / Hokkaido / Sweetwater nights.
■ **LP** . . . . . . . . . . . . . . . . . . . . .204719
Arista / Jun '82.
■ **CD** . . . . . . . . . . . . . . . . . . . GRD 9511
GRP / Aug '88.
■ **CD** . . . . . . . . . . . . . . . . . . GRP 95112
GRP / Jan '93.

### PRESENTS THE GRP ALL-STAR BIG BAND.
**Tracks:** Oleo / My man's gone now / Sing, sing, sing / Manteca / Blues for Howard / Cherokee / Blue train / 'S wonderful / Sister Sadie.
CD . . . . . . . . . . . . . . . . . . . . . GRP 97402
GRP / Oct '93 / BMG / New Note.

### PRESENTS THE GRP ALL-STAR BIG BAND.
**Tracks:** Not Advised.
VHS . . . . . . . . . . . . . . . . . . . . GRV 9740
GRP / Oct '93 / BMG / New Note.

### STICKS AND STONES (Grusin, Dave & Don).
**Tracks:** Not Advised.
■ **LP** . . . . . . . . . . . . . . . . . . . GRP 91051
■ **MC** . . . . . . . . . . . . . . . . . . GRPM 91051

---

■ **CD** . . . . . . . . . . . . . . . . . . . GRPD 9562
GRP / Jul '88.

### SUPER LIVE 2 (Grusin, Dave/Lee Ritenour/Chick Corea).
**Tracks:** Not Advised.
■ **LP** . . . . . . . . . . . . . . . . . . . . . .A 1650
■ **CD** . . . . . . . . . . . . . . . . . . . . . .D 1650
■ **MC** . . . . . . . . . . . . . . . . . . . . . .C 1650
GRP / Feb '88.

## Guinn

### GUINN.
**Tracks:** Dreamin' / Open your door / I can't live without you / Slow down / Sincerely / People will be people / Give everything you got for love.
■ **LP** . . . . . . . . . . . . . . . . . . . . ZL 72418
■ **MC** . . . . . . . . . . . . . . . . . . . ZK 72418
Motown / Jun '86.

### OPEN YOUR DOOR.
**Tracks:** Open your door / Sincerely.
■ **7"** . . . . . . . . . . . . . . . . . . . .GUINN 1
■ **12"** . . . . . . . . . . . . . . . . . . .GUINN 1T
Motown / Apr '86.

### PEOPLE WILL BE PEOPLE.
**Tracks:** People will be people / Dreamin'.
■ **12"** . . . . . . . . . . . . . . . . . . . GUNNT 2
■ **7"** . . . . . . . . . . . . . . . . . . . . GUNN 2
Motown / Jul '86.

## Guthrie, Gwen

### AIN'T NOTHIN' GOIN' ON BUT THE RENT.
**Tracks:** Ain't nothin' goin' on but the rent (remix) / Ain't nothin' goin' on but the rent.
■ **CD Single** . . . . . . . . . . . . PZCD 276
■ **MC Single** . . . . . . . . . . . . POCS 276
■ **12"** . . . . . . . . . . . . . . . . . . . . .PZ 276
Polydor / Aug '93.

### AIN'T NOTHIN' GOIN' ON BUT THE RENT (OLD GOLD).
**Tracks:** Ain't nothin' goin' on but the rent / (They long to be) close to you.
■ **12"** . . . . . . . . . . . . . . . . . . . .OG 4084
Old Gold / Nov '88.

### AIN'T NOTHING GOIN' ON BUT THE RENT.
**Tracks:** Ain't nothin' goin' on but the rent / Passions eyes.
■ **12"** . . . . . . . . . . . . . . . . . . POSPX 807
■ **7"** . . . . . . . . . . . . . . . . . . . POSP 807
Boiling Point / Jul '86.

### CAN'T LOVE YOU TONIGHT.
**Tracks:** Can't love you tonight / Surgeon General's funky 4-4 beat.
■ **12"** . . . . . . . . . . . . . . . . . . W 7990T
■ **7"** . . . . . . . . . . . . . . . . . . . W 7990
WEA / Apr '88.

### CLOSE TO YOU.
**Tracks:** Close to you / You touch my life / Save your love for me (Extra track available on 12" version only).
■ **7"** . . . . . . . . . . . . . . . . . . . POSP 822
■ **12"** . . . . . . . . . . . . . . . . . . POSPX 822
Polydor / Sep '86.

### EYES (YOU NEVER REALLY CARED).
**Tracks:** Eyes (You never really cared).
■ **12"** . . . . . . . . . . . . . . . . . . HTR 1001
■ **CD Single** . . . . . . . . . . . . CDHTR 1001
Total / Oct '92.

### FAMILY AFFAIR.
**Tracks:** Family affair / Peek-a-boo / It should have been you.
■ **12"** . . . . . . . . . . . . . . . . . . 12 BRW 86
■ **7"** . . . . . . . . . . . . . . . . . . . BRW 86
4th & Broadway / Jan '88.

### FOR YOU.
**Tracks:** For you / Peek-a-boo.
■ **12"** . . . . . . . . . . . . . . . . . . 12WIP 6827
■ **7"** . . . . . . . . . . . . . . . . . . . WIP 6827
Island / Oct '82.

### FRIENDS AND LOVERS (Guthrie, Gwen & Boris Gardiner).
**Tracks:** Friends and lovers.
■ **12"** . . . . . . . . . . . . . . . . . . . CRT 1
■ **7"** . . . . . . . . . . . . . . . . . . . . .CR 1
Creole / Aug '87.

### GOOD TO GO LOVER.
**Tracks:** Close to you / Outside in the rain / Good to go lover / You touch my life / Ain't nothin' goin' on

but the rent / I still want you / Stop holding back / Passion eyes.
- **LP** . . . . . . . . . . . . . . . . . . . **POLD 5201**
- **MC** . . . . . . . . . . . . . . . . . . . **POLDC 5201**
- **CD** . . . . . . . . . . . . . . . . . . . **829 532-2**

Polydor / Oct '86.

## GOOD TO GO LOVER.
**Tracks:** Good to go lover / Outside in the rain (US remix).
- **12"** . . . . . . . . . . . . . . . . . . . **POSPX 841**
- **7" Set** . . . . . . . . . . . . . . . . . **POSPD 841**
- **7"** . . . . . . . . . . . . . . . . . . . **POSP 841**

Boiling Point / Feb '87.

## GWEN GUTHRIE.
**Tracks:** Not Advised.
- **LP** . . . . . . . . . . . . . . . . . . . **ILPS 9699**
- **MC** . . . . . . . . . . . . . . . . . . . **ICT 9690**

Island / Jan '86.

## HOPSCOTCH.
**Tracks:** Hopscotch / You're the one.
- **12"** . . . . . . . . . . . . . . . . . . **12 IS 106**
- **7"** . . . . . . . . . . . . . . . . . . . **IS 106**

Island / Jul '83.

## IT SHOULD HAVE BEEN YOU.
**Tracks:** It should have been you / God don't like ugly.
- **12"** . . . . . . . . . . . . . . . . . . **12WIP 6757**
- **7"** . . . . . . . . . . . . . . . . . . . **WIP 6757**

Island / Apr '82.

## JUST FOR YOU.
**Tracks:** Put your love in control / Love in moderation / Just for you / I gotta have you / Feel it no more / Oh Donny no / Joy riders / Thrill me.
- **LP** . . . . . . . . . . . . . . . . . . . **BRLP 505**
- **MC** . . . . . . . . . . . . . . . . . . . **BRCA 505**

4th & Broadway / Mar '85.
- **LP** . . . . . . . . . . . . . . . . . . . **BRLM 505**
- **MC** . . . . . . . . . . . . . . . . . . . **BRCM 505**

4th & Broadway / Apr '87.

## LIFELINE.
**Tracks:** Destiny / Too many fish in the sea / Rockin' chair / What would I do without you / Bye bye lover / Don't take your love from me / Can't love you tonight / Once more with feeling / Send me somebody.
- **CD** . . . . . . . . . . . . . . . . . . . **9256982**
- **LP** . . . . . . . . . . . . . . . . . . . **WX 154**
- **MC** . . . . . . . . . . . . . . . . . . . **WX 154C**

WEA / May '88.

## LOVE IN MODERATION.
**Tracks:** Love in moderation / Padlock / Motivation (Only on 12" single.).
- **7"** . . . . . . . . . . . . . . . . . . . **BRW 17**
- **12"** . . . . . . . . . . . . . . . . . . **12 BRW 17**

4th & Broadway / Jan '85.

## MISS MY LOVE.
**Tracks:** Miss my love / Miss my love (inst).
- **12"** . . . . . . . . . . . . . . . . . . **W 9763T**
- **7"** . . . . . . . . . . . . . . . . . . . **W 9763**

Reprise / Nov '90.

## OUTSIDE IN THE RAIN.
**Tracks:** Outside in the rain / I still want you.
- **12"** . . . . . . . . . . . . . . . . . . **POSBX 841**
- **7"** . . . . . . . . . . . . . . . . . . . **POSB 841**

Boiling Point / Nov '86.

## PADLOCK.
**Tracks:** Peanut butter prelude / Hopscotch / Seventh heaven / Getting hot / Peanut butter / Padlock.
- **MC** . . . . . . . . . . . . . . . . . . . **IMC 2**
- **LP** . . . . . . . . . . . . . . . . . . . **IMA 2**

Garage (1) / May '85.

## PORTRAIT: GWEN GUTHRIE.
**Tracks:** Peanut butter / Seventh heaven / You're the one / Family affair / Hopscotch / Younger than me / Padlock / Oh what a life.
- **MC** . . . . . . . . . . . . . . . . . . . **ICT 9758**
- **LP** . . . . . . . . . . . . . . . . . . . **ILPS 9758**

Island / Aug '83 / PolyGram.

## SEVENTH HEAVEN.
**Tracks:** Seventh heaven / It should have been you / Getting hot (Extra track available on 12").
- **7"** . . . . . . . . . . . . . . . . . . . **BRW 52**
- **12"** . . . . . . . . . . . . . . . . . . **12 BRW 52**

4th & Broadway / Sep '86.

## THEY LONG TO BE CLOSE TO YOU.
**Tracks:** (They long to be) close to you.
- **7"** . . . . . . . . . . . . . . . . . . . **POSP 822**

Boiling Point / Oct '86.

## THIS CHRISTMAS EVE.
**Tracks:** This Christmas eve.
- **12"** . . . . . . . . . . . . . . . . . . **HOTT 1**
- **CD Single** . . . . . . . . . . . . . . . **HOTD 1**
- **MC Single** . . . . . . . . . . . . . . . **HOTC 1**

Hot Time / Nov '93.

## TICKET TO RIDE.
**Tracks:** Ticket to ride / Peek-a-boo / Younger than me / Oh what a life / It should have been you / You're the one / Family affair / Seventh heaven.
- **CD** . . . . . . . . . . . . . . . . . . . **BRCD 516**
- **LP** . . . . . . . . . . . . . . . . . . . **BRLP 516**
- **MC** . . . . . . . . . . . . . . . . . . . **BRCA 516**

4th & Broadway / Feb '88.

## Guy

## AWAKENING OF THE DEVIL.
**Tracks:** Not Advised.
- **VHS** . . . . . . . . . . . . . . . . . . **MANIA 1001**

Animania / Jul '94 / Total.

## DO ME RIGHT.
**Tracks:** Do me right.
- **12"** . . . . . . . . . . . . . . . . . . **MCST 1551**

MCA / Jul '91.
- **12" Remix** . . . . . . . . . . . . . . . **MCSX 1551**

Geffen / Jul '91.
- **7"** . . . . . . . . . . . . . . . . . . . **MCS 1551**
- **CD Single** . . . . . . . . . . . . . . . **MCSTD 1551**

MCA / Jul '91.

## FUTURE, THE.
**Tracks:** Not Advised.
- **MC** . . . . . . . . . . . . . . . . . . . **MCGC 6119**
- **CD** . . . . . . . . . . . . . . . . . . . **DMCG 6119**
- **LP** . . . . . . . . . . . . . . . . . . . **MCG 6119**

MCA / Nov '90.

## GROOVE ME.
**Tracks:** Groove me.
- **12"** . . . . . . . . . . . . . . . . . . **MCAT 1331**
- **7"** . . . . . . . . . . . . . . . . . . . **MCA 1331**

MCA / Apr '89.

## GUY.
**Tracks:** Not Advised.
- **LP** . . . . . . . . . . . . . . . . . . . **MCA 42176**

MCA / Jul '88.
- **CD** . . . . . . . . . . . . . . . . . . . **DMCG 6043**
- **LP** . . . . . . . . . . . . . . . . . . . **MCG 6043**
- **MC** . . . . . . . . . . . . . . . . . . . **MCGC 6043**

MCA / Apr '89.

## HER.
**Tracks:** Her.
- **12"** . . . . . . . . . . . . . . . . . . **MCST 1528**
- **7"** . . . . . . . . . . . . . . . . . . . **MCS 1528**
- **CD Single** . . . . . . . . . . . . . . . **MCSTD 1528**
- **MC Single** . . . . . . . . . . . . . . . **MCSTC 1528**

MCA / Apr '91.

## MY FANTASY (Guy Featuring Teddy Riley).
**Tracks:** My fantasy.
- **7"** . . . . . . . . . . . . . . . . . . . **MCA 1353**
- **CD Single** . . . . . . . . . . . . . . . **DMCAT 1353**
- **12"** . . . . . . . . . . . . . . . . . . **MCAT 1353**

MCA / Jul '89.

## Gypsies

## JERK IT.
**Tracks:** Jerk it / Diamonds, rubies, gold and fame.
- **7"** . . . . . . . . . . . . . . . . . . . **201785**

CBS / Jul '65.

# H

## H-Town

### FEVER FOR DA FLAVOR.
Tracks: Introduction / Can't fade da H / Treat U right / Fever for da flavor / Sex me / H-town bounce / Keepin' my composure / Interlude / Lick U up / Knockin' da boots / Won't U come back / Baby I wanna.
LP . . . . . . . . . . . . . . . . . . . . . . . . . .110701
Musidisc / Jun '93 / Vital Distribution / Discovery / A.D.A. Distribution / Harmonia Mundi (UK).
CD . . . . . . . . . . . . . . . . . . . . . . . . . .110702
MC . . . . . . . . . . . . . . . . . . . . . . . . . .110704
Musidisc / Apr '94 / Vital Distribution / Discovery / A.D.A. Distribution / Harmonia Mundi (UK).

### FLAVOR EP.
Tracks: Baby I wanna / Treat u right / Knockin' da boots.
12″. . . . . . . . . . . . . . . . . . . . . . . . . .112226
CD Single . . . . . . . . . . . . . . . . . . . . . .112222
Musidisc / Mar '94 / Vital Distribution / Discovery / A.D.A. Distribution / Harmonia Mundi (UK).

### KNOCKIN' DA BOOTS.
Tracks: Knockin' da boots (mixes) / H-town bounce (mixes).
■ 12″. . . . . . . . . . . . . . . . . . . . . . . . .110716
■ CD Single . . . . . . . . . . . . . . . . . . . . .110712
Musidisc / Jun '93.

## Hairston, Curtis

### CHILLIN' OUT.
Tracks: Hold on (for me) / Chillin' out.
■ 12″. . . . . . . . . . . . . . . . . . . . . . . .A 9335 T
■ 7″ . . . . . . . . . . . . . . . . . . . . . . . . .A 9335
Atlantic / Nov '86.

### CURTIS HAIRSTON.
Tracks: Chillin' out / Let's make love tonight / You're my shining star / Hold on (for me) / All we have is love / Take charge / Morning after / Let me change your mind.
■ LP . . . . . . . . . . . . . . . . . . . . . . . .781 693-1
■ MC . . . . . . . . . . . . . . . . . . . . . . . .781 693-4
Atlantic / Jan '87.

### I WANT YOU (ALL TONIGHT).
Tracks: I want you(all tonight).
■ 12″. . . . . . . . . . . . . . . . . . . . . . . .RCAT 368
■ 7″ . . . . . . . . . . . . . . . . . . . . . . . . .RCA 368
RCA / Oct '83.
■ 12″. . . . . . . . . . . . . . . . . . . . . . . . .PT 40170
■ 7″ . . . . . . . . . . . . . . . . . . . . . . . . .PB 40169
RCA / Jun '85.

### I WANT YOUR LOVIN' (JUST A LITTLE BIT).
Tracks: I want your lovin' (just a little bit).
■ 12″. . . . . . . . . . . . . . . . . . . . . . . . .LONX 66
■ 7″ . . . . . . . . . . . . . . . . . . . . . . . . . .LON 66
London / Apr '85.

### MORNING AFTER, THE.
Tracks: Morning after.
■ 12″. . . . . . . . . . . . . . . . . . . . . . . . .A 9280 T
■ 7″ . . . . . . . . . . . . . . . . . . . . . . . . .A 9280
Atlantic / Feb '87.

## Hakim, Omar

### RHYTHM DEEP.
Tracks: Crucial 2 groove / Rhythm deep / Real side / Love is here to stay / Tears / Isolated lonely / Take my heart / Amethyst secrets / Angel delight / Constructive criticism / Sun always shines / Mystic's glance.
■ LP . . . . . . . . . . . . . . . . . . . . . .GRP 95851
■ CD . . . . . . . . . . . . . . . . . . . . . .GRP 95852
■ MC . . . . . . . . . . . . . . . . . . . . . .GRP 95854
GRP / Apr '89.

## Hale, Willie

### BEAVER FEVER (Hale, Willie 'Little Beaver').
Tracks: Thank you for my life / Don't get tired of me / I feel like crying / Party times / Groove on / Katy / Pearl.
■ LP . . . . . . . . . . . . . . . . . . . . . .TKR 83392
TK / Mar '81.

---

### GROOVE ON (Hale, Willie 'Little Beaver').
Tracks: Groove on / Party times.
■ 12″. . . . . . . . . . . . . . . . . . . . .TKR 137587
■ 7″ . . . . . . . . . . . . . . . . . . . . . . .TKR 7587
TK / Nov '80.

## Hall, Aaron

Guy graduate who released belated solo debut *The Truth* at close of 1993, having contributed to *Boomerang* soundtrack in '92 and scored U.S. R&B No. 1 smash with *Don't Be Afraid* Profile was maintained in '94 with appearance on *Above the Rim* soundtrack and duet with brother Damien on latter's debut, *Straight to the Point*.

### DON'T BE AFRAID.
Tracks: Don't be afraid.
■ 12″. . . . . . . . . . . . . . . . . . . . .MCST 1632
MCA / May '92.

### DON'T BE AFRAID (REMIX).
Tracks: Don't be afraid.
■ 12″ Remix. . . . . . . . . . . . . . . . . .MCSX 1631
MCA / May '92.

### TRUTH, THE.
Tracks: Prologue / Do anything / Open up / Get a little freaky with me / Pick up the phone / Don't be afraid (jazz you up version) / Intil I found you / You keep me crying (interlude) / Don't be afraid (introduction) / Don't be afraid (sex your down some mo' version) / Let's make love / When you need me / I miss you / Until the end of time / Epilogue.
CD . . . . . . . . . . . . . . . . . . . . . .MCD 10810
MC . . . . . . . . . . . . . . . . . . . . . .MCC 10810
■ LP . . . . . . . . . . . . . . . . . . . . .MCA 10810
MCA / Nov '93 / BMG.

## Hall, Randy

### I BELONG TO YOU.
Tracks: I've been watching you / Real man / I belong to you / Gentleman / Older woman, younger man / Feel my eyes / Glamour boys / She's my little star / I want to touch you.
■ LP . . . . . . . . . . . . . . . . . . . . . .MCF 3236
■ MC . . . . . . . . . . . . . . . . . . . . .MCFC 3236
MCA / Aug '84.

### I'VE BEEN WATCHING YOU.
Tracks: I've been watching you.
■ 12″. . . . . . . . . . . . . . . . . . . . .MCAT 912
■ 7″ . . . . . . . . . . . . . . . . . . . . . .MCA 912
MCA / Nov '84.

## Hambric, Billy

### SHE SAID GOODBYE.
Tracks: She said goodbye / I found true love.
■ 7″ . . . . . . . . . . . . . . . . . . . . . . .GRP 139
Grapevine (Northern Soul) / Dec '79.

## Hamilton, Edward

### BABY DON'T YOU WEEP (Hamilton, Edward & Arabians).
Tracks: Baby don't you weep / I'm gonna love you.
■ 7″ . . . . . . . . . . . . . . . . . . . . . . .GRP 134
Grapevine (Northern Soul) / Feb '80.

### BE CAREFUL GIRL.
Tracks: Be careful girl.
■ 12″. . . . . . . . . . . . . . . . . . . . . . .HL 002
Hot Line / '79.

## Hamilton, Roy

### THERE SHE IS.
Tracks: There she is / Panic on.
■ 7″ . . . . . . . . . . . . . . . . . . . . .MGM 1251
MGM (EMI) / '64.

### THOUSAND TEARS AGO, A.
Tracks: Thousand tears ago / Sweet violet.
■ 7″ . . . . . . . . . . . . . . . . . . . . .MGM 1268
MGM (EMI) / Mar '64.

---

### UNCHAINED.
Tracks: Don't let go / Great romance / I need your lovin' / Jungle fever / I'm gonna sit right down and cry / I'm on my way back home / Unchained melody / Ebb tide / Clock / I'll come running back to you / Since I fell for you / You're gonna need magic / Hurt / Don't come crying to me / You can have her / You'll never walk alone.
■ LP . . . . . . . . . . . . . . . . . . . . .CRB 1200
Charly R&B / Sep '88.

## Hamilton, Roy

### HOLD ON TIGHT.
Tracks: Hold on tight.
■ 7″ . . . . . . . . . . . . . . . . . . . . . .ECX 535
Excaliber / Nov '83.

### HOLD ONTO THIS MOOD.
Tracks: Hold onto this mood / Hold onto this mood (inst).
■ 12″ Remix. . . . . . . . . . . . . . . . .BRWX 67
■ 7″ . . . . . . . . . . . . . . . . . . . . . .BRW 67
■ 12″. . . . . . . . . . . . . . . . . . . .12 BRW 67
4th & Broadway / May '87.

### HOLD TIGHT.
Tracks: Hold tight.
■ 7″ . . . . . . . . . . . . . . . . . . . . . .EXC 535
■ 12″. . . . . . . . . . . . . . . . . . . . .EXCL 535
PRT / Apr '84.

### HOW DO YOU DO.
Tracks: How do you do / How do you do(instrumental mix).
■ 12″. . . . . . . . . . . . . . . . . . . . .EXCL 534
■ 7″ . . . . . . . . . . . . . . . . . . . . . .EXC 534
PRT / Jul '83.

### TAKE YOUR TIME.
Tracks: Take your time.
■ 12″. . . . . . . . . . . . . . . . . . . . .EXCL 522
■ 7″ . . . . . . . . . . . . . . . . . . . . . .EXC 522
PRT / Oct '82.

## Hammond, Clay

### STREETS WILL LOVE YOU.
Tracks: Streets will love you / License to steal / Too many irons in the fire / I know what love is / They don't makeum no more / Ask me for what you want / Part time love / Monkey.
CD . . . . . . . . . . . . . . . . . . . . .EJRCD 4014
■ LP . . . . . . . . . . . . . . . . . . . . . .EJR 4014
MC . . . . . . . . . . . . . . . . . . . .EJRMC 4014
Evejim / Nov '89 / Ichiban Records (UK) / Backs Distribution.

### STREETS WILL LOVE YOU.
Tracks: Streets will love you / License to steal.
■ 7″ . . . . . . . . . . . . . . . . . . . . . . .89 509
Evejim / Nov '89.

### TAKING HIS TIME.
Tracks: I'll make it up to you / Take your time / Something better / I'm gonna be sweeter / You brought it all on yourself / Love made the whole world multiply / Suzy do it better than you / Good side of my girl / You messed up my mind / My jealous girl / Do right woman / Left me cryin' / Gonna be some changes / I got a letter this morning / My sweet baby is coming home.
■ LP . . . . . . . . . . . . . . . . . . . . .KENT 081
Kent / Aug '88.

## Hammond, Fred

### DELIVERANCE.
Tracks: Not Advised.
CD . . . . . . . . . . . . . . . . . . . . .CDO 2978
Benson (USA) / May '93 / Word Records (UK).

## Hammond, Johnny

### BREAKOUT.
Tracks: It's too late / Workin' on a groovy thing / Never can say goodbye / Blues selah / Breakout.
LP . . . . . . . . . . . . . . . . . . . . . . . .KUL 3
Kudu / Aug '72.

■ DELETED

## GEARS/FOREVER TAURUS.
Tracks: Tell me what to do / Los conquistadores chocolates / Lost on 23rd Street / Shifting gears / Can't we smile / Old devil moon / Countdown / Walk in sunshine / Ghetto samba / Cosmic voyager / My ship / Forever Taurus.
■ CD Set . . . . . . . . . . . . . . . CDBPGD 037
BGP / Oct '92 / Pinnacle.

## Hancock, Herbie

Chicago-born, classically-trained keyboard player who studied engineering but quit for musical career. A member of jazz trumpeter Donald Byrd's band in early '60s, he then established parallel careers as solo artist and Miles Davis sideman. Inspired by Davis' excursions into rock, Hancock quit for similarly-inclined solo career; 1969 album *The Prisoner* was his first to include electric piano. He also began to dabble in jazz-funk. As disco gathered pace, Hancock scored first major commercial success with funky *Head Hunters* album, setting blueprint for follow-ups. 1978 U.K. hit single *I Thought It Was You* terminated his association with jazz; subsequent efforts were dance-orientated, peaking with 1983's hiphop extravaganza *Rockit*, a collaboration with Material. However, he won Oscar in 1986 for work on the soundtrack to Tavernier's jazz epic *Round Midnight*.

## AUTO DRIVE.
Tracks: Autodrive / Bomb.
■ 12" . . . . . . . . . . . . . . . . . . TA 3802
■ 7" . . . . . . . . . . . . . . . . . . .A 3802
CBS / Oct '83.

## BEST OF HERBIE HANCOCK.
Tracks: Doin' it / I thought it was you / Chameleon / Hang up your hang ups / You bet your love / Tell everybody.
■ LP . . . . . . . . . . . . . . . . . CBS 32526
MC. . . . . . . . . . . . . . . . . . .40 32526
CBS / Nov '84 / Sony.

## BEST OF HERBIE HANCOCK - THE BLUE NOTE YEARS.
Tracks: Watermelon man / Driftin' (CD only.) / Maiden voyage / Dolphin dance / One finger snap / Canteloupe island / Riot / Speak like a child / King cobra (CD only.).
CD. . . . . . . . . . . . . . . . . . .BNZ 143
■ LP . . . . . . . . . . . . . . . . . . B1 91142
Blue Note / Dec '88 / EMI.

## BY ALL MEANS.
Tracks: By all means / Do I have to.
■ 12" . . . . . . . . . . . . . . . . . . EXCL 509
■ 7" . . . . . . . . . . . . . . . . . . EXC 509
Excaliber / Jul '87.

## BY ALL MEANS (Hancock, Herbie & Alphonse Mouzon).
Tracks: Do I have to / Space invaders / Next time we love / Jogger / By all means.
■ LP . . . . . . . . . . . . . . . . . MPS 68 266
MPS Jazz / Apr '81.
■ CD . . . . . . . . . . . . . . . . . 817 485-2
Verve / Apr '84.

## CANTALOUPE ISLAND.
Tracks: Cantaloupe island / Watermelon man / Driftin' / Blind man / What it I don't / Maiden voyage.
CD. . . . . . . . . . . . . . . . . CDP 8293312
Blue Note / Jul '94 / EMI.

## COLLECTION: HERBIE HANCOCK.
Tracks: Chameleon / Watermelon man / Maiden voyage / I thought it was you / No means yes / Tell everybody / Rockit / Autodrive / Hard rock / Round midnight.
■ CD. . . . . . . . . . . . . . . . . CCSCD 283
■ MC. . . . . . . . . . . . . . . . . CCSMC 283
Castle Collector Series / Feb '91.

## CROSSINGS.
Tracks: Sleeping giant / Quasar / Water torture.
■ LP . . . . . . . . . . . . . . . . . K 46164
WEA / Jun '78.

## EMPYREAN ISLES.
Tracks: One finger snap / Oliloqui vall'     Canteloupe Island / Egg / One finger snap / Hoy (CD only.) / Oliloqui valley (alt. take) (CD only.).
■ LP . . . . . . . . . . . . . . . . . BST 84175
■ CD . . . . . . . . . . . . . . . . . .BNZ 185
Blue Note / Jul '89.

## EVENING WITH .., AN (Hancock, Herbie & Chick Corea).
Tracks: Homecoming / Ostinato / Hook / Bouquet / Maiden voyage / La fiesta.
■ Double LP. . . . . . . . . . . . . . 2672049
Polydor / Dec '79.

## EVENING WITH HERBIE HANCOCK AND CHICK COREA, AN (Hancock, Herbie & Chick Corea).
Tracks: Someday my Prince will come / Liza / Button up / February moments / Maiden voyage / La fiesta.
■ Double LP . . . . . . . . . . . . . CBS 88329
CBS / '79.

## FAT ALBERT ROTUNDA.
Tracks: Wiggle waggle / Fat mama / Tell me a bedtime story / Oh' here he comes / Jessica / Fat Albert Rotunda / Li'l brother.
■ LP . . . . . . . . . . . . . . . . . K 46039
WEA / '88.

## FEETS DON'T FAIL ME NOW.
Tracks: You bet your love / Trust me / Tell everybody / Ready or not / Honey from the jar / Knee deep.
■ LP . . . . . . . . . . . . . . . . . CBS 83491
CBS / Feb '79.
■ CD . . . . . . . . . . . . . . . . . CD 83491
CBS / Sep '85.
CD. . . . . . . . . . . . . . . . . .983311 2
Pickwick/Sony Collector's Choice / Oct '93 / Pickwick / Pinnacle.

## FUTURE SHOCK.
Tracks: Rockit / Future shock / TFS / Earthbeat / Autodrive / Rough.
■ LP . . . . . . . . . . . . . . . . . CBS 25540
■ MC. . . . . . . . . . . . . . . . . .40 25540
CBS / Aug '83.
■ LP . . . . . . . . . . . . . . . . . 4506251
■ MC. . . . . . . . . . . . . . . . . 4506254
CBS / Apr '87.
■ CD . . . . . . . . . . . . . . . .CDCBS 25540
CBS / '88.

## FUTURE SHOCK.
Tracks: Future shock.
■ 7" . . . . . . . . . . . . . . . . . .A 4075
CBS / Jan '84.

## GO FOR IT.
Tracks: Go for it / Making love.
■ 7" . . . . . . . . . . . . . . . . . CBS 8329
CBS / Apr '80.

## HANCOCK ALLEY.
Tracks: Jammin' with Herbie / Herbie's blues / Rock your soul / Scoochie / Cycles / Witch fire.
■ LP . . . . . . . . . . . . . . . . .MAN 5021
Manhattan Records / Jun '80.

## HARDROCK.
Tracks: Hardrock / T.F.S.
■ 12" . . . . . . . . . . . . . . . . . TA 4616
■ 7" . . . . . . . . . . . . . . . . . .A 4616
CBS / Aug '84.

## HEADHUNTERS.
Tracks: Chameleon / Watermelon man / Sly / Vein melter.
■ LP . . . . . . . . . . . . . . . . . CBS 32008
CBS / Apr '84.
■ CD . . . . . . . . . . . . . . . . . CD 65928
CBS / Jul '84.

## HERBIE HANCOCK AND THE ROCKIT BAND (Hancock, Herbie & The Rockit Band).
Tracks: Not Advised.
VHS . . . . . . . . . . . . . . . . . .661950
CBS / Oct '84 / Sony.

## HERBIE HANCOCK: GREATEST HITS.
Tracks: Doin' it / Thought it was you / Chameleon / Hang up your hang ups / You bet your love / Tell everybody.
■ LP . . . . . . . . . . . . . . . . . CBS 84106
MC. . . . . . . . . . . . . . . . . . .40 84106
CBS / Jan '80 / Sony.

## HOT AND HEAVY.
Tracks: Hot piano / Live and awake / Night walkers / Scoochie / Cycles / Witch fire (end s1) / Jammin' with erbie / Herbie's blues / Rock your soul / Afro boogie / Far out / Hot and heavy.
■ LP . . . . . . . . . . . . . . . . . CBR 1030
MC. . . . . . . . . . . . . . . . . . KCBR 1030
Premier (Sony) / '84 / Sony / Pinnacle.
■ LP . . . . . . . . . . . . . . . . . SJAZZ 4
MC. . . . . . . . . . . . . . . . . . SJAZZC 4
Star Jazz (USA) / Apr '86 / Charly.

## I THOUGHT IT WAS YOU.
Tracks: I thought it was you.
■ 7" . . . . . . . . . . . . . . . . . CBS 6530
CBS / May '82.

## I THOUGHT IT WAS YOU (OLD GOLD).
Tracks: I thought it was you / You bet your love.
■ 7" . . . . . . . . . . . . . . . . . .OG 9561
Old Gold / Sep '85.

## INVENTIONS AND DIMENSIONS.
Tracks: Succotash / Triangle / Jack rabbit / Mimosa / Jump ahead.
■ CD . . . . . . . . . . . . . . . . . .BNZ 154
■ LP . . . . . . . . . . . . . . . . . B1 84147
Blue Note / Apr '89.

## JAZZ COLLECTION, A.
Tracks: Liza / I fall in love too easily / Nefertiti / Someday my Prince will come / 'round midnight / Well you needn't / Parade / Eye of the hurricane / Maiden voyage.
MC. . . . . . . . . . . . . . . . . . 4679014
Columbia / Jun '91 / Sony.
■ CD . . . . . . . . . . . . . . . . . 4679012
Columbia / Jan '92.

## LITE ME UP.
Tracks: Lite me up / Bomb / Gettin' to the good part / Paradise / Can't hide your love / Fun tracks / Motormouth / Give it all your heart.
■ LP . . . . . . . . . . . . . . . . . CBS 32474
CBS / Jul '84.

## LITE ME UP.
Tracks: Lite me up / Satisfied with love.
■ 7" . . . . . . . . . . . . . . . . . .A 2222
CBS / Nov '82.

## LIVE IN NEW YORK.
Tracks: Not Advised.
CD . . . . . . . . . . . . . . . . . . JD 1274
Jazz Door / Nov '94 / Charly / Koch International / A.D.A. Distribution.

## MAGIC WINDOWS.
Tracks: Magic number / Tonight's the night / Everybody's broke / Help yourself / Satisfied with love / Twilight clone.
■ LP . . . . . . . . . . . . . . . . . CBS 85144
CBS / Nov '81.

## MAIDEN VOYAGE.
Tracks: Maiden voyage / Eye of the hurricane / Little one / Survival of the fittest / Dolphin dance.
MC. . . . . . . . . . . . . . . . . TCBST 841954
Blue Note / Mar '84 / EMI.
CD . . . . . . . . . . . . . . . CDP 746 339 2
EMI / Jan '86 / EMI.
■ MC. . . . . . . . . . . . . . . TCBST 84195
Blue Note / Mar '86.
CD. . . . . . . . . . . . . . . . . . BNZ 40
Blue Note / Jul '87 / EMI.
■ LP . . . . . . . . . . . . . . . . . BST 84195
Blue Note / Jul '89.

## MONSTER.
Tracks: Saturday night / Stars in your eyes / Go for it / Don't hold it in / Making love / It all comes round.
■ LP . . . . . . . . . . . . . . . . . CBS 84237
CBS / Jun '80.

## MR HANDS.
Tracks: Spiralling prism / Calypso / Just around the corner / 4 a.m. / Shifless shuffle / Textures.
MC. . . . . . . . . . . . . . . . . . .40 84638
CBS / Nov '80 / Sony.

## MWANDISHI.
Tracks: Ostinato (suite for Angela) / You'll know when you get there / Wandering spirit song.
■ LP . . . . . . . . . . . . . . . . . K 46077
WEA / '88.

## MY POINT OF VIEW.
Tracks: Blind man, blind man / Tribute to someone / King Cobra / Pleasure is mine / And what if I don't.
■ LP . . . . . . . . . . . . . . . . . BST 84126
Blue Note / Oct '84.
■ CD . . . . . . . . . . . . . . . . . BNZ 44
Blue Note / Apr '88.

## NIGHT WITH HERBIE.
Tracks: Hot piano / Live and awake / Night walkers / Afro boogie / Far out / Hot heavy.
■ LP . . . . . . . . . . . . . . . . .MAN 5027
Manhattan Records / Aug '80.

## PALM GREASE.
Tracks: Palm grease / Butterfly.
■ 7" . . . . . . . . . . . . . . . . . CBS 3059
CBS / Jan '75.

## PERFECT MACHINE.
**Tracks:** Perfect machine / Obsession / Vibe alive / Beat wise / Maiden voyage / Chemical residue.
■ LP . . . . . . . . . . . . . . . . . . . . . . 4606791
■ MC . . . . . . . . . . . . . . . . . . . . . . 4606794
■ CD . . . . . . . . . . . . . . . . . . . . . . 4606792
CBS / Jun '88.

## PRISONER, THE.
**Tracks:** I have a dream / Prisoner / Fire water / He who lives in fear / Promise of the sun.
■ LP . . . . . . . . . . . . . . . . . . . . . BST 84321
Blue Note / May '70.
■ CD . . . . . . . . . . . . . . . . . . . . . . BNZ 43
Blue Note / Aug '87.

## QUARTET.
**Tracks:** Well you needn't / Round midnight / Clear ways / Quick sketch / Eye of the hurricane / Parade / Sorcerer / Pee Wee / I fall in love too easily.
■ LP . . . . . . . . . . . . . . . . . . . . . . 22219
CBS / '84.

## QUARTET WITH WYNTON MARSALIS.
**Tracks:** Well you needn't / 'Round midnight / Clear ways / Quick sketch / Eye of the hurricane / Parade / Sorcerer / Pee wee / I fall in love too easily.
CD . . . . . . . . . . . . . . . . . . . . . . .465626 2
Columbia / Nov '93 / Sony.

## ROCKIT.
**Tracks:** Rockit / Rough.
■ 12" . . . . . . . . . . . . . . . . . . . . . . TA 3577
■ 7" . . . . . . . . . . . . . . . . . . . . . . .A 3577
CBS / '83.

## ROCKIT (OLD GOLD).
**Tracks:** Rockit / You bet your love / I thought it was you / Future shock.
■ 12" . . . . . . . . . . . . . . . . . . . . . .OG 4001
Old Gold / Feb '86.

## SONGS FOR MY FATHER.
**Tracks:** Not Advised.
■ MC . . . . . . . . . . . . . . . . . . . 4BN 84195
Blue Note / Sep '87.

## SOUND-SYSTEM.
**Tracks:** Hardrock / Metal beat / Karabali / Junku / People are changing / Sound-system / Rockit (Extra track available on cassette only.) / Autodrive (Extra track available on cassette only.) / Future shock (Extra track available on cassette only.) / TFS (Extra track available on cassette only.) / Rough (Extra track available on cassette only.) / Chameleon (Extra track available on cassette only.).
■ CD . . . . . . . . . . . . . . . . . . . CD 26062
CBS / Dec '85.
■ LP . . . . . . . . . . . . . . . . . . CBS 32805
MC. . . . . . . . . . . . . . . . . . . . .40 32805
CBS / Aug '86 / Sony.

## SPEAK LIKE A CHILD.
**Tracks:** Riot / Speak like a child / First trip / Toys / Goodbye to childhood / Sorcerer.
■ LP . . . . . . . . . . . . . . . . . . . . BST 84279
Blue Note / Sep '68.
■ CD . . . . . . . . . . . . . . . . . . . . . BNZ 41
Blue Note / Jun '87.

## SUNLIGHT.
**Tracks:** I thought it was you / Come running to me / Sunlight / No means yes / Good question.
■ LP . . . . . . . . . . . . . . . . . . . . CBS 82240
■ MC . . . . . . . . . . . . . . . . . . . .40 82240
CBS / Jul '78.

## TAKIN' OFF.
**Tracks:** Watermelon man / Three bags full / Empty pockets / Maze / Driftin' / Alone and I.
■ LP . . . . . . . . . . . . . . . . . . . . BST 84109
Blue Note / Jul '82.
■ CD . . . . . . . . . . . . . . . . . . . . . BNZ 42
Blue Note / May '87.
■ MC . . . . . . . . . . . . . . . . . . 4BN 84109
Blue Note / Sep '87.

## TELL EVERYBODY.
**Tracks:** Tell everybody / Trust me.
■ 12" . . . . . . . . . . . . . . . . . . .CBS 127229
■ 7" . . . . . . . . . . . . . . . . . . . . CBS 7229
CBS / Apr '79.

## THIRD PLANE (Hancock, Herbie/Ron Carter/Tony Williams).
**Tracks:** Not Advised.
CD . . . . . . . . . . . . . . . . . . . .CA 98 134
Carrere (France) / '86.

## THRUST.
**Tracks:** Not Advised.
■ LP . . . . . . . . . . . . . . . . . . . . CBS 80193
CBS / Oct '74.

## VIBE ALIVE.
**Tracks:** Vibe alive / Vibe alive (ext. dance remix) (Available on 12" version only.) / Vibe alive (bonus beats) (Track on 12" version only.) / Maiden voyage.
■ 12" . . . . . . . . . . . . . . . . . . . . 6514328
■ 7" . . . . . . . . . . . . . . . . . . . . . 6514327
■ CD Single . . . . . . . . . . . . . . . . 6514329
CBS / May '88.

## VILLAGE LIFE.
**Tracks:** Moonlight / Ndan ndan nyaria / Early warning / Kanatente.
■ LP . . . . . . . . . . . . . . . . . . . . CBS 23697
CBS / '86.

## YOU BET YOUR LOVE.
**Tracks:** You bet your love / Knee deep.
■ 7" . . . . . . . . . . . . . . . . . . . . .CBS 7010
CBS / Feb '79.

## YOU BET YOUR LOVE (OLD GOLD).
**Tracks:** Rockit / You bet your love / I thought it was you.
CD Single . . . . . . . . . . . . . . . . . .OG 6502
Old Gold / Jul '90 / Pickwick.

# Handy, John

## ALL ABOARD (Handy, Capt. John & His New Orleans Stompers).
**Tracks:** Not Advised.
■ LP . . . . . . . . . . . . . . . . . . . . . GHB 42
GHB / Jun '86.

## ALL ABOARD WITH JIM ROBINSON (Handy, Capt. John).
**Tracks:** Not Advised.
■ LP . . . . . . . . . . . . . . . . . . . . . GHB 43
GHB / Jun '88.

## ALL ABOARD WITH RIMMINGTON (Handy, Capt. John).
**Tracks:** Not Advised.
■ LP . . . . . . . . . . . . . . . . . . . . . GHB 41
GHB / Jun '88.

## CAPT. JOHN HANDY & EASY RIDERS JAZZBAND.
**Tracks:** Not Advised.
CD . . . . . . . . . . . . . . . . . . . . .BCD 325
GHB / Apr '94 / Jazz Music.

## CAPT. JOHN HANDY & HIS NEW OR-LEANS STOMPERS VOL.1 (Handy, Capt. John).
**Tracks:** Not Advised.
CD . . . . . . . . . . . . . . . . . . . . . BCD 41
GHB / Aug '94 / Jazz Music.

## CAPT. JOHN HANDY & HIS NEW OR-LEANS STOMPERS VOL.2 (Handy, Capt. John & His New Orleans Stompers).
**Tracks:** Not Advised.
CD . . . . . . . . . . . . . . . . . . . . . BCD 42
GHB / Aug '94 / Jazz Music.

## CAPT. JOHN HANDY/GEOFF BULL/BARRY MARTYN'S BAND (Handy, Capt. John, Geoff Bull, Barry Martyn).
**Tracks:** Not Advised.
■ LP . . . . . . . . . . . . . . . . . . . . GHB 166
GHB / Feb '87.

## HARD WORK.
**Tracks:** Not Advised.
■ LP . . . . . . . . . . . . . . . . . . . .IMPL 8038
Impulse Jazz / Aug '76.

## HARD WORK.
**Tracks:** Hard work / Young enough to dream.
■ 12" . . . . . . . . . . . . . . . . . . . .MCAT 626
■ 7" . . . . . . . . . . . . . . . . . . . . MCA 626
MCA / May '82.

## LEGENDARY HANDY SESSIONS (LONDON).
**Tracks:** Not Advised.
■ LP . . . . . . . . . . . . . . . . . . . . GHB 251
GHB / Apr '89.

## RIGHT THERE.
**Tracks:** Not Advised.
■ LP . . . . . . . . . . . . . . . . . . . . MLP 3010
Gull / Apr '84.

## VERY FIRST RECORDINGS.
**Tracks:** Not Advised.
CD . . . . . . . . . . . . . . . . . . . . . AMCD 51
American Music / Apr '94 / Jazz Music.

## WHERE GO THE BOATS (Handy, John & Lee Ritenour).
**Tracks:** Not Advised.
CD . . . . . . . . . . . . . . . . . . . . INAK 861 CD
Inak / '88 / Koch International / New Note.

## WITH THE CLAUDE HOPKINS BAND (Handy, Capt. John).
**Tracks:** Not Advised.
■ LP . . . . . . . . . . . . . . . . . . . . NL 89503
RCA (France) / Feb '85.

# Happy Cats

## THESE BOOTS ARE MADE FOR WALKIN'.
**Tracks:** These boots are made for walkin' / Destroy that boy.
■ 7" . . . . . . . . . . . . . . . . . . . . .GRP 110
Grapevine (Northern Soul) / '78.

# Hardcastle, Paul

## 19.
**Tracks:** 19 / Fly by night / Don't waste my time.
■ 12" . . . . . . . . . . . . . . . . . .CHS 122860
■ 7" . . . . . . . . . . . . . . . . . . . CHS 2860
■ MC Single . . . . . . . . . . . . . ZCHS 2860
Chrysalis / Apr '85.
■ 12" . . . . . . . . . . . . . . . . . . . .OG 4236
Pickwick / Sep '92.

## ARE YOU READY (Hardcastle, Paul Sound Syndicate).
**Tracks:** Are you ready / Dark star.
■ 12" . . . . . . . . . . . . . . . . . . ONE 6605
■ 7" . . . . . . . . . . . . . . . . . . ONE 6105
■ CD Single . . . . . . . . . . . . . . ONE 6905
K-Tel / May '89.

## DON'T WASTE MY TIME.
**Tracks:** Don't waste my time / Moonhopper / Loiter-ing with intent (On 12" version only.).
■ 7" . . . . . . . . . . . . . . . . . . . . . PAUL 1
■ 12" . . . . . . . . . . . . . . . . . . . PAULX 1
Chrysalis / Jan '86.

## EAT YOUR HEART OUT.
**Tracks:** Eat your heart out.
■ 12" . . . . . . . . . . . . . . . . . .COOLX 102
■ 7" . . . . . . . . . . . . . . . . . . .COOL 102
Cool Tempo / Nov '84.

## FOOLIN' YOURSELF.
**Tracks:** Foolin' yourself / King Tut / Strollin' (On 12" version only.).
■ 12" . . . . . . . . . . . . . . . . . . . PAULX 2
■ 7" . . . . . . . . . . . . . . . . . . . . PAUL 2
Chrysalis / Jun '86.

## FORTY YEARS.
**Tracks:** Forty years / Movin' sound / Nineteen (on CD version only.) / Nineteen (the final story) (on CD version only.).
■ 12" . . . . . . . . . . . . . . . . . . . PAULX 5
■ 7" . . . . . . . . . . . . . . . . . . . . PAUL 5
■ CD Single . . . . . . . . . . . . . . PAULCD 5
Chrysalis / May '88.

## GUILTY.
**Tracks:** Guilty.
■ 7" . . . . . . . . . . . . . . . . . . . . .TOCO 2
Total Control / Jul '84.

## JUST FOR MONEY.
**Tracks:** Just for money / Back in time.
■ 12" . . . . . . . . . . . . . . . . . . . CASHX 1
■ 7" . . . . . . . . . . . . . . . . . . . . CASH 1
Chrysalis / Nov '85.

## LIVING FOR YOU (Hardcastle, Paul & Jaki Graham).
**Tracks:** Living for you.
■ 7" . . . . . . . . . . . . . . . . . . . . . KTS 1
Kiss The Sky / Jan '91.

## NO WINNERS.
**Tracks:** Not Advised.
■ LP . . . . . . . . . . . . . . . . . . . . CDL 1549
■ MC . . . . . . . . . . . . . . . . . . ZCDL 1549
■ CD . . . . . . . . . . . . . . . . . . CCD 1549
Chrysalis / May '88.

## PAPA'S GOT A BRAND NEW PIGBAG.
**Tracks:** Papa's got a brand new pig bag.
■ 12" . . . . . . . . . . . . . . . . . . .KAZ 50T

■ DELETED

■ 7″ . . . . . . . . . . . . . . . . . . . . . . KAZ 50
Kaz / Jul '85.

## PAUL HARDCASTLE.
**Tracks:** In the beginning / 19 / King Tut / Don't waste my time / Central Park / Just for money / Moonchopper / Better / Strollin' / Rain forest.
■ MC . . . . . . . . . . . . . . . . . . . . ZCHR 1517
■ LP . . . . . . . . . . . . . . . . . . . . . CHR 1517
Chrysalis / Nov '85.
■ CD . . . . . . . . . . . . . . . . . . . . . CCD 1517
Chrysalis / Apr '86.

## RAIN FOREST.
**Tracks:** Rain forest / Forest fire.
■ 12″ . . . . . . . . . . . . . . . . . . . . . . . BRT 8
Blue Bird (2) / Aug '84.
■ 12″ . . . . . . . . . . . . . . . . . . . . . . BRT 15
■ 7″ . . . . . . . . . . . . . . . . . . . . . . . BR 15
Blue Bird (2) / Jun '85.

## RAINFOREST (OLD GOLD).
**Tracks:** Rainforest / You're the one for me / Guilty / Daybreak / AM.
12″ . . . . . . . . . . . . . . . . . . . . . . . OG 4191
Old Gold / Sep '90 / Pickwick.

## SOUND SYNDICATE.
**Tracks:** Not Advised.
■ CD . . . . . . . . . . . . . . . . . . . . . NCD 3431
K-Tel / '88.

## WALK IN THE NIGHT.
**Tracks:** Walk in the night / Star wars / Just passin' through (Extra track on 12″ version.).
■ 12″ . . . . . . . . . . . . . . . . . . . . . PAULX 4
■ 7″ . . . . . . . . . . . . . . . . . . . . . . PAUL 4
Chrysalis / Mar '88.

## WIZARD, THE.
**Tracks:** Wizard, The (part 1) / Wizard, The (part 2).
■ 12″ . . . . . . . . . . . . . . . . . . . . . PAULX 3
■ 7″ . . . . . . . . . . . . . . . . . . . . . . PAUL 3
Chrysalis / Sep '86.

## WIZARD, THE.
**Tracks:** Nineteen / Don't waste my time / Just for the money / Wizard / Eat your heart out / Foolin' yourself / Walk in the night / 40 years / King Tut / Central Park / Moonhopper.
■ CD . . . . . . . . . . . . . . . . . . . . . CCDD 1885
■ MC . . . . . . . . . . . . . . . . . . . . CCMC 1885
Chrysalis / Mar '93.

## YOU'RE THE ONE FOR ME.
**Tracks:** You're the one for me.
■ 12″ . . . . . . . . . . . . . . . . . . . . . TOCO 1
Total Control / Mar '84.

## ZERO ONE.
**Tracks:** Forest fire / Panic / Rain forest / Sound chaser / Zero one / Ready-ready go / Drum beat / Hip hop beat.
■ LP . . . . . . . . . . . . . . . . . . . . . LPBR 1003
Blue Bird (2) / Feb '85.
■ CD . . . . . . . . . . . . . . . . . . . . . CDBR 1003
Blue Bird (2) / Jul '86.

# Harewood, Dorian

## LOVE WILL STOP CALLING.
**Tracks:** Not Advised.
CD . . . . . . . . . . . . . . . . . . . . . . CDER 1001
LP . . . . . . . . . . . . . . . . . . . . . . . . ER 1001
MC . . . . . . . . . . . . . . . . . . . . . . ZCER 1001
Ichiban / Nov '88 / A.D.A. Distribution / Pinnacle / ACD Trading Ltd. / Koch International / Direct Distribution.

## SHOW ME (ONE MORE TIME).
**Tracks:** Show me (one more time) / No excuses.
■ 12″ . . . . . . . . . . . . . . . . . . . . . 12 PO 17
■ 7″ . . . . . . . . . . . . . . . . . . . . . . 7 PO 17
Ichiban / Nov '88.

# Harp, Everette

## COMMON GROUND.
**Tracks:** Strutt / Feel so right / Jeri's song / You make me feel brand new / Stay with me / I'm sorry / Sending my love / Love you to the letter / Perfect day (Tessa's smile) / Where do we go / Coming home / Common ground / Song for toots.
CD . . . . . . . . . . . . . . . . . . . . . CDP 7892972
Blue Note / Aug '94 / EMI.

## EVERETTE HARP.
**Tracks:** Full circle / More than you'll ever know / There's still hope / Thank you for all your love / Let's wait a while / Remember my love / Funk a le gonk / When I think of you / He'll never leave / If I had to live my life without you / You made it better / Freefall Tomorrow.

■ LP . . . . . . . . . . . . . . . . . . . . . . B1 96242
■ CD . . . . . . . . . . . . . . . . . . . . CDP 7962422
Blue Note / Aug '92.

# Harper, Bud

## MR. SOUL.
**Tracks:** Mr. Soul / Let me love you.
■ 7″ . . . . . . . . . . . . . . . . . . . . . . VP 9252
Vocalion / Nov '65.

# Harriet

## TEMPLE OF LOVE.
**Tracks:** Temple of love / Animal.
■ 12″ . . . . . . . . . . . . . . . . . . . . . YZ 505T
■ 7″ . . . . . . . . . . . . . . . . . . . . . . YZ 505W
■ 7″ . . . . . . . . . . . . . . . . . . . . . . . YZ 505
■ CD Single . . . . . . . . . . . . . . . . YZ 505CD
■ MC Single . . . . . . . . . . . . . . . . . YZ 505C
East West / Aug '90.

## WOMAN TO MAN.
**Tracks:** Temple of love / Magic bed / Takes a little time / Only the lonely/Good girl / Woman to man / Fool am I / Wish.
CD . . . . . . . . . . . . . . . . . . . . . 9031721102
■ LP . . . . . . . . . . . . . . . . . . . . . WX 358
MC . . . . . . . . . . . . . . . . . . . . . WX 358C
East West / Oct '90 / WEA.

## WOMAN TO MAN.
**Tracks:** Woman to man / Money talking / What you gonna do (CD single & cassingle only.).
■ 12″ . . . . . . . . . . . . . . . . . . . . . YZ 535 T
■ 7″ . . . . . . . . . . . . . . . . . . . . . . YZ 535
■ CD Single . . . . . . . . . . . . . . . . YZ 535 CD
■ MC Single . . . . . . . . . . . . . . . . . YZ 535 C
WEA / Oct '90.

# Harris, Betty

## RIDE YOUR PONY.
**Tracks:** Ride your pony.
■ 7″ . . . . . . . . . . . . . . . . . . . . . . CTD 102
Charly / Jul '80.

## SOUL PERFECTION.
**Tracks:** Ride your pony / What a sad feeling / Bad luck / I'm gonna git ya / Show it / Can't last much longer / I don't wanna hear it / Sometime / Mean man / Lonely hearts / Hook line 'n' sinker / What'd I do wrong / Trouble with my lover / Nearer to you / I'm evil tonight / 12 red roses.
■ LP . . . . . . . . . . . . . . . . . . . . . ACLP 6007
B & C / Jun '69.

# Harris, Damon

## IT'S MUSIC.
**Tracks:** It's music / Ride on.
■ 7″ . . . . . . . . . . . . . . . . . . . . . . FTC 165
Fantasy / Jan '79.

## SILK.
**Tracks:** Silk / Funday.
■ 7″ . . . . . . . . . . . . . . . . . . . . . . FTC 172
Fantasy / '79.

# Harris, Eddie

## BEST OF EDDIE HARRIS, THE.
**Tracks:** Not Advised.
CD . . . . . . . . . . . . . . . . . . . . . 756781370-2
Atlantic / Jun '93 / WEA.

## BLACK SAX.
**Tracks:** Not Advised.
■ Double LP . . . . . . . . . . . . . . GNPS 2-2073
GNP Crescendo / '88.

## EDDIE (Harris, Eddie, Ralph Armstrong, Sherman Ferguson).
**Tracks:** Not Advised.
■ LP . . . . . . . . . . . . . . . . . . . . . . SJP 244
Timeless (Jazz) / Oct '86.

## EXODUS TO JAZZ.
**Tracks:** Exodus / Alicia / Gone home / A.T.C. / A.M. Blues / Little girl blue / Velocity / W.P.
■ LP . . . . . . . . . . . . . . . . . . . . . . ATS 10

■ MC . . . . . . . . . . . . . . . . . . . . TCATS 10
Atlantis / Apr '87.

## GET ON DOWN.
**Tracks:** Get on down / Time to do your own thing.
■ 7″ . . . . . . . . . . . . . . . . . . . . . K 10631
Atlantic / Jul '75.

## GET ON UP AND DANCE.
**Tracks:** Get on up and dance / Why must we part.
■ 7″ . . . . . . . . . . . . . . . . . . . . . K 10741
Atlantic / Apr '76.

## I'M TIRED OF DRIVING.
**Tracks:** Two times two equals love / You are the one / Songbird / I'm tired of driving / Loneliest monk / Theme for the foxy ladies / You stole my heart / There was a time / What's wrong with the world today.
■ LP . . . . . . . . . . . . . . . . . . . . . PL 12942
RCA / '79.

## LISTEN HERE.
**Tracks:** Funkaroma / I need some money / Listen here hi life / People get funny when they get a little money / Is it in / How can I find some way to show you / Walkin' the walk / Fusion jazz dance.
CD . . . . . . . . . . . . . . . . . . . ENJACD 70792
Enja (Germany) / Jun '93 / New Note.

## LIVE IN BERLIN.
**Tracks:** Not Advised.
CD . . . . . . . . . . . . . . . . . . . . CDSJP 289
■ LP . . . . . . . . . . . . . . . . . . . . . SJP 289
Timeless (Jazz) / May '89 / New Note / Jazz Music.

## SILVER CYCLES.
**Tracks:** Free at last / 1974 blues / Smoke signals / Coltrane's view / I'm gonna leave you by yourself / Silver cycles / Little bit / Electric ballad / Infrapolations.
■ LP . . . . . . . . . . . . . . . . . . . . . 588 177
Atlantic / Apr '69.

## STEPS UP (Harris, Eddie quartet).
**Tracks:** Not Advised.
■ LP . . . . . . . . . . . . . . . . . . . . . SCS 1151
Steeplechase (USA) / Sep '81.

## SWISS MOVEMENT (Harris, Eddie & Les McCann).
**Tracks:** Compared to what / Cold duck time / Kathleen's theme / You got it in your soulness / Generation gap.
■ LP . . . . . . . . . . . . . . . . . . . . . K 50405
Atlantic.
CD . . . . . . . . . . . . . . . . . . . . . K781 365 2
Atlantic / '88 / WEA.
CD . . . . . . . . . . . . . . . . . . . . .756781365-2
Atlantic / Apr '94 / WEA.

## TALE OF TWO CITIES.
**Tracks:** Chicago serenade / Cherokee / Lover man / Sonnymcon (for two) / I can't get started with you / Illusionary dreams / Don't let me go / Listen here.
■ CD . . . . . . . . . . . . . . . . . . . . . VNCD 3
■ LP . . . . . . . . . . . . . . . . . . . . . VNLP 3
■ MC . . . . . . . . . . . . . . . . . . . . . VNTC 3
Virgin / Feb '91.

## THERE WAS A TIME (Echo of Harlem).
**Tracks:** Love letters / Historia de un amor / Autumn in New York / Photographs of you / Song is you / Harlem nocturne / There was a time (Echo of Harlem) / Lover come back to me.
■ CD . . . . . . . . . . . . . . . . . . . . . 6068-2
Enja (Germany) / Apr '91.

# Harris, Gene

## AT LAST (Harris, Gene & Scott Hamilton Quintet).
**Tracks:** You are my sunshine / It never entered my mind / After you've gone / Lamp is low / At last / Blues for Gene / I fall in love too easily / Some of these days / Stairway to the stars / Sittin' in the sandtrap.
CD . . . . . . . . . . . . . . . . . . . . . CCD 4434
MC . . . . . . . . . . . . . . . . . . . . . CJ 434 C
Concord / Nov '90 / New Note.

## BLACK AND BLUE (Harris, Gene Quartet).
**Tracks:** Another star / Black and blue / c.c. rider / Hot today / Best things in life are free / Nobody knows you (when you're down and out) / It might as well be Spring / Blue bossa / Song is you / Will you still be mine.
CD . . . . . . . . . . . . . . . . . . . . . CCD 4482
MC . . . . . . . . . . . . . . . . . . . . . CJ 482C
Concord / Oct '91 / New Note.

## FUNKY GENE'S.
**Tracks:** Blues for Basie / Trouble with hello is good-bye / Old funky Gene's / Everything happens to me / Nice 'n' easy / Ahmad's blues / Bye bye blues / Children of Sanchez / Blues in Hoss's flat.
CD. . . . . . . . . . . . . . . . . . . . . . . . . . . CCD 4609
Concord / Sep '94 / New Note.

## GENE HARRIS & THE PHILIP MORRIS SUPERBAND (Harris, Gene & The Philip Morris Superband).
**Tracks:** Surrey with the fringe on top / Creme de menthe (on CD only) / When it's sleepy time down South / Love is here to stay / I'm just a lucky so and so / Serious grease (on CD only) / Like a lover (on CD only) / Old man river / Do you know what it means to New Orleans (on 12" only) / Porgy and Bess (medley) / You're my everything / There is no greater love / Things ain't what they used to be.
CD. . . . . . . . . . . . . . . . . . . . . . . . . . . CCD 4397
■ LP . . . . . . . . . . . . . . . . . . . . . . . . . . CJ 397
MC. . . . . . . . . . . . . . . . . . . . . . . . . CJ 397C
Concord Jazz / Nov '89 / New Note.

## GENE HARRIS TRIO PLUS ONE, THE.
**Tracks:** Gene's lament / Uptown sop / Things ain't what they used to be / Yours is my heart alone / Battle hymn of the Republic.
CD. . . . . . . . . . . . . . . . . . . . . . . . . . . CCD 4303
LP . . . . . . . . . . . . . . . . . . . . . . . . . . . CJ 303
Concord Jazz / Sep '90 / New Note.

## LIKE A LOVER (Harris, Gene Quartet).
**Tracks:** Like a lover / Misterioso / Strollin' / Until the real thing comes along / Jeannie / I can't stop loving you / You make me feel so young / Oh, look at me now / Wrap your troubles in dreams.
CD. . . . . . . . . . . . . . . . . . . . . . . . . . . CCD 4526
Concord / Oct '92 / New Note.

## LISTEN HERE (Harris, Gene Quartet).
**Tracks:** His masquerade / I've got a feeling I'm falling in love / Blues for Jezebel / Lullabye / This can't be love / Don't be that way / Listen here / Sweet and lovely / Song is ended / To you.
CD. . . . . . . . . . . . . . . . . . . . . . . . . . . CCD 4385
LP . . . . . . . . . . . . . . . . . . . . . . . . . . . CJ 385
MC. . . . . . . . . . . . . . . . . . . . . . . . . CJ 385C
Concord Jazz / Sep '90 / New Note.

## LITTLE PIECE OF HEAVEN, A (Harris, Gene Quartet).
**Tracks:** Blues in baxter's pad / Scotch & soda / Take the 'A' train / My little suede shoes / Blues for ste chapelle / Ma he's making eyes at me / Pensativa / How long has this been going on / Old dog blues / Ode to Billy Joe / Sentimental journey.
CD. . . . . . . . . . . . . . . . . . . . . . . . . . . CCD 4578
Concord / Nov '93 / New Note.

## TRIBUTE TO COUNT BASIE (Harris, Gene All Star Big Band).
**Tracks:** Captain Bill / Night mist blues / Swingin' the blues / When did you leave Heaven / Blue and sentimental / Riled up / Masquerade is over / Dejection blues.
CD. . . . . . . . . . . . . . . . . . . . . . . . . . . CCD 4337
■ LP . . . . . . . . . . . . . . . . . . . . . . . . . . CJ 337
MC. . . . . . . . . . . . . . . . . . . . . . . . . CJC 337
Concord Jazz / May '88 / New Note.

## WORLD TOUR 1990 (Harris, Gene & The Philip Morris Superband).
**Tracks:** Airmail special / Lonely bottles / Child is born / Buhaina Buhaina / Don't get around much anymore / Lover (CD only.) / In the wee small hours of the morning / Tricrotism (CD only.) / Centerpiece (CD only.) / Dear blues / Nica's dream / Girl talk / Battle royal / Warm valley.
CD. . . . . . . . . . . . . . . . . . . . . . . . . . . CCD 4443
MC. . . . . . . . . . . . . . . . . . . . . . . . . . CJ 443C
Concord / Feb '91 / New Note.

# Harris, Major

Having served in Delfonics from 1971 to '73, Harris struck out on his own with double-platinum *Love Won't Let Me Wait*. Single featured (uncredited) Barbara Ingram, whose moaning suggested either ecstasy or severe asthma, and was later covered by Luther Vandross. Further albums on Atlantic yielded no such successes and Harris descended into late '70s vacuum. He scored one-off comeback in '83 with *All My Life* and was last spotted in reformed Delfonics.

## ALL MY LIFE.
**Tracks:** All my life.
■ 12". . . . . . . . . . . . . . . . . . . . . . . LONX 37
■ 7". . . . . . . . . . . . . . . . . . . . . . . . . LON 37
London / Nov '83.

## GOTTA MAKE UP YOUR MIND.
**Tracks:** Gotta make up your mind.
■ 12". . . . . . . . . . . . . . . . . . . . . MKHAN 29
■ 7". . . . . . . . . . . . . . . . . . . . . . . . KHAN 29
Streetwave / Oct '84.

## I BELIEVE IN LOVE.
**Tracks:** I believe in love.
■ 12". . . . . . . . . . . . . . . . . . . . . MKHAN 35
Streetwave / Jan '85.

## I WANT YOUR LOVE.
**Tracks:** I want your love.
■ 12". . . . . . . . . . . . . . . . . . . . . . . VIBE 1T
■ 7". . . . . . . . . . . . . . . . . . . . . . . . . VIBE 1
Buzz Int. / Feb '84.

## JUST A THING THAT I DO.
**Tracks:** Just a thing that I do / Loving you is mellow.
■ 7". . . . . . . . . . . . . . . . . . . . . . . . K 10690
Atlantic / Jan '75.

## LOVE WON'T LET ME WAIT.
**Tracks:** Love won't let me wait / After loving you.
■ 7". . . . . . . . . . . . . . . . . . . . . . . . K 10585
Atlantic / Aug '75.

## LOVE WON'T LET ME WAIT (OLD GOLD).
**Tracks:** Love won't let me wait / Patches.
■ 7". . . . . . . . . . . . . . . . . . . . . . . . OG 9913
Old Gold / '89.

# Harris, Rahni
## SIX MILLION STEPS (WEST RUNS SOUTH).
**Tracks:** Six million steps (west runs south) / Six million steps (west runs south) (version).
■ 7". . . . . . . . . . . . . . . . . . . . . . . 6007 198
Mercury / Dec '78.

# Harris, Simon
## (I'VE GOT YOUR) PLEASURE CONTROL.
**Tracks:** (I've got your) pleasure control.
■ 12". . . . . . . . . . . . . . . . . . . . . . . . FX 106
■ 7". . . . . . . . . . . . . . . . . . . . . . . . . . F 106
■ 12". . . . . . . . . . . . . . . . . . . . . . . FXR 106
■ CD Single. . . . . . . . . . . . . . . . . . FCD 106
■ MC Single. . . . . . . . . . . . . . . . . . FCS 106
FFRR / Jun '89.

## ANOTHER MONSTER JAM.
**Tracks:** Another monster jam / Another monster jam (radio edit) (On 7" and CD single only.) / Another monster jam (radio instrumental) (On 7" only.) / Another monster jam (monster jam) (Not on 7".) / Breakdown (On 12" and cassingle only.) / Another monster jam (bonus beats) (On 12" and cassingle only.) / Another monster jam (dub) (Not on 7".)
■ 12". . . . . . . . . . . . . . . . . . . . . . . . FX 116
■ CD Single. . . . . . . . . . . . . . . . . . FCD 116
■ MC Single. . . . . . . . . . . . . . . . . . FCS 116
■ 7". . . . . . . . . . . . . . . . . . . . . . . . . . F 116
FFRR / Nov '89.

## BAD ON THE MIKE.
**Tracks:** Bad on the mike / Drumapella / Sample breakdown / Bad beats.
■ 12". . . . . . . . . . . . . . . . . . . . . . LONX 162
London / Oct '87.

## BASS.
**Tracks:** Bass (how low can you go) / From the vaults of good times / Sexy lady / Official voice of hip hop / Run 4 cover / Wheels of steel / (I've got your) pleasure control / London's finest / Stardate / Final frontier / We're gonna dance / Another monster jam / It is scratched / Here comes that sound (demolition album mix) / Feel.
■ LP . . . . . . . . . . . . . . . . . . . . . . 828 153-1
■ MC . . . . . . . . . . . . . . . . . . . . . . 828 153-4
■ CD . . . . . . . . . . . . . . . . . . . . . . 828 153-2
FFRR / Aug '90.

## BASS (HOW LOW CAN YOU GO).
**Tracks:** Bass (how low can you go) / Playback. The (edit) (Track on 7".) / Bass (how low can you go) (Bomb the house mix) (Track on 12".) / Bass (how low can you go)(Inst.) (Track on 12".).
■ 12". . . . . . . . . . . . . . . . . . . . . . . . FFRX 4
■ 7". . . . . . . . . . . . . . . . . . . . . . . . . FFR 4
■ 12" Remix. . . . . . . . . . . . . . . . . . FFRXR 4
FFRR / Mar '88.
■ CD Single. . . . . . . . . . . . . . . . . . FFRCD 4
FFRR / May '88.

## BEATS, BREAKS & SCRATCHES (BOX SET).
**Tracks:** Not Advised.
■ LP Set. . . . . . . . . . . . . . . . . . MOMIXBOX
Music Of Life / Nov '89.

## BEATS, BREAKS & SCRATCHES VOL. 1.
**Tracks:** Not Advised.
■ LP . . . . . . . . . . . . . . . . . . . . . . MOMIX 1
Music Of Life / Jun '87.

## BEATS, BREAKS & SCRATCHES VOL. 10.
**Tracks:** Not Advised.
CD. . . . . . . . . . . . . . . . . . . . . . MOLCD 027
LP . . . . . . . . . . . . . . . . . . . . . . MOLLP 027
Music Of Life / Mar '93 / Grapevine Distribution.

## BEATS, BREAKS & SCRATCHES VOL. 11.
**Tracks:** Not Advised.
CD. . . . . . . . . . . . . . . . . . . . . . . MOLCD 31
LP . . . . . . . . . . . . . . . . . . . . . . . MOLLP 31
Music Of Life / Oct '93 / Grapevine Distribution.

## BEATS, BREAKS & SCRATCHES VOL. 2.
**Tracks:** Not Advised.
■ LP . . . . . . . . . . . . . . . . . . . . . . MOMIX 2
Music Of Life / Oct '88.

## BEATS, BREAKS & SCRATCHES VOL. 3.
**Tracks:** Not Advised.
■ LP . . . . . . . . . . . . . . . . . . . . . . MOMIX 3
Music Of Life / Mar '89.

## BEATS, BREAKS & SCRATCHES VOL. 4.
**Tracks:** Life beats / Dopin' drums / Groove beats / Hold tight / Funky break / Ruff loop / Samurai beats / Heavy loop / Mardi gras / Big beats / Impeach / Compton loop / Course beat / Effects and scratches.
■ LP . . . . . . . . . . . . . . . . . . . . . . MOMIX 4
Music Of Life / Sep '89.

## BEATS, BREAKS & SCRATCHES VOL. 5.
**Tracks:** Not Advised.
LP . . . . . . . . . . . . . . . . . . . . . . . MOMIX 5
Music Of Life / Sep '90 / Grapevine Distribution.

## BEATS, BREAKS & SCRATCHES VOL. 6.
**Tracks:** Not Advised.
LP . . . . . . . . . . . . . . . . . . . . . . . MOMIX 6
Music Of Life / Dec '90 / Grapevine Distribution.

## BEATS, BREAKS & SCRATCHES VOL. 7.
**Tracks:** Not Advised.
CD. . . . . . . . . . . . . . . . . . . . . . MOMIX 7CD
LP . . . . . . . . . . . . . . . . . . . . . . . MOMIX 7
Music Of Life / Jun '91 / Grapevine Distribution.

## BEATS, BREAKS & SCRATCHES VOL. 8.
**Tracks:** Not Advised.
CD. . . . . . . . . . . . . . . . . . . . . . MOMIX 8CD
LP . . . . . . . . . . . . . . . . . . . . . . . MOMIX 8
Music Of Life / Nov '91 / Grapevine Distribution.

## BEATS, BREAKS & SCRATCHES VOL. 9.
**Tracks:** Soul sisters / Lastnight / Light soul / Bass, uh hah / Slow & heavy bass / Jazz bass / Best end / Alright bass / All alone / Pop drums / Downtown beat / Disco kitch / Country drummin' / FX & scratches.
LP . . . . . . . . . . . . . . . . . . . . . . . MOMIX 9
Music Of Life / Oct '92 / Grapevine Distribution.

## BEATS, BREAKS & SCRATCHES VOLS. 1 & 2.
**Tracks:** Not Advised.
CD Set . . . . . . . . . . . . . . . . . MOMIX 1/2CD
Music Of Life / '89 / Grapevine Distribution.

## BEATS, BREAKS & SCRATCHES VOLS. 3 & 4.
**Tracks:** Not Advised.
CD Set . . . . . . . . . . . . . . . . . MOMIX 3/4CD
Music Of Life / '89 / Grapevine Distribution.

## BEST OF BEATS, BREAKS AND SCRATCHES.
**Tracks:** Not Advised.
CD. . . . . . . . . . . . . . . . . . . . . .MOBEST 1CD
LP . . . . . . . . . . . . . . . . . . . . . . MOBEST 1
LP P.Disc . . . . . . . . . . . . . . . . . MOBEST 1P
Music Of Life / Jun '92 / Grapevine Distribution.

## DISTURBING THE PEACE.
**Tracks:** Theme from disturbing the peace / Time / Rock right now / Ragga house (All night long) / This is serious / Don't stop the music / Shock the house / Right here, right now / Twilight / Runaway love / Ragga house.
CD. . . . . . . . . . . . . . . . . . . . . . DISTURB 1CD
LP . . . . . . . . . . . . . . . . . . . . . . DISTURB 1
MC. . . . . . . . . . . . . . . . . . . . . . DISTURB 1C
Living Beat / Nov '90 / Grapevine Distribution.

■ DELETED

## DON'T STOP THE MUSIC.
**Tracks:** Don't stop the music / Ragga house.
■ 12"  . . . . . . . . . . . . . . . . . . . . SMASH 10
■ 7"  . . . . . . . . . . . . . . . . . . . 7 SMASH 10
■ CD Single . . . . . . . . . . . . . . SMASH 10CD
Living Beat / Jul '90.

## HERE COMES THAT SOUND.
**Tracks:** Here comes that sound / Only a demo /
Perfect beat (Only on the 12" version.) / Acid fingers
breakdown (Only on the 12" version.).
■ 12"  . . . . . . . . . . . . . . . . . . . . . . .FFRX 12
■ 12" Remix. . . . . . . . . . . . . . . . . .FFRXR 12
■ 7"  . . . . . . . . . . . . . . . . . . . . . . . .FFR 12
FFRR / Sep '88.

## RAGGA HOUSE (ALL NIGHT LONG)
(Harris, Simon & Daddy Freddy).
**Tracks:** Ragga house (all night long) / Ragga house
(all night long) (version) / Ragga house (all night
long) (remix).
■ 12"  . . . . . . . . . . . . . . . . . . . . . SMASH 9
■ 12" Remix. . . . . . . . . . . . . . . . . . SMASH 9R
■ 7"  . . . . . . . . . . . . . . . . . . . . 7 SMASH 9
■ CD Single. . . . . . . . . . . . . . . SMASH 9 CD
■ MC Single. . . . . . . . . . . . . . . SMASH 9 C
Living Beat / Feb '90.

## ROLLIN' WITH THE PUNCHES.
**Tracks:** Rollin' with the punches.
■ 12"  . . . . . . . . . . . . . . . . . . . . . SMASH 24
■ CD Single . . . . . . . . . . . . . . .SMASH 24CD
Music Of Life / Jun '92.

## STRETCHBEATS VOL 1.
**Tracks:** Not Advised.
■ LP  . . . . . . . . . . . . . . . . . . . . . STARMIX 2
Sailtrack / Aug '91 / Pinnacle.

## SUMMERTIME.
**Tracks:** Summertime.
■ 12"  . . . . . . . . . . . . . . . . . . . . . SMASH 20
Living Beat / Oct '91.

## TIME (Harris, Simon Featuring Leslie Lyrics).
**Tracks:** Time / Time (version).
■ 12"  . . . . . . . . . . . . . . . . . . . . . SMASH 11
■ 7"  . . . . . . . . . . . . . . . . . . . . .7SMASH 11
■ CD Single . . . . . . . . . . . . . . .SMASH 11CD
Living Beat / Aug '90.

## Harrison, Danny

### SPEAK OF THE DEVIL.
**Tracks:** Speak of the devil / I'm a rollin' stone.
■ 7"  . . . . . . . . . . . . . . . . . . . . . . . Q 72479
Coral / May '65.

## Hart, Cajun

### GOT TO FIND A WAY.
**Tracks:** Got to find a way / Lovers prayer.
■ 7"  . . . . . . . . . . . . . . . . . . . . . . . .WB 7258
WEA / '69.

## Hartman, Dan

### BOOGIE ALL SUMMER.
**Tracks:** Boogie all Summer.
■ 7"  . . . . . . . . . . . . . . . . . . . . . . SKY 7741
Blue Sky / Nov '79.

### FREE RIDE.
**Tracks:** Free ride / Love strong.
■ 7"  . . . . . . . . . . . . . . . . . . . . . . SKY 8562
Blue Sky / Jun '80.

### GET OUTTA TOWN.
**Tracks:** Get outta town / I can dream about you.
■ 12"  . . . . . . . . . . . . . . . . . . . . .MCAT 982
■ 7"  . . . . . . . . . . . . . . . . . . . . . .MCA 982
MCA / Nov '85.

### HANDS DOWN.
**Tracks:** Hands down / Hands up.
■ 7"  . . . . . . . . . . . . . . . . . . . . . . SKY 7896
Blue Sky / Oct '79.

### I CAN DREAM ABOUT YOU.
**Tracks:** We are the young / I can dream about you /
Shy hearts / I'm not a rolling stone / Rage to live /
Name of the game / Power of a good love / Second
nature / I can't get enough / Electricity.
■ LP  . . . . . . . . . . . . . . . . . . . . . MCF 3239
■ CD  . . . . . . . . . . . . . . . . . . . . . DIDX 200
■ MC  . . . . . . . . . . . . . . . . . . . . MCFC 3239
MCA / Jan '85.

### I CAN DREAM ABOUT YOU.
**Tracks:** I can dream about you / Instant replay.
■ 12"  . . . . . . . . . . . . . . . . . . . . .MCAT 988

### (continued column 2)

■ 12"  . . . . . . . . . . . . . . . . . . . . .MCAX 988
■ 7"  . . . . . . . . . . . . . . . . . . . . . .MCA 988
MCA / Sep '85.

## INSTANT REPLAY.
**Tracks:** Instant replay / Countdown-this is it / Double-
O-Love / Chocolate box / Love is a natural / Time
and space.
■ LP  . . . . . . . . . . . . . . . . . . . . . SKY 83265
Blue Sky / Jan '79.
■ MC.  . . . . . . . . . . . . . . . . . .40 32713
■ LP  . . . . . . . . . . . . . . . . . . . SKY 32713
Blue Sky / Feb '86.
CD.  . . . . . . . . . . . . . . . . . . . . .983383 2
Pickwick / Feb '94 / Pickwick.

## INSTANT REPLAY.
**Tracks:** Instant Replay / Instant replay (version).
■ 7"  . . . . . . . . . . . . . . . . . . . . . SKY 6706
Sky / Oct '78.

## NEW GREEN/CLEAR BLUE.
**Tracks:** Sigh of relief / Romance / New green/clear
blue / Swan / Beautiful mist / Alpha waves / Adrift in
a red sky / Scaramanga / Soviet nights / Hope of no
end / Home.
■ LP  . . . . . . . . . . . . . . . . . . . . . 209 937
■ MC.  . . . . . . . . . . . . . . . . . . . . 409 937
■ CD  . . . . . . . . . . . . . . . . . . . . . 259 937
RCA / Aug '89.

## RELIGHT MY FIRE.
**Tracks:** Relight my fire / Vertigo.
■ 12"  . . . . . . . . . . . . . . . . . . . . .138104
■ 7"  . . . . . . . . . . . . . . . . . . . . . SKY 8104
Blue Sky / Jan '80.

## SECOND NATURE.
**Tracks:** Second Nature / I can't get enough.
■ 12"  . . . . . . . . . . . . . . . . . . . . .MCAT 957
■ 7"  . . . . . . . . . . . . . . . . . . . . . .MCA 957
MCA / May '85.

## THIS IS IT.
**Tracks:** This is it / Countdown.
■ 7"  . . . . . . . . . . . . . . . . . . . . . SKY 6999
Blue Sky / Jan '79.

## TIME AND SPACE.
**Tracks:** Time and space / Double o love.
■ 7"  . . . . . . . . . . . . . . . . . . . . . SKY 7221
Blue Sky / '79.

## WAITING TO SEE YOU.
**Tracks:** Waiting to see you.
■ 12"  . . . . . . . . . . . . . . . . . . . . . TA 7186
Epic / Aug '86.

## WE ARE THE YOUNG.
**Tracks:** Not Advised.
■ CD  . . . . . . . . . . . . . . . . . . . . DMCA 111
MCA.

## WE ARE THE YOUNG.
**Tracks:** We are the young / I'm not a rolling stone.
■ 12"  . . . . . . . . . . . . . . . . . . . . .MCAT 924
■ 7"  . . . . . . . . . . . . . . . . . . . . . .MCA 924
MCA / Jan '85.

## Harvey, Dee

### JUST AS I AM.
**Tracks:** Leave well enough alone / All that you want /
Star / How can we be friends / Just as I am / What's
next / I don't know yet / Like an echo / Nothing but
emotion / Tie that binds.
■ LP  . . . . . . . . . . . . . . . . . . . . . ZL 72761
■ CD  . . . . . . . . . . . . . . . . . . . . . ZD 72761
■ MC.  . . . . . . . . . . . . . . . . . . . . ZK 72761
Motown / Sep '91.

## Harvey, Steve

### I'M THE ONE.
**Tracks:** I'm the one / I'm the one (dub version).
■ 12"  . . . . . . . . . . . . . . . . . . . . .AMY 701
■ 7"  . . . . . . . . . . . . . . . . . . . . . .AM 701
A&M / Oct '90.

### SOMETHING SPECIAL.
**Tracks:** Something special.
■ 12"  . . . . . . . . . . . . . . . . . . . . .LONX 25
■ 7"  . . . . . . . . . . . . . . . . . . . . . .LON 25
London / May '83.

### TONIGHT.
**Tracks:** Tonight.
■ 12"  . . . . . . . . . . . . . . . . . . . . .LONX 36
■ 7"  . . . . . . . . . . . . . . . . . . . . . .LON 36
London / Oct '83.

## Haskins, Fuzzy

### WHOLE NOTHER/RADIO ACTIVE THANG.
**Tracks:** Tangerine green / Cookie jar / Mr Junk man /
I can see myself in you / Fuz and da boog / Which
way do I disco / Love's now is forever / Sometimes I
rock and roll / I'll be loving you / Right back where I
started from / Not yet / I think I got my thang together
/ This situation called love / Gimme back (Some of
the love you got from me) / Things we used to do /
Woman / Sinderilla / Silent day.
CD  . . . . . . . . . . . . . . . . . . . CDSEWD 093
Westbound / Sep '94 / Pinnacle.

## Hatcher, Roger

### WE'RE GONNA MAKE IT.
**Tracks:** We're gonna make it / High blood pressure.
■ 7"  . . . . . . . . . . . . . . . . . . . . . .CHEW 5
Mint / Feb '76.

## Hathaway, Donny

Though born in Chicago, Donny grew up in
St Louis, Missouri with his grandmother,
Martha Cromwell herself a successful local
gospel singer. In his teens he studied music
at Washington's Howard University, becoming a close friend of singer Roberta Flack
and sharing a room with Leroy Hutson later
to become lead vocalist in The Impressions.
Always blending soul and jazz with his natural inclination to church music, Hathaway
performed on the local club circuit, where a
meeting with Chicago artist/writer/producer
Curtis Mayfield led to regular work at Mayfield's flourishing Curtom Records label.
Hathaway's first recordings were duets with
June Conquest and after productions on
The Staple Singers, Jerry Butler and Carla
Thompson, he signed as a solo act to Atlantic Records. Hathaway's first album, *Donny
Hathaway*, rapidly established him as an
artist of stature, his co-composition with
Leroy Hutson, the classic *The Ghetto* becoming a hit 45. Further albums throughout
the '70s are seen as landmarks in soul-
gospel performance, *Everything Is Everything*, *Extensions Of A Man* and a live album
in the mid-decade earning him high public
regard from such as Aretha Franklin. Few of
his own singles were hits however, Hathaway enjoying his best chart positions duetting
with labelmate Roberta Flack. In '72 *Where
Is The love* was an international hit, while,
six years later, *The Closer I Get To You*,
also made the UK top 50. But Hathaway was
far from happy in his personal life. His
father had a history of mental illness and by
the end of the decade it seems Donny had
also succumbed to schizophrenia. In January '79, shortly after recording his vocal
onto the song *Back Together Again*, another
duet with Flack he threw himself to his
death from a New York hotel bedroom.

### BEST OF DONNY HATHAWAY.
**Tracks:** You were meant for me / Song for you /
You've got a friend / Someday we'll all be free /
Giving up / Where is the love / Ghetto / Valdez in the
country / This Christmas.
■ LP  . . . . . . . . . . . . . . . . . . . . . K 50525
Atco / '84.

### CLOSER I GET TO YOU, THE (see under Flack, Roberta).

### DONNY HATHAWAY.
**Tracks:** Giving up / Song for you / Little girl / He ain't
heavy, he's my brother / Magnificent sanctuary band
/ She is my lady / I believe in music / Take a love
song / Put your hand in the hand.
■ LP  . . . . . . . . . . . . . . . . . . . . . 2400143
Atlantic / Sep '71.

### DONNY HATHAWAY COLLECTION, A.
**Tracks:** Song for you / I love you more than you'll
ever know / You were meant for me / Back together
again / Where is the love / For all we know /
Someday we'll all be free / Giving up / Closer I get to
you / You are my heaven / What's goin' on / Ghetto /
To be young, gifted and black / You've got a friend /
This Christmas.
■ CD  . . . . . . . . . . . . . . . . . . 7567820922
Atlantic / Apr '93 / WEA.

### DONNY HATHAWAY LIVE.
**Tracks:** What's going on / Ghetto / Hey girl / You've
got a friend / Little ghetto boy / We're still friends /
Jealous guy / Voices inside (everything).
■ LP  . . . . . . . . . . . . . . . . . . . . . K 40369
Atlantic.

## EVERYTHING IS EVERYTHING.

**Tracks:** Voices inside / Je vous aime / I believe to my soul / Misty / Sugar Lee / Tryin' times / Thank you master / Ghetto / To be young, gifted and black.
■ LP . . . . . . . . . . . . . . . . . . . . . . .2465 019
Atco / Apr '71.

## EXTENSION OF A MAN.

**Tracks:** I love the lord; He heard my cry (parts 1 & 2) / Someday we'll all be free / Flying easy / Valdez in the country / I love you more than you'll ever know / Come little children / Love, love, love / Slums / Magdalena / I know it's you.
■ LP . . . . . . . . . . . . . . . . . . . . . . . SD 7029
Atco / '73.

## WHERE IS THE LOVE (see under Flack, Roberta).

## YOU'VE GOT A FRIEND (see under Flack, Roberta).

# Hathaway, Lalah

## BABY DON'T CRY.

**Tracks:** Baby don't cry / Heaven knows.
■ CD Single . . . . . . . . . . . . . . .VUSCD 35
■ 7" . . . . . . . . . . . . . . . . . . . . . . . .VUS 35
■ 12" . . . . . . . . . . . . . . . . . . . . . .VUST 35
Virgin / Jan '91.

## HEAVEN KNOWS.

**Tracks:** Heaven knows / U godit gowin on.
■ 12" . . . . . . . . . . . . . . . . . . . . . .VUST 28
■ 12" . . . . . . . . . . . . . . . . . . . . .VUSTP 28
■ 7" . . . . . . . . . . . . . . . . . . . . . . . VUS 28
■ CD Single . . . . . . . . . . . . . . .VUSCD 28
■ MC Single . . . . . . . . . . . . . . . VUSC 28
Virgin / Sep '90.

## LALAH HATHAWAY.

**Tracks:** Somethin' / Heaven knows / Baby don't cry / Smile / U godit gowin on / Obvious / Stay home tonight / I'm coming back / Sentimental / I gotta move on.
■ LP . . . . . . . . . . . . . . . . . . . . . .VUSLP 24
■ MC . . . . . . . . . . . . . . . . . . . . .VUSMC 24
■ CD . . . . . . . . . . . . . . . . . . . . .CDVUS 24
Virgin / Oct '90.

# Havens, Richie

## ALARM CLOCK.

**Tracks:** Here comes the sun / To give all your love away / Younger men grow older / Girls don't run away / End of the season / Some will wait / Patient lady / Missing train / Alarm clock.
■ LP . . . . . . . . . . . . . . . . . . . . .2310 080
Polydor / Mar '71.

## CUTS TO THE CHASE.

**Tracks:** They dance alone / Times they are a' changin / Lives in the balance / Hawk / Old love / At a glance.
CD. . . . . . . . . . . . . . . . . . . . ESSCD 212
MC. . . . . . . . . . . . . . . . . . . . ESSMC 212
Essential / Jun '94 / Total / BMG.

## DEATH AT AN EARLY AGE.

**Tracks:** Death at an early age / Moonlight rain.
■ 7" . . . . . . . . . . . . . . . . . . . . . . CX 5381
Connexion / Jun '83.

## LIVE ON STAGE.

**Tracks:** From the prison / Younger men grow older / Old friends / God bless this child / High flyin' bird / Tupelo honey / Just like a woman / Handsome Johnny / Where have all the flowers gone / Rocky racoon / Teach your children / Minstrel from Gault / Freedom.
■ LP . . . . . . . . . . . . . . . . . . . . .2659 015
Polydor / Nov '72.

## MIRAGE.

**Tracks:** Live it up / Shadows of the past / i don't complain / Touch the sky / Billy John / We all wanna boogie / Avalon / Aviation man / Nobody left to crown / End.
■ LP . . . . . . . . . . . . . . . . . . . AMLH 64641
A&M / Nov '77.

## MIXED BAG.

**Tracks:** High flyin bird / I can't make it anymore / Morning morning / Adam / Follow / Three day eternity / Sand / Handsome Johnny / San francisco bay blues / Just like a woman / Eleanor Rigby.
■ LP . . . . . . . . . . . . . . . . . . . .SVLP 6008
Verve / Feb '69.
CD. . . . . . . . . . . . . . . . . . . . . 835 210-2
Polydor / May '88 / PolyGram.

## RICHARD B. HAVENS 1983.

**Tracks:** Stop pulling and pushing me / For Haven's sake / Strawberry fields forever / What more can I say John / I pity the poor immigrant / Lady Madonna / Priests / Indian rope man / Cautiously / Just above my hobby horse's head / She's leaving home / Putting out the vibration / Parable of Ramon / With a little help from my friends / Wear your love like heaven / Run shaker life / Do you feel good.
■ LP . . . . . . . . . . . . . . . . . . . . . SVLP 6014
Verve / May '69.

## RICHIE HAVENS SINGS BEATLES AND DYLAN.

**Tracks:** Not Advised.
CD . . . . . . . . . . . . . . . . . . . . . RCD 20035
Rykodisc / May '92 / Vital Distribution / Topic Records / Direct Distribution / C.M. Distribution / A.D.A. Distribution.

## SIMPLE THING.

**Tracks:** Not Advised.
CD . . . . . . . . . . . . . . . . . . . . . .RBD 400
■ LP . . . . . . . . . . . . . . . . . . . . . . RBI 400
MC . . . . . . . . . . . . . . . . . . . . . .RBC 400
Start / Jun '87 / THE / Koch International.

## SOMETHIN' ELSE AGAIN.

**Tracks:** No opportunity necessary / Inside of him / Klan / Sugarplums / Don't listen to me / From the prison / Maggie's farm / Somethin' else again / New city / Run shaker life.
■ LP . . . . . . . . . . . . . . . . . . . . . SVLP 6005
Verve / Mar '68.

## STATE OF MIND.

**Tracks:** No opportunity necessary, no experience needed / Lady Madonna / Klan / Ring around the moon / Inside of him / Strawberry fields forever / Run shaker life / There's a hole in the future / Handsome Johnny / Stop pulling and pushing me / Indian rope man / High flyin' bird.
■ LP . . . . . . . . . . . . . . . . . . . . .2304050
Verve / Dec '71.

# Hawkins, Edwin

## BEST OF THE EDWIN HAWKINS SINGERS (Hawkins, Edwin Singers).

**Tracks:** Oh happy day / Jubilation / Someday / Every man wants to be free / Lean on me / Ooh, child / I'm coming through / Blowin' in the wind.
■ LP . . . . . . . . . . . . . . . . . . . 252 213-1
MC. . . . . . . . . . . . . . . . . . . . 252 213-4
Buddah / Jul '85.

## IMAGINE HEAVEN.

**Tracks:** Not Advised.
■ LP . . . . . . . . . . . . . . . . . . . . . LN 1501
IMS / Mar '82.

## LIVE WITH THE OAKLAND SYMPHONY ORCHESTRA.

**Tracks:** Fanfare overture / Worship the Lord / Come to me / Talk / Gift of song / Oh happy day / Call him, he'll be there / I need to pray.
■ LP . . . . . . . . . . . . . . . . . . . MYR 1112
MC . . . . . . . . . . . . . . . . . . . .MC 1112
Myrrh / May '82 / Word Records (UK) / Sony.

## OH HAPPY DAY (Hawkins, Edwin Singers).

**Tracks:** Oh happy day.
■ 7" . . . . . . . . . . . . . . . . . . . . 201 048
Buddah / May '69.

## OH HAPPY DAY (Best of Edwin Hawkins) (Hawkins, Edwin Singers).

**Tracks:** Oh happy day / To my father's house / Lord don't move that mountain / Children get together / I heard the voice of Jesus say / Precious memories / Joy, joy / He's a friend of mine / I'm going through / Footprints of Jesus / All you need / Jesus / I shall be free / Mine all mine / My Lord is coming back.
CD . . . . . . . . . . . . . . . . . . . NEMCD 636
Sequel / Jun '93 / Total / BMG.

## OH HAPPY DAY (OLD GOLD) (Hawkins, Edwin Singers).

**Tracks:** Oh happy day / Brand new key.
■ 7" . . . . . . . . . . . . . . . . . . . .OG 9802
Old Gold / Oct '88.

# Hayes, Isaac

Self-styled 'Black Moses' moved from Tennessee to Memphis, joining Stax in early '60s. Originally a backing musician, Hayes developed fruitful songwriting union with David Porter; pair's breakthrough was Sam & Dave hit *Hold On I'm Comin'*, other smashes including *Soul Man* and Carla

Thomas' *B-A-B-Y*. Disintegration of Sam & Dave's partnership spelt end for their songwriting producers and Hayes went solo, hitting big time with *Hot Buttered Soul* in '69. Album's lavish productions - notably *By the Time I Get to Phoenix* - were innovative and highly influential. Fourth album, *Shaft* soundtrack, cemented reputation; winning four Grammies and an Oscar, and spawning transatlantic smash *Theme from Shaft*. However, Hayes' soul supremo status was usurped by Barry White; success - bar U.K. no. 10 *Disco Connection* - waned, and he was bankrupt by '78 (collaboration with Millie Jackson on '79's *Royal Rappin'* was motivated as much by common ground as financial and commercial necessity). Fortunes improved when *Don't Let Go* made U.S. Top 20 and his songs were successfully revived by Rachel Sweet, Dionne Warwick and Blues Brothers. Starring role in hit movie *Escape From New York* presaged TV acting career; musical comebacks have been largely unsuccessful. However, Hayes' *I Can't Turn Around* was remodelled for Farley Jackmaster Funk's pioneering '86 house smash *Love Can't Turn Around*.

## BEST OF ISAAC HAYES VOL 2.

**Tracks:** Not Advised.
CD . . . . . . . . . . . . . . . . . . . . FCD 60002
London / Apr '87 / PolyGram.

## BEST OF SHAFT (Film soundtrack).

**Tracks:** Shaft, Theme from / Walk from Regio's / Ellie's love theme / Cafe Regio's / Early Sunday morning / Soulsville / Bumpy's blues / Do your thing / End theme.
■ LP . . . . . . . . . . . . . . . . . . .STAXL 5012
MC . . . . . . . . . . . . . . . . . . . STAXK 5012
Stax / Oct '81 / Pinnacle.
■ LP . . . . . . . . . . . . . . . . . . . . . 1052504
Stax / Jun '86.

## BLACK MOSES.

**Tracks:** Never can say goodbye / (They long to be) close to you / Nothing takes the place of you / Man's temptation / Part time love / Ike's rap IV / Brand new me / Going in circles / Never gonna give you up / Ike's rap II / Help me love / Need to belong / Good love / Ike's rap III / Your love is so doggone good / For the good times / I'll never fall in love again.
■ Double LP . . . . . . . . . . . . . . . .2628 004
Stax / Feb '72.
CD Set . . . . . . . . . . . . . . . . CDSXE2 033
Stax / Aug '90 / Pinnacle.

## BLUE HAYES.

**Tracks:** Precious, precious / When I fall in love / I just want to make love to you / Rock me baby / Going to Chicago blues / Misty / You don't know like I know.
■ LP . . . . . . . . . . . . . . . . . . . . .2465 016
Buddah / Nov '70.

## CHOCOLATE CHIP.

**Tracks:** Chocolate chip.
■ 7" . . . . . . . . . . . . . . . . . . . . ABC 4076
Anchor (1) / Aug '75.

## CHRONICLE.

**Tracks:** Shaft / Walk on by / Ain't that loving you / Men / I stand accused / Do your thing / Never can say goodbye / Joy / By the time I get to Phoenix.
■ LP . . . . . . . . . . . . . . . . . . . . STM 7003
Stax / Apr '78.

## DISCO CONNECTION.

**Tracks:** Disco connection.
■ 7" . . . . . . . . . . . . . . . . . . . . ABC 4100
ABC Records / Apr '76.

## DON'T LET GO.

**Tracks:** Don't let go / You can't hold your woman.
■ 12" . . . . . . . . . . . . . . . . . . .STEPX 4
■ 7" . . . . . . . . . . . . . . . . . . . . . STEP 4
Polydor / Dec '79.

## DON'T LET GO.

**Tracks:** Don't let go / What does it take / Few more kisses to go / Fever / Someone who will take the place of you.
■ LP . . . . . . . . . . . . . . . . . . . . .2480510
Polydor / Nov '79.

## FOR THE SAKE OF LOVE.

**Tracks:** Just the way your are / Believe in me / If we ever needed peace / Shaft II / Zeke the freak / Don't let me be lonely tonight.
■ LP . . . . . . . . . . . . . . . . . . . . 248 047 5
Polydor / Jan '79.

■ DELETED

## GOLDEN HOUR PRESENTS ISAAC HAYES.
Tracks: Not Advised.
- LP .................................. GH 844
Golden Hour / Mar '76.

## HEY GIRL.
Tracks: Ike's rap / Hey Fred / Hey girl.
- 12" .................................. 6502366
- 7" .................................. 6502367
CBS / Nov '86.

## HIS GREATEST HITS.
Tracks: Walk on by / Joy / Never can say goodbye / Man, Theme from / By the time I get to Phoenix / Shaft, Theme from / Let's stay together / Do your thing / Ain't that lovin' you / Look of love / I stand accused.
- LP .................................. STX 88003
Stax / Nov '80.

## HOT BUTTERED SOUL.
Tracks: Walk on by / Hyperbolicsyllabicsesquedaiymistic / One woman / By the time I get to Phoenix.
- LP .................................. SXATS 1028
Stax / Jan '70.
- LP .................................. 2325011
Stax / Jun '71.
- LP .................................. STAXL 5002
MC. .................................. STAXK 5002
Stax / Aug '81 / Pinnacle.
- LP .................................. SXE 005
Stax / Nov '87.
- LP .................................. SX 005
Stax / Dec '88.
- CD .................................. CDSXE 005
Stax / May '91 / Pinnacle.

## HOTBED.
Tracks: Use me / I'm gonna have to tell her / Ren commandments of love / Feel like makin' love / Hobosac and me.
- CD .................................. CDSXE 105
Stax / Jul '94 / Pinnacle.

## I AIN'T NEVER.
Tracks: I ain't never / Shaft / Love has been good to us.
- 7" .................................. 2141262
Polydor / Jun '80.

## IN THE BEGINNING.
Tracks: Precious, precious / When I fall in love / I just want to make love to you / Rock me baby / Going to Chicago blues / Misty / You don't know like I know.
- LP .................................. K 40327
Atlantic / Apr '72.

## ISAAC HAYES MOVEMENT, THE.
Tracks: I stand accused / One big unhappy family / I just don't know what to do with myself / Something.
- LP .................................. 2325014
Stax / Jul '71.
- CD .................................. CDSXE 025
- LP .................................. SXE 025
Stax / Feb '90 / Pinnacle.

## ISAAC'S MOODS.
Tracks: Ike's mood / Soulsville / Joy Part 1 / If loving you is wrong I don't want to be right / Never can say goodbye / Shaft, Theme from / Ike's rap IV / Brand new me / Do your thing / Walk on by / I stand accused / Ike's rap I (On CD only) / Hyperbolicsyllabicsesquedalymistic (On CD only) / Ike's rap III (On CD only) / Ike's rap II (On CD only).
- CD .................................. CDSX 011
- LP .................................. SX 011
MC. .................................. SXC 011
Stax / Apr '88 / Pinnacle.

## JOY.
Tracks: Joy / I love you that's all / Man will be a man / Feeling keeps on coming / I'm gonna make it (without you).
- CD .................................. CDSXE 047
Stax / May '92 / Pinnacle.

## LIFETIME THING.
Tracks: I'm gonna make you love me / Three times a lady / Fugitive / Lifetime thing / Summer / I'm so proud.
- LP .................................. 231 107 4
Polydor / Oct '81.

## LIGHT MY FIRE.
Tracks: Light my fire / Feeling alright / Windows of the world / Look of love / It's too late / Rock me baby / Call it stormy Monday / Type thang / First time ever I saw your face.
- LP .................................. STM 7008
Stax / Feb '80.

## LIVE AT THE SAHARA TAHOE.
Tracks: Shaft, Theme from / Come on / Light my fire / Ike's rap / Never can say goodbye / Windows of the world / Look of love / Ellie's love theme / Use me / Do your thing / Men, The (Theme from) / It's too late / Rock me baby / Stormy Monday blues / Type thang / First time ever I saw your face / Ike's rap VI / Ain't no sunshine / Feelin' alright.
- LP .................................. MPS 88004
MC. .................................. MPS 588004
Stax / Nov '86 / Pinnacle.
- CD Set .................................. CDSXE 2053
Stax / Jul '92 / Pinnacle.

## LOVE ATTACK.
Tracks: Love attack / Let me be your everything / Showdown / Eye of the storm / Accused rap / I stand accused '88 / She's got a way / Foreplay rap / Love won't let me wait.
- CD .................................. 4625152
- LP .................................. 4625151
- MC. .................................. 4625154
CBS / Nov '88.

## MAN AND A WOMAN, A (Hayes, Isaac & Dionne Warwick).
Tracks: Not Advised.
- Double LP .................................. ABCD 613
ABC Records / Mar '77.

## MOONLIGHT LOVIN'.
Tracks: Moonlight lovin' / It's heaven to me.
- 7" .................................. 206 690 4
Polydor / May '78.

## MOVEMENT.
Tracks: I stand accused / One big unhappy family / I just don't know what to do with myself / Something.
- LP .................................. SXATS 1032
Stax / Jul '70.
- LP .................................. 2325 014
Polydor / Mar '71.

## NEVER CAN SAY GOODBYE.
Tracks: Never can say goodbye / I can't help it.
- 7" .................................. 2025 029
Stax / Jul '71.

## NEW HORIZON.
Tracks: Stranger in paradise / Moonlight lovin' / Don't take your love away / Out of the ghetto / It's heaven to me.
- LP .................................. 2391313
Polydor / Jan '78.

## ONCE AGAIN.
Tracks: It's all in the game / Ike's rap VII / This time I'll be sweeter / I ain't never / Wherever you are / Love has been good to me.
- LP .................................. 2480538
Polydor / Jul '80.

## SHAFT, THEME FROM.
Tracks: Shaft, Theme from / Men, The (theme from) (Available on 12" and CD single only) / Walk on by (Only on CD single.) / Type thang (Available on 12" and CD single only).
- 7" .................................. STAX 1009
Stax / Mar '82.
- 7" .................................. STAX 810
Stax / Aug '87.
- 12" .................................. SEWT 701
- CD Single .................................. CDSEWT 701
- 7" .................................. SEWS 701
South Bound / May '89.

## TO BE CONTINUED.
Tracks: Ike's rap 1 / Our day will come / Look of love / Ike's mood 1 / You've lost that lovin' feelin' / Runnin' out of fools.
- LP .................................. 2325 026
Stax / Apr '71.
- LP .................................. STAXL 5008
- MC. .................................. STAXK 5008
Stax / Oct '81 / Pinnacle.
- CD .................................. CDSXE 030
Stax / Feb '91 / Pinnacle.

## U-TURN.
Tracks: If you want my lovin' / Flash backs / You turn me on / Ike's rap VIII / Can't take my eyes off you / Thing for you / Thank God for love.
- LP .................................. 4501551
CBS / Dec '86.

## ZEKE THE FREAK.
Tracks: Zeke the freak / If we ever needed peace.
- 7" .................................. POSP 23
Polydor / Feb '79.

## Haynes, Victor

### CALLIN' UP.
Tracks: Callin' up.
- 12" .................................. EXPAND 40
Passion/Debut/Scratch Music / Aug '93.

### DON'T WANT NOBODY ELSE.
Tracks: Don't want nobody else.
12" .................................. EXPAND 51
Skratch (2) / Oct '94 / 3MV / Sony.

## Haywood, Leon

### BABY RECONSIDER.
Tracks: Baby reconsider / Would I.
- 7" .................................. FTC 151
Fantasy / Feb '78.

### BELIEVE HALF OF WHAT YOU SEE.
Tracks: Believe half of what you see / Day I laid eyes on you.
- 7" .................................. BTC 2146
20th Century / Jan '75.

### DON'T PUSH IT DON'T FORCE IT.
Tracks: Don't push it don't force it / Who you been giving it up to.
- 12" .................................. TCD 2443
- 7" .................................. TC 2443
20th Century / Mar '80.

### DOUBLE MY PLEASURE.
Tracks: Double my pleasure / It's gonna be alright.
- 7" .................................. MCA 353
MCA / Mar '78.

### EVER SINCE YOU WERE SWEET SIXTEEN.
Tracks: Ever since you were sweet sixteen / Skate a while.
- 7" .................................. VL 9288
Vocalion / May '67.

### I WANNA DO SOMETHING FREAKY TO YOU.
Tracks: I wanna do something freaky to you / I know what love is.
- 7" .................................. BTC 2228
20th Century / Nov '75.

### IF YOU'RE LOOKING FOR A NIGHT OF FUN.
Tracks: If you're looking for a night of fun / That's what time it is.
- 12" .................................. TCD 2454
- 7" .................................. TC 2454
20th Century / Jun '80.

### INTIMATE.
Tracks: Let me make it good to you / Dream dream / Strokin' / Let's get it on / Streets will love you to death / I'm your knight in shining armor / They don't make 'em no more like you / It's got to be me.
- LP .................................. CBS 81774
CBS / Feb '77.

### IT'S GOT TO BE MELLOW.
Tracks: Mercy, mercy, mercy / It's got to be mellow / Yesterday / I can't stop loving you / Nobody knows you when you're down and out / Tennessee waltz / Ode to Billy joe pts 1 and 2 / Cornbread and buttermilk / 'Round midnight.
- LP .................................. MUPS 369
MCA / May '69.

### IT'S ME AGAIN.
Tracks: T.V. mama / Desire / I'll always be around / Secret rendezvous / I'm out to catch / Keep it in the family / I wanta do something freaky to you / Steppin' out.
- LP .................................. 810 304-1
Casablanca / Sep '83.

### NATURALLY.
Tracks: Don't push it, don't force it / Daydream / That's what time it is / Love is what we came here for / If you're looking for a night of fun / Who you been giving it up to / Lover's rap.
- LP .................................. T 613
20th Century / Jul '80.

## Haywoode, Emma

### DON'T POISON ME.
Tracks: Don't poison me.
- 12" .................................. BOSS 12008
- 7" .................................. BOSS 008
Boss / Nov '91.

- DELETED

## NEED YOUR LOVIN'.
Tracks: Need your lovin'.
■ 12" . . . . . . . . . . . . . . . . . . . . . . . BOSS 12001
Boss / Feb '90.

### Headhunters

## IMPOSSIBLE.
Tracks: Impossible / Strait-jacket.
■ 7" . . . . . . . . . . . . . . . . . . . . . . . . . XS 005
Shout / Dec '83.

## INDUSTRIAL WARFARE.
Tracks: Not Advised.
■ LP . . . . . . . . . . . . . . . . . . . . . . . . . LX 004
Shout / Aug '83.

## WAY OF THE SOUTH.
Tracks: Way of the south.
■ 12" . . . . . . . . . . . . . . . . . . . . . . . QST 009
Quiet / Jun '86.

## WIPE OUT THE FUNK.
Tracks: Wipe out the funk.
■ 12" . . . . . . . . . . . . . . . . . . . . . . . XW 1201
Shout / Oct '82.

### Headin' South

## SEARCHIN'.
Tracks: Searchin (Part 1) / Searchin (Part 2) / Cloudburst / Searchin (Instrumental).
■ 12" . . . . . . . . . . . . . . . . . . . . . . . CUP 001
Clean Up Records / Nov '92.

### Heard, Larry

## BLACK OCEANS.
Tracks: Black oceans / Burning for you / What can you do.
12" . . . . . . . . . . . . . . . . . . . . . . . . BMI 015
Black Market International / Mar '94 / Soul Trader Ltd.

### Heatwave

## ALWAYS AND FOREVER.
Tracks: Always and Forever.
■ 7" . . . . . . . . . . . . . . . . . . . . . . . . GT 236
GTO / Nov '78.

## BOOGIE NIGHTS.
Tracks: Not Advised.
CD . . . . . . . . . . . . . . . . . . . . . . . . . JHD 028
MC . . . . . . . . . . . . . . . . . . . . . . . MCJHD 028
IMD / Jun '92 / BMG.

## BOOGIE NIGHTS.
Tracks: Boogie nights / Too hot to handle.
■ 7" . . . . . . . . . . . . . . . . . . . . . . . . GT 77
GTO / Jan '77.
■ 7" . . . . . . . . . . . . . . . . . . . . . . . EPCA 2965
Epic / Nov '82.
■ 7" . . . . . . . . . . . . . . . . . . . . . . . . A 4592
Epic / Jun '84.

## BOOGIE NIGHTS (OLD GOLD).
Tracks: Boogie nights / Always and forever.
■ 7" . . . . . . . . . . . . . . . . . . . . . . . OG 9395
Old Gold / Jun '84.
■ 12" . . . . . . . . . . . . . . . . . . . . . . . OG 4144
Old Gold / Nov '89.

## CANDLES.
Tracks: Gangsters of the groove / Jitterbuggin' party suite / Turn around / Posin' till closin' / All I am / Dreamin' you / Goin' crazy / Where did I go wrong.
■ LP . . . . . . . . . . . . . . . . . . . . . . . GTLP 047
GTO / Feb '81.

## CENTRAL HEATING.
Tracks: Not Advised.
■ LP . . . . . . . . . . . . . . . . . . . . . . . GTLP 027
■ MC . . . . . . . . . . . . . . . . . . . . . . GTMC 027
GTO / Apr '78.

## CURRENT.
Tracks: Lettin' it loose / State to state / Look after love / Naturally / Big guns / Find it in your heart / Hold on to the one / Mind what you find.
■ LP . . . . . . . . . . . . . . . . . . . . . . . EPC 85812
Epic / Jul '82.

## DANCE HITS.
Tracks: Boogie nights / Look after love / Always and forever / Groove line / Mind blowing decisions / Razzle dazzle / Gangsters of the groove / Jitterbuggin' / Naturally / Too hot to handle / Lettin' it loose / Posin' till closin' / Super soul sister / Hold on to the one / Mind what you find / Big guns.
CD . . . . . . . . . . . . . . . . . . . . . . . . 9827392

---

Pickwick/Sony Collector's Choice / Mar '94 / Pickwick / Pinnacle.

## FEEL LIKE MAKIN' LOVE (Heatwave & Jocelyn Brown).
Tracks: Feel like makin' love / Sweet delight / Cover discover.
■ 12" . . . . . . . . . . . . . . . . . . . . . . 12HW 3
■ 7" . . . . . . . . . . . . . . . . . . . . . . . HW 3
■ CD Single . . . . . . . . . . . . . . . . . . HWCD 3
■ MC Single . . . . . . . . . . . . . . . . . . HWC 3
Brothers Organisation / Oct '90.

## GANGSTERS OF THE GROOVE.
Tracks: Gangsters of the groove / Someone like you.
■ 12" . . . . . . . . . . . . . . . . . . . . . GT 13 285
■ 7" . . . . . . . . . . . . . . . . . . . . . . . GT 285
GTO / Jan '81.

## GANGSTERS OF THE GROOVE (OLD GOLD).
Tracks: Groove line / Mind blowing decisions / Too hot to handle / Gangsters of the groove.
■ 12" . . . . . . . . . . . . . . . . . . . . . . OG 4003
Old Gold / Feb '86.

## GANGSTERS OF THE GROOVE - 90'S MIX.
Tracks: Mind blowing decisions / Ain't no half steppin' / I surrender / Gangsters of the groove / Sweet delight / Razzle dazzle / Time out / Feel like makin' love / Groove line / Too hot to handle / Cover discover / Boogie nights / Jitterbuggin' / Always and forever.
■ MC Set . . . . . . . . . . . . . . . . . . STAC 2434
■ LP . . . . . . . . . . . . . . . . . . . . . STAR 2434
■ CD . . . . . . . . . . . . . . . . . . . . . TCD 2434
Telstar/Ronco / Oct '90.

## GREATEST HITS: HEATWAVE.
Tracks: Boogie nights / Always and forever / Lettin' it loose / Look after love / Groove line / Gangsters of the groove / Posin' 'til closin' / Big guns.
■ MC . . . . . . . . . . . . . . . . . . . . . .40 32503
■ LP . . . . . . . . . . . . . . . . . . . . . EPC 32503
Epic / '84.

## GROOVE LINE, THE.
Tracks: Groove line.
■ 7" . . . . . . . . . . . . . . . . . . . . . . . GT 115
GTO / Jan '78.

## HEATWAVE (EP).
Tracks: Boogie nights / Always and forever / Gangsters of the groove / Groove line.
MC . . . . . . . . . . . . . . . . . . . EPC A 40 2631
Epic / Aug '82 / Sony.

## HOT PROPERTY.
Tracks: Not Advised.
■ LP . . . . . . . . . . . . . . . . . . . . . . GTLP 039
■ MC . . . . . . . . . . . . . . . . . . . . . .GTMC 039
GTO / May '79.

## JITTERBUGGIN'.
Tracks: Jitterbuggin' / Wack that axe (on 12" only) / Goin' crazy.
■ 12" . . . . . . . . . . . . . . . . . . . . . GT 13290
■ 7" . . . . . . . . . . . . . . . . . . . . . . . GT 290
GTO / Mar '81.

## LETTIN' IT LOOSE.
Tracks: Lettin' it loose / Mind what you find.
■ 12" . . . . . . . . . . . . . . . . . . . . EPCA 132414
■ 7" . . . . . . . . . . . . . . . . . . . . . EPCA 2414
Epic / Jun '82.

## MAXIMUM HEAT.
Tracks: Boogie nights / Groove line / All I am / Too hot to handle / Mind-blowing decisions / Star of the story (X) / Posin' 'til closin' / Always and forever / Where did I go wrong / Razzle dazzle / Jitterbuggin' / Gangsters of the groove.
■ LP . . . . . . . . . . . . . . . . . . . . . SHM 3131
■ MC . . . . . . . . . . . . . . . . . . . . . HSC 3131
Hallmark / Nov '83.

## MIND BLOWING DECISIONS.
Tracks: Mind blowing decisions / Beat your booty.
■ 7" . . . . . . . . . . . . . . . . . . . . . . . GT 226
GTO / Jun '78.
■ 12" . . . . . . . . . . . . . . . . . . . . . PSXT 01
■ CD Single . . . . . . . . . . . . . . . . . . PSXS 01
Parasol / Aug '93.

## MIND BLOWING DECISIONS (2).
Tracks: Mind blowing decisions.
■ 7" . . . . . . . . . . . . . . . . . . . . . . . HW 1
■ CD Single . . . . . . . . . . . . . . . . . . HWCD 1
■ MC Single . . . . . . . . . . . . . . . . . . HWC 1
■ 12" . . . . . . . . . . . . . . . . . . . . . 12HW 1
Brothers Organisation / Aug '90.

---

## POSING TILL CLOSING.
Tracks: Posing till closing / Where did I go wrong.
■ 7" . . . . . . . . . . . . . . . . . . . . . . . GT 29
GTO / Jun '81.

## POWER CUTS (All Their Hottest Hits).
Tracks: Boogie nights / Jitterbuggin' / Too hot to handle / Look after love / Big guns / Groove line / Mind blowing decisions / Always and forever / Posin' til closin' / Razzle dazzle / Lettin' it loose / Gangsters of the groove.
■ LP . . . . . . . . . . . . . . . . . . . . . EPC 25191
Epic / '83.
■ CD . . . . . . . . . . . . . . . . . . . . . 468921:
■ MC . . . . . . . . . . . . . . . . . . . . . 468921:
Epic / Oct '91.

## RAZZLE DAZZLE.
Tracks: Razzle dazzle.
■ 7" . . . . . . . . . . . . . . . . . . . . . . . GT 24
GTO / May '79.

## SOUND OF SOUL.
Tracks: Too hot to handle / Ain't no half steppin' Lay it on me / Boogie nights / Central heating / Min blowing decisions / Happiness togetherness Groove line / Put the word out / Jitterbuggin' / Wher did I go wrong / Gangsters of the groove / Always and forever.
CD . . . . . . . . . . . . . . . . . . . . . BLATCD 1
MC . . . . . . . . . . . . . . . . . . . . . BLATMC 1
■ LP . . . . . . . . . . . . . . . . . . . . . BLATLP 1
Blatant / May '89 / Roots Records.

## STRAIGHT FROM THE HEART.
Tracks: Straight from the heart / Introducing my love
■ 12" . . . . . . . . . . . . . . . . . . . . . SITYT :
■ 7" . . . . . . . . . . . . . . . . . . . . . . SITY :
Soul City / Oct '87.

## TOO HOT TO HANDLE.
Tracks: Not Advised.
■ LP . . . . . . . . . . . . . . . . . . . . . GTLP 013
GTO / Nov '76.
■ LP . . . . . . . . . . . . . . . . . . . . . EPC 32191
Epic / Oct '82.

## TOO HOT TO HANDLE.
Tracks: Too hot to handle / Slip your disc to this.
■ 7" . . . . . . . . . . . . . . . . . . . . . . . GT 9
GTO / May '77.

## WHO DAT.
Tracks: Who dat / Turn the clock back.
■ 12" . . . . . . . . . . . . . . . . . . . . . SITYT 1
■ 7" . . . . . . . . . . . . . . . . . . . . . . SITY :
Soul City / Jul '88.

### Heaven & Earth

## DEDICATION.
Tracks: Not Advised.
■ CD . . . . . . . . . . . . . . . . . . . . . 781 850-:
Atlantic / '88.

### Hebb, Bobby

## LOVE LOVE LOVE.
Tracks: Love love love.
■ 7" . . . . . . . . . . . . . . . . . . . . . .6051 023
Philips / Aug '72.

## SUNNY.
Tracks: Sunny.
■ 7" . . . . . . . . . . . . . . . . . . . . . . BF 1503
Philips / Sep '66.

## SUNNY (OLD GOLD).
Tracks: Sunny / Na na hey hey kiss him goodbye.
■ 7" . . . . . . . . . . . . . . . . . . . . . .OG 9491
Old Gold / Jan '85.

### Height, Donald

## 365 DAYS.
Tracks: 365 Days / I'm willing to wait.
7" . . . . . . . . . . . . . . . . . . . . . HLZ 10116
London / Feb '67 / PolyGram.

### Helms, Jimmy

## DON'T COOL YOUR LOVE.
Tracks: Don't cool your love / Don't want to lose you
■ 7" . . . . . . . . . . . . . . . . . . . . . 7N 45503
Pye / Jul '75.

## GONNA MAKE YOU AN OFFER YOU CAN'T REFUSE.
Tracks: Gonna make you an offer you can't refuse.
■ 7" . . . . . . . . . . . . . . . . . . . . . . BUG 27
Cube / Feb '73.

■ DELETED

## GONNA MAKE YOU AN OFFER YOU CAN'T REFUSE (2).
Tracks: Gonna make you an offer you can't refuse / So long love.
■ 12" .................... HBUG 98
■ 7" ..................... BUG 98
Cube / Jan '84.

## PUTTING IT DOWN TO THE WAY I FEEL ABOUT YOU.
Tracks: Putting it down to the way I feel about you / Uncertain.
■ 7" ..................... 7N 45679
Pye / Mar '77.

# Henderson, Eddie

## CYCLOPS.
Tracks: Cyclops / Cyclops (version).
■ 7" ..................... CL 16034
Capitol / Jan '79.

## PRANCE ON.
Tracks: Prance on / Say you will.
■ 12" .................... 12CL 16015
■ 7" ..................... CL 16015
Capitol / Oct '78.

## RUNNIN' TO YOUR LOVE.
Tracks: Runnin to your love / Sunchaser / Hibby / This band is hot / Please your mind / Moon / Marlana.
■ LP ..................... EST 11984
Capitol / '79.

## RUNNIN' TO YOUR LOVE.
Tracks: Runnin' to your love / Hibby.
■ 12" .................... 12CL 16099
■ 7" ..................... CL 16099
Capitol / Aug '79.

## SAY YOU WILL.
Tracks: Say you will / Funk surgeon.
■ 7" ..................... CL 15937
Capitol / Sep '77.

## THINK OF ME (Henderson, Eddie Quintet).
Tracks: Not Advised.
CD ...................... SCCD 31264
Steeplechase (USA) / Oct '90 / Cadillac.

# Henderson, Finis

## FINIS.
Tracks: Skip to my lou / Making love / Lovers / You owe it all to love / Blame it on the night / Percussion intro - call me / Vina del mar / Crush on you / I'd rather be gone / School girl.
■ LP ..................... STML 12191
■ MC ..................... CSTML 12191
Motown / Jul '83.

## SKIP TO MY LOU.
Tracks: Skip to my lou / I'd rather be gone.
■ 12" .................... TMGT 1304
■ 7" ..................... TMG 1304
Motown / Jul '83.

# Henderson, Michael

In the admittedly small field of bass-playing child prodigies, Michael Henderson reigned supreme. Only 13 when he played with the Fantastic Four, Detroit Emeralds and Billy Preston, Henderson had yet to turn 20 when he began seven year association with Miles Davis (having previously toured with Aretha and Stevie). His solo career got underway when he teamed up with Norman Connors, on whose U.S. hit You Are My Starship Henderson sang lead; series of albums on Buddah followed. Although he never became a major star, Henderson could boast a star-studded career; later associations including Phyllis Hyman, Bobby Womack, the Dramatics and Cherelle.

## BEST OF MICHAEL HENDERSON.
Tracks: Be my girl / I can't help it / In the night time / To be loved / (We are here) / You are my starship / Make me feel better / Let me love you / You haven't made it to the top / Take me i'm yours / Do it all / Wide reciever / Valentine love / Reach out for me / Am I special.
CD ...................... NEXCD 117
■ LP ..................... NEXLP 117
■ MC ..................... NEXMC 117
Sequel / May '90 / Total / BMG.

## DO IT ALL.
Tracks: Playing on the real thing / Everybody wants to now / To be loved / Do it all / In the Summertime / Wait until the rain / Riding.
■ LP ..................... BDLP 4006
Buddah / Nov '79.

## FICKLE.
Tracks: Fickle / Feeling like myself once again / One step at a time / Thin walls / You wouldn't have to work at all / Assault with a friendly weapon / Love will find a way / Whip it / Fickle (instrumental version).
■ LP ..................... BDLP 4070
Buddah / Jul '83.

## FICKLE.
Tracks: Fickle.
■ 12" .................... BDSL 501
■ 7" ..................... BDS 501
Buddah / May '83.

## GOIN' PLACES.
Tracks: Whip it / Going places / Let me love you / I can't help it / I'll be understanding / At the concert / Won't you be mine.
■ LP ..................... BDLH 5018
Buddah / Jan '78.

## IN THE NIGHT TIME.
Tracks: Take me I'm yours / We can go on / Happy / In the night time / Whisper in my ear / Am I special / Yours truly, indiscreetly / One to one.
■ LP ..................... BDLP 4055
Buddah / Sep '78.

## TAKE ME I'M YOURS.
Tracks: Take me I'm yours / Let me love you.
■ 7" ..................... BDS 477
Buddah / Aug '78.

## WIDE RECEIVER.
Tracks: You're my choice / Make me feel like / Reach out for me / Wide receiver / I don't need nobody else / What I'm feeling (for you) / Ask the lonely / There's no one like you / Prove it.
■ LP ..................... BDLP 4065
Buddah / Oct '80.

## WIDE RECEIVER.
Tracks: Wide receiver / I can't help it.
■ 12" .................... BDSL 494
■ 7" ..................... BDS 494
Buddah / Sep '80.

# Henderson, Wayne

## BACK TO THE GROOVE (Henderson, Wayne & the Next Crusade).
Tracks: Rosa Cafe / Right on brother man / Arcoiris (rainbow) / 1990 BC (The grand dance) / Joshua / Urban jungle / Down home transitions / TNT / Lady in waiting / Alfie.
CD ...................... PAR 2013CD
Par / Aug '93 / New Note.

## DANCIN' LOVE AFFAIR.
Tracks: Dancin' love affair / So in love with you.
■ 12" .................... STEPX 7
■ 7" ..................... STEP 7
Polydor / Nov '79.

## HOT STUFF.
Tracks: Hot stuff / Living on a dream.
■ 7" ..................... 2066947
Polydor / Sep '78.

## PRIME TIME (see under Ayers, Roy).

## RUGBY GUITAR.
Tracks: Not Advised.
CD ...................... FF 542CD
MC ...................... FF 542C
Flying Fish / '92 / Cadillac / Roots Records / Projection / C.M. Distribution / Direct Distribution / Jazz Music / Duncans / A.D.A. Distribution.

## SKETCHES OF LIFE (Henderson, Wayne & the Next Crusade).
Tracks: Strange love / We're gonna rock your sock off / Men cry too / I'll take you there / Color of love / Just because its jazz / (Don't mean ya can't dance) / Portrait of a dream / Ancestral chant / For old time sake / Survival.
CD ...................... PAR 2021
Par / Nov '93 / New Note.

## ALTERNATIONS.
Tracks: You're the only one that I ever needed / Snakes alive / Propaganda / Night ain't long enough / Bandit / Love it / King of hearts / Casanova / Alternations.
■ LP ..................... SPART 1104
Arista / Oct '79.

## ART OF DEFENCE, THE.
Tracks: I sweat (going through the motions) / Soft targets / Life / I want you.
■ LP ..................... PL 84999
MC ...................... PK 84999
RCA / May '84 / BMG.

## BABY GO GO.
Tracks: Baby go go / Drive me wild.
■ 12" .................... 12 EA 238
■ 7" ..................... EA 238
EMI-America / Sep '87.

## FEMALE TROUBLE.
Tracks: I know what you need / Big fun / Baby go go / Rhythm of change / Why should I cry / Too hot to handle / Winds of change / Female trouble / Drive me wild.
■ CD ..................... CDP 746 550-2
■ LP ..................... AML 3120
■ MC ..................... TCAML 3120
EMI-America / Jun '87.

## HEART OF A WOMAN.
Tracks: Heart of a woman / To the bone.
■ 12" .................... RCAT 430
■ 7" ..................... RCA 430
RCA / Jul '84.

## HEAT, THE.
Tracks: Revolutionary dance / Girl like that / Heat / I need love / If looks could kill / Rock this house / Time.
■ LP ..................... PL 85465
■ MC ..................... PK 85465
RCA / Sep '85.

## I SWEAT.
Tracks: I sweat.
■ 12" .................... ARIST 12628
■ 7" ..................... ARIST 628
Arista / Jul '85.

## I SWEAT (GOING THROUGH THE MOTIONS).
Tracks: I sweat (going through the motions) / Living on the border.
■ 12" .................... RCAT 400
■ 7" ..................... RCA 400
RCA / May '84.

## I'M WINNING.
Tracks: I'm winning / Take a chance.
■ 7" ..................... EPC 5653
Epic / Aug '77.

## IF LOOKS COULD KILL (D.O.A.).
Tracks: If looks could kill (D.O.A) / Het - part 2.
■ 12" .................... PT 49940
■ 7" ..................... PB 49939
RCA / Sep '85.

## KEEP IT CONFIDENTIAL.
Tracks: Keep it confidential / B-boys.
■ 12" .................... RCAT 356
■ 7" ..................... RCA 356
RCA / Aug '83.

## LOVE IT.
Tracks: Love it / King of hearts.
■ 7" ..................... ARIST 313
Arista / Oct '79.

## NONA.
Tracks: Winning / Everybody wants to be somebody / Tax exile / Tout de suite mam'selle / Problem / Once again / Too late to run / Will you be there / Leaving here today.
■ LP ..................... EPC 82120
Epic / Oct '77.

## SKINDIVER.
Tracks: Off the coast to you / Women who fly / No emotion / Love is kind / Tears / Skindiver / 6th sense / Through the wire / Interior voices / New desire.
■ LP ..................... 210 045
■ MC ..................... 410 045
■ CD ..................... 260 045
RCA / Aug '89.

## SNAKES ALIVE.
Tracks: Snakes alive / We can go.
■ 7" ..................... ARIST 288
Arista / Sep '79.

## WHY SHOULD I CRY.
**Tracks:** Why should I cry / Funkyland / Why should I cry (boo-hoo mix) (extra track on extended 12" only) / Why should I cry (dub boo-hoo mix) (extra track on extended 12" only).
■ 7" . . . . . . . . . . . . . . . . . . . . . . . . . . EA 234
■ 12" . . . . . . . . . . . . . . . . . . . . . 12 EAX 234
■ 12" . . . . . . . . . . . . . . . . . . . . . 12EA 234
EMI-America / May '87.

## WINDS OF CHANGE (Mandela to Mandela).
**Tracks:** Winds of change / Too hot too handle / Female trouble.
■ 12" . . . . . . . . . . . . . . . . . . . . . . . . 12MT 34
■ 7" . . . . . . . . . . . . . . . . . . . . . . . . . MT 34
EMI-Manhattan / Mar '88.

## WOMEN WHO FLY.
**Tracks:** Women who fly / Interior voices.
■ CD Single . . . . . . . . . . . . . . . . . . . .662645
■ 12" . . . . . . . . . . . . . . . . . . . . . . . .612645
■ 7" . . . . . . . . . . . . . . . . . . . . . . . .112645
Private Music / Sep '89.

## YOU'RE THE ONLY ONE THAT I EVER NEEDED.
**Tracks:** You're the only one that I ever needed / Casanova.
■ 7" . . . . . . . . . . . . . . . . . . . . . .ARIST 253
Arista / May '79.

## Henry, Clarence

## AIN'T GOT NO HOME (Henry, Clarence 'Frogman').
**Tracks:** Ain't got no home / Country boy / But I do / You always hurt the one you love.
■ 7" . . . . . . . . . . . . . . . . . . . . . CHES 4003
Chess (PRT) / Jul '85.

## AIN'T GOT NO HOME (Henry, Clarence 'Frogman').
**Tracks:** Ain't got no home / Baby ain't that love.
■ 7" . . . . . . . . . . . . . . . . . . . . . HLU 10025
London-American / Mar '66.

## BEST OF CLARENCE 'FROGMAN' HENRY (Henry, Clarence 'Frogman').
**Tracks:** (I don't know why) But I do / That's my desire / Just my baby and me / If I didn't care / Standing in the need of love / Why can't you / Since I met you baby / I'm just the jealous kind / Please Mr. Boss-man / Ain't got no home / Lonely street / See saw / Glory of love / Made me love you / Little too much love / Your picture / Troublesm troubles / You always hurt the one you love.
CD . . . . . . . . . . . . . . . . . . . MCLD 19226
MC . . . . . . . . . . . . . . . . . . . MCLC 19226
MCA / Sep '93 / BMG.

## BUT I DO (Henry, Clarence 'Frogman').
**Tracks:** But I do.
■ 7" . . . . . . . . . . . . . . . . . . . . . 7N 25078
Pye International / May '61.
■ 7" . . . . . . . . . . . . . . . . . . . . . FBS 19
Flashback / Jan '83.
■ CD Single . . . . . . . . . . . . . . . MCSTD 1797
MCA / Jun '93.

## BUT I DO (Henry, Clarence 'Frogman').
**Tracks:** Ain't got no home / It won't be long / I found a home / Baby baby please / Never never / Oh Mickey / But I do / Just my baby and me / Live it right / I want to be a movie star / Steady date / Oh why / Little Suzy / You always hurt the one you love / I love you, yes I do / Lonely street / Your picture / I wish I could say the same / Standing in the need of love / Little too much / On bended knees / Jealous kind / Dream myself a sweetheart / Lost without you / Takes two to Tango / Long lost and worried / Looking back.
CD . . . . . . . . . . . . . . . . . . . .CDRED 13
Charly / Jun '89 / Charly.

## BUT I DO (Henry, Clarence 'Frogman').
**Tracks:** Not Advised.
CD . . . . . . . . . . . . . . . . . . . . CPCD 8007
Charly / Feb '94 / Charly.

## I DON'T KNOW WHY (Henry, Clarence 'Frogman').
**Tracks:** I don't know why / You always hurt the one you love.
■ 7" . . . . . . . . . . . . . . . . . . . . . .JB 015
Juke Box (Re-issue) / Mar '82.

## LEGENDARY CLARENCE 'FROGMAN' HENRY (Henry, Clarence 'Frogman').
**Tracks:** Not Advised.
■ LP . . . . . . . . . . . . . . . . . . . . STLP 3001

MC. . . . . . . . . . . . . . . . . . . . . STK 3001
Silvertown / Nov '83 / Silvertown Records.

## LITTLE GREEN FROG (Henry, Clarence 'Frogman').
**Tracks:** Loving cajun style (cajun honey) / Cheatin' traces / Ain't got no home (1) / Think it over / Baby ain't that love / Heartaches by the number / Have you ever been lonely / Little green frog / You can't hide a tear / I told my pillow / I might as well / Don't take it so hard / Tore up over you / Ain't got no home / Ain't got no home (2).
LP . . . . . . . . . . . . . . . . . . . . BFX 15278
Bear Family / Sep '87 / Rollercoaster Records / Swift / Direct Distribution / Topic Records.

## LONELY STREET (Henry, Clarence 'Frogman').
**Tracks:** Lonely street / Why can't you.
■ 7" . . . . . . . . . . . . . . . . . . . . . 7N 25108
Pye International / Sep '61.

## NEW RECORDINGS (Henry, Clarence 'Frogman').
**Tracks:** Not Advised.
■ LP . . . . . . . . . . . . . . . . . . . . .CFH 101
Clarence Frogman Henry / Apr '79.

## THAT OLDE PIANO (Henry, Clarence 'Frogman').
**Tracks:** That olde piano / Keep your hands off her.
■ 7" . . . . . . . . . . . . . . . . . . . . . KOR 20
Rockney / Aug '83.

## YOU ALWAYS HURT THE ONE YOU LOVE (Henry, Clarence 'Frogman').
**Tracks:** But I do / I want to be a movie star / Oh why / Your picture / Live it right / Never, never / Ain't got no home / You always hurt the one you love / Little Suzy / I love you, yes I do / Steady date / Just my baby and me / Oh Mickey.
■ LP . . . . . . . . . . . . . . . . . . . . GCH 8121
Chess (Charly) / '89.

## YOU ALWAYS HURT THE ONE YOU LOVE (Henry, Clarence 'Frogman').
**Tracks:** You always hurt the one you love.
■ 7" . . . . . . . . . . . . . . . . . . . . . 7N 25089
Pye International / Jul '61.

## Henry, Pauline

## CAN'T TAKE YOUR LOVE.
**Tracks:** Can't take your love / Can't take your love (mixes) / Watch the miracle start / Watch the miracle start (mixes).
■ 12" . . . . . . . . . . . . . . . . . . . .659990 6
■ 7" . . . . . . . . . . . . . . . . . . . . .659990 7
■ CD Single . . . . . . . . . . . . . . . .659990 2
■ MC Single . . . . . . . . . . . . . . . .659990 4
Sony Soho2 / Jan '94.

## FEEL LIKE MAKING LOVE.
**Tracks:** Feel like makin' love / Feel like making love (Mixes) / Love comes to mind (Available on CDS only).
■ 12" . . . . . . . . . . . . . . . . . . . .659797 6
■ 7" . . . . . . . . . . . . . . . . . . . . .659797 7
■ CD Single . . . . . . . . . . . . . . . .659797 2
■ MC Single . . . . . . . . . . . . . . . .659797 4
Sony Soho2 / Oct '93.

## PAULINE.
**Tracks:** Revolution / Baby I know / Too many people / Feel like making love / Now I've been to paradise / Can't take your love / I've got a feeling / Watch the miracle start / Touch of your hand / Now that I've found you / Revolution (Louie Louie Remix).
CD . . . . . . . . . . . . . . . . . . . .474744 2
LP . . . . . . . . . . . . . . . . . . . .474744 1
MC. . . . . . . . . . . . . . . . . . . .474744 4
Sony Soho2 / Feb '94 / Sony.

## TOO MANY PEOPLE.
**Tracks:** Too many people / Revolution / Too many people (mixes) (On CD single & 12" only).
■ 12" . . . . . . . . . . . . . . . . . . . .659594 6
■ CD Single . . . . . . . . . . . . . . . .659594 2
■ MC Single . . . . . . . . . . . . . . . .659594 4
Sony Soho2 / Sep '93.

## WATCH THE MIRACLE START.
**Tracks:** Watch the miracle start / Feel like making love / Watch the miracles start (Mixes).
■ 12" . . . . . . . . . . . . . . . . . . . .660277 6
■ 7" . . . . . . . . . . . . . . . . . . . . .660277 7
■ CD Single . . . . . . . . . . . . . . . .660277 2
■ MC Single . . . . . . . . . . . . . . . .660277 4
Sony Soho2 / May '94.

## Hewett, Howard

## ALLEGIANCE.
**Tracks:** To thee I pray: intro / Save your sex for me / Allegiance / Can we try again / How fast forever goes / Can't get over your love / To thee I pray interlude / Say you will / Take it to the highest / From this day on / Ronnie-O / Masquerade / Just like woman / To thee I pray.
CD . . . . . . . . . . . . . . . . . . . . 755961393
MC. . . . . . . . . . . . . . . . . . . . 755961393
WEA / Nov '92 / WEA.

## FOREVER AND EVER.
**Tracks:** Strange relationship / Natural love / Once twice, three times / You'll find another man / Forever and ever / Shakin' my emotion / Share a love / Thi time / Challenge / Goodbye good friend.
CD . . . . . . . . . . . . . . . . . . . .K 960779
■ LP . . . . . . . . . . . . . . . . . . . .K 960779
MC. . . . . . . . . . . . . . . . . . . .K 960779
Elektra / Mar '88 / WEA.

## HOWARD HEWETT.
**Tracks:** When will it be / Show me / If I could on have that day back / (Let me show you) how to fall i love / I do / More I get (the more I want) / Let's ge deeper / Shadow / I know you'll be comin' back Don't give in / Jesus.
CD . . . . . . . . . . . . . . . . . . . . 755960904
■ LP . . . . . . . . . . . . . . . . . . . 755960904
■ MC. . . . . . . . . . . . . . . . . . . 755960904
Elektra / Apr '90 / WEA.

## I COMMIT TO LOVE.
**Tracks:** I'm for real / Last forever / I commit to love In a crazy way / Love don't wanna wait / Got 2 go,I Eye on you / Let's try it all over again / Say Amen
■ LP . . . . . . . . . . . . . . . . . . . . 960487
MC. . . . . . . . . . . . . . . . . . . . 960487
Elektra / Sep '86 / WEA.

## I'M FOR REAL.
**Tracks:** I'm for real / Eye on you.
■ 7" . . . . . . . . . . . . . . . . . . . . . EKR 4
■ 12" . . . . . . . . . . . . . . . . . . . . . EKR 47
Elektra / Aug '86.

## STAY (AFTER MIDNIGHT MIX).
**Tracks:** Stay (after midnight mix) / Eye on you.
■ 12" . . . . . . . . . . . . . . . . . . . . . EKR 51
■ 7" . . . . . . . . . . . . . . . . . . . . . EKR 5
Elektra / Feb '87.

## Hi-Five

## FAITHFUL.
**Tracks:** Not Advised.
CD . . . . . . . . . . . . . . . . . . . . . CHIP 14
LP . . . . . . . . . . . . . . . . . . . . . HIP 14
MC. . . . . . . . . . . . . . . . . . . . . HIPC 14
Jive / Jan '94 / BMG.

## HI FIVE.
**Tracks:** Not Advised.
CD . . . . . . . . . . . . . . . . . . . . . CHIP 10
■ LP . . . . . . . . . . . . . . . . . . . . . HIP 10
■ MC. . . . . . . . . . . . . . . . . . . . . HIPC 10
Jive / Feb '91 / BMG.

## I CAN'T WAIT ANOTHER.
**Tracks:** I can't wait another.
■ 12" . . . . . . . . . . . . . . . . . . . .JIVET 28
■ 7" . . . . . . . . . . . . . . . . . . . . .JIVE 28
■ CD Single . . . . . . . . . . . . . . . JIVECD 28
Jive / Sep '91.

## I JUST CAN'T HANDLE IT.
**Tracks:** I just can't handle it.
■ 7" . . . . . . . . . . . . . . . . . . . . .JIVE 26
■ 12" . . . . . . . . . . . . . . . . . . . .JIVET 26
■ CD Single . . . . . . . . . . . . . . . JIVECD 26
Jive / Jan '91.

## I LIKE THE WAY.
**Tracks:** Not Advised.
■ 12" . . . . . . . . . . . . . . . . . . . .JIVET 32
■ 7" . . . . . . . . . . . . . . . . . . . . .JIVE 32
■ MC Single. . . . . . . . . . . . . . . JIVEC 32
■ CD Single . . . . . . . . . . . . . . . JIVECD 32
Jive / Dec '92.

## I LIKE THE WAY (THE KISSING GAME).
**Tracks:** I like the way (the kissing game).
■ 12" . . . . . . . . . . . . . . . . . . . .JIVET 27
■ 7" . . . . . . . . . . . . . . . . . . . . .JIVE 27
■ CD Single . . . . . . . . . . . . . . . JIVECD 27
Jive / May '91.

## JUST ANOTHER GIRLFRIEND.
**Tracks:** Just another girlfriend.
■ 7" . . . . . . . . . . . . . . . . . . . . .JIVE 26
Jive / Nov '91.

■ DELETE

## KEEP IT GOIN' ON.
Tracks: Not Advised.
CD . . . . . . . . . . . . . . . . . . . . . . . CHIP 131
■ LP . . . . . . . . . . . . . . . . . . . . . . HIP 131
MC . . . . . . . . . . . . . . . . . . . . . . HIPC 131
Jive / Nov '92 / BMG.

## NEVER SHOULD HAVE LET YOU GO.
Tracks: Never should have let you go.
■ 7" . . . . . . . . . . . . . . . . . . . . . .JIVE 342
Jive / Nov '93.

## SHE'S PLAYING HARD TO GET.
Tracks: She's playing hard to get.
■ 12" . . . . . . . . . . . . . . . . . . . .JIVET 316
■ CD Single . . . . . . . . . . . . . . .JIVECD 316
■ 7" . . . . . . . . . . . . . . . . . . . . . .JIVE 316
■ MC Single . . . . . . . . . . . . . . .JIVEC 316
Jive / Oct '92.

## UNCONDITIONAL LOVE.
Tracks: Unconditional love.
■ 7" . . . . . . . . . . . . . . . . . . . . . .JIVE 336
■ MC Single . . . . . . . . . . . . . . .JIVEC 336
■ 12" . . . . . . . . . . . . . . . . . . . .JIVET 336
■ CD Single . . . . . . . . . . . . . .JIVECD 336
Jive / Jun '93.

## Hi-Gloss

### YOU'LL NEVER KNOW.
Tracks: Not Advised.
■ LP . . . . . . . . . . . . . . . . . . . . EPC 85318
MC . . . . . . . . . . . . . . . . . . . .40 85318
Epic / Sep '81 / Sony.

### YOU'LL NEVER KNOW.
Tracks: You'll never know / totally yours.
■ 12" . . . . . . . . . . . . . . . . . .EPCA 131387
■ 7" . . . . . . . . . . . . . . . . . . . EPCA 1387
Epic / Jul '81.

## Hi-Rhythm

### ON THE LOOSE.
Tracks: On the loose / Superstar / Since you've been
gone / Purple raindrops / I remember, do you / Save
all my lovin' / You got me comin' / Skinny dippin'.
■ LP . . . . . . . . . . . . . . . . . . . .SHU 8506
London-American / Feb '77.

## Hi-Tension

### AUTUMN LOVE.
Tracks: Autumn love / Unspoken.
■ 7" . . . . . . . . . . . . . . . . . . . . WIP 6462
Island / Nov '78.

### BRITISH HUSTLE.
Tracks: British hustle / Peace on Earth.
■ 7" . . . . . . . . . . . . . . . . . . . . WIP 6446
Island / Aug '78.

### BRITISH HUSTLE - THE BEST OF DAVID JOSEPH & HI-TENSION (see under Joseph, David).

### FUNKTIFIED.
Tracks: Funktified / Latin inspiration.
■ 12" . . . . . . . . . . . . . . . . . 12XWIP 6489
Island / May '79.

### HAPPY.
Tracks: Happy / Shock girl.
■ 12" . . . . . . . . . . . . . . . . . . MKHAN 30
■ 7" . . . . . . . . . . . . . . . . . . . KHAN 30
Streetwave / Oct '84.

### HI TENSION.
Tracks: You're my girl / Searchin' / Autumn love /
Power and lightning / Unspoken / British hustle / If it
moves you / Hi tension / Peace on Earth.
■ LP . . . . . . . . . . . . . . . . . . ILPS 9564
Island / Dec '78.

### HI TENSION.
Tracks: Hi Tension / Girl I betcha.
■ 7" . . . . . . . . . . . . . . . . . . . . WIP 6422
Island / May '78.

### HOW D'YOU FEEL.
Tracks: How d'you feel / Lyin' low.
■ 12" . . . . . . . . . . . . . . . . . 12EMI 5303
■ 7" . . . . . . . . . . . . . . . . . . . EMI 5303
EMI / May '82.

### RAT RACE.
Tracks: Rat race / In the dark.
■ 12" . . . . . . . . . . . . . . . . . . . MKHAN 13

■ DELETED

---

■ 7" . . . . . . . . . . . . . . . . . . . . KHAN 13
Streetwave / May '84.

### THERE'S A REASON.
Tracks: There's a reason / If it moves you.
■ 12" . . . . . . . . . . . . . . . . . . 12WIP 6493
■ 7" . . . . . . . . . . . . . . . . . . . WIP 6493
Island / Sep '79.

### WE'VE GOT THE FUNK.
Tracks: We've got the funk / Objects.
■ 12" . . . . . . . . . . . . . . . . . 12EMI 5225
■ 7" . . . . . . . . . . . . . . . . . . . EMI 5225
EMI / Sep '81.

## Hicks, D'Atra

### D'ATRA HICKS.
Tracks: Sweet talk / You make me want to give it up /
Something about you / Palm of your hand / Until
forever (Theme from 'Everybody's All-American'.) /
Love and happiness / Heart of gold / I wanna be
loved / If my heart could lie / Wait / One touch (leads
to another) / Everything I feel / Sweet talk (ext. mix)
(CD only.)
■ CD . . . . . . . . . . . . . . . . . CDEST 2104
■ LP . . . . . . . . . . . . . . . . . . EST 2104
■ MC . . . . . . . . . . . . . . . . . TCEST 2104
Capitol / Aug '89.

### SWEET TALK.
Tracks: Sweet talk / Sweet talk (inst.) (7" only.) /
Sweet talk (Sweet revenge mix) (12" only.) / Sweet
talk (ext.) (12" only.)
■ 12" . . . . . . . . . . . . . . . . . . 12CL 545
■ 12" . . . . . . . . . . . . . . . . . 203 491 6
■ 7" . . . . . . . . . . . . . . . . . . 203 491 7
■ 7" . . . . . . . . . . . . . . . . . . . CL 545
■ CD Single . . . . . . . . . . . . . . CDCL 545
Capitol / Oct '89.

## Hicks, Joe

### SOMETHING SPECIAL (Hicks, Joe & Jimmy Hughes).
Tracks: Team / Nobody knows you (when you're
down and out) / Train of thought / Rock me baby /
Could it be love / Rusty ol' halo / All in / Water water
/ Ruby Dean / I like everything about you / Let 'em
down baby / I'm so glad / Lay it on the line / Sweet
things you do / Chains of love / I'm not ashamed to
beg or plead / It's all up to you / Lock me up / What
side of the door / Peeped around yonder's bend /
Just ain't as strong as I used to be / Did you forget.
CD . . . . . . . . . . . . . . . . . . CDSXD 098
Stax / Jul '93 / Pinnacle.

### TAKE ME HOME.
Tracks: Take me home / Soul meeting.
■ 12" . . . . . . . . . . . . . . . . . . .HL 006
Hit Line / '78.

## Hicks, Marva

### MARVA HICKS.
Tracks: Never been in love before / Searchin for the
love / Got you where I want / Never say never / One
good reason (Edit) / Strong is our love / What is love
/ In love with love / Conviction / Life without you.
CD . . . . . . . . . . . . . . . . . . 8472092
■ LP . . . . . . . . . . . . . . . . . . 8472091
■ MC . . . . . . . . . . . . . . . . . . 8472094
Urban / Mar '91 / PolyGram.

## High Fashion

### FEELIN' LUCKY LATELY.
Tracks: Feeling lucky lately / You're the winner /
Hold on / Next to you / Have you heard the news /
When the lover strikes / I want to be your everything
/ Brainy children.
■ LP . . . . . . . . . . . . . . . . . . EST 12214
■ MC . . . . . . . . . . . . . . . . . TCEST 12214
Capitol / Aug '82.

### FEELIN' LUCKY LATELY.
Tracks: Feeling lucky lately / Brainy children.
■ 12" . . . . . . . . . . . . . . . . . . 12CL 250
■ 7" . . . . . . . . . . . . . . . . . . . CL 250
Capitol / May '82.

## High Inergy

### FIRST IMPRESSIONS.
Tracks: First impressions / Could this be love.
■ 7" . . . . . . . . . . . . . . . . . . TMG 1268
Motown / Jun '82.

### HE'S A PRETENDER.
Tracks: He's a pretender (part 1) / He's a pretender
(part 2) / Don't let up on the groove.

---

■ 12" . . . . . . . . . . . . . . . . . TMGT 1294
■ 7" . . . . . . . . . . . . . . . . . . TMG 1294
Motown / Feb '83.

### HIGH INERGY.
Tracks: Goin' thru the motions / All of you / Heaven's
just a step away / Fill the need in me / Devotion / I
just wanna dance with you / Now that there's you /
Don't park your loving / Soakin' wet.
■ LP . . . . . . . . . . . . . . . . . .STML 12157
Motown / Oct '81.

### HOLD ON TO MY LOVE.
Tracks: I can't help myself / Sweet man / Make me
yours / Hold on to my love / If I love you tonight /
Boomerang love / I'm a believer / It was you babe.
■ LP . . . . . . . . . . . . . . . . . .STML 12144
Motown / Oct '81.

### HOLD ON TO MY LOVE.
Tracks: Hold on to my love / If i love you tonight.
■ 7" . . . . . . . . . . . . . . . . . . TMG 1214
Motown / Oct '81.

### I JUST WANNA DANCE WITH YOU.
Tracks: I just wanna dance with you / Take my life.
■ 7" . . . . . . . . . . . . . . . . . . TMG 1234
Motown / Oct '81.

### LOVE IS ALL YOU NEED.
Tracks: Love is all you need / Save it for a rainy day.
■ 7" . . . . . . . . . . . . . . . . . . TMG 1103
Motown / Mar '78.

### LOVIN' FEVER.
Tracks: Lovin' fever / Beware.
■ 7" . . . . . . . . . . . . . . . . . . TMG 1122
Motown / Oct '78.

### MAKE ME YOURS.
Tracks: Make me yours / I love makin' love.
■ 7" . . . . . . . . . . . . . . . . . . TMG 1205
Motown / Oct '81.

### SHOULDA GONE DANCIN'.
Tracks: Shoulda gone dancin' / I've got what you
need / Come and get it / Midnight music man / Let
yourself go / Love of my life / Too late.
■ LP . . . . . . . . . . . . . . . . . .STML 12111
Motown / '79.

### SHOULDA GONE DANCIN'.
Tracks: Shoulda gone dancin' / Peaceland.
■ 12" . . . . . . . . . . . . . . . . . 12TMG 1142
■ 7" . . . . . . . . . . . . . . . . . . TMG 1142
Motown / May '79.

### SO RIGHT.
Tracks: Journey to love / Don'tcha love it / Wrong
man right touch / Wanna be your lady / First impres-
sions / So right / Show me how / Tired of being alone
/ Take a chance / Match point.
■ LP . . . . . . . . . . . . . . . . . .STML 12170
Motown / Aug '82.

### STEPPIN' OUT.
Tracks: Lovin' fever / Hi / You captured my heart /
Didn't wanna tell you / Every time I see you I go wild
/ Fly little blackbird / Beware / We are the future /
Paceland.
■ LP . . . . . . . . . . . . . . . . . .STML 12090
Motown / Sep '78.

### TURNIN' ON.
Tracks: Love is all you need / You can't turn me off /
Some kinda magic / Searchin' / Ain't no love left /
Let me get close to you / Save it for a rainy day /
High school / Could this be love.
■ LP . . . . . . . . . . . . . . . . . .STML 12074
Motown / Jan '78.

### YOU CAN'T TURN ME OFF.
Tracks: You can't turn me off / Let me get close to
you.
■ 7" . . . . . . . . . . . . . . . . . . TMG 1087
Motown / Oct '77.

## Hightower, Donna

### FABULOUS MISS DONNA HIGHTOWER, THE.
Tracks: Perfidia / Maybe you'll be there / Lover
come back to me / There I've said it again / Because
of you / Don't take your love from me / C'est la vie /
Too young / Baby get lost / I get a kick out of you /
Anytime, anyday, anywhere / Trouble in my mind.
■ LP . . . . . . . . . . . . . . . . . . FA 2051
Ember / Apr '68.

### IF YOU HOLD MY HAND.
Tracks: If you hold my hand / I made my bed.
■ 7" . . . . . . . . . . . . . . . . . . F 23160
Decca / Apr '71.

## Hightower, Rosetta

### GO PRAY FOR TOMORROW.
Tracks: Go pray for tomorrow / Give me just a little more time.
■ 7"..........................CBS 7068
CBS / Mar '71.

### WE FOUND LOVE TODAY.
Tracks: We found love today / Emergency.
■ 7"..........................IMA 001
Mirage (USA) / Feb '81.

## Hilary

### DO IT.
Tracks: Do it / Sundancers.
■ 12"..........................CBS 127215
■ 7"..........................CBS 7315
CBS / May '79.

## Hill, Bunker

### HIDE & GO SEEK PT.1.
Tracks: Hide & go seek Pt. 1.
■ 7"..........................SS 135
Stateside / '62.

## Hill, Jessie

### Y'ALL READY NOW?.
Tracks: Ooh poo pah doo / Why holler / Whip it on me / I got mine / Get in touch / Oogsey moo / I need your love / Pot's on strike / Popcorn pop pop / Scoop scoobie doobie / High head blues / Can't get enough (of that ooh poo pah do) / In my mind / Candy / Sweet jelly roll.
■ LP..........................CRB 1169
MC..........................TCCRB 1169
Charly R&B / Dec '87 / Charly.
CD..........................CDCHARLY 262
Charly R&B / Apr '91 / Charly.

## Hill, Lonnie

### COULD IT BE LOVE.
Tracks: Could it be love / Step on out.
■ 12"..........................TENT 117
■ 7"..........................TEN 117
10 / May '86.

### GALVASTON BAY.
Tracks: Galveston Bay / My sweet love.
■ 12"..........................TEN 111-12
■ 7"..........................TEN 111
10 / Jun '86.

### YOU GOT ME RUNNIN'.
Tracks: Keep on dancing / Step on out / Mr. Music man / Something special to me / Galveston bay / Could it be love / My sweet love / Close to you / You got me running / Hard times.
■ MC..........................CXID 13
■ LP..........................XID 13
10 / Jun '88.

## Hill, Z.Z.

Born Arzel Hill in 1940, this bluesy soul singer's adopted name was later echoed by fellow Texans ZZ Top. But when the bearded wonders made it big in the late '70s, Hill's career was on the slide. He'd recorded for the Kent label in the '60s, then formed modestly-monickered Hill records. R&B hit *Don't Make Me Pay For His Mistakes* won him a deal with United Artists, for whom he recorded two albums before switching to CBS. Tenure there yielded three albums before he returned to smaller-scale blues market before moving to Hi! and then Malaco Records. Hill died in the mid-'80s.

### BEST OF..Z Z HILL.
Tracks: Next room / Down Home Blues / Please don't let our good thing end / Right arm for your love / Open house at my house / Someone else is steppin' in / Shade tree mechanic / Three into two won't go / Stop you from givin' me the blues / Friday is my day.
■ LP..........................MALP 006
Malaco / Sep '86.
CD..........................MALCD 342
Malaco / Apr '87 / C.M. Distribution / Charly / Pinnacle.

### BLUESMASTER.
Tracks: Not Advised.
■ LP..........................MAL 7420
Malaco / Dec '84.

### BRAND NEW.
Tracks: It ain't no use / Ha ha / Second chance / Our love is getting better / Faithful & true / Chokin' kind / Hold back / Man needs a woman / Early in the morning / I think I'd do that.
■ LP..........................2916013
Mojo / '72.

### BRAND NEW Z.Z. HILL, THE.
Tracks: It ain't no use / Ha ha (laughing song) / Second chance / Our love is getting better / Faithful and true / Chockin' kind / Hold back (one man at a time) / Man needs a woman (woman needs a man) / Early in the morning / I think I'd do it / She's all I got / Raining on a sunny day / Sweeter than sweetness / Sidewalks, fences and walls / I did the woman wrong / Yours love / Laid back and easy / You and me together forever / Ain't nothin' in the news (but the blues) / Did I come back to soon (or stay away too long) / Wy whole world has ended (without you) / Cuss the wind.
CD..........................CDCHD 532
Ace / Jun '94 / Pinnacle / Complete Record Co. Ltd.

### CHEATING IN THE NEXT ROOM.
Tracks: Cheating in the next room / Right arm for your love.
■ 7"..........................MAL 002
Malaco / Jun '82.

### DOWN HOME.
Tracks: Not Advised.
■ LP..........................MAL 7406
MC..........................MALC 7406
Malaco / May '82 / C.M. Distribution / Charly / Pinnacle.

### DOWN HOME SOUL OF Z.Z. HILL, THE.
Tracks: Baby I'm sorry / I need someone (to love me) / Have mercy someone / Kind of love I want / Hey little girl / I found love / No more doggin' / You can't hide a heartache / That's it / Happiness is all I need / Everybody has to cry / Nothing can change this love / Set your sights higher / Steal away / You're gonna need my loving / You're gonna make me cry / Oh darling / If I could do it all over / You don't love me / You won't hurt no more / What more / You got what I need.
CD..........................CDKEN 099
Kent / Sep '92 / Pinnacle.

### DOWNHOME BLUES.
Tracks: Not Advised.
CD..........................MALCD 7406
Malaco / Mar '93 / C.M. Distribution / Charly / Pinnacle.

### DUES PAID IN FULL.
Tracks: Happiness is all I need / Hey little girl / I need someone (to love me) / You don't love me / If I could do it all over again / Everybody has to cry / Kind of love I want / That's it / What more / Oh darling / Have mercy, someone / I found love / Set your sights higher / You got what I need.
■ LP..........................KENT 018
Kent / Apr '84.

### GREATEST HILLS.
Tracks: Not Advised.
■ LP..........................MALP 7437
Malaco Gospel / '89.
CD..........................MALCD 7437
Malaco / Mar '93 / C.M. Distribution / Charly / Pinnacle.

### I KEEP ON LOVIN' YOU.
Tracks: I keep on lovin' you / Whoever's thrilling you is killing me.
■ 7"..........................UP 35727
United Artists / Jan '75.

### I'M A BLUES MAN.
Tracks: Not Advised.
■ LP..........................MAL 7415
Malaco / Nov '83.

### IN MEMORIAM.
Tracks: Not Advised.
■ LP..........................MAL 7426
Malaco / Jun '85.

### MAN NEEDS A WOMAN, A.
Tracks: Blues at the opera(Communication in regards to circumstances / Act 1, Scene 1 - It Ain't no use / Act 1, Scene 2 - Ha Ha(Laughing song) / Act 2, Scene 1 - Second chance / Act 2, Scene 2 - Our love is getting better / Act 3 - Finale,Faithful and true / Chockin' kind / Hold back (one man at a time) / Man needs a woman, (a woman needs a man) / Early in the morning / I think I'd do it.
■ LP..........................TOP 138
MC..........................KTOP 138
Topline / May '86 / Charly.

### RHYTHM & THE BLUES, THE.
Tracks: Someone else is steppin' in / What am gonna tell her / Open house at my house / Who you been giving it to / That fire is hot / Wang dang doodle / Outside thang / You're gonna be a woman / Help me, I'm in need / Get you some business.
■ LP..........................MAL 741
Malaco / '88.

### WHOEVER'S THRILLING YOU (Is killing me).
Tracks: Am I groovin' you / 'Cause I love you / Love in the street / I don't need half a love / Ain't nothing you can do / I've got to get you back / Two sides to every story / That ain't the way to make love / I keep on lovin' you / Look what you've done / Whoever's thrilling you (is killing me) / My turn.
■ MC..........................TCSSL 600
■ LP..........................SSL 600
Stateside / Sep '86.

### Z.Z. HILL.
Tracks: Not Advised.
■ LP..........................MAL 740
MC..........................MALC 740
Malaco / May '82 / C.M. Distribution / Charly / Pinnacle.

## Hines, Gregory

### GREGORY HINES.
Tracks: That girl wants to dance with me / Love don love you anymore / You need somebody / This is what I believe / I'm gonna get to you / There's nothing better than love / Gloria my love / So much better now.
■ CD..........................4610272
■ LP..........................461027
■ MC..........................4610274
Epic / Aug '88.

### THAT GIRL WANTS TO DANCE (WITH ME).
Tracks: That girl wants to dance with me.
■ 12"..........................6528120
■ 7"..........................6528127
■ CD Single..........................6538122
Epic / Jul '88.

### THERE'S NOTHING BETTER THAN LOVE
(see under Vandross, Luther).

### YOU NEED SOMEBODY.
Tracks: You need somebody / You need somebody (instrumental) / There's nothing better than love (Only on 12"version and CD single) / That girl wants to dance with me (Only on 12" version & CD single.)
■ 12"..........................6531096
■ 7"..........................6531097
■ CD Single..........................6531092
Epic / Oct '88.

## Hines, Marcia

### LET THE MUSIC PLAY.
Tracks: Let the music play / April sun in Cuba / Save the last dance for me.
■ 12"..........................GOT 392
Logo / Oct '80.

### OOH CHILD.
Tracks: Ooh child / Dance you fool, dance.
■ 7"..........................GO 37
Logo / Mar '80.

### SAVE THE LAST DANCE FOR ME.
Tracks: Save the last dance for me / Moments.
■ 7"..........................GO 383
Logo / Mar '80.

### SIGNED, SEALED, DELIVERED, I'M YOURS.
Tracks: Signed, sealed, delivered, I'm yours / I've got the music in me.
■ 7"..........................GO 328
Logo / Mar '79.

### SOMETHING'S MISSING.
Tracks: Something's missing / Moments.
■ 7"..........................GO 373
Logo / Nov '79.

### TAKE IT FROM THE BOYS.
Tracks: Your love still brings me to my knees / Love me like the last time / Take it from the boys / Many rivers to cross / What a bitch is love / I was free / Just this one time / Dance goes on / It don't take much / Taking it all in stride.
■ LP..........................LOGO 1034
MC..........................KLOGO 1034
Logo / Mar '82 / C.M. Distribution.

■ DELETED

### TAKING IT ALL IN STRIDE.
**Tracks:** Taking it all in stride / Take it from the boys.
■ 7" . . . . . . . . . . . . . . . . . . . . . . . . GO 405
Logo / Dec '81.

### WHAT A BITCH IS LOVE.
**Tracks:** What a bitch is love / I like it.
■ 7" . . . . . . . . . . . . . . . . . . . . . . . . GO 411
Logo / Feb '82.

### YOUR LOVE STILL BRINGS ME TO MY KNEES.
**Tracks:** Your love still brings me to my knees / All the things we do when were alone.
■ 7" . . . . . . . . . . . . . . . . . . . . . . . . GO 403
Logo / Jul '81.

## Hinton, Joe

### JUST A KID NAMED JOE.
**Tracks:** Just a kid named Joe / Pledging my love.
■ 7" . . . . . . . . . . . . . . . . . . . . . . . . VP 9258
Vocalion / Jan '66.

## Hiroshima

### ANOTHER PLACE.
**Tracks:** One wish / Save yourself for me / Another place / I do remember / Game / Undercover / Stay away / What's it to ya / Touch & go.
■ LP . . . . . . . . . . . . . . . . . . . . . . EPC 26916
■ MC . . . . . . . . . . . . . . . . . . . . . . .40 26916
Epic / Jun '86.

### CRUISIN' J-TOWN.
**Tracks:** Cruisin' J-Town / Warriors / Lion dance.
■ 12" . . . . . . . . . . . . . . . . . . . . . . . T 12388
Arista / Jan '81.

### LION DANCE.
**Tracks:** Lion dance / Roomful of mirrors.
■ 12" . . . . . . . . . . . . . . . . . . . ARIST 12340
■ 7" . . . . . . . . . . . . . . . . . . . . . . .ARIST 340
Arista / Mar '80.

### ODORI.
**Tracks:** Not Advised.
■ LP . . . . . . . . . . . . . . . . . . . . . . SPART 1155
Arista / Nov '80.

### SELF MUTILATION.
**Tracks:** Self mutilation.
12" . . . . . . . . . . . . . . . . . . . . . DREAM 02
Dream Inn / Jun '94 / SRD.

### SEND YOUR LOVE TO ME.
**Tracks:** Another place / Send your love to me.
■ 7" . . . . . . . . . . . . . . . . . . . . . . . .A 7113
Epic / Apr '86.

## Hit Pack

### NEVER SAY NO TO YOUR BABY.
**Tracks:** Never say no to your baby / Let's dance.
■ 7" . . . . . . . . . . . . . . . . . . . . . . TMG 513
Tamla Motown / '65.

## Hodges, James & Smith

### DANCING IN THE STREET.
**Tracks:** Dancing in the street / Ain't that peculiar.
■ 7" . . . . . . . . . . . . . . . . . . . . HLU 10573
London-American / Aug '79.

### SITUATION.
**Tracks:** Situation / People needing people.
■ 7" . . . . . . . . . . . . . . . . . . . . HLU 10548
London-American / May '77.

## Hoggard, Jay

### DAYS LIKE THESE.
**Tracks:** Not Advised.
■ CD . . . . . . . . . . . . . . . . . . . . . . GRD 9516
GRP / Sep '88.

### FOUNTAIN.
**Tracks:** Sweet potato / Stompin' at the Savoy / Pre-ude to a kiss / Starting over / Fables of faubus / Epistrophy / Fountain / My one and only love.
MC . . . . . . . . . . . . . . . . . . . . . MC 5450
■ CD . . . . . . . . . . . . . . . . . . . . MCD 5450
Muse / Aug '92 / New Note / Jazz Horizons / C.M. Distribution.

### IN THE SPIRIT.
**Tracks:** Bye ya / Prayin' out loud / Stolen moments / In the spirit of Eric Dolphy / Andrew / Gazzelonie / De pois do amour o vazio / Without a song.

■ DELETED

■ CD . . . . . . . . . . . . . . . . . . . . . MCD 5476
Muse / Aug '93.

### LITTLE TIGER, THE.
**Tracks:** Not Advised.
CD . . . . . . . . . . . . . . . . . . . . . MCD 5410
LP . . . . . . . . . . . . . . . . . . . . . . MR 5410
Muse / Sep '92 / New Note / Jazz Horizons / C.M. Distribution.

### LOVE SURVIVES.
**Tracks:** Don't quit / Pacific vibes / Felice / Love survives / Sailing / As if in a dream / God is capable of everything.
■ LP . . . . . . . . . . . . . . . . . . . . . GR 8204
Gramavision / May '83.

### OVERVIEW.
**Tracks:** Not Advised.
CD . . . . . . . . . . . . . . . . . . . . . MCD 5383
LP . . . . . . . . . . . . . . . . . . . . . . MR 5383
Muse / Sep '92 / New Note / Jazz Horizons / C.M. Distribution.

### RAINFOREST.
**Tracks:** Not Advised.
■ LP . . . . . . . . . . . . . . . . . . . . .1014 007
Contemporary Jazz / Jul '81.

## Holiday, Jimmy

### EVERYBODY NEEDS HELP.
**Tracks:** Baby boy's in love (Mono) / Yesterday died / Man ain't nothin' without a woman / I'm in love with you / Spread your love / Baby I love you / In the eyes of my girl / I don't want to hear it anymore / Turning point / I'm gonna help hurry my brothers home (Mono) / We forgot about love / Everybody needs help / Ready, willing and able / I've got to live while I can / I'm gonna use what I got (to get what I need) / Beauty of a girl in love (Mono).
MC . . . . . . . . . . . . . . . . . . . TC-SSL 6010
■ LP . . . . . . . . . . . . . . . . . . . . SSL 6010
Stateside / Sep '86 / EMI.

### GIVE ME YOUR LOVE.
**Tracks:** Give me your love / Turning point.
■ 7" . . . . . . . . . . . . . . . . . . . . LIB 12048
Liberty / Jan '67.

### READY, WILLING AND ABLE (Holiday, Jimmy & Clydie King).
**Tracks:** Ready, willing and able / We got a good thing goin'.
■ 7" . . . . . . . . . . . . . . . . . . . . LIB 12058
Liberty / Jun '67.

### SPREAD YOUR LOVE.
**Tracks:** Spread your love / Turning points / Baby I love you / Give me your love / You won't get away / Nobody's fault but your own / Everybody needs help / Got to live while I can / We got a good thing goin' (and 5 others).
■ LP . . . . . . . . . . . . . . . . . . . MLS 40010
Minit / Nov '68.

## Holland & Dozier

### DON'T LEAVE ME.
**Tracks:** Don't leave me / I'm so glad.
■ 12" . . . . . . . . . . . . . . . . . . . HDH 459T
■ 7" . . . . . . . . . . . . . . . . . . . .HDH 459
HDH / Aug '84.

### WHY CAN'T WE BE LOVERS.
**Tracks:** Why can't we be lovers.
■ 7" . . . . . . . . . . . . . . . . . . . . INV 525
Invictus / Oct '72.
■ 7" . . . . . . . . . . . . . . . . . . . . HDH 4513
HDH / Feb '85.

## Holland, Eddie

### IF IT'S LOVE (IT'S ALL RIGHT).
**Tracks:** If it's love (it's all right).
■ 7" . . . . . . . . . . . . . . . . . . . . CBA 1808
Oriole / '63.

## Holliday, Jennifer

### AND I'M TELLING YOU I'M NOT GOING.
**Tracks:** And I'm telling you I'm not going / Fake your way to the top.
■ 7" . . . . . . . . . . . . . . . . . . . GEFA 2644
Geffen / Aug '82.

### FEEL MY SOUL.
**Tracks:** Just let me wait / I am ready now / This game of love / I am love / Shine a light / Just for a while / My sweet delight / Change is gonna come / This day.

■ LP . . . . . . . . . . . . . . . . . . . . . 9040141
■ MC . . . . . . . . . . . . . . . . . . . . . 9040144
Geffen / Sep '86.
■ CD . . . . . . . . . . . . . . . . . . . . . 9040142
Geffen / '88.

### GET CLOSE TO MY LOVE.
**Tracks:** New at it / He ain't special / Get close to my love / Read it in my eyes / Ain't it just like love / Heart on the line / I never thought I'd fall in love again / Givin' up.
■ LP . . . . . . . . . . . . . . . . . . . . . 9241501
■ CD . . . . . . . . . . . . . . . . . . . . . 9241502
■ MC . . . . . . . . . . . . . . . . . . . . . 9241504
Geffen / Sep '87.

### HARD TIME FOR LOVERS.
**Tracks:** Hard time for lovers / Pretender.
■ 12" . . . . . . . . . . . . . . . . . . . . TA 6408
■ 7" . . . . . . . . . . . . . . . . . . . . .A 6408
Geffen / Sep '85.

### I AM CHANGING.
**Tracks:** I am changing / Cadillac car.
■ 7" . . . . . . . . . . . . . . . . . . . GEFA 2895
Geffen / Oct '82.

### I AM LOVE.
**Tracks:** I am love.
■ 12" . . . . . . . . . . . . . . . . . . . . TA 3704
■ 7" . . . . . . . . . . . . . . . . . . . . .A 3704
Geffen / Feb '84.

### I'M ON YOUR SIDE.
**Tracks:** I'm on your side / It's in there / Raise the roof / Dream with your name on it / Guilty / It will haunt me / Love stories / Is it love / I fall apart / More 'n' more.
CD . . . . . . . . . . . . . . . . . . . . . .261519
■ LP . . . . . . . . . . . . . . . . . . . . .211519
■ MC . . . . . . . . . . . . . . . . . . . . .411519
Arista / Sep '91 / BMG.

### SAY YOU LOVE ME.
**Tracks:** You're the one / What kind of love is this / No frills love / Hard time for lovers / Say you love me / I rest my case / Dreams never die / Just a matter of time / He's a pretender / Come sunday.
■ LP . . . . . . . . . . . . . . . . . . . GEF 26564
Geffen / Oct '85.

### SHINE A LIGHT.
**Tracks:** Shine a light / Heart strings.
■ 7" . . . . . . . . . . . . . . . . . . . . .A 3867
Geffen / Oct '83.

## Holliman, Clarence

### SEE THERE (see under Fran, Carol).

### SOUL SENSATION (see under Fran, Carol).

## Holloway, Brenda

### ARTISTRY OF BRENDA HOLLOWAY.
**Tracks:** Unchained / Operator / I'll be available / Where were you / Every little bit hurts / Too proud to cry / I'll always love you (and 9 others).
■ LP . . . . . . . . . . . . . . . . . . . .STML 11083
Tamla Motown / Nov '68.

### EVERY LITTLE BIT HURTS.
**Tracks:** Every little bit hurts.
■ 7" . . . . . . . . . . . . . . . . . . . . .SS 307
Stateside / '64.

### GIVE ME A LITTLE INSPIRATION.
**Tracks:** Give me a little inspiration / Give me a little inspiration (version).
■ 12" . . . . . . . . . . . . . . . . . . . . MARE 53
■ 7" . . . . . . . . . . . . . . . . . . . MARES 53
Nightmare / Jun '88.

### HURT A LITTLE EVERYDAY.
**Tracks:** Hurt a little everyday / Where were you.
■ 7" . . . . . . . . . . . . . . . . . . . . TMG 581
Tamla Motown / Nov '66.

### JUST LOOK WHAT YOU'VE DONE.
**Tracks:** Just look what you've done / When I'm gone.
■ 7" . . . . . . . . . . . . . . . . . . . . ZB 41911
Motown / Apr '88.

### OPERATOR.
**Tracks:** Operator.
■ 7" . . . . . . . . . . . . . . . . . . . . TMG 519
Tamla Motown / '65.

### STARTING THE HURT ALL OVER AGAIN.
**Tracks:** Starting the hurt all over again.
■ 7" . . . . . . . . . . . . . . . . . . . . TMG 608
Tamla Motown / '67.

## TOGETHER TILL THE END OF TIME.
Tracks: Together till the end of time / Sad song.
■ 7" .............................. TMG 556
Tamla Motown / Mar '66.

## WHEN I'M GONE.
Tracks: When I'm gone.
■ 7" .............................. TMG 508
Tamla Motown / '65.

## Holloway, Loleatta

Uncredited and unpaid use of her voice on Black Box's 1989 smash *Ride On Time* finally brought Loleatta Holloway into limelight. From gospel roots, including mid-'60s tenure with the Caravans, she developed solo career, highlight of which is regarded as Sam Dees-penned *Cry To Me* ('75). Moving from soul to dance, she scored disco hits in late '70s and recorded with likes of Norman Harris and Dan Hartman; collaboration with latter, *Love Sensation* on Salsoul, was one plundered by Black Box. Her later recordings tend to be in independent dance field.

## CRY TO ME.
Tracks: Cry to me.
■ 12" .............................. RCAT 413
■ 7" .............................. RCA 413
RCA / Jun '84.

## CRY TO ME.
Tracks: Cry to me / I know where you're coming from / Show must go on / World don't owe you nothing / Just be true to me / Something about the way I feel / I'll be gone / I can't help myself / Casanova / H.E.L.P.M.E.M.Y.L.O.R.D.
■ LP .............................. AA 2008
Aware / '75.

## DREAMIN'.
Tracks: Dreamin' / Is it just a man's way.
■ 7" .............................. SZ 2022
Salsoul / Mar '77.

## HEARTSTEALER.
Tracks: Heartstealer.
■ 12" .............................. SDY 11
Saturday / Jan '90.

## HIT AND RUN/LOVE SENSATION.
Tracks: Hit and run / Love sensation.
■ 12" .............................. 12 SALSA 1
Salsoul / Apr '93.

## LOLEATTA.
Tracks: Hit and run / Is it just a man's way / We're getting stronger / Dreamin' / Ripped off / Worn out broken heart / That's how heartaches are made / What now.
■ LP .............................. SZS 5513
Salsoul / May '77.
CD .............................. CPCD 8063
LP .............................. CPLP 8063
Charly / Nov '94 / Charly.

## LOVE SENSATION.
Tracks: Love sensation / Hit and run.
■ 7" .............................. SAL 6
Salsoul / Sep '80.
■ 12" .............................. SALT 105
■ 7" .............................. SAL 105
Salsoul / Jan '84.

## QUEEN OF THE NIGHT.
Tracks: Catch me on the rebound / Only you / Good good feeling / Mama don't, papa won't / I may not be there when you want me / You light up my life / Two sides to every story / I'm in love.
■ LP .............................. SSLP 1509
Salsoul / Oct '78.

## QUEENS ANTHEM, THE.
Tracks: Queens anthem.
12" .............................. SIXT 118
CD Single .............................. SIXCD 118
Six6 / Aug '94 / Sony / 3MV.

## STAND UP.
Tracks: Stand up (Mixes).
■ 12" .............................. SIXT 111
■ CD Single .............................. SIXCD 111
■ MC Single .............................. SIXC 111
Six6 / Feb '94.

## STRONG ENOUGH EP.
Tracks: Strong enough / From this moment on / Reach out of the darkness / In control / Have no doubt.
■ CD Single .............................. EKT 108CD
■ EP .............................. EKT 108

■ MC Single .............................. EKT 108C
Select / Jun '92.

## YOU LIGHT UP MY LIFE.
Tracks: You light up my life / Only you.
■ 7" .............................. SSOL 111
Salsoul / Aug '78.

## Holman, Eddie

## EDDIE'S MY NAME.
Tracks: This can't be true / You can tell / I surrender / Return to me / Don't stop now / I'll cry 1000 tears / Where I'm not wanted / Hurt / Peace of mind / Never let me go / Been so long / Sexy Ed here wants a lonely girl / Eddie's my name / Sweet memories / Stay mine for heaven's sake / Free country, A / You know that I will / Am I a loser / I'm not gonna give up / I'll cry 1000 tears (unreleased version).
CD .............................. GSCD 031
LP .............................. GSLP 031
Goldmine / Dec '93 / Vital Distribution.

## HEY THERE LONELY GIRL.
Tracks: Hey there lonely girl.
■ 7" .............................. ABC 4012
ABC Records / Oct '74.

## HEY THERE LONELY GIRL (OLD GOLD).
Tracks: Hey there lonely girl.
■ 7" .............................. OG 9218
Old Gold / Jul '82.

## I LOVE YOU.
Tracks: I love you / I surrender.
■ 7" .............................. ACT 4547
Action / '69.

## I SURRENDER.
Tracks: I surrender / Just one more chance.
■ 7" .............................. TOWN 109
Kent / Jun '85.

## NIGHT TO REMEMBER.
Tracks: You make my life complete / Time will tell / Immune to love / This will be a night to remember / Beauty and the beast / No need to say goodbye / No price / Love is all I need / You against you.
■ LP .............................. SZS 5511
Salsoul / Sep '77.

## NIGHT TO REMEMBER, A.
Tracks: Not Advised.
CD .............................. CPCD 8061
LP .............................. CPLP 8061
Charly / Nov '94 / Charly.

## SINCE I DON'T HAVE YOU.
Tracks: Since I don't have you / I love you.
■ 7" .............................. ABC 4032
ABC Records / Jan '75.

## SWEET MEMORIES (Holman, Eddie & The Larks).
Tracks: This can't be true / You can tell / I surrender / Return to me / Don't stop now / 1000 tears / Where I'm not wanted / Hurt / Why do fools fall in love again / Been so long / Somewhere waits a lonely girl / Eddie's my name / Sweet memories.
LP .............................. E 001
Universal Love / Jan '92.

## THIS CAN'T BE TRUE.
Tracks: This can't be true / Free country.
■ 7" .............................. P 960
Cameo Parkway / Mar '66.

## UNITED.
Tracks: United / Eternal love / Give it all to the Lord / I asked Jesus / Thank you for saving me / Holy ghost / Breathe on me Lord.
■ LP .............................. GNC 1001
New Cross / Jun '85.

## Honey Cone

## ARE YOU MAN ENOUGH.
Tracks: Not Advised.
CD .............................. HDHCD 507
HDH / Nov '91 / Pinnacle.

## GIRLS IT AIN'T EASY.
Tracks: While you're out looking for sugar / Girls it ain't easy / When will it end / Feeling's gone / You made me come to you / Take me with you / Are you man enough, are you strong enough / Want ads / My mind's on leaving, but my heart won't let me go / We belong together / Sunday morning people / Take my love / Deaf, blind, paralyzed / Day I found myself.
■ LP .............................. HDH LP 004
HDH / May '84.

## HONEY CONE.
Tracks: Sunday morning people / Son of a preacher man / Take me with you / Girls it ain't easy / You've made me so very happy / Are you man enough, are you strong enough / Aquarius / Take my love / While you're looking for sugar / My mind's on leaving but my heart won't let me go / Feeling's gone.
■ LP .............................. SHW 5002
Hot Wax / Jan '71.

## SOULFUL TAPESTRY.
Tracks: One monkey don't stop no show / Don't count your chickens / Little more / Stick-up / Want ads / Who's it gonna be / How does it feel / V.I.P. / Day I found myself / All the Kings horses.
■ LP .............................. SHW 5005
Hot Wax / Sep '72.

## SWEET REPLIES.
Tracks: Want ads / You made me come to you / Blessed be our love / Are you man enough, are you strong enough / When will it end / Feeling's gone / Sunday morning people / Deaf, blind, paralysed / Take me with you / My mind's on leaving, but my heart won't let me go / We belong together / Day I found myself.
■ LP .............................. SHW 5004
Hot Wax / Sep '71.

## WANT ADS.
Tracks: Girls it ain't easy / Want ads.
■ 7" .............................. HDH 454
HDH / May '84.

## Hooker, Frank

## ROCK ME (Hooker, Frank & Positive People).
Tracks: Looking for my no. 1 love.
■ 12" .............................. DJR 18009
■ 7" .............................. DJS 10931
DJM / Jan '80.

## THIS FEELIN' (Hooker, Frank & Positive People).
Tracks: This feelin' / I wanna know your name.
■ 12" .............................. DJR 18012
■ 7" .............................. DJS 10947
DJM / '88.

## Hopkins, Linda

## HOW BLUE CAN YOU GET.
Tracks: Not Advised.
■ LP .............................. PA 8034
Palo Alto / Jan '84.
MC. .............................. PAC 8034
Palo Alto / Jul '86.

## SHIVER AND SHAKE.
Tracks: Shiver and shake / Rock and roll blues / My loving baby / I can't / It took a long long time baby / Empty bed blues / Trouble in mind / Willow weep for me / Come back baby / Mama needs your loving baby / I'm going to cry right out of my mind / Danny boy / Is this goodbye / Get off my wagon / Three time loser / Tears of joy.
■ LP .............................. OFF 6032
Official.

## Horne, Jimmy 'Bo'

## BEST OF JIMMY BO HORNE.
Tracks: Dance across the floor / You get me hot / Gimme some / Going home for love / Let me / Spank / Get happy / I get lifted / Without you / Is it in.
■ LP .............................. TKR 83391
TK / Mar '81.

## DANCE ACROSS THE FLOOR.
Tracks: Dance across the floor / It's your sweet love.
■ 7" .............................. TKR 6208
TK / Jul '78.

## DANCE ACROSS THE RIVER.
Tracks: Dance across the river / Get happy / Gimme some / I wanna go home with you / Don't worry about it / It's your sweet love / Let me be your lover / Ask the birds and the bees.
■ LP .............................. TKR 82533
TK / Oct '78.

## GET HAPPY.
Tracks: Get happy / It's your sweet love.
■ 7" .............................. XB 2173
TK / May '77.

## IS IT IN.
Tracks: Is it in / Spank.
■ 12" .............................. TKR 137586
■ 7" .............................. TKR 7586
TK / Nov '80.

## WITHOUT YOU.
Tracks: Without you / Going home for love.
■ 7" . . . . . . . . . . . . . . . . . . . . . . . . . TKR 7575
TK / Apr '80.

## YOU'RE SO GOOD TO ME.
Tracks: You're so good to me / You're so good to me (version).
■ 12" . . . . . . . . . . . . . . . . . . . . SUNYL 102
Sunny View (USA) / Jan '84.

## Horne Section

## LADY SHINE.
Tracks: Lady shine.
■ 12" . . . . . . . . . . . . . . . . . . . . 12 BRW 10
■ 7" . . . . . . . . . . . . . . . . . . . . . . BRW 10
4th & Broadway / Aug '84.

## Hot Chocolate

## ARE YOU GETTING ENOUGH (of what makes you happy)?).
Tracks: Are you getting enough happiness / I've got you on my mind.
■ 12" . . . . . . . . . . . . . . . . . . . . 12RAK 318
■ 7" . . . . . . . . . . . . . . . . . . . . . .RAK 318
RAK / Jun '80.

## BROTHER LOUIE.
Tracks: Brother Louie.
■ 7" . . . . . . . . . . . . . . . . . . . . . .RAK 149
RAK / Mar '73.

## CHANCES.
Tracks: Chances / Nights to remember.
■ 7" . . . . . . . . . . . . . . . . . . . . . .RAK 350
RAK / Sep '82.

## CHERI BABE.
Tracks: Cheri babe.
■ 7" . . . . . . . . . . . . . . . . . . . . . .RAK 188
RAK / Oct '74.

## CHILD'S PRAYER, A.
Tracks: Child's prayer.
■ 7" . . . . . . . . . . . . . . . . . . . . . .RAK 212
RAK / Aug '75.

## CICERO PARK.
Tracks: Not Advised.
■ LP . . . . . . . . . . . . . . . . . . . . SRAK 507
RAK / Jul '74.

## CLASS.
Tracks: Love me to sleep / Losing you / Gotta give up your love / Walking on the moon / Green shirt / Children of spacemen / Brand new Christmas / Are you getting enough happiness.
■ LP . . . . . . . . . . . . . . . . . . . . SRAK 543
RAK / Dec '80.
■ LP . . . . . . . . . . . . . . . . . . FA 41 3111 1
■ MC . . . . . . . . . . . . . . . . . . FA 41 3111 4
Fame / Sep '84 / EMI.

## DISCO QUEEN.
Tracks: Disco queen.
■ 7" . . . . . . . . . . . . . . . . . . . . . .RAK 202
RAK / Aug '75.

## DON'T STOP IT NOW.
Tracks: Don't stop it now.
■ 7" . . . . . . . . . . . . . . . . . . . . . .RAK 230
RAK / Mar '76.

## EMMA.
Tracks: Emma.
■ 7" . . . . . . . . . . . . . . . . . . . . . .RAK 168
RAK / Mar '74.

## EVERY 1'S A WINNER.
Tracks: Every 1's a winner.
■ 7" . . . . . . . . . . . . . . . . . . . . . .RAK 270
RAK / Feb '78.

## EVERY 1'S A WINNER.
Tracks: Every 1's a winner (groove mix) / So you win again.
■ 12" . . . . . . . . . . . . . . . . . . . . 12EMI 5607
■ 7" . . . . . . . . . . . . . . . . . . . . . . EMI 5607
EMI / Mar '87.

## EVERY 1'S A WINNER.
Tracks: Every 1's a winner / Confetti day / Love is the answer one more time / Sometimes it hurts to be a friend / So you win again / Stay with me / Runaway girl / I'm gonna make you feel like a woman / Put your love in me.
■ LP . . . . . . . . . . . . . . . . . . . . SRAK 531
RAK / Apr '78.

## GIRL CRAZY.
Tracks: Girl crazy / Bed games.
■ 7" . . . . . . . . . . . . . . . . . . . . . .RAK 341
RAK / Apr '82.

## GOING THROUGH THE MOTIONS.
Tracks: Going through the motions / I just love what you're doin' / Dreaming of you / Dance / Mindless boogie / Night ride / Congas man.
■ LP . . . . . . . . . . . . . . . . . . . . SRAK 536
RAK / Jul '79.

## GOING THROUGH THE MOTIONS.
Tracks: Going through the motions.
■ 7" . . . . . . . . . . . . . . . . . . . . . .RAK 296
RAK / Jun '78.

## GREATEST HITS: HOT CHOCOLATE.
Tracks: Not Advised.
VHS . . . . . . . . . . . . . . . . . . UNKNOWN
Video Collection / '85 / Gold & Sons / Video Collection / THE.

## GREATEST HITS: HOT CHOCOLATE (2).
Tracks: Love is life / You could've been a lady / I believe (in love) / You'll always be a friend / Brother Louie / Rumours / Emma / Cheri babe / Disco queen / Child's prayer / You sexy thing / Don't stop it now / Man to man / Heaven is in the back seat of my cadillac.
■ LP . . . . . . . . . . . . . . . . . . . . SRAK 524
■ LP . . . . . . . . . . . . . . . . . . . . ATAK 50
■ MC . . . . . . . . . . . . . . . . . . TCATAK 50
RAK / Oct '76.
CD . . . . . . . . . . . . . . . . . . CDMFP 6009
MC . . . . . . . . . . . . . . . . . . TCMFP 5801
■ LP . . . . . . . . . . . . . . . . . . MFP 5801
MFP / Sep '87 / EMI.

## HEART AND SOUL OF HOT CHOCOLATE.
Tracks: Love is life / Rumours / Disco queen / Cheri babe / You'll never be so wrong / You could of been a lady.
■ CD . . . . . . . . . . . . . . . . . . KNCD 12056
■ MC . . . . . . . . . . . . . . . . . . KNMC 12056
Knight / Jul '91.

## HEARTACHE NO.9.
Tracks: Heartache no.9 / One life / Extended mix (On 12' version only.) / Heartache no.9 (Dub) (On 12' version only.).
■ 12" . . . . . . . . . . . . . . . . . . . . 12RAK 386
■ 7" . . . . . . . . . . . . . . . . . . . . . .RAK 386
RAK / Mar '86.

## HEAVEN IS IN THE BACK SEAT OF MY CADILLAC.
Tracks: Heaven is in the back seat of my Cadillac.
■ 7" . . . . . . . . . . . . . . . . . . . . . .RAK 240
RAK / Jul '76.

## HOT CHOCOLATE.
Tracks: Not Advised.
■ LP . . . . . . . . . . . . . . . . . . . . SRAK 516
RAK / Oct '75.

## I BELIEVE (IN LOVE).
Tracks: I believe (in love).
■ 7" . . . . . . . . . . . . . . . . . . . . . .RAK 118
RAK / Jul '71.

## I GAVE YOU MY HEART (DIDN'T I).
Tracks: I gave you my heart (didn't I) / Jeannie.
■ 7" . . . . . . . . . . . . . . . . . . . . . .RAK 369
RAK / Feb '84.

## I'LL PUT YOU TOGETHER AGAIN.
Tracks: I'll put you together again.
■ 7" . . . . . . . . . . . . . . . . . . . . . .RAK 286
RAK / Nov '78.

## I'M SORRY.
Tracks: I'm sorry / Love is a good thing.
■ 7" . . . . . . . . . . . . . . . . . . . . . .RAK 366
RAK / Nov '83.

## IT STARTED WITH A KISS.
Tracks: It started with a kiss / Emotion explosion.
■ 7" . . . . . . . . . . . . . . . . . . . . . .RAK 344
RAK / Jun '82.

## IT STARTED WITH A KISS.
Tracks: It started with a kiss / You sexy thing / Every 1's a winner.
■ CD Single . . . . . . . . . . . . . . . . EMCT 7
■ CD Single . . . . . . . . . . . . . . . CDEMCTS 7
■ CD Single . . . . . . . . . . . . . . . CDEMCT 7
■ MC Single . . . . . . . . . . . . . . . TCEMCT 7
EMI / Feb '93.

## LOSING YOU.
Tracks: Losing you / Children of spacemen.
■ 7" . . . . . . . . . . . . . . . . . . . . . .RAK 328
RAK / Feb '81.

## LOVE IS LIFE.
Tracks: Love is life.
■ 7" . . . . . . . . . . . . . . . . . . . . . .RAK 103
RAK / Jul '70.

## LOVE ME TO SLEEP.
Tracks: Love me to sleep / Girl is a fox.
■ 7" . . . . . . . . . . . . . . . . . . . . . .RAK 324
RAK / Nov '80.

## LOVE SHOT.
Tracks: Sexy Caribbean girl / Let's try again / Secret hideaway / Tears on the telephone / Jeannie / I'm sorry / Friend of mine / Touch the night / Love is a good thing / I gave you my heart (didn't I).
■ LP . . . . . . . . . . . . . . . . . . SRAK 1653831
RAK / Oct '83.

## MAN TO MAN.
Tracks: Not Advised.
■ LP . . . . . . . . . . . . . . . . . . . . SRAK 522
■ MC . . . . . . . . . . . . . . . . . . TC SRAK 522
RAK / Jul '76.

## MAN TO MAN.
Tracks: Man to man.
■ 7" . . . . . . . . . . . . . . . . . . . . . .RAK 238
RAK / Jun '76.

## MINDLESS BOOGIE.
Tracks: Mindless boogie / Don't turn it off.
■ 12" . . . . . . . . . . . . . . . . . . . . 12RAK 292
■ 7" . . . . . . . . . . . . . . . . . . . . . .RAK 292
RAK / Apr '79.

## MYSTERY.
Tracks: Girl crazy / Mystery / Are you getting enough happiness / No tears / Chances / It started with a kiss / You'll never be so wrong / No doubt about it / One night's not enough.
■ LP . . . . . . . . . . . . . . . . . . . . SRAK 549
RAK / Oct '82.

## NO DOUBT ABOUT IT.
Tracks: No doubt about it / Gimme some of your loving.
■ 12" . . . . . . . . . . . . . . . . . . . . 12RAK 310
■ 7" . . . . . . . . . . . . . . . . . . . . . .RAK 310
RAK / Apr '80.

## PUT YOUR LOVE IN ME.
Tracks: Put your love in me.
■ 7" . . . . . . . . . . . . . . . . . . . . . .RAK 266
RAK / Nov '77.

## REST OF THE BEST OF HOT CHOCOLATE, THE.
Tracks: Heaven is in the back seat of my cadillac / Man to man / You could've been a lady / Rumours / Mary-Anne / You'll always be a friend / Mindless boogie / Heartache no. 9 (remix) / Cheri babe / Going through the motions / Blue night / Every 1's a winner (remix) / You'll never be so wrong / I'm sorry / Chances / Tears on the telephone / Love me to sleep / You sexy thing (remix).
CD . . . . . . . . . . . . . . . . . . CDGO 2060
MC . . . . . . . . . . . . . . . . . . TCGO 2060
EMI / Sep '94 / EMI.

## RUMOURS.
Tracks: Rumours.
■ 7" . . . . . . . . . . . . . . . . . . . . . .RAK 157
RAK / Jul '73.

## SO YOU WIN AGAIN.
Tracks: So you win again / Part of being with you.
■ 7" . . . . . . . . . . . . . . . . . . . . . .RAK 259
RAK / May '77.

## TEARS ON THE TELEPHONE.
Tracks: Tears on the telephone / It's my birthday.
■ 7" . . . . . . . . . . . . . . . . . . . . . .RAK 363
RAK / Sep '83.

## THEIR GREATEST HITS.
Tracks: You sexy thing / It started with a kiss / Brother Louie / Girl crazy / So you win again / Put your love in me / Love is life / I'll put you together again / No doubt about it / Every 1's a winner / Emma / I gave you my heart (Didn't I) / You could've been a lady / Disco Queen / Don't stop it now / Child's prayer / What kinda boy for girl' / I believe (In love) / Are you getting enough happiness.
CD . . . . . . . . . . . . . . . . . . CDEMTV 73
MC . . . . . . . . . . . . . . . . . . TCEMTV 73
■ LP . . . . . . . . . . . . . . . . . . EMTV 73
EMI / Mar '93 / EMI.

## TWENTY HOTTEST HITS.
**Tracks:** So you win again / You sexy thing / Put your love in me / Love is life / You'll always be a friend / Rumours / I believe / Child's prayer / Don't stop it now / I'll put you together again / Emma / Brother Louie / Man to man / Cheri babe / Mindless boogie / You could've been a lady / Going through the motions / Heaven is in the back seat of my Cadillac / Disco queen / Every 1's a winner.
- ■ LP . . . . . . . . . . . . . . . . . . . . . . . . ATAK 134
- ■ LP . . . . . . . . . . . . . . . . . . . . . . . . EMTV 22
- ■ MC. . . . . . . . . . . . . . . . . . . . . TC EMTV 22

EMI / Dec '79.
- ■ MC. . . . . . . . . . . . . . . . . . . . . TCATAK 134
- ■ CD . . . . . . . . . . . . . . . . . . . . . . . . CZ 213

EMI / Jul '89.

## VERY BEST OF HOT CHOCOLATE, THE.
**Tracks:** It started with a kiss / So you win again / I gave you my heart (Didn't I) / No doubt about it / Brother Louie / Tears on the telephone / Chances / You could've been a lady / Every 1's a winner / Girl crazy / You sexy thing / I'll put you together again / Are you getting enough happiness / Emma / What kinda boy you looking for (girl) / Heaven is in the back seat of my cadillac.
- ■ LP . . . . . . . . . . . . . . . . . . . . . . . . EMTV 42
- ■ CD . . . . . . . . . . . . . . . . . . CDP 746 375 2
- ■ MC. . . . . . . . . . . . . . . . . . . . . TCEMTV 42

EMI / Feb '87.

## VERY BEST OF HOT CHOCOLATE, THE.
**Tracks:** You sexy thing / Emma / Put your love in me / So you win again / It started with a kiss.
- ■ VHS . . . . . . . . . . . . . . . . . . . . . . . .PM 0032

Video Collection / Mar '87 / Gold & Sons / Video Collection / THE.
- ■ VHS . . . . . . . . . . . . . . . . . . . . . . . .MC 2002

Music Club Video / Sep '89 / Video Collection / Gold & Sons / THE.

## WHAT KINDA BOY YOU LOOKING FOR (GIRL).
**Tracks:** What kinda boy you looking for (girl) / Got to get back to work.
- ■ 7" . . . . . . . . . . . . . . . . . . . . . . . .RAK 357

RAK / Apr '83.

## YOU COULD'VE BEEN A LADY.
**Tracks:** You could've been a lady.
- ■ 7" . . . . . . . . . . . . . . . . . . . . . . . .RAK 110

RAK / Feb '71.

## YOU SEXY THING.
**Tracks:** You sexy thing.
- ■ 7" . . . . . . . . . . . . . . . . . . . . . . . .RAK 221

RAK / Oct '75.

## YOU SEXY THING.
**Tracks:** You sexy thing / No doubt about it.
- ■ 7" . . . . . . . . . . . . . . . . . . . . . . . .G45 12

EMI Golden 45's / Mar '84.

## YOU SEXY THING (1990).
**Tracks:** You sexy thing (1990) / Everyone's a winner (1990) / Heaven's in the back seat of my Cadillac (Not on 7" single.).
- ■ 12" . . . . . . . . . . . . . . . . . . . . . . . .HNC T4
- ■ 7" . . . . . . . . . . . . . . . . . . . . . . . .HNC 4

Different Class / Jun '90.

## YOU SEXY THING (2ND RE-ISSUE).
**Tracks:** You sexy thing / Every 1's a winner.
- ■ 12" . . . . . . . . . . . . . . . . . . . . .12EMI 5592
- ■ 12" Remix. . . . . . . . . . . . . . . . . . EMIX 5592
- ■ 7" . . . . . . . . . . . . . . . . . . . . . . EMI 5592

EMI / Jan '87.

## YOU'LL ALWAYS BE A FRIEND.
**Tracks:** You'll always be a friend.
- ■ 7" . . . . . . . . . . . . . . . . . . . . . . . .RAK 139

RAK / Sep '72.

## YOU'LL NEVER BE SO WRONG.
**Tracks:** You'll never be so wrong / Robot love.
- ■ 12" . . . . . . . . . . . . . . . . . . . . .12RAK 331
- ■ 7" . . . . . . . . . . . . . . . . . . . . . . . .RAK 331

RAK / Apr '81.

# Hot House

## CRAZY.
**Tracks:** Crazy / My boys arms / Pull over (on 12" only.) / Way that we walk (Available on CD only.)
- ■ 12" . . . . . . . . . . . . . . . . . . . . . PT 42114
- ■ 7" . . . . . . . . . . . . . . . . . . . . . . PB 42113
- ■ CD Single. . . . . . . . . . . . . . . . . . PD 42114

RCA / Jun '88.

## DON'T COME TO STAY.
**Tracks:** Don't come to stay / Love, rich, cash, poor de-construction / That's when I'll stop loving you (Only on 12").

---

- ■ 12" . . . . . . . . . . . . . . . . . . . . . PT 42234
- ■ 7" . . . . . . . . . . . . . . . . . . . . . . PB 42233
- ■ CD Single. . . . . . . . . . . . . . . . . . PD 42234

RCA / Sep '88.

## DON'T COME TO STAY.
**Tracks:** Don't come to stay / Me and you.
- ■ 12" . . . . . . . . . . . . . . . . . . . . . . M 6212
- ■ 7" . . . . . . . . . . . . . . . . . . . . . . . M 621

Construction / Nov '86.
- ■ 7" . . . . . . . . . . . . . . . . . . . . . . CHEZ 1

RCA / Jul '88.

## EVERYTHING YOU SAID.
**Tracks:** Everything you said / All comes down.
- ■ 12" . . . . . . . . . . . . . . . . . . . . . PT 42846
- ■ 7" . . . . . . . . . . . . . . . . . . . . . . PB 42845
- ■ CD Single. . . . . . . . . . . . . . . . . . PD 42846

De-Construction / May '89.

## HARD AS I TRY.
**Tracks:** Hard as I try / Person who's taking you home / Home boy (Only on CD single and 12".) / Don't come to stay (Only on CD single.).
- ■ 12" . . . . . . . . . . . . . . . . . . . . . PT 42658
- ■ 7" . . . . . . . . . . . . . . . . . . . . . . PB 42657
- ■ CD Single. . . . . . . . . . . . . . . . . . PD 42658

De-Construction / Mar '89.

## LOSING THE FEELING.
**Tracks:** Losing the feeling.
- ■ 12" . . . . . . . . . . . . . . . . . . . . . PT 43512
- ■ 7" . . . . . . . . . . . . . . . . . . . . . . PB 43511
- ■ CD Single. . . . . . . . . . . . . . . . . . PD 43512

RCA / May '90.

## MOVERS AND SHAKERS.
**Tracks:** Responsible / Taking you home / Never, never fall / Waiting for that train to come / Losing the feeling / Crawl to me / All my own / Everything you said / Twenty six hours / All comes down.
- ■ CD . . . . . . . . . . . . . . . . . . . . . PD 74660
- ■ LP . . . . . . . . . . . . . . . . . . . . . PL 74660
- ■ MC. . . . . . . . . . . . . . . . . . . . . PK 74660

RCA / Jun '90 / BMG.

## SOUTH.
**Tracks:** Way that we walk / Don't come to stay / Hard as I try / Home boy / Jealous kind / Same place, same time / Me and you / Crazy / Catch before we fall / Evening with the blues / That's when I'll stop loving you (CD/cassette only) / My boy's arms (CD/cassette only).
- ■ CD . . . . . . . . . . . . . . . . . . . . . PD 71855
- ■ LP . . . . . . . . . . . . . . . . . . . . . PL 71855
- ■ MC. . . . . . . . . . . . . . . . . . . . . PK 71855

RCA / Oct '88 / BMG.
- ■ CD . . . . . . . . . . . . . . . . . . .74321 19318-2

RCA / Apr '94 / BMG.

## WAY WE TALK, THE.
**Tracks:** Way we talk.
- ■ 7" . . . . . . . . . . . . . . . . . . . . . . CHEZ 2
- ■ 12" . . . . . . . . . . . . . . . . . . . . . CHEZT 2

Construction / Aug '87.

# Hot Streak

## BODY WORK.
**Tracks:** Body work / Body work (inst).
- ■ 12" . . . . . . . . . . . . . . . . . . . . POSPX 642
- ■ 7" . . . . . . . . . . . . . . . . . . . . . POSP 642

Polydor / Aug '83.
- ■ 12" . . . . . . . . . . . . . . . . . . . . POSPX 821
- ■ 7" . . . . . . . . . . . . . . . . . . . . . POSP 821

Boiling Point / Sep '86.

## BODY WORK (OLD GOLD).
**Tracks:** Body work / Go deh yaka (Go to the top).
- ■ 12" . . . . . . . . . . . . . . . . . . . . . .OG 4045

Old Gold / Feb '88.

# Houston, Cissy

Founding member of Houston dynasty, Cissy was born in 1932 in New Jersey. First exposure came with family gospel group Drinkard Sisters, which at various times included Judy Clay and Cissy's nieces Dee Dee and Dionne Warwick. She became lead singer of Sweet Inspirations, who backed stars including Solomon Burke, Wilson Pickett, Aretha Franklin and Elvis Presley, as well as scoring soul hits of their own. When group split in 1970, Cissy embarked on solo career but devoted most of decade to raising family and serving as music director at New Hope Baptist Church in Newark. Well-respected in soul community, she latterly duetted with Luther Vandross and daughter Whitney.

## BREAK IT TO ME GENTLY.
**Tracks:** Break it to me gently / Gonna take the easy way out.
- ■ 7" . . . . . . . . . . . . . . . . . . . . . . EMI 5049

EMI / Mar '80.

## CISSY HOUSTON.
**Tracks:** I just don't know what to do with myself / Didn't we / I'll be there / Any guy / When something is wrong with my baby / Be my baby / This empty place / Long and winding road / He/I believe.
- ■ LP . . . . . . . . . . . . . . . . . . . . . . 6310205

Janus / Nov '71.

## CISSY HOUSTON.
**Tracks:** Tomorrow / Morning much better / You song / Love is holding on / He ain't heavy, he's my brother / It never really ended / Make it easy on yourself / Things to do / Love is something that leads you.
- ■ LP . . . . . . . . . . . . . . . . . . . . . PVLP 1036

Private Stock / Dec '77.

## IT DOESN'T ONLY HAPPEN AT NIGHT.
**Tracks:** It doesn't only happen at night.
- ■ 7" . . . . . . . . . . . . . . . . . . . . . . EMI 505

EMI / May '80.

## LONG AND WINDING ROAD.
**Tracks:** I just don't know what to do with myself / Didn't we / I'll be there / Any guy / When something is wrong with my baby / Be my baby / This empty place / Long and winding road / He I believe.
- ■ LP . . . . . . . . . . . . . . . . . . . . .NSPL 28146

Pye / Apr '71.

## LONG AND WINDING ROAD.
**Tracks:** Long and winding road / Be my baby.
- ■ 7" . . . . . . . . . . . . . . . . . . . . . 7N 25548

Pye / Mar '71.

## MAMA'S COOKIN'.
**Tracks:** Midnight train to Georgia / Nothing can stop me / Making love / It's not easy / Any guy / Long and winding road / Don't wonder why / I just don't know what to do with myself / This empty place / Only time you say you love me / I love you / Will you love me tomorrow / I'll be there / Be my baby / I believe Down in the boondocks.
- ■ LP . . . . . . . . . . . . . . . . . . . . . CRB 115
- ■ MC. . . . . . . . . . . . . . . . . . . . TCCRB 115

Charly R&B / Jun '87 / Charly.

## MORNING MUCH BETTER.
**Tracks:** Morning much better / It never really ended.
- ■ 7" . . . . . . . . . . . . . . . . . . . . . .PVT 12

Private Stock / Nov '77.

## PRESENTING.
**Tracks:** I just don't know what to do with myself / Didn't we / I'll be there / Any guy / When something is wrong with my baby / Be my baby / This empty place / Long and winding road / He / I believe.
- ■ LP . . . . . . . . . . . . . . . . . . . . . SMLP 86

Major Minor / May '70.

## STEP ASIDE FOR A LADY.
**Tracks:** Break it to me gently / You're the fire / It doesn't only happen at night / Just one man / Step aside for a lady / What I miss / Gonna take the easy way out.
- ■ LP . . . . . . . . . . . . . . . . . . . . . EMC 3321

EMI / Apr '80.

## THINK IT OVER.
**Tracks:** Think it over / Umbrella song, An.
- ■ 7" . . . . . . . . . . . . . . . . . . . . . .PVT 164

Private Stock / Jul '78.

## THINK IT OVER.
**Tracks:** Not Advised.
- ■ LP . . . . . . . . . . . . . . . . . . . . . PVLP 104

Private Stock / Nov '78.

## TOMORROW.
**Tracks:** Tomorrow / Love is holding on.
- ■ 7" . . . . . . . . . . . . . . . . . . . . . .PVT 104

Private Stock / Jul '77.

## WITH YOU I COULD HAVE IT ALL.
**Tracks:** With you I could have it all / What you gonna do / (Dance Mix) / Ballad (Extra track on 12" version only.).
- ■ 12" . . . . . . . . . . . . . . . . . . . . . CRT 86
- ■ 7" . . . . . . . . . . . . . . . . . . . . . . CR 86

Creole / Feb '86.

## YOUR SONG.
**Tracks:** Your song / Love is holding on.
- ■ 7" . . . . . . . . . . . . . . . . . . . . . .PVT 136

Private Stock / Feb '78.

## Houston, Thelma

Having originally aimed for Hollywood stardom, Houston turned to music after stint with gospel group Art Reynolds Singers. Her 1969 debut, *Sunshower*, was written and produced by then red-hot Jim Webb, but stiffed. Houston spent next seven years winning considerable acclaim but no successes. Breakthrough finally came in '77 with U.S. No. 1 *Don't Leave Me This Way*, an old Harold Melvin track remodelled for dancefloor (original was promptly reissued and charted higher than Houston's in U.K.). She failed to consolidate new-found fame, although LP of duets with Jerry Butler fared moderately well. Subsequent success was sporadic and modest, despite backing of first Motown, then RCA and MCA.

### 96 TEARS.
Tracks: 96 tears / There's no runnin' away from love.
■ 12" . . . . . . . . . . . . . . . . . . . . . RCAT 120
■ 7" . . . . . . . . . . . . . . . . . . . . . .RCA 120
RCA / Sep '81.

### ANY WAY YOU LIKE IT.
Tracks: Anyway you like it / Don't leave me this way / Don't know why I love you / Come to me / Don't make me pay (for another girl's mistake) / Sharing something perfect between ourselves / If it's the last thing I do / Differently.
■ LP . . . . . . . . . . . . . . . . . . . . STML 12049
Motown / Jan '77.
■ LP . . . . . . . . . . . . . . . . . . . . . STMS 5067
■ MC . . . . . . . . . . . . . . . . . . . . .CSTMS 5067
Motown / Aug '82.

### BEST OF THELMA HOUSTON.
Tracks: Don't leave me this way / Love machine / Saturday night, Sunday morning / Today will soon be yesterday / Jumpin' Jack Flash / If it's the last thing I do / I can't go back there again / Me and Bobby McGhee / You've been doing wrong for so long / Stealin' in the name of the Lord / No one's gonna be a fool forever / Piano man / I'm just a part of yesterday / I'm here again.
■ CD . . . . . . . . . . . . . . . . . . . . . WD 72774
Motown / Dec '91.

### BREAKWATER CAT.
Tracks: Suspicious minds / Down the backstairs of my life / Understand your man / Lost and found / Something we may never know / Breakwater cat / Long lasting love / Before there could be me / Gone / What was that song.
■ MC. . . . . . . . . . . . . . . . . . . . . . FK 13500
■ LP . . . . . . . . . . . . . . . . . . . . . . PL 13500
RCA / Mar '80.

### DEVIL IN ME.
Tracks: I'm here again / It's just me feeling good / I can't go on living without your love / Triflin' / Give me something to believe in / Memories / I've got the devil in me / Baby I love you too much / Your eyes.
■ LP . . . . . . . . . . . . . . . . . . . . STML 12075
Motown / Jan '78.

### DON'T LEAVE ME THIS WAY.
Tracks: Don't leave me this way / Today will soon be yesterday.
■ 7" . . . . . . . . . . . . . . . . . . . . . TMG 1060
Motown / Oct '81.

### DON'T LEAVE ME THIS WAY.
Tracks: Don't leave me this way / If you feel it.
■ 7" . . . . . . . . . . . . . . . . . . . . . TMG 1382
■ 12" . . . . . . . . . . . . . . . . . . . . TMGT 1382
Motown / Apr '85.

### DON'T PITY ME.
Tracks: Don't pity me / It's just me feeling good.
■ 7" . . . . . . . . . . . . . . . . . . . . . TMG 1117
Motown / Sep '78.

### I CAN'T GO ON LIVING WITHOUT YOUR LOVE.
Tracks: I can't go on living without your love / Anyway you like it.
■ 7" . . . . . . . . . . . . . . . . . . . . . TMG 1102
Motown / Mar '78.

### I GUESS IT MUST BE LOVE.
Tracks: I guess it must be love / Working girl.
■ 12" . . . . . . . . . . . . . . . . . . . . MCAT 940
■ 7" . . . . . . . . . . . . . . . . . . . . . MCA 940
MCA / Feb '85.

### I'VE GOT THE MUSIC IN ME (Houston, Thelma & Pressure Cooker).
Tracks: Not Advised.
■ LP . . . . . . . . . . . . . . . . . . . . . . ST 200
Sheffield Treasury / Oct '82.

### CD . . . . . . . . . . . . . . . . . . . . . . .CD 2
Sheffield Treasury / '88.

### IF YOU FEEL IT.
Tracks: If you feel it / Hollywood.
■ 12" . . . . . . . . . . . . . . . . . . . . . RCAT 77
■ 7" . . . . . . . . . . . . . . . . . . . . . . RCA 77
RCA / May '81.

### IT'S A LIFETIME THING (Houston, Thelma & Jerry Butler).
Tracks: It's a lifetime thing / Only the beginning.
■ 7" . . . . . . . . . . . . . . . . . . . . . TMG 1074
Motown / '77.

### NEVER GONNA BE ANOTHER ONE.
Tracks: Never give you up / Too many teardrops / Ninety-six tears / There's no runnin' away from love / Never gonna be another one / If you feel it / Don't make me over / Hollywood.
■ LP . . . . . . . . . . . . . . . . . . . . . RCALP 5035
■ MC . . . . . . . . . . . . . . . . . . . . . RCAK 5035
RCA / Jun '81.

### QUALIFYING HEATS.
Tracks: Not Advised.
■ LP . . . . . . . . . . . . . . . . . . . . . MCF 3243
MCA / Aug '87.

### READY TO ROLL.
Tracks: Saturday night, Sunday morning / Love is comin' on / I wanna start my life all over again / Midnight Mona / Pardon me / Everybody's got a story / Strange / Am I expecting too much / Can't we try.
■ LP . . . . . . . . . . . . . . . . . . . . STML 12098
Motown / Dec '78.

### RIDE TO THE RAINBOW.
Tracks: Saturday night, Sunday morning / I wanna be back in love again / Love machine / Imaginary paradise / Just a little piece of you / Ride to the rainbow / Paying for it with my heart / Give it to me.
■ LP . . . . . . . . . . . . . . . . . . . . STML 12117
Motown / '79.

### SATURDAY NIGHT, SUNDAY MORNING.
Tracks: Saturday night, Sunday morning / I'm not strong enough.
■ 7" . . . . . . . . . . . . . . . . . . . . . TMG 1130
Motown / Jan '79.

### SUNSHOWER.
Tracks: Sunshower / Everybody gets to go to the moon / To make it easier on you / Didn't we / Crazy mixed-up girl / Someone is standing outside / Jumpin' Jack Flash / This is where I came in / Pocketful of keys / This is your life / Cheap lovin' / If this was the last song.
■ LP . . . . . . . . . . . . . . . . . . . . . SSL 5010
Stateside / Nov '69.
■ LP . . . . . . . . . . . . . . . . . . . . . SPB 1053
Probe / Jun '72.
■ LP . . . . . . . . . . . . . . . . . . . . . ABCL 5061
ABC Records / May '77.
■ LP . . . . . . . . . . . . . . . . . . . . . STMS 5030
■ MC. . . . . . . . . . . . . . . . . . . . . CSTMS 5030
Motown / Oct '81.

### SUSPICIOUS MIND.
Tracks: Suspicious mind / Gone.
■ 7" . . . . . . . . . . . . . . . . . . . . . PB 1913
RCA / Mar '80.

### THELMA & JERRY (Houston, Thelma & Jerry Butler).
Tracks: Only the beginning / And you've got me / It's a lifetime thing / If you leave me now/Love so right / I love you through windows / Joy inside my tears / Sweet love I've found / Let's pretend / Let's get together.
■ LP . . . . . . . . . . . . . . . . . . . . STML 12063
Motown / Aug '77.

### THELMA HOUSTON.
Tracks: No one's gonna be a fool forever / Black California / I ain't going nowhere / Nothing left to me / Stealing in the name of the Lord / Blackberries / And I thought you love me / I ain't that easy to lose / What if / There's no such thing as love / Me & Bobby McGee / I'm letting go / Do something about it / And I never did.
■ LP . . . . . . . . . . . . . . . . . . . . . MWS 7003
Mowest / Feb '73.
■ LP . . . . . . . . . . . . . . . . . . . . . MCF 3165
MCA / May '83.

### TWO TO ONE (Houston, Thelma & Jerry Butler).
Tracks: If it would never end / Find a way / We owe it to ourselves / I'm not strong enough / Never gonna get enough / Don't pity me / Chicago send her home / You gave me love.

### LP . . . . . . . . . . . . . . . . . . . . . .STML 12092
Motown / Sep '78.

### WORKING GIRL.
Tracks: Working girl / Running in circles.
■ 12" . . . . . . . . . . . . . . . . . . . . MCAT 813
■ 7" . . . . . . . . . . . . . . . . . . . . . MCA 813
MCA / May '83.

### YOU USED TO HOLD ME SO TIGHT.
Tracks: You used to hold me so tight.
■ 12" . . . . . . . . . . . . . . . . . . . . MCAT 932
■ 7" . . . . . . . . . . . . . . . . . . . . . MCA 932
MCA / Nov '84.

## Houston, Whitney

Among the most commercially-successful singers of all-time, Whitney Houston - born in New Jersey 1963 to Cissy Houston - topped impressive list of achievements with best-selling single *I Will Always Love You* from the film *The Bodyguard*, and already multi-platinum superstar into household name. Previously, Houston was first female artist in the history of the Billboard Charts to have an album enter at No. 1, scored record-breaking seven consecutive U.S. chart-toppers, and still found time to duet with Aretha Franklin and Teddy Pendergrass and marry Bobby Brown (and, inevitably, score hit duet with him as well). Dismissed by purists for none-too-subtle approach to ballads, Houston is arguably best-served by infectious dance classics like *How Will I Know*, *I Wanna Dance With Somebody* and *So Emotional*.

### ALL THE MAN THAT I NEED.
Tracks: All the man that I need / Dancing on the smooth edge.
■ 7" . . . . . . . . . . . . . . . . . . . . . .113981
■ 12" . . . . . . . . . . . . . . . . . . . . .614000
■ 7" . . . . . . . . . . . . . . . . . . . . . .114000
■ CD Single . . . . . . . . . . . . . . . . . .664000
■ MC Single. . . . . . . . . . . . . . . . . .411307
Arista / Dec '90.

### DIDN'T WE ALMOST HAVE IT ALL.
Tracks: Didn't we almost have it all.
■ 12" . . . . . . . . . . . . . . . . . . . . . RIST 31
■ 7" . . . . . . . . . . . . . . . . . . . . . . RIS 31
Arista / Aug '87.

### GREATEST LOVE OF ALL.
Tracks: Greatest love of all / Thinking about you / Shock me (On 12" version only).
■ 12" . . . . . . . . . . . . . . . . . . . . ARIST 12658
■ 7" . . . . . . . . . . . . . . . . . . . . . .ARIST 658
Arista / Mar '86.

### HOLD ME (Houston, Whitney & Teddy Pendergrass).
Tracks: Hold me / Love.
■ 7" . . . . . . . . . . . . . . . . . . . . . . EKR 32
Elektra / Jan '86.

### HOW WILL I KNOW.
Tracks: How will I know / Someone for me.
■ 12" . . . . . . . . . . . . . . . . . . . . ARIST 12656
■ 7" . . . . . . . . . . . . . . . . . . . . . .ARIST 656
Arista / Jan '86.

### I BELONG TO YOU.
Tracks: I belong to you.
■ 12" . . . . . . . . . . . . . . . . . . . . .614727
■ 7" . . . . . . . . . . . . . . . . . . . . . .114727
■ CD Single . . . . . . . . . . . . . . . . . .664727
Arista / Sep '91.

### I HAVE NOTHING.
Tracks: I have nothing.
■ 12" . . . . . . . . . . . . . . . . . . 7432114614-1
■ CD Single. . . . . . . . . . . . . . 7432114614-2
■ MC Single. . . . . . . . . . . . . . 7432114614-4
■ 7" . . . . . . . . . . . . . . . . . . 7432114614-7
Arista / Apr '93.

### I WANNA DANCE WITH SOMEBODY.
Tracks: I wanna dance with somebody / Moment of truth.
■ CD Single . . . . . . . . . . . . . . . . . RISCD 1
■ 12" . . . . . . . . . . . . . . . . . . . . . RIST 1
■ 7" . . . . . . . . . . . . . . . . . . . . . . RIS 1
Arista / May '87.

### I WANNA DANCE WITH SOMEBODY.
Tracks: Not Advised.
■ VHS . . . . . . . . . . . . . . . . . . . . VCRIS 1
Chart Attack (Video) / Sep '87 / Pinnacle.

### I WILL ALWAYS LOVE YOU.
Tracks: Jesus loves me / Do you hear what I hear (On CDs only) / I will always love you.

■ 12"................74321 12065-1
Arista / Oct '92.
■ 7"................74321 12065-1
■ CD Single................74321 12065-2
■ MC Single................74321 12065-4
Arista / Dec '93.

### I'M EVERY WOMAN.
Tracks: I'm every woman / I'm every woman (mixes).
■ 7"................74321 13150-7
■ CD Single................74321 13150-2
■ MC Single................74321 13150-4
■ 12"................74321 13150-1
Arista / Feb '93.

### I'M YOUR BABY TONIGHT.
Tracks: I'm your baby tonight / My name is not Susan / All the man that I need / Lover for life / Anymore / Miracle / I belong to you / Who do you love / We didn't know / After we make love / I'm knockin'.
CD................261039
■ LP................211039
MC................411039
Arista / Nov '90 / BMG.
DCC................782218616-5
Arista / Nov '93 / BMG.

### I'M YOUR BABY TONIGHT.
Tracks: I'm your baby tonight / I'm knockin' / I'm your baby tonight (extended remix) (Available on 12" and CD single format only.) / Feels so good (Available on 12" and CD single format only.).
■ 12"................613594
■ 12"................613817
■ 7"................113594
■ CD Single................663594
■ MC Single................411180
Arista / Oct '90.

### IT ISN'T, IT WASN'T, IT AIN'T NEVER GONNA BE (see under Franklin, Aretha).

### LIVE IN CONCERT.
Tracks: I wanna dance with somebody (who loves me) / Saving all my love for you / How will I know / Love medley / Didn't we almost have it all / House is not a home / Where do broken hearts go / All the man that I need / My name is not Susan / Anymore / Song for you / Revelation / Who do you love / I'm your baby tonight / Greatest love of all.
Laser Disc................781137
VHS................791.137
BMG Video / Sep '91 / BMG.

### LOVE WILL SAVE THE DAY.
Tracks: Love will save the day / Hold me / Love will save the day (dub).
■ 7"................111576B
■ CD Single................661516
■ 12"................611516
■ 7"................111516
Arista / May '88.

### MY NAME IS NOT SUSAN.
Tracks: My name is not Susan.
■ 12"................614510
■ 7"................114510
■ MC Single................411885
■ CD Single................664510
Arista / Jul '91.

### NO.1 VIDEO HITS, THE.
Tracks: You give good love / Saving all my love for you / How will I know / Greatest love of all.
■ VHS................RVT 11001
RCA / Oct '86.
VHS................790 477
BMG / Nov '90 / BMG.

### ONE MOMENT IN TIME.
Tracks: One moment in time.
■ CD Single................661613
■ 12"................611613
■ 7"................111613
Arista / Sep '88.

### QUEEN OF THE NIGHT.
Tracks: Queen of the night / Queen of the night (mixes).
■ CD Single................74321 16930-2
■ 12"................74321 16930-1
■ 7"................74321 16930-7
■ MC Single................74321 16930-4
Arista / Oct '93.

### RUN TO YOU.
Tracks: Run to you / After we make love / For the love of you (Available on CDS only.).
■ 7"................74321 153337
■ CD Single................74321 153332
■ CD Single................74321 158952
■ MC Single................74321 153334
Arista / Jul '93.

### SAVING ALL MY LOVE FOR YOU.
Tracks: Saving all my love for you / All at once.
■ 12"................ARIST 12640
■ 7"................ARIST 640
Arista / Oct '85.

### SO EMOTIONAL.
Tracks: So emotional / For the love of you / So emotional (extended) / So emotional (dub) / Didn't we almost have it all (live).
■ 7" P.Disc................RISP 43
■ 7"................RIS 43
■ CD Single................RISCD 43
■ 12"................RIST 43
Arista / Nov '87.

### SOMEONE FOR ME.
Tracks: Someone for me / Greatest love of all.
■ 12"................ARIST 12614
■ 7"................ARIST 614
Arista / Apr '85.

### WE'VE GOT SOMETHING (see under Brown, Bobby (1)).

### WHERE DO BROKEN HEARTS GO.
Tracks: Where do broken hearts go / Where you are / If you say my eyes are beautiful (Extra track on 12". Duet with Jermaine Jackson.).
■ 12"................609793
■ 7"................109793
Arista / Feb '88.

### WHITNEY.
Tracks: I wanna dance with somebody / Just the lonely talking again / Love will save the day / Didn't we almost have it all / So emotional / Where you are / Love is a contact sport / You're still my man / For the love of you / Where do broken hearts go / I know him so well.
CD................258141
■ LP................208141
MC................408141
Arista / May '87 / BMG.
DCC................782218405-5
Arista / Nov '93 / BMG.

### WHITNEY HOUSTON.
Tracks: How will I know / Take good care of my heart (Duet with Jermaine Jackson.) / Greatest love of all / Hold me (Duet with Teddy Pendergrass.) / You give good love / Thinking about you / Someone for me / Saving all my love for you / Nobody loves me like you do (Duet with Jarmaine Jackson.) / All at once.
■ LP................206978
MC................406978
Arista / Dec '85 / BMG.
CD................610359
Arista / Aug '86 / BMG.
DCC................782218212-5
Arista / Nov '93 / BMG.

### YOU GIVE GOOD LOVE.
Tracks: You give good love / How will I know.
■ 12"................ARIST 12625
■ 7"................ARIST 625
Arista / Jul '85.

## Howard, George

### ASPHALT GARDENS.
Tracks: Not Advised.
■ LP................PA 8035
MC................PAC 8035
Palo Alto / Jan '84.

### DANCING IN THE SUN.
Tracks: Love will find a way / Dancing in the sun / Quiet as it's kept / In love / Telephone / Stay with me / Moods.
■ CD................GRD 9626
■ MC................GRC 9626
GRP / Nov '90.

### DO I EVER CROSS YOUR MIND?.
Tracks: Just the way I feel / Try again / Cross your mind / Stay here with me / Shadow / Partly cloudy / Spirit / Modern love / Jo Jo / Mind bender.
■ MC................GRP 96694
■ CD................GRP 96692
GRP / May '92.

### HOME FAR AWAY, A.
Tracks: Miracle / If you were mine / Doria / Until tomorrow / You can make the story right / Grover's groove / No ordinary love / Home far away / For our fathers / Renewal.
CD................GRP 97802
GRP / Jul '94 / BMG / New Note.

### LOVE AND UNDERSTANDING.
Tracks: Hopscotch / Only here for a minute / Baby, come to me / Interlude / Love and understanding /

Everything I miss at home / Love struck / Talk to the drum / Red, black and blue / Broad Street.
■ LP................GR 9629
■ CD................GRD 9629
■ MC................GRC 9629
GRP / Feb '91.
■ CD................GRP 96292
GRP / Jul '92.

### LOVE WILL FOLLOW.
Tracks: Love will follow / September rain / Slow walking / Raiders / It can't be forever / That's just what it is / Come with me.
■ CD................GRP 96592
■ MC................GRP 96594
GRP / Oct '91.

### NICE PLACE TO BE, A.
Tracks: No no / Jade's world / Sweetest taboo / Nice place to be / Let's live in harmony / Pretty face / Spenser for hire / Stanley's groove.
■ MC................MCF 3330
■ LP................IMCA 5855
■ CD................MCAD 5855
■ MC................MCFC 3330
■ MC................IMCAC 5855
MCA / Feb '87.

### PERSONAL.
Tracks: I want you for myself / Shower you with love / Uptown / You and me / I'm in effect / You only come out at night / Personally / Fakin' feeling / Got it goin' on / Piano in the dark.
■ LP................MCA 6335
■ CD................MCAD 6335
MCA / Apr '90.

### STEPPIN' OUT.
Tracks: Not Advised.
■ LP................PA 201
MC................PAC 201
Palo Alto / Jul '86.
■ CD................GRP 96862
GRP / Jul '89.

### WHEN SUMMER COMES.
Tracks: When summer comes / Grazin' in the grass / Just for tonight / Hard times / Three minute warning / Family / Only / When a child smiles / Reach / Out in the cold.
CD................GRP 97242
GRP / Aug '93 / BMG / New Note.

## Howard, Miki

### COME SHARE MY LOVE.
Tracks: Come share my love / Love will find a way / Imagination / Come back to me lover / I can't wait (to see you alone) / I surrender / Mr. Friend / You better be ready to love me / Do you want my love.
■ LP................K 781 688-1
■ MC................K 781 688-4
Atlantic / Feb '87.

### COME SHARE MY LOVE.
Tracks: Come share my love.
■ 12"................A 9351 T
■ 7"................A 9351
WEA / Feb '87.

### FEMME FATALE.
Tracks: Good morning heartache / This better earth / Hope that we can be together soon / Shining through / But I love you / Ain't nobody like you / I've been through it / Release me / Thank you for takin' me to Africa / Cigarette ashes on the floor.
CD................7599244524
MC................7599244524
Giant / Oct '92 / BMG.

### IMAGINATION.
Tracks: Imagination / You better be ready to love me.
■ 12"................A 9284 T
■ 7"................A 9284
Atlantic / Apr '87.

### LOVE CONFESSIONS.
Tracks: Baby, be mine / You've changed / That's what love is / In too deep / Crazy / Bitter love / I wanna be there / Reasons / Love confession.
■ LP................K 781 810 1
■ MC................K 781 810 4
Atlantic / Nov '87.

### MIKI HOWARD.
Tracks: Not Advised.
CD................782024 2
■ LP................782024 1
MC................782024 4
WEA / '89 / WEA.

**UNTIL YOU COME BACK TO ME.**
Tracks: Until you come back to me.
■ 7"........................A 7935
Atlantic / May '90.

## Hudmon, R.B.

**HOW CAN I BE A WITNESS.**
Tracks: How can I be a witness / If you don't cheat on me.
■ 7"........................K 10742
Atlantic / Apr '76.

## Hudson, Al

**DANCE, GET DOWN (Hudson, Al & The Partners).**
Tracks: Dance, get down / How do you do.
■ 7".......................ABC 4229
ABC Records / Aug '78.

**DON'T THINK ABOUT IT.**
Tracks: Don't think about it / Don't think about it (bass appella).
■ 12".....................MCAT 1097
■ 7".......................MCA 1097
MCA / Jun '87.

**HAPPY FEET.**
Tracks: Not Advised.
■ LP.......................MCF 3015
MCA / '79.

**IF YOU FEEL LIKE DANCIN' (Hudson, Al & Soul Partners).**
Tracks: If you feel like dancin' / If you get caught.
■ 7".......................ABC 4203
ABC Records / Feb '78.

**IX.**
Tracks: Don't think about it / Who does she think she is / You better quit / Starry eyes / Whammy / Set it out / Stole my heart / I can't help myself / Oh girl.
■ LP.......................MCF 3343
■ MC.......................MCFC 3343
MCA / Nov '86.

**LADY YOU ARE.**
Tracks: Lady you are / Can't get enough of your love.
■ 12".....................MCAT 883
■ 7".......................MCA 883
MCA / Apr '84.

**LET'S TALK.**
Tracks: Let's talk.
■ 12".....................MCAT 972
■ 7".......................MCA 972
MCA / Jun '85.

**LOVE IS ONE WAY.**
Tracks: Love is / My lady / All over again / Get it over / Push / I didn't mean to break your heart / Be serious / Wait until tomorrow.
■ LP.......................MCF 3094
MCA / Feb '81.

**MR GROOVE.**
Tracks: Mr. Groove / Lady you are.
■ 7".......................MCA 890
■ 12".....................MCAT 890
MCA / Jun '84.

**MUSIC.**
Tracks: Music / Tonight.
■ 7".......................MCA 542
MCA / Nov '79.

**NEW BEGINNING, A (Hudson, Al & One Way).**
Tracks: Driving me crazy / Weekend lover / Let's talk / Get up off it / Say you will / Love at the count of 3 / Pleasure seekers / U, me & the other guy / You're not my problem / Must'a been crazee.
■ CD.......................CDP 748 990 2
■ LP.......................EST 2074
■ MC.......................TCEST 2074
Capitol / Oct '88.

**NOW THAT I FOUND YOU.**
Tracks: Now that I found you / Rock.
■ 12".....................MCAT 553
■ 7".......................MCA 553
MCA / Mar '80.

**ONE WAY.**
Tracks: Music.
■ LP.......................MCF 3043
MCA / Jan '80.

**WHO'S FOOLING WHO?.**
Tracks: Who's foolong who / Sweet lady / Cutie pie.
■ LP.......................MCF 3130

■ MC.......................MCFC 3130
MCA / Mar '82.

**WRAP YOUR BODY.**
Tracks: Not Advised.
■ LP.......................MCF 3263
■ MC.......................MCFC 3263
MCA / Jul '85.

**YOU BETTER QUIT.**
Tracks: You better quit / Oh girl.
■ 12".....................MCAT 1142
■ 7".......................MCA 1142
MCA / Apr '87.

**YOU CAN DO IT (Hudson, Al & The Partners).**
Tracks: You can do it / Happy feet.
■ 7".......................MCA 511
MCA / Aug '79.

## Hudson, Dave

**NIGHT AND DAY.**
Tracks: You make me feel / Now that love has gone / Love and happiness / Translover / Let's get back together / Thin line / Love in the fast lane / Just a feeling / That's what dreams are made of / Night and day.
CD.......................WAY 269507-2
MC.......................WAY 269507-4
Waylo / Apr '90 / Charly.
■ CD.......................TLCD 583
■ LP.......................TRPL 125
Timeless (Soul) / Jan '90.

**WHO BABY.**
Tracks: Who baby.
■ 12".....................RED 006
Redman International / May '84.

## Hudson, David

**HONEY HONEY.**
Tracks: Honey honey / Come back baby.
■ 7".......................TKR 7583
TK / Sep '80.

## Hudson, Lavine

**ALL I NEED.**
Tracks: All I need / Turned away.
■ 12".....................TENX 339
■ 7".......................TEN 339
■ CD Single...............TENCD 339
■ CD Single...............TENC 339
10 / Apr '91.

**BETWEEN TWO WORLDS.**
Tracks: Keep your mind / All I need / Let's build a world / Nature / Tell me why / You're still loved / Turned away / Little sensitivity / Hold on thru' the night / Heartless generation / Bring back the love / You're still loved (reprise) / Stand.
■ CD.......................DIXCD 103
■ LP.......................DIX 103
■ MC.......................CDIX 103
10 / Jun '91.

**FLESH OF MY FLESH (WHAT I WANT THE WORLD TO KNOW).**
Tracks: Flesh of my flesh (Not on CD) / Testimony (On all versions) / Intervention (sanctified remix) (On CD only).
■ 7".......................VS 1096
■ CD Single...............VSCD 1096
■ 12".....................VST 1096
Virgin / Jul '88.

**INTERVENTION.**
Tracks: Intervention / Flesh of my flesh / Create in me a clean heart / Can't see you / Material world / Learning how to love / Prodigal boy / Home / Does Jesus care / Celebrate.
■ CD.......................CDV 2529
■ LP.......................V 2529
■ MC.......................TCV 2529
Virgin / Jun '88.

**INTERVENTION.**
Tracks: Intervention (On all versions except VSTR/ VCDR 1067) / It's me (On all versions except VSTR/ VSCDR 1067) / Home (On VSCDR 1067 only) / Testimony (On VSTR 1067 only).
■ 12" Remix...............VSR 1067
■ CD Single...............VSCDR 1067
■ 12".....................VST 1067
■ 12" Remix...............VSTR 1067
■ 7".......................VS 1067
■ 7".......................VSE 1067
■ CD Single...............VSCD 1067
Virgin / Dec '88.

**LITTLE SENSITIVITY, A.**
Tracks: Little sensitivity / Child's heat.
■ 12".....................TENX 351
■ 7".......................TEN 351
■ CD Single...............TENCD 351
10 / Jun '91.

## Hudson People

**BOOGIE ON DOWN TOWN.**
Tracks: Boogie on down town.
■ 7".......................VS 301
Virgin / Nov '79.

**BOY SCOUT.**
Tracks: Boy scout / Hudson's funked it again.
■ 7".......................BP 350
Liberty / May '80.

**TRIP TO YOUR MIND.**
Tracks: Trip to your mind / Trip to your mind (version).
■ 12".....................ENY 2712
■ 7".......................ENY 27
Ensign / Jun '79.

## Hudsons

**DON'T TRY TO FIGHT IT.**
Tracks: Don't try to fight it / You keep me up.
■ 12".....................TA 3373
■ 7".......................A 3373
Epic / Jun '83.

**ONE'S MAN MEAT.**
Tracks: One man's meat / Heat got you down.
■ 12".....................12 WCH 1
■ 7".......................WCH 1
Wheelchair / Jan '86.

**SHOW ME YOU CARE.**
Tracks: Show me you care.
■ 12".....................STRA 132711
■ 7".......................STRA 2711
Streetwave / Sep '82.

## Hues Corporation

**I'LL TAKE A MELODY.**
Tracks: I'll take a melody / Into my music.
■ 7".......................RCA 2514
RCA / Jan '75.

**ROCK THE BOAT.**
Tracks: Rock the boat.
■ 7".......................APBO 0232
RCA / Jun '74.
■ 7".......................GOLD 504
Soul Train / Jul '81.

**ROCK THE BOAT (OLD GOLD).**
Tracks: Rock the boat / Rockin' soul (Available on 12" only) / Ms. Grace / You little trust maker.
■ 12".....................OG 4030
Old Gold / Dec '87.

**ROCKIN' SOUL.**
Tracks: Rockin' soul.
■ 7".......................PB 10066
RCA / Sep '74.

## Huff, Leon

Although his one solo album hardly does justice to Huff's importance, the title *Here To Create Music* could not be more appropriate. In 1964, working as a pianist for Leiber & Stoller, Huff played on Candy & The Kisses' *The 81*; forging a partnership with the song's composer Kenny Gamble. Originally a production duo, the pair set up their own labels: Excel, Gamble, Neptune (through Chess) and finally - under the Columbia umbrella - Philadelphia International Records. PIR succeeded Motown as the leading soul label, yielding classics by - among many others - Billy Paul, Harold Melvin, the O'Jays and the Three Degrees. Their trademark 'Philly sound' also won them a lucrative career as outside producers, for acts including Jerry Butler and Johnny Mathis. The PIR ship ran aground in '82, despite successes with Teddy Pendergrass and The Jones Girls - but Gamble & Huff had already written themselves into soul history.

**HERE TO CREATE MUSIC.**
Tracks: Your body won't move if you can't feel.. / I ain't jivin', I'm jammin' / No greater love / Tight money / Tasty / Low down hard time blues / This one's for us / Latin spirit.

■ LP . . . . . . . . . . . . . . . . . . . . . PIR 84530
Philadelphia Int. / Jan '81.

## Hugh, Grayson

**HOW 'BOUT US? (see under Wright, Betty).**

**TALK IT OVER.**
Tracks: Talk it over / Empty as the wind.
■ 12" . . . . . . . . . . . . . . . . . . . . . PT 49484
■ 7" . . . . . . . . . . . . . . . . . . . . . PB 49483
■ CD Single . . . . . . . . . . . . . . . PD 49484
RCA / Jul '89.

## Hughes, Freddie

**BABY BOY.**
Tracks: Baby boy / Purple haze.
■ 7" . . . . . . . . . . . . . . . . . . . . . BR 37
Brunswick / Aug '76.

## Hughes, Jimmy

**SHOT OF RHYTHM AND BLUES, A.**
Tracks: Shot of rhythm and blues.
■ 7" . . . . . . . . . . . . . . . . . . . . .CTD 103
Charly / Jul '80.

**SOMETHING SPECIAL.**
Tracks: I like everything about you / Let 'em down, baby / I'm so glad / Lay it on the line / Sweet things you do / Chains of love / I'm not ashamed to beg or plead / It's all up to you / Lock me up / What side of the door / Peeped around yonder's bend.
■ LP . . . . . . . . . . . . . . . . . . . .SXATS 1010
Stax / Nov '69.

**SOUL NEIGHBOURS (Hughes, Jimmy & Joe Simon).**
Tracks: Shot of rhythm and blues / Neighbour, neighbour / There is something on your mind / I tried to tell you / Stormy Monday blues / I'm getting better / Try me / Steal away / Say (that your love is true) / My adorable one / When your near / Whoopee / When I'm gone / I keep remembering / Bring it on home to me / Let's do it over.
■ LP . . . . . . . . . . . . . . . . . . . . . CRB 1086
Charly R&B / Nov '84.

## Hugo & Luigi

**LA PLUME DE MA TANTE.**
Tracks: La plume de ma tante.
■ 7" . . . . . . . . . . . . . . . . . . . . . RCA 1127
RCA / Jun '59.

## Humphrey, Bobbi

**BEST OF BOBBI HUMPHREY, THE.**
Tracks: New York times / Uno Esta / Harlem River Drive / Mestizo eyes / Ladies Day / Blacks & blues / Trip / Fun House / Chicago dawn / You make me feel so good.
■ CD . . . . . . . . . . . . . . . . . . CDP 780 503 2
■ LP . . . . . . . . . . . . . . . . . . . . B1 80503
Blue Note / Feb '93.

**NOW WAY.**
Tracks: Now way / Now way (Instrumental).
■ 12" . . . . . . . . . . . . . . . . . . . . .JABX 39
■ 7" . . . . . . . . . . . . . . . . . . . . . JAB 39
Club / Sep '86.

## Hunt, Geraldine

**CAN'T FAKE THE FEELING.**
Tracks: Can't fake the feeling.
■ 12" . . . . . . . . . . . . . . . . . . . . . FIZY 501
Champagne / Oct '80.
■ 7" . . . . . . . . . . . . . . . . . . . . . FIZZ 501
Champagne / Sep '80.

## Hunt, Tommy

**CRACKIN' UP.**
Tracks: Crackin' up.
■ 7" . . . . . . . . . . . . . . . . . . . . . SRL 1132
Spark (3) / Oct '75.

**LOVIN' ON THE LOSING SIDE.**
Tracks: Lovin' on the losing side.
■ 7" . . . . . . . . . . . . . . . . . . . . . SRL 1146
Spark (3) / Aug '76.

**LOVING ON THE LOSING SIDE.**
Tracks: Loving on the losing side / Love is getting stronger / Stop.

■ 7" . . . . . . . . . . . . . . . . . . . . . CC 11
Casino Classics / Nov '79.

**NEVER CAN SAY GOODBYE.**
Tracks: Never can say goodbye / Sign on the dotted line / You've got me where you want me.
■ 7" . . . . . . . . . . . . . . . . . . . . . CC 15
Casino Classics / Nov '79.

**ONE FINE MORNING.**
Tracks: One fine morning.
■ 7" . . . . . . . . . . . . . . . . . . . . . SRL 1148
Spark (3) / Nov '76.

**STOP THE BUS.**
Tracks: Stop the bus / Susanna baby.
■ 7" . . . . . . . . . . . . . . . . . . . . . RK 1012
RK / Sep '78.

**WORK SONG, THE.**
Tracks: Work song / Please stay.
■ 7" . . . . . . . . . . . . . . . . . . . . . TOWN 103
Kent / Jun '85.

**YOUR MAN.**
Tracks: Lover / This and only this / I am a witness / Human / Your man / Don't make me over / She'll hurt you too / Didn't I tell you / It's all a bad dream / Make the night a little longer / Oh Lord what are you doing to me / Parade of broken hearts / I might like it / You made a man out of me / Just a little taste of your sweet lovin' / Promised land.
■ LP . . . . . . . . . . . . . . . . . . . . . KENT 059
Kent / Oct '86.

## Hunt, Willie Amos

**WOULD YOU BELIEVE.**
Tracks: Would you believe / My baby wants to dance.
■ 7" . . . . . . . . . . . . . . . . . . . . .602003
Camp / '67.

## Hunter, Herbert

**JOB OPENING.**
Tracks: Job opening.
■ 7" . . . . . . . . . . . . . . . . . . . . . QC 001
Queen City / '81.

## Hunter, Ivory Joe

**16 GREATEST HITS.**
Tracks: Not Advised.
CD . . . . . . . . . . . . . . . . . . . .KCD 000605
King / Sep '92 / New Note / Koch International.

**7TH STREET BOOGIE (1949-1950).**
Tracks: 7th Street boogie / Boogin' in the basement / High cost low pay blues / Siesta with sonny / I quit my pretty mama / Don't fall in love with me / I got your water on / Leave her alone / Blues at sunrise / Reconversion blues / Giving blues / Send me pretty mama / Woo wee blues / What did you do to me / S P Blues / Don't you believe her.
■ LP . . . . . . . . . . . . . . . . . . . . . KIX 4
Route 66 (Sweden) / Jun '80.
CD . . . . . . . . . . . . . . . . . . . . . RBD 4
Route 66 (Sweden) / Apr '91 / Swift / Wellard.

**ARTISTRY OF IVORY JOE HUNTER, THE.**
Tracks: If you want my love / In memories / If you were my love / Lonesome cold blooded woman / How about me / I'm cuttin' out / I need you so / My baby's gone / I'm lost without you.
■ LP . . . . . . . . . . . . . . . . . . . . . BDL 1016
Bulldog Records / '82.

**HITS, THE.**
Tracks: Blues at sunrise / Pretty mama blues / Don't fall in love with me / Waiting in vain / Guess who / Landlord blues / Jealous heart / I almost lost my mind / I quit my pretty mama / S.P. blues / I need you so / It's a sin / Since I met you baby / Empty arms / Love's a hurting game / City lights.
■ LP . . . . . . . . . . . . . . . . . . . . . OFF 6040
Official / Jun '87.

**I HAD A GIRL.**
Tracks: Boogin' in the rain / I love my man / Mean woman blues / False friend blues / I like it / Stop rocking that train / Please don't cry any more / I had a girl / Let me dream / Gimme a pound o' ground / Where shall I go / It's a sin / I'm yours until eternity / U name it.
■ LP . . . . . . . . . . . . . . . . . . . . . KIX 25
Route 66 (Sweden) / Aug '87.

**IVORY JOE HUNTER SINGS 16 OF HIS GREATEST HITS.**
Tracks: Jealous heart / I quit my pretty mama / Waiting in vain / No money / No luck blues / Too late

/ I like it / I have no reason to complain / Lying woman / Guess who / In time / Code song / Please don't cry anymore / Don't fall in love with me / False friend blues / It's you just you / Changing blues.
■ LP . . . . . . . . . . . . . . . . . . . . . SING 605
Sing / Dec '87.
■ LP . . . . . . . . . . . . . . . . . . . . . KLP 605
King / Oct '88.
CD . . . . . . . . . . . . . . . . . . . . . KCD 605
King / Mar '90 / New Note / Koch International.

**JUMPING AT THE DEWDROP.**
Tracks: Jumping at the dew drop / Blues at midnight / Are your hep / You're always looking for / She's a killer / We're gonna boogie / Old gal and new gal blues / Old man's boogie / If you see my baby / You lied.
■ LP . . . . . . . . . . . . . . . . . . . . . KIX 15
Route 66 (Sweden) / Aug '87.

**SINCE I MET YOU BABY.**
Tracks: Not Advised.
■ LP . . . . . . . . . . . . . . . . . . . . . 830 897-1
Mercury / '88.

**THIS IS IVORY JOE.**
Tracks: Welcome home / City lights / Stolen moments / Cottage for sale / Guess who / Old fashioned love / Pretty mama blues / Can I forget you / I love you so much / Darling I need you / Did you mean it / My search was ended.
LP . . . . . . . . . . . . . . . . . . . . . CH 97
Ace / Nov '93 / Pinnacle / Complete Record Co. Ltd.

## Hurtt, Phil

**BOOGIE CITY.**
Tracks: Boogie city / Ph Factor boogie.
■ 12" . . . . . . . . . . . . . . . . . . . .12FTC 174
■ 7" . . . . . . . . . . . . . . . . . . . . . FTC 174
Fantasy / May '79.

**GIVING IT BACK.**
Tracks: Giving it back.
■ 7" . . . . . . . . . . . . . . . . . . . . . FTC 161
Fantasy / Oct '78.

**GIVING IT BACK.**
Tracks: Giving it back / Teach them well / Lovin' / Give us what we want / Heaven / Where the love is / Lady / Let your hair down / That's the way the story goes / Please don't come home.
■ LP . . . . . . . . . . . . . . . . . . . . . FT 546
Fantasy / Sep '78.

**PH FACTOR.**
Tracks: Boogie city / PH Factor / I've got the power / I think it's about time / Don't let this moment get away / I'm in love again / Let it flow.
■ LP . . . . . . . . . . . . . . . . . . . . . FT 561
Fantasy / '79.

## Hutch, Willie

Having proved his hit-making credentials as songwriter for Fifth Dimension and arranger for Jackson Five, Hutch was invited to join Motown on permanent basis. He produced Smokey Robinson's first post-Miracles album and established own name with soundtrack The Mack. After stint on Whitfield label, he returned to Motown in '82, and finally cracked U.K. chart with In And Out. However, he remains better-known for behind-the-scenes work with acts such as Four Tops.

**COME AND DANCE WITH ME.**
Tracks: Come and dance with me / Easy does it.
■ 7" . . . . . . . . . . . . . . . . . . . . . LV 10
WEA / Feb '79.

**HAVIN' A HOUSE PARTY.**
Tracks: Willie's boogie / We gonna have a house party / What you gonna do after the party / I can sho' give you love / I never had it so good / We gonna party tonight / After love is gone / Soul strut / Train of love.
■ LP . . . . . . . . . . . . . . . . . . . .STML 12069
Motown / Sep '77.

**IN & OUT.**
Tracks: In and out / Slick / Brother's gonna work it out / Sunshine lady / Get ready for the party / You sure know how to love your man / Them of Foxy Brown / Love power / Tell me why has our love turned cold / Shake it / Party down / If you ain't got no money (you can't get no honey) / We gonna party tonight / What you gonna do after the party.
■ LP . . . . . . . . . . . . . . . . . . . . . STMR 9019
■ MC . . . . . . . . . . . . . . . . . . . CSTMR 9019
Motown / Feb '83.

### IN & OUT.
Tracks: In and out / Brothers gonna work it out.
■ 12" . . . . . . . . . . . . . . . . . . . . TMGT 1285
■ 7" . . . . . . . . . . . . . . . . . . . . . TMG 1285
Motown / Nov '82.

### IN TUNE.
Tracks: All hell broke loose / Paradise / All Ameri-
can funkathon / Anything is possible if you believe in
love / Come on and dance with me / Easy does it /
Hip shakin' sexy lady / Nothing lasts forever.
■ LP . . . . . . . . . . . . . . . . . . . . . K 56559
Whitfield (USA) / Feb '79.

### KEEP ON JAMMIN.
Tracks: Keep on jammin' / In and out.
■ 12" . . . . . . . . . . . . . . . . . . . . ZT 40174
■ 7" . . . . . . . . . . . . . . . . . . . . . ZB 40173
Motown / Jun '85.

### LOVE POWER.
Tracks: Love power / Get ready for the get down.
■ 7" . . . . . . . . . . . . . . . . . . . . . TMG 1008
Tamla Motown / Oct '75.

### LOVE RUNS OUT.
Tracks: Love runs out / Lend a hand.
■ 7" . . . . . . . . . . . . . . . . . . . . . ABC 4206
ABC Records / Mar '78.

### MAKING A GAME OUT OF LOVE.
Tracks: Not Advised.
■ LP . . . . . . . . . . . . . . . . . . . . . ZL 72378
■ MC . . . . . . . . . . . . . . . . . . . . . ZK 72378
Motown / Jul '85.

### PARTY DOWN.
Tracks: Party down / Slick.
■ 12" . . . . . . . . . . . . . . . . . . . . TMGT 1293
■ 7" . . . . . . . . . . . . . . . . . . . . . TMG 1293
Motown / Feb '83.

## Hutson, Leroy

### ALL BECAUSE OF YOU.
Tracks: All because of you / Lucky fellow.
■ 7" . . . . . . . . . . . . . . . . . . . . . K 16536
WEA / Apr '75.
■ 12" . . . . . . . . . . . . . . . . . . . . 12CUR 105
Curtom / Feb '90.

### LEROY HUTSON.
Tracks: All because of you / I bless the day it's
different / Cool out / Lucky fellow / Can't stay away /
So much love.
■ LP . . . . . . . . . . . . . . . . . . . . . K 56139
WEA / Jun '75.

### SHADES OF LOVE (EP).
Tracks: Shades of love.
■ 12" . . . . . . . . . . . . . . . . . . . . EXPAND 24
Expansion / Apr '92.

### THERE'S MORE WHERE THIS CAME FROM.
Tracks: Love the feeling / So nice / More where that
came from / Never know what you can do (give it a
try) / Lover's holiday / Get to this (you'll get to me) /
Ghetto '74 / After the fight / Heaven right here (on
earth) / When you smile.
LP . . . . . . . . . . . . . . . . . . . . . . CUR 2004
Curtom / Jun '89 / ACD Trading Ltd. / Pinnacle /
Koch International.
CD . . . . . . . . . . . . . . . . . . . . . . CUR 2004CD
Curtom / Mar '94 / ACD Trading Ltd. / Pinnacle /
Koch International.
MC . . . . . . . . . . . . . . . . . . . . . . CUR 2004C
Curtom / Mar '94 / ACD Trading Ltd. / Pinnacle /
Koch International.

### UNFORGETTABLE.
Tracks: Unforgettable / Funk in my life / Right or
wrong / So nice / Lonely without you / More where
that came from.
■ LP . . . . . . . . . . . . . . . . . . . . . RSS 15
RSO / Dec '79.

## Hyman, Phyllis

Despite infrequent and lowly placings on
pop charts, Hyman has acquired solid reputation as dance diva. She made first splash
as singer on Norman Connor's cover of
Stylistics' *Betcha By Golly Wow* in '76. Producer Connors was succeeded in 1979 by
James Mtume/Reggie Lucas for *You Know
How To Love Me* album; title track of which
became U.K. hit. Subsequent albums included *Goddess Of Love*, with Narada Michael Walden/Thom Bell at the helm, and
*Living All Alone*. Latter was debut for Philadelphia International label and boasted
Loose Ends' *Ain't You Had Enough Love*.
Recent years have seen Hyman return to
Arista, sing with artists ranging from Barry
Manilow to Grover Washington, and main-
tain career as film and stage actress.

### BEST OF PHYLLIS HYMAN.
Tracks: You know how to love me / Love too good to
last / We should be lovers / Answer is you / Be
careful / Under your spell / Don't tell me tell her /
Living inside your love / Why did you turn me on /
Gonna make changes.
■ LP . . . . . . . . . . . . . . . . . . . . . .207830
■ MC . . . . . . . . . . . . . . . . . . . . . .407830
Arista / Sep '86.

### BEST OF PHYLLIS HYMAN (2) (Buddah years).
Tracks: Loving you - losing you / No one can love
you more / One thing on my mind / I don't want to
lose you / Deliver the love / Night bird gets the love /
Beautiful man of mine / Children of the world / Living
inside your love / Sweet music / Answer is you /
Love is free / Sing a song / Soon come again / Be
careful (how you treat my love).
CD . . . . . . . . . . . . . . . . . . . . . . NEXCD 138
■ LP . . . . . . . . . . . . . . . . . . . . . NEXLP 138
Sequel / Oct '90 / Total / BMG.

### CAN'T WE FALL IN LOVE AGAIN.
Tracks: You sure look good to me / Don't tell me /
Tell her / I ain't asking / Can't we fall in love again /
Love too good to last / Tonight you and me / Sun-
shine in my life / Just another face in the crowd.
■ LP . . . . . . . . . . . . . . . . . . . . . SPART 1154
Arista / '82.

### GODDESS OF LOVE.
Tracks: Ridin' the tiger / Goddess of love / Why did
you turn me on / Your move, my heart / Let someone
love you / Falling star / We should be lovers / Just
me and you / Just 25 miles to anywhere.
■ LP . . . . . . . . . . . . . . . . . . . . . .205543
MC . . . . . . . . . . . . . . . . . . . . . . .405543
Arista / Jun '83 / BMG.

### LIVING ALL ALONE.
Tracks: Living all alone / First time together / If you
want me / Slow dancing / Old friend / You just don't
know / Ain't you had enough love / Screaming at the
moon / What you won't do for love.
■ MC . . . . . . . . . . . . . . . . . . . . . TCPHIL 4001
■ LP . . . . . . . . . . . . . . . . . . . . . PHIL 4001
Philadelphia Int. / Sep '86.

### LIVING INSIDE YOUR LOVE.
Tracks: Living inside your love / Loving you, losing
you.
■ 12" . . . . . . . . . . . . . . . . . . . . BDSL 487
■ 7" . . . . . . . . . . . . . . . . . . . . . BDS 487
Buddah / Nov '79.

### LOVING YOU, LOSING YOU.
Tracks: Loving you, losing you / Betcha by golly
wow.
■ 12" . . . . . . . . . . . . . . . . . . . . BDSL 493
■ 7" . . . . . . . . . . . . . . . . . . . . . BDS 493
Buddah / Mar '80.

### PHYLLIS HYMAN.
Tracks: Loving you, losing you / No one can love you
more / One thing on my mind / I don't want to lose
you / Deliver the love / Was yesterday such a long
time ago / Night bird gets the love / Beautiful man of
mine / Children of the world.

■ LP . . . . . . . . . . . . . . . . . . . . . BDLP 4046
Buddah / Nov '77.

### RIDIN' THE TIGER.
Tracks: Ridin' the tiger.
■ 12" . . . . . . . . . . . . . . . . . . . . ARIST 12535
■ 7" . . . . . . . . . . . . . . . . . . . . . .ARIST 535
Arista / May '83.

### SCREAMING AT THE MOON.
Tracks: Screaming at the moon / Ain't you had
enough love.
■ 12" . . . . . . . . . . . . . . . . . . . . 12PIR 4
■ 7" . . . . . . . . . . . . . . . . . . . . . PIR 4
Philadelphia Int. / Mar '87.

### SCREAMING AT THE MOON (EXT REMIX).
Tracks: Screaming at the moon (ext remix) / Screaming at the moon / Ain't you had enough love / Ain't
you had enough love (ext) / Ain't you had enough
love (percussapella version).
■ Special . . . . . . . . . . . . . . . . . . 12PIRD 4
Philadelphia Int. / Apr '87.

### SING A SONG.
Tracks: Living inside your love / Sweet music /
Answer is you / Love is free / Sing a song / Gonna
make changes / Soon come again / Be careful /
Here's that rainy day.
■ LP . . . . . . . . . . . . . . . . . . . . . BDLP 4058
Buddah / '79.

### TONIGHT YOU AND ME.
Tracks: Tonight you and me.
■ 7" . . . . . . . . . . . . . . . . . . . . . .ARIST 444
Arista / Nov '81.

### UNDER HER SPELL.
Tracks: Loving you, losing you / Can't we fall in love
again / Why did you turn me on / You sure look good
to me / Let someone love you / Just another face in
the crowd / You know how to love me / Under your
spell / Don't tell me, tell her / Betcha by golly wow /
Love too good to last / Complete me / Your move, my
heart / Kiss you all over.
■ LP . . . . . . . . . . . . . . . . . . . . . .210620
■ MC . . . . . . . . . . . . . . . . . . . . . .410620
■ CD . . . . . . . . . . . . . . . . . . . . . .260620
Arista / Apr '90.

### UNDER YOUR SPELL.
Tracks: Under your spell / Kiss you all over / Hold on
(Only on 12" single.).
■ 12" . . . . . . . . . . . . . . . . . . . . ARIST 12343
■ 7" . . . . . . . . . . . . . . . . . . . . . .ARIST 343
Arista / May '80.

### UNDER YOUR SPELL (OLD GOLD).
Tracks: Under your spell / Rainbow.
■ 12" . . . . . . . . . . . . . . . . . . . . .OG 4510
Old Gold / Apr '89.

### YOU KNOW HOW TO LOVE ME.
Tracks: You know how to love me / We should be
lovers / Riding the tiger (Extra track on 12" version
only.) / Give a little more.
■ 12" . . . . . . . . . . . . . . . . . . . . ARIST 12323
■ 7" . . . . . . . . . . . . . . . . . . . . . .ARIST 323
Arista / Jan '80.
■ 7" . . . . . . . . . . . . . . . . . . . . . .ARIST 669
■ 12" . . . . . . . . . . . . . . . . . . . . ARIST 12669
Arista / Aug '86.

### YOU KNOW HOW TO LOVE ME.
Tracks: Not Advised.
■ LP . . . . . . . . . . . . . . . . . . . . . SPART 1114
Arista / Mar '80.

### YOU KNOW HOW TO LOVE ME (OLD GOLD).
Tracks: You know how to love me / Don't tell me tell
her.
■ 12" . . . . . . . . . . . . . . . . . . . . .OG 4067
Old Gold / '88.

### YOU SURE LOOK GOOD TO ME.
Tracks: You sure look good to me / Sunshine in my
life.
■ 7" . . . . . . . . . . . . . . . . . . . . . .ARIST 424
Arista / '82.

# I

## I Level

### GIVE ME.
**Tracks:** Give me.
- 12" ........................ VS 523-12
- 7" .......................... VS 523

Virgin / Aug '82.

### I LEVEL.
**Tracks:** Minefield / Treacle / Heart aglow / Stone heart / Woman / Give me / No. 4 / Teacher / Music / Face again.
- LP ......................... V 2270

Virgin / Jul '83.
- MC ....................... OVEDC 127
- LP ...................... OVED 127

Virgin / Aug '88.

### IN THE RIVER.
**Tracks:** In the river / Strangers / In the river (acapella) (Only on 12" single.).
- 12" ....................... VS 681 12
- 7" ......................... VS 681

Virgin / Jun '84.

### IN THE SAND.
**Tracks:** In the sand / Latin antics.
- 12" ....................... VS 718 12
- 7" ......................... VS 718

Virgin / Feb '85.

### MINEFIELD.
**Tracks:** Minefield / Number 4 / Give me.
- 12" ....................... VS 563 12
- 7" ......................... VS 563

Virgin / Apr '83.

### MINEFIELD (OLD GOLD).
**Tracks:** Minefield / River.
- 12" ........................ OG 4112

Old Gold / Mar '89.

### OUR SONG.
**Tracks:** Our song.
- 7" .......................... VS 699

Virgin / Jul '84.

### SHAKE.
**Tracks:** New day / In the river / Into another world / Keep me running / In the sand / Our song / Had enough / Drums / Cat amongst the pigeons.
- MC ....................... TCV 2320
- LP ......................... V 2320

Virgin / Feb '85.
- LP ...................... OVED 179

Virgin / '88.

### STONE HEART.
**Tracks:** Stone heart / Historical nights / Wagon (on 12" only).
- 12" ....................... VS 626 12
- 7" ......................... VS 626

Virgin / Aug '83.

### TEACHER.
**Tracks:** Teacher / All my love.
- 12" ....................... VS 595 12
- 7" ......................... VS 595

Virgin / Jun '83.

## Identity Crisis

### ELOISE.
**Tracks:** Eloise.
- 7" ......................... FMR 1

FMR / Sep '82.

## Ikettes

### (NEVER MORE) LONELY FOR YOU.
**Tracks:** (Never more) lonely for you / Sally go round the roses.
- 7" ....................... BM 56516

Polydor / Mar '66.

### FINE, FINE, FINE.
**Tracks:** (He's gonna be) Fine, fine, fine / Can't sit down / Don't feel sorry for me / Camel walk / Blue on blue / I'm so thankful / You're trying to make me lose my mind / Sally go 'round the roses / Peaches and cream / Never more will I be lonely for you / Not that I recall / Your love is me / Biggest players / How

come / Nobody loves me / It's been so long / Through with you (On CD only) / Cheater (On CD only) / I'm leaving you (On CD only) / You're still my baby (On CD only) / Give me a chance (try me) (On CD only) / Love of my man (live) (On CD only) / Living for you (On CD only) / I love the way you love (live) (On CD only).
- LP ......................... KENT 063

Kent / Jan '87.
- CD ...................... CDKEN 063

Kent / Sep '92 / Pinnacle.

### I'M SO THANKFUL.
**Tracks:** I'm so thankful / Don't feel sorry for me.
- 7" ....................... BM 56506

Polydor / Jan '66.

### PEACHES 'N' CREAM.
**Tracks:** Peaches'n'cream / Biggest players.
- 7" ......................... SS 407

Stateside / '65.

### WHAT'CHA GONNA DO.
**Tracks:** What'cha gonna do / Down down.
- 7" ....................... HLU 10081

London / Jun '66.

## Imagination

### BEST OF IMAGINATION.
**Tracks:** Not Advised.
- CD ..................... ADEHCD 787

Arcade / May '88.

### BEST OF IMAGINATION.
**Tracks:** Not Advised.
- CD ....................... OPTMCD 010
- MC ....................... OPTMC 010

Icon / Jun '93 / Pinnacle.

### BODY TALK.
**Tracks:** Tell me do you want my love / Flashback / I'll always love you (but don't look back) / In and out of love / Body talk / So good, so right / Burning up.
- MC ....................... ZCRB 1001

R & B / Oct '81.
- CD ...................... CDRBL 7775

R & B / '86.
- CD ........................ ND 74322
- MC ........................ NK 74322

RCA / Apr '91.

### BODY TALK.
**Tracks:** Body talk.
- 12" ........................ RBL 201
- 7" ......................... RBS 201

R & B / May '81.

### CHANGES.
**Tracks:** Changes / So good, so right.
- 12" ....................... RBSL 213
- 7" ......................... RBS 213
- 7" P.Disc .................. RBP 213

R & B / Nov '82.

### CLOSER.
**Tracks:** I know what love is / Hold me in your arms / Paranoia / Where are you now / Last time / For members only / Instinctual / Who (tell me who) / Over / Hot nights / Skin time / Closer / Operator (On cassette/compact disc only.) / Touch (part 1) (On compact disc only.).
- LP ......................... PL 71508
- CD ........................ PD 71508
- MC ........................ PK 71508

RCA / Oct '87.

### COLLECTION: IMAGINATION.
**Tracks:** Just an illusion / Music and lights / So good so right / Flashback / Body talk / Looking at midnight / In the heat of the night / In and out of love / Burnin' up.
- MC ........................ NK 75001
- CD ........................ ND 75001

Arista / Jun '92.

### FASCINATION OF THE PHYSICAL, THE.
**Tracks:** Not Advised.
- CD .................... BLM 3300292

Capital City / Sep '92 / Grapevine Distribution.

### FLASHBACK.
**Tracks:** Flashback / Just an illusion / In and out of love / In the heat of the night / Looking at midnight / State of love / Music and lights / New dimensions / Heart 'n' soul / Burnin' up / Instinctualk / Changes / Thank you my love / Body talk.
- CD ....................... PWKS 4122
- MC ..................... PWKMC 4122

Pickwick / Oct '92 / Pickwick.

### FLASHBACK.
**Tracks:** Not Advised.
- 12" ........................ RBL 206
- 7" ......................... RBS 206

R & B / Nov '81.

### FOUND MY GIRL.
**Tracks:** Found my girl / In and out of love.
- 12" ....................... RBL 1800
- 7" ........................ RBS 1800

R & B / Apr '85.

### HOLD ME IN YOUR ARMS.
**Tracks:** Hold me in your arms / Instinctual (US remix) / Operator (Only on 12" version.).
- 12" ....................... PT 42058
- 7" ......................... PB 42057

RCA / May '88.

### I KNOW WHAT LOVE IS.
**Tracks:** I know what love is / One day I found me.
- 12" ....................... PT 41564
- 7" ......................... PB 41563

RCA / Sep '87.

### I LIKE IT.
**Tracks:** I like it.
- 12" ........................ LEET 1
- 7" ......................... LEEE 1
- CD Single .................. LEED 1
- MC Single ................. LEEM 1

Capital City / Feb '92.

### I'LL ALWAYS LOVE YOU.
**Tracks:** I'll always love you / Burning up.
- 7" ......................... RBS 205

R & B / Nov '81.

### IMAGINATION GOLD.
**Tracks:** Flashback / Music and lights / Body talk / Changes / Looking at midnight / Just an illusion / Burning up / In and out of love / New dimension / In the heat of the night.
- LP ....................... RBLP 1006
- MC ...................... ZCRB 1006

R & B / Nov '84.

### IMAGINATION IN CONCERT.
**Tracks:** Changes / Flashback / Shoo be doo da / Point of no return / In and out of love / State of love / Music and lights / Need to be free / Body talk / New dimensions / Burning up / Just an illusion.
- VHS ....................... VC 4011

Video Collection / May '87 / Gold & Sons / Video Collection / THE.
- VHS ........................ 6147

Peppermint Music / '88.
- VHS ....................... RV 002

Renegade Video / Feb '91.

### IN AND OUT OF LOVE.
**Tracks:** In and out of love / In and out of love (instrumental).
- 12" ....................... RBSL 202
- 7" ......................... RBS 202

R & B / Sep '81.

### IN THE HEAT OF THE NIGHT.
**Tracks:** In the heat of the night / Heart 'n' soul / Music and lights / All night loving / Just an illusion / All I want to know / One more love / Changes.
- LP ....................... RBLP 1002
- MC ...................... ZCRB 1002

R & B / Sep '82.

### IN THE HEAT OF THE NIGHT.
**Tracks:** In the heat of the night.
- 12" ........................ RBS 211

■ DELETED

■ *7"* . . . . . . . . . . . . . . . . . . .RBS 211
R & B / Aug '82.

**INSTINCTUAL.**
Tracks: Instinctual / Touch.
■ *12"* . . . . . . . . . . . . . . . . . PT 41698
■ *7"* . . . . . . . . . . . . . . . . . . PB 41697
RCA / Dec '87.

**JUST AN ILLUSION.**
Tracks: Just an illusion.
■ *12"* . . . . . . . . . . . . . . . . . .RBL 208
■ *7"* . . . . . . . . . . . . . . . . . .RBS 208
R & B / Feb '82.

**JUST AN ILLUSION (1989 REMIX).**
Tracks: Just an illusion.
■ *12"* . . . . . . . . . . . . . . HONEY (T)10
■ *7"* . . . . . . . . . . . . . . . .HONEY 10
■ *CD Single* . . . . . . . . . . . HONEY (D)10
Honeybee / Oct '89.

**JUST AN ILLUSION (OLD GOLD).**
Tracks: Just and illusion / Body talk.
*12"* . . . . . . . . . . . . . . . . . . .OG 4196
Old Gold / Nov '90 / Pickwick.

**LAST DAYS OF SUMMER.**
Tracks: Last days of summer / Sho be doo be dabba doo be (Only on 12" single.) / Last days of summer (version).
■ *12"* . . . . . . . . . . . . . . . . . RBL 1802
■ *7"* . . . . . . . . . . . . . . . . . RBS 1802
R & B / Aug '85.

**LAST TIME, THE.**
Tracks: Touch / Last time.
■ *12"* . . . . . . . . . . . . . . . . . PT 41472
■ *7"* . . . . . . . . . . . . . . . . . PB 41471
RCA / Aug '87.

**LIKE IT IS.**
Tracks: Not Advised.
*CD* . . . . . . . . . . . . . . . . . . . SMD 985
■ *LP* . . . . . . . . . . . . . . . . . . SMR 985
*MC.* . . . . . . . . . . . . . . . . . . SMC 985
Stylus / Aug '89.

**LOOKING AT MIDNIGHT.**
Tracks: Looking at midnight / Follow me.
■ *12"* . . . . . . . . . . . . . . . . . .RBL 214
■ *7"* . . . . . . . . . . . . . . . . . .RBS 214
R & B / May '83.

**LOVE SONGS, THE.**
Tracks: Body talk / Heart 'n' soul / Changes / In and out of love / One more love / Hold me in your arms / In the heat of the night / Sunshine / So good so right / Looking at midnight / Closer / Thank you love.
*CD* . . . . . . . . . . . . . . . . . . ND 74483
■ *LP* . . . . . . . . . . . . . . . . . NL 74483
■ *MC.* . . . . . . . . . . . . . . . . NK 74483
RCA / Feb '90 / BMG.

**LOVE'S TAKING OVER.**
Tracks: Love's taking over / Love's taking over (sensitive mix) (Available on 12" and CD only) / Love's taking over (club mix) (Available on 12" and CD only) / Instinctual (Available on CD only).
■ *7"* . . . . . . . . . . . . . . . . . PB 42659
■ *12"* . . . . . . . . . . . . . . . . . PT 42660
■ *CD Single* . . . . . . . . . . . . . PD 42660
RCA / Jun '89.

**MUSIC AND LIGHTS.**
Tracks: Music and lights.
■ *12"* . . . . . . . . . . . . . . . . . RBSL 210
■ *7"* . . . . . . . . . . . . . . . . . .RBS 210
R & B / Jun '82.

**MUSIC AND LIGHTS (OLD GOLD).**
Tracks: Music and lights / Flashback.
*12"* . . . . . . . . . . . . . . . . . . .OG 4202
Old Gold / Jun '91 / Pickwick.

**NEW DIMENSIONS.**
Tracks: New dimension / I'll always love you.
■ *12"* . . . . . . . . . . . . . . . . . .RBL 216
■ *7"* . . . . . . . . . . . . . . . . . .RBS 216
R & B / Oct '83.

**NIGHT DUBBING.**
Tracks: Flashback / Just an illusion / Music and lights / So good, so right / Body talk / Heart 'n' soul / Changes / Burning up.
■ *LP* . . . . . . . . . . . . . . . . . RBDUB 1
*MC.* . . . . . . . . . . . . . . . . . ZCDUB 1
R & B / May '83.

**SCANDALOUS.**
Tracks: New dimension / State of love / Point of no return / When I see the fire / Shoo be doo da dabba doobee / Wrong in love / Looking at midnight / Need to be free.

■ *LP* . . . . . . . . . . . . . . . . . RBLP 1004
*MC.* . . . . . . . . . . . . . . . . . ZCRP 1004
R & B / Nov '83.

**STATE OF LOVE.**
Tracks: State of love / Wrong in love.
■ *12"* . . . . . . . . . . . . . . . . . .RBL 218
■ *7"* . . . . . . . . . . . . . . . . . .RBS 218
■ *7" P.Disc.* . . . . . . . . . . . . . .RBP 218
R & B / May '84.

**SUNSHINE.**
Tracks: Sunshine / Triology / Streetmix (medley) (Extra track on double 12" single only) / Body talk (live version) (Extra track on double 12" single only).
■ *12"* . . . . . . . . . . . . . . . . . RBL 1804
■ *7"* . . . . . . . . . . . . . . . . . RBS 1804
■ *7" Set* . . . . . . . . . . . . . . . RBLX 1804
R & B / Apr '86.

**THANK YOU MY LOVE.**
Tracks: Thank you my love / Point of no return.
■ *12"* . . . . . . . . . . . . . . . . . RBL 219
■ *7"* . . . . . . . . . . . . . . . . . .RBS 219
R & B / Oct '84.
■ *12" P.Disc.* . . . . . . . . . . . . .RBX 219
R & B / Feb '85.

## Imperials

**BEST OF LITTLE ANTHONY & THE IMPERIALS (Little Anthony & The Imperials).**
Tracks: Tears on my pillow / Two people in the world / So much / Diary (CD only) / It's not for me (CD only.) / Wishful thinking / Prayer and a juke box / I'm alright (CD only.) / Shimmy, shimmy, ko-ko-bop / My empty room / I'm taking a vacation from love / Please say you want me / Traveling stranger (CD only.) / I'm on the outside (looking in) / Goin' out of my head / Hurt so bad / Take me back / I miss you so.
■ *MC.* . . . . . . . . . . . . . . . . TCROU 5002
■ *LP* . . . . . . . . . . . . . . . . . ROU 5002
■ *CD* . . . . . . . . . . . . . . . . . . CZ 242
Roulette (EMI) / Nov '89.

**BETTER USE YOUR HEAD (Little Anthony & The Imperials).**
Tracks: Better use your head.
■ *7"* . . . . . . . . . . . . . . . . . . UP 1137
United Artists / '66.
■ *7"* . . . . . . . . . . . . . . . . . UP 36118
United Artists / '76.

**DO WHAT I GOTTA DO.**
Tracks: Do what i gotta do / Dance with me.
■ *7"* . . . . . . . . . . . . . . . . . .PX 274
Power Exchange / Jun '78.

**FOLLOW MAN WITH MUSIC (Little Anthony & The Imperials).**
Tracks: Not Advised.
■ *LP* . . . . . . . . . . . . . . . . . . .KL 025
Word (UK) / '74.

**GOIN' OUT OF MY HEAD.**
Tracks: Goin' out of my head / I just wanna be your lovin' man.
■ *7"* . . . . . . . . . . . . . . . . . TAM 101
EMI / Feb '79.

**HURT (Little Anthony & The Imperials).**
Tracks: Hurt / Never again.
■ *7"* . . . . . . . . . . . . . . . . . . UP 1126
United Artists / '66.

**HURT SO BAD (Little Anthony & The Imperials).**
Tracks: Hurt so bad / Reputation.
■ *7"* . . . . . . . . . . . . . . . . . . UP 1083
United Artists / '65.

**LET THE WIND BLOW (Little Anthony & The Imperials).**
Tracks: Not Advised.
■ *LP* . . . . . . . . . . . . . . . . MYRR 1196
*MC.* . . . . . . . . . . . . . . . . MYRC 1196
Myrrh / Aug '85 / Word Records (UK) / Sony.

**MAKE IT EASY ON YOURSELF (Little Anthony & The Imperials).**
Tracks: Make it easy on yourself / Goin' out of my head.
■ *7"* . . . . . . . . . . . . . . . . . . UP 1073
United Artists / '64.

**ONE MORE SONG FOR YOU (Little Anthony & The Imperials).**
Tracks: What can I do for you / I'm forgiven / All my life / Livin' without your love / Closer than ever / One more song for you / Higher power / More like you.
■ *LP* . . . . . . . . . . . . . . . . . DAY 4004

*MC.* . . . . . . . . . . . . . . . . TC DAY 4004
Dayspring / May '82 / Word Records (UK) / Sony.

**OUTSIDE LOOKIN' IN.. (Little Anthony & The Imperials).**
Tracks: I'm on the outside looking in / Goin' out of my head / Hurt so bad / Take me back / I miss you so / Out of sight out of mind / Hurt / Ten commandments of love / Better use your head / Gonna fix you good (every time you're bad) / It's not the same / I'm hypnotized / You better take it easy baby / Help me find a way (to say I love you) / Yesterday has gone / World of darkness.
■ *MC.* . . . . . . . . . . . . . . . EG 2602914
■ *LP* . . . . . . . . . . . . . . . EG 2602911
Liberty / Oct '84.

**PRIORITY (Little Anthony & The Imperials).**
Tracks: Trumpet of Jesus / Come back and finish what you started / I'd rather believe in you / Any good time at all / Be still my soul / There's no time till you take it / Pieces / Into my life / Seek ye first.
■ *LP* . . . . . . . . . . . . . . . . . DAY 4005
*MC.* . . . . . . . . . . . . . . . TC DAY 4005
Dayspring / May '82 / Word Records (UK) / Sony.

**SHIMMY SHIMMY KOKO POP (Little Anthony & The Imperials).**
Tracks: Shimmy shimmy koko pop / I'm still in love with you.
■ *7"* . . . . . . . . . . . . . . . . . .JAR 256
Top Rank (1) / Jan '60.

**TEARS ON MY PILLOW (Little Anthony & The Imperials).**
Tracks: Tears on my pillow / Two people in the world.
■ *7"* . . . . . . . . . . . . . . . . . HLH 8704
London / Aug '58.

**TIME TO GET IT TOGETHER (Little Anthony & The Imperials).**
Tracks: Not Advised.
■ *LP* . . . . . . . . . . . . . . . . . . KLO 12
Key / '74.

**WHERE YOU GONNA FIND SOMEBODY LIKE ME.**
Tracks: Where you gonna find somebody like me / Another star.
■ *7"* . . . . . . . . . . . . . . . . . .PX 270
Power Exchange / Mar '78.

**WHO'S GONNA LOVE ME.**
Tracks: Who's gonna love me / Can you imagine.
■ *7"* . . . . . . . . . . . . . . . . . .PX 266
Power Exchange / Nov '77.

## Impressions

Impressions were formed in 1958 by Curtis Mayfield (then 15) and singer Jerry Butler. First hit, *For Your Precious Love*, was credited to Jerry Butler & The Impressions, landing former with high profile and consequent enthusiasm for solo career. Mayfield became unchallenged leader, guiding band from doo-wop/R&B origins towards soul and pop. Run of hits began at end of '61 with *Gypsy Woman*; subsequently covered by artists ranging from Ry Cooder to Bobby Womack. By mid-'60s, Chicago-based band faced stiff competition from Detroit's Motown and Memphis' Stax/Volt, but returned to form in '68 by addressing trio of hits to black consciousness issues. Mayfield quit in '70 for successful solo career; Impressions struggled on, eventually scoring hit with aptly titled *Finally Got Myself Together*. Lack of U.K. interest was rectified at end of 1975, when *First Impressions* made Top 20. Band faded into obscurity during disco era, making occasional, low-key comebacks in ensuing decades.

**16 GREATEST HITS: IMPRESSIONS.**
Tracks: Not Advised.
■ *LP* . . . . . . . . . . . . . . . . . . AB 727
ABC Records / '77.

**AIN'T GOT TIME.**
Tracks: Ain't got time / I'm so proud.
■ *7"* . . . . . . . . . . . . . . . . . 2011069
Buddah / Apr '71.

**ALL THE BEST (Impressions Feat. Curtis Mayfield).**
Tracks: Gypsy woman / It's all right / People get ready / Talking about my baby / I'm so proud / You must believe me / Woman's got soul / I've been trying / Amen / You've been cheating / I'm the one who loves you / We're a winner / Keep on pushing /

Right on time / Move on up / Freddie's dead / First impressions.

CD . . . . . . . . . . . . . . . . . . . . . . . **PWKS 4206**
MC . . . . . . . . . . . . . . . . . . . . . . **PWKMC 4206**
Pickwick / May '94 / Pickwick.

## AMEN.

**Tracks:** Gipsy woman / Keep on pushin' / I'm so proud / Say you love me / I've been tryin' / Amen / Choice of colours / Fool for you / Wherever she leadeth me / Mighty mighty spade and whitey / Gone away / This is my country.

■ LP . . . . . . . . . . . . . . . . . . . . . . . .2359 009
Buddah / Nov '70.

## BEST OF THE IMPRESSIONS.

**Tracks:** Not Advised.

■ LP . . . . . . . . . . . . . . . . . . . . . . . . **AB 654**
ABC Records / '77.

## BIG SIXTEEN - VOL. 2.

**Tracks:** You've been cheatin' / Lonely man / Never too much love / You'll want me back / Just one kiss from you / I've been trying / Since I lost the one I love / Don't cry my love / Falling in love with you / I've found that I've lost / I need a love / Can't satisfy / This must end.

■ LP . . . . . . . . . . . . . . . . . . . . . . .SSL 10279
Stateside / Jul '69.

## CHECK OUT YOUR MIND.

**Tracks:** Check out your mind / Can't you see / You're really something Sadie / Do you want to win / You'll be always mine / Only you / Baby turn on to me / Madam Mary / We must be in love / Say you love me.

■ LP . . . . . . . . . . . . . . . . . . . . . . . .2318 017
Buddah / Feb '71.

## DEFINITIVE IMPRESSIONS, THE.

**Tracks:** Gypsy woman / Grow closer together / Little young lover / Minstrel and queen / I'm the one who loves you / Sad, sad girl and boy / It's all right / Talking about my baby / I'm so proud / Keep on pushing / I've been trying / Girl you don't know me / I made a mistake / You must believe me / Amen / People get ready / Woman's got soul / Meeting over yonder / I need you / Just one kiss from you / You've been cheatin' / Since I lost the one I love / I can't satisfy / You always hurt me / I can't stay away from you / We're a winner / We're rolling on / I loved and I lost.

CD . . . . . . . . . . . . . . . . . . . . . . **CDKEND 923**
Kent / Oct '89 / Pinnacle.

## FAN THE FIRE.

**Tracks:** Fan the fire / I don't wanna lose your love / Love love love / You're mine / I surrender / Take everything / I don't mind / For your precious love.

■ LP . . . . . . . . . . . . . . . . . . . . . . . . **T 624**
MC . . . . . . . . . . . . . . . . . . . . . . . . **C 624**
20th Century / Sep '81.

## FAN THE FIRE.

**Tracks:** Fan the flame / For your precious love.

■ 7" . . . . . . . . . . . . . . . . . . . . . . . . **TC 2500**
■ 12" . . . . . . . . . . . . . . . . . . . . . . **TCD 2500**
20th Century / Aug '81.

## FINALLY GOT MYSELF TOGETHER.

**Tracks:** Not Advised.

■ LP . . . . . . . . . . . . . . . . . . . . . . **BDLP 4003**
Buddah / Sep '74.

## FIRST IMPRESSIONS.

**Tracks:** Sooner or later / Same thing it took / Old before my time / First impressions / Groove / I'm so glad / How high is high / Why must a love song be a sad song.

■ LP . . . . . . . . . . . . . . . . . . . . . . . . **RSS 9**
RSO / '79.

## FIRST IMPRESSIONS.

**Tracks:** First impressions / Sunshine.

■ 7" . . . . . . . . . . . . . . . . . . . . . . . **K 16638**
Curtom / Nov '75.
■ 12" . . . . . . . . . . . . . . . . . . . . **12CUR 103**
Curtom / Feb '90.

## FOR YOUR PRECIOUS LOVE.

**Tracks:** For your precious love / Sweet was the wine / Come back my love / At the county fair / That you love me / Gift of love / Senorita / Let me know / Don't drive me away / Lover's lane / Believe in me / Young lover / Long time ago / Lovely one.

■ LP . . . . . . . . . . . . . . . . . . . . . . . **JOY 104**
Joy / Aug '68.
■ LP . . . . . . . . . . . . . . . . . . . . . . **DJB 26086**
DJM / Nov '76.
CD . . . . . . . . . . . . . . . . . . . . . . **CDCD 1105**
Charly / Jul '93 / Charly.

## GREATEST HITS: IMPRESSIONS.

**Tracks:** Not Advised.

## GYPSY WOMAN.

**Tracks:** Gypsy woman.

■ 7" . . . . . . . . . . . . . . . . . . . . . **45POP 961**
H.M.V. / '61.

## IMPRESSIONS, THE.

**Tracks:** It's all right / Gypsy woman / Grow closer together / Little young lover / You've come home / Never let me go / Minstrel and Queen / I need your love / I'm the one who loves you / Sad sad girl and boy / As long as you love me / Twist and limbo.

■ LP . . . . . . . . . . . . . . . . . . . . . . **KENT 005**
Kent / Sep '83.

## KEEP ON PUSHING.

**Tracks:** Keep on pushing / I've been trying / I ain't supposed to / Dedicate my song to you / Long long winter / Somebody help me / Amen / I thank heaven / Talking about my baby / Don't let it hide / I love you (yeah) / I made a mistake.

■ LP . . . . . . . . . . . . . . . . . . . . . . **KENT 009**
Kent / Oct '83.

## LASTING IMPRESSIONS.

**Tracks:** Sooner or later / Same thing it took / Old before my time / First impressions / Loving power / Sunshine / I can't wait to see you / If you have to ask.

LP . . . . . . . . . . . . . . . . . . . . . . **CUR 2006**
MC . . . . . . . . . . . . . . . . . . . . . **CURMC 2006**
Curtom / Oct '89 / ACD Trading Ltd. / Pinnacle / Koch International.
CD . . . . . . . . . . . . . . . . . . . . . **CURCD 2006**
Curtom / Oct '94 / ACD Trading Ltd. / Pinnacle / Koch International.

## LOVING POWER.

**Tracks:** Loving power / Sunshine / I can't wait to see you / If you have to ask / You can't be wrong / I wish I'd stayed in bed / Keep on trying.

■ LP . . . . . . . . . . . . . . . . . . . . . . . **RSS 10**
RSO / '79.

## NEVER ENDING IMPRESSIONS, THE.

**Tracks:** Sister love / Little boy blue / Satin doll / Girl don't you know me / I gotta keep on moving / You always hurt the one you love / That's what love will do / I'm so proud / September song / Lemon Tree / Ten to one / Woman who loves me.

■ LP . . . . . . . . . . . . . . . . . . . . . . **KENT 008**
Kent / Oct '83.

## ORIGINALS.

**Tracks:** Not Advised.

■ Double LP . . . . . . . . . . . . . . . . . **ABSD 303**
ABC Records / Nov '76.

## PEOPLE GET READY.

**Tracks:** Woman's got soul / Emotions / Sometimes I wonder / We're in love / Just another dance / Can't work no longer / People get ready / I've found that I've lost / Hard to believe / See the real me / Get up and move / You must believe me.

■ LP . . . . . . . . . . . . . . . . . . . . . . **KENT 012**
Kent / Nov '83.

## RIGHT ON TIME.

**Tracks:** It's alright / Gypsy woman / Right on time / Talking about my baby / Never let me go / I've been trying / Emotions / People get ready / Riding high / Can't work no longer / You've come home / You must believe me / Man's temptation / Nothing can stop me / Don't cry my love / It's all over.

■ LP . . . . . . . . . . . . . . . . . . . . . . **CRB 1063**
Charly R&B / Nov '83.

## SINCE I LOST THE ONE I LOVE.

**Tracks:** Since I lost the one I love / Falling in love with you.

■ 7" . . . . . . . . . . . . . . . . . . . . . . **POP 1516**
H.M.V. / Mar '66.

## SOONER OR LATER.

**Tracks:** Sooner or later / Miracle woman.

■ 7" . . . . . . . . . . . . . . . . . . . . . **K 16563**
WEA / Jun '75.

## SOULFULLY.

**Tracks:** Woman's got soul / Meeting over yonder / People get ready / You've been cheatin'.

■ LP . . . . . . . . . . . . . . . . . . . . . .7 EG 8954
H.M.V. / Sep '66.

## THIS IS MY COUNTRY.

**Tracks:** They don't know / Stay close to me / I'm loving nothing / Love's happening / Gone away / You want somebody else / So unusual / My woman's love / Fool for you / This is my country.

■ LP . . . . . . . . . . . . . . . . . . . . . . . .203012
Buddah / Mar '69.

## TIMES HAVE CHANGED.

**Tracks:** Stop the war / Times have changed / Inner City blues / Our love goes on and on / Potent love /

Need to belong to someone / This love's for real / Love me.

■ LP . . . . . . . . . . . . . . . . . . . . . . . .2318059
Buddah / Jun '72.

## TOO SLOW.

**Tracks:** Too slow / No one else.

■ 7" . . . . . . . . . . . . . . . . . . . . . . **POP 1526**
H.M.V. / Mar '66.

## WE'RE A WINNER.

**Tracks:** Moonlight shadows / Let me tell the world / I'm gettin' ready / Nothing can stop me / Man oh man / You've got me runnin' / It's hard to believe / We're a winner / Let it be me / No one to love / Little brown boy / I loved and I lost / Romancing to the folk song / Up and away.

■ LP . . . . . . . . . . . . . . . . . . . . . .SSL 10239
Stateside / Jul '68.
■ LP . . . . . . . . . . . . . . . . . . . . . . . **AB 635**
ABC Records / '77.

## YOU ALWAYS HURT ME.

**Tracks:** You always hurt me / Little girl.

■ 7" . . . . . . . . . . . . . . . . . . . . . . **POP 1581**
H.M.V. / Mar '67.

## YOU'VE BEEN CHEATIN'.

**Tracks:** You've been cheatin' / Just one kiss from you.

7" . . . . . . . . . . . . . . . . . . . . . . . **POP 1498**
H.M.V. / Jan '66 / EMI.

## YOUNG MODS' FORGOTTEN STORY.

**Tracks:** Young mods' forgotten story / Choice of colours / Girl I find / Wherever you leadeth me / My deceiving heart / Seven years / Love's miracle / Jealous man / Soulful love / Mighty mighty.

■ LP . . . . . . . . . . . . . . . . . . . . . . . .2359 003
Buddah / Aug '70.
CD . . . . . . . . . . . . . . . . . . . . . **CUR 2013CD**
MC . . . . . . . . . . . . . . . . . . . . . **CUR 2013MC**
Curtom / Mar '94 / ACD Trading Ltd. / Pinnacle / Koch International.

## YOUR PRECIOUS LOVE.

**Tracks:** Sweet was the wind / For your precious love / Lovers Lane / Don't drive me away / Gift of love / At the county fair / Come back my love / Love me / Little young lover / Lonely one / Long time ago / Senorita, I love you / Say that you love me / New love (I found a love).

■ LP . . . . . . . . . . . . . . . . . . . . . . .TOP 179
MC . . . . . . . . . . . . . . . . . . . . . . **KTOP 179**
Topline / Aug '87 / Charly.

# Incognito

Originally a spinoff from London jazz-funkers Light Of The World (who also spawned Beggar & Co), Incognito first charted with 1980's *Parisienne Girl*. Subsequent efforts were less successful and group petered out amidst similarly under-subscribed solo efforts. In '91, guitarist Jean Paul Maunick reformed Incognito with Linda Muriel and signed to Talkin' Loud. Any previous achievements were eclipsed by Top 10 placing for cover of Ronnie Laws' *Always There*, featuring Jocelyn Brown. Another smash, *Don't You Worry 'Bout A Thing*, consolidated their position; Incognito remain one of Brit-funk's few success stories. Public demand for Beggar & Co revival has been curiously underwhelming.

## ALWAYS THERE.

**Tracks:** Always there (7" & 12" remix only) / Journey into sunlight (Not on remix).

■ 12" . . . . . . . . . . . . . . . . . . . . .TLKX 10
■ 12" . . . . . . . . . . . . . . . . . . . . .TLKXR 10
■ 7" . . . . . . . . . . . . . . . . . . . . . . TLK 10
■ CD Single . . . . . . . . . . . . . . . . .TLKCD 10
Talkin' Loud / Jun '91.

## CAN YOU FEEL ME.

**Tracks:** Can you feel me / Glide.

■ 12" Remix . . . . . . . . . . . . . . . . . **TKLX 4**
■ 12" . . . . . . . . . . . . . . . . . . . . . **TLKX 4**
■ 7" . . . . . . . . . . . . . . . . . . . . . . **TLK 4**
Talkin' Loud / Nov '90.

## CHANGE.

**Tracks:** Change.

■ 12" . . . . . . . . . . . . . . . . . . . . .TLKX 26
■ 7" . . . . . . . . . . . . . . . . . . . . . TLK 26
■ CD Single . . . . . . . . . . . . . . . . .TLKCD 26
■ MC Single. . . . . . . . . . . . . . . .TLKMC 26
Talkin' Loud / Aug '92.

## CRAZY FOR YOU (Incognito featuring Chyna).

**Tracks:** Crazy for you / Love is the colour.

■ 12". . . . . . . . . . . . . . . . . . . . . .TLKX 14

■ DELETED

■ 7" . . . . . . . . . . . . . . . . . . . . TLK 14
■ CD Single. . . . . . . . . . . . . . . .TLKCD 14
■ MC Single. . . . . . . . . . . . . . . .TLKMC 14
Talkin' Loud / Aug '91.

## DON'T YOU WORRY 'BOUT A THING.
**Tracks:** Don't you worry 'about a thing.
■ 12" . . . . . . . . . . . . . . . . . . . .TLKX 21
■ 7" . . . . . . . . . . . . . . . . . . . . TLK 21
■ MC Single. . . . . . . . . . . . . . . .TLKMC 21
■ CD Single. . . . . . . . . . . . . . . .TLKCD 21
Talkin' Loud / Jun '92.

## GIVIN' IT UP.
**Tracks:** Givin' it up / Givin' it up (mixes).
■ 12" . . . . . . . . . . . . . . . . . . . .TLKX 44
■ 7" . . . . . . . . . . . . . . . . . . . . TLK 44
■ CD Single. . . . . . . . . . . . . . . .TLKCD 44
■ MC Single. . . . . . . . . . . . . . . .TLKMC 44
Talkin' Loud / Nov '93.

## HAPPY DAYS.
**Tracks:** Happy days / Parachute song.
■ 7" . . . . . . . . . . . . . . . . . . . . SAT 115
Satril / Dec '76.

## INCOGNITO.
**Tracks:** Incognito / Shine on.
■ 7" . . . . . . . . . . . . . . . . . . . . ENY 211
■ 12" . . . . . . . . . . . . . . . . . . . . ENYT 211
Ensign / Jun '81.

## INSIDE LIFE.
**Tracks:** Metropolis / Smile / One step to a miracle /
Can you feel me / Gypsy / Inside life / Love is the
colour / Sketches in the dark / Soho / Always there.
CD. . . . . . . . . . . . . . . . . . . . . . . . 8485462
■ LP . . . . . . . . . . . . . . . . . . . . . . 8485461
■ MC. . . . . . . . . . . . . . . . . . . . . . 8485464
Talkin' Loud / Jul '91 / PolyGram.

## INSIDE LIFE.
**Tracks:** Inside life / Promise you the moon.
■ 12" . . . . . . . . . . . . . . . . . . . . TLKX 7
■ 7" . . . . . . . . . . . . . . . . . . . . TLK 7
■ CD Single. . . . . . . . . . . . . . . .TLKCD 7
Talkin' Loud / Apr '91.

## JAZZ FUNK.
**Tracks:** Shine on / Wake up the city / Why don't you
believe / Chase the clouds away / Interference /
Incognito / Sunburn / Smile of a child / Walking on
wheels.
■ LP . . . . . . . . . . . . . . . . . . . . . ENVY 504
■ MC. . . . . . . . . . . . . . . . . . . . . ENCAS 504
Ensign / Apr '81.

## NORTH LONDON BOY.
**Tracks:** North London boy / Second chance.
■ 7" . . . . . . . . . . . . . . . . . . . . ENY 221
■ 12" . . . . . . . . . . . . . . . . . . . . ENYT 221
Ensign / Nov '81.

## PARISIENNE GIRL.
**Tracks:** Parisienne girl.
■ 7" . . . . . . . . . . . . . . . . . . . . ENY 44
Ensign / Nov '80.

## PIECES OF A DREAM.
**Tracks:** Pieces of a dream / Pieces of a dream
(mixes).
■ 12" Remix. . . . . . . . . . . . . . . .TLKXX 46
■ 12" . . . . . . . . . . . . . . . . . . . .TLKX 46
■ CD Single. . . . . . . . . . . . . . . .TLKCD 46
■ MC Single. . . . . . . . . . . . . . . .TLKMC 46
Talkin' Loud / Jan '94.

## POSITIVITY.
**Tracks:** Still a friend of mine / Smiling faces / Keep
the fires burning / Do right / Positivity / Talkin' loud /
Deep waters / Where do we go from here / Giving it
up / Thinking about tomorrow.
CD. . . . . . . . . . . . . . . . . . . . . . . .518260-2
LP . . . . . . . . . . . . . . . . . . . . . . . .518260-1
MC. . . . . . . . . . . . . . . . . . . . . . . .518260-4
Talkin' Loud / Nov '93 / PolyGram.

## STILL A FRIEND OF MINE.
**Tracks:** Still a friend of mine.
■ 12" . . . . . . . . . . . . . . . . . . . .TLKX 42
■ 7" . . . . . . . . . . . . . . . . . . . . TLK 42
■ CD Single. . . . . . . . . . . . . . . .TLKCD 42
■ MC Single. . . . . . . . . . . . . . . .TLKMC 42
Talkin' Loud / Aug '93.

## TRIBES, VIBES AND SCRIBES.
**Tracks:** Colibri / Change / River in my dreams / Don't
you worry 'bout a thing / Magnet ocean / I love what
you do for me / Closer to the feeling / L'Arc en ciel
de miles / Need to know / Pyramids / Tribal vibes.
CD. . . . . . . . . . . . . . . . . . . . . . . . 5123632
MC. . . . . . . . . . . . . . . . . . . . . . . 5123634
■ LP . . . . . . . . . . . . . . . . . . . . . . 5123631
Talkin' Loud / Jun '92 / PolyGram.

## Incredible Bongo Band

### BONGO ROCK '73.
**Tracks:** Bongo rock '73 / Bongolia.
■ 7" . . . . . . . . . . . . . . . . . . . . DJS 383
DJM / Jun '75.

## Incredibles

### HEART & SOUL.
**Tracks:** Heart and soul / For sentimental reasons /
Lost without you / Standing here crying / I'll make it
easy / Miss Treatment / Without a word / All of a
sudden / Another dirty deal / There's nothing else to
say baby / Fool, fool, fool (version 1) / Stop the
raindrops / I found another love / Crying heart (version 1) / Without a word (45 version) / Standing here
crying (2) / Miss Treatment (45 version ) / I can't get
over losing your love / Fool, fool, fool (version 2).
CD. . . . . . . . . . . . . . . . . . . . . . . .GSCD 018
Goldmine / Jul '93 / Vital Distribution.

### HEART AND SOUL.
**Tracks:** Not Advised.
■ LP . . . . . . . . . . . . . . . . . . . . . CLP 512
Contempo (1) / Oct '74.

### THERE'S NOTHING ELSE TO SAY.
**Tracks:** There's nothing else to say / I can't get over
losing your love.
■ 7" . . . . . . . . . . . . . . . . . . . . SS 2053
Stateside / '67.

## Indeep

### GIRL'S GOT SOUL.
**Tracks:** Girl's got soul / Night the boy learned to
dance.
■ 12" . . . . . . . . . . . . . . . . . . . .BKSL 12
■ 7" . . . . . . . . . . . . . . . . . . . . BKS 12
Beckett / Jun '84.

### INDEEP.
**Tracks:** Buffalo Bill / Love is like a gun / Last night a
DJ saved my life / Slow down / Lipstick politics /
When boys talk / There it is.
■ LP . . . . . . . . . . . . . . . . . . . . .SNYLP 1001
Sound Of New York (USA) / Jun '83.

### LAST NIGHT A DJ SAVED MY LIFE.
**Tracks:** Last night a DJ saved my life / D.J. delight.
■ 12" . . . . . . . . . . . . . . . . . . . .SNYL 1
■ 7" . . . . . . . . . . . . . . . . . . . . SNY 1
Sound Of New York (USA) / Jan '83.
■ 12" . . . . . . . . . . . . . . . . . . . .BLUE 008
Deejay (USA) / Nov '87.

### PYJAMA PARTY TIME.
**Tracks:** Girls got soul / Night the boy learned how to
dance / Ten reasons why I can't be free / If you want
it / You got to rock it / I got my rights / Record keeps
spinning / Pyjama party time.
■ LP . . . . . . . . . . . . . . . . . . . . . BKLP 5681
■ MC. . . . . . . . . . . . . . . . . . . . . ZCBK 5681
Beckett / Apr '84.

### RECORD KEEPS SPINNING.
**Tracks:** Record keeps spinning / Record keeps spinning (version).
■ 12" . . . . . . . . . . . . . . . . . . . .BKSL 11
■ 7" . . . . . . . . . . . . . . . . . . . . BKS 11
Beckett / Jan '84.

### WHEN BOY'S TALK.
**Tracks:** When boy's talk.
■ 12" . . . . . . . . . . . . . . . . . . . .SNYL 3
■ 7" . . . . . . . . . . . . . . . . . . . . SNY 3
Sound Of New York (USA) / Apr '83.

## Independents

Short-lived outfit who enjoyed rapid succession of U.S. smashes from '73, including
*Leaving Me, It's All Over, First Time We
Met, Just As Long As You Need Me* and *I
Want To Be There*. Band split when
founders Chuck Jackson and Marvin Yancey decided to re-direct their writing and
producing skills into other performers, such
as Natalie Cole.

### FIRST TIME WE MET (The Greatest Hits).
**Tracks:** I found love on a rainy day / First time we
met / I just want to be there / Leaving me / It's all
over / Let this be a lesson to you / No wind no rain /
Just as long as you need me (Parts 1&2) / Sara Lee /
Baby I've been missing you / Couldn't hear nobody
say (I love you like I do).
■ LP . . . . . . . . . . . . . . . . . . . . . CRB 1146
Charly R&B / Nov '86.

## Index

### FUNKIN' FOR YOU.
**Tracks:** Funkin for you (mixes) / Made in voyage.
■ 12" . . . . . . . . . . . . . . . . . . . .BBJ 006T
Black On Black / Oct '94 / Vital Distribution.

### I'M GONNA GET YOU.
**Tracks:** I'm gonna get you / Computer love.
■ 7" . . . . . . . . . . . . . . . . . . . . .DJS 10933
DJM / Feb '80.

### LOVE YOU'VE BEEN FAKIN'.
**Tracks:** Love you've been fakin'.
■ 12" . . . . . . . . . . . . . . . . . . . . EXCL 521
■ 7" . . . . . . . . . . . . . . . . . . . . .EXC 521
Excaliber / Aug '82.

### STARLIGHT.
**Tracks:** Starlight / Virgin.
■ 7" . . . . . . . . . . . . . . . . . . . . SHACK 8
Record Shack / Sep '81.

## Ingram

### NIGHT STALKERS.
**Tracks:** Night stalkers / With you / Drivin' me crazy /
When you're hot you're hot / Just for you / I like it /
Fantasy / Hot body.
■ LP . . . . . . . . . . . . . . . . . . . . . OELP 1
Other End / May '84.

### SMOOTHIN' GROOVIN'.
**Tracks:** Smoothin' groovin' / D.J.'s delight.
■ 12" . . . . . . . . . . . . . . . . . . . . WAVEL 3
■ 7" . . . . . . . . . . . . . . . . . . . . WAVE 3
Streetwave / Jun '83.

### WE LIKE TO DO IT.
**Tracks:** We like to do it / Groovin' on a groove.
■ 12" . . . . . . . . . . . . . . . . . . . . WAVEL 5
Streetwave / Jul '83.

### WHEN YOU'RE HOT YOU'RE HOT.
**Tracks:** When you're hot you're hot.
■ 7" . . . . . . . . . . . . . . . . . . . . OET 1
Other End / May '84.

### WITH YOU.
**Tracks:** With you.
■ 12" . . . . . . . . . . . . . . . . . . . . 12 OET 2
■ 7" . . . . . . . . . . . . . . . . . . . .7 OET 2
Other End / Jun '84.

## Ingram, James

Having left Ohio to seek fame and fortune in
L.A., Ingram was plucked from obscurity by
Quincy Jones after several years of otherwise fruitless gigging and recording. Starring role on Q's *The Dude* album set pattern
for Ingram's career; his best-known work
being duets with artists including Patti Austin (*Baby Come To Me*, '82), Michael McDonald (*Ya Mo B There*, '84) and Linda Ronstadt (*Somewhere Out There*, '87). Enduring
association with Jones led to Ingram-com-
posed *P.Y.T.* on *Thriller* and impressive
turns on *We Are The World* and *Back On
The Block*. Ingram's recent work, for which
he switched from Qwest to Warner Bros.,
has done little to raise his profile.

### ALWAYS.
**Tracks:** Always (Instrumental).
■ 12" . . . . . . . . . . . . . . . . . . . .W 8669T
■ 7" . . . . . . . . . . . . . . . . . . . . W 8669
Qwest / Jul '86.

### ALWAYS YOU.
**Tracks:** Someone like you / Let me love you this way
/ Always you / Treat her right / Baby's born / This is
the night / You never know what you've got / Too
much from this heart / Sing for the children / Any
kind of love.
CD. . . . . . . . . . . . . . . . . . . . . . .936245275-2
MC. . . . . . . . . . . . . . . . . . . . . . .936245275-4
Warner Bros. / May '93 / WEA.

### BETTER WAY'.
**Tracks:** Better way.
■ 12" . . . . . . . . . . . . . . . . . . . . MCAT 1182
■ 7" . . . . . . . . . . . . . . . . . . . . .MCA 1182
MCA / Aug '87.

### I DIDN'T HAVE THE HEART.
**Tracks:** I didn't have the heart / Baby be mine.
■ 12" . . . . . . . . . . . . . . . . . . . . W 9911 T
■ 7" . . . . . . . . . . . . . . . . . . . . W 9911
■ CD Single. . . . . . . . . . . . . . . . W 9911 CD
■ MC Single. . . . . . . . . . . . . . . . W 9911 C
WEA / Oct '90.

## IT'S REAL.
Tracks: It's real / Call on me / Love come down / Love one day at a time / Someday we'll all be free / I wanna come back / So fine / (You make me feel like a) natural man / I don't have the heart / When was the last time music made.
- ■ LP . . . . . . . . . . . . . . . . . . . WX 280
- ■ MC. . . . . . . . . . . . . . . . . . . WX 280C
WEA / Jun '89 / WEA.
- ■ CD . . . . . . . . . . . . . . . . . . K 925924 2
- ■ LP . . . . . . . . . . . . . . . . . . K 925924 1
- ■ MC. . . . . . . . . . . . . . . . . . K 925924 4
WEA / May '89 / WEA.

## IT'S REAL.
Tracks: It's real / Aren't you tired.
- ■ 12" . . . . . . . . . . . . . . . . . .W 2975T
- ■ 7" . . . . . . . . . . . . . . . . . . W 2975
- ■ CD Single . . . . . . . . . . . . . .W 2975CD
- ■ MC Single . . . . . . . . . . . . . .W 2975C
WEA / Jun '89.

## IT'S YOUR NIGHT.
Tracks: Party animal / Yah mo B there / She loves me (the best that I can be) / Try your love again / Whatever we imagine / One more rhythm / There's no easy way / It's your night / How do you keep the music playing.
- ■ MC . . . . . . . . . . . . . . . . . .923970 4
- ■ LP . . . . . . . . . . . . . . . . . .923970 1
Qwest / Nov '83.
- ■ CD . . . . . . . . . . . . . . . . . .923970 2
Qwest / '86 / WEA.

## IT'S YOUR NIGHT.
Tracks: It's your night / She loves me.
- ■ 12" . . . . . . . . . . . . . . . . . .W 9026T
- ■ 7" . . . . . . . . . . . . . . . . . . W 9026
WEA / Mar '85.

## NEVER FELT SO GOOD.
Tracks: Always / Never felt so good / Red hot lover / Lately / Wings of my heart / Trust me / Tuff / Say hey / Love's been here and gone / Right back.
- ■ CD . . . . . . . . . . . . . . . . . .925424 2
Qwest / '86.
- ■ LP . . . . . . . . . . . . . . . . . . WX 44
- ■ MC . . . . . . . . . . . . . . . . . . WX 44 C
Qwest / Aug '86.

## PARTY ANIMAL.
Tracks: Party animal / Come a da my place.
- ■ 12" . . . . . . . . . . . . . . . . . .W 9493T
- ■ 7" . . . . . . . . . . . . . . . . . . W 9493
Qwest / Oct '83.

## POWER OF GREAT MUSIC, THE.
Tracks: Where did my heart go / How do you keep the music playing / Just once / Somewhere out there / I don't have the heart / There's no easy way / Get ready / Baby come to me / One hundred ways / Yah mo be there / Remember the dream / Whatever we imagine.
- CD. . . . . . . . . . . . . . . . . . 7599267002
- MC. . . . . . . . . . . . . . . . . . 7599267004
WEA / Mar '94 / WEA.

## SHE LOVES ME.
Tracks: She loves me / It's your night / Try your love again (Only on 12" single.).
- ■ 12" . . . . . . . . . . . . . . . . . . W 9287 T
- ■ 7" . . . . . . . . . . . . . . . . . . W 9287
Qwest / Jun '84.

## WHATEVER WE IMAGINE.
Tracks: Whatever we imagine / It's your night.
- ■ 7" . . . . . . . . . . . . . . . . . . W 9165
Qwest / Sep '84.

## YAH MO BE THERE (Ingram, James & Michael McDonald).
Tracks: Yah mo B there / Come-a da machine to take-a my place.
- ■ 7" . . . . . . . . . . . . . . . . . . W 9394
- ■ 12" . . . . . . . . . . . . . . . . . . W 9394 T
Qwest / Jan '85.

## YAH MO BE THERE (OLD GOLD).
Tracks: Yah mo be there / Baby come to me.
- ■ 7" . . . . . . . . . . . . . . . . . .OG 9908
Old Gold / '89.

<hr>

## Ingram, Luther

One of the great cult soul voices, Ingram hails from Jackson, Tennessee. He learnt his vocal techniques, as always, in local churches before moving up to New York in search of R&B success. Signed by the Stax-distributed independent Koko label, he achieved notoriety straight away: his album *I've Been Here All The Time* rode the soul chart while a single from his second album,

*If Loving You Is Wrong (I Don't Want To Be Right)* made number one in '72. It also sold in excess of 50,000 copies as an import in the UK. Like many others, Ingram suffered from the financial collapse of Stax; but re-surfaced in '78, still on Koko, with a pair of albums most soul fans consider amongst the best in their collections: *Let's Steal Away To The Hideaway* and *Do You Love Somebody*. Neither was staggeringly successful and Ingram disappeared again until '86 when the hip hop label, Profile issued *Luther Ingram*, another rather good album from the man.

## I LIKE THE FEELING.
Tracks: Not Advised.
- CD. . . . . . . . . . . . . . . URG 4119CD
- MC. . . . . . . . . . . . . . . URG 4119MC
Ichiban / Feb '94 / A.D.A. Distribution / Pinnacle / ACD Trading Ltd. / Koch International / Direct Distribution.

## IF LOVING YOU IS WRONG (I DON'T WANT TO BE RIGHT).
Tracks: If loving you is wrong (I don't want to be right) / Do you love somebody / Always / Let's steal away to the hideaway / Get to me / Sweet inspiration / I'll just call you honey / Help me love / I remember / I'll be your shelter in time of storm / You got to give love to get love / Missing you / Oh baby, you can depend on me / I'm trying to sing a message to you.
- CD . . . . . . . . . . . . . . CDCHARLY 303
Charly / Nov '91 / Charly.

## LET'S STEAL AWAY TO THE HIDEAWAY.
Tracks: Let's steal away to the hideaway / That's the way love is / Sweet inspiration / I'm gonna be the best thing / I like the feeling / All that shines / What goes around comes around / It's too much / Your love is something special / I've got your love in my life.
- ■ LP . . . . . . . . . . . . . . . . . . KOA 1300
Koko / '76.

<hr>

## Inner Life

## LET'S CHARGE IT UP.
Tracks: Let's charge it up.
- ■ 12" . . . . . . . . . . . . . . . 12 PER 3901
- ■ 7" . . . . . . . . . . . . . . . PERS 3901
Personal / Apr '85.

## NO WAY.
Tracks: No way / No way (version).
- ■ 12" . . . . . . . . . . . . . . . 12PER 101
- ■ 7" . . . . . . . . . . . . . . . PERS 101
Personal / Apr '84.

## SPRING RAIN / MOMENT OF MY LIFE (see under Silvetti).

<hr>

## Innocence

## BELIEF.
Tracks: Silent voice / Let's push it / Reflections / Natural thing / Matter of fact / Higher ground / Remember the day / Moving upwards / Come together / Reprise.
- CD. . . . . . . . . . . . . . . . . . CCD 1797
- MC. . . . . . . . . . . . . . . . . . ZCTLP 20
- ■ LP . . . . . . . . . . . . . . . . . .CTLP 20
Cool Tempo / Oct '90 / EMI.

## BUILD.
Tracks: Family ties / I'll be there / Build / Looking for someone / Solitude / Family ties(Reprise) / One love in my lifetime / Promise of love / Hold on / Respect / No sacrifice / Build (reprise).
- CD . . . . . . . . . . . . . . . . . . CTCD 26
- ■ LP . . . . . . . . . . . . . . . . . .CTLP 26
- ■ MC . . . . . . . . . . . . . . . . . .CTTC 26
Cool Tempo / Oct '92 / EMI.

## I'LL BE THERE.
Tracks: I'll be there.
- ■ 12" . . . . . . . . . . . . . . . . . COOLX 255
- ■ 7" . . . . . . . . . . . . . . . . . . COOL 255
- ■ CD Single . . . . . . . . . . . . . COOLCD 255
- ■ MC Single . . . . . . . . . . . . . COOLMC 255
Cool Tempo / Jun '92.

## LET'S PUSH IT.
Tracks: Let's push it (big beat mix) (Only on 12" and CD single) / Let's push it (belief mix) (Only on 12" single) / Silent voice (saxovana) (Only on 12" and CD single) / Let's push it (dub version) (Only on 7" and MC single) / Let's push it (7" version) (Only on CD single).
- ■ 12" . . . . . . . . . . . . . . . . . COOLX 220
- ■ 7" . . . . . . . . . . . . . . . . . . COOL 220
- ■ CD Single . . . . . . . . . . . . . COOLCD 220

- ■ MC Single . . . . . . . . . . . . . COOLMC 220
Cool Tempo / Oct '90.

## MATTER OF FACT, A.
Tracks: Matter of fact / Reflections.
- ■ 7" . . . . . . . . . . . . . . . . . .COOL 223
- ■ 12" . . . . . . . . . . . . . . . . . COOLX 223
- ■ 12" Remix . . . . . . . . . . . . . COOLXR 223
- ■ CD Single . . . . . . . . . . . . . COOLCD 223
- ■ MC Single . . . . . . . . . . . . . COOLMC 223
Cool Tempo / Nov '90.

## NATURAL THING.
Tracks: Natural thing / Natural thing (dub version).
- ■ 12" . . . . . . . . . . . . . . . . . COOLX 201
- ■ 12" Remix . . . . . . . . . . . . . COOLXR 201
- ■ 7" . . . . . . . . . . . . . . . . . .COOL 201
- ■ CD Single . . . . . . . . . . . . . COOLCD 201
Cool Tempo / Feb '90.

## ONE LOVE IN MY LIFETIME.
Tracks: One love in my lifetime / Matter of fact (7" & MC only.) / Respect (CD only.) / Let's push it.
- ■ 12" . . . . . . . . . . . . . . . . . COOLX 263
- ■ 7" . . . . . . . . . . . . . . . . . .COOL 263
- ■ MC Single . . . . . . . . . . . . . TCCOOL 263
- ■ CD Single . . . . . . . . . . . . . COOLCD 263
Cool Tempo / Sep '92.

## REMEMBER THE DAY.
Tracks: Remember the day (Not on 12") / Remember the day (ambient mix) / Remember the day (final mix) (12" & CD single only.) / Remember the day (dub mix) (12" only.).
- ■ 7" . . . . . . . . . . . . . . . . . .COOL 226
- ■ 12" . . . . . . . . . . . . . . . . . COOLX 226
- ■ CD Single . . . . . . . . . . . . . COOLCD 226
- ■ MC Single . . . . . . . . . . . . . COOLMC 226
Cool Tempo / Mar '91.

## SILENT VOICE.
Tracks: Silent voice.
- ■ 7" . . . . . . . . . . . . . . . . . .COOL 212
- ■ 12" . . . . . . . . . . . . . . . . . COOLX 212
- ■ 12" Remix . . . . . . . . . . . . . COOLXR 212
- ■ CD Single . . . . . . . . . . . . . COOLCD 212
- ■ MC Single . . . . . . . . . . . . . COOLMC 212
Cool Tempo / Jul '90.

<hr>

## Instant Funk

## CRYIN'.
Tracks: Crying / Dark vader.
- ■ . . . . . . . . . . . . . . . . . . SSOL 118
Salsoul / Apr '79.

## EVERYBODY.
Tracks: Everybody / You want my love.
- ■ 12" . . . . . . . . . . . . . . . . . . SALT 8
- ■ 7" . . . . . . . . . . . . . . . . . . SAL 8
Salsoul / Nov '80.

## FLOAT LIKE A BUTTERFLY.
Tracks: Float like a butterfly.
- ■ 7" . . . . . . . . . . . . . . . . . PIR 4291
Philadelphia Int. / May '76.

## FUNK IS ON, THE.
Tracks: It's cool / Funk is on / Funk 'n' roll / You want my love / What can I do for you / Everybody / Can you see where I'm coming from / You're not getting older.
- ■ LP . . . . . . . . . . . . . . . . . . SALP 4
Salsoul / Nov '80.

## GOT MY MIND MADE UP.
Tracks: Got my mind made up / Crying / Never let it go away / Don't you wanna party / Wide world of sports / Darth Vader / You say you want me to stay / I'll be doggone.
- ■ LP . . . . . . . . . . . . . . . . . SSLP 1511
Salsoul / Mar '79.

## GOT MY MIND MADE UP.
Tracks: Got my mind made up / Wide world of sports.
- ■ 7" . . . . . . . . . . . . . . . . . SSOL 114
Salsoul / Jan '79.

## INSTANT FUNK.
Tracks: Blazin' / Who took away the funk / No stoppin' that rockin' / Smack dab in the middle / You're gonna get yours / Hard day's night / Easy come, easy go / I'll be good to you.
- ■ LP . . . . . . . . . . . . . . . . . XL 13227
Salsoul / Mar '83.

## WHY DON'T YOU THINK ABOUT ME.
Tracks: Why don't you think about me / Slam dunk the funk / I got my mind made up.
- ■ 12" . . . . . . . . . . . . . . . . . .BATTL 1
Battersea / Jun '82.

■ DELETED

## Interaction

**SHOW EM HOW WE DO IT (Interaction & Michelle Weeks).**
Tracks: Show em how we do it (mixes).
12″. . . . . . . . . . . . . . . . . . . . . SLIP 011
12″ Remix. . . . . . . . . . . . . . .SLIP 011R
CD Single. . . . . . . . . . . . . . .SLIP 011CD
Slip'n'Slide / Sep '94 / Vital Distribution.

## Intrigue

**HEAVEN MADE.**
Tracks: Heaven made / Ropes.
■ 12″. . . . . . . . . . . . . . . . . . .12PRO 1
■ 7″ . . . . . . . . . . . . . . . . . . . . PRO 1
Project / Jun '85.

**I LIKE IT.**
Tracks: I like it.
■ 12″. . . . . . . . . . . . . . . . . .PRESSD 1003
Pressure / Feb '83.

**LET SLEEPING DOGS LIE.**
Tracks: Let sleeping dogs lie.
■ 12″. . . . . . . . . . . . . . . . . . . .MPRT 2
■ 7″ . . . . . . . . . . . . . . . . . . . .MPR 2
Music Power / Sep '84.

**NO TURNING BACK.**
Tracks: No turning back / Call of the heart.
■ 12″. . . . . . . . . . . . . . . . . . . .MPRT 1
■ 7″ . . . . . . . . . . . . . . . . . . . .MPR 1
Music Power / Apr '84.

**TOGETHER FOREVER.**
Tracks: Fly girl / Fly girl (dance mix) / Together forever.
■ 7″ . . . . . . . . . . . . . . . . . . .COOL 153
■ 12″. . . . . . . . . . . . . . . . . .COOLX 153
Cool Tempo / Sep '87.

## Intruders

Philadelphia band that achieved its greatest success with 1968 million selling single *Cowboys To Girls*. Having produced an early single on the Musicor label, Leon Huff signed the Intruders to Gamble Records (formerly Excel), owned by himself and Kenny Gamble; pair subsequently produced all their chart hits. Later minor hits included *Win, Place Or Show (She's A Winner)* - U.K. No. 14 in '74 - and *I'll Always Love My Mama* - U.S. R&B No. 6 in 1975. The band boosted their popularity with appearances on local Philadelphia TV shows in the early '70s but were later somewhat eclipsed by artists such as the O'Jays and Stylistics.

**(WIN SHOW OR PLACE) SHE'S A WINNER.**
Tracks: (Win show or place) She's a winner / Memories are here to stay.
■ 7″ . . . . . . . . . . . . . . . . . . PIR 2212
Philadelphia Int. / Jun '74.

**(WIN SHOW OR PLACE) SHE'S A WINNER (OLD GOLD).**
Tracks: (Win show or place) she's a winner / I'll always love my momma.
7″. . . . . . . . . . . . . . . . . . .OG 9958
Old Gold / '92 / Pickwick.

**I'LL ALWAYS LOVE MY MAMA.**
Tracks: I'll always love my mama.
■ 7″ . . . . . . . . . . . . . . . . . . PIR 2147
Philadelphia Int. / Apr '74.

**WARM AND TENDER LOVE.**
Tracks: Warm and tender love.
■ 12″. . . . . . . . . . . . . . . . . . MKHAN 43
■ 7″ . . . . . . . . . . . . . . . . . . KHAN 43
Streetwave / May '85.

**WHO DO YOU LOVE.**
Tracks: Not Advised.
■ CD . . . . . . . . . . . . . . . . . . MKCD 006
PRT / '88.

**WHO DO YOU LOVE.**
Tracks: Who do you love / It's alright.
■ 12″. . . . . . . . . . . . . . . . . . MKHAN 50
Streetwave / Jul '85.

**WHO DO YOU LOVE.**
Tracks: Who do you love.
■ 12″. . . . . . . . . . . . . . . . . . MKHAN 34
Streetwave / Nov '83.
■ 7″ . . . . . . . . . . . . . . . . . . KHAN 34
Streetwave / Dec '84.

**WHO DO YOU LOVE** (see under Rae, Fonda).

## Invisible Man's Band

**ALL NIGHT THING.**
Tracks: All night thing.
■ 12″. . . . . . . . . . . . . . . . . .12WIP 6571
■ 7″ . . . . . . . . . . . . . . . . . . WIP 6571
Island / Jun '80.

**INVISIBLE MAN'S BAND.**
Tracks: Full moon / All night thing / X country / 9 x's out of ten / Rent strike / Love can't come/love has come.
■ LP . . . . . . . . . . . . . . . . . . ILPS 9537
Island / Jul '80.

**LOVE CAN'T COME (PART 1).**
Tracks: Love can't come (part 1) / Love can't come (part 2) / 9 x's out of ten.
■ 12″. . . . . . . . . . . . . . . . . .12WIP 6642
Island / Aug '80.

## Ioni

**SENTENCE OF LOVE.**
Tracks: Sentence of love / Daydream.
■ 12″. . . . . . . . . . . . . . . . . . AMY 162
■ 7″ . . . . . . . . . . . . . . . . . . AM 162
■ CD Single . . . . . . . . . . . . . . AMCD 162
■ MC Single. . . . . . . . . . . . . . AMMC 162
A&M / Jan '93.

**WE ARE ALL FREE.**
Tracks: We are all free.
■ 12″. . . . . . . . . . . . . . . . . .580285-1
■ 7″ . . . . . . . . . . . . . . . . . .580285-7
■ CD Single . . . . . . . . . . . . . .580285-2
■ MC Single. . . . . . . . . . . . . .580285-4
A&M / Jun '93.

**YOU OUGHTA BE IN PICTURES.**
Tracks: You oughta be in pictures / Taste it.
12″. . . . . . . . . . . . . . . . . .580669-1
7″ . . . . . . . . . . . . . . . . . .580668-7
CD Single . . . . . . . . . . . . . .580669-2
MC Single . . . . . . . . . . . . . .580668-4
A&M / Jul '94 / PolyGram.

## Ipso Facto

**GIVE IT TO HER.**
Tracks: Give it to her.
■ 12″. . . . . . . . . . . . . . . . . . IF 884
Zodiac / Sep '84.

**GLASS TIGERS.**
Tracks: Glass tigers.
■ 7″ . . . . . . . . . . . . . . . . . . IF 985
Zodiac / May '85.

**LOVE CAN MAKE YOU FEEL SO HAPPY.**
Tracks: Love can make you feel so happy.
■ 12″. . . . . . . . . . . . . . . . . DEBTX 3134
Debut (2) / Nov '91.

**MANNEQUIN.**
Tracks: Mannequin.
■ 7″ . . . . . . . . . . . . . . . . . .IFV 83
If / Sep '84.

**MOVIN' ON.**
Tracks: Movin' on.
■ 12″. . . . . . . . . . . . . . . . . DEBTX 3115
Debut (2) / Jun '91.

**NOIR DIOR.**
Tracks: Noir dior.
■ 7″ . . . . . . . . . . . . . . . . . . IF 784
If / Sep '84.

## Irby, Joyce

**MAXIMUM THRUST (Irby, Joyce Fenderella).**
Tracks: Mr. D.J. I'm available / She's not my lover / I love you / Let's do it / Maximum thrust / Guardian angel / I'll be there / Go go girl.
■ CD . . . . . . . . . . . . . . . . . . ZD 72662
■ LP . . . . . . . . . . . . . . . . . . ZL 72662
■ MC . . . . . . . . . . . . . . . . . . ZK 72662
Motown / Jul '89.

**MR D.J.**
Tracks: Mr. D.J. / Mr. D.J. (mix).
■ 12″. . . . . . . . . . . . . . . . . . ZT 42772
■ 7″ . . . . . . . . . . . . . . . . . . ZB 42771
■ CD Single . . . . . . . . . . . . . . ZD 42772
Motown / May '89.

## Irini

**24/7 LOVE.**
Tracks: 24/7 Love.
■ 12″. . . . . . . . . . . . . . . . . . SCGT 101
■ CD Single . . . . . . . . . . . . . . SCGCD 101
■ MC Single . . . . . . . . . . . . . . SCGTC 101
SCG Records / May '93.

**DON'T LET THEM KNOW.**
Tracks: Don't let them know.
CD Single . . . . . . . . . . . . . . SCGCD 102
SCG Records / Feb '94 / Jetstar.

**LOVE ON MY MIND.**
Tracks: Love on my mind (Mixes).
12″. . . . . . . . . . . . . . . . . .HIIT 021
Here It Is / Apr '94 / Jetstar.

## Irvine, Weldon

**IN HARMONY.**
Tracks: Not Advised.
■ LP . . . . . . . . . . . . . . . . . . SES 19749
Code O / Oct '75.

## Ish

**FASTER THAN A SPEEDING BULLET.**
Tracks: Faster than a speeding bullet / Don't stop.
■ 7″ . . . . . . . . . . . . . . . . . . TKR 7540
TK / Apr '79.

**ON THIS CORNER.**
Tracks: You're my only lover / I could love you / You're my favourite thing to do / On this corner / Holy night / More than I can bear / It ain't necessarily so / Chase the lace / Femininity.
■ LP . . . . . . . . . . . . . . . . . . GEF 26967
■ MC . . . . . . . . . . . . . . . . . . 4026967
Geffen / Apr '86.

**YOU'RE MY ONLY LOVER.**
Tracks: You're my only lover / It ain't necessarily so.
■ 7″ . . . . . . . . . . . . . . . . . .A 7029
Geffen / Apr '86.

## Isis

**HAIL THE WORD.**
Tracks: Hail the word.
■ 12″. . . . . . . . . . . . . . . . . .12 BRW 224
■ 7″ . . . . . . . . . . . . . . . . . . BRW 224
■ CD Single . . . . . . . . . . . . . .BRCD 224
4th & Broadway / Jun '91.

**REBEL SOUL.**
Tracks: Rebel soul / Face the bass / Great pimpstress / In the mind of one / Hail the words of Isis / To the crossroads / Power of myself is moving / Wizard of optics / House of Isis / State of mind.
CD. . . . . . . . . . . . . . . . . .BRCD 571
■ LP . . . . . . . . . . . . . . . . . . BRLP 571
■ MC . . . . . . . . . . . . . . . . . .BRCA 571
4th & Broadway / Mar '91 / PolyGram.

**REBEL SOUL.**
Tracks: Rebel soul / Face the bass.
■ 7″ . . . . . . . . . . . . . . . . . . BRW 190
4th & Broadway / Nov '90.

## Isley Brothers

Isley Brothers - O'Kelly, Ronald and Rudolph - began as gospel singers in Cincinnati. Moving to New York in 1957, they followed lead of such gospel greats as Sam Cooke in switching to secular style. Early career contained three pop landmarks: *Shout, Twist And Shout* and early appearance of up-and-coming session guitarist James Hendrix. Mixed fortunes received boost in 1966, when they reached U.S. No. 12 with *This Old Heart Of Mine*, written by Motown's golden Holland/Dozier/Holland team; single was belated U.K. smash in late '68. Isleys quit Motown in '69, to take control of their output; second classic period was heralded by self-penned *It's Your Thing*. Now boasting younger brother and hot guitarist Ernie, group forged successful path for rock-soul fusion with hits like *That Lady, Summer Breeze, Fight The Power* and *Harvest For The World*. In the late '70s, the Isleys were overtaken by disco. However, they remain a popular concert attraction; 1994 tour line-up boasted soul diva (and Ronald's wife) Angela Winbush. Their influence can be heard in Prince's early work (soft soul and hard rock guitar) and innumerable cover versions.

## 20 GOLDEN PIECES: ISLEY BROTHERS.
**Tracks:** Drag / I need love / Don't be jealous / Rockin' McDonald / This is the end / Don't you feel / Hold on baby / I say love / I'm laughing to keep from crying / Let's twist again / Never leave me baby / Nobody but me / Right now / Rubberleg twist / Spanish twist / Snake / Time after time / Twist and shout / Twistin' with Linda / You better come home.
- ■ LP ....................... **BDL 2032**
- MC. ....................... **AJKL 2032**

Bulldog Records / Apr '83 / President Records / Jazz Music / Wellard / TKO Records Ltd.

## 3 + 3.
**Tracks:** That lady / Don't let me be lonely tonight / If you were there / You walk your way / Listen to the music / What it comes down to / Sunshine (go away today) / Summer breeze / Highways of my life.
- ■ LP ....................... **EPC 32039**
- ■ MC. ....................... **.40 32039**
- CD ....................... **.982651-2**

Pickwick/Sony Collector's Choice / Mar '94 / Pickwick / Pinnacle.

## 6 TRACK HITS: ISLEY BROTHERS.
**Tracks:** Listen to the music / Brown eyed girl / Harvest for the world / Under the influence of love / You still feel the need / Don't let me be lonely tonight.
- ■ EP ....................... **7SR 5026**
- MC. ....................... **7SC 5026**

Scoop 33 / Sep '83.

## BATTLE OF THE GROUPS.
**Tracks:** Not Advised.
- CD ....................... **NEMCD 691**

Sequel / Aug '94 / Total / BMG.

## BEHIND A PAINTED SMILE.
**Tracks:** Behind a painted smile.
- ■ 7" ....................... **TMG 693**

Tamla Motown / May '69.

## BEHIND A PAINTED SMILE.
**Tracks:** Behind a painted smile / Got to have you back / Take me in your arms / Catching up on time / Save me from this misery / Little Miss Sweetness / Good times / All because I love you / That's the way love is / Tell me it's just a rumour baby / Why when love is gone / One too many heartaches / Whispers.
- ■ LP ....................... **STML 11112**

Tamla Motown / Jul '69.

## BETWEEN THE SHEETS.
**Tracks:** Choosy lover / Touch me / I need your body / Between the sheets / Let's make love tonight / Ballad for the fallen soldier / Slow down children / Way out love / Gettin' over / Rock you good.
- MC. ....................... **.40 25419**
- ■ LP ....................... **EPC 25419**

Epic / Jul '83 / Sony.

## BETWEEN THE SHEETS.
**Tracks:** Between the sheets / That lady.
- ■ 7" ....................... **.A 3513**
- ■ 12" ....................... **TA 3513**

Epic / Jun '83.

## BROTHERS IN SOUL.
**Tracks:** Twist and shout / Rockin' McDonald / Drag / Don't be jealous / This is the end / Twistin' with Linda / Spanish twist / Let's twist again / Rubber leg twist / Shake it with me baby / Nobody but me / Snake / Hold on baby / Don't you feel / You better come home / I say love / I'm laughing to keep from crying / Time after time / Right now / Never leave me baby / Long tall Sally.
- CD ....................... **CDCD 1107**

Charly / Jul '93 / Charly.

## BROTHERS ISLEY.
**Tracks:** It turned you on / Vacuum cleaner / I got to get myself together / Was it good to you / Blacker the berrie / My little girl / Get down off the train / Holding on / Feels like the world.
- ■ LP ....................... **SSL 10300**

Stateside / Jun '70.

## CHOOSY LOVER.
**Tracks:** Choosy lover.
- ■ 12" ....................... **TA 3690**
- ■ 7" ....................... **.A 3690**

Epic / Aug '83.

## COLDER ARE MY NIGHTS.
**Tracks:** Colder are my nights / Colder are my nights (Instrumental).
- ■ 12" ....................... **W 8860T**
- ■ 7" ....................... **W 8860**

WEA / Jan '86.

## COMPLETE UA SESSIONS, THE (Legends of Rock & Roll Series).
**Tracks:** Surf and shout / Please, please, please / She's the one / Tango / What'cha gonna do / Stagger Lee / You'll never leave him / Let's go, let's go, let's go / She's gone / Shake it with me baby / Long tall Sally / Do the twist / My little girl / Open up her eyes / Love is a wonderful thing / Footprints in the snow / Who's that lady / Basement / Conch / My little girl (2).
- CD ....................... **CZ 421**

EMI / Apr '91 / EMI.

## COMPLETE VICTOR SESSIONS, THE.
**Tracks:** Rock around the clock / He's got the whole world in his hands / Turn to me / Respectable / Open your heart / St. Louis blues (Track on CD only.) / Ring a ling a ling / I'm gonna knock on your door / That lucky old sun / Not one minute more / When the saints go marching in / Tell me who / How deep is the ocean / Gypsy love song (Track on CD only.) / Yes indeed / Say you love me too / Without a song / Shout (part 1 & 2).
- CD ....................... **ND 90540**
- MC. ....................... **NK 90540**

RCA / Mar '91.

## DON'T SAY GOODNIGHT, IT'S TIME FOR LOVE.
**Tracks:** Don't say goodnight it's time for love / Don't say goodnight it's time for love (part 2.
- ■ 7" ....................... **EPC 8664**

Epic / Jun '80.

## FLIPHITS (EP).
**Tracks:** This old heart fo mine / I guess I'll always love you / Behind a painted smile / Put yourself in my place.
- ■ MC Single. ....................... **CTME 2033**

Motown / Jul '83.

## FOREVER GOLD.
**Tracks:** That lady / Live it up / Hello it's me / (At your best) You are love / Fight the power / For the love of you / Hope you feel better love / Highways of my life / Harvest for the world / Summer breeze.
- MC. ....................... **.40 32238**
- ■ LP ....................... **EPC 32238**

Epic / '84 / Sony.
- CD ....................... **CD 32238**

Epic / '91 / Sony.
- CD ....................... **.477502 2**

Epic / Oct '94 / Sony.

## GO ALL THE WAY.
**Tracks:** Go all the way / Say you will / Pass it on / Here we go again / Don't say goodnight / It's time for love / Belly dancer.
- ■ LP ....................... **EPC 86110**
- MC. ....................... **.40 86110**

Epic / May '80 / Sony.

## GO FOR YOUR GUNS.
**Tracks:** Not Advised.
- ■ LP ....................... **EPC 86027**

Epic / May '77.

## GOT TO HAVE YOU BACK.
**Tracks:** Got to have you back / Just ain't enough love.
- ■ 7" ....................... **TMG 606**

Tamla Motown / May '67.

## GRAND SLAM.
**Tracks:** Tonight is the night / I once had your love (and I can't let go) / Hurry up and wait / Young girls / Party night / Don't let go / Who said.
- ■ LP ....................... **EPC 84914**
- MC. ....................... **.40 84914**

Epic / Apr '81 / Sony.

## GREATEST HITS.
**Tracks:** This old heart of mine / Put yourself in my place / That's the way love is / Take me in your arms / Take some time out for love / I hear a symphony / Behind a painted smile / Little Miss Sweetness / Stop in the name of love / Got to have you back / Who could ever doubt my love / Nowhere to run.
- ■ LP ....................... **SRS 5043**

Starline / Oct '70.

## GREATEST HITS: ISLEY BROTHERS (Volume 1).
**Tracks:** That lady / Groove with you / For the love of you / Footsteps in the dark / Between the sheets / It's your thing / Fight the power / Live it up.
- ■ LP ....................... **EPC 32443**
- ■ MC. ....................... **.40 32443**

Epic / Jun '84.

## GREATEST HITS: ISLEY BROTHERS.
**Tracks:** This old heart of mine / That lady / Summer breeze / Listen to the music / Behind a painted smile

/ For the love of you / Highways of my life / It's a disco night (Rock don't stop) / Dancin' around the world / I guess I'll always love you / It's your thing / Between the sheets / Caravan of love.
- ■ CD ....................... **TCD 2306**
- ■ LP ....................... **STAR 2306**
- ■ MC. ....................... **STAC 2306**

Telstar/Ronco / Feb '88.

## HARVEST FOR THE WORLD.
**Tracks:** Harvest for the world / Prelude / People of today / Who loves you better / You are love / Let me down easy / So you wanna stay down / You still feel the need.
- ■ LP ....................... **EPC 81268**

Epic / Aug '76.
- ■ LP ....................... **EPC 32652**
- ■ MC. ....................... **.40 32652**

Epic / Jun '85.

## HARVEST FOR THE WORLD.
**Tracks:** Harvest for the world / Who loves you better (parts 1 & 2) (on 12" only) / Summer breeze (Only on (6531547) 7".).
- ■ 7" ....................... **EPC 4369**

Epic / Jul '76.
- ■ 7" ....................... **CBS 8862**

CBS / May '82.
- ■ 7" ....................... **.A 7234**

Epic / Jun '86.
- ■ 7" ....................... **6531547**

Epic / Oct '88.

## HARVEST FOR THE WORLD (OLD GOLD).
**Tracks:** Harvest for the world / Who loves you better (Part 1) / Who loves you better (Part 2).
- ■ 12" ....................... **OG 4069**

Old Gold / Jul '88.

## HEAT IS ON, THE.
**Tracks:** Not Advised.
- ■ LP ....................... **69139**

Epic / Jun '75.

## HIGHWAYS OF MY LIFE.
**Tracks:** Highways of my life.
- ■ 7" ....................... **EPC 1980**

Epic / Jan '74.

## HIGHWAYS OF MY LIFE (OLD GOLD).
**Tracks:** Highways of my life / Harvest for the world.
- ■ 7" ....................... **OG 9311**

Old Gold / Apr '83.

## I GUESS I'LL ALWAYS LOVE YOU.
**Tracks:** I guess I'll always love you / Take some time out for love.
- ■ 7" ....................... **TMG 572**

Tamla Motown / Sep '66.
- ■ 7" ....................... **TMG 979**

Tamla Motown / Jun '75.

## INSIDE YOU.
**Tracks:** Inside you / Baby hold on / Don't hold back you love / First love / Love merry go round / Welcome into my heart / Love zone.
- ■ LP ....................... **EPC 85252**

Epic / Dec '81.

## INSIDE YOU.
**Tracks:** Inside you / Love zone.
- ■ 12" ....................... **EPCA 131741**
- ■ 7" ....................... **EPCA 1741**

Epic / Jan '80.

## ISLEY BROTHERS.
**Tracks:** Tell me it's just a rumour baby / You've got so much to shout about / It moves me to tears / Why when love is gone / Trouble / No good without you / Whispers / All because I love you / Leaving here / One too many heartaches / Share a little love with me / I can't help it.
- ■ LP ....................... **SRS 5098**

Starline / Feb '72.

## IT'S A DISCO NIGHT (OLD GOLD).
**Tracks:** It's a disco night (rock don't stop) / That lady / Summer breeze / It's your thing (Not on CD single.)
- ■ 12" ....................... **OG 4006**

Old Gold / Feb '86.
- CD Single. ....................... **OG 6506**

Old Gold / Jul '90 / Pickwick.

## IT'S A DISCO NIGHT (ROCK DON'T STOP).
**Tracks:** It's a disco night (Rock don't stop).
- ■ 7" ....................... **EPC 7911**

Epic / Nov '79.

## IT'S OUR THING.
**Tracks:** I know who you been sockin' it to / Somebody been messin' / Save me / I must be losing my touch / Feel like the world / It's your thing / Give the

women what they want / Love is what you make it / Don't give it away / He's got your love.
■ **LP** . . . . . . . . . . . . . . . . . . . **SMLP 59**
Major Minor / Jul '69.

### IT'S YOUR THING.
**Tracks:** It's your thing.
■ **7"** . . . . . . . . . . . . . . . . . . . **MM 621**
Major Minor / Jun '69.

### LET'S GO.
**Tracks:** Surf and shout / Please please please / She's the one / Tango / Whatcha gonna do / stagger lee / You'll never leave him / Let's go, let's go, lets go / She's gone / Shake it with me baby / Long tall Sally / Do the twist / Who's that lady / My little girl / Love is a wonderful thing / Open up your eyes.
■ **MC** . . . . . . . . . . . . . . . . **TCSSL 6001**
■ **LP** . . . . . . . . . . . . . . . . . **SSL 6001**
Stateside / Mar '86.

### LIFE IN THE CITY.
**Tracks:** Life in the city.
■ **7"** . . . . . . . . . . . . . . . . . . **EPC 7757**
Epic / Aug '79.

### LIVE.
**Tracks:** Here we go again / Between the sheets / Smooth sailin' tonight / Voyage to Atlantis / Take me to the next phase / Choosey lover / Footsteps in the dark / Groove with you / Hello, it's me / Don't say goodnight (It's time for love) / Spend the night / Who's that lady / It's your thing / Shout / For the love / Fight the power / Make me say it again.
**CD**. . . . . . . . . . . . . . . . . . **7559615382**
**MC**. . . . . . . . . . . . . . . . . . **7559615384**
Elektra / Sep '93 / WEA.

### LIVE IT UP.
**Tracks:** Not Advised.
■ **LP** . . . . . . . . . . . . . . . . . **EPC 80317**
Epic / Sep '74.

### MASTERPIECE.
**Tracks:** May I / My best was good enough / If leaving me is easy / You never know when you;re gonna fall in love / Stay gold / Colder are my nights / Come to me / Release your love / Most beautiful girl.
■ **MC**. . . . . . . . . . . . . . . . .**925347 4**
■ **LP** . . . . . . . . . . . . . . . . .**925347 1**
WEA / Dec '85.
■ **LP** . . . . . . . . . . . . . . . . .**825347 1**
WEA / Feb '86.

### MIDNIGHT SKY.
**Tracks:** Midnight sky.
■ **7"** . . . . . . . . . . . . . . . . . **EPC 3034**
Epic / Jan '75.

### MOTOWN'S GREATEST HITS: ISLEY BROTHERS.
**Tracks:** This old heart of mine / Just ain't enough love / Put yourself in my place / I guess I'll always love you / There's no love left / It's out of the question / Take some time out for love / Whispers / Nowhere to run / Who could ever doubt my love / Behind a painted smile / That's the way love is / Tell me it's just a rumour baby / Take me in your arms / Got to have you back / Little Miss Sweetness / My love is your love (forever) / Why when the love has gone / All because I love you / I hear a symphony.
■ **LP** . . . . . . . . . . . . . . . . . **WL 72516**
■ **MC**. . . . . . . . . . . . . . . . . **WK 72516**
Motown / Feb '87.
■ **CD** . . . . . . . . . . . . . . . . . **WD 72516**
**CD**. . . . . . . . . . . . . . . . . .**530053-2**
■ **MC**. . . . . . . . . . . . . . . . .**530053-4**
Motown / Jan '92 / PolyGram.

### PEARLS FROM THE PAST - ISLEY BROTHERS.
**Tracks:** Not Advised.
**CD**. . . . . . . . . . . . . . . . . **KLMCD 009**
Scratch / Nov '93 / Scratch Records / BMG / Grapevine Distribution.

### PRIDE.
**Tracks:** Pride / Pride (version).
■ **7"** . . . . . . . . . . . . . . . . . **EPC 5105**
Epic / May '77.

### PUT YOURSELF IN MY PLACE.
**Tracks:** Put yourself in my place.
■ **7"** . . . . . . . . . . . . . . . . . **TMG 708**
Tamla Motown / Jul '69.

### REAL DEAL.
**Tracks:** Real deal / Are you with me / Stone cold lover / It's alright with me / All in my lover's eye / I'll do it all for you / Under the influence.
■ **LP** . . . . . . . . . . . . . . . . . **EPC 85790**
Epic / Oct '82.

### SHOUT.
**Tracks:** Shout / Respectable / Tell me who.
■ **12"** . . . . . . . . . . . . . . . . . **PC 9411**
RCA / Aug '79.

### SHOUT.
**Tracks:** Shout (part 1) / Shout (part 2) / Tell me who / How deep is the ocean (1) / Respectable (1) / Say you love me too / Open up your heart / He's got the whole world in his hands / Without a song / Yes indeed / Ring-a-ling-a-ling / That lucky old sun / How deep is the ocean (2) / Respectable (2) / When the saints go marching in / Gypsy love song / St. Louis blues / Rock around the clock / Turn to me / Not one minute more / I'm gonna knock on your door.
**CD**. . . . . . . . . . . . . . . . . **BCD 15425**
Bear Family / Dec '88 / Rollercoaster Records / Swift / Direct Distribution / Topic Records.

### SHOUT.
**Tracks:** Shout / When the saints go marching in / St. Louis blues / How indeed / How deep is the ocean / Ring-a-ling-a-ling / He's got the whole world in his hands / That lucky old sun / Respectable / Without a song.
■ **LP** . . . . . . . . . . . . . . . . . **INTS 1098**
RCA / Nov '70.

### SHOUT AND TWIST WITH RUDOLPH, RONALD AND O'KELLY.
**Tracks:** Twist and shout / Nobody but me / Crazy love / Snake / Make it easy on yourself / Right now / You better come home / Twistin' with Linda / Never leave me baby / Two stupid feet / Time after time / Let's twist again / Wah watusi / I say love / Rubberleg twist / Hold on baby / I'm laughing to keep from crying / Don't you feel / Spanish twist.
**CD**. . . . . . . . . . . . . . . . . .**CDCH 928**
Ace / Apr '90 / Pinnacle / Complete Record Co. Ltd.

### SHOWDOWN.
**Tracks:** Showdown / Groove with you / Ain't givin' up no love / Rockin' with fire / Take me to the next phase / Coolin' me out / Fun and games / Love lover.
■ **LP** . . . . . . . . . . . . . . . . . **EPC 86039**
Epic / Jun '78.

### SMOOTH SAILIN'.
**Tracks:** Everything is alright / Dish it out / It takes a good woman / Send a message / Smooth sailin' tonight / Somebody I used to know / Come my way / I wish.
■ **LP** . . . . . . . . . . . . . . . . . **K 925586 1**
■ **MC**. . . . . . . . . . . . . . . . . **K 925586 4**
WEA / Jul '87 / WEA.

### SOUL KINGS VOL.1.
**Tracks:** Twist and shout / Time after time / I say love / Right now / Drag / Don't be jealous / Rockin' McDonald / Let's twist again / Nobody but me / Crazy love / You better come home / Shake it with me baby.
**CD**. . . . . . . . . . . . . . . . . . **SMS 056**
Pickwick / Oct '92 / Pickwick.

### SOUL ON THE ROCKS.
**Tracks:** Got to have you back / That's the way love is / Whispers / Tell me it's just a rumour / One too many heartaches / It's out of the question / Why when love is gone / Save me from this misery / Little Miss Sweetness / Good things / Catching up on time / Behind the painted smile.
■ **LP** . . . . . . . . . . . . . . . . . **STML 11066**
Tamla Motown / Feb '68.

### SOUND OF SOUL, THE.
**Tracks:** You walk your way / Don't let me be lonely tonight / Heat is on / Go for your guns / Brown eyed girl / Harvest for the world / Put a little love in your heart / I say you will / Live it up / Summer breeze / That lady / If you were here tonight.
**CD**. . . . . . . . . . . . . . . . . **BLATCD 10**
**MC**. . . . . . . . . . . . . . . . . **BLATMC 10**
■ **LP** . . . . . . . . . . . . . . . . . **BLATLP 10**
Blatant / Mar '89 / Roots Records.

### SPEND THE NIGHT.
**Tracks:** Spend the night (ce soir) / You'll never walk alone / One of a kind / Real woman / Come together / If you ever need somebody / Baby come back home / One of a kind (reprise).
■ **CD** . . . . . . . . . . . . . . . . . **K 9259402**
■ **LP** . . . . . . . . . . . . . . . . . **K 9259401**
■ **MC**. . . . . . . . . . . . . . . . . **K 9259404**
WEA / Aug '89.

### SUMMER BREEZE.
**Tracks:** Summer breeze.
■ **7"** . . . . . . . . . . . . . . . . . **EPC 2244**
Epic / May '74.

### SUPER HITS.
**Tracks:** This old heart of mine / Just ain't enough love / Put yourself in my place / I guess I'll always love you / There's no love left / It's out of the question / Take some time out for love / I hear a symphony / Behind the painted smile / That's the way love is / Tell me it's just a rumour baby / Take me in your arms / Got to have you back / Little Miss Sweetness / All because I love you / When love is gone.
■ **LP** . . . . . . . . . . . . . . . . . **UNKNOWN**
Motown / Oct '81.

### TAKE ME TO THE NEXT PHASE.
**Tracks:** Take me to the next phase.
■ **7"** . . . . . . . . . . . . . . . . . **EPC 6292**
Epic / May '78.

### TAKE SOME TIME OUT.
**Tracks:** Twist and shout / I say love / Hold on baby / Right now / Rubberleg twist / Snake / You better come home / Never leave me baby / Spanish twist / Time after time / Let's twist again / Don't you feel.
■ **LP** . . . . . . . . . . . . . . . . . **MAL 894**
Marble Arch / Feb '69.

### TAKE SOME TIME OUT FOR LOVE.
**Tracks:** Take some time out for love / Who could ever doubt my love.
■ **7"** . . . . . . . . . . . . . . . . . **TMG 566**
Tamla Motown / '66.

### THAT LADY.
**Tracks:** That lady.
■ **7"** . . . . . . . . . . . . . . . . . **EPC 1704**
Epic / Sep '73.

### THAT LADY (OLD GOLD).
**Tracks:** That lady / Summer breeze.
■ **7"** . . . . . . . . . . . . . . . . . **OG 9317**
Old Gold / Apr '83.

### THIS OLD HEART OF MINE.
**Tracks:** Nowhere to run / Stop in the name of love / This old heart of mine / Take some time out for love / I guess I'll always love you / Baby don't you do it / Who could ever doubt my love / There's no love left / Seek and you shall find.
■ **LP** . . . . . . . . . . . . . . . . . **STML 11034**
Tamla Motown / Dec '68.
■ **LP** . . . . . . . . . . . . . . . . . **STMS 5026**
■ **MC**. . . . . . . . . . . . . . . . . **CSTMS 5026**
Motown / Oct '81.
■ **LP** . . . . . . . . . . . . . . . . . **WL 72078**
Motown / '86.

### THIS OLD HEART OF MINE.
**Tracks:** This old heart of mine / Behind a painted smile.
■ **7"** . . . . . . . . . . . . . . . . . **TMG 937**
Tamla Motown / Jan '75.
■ **7"** . . . . . . . . . . . . . . . . . **TMG 1050**
Tamla Motown / Sep '76.

### THIS OLD HEART OF MINE (Isley Brothers/Impressions.
**Tracks:** Not Advised.
**CD**. . . . . . . . . . . . . . . . . **RMB 75051**
**MC**. . . . . . . . . . . . . . . . . **RMB 45051**
Remember / Nov '93 / Midland Records / BMG.

### THIS OLD HEART OF MINE.
**Tracks:** This old heart of mine / There's no love left.
■ **7"** . . . . . . . . . . . . . . . . . **TMG 555**
Tamla Motown / Apr '66.

### TIMELESS.
**Tracks:** It's your thing / Love the one you're with / I know who you've been socking it to / Get into something / I need you / Work to do / Brother, brother / Keep on doin' / I turned you on / Put a little love in your heart / Pop that thang / Lay, lady, lay / Spill the wine / Fire and rain / Freedom / Ohio / Machine gun / Nothing to do but today / Lay away.
■ **Double LP.** . . . . . . . . . . . . . . **EPC 88327**
Epic / Feb '79.

### TONIGHT IS THE NIGHT.
**Tracks:** Tonight is the night / Who said.
■ **7"** . . . . . . . . . . . . . . . . . **EPC A 1122**
Epic / Apr '81.

### TRACKS OF LIFE.
**Tracks:** Get my licks in / No axe to grind / Searching for a miracle / Sensitive lover / Bedroom eyes / Lost in your love / Whatever turns you on / Morning love / Dedicate this song / Red hot / Koolin' out / Brazilian wedding song / I'll be there / Turn on the moon.
**CD**. . . . . . . . . . . . . . . . . **7599266202**
**MC**. . . . . . . . . . . . . . . . . **7599266204**
WEA / Jun '92 / WEA.

■ **DELETED**

## TWIST AND SHOUT.
Tracks: Twistin' with Linda / Time after time / Never leave me baby / Let's twist again / Snake / Twist and shout / Nobody but me / You better come home / I say love / Rubberleg twist.
MC.............................. ORC 009
Orchid Music / Feb '82 / Pinnacle.
■ CD.............................. NCD 5162
K-Tel / '88.

## TWIST AND SHOUT.
Tracks: Twist and shout.
■ 7"..............................SS 112
Stateside / Jul '63.
■ 7"..............................DJS 640
DJM / Feb '76.

## VOYAGE TO ATLANTIS.
Tracks: Voyage to Atlantis / Tell me when you need it again.
■ 7".............................. EPC 5443
Epic / Jul '77.

## WARPATH.
Tracks: Warpath / I got to find me one.
■ 7".............................. SS 2188
Stateside / May '71.

## WINNER TAKES ALL.
Tracks: I wanna be with you / Liquid love / Winner takes all / Life in the city / It's a disco night (rock don't stop) / What you do to me / Let's fall in love / How lucky I am / You're the key to my heart / You're beside me / Let me into your life / Love comes and goes / Go for what you know / Mind over matter.
■ Double LP............... EPC 88460
■ MC Set.....................40 88460
Epic / Jul '79.

## WINNER TAKES ALL.
Tracks: Winner takes all / Fun and games.
■ 7".............................. EPC 7795
Epic / Jan '80.

### Isley-Jasper-Isley

## BROADWAY'S CLOSER TO SUNSET BLVD.
Tracks: Sex drive / Serve you right / I can't get over losing you / Kiss and tell / Love is gonna last forever / Broadway's closer to Sunset Boulevard / Look the other way / Break this chain.
■ LP.............................. EPC 26307
Epic / Jan '85.
■ LP..............................4503591
MC...............................4503594
Epic / Jan '87 / Sony.

## CARAVAN OF LOVE.
Tracks: Dancin' around the world / Insatiable woman / I can hardly wait / Liberation / Caravan of love / If you believe in love / High heel syndrome.
■ LP.............................. EPC 26656
MC...............................40 26656
Epic / Oct '85 / Sony.

## CARAVAN OF LOVE.
Tracks: Caravan of love / I can't get over losing you.
■ 12".............................. TA 6612
■ 7"..............................A 6612
Epic / Nov '85.

## CARAVAN OF LOVE (OLD GOLD).
Tracks: Caravan of love / Voyage to Atlantis.
■ 7"..............................OG 4076
Old Gold / Aug '88.

## DIFFERENT DRUMMER.
Tracks: Different drummer / 8th wonder of the world / Blue rose / Do it right / Givin' you back the love / Once in a lifetime lady / For the sake of love / Brother to brother / I wanna be yours.
■ LP..............................4501431
MC...............................4501434
Epic / May '87 / Sony.

## EIGHTH WONDER OF THE WORLD.
Tracks: Eighth wonder of the world / Broadway's closer to Sunset Boulevard.
■ 12"..............................6507508
■ 12"..............................6507506
■ 7"..............................6507507
Epic / Apr '87.

## INSATIABLE WOMAN.
Tracks: Insatiable woman / Break this chain / Caravan of love / I can't get over losing you.
■ 12".............................. TA 6861
■ 7"..............................A 6861
■ 7" Set..............................DTA 6861
Epic / Feb '86.

## KISS AND TELL.
Tracks: Kiss and tell.
■ 12".............................. TX 6081
■ 7"..............................A 6081
Epic / Apr '85.

## LOOK THE OTHER WAY.
Tracks: Look the other way / Look the other way (pt 2).
■ 12".............................. TA 4933
■ 7"..............................A 4933
Epic / Nov '84.

### Ivory, Jackie

## HI HEEL SNEAKERS.
Tracks: High heel sneakers / Do it to death.
■ 7"..............................AT 4075
Atlantic / Mar '66.

### Izit

## DON'T GIVE UP NOW.
Tracks: Don't give up now.
■ 12".............................. TNG 12003
Revolver / Jul '92.

## EVERYWHERE E.P.
Tracks: Izit everywhere Pt.2 (Radio edit) (Features on CDS only.) / Izit everywhere Pt.2 (Full length) / Elijah's blue / Delta freestyle jam / Male stripper.
12".............................. TNG 12012
CD Single............... TNGCDS 012
Tongue 'N' Groove / Sep '94 / Vital Distribution.

## MAKE WAY FOR THE ORIGINALS.
Tracks: Make way for the originals.
■ 12".............................. OPT12 014
■ 7".............................. OPT7 014
Optimism / Dec '94.

## ONE BY ONE/DON'T GIVE UP NOW.
Tracks: One by one (mixes) / Don't give up now (mixes).
■ 12".............................. TNG 12004
Tongue 'N' Groove / Jun '93.

## SAY YEAH - REMIXES.
Tracks: Say yeah (mixes).
12".............................. TNG 12008
Tongue 'N' Groove / Mar '94 / Vital Distribution.

## STORIES.
Tracks: Stories (I've a novella edit.) (Not on 12".) / Now I know (On 7" only.) / Stories (I've a novella mix) (Not on 7".) / Stories (Jackanory mix) (On 12" only.) / Stories (stories mix) (Not on 7".).
■ 12"..............................FX 122
■ 7"..............................F 122
■ CD Single..............................FCD 122
■ MC Single..............................FCS 122
FFRR / Nov '89.

## WHOLE AFFAIR.
Tracks: Izit everywhere / Sharing our lives / Bird of paradise / Bio white & the 7 chords / One by one / Say yeah / Whole affair, The (part 1) / Sugar & spice / Don't give up now / Rhyme of the ancient groove / Whole affair (part 2).
CD.............................. TNGCD 001
LP.............................. TNGLP 001
Tongue 'N' Groove / Oct '93 / Vital Distribution.

# J

## J & J

### BALLET, THE.
Tracks: Ballet.
- 12" ..................... BB 038
Beat Box / Apr '91.
- 12" ..................... BB 03
Beat Box / Mar '92.

## J.B. Allstars

### I LIKE IT LIKE THAT.
Tracks: I like it like that / I like it like that (version).
- 12" ..................... HNT 1001
- 7" ..................... HN 7001
Hi-Note / Nov '89.

## J.B.'s

### GRUNT, THE.
Tracks: Grunt, The (part 1) / Grunt, The (part 2).
- 7" ..................... 2027 002
Mojo / Jul '71.
- 7" ..................... 45-6317
King (USA) / Mar '87.

### STAND EASY.
Tracks: Stand easy.
12" ..................... B2B 12008
Back 2 Basics / Jul '94 / SRD.

## Jabara, Paul

### DISCO WEDDING.
Tracks: Disco wedding / Honeymoon.
- 12" ..................... CANL 160
- 7" ..................... CAN 160
Casablanca / Sep '79.

### KEEPING TIME.
Tracks: Didn't the time go fast / Saturday matinee / Trapped in a stairway / Take good care of my baby / What's a girl to do / Dancin' / Last dance / Pleasure island / Something's missing.
- LP ..................... CAL 2029
Casablanca / Sep '78.

### SATURDAY MATINEE.
Tracks: Saturday matinee / Disco queen.
- 7" ..................... CAN 133
Casablanca / Nov '78.

### SHUT OUT.
Tracks: Shut out / Hungry for love.
- 7" ..................... CAN 109
Casablanca / Sep '77.

### THIRD ALBUM.
Tracks: Disco wedding / Honeymoon in Puerto Rico / Disco divorce / Foggy day / Never lose your sense of humour / Just you and me.
- LP ..................... CAL 2056
Casablanca / '79.

## Jackson Sisters

### BOY YOU'RE DYNAMITE.
Tracks: Boy you're dynamite / Shake her loose.
- 7" ..................... CBS 2896
CBS / Jan '75.

### I BELIEVE IN MIRACLES.
Tracks: I believe in miracles / Boy you're dynamite / Why can't we be more than friends.
- 7" ..................... URB 4
- 12" ..................... URBX 4
Urban / Jun '87.

## Jackson, Brian

### 1980 (see under Scott-Heron, Gil).

### BOTTLE, THE (see under Scott-Heron, Gil).

## Jackson, Charles

### PASSIONATE BREEZES.
Tracks: Passionate breezes / Love of you / Ooh child / I'm in heaven / You are so beautiful / Train / Tonight's the night / Get on down / I really want you.
- LP ..................... EST 11775
Capitol / Aug '78.

### TRAIN.
Tracks: Train / Passionate breezes.
- 7" ..................... CL 16068
Capitol / Nov '79.

## Jackson, Chuck

No sooner had doo-wop outfit Del-Vikings scored their biggest hit with *Come Go With Me* (U.S. No. 4, 1957), than lead singer Jackson quit to go solo. After variety of unsuccessful releases, he was signed by Shirelles' producer Luther Dixon to New York label Wand. Series of R&B hits ensued, often written by Burt Bacharach, with *Any Day Now* crossing over to pop chart. He also duetted with Maxine Brown on three songs. Ill-advised stint at Motown from '67-'71 saw lowering of profile that continued through '70s; despite one-off hit *I Only Get This Feeling* on All-Platinum in '73. He resurfaced in '80s; singing with Gary U.S. Bonds and at George Bush's inauguration, and recording acclaimed *All Over The World*.

### ALL OVER THE WORLD.
Tracks: All over the world.
- 7" ..................... MARES 103
Nightmare / Jul '89.
- 12" ..................... DEBTX 3119
- 7" ..................... DEBT 3119
- MC Single. ..................... DEBTMC 3119
Debut (2) / Jul '91.

### ANY DAY NOW.
Tracks: Any day now / Same old story / I don't want to cry / In real life / I wake up crying / Breaking point / What'cha gonna say tomorrow / Getting ready for heartbreak / Make the night a little longer / Tell him I'm not home / I keep forgettin' / I'm your man / Hand it over / Since I don't have you / I need you / If I didn't love you / Good things come to those who wait / These chains of love / Shame on me / Something you got.
- LP ..................... DJM 22074
DJM / Sep '77.

### CHUCK JACKSON ARRIVES.
Tracks: Man in you / Your wonderful love / Lonely lonely man am I / Ain't no sun since you've been gone / I can't go on sharing your love / Forgive my jealousy / To see the sun again / What am I gonna do without you / I like everything about you / We'll find a way / Where you gonna run to now / Girls girls girls.
- LP ..................... STML 11071
Tamla Motown / Jun '68.

### ENCORE/MR. EVERYTHING.
Tracks: Tell him I'm not home / Blue holiday / Tomorrow / Two stupid feet / This broken heart (that you gave me) / Don't believe him, Donna / King of the Mountain / Invisible / Another day / Listen / Go on Yak Yak / Getting ready for the heartbreak / Since I don't have you / I just don't know what to do with myself / I need you / I'm your man / Human / Love is a many splendored thing / Work song / If I didn't love you / Something you've got / D-5 / Somebody new / Tears of joy.
CD ..................... CDKEND 110
Kent / Aug '94 / Pinnacle.

### GOIN' BACK TO.
Tracks: Are you lonely for me baby / Honey come back / Can you feel it, babe / Loving you is sweeter than ever / Cry like a baby / You keep running away / Can I change my mind / I'd still love you / Chokin' kind / Day my world stood still / No more water in the well / Rosalind.
- LP ..................... STML 11117
Tamla Motown / Sep '69.

### GOOD THINGS.
Tracks: Tell him I'm not home / Beg me / I keep forgettin' / Millionaire / Hand it over / Two stupid feet / Make the night a little longer / I wake up crying / I'm your man / Castanets / Who's gonna pick up the pieces / Good things come to those who wait / I don't want to cry / Breaking point / Any other way / Any day now / Since I don't have you / They don't give medals (to yesterday's heroes) / Where do I go from here / These chains of love (are breaking me down) / What's with this loneliness / Forget about me / I just don't know what to do with myself / I can't stand to see you cry.
CD ..................... CDKEND 935
Kent / Aug '90 / Pinnacle.

### GREAT CHUCK JACKSON, THE.
Tracks: Hula lua / I'm yours / Ooh, baby / Judy's eyes / Judy's eyes (instrumental) / Come on, squeeze me (my darling) / This is it / Let's push Mr. Pride aside / Let's push Mr. Pride aside (instrumental - slow) / Let's push Mr. Pride aside (instrumental - fast).
- LP ..................... BDL 1015
Bulldog Records / Jul '82.

### I DIDN'T WANT TO CRY.
Tracks: I didn't want to cry / Tell him I'm not home / I wake up crying / Any day now / I keep forgettin' / Beg me / Millionaire / Hand it over / They don't give medals / Since I don't have you / Breaking point / Any other way / These chains of love / I just don't know what to do with myself / Forget about me / I'm your man.
CD ..................... CDCD 1025
Charly / Mar '93 / Charly.

### I DON'T WANT TO CRY/ANY DAY NOW.
Tracks: I don't want to cry / Tears on my pillow / My willow tree / In between tears / Tear of the year / I cried for you / Lonely teardrops / Don't let the sun catch you crying / Salty tears / I wake up crying / Tear / Man ain't supposed to cry / I keep forgettin' / Any day now / Just once / Same old story / Watcha gonna say tomorrow / Make the night a little longer / Who's gonna pick up the pieces / In real life / Angel of angels / Breaking point / Prophet / Everybody needs love.
CD ..................... CDKEND 107
Kent / Aug '93 / Pinnacle.

### I'VE GOT THE NEED.
Tracks: I've got the need / Beautiful woman.
- 7" ..................... 6146310
All Platinum / Nov '75.

### MR EMOTION.
Tracks: I keep forgettin' / Tell him I'm not home / Any other way / I need you / I'm your man / Make the night a little longer / Getting ready for the heartbreak / I just don't know what to do with myself / Hand it over / Good things come to those who wait / Chains of love / Two stupid feet / Any day now / Look over your shoulder / I forgot to tell her / Since I don't have you.
- LP ..................... KENT 033
Kent / Jan '85.

### POWERFUL SOUL, A.
Tracks: Millionaire / Beg me / Breaking point / Who's gonna pick up the pieces / If I didn't love you / I wake up crying / Forget about me / Prophet / Little by little / I've got to be strong / I don't want to cry / This broken heart / Don't believe him, Donna / They don't give medals / Love of my girl / I can't stand to see you cry.
- LP ..................... KENT 073
Kent / Sep '87.

### THESE CHAINS OF LOVE.
Tracks: These chains of love / Any day now.
- 7" ..................... DDS 170
Pye Disco Demand / Jul '75.

## Jackson, Deon

### HIS GREATEST.
Tracks: Not Advised.
- LP ..................... SS 8020
Solid Smoke (USA) / Jul '84.

### LOVE MAKES THE WORLD GO ROUND.
Tracks: Love makes the world go round / You said you loved me.

■ DELETED

■ 7" . . . . . . . . . . . . . . . . . . . . . . AT 4070
Atlantic / Feb '66.

## LOVE MAKES THE WORLD GO ROUND.
**Tracks:** Love makes the world go round / I can't go on.
■ 7" . . . . . . . . . . . . . . . . . . . . . CS 9031
Contempo (2) / Jun '75.

## LOVE TAKES A LONG TIME GROWING.
**Tracks:** Love takes a long time growing / Hush little baby.
■ 7" . . . . . . . . . . . . . . . . . . . . .584012
Atlantic / Jun '66.

## Jackson, Freddie

Former church singer, banker and Mystic Merlin (*Mr Magician*) leader Jackson has enjoyed unspectacular but consistent career since *Rock Me Tonight* broke in '85. He coasted through late '80s, collaborating with likes of Melba Moore and Will Downing; then hit again in '92 with cover of *Me & Mrs Jones*. However, this marked end of his tenure with Capitol Records and, after two less successful sets for RCA, Jackson signed with Scotti Bros in '94. Debut for label is expected in early '95.

## CRAZY (FOR ME).
**Tracks:** Crazy (for me)- Radio edit / Crazy (for me) - The done properly dub / Crazy (for me) - The done properly mix (12" & CD single only).
■ 12" . . . . . . . . . . . . . . . . . 12CL 510
■ 7" . . . . . . . . . . . . . . . . . . .CL 510
■ CD Single . . . . . . . . . . . . . .CDCL 510
Capitol / Sep '88.

## DO ME AGAIN.
**Tracks:** Don't it feel good / Love me down / Main course / It takes two / I'll be waiting for you / Don't say you love me / Do me again / Live for the moment / Second time for love / I can't take it / All over you (Not on album.).
■ LP . . . . . . . . . . . . . . . . . . EST 2134
MC. . . . . . . . . . . . . . . . . . TCEST 2134
■ CD . . . . . . . . . . . . . . . . . CDEST 2134
Capitol / Nov '90 / EMI.

## DON'T LET LOVE SLIP AWAY.
**Tracks:** Nice 'n' slow / Hey lover / Don't let love slip away / Crazy (for me) / One heart too many / If you don't know me by now / You and I got a thang / Special guy / Yes, I need you / It's gonna take a long, long time.
CD . . . . . . . . . . . . . . . . . . CDEST 2067
■ LP . . . . . . . . . . . . . . . . . . EST 2067
■ MC. . . . . . . . . . . . . . . . . TCEST 2067
Capitol / Jul '88 / EMI.
CD . . . . . . . . . . . . . . . . . . . CZ 401
■ LP . . . . . . . . . . . . . . . . . ATAK 171
MC. . . . . . . . . . . . . . . . . . TCATAK 171
Capitol / Mar '91 / EMI.

## GREATEST HITS OF FREDDIE JACKSON.
**Tracks:** Do me again / Rock me tonight / I don't want to lose your love / I could use a little love (right now) / Jam tonight / Nice and slow / You are my lady / Love me down / Have you ever loved somebody / Hey lover / Love is just a touch away / Tasty love / Christmas forever.
CD. . . . . . . . . . . . . . . . . . CDEST 2226
MC. . . . . . . . . . . . . . . . . TCEST 2226
Capitol / Feb '94 / EMI.

## HAVE YOU EVER LOVED SOMEBODY.
**Tracks:** Have you ever loved somebody (Double pack.) / Tasty love (inst) (Double pack.) / Rock me tonight (for old time's sake) (Double pack.) / Have you ever loved somebody (inst mix) (Double pack.).
■ 7" Set . . . . . . . . . . . . . . . . .CLD 437
■ 12" . . . . . . . . . . . . . . . . . 12CL 437
■ 7" . . . . . . . . . . . . . . . . . . .CL 437
Capitol / Jan '87.

## HE'LL NEVER LOVE YOU LIKE I DO.
**Tracks:** He'll never love you (like I do)(maserati mix) (Extra track on 12" version only) / I wanna say I love you / He'll never love you (like I do) / Tasty love / Have you ever loved somebody / Look around / Jam tonight / Just like the first time / I can't let you go / I don't want to lose your love.
■ 12" . . . . . . . . . . . . . . . . . 12CL 387
■ 7" . . . . . . . . . . . . . . . . . . .CL 387
Capitol / Apr '86.

## HERE IT IS.
**Tracks:** Was it something / Comin' home ll u / Here it is / How does it feel / Givin' my love / Paradise / Make love easy / Addictive 2 touch / I love / My family.
CD. . . . . . . . . . . . . . . . . 7863 66318-2

MC. . . . . . . . . . . . . . . . . 7863 66318-4
RCA / Jan '94 / BMG.

## JAM TONIGHT.
**Tracks:** Jam tonight.
■ 12" Remix . . . . . . . . . . . . . 12CLS 461
■ 12" . . . . . . . . . . . . . . . . . 12CL 461
■ 7" . . . . . . . . . . . . . . . . . .CL 461
Capitol / Sep '87.

## JUST LIKE THE FIRST TIME.
**Tracks:** You are my love / Tasty love / Have you ever loved somebody / Look around / Jam tonight / Just like the first time / I can't let you go / I don't want to lose your love / Still waiting / Janay.
MC. . . . . . . . . . . . . . . . .TCEST 2023
■ LP . . . . . . . . . . . . . . . . . EST 2023
Capitol / Oct '86 / EMI.
CD . . . . . . . . . . . . . . . . . . CZ 118
Capitol / Jan '87 / EMI.

## LITTLE BIT MORE, A (Jackson, Freddie & Melba Moore).
**Tracks:** Little bit more / It's been so long / Calling.
■ 12" . . . . . . . . . . . . . . . . . 12CL 446
■ 7" . . . . . . . . . . . . . . . . . . .CL 446
Capitol / May '87.

## LOVE ME DOWN.
**Tracks:** Love me down (radio edit) (Not on 12") / All over you (From the Original Motion Picture Soundtrack 'Def By Temptation'.) / Love me down (LP version) (Not on 7".) / Love me down (inst). (12" only.)
■ 12" . . . . . . . . . . . . . . . . . 12CL 611
■ 7" . . . . . . . . . . . . . . . . . . .CL 611
■ CD Single . . . . . . . . . . . . . .CDCL 611
Capitol / Mar '91.

## MAKE LOVE EASY.
**Tracks:** Make love easy.
■ 12" . . . . . . . . . . . . . . . 7432117916-1
■ 7" . . . . . . . . . . . . . . . 7432117916-7
■ CD Single . . . . . . . . . . . 7432117916-2
■ MC Single . . . . . . . . . . . 7432117916-4
RCA / Dec '93.

## ME AND MRS JONES.
**Tracks:** Me and Mrs Jones.
■ 12" . . . . . . . . . . . . . . . . . 12CL 668
■ 7" . . . . . . . . . . . . . . . . . . .CL 668
■ CD Single . . . . . . . . . . . . . .CDCL 668
■ MC Single . . . . . . . . . . . . . .TCCL 668
EMI / Sep '92.

## NICE 'N' SLOW.
**Tracks:** Nice 'n' slow / You are my love / Nice 'n' slow (ext. version)* / Nice 'n' slow (radio remix)*.
■ 12" . . . . . . . . . . . . . . . . . 12CL 502
■ 7" . . . . . . . . . . . . . . . . . . .CL 502
■ CD Single . . . . . . . . . . . . . .CDCL 502
Capitol / Jun '88.

## ROCK ME TONIGHT.
**Tracks:** He'll never love you (like I do) / Love is just a touch away / I wanna say I love you / You are my lady / Rock me tonight (for old times sake) / Sing a song of love / Calling / Good morning heartache.
■ LP . . . . . . . . . . . . . . . . . . FRED 1
MC. . . . . . . . . . . . . . . . . . .TCFRED 1
Capitol / May '85 / EMI.
CD . . . . . . . . . . . . . . . CDP 746 170 2
Capitol / Jan '86 / EMI.
CD . . . . . . . . . . . . . . . . . . CZ 364
■ LP . . . . . . . . . . . . . . . . . ATAK 160
MC. . . . . . . . . . . . . . . . . TCATAK 160
EMI / Oct '90 / EMI.

## ROCK ME TONIGHT (FOR OLD TIMES SAKE).
**Tracks:** Rock me tonight (for old times sake) / Rock me tonight (for old times sake)(groove version).
■ 7" . . . . . . . . . . . . . . . . . .CL 358
■ 12" . . . . . . . . . . . . . . . . . 12CL 358
Capitol / Feb '86.

## ROCK ME TONIGHT (OLD GOLD).
**Tracks:** Rock me tonight / Have you ever loved somebody.
CD Single . . . . . . . . . . . . . . .OG 6621
Old Gold / Jun '92 / Pickwick.

## TASTY LOVE.
**Tracks:** Tasty love / I wanna say I love you.
■ 7" . . . . . . . . . . . . . . . . . .CL 428
■ 12" . . . . . . . . . . . . . . . . . 12CL 428
Capitol / Sep '86.

## TIME FOR LOVE.
**Tracks:** I could use a little love (right now) / Time for love tonight / Chivalry / Trouble / Can I touch you / All I'll ever ask / Will you be there / Come with me tonight / Can we try / Me and Mrs Jones / Live my life without you.

CD . . . . . . . . . . . . . . . . . . CDEST 2178
■ LP . . . . . . . . . . . . . . . . . . EST 2178
■ MC. . . . . . . . . . . . . . . . .TCEST 2178
Capitol / Sep '92 / EMI.

## YOU ARE MY LADY.
**Tracks:** You are my lady / I wanna say I love you.
■ EP . . . . . . . . . . . . . . . . . .CLD 379
■ 12" . . . . . . . . . . . . . . . . . 12CL 379
■ 7" . . . . . . . . . . . . . . . . . .CL 379
Capitol / Oct '85.

## Jackson, J.J.

## BUT IT'S ALRIGHT.
**Tracks:** But it's alright / Do the boogaloo.
■ 7" . . . . . . . . . . . . . . . . . . 56718
Polydor / Oct '66.

## COME SEE ME.
**Tracks:** Come see me / Try me.
■ 7" . . . . . . . . . . . . . . . . . .JH 329
Strike (60's) / Apr '67.

## GREAT J.J. JACKSON, THE.
**Tracks:** But it's alright / Try me / That ain't right / You've got me dizzy / Change is gonna come / I dig girls / Come and see me (I'm your man) / Stones that I throw / Give me back the love / Ain't too proud to beg / Love is a hurting thing / Boogaloo baby / Let it out.
■ 7" . . . . . . . . . . . . . . . . . .SEE 281
See For Miles / '89.
CD . . . . . . . . . . . . . . . . . .SEECD 281
See For Miles / Feb '94 / Pinnacle.

## GREATEST LITTLE SOUL BAND IN THE LAND.
**Tracks:** Tobacco road / Tenement halls / J.J.'s bag / In the same old way / Change is gonna come / Fat, black and together / Win lose or draw / That's woman loving her man.
■ LP . . . . . . . . . . . . . . . . . .SAK 100
MCA / Jun '69.

## Jackson, Jackie

## JACKIE JACKSON.
**Tracks:** Not Advised.
■ LP . . . . . . . . . . . . . . . . .STML 11249
Tamla Motown / '74.

## Jackson, Janet

Janet Jackson is only serious rival for brother Michael's commercial superiority. Early career included successful stints on U.S. TV (including *Diff'rent Strokes* and *Fame*) and uncelebrated albums, *Janet Jackson* and *Dream Street*, before 1986's *Control* provided lift-off for superstardom. A&M urban music director John McClain teamed Jackson with producers Jam & Lewis; result was collection of fine dance songs, five of which went Top 10 in the U.S. However, success of *Control* was eclipsed by 1989's *Rhythm Nation 1814*, arguably the best album to bear Jackson name since *Off the Wall*. Continuing family's record-breaking tradition, *Rhythm Nation* became first album to spawn seven Top 5 U.S. hits. Recorded a duet with Luther Vandross, *Best Things In Life Are Free* for soundtrack of Damon Wayon's *Mo Money*, which reached No. 2 in the UK singles chart in 1992. Multi-million dollar signing to Virgin paid off when '93's *Janet* - another pounding production by Jam & Lewis - beat Michael's first week sales record and initiated another run of hits. A charismatic, influential and talented performer, Janet Jackson can now fairly lay claim to Madonna's female pop supremacy.

## AGAIN.
**Tracks:** Again / Again (mix).
■ 7" . . . . . . . . . . . . . . . . . . VS 1481
■ CD Single . . . . . . . . . . . . . VSCDX 1481
■ CD Single . . . . . . . . . . . . . VSCDE 1481
■ MC Single . . . . . . . . . . . . . VSC 1481
Virgin / Oct '93.

## ALRIGHT.
**Tracks:** Alright.
■ 12" . . . . . . . . . . . . . . . . . USAT 693
■ 7" . . . . . . . . . . . . . . . . . USAS 693
■ 7" . . . . . . . . . . . . . . . . . .USA 693
■ CD Single . . . . . . . . . . . . . USACD 693
■ MC Single . . . . . . . . . . . . . USAMC 693
A&M / Jun '90.

■ DELETED

## ANY TIME, ANY PLACE.
Tracks: Any time, any place / Any time, any place (Mixes) / Throb / And on and on (Features on MCS & VSCDT 1501 only).
| | |
|---|---|
| ■ 12"................... | VST 1501 |
| CD Single................ | VSCDG 1501 |
| CD Single................ | VSCDT 1501 |
| MC Single................ | VSC 1501 |

Virgin / Jun '94 / EMI.

## BECAUSE OF LOVE.
Tracks: Because of love (Mixes).
| | |
|---|---|
| ■ 12"................... | VST 1488 |
| ■ 7"................... | VS 1488 |
| ■ CD Single............. | VSCDG 1488 |
| ■ MC Single............. | VSC 1488 |

Virgin / Feb '94.

## BEST THINGS IN LIFE ARE FREE, THE (see under Vandross, Luther).

## BLACK CAT.
Tracks: Black cat / 1812 megamix.
| | |
|---|---|
| ■ 12"................... | AMY 587 |
| ■ 12"................... | AMX 587 |
| ■ 7"................... | AM 587 |
| ■ CD Single............. | AMCD 587 |
| ■ MC Single............. | AMMC 587 |

A&M / Aug '90.

## COME BACK TO ME.
Tracks: Come back to me / Alright.
| | |
|---|---|
| ■ 12"................... | USAT 681 |
| ■ 12"................... | USAF 681 |
| ■ 12"................... | USAD 681 |
| ■ 7"................... | USAB 681 |
| ■ 7"................... | USA 681 |
| ■ CD Single............. | USACD 681 |
| ■ MC Single............. | USAMC 681 |

A&M / Jan '90.

## COME GIVE YOUR LOVE TO ME.
Tracks: Come give your love to me / Magic is working.
| | |
|---|---|
| ■ 12"................... | AMSX 8303 |
| ■ 7"................... | AMS 8303 |

A&M / Jan '83.

## CONTROL.
Tracks: Control / What have you done for me lately / You can be mine / Pleasure principle / When I think of you / He doesn't know I'm alive / Let's wait awhile / Funny how time flies / Nasty.
| | |
|---|---|
| ■ LP................... | AMA 5106 |
| ■ CD................... | CDA 5106 |
| ■ MC................... | AMC 5106 |

A&M / '86.

## CONTROL.
Tracks: Control.
| | |
|---|---|
| ■ 12"................... | AMY 359 |
| ■ 7"................... | AM 359 |

A&M / Oct '86.

## CONTROL - THE REMIXES.
Tracks: Control (video mix) / When I think of you (dance remix) / Pleasure principle (the long vocal mix) / Pleasure principle (the shep pettibone mix) / What have you done for me lately (extended mix) / Nasty (cool summer mix part two) / Let's wait awhile (remix).
| | |
|---|---|
| ■ CD................... | MIX CD 1 |
| ■ MC................... | MIX MC 1 |
| ■ LP................... | MIX LP 1 |

A&M / Nov '87.
| | |
|---|---|
| CD................... | CDMID 149 |

A&M / Aug '91 / PolyGram.
| | |
|---|---|
| MC................... | CMID 149 |

A&M / Oct '92 / PolyGram.

## CONTROL - THE VIDEOS.
Tracks: Nasty / What have you done for me lately / When I think of you / Control / Pleasure principle / Let's wait awhile.
| | |
|---|---|
| ■ VHS................... | AMV 838 |

A&M Sound Pictures / '87.

## DON'T MESS UP THIS GOOD THING.
Tracks: Don't mess up this good thing / Young love.
| | |
|---|---|
| ■ 12"................... | AMX 112 |
| ■ 7"................... | AM 112 |

A&M / May '83.

## DREAM STREET.
Tracks: Don't stand another chance / Two to the power / Pretty boy / Dream Street / Communication / Fast girls / Hold back the tears / All my love to you / If it takes all night.
| | |
|---|---|
| ■ LP................... | AMA 4962 |
| ■ MC................... | AMC 4962 |

A&M / Oct '84.

## ESCAPADE (WE'VE GOT IT MADE).
Tracks: Escapade (we've got it made) / Escapade (we've got it made) (version).
| | |
|---|---|
| ■ 12"................... | USAF 684 |
| ■ 12"................... | USAT 684 |
| ■ 7"................... | USA 684 |
| ■ 7" P.Disc............. | USAP 684 |
| ■ CD Single............. | USACD 684 |
| ■ MC Single............. | USAMC 684 |

Breakout / Mar '90.

## FUNNY HOW TIME FLIES (WHEN YOU'RE HAVING FUN).
Tracks: Funny how time flies / When I think of you / Nasty (cool summer mix part one).
| | |
|---|---|
| ■ 7"................... | USA 613 |

Breakout / '87.

## IF.
Tracks: If / One more chance (Available on 7 and MCS only) / If (mixes).
| | |
|---|---|
| ■ 12"................... | VST 1474 |
| ■ CD Single............. | VSCDT 1474 |
| ■ 7"................... | VS 1474 |
| ■ MC Single............. | VSC 1474 |

Virgin / Jul '93.

## JANET.
Tracks: Morning / That's the way love goes / You know.. / You want this / Be a good boy / Be a good boy.. / If / Back / This time / Go on Miss Janet / Throb / What'll I do / Lounge / Funky big band / Racism / New agenda / Love pt.2 / Because of love / Wind / Again / Another lover / Where are you now / Hold on baby / Body that loves you / Rain / Any time, any place / Are you still up / Sweet dreams.
| | |
|---|---|
| CD................... | CDV 2720 |
| LP................... | V 2720 |
| MC................... | TCV 2720 |

Virgin / May '93 / EMI.

## JANET JACKSON.
Tracks: Say you do / You'll never find (a love like mine) / Young love / Love and my best friend / Don't mess up a good thing / Forever yours / Magic is working / Come give your love to me.
| | |
|---|---|
| ■ LP................... | AMLH 64907 |
| ■ MC................... | CAM 64907 |

A&M / Jan '83.
| | |
|---|---|
| CD................... | CDMID 114 |
| MC................... | CMID 114 |

A&M / Oct '92 / PolyGram.

## LET'S WAIT AWHILE.
Tracks: Let's wait awhile / Nasty (cool summer mix part one) / Nasty (original mix) / Control / Let's wait awhile (remix).
| | |
|---|---|
| ■ 7"................... | USA 601 |
| ■ 7" Set............... | USAD 601 |

Breakout / Mar '87.

## LOVE WILL NEVER DO WITHOUT YOU.
Tracks: Love will never do without you.
| | |
|---|---|
| ■ 12"................... | AMY 700 |
| ■ 7"................... | AM 700 |
| ■ CD Single............. | AMCD 700 |
| ■ MC Single............. | AMMC 700 |

A&M / Sep '90.

## MISS YOU MUCH.
Tracks: Miss you much / You need me.
| | |
|---|---|
| ■ 12"................... | USAT 663 |
| ■ 7"................... | USA 663 |
| ■ 7"................... | USAS 663 |
| ■ CD Single............. | USACD 663 |
| ■ MC Single............. | USATC 663 |

A&M / Aug '89.

## NASTY.
Tracks: Nasty / You'll never find (a love like mine).
| | |
|---|---|
| ■ 7"................... | AM 316 |

A&M / May '86.

## PLEASURE PRINCIPLE, THE.
Tracks: Pleasure principle / Pleasure principle (mixes).
| | |
|---|---|
| ■ 12"................... | USAT 604 |
| ■ 7"................... | USA 604 |
| ■ MC Single............. | USATC 604 |

Breakout / May '87.

## RHYTHM NATION.
Tracks: Rhythm nation.
| | |
|---|---|
| ■ 12"................... | USAT 673 |
| ■ 7"................... | USAS 673 |
| ■ 7"................... | USA 673 |
| ■ CD Single............. | USACD 673 |
| ■ MC Single............. | USATC 673 |

A&M / Oct '89.

## RHYTHM NATION 1814.
Tracks: Rhythm nation / State of the world / Knowledge / Miss you much / Love will never do (without

you) / Livin' in a world (they didn't make) / Alright / Escapade / Black cat / Lonely / Come back to me / Someday is tonight.
| | |
|---|---|
| CD................... | CDA 3920 |
| MC................... | AMC 3920 |
| ■ LP................... | AMA 3920 |

A&M / Sep '89 / PolyGram.

## RHYTHM NATION 1814.
Tracks: Miss you much / Rhythm nation / Black Cat / Knowledge.
| | |
|---|---|
| VHS................... | AMV 00855 |

A&M Sound Pictures / Nov '89 / Gold & Sons / PolyGram Music Video / THE.
| | |
|---|---|
| VHS................... | AMV 855 |

Channel 5 / Apr '90 / Channel 5 Video / P.R.O. Video / Gold & Sons.

## RHYTHM NATION 1814 (SPECIAL EDITION).
Tracks: Miss you much ( Sheps house mix) (On 1814 Bonus beats only. (previously unreleased)) / You need me (On 1814 Bonus beats only.) / Skin games (On 1814 Bonus beats only. (previously unreleased)) / Come back to me (inst.) (On 1814 Bonus beats only. (previously unreleased)) / 1814 megamix (On 1814 Bonus beats only.).
| | |
|---|---|
| ■ CD................... | AMAD 3920 |
| ■ LP P.Disc............. | AMAP 3920 |
| ■ MC Set............... | AMAC 3920 |

A&M / Sep '90.

## RHYTHM NATION COMPILATION, THE.
Tracks: Miss you much / Rhythm nation / Escapade / Alright / Come back to me / Black cat / Love will never do (without you) / Epilogue.
| | |
|---|---|
| VHS................... | AMV 874 |

A&M Sound Pictures / Nov '90 / Gold & Sons / PolyGram Music Video / THE.
| | |
|---|---|
| VHS................... | CFV 10892 |

Channel 5 / Oct '90 / Channel 5 Video / P.R.O. Video / Gold & Sons.

## THAT'S THE WAY LOVE GOES.
Tracks: That's the way love goes / That's the way love goes (mixes).
| | |
|---|---|
| ■ 12"................... | VST 1460 |
| MC Single............. | VSC 1460 |
| ■ 7"................... | VS 1460 |
| ■ CD Single............. | VSCDG 1460 |

Virgin / Apr '93.

## WHAT HAVE YOU DONE FOR ME LATELY.
Tracks: What have you done for me lately / Young love.
| | |
|---|---|
| ■ 12"................... | AMY 308 |
| ■ 7"................... | AM 308 |

A&M / Mar '86.

## WHEN I THINK OF YOU.
Tracks: When I think of you / Come give your love to me.
| | |
|---|---|
| ■ 12"................... | AMY 337 |
| ■ 7"................... | AM 337 |

A&M / Jul '86.

## YOU WANT THIS.
Tracks: You want this (mixes) / New agenda (On VSCDT 1519 only) / 70's love groove (On VSC 1519/ VSCDG 1519 only) / And on and on (On VSC 1519/ VSCDT 1519 only).
| | |
|---|---|
| 12"................... | VST 1519 |
| CD Single................ | VSCDG 1519 |
| CD Single................ | VSCDT 1519 |
| MC Single................ | VSC 1519 |

Virgin / Oct '94 / EMI.

---

# Jackson, Jermaine

Until Janet's breakthrough, Jermaine was only Jackson to present even minor threat to Michael's supremacy; scoring 1973 U.S. hit with cover of Shep & The Limelites' '61 smash *Daddy's Home*. When Jacksons quit Motown in '75, Jermaine remained on label; decision probably unconnected to his marriage to boss' daughter Hazel Gordy. While brothers' fortunes soared on Epic, Jermaine's plummeted; revived only by Stevie Wonder/Lee Garrett-penned 1980 smash *Let's Get Serious*. Less predictable collaboration, with new-wavers Devo on *Let Me Tickle Your Fancy*, returned him to U.S. charts in 1982. Jermaine finally quit Motown for Arista in 1984, and reunited with brothers for mercenary *Victory* tour and album. Final flush of solo success came in early '85 with hit ballad *Do What You Do*. He returned to headlines, though not charts, with Michael-baiting *Word To The Badd* single in '92; taken from LA & Babyface-produced *La Face* album.

## BURNIN' HOT.
Tracks: Burnin' hot / Castles of sand.
- 12"........................ 12TMG 1194
- 7"........................... TMG 1194

Motown / Oct '81.

## COVER STORY.
Tracks: Not Advised.
- VHS........................... SV 1808

Stylus Video / Feb '90 / EMI / Pinnacle / THE / Gold & Sons.

## DO WHAT YOU DO.
Tracks: Do what you do / Tell me I'm not dreaming / When the rain begins to fall (Only on 12" single.).
- 12"....................... ARIST 12609
- 7"......................... ARIST 609

Arista / Jan '85.

## DO YOU REMEMBER ME.
Tracks: Do you remember me (USA mix) (12" version also includes "Bonus Beats" mix and "Dub Mix" of title.) / Voices in the dark.
- 12"....................... ARIST 12664
- 12" Remix................. ARIST 22664
- 7"......................... ARIST 664

Arista / May '86.

## DON'T TAKE IT PERSONAL.
Tracks: Climb out / Don't take it personal / Make it easy on love / So right / I'd like to get to know you / Two ships (in the night) / Rise to the occasion / (C'mon) feel the need / Next to you / Don't make me wait.
- LP............................210230
- CD............................260230
- MC............................410230

Arista / Nov '89.

## DON'T TAKE IT PERSONAL.
Tracks: Don't take it personal / Clean up your act.
- 12"............................612634
- 7".............................112634
- CD Single.....................662634
- MC Single.....................410634

Arista / Sep '89.

## DYNAMITE.
Tracks: Dynamite / Sweetest sweetest / Tell me I'm not dreaming / Escape from the planet of the ant men / Come to me (one way or another) / Do what you do / Some things are private / Oh Mother.
- CD............................610150
- MC............................406317

Arista / Mar '85.

## DYNAMITE.
Tracks: Dynamite / Tell me I'm not dreaming / Come to me (one way or another).
- 12"........................... JJK 122
- 7"............................. JJK 2

Arista / Jul '84.

## DYNAMITE.
Tracks: Not Advised.
- VHS......................... RVT 20791

RCA/Columbia (Video) / '88 / Gold & Sons / THE / Sony.

## DYNAMITE (JELLY BEAN REMIX).
Tracks: Dynamite (jelly bean remix) / Take good care of my heart.
- 12"....................... ARIST 12616
- 7"......................... ARIST 616

Arista / May '85.

## FEEL THE FIRE.
Tracks: Feel the fire / You need to be loved / Strong love / Git up and dance / I love you more / Happiness is / Some kind of woman / Got to get to you girl / Take time.
- LP........................STML 12067

Motown / Sep '77.

## GREATEST HITS AND RARE CLASSICS.
Tracks: Daddy's home / That's how love goes / You're in good hands / Let's be young tonight / You need to be loved / Castles of sand / Where are you now / You're supposed to keep your love for me / Let's get serious / Litle girl don't you worry / You like me don't you / I'm just too shy / Let me tickle your fancy / Paradise in your eyes / Very special part / Burnin' hot.
- CD......................... WD 72706

Motown / Dec '91.

## I LIKE YOUR STYLE.
Tracks: I gotta have you / I'm just too shy / You're givin' me the run around / Paradise in your eyes / Is it always gonna be like this / Signed, sealed, delivered (I'm yours) / Maybe next time / I can't take no more / It's still undone / I'm my brother's keeper.
- LP........................STML 12160

- MC..........................CSTML 12160

Motown / Oct '81.

## I THINK IT'S LOVE.
Tracks: I think it's love / Voices in the dark.
- 12"....................... ARIST 12655
- 7"..........................ARIST 655

Arista / Feb '86.

## I'M JUST TOO SHY.
Tracks: I'm just too shy / All because of you.
- 7"........................... TMG 1242

Motown / Nov '81.

## JERMAINE.
Tracks: Pieces fit / You like me don't you / Little girl don't you worry / All because of you / You've changed / First you laugh then you cry / I miss you so / Can I change my mind / Beautiful morning.
- LP........................STML 12147
- MC.......................CSTML 12147

Motown / Oct '81.

## JERMAINE.
Tracks: That's how love goes / I'm in a different world / Homeward bound / Take me in your arms / I only have eyes for you / I let love pass me by / Live it up / If you were my woman / Ain't that peculiar / Daddy's home.
- LP........................STML 11221

Tamla Motown / Feb '73.

## LET ME TICKLE YOUR FANCY.
Tracks: Let me tickle your fancy / Very special part / Uh, uh, I didn't do it / You belong to me / You moved a mountain / Running / Messing around / This time / There's a better way / I like your style.
- LP........................STML 12174

Motown / Oct '82.

## LET ME TICKLE YOUR FANCY.
Tracks: Let me tickle your fancy / Maybe next time.
- 12"........................... TMGT 1276
- 7"........................... TMG 1276

Motown / Aug '82.

## LET'S GET SERIOUS.
Tracks: Let's get serious / Where are you now / You got to hurry girl / We can put it back together / Burnin' hot / You're supposed to keep your love for me / Feelin' free.
- LP........................STML 12127
- MC.......................CSTML 12127

Motown / Oct '81.
- MC.......................... WK 72258
- LP.......................... WL 72258

Motown / Apr '85.
- CD......................... 530 217-2

Polydor / Sep '93 / PolyGram.

## LET'S GET SERIOUS.
Tracks: Let's get serious / Je vous aime beaucoup.
- 12"...................... 12TMG 1183
- 7"........................... TMG 1183

Motown / May '80.

## LITTLE GIRL DON'T YOU WORRY.
Tracks: Little girl don't you worry / We can put it back together.
- 12"......................... TMGT 1212
- 7"........................... TMG 1212

Motown / Oct '81.

## PARADISE IN YOUR EYES.
Tracks: Paradise in your eyes / I'm my brother's keeper.
- 7"........................... TMG 1253

Motown / Feb '82.

## PERFECT.
Tracks: Perfect.
- 12"....................... ARIST 12619
- 7"..........................ARIST 619

Arista / Apr '85.

## PRECIOUS MOMENTS.
Tracks: Do you remember me / Lonely won't leave me alone / Give a little love / Precious moments / I think it's love / Our love story / I hear heartbeat / If you say my eyes are beautiful (With Whitney Houston.) / Voices in the dark / Words into action.
- LP............................207087
- MC............................407087

Arista / Jul '86.
- CD............................610487

Arista / Apr '88.
- LP............................209062
- MC............................409062
- CD............................259062

Arista / May '88.

## SWEETEST SWEETEST.
Tracks: Sweetest sweetest / Come to me (one way or another).

- 12"........................... JJK 121
- 7"............................. JJK 1
- 7" P.Disc....................JJKPD 1

Arista / Apr '84.

## VERY SPECIAL PART.
Tracks: Very special part / You're giving me the runaround.
- 12"......................... TMGT 1286
- 7"........................... TMG 1286

Motown / Nov '82.

## WHEN THE RAIN BEGINS TO FALL
(Jackson, Jermaine & Pia Zadora).
Tracks: When the rain begins to fall.
- 12"....................... ARIST 12584
- 7"..........................ARIST 584

Arista / Sep '84.

## YOU LIKE ME DON'T YOU.
Tracks: You like me don't you.
- 12"......................... TMGT 1222
- 7"........................... TMG 1222

Motown / Oct '81.

## YOU MOVED A MOUNTAIN.
Tracks: You moved a mountain / Running.
- 7"........................... TMG 1303

Motown / Apr '83.

## YOU SAID.
Tracks: You said, you said / Rebel (with a cause) / I dream, I dream (Prelude) / I dream, I dream / We're making whoopee / Treat you right / Lovers holiday / Secrets / True lovers / Don't you deserve someone / Word to the badd / You said, you said (extended version).
- LP............................212.269
- CD............................262.269
- MC............................412.269

Arista / Mar '92.

## YOU'RE SUPPOSED TO KEEP YOUR LOVE..
Tracks: You're supposed to keep your love...
- 7"........................... TMG 1201

Motown / Oct '81.

## Jackson, Jerry

## IT'S ROUGH OUT THERE.
Tracks: It's rough out there / I'm gonna paint a picture.
- 7"............................. P 100

Cameo Parkway / Jun '66.

## Jackson, Latoya

## BAD GIRL.
Tracks: Sexual feeling / You and me / He's my brother / Restless heart / Playboy / You can count on me / Somewhere / Bad girl / Be my lover / He's so good to me / Do the salsa / Piano man.
- CD..........................CDTB 127

Magnum Force / Feb '92 / THE / Jazz Music / Hot Shot.

## HEART DON'T LIE.
Tracks: Think twice / Heart don't lie / Bet'cha gonna need my lovin' / Private joy / Hot potato / I like everything you're doin' / Frustration / Without you.
- LP......................... EPC 25992

Epic / Aug '84.

## HEART DON'T LIE.
Tracks: Heart don't lie / Without you.
- 12"........................... TA 4369
- 7"............................. A 4369

Epic / May '84.

## HOT POTATO.
Tracks: Hot potato / Think twice.
- 12"........................... TA 4679

Epic / Sep '84.

## IF YOU FEEL THE FUNK.
Tracks: If you feel the funk / Lovely is she.
- 12"....................... POSPX 197
- 7"......................... POSP 197

Polydor / Nov '80.

## LATOYA.
Tracks: You're gonna get rocked / You blew / Such a wicked love / Not giving up on love / If I could get to you / Turn on the radio / Just say no / Does it really matter / (Tell me) he really means nothing to you at all / (Ain't nobody loves you) like I do.
- CD.......................... PD 88502
- LP.......................... PL 88502
- MC.......................... PK 88502

RCA / Nov '88.

■ DELETED

## OOPS OH NO CLUB MIX.
Tracks: Oops oh no club mix.
- 12"...................................MOLIF 7
- 7".....................................MOL 7
Music Of Life / Oct '86.

## SIZZLING SENSATION, A.
Tracks: Not Advised.
VHS..................................PIV 2126
Pickwick Video / Apr '90 / THE / Gold & Sons.

## SPOTLIGHT ON LATOYA JACKSON.
Tracks: Sexual feeling / You and me / He's my brother / Be my lover / Piano man / Restless heart / Do the salsa / Playboy / He's so good to me / Somewhere / Bad girl / You can count on me.
CD..................................HADCD 111
MC..................................HADMC 111
Javelin / Feb '94 / THE.

## STAY THE NIGHT.
Tracks: Stay the night / Camp Kuchi Kaiai.
- 7"...................................POSP 332
Polydor / Oct '81.

## YOU'RE GONNA GET ROCKED.
Tracks: You're gonna get rocked / Does it really matter.
- 12"...................................PT 49528
- 7"....................................PB 49527
RCA / Sep '88.

---

## Jackson, Mahalia

New Orleans-born singer who sang in father's church choir from age 5 and led own groups after moving to Chicago in 1927. Recorded for Apollo (1945-54), notably multi million-selling *Move On Up A Little Higher*, and performed acclaimed concerts at Carnegie Hall and on 1952 European tour. Many fine albums for Columbia from 1954 included *What The World Needs Now*, featuring her readings of *Abraham, Martin & John* and *Put A Little Love In Your Heart*. Striking appearance in 1962 film *Jazz On A Summer's Day* effectively concluded career, though she continued as businesswoman and civil rights campaigner until her death in '72. Aretha Franklin, who cited Jackson as influence, sang at her funeral.

## 20 GREATEST HITS: MAHALIA JACKSON.
Tracks: Not Advised.
- LP.....................................20120
MC......................................40120
Astan / Nov '84.

## BEST-LOVED HYMNS OF DR MARTIN LUTHER KING.
Tracks: We shall overcome / Take my hand precious Lord / Just a closer walk with Thee / There is a balm in Gilead / Old rugged cross / Rock of ages / How I got over / If I can help somebody / He's got the whole world in his hands / An evening prayer.
- LP.....................................63369
CBS / Jun '69.

## GOSPEL.
Tracks: Tell it, sing it, shout it / Somebody touched me / Only hope we have / There is power in the blood / I asked the Lord / Hold me / Give me that old time religion / Leaning on the everlasting arms / Only believe / To me it's so wonderful / I'll never turn back no more / Highway up to Heaven / Trust in God / Lord search my heart / Where he leads me / Hallelujah 'tis done / Thank you, Jesus / Never look down / You can't hurry God / It's my desire / He knows how much we can bear / My Lord.
- Double LP............................VJD 537
Vogue Jazz (France) / Sep '77.

## GOSPELS, SPIRITUALS AND HYMNS.
Tracks: Not Advised.
CD Set................................468663 2
MC Set................................468663 4
Columbia / May '94 / Sony.

## HE'S GOT THE WHOLE WORLD IN HIS HANDS.
Tracks: Not Advised.
CD..................................JW 77004
Jazz World / '90 / New Note / Target Sales & Marketing.

## I'M ON MY WAY.
Tracks: Not Advised.
CD...................................CD 12509
MC...................................MC 12509

---

Music Of The World / Nov '92 / Flexitron Ltd. / Direct Distribution / C.M. Distribution / Impetus Records / Ross Records / Duncans / BMG.

## I'VE DONE MY WORK.
Tracks: He's got the whole world in his hands / Every time I feel the Spirit / Upper room / We shall overcome / House I live in (that's America to me) / Go tell it on the mountain / Down by the riverside / Joshua fit de battle of Jerico / When the saints go marching in / Keep your hands on the plough / Nobody knows the trouble I've seen / Deep river / Holy City / Crying in the chapel / You'll never walk alone.
- LP....................................WST 9630
MC.....................................WC 9630
Word (UK) / May '85 / Word Records (UK) / Sony.

## IN THE UPPER ROOM.
Tracks: Not Advised.
CD..................................VGCD 600061
Vogue / '86 / BMG.

## JAZZ TIME VOL.16.
Tracks: Not Advised.
- LP....................................502716
Vogue / '88.

## JESUS IS WITH ME.
Tracks: Not Advised.
- LP.....................................20081
MC......................................40081
Astan / Nov '84.

## LIVE IN ANTIBES 1968.
Tracks: Not Advised.
- LP.....................................FC 122
France's Concert / May '89.
CD.....................................FCD 122
France's Concert / Jul '94 / Jazz Music / BMG.

## MAHALIA (Mahalia Jackson 1911-1972).
Tracks: Not Advised.
- VHS..................................HEN 2049
Hendring Video / Mar '90.

## MAHALIA JACKSON.
Tracks: Not Advised.
- LP..................................EMB 31383
MC...................................40.31383
Ember / Jun '84 / TKO Records Ltd / President Records.

## MAHALIA JACKSON COLLECTION (20 golden greats).
Tracks: Nobody knows the trouble I've seen / Go tell it on the mountain / Come to Jesus / My story / I believe / In the upper room / Run all the way / Shall I meet you over yonder / Beautiful tomorrow / Last mile on the way / Walkin' to Jerusalem / Bless this house / I'm on my way to Canaan / Lord's Prayer / He's my light / Even me / It is no secret / Hand of God / Jesus is with me / Get away Jordan.
- LP..................................DVLP 2006
MC..................................DVMC 2006
Deja Vu / Aug '85 / Jazz Music / Music Collection International.

## MAHALIA JACKSON STORY, THE.
Tracks: Get away Jordan / Go tell it on the mountain / Lord's prayer / He's got the whole world in his hands / Shall I meet you over yonder / Evening prayer, An / I'm going to live the life I sing about / City called heaven / It don't cost very much / Nobody knows the trouble I've seen / Didn't it rain / He's my light / Joshua fit de battle of Jerico / I believe / Come to Jesus / My story / My God is real / Beautiful tomorrow / Last mile on the way / Even me / Hands of God / Walk over God's heaven / I'm on my way / Jesus is with me / Walkin' to Jerusalem.
CD Set................................DVRECD 23
MC Set................................DVREMC 23
Deja Vu / May '89 / Jazz Music / Music Collection International.

## MAHALIA JACKSON, VOL 1.
Tracks: Tell it, sing it, shout it / Somebody touched me / Only hope we have / There is power in the blood / I asked the Lord / Hold me / Give me that old time religion / Leaning on the everlasting arms / He's sweet, I know / Somebody bigger than you / Only believe / To me it's so wonderful.
- LP.....................................JR 115
Jazz Reactivation / Jan '82.

## MAHALIA JACKSON, VOL 2.
Tracks: I'll never turn back no more / Highway up to Heaven / Lord search my soul / I trust in God / Where he leads me / Hallelujah / 'Tis done / Thank you, Jesus / Never look down / You can't hurry God / It's my desire / He knows how much we can bear / My Lord.
- LP.....................................JR 134
Jazz Reactivation / May '83.

---

## MEMORIAL.
Tracks: Not Advised.
- Double LP............................400010
Vogue / Oct '88.

## MY STORY.
Tracks: Not Advised.
- LP.....................................20080
MC......................................40080
Astan / Nov '84.

## MY TASK.
Tracks: My task / Amazing grace / God is so good / Walk in Jerusalem / Satisfied mind / Whither thou goest / It is no secret / Then the answer came / My friend / Bible tells me so / Somebody bigger than you and I / He calmed the ocean / For my good fortune / I've done my work / How I got over / That's what he's done for me.
- LP..................................WRD 3011
MC..................................TCWR 3011
Word (UK) / May '85 / Word Records (UK) / Sony.

## NOBODY KNOWS THE TROUBLE I'VE SEEN.
Tracks: Not Advised.
CD..................................VG 670216
Vogue / Jul '89 / BMG.

## PORTRAIT.
Tracks: Not Advised.
MC..................................WSC 99014
- CD...................................CD 99014
World Star Collection / Sep '93 / BMG.

## QUEEN OF GOSPEL.
Tracks: Not Advised.
CD..................................MCCD 122
MC..................................MCTC 122
Music Club / Aug '93 / Gold & Sons / THE / Video Collection / C.M. Distribution.

## QUEEN OF GOSPEL, THE.
Tracks: Not Advised.
- LP.................................ENT LP 13029
Entertainers / Nov '87.
CD.................................GOJCD 53028
Giants Of Jazz / Mar '92 / Wellard / Swift / Target / Jazz Music / BMG.
MC.................................ENT MC 13029
Entertainers / Mar '92 / BMG.

## SILENT NIGHT.
Tracks: Silent night / Go tell it on the mountain / Bless this house.
- LP.....................................6.24480
Teldec (1) / Dec '81.

## WARM AND TENDER SOUL OF MAHALIA JACKSON.
Tracks: In the upper room / City called Heaven / Run all the way / Go tell it on the mountain / I'm on my way to Canaan / I bow on my knees / Shall I meet you over yonder / Beautiful tomorrow / It is no secret / Hands of God / Jesus is with me / Nobody knows the trouble I've seen / Even me / Get away Jordan / Last mile on the way / Bless this house / Walkin' to Jerusalem / My story / I believe / Dig a little deeper / Lord's prayer / Come to Jesus / He's my light.
- Double LP............................SM 3763/2
Joker (USA) / Apr '81.

## WARM AND TENDER SOUL OF MAHALIA JACKSON VOL.1.
Tracks: Not Advised.
- LP....................................SM 3609
MC.....................................MC 3609
Joker (USA) / '88 / C.M. Distribution / Jazz Horizons / Jazz Music.

## WARM AND TENDER SOUL OF MAHALIA JACKSON VOL.2.
Tracks: Not Advised.
- LP....................................SM 3610
Joker (USA) / Apr '81.

## WE SHALL OVERCOME.
Tracks: Rusty bell / If I could help somebody / Didn't it rain / Holding my saviour's hand / This is my faith / Elijah rock / We shall overcome / We have come a mighty long way / How I got over / I would rather have Jesus / Down by the riverside / It's in my heart / Come on children, let us sing.
CD..................................CDCD 1129
Charly / Nov '93 / Charly.

## WHEN THE SAINTS GO MARCHING IN.
Tracks: I'm going to live the life I sing about in my song / When I wake up in glory / Jesus met the woman at the well / Oh Lord is it / I will move on up a little higher / When the saints go marching in / Jesus out of the depths / Walk over God's heaven / Keep your hands on the plough / Didn't it rain.

■ LP. . . . . . . . . . . . . . . . . . . . . . . . . . 4508691
■ MC. . . . . . . . . . . . . . . . . . . . . . . . . . 4508694
CBS / Jul '87.

# Jackson, Michael

Michael Jackson confirmed his place among legends of the 20th century in March 1984, when *Thriller* sailed past Bing Crosby's *White Christmas* to become the best-selling recording of all time. By mid-85, its global sales were estimated at 40 million; the culmination of an exceptional career. Born in Gary, Indiana in 1958, Michael was five when he joined his elder brothers' group; at six, he became lead vocalist. The group won several talent contests before being signed by Tamla Motown and groomed for stardom. In 1970, The Jackson 5 made history by becoming the only act to top the US Hot 100 with their first four singles. Within a year, Michael was launched on a simultaneous solo career; the highlight of which was his first solo chart-topper, *Ben*. The Jacksons' career at Motown coasted along in less spectacular fashion, before they left for Epic; returning in '77 with a new series of hits. Buoyed by success, Michael signed up for a remake of *Wizard Of Oz*, the only useful result of which was teaming with veteran musical director, Quincy Jones. Union produced '79's flawless *Off The Wall*, which deservedly held best-selling album by a black artist title until *Thriller*. His subsequent career has been well-documented, with various controversies obscuring Jackson's phenomenal commercial and artistic triumphs. *Bad* and *Dangerous* were undeniably contrived, but nonetheless spawned more hits and sales than virtually all his contemporaries.

## 12" TAPE: MICHAEL JACKSON.
Tracks: Billie Jean / Beat it / Wanna be startin' something / Thriller / P.Y.T. (pretty young thing).
MC. . . . . . . . . . . . . . . . . . . . . . . . . . 4501274
Epic / Sep '86 / Sony.

## 18 GREATEST HITS.
Tracks: Not Advised.
■ CD. . . . . . . . . . . . . . . . . . . . WD 72629
■ LP. . . . . . . . . . . . . . . . . . . . . WL 72629
■ MC. . . . . . . . . . . . . . . . . . . . WK 72629
Motown / Jun '88.

## 18 GREATEST HITS: MICHAEL JACKSON (Jackson, Michael & Jackson Five).
Tracks: One day in your life / Lookin' through the windows / Got to be there / Doctor my eyes / Ben / ABC / We're almost there / Skywriter / Rockin' robin / Happy / Ain't no sunshine / I'll be there / I want you back / Love you save / We've got a good thing going / Mama's pearl / Hallelujah day / Never can say goodbye.
■ LP. . . . . . . . . . . . . . . . . . . STAR 2232
MC. . . . . . . . . . . . . . . . . . . . STAC 2232
Telstar/Ronco / Jul '83 / BMG.
■ CD. . . . . . . . . . . . . . . . . . . TCD 2232
Telstar/Ronco / '86.

## ABC (Jackson, Michael & Jackson Five).
Tracks: ABC.
■ 7". . . . . . . . . . . . . . . . . . . . ZB 41941
Motown / Apr '88.

## AIN'T NO SUNSHINE.
Tracks: Rockin' robin / Johnny Raven / Shoo-be-doo-be-doo-da-day / Happy / Too young / Up again / With a child's heart / Ain't no sunshine / Euphoria / Morning glow / Music and me / All the things you are / Cinderella stay awhile / We've got forever.
■ LP. . . . . . . . . . . . . . . . . . . . TMS 3511
■ MC. . . . . . . . . . . . . . . . . . . TMC 3511
Motown / Jun '82.
■ LP. . . . . . . . . . . . . . . . . . . . . . 20038
■ MC. . . . . . . . . . . . . . . . . . . . . . 40038
Astan / Nov '84.

## AIN'T NO SUNSHINE.
Tracks: Ain't no sunshine / I wanna be.
■ 7". . . . . . . . . . . . . . . . . . . . TMG 826
Tamla Motown / Jul '72.

## ANOTHER PART OF ME.
Tracks: Another part of me / Another part of me (inst.).
■ 7". . . . . . . . . . . . . . . . . . . . 6528449
Epic / '88.
■ 12" Remix. . . . . . . . . . . . . . 6528446
■ 12" Remix. . . . . . . . . . . . . . 6528442
■ 7". . . . . . . . . . . . . . . . . . . . .652844 0
Epic / Aug '88.
■ CD Single. . . . . . . . . . . . . . 6530042
Epic / Sep '88.

## ANTHOLOGY - MICHAEL JACKSON (Volumes 1 & 2).
Tracks: Got to be there / Rockin' robin / Ain't no sunshine / Maria (you were the only one) / I wanna be where you are / Girl don't take your love from me / Love is here and now you're gone / People make the world go 'round / Shoo-be-doo-be-doo-da-day / With a child's heart / Everybody's somebody's fool / In our small way / All the things you are / You can cry on my shoulder / Maybe tomorrow / I'll be there / Never can say goodbye / It's too late to change the time / Dancing machine / When I come of age / Dear Michael / Music and me / You are there / One day in your life / Love's gone bad / That's what love is made of / Who's looking for a lover / Lonely teardrops / We're almost there / Take me back / Just a little bit of you / Melodie / I'll come home to you / If n'I was God / Happy / Don't let it get you down / Call on me / To make my father proud / Farewell my summer love.
■ CD. . . . . . . . . . . . . . . . . . . ZD 72530
Motown / Jan '87.
■ CD. . . . . . . . . . . . . . . . . . . WD 72530
Motown / Mar '89.
CD. . . . . . . . . . . . . . . . . . . .530178-2
Motown / Jan '93 / PolyGram.

## BAD.
Tracks: Bad / Way you make me feel / Speed demon / Liberian girl / Just good friends / Another part of me / Man in the mirror / I just can't stop loving you / Dirty Diana / Smooth criminal.
■ CD P.Disc. . . . . . . . . . . . . . 4502909
■ LP P.Disc. . . . . . . . . . . . . . 4502900
Epic / Nov '87.
CD. . . . . . . . . . . . . . . . . . . . 4502902
■ LP. . . . . . . . . . . . . . . . . . . 4502901
Epic / Sep '87 / Sony.
MC. . . . . . . . . . . . . . . . . . . . 4502904
Epic / Dec '88 / Sony.
MiniDisc. . . . . . . . . . . . . . . .450290-3
Epic / Feb '93 / Sony.

## BAD.
Tracks: Bad.
■ MC Single. . . . . . . . . . . . . . 6511554
■ 12". . . . . . . . . . . . . . . . . . . 6511006
■ 12". . . . . . . . . . . . . . . . . . . 6511556
■ 7". . . . . . . . . . . . . . . . . . . . 6511557
CBS / Sep '87.

## BEAT IT.
Tracks: Beat it.
■ 12". . . . . . . . . . . . . . . . . . . . TA 3258
■ 7". . . . . . . . . . . . . . . . . . EPCA 3258
Epic / Apr '83.

## BEN.
Tracks: Ben / Greatest show on earth / People make the world go round / We've got a good thing going / Everybody's somebody's fool / My girl / What goes around comes around / In our small way / Shee be doo be doo a day / You can cry on my shoulder.
■ LP. . . . . . . . . . . . . . . . . STML 11220
Tamla Motown / Jan '73.
■ LP. . . . . . . . . . . . . . . . . . STMS 5008
■ MC. . . . . . . . . . . . . . . . CSTMS 5008
Motown / Oct '81.
■ LP. . . . . . . . . . . . . . . . . . WL 72069
■ MC. . . . . . . . . . . . . . . . . WK 72069
Motown / May '84.
■ CD. . . . . . . . . . . . . . . . . . WD 72069
Motown / Feb '90.
CD. . . . . . . . . . . . . . . . . . 530 163-2
Polydor / Sep '93 / PolyGram.

## BEN.
Tracks: Ben / Abraham, martin and john.
■ 7". . . . . . . . . . . . . . . . . . . . TMG 834
Tamla Motown / Nov '72.

## BEST OF MICHAEL JACKSON.
Tracks: Got to be there / Ain't no sunshine / My girl / Ben / Greatest show on earth / I wanna be where you are / Happy / Rockin' robin / Just a little bit of you / One day in your life / Music and me / In our small way / We're almost there / Morning glow.
■ LP. . . . . . . . . . . . . . . . . . STMR 9009
■ MC. . . . . . . . . . . . . . . . CSTMR 9009
Motown / Oct '81.
■ CD. . . . . . . . . . . . . . . . . . WD 72063
■ LP. . . . . . . . . . . . . . . . . . WL 72063
■ MC. . . . . . . . . . . . . . . . . WK 72063
Motown / '85.

## BILLIE JEAN.
Tracks: Billie Jean / You can't win (part I).
■ 7". . . . . . . . . . . . . . . . . . EPCA 3084
Epic / Jan '83.

## BLACK OR WHITE.
Tracks: Black or white / Black or white (instrumental) / Smooth criminal (Only on CD Single.).
■ 12". . . . . . . . . . . . . . . . . . . 6575986
■ 7". . . . . . . . . . . . . . . . . . . . 6575987
■ CD Single. . . . . . . . . . . . . . 6575982
■ MC Single. . . . . . . . . . . . . . 6575984
Epic / Nov '91.

## BLACK OR WHITE (CLIVILLES & COLE REMIXES).
Tracks: Black or white.
■ 12". . . . . . . . . . . . . . . . . . . 6577316
■ CD Single. . . . . . . . . . . . . . 6577312
Epic / Jan '92.

## COMPACT COMMAND PERFORMANCES: 18 GREATEST HITS (Jackson, Michael & Jackson Five).
Tracks: I wanna be where you are / With a child's heart / One day in your life / Who's loving you / Love you save / Never can say goodbye / Maybe tomorrow / Sugar daddy / Lookin' through the windows / Get it together / Dancing machine / Got to be there / Ben / ABC / Rockin' robin / I'll be there / I want you back / Mama's pearl.
CD. . . . . . . . . . . . . . . . . MCD 06070 MD
Motown / May '84 / PolyGram.
■ CD. . . . . . . . . . . . . . . . . . WD 72420
Motown / Oct '87.

## DANGEROUS.
Tracks: Jam / Why you wanna trip on me / In the closet / She drives me wild / Remember the time / Can't let her get away / Heal the world / Black or white / Who is it / Give in to me / Will you be there / Keep the faith / Gone too soon / Dangerous.
CD. . . . . . . . . . . . . . . . . . . . 4658022
■ LP. . . . . . . . . . . . . . . . . . . 4658021
MC. . . . . . . . . . . . . . . . . . . . 4658024
Epic / Nov '91 / Sony.
MiniDisc. . . . . . . . . . . . . . . .465802-3
Epic / Feb '93 / Sony.

## DANGEROUS - THE SHORT FILMS.
Tracks: Not Advised.
VHS . . . . . . . . . . . . . . . . . . .491642
Sony Music Video / Nov '93 / Sony.

## DANGEROUS/OFF THE WALL.
Tracks: Not Advised.
CD Set . . . . . . . . . . . . . . . . .4658022 D
Epic / Feb '93 / Sony.

## DIRTY DIANA.
Tracks: Dirty Diana / Dirty Diana (instrumental) / Bad (dance extended mix) (Features the song 'False Fade').
■ 12". . . . . . . . . . . . . . . . . . . 6515468
■ 12". . . . . . . . . . . . . . . . . . . 6528646
■ 7". . . . . . . . . . . . . . . . . . . . 6515467
■ 7". . . . . . . . . . . . . . . . . . . . 6515460
■ CD Single. . . . . . . . . . . . . . 6515469
Epic / Jul '88.

## DON'T STOP 'TIL YOU GET ENOUGH.
Tracks: Don't stop 'til you get enough / Wanna be startin' something.
■ 7". . . . . . . . . . . . . . . . . . . . EPC 7763
Epic / Sep '79.
■ 7". . . . . . . . . . . . . . . . . . . . CBS 8856
CBS / Apr '82.

## EASE ON DOWN THE ROAD (Jackson, Michael & Diana Ross).
Tracks: Ease on down the road / Poppy girls.
■ 7". . . . . . . . . . . . . . . . . . . . MCA 396
MCA / Nov '78.
■ 7". . . . . . . . . . . . . . . . . . . . MCA 898
MCA / Jun '84.

## FAREWELL MY SUMMER LOVE.
Tracks: Don't let it get you down / You've really got a hold on me / Melodie / Touch the one you love / Girl you're so together / Farewell my summer love / Call on me / Here I am / To make my father proud.
■ LP. . . . . . . . . . . . . . . . . . . ZL 72227
■ MC. . . . . . . . . . . . . . . . . . ZK 72227
Motown / Aug '84.
■ LP. . . . . . . . . . . . . . . . . . WL 72630
■ MC. . . . . . . . . . . . . . . . . WK 72630
Motown / Jun '88.
■ CD. . . . . . . . . . . . . . . . . . WD 72630
Motown / Oct '89.

## FAREWELL MY SUMMER LOVE.
Tracks: Farewell my summer love / Call on me.
■ 12". . . . . . . . . . . . . . . . . TMGT 1342
■ 7". . . . . . . . . . . . . . . . . . TMG 1342
Motown / May '84.

■ DELETED

## FLIPHITS (EP).
Tracks: One day in your life / Got to be there / Ben / Ain't no sunshine.
- ■ **MC Single.** . . . . . . . . . . . . . . . . CTME 2035

Motown / Jul '83.

## FOREVER MICHAEL.
Tracks: We're almost there / Take me back / One day in your life / Cinderella, stay awhile / We've got forever / Just a little bit of you / You are there / Dapper Dan / Dear Michael / I'll come home to you.
- ■ **LP** . . . . . . . . . . . . . . . . . . . . STMS 5095
- ■ **MC.** . . . . . . . . . . . . . . . . . . CSTMS 5095

Motown / Jun '83.
- ■ **LP** . . . . . . . . . . . . . . . . . . . . WL 72121
- ■ **MC.** . . . . . . . . . . . . . . . . . . . WK 72121

Motown / '88.
- ■ **CD** . . . . . . . . . . . . . . . . . . . . WD 72121

Motown / Mar '90.

## GET IT (see under Wonder, Stevie).

## GIRL YOU'RE SO TOGETHER.
Tracks: Girl you're so together / Touch the one you love.
- ■ **12″** . . . . . . . . . . . . . . . . . . . TMGT 1355
- ■ **7″** . . . . . . . . . . . . . . . . . . . . TMG 1355

Motown / Aug '84.

## GIRLFRIEND.
Tracks: Girlfriend.
- ■ **7″** . . . . . . . . . . . . . . . . . . . . EPC 8782

Epic / Jul '80.

## GIVE IN TO ME.
Tracks: Give in to me / Dirty Diana / Beat it (Features on CDs only).
- ■ **7″** . . . . . . . . . . . . . . . . . . . .659069 7
- ■ **CD Single.** . . . . . . . . . . . . . .659069 2
- ■ **MC Single.** . . . . . . . . . . . . . .659069 4

Epic / Feb '93.

## GONE TOO SOON.
Tracks: Gone too soon / Human nature (On CD single & 12″ only) / She's out of my life (On CD single & 12″ only) / Thriller (On CD single & 12″ only).
- ■ **12″** . . . . . . . . . . . . . . . . . . .659976 6
- ■ **7″** . . . . . . . . . . . . . . . . . . . .659976 7
- ■ **CD Single.** . . . . . . . . . . . . . .659976 2
- ■ **MC Single.** . . . . . . . . . . . . . .659976 4

Epic / Dec '93.

## GOT TO BE THERE.
Tracks: Ain't no sunshine / I wanna be where you are / Girl don't take your love from me / In our small way / Got to be there / Rockin' robin / Wings of my love / Maria (you were the only one) / Love is here and now you're gone / You've got a friend.
- ■ **LP** . . . . . . . . . . . . . . . . . . . .STML 11205

Tamla Motown / Jun '72.
- ■ **LP** . . . . . . . . . . . . . . . . . . . . STMS 5007
- ■ **MC.** . . . . . . . . . . . . . . . . . . CSTMS 5007

Motown / Oct '81.
- ■ **LP** . . . . . . . . . . . . . . . . . . . . WL 72068

Motown / '86.
- ■ **CD** . . . . . . . . . . . . . . . . . . . . WD 72068

Motown / Jun '89.

CD . . . . . . . . . . . . . . . . . . . . . . . . 5301622

Motown / Aug '93 / PolyGram.

## GOT TO BE THERE.
Tracks: Got to be there / Rockin' robin.
- ■ **7″** . . . . . . . . . . . . . . . . . . . . TMG 797

Tamla Motown / Feb '72.
- ■ **7″** . . . . . . . . . . . . . . . . . . . . TMG 973

Tamla Motown / May '75.
- ■ **7″** . . . . . . . . . . . . . . . . . . . . TMG 994

Tamla Motown / Oct '75.

## GOT TO BE THERE/BEN (2 Classic albums).
Tracks: Ain't no sunshine / I wanna be where you are / Girl don't take your love from me / In your own small way / Got to be there / Rockin' robin / Love is here and now you're gone / Wings of love / Maria, you were the only one / You've got a friend / Ben / Greatest show on earth / People make the world go round / We've got a good thing going / Everybody's fool / My girl / What goes around comes around / In our small way / You can cry on my shoulder / Shoo-be-doo-be-doo-da-day.
- ■ **CD** . . . . . . . . . . . . . . . . . . . . ZD 72468

Motown / Nov '86.

## GREAT LOVE SONGS OF MICHAEL JACKSON.
Tracks: Got to be there / I wanna be where you are / In our small way / Girl don't take your love from me / Maria / Love is here and now you're gone / Happy / I'll come home to you / You are there / One day in our life.
- ■ **LP** . . . . . . . . . . . . . . . . . . . . WL 72289
- ■ **MC.** . . . . . . . . . . . . . . . . . . . WK 72289

Motown / Nov '84.
- ■ **CD** . . . . . . . . . . . . . . . . . . . . WD 72289

Motown / Nov '89.

## GREATEST ORIGINAL HITS.
Tracks: Off the wall / Don't stop, till you got enough / Rock with me / Stay out of my life.
- ■ **EP** . . . . . . . . . . . . . . . . . . . . EPCA 2906

Epic / Mar '83.

## HAPPY.
Tracks: Happy / We're almost there.
- ■ **7″** . . . . . . . . . . . . . . . . . . . . TMG 986

Tamla Motown / Sep '75.

## HEAL THE WORLD.
Tracks: Heal the world / She drives me wild / Man in the mirror (On CDs only) / Wanna be startin' something (remix) (On 12″ only) / Don't stop 'til you get enough)(remix) (On 12″ only) / Rock with you (remix (On 12″ only) / Don't stop til you get enough (Roger Underground solution).
- ■ **12″** . . . . . . . . . . . . . . . . . . .658488-8
- ■ **7″** . . . . . . . . . . . . . . . . . . . .658488-7
- ■ **CD Single.** . . . . . . . . . . . . . .658488-5
- ■ **MC Single.** . . . . . . . . . . . . . .658488-4

Epic / Dec '92.

## I JUST CAN'T STOP LOVING YOU (Jackson, Michael & Siedah Garrett).
Tracks: I just can't stop loving you / Baby be mine.
- ■ **12″** . . . . . . . . . . . . . . . . . . . 6502026
- ■ **7″** . . . . . . . . . . . . . . . . . . . . 6502020
- ■ **7″** . . . . . . . . . . . . . . . . . . . . 6502027

Epic / Aug '87.

## I SAW MOMMY KISSING SANTA CLAUS.
Tracks: I saw Mommy kissing Santa Claus / Santa Claus is coming to town / Up on the house top / Frosty the Snowman.
- ■ **7″** . . . . . . . . . . . . . . . . . . . . ZB 41655

Motown / Nov '87.

## I WANT YOU BACK (Jackson, Michael & Jackson Five).
Tracks: I want you back / Never can say goodbye.
- ■ **12″** . . . . . . . . . . . . . . . . . . . ZT 41914
- ■ **7″** . . . . . . . . . . . . . . . . . . . . ZB 41913

Motown / Apr '88.

## IN THE CLOSET.
Tracks: In the closet.
- ■ **12″** . . . . . . . . . . . . . . . . . . . 6580186
- ■ **7″** . . . . . . . . . . . . . . . . . . . . 6580187
- ■ **CD Single.** . . . . . . . . . . . . . . 6580182
- ■ **MC Single.** . . . . . . . . . . . . . . 6580184

Epic / Apr '92.

## JAM.
Tracks: Jam / Jam (mix).
- ■ **12″** . . . . . . . . . . . . . . . . . . . 6583606
- ■ **7″** . . . . . . . . . . . . . . . . . . . . 6583607
- ■ **CD Single.** . . . . . . . . . . . . . . 6583602
- ■ **MC Single.** . . . . . . . . . . . . . . 6583604

Epic / Sep '92.

## JUST A LITTLE BIT OF YOU.
Tracks: Just a little bit of you / Dear Michael.
- ■ **7″** . . . . . . . . . . . . . . . . . . . . TMG 1006

Tamla Motown / Oct '75.

## LEAVE ME ALONE.
Tracks: Leave me alone / Human nature / Don't stop 'til you get enough / Wanna be startin' something (extended).
- ■ **MC Single.** . . . . . . . . . . . . . . 6546724
- ■ **12″** . . . . . . . . . . . . . . . . . . . 6546726
- ■ **7″** . . . . . . . . . . . . . . . . . . . . 6546720
- ■ **7″** . . . . . . . . . . . . . . . . . . . . 6546727
- ■ **CD Single.** . . . . . . . . . . . . . . 6546722

Epic / Feb '89.

## LEGEND.
Tracks: Not Advised.
- ■ **CD** . . . . . . . . . . . . . . . . . . . 295 706/7

EMS / Jul '90.

## LEGEND CONTINUES, THE.
Tracks: Beat it / Thriller / ABC / Ease on down the road / Heartbreak hotel.

VHS . . . . . . . . . . . . . . . . . . . . . MJ 1000

Video Collection / Jun '88 / Gold & Sons / Video Collection / THE.

## LEGEND CONTINUES/MAKING OF THRILLER, THE.
Tracks: Not Advised.

VHS . . . . . . . . . . . . . . . . . . . . . VC 4116

Video Collection / Jul '92 / Gold & Sons / Video Collection / THE.

## LIBERIAN GIRL.
Tracks: Liberian girl / Girlfriend / You can't win (Only on 12″ single. (654947 1).).

- ■ **12″** . . . . . . . . . . . . . . . . . . . 6549478
- ■ **12″** . . . . . . . . . . . . . . . . . . . 6549471
- ■ **7″** . . . . . . . . . . . . . . . . . . . . 6549470
- ■ **7″** . . . . . . . . . . . . . . . . . . . . 6549479
- ■ **CD Single** . . . . . . . . . . . . . . . 6549472
- ■ **MC Single** . . . . . . . . . . . . . . . 6549474

Epic / Jul '89.

## LOOKING BACK TO YESTERDAY.
Tracks: When I come of age / Teenage symphony / I hear a symphony / Give me half a chance / Loves gone bad / Lonely teardrops / You're good for me / That's what love is made of / I like the way you are (don't change your love on me) / She's lookin' for a lover / If I was God.
- ■ **LP** . . . . . . . . . . . . . . . . . . . . WL 72424
- ■ **MC.** . . . . . . . . . . . . . . . . . . . WK 72424

Tamla Motown / Jul '86.

## LOVE SONGS: MICHAEL JACKSON & DIANA ROSS (Jackson, Michael & Diana Ross).
Tracks: I'm still waiting / Got to be there / Touch me in the morning / Ain't no sunshine / All of my life / Farewell my summer love / Love hangover / Ben / One day in your life / Ain't no mountain high enough / I'll be there / Endless love / Never can say goodbye / Reach out and touch somebody's hand / Girl you're so together / Do you know where you're going to.
- ■ **LP** . . . . . . . . . . . . . . . . . . . . WL 72691
- ■ **CD** . . . . . . . . . . . . . . . . . . . . WD 72691
- ■ **MC.** . . . . . . . . . . . . . . . . . . . WK 72691

Motown / Oct '90.

## MAKING OF THRILLER.
Tracks: Not Advised.

VHS . . . . . . . . . . . . . . . . . . . . . MA 11000

Vestron Music Video / Oct '86 / Sony / Gold & Sons / THE.

## MAN IN THE MIRROR.
Tracks: Man in the mirror / Man in the mirror (album mix) / Man in the mirror (instrumental).
- ■ **7″** . . . . . . . . . . . . . . . . . . . . 6513387
- ■ **7″ P.Disc** . . . . . . . . . . . . . . . 6513389
- ■ **12″** . . . . . . . . . . . . . . . . . . . 6513386
- ■ **7″** . . . . . . . . . . . . . . . . . . . . 6513387
- ■ **CD Single** . . . . . . . . . . . . . . . 6513382

Epic / Feb '88.

## MICHAEL JACKSON.
Tracks: Not Advised.

MC. . . . . . . . . . . . . . . . . . . EPC A 40 2906

Epic / Dec '82 / Sony.

## MICHAEL JACKSON AND THE JACKSON FIVE LIVE (Jackson, Michael & The Jackson Five).
Tracks: Introduction / We're gonna have a good time / Lookin' through the windows / Got to be there / I want you back / ABC / Love you save / Daddy's home / Superstition / Ben / Papa was a rollin' stone / That's how love goes / Never can say goodbye / Ain't that peculiar / I wanna be where you are.

MC. . . . . . . . . . . . . . . . . . . . WK 72641
- ■ **LP** . . . . . . . . . . . . . . . . . . . . WL 72641

Motown / Jul '88 / PolyGram.
- ■ **CD** . . . . . . . . . . . . . . . . . . . . WD 72641

Motown / Jan '89.

## MICHAEL JACKSON MIX, THE.
Tracks: Ben / Ain't no sunshine / Never can say goodbye / Got to be there / Happy (Love theme from lady sings) / I'll be there / We're almost there / People make the world go round / Who's loving you / I was made to love her / You've got a friend / Girl don't take your love from me / We've got a good thing going / I'll come home to you / ABC / I want you back / Get it together / Boogie man / Just a little bit of you / Love you save / Farewell my summer love / Love is here and now you're gone / Hallelujah day / Skywriter / Lookin' through the windows / Sugar daddy / Don't let it get you down / Girl you're so together / Mama's pearl / My girl / Dancing machine / Shoo-be-doo-be-doo-da-day / Doctor my eyes / Rockin' robin / Little bitty pretty one.

CD Set . . . . . . . . . . . . . . . . . . SMD 745
- ■ **Double LP.** . . . . . . . . . . . . . . SMR 745

MC Set . . . . . . . . . . . . . . . . . . SMC 745

Stylus / Dec '87.

## MICHAEL JACKSON SINGLES SET.
Tracks: Man in the mirror / Man in the mirror (instrumental) / Dirty Diana / Dirty Diana (instrumental) / Way you make me feel / Way you make me feel, The (instrumental) / I just can't stop loving you / Baby be mine / Bad / Bad (dance radio).
- ■ **7″ Set** . . . . . . . . . . . . . . . . . . .MJ 5

Epic / Jul '88.

**MICHAEL JACKSON TOUR SOUVENIR PACK.**
**Tracks:** Not Advised.
■ **CD** . . . . . . . . . . **MJ 4**
Epic / Sep '92.

**MOONWALKER.**
**Tracks:** Not Advised.
**VHS** . . . . . . . . . . **084 248 3**
4 Front / Feb '92 / PolyGram Video.
**Laser Disc** . . . . . . . . . . **PLFEB 30171**
Pioneer LDCE / Jun '92 / Video Collection / THE.

**MOTOWN'S GREATEST HITS: MICHAEL JACKSON.**
**Tracks:** I want you back (PWL Mix) / Doctor my eyes / One day in your life / Lookin through the windows / Got to be there / I'll be there / Love you save / Abc (A B C) / Rockin Robin / Happy (Love theme from lady sings the blues) / Ben / Never can say goodbye / Farewell my summer love / Original version/I want you back / Mama's pearl / Ain't no sunshine / Girl you're so together / Hallelujah day / Skywriter / We're almost there.
**CD** . . . . . . . . . . **5300142**
**MC** . . . . . . . . . . **5300144**
■ **LP** . . . . . . . . . . **5300141**
Motown / Feb '92 / PolyGram.

**MUSIC AND ME.**
**Tracks:** With a child's heart / Up again / All the things you are / Happy / Too young / Doggin' around / Johnny Raven / Euphoria / Morning glow / Music and me / Rockin' Robin.
■ **LP** . . . . . . . . . . **WL 72291**
■ **MC** . . . . . . . . . . **WK 72291**
Motown / Nov '84.
**CD** . . . . . . . . . . **550078-2**
**MC** . . . . . . . . . . **550078-4**
Spectrum (1) / May '93 / PolyGram.

**OFF THE WALL.**
**Tracks:** Don't stop til you get enough / Rock with you / Working day and night / Get on the floor / Off the wall / Girlfriend / She's out of my life / I can't help it / It's the falling in love / Burn this disco out.
■ **LP** . . . . . . . . . . **EPC 83468**
Epic / Sep '79.
**CD** . . . . . . . . . . **CD 83468**
Epic / '83 / Sony.
■ **LP** . . . . . . . . . . **4500861**
**MC** . . . . . . . . . . **4500864**
Epic / Nov '86 / Sony.

**OFF THE WALL.**
**Tracks:** Off the wall / Working day and night.
■ **7"** . . . . . . . . . . **EPC 8046**
Epic / Nov '79.
■ **7"** . . . . . . . . . . **CBS 8046**
CBS / Apr '82.

**ONE DAY IN YOUR LIFE.**
**Tracks:** One day in your life / We're almost there / You're my best friend, my love / Don't say goodbye again / Take me back / It's too late to change the time / We've got a good thing going / You are there / Doggin' around / Dear Michael / Girl, don't take your love from me / I'll come home to you.
■ **LP** . . . . . . . . . . **STML 12158**
■ **MC** . . . . . . . . . . **CSTML 12158**
Motown / Oct '81.

**ONE DAY IN YOUR LIFE.**
**Tracks:** One day in your life / Take me back.
■ **7"** . . . . . . . . . . **TMG 976**
Tamla Motown / Jun '75.

**ORIGINAL SOUL OF MICHAEL JACKSON.**
**Tracks:** Twenty five miles / Dancing machine / It's too late to change the time / Ain't no sunshine / Melodie / Got to be there / Doggin' around / Rockin' robin / If I don't love you this way / You've got a friend / Forever came today.
■ **LP** . . . . . . . . . . **ZL 72622**
■ **MC** . . . . . . . . . . **ZK 72622**
■ **CD** . . . . . . . . . . **ZD 72622**
Motown / Feb '88.

**P.Y.T (pretty young thing).**
**Tracks:** P.Y.T. (pretty young thing) / Heartbreak hotel.
■ **7"** . . . . . . . . . . **A 4136**
■ **12"** . . . . . . . . . . **TA 4136**
CBS / Mar '84.

**REMEMBER THE TIME.**
**Tracks:** Remember the time / Come together.
■ **12"** . . . . . . . . . . **6577746**
■ **7"** . . . . . . . . . . **6577747**
■ **CD Single** . . . . . . . . . . **6577742**
■ **MC Single** . . . . . . . . . . **6577744**
Epic / Feb '92.

**ROCK WITH YOU.**
**Tracks:** Rock with you / Get on the floor / You can't win.
■ **12"** . . . . . . . . . . **EPC 13 8206**
■ **7"** . . . . . . . . . . **EPC 8206**
Epic / Feb '80.
■ **7"** . . . . . . . . . . **CBS 8206**
CBS / Apr '82.

**ROCKIN' ROBIN.**
**Tracks:** Rockin' robin / Love is here and now you're gone.
■ **7"** . . . . . . . . . . **TMG 816**
Tamla Motown / May '72.

**SAY SAY SAY (Jackson, Michael & Paul McCartney).**
**Tracks:** Say say say / Ode to a koala bear.
■ **12"** . . . . . . . . . . **12R 6062**
■ **7"** . . . . . . . . . . **R 6062**
Parlophone / Oct '83.

**SHE'S OUT OF MY LIFE.**
**Tracks:** She's out of my life / Push me away.
■ **7"** . . . . . . . . . . **EPC 8384**
Epic / May '80.

**SINGLES PACK.**
**Tracks:** Don't stop till you get enough / Off the wall / Rock with you / Wanna be startin' something / Thriller / She's out of my life / Girl is mine / Billie Jean / Beat it.
■ **7"** . . . . . . . . . . **MJ 1**
Epic / Nov '83.

**SMOOTH CRIMINAL.**
**Tracks:** Smooth criminal / Smooth criminal (instrumental) (Only on 7" single.) / Smooth criminal (extended dance mix) (Only on 12" version & CD single.) / Smooth criminal (dance mix dub) (Only on 12" version.) / Smooth criminal (a cappella) (Only on 12" version & CD single.) / Smooth criminal (Annie mix) (Only on CD single.).
■ **12"** . . . . . . . . . . **6530268**
■ **12"** . . . . . . . . . . **6530261**
■ **12"** . . . . . . . . . . **6531706**
■ **7"** . . . . . . . . . . **6530260**
■ **7"** . . . . . . . . . . **6530267**
■ **CD Single** . . . . . . . . . . **6530262**
Epic / Nov '88.

**THRILLER.**
**Tracks:** Wanna be startin' something / Baby be mine / Girl is mine / Thriller / Beat it / Billie Jean / Human nature / P.Y.T. (pretty young thing) / Lady in my life.
■ **LP** . . . . . . . . . . **EPC 85930**
**MC** . . . . . . . . . . **40 85930**
Epic / Dec '82 / Sony.
**CD** . . . . . . . . . . **CD 85930**
Epic / '83 / Sony.
■ **LP P.Disc** . . . . . . . . . . **EPC 11 85930**
Epic / Jul '83.
**MiniDisc** . . . . . . . . . . **85930-3**
Epic / Feb '93 / Sony.

**THRILLER.**
**Tracks:** Thriller / Things I do for you / Thriller (inst).
■ **12"** . . . . . . . . . . **TA 3643**
■ **7"** . . . . . . . . . . **A 3643**
Epic / Nov '83.

**UNAUTHORISED.**
**Tracks:** Not Advised.
**VHS** . . . . . . . . . . **VVC 1071**
Virgin Vision / Jun '92 / Gold & Sons / THE.

**WANNA BE STARTIN' SOMETHING.**
**Tracks:** Wanna be startin' something / Rock with you.
■ **12"** . . . . . . . . . . **TA 3427**
■ **7"** . . . . . . . . . . **A 3427**
Epic / Jun '83.

**WAY YOU MAKE ME FEEL, THE.**
**Tracks:** Way you make me feel / Way you make me feel, The (instrumental) / Way you make me feel, The (dance ext. mix) (Available on 12" only) / Way you make me feel, The (dub version) (Available on 12" only) / Way you make me feel, The (acapella) (Available on 12" only).
■ **12"** . . . . . . . . . . **6512758**
■ **7"** . . . . . . . . . . **6512753**
■ **7"** . . . . . . . . . . **6512757**
■ **CD Single** . . . . . . . . . . **6512759**
Epic / Nov '87.

**WE'RE ALMOST THERE.**
**Tracks:** We're almost there / We've got a good thing going.
■ **7"** . . . . . . . . . . **TMG 977**
Tamla Motown / Jun '75.

**WHO IS IT.**
**Tracks:** Who is it / Rock with you / You get get enough (Only available on CD Single.).
■ **CD Single** . . . . . . . . . . **6581792**
■ **12"** . . . . . . . . . . **6581796**
■ **7"** . . . . . . . . . . **6581797**
■ **MC Single** . . . . . . . . . . **6581794**
Epic / Jul '92.

**WILL YOU BE THERE.**
**Tracks:** Will you be there / Girlfriend / Man in the mirror (Only on CD Single) / Will you be there (album version) (Only on CD Single).
■ **7"** . . . . . . . . . . **659222 7**
■ **CD Single** . . . . . . . . . . **659222 2**
■ **MC Single** . . . . . . . . . . **659222 4**
Sony Music / Jun '93.

**YOU CAN'T WIN.**
**Tracks:** You can't win / You can't win (version).
■ **12"** . . . . . . . . . . **EPC 12 7135**
■ **7"** . . . . . . . . . . **EPC 7135**
Epic / May '79.

**YOU CAN'T WIN (PART 1).**
**Tracks:** You can't win (part 1) / Billie Jean.
■ **CD Single** . . . . . . . . . . **6516613**
Epic / '88.

## Jackson, Millie

Millie Jackson is a true soul star. The biggest of her handful of minor U.K. chart entries was a 1985 duet with Elton John, and crossover successes at home have been equally underwhelming. After 1973 U.S. hit *Hurts So Good* (from *Cleopatra Jones* movie), Jackson disappeared from the pop chart. But to soul fans she remained a major star; infamous for forthright lyrics and acclaimed for vocal power. An outrageous stage act precluded her from the stardom enjoyed by contemporaries Tina Turner and Chaka Khan, and obscured her less explicit output. Jackson's willingness to compromise and mellowing with age may be gauged by 1989 album *Back To The Shit*.

**21 OF THE BEST (1971-1983).**
**Tracks:** Child of God / Ask me what you want / My man, a sweet man / Breakaway / It hurts so good / How do you feel the morning after / (If loving you is wrong) I don't want to be right / Loving arms / Bad risk / You can't turn me off (in the middle of turning me on) / If you're not back in love by Monday / All the way lover / Go out and get some (get it out 'cha system) / Keep the home fire burnin' / Never change lovers in the middle of the night / Kiss you all over / This is it (part 2) / It's gonna take some time this time / Do you wanna make love / Blues don't get tired of me / I feel like walkin' in the rain.
**CD** . . . . . . . . . . **CDSEWD 100**
South Bound / Sep '94 / Pinnacle.

**AN IMITATION OF LOVE.**
**Tracks:** Hot, wild, unrestricted, crazy love / Wanna be your lover / Love is a dangerous game / Cover me (wall to wall) / Mind over matter / It's a thing / I need to be by myself / I fell in love.
■ **LP** . . . . . . . . . . **HIP 43**
■ **MC** . . . . . . . . . . **HIPC 43**
■ **CD** . . . . . . . . . . **CHIP 43**
Jive / Nov '86.

**BACK TO THE SH.T.**
**Tracks:** Not Advised.
■ **LP** . . . . . . . . . . **HIP 77**
■ **MC** . . . . . . . . . . **HIPC 77**
■ **CD** . . . . . . . . . . **CHIP 77**
Jive / Jun '89.

**BEST OF MILLIE JACKSON.**
**Tracks:** It hurts so good / How do you feel the morning after / My man, a sweet man / Get your love right / There you are / I still love you / If loving you is wrong I don't want to be right / Breakaway / Summer / Child of God / Loving arms.
■ **LP** . . . . . . . . . . **2391 247**
■ **MC** . . . . . . . . . . **3177 247**
Spring / Dec '76.

**CAUGHT UP.**
**Tracks:** If loving you is wrong I don't want to be right / Rap / All I want is a fighting chance / I'm tired of hiding / It's all over but the shouting / So easy going so hard coming back / I'm through trying to prove my love to you / Summer (first time).
■ **LP** . . . . . . . . . . **2391 147**
Polydor / Feb '75.
■ **LP** . . . . . . . . . . **TANLP 2**
**MC** . . . . . . . . . . **ZCTAN 2**
Important / Sep '85.
**CD** . . . . . . . . . . **CDSEWM 003**
**MC** . . . . . . . . . . **SEWC 003**
■ **LP** . . . . . . . . . . **SEW 003**
South Bound / Jun '89 / Pinnacle.

## DIDN'T I BLOW YOUR MIND.
**Tracks:** Didn't I (blow your mind this time) / Be a sweetheart.
■ 7″ . . . . . . . . . . . . . . . . . . . . . . . POSP 126
Polydor / Mar '80.

## E.S.P. (Extra Sexual Persuasion).
**Tracks:** Sexercise (Parts 1 & 2) / This girl could be dangerous / Slow tongue (Working your way down) / Why me / I feel like walking in the rain / Too easy being easy / Slow tongue / You're working me.
■ LP . . . . . . . . . . . . . . . . . K 250382 1
■ MC . . . . . . . . . . . . . . . . K 250382 4
Sire / Feb '84.
■ CD . . . . . . . . . . . . . . . .K 9255412
WEA / Sep '87.
CD . . . . . . . . . . . . . . . . .CDSEWM 093
South Bound / Apr '94 / Pinnacle.

## FEELIN' BITCHY.
**Tracks:** All the way lover / Lovin' your good thing away / Angel in your arms / Little taste of outside love / You created a monster / Cheatin' is / If you're not back in love by Monday / Feeling like a woman.
■ LP . . . . . . . . . . . . . . . . . . .2391 301
■ MC . . . . . . . . . . . . . . . . . .3177 301
Spring / Oct '77.
CD . . . . . . . . . . . . . . . . . .CDSEWM 042
South Bound / Oct '91 / Pinnacle.

## FEELS LIKE THE FIRST TIME (Jackson, Millie & Isaac Hayes).
**Tracks:** Feels like the first time / Sweet music.
■ 12″ . . . . . . . . . . . . . . . . . .POSPX 87
■ 7″ . . . . . . . . . . . . . . . . . . . POSP 87
Polydor / Nov '79.

## FOR MEN ONLY.
**Tracks:** This is where I came in / This is it / If that don't turn you on / I wish that I could hurt that way again / Fool's affair / You must have known I needed love / Despair / Not on your life / Ain't no coming back.
■ LP . . . . . . . . . . . . . . . . . . .2391 460
MC . . . . . . . . . . . . . . . . . . . .3177 460
Spring / Jan '80 / C.M. Distribution / A.D.A. Distribution.
CD . . . . . . . . . . . . . . . . . .CDSEWM 070
South Bound / Jun '93 / Pinnacle.

## FREE AND IN LOVE.
**Tracks:** House for sale / I'm free / Tonight I'll shoot the moon / There you are / Do what makes the world go round / Bad risk / I feel like making love / Ninety love affair / I'm in love again.
■ LP . . . . . . . . . . . . . . . . . . .2391 215
■ MC . . . . . . . . . . . . . . . . . .3177 215
Spring / May '76.
CD . . . . . . . . . . . . . . . . . .CDSEW 032
■ LP . . . . . . . . . . . . . . . . . . .SEW 032
■ MC . . . . . . . . . . . . . . . . . .SEWC 032
South Bound / Aug '90 / Pinnacle.

## GET IT OUTCHA SYSTEM.
**Tracks:** Go out and get some (get it out'cha system) / Keep the home fire burnin' / Logs and thangs / Put something down on it / Here you come again / Why say you're sorry / He wants to hear the words / I just wanna be with you / Sweet music man.
■ MC . . . . . . . . . . . . . . . . . .3177 356
Spring / Jul '78.
CD . . . . . . . . . . . . . . . . . .CDSEWM 046
South Bound / Mar '92 / Pinnacle.

## HARD TIMES.
**Tracks:** Blufunkes / Special occasion / I don't want to cry / We're gonna make it / Hard times / Blues don't get tired of me / Mess on your hands / Finger rap / Mess on your hands (reprise) / Finger rap (reprise) / Feel love comin' on.
■ LP . . . . . . . . . . . . . . . . . . .2391 555
MC . . . . . . . . . . . . . . . . . . . .3177 555
Spring / Oct '82 / C.M. Distribution / A.D.A. Distribution.
South Bound / Mar '94 / Pinnacle.
CD . . . . . . . . . . . . . . . . . .CDSEWM 090

## HOT, WILD, UNRESTRICTED CRAZY LOVE.
**Tracks:** Hot, wild, unrestricted crazy love / Hot, wild, unrestricted crazy love (instrumental).
■ 12″ . . . . . . . . . . . . . . . . . .JIVET 131
■ 7″ . . . . . . . . . . . . . . . . . . .JIVE 131
Jive / Sep '86.

## HOUSE FOR SALE.
**Tracks:** House for sale / There you are.
■ 7″ . . . . . . . . . . . . . . . . . . .2066713
Spring / Mar '83.

## I FEEL LIKE WALKING IN THE RAIN.
**Tracks:** I feel like walking in the rain / Why me.
■ 7″ . . . . . . . . . . . . . . . . . . . . MW 1

Sire / Feb '84.
■ 7″ . . . . . . . . . . . . . . . . . . . W 9348
■ 12″ . . . . . . . . . . . . . . . . . .W 9348T
WEA / Mar '85.

## I GOT TO TRY IT ONE TIME.
**Tracks:** How do you feel the morning after / Get your love right / My love is so fly / Letter full of tears / Watch the one who brings you the news / I got to try it one time / Gospel truth / One night stand / I gotta do something about myself / In the wash.
CD . . . . . . . . . . . . . . . . . .CDSEW 023
■ LP . . . . . . . . . . . . . . . . . .SEW 023
■ MC . . . . . . . . . . . . . . . . . .SEWC 023
South Bound / Feb '90 / Pinnacle.

## I HAD TO SAY IT.
**Tracks:** I had to say it / I ain't no glory story.
■ 12″ . . . . . . . . . . . . . . . . . .POSPX 223
■ 7″ . . . . . . . . . . . . . . . . . . . POSP 223
Spring / Jan '81.

## I HAD TO SAY IT.
**Tracks:** I had to say it / Loving arms / Rap / Stranger / I ain't no glory story / It's gonna take some time this time / Fancy this / Ladies first / Somebody's love died here last night / You owe me that much.
MC . . . . . . . . . . . . . . . . . . . .3177 495
Spring / Dec '80 / C.M. Distribution / A.D.A. Distribution.
CD . . . . . . . . . . . . . . . . . .CDSEWM 086
South Bound / Nov '93 / Pinnacle.

## IF LOVING YOU IS WRONG.
**Tracks:** If loving you is wrong / Rap.
■ 7″ . . . . . . . . . . . . . . . . . . . 2066536
Polydor / Jan '75.

## IF YOU'RE NOT BACK IN LOVE BY MONDAY.
**Tracks:** If you're not back in love by Monday / Little taste of outside love.
■ 7″ . . . . . . . . . . . . . . . . . . . 2066843
Spring / Jan '78.

## IT HURTS SO GOOD.
**Tracks:** I cry / Hypocrisy / Two-faced world / It hurts so good / Don't send nobody else / Hypocrisy (reprise) / Good to the very last drop / Help yourself / Love doctor / Now that you got it / Close my eyes / Breakaway (reprise).
CD . . . . . . . . . . . . . . . . . .CDSEW 019
MC . . . . . . . . . . . . . . . . . . . .SEWC 019
■ LP . . . . . . . . . . . . . . . . . .SEW 019
South Bound / Nov '89 / Pinnacle.

## IT'S GONNA TAKE TIME THIS TIME.
**Tracks:** It's gonna take time this time / Kiss you all over.
■ 12″ . . . . . . . . . . . . . . . . . .TAN 001
■ 7″ . . . . . . . . . . . . . . . . . . . PAN 001
Important / Mar '85.

## JUST A LIL' BIT COUNTRY.
**Tracks:** I can't stop loving you / Till I get it right / Pick me up on your way down / Loving you / I laughed a lot / Love on the rocks / Standing in your line / Rose coloured glasses / It meant nothing to me / Anybody that don't like Millie Jackson.
CD . . . . . . . . . . . . . . . . . .CDSEWM 089
South Bound / Jan '94 / Pinnacle.

## KISS YOU ALL OVER.
**Tracks:** Kiss you all over / Once you've had it.
■ 7″ . . . . . . . . . . . . . . . . . . . 2095091
Spring / '79.

## LIVE AND OUTRAGEOUS.
**Tracks:** Passion / Horse or a mule / Lover & girlfriends / Don't you ever stop / I had to say it / Still / Ugly man / This is it.
■ LP . . . . . . . . . . . . . . . . . . .2391 540
Spring / Mar '82.

## LIVE AND UNCENSORED.
**Tracks:** Keep the home fires burning / Logs and thangs / Put something down on it / Da ya think I'm sexy / Just when I needed you most / What am I waiting for / I still love you / All the way lover / Soaps / Hold the line / Be a sweetheart / Didn't I (blow your mind this time) / Give it up / Moment's pleasure / If loving you is wrong / I don't want to be right / Rap / Never change lovers / Sweet music man / It hurts so good.
■ Double LP . . . . . . . . . . . . . .2683 073
MC . . . . . . . . . . . . . . . . . . . .3571 011
Polydor / Jan '80 / PolyGram.
■ LP . . . . . . . . . . . . . . . . . . .TANLP 1
Important / Mar '85.

## LIVE AND UNCENSORED/LIVE AND OUTRAGEOUS.
**Tracks:** Keep the home fire burnin' / Logs and thangs / Put something down on it / Da ya think I'm

sexy / Just when I needed you most / Phuck u symphony / What am I waiting for / I still love you (you still love me) / All the way lover / Soaps / Hold the line / Be a sweetheart / Didn't I (blow your mind this time) / Give it up / Moment's pleasure / (If loving you is wrong) I don't want to be ri / Rap / Never change lovers in the middle of the night / Sweet music man / It hurts so good / Passion (On CD only) / Horse or mule (On CD only) / Lovers and girlfriends (On CD only) / Don't you ever stop loving me (On CD only) / I had to say it (On CD only) / Still (On CD only) / Ugly men (On CD only) / This is it (On CD only).
CD Set . . . . . . . . . . . . . . . .CDSEW2 038
■ Double LP . . . . . . . . . . . . .SEW2 038
■ MC Set . . . . . . . . . . . . . . SEWC2 038
South Bound / Mar '91 / Pinnacle.

## LOVE IS A DANGEROUS GAME.
**Tracks:** Love is a dangerous game.
■ CD Single . . . . . . . . . . . . . . .C135
Jive / '87.

## LOVING ARMS.
**Tracks:** Loving arms / Leftovers.
■ 7″ . . . . . . . . . . . . . . . . . . . POSP 254
Polydor / Apr '81.

## LOVINGLY YOURS.
**Tracks:** You can't turn me off / Something 'bout cha / I'll continue to love you / I can't say goodbye / Love of your own / I'll live my love for you / Body movements / From her arms to mine / Help me finish my song / I'll be rolling.
■ LP . . . . . . . . . . . . . . . . . . .2391 252
Spring / Feb '77.
CD . . . . . . . . . . . . . . . . . .CDSEWM 037
South Bound / Feb '91 / Pinnacle.

## MILLIE JACKSON.
**Tracks:** If this is love / I ain't giving up / I miss you baby / Child of God / Ask me what you want / My man, a sweet man / You're the joy of my life / I gotta get away from my own self / I just can't stand it / Strange things.
■ LP . . . . . . . . . . . . . . . . . . .2918005
Mojo / Jan '73.
CD . . . . . . . . . . . . . . . . . .CDSEW 009
■ LP . . . . . . . . . . . . . . . . . .SEW 009
■ MC . . . . . . . . . . . . . . . . . .SEWC 009
South Bound / Aug '89 / Pinnacle.

## MOMENT'S PLEASURE, A.
**Tracks:** Never change lovers in the middle of the night / Seeing you again / Kiss you all over / Moment's pleasure / What went wrong last night / Rising cost of love / We got to hit it off / Once you've had it.
■ MC . . . . . . . . . . . . . . . . . .3177 395
■ LP . . . . . . . . . . . . . . . . . . .2391395
Spring / Apr '79.
CD . . . . . . . . . . . . . . . . . .CDSEWM 053
Westbound / Sep '92 / Pinnacle.

## MY MAN, A SWEET MAN.
**Tracks:** My man, a sweet man / Here you come again / All the way lover / I'm a lover / Of your love.
■ 7″ . . . . . . . . . . . . . . . . . . .2093 002
Mojo / Jul '71.
■ 7″ . . . . . . . . . . . . . . . . . . .2093 022
Mojo / Nov '72.
■ 12″ . . . . . . . . . . . . . . . . . .POSPX 29
■ 7″ . . . . . . . . . . . . . . . . . . . POSP 29
Polydor / Feb '79.
■ 7″ . . . . . . . . . . . . . . . . . . .SEWS 702
■ CD Single . . . . . . . . . . . . . .CDSEWT 702
South Bound / Oct '89.

## NEVER CHANGE LOVERS IN THE MIDDLE OF THE NIGHT.
**Tracks:** Never change lovers in the middle of the night.
■ 7″ . . . . . . . . . . . . . . . . . . . POSP 51
Polydor / May '79.

## ROYAL RAPPIN'S (Jackson, Millie & Isaac Hayes).
**Tracks:** Sweet music, soft lights and you / Feels like the first time / You never cross my mind / Love changes / I changed my mind / Do you wanna make love / If I had my way / If you had your way / You needed me.
■ LP . . . . . . . . . . . . . . . . . . .2480516
Polydor / Nov '79.
CD . . . . . . . . . . . . . . . . . .CDSEWM 059
South Bound / Jan '93 / Pinnacle.

## SOMETHING YOU CAN FEEL.
**Tracks:** Something you can feel.
■ 12″ . . . . . . . . . . . . . . . . . .JIVET 175
■ 7″ . . . . . . . . . . . . . . . . . . .JIVE 175
Jive / May '88.

■ DELETED

213

## SPECIAL OCCASION.
**Tracks:** Special occaision / Blues don't get tired of me.
■ 7"...............................POSP 524
Polydor / Nov '82.

## STILL CAUGHT UP.
**Tracks:** Loving arms / Making the best of a bad situation / Memory of a wife / Tell her it's over / Do what makes you satisfied / You can't stand the thought of another me / Leftovers / I still love you (you still love me).
■ LP.................................2391 183
Polydor / Sep '75.
■ LP................................TANLP 3
MC.................................ZCTAN 3
Important / Sep '85.
CD.............................CDSEW 027
MC..............................SEWC 027
■ LP.............................SEW 027
South Bound / Jul '90 / Pinnacle.

## SWEET MUSIC MAN.
**Tracks:** Sweet music man / Feeling like a woman.
■ 7".................................2066973
Spring / Sep '78.

## THIS IS IT.
**Tracks:** This is it / Not on your life.
■ 7"...............................POSP 159
Polydor / Aug '80.

## TIDE IS TURNING, THE.
**Tracks:** Tide is turning / Are you that someone / You knocked the love (right outta..) / Let me show you / Something you can feel / In my dreams / Cover me (wall to wall) / I almost believed you.
■ LP...................................HIP 65
■ MC.................................HIPC 65
■ CD.................................CHIP 65
Jive / Jun '88.

## WANNA BE YOUR LOVER.
**Tracks:** Wanna be your lover / Mind over matter.
■ 12"...............................JIVET 142
■ 7"................................JIVE 142
Jive / May '87.

## YOUNG MAN, OLDER WOMAN.
**Tracks:** Not Advised.
CD................................ICH 1159CD
MC................................ICH 1159MC
Ichiban / Feb '94 / A.D.A. Distribution / Pinnacle / ACD Trading Ltd. / Koch International / Direct Distribution.

## Jackson, Rebbie

### CENTIPEDE.
**Tracks:** Centipede / Come alive, it's saturday night / Hey boy / Open up my love / Play me i'm a jukebox / I feel for you / Fork in the road / Ready for love.
■ LP..............................CBS 25926
CBS / Dec '84.

### CENTIPEDE.
**Tracks:** Centipede.
■ 12"................................TA 4528
■ 7"..................................A 4528
CBS / Jan '85.

### REACTION.
**Tracks:** Reaction / Reaction (instrumental).
■ 12"................................TA 7323
■ 7"..................................A 7323
CBS / Sep '86.

### REACTION.
**Tracks:** Reaction / Ain't no way to love / Ticket to love / You don't know what you're missing / You send the rain away / If you don't call (You don't care) / Always wanting something / Tonight I'm yours / Lessons (In the fine art of love).
■ LP...............................CBS 26961
■ MC.............................40 26961
CBS / Sep '86.

## Jackson, Tony

### LOVE BLIND.
**Tracks:** Love blind.
■ 12"...............................12CAG 2
■ 7"................................CAG 2
Cedar / Sep '84.

### LOVE I LOST, THE.
**Tracks:** Love I lose / Secretary in love.
■ 12"...............................OPINT 24
■ 7"................................OPIN 24
Opium / Jul '88.

## NEW YEAR'S RESOLUTION.
**Tracks:** New year's resolution.
■ 12"...............................12XMAS 1
■ 7"...............................XMAS 1
Cedar / Dec '84.

## SNOWY WHITE CHRISTMAS.
**Tracks:** Snowy white Christmas / New Years resoloution.
■ 12"...............................XMAS 121
Cedar / Oct '84.

## STEPPIN' OUT OF THE GROOVE.
**Tracks:** Steppin' out of the groove.
■ 7"....................................SW 6
Switch / Aug '83.

## SUMMER GROOVE.
**Tracks:** Summer groove.
■ 12"...............................12CAG 1
■ 7"................................CAG 1
Cedar / Jul '84.

## Jackson, Walter

### BABY I LOVE YOUR WAY.
**Tracks:** Baby I love your way / What would you do.
■ 7"................................UP 36250
United Artists / May '77.

### FEELING GOOD.
**Tracks:** Too shy to say / Play in the band / Welcome home / Please pardon me / Love is lovelier / Love woke me up this morning / Feelings / Words / I've got it bad feelin' good / Someone saved my life today.
■ LP................................UAS 30019
United Artists / Feb '77.

### IT'S COOL.
**Tracks:** It's cool / Magic man / If i had my way / Feelings / Tell me when it hurts / I won't remember ever loving you / Baby I love your way / Someone saved my life tonight / Got to find me an angel / Come to me / Open up your heart / Unchained melody / Love woke me up this morning / At last.
CD.............................CDCHARLY 305
Charly R&B / Feb '92 / Charly.

### MANHATTAN SKYLINE.
**Tracks:** Manhattan skyline / If I could see myself.
■ 7"................................UP 36384
United Artists / Apr '78.

### PORTRAIT OF WALTER JACKSON, A.
**Tracks:** Not Advised.
■ LP...............................BRLP 1001
Blue Bird (2) / Nov '84.

### SPEAK HER NAME.
**Tracks:** Speak her name / They don't give medals.
■ 7"................................DB 8154
Columbia / Mar '67.

### TOUCHING IN THE DARK.
**Tracks:** Touching in the dark.
■ 12"................................BRT 11
■ 7"...................................BR 11
Blue Bird (2) / Dec '84.

## Jacksons

By 1975, the success that Jackie, Tito, Marlon, Michael and Jermaine had enjoyed on Tamla as the Jackson Five was on the wane. Leaving Motown and Jermaine behind, group recruited sixth brother Randy (too young to join original group) and signed to Epic as the Jacksons (Motown retained rights to former moniker). Teamed with Gamble & Huff, they stormed back in '77 with U.S. million-seller Enjoy Yourself. Follow-up Show You The Way To Go returned them to limelight across Atlantic, becoming their first U.K. No. 1. Further success came with 1978 Destiny album and attendant smashes, Blame It On The Boogie and Shake Your Body (Down To The Ground). Following Michael's graduation into superstardom, Jacksons regrouped at close of 1980 for Triumph. Album fared well and yielded several hits - notably Can You Feel It? - but was inevitably overshadowed by Off The Wall, problem that escalated post-Thriller. '84 Victory album and tour were purely mercenary exercises, after which Michael refused to work with his brothers. Group continued with predictably diminished returns in late '80s, although 2300 Jackson Street boasted production by Teddy Riley and LA & Babyface.

## 2300 JACKSON STREET.
**Tracks:** Art of madness / Nothin' (that compares 2 U) / Maria / Private affair / 2300 Jackson Street / Harle / She / Alright with me / Play it up / Midnigh rendezvous / If you'd only believe.
■ CD................................463352
■ LP................................463352
■ MC................................463352
Epic / Jun '89.

## 2300 JACKSON STREET.
**Tracks:** 2300 Jackson Street (edit) (On 7" only) When I look at you / Keep her (On 12" & CD single.) 2300 Jackson Street (album version) (On 12" & C single.) / Please come back to me when I look at yo (Only on 12" (655206 )).
■ 12"...............................655206
■ 12"...............................655206
■ 7"................................655206
■ CD Single.........................655206
■ MC Single.........................655206
Epic / Aug '89.

## BLAME IT ON THE BOOGIE.
**Tracks:** Blame it on the boogie / Do what you wanna
■ 7"................................EPC 668
Epic / Sep '78.

## BODY.
**Tracks:** Body.
■ 7"..................................A 488
Epic / Nov '84.

## CAN YOU FEEL IT.
**Tracks:** Can you feel it / Wondering who / Shake you body (On 12" only).
■ 12"..............................EPC 13-955
■ 7"................................EPC 955
Epic / Feb '81.

## CAN YOU FEEL IT (OLD GOLD).
**Tracks:** Can you feel it / Walk right now.
12"................................OG 419
Old Gold / Sep '90 / Pickwick.

## DESTINY.
**Tracks:** Blame it on the boogie / Push me away Things I do for you / Shake your body / Destiny Bless his soul / All night dancin' / That's what yo get.
■ LP................................EPC 8320
Epic / May '79.
■ LP................................EPC 3238
Epic / '84.
■ MC.............................40 3238
■ CD...............................CD 3238
Epic / Jun '89.

## DESTINY.
**Tracks:** Destiny / That's what you get.
■ 7"................................EPC 698
Epic / Feb '79.

## DREAMER.
**Tracks:** Dreamer.
■ 7"................................EPC 545
Epic / Aug '77.

## ENJOY YOURSELF.
**Tracks:** Enjoy yourself.
■ 7"................................EPC 506
Epic / Apr '77.

## EVEN THOUGH YOU'VE GONE.
**Tracks:** Even though you've gone / Different kind o lady.
■ 7"................................EPC 591
Epic / Feb '78.

## GOIN' PLACES.
**Tracks:** Music's takin' over / Goin' places / Differen kind of lady / Even though you're gone / Jump for jo / Heaven knows I love you, girl / Man of war / D what you wanna / Find me a girl.
■ LP................................EPC 8603
Epic / Dec '77.
MC................................982836
Pickwick / Oct '92 / Pickwick.
CD................................982836
Pickwick/Sony Collector's Choice / May '94 / Pic wick / Pinnacle.

## GOIN' PLACES.
**Tracks:** Going places.
■ 7"................................EPC 573
Epic / Nov '77.

## HEARTBREAK HOTEL.
**Tracks:** Heartbreak hotel / Different kind of lady.
■ 7"................................EPC 939
Epic / Dec '80.

■ DELETE

Carleen Anderson - True Spirit (Clrca 1994)

Anita Baker - Compositions (Elektra 1990)

Anita Baker - Rapture (Elektra 1986)

Bobby Bland - His California Album (Probe 1973)

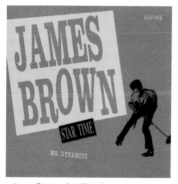

James Brown - Star Time Boxed Set (Disc 1)
(Polydor 1991)

G.C. Cameron - Give Me Your Love
(Malaco 1988)

Sam Cooke - The Man, His Music (RCA 1986)

Sam Dees - The Show Must Go On
(Atlantic 1973)

**Plate 1**

The Dells Vs. The Dramatics (Cadet 1974)

Will Downing - A Dream Fulfilled
(4th & Broadway 1991)

Lamont Dozier - Black Bach (ABC 1974)

Lamont Dozier - Peddlin' Music On The Side
(Warner 1977)

Earth, Wind And Fire (CBS 1977)

Earth, Wind And Fire - That's The Way Of The
World (CBS 1975)

Aretha Franklin - 30 Greatest Hits (Atlantic 1985)

Marvin Gaye - Here, My Dear (Motown 1979)

Plate 2

Marvin Gaye - Let's Get It On (Motown 1973)

Marvin Gaye - What's Going On
(Tamla Motown 1971)

Al Green - Al Green Is Love/Full Of Fire
(Hi! 1975/6)

Al Green - I'm Still In Love With You/Call Me
(Hi! 1972/3)

Donny Hathaway - Everything Is Everything
(Atlantic 1971)

Michael Henderson - Do It All (Buddah 1979)

Z.Z. Hill - The Rhythm And The Blues
(Malaco 1988)

Eddie Hinton - Very Extremely Dangerous
(Capricorn 1978)

**Plate 3**

Loleatta Holloway - Cry To Me (Aware 1975)

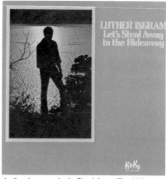

Luther Ingram - Let's Steal Away The Hideaway
(Koko 1976)

Millie Jackson - Caught Up (Polydor 1974)

Millie Jackson - Still Caught Up (Polydor 1975)

Al Jarreau - We Got By (Reprise 1975)

Linda Jones - Your Precious Love (Sequel 1991)

Latimore - It Ain't Where You Been.... (TK 1977)

Laura Lee (Buddah 1972)

**Plate 4**

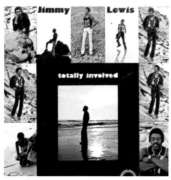

Jimmy Lewis - Totally Involved (Hot Atlanta 1974)

Teena Marie - It Must Be Magic (Motown 1981)

Teena Marie - Starchild (Epic 1984)

Curtis Mayfield - Back To The World
(Curtom 1973)

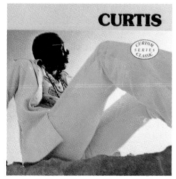

Curtis Mayfield - Curtis (Curtom 1970)

Curtis Mayfield - There's No Place Like America
Today (Curtom 1975)

Curtis Mayfield - Superfly O.S.T. (Curtom 1972)

Harold Melvin & The Bluenotes - To Be True
(Philadelphia 1975)

**Plate 5**

Me'shell NdegeOcello - Plantation Lullabies
(Maverick 1993)

Neville Brothers - Yellow Moon (A&M 1989)

The O'Jays - Ship Ahoy (Philadelphia 1975)

Parliament - Mothership Connection
(Casablanca 1975)

Teddy Pendergrass (Philadelphia 1979)

Esther Phillips (Kudu 1978)

Prince - Sign 'O' The Times (Paisley Park 1987)

Otis Redding - Otis Blue (Atlantic 1965)

**Plate 6**

Rufus & Chaka Khan - Ask Rufus (MCA 1977)

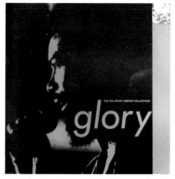

Gil Scott-Heron - Glory (Arista 1990)

The Soul Children - Friction (Stax 1974)

Staple Singers - Be What You Are (Stax 1973)

Staple Singers - Be Altitude: Respect Yourself
(Stax 1972)

Johnnie Taylor - Chronicle (Stax 1978)

Luther Vandross - Forever, For Always, For Love
(Epic 1982)

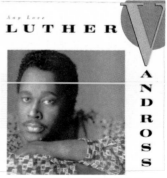

Luther Vandross - Any Love (Epic 1988)

**Plate 7**

Caron Wheeler - UK Blak (RCA 1990)

Bobby Womack - Looking For Love Again
(EMI-Manhattan 1974)

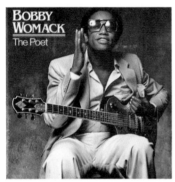

Bobby Womack - The Poet (Beverly Glen 1981)

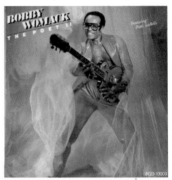

Bobby Womack - The Poet II (Beverly Glen 1984)

Stevie Wonder - Innervisions
(Tamla Motown 1973)

Stevie Wonder - Songs In The Key Of Life
(Motown 1976)

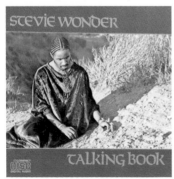

Stevie Wonder - Talking Book
(Tamla Motown 1972)

Young Disciples - Road To Freedom
(Talkin' Loud 1991)

**Plate 8**

## I'LL BE THERE (Jackson Five).
Tracks: I'll be there / ABC.
- 7" . . . . . . . . . . . . . . . . . . . TMG 758
Tamla Motown / Nov '70.
- 7" . . . . . . . . . . . . . . . . . . . TMG 969
Tamla Motown / May '75.

## JACKSONS IN CONCERT.
Tracks: Not Advised.
- VHS . . . . . . . . . . . . . . . . . . . V 158 B
VCL / Jan '84.

## JACKSONS, THE.
Tracks: Enjoy yourself / Think happy / Good times / Keep on dancing / Blues away / Show you the way to go / Living together / Strength of one man / Dreamer / Style of life.
- LP . . . . . . . . . . . . . . . . . . EPC 86009
Epic / Jul '77.
- LP . . . . . . . . . . . . . . . . . . EPC 88562
Epic / Dec '81.
- LP . . . . . . . . . . . . . . . . . . EPC 32101
Epic / May '82.
- LP . . . . . . . . . . . . . . . . . . CBS 32101
CBS / '88.
- CD . . . . . . . . . . . . . . . . . . CD 32101
- CD . . . . . . . . . . . . . . . . . . . 9827382
Pickwick/Sony Collector's Choice / Jun '94 / Pickwick / Pinnacle.

## LOVELY ONE.
Tracks: Lovely one / Can you feel it.
- 7" . . . . . . . . . . . . . . . . . . . EPC 9302
Epic / Oct '80.

## MAYBE TOMORROW (Jackson Five).
Tracks: Maybe tomorrow / She's good / Never can say goodbye / Wall / Petals / Sixteen candles / (We've got) Blue skies / My little baby / It's great to be here / Honey chile / I will find a way.
- LP . . . . . . . . . . . . . . . . . .STML 11188
Tamla Motown / Oct '71.
- CD . . . . . . . . . . . . . . . . . . . 5301612
Motown / Aug '93 / PolyGram.

## MUSIC'S TAKIN' OVER.
Tracks: Music's takin' over / Man of war.
- 7" . . . . . . . . . . . . . . . . . . . EPC 6263
Epic / Apr '78.

## NOTHIN' (THAT COMPARES 2 U).
Tracks: Nothin (that compares 2 U) (the mix) / Nothin (that compares 2 U) (extended version) / Nothin (that compares 2 U) (choice dub) / Heartbreak hotel / Alright with me.
- 12" . . . . . . . . . . . . . . . . . . . 6548081
- 12" . . . . . . . . . . . . . . . . . . . 6548086
- 7" . . . . . . . . . . . . . . . . . . . 6549098
- 7" . . . . . . . . . . . . . . . . . . . 6548087
- CD Single . . . . . . . . . . . . . . . 6548082
- MC Single . . . . . . . . . . . . . . . 6548084
Epic / Apr '89.

## ORIGINAL CLASSIC ALBUM.
Tracks: Not Advised.
- CD . . . . . . . . . . . . . . . . . . . 9826402
Pickwick/Sony Collector's Choice / Nov '91 / Pickwick / Pinnacle.

## SHAKE YOUR BODY (DOWN TO THE GROUND).
Tracks: Shake your body.
- 7" . . . . . . . . . . . . . . . . . . . CBS 7181
CBS / Apr '82.

## SHAKE YOUR BODY (DOWN TO THE GROUND) (OLD GOLD).
Tracks: Shake your body (down to the ground) / Blame it on the boogie.
- 12" . . . . . . . . . . . . . . . . . . .OG 4142
Old Gold / Nov '89.

## SHAKE YOUR BODY DOWN (TO THE GROUND).
Tracks: Shake your body.
- 7" . . . . . . . . . . . . . . . . . . . EPC 7181
Epic / Mar '79.

## SHOW YOU THE WAY TO GO.
Tracks: Show you the way to go / Blame it on the boogie.
- 7" . . . . . . . . . . . . . . . . . . . EPC 5266
Epic / Jun '77.

## THINGS I DO FOR YOU.
Tracks: Things I do for you / Don't stop till you get enough.
- 12" . . . . . . . . . . . . . . . . . . . TA 4431
Epic / Jun '84.
- 7" . . . . . . . . . . . . . . . . . . . .A 4431
Epic / Jun '84.
- 7" . . . . . . . . . . . . . . . . . . . EPCA 1902
Epic / Dec '81.

## TIME OUT FOR THE BURGLAR.
Tracks: Time out for the burglar / News at 11.
- 12" . . . . . . . . . . . . . . . . . . . MCAS 1129
MCA / Feb '87.

## TIME WAITS FOR NO ONE.
Tracks: Time waits for no one / Give it up.
- 7" . . . . . . . . . . . . . . . . . . . EPCA 1579
Epic / Sep '81.

## TORTURE.
Tracks: Torture / Show you the way to go / Blame it on the boogie.
- 12" . . . . . . . . . . . . . . . . . . . TA 4675
Epic / Aug '84.
- 7" . . . . . . . . . . . . . . . . . . . .A 4675
Epic / Aug '84.

## TRIUMPH.
Tracks: Can you feel it / Lovely one / Your ways / Everybody / This place hotel / Time waits for no one / Walk right now / Give it up / Wondering who.
- LP . . . . . . . . . . . . . . . . . . EPC 86112
Epic / Oct '80.
- LP . . . . . . . . . . . . . . . . . . EPC 32366
Epic / Jun '85.
- MC . . . . . . . . . . . . . . . . . . .40 32366
Epic / Jun '85.
- CD . . . . . . . . . . . . . . . . . . CD 86112
CBS / Nov '87.
- CD . . . . . . . . . . . . . . . . . . .986640 2
Pickwick/Sony Collector's Choice / Mar '94 / Pickwick / Pinnacle.

## VICTORY.
Tracks: Torture / Wait / One more chance / Be not always / State of shock / We can change the world / Hurt / Body.
- LP . . . . . . . . . . . . . . . . . . EPC 86303
Epic / Jul '84.
- CD . . . . . . . . . . . . . . . . . . CD 86303
Epic / May '87.
- LP . . . . . . . . . . . . . . . . . . .4504501
Epic / Sep '94 / Sony.
- CD . . . . . . . . . . . . . . . . . . .450450-2
- MC . . . . . . . . . . . . . . . . . . .4504504
Epic / Sep '94 / Sony.

## WAIT.
Tracks: Wait / She's out of my life.
- 12" . . . . . . . . . . . . . . . . . . . TA 6105
Epic / Mar '85.
- 7" . . . . . . . . . . . . . . . . . . . .A 6105
Epic / Mar '85.

## WALK RIGHT NOW.
Tracks: Walk right now / Your ways.
- 7" . . . . . . . . . . . . . . . . .EPC A 1294
Epic / Jul '81.
- 12" . . . . . . . . . . . . . . . . . . EPC 13-1294
Epic / Jun '81.

# Jacobs, Debbie

## HIGH ON YOUR LOVE.
Tracks: High on your love / I can never forget a friend.
- 7" . . . . . . . . . . . . . . . . . . . MCA 597
MCA / Jun '80.

## UNDERCOVER LOVER.
Tracks: Undercover lover / Think I'm falling in love.
- 7" . . . . . . . . . . . . . . . . . . . MCA 520
MCA / Aug '79.

# Jacobs, Hank

## SO FAR AWAY.
Tracks: So far away / Out of sight / Hank's groove / Summertime.
- 7" . . . . . . . . . . . . . . . . . . . ENS 5
Ensign / Oct '83.

# Jade

## DON'T WALK AWAY.
Tracks: Don't walk away / Don't walk away (mixes).
- 12" . . . . . . . . . . . . . . . . . .W 0160T
- 7" . . . . . . . . . . . . . . . . . . . W 0160
- CD Single . . . . . . . . . . . . . . .W 0160CD
- MC Single . . . . . . . . . . . . . . .W 0160C
Giant / Mar '93.

## I CAN'T BELIEVE IT'S OVER.
Tracks: I can't believe it's over / Blue jade (Extra track on 12" version only).

- 12" . . . . . . . . . . . . . . . . . . . TWD 1953
Master Funk / Oct '86.

## I WANNA LOVE YOU.
Tracks: I wanna love you / Don't walk away / I wanna love you (mixes) (On CD Single and 12" only).
- 12" . . . . . . . . . . . . . . . . . .W 0140T
- 7" . . . . . . . . . . . . . . . . . . . W 0140
- CD Single . . . . . . . . . . . . . . .W 0140CD
WEA / Nov '92.
- 12" . . . . . . . . . . . . . . . . 74321 151661
- 7" . . . . . . . . . . . . . . . . 74321 151667
- CD Single . . . . . . . . . . . . 74321 151661
- MC Single . . . . . . . . . . . . 74321 151664
Arista / Jun '93.

## JADE.
Tracks: Not Advised.
- 12" . . . . . . . . . . . . . . . . . . . ZEN 1204
Ninja Tune / Sep '92.

## JADE TO THE MAX.
Tracks: Don't walk away / I wanna love you / I want 'cha baby / That boy / Out with the girls / Hold me close / One woman / Give me what I'm missing / Looking for Mr. Do Right / Don't ask my neighbor / Blessed.
- CD . . . . . . . . . . . . . . . . .759924466-2
- MC . . . . . . . . . . . . . . . . .759924466-4
WEA / Mar '93 / WEA.

## MIND BODY AND SONG.
Tracks: When will I see you again (intro) / Everyday of the week / Hangin' / What's goin' on / 5432 (Yo-Time is up) / I like the way / Do you want me / If the mood is right / Bedroom / If the lovin' ain't good / Let's get it on / It's on / There's not a man / Everything / Mind body and song.
- CD . . . . . . . . . . . . . . . . 74321 22605 26
- MC . . . . . . . . . . . . . . . . 74321 22605 40
Giant / Oct '94 / BMG.

## MIND, BODY & SONG.
Tracks: Not Advised.
- CD . . . . . . . . . . . . . . . . .7432122605-2
- MC . . . . . . . . . . . . . . . . .7432122605-4
Giant / Nov '94 / BMG.

## MR JOY.
Tracks: Mr. Joy / Don't love / Let me / Sweet love (Instrumental) / Freak / Sweet love.
- CD . . . . . . . . . . . . . . . . . . . TLCD 447
- LP . . . . . . . . . . . . . . . . . . . TRPL 119
Timeless (Soul) / Oct '89.

## ONE WOMAN.
Tracks: One woman / Don't walk away / One woman (remix) (On 12" & CD single only) / Don't walk away (remix) (On CD single & 12" only).
- 12" . . . . . . . . . . . . . . . . .7432116512-1
- CD Single . . . . . . . . . . . . .7432116512-2
- MC Single . . . . . . . . . . . . .7432116512-4
- 7" . . . . . . . . . . . . . . . . .7432116512-7
Giant / Sep '93.

# Jamariah

## BEVERLY.
Tracks: Beverly / Don't go trippin over me / Let's turn the lights down low.
- 12" . . . . . . . . . . . . . . . . .EXPAND 46
Expansion / Jul '93.

# James, Etta

L.A.-born R&B singer who rose to prominence on the Johnny Otis show in 1955. Her first major single was *Dance With Me Henry*; followed by a series of successes on Chess label from 1960 to the mid-'70s. Among them were two classics: a version of the much-covered *I'd Rather Go Blind* and *Tell Mama* - her biggest U.S. hit. Both were recorded at Muscle Shoals studio in '68. James finally kicked a career-long heroin addiction - documented in her *Out On The Streets, Again* - in the mid-'80s, and signed to Island. Her first album of the '90s, *Stickin' To My Guns*, reunited her with the Muscle Shoals studio.

## AT LAST.
Tracks: Anything to say you're mine / My dearest darling / Trust in me / Sunday kind of love / Tough Mary / I just want to make love to you / At last / All I could do was cry / Stormy weather / Girl of my dreams.
- LP . . . . . . . . . . . . . . . . . . . GCH 8036
- MC . . . . . . . . . . . . . . . . . . GCHK 78036
Chess (Charly) / Oct '87 / Charly.
- CD . . . . . . . . . . . . . . . . . . . CHD 9266
- LP . . . . . . . . . . . . . . . . . . . CH 9266
Chess (MCA) / Jul '90.

**CD** . . . . . . . . . . . . . . . . . . . . . .CHLD 19168
Chess (MCA) / Nov '91 / BMG.
**CD** . . . . . . . . . . . . . . . . . . . . . .CDCD 1053
Charly / Mar '93 / Charly.

## AVENUE D (James, Etta & David A Stewart).
**Tracks:** Avenue D / My head is a city / Avenue D (Kevorkian remix) / Avenue D (Avenue dub) / Avenue D (sound assassins mix).
■ **12"** . . . . . . . . . . . . . . . . . . . . . 12CL 533
■ **7"** . . . . . . . . . . . . . . . . . . . . . .CL 533
Capitol / May '89.

## BACK IN THE BLUES.
**Tracks:** Tell mama / Pushover / All I could do was cry / My dearest darling / At last / I'd rather go blind / Trust in me / Sunday kind of love / Something's got a hold on me / Stop the wedding.
**CD** . . . . . . . . . . . . . . . . . . . . . 26 10 102
**MC** . . . . . . . . . . . . . . . . . . . . . 26 10 104
Dillion / '92 / Sound Solutions.

## BLUES IN THE NIGHT (James, Etta & Eddie 'Cleanhead' Vinson).
**Tracks:** Kidney stew / Railroad porter blues / Something's got a hold on me / Medley: at last / Trust in me / Sunday kind of love / I just wanna make love to you / Please send me someone to love / Love man / Misty.
■ **LP** . . . . . . . . . . . . . . . . . . . . . . F 9647
**MC** . . . . . . . . . . . . . . . . . . . . . . 5F 9647
Fantasy / Nov '86 / Pinnacle / Jazz Music.
**CD** . . . . . . . . . . . . . . . . . . . . . .FCD 9647
Ace / Apr '94 / Pinnacle / Complete Record Co. Ltd.

## CHESS MASTERS.
**Tracks:** Not Advised.
■ **LP** . . . . . . . . . . . . . . . . . . . . CXMP 2000
Chess (PRT) / Apr '81.

## CHESS MASTERS.
**Tracks:** Tell Mama / I'd rather go blind / Watchdog / Love of my man / I'm gonna take what he's got / Some rope / Security / Steal away / My mother in law / Don't lose your good thing / It hurts me so much / Just a little bit / Something's got a hold on me / Baby what you want me to do / What I'd say / Money / Seven day fool / Sweet little angel / Ooh poo pah doo / Woke up this morning.
■ **LP Set** . . . . . . . . . . . . . . . . . .CXMD 4017
Chess (PRT) / Apr '83.

## CHICAGO GOLDEN YEARS.
**Tracks:** Not Advised.
■ **Double LP** . . . . . . . . . . . . . . . . . .427014
Vogue / Oct '88.

## COME A LITTLE CLOSER.
**Tracks:** Out on the street again / Mama told me / You give me what I want / Come a little closer / Let's burn down the cornfield / Powerplay / Feeling uneasy / St. Louis blues / Gonna have some fun tonight / Sooki sooki.
■ **LP** . . . . . . . . . . . . . . . . . . . . GCH 8047
**MC** . . . . . . . . . . . . . . . . . . . . GCHK 78047
Chess (Charly) / May '88 / Charly.

## DEEP IN THE NIGHT.
**Tracks:** Laying beside you / Piece of my heart / Only women bleed / Take it to the limit / Lovesick blues / Strange man / Sugar on the floor / Sweet touch of love / I'd rather go blind.
■ **LP** . . . . . . . . . . . . . . . . . . . . . K 56492
WEA / Jul '78.

## ETTA JAMES LIVE.
**Tracks:** Not Advised.
**CD** . . . . . . . . . . . . . . . . . . 598 1099 20
Tomato (1) / Jul '94 / RTM / Pinnacle.

## GOLDEN DECADE.
**Tracks:** You got it / In the basement / Baby what you want me to do / Sunday kind of love / Lovin' more everyday / 842-2089 / Pay back / I'd rather go blind / Tell Mama / Something's got a hold on me / Security / At last / Stop the wedding / Two sides / Losers weepers / Pushover.
■ **LP** . . . . . . . . . . . . . . . . . . . . . 6710126
Chess / Dec '72.

## GOOD ROCKIN' MAMA.
**Tracks:** Dance with me Henry / Do something crazy / Woman / I hope you're satisfied / Strange things happening / Good rockin' daddy / Hey Henry / That's all / I'm a fool.
■ **LP** . . . . . . . . . . . . . . . . . . . . 10 CH 33
Ace / May '81.

## GOOD ROCKIN' MAMA/TUFF LOVER.
**Tracks:** Good rockin' mama / Dance with me Henry / Do something crazy / Woman / I hope you're satisfied / Strange things happening / Good rockin' daddy / Hey Henry / I'm a fool / That's all / Tough lover /

Pick-up / By the light of the silvery moon / Fools we mortals be / Come what may / Good lookin' / Tears of joy / Shortnin' bread rock / Baby every night / Then I'll care / Market place.
**MC Set** . . . . . . . . . . . . . . . . . . .CHC 803
Ace / Feb '85 / Pinnacle / Complete Record Co. Ltd.

## GOSPEL SOUL OF ETTA JAMES.
**Tracks:** Not Advised.
**CD** . . . . . . . . . . . . . . . . . . . . KWEST 5403
Disky / Sep '93 / THE.

## HER GREATEST SIDES VOL.1.
**Tracks:** Tell mama / Something's got a hold on me / Pushover / Only time will tell / Stop the wedding / Security / I'd rather go blind / Trust in me / Sunday kind of love / My dearest darling / At last / Waiting for Charlie to come home / All I could do was cry / Fool that I am.
■ **LP** . . . . . . . . . . . . . . . . . . . . GCH 8015
**MC** . . . . . . . . . . . . . . . . . . . . GCHK 78015
Chess (Charly) / '87 / Charly.

## I GOT THE WILL.
**Tracks:** I got the will / Come to Mama / One night (Available on 10" and CD only).
■ **10"** . . . . . . . . . . . . . . . . . . . . 10 IS 418
■ **7"** . . . . . . . . . . . . . . . . . . . . . IS 418
■ **CD Single** . . . . . . . . . . . . . . . . . CID 418
Island / Jul '89.

## I PREFER YOU.
**Tracks:** I prefer you / I'm so glad.
■ **7"** . . . . . . . . . . . . . . . . . . . . CRS 8052
Chess / Jan '67.

## JUICY PEACHES.
**Tracks:** Next door to the blues / Pay back / Two sides to every story / Loving you more every day / That's all I want from you / It must be your love / Don't pick me for your fool / Do right woman / I worship the ground you walk on / You got it / Almost persuaded / Tighten up your own thing / Losers weepers / I found a love.
■ **LP** . . . . . . . . . . . . . . . . . . . . GCH 8116
Chess (Charly) / '89.

## LATE SHOW, THE (James, Etta & Eddie 'Cleanhead' Vinson).
**Tracks:** Cleanhead blues / Old maid boogie / Home boy / Cherry red / Baby what you want me to do / Sweet little angel / I'd rather go blind / Teach me tonight / Only women bleed / He's got the whole world in his hand.
**CD** . . . . . . . . . . . . . . . . . . . . .FCD 9655-2
Ace / Apr '94 / Pinnacle / Complete Record Co. Ltd.

## LEGENDARY HITS.
**Tracks:** Not Advised.
**CD** . . . . . . . . . . . . . . . . . . . . . 90152-2
Jazz Archives (USA) / Oct '92 / Jazz Music / Discovery / Cadillac.

## LIVE AT MONTREUX.
**Tracks:** Hot Pants Road / Tell mama / I'd rather go blind / Something's got a hold on me / Damn your eyes / Breaking up somebody's home / Baby what you want me to do / Hoochie coochie man / I got the will / Sugar on the floor.
**VHS** . . . . . . . . . . . . . . . . . . . . IVA 052
Island Visual Arts / Jul '90 / PolyGram / THE.

## LIVE AT MONTREUX: ETTA JAMES.
**Tracks:** Not Advised.
**VHS** . . . . . . . . . . . . . . . . . . . . 0829363
Polygram Music Video / '92 / PolyGram.

## MISS PEACHES SINGS THE SOUL.
**Tracks:** Not Advised.
**CD** . . . . . . . . . . . . . . . . . . . . . TS 21
That's Soul / Apr '94 / BMG.

## MYSTERY LADY.
**Tracks:** Don't explain / You've changed / Man I love / I don't stand a ghost of a chance (with you) / Embraceable you / How deep is the ocean / (I'm afraid) The masquerade is over / Body and soul / Very thought of you / Lover man (Oh where can you be) / I'll be seeing you.
**CD** . . . . . . . . . . . . . . . . . 1005 82114-2
Private Music / Apr '94 / Silver Sounds (CD) / BMG.

## ON CHESS.
**Tracks:** Not Advised.
**CD** . . . . . . . . . . . . . . . . . . VGCD 600 175
Vogue / Oct '88 / BMG.

## PEACHES.
**Tracks:** Lovin' you more every day / I'd rather go blind / Only time will tell / At last / All I could do was cry / Stop the wedding / Two sides / Pushover / Losers weepers / Security / Tell Mama / Something's gotta hold on me / Sunday kind of love / Next door to the blues / Trust in me (and many more).

■ **LP Set** . . . . . . . . . . . . . . . . . . .66710
Chess / Oct '71.

## PIECE OF MY HEART.
**Tracks:** Piece of my heart / Lovesick blues.
■ **7"** . . . . . . . . . . . . . . . . . . . . . K 171
WEA / Jun '78.

## R & B DYNAMITE.
**Tracks:** W.O.M.A.N. / Number one / I'm a fool / Strange things happening / Hey Henry / I ho you're satisfied / Good rockin' daddy / Sunshine love / That's all / How big a fool / Market place Tough lover / Do something crazy / Be my love dovey / Nobody loves you (like me) / Hickory dicko dock / You know what I mean / Wallflower / Bat baby, every night / We're in love / Tears of jo (Available on CD and cassette only) / Pick-up (Ava able on CD and cassette only).
**MC** . . . . . . . . . . . . . . . . . . . . .CHC 2
Ace / Jun '87 / Pinnacle / Complete Record Co. Lt
**CD** . . . . . . . . . . . . . . . . . . . . .CDCH 2
■ **LP** . . . . . . . . . . . . . . . . . . . . . CH 2
Ace / Nov '93 / Pinnacle / Complete Record Co. Lt

## R & B QUEEN.
**Tracks:** My one and only / Pick-up / I'm a fool / the light of the silvery moon / Come what may That's all / Tough lover / Dance with me Henry Tears of joy / Baby baby every night / Do somethi crazy / Market place.
■ **LP** . . . . . . . . . . . . . . . . . . . . GEM 0
■ **MC** . . . . . . . . . . . . . . . . . . . . GEMC 0
Crown / Feb '86.

## RIGHT TIME, THE.
**Tracks:** I sing the blues / Love and happiness Evening of love / Wet match / You're taking another man's place / Give it up / Let it rock / nine nine and a half (won't do) / You've got me / Nightin is the rightime / Down home blues.
**CD** . . . . . . . . . . . . . . . . . . . 755961347
**MC** . . . . . . . . . . . . . . . . . . . 755961347
WEA / Oct '92 / WEA.

## ROCKS THE HOUSE.
**Tracks:** Something's got a hold on me / Baby wha you want me to do / What I say / Money / Seven da fool / Sweet little angel / Ooh poo pah doo / Woke u this morning.
■ **LP** . . . . . . . . . . . . . . . . . . . . GCH 803
**MC** . . . . . . . . . . . . . . . . . . . . GCHK 7803
Chess (Charly) / Apr '88.

## SEVEN YEAR ITCH.
**Tracks:** I got the will / Jump into the fire / Shake ground / Come to Mama / Damn your eyes / Breaki up somebody's home / Jealous kind / How strong a woman / It ain't always what you do / One night
■ **LP** . . . . . . . . . . . . . . . . . . . . ILPS 992
**MC** . . . . . . . . . . . . . . . . . . . . .ICT 992
■ **CD** . . . . . . . . . . . . . . . . . . . . CID 992
Island / Mar '89 / PolyGram.

## SOMETHING'S GOT A HOLD.
**Tracks:** Not Advised.
**CD** . . . . . . . . . . . . . . . . . . . . . CDRB
Charly R&B / Apr '94 / Charly.

## SOMETHING'S GOT A HOLD ON M (Vol. 2).
**Tracks:** Not Advised.
**CD** . . . . . . . . . . . . . . . . . . . . RTS 3303
■ **MC** . . . . . . . . . . . . . . . . . . . . RTS 4303
Roots / May '92 / Pinnacle / Target.

## SOULFUL MISS PEACHES.
**Tracks:** Tell Mama / I'd rather go blind / Security I'm loving you more everyday / Mellow fellows / I the basement, part 1 (Duet with Sugar Pie De Santo / Love of my man / Same rope / I'm gonna take wha he's got / Just a little bit / Steal away / I'm waiting fo Charlie to come home / You got it / Almost per suaded / I got you babe / Losers, weepers / All th way down / Let's burn down the cornfield / Feelin uneasy / Out on the street, again.
**CD** . . . . . . . . . . . . . . . . . . . . CPCD 801
Charly / Feb '94 / Charly.

## STICKIN' TO MY GUNS.
**Tracks:** Not Advised.
**CD** . . . . . . . . . . . . . . . . . . . . . CID 995
■ **LP** . . . . . . . . . . . . . . . . . . . . .ILPS 995
■ **MC** . . . . . . . . . . . . . . . . . . . . .ICT 995
Island / Apr '90 / PolyGram.

## STICKING TO MY GUNS.
**Tracks:** Not Advised.
**CD** . . . . . . . . . . . . . . . . . . . . IMCD 19
Island Masters / Jul '94 / PolyGram.

■ DELETE

## AKE IT TO THE LIMIT.
racks: Take it to the limit / Strange man.
■ 7″ . . . . . . . . . . . . . . . . . . . . . K 17224
WEA / Sep '78.

## ELL MAMA.
racks: If I can't have you / Spoonful / Nobody but
ou / Next door to the blues / Something's got a hold
n me / (You better) do right / I'm loving you more
veryday / Breaking point / Mellow fellow / Steal
way / Just a little bit / Don't lose your good thing /
Watch dog / I'm gonna take what he's got / I'd rather
o blind / Love of my man / It hurts me so much /
ame rope / I got you babe / I worship the ground
ou walk on / You got it / Fire / Miss Pitiful.
O . . . . . . . . . . . . . . . . . . . . . CDRED 7
harly / Oct '88 / Charly.
■ CD . . . . . . . . . . . . . . . . . . CHD 9269
hess (MCA) / Feb '90.
O . . . . . . . . . . . . . . . . . . .CHLD 19035
hess (MCA) / Apr '92 / BMG.

## ELL MAMA.
racks: Tell mama / Security / Something's got a
old on me / I'd rather go blind.
■ 7″ . . . . . . . . . . . . . . . . . . CHES 4005
hess (PRT) / Jul '85.

## ELL MAMA.
racks: I'd rather go blind / Watchdog / Love of my
an / Tell mama / Gonna take what he's got / Same
ope / Security / Steal away / My mother-in-law /
on't lose your good thing / It hurts me so much /
ust a little bit.
■ LP . . . . . . . . . . . . . . . . . . . CRL 4536
hess / May '68.

## ELL MAMA VOL.1.
racks: Not Advised.
O . . . . . . . . . . . . . . . . . . . RTS 33003
C. . . . . . . . . . . . . . . . . . . . RTS 43003
oots / Nov '90 / Pinnacle / Target.

## HIS COUNTRY'S ROCKIN'.
racks: Not Advised.
HS . . . . . . . . . . . . . . . . . MMGVE 002
agnum / Jun '93 / THE.

## UFF LOVER.
racks: Tough lover / Pick-up / By the light of the
very moon / Fools we mortals be / Come what may
Dance with me Henry / Good lookin' / Tears of joy /
hortnin' bread rock / Baby every night / Then I'll
are / Market place.
. . . . . . . . . . . . . . . . . . . . . CH 73
ce / Nov '93 / Pinnacle / Complete Record Co. Ltd.

## James, Jimmy

## IN'T LOVE GOOD (James, Jimmy &
he Vagabonds).
racks: Ain't love good / Don't know what I'm gonna
o.
■ 7″ . . . . . . . . . . . . . . . . . . 7N 35349
ccadilly / Jun '66.

## ANCIN TILL DAWN.
acks: I can't stop my feet from dancin' / Be what
ou, wanna be / If you think funk is junk you're drunk
Till I can't take it anymore / Girl, I really love you /
ow that you've gone / You made love again / Tell
e world.
MC. . . . . . . . . . . . . . . . . . . .ZNC 101
■ LP . . . . . . . . . . . . . . . . . . . N 101
RT / Jul '79.

## OLDEN HOUR OF JIMMY JAMES
ames, Jimmy & The Vagabonds).
acks: Now is the time / Disco fever / Red red wine /
uspicious love / Stay with me / I want you so much /
hatever happened to the love we knew / You don't
and a chance / I'll go where your music takes me /
ancing to the music of love / Till I can't take
nymore / Let's have fun / I know you don't love me
at you got me anyway / Never had this dream
efore / Your love keeps haunting me / Come lay
me lovin' on me / Chains of love.
■ LP . . . . . . . . . . . . . . . . . . GH 679
olden Hour / Mar '79.

## ELP YOURSELF (James, Jimmy & The
agabonds).
acks: Help yourself.
■ 7″ . . . . . . . . . . . . . . . . . . TR 7806
ojan / '70.

## I DIDDLEY DEE DUM DUM.
acks: Hi diddley dee dum dum / Come to me softly.
■ 7″ . . . . . . . . . . . . . . . . . . 7N 35320
ccadilly / May '66.

## I CAN'T GET BACK HOME TO MY BABY.
Tracks: I can't get back home to my baby / Hungry
for love.
■ 7″ . . . . . . . . . . . . . . . . . . 7N 35360
Piccadilly / Jan '67.

## I'LL GO WHERE YOUR MUSIC TAKES
ME.
Tracks: I'll go where your music takes me.
■ 7″ . . . . . . . . . . . . . . . . . . 7N 45585
Pye / Apr '76.

## I'LL GO WHERE YOUR MUSIC TAKES
ME (OLD GOLD).
Tracks: I'll go where your music takes me / Now is
the time.
■ 7″ . . . . . . . . . . . . . . . . . .OG 9137
Old Gold / Jul '82.

## IF YOU THINK THAT FUNK IS JUNK
YOU'RE DRUNK.
Tracks: If you think that funk is junk you're drunk /
Let's go disco.
■ 7″ . . . . . . . . . . . . . . . . . . 7N 46195
Pye / Apr '79.

## LIFE.
Tracks: Life / Whatcha gonna do.
■ 7″ . . . . . . . . . . . . . . . . . . 7N 45665
Pye / Feb '77.

## LOVE FIRE.
Tracks: Love fire / Live for the night.
■ 7″ . . . . . . . . . . . . . . . . . .ERC 110
■ 12″ . . . . . . . . . . . . . . . . . .ERCL 110
ERC / Apr '84.

## NO GOOD TO CRY.
Tracks: No good to cry / You showed me the way.
■ 7″ . . . . . . . . . . . . . . . . . . 7N 35374
Piccadilly / May '67.

## NO HOLDS BARRED (see under Wash-
ington, Geno).

## NOW IS THE TIME.
Tracks: Now is the time / I'll go where your music
takes me / Missing you.
■ 7″ . . . . . . . . . . . . . . . . . . 7N 45606
Pye / Jul '76.
■ 12″ . . . . . . . . . . . . . . . . . .NINE 5
■ 7″ . . . . . . . . . . . . . . . . . . NINE 75
Nine O Nine / May '87.

## NOW THAT YOU'VE GONE.
Tracks: Now that you've gone / Girl I really love you.
■ 7″ . . . . . . . . . . . . . . . . . .7P 116
PRT / Jul '79.

## REACH OUT.
Tracks: Reach out / Now is the time.
■ 12″ . . . . . . . . . . . . . . . . . .ERCL 119
■ 7″ . . . . . . . . . . . . . . . . . .ERC 119
ERC / Aug '84.

## RED RED WINE (James, Jimmy & The
Vagabonds).
Tracks: Red red wine.
■ 7″ . . . . . . . . . . . . . . . . . . 7N 17579
Pye / Sep '68.

## RIVERBOAT JENNY.
Tracks: River boat Jenny / If I wasn't black (would I
be white).
■ 7″ . . . . . . . . . . . . . . . . . . CS 2095
Contempo (1) / Oct '76.

## YOU DON'T STAND A CHANCE IF YOU
CAN'T DANCE (James, Jimmy & The
Vagabonds).
Tracks: You don't stand a chance if you can't dance.
■ 7″ . . . . . . . . . . . . . . . . . . 7N 45443
Pye / Jan '75.

## YOU MADE ME LOVE AGAIN.
Tracks: You made me love again / Dreams.
■ 7″ . . . . . . . . . . . . . . . . . . 7N 46039
Pye / Jan '78.

## James, Josie

## CALL ME (WHEN YOU NEED MY LOVE).
Tracks: Call me (when you need my love) / Win your
love.
■ 12″ . . . . . . . . . . . . . . . . . .12TPL 1
■ 7″ . . . . . . . . . . . . . . . . . .7TPL 1
TPL / Aug '85.

## DANCE YOU UP.
Tracks: Dance you up.
■ 12″ . . . . . . . . . . . . . . . . . 12 TPL 2

■ 7″ . . . . . . . . . . . . . . . . . . TPLO 2
One Little Indian / Aug '86.

## MORNING GLOW.
Tracks: Not Advised.
■ 12″ . . . . . . . . . . . . . . . .EXPAND 32
Expansion / Oct '92.

## WIN YOUR LOVE.
Tracks: Win your love.
■ 12″ . . . . . . . . . . . . . . . .EXPAND 28
Expansion / Jun '92.

## James, Rick

Before Prince started selling, Rick James
ruled punk-funk: his 1981 *Street Songs* album spent over a year on U.S. charts, yielding enormous *Super Freak* single, which in
turn kickstarted MC Hammer's career as
source of *You Can't Touch This*. Born in
New York, teenage James absconded from
U.S. Navy to Canada (hence one of soul's
least plausible teamings: Toronto band My-
nah Birds, featuring Rick James and Neil
Young). He later graduated from backroom
boy to recording artist at Motown; debut
*Come Get It* was first of three hit LPs in '78.
He also helped Teena Marie up first rungs
of fame's ladder. Early '80s were less pro-
sperous: he was eclipsed by arch-rival
Prince and sandbagged by addiction, but
still mastermind success of Mary Jane
Girls (named after one of his own songs),
who made classic *All Night Long*. Fortunes
improved in '84/'85, notably with *Glow* album, but conflicts with Motown caused him
to jump ship. *Loosey's Rap* was hit on new
label Reprise, but sadly proved to be his
last major success before old bad habits
dragged career down once more.

## 17.
Tracks: 17.
■ 12″ . . . . . . . . . . . . . . . . . TMGT 1348
■ 7″ . . . . . . . . . . . . . . . . . .TMG 1348
Motown / Jul '84.

## BIG TIME.
Tracks: Big time / Island lady.
■ 12″ . . . . . . . . . . . . . . . . 12TMG 1198
Motown / Aug '80.
■ 7″ . . . . . . . . . . . . . . . . . .TMG 1198
Motown / Oct '81.

## BUSTIN' OUT.
Tracks: Bustin' out / Sexy lady.
■ 7″ . . . . . . . . . . . . . . . . . .TMG 1147
Motown / Jun '79.

## BUSTIN' OUT OF L SEVEN.
Tracks: Bustin' out / High on your love suite / One
more shot of your love / Love interlude / Spacey love
/ Cop 'n' blow / Jefferson ball / Fool on the street.
■ LP . . . . . . . . . . . . . . . . . .STML 12104
Motown / Oct '81.

## CAN'T STOP.
Tracks: Can't stop / Oh what a night for luv.
■ 12″ . . . . . . . . . . . . . . . . . TMG 1378T
■ 7″ . . . . . . . . . . . . . . . . . .TMG 1378
Motown / Mar '85.

## COLD BLOODED.
Tracks: Doin' it / U bring the freak out / 123 (U, her
and me) / Cold blooded / New York town / Pimp the
simp / Ebony eyes / Tell me what you want.
■ LP . . . . . . . . . . . . . . . . . . STMA 8038
Motown / Sep '83.

## COLD BLOODED (2 PARTS).
Tracks: Cold blooded (part 1) / Cold blooded (part 2).
■ 12″ . . . . . . . . . . . . . . . . . TMGT 1314
■ 7″ . . . . . . . . . . . . . . . . . .TMG 1314
Motown / Aug '83.

## COME GET IT.
Tracks: Stone city band / Hi / You and I / Sexy lady /
Dream maker / Be my lady / Mary Jane / Hollywood.
■ LP . . . . . . . . . . . . . . . . . .STML 12085
Motown / Jul '78.
■ LP . . . . . . . . . . . . . . . . . . STMS 5078
MC. . . . . . . . . . . . . . . . . . . CSTMS 5078
Motown / Oct '82 / PolyGram.

## DANCE WIT ME.
Tracks: Dance wit me.
■ 12″ . . . . . . . . . . . . . . . . . TMGT 1266
■ 7″ . . . . . . . . . . . . . . . . . .TMG 1266
Motown / Jun '82.

## EBONY EYES (James, Rick & Friend).
Tracks: Ebony eyes / 123 (U. her and me) / Standing
on the top.

■ 12". . . . . . . . . . . . . . . . . . . TMGT 1327
■ 7" . . . . . . . . . . . . . . . . . . . . TMG 1327
Motown / Jan '84.

## FIRE IT UP.
**Tracks:** Fire it up / Love gun / Lovin you is a pleasure / Love in the night / Come into my life / Stormy love / When love is gone.
■ LP. . . . . . . . . . . . . . . . . . STML 12128
Motown / Oct '81.

## FLAG, THE.
**Tracks:** Freak flag / Forever and a day / Sweet and sexy thing / Free to be me / Save it for me / R U experienced / Funk in America / Slow and easy / Oma raga / Painted pictures / Silly little man.
■ CD. . . . . . . . . . . . . . . . . . ZD 72443
Motown / '86.
■ LP . . . . . . . . . . . . . . . . . . ZL 72443
■ MC . . . . . . . . . . . . . . . . . . ZK 72443
Motown / Jun '86.

## FOOL ON THE STREET.
**Tracks:** Fool on the street / Jefferson ball.
■ 7" . . . . . . . . . . . . . . . . . . . TMG 1156
Motown / Sep '79.

## GARDEN OF LOVE.
**Tracks:** Big time / Don't give up on love / Island lady / Gettin' it on / Summer love / Mary go round / Gettin' it on (Reprise).
■ LP . . . . . . . . . . . . . . . . . . STML 12141
Motown / Oct '81.

## GHETTO LIFE.
**Tracks:** Ghetto life / Below the funk.
■ 12". . . . . . . . . . . . . . . . . . TMGT 1250
■ 7" . . . . . . . . . . . . . . . . . . . TMG 1250
Motown / Jan '82.

## GIVE IT TO ME BABY.
**Tracks:** Give it to me baby / Don't give up on love.
■ 12". . . . . . . . . . . . . . . . . . TMGT 1229
■ 7" . . . . . . . . . . . . . . . . . . . TMG 1229
Motown / Oct '81.

## GLOW.
**Tracks:** Not Advised.
■ 7" . . . . . . . . . . . . . . . . . . . ZB 40223
■ 12". . . . . . . . . . . . . . . . . . ZT 40224
Motown / Jun '85.
■ LP . . . . . . . . . . . . . . . . . . ZL 72362
■ MC . . . . . . . . . . . . . . . . . . ZK 72362
Motown / May '85.

## GREATEST HITS: RICK JAMES.
**Tracks:** Super freak / You turn me on / You and I / Mary Jane / Ebony eyes / Give it to me baby / Dance wit me / Cold blooded / 17.
■ LP . . . . . . . . . . . . . . . . . . WL 72427
■ MC . . . . . . . . . . . . . . . . . . WK 72427
Motown / Aug '86.
■ CD . . . . . . . . . . . . . . . . . . WD 72427
Motown / Apr '88.
MC. . . . . . . . . . . . . . . . . . . 5300982
■ CD . . . . . . . . . . . . . . . . . . 5300984
Motown / Jul '93 / PolyGram.

## HARD TO GET.
**Tracks:** Hard to get / My love / Give it me.
■ 12". . . . . . . . . . . . . . . . . . TMGT 1277
■ 7" . . . . . . . . . . . . . . . . . . . TMG 1277
Motown / Aug '82.

## HIGH ON YOUR LOVE SUITE.
**Tracks:** High on your love suite.
■ 7" . . . . . . . . . . . . . . . . . . . TMG 1137
Motown / '79.

## KICKIN'.
**Tracks:** Not Advised.
■ CD. . . . . . . . . . . . . . . . . . 926077 2
WEA / '89.

## LOOSEY'S RAP.
**Tracks:** Loosey's rap.
■ 12". . . . . . . . . . . . . . . . . . W 7885T
■ 7" . . . . . . . . . . . . . . . . . . . W 7885
WEA / May '88.

## LOVE GUN.
**Tracks:** Love gun / Stormy love.
■ 7" . . . . . . . . . . . . . . . . . . . TMG 1174
Motown / Jan '80.

## MARY JANE.
**Tracks:** Mary Jane / Dream maker.
■ 7" . . . . . . . . . . . . . . . . . . . TMG 1121
Motown / Oct '78.

## REFLECTIONS OF RICK.
**Tracks:** 17 / Oh what a night / You turn me on / Fire and desire / Bustin' out / You & I / Mary Jane / Dance wit' me / Give it to me baby / Super freak.

■ LP . . . . . . . . . . . . . . . . . . ZL 72174
■ MC . . . . . . . . . . . . . . . . . . ZK 72174
■ CD . . . . . . . . . . . . . . . . . . ZD 72174
Motown / Aug '84.

## STREET SONGS.
**Tracks:** Give it to me baby / Ghetto life / Make love to me / Mr. Policeman / Super freak / Fire and desire / Call me up / Below the funk.
■ LP . . . . . . . . . . . . . . . . . . STML 12153
■ MC . . . . . . . . . . . . . . . . . . CSTML 12153
Motown / Oct '81.
■ LP . . . . . . . . . . . . . . . . . . ZL 72036
■ MC . . . . . . . . . . . . . . . . . . ZK 72036
RCA / '86.
■ CD . . . . . . . . . . . . . . . . . . 530 218-2
Polydor / Sep '93 / PolyGram.

## STREET SONGS/THROWIN' DOWN (2 Classic albums).
**Tracks:** Give it to me baby / Ghetto life / Make love to me / Mr. Policeman / Super freak / Fire and desire / Call me / Below the funk (pass the J) / Dance wit' me / Money talks / Teardrops / Throwdown / Standing on the top / Hard to get / Happy / 69 times / My love.
■ CD . . . . . . . . . . . . . . . . . . ZD 72474
Motown / Dec '86.

## SUMMER LOVE.
**Tracks:** Summer love / Gettin' it on.
■ 12". . . . . . . . . . . . . . . . . . TMGT 1209
■ 7" . . . . . . . . . . . . . . . . . . . TMG 1209
Motown / Oct '81.

## SUPER FREAK (PART 2).
**Tracks:** Super freak (part 2) / Fire and desire.
■ 7" . . . . . . . . . . . . . . . . . . . TMG 1241
■ 12". . . . . . . . . . . . . . . . . . TMGT 1241
Motown / Nov '82.

## SWEET AND SEXY THING.
**Tracks:** Sweet and sexy thing.
■ 7" . . . . . . . . . . . . . . . . . . . ZB 40755
■ 12". . . . . . . . . . . . . . . . . . ZT 40756
Motown / Jun '86.

## THROWIN' DOWN.
**Tracks:** Dance wit' me / Money talks / Teardrops / Throwdown / Standing on the top / Hard to get / Happy / 69 times / My love.
■ LP . . . . . . . . . . . . . . . . . . STML 12167
■ MC . . . . . . . . . . . . . . . . . . CSTML 12167
Motown / Jun '82.

## WONDERFUL.
**Tracks:** Wonderful / Judy / Loosey's rap / So tight / Sexual luv affair / Love's fire / I believe in you / In the girls room / Hypnotize / Sherry baby.
■ CD . . . . . . . . . . . . . . . . . . WX 156CD
WEA / Aug '88.
■ CD . . . . . . . . . . . . . . . . . . 925659 1
■ LP . . . . . . . . . . . . . . . . . . WX 156
■ MC . . . . . . . . . . . . . . . . . . WX 156C
Reprise / Jun '88.

## YOU AND I.
**Tracks:** You and I / Hollywood.
■ 7" . . . . . . . . . . . . . . . . . . . TMG 1110
Motown / Oct '81.

## YOU TURN ME ON.
**Tracks:** You turn me on.
■ 12". . . . . . . . . . . . . . . . . . TMGT 1359
■ 7" . . . . . . . . . . . . . . . . . . . TMG 1359
Motown / Oct '84.

## James, T.C.

## GET UP ON YOUR FEET (James, T.C. & The Fist O'Funk Orchestra).
**Tracks:** Get up on your feet / Dance all over the world.
■ 7" . . . . . . . . . . . . . . . . . . . EMI 2779
EMI / Apr '78.

## GET UP ON YOUR FEET (James, T.C. & The Fist O'Funk Orchestra).
**Tracks:** Get up on your feet / Tonight / Bumpsie's whipping cream / It's so nice / Dance all over the world / Today today / I've been looking for somebody.
■ LP . . . . . . . . . . . . . . . . . . EMC 3251
EMI / Jul '78.

## Jamiroquai

## BLOW YOUR MIND.
**Tracks:** Blow your mind (part 1&2) (On 12" & CD Single only) / Blow your mind (part 1) (On 7" only) / Hocked up / When you gonna learn (On CD Single only).
■ 12". . . . . . . . . . . . . . . . . . 659297-6
■ CD Single. . . . . . . . . . . . . . . 659297-2

■ MC Single. . . . . . . . . . . . . . . 659297
Sony Soho2 / Jun '93.

## EMERGENCY ON PLANET EARTH.
**Tracks:** When you gonna learn / Too young to die / Hooked up / If I like it, I do it / Music of the mind / Emergency on planet Earth / Whatever it is I ju can't stop / Blow your mind / Revolution 1993 / Diddin' out.
MiniDisc. . . . . . . . . . . . . . . . 474069
Sony Soho2 / Aug '93 / Sony.
CD. . . . . . . . . . . . . . . . . . . 474069
LP . . . . . . . . . . . . . . . . . . . 474069
MC. . . . . . . . . . . . . . . . . . . 474069
Sony Soho2 / Jun '93 / Sony.

## EMERGENCY ON PLANET EARTH.
**Tracks:** Emergency on planet Earth (Not available o 12) / Emergency on planet Earth (mix) / If I like it, I d it (acoustic version) / Revolution 1993 (demo) (Avai able on CDS only).
■ 12". . . . . . . . . . . . . . . . . . 659578
■ CD Single . . . . . . . . . . . . . . 659578
■ MC Single. . . . . . . . . . . . . . . 659578
Sony Soho2 / Aug '93.

## RETURN OF THE SPACE COWBOY.
**Tracks:** Just another story / Stillness in time / Ha the man / Light years / Manifest destiny / Kids / M Moon / Scam / Journey to Arnhemland / Mornin glory / Space cowboy.
CD. . . . . . . . . . . . . . . . . . . 477813-
LP . . . . . . . . . . . . . . . . . . . 477813-
MC. . . . . . . . . . . . . . . . . . . 477813-
Sony Soho2 / Oct '94 / Sony.

## SPACE COWBOY.
**Tracks:** Space cowboy / Journey to Arnhemland (O 12"/CD only) / Space cowboy (stoned again) (On 12 only) / Kids (Not on 12") / Space cowboy (demo) (O CD only).
12". . . . . . . . . . . . . . . . . . . 660851
CD Single . . . . . . . . . . . . . . . 660851
MC Single . . . . . . . . . . . . . . . 660851
Sony Soho2 / Sep '94 / Sony.

## TOO YOUNG TO DIE.
**Tracks:** Too young to die (Extended version) / To young to die Mixes.
■ MC Single. . . . . . . . . . . . . . . 659011
■ 12". . . . . . . . . . . . . . . . . . 659011
■ CD Single . . . . . . . . . . . . . . 659011
Sony Soho2 / Mar '93.

## WHEN YOU GONNA LEARN.
**Tracks:** When you gonna learn / When you gonn learn (mixes) (Not available on MCS) / Didgin' ot (Not available on 12) / Too young to die (live) (Avai able on CDS only).
■ 12". . . . . . . . . . . . . . . . . . JAZID 046
■ 7" . . . . . . . . . . . . . . . . . . . JAZID 04
■ CD Single . . . . . . . . . . . . . . JAZID 046C
■ MC Single. . . . . . . . . . . . . . . JAZID 046M
Acid Jazz / Feb '93.
■ 12". . . . . . . . . . . . . . . . . . 659695
■ CD Single . . . . . . . . . . . . . . 659695
■ MC Single. . . . . . . . . . . . . . . 659695
Sony Soho2 / Sep '93.

## Jammer, Joe

## BAD NEWS.
**Tracks:** You can't hide it / Never again / Count on m / On the other side / I'm sorry / In the city / Last nigh / Missed my train / Your hurting me / Look befor you leap / Rising sun.
■ LP . . . . . . . . . . . . . . . . . . SRZA 851
Regal Zonophone / Feb '73.

## Jammers

## BE MINE TONIGHT.
**Tracks:** Be mine tonight / What have you got to lose And you know that.
■ 12". . . . . . . . . . . . . . . . . . SALT 10
■ 7" . . . . . . . . . . . . . . . . . . . SAL 10
Salsoul / Dec '82.

## Jarmels

## COMPLETE JARMELS,THE.
**Tracks:** Little bit of soap / She loves to dance / One by one / Keep your mind on me / Come on girl (it' time to smile again) / Why am I a fool for you / Wa you look tonight / Little lonely one / Gee oh gosh Red sails in the sunset / Loneliness / I'll follow you You don't believe a word I say / Little bug.
■ LP . . . . . . . . . . . . . . . . . . CH 17
Ace / Mar '86.

■ DELETE

## Jarreau, Al

Milwaukee-born singer who came to prominence in early '70s jazz scene. Having established a larger following by dabbling in soul, MoR and pop, Jarreau peaked in 1981 with U.S. Top 20 single *We're In This Love Together* and LP *Breakin' Away*. Follow-up, *Jarreau* (titled *Trouble In Paradise* in U.S.), yielded *Mornin'*; his biggest UK hit until theme from TV's *Moonlighting* made Top 10 in '87. 1994 album, *Tenderness*, boasted all-star line-up, including saxophonists Michael Brecker and David Sanborn, but unfortunately set them to work on distinctly unswinging songs by the Beatles and Elton John.

### AIN'T NO SUNSHINE.
Tracks: Ain't no sunshine / Lean on me / Use me / Kissing my love / Grandma's hands / You / Lonely town / Lonely street / Same love that made me laugh.
■ LP . . . . . . . . . . . . . . . . . . . BMLP 1011
Blue Moon (1) / '84.
□ CD . . . . . . . . . . . . . . . . . . CDBM 1011
Blue Moon (1) / Jun '88 / Roots Records / Jazz Music / Swift / Projection / THE / Hot Shot.
■ LP . . . . . . . . . . . . . . . . . . . 226 2233
■ MC . . . . . . . . . . . . . . . . . . . 216 2233
Street Life / May '88.
□ CD . . . . . . . . . . . . . . . . . . CDSGP 031
■ MC . . . . . . . . . . . . . . . . . CASSGP 031
Prestige / Oct '92 / Total / BMG.

### AL JARREAU.
Tracks: Not Advised.
■ LP . . . . . . . . . . . . . . . . . . . AZ 2467
■ MC . . . . . . . . . . . . . . . . . . . C 467
Disc AZ (France) / Aug '84 / Pinnacle.

### AL JARREAU LIVE.
Tracks: Not Advised.
□ CD . . . . . . . . . . . . . . . . . . . ZET 531
Zeta / Dec '90.

### ALL FLY HOME.
Tracks: Thinkin' about it too / I'm home / Brite 'n' sunny babe / I do / Fly / Wait a little while / She's leaving home / All / (Sittin' on) The dock of the bay.
■ LP . . . . . . . . . . . . . . . . . . . K 56546
WEA / Dec '78.

### ALL FLY HOME/THIS TIME.
Tracks: Not Advised.
■ MC Set . . . . . . . . . . . . . . . . .923948 4
WEA / Nov '83.

### ALL OR NOTHING AT ALL.
Tracks: All or nothing at all.
■ 12" . . . . . . . . . . . . . . . . . . .U 7663T
■ 7" . . . . . . . . . . . . . . . . . . .U 7663
■ CD Single . . . . . . . . . . . . . . U 7663CD
WEA / Apr '89.

### BLUE ANGEL.
Tracks: Blue angel.
■ 12" . . . . . . . . . . . . . . . . . . 9031775690
■ 7" . . . . . . . . . . . . . . . . . . 9031775687
■ CD Single . . . . . . . . . . . . . . 9031775684
East West / May '92.

### BOOGIE DOWN.
Tracks: Boogie down / Our love.
■ 12" . . . . . . . . . . . . . . . . . . I 9814 T
■ 7" . . . . . . . . . . . . . . . . . . .U 9814
WEA / Sep '83.

### BREAKIN' AWAY.
Tracks: Closer to your love / My old friend / We're in this love together / Easy / Our love / Breakin' away / Roof garden / Blue rondo a la turk / Teach me tonight.
■ LP . . . . . . . . . . . . . . . . . . . K 56917
■ MC . . . . . . . . . . . . . . . . . . . K4 56917
WEA / Aug '81.
□ CD . . . . . . . . . . . . . . . . . . . 256 917
WEA / '83.

### CLOSER TO YOUR LOVE.
Tracks: Closer to your love / Love is real.
■ 12" . . . . . . . . . . . . . . . . . . K 17876T
■ 7" . . . . . . . . . . . . . . . . . . . K 17876
WEA / Nov '81.

### DAY BY DAY (see under Shakatak).

### GLOW.
Tracks: Rainbow in your eyes / Your song / Agua de beber / Have you seen the child / Hold on me / Fire and rain / Somebody's watching you / Milwaukee how.
■ LP . . . . . . . . . . . . . . . . . . . K 54073
Reprise (USA) / Jul '77.

### HEARTS HORIZON.
Tracks: All or nothing at all / So good / All of my love / Pleasure over pain / Yo jeans / Way to your heart / One way / 10 K HI / I must have been a fool / More love / Killer love / Heart's horizon.
□ CD . . . . . . . . . . . . . . . . . . . 2559752
■ LP . . . . . . . . . . . . . . . . . . . WX 230
■ MC . . . . . . . . . . . . . . . . . . . WX 230C
WEA / Nov '88.

### HEAVEN AND EARTH.
Tracks: What you do to me / It's not hard to love you / Blue angel / Heaven and earth / Superfine love / Whenever I hear your name / Love of my life / If I break / Blue in green (tapestry) Part 1 / Blue in green (tapestry) part 2.
CD . . . . . . . . . . . . . . . . . . . 9031774662
MC . . . . . . . . . . . . . . . . . . . 9031774664
WEA / Jul '92 / WEA.

### HIGH CRIME.
Tracks: Raging waters / Imagination / Murphy's law / Tell me / After all / High crime / Let's pretend / Sticky wicket / Love speaks louder than words / Falling.
□ CD . . . . . . . . . . . . . . . . . . .250807 2
■ LP . . . . . . . . . . . . . . . . . . .250807 1
■ MC . . . . . . . . . . . . . . . . . . .250807 4
WEA / Nov '84.

### IN LONDON.
Tracks: Raging waters / Black and blue / I will be here for you / Let's pretend / High crime / Roof garden / Teach me tonight / We're in this love together.
■ LP . . . . . . . . . . . . . . . . . . .252369 1
■ MC . . . . . . . . . . . . . . . . . . .252369 4
□ CD . . . . . . . . . . . . . . . . . . .252369 2
WEA / Nov '85.

### IN LONDON.
Tracks: Not Advised.
■ VHS . . . . . . . . . . . . . . . . . .252233 3
WEA / Jun '86.

### JARREAU.
Tracks: Mornin' / Boogie down / I will be here for you / Save me / Step by step / Black and blue / Trouble in paradise / Not like this / Love is waiting.
■ MC . . . . . . . . . . . . . . . . . . . U 00704
■ LP . . . . . . . . . . . . . . . . . . .U 0070
WEA / Apr '83.
□ CD . . . . . . . . . . . . . . . . . . . U 00702
WEA / Jan '84.

### JAZZ SINGER, THE.
Tracks: Not Advised.
■ LP . . . . . . . . . . . . . . . . . . . MA 18128
MC . . . . . . . . . . . . . . . . . .MAMC 9181285
Masters (Holland) / Dec '88.

### L IS FOR LOVER.
Tracks: Tell me what I gotta do / Says / Pleasure / Golden girl / Across the midnight sky / No ordinary romance / L is for lover / Real tight.
□ CD . . . . . . . . . . . . . . . . . . .253080 2
■ LP . . . . . . . . . . . . . . . . . . .253080 1
■ MC . . . . . . . . . . . . . . . . . . .253080 4
WEA / Oct '86.

### L IS FOR LOVER.
Tracks: L is for lover.
■ 12" . . . . . . . . . . . . . . . . . . .U 8612T
■ 7" . . . . . . . . . . . . . . . . . . .U 8612
WEA / Oct '86.

### LET'S PRETEND.
Tracks: Let's pretend / I keep calling.
■ 12" . . . . . . . . . . . . . . . . . . .W 9257T
■ 7" . . . . . . . . . . . . . . . . . . . W 9257
WEA / Nov '84.

### LET'S PRETEND (LIVE).
Tracks: Let's pretend (live).
■ 12" . . . . . . . . . . . . . . . . . . U 8911 T
■ 7" . . . . . . . . . . . . . . . . . . .U 8911
WEA / Sep '85.

### LOOK TO THE RAINBOW (LIVE).
Tracks: Letter perfect / Rainbow in your eyes / One good turn / Could you believe / Burst in with the dawn / Better than anything / So long girl / Look to the rainbow / You don't see me / Take five / Loving you / We got by.
■ Double LP . . . . . . . . . . . . . . . K 66059
WEA / May '77.

### LOVE IS WAITING.
Tracks: Love is waiting / Christmas song / Blue rondo a la Turk.
■ 12" . . . . . . . . . . . . . . . . . . U 9744T
■ 7" . . . . . . . . . . . . . . . . . . .U 9744
WEA / Dec '83.

### MANIFESTO.
Tracks: Not Advised.
■ LP . . . . . . . . . . . . . . . . . . . MA 181285
Masters (Holland) / '88.

### MASQUERADE IS OVER, THE.
Tracks: My favourite things / Stockholm sweetnin' / Sleeping bee / Masquerade is over / Sophisticated lady / Joey / Come rain or come shine / One note samba.
■ LP . . . . . . . . . . . . . . . . . . . B 90136
MC . . . . . . . . . . . . . . . . . . . MB 990136
Happy Bird (Germany) / Jun '83.
CD . . . . . . . . . . . . . . . . . . . CDBM 079
■ LP . . . . . . . . . . . . . . . . . . .BMLP 079
Blue Moon (1) / Nov '89 / Roots Records / Jazz Music / Swift / Projection / THE / Hot Shot.

### MOONLIGHTING.
Tracks: Moonlighting / Golden girl (lp version).
■ 7" . . . . . . . . . . . . . . . . . . .U 8407
■ 12" . . . . . . . . . . . . . . . . . . U 8407 T
WEA / Feb '87.

### MORNIN'.
Tracks: Mornin' / Not like this / Roof garden.
■ 12" . . . . . . . . . . . . . . . . . . U 9929 T
■ 7" . . . . . . . . . . . . . . . . . . .U 9929
WEA / Apr '83.

### OUR LOVE.
Tracks: Our love / Roof garden.
■ 7" . . . . . . . . . . . . . . . . . . . K17907
WEA / Feb '82.

### RAGING WATERS.
Tracks: Raging waters / Too hot.
■ 12" . . . . . . . . . . . . . . . . . . .W 9145T
■ 7" . . . . . . . . . . . . . . . . . . . W 9145
WEA / Apr '85.

### REPLAY OF AL JARREAU.
Tracks: Not Advised.
■ LP . . . . . . . . . . . . . . . . . . . FEDB 5003
MC . . . . . . . . . . . . . . . . . . . CFEDB 5003
Sierra / Feb '85.

### SINGS BILL WITHERS.
Tracks: Ain't no sunshine / Lean on me / Use me / Missing my love / Grandma's hands / You / Lonely town, lonely street / That same love that made me laugh.
■ LP . . . . . . . . . . . . . . . . . . .TOP 173
MC . . . . . . . . . . . . . . . . . . . KTOP 173
Topline / Apr '87 / Charly.
CD . . . . . . . . . . . . . . . . . . . CDCD 1196
Charly / Sep '94 / Charly.

### SO GOOD.
Tracks: So good / Pleasure over pain / Mornin' (12" only).
■ 12" . . . . . . . . . . . . . . . . . . .W 7664T
■ 7" . . . . . . . . . . . . . . . . . . . W 7664
WEA / Dec '88.

### SPIRITS AND FEELINGS.
Tracks: Ain't no sunshine / Lean on me / Use me / Kissing my love / Grandma's hands / You / Lonely town, lonely street / Same love that made me laugh.
■ LP . . . . . . . . . . . . . . . . . . . B 90168
Happy Bird (Germany) / May '84.

### SPOTLIGHT ON AL JARREAU.
Tracks: Ain't no sunshine / Kissing my love / You / Same love that made me laugh / Rainbow in your eyes / Grandma's hands / Lonely town, lonely street / Lean on me / One good turn / We got by / Use me (till you use me up) / Loving you / Letter perfect.
CD . . . . . . . . . . . . . . . . . . .HADCD 115
MC . . . . . . . . . . . . . . . . . . .HADMC 115
Javelin / Feb '94 / THE.

### TELL ME WHAT I GOTTA DO.
Tracks: Tell me what I gotta do / Roof garden.
■ 12" . . . . . . . . . . . . . . . . . . U 8523T
WEA / Nov '86.
■ 7" . . . . . . . . . . . . . . . . . . .U 8523
WEA / Apr '87.

### TENDERNESS.
Tracks: Mas que nada / Try a little tenderness / Your song / My favorite things / She's leaving home / Summertime / We got by / Save your love for me / You don't see me / Wait for the magic / Dinosaur / Go away little girl.
CD . . . . . . . . . . . . . . . . . . .450993778-2
MC . . . . . . . . . . . . . . . . . . .450993778-4
Warner Bros. / Jun '94 / WEA.

### TENDERNESS.
Tracks: Not Advised.
VHS . . . . . . . . . . . . . . . . . . .4509961623
Warner Music Video / Jun '94 / WEA.

## THIS TIME.
**Tracks:** Never givin' up / Gimme what you got / This time / Your sweet love / Alonzo / Spain / Distracted / Love is real / Change your mind.
■ **LP** .............................. K 56804
WEA / Jun '80.

## TROUBLE IN PARADISE.
**Tracks:** Trouble in paradise / Save me.
■ **12"** .............................. U 9871 T
■ **7"** ................................ U 9871
WEA / Jul '83.

## WE GOT BY.
**Tracks:** Spirit / We got by / Susan's song / You don't see me / Lock all the gates / Raggedy Ann / Letter perfect / Sweet potato pie / Aladdin's lamp.
**CD** ................................. 2224-2
Warner Bros. / '75 / WEA.
■ **LP** ............................... K 54045
Reprise (USA) / Jun '77.

## WE'RE IN THIS LOVE TOGETHER.
**Tracks:** We're in this love together / Easy.
■ **12"** ............................. K 17849T
■ **7"** ............................... K 17849
WEA / Sep '81.

## YOU.
**Tracks:** Not Advised.
■ **LP** ................................ PLP 19
**MC.** ................................ PMC 19
Platinum (W.Germany) / Oct '85.

# Jasper, Chris

## ONE MORE TIME.
**Tracks:** One more time / Givin' my all.
■ **7"** ............................... 6515107
CBS / Apr '88.

## ONE TIME LOVE.
**Tracks:** One time love.
■ **12"** .............................. 6615106
■ **7"** ............................... 6615107
CBS / '88.

## SUPERBAD.
**Tracks:** Superbad / Givin' my all / One time love / Earthquake / Like I do / Dance for the dollar / Son of man / My soul train.
■ **LP** ............................... 4607061
■ **CD** .............................. 4607062
■ **MC.** ............................. 4607064
Epic / Mar '88.

## TIME BOMB.
**Tracks:** First time / Hit on you / In your face / Margie / It's workin' / Time bomb / Sanctified you.
■ **CD** .............................. 4654602
■ **LP** .............................. 4654601
■ **MC.** ............................. 4654604
Epic / Oct '89.

# Javells

## GOODBYE NOTHING TO SAY (Javells & Nosmo King).
**Tracks:** Goodbye nothing to say.
■ **7"** .............................. DDS 2003
Pye Disco Demand / Nov '74.

## LOVING YOU IS EASY.
**Tracks:** Loving you is easy / Only the beginning.
■ **7"** .............................. 7N 45435
Pye / Feb '75.

# Jay & The Techniques

## APPLES, PEACHES, PUMPKIN PIE.
**Tracks:** Apples, peaches, pumpkin pie / Stronger than dirt.
■ **7"** ................................ BF 1597
Philips / Jul '67.

# Jaye, Miles

## HEAVEN.
**Tracks:** Heaven / Lets start over.
■ **12"** ............................. 12 BRW 133
■ **12" Remix.** ....................... BRW 133X
■ **12" Remix.** ................... 12 BRW 133X
■ **7"** ................................ BRW 133
■ **CD Single.** ....................... BRCD 133
4th & Broadway / Jun '89.

## I'VE BEEN A FOOL FOR YOU.
**Tracks:** I've been a fool for you / Happy 2 have U / Let's start over (Extra track available on 12" only).
■ **12"** ............................. 12 BRW 92

■ **7"** ............................... BRW 92
4th & Broadway / Apr '88.

## IRRESISTIBLE.
**Tracks:** Irresistible / Objective / Next time / Slo-dance / Message / Neither one of us / Interlude / I'll be there / Heaven / Love in the night.
■ **LP** ............................... BRLP 531
■ **MC.** ............................. BRCA 531
■ **CD** .............................. BRCD 531
4th & Broadway / May '89.

## JUST BE GOOD TO ME.
**Tracks:** Just be good to me / Heaven (Only on 12" & CD single.) / Sensuous.
■ **12"** ............................. 12 BRW 233
■ **7"** ............................... BRW 233
■ **CD Single.** ....................... BRCD 233
4th & Broadway / Aug '91.

## LET'S START OVER.
**Tracks:** Let's start over / Lazy love.
■ **12"** ............................. 12 BRW 81
■ **7"** ............................... BRW 81
4th & Broadway / Nov '87.

## MILES.
**Tracks:** Let's start over / Lazy love / Special thing / I've been a fool for you / I cry for you / Come home / Happy 2 have U / Desiree.
■ **CD** .............................. BRCD 515
■ **LP** ............................... BRLP 515
■ **MC.** ............................. BRCA 515
4th & Broadway / Nov '87.
**MC.** ................................ ICM 2031
■ **CD** .............................. IMCD 101
Island / Feb '90 / PolyGram.

## OBJECTIVE.
**Tracks:** Objective (On CD only).
■ **12"** ............................. 12 BRW 142
■ **7"** ............................... BRW 142
■ **CD Single.** ....................... BRCD 142
4th & Broadway / Jul '89.

## STRONG.
**Tracks:** Not Advised.
■ **LP** ............................... BRLP 573
■ **MC.** ............................. BRCA 573
■ **CD** .............................. BRCD 573
4th & Broadway / Jun '91.

# Jefferson, Marshall

## DO THE DO.
**Tracks:** Do the do.
■ **12"** ............................. DJINT 10
DJ International / Apr '89.

## HOUSE MUSIC ANTHEM, THE.
**Tracks:** House music anthem / Move your body.
■ **7"** ............................... TARTS 3
Affair / Oct '86.

## MOVE YOUR BODY (90 REMIX).
**Tracks:** Move your body.
■ **12"** ............................. TRAXT 4
■ **7"** ............................... TRAXS 4
Radical / Dec '89.

## OPEN YOUR EYES (Marshall Jefferson Presents Truth).
**Tracks:** Open your eyes / Open your eyes (version).
■ **7"** ............................... FFRR 18
■ **12"** ............................. FFRX 18
FFRR / Dec '88.

# Jeffreys, Garland

## 35 MILLIMETER DREAMS.
**Tracks:** 35 millimeter dreams / Ghost writer.
■ **7"** ............................... AMS 7290
A&M / May '77.

## AMERICAN BOY AND GIRL.
**Tracks:** Not Advised.
■ **LP** ............................... AMLH 64778
A&M / Sep '79.

## CHRISTINE.
**Tracks:** Christine / Scapegoat club.
■ **7"** ............................... EPC 9577
Epic / Feb '81.

## DON'T CALL ME BUCKWHEAT.
**Tracks:** Moonshine in the cornfield / Welcome to the world / Don't call me Buckwheat / Color line / Hail hail rock'n'roll / I was afraid of Malcolm / Bottle of love / Answer / Racial repertoire / Spanish blood / Lonelyville / Murder jubilee / I'm not a know it all.
**CD.** ................................ PD 90588
**MC.** ................................ PK 90588
■ **LP** ............................... PL 90588

RCA / Nov '91 / BMG.
**DCC.** ............................... 078636111
RCA / Jan '93 / BMG.

## ESCAPE ARTIST.
**Tracks:** Modern lovers / Christine / Ghost of chance / 96 tears / Innocent / True confessions / R.O.C.K / Graveyard rock / Mystery kids / Jump.
■ **LP** ............................... EPC 848
Epic / Mar '81.

## GHOST WRITER.
**Tracks:** Rough and ready / I may not be your kind / New York skyline / Cool down boy / Ghost writer / Lift me up / Who-O / Wild in the streets / 35 millimeter / Dreams / Spanish town.
■ **LP** ............................... AMLH 648
A&M / Apr '77.

## GUTS FOR LOVE.
**Tracks:** Real man / Surrender / Fidelity / Rebel love / Dance up / Guts for love / Shout / What does it take / Loneliness / El Salvador / American backslide.
■ **LP** ............................... EPC 250
Epic / Feb '83.

## HAIL HAIL ROCK 'N' ROLL.
**Tracks:** Hail hail rock 'n' roll / Bottle of love.
■ **12"** ............................. PT 491
■ **7"** ............................... PB 491
■ **CD Single.** ....................... PD 491
■ **MC Single.** ....................... PK 491
RCA / Jan '92.

## MATADOR & MORE.
**Tracks:** Livin' for me / I may not be your kind / One eyed Jack / No woman, no cry / Shoot the moonlight / Ghost writer / Matador / Wild in the streets / Keep on trying / Ship of fools / New York skyline / Spanish town.
**CD.** ................................ 397 179
■ **LP** ............................... 397 179
**MC.** ................................ 397 179
A&M / Oct '91 / PolyGram.

## NINETY SIX TEARS.
**Tracks:** Ninety six tears / Escape goat dub.
■ **7"** ............................... EPC A 10
Epic / Mar '81.

## ONE-EYED JACK.
**Tracks:** She didn't lie / Keep on trying / Reelin' / Haunted house / One eyed Jack / Scream in the night / No woman to cry / Oh my soul / Desperation drive / Been there and back.
■ **LP** ............................... AMLH 646
A&M / Apr '78.

## ROCK 'N' ROLL ADULT.
**Tracks:** Wild in the street / 96 tears / I may not be your kind / Matador / R.O.C.K. / 35 millimeter / Dreams / Bound to get ahead someday / Cool down boy.
■ **LP** ............................... EPC 8530
Epic / Jan '82.

## WILD IN THE STREETS.
**Tracks:** Wild in the streets / Cool down boy.
■ **7"** ............................... AMS 730
A&M / Aug '77.

# Jeffries, Michael

## MICHAEL JEFFRIES.
**Tracks:** Not thru being with you / Jealous heart / We loved / Stop in the name of us / 99 lies / Teach me / I'm waiting / Baby don't ya go / Trade dreams / I don't get no better than this.
■ **CD** .............................. 925925
■ **LP** ............................... 925925
■ **MC.** ............................. 925925
WEA / Jan '90.

## NOT THRU BEING WITH YOU (Jeffries Michael with Karyn White).
**Tracks:** Not thru being with you / Not thru being with you (instrumental).
■ **12"** ............................. W 2792
■ **7"** ............................... W 279
■ **CD Single.** ....................... W 2797C
WEA / Feb '90.

## RAZZLE DAZZLE (Jeffries, Michael James Newton Howard).
**Tracks:** Razzle dazzle / Half time / Razzle dazzle (Instrumental).
■ **7"** ................................ W 868
■ **12"** ............................. W 8681
WEA / May '86.

## Jellybean

### COMING BACK FOR MORE PART 1.
Tracks: Coming back for more(Part 1).
- 7" . . . . . . . . . . . . . . . . . . . . . . . . . JEL 4
- 12" . . . . . . . . . . . . . . . . . . . . . . . . JELX 4
Chrysalis / Aug '88.

### JINGO.
Tracks: Jingo.
- 7" . . . . . . . . . . . . . . . . . . . . . . . . . JEL 2
- 12" . . . . . . . . . . . . . . . . . . . . . . . . JELX 2
Chrysalis / Oct '87.

### JUST A MIRAGE.
Tracks: Just a mirage / Just a mirage (dub) / Who found who? (UK house mix) (extra track on 12" version only).
- 7" . . . . . . . . . . . . . . . . . . . . . . . . . JEL 3
- 12" . . . . . . . . . . . . . . . . . . . . . . . . JELX 3
Chrysalis / Feb '88.

### JUST VISITING THIS PLANET.
Tracks: Little too good to me / Who found who / Just a mirage / Am I dreaming / Real thing / Walking in my sleep / Hypnotised / Jingo.
- CD . . . . . . . . . . . . . . . . . . . . . . . CCD 1569
- LP . . . . . . . . . . . . . . . . . . . . . . . CHR 1569
- MC . . . . . . . . . . . . . . . . . . . . . . . ZCHR 1569
Chrysalis / Oct '87 / EMI.

### REAL THING, THE.
Tracks: Real thing / Real thing, The (inst).
- 12" . . . . . . . . . . . . . . . . . . . . . CHS 123167
- 7" . . . . . . . . . . . . . . . . . . . . . . CHS 3167
Chrysalis / Sep '87.

### ROCKS THE HOUSE (12" mixes).
Tracks: Coming back for more / Jingo / Just a mirage / Little too good to me / Who found who / Was dog a doughnut / Mirage / Sidewalk talk / Anyway you like / Real thing (Not on CD.).
- CD . . . . . . . . . . . . . . . . . . . . . . . . CDJB 1
- LP . . . . . . . . . . . . . . . . . . . . . . . . . CJB 1
- MC . . . . . . . . . . . . . . . . . . . . . . . ZCJB 1
Chrysalis / Aug '88.

### SIDEWALK TALK.
Tracks: Sidewalk talk / Was dog a doughnut / Sidewalk talk (Funhouse remix) (Extra track on 12" Remix version only) / Was dog a doughnut (remix) (Extra track on 12" Remix version only.).
- 12" Remix . . . . . . . . . . . . . . . . . 12 EAX 310
- 7" . . . . . . . . . . . . . . . . . . . . . . . EA 210
- 12" . . . . . . . . . . . . . . . . . . . . . .12 EA 210
EMI-America / Jan '86.

### SPILLIN' THE BEANS.
Tracks: What's it gonna be / Do you love as good as you look / Spillin' the beans / What's up / Not this time / Don't let love come between us / Love is a contact sport / Tightrope / Absent minded lover / Don't let it go to your heart / Secret weapon (Available on CD only).
- CD . . . . . . . . . . . . . . . . . . . . . . . 7567821802
- LP . . . . . . . . . . . . . . . . . . . . . . . 7567821801
- MC . . . . . . . . . . . . . . . . . . . . . . . 7567821804
Atlantic / Feb '91 / WEA.

### WHAT'S IT GONNA BE.
Tracks: What's it gonna be / What's it gonna be (version).
- 12" . . . . . . . . . . . . . . . . . . . . . . . A 7769T
- 7" . . . . . . . . . . . . . . . . . . . . . . . . A 7769
- CD Single . . . . . . . . . . . . . . . . . . A 7769CD
- MC Single . . . . . . . . . . . . . . . . . . A 7769C
East West / Jan '91.

### WHO FOUND WHO (Jellybean & Elisa Fiorillo).
Tracks: Who found who (7" edit) (On 7" single only.) / Who found who (uptown dub) (On 7" single only.) / Who found who (club mix) (On 12" single only.) / Real thing (El Barrio mix) (On 12" single only.) / ing (Hot Salsa piano dub) (On 12" single only.).
- 7" . . . . . . . . . . . . . . . . . . . . . . . . JEL 1
- 12" . . . . . . . . . . . . . . . . . . . . . . . JELX 1
Chrysalis / Nov '87.

### WOTUPSKI.
Tracks: Compromise / Sidewalk talk / Dancing on the e / Was dog a doughnut / Mexican.
- MC . . . . . . . . . . . . . . . . . . . . . . EE 2402314
- LP . . . . . . . . . . . . . . . . . . . . . . EE 2402311
EMI-America / Oct '84.

## Jenkins, Johnny

### TON TON MACOUTE.
Tracks: I walk on gilded splinters / Leaving trunk / Blind bats & swamp rats / Rollin' stone / Sick & tired / Down along the cove / Bad news / Dimples / Voodoo in you.

- LP . . . . . . . . . . . . . . . . . . . . . . . K 40105
Atlantic / Aug '72.

## Jenkins, Keshia

### I NEED SOMEBODY.
Tracks: I need somebody / I need somebody (version).
- 12" . . . . . . . . . . . . . . . . . . . . . CBE 1222
- 7" . . . . . . . . . . . . . . . . . . . . . . .CBE 722
City Beat / Apr '88.

### STILL WAITING.
Tracks: Still waiting.
- 12" . . . . . . . . . . . . . . . . . . . . . PROFT 250
- 7" . . . . . . . . . . . . . . . . . . . . . PROF 250
Profile (USA) / May '89.

## Jerome, Steve

### DON'T KEEP HAUNTING ME.
Tracks: Don't keep haunting me / Kiss and tell.
- 12" . . . . . . . . . . . . . . . . . . . . . . NEED 1
- 7" . . . . . . . . . . . . . . . . . . . . . 7 NEED 1
Needle / Aug '87.

### SONG THAT NEVER DIES.
Tracks: Song that never dies / Token.
- 7" . . . . . . . . . . . . . . . . . . . . .DJS 10941
DJM / Jun '80.

## Jeter, Genobia

### GENOBIA.
Tracks: Sunshine / Peace of mind / Together / Blessing in disguise / I just want what's mine / We got love / All of my love / Take a look.
- LP . . . . . . . . . . . . . . . . . . . . . . . PL 85897
- MC . . . . . . . . . . . . . . . . . . . . . . PK 85897
RCA / Oct '86.

### HEAVEN.
Tracks: Not Advised.
LP . . . . . . . . . . . . . . . . . . . . . . . SL 14547
Savoy / Apr '90 / Jazz Music / Wellard / Savoy Records / Conifer Records.

### THINGS HAVE 'GOT' TO GET BETTER.
Tracks: Not Advised.
LP . . . . . . . . . . . . . . . . . . . . . . . SL 14597
Savoy / Apr '90 / Jazz Music / Wellard / Savoy Records / Conifer Records.

## Jezebells

### TAINTED LOVE.
Tracks: Tainted love / Torch is back.
- 7" . . . . . . . . . . . . . . . . . . . . . DDS 2006
Pye Disco Demand / Apr '75.

## Jharris

### MY BABY E.P.
Tracks: My baby / You're the one / Come take my love / Dream come true / Be my girl.
- 12" . . . . . . . . . . . . . . . . . . . . . ATEP 014
About Time / Jul '92.

## Jhovan

### FOR DA RECORD.
Tracks: For da record.
12" . . . . . . . . . . . . . . . . . . . . . . . CON 15
Conscious / Mar '94 / Vital Distribution / Jetstar.

## Jiani, Carol

### ASK ME.
Tracks: Ask me / Kicking the habit.
- 12" . . . . . . . . . . . . . . . . . . . . . EXCL 523
Excaliber / Sep '82.

### HIT'N'RUN LOVER.
Tracks: Hit and run lover / Hit and run lover (instrumental) / Hit and run lover (version) / All the people of the world.
- 12" . . . . . . . . . . . . . . . . . . . . . FIZY 506
- 7" . . . . . . . . . . . . . . . . . . . . . . FIZZ 506
Champagne / Apr '81.
- 12" . . . . . . . . . . . . . . . . . . . . PASH 85(12)
Passion (1) / Sep '88.

### SUCH A JOY HONEY.
Tracks: Such a joy honey / Such a joy honey (instrumental).
- 7" . . . . . . . . . . . . . . . . . . . . .MCA 1130
MCA / Mar '87.

### TOUCH AND GO LOVER.
Tracks: Touch and go lover / Love now play later.
- 12" . . . . . . . . . . . . . . . . . . . . . MKHAN 7

- 7" . . . . . . . . . . . . . . . . . . . . . . . KHAN 7
Streetwave / Mar '84.

## Jive Five

### OUR TRUE STORY.
Tracks: My true story / Do you hear wedding bells / Beggin' you please / Rain / Johnny never knew / People from another world / What time is it / When I was single / These golden rings / Girl with the wind in her hair / I don't want to be without you baby / No not again / You know what I would do / Never never / Hully gully callin' time / Hurry back.
- LP . . . . . . . . . . . . . . . . . . . . . . . CH 76
Ace / Aug '83.
- CD . . . . . . . . . . . . . . . . . . . . . . CDCH 76
Ace / Aug '91 / Pinnacle / Complete Record Co. Ltd.

### WAY BACK.
Tracks: Not Advised.
- LP . . . . . . . . . . . . . . . . . . . . . .ASR 801
Ambient Sound / Apr '85.

## Jodeci

Swingbeat quartet with gospel backgrounds, reportedly signed to MCA after impromptu live audition in label's New York offices. Group came to prominence in 1992 with double platinum *Forever My Lady* album, which boasted writing input from Al B. Sure and won them four U.S. hits - notably gold-certified *Come & Talk To Me* - and Soul Train award. Having maintained profile with contributions to *Who's the Man* and *Fried Green Tomatoes* soundtracks, and the arrest of two members for sex and weapons offences, Jodeci pushed to forefront of swing with superb *Diary Of A Mad Band*. Released at close of '93, album has yet to leave U.S. charts. Mainman Devante Swing is now an in-demand producer, working with acts ranging from Jodeci wannabes H-Town to Aerosmith, and masterminding Xscape-ish Sista. Early Jodeci member Dave Hollister is now with Blackstreet.

### CHERISH.
Tracks: Cherish.
- 12" . . . . . . . . . . . . . . . . . MCST 1726
- 7" . . . . . . . . . . . . . . . . . . MCS 1726
- CD Single . . . . . . . . . . . . . . MCSD 1726
- MC Single . . . . . . . . . . . . . . MCSC 1726
MCA / Jan '93.

### CRY FOR YOU.
Tracks: Not Advised.
- 12" . . . . . . . . . . . . . . . . . MCST 1951
- 7" . . . . . . . . . . . . . . . . . . MCSR 1951
- CD Single . . . . . . . . . . . . . . MCSTD 1951
- MC Single . . . . . . . . . . . . . . MCSC 1951
MCA / Nov '93.

### DIARY OF A MAD BAND.
Tracks: My heart belongs to you / Cry for you / Feenin' / What about us / Ride & slide / Alone / You got it / Won't waste you / In the meanwhile / Gimme all you got / Sweaty / Jodecial hotline / Lately (Not available on LP) / Let's go through the motions (Not available on LP) / Success (Available on CD only).
- CD . . . . . . . . . . . . . . . . . . MCD 11019
- MC . . . . . . . . . . . . . . . . . . MCC 11019
- LP . . . . . . . . . . . . . . . . . . MCA 11019
MCA / Dec '93 / BMG.

### FEENIN.
Tracks: Feenin.
- 12" . . . . . . . . . . . . . . . . . MCST 1984
- 12" Remix . . . . . . . . . . . . . . MCSX 1984
- CD Single . . . . . . . . . . . . . . MCSTD 1984
- MC Single . . . . . . . . . . . . . . MCSC 1984
MCA / Jul '94.

### FOREVER MY LADY.
Tracks: Not Advised.
- CD . . . . . . . . . . . . . . . . . . MCAD 10534
- MC . . . . . . . . . . . . . . . . . . MCAC 10534
- LP . . . . . . . . . . . . . . . . . . MCA 10534
MCA / May '92 / BMG.

## Joe

### ALL OR NOTHING.
Tracks: All or nothing / One for me.
12" . . . . . . . . . . . . . . . . . . . . . . JOEX 3
CD Single . . . . . . . . . . . . . . . . . . JOEDD 3
CD Single . . . . . . . . . . . . . . . . . . JOECD 3
MC Single . . . . . . . . . . . . . . . . . . JOEMC 3
Mercury / Aug '94 / PolyGram.

### EVERYTHING.
Tracks: One for me / I'm in luv / All or nothing / It's alright / If loving you is wrong / What's on your mind

/ Finally back / Get a little closer / I can do it right /
Everything / Baby don't stop / Do me.

| | |
|---|---|
| CD | .518807-2 |
| LP | .518807-1 |
| MC | .518807-4 |

Vertigo / Feb '94 / PolyGram.

## I'M IN LUV.

**Tracks:** I'm in luv.

| | |
|---|---|
| ■ 12" | JOEX 1 |
| ■ 7" | JOE 1 |
| ■ CD Single | JOECD 1 |
| ■ MC Single | JOEC 1 |

Vertigo / Dec '93.

## ONE FOR ME, THE.

**Tracks:** One for me (Mixes) / I'm in luv (On JOEDD 2 only) / Do me (ON JOEDD 2 only).

| | |
|---|---|
| ■ 12" | JOEX 2 |
| ■ CD Single | JOECD 2 |
| ■ CD Single | JOEDD 2 |
| ■ MC Single | JOE 2 |

Mercury / Apr '94.

# Joe Public

## I'VE BEEN WATCHING.

**Tracks:** I've been watchin'.

| | |
|---|---|
| ■ CD Single | .658765-2 |
| ■ 12" | .658765-6 |
| ■ 7" | .658765-7 |
| ■ MC Single | .658765-4 |

Columbia / Nov '92.

## JOE PUBLIC.

**Tracks:** Live and learn / I've been watchin' / I miss you / I gotta thang / Anything / This one's for you / I like it / Touch you / Do you everynite / When I look in your eyes.

| | |
|---|---|
| ■ LP | 4691731 |
| ■ CD | 4691732 |
| ■ MC | 4691734 |

Columbia / Jul '92.

## LIVE AND LEARN.

**Tracks:** Live and learn.

| | |
|---|---|
| ■ 7" | 6575267 |
| ■ 12" | 6575266 |
| ■ CD Single | 6575262 |
| ■ MC Single | 6575264 |

Columbia / Jul '92.

# John, Leee

## ROCK ME SLOW.

**Tracks:** Rock me slow / Rock me slow (instrumental) / Honey I'm yours (Extra track on 12" version only).

| | |
|---|---|
| ■ 12" | RBS 1805 |
| ■ 7" | RBL 1805 |

R & B / Aug '86.

# John, Mable

## STAY OUT OF THE KITCHEN.

**Tracks:** Stay out of the kitchen / Left over love / Able Mable / Shouldn't I love him / Catch that man / Ain't giving it up / Running out / Love tornado / Bigger and better / Sweet devil / It's catching / Drop on in / That woman will give it a try / That's what my love can do / I love you more than words can say / Have your cake / Be warm to me / I taught you how / If you give up what you got (see what you lost) / Don't get caught / Man's too busy / I'm a big girl now / To love what I want, and want what I love / Sorry about that / I need your love so bad.

| | |
|---|---|
| CD | CDSXD 048 |

Stax / Sep '92 / Pinnacle.

## TIME STOPS.

**Tracks:** Time stops.

| | |
|---|---|
| ■ 12" | 12MOTC 60 |

Motor City / Nov '91.

# Johnson, Al

## I'M BACK FOR MORE.

**Tracks:** I'm back for more / You are my personal angel.

| | |
|---|---|
| ■ 7" | CBS 8545 |

CBS / May '80.

# Johnson, General

## CAN'T NOBODY LOVE ME LIKE YOU DO.

**Tracks:** Can't nobody love me like you do / Lies.

| | |
|---|---|
| ■ 7" | .ARIST 237 |

Arista / Feb '79.

## DON'T WALK AWAY.

**Tracks:** Don't walk away / Lies.

| | |
|---|---|
| ■ 7" | .ARIST 166 |

Arista / Feb '78.

## GENERALLY SPEAKING.

**Tracks:** Saginaw county line / God's gift to man / It was almost something / Every couple's not a pair / All we need is understanding / Everything's Tuesday / I never get tired of you / My credit didn't go through / Things are bound to get better later on / Mary Lou Thomas.

| | |
|---|---|
| ■ LP | SVT 1008 |

Invictus / Feb '73.

## SHERO (Johnson, General & Chairmen Of The Board).

**Tracks:** Shero.

| | |
|---|---|
| MC Single | MCS 93-630 |

Ichiban / Feb '94 / A.D.A. Distribution / Pinnacle / ACD Trading Ltd. / Koch International / Direct Distribution.

## WHAT GOES AROUND COMES AROUND (Johnson, General & Chairmen Of The Board).

**Tracks:** Not Advised.

| | |
|---|---|
| CD | SUR 4168 |
| MC | SUR 4168MC |

Ichiban / Feb '94 / A.D.A. Distribution / Pinnacle / ACD Trading Ltd. / Koch International / Direct Distribution.

# Johnson, Howard

## DOIN' IT MY WAY.

**Tracks:** My way / Jump into the fire / Let's take time out / Missing you / Much too much / You're the one I've needed / Let this dream be real / Everywhere I go.

| | |
|---|---|
| ■ LP | AMLX 64961 |
| ■ MC | CXM 64961 |

A&M / Nov '83.

## KEEPIN' LOVE NEW.

**Tracks:** So fine / Take me through the night / This heaven / Jam song / Keepin' love new / So glad you're my lady / Say you wanna / Forever falling in love.

| | |
|---|---|
| ■ LP | AMLH 64895 |

A&M / Sep '82.

## KEEPIN' LOVE NEW.

**Tracks:** Keepin' love new / So fine.

| | |
|---|---|
| ■ 7" | USAF 1221 |

A&M / Aug '82.

## KNEES.

**Tracks:** Knees / Why sleep alone tonight.

| | |
|---|---|
| ■ 12" | AMY 282 |
| ■ 7" | AM 282 |

A&M / Oct '85.

## LET'S TAKE TIME OUT.

**Tracks:** Let's take time out / Everywhere I go / Take me thru' the night.

| | |
|---|---|
| ■ 12" | AMX 154 |
| ■ 7" | AM 154 |

A&M / Sep '83.

## SAY YOU WANNA.

**Tracks:** Say you wanna / Jam song.

| | |
|---|---|
| ■ 12" | USAF 1226 |

Funk America / Jan '83.

## SO FINE.

**Tracks:** So fine / Keepin' love new.

| | |
|---|---|
| ■ 7" | USA 1221 |

A&M / Sep '82.

## STAND UP.

**Tracks:** Stand up / So fine.

| | |
|---|---|
| ■ 12" | AMY 266 |
| ■ 7" | AM 266 |

A&M / Aug '85.

# Johnson, Jesse

## BE YOUR MAN.

**Tracks:** Be your man / Special love.

| | |
|---|---|
| ■ 12" | AMY 244 |
| ■ 7" | AM 244 |

A&M / Apr '85.

## CAN YOU HELP ME.

**Tracks:** Can you help me / Free world.

| | |
|---|---|
| ■ 12" | AMY 259 |
| ■ 7" | AM 259 |

A&M / Jun '85.

## CRAZAY.

**Tracks:** Crazay / I'm your man.

| | |
|---|---|
| ■ 12" | AMY 360 |
| ■ 7" | AM 360 |

A&M / Nov '86.

## EVERY SHADE OF LOVE.

**Tracks:** Not Advised.

| | |
|---|---|
| ■ LP | UNKNOWN |

Breakout / Jul '88.

## EVERY SHADE OF LOVE.

**Tracks:** Every shade of love / Lovestruck.

| | |
|---|---|
| ■ 12" | USAT 637 |
| ■ 7" | .USA 637 |

Breakout / Sep '88.

## I WANT MY GIRL (Johnson, Jesse Revue).

**Tracks:** I want my girl / Fast girls.

| | |
|---|---|
| ■ 7" | AM 270 |

A&M / Sep '85.

## JESSE JOHNSON'S REVUE.

**Tracks:** Be your man / I want my girl / She won't let go / Just too much / Let's have some fun / Can you help me / Special love / She's a doll.

| | |
|---|---|
| ■ LP | .AMA 5024 |
| MC | .AMC 5024 |

A&M / '87 / PolyGram.

## LOVESTRUCK.

**Tracks:** Lovestruck / Do yourself a favour.

| | |
|---|---|
| ■ 12" | USAT 628 |
| ■ 7" | .USA 628 |

Breakout / May '88.

## SHADES OF LOVE.

**Tracks:** Lovestruck / So misunderstood / I'm the one / Color shock / Every shade of love / Everybody wants somebody to love / I'm just wanting you / Stop look listen.

| | |
|---|---|
| ■ CD | CDA 5188 |
| ■ LP | .AMA 5188 |
| ■ MC | .AMC 5188 |

A&M / Apr '88.

## SHE (I CAN'T RESIST).

**Tracks:** She (I can't resist) / She (I can't resist) (Version) / Crazay (Only available on 12" version).

| | |
|---|---|
| ■ 12" | AMY 382 |
| ■ 7" | AM 382 |

A&M / Feb '87.

## SHOCKADELICA.

**Tracks:** Change your mind / She / Addiction / Baby let's kiss / Better way / Tonight / Crazay / Do yourself a favour / Burn you up / Black in America.

| | |
|---|---|
| ■ CD | CDA 5122 |
| ■ LP | .AMA 5122 |
| ■ MC | .AMC 5122 |

A&M / Oct '86.

| | |
|---|---|
| CD | 395 122-2 |

A&M / Aug '89 / PolyGram.

# Johnson, Jimmy

## BAR ROOM PREACHER.

**Tracks:** Not Advised.

| | |
|---|---|
| MC | ALCS 4744 |

Alligator / Aug '92 / Topic Records / Direct Distribution / C.M. Distribution / A.D.A. Distribution / Jazz Music.

| | |
|---|---|
| CD | ALCD 4744 |

Alligator / May '93 / Topic Records / Direct Distribution / C.M. Distribution / A.D.A. Distribution / Jazz Music.

## HEAP SEE.

**Tracks:** Not Advised.

| | |
|---|---|
| ■ LP | 3372 |

Blue Phoenix / Jan '85.

## I DIDN'T GIVE A DAMN IF WHITES BOUGHT IT, VOL.2.

**Tracks:** Pepper's hangout / Looking for my baby / Pretty baby / High heel sneakers / When my first wife quit me.

| | |
|---|---|
| ■ LP | .RL 05 |

Red Lightnin' / Oct '84.

## JOHNSON'S WHACKS.

**Tracks:** Not Advised.

| | |
|---|---|
| ■ LP | .DL 64 |

Delmark (USA) / Dec '88.

| | |
|---|---|
| CD | DD 64 |

■ DELETED

Delmark (USA) / Dec '89 / Cadillac / Swift / A.D.A. Distribution / Topic Records / Direct Distribution / Jazz Music / C.M. Distribution.

### NORTH/SOUTH (Johnson, Jimmy Band).
Tracks: Not Advised.
■ LP . . . . . . . . . . . . . . . . . . . . . . . .DL 647
Delmark (USA) / Dec '88.

## Johnson, Johnny

### BLAME IT ON THE PONY EXPRESS (Johnson, Johnny & Bandwagon).
Tracks: Blame it on the pony express.
■ 7" . . . . . . . . . . . . . . . . . . . BELL 1128
Bell / Nov '70.

### BREAKIN' DOWN THE WALLS OF HEARTACHE (Johnson, Johnny & Bandwagon).
Tracks: Breakin' down the walls of heartache / Dancing master.
■ 7" . . . . . . . . . . . . . . . . . . . . . . .583670
Direction (CBS) / Oct '68.
■ 7" . . . . . . . . . . . . . . . . . . . . EPC 8315
Epic / Mar '80.

### HONEY BEE (Johnson, Johnny & Bandwagon).
Tracks: Honey bee / I don't know why.
■ 7" . . . . . . . . . . . . . . . . . . . . . . INT 507
EMI International / Jan '75.

### JOHNNY B.BAD.
Tracks: Tanqueray / Hush oh hus / Johnnie B.Bad / Creek mud / Fault line tremor / Stepped in what / Can you stand it / Key to the highway / Blues [8]X572 / Baby what's wrong / Cow cow blues / Movin' out.
CD . . . . . . . . . . . . . . . . . . . . . 7559611492
MC . . . . . . . . . . . . . . . . . . . . . 7559611494
Elektra / Sep '91 / WEA.

### JOHNNY JOHNSON & THE BANDWAGON.
Tracks: When love has gone away / Stoned soul picnic / Breakin' down the walls of heartache / I wish it would rain / You blew your cool / You / People got to be free / Girl from Harlem / Are you ready for this / I ain't lyin' / Don't let it in / Baby make your own sweet music.
LP . . . . . . . . . . . . . . . . . . . . . . 8 63500
Direction / Feb '69.

### LET'S HANG ON (Johnson, Johnny & Bandwagon).
Tracks: Let's hang on.
■ 7" . . . . . . . . . . . . . . . . . . . . . . .584180
Direction (CBS) / May '69.

### SOUL SURVIVOR (Johnson, Johnny & Bandwagon).
Tracks: On the Pony Express / Love is blue / Gasoline Alley bred / He ain't heavy, he's my brother / Sweet inspiration / In the bad, bad old days / United we stand / Games people play / Something / Pride comes before a fall / Never let her go.
■ LP . . . . . . . . . . . . . . . . . . . . SBLL 138
Bell / Dec '70.

### SWEET INSPIRATION (Johnson, Johnny & Bandwagon).
Tracks: Sweet inspiration.
■ 7" . . . . . . . . . . . . . . . . . . . . BELL 1111
Bell / Jul '70.

### YOU (Johnson, Johnny & Bandwagon).
Tracks: You.
■ 7" . . . . . . . . . . . . . . . . . . . . . . .583923
Direction (CBS) / Feb '69.

## Johnson, L.V.

### I GOT THE TOUCH.
Tracks: I got the touch / Take a little time to know her / Are you serious / I don't want to lose your love / What do you mean love ain't got nothing to do / I am missing you / I just can't get over you / Stroking kind (choking kind).
LP . . . . . . . . . . . . . . . . . . . . . ICH 1112
MC . . . . . . . . . . . . . . . . . . . ICH 1112MC
Ichiban / Jul '91 / A.D.A. Distribution / Pinnacle / ACD Trading Ltd. / Koch International / Direct Distribution.
CD . . . . . . . . . . . . . . . . . . . .CDICH 1112
Ichiban / Oct '93 / A.D.A. Distribution / Pinnacle / ACD Trading Ltd. / Koch International / Direct Distribution.

### IT'S SO COLD AND MEAN.
Tracks: Get him out of your system / It's so cold and mean (the drug scene) / One in a million you / Blues

in the north / It's not my time / Make you mine / Steal away / How can I live without you.
LP . . . . . . . . . . . . . . . . . . . . . . ICH 1050
MC . . . . . . . . . . . . . . . . . . . .ZCICH 1050
Ichiban / Dec '89 / A.D.A. Distribution / Pinnacle / ACD Trading Ltd. / Koch International / Direct Distribution.
CD . . . . . . . . . . . . . . . . . . . .CDICH 1050
Ichiban / Oct '93 / A.D.A. Distribution / Pinnacle / ACD Trading Ltd. / Koch International / Direct Distribution.

### IT'S SO COLD AND MEAN.
Tracks: It's so cold & mean / It's so cold & mean (inst.).
■ 7" . . . . . . . . . . . . . . . . . . . . . . 89173
Ichiban / Nov '89.

### ONE IN A MILLION YOU.
Tracks: One in a million you / Steal away.
■ 7" . . . . . . . . . . . . . . . . . . . . . . 90203
CMC / Apr '90.

### UNCLASSIFIED.
Tracks: Not Advised.
CD . . . . . . . . . . . . . . . . . . . .ICH 1137CD
MC . . . . . . . . . . . . . . . . . . . ICH 1137MC
Ichiban / May '94 / A.D.A. Distribution / Pinnacle / ACD Trading Ltd. / Koch International / Direct Distribution.

## Johnson, Lorraine

### FEED THE FLAME.
Tracks: I'm learning to dance all over again / Nobody's wrong / More I get, the more I want / Feed the flame / Who do you think you're fooling / Save me your love.
■ LP . . . . . . . . . . . . . . . . . . . . EPC 83591
Epic / '79.

### FEED THE FLAME.
Tracks: Feed the flame / Who do you think you're fooling.
■ 7" . . . . . . . . . . . . . . . . . . . . EPC 7089
Epic / Mar '79.

## Johnson, Lou

### AIN'T GONNA BE THAT WAY.
Tracks: Ain't gonna be that way.
■ 7" . . . . . . . . . . . . . . . . . . . . HLT 9156
London-American / Aug '60.

### I LOVE THE WAY YOU LOVE.
Tracks: I love the way you love.
■ 7" . . . . . . . . . . . . . . . . . . . . HLT 9109
London-American / May '60.

### MESSAGE TO MARTHA.
Tracks: Message to Martha.
■ 7" . . . . . . . . . . . . . . . . . . . . HL 9929
London-American / Nov '64.

### UNSATISFIED.
Tracks: Unsatisfied / Time to love, a time to cry.
■ 7" . . . . . . . . . . . . . . . . . . . . HLX 9994
London-American / '65.

## Johnson, Louis

### PASSAGE.
Tracks: Have you heard the word / You can't be livin' / Faith walking people / I see the light / Great flood / Open up your heart / Power / Love eyes / Sun will come again.
■ LP . . . . . . . . . . . . . . . . . . . AMLH 64851
A&M / Mar '81.

## Johnson, Marv

### EARLY CLASSICS.
Tracks: You got what it takes / I love the way you love / Come to me.
■ LP . . . . . . . . . . . . . . . . . . . . LBR 1008
Liberty / Jan '80.

### I MISS YOU BABY.
Tracks: I miss you baby.
■ 7" . . . . . . . . . . . . . . . . . . . . TMG 713
Tamla Motown / Nov '69.

### I'LL PICK A ROSE FOR MY ROSE.
Tracks: I'll pick a rose for my rose.
■ 7" . . . . . . . . . . . . . . . . . . . . TMG 680
Tamla Motown / Jan '69.

### I'LL PICK A ROSE FOR MY ROSE.
Tracks: I'll pick a rose for my rose / I'm not a plaything / Just the way you are / Sleep / Bad girl / Everybody's gotta pay some dues / So glad you

chose me / I wish I liked you / I miss you baby / Why do you want to let me go / You got the love I love.
■ LP . . . . . . . . . . . . . . . . . . . .STML 11111
Tamla Motown / Jun '69.

### WHY DO YOU WANT TO LET ME GO.
Tracks: Why do you want to let me go.
■ 7" . . . . . . . . . . . . . . . . . . . . TMG 525
Tamla Motown / '65.

### YOU GOT WHAT IT TAKES.
Tracks: You got what it takes.
■ 7" . . . . . . . . . . . . . . . . . . . . HLT 9013
London-American / Feb '60.

## Johnson, Norman

### OUR LOVE WILL GROW (Johnson, Norman & Showmen).
Tracks: Our love will grow / You're everything.
■ 7" . . . . . . . . . . . . . . . . . . . . ACT 4529
Action / '69.

## Johnson, Orlando

### JUST A KISS.
Tracks: Just a kiss.
■ 12" . . . . . . . . . . . . . . . . . . . . .XTCT 12
■ 7" . . . . . . . . . . . . . . . . . . . . XTC 12
Ecstasy / Mar '85.

### TURN THE MUSIC ON (Johnson, Orlando & Trance).
Tracks: Turn the music on.
■ 12" . . . . . . . . . . . . . . . . . . .12MAG 246
■ 7" . . . . . . . . . . . . . . . . . . . MAG 246
Magnet / Jul '83.

## Johnson, Paul

### ARE WE STRONG ENOUGH.
Tracks: Are we strong enough / Intimate friends / Where can you be.
■ 12" . . . . . . . . . . . . . . . . . . .PJOHNT 3
■ 12" . . . . . . . . . . . . . . . . . . .PJOHNQ 3
■ 7" . . . . . . . . . . . . . . . . . . . PJOHN 3
■ EP . . . . . . . . . . . . . . . . . . .PJOHN E3
CBS / Jul '87.

### BURNIN'.
Tracks: Burnin' / Wonder of you.
■ 12" . . . . . . . . . . . . . . . . . . .PJOHNT 5
■ 7" . . . . . . . . . . . . . . . . . . . PJOHN 5
■ EP . . . . . . . . . . . . . . . . . . .PJOHN E5
■ CD Single . . . . . . . . . . . . . . PJOHNC 5
CBS / Jan '88.

### DON'T MAKE ME WAIT TOO LONG.
Tracks: Don't make me wait too long / Father father / Don't make me wait too long (Not on 7" single.) / Where can you be (Not on 7' single.) / Don't make me wait too long (Full length mix) / Don't make me wait too long (Spiritual mix) / You're no good (Deep house mix).
■ 12" . . . . . . . . . . . . . . . . . . . PJOHN Q9
■ 12" . . . . . . . . . . . . . . . . . . . PJOHN T9
■ 7" . . . . . . . . . . . . . . . . . . . PJOHN 9
■ CD Single . . . . . . . . . . . . . . PJOHN C9
■ MC Single . . . . . . . . . . . . . . PJOHN M9
CBS / Jun '90.

### EVERY KINDA PEOPLE.
Tracks: Burnin' / Every kinda people / Believer / Burnin' (extended mix).
■ 12" P.Disc . . . . . . . . . . . . . . .PJOHNT 6
■ 7" P.Disc . . . . . . . . . . . . . . . PJOHN 6
■ CD Single . . . . . . . . . . . . . . PJOHN C6
CBS / Mar '88.

### FEAR OF FALLING.
Tracks: Fear of falling / That was yesterday / Fear of falling (live) / Tell me something good (live).
■ 12" . . . . . . . . . . . . . . . . . . .PJOHN T4
■ 7" . . . . . . . . . . . . . . . . . . . PJOHN 4
■ 7" . . . . . . . . . . . . . . . . . . . PJOHN Q4
CBS / Oct '87.

### HALF A WORLD AWAY.
Tracks: Half a world away / Where can you be (Not on CBS PJON 52) / When love comes calling* (* On PJON 52 only).
■ 12" . . . . . . . . . . . . . . . . . . .PJON 52
■ 12" . . . . . . . . . . . . . . . . . . .PJOHNT 2
■ 7" . . . . . . . . . . . . . . . . . . . PJOHN 2
CBS / May '87.

### MASQUERADE.
Tracks: Masquerade (Only on 7" and CD single.) / Personal (Only on 7" and CD single.) / Masquerade (extended version) (Only on 12" and CD single.) / You're no good (deep house mix) (Only on 12" single.) / You're no good (Only on CD single.) / New love (Only on EP) / Where can you be (Only on EP).

| | |
|---|---|
| ■ 12″ | .PJOHNT 8 |
| ■ 7″ | .PJOHN 8 |
| ■ CD Single | .PJOHNC 8 |
| ■ EP | .PJOHNE 8 |

CBS / Jul '89.

## NO MORE TOMORROWS.
**Tracks:** No more tomorrows / I don't care / No more tomorrows (extended) (On CD & 12″ only.) / Hold on I'm coming (On CD & 12″ only.) / That was yesterday (On CD only).

| | |
|---|---|
| ■ 12″ | .PJOHN T7 |
| ■ 12″ | .PJOHN Q7 |
| ■ 7″ | .PJOHN 7 |
| ■ CD Single | .PJOHN C7 |
| ■ EP | .PJOHN E7 |

CBS / Feb '89.

## PAUL JOHNSON.
**Tracks:** When love comes calling / Fear of falling / New love / Every kinda people / Intimate friends / Burnin' / Heaven is 10 zillion light years away / Are we strong enough / Half a world away.

| | |
|---|---|
| CD | .4506402 |
| ■ LP | .4506401 |
| ■ MC | .4506404 |

CBS / Feb '88 / Sony.

## PAUL JOHNSON / PERSONAL.
**Tracks:** When love comes calling / Fear of falling / New love / Every kinda people / Intimate friends / Burnin' / Heaven is 10 zillion light years away / Are we strong enough / Half a world away / Best think it over / No more tomorrows / Masquerade / In a circle / Who shot Cupid / Sweet Marinda / Not enough love in the world / You're no good / Father, Father / Me oh my.

| | |
|---|---|
| ■ CD Set. | .4661482 |
| ■ Double LP. | .4661481 |
| ■ MC Set | .4661484 |

CBS / Nov '89.

## PERSONAL.
**Tracks:** Best think it over / No more tomorrows / Masquerade / In a circle / Who shot cupid / Sweet Marinda / Not enough love in the world / You're no good / Father? Father / Me oh my.

| | |
|---|---|
| CD | .4632842 |
| ■ LP | .4632841 |
| ■ MC | .4632844 |

CBS / Mar '89.

## WHEN LOVE COMES CALLING.
**Tracks:** When love comes calling / Don't pass me by.

| | |
|---|---|
| ■ 12″ | .PJOHNT 1 |
| ■ 7″ | .PJOHN 1 |

CBS / Jan '87.

## Johnson, Roy Lee

### BOOGALOO NO.3.
**Tracks:** Boogaloo no.3 / So Anna just love me.

| | |
|---|---|
| ■ 7″ | .ACT 4518 |

Action / '68.

## Johnson, Ruby

### I'LL RUN YOUR HURT AWAY.
**Tracks:** I'll run your heart away / What more can a woman do / Won't be long / Love of my man / Why not give me a chance / It's not that easy / Don't play that song (you lied) / Come to me my darling / It's better to give than to receive / keep on keepin' on / How strong is my love / Need your love so bad / Left over love / I'd better check on myself / I'd rather fight than switch / No no no / If I ever needed love (I sure do need it now) / When my love comes down / Weak spot.

| | |
|---|---|
| CD | .CDSXD 049 |

Stax / Mar '93 / Pinnacle.

## Johnson, Shirley

### LOOKING FOR LOVE.
**Tracks:** Not Advised.

| | |
|---|---|
| CD | .AP 094CD |
| MC. | .AP 094C |

Appaloosa / Jul '94 / A.D.A. Distribution.

## Johnson, Syl

By day a mild-mannered student at Chicago's Boston School of Music, by night a blues-blasting guitarist with Muddy Waters, Howlin' Wolf and others, Johnson further paid his dues with seven year-stint in Junior

Wells' band. Stepping out solo in '62, he tapped R&B hit vein with *C'mon Sock It To Me* and *Is It Because I'm Black.* Signed to Hi by Willie Mitchell, he topped R&B chart with *I'm Still Here* in 1970, although subsequent albums tended to more blues-orientated. Johnson made minor splash on U.K. scene in '82 with *Ms Fine Brown Fame.*

## A SIDES, THE.
**Tracks:** Love you left behind / I wanna satisfy your every need / We did it / Back for a taste of your love / I'm yours / Let yourself go / I want to take you home (to see mama) / Take me to the river / I only have love / Star bright, star lite / You make me leave home / Fonk you / Stand by me / Mystery lady.

| | |
|---|---|
| CD | .HILOCD 06 |

Hi / Mar '94 / Pinnacle.

## BACK FOR A TASTE OF YOUR LOVE.
**Tracks:** Not Advised.

| | |
|---|---|
| CD | .HIUKCD 142 |

Hi / Jun '93 / Pinnacle.

## BRINGS OUT THE BLUES IN ME.
**Tracks:** Brings out the blues in me / How you need to be loved / Last night was the night / Got my eyes on you / Liberated lady / Sock it to me / Is it because I'm black / Crazy people.

| | |
|---|---|
| ■ LP | .FLY 569 |

Flyright / Apr '86.

## IS IT BECAUSE I'M BLACK.
**Tracks:** Come on sock it to me / Dresses too short / I can take care of business / I'll take those skinny legs / I resign / Get ready / I feel an urge / I take care of homework / Is it because I'm black / Concrete reservation / Walk a mile in my shoes / I'm talkin' 'bout freedom / Right on / Different strokes (On CD only) / Going to the shack (On CD only) / One way to nowhere (On CD only) / Thank you baby (On CD only) / One way ticket to nowhere (On CD only) / Kiss by kiss (On CD only) / Same kind of thing (On CD only).

| | |
|---|---|
| ■ LP | .CRB 1125 |

Charly R&B / Aug '86.

| | |
|---|---|
| CD | .CPCD 8011 |

Charly / Feb '94 / Charly.

## LET YOURSELF GO.
**Tracks:** Let yourself go / Please don't give up on me.

| | |
|---|---|
| ■ 7″ | .HLU 10476 |

London / Jan '75.

## LOVE CHIMES, THE.
**Tracks:** Back for a taste of your love / We did it / I'm yours / Don't do it / I hear the love chimes / Anyway the wind blows / Love you left behind / I want to take you home (to see Mama) / Feeling frisky / Let yourself go / I let a good girl go / Wind, blow her back my way / You don't know me / I hate I walked away / Please don't give up on me.

| | |
|---|---|
| ■ LP | .HIUKLP 404 |

Hi / Jul '86.

## MS. FINE BROWN FAME.
**Tracks:** Ms. Fine Brown frame / Keep on loving me / They can't see your good side / Grooves me / Sweet thing / You don't have to go / It ain't easy.

| | |
|---|---|
| ■ LP | .EPC 25300 |

Epic / Apr '83.

## MS. FINE BROWN FRAME.
**Tracks:** Ms. Fine brown frame / You don't have to go.

| | |
|---|---|
| ■ 12″ | .EPCA 133016 |
| ■ 7″ | .EPCA 3016 |

Epic / Jan '73.

## MUSIC TO MY EARS.
**Tracks:** Not Advised.

| | |
|---|---|
| CD | .HIUKCD 117 |

Demon / Jul '91 / Pinnacle / A.D.A. Distribution.

## STUCK IN CHICAGO.
**Tracks:** Watch what you do to me / Diamond in the rough / I only have love / Bustin' up or bustin' out / Stuck in Chicago / Keeping down confusion / 'Bout to make me leave home / Take me to the river / Music to my ears / Steppin' out / Could I be falling in love / It ain't easy / That's just my luck / Star bright, star lite.

| | |
|---|---|
| ■ LP | .HIUKLP 424 |

Hi / '88.

## TOTAL EXPLOSION & UPTOWN SHAKEDOWN.
**Tracks:** Only have love, I / Bustin' up or bustin' out / Star bright, star light / Watch what you do to me / Steppin' out / Take me to the river / It ain't easy / 'Bout to make me leave home / That's just my luck / Mystery lady / Let's dance for love / Gimme little sign / You're the star of the show / Blue water / Who's gonna love you / Otis Redding medley.

| | |
|---|---|
| CD | .HIUKCD 143 |

Demon / Jun '93 / Pinnacle / A.D.A. Distribution.

## Johnson, Troy

### GETTING A GRIP ON LOVE.
**Tracks:** You make me lose my head / If you've got the heart / Mesmerized / Just get a grip / It's my groove / It's you / Wonders of your love / Time will tell / Honest lover.

| | |
|---|---|
| ■ LP | .ZL 72416 |
| ■ MC | .ZK 72416 |

Motown / Jul '86.

## Johnston, Sabrina

### FRIENDSHIP.
**Tracks:** Friendship.

| | |
|---|---|
| ■ 12″ | .YZ 637T |
| ■ 7″ | .YZ 637 |
| ■ CD Single | .YZ 637CD |
| ■ MC Single | .YZ 637C |

East West / Nov '91.

### I WANNA SING.
**Tracks:** I wanna sing.

| | |
|---|---|
| ■ 12″ | .YZ 661 T |
| ■ 7″ | .YZ 661 |
| ■ CD Single | .YZ 661 CD |
| ■ MC Single | .YZ 661 C |

East West / Jun '92.

### PEACE.
**Tracks:** Peace.

| | |
|---|---|
| ■ 12″ | .YZ 616T |
| ■ 7″ | .YZ 616 |
| ■ CD Single | .YZ 616CD |
| ■ MC Single | .YZ 616C |

East West / Aug '91.

### PEACE.
**Tracks:** Not Advised.

| | |
|---|---|
| CD | .9031763532 |
| ■ LP | .WX 455 |
| MC. | .WX 455C |

East West / Aug '92 / WEA.

### SATISFY MY LOVE.
**Tracks:** Satisfy my love.

| | |
|---|---|
| 12″ | .CHAMP 12311 |
| CD Single | .CHAMPCD 311 |
| MC Single | .CHAMPK 311 |

Champion / Aug '94 / BMG.

## Joli, France

### ATTITUDE.
**Tracks:** Walking into a heartache / Nasty love / I want you with me / Dumb blonde / Girl in the '80s / Standing in the shadows of love / Mad about the boy / Blue eyed technology / You're not alone.

| | |
|---|---|
| ■ LP | .EPC 25721 |
| MC. | .40 25721 |

Epic / Nov '83 / Sony.

### COME TO ME.
**Tracks:** Come to me / Let go.

| | |
|---|---|
| ■ 7″ | .ARO 204 |

Ariola / Nov '79.

### FEEL LIKE DANCING.
**Tracks:** Feel like dancing / Tough luck.

| | |
|---|---|
| ■ 7″ | .ARO 240 |

Ariola / Aug '80.

### GIRL IN THE 80S.
**Tracks:** Girl in the 80s / Inside my mind.

| | |
|---|---|
| ■ 7″ | .A 3795 |

Epic / Nov '83.

## Jomanda

### GOT A LOVE FOR YOU.
**Tracks:** Got a love for you.

| | |
|---|---|
| ■ 12″ | .W 0040T |
| ■ MC Single | .W 0040C |
| ■ 7″ | .W 0040 |
| ■ CD Single | .W 0040CD |

Giant / Jun '91.

### I LIKE IT.
**Tracks:** I like it / I like it (mixes).

| | |
|---|---|
| ■ 12″ Remix | .A 8377T |
| ■ 12″ Remix. | .A 8377TX |
| ■ 7″ | .A 8377 |
| ■ CD Single | .A 8377CD |

East West / Aug '93.

### JOMANDA.
**Tracks:** Not Advised.

| | |
|---|---|
| CD | .7567805482 |

**MC.** . . . . . . . . . . . . . . . 7567805484
East West / Sep '93 / WEA.

## MAKE MY BODY ROCK.
Tracks: Make my body rock.
- 12" Remix. . . . . . . . . . . . . PT 42750R
- 12" . . . . . . . . . . . . . . . . . PT 42750
- 7" . . . . . . . . . . . . . . . . . . PB 42749
- CD Single . . . . . . . . . . . . . PD 42750
RCA / Apr '89.

## NEVER.
Tracks: Never / Never (Mixes).
- 12" . . . . . . . . . . . . . . . . . A 8347T
- 7" . . . . . . . . . . . . . . . . . . A 8347
- CD Single . . . . . . . . . . . . A 8347CD
- MC Single . . . . . . . . . . . . A 8347C
Atlantic / Oct '93.

## NUBIA SOUL.
Tracks: Never / Don't deny / Just a little more time / I like it / I cried the tears / Does the music love you / Life / What you go through for love / Island / Don't fight the feelings / Kiss you / Back to you / Gotta be with you.
**CD.** . . . . . . . . . . . . . . . .756780548-2
**MC.** . . . . . . . . . . . . . . . .756780548-4
Atlantic / Dec '93 / WEA.

## SHARE.
Tracks: Share.
- 12" . . . . . . . . . . . . . . . . . YZ 547 T
- 7" . . . . . . . . . . . . . . . . . . .YZ 547
- CD Single . . . . . . . . . . . . YZ 547 CD
- MC Single . . . . . . . . . . . . YZ 547 C
East West / Dec '90.

## SOMEONE TO LOVE ME.
Tracks: Make my body rock / Someone to love me / Share / Don't you want my love / You knew / Boy / Dance / Got a love for you / It ain't no big thing / When love hurts / True meaning of love / What's the deal (Not available on LP) / I will always be there for you (Not available on LP) / Without you (Available on CD only).
**CD.** . . . . . . . . . . . . . . . . . 7599244142
- LP . . . . . . . . . . . . . . . . . 7599244141
**MC.** . . . . . . . . . . . . . . . . . 7599244144
Sire / Jul '91 / WEA.

# Jonah, Julian

## BETTER DAY (Jonah, Julian & Linda Muriel).
Tracks: Better day / Better day (instrumental) / Jealousy and lies (Available on 12" only).
- 12" . . . . . . . . . . . . . . . . COOLX 193
- 7" . . . . . . . . . . . . . . . . . COOL 193
Cool Tempo / Oct '89.

## HOT TO TOUCH.
Tracks: Hot to the touch / Dreaming.
- 12" . . . . . . . . . . . . . . . . 12 TOCO 8
- 7" . . . . . . . . . . . . . . . . . . TOCO 8
Total Control / Jun '86.

## IT'S A JUNGLE OUT THERE.
Tracks: It's a jungle out there (Not on 12") / Just a love thing.
- CD Single . . . . . . . . . . . COOLCD 208
- MC Single . . . . . . . . . . . COOLMC 208
Cool Tempo / Aug '90.
- 12" . . . . . . . . . . . . . . . . COOLX 208
- 7" . . . . . . . . . . . . . . . . . COOL 208
Cool Tempo / Jul '90.

## JEALOUSY AND LIES.
Tracks: Jealousy and lies / Jealousy and lies (instrumental).
- 12" . . . . . . . . . . . . . . . . COOLX 157
- 7" . . . . . . . . . . . . . . . . . COOL 157
Cool Tempo / Apr '88.

## WELCOME TO THE DISCO.
Tracks: Welcome to the disco.
- 12" . . . . . . . . . . . . . . . . . BUMP 11
Bump 'n' Hustle / Jun '92.

# Jones, Bobby

## HILL COUNTRY SUITE.
Tracks: Not Advised.
- LP . . . . . . . . . . . . . . . . . ENJA 2046
Enja (Germany) / Jan '82.

## SOUL SET FREE (Jones, Bobby & New Life).
Tracks: This little light of mine / He believes in me / Close to you / I won't give up / Movin' on / Martin / No one can match your love / Soul set free / Celebration.
- LP . . . . . . . . . . . . . . . . .MYR 1115

**MC.** . . . . . . . . . . . . . . . .MC 1115
Myrrh / May '82 / Word Records (UK) / Sony.

# Jones, Booker T.

## BOOKER T & PRISCILLA (Booker T & Priscilla).
Tracks: Wedding song / She / Indian song / Sea gull / Cool black dream / Sweet child you're not alone / He / Sister Babe / Earth children / Water brothers / For Priscilla / Delta song / Why / Mississippi voodoo / Medley from the Jones Ranch / Funny honey / California girl / Sun don't shine / Ole man trouble.
- LP Set. . . . . . . . . . . . . AMLH 63504
A&M / Oct '71.

## LET'S GO DANCIN'.
Tracks: Let's go dancing / Knockin' on Heaven's door.
- 12" . . . . . . . . . . . . . . . . AMS 7415
A&M / Feb '79.

## TRY AND LOVE AGAIN.
Tracks: I'll put some love / Ain't that peculiar / Let's go dancin' / Someday we'll be together / I was made to love her / Knockin' on heaven's door / We could fly / Superlove / Try and love again.
- LP . . . . . . . . . . . . . . . . AMLH 64720
A&M / Nov '78.

# Jones, Brenda Lee

## YOU'RE THE LOVE OF MY LIFE.
Tracks: You're the love of my life / Thread your needle.
- 7" . . . . . . . . . . . . . . . . . . . USA 8
UK / Apr '75.

# Jones, Charlie L.

## CHARLIE L. JONES.
Tracks: Pretty little sexy thing / I thought I was over you / Crazy over you / Love on the beach / Troubles is troubling me / It's how love should be / Now I know how love is / Blues all over / Let's have a good time / Just a smile / Woo-baby you're so sweet.
- LP . . . . . . . . . . . . . . . . . TRPL 117
Timeless (Soul) / Jan '90.

# Jones, Doris

## CAN'T YOU SEE THAT SMILE ON MY FACE.
Tracks: Can't you see my face / Time on my hands.
- 7" . . . . . . . . . . . . . . . . . UP 36339
United Artists / Feb '78.

## NO WAY OUT.
Tracks: No way out / No way out (part 2).
- 7" . . . . . . . . . . . . . . . . . UP 36259
United Artists / Jun '77.

## SUDDENLY I'M ALIVE.
Tracks: Suddenly I'm alive / Possessed.
- 7" . . . . . . . . . . . . . . . . . UP 36380
United Artists / May '78.

# Jones Girls

Former Diana Ross backing singers Shirley, Valorie and Brenda Jones breezed into limelight on Philadelphia International label: Kenny Gamble-produced debut *You Gonna Make Me Love Somebody Else* made U.S. Top 40 in '79. Dismissed as ersatz Emotions, group nonetheless became dance favourites; although declining fortunes prompted lengthy sabbatical from 1984 and 1992 album *Coming Back* appears to have been trio's last gasp. Shirley Jones returned in 1994 with second solo album *With You*, including remake of group's biggest hit *Nights Over Egypt*.

## ARTISTS SHOWCASE: JONES GIRLS.
Tracks: You gonna make me love somebody else / 2 win u back / At peace with woman / Knockin' / Keep it coming / Get as much love as you can / Life goes on / Nights over Egypt.
- LP . . . . . . . . . . . . . . . . . MUSIC 4
**MC.** . . . . . . . . . . . . . . . . ZCMUS 4
Street Sounds / Jul '86 / BMG / Total.

## AT PEACE WITH WOMAN.
Tracks: At peace with woman / When I'm gone.
- 7" . . . . . . . . . . . . . . . . .PIRA 1030
Philadelphia Int. / Mar '81.

## COMING BACK.
Tracks: Not Advised.
**CD.** . . . . . . . . . . . . . . . .ARPCD 02

**MC.** . . . . . . . . . . . . . . . . ARPMC 02
- LP . . . . . . . . . . . . . . . . . ARPLP 02
ARP / Oct '92 / Jetstar.

## GET AS MUCH LOVE AS YOU CAN.
Tracks: That man of mine / Get as much love as you can / Nights over Egypt / Love don't ever say good-bye / ASAP / Let's be friends first / World will sing our song / You're breaking my heart.
- LP . . . . . . . . . . . . . . . . . PIR 85347
Philadelphia Int. / Apr '82.

## JONES GIRLS.
Tracks: This feelings killing me / You made me love you / Show love today / You gonna make love somebody else / Life goes on / Who can I run to / We're a melody / I'm at your mercy.
- LP . . . . . . . . . . . . . . . . . PIR 83831
Philadelphia Int. / '79.

## KEEP IT COMING.
Tracks: Keep it coming / Won't let you take it back / Why you wanna do that to me / You can't have my love / Better things to do / Love is comin' atcha / Ah ah ah ah / Right stuff.
- LP . . . . . . . . . . . . . . . . . PIR 25487
Philadelphia Int. / Jul '84.

## NIGHTS OVER EGYPT.
Tracks: Nights over Egypt / ove don't ever say goodbye.
- 12" . . . . . . . . . . . . . . PIR A13 2031
- 7" . . . . . . . . . . . . . . . .PIR A2031
Philadelphia Int. / Feb '82.

## NIGHTS OVER EGYPT (OLD GOLD).
Tracks: Nights over Egypt / You can't my love.
- 12" . . . . . . . . . . . . . . . . .OG 4071
Old Gold / Jul '88.

## ON TARGET.
Tracks: Let's hit it (dialogue) / On target / Win U back / Baby, I'm yours / Knockin' / I can make a difference / What a fool / Curious / I'm a woman here.
- LP . . . . . . . . . . . . . . . . . PL 84817
**MC.** . . . . . . . . . . . . . . . . PK 84817
RCA / Oct '83 / BMG.

## ON TARGET.
Tracks: On target / Curious.
- 12" . . . . . . . . . . . . . . . . RCAT 364
- 7" . . . . . . . . . . . . . . . . .RCA 364
RCA / Nov '83.

## YOU MADE ME LOVE YOU.
Tracks: You made me love you / I'm at your mercy.
- 7" . . . . . . . . . . . . . . . . . PIR 7843
Philadelphia Int. / Sep '79.

## YOU'RE GONNA MAKE ME LOVE SO-MEBODY ELSE.
Tracks: You're gonna make me love somebody else / Who can I run to.
- 7" . . . . . . . . . . . . . . . . . PIR 7361
Philadelphia Int. / '79.

# Jones, Glenn

Jones had carved a successful niche in the gospel genre when he was brought to the attention of veteran producer Norman Connors. Having sung and toured with Connors, Jones signed to RCA; his solo debut won fans on both sides of the Atlantic. After further collaborations with Leon Sylvers and Dionne Warwick, his third, eponymous album became his first U.K. chart entry - an achievement he has yet to repeat, despite latterly recording for Atlantic and WEA.

## ALL FOR YOU.
Tracks: Not Advised.
**CD.** . . . . . . . . . . . . . . . . CHIP 74
- LP . . . . . . . . . . . . . . . . . HIP 74
- MC . . . . . . . . . . . . . . . . HIPC 74
Jive / May '90 / BMG.

## BEST OF GLENN JONES, THE.
Tracks: Not Advised.
- CD . . . . . . . . . . . . . . . CHIP 129
Jive / Jul '93.

## FINESSE.
Tracks: Finesse / You're the only one I love / Show me / It hurts too much / Meet me half way there / Bring back your love / Everlasting love / On the floor.
- MC . . . . . . . . . . . . . . . . PK 88036
- LP . . . . . . . . . . . . . . . . . PL 88036
RCA / Nov '84.
- CD . . . . . . . . . . . . . . . . ND 88036
- LP . . . . . . . . . . . . . . . . . NL 88036
- MC . . . . . . . . . . . . . . . . NK 88036
RCA / Jun '91.

- DELETED

225

## GLENN JONES.
Tracks: Not Advised.
■ LP . . . . . . . . . . . . . . . . . . . . HIP 51
■ MC . . . . . . . . . . . . . . . . . . . HIPC 51
Jive / Oct '87.

## HERE I AM.
Tracks: Not Advised.
CD . . . . . . . . . . . . . . . . . . .756782513-2
LP . . . . . . . . . . . . . . . . . . .756782513-1
MC . . . . . . . . . . . . . . . . . . .756782513-4
Warner Bros. / Apr '94 / WEA.

## HERE I GO AGAIN.
Tracks: Here I go again / I've been searchin' (nobody like you) / Call me / Good thang / Open up your heart / Way you do / Baby come to me / In you / Love is forever / Get it right / Say yeah.
CD . . . . . . . . . . . . . . . . . . . 7567823522
Atlantic / Mar '92 / WEA.
■ LP . . . . . . . . . . . . . . . . . . 7567823521
MC . . . . . . . . . . . . . . . . . . . 7567823524
Atlantic / May '92 / WEA.

## I AM SOMEBODY.
Tracks: I am somebody.
■ 12" . . . . . . . . . . . . . . . . . .RCAT 318
■ 7" . . . . . . . . . . . . . . . . . . .RCA 318
RCA / Feb '83.

## I AM SOMEBODY (OLD GOLD).
Tracks: I am somebody / Keep on doin' (what you're doin').
■ 12" . . . . . . . . . . . . . . . . . .OG 4096
Old Gold / Jan '89.

## LIVING IN THE LIMELIGHT.
Tracks: Living in the limelight / Love me through the night.
■ 12" . . . . . . . . . . . . . . . . . .JIVET 166
■ 7" . . . . . . . . . . . . . . . . . . .JIVE 166
Jive / Apr '88.

## STAY.
Tracks: Stay.
■ 12" . . . . . . . . . . . . . . . . . .JIVET 247
■ 7" . . . . . . . . . . . . . . . . . . .JIVE 247
■ CD Single . . . . . . . . . . . . . JIVECD 247
Jive / Apr '90.

## TAKE IT FROM ME.
Tracks: Stay / Set the night on fire / Love will show us how / Be my lady / Giving myself to you / All work and no play / Dangerous / Take it from me.
MC . . . . . . . . . . . . . . . . . . . PK 85807
■ LP . . . . . . . . . . . . . . . . . . PL 85807
RCA / Aug '86 / BMG.

## WE'VE ONLY JUST BEGUN (The romance is not over).
Tracks: We've only just begun / We've only just begun (version).
■ 7" . . . . . . . . . . . . . . . . . . .JIVE 151
■ 12" . . . . . . . . . . . . . . . . . .JIVET 151
■ CD Single . . . . . . . . . . . . . JIVECD 151
Jive / Sep '87.

## Jones, Gloria

## BRING ON THE LOVE.
Tracks: Bring on the love / Cry baby.
■ 7" . . . . . . . . . . . . . . . . . . CL 16014
Capitol / Sep '78.

## FINDERS KEEPERS.
Tracks: Finders keepers / Run one flight of stairs.
■ 7" . . . . . . . . . . . . . . . . . . .SS 555
Stateside / '66.

## GET IT ON.
Tracks: Get it on / Get in on (version).
■ 7" . . . . . . . . . . . . . . . . . . EMI 2437
EMI / Apr '76.

## GO NOW.
Tracks: Go now / Drive me crazy (disco lady).
■ 7" . . . . . . . . . . . . . . . . . . EMI 2570
EMI / Feb '77.

## HEARTBEAT.
Tracks: Heartbeat (part 1) / Heartbeat (part 2).
■ 7" . . . . . . . . . . . . . . . . . . CL 15429
Capitol / Jan '66.

## LISTEN TO ME.
Tracks: Listen to me.
■ 7" . . . . . . . . . . . . . . . . . . BP 380
Liberty / Nov '80.

## TAINTED LOVE.
Tracks: Tainted love / Touch of venus.
■ 12" . . . . . . . . . . . . . . . . . 12 HEAT 6
■ 7" . . . . . . . . . . . . . . . . . . HEAT 6

Inferno (1) / Jan '82.
■ 7" . . . . . . . . . . . . . . . . . . SP 8303
Rockhouse / Feb '83.
■ 7" . . . . . . . . . . . . . . . . . . SS 3010
Soul Stop / Oct '84.

## WINDSTORM.
Tracks: Bring on the love / Windstorm / If the roses don't come / Blue light microphone / Hooked on you baby / Vaya con Dios / Kiss me, kiss me, kiss me / Woman is a woman.
■ LP . . . . . . . . . . . . . . . . . . EMC 3290
EMI / Jan '79.
■ LP . . . . . . . . . . . . . . . . . . SWK 2002
Sidewalk / Mar '79.

## WINDSTORM.
Tracks: Windstorm / Blue light microphone.
■ 7" . . . . . . . . . . . . . . . . . . SID 104
Sidewalk / Mar '79.

## Jones, Grace

## AMADO MIO.
Tracks: Amado mio (Brazilian mix - radio edit) (7" only.) / Amado mio (radio edit) (7" only.) / Amado mio (Brazilian mix) (Not on 7".) / Amado mio (28th Street crew club mix) (Not on 7".) / Amado mio (28th Street crew dub mix) (Not on 7".).
■ 12" . . . . . . . . . . . . . . . . . 12CL 571
■ 7" . . . . . . . . . . . . . . . . . . CL 571
■ CD Single . . . . . . . . . . . . . CDCL 571
Capitol / Apr '90.

## APPLE STRETCHING, THE.
Tracks: Apple stretching / Nipple to the bottle.
■ 12" . . . . . . . . . . . . . . . . . 12WIP 6779
■ 7" . . . . . . . . . . . . . . . . . . WIP 6779
Island / Oct '82.

## BULLETPROOF HEART.
Tracks: Driving satisfaction / Kicked around / Love on top of love / Paper plan / Crack attack / Bulletproof heart / On my way / Dream (Cassette & CD only.) / Seduction surrender / Someone to love / Don't cry freedom (CD only.) / Amado mio.
■ CD . . . . . . . . . . . . . . . . . .CDESTU 2106
■ LP . . . . . . . . . . . . . . . . . . ESTU 2106
■ MC . . . . . . . . . . . . . . . . . TCESTU 2106
Capitol / Oct '89.

## DEMOLITION MAN.
Tracks: Demoliton man / Bullshit / Warm leatherette.
■ 12" . . . . . . . . . . . . . . . . . 12WIP 6673
■ 7" . . . . . . . . . . . . . . . . . . WIP 6673
Island / Feb '81.

## FAME.
Tracks: Not Advised.
■ LP . . . . . . . . . . . . . . . . . . ILPS 9525
Island / Jul '78.
CD . . . . . . . . . . . . . . . . . . . 5501322
MC . . . . . . . . . . . . . . . . . . . 5501324
Spectrum (1) / Oct '93 / PolyGram.

## GRACE JONES: INTERVIEW PICTURE DISC.
Tracks: Not Advised.
■ LP P.Disc . . . . . . . . . . . . . BAK 2007
Baktabak / May '87.

## HUNTER GETS CAPTURED BY THE GAME.
Tracks: Hunter gets captured by the game / Hunter gets captured by the game (part 2) / Warm leatherette (Only on 12" single.)
■ 12" . . . . . . . . . . . . . . . . . 12 WIP 6645
■ 7" . . . . . . . . . . . . . . . . . . WIP 6645
Island / Sep '80.

## I NEED A MAN.
Tracks: I need a man / I need a man (version).
■ 7" . . . . . . . . . . . . . . . . . . .2058 898
Polydor / Jul '77.

## I'M NOT PERFECT (BUT I'M PERFECT FOR YOU).
Tracks: I'm not perfect (but I'm perfect for you) / I'm not perfect (perfectly extended remix) (Track on 12" single only.) / I'm not perfect (Instrumental version) (Track on 12" single only.) / Scary but fun.
■ 12" . . . . . . . . . . . . . . . . . .12MT 15
■ 12" P.Disc. . . . . . . . . . . . . 12MTP 15
■ 7" . . . . . . . . . . . . . . . . . . MT 15
EMI-Manhattan / Nov '86.

## I'VE SEEN THAT FACE BEFORE.
Tracks: I've seen that face before / Libertango.
■ 7" . . . . . . . . . . . . . . . . . . WIP 6700
Island / Aug '81.

## INSIDE STORY.
Tracks: I'm not perfect (but I'm perfect for you) / Hollywood liar / Chan hitch-hikes to Shanghai / Victor should have been a jazz musician / Party girl / Crush / Barefoot in Beverly Hills / Scary but fun / White collar crime / Inside story.
■ LP . . . . . . . . . . . . . . . . . . MTL 1007
■ MC . . . . . . . . . . . . . . . . . TCMTL 1007
EMI-Manhattan / Nov '86.
■ CD . . . . . . . . . . . . . . . . . .BU 8
EMI / Nov '86.

## ISLAND LIFE.
Tracks: Slave to the rhythm / Pull up to the bumper / Private life / La vie en rose / I need a man / My Jamaican guy / Walking in the rain / Libertango / Love is the drug / Do or die / I've seen that face before.
■ CD . . . . . . . . . . . . . . . . . . CID 132
■ LP . . . . . . . . . . . . . . . . . . GJ 1
■ MC . . . . . . . . . . . . . . . . . GJC 1
Island / Nov '85.
CD . . . . . . . . . . . . . . . . . . .IMCD 16
MC . . . . . . . . . . . . . . . . . . . ICM 2030
■ LP . . . . . . . . . . . . . . . . . . ILPM 2030
Island / Apr '91 / PolyGram.

## LIVING MY LIFE.
Tracks: My Jamaican guy / Nipple to the bottle / Apple stretching / Everybody hold still / Cry now - laugh later / Inspiration / Unlimited capacity for love.
MC . . . . . . . . . . . . . . . . . . .ICT 9722
■ LP . . . . . . . . . . . . . . . . . . ILPS 9722
Island / Nov '82 / PolyGram.
■ LP . . . . . . . . . . . . . . . . . . ILPM 9722
MC . . . . . . . . . . . . . . . . . . . ICM 9722
Island / Feb '87 / PolyGram.
CD . . . . . . . . . . . . . . . . . . .IMCD 18
Island / Jun '89 / PolyGram.
MC . . . . . . . . . . . . . . . . . . . 842 615 4
Island / '90 / PolyGram.

## LOVE IS THE DRUG.
Tracks: Love is the drug (remix) / Living my life / Apple stretching (Track on 12" version only.)
■ 7" P.Disc . . . . . . . . . . . . . ISP 266
■ 12" . . . . . . . . . . . . . . . . . ISG 266
■ 12" P.Disc. . . . . . . . . . . . . 12ISP 266
■ 7" . . . . . . . . . . . . . . . . . . IS 266
Island / Feb '86.

## LOVE ON TOP OF LOVE - KILLER KISS.
Tracks: Love on top of love - killer kiss (Not on 12".) / On my way (7" only.) / Love on top of love - killer kiss (Garage house mix) (Not on 7".) / Love on top of love - killer kiss (club mix) (12" only.) / Love on top of love - killer kiss (dub mix) (12" only.) / Love on top of love - killer kiss (swing mix) (CD single only.).
■ 12" . . . . . . . . . . . . . . . . . 12CL 557
■ 7" . . . . . . . . . . . . . . . . . . CL 557
■ CD Single . . . . . . . . . . . . . CDCL 557
Capitol / Nov '89.

## MY JAMAICAN GUY.
Tracks: My Jamaican guy / Cry now, laugh later.
■ 12" . . . . . . . . . . . . . . . . . 12 IS 103
■ 7" . . . . . . . . . . . . . . . . . . IS 103
■ 7" P.Disc . . . . . . . . . . . . . ISP 103
Mar '83.

## NIGHTCLUBBIN'.
Tracks: Feel up / Walking in the rain / Pull up to the bumper / Use me / Art groupie / Libertango / I've done it again.
■ LP . . . . . . . . . . . . . . . . . . ILPS 9624
Island / May '81.
■ LP . . . . . . . . . . . . . . . . . . .ILPM 9624
MC . . . . . . . . . . . . . . . . . . . ICM 9624
■ CD . . . . . . . . . . . . . . . . . .CID 9624
Island / Jan '87 / PolyGram.
CD . . . . . . . . . . . . . . . . . . .IMCD 17
Island / Jun '89 / PolyGram.
MC . . . . . . . . . . . . . . . . . . . 842 368 4
Island / '90 / PolyGram.

## ON YOUR KNEES.
Tracks: On your knees / Don't mess with the messer.
■ 12" . . . . . . . . . . . . . . . . . 12WIP 6511
Island / Aug '79.

## ONE MAN SHOW, A.
Tracks: Warm leatherette / Walking in the rain / Feel up / La vie en rose / Demolition man / Pull up to the bumper / Private life / My Jamaican guy / Living my life / Libertango.
VHS . . . . . . . . . . . . . . . . . . IPV 005 SV
Island Pictures / Nov '82 / PolyGram.
VHS . . . . . . . . . . . . . . . . . . CFV 05912
Channel 5 / '88 / Channel 5 Video / P.R.O. Video / Gold & Sons.
VHS . . . . . . . . . . . . . . . . . . IVA 023

■ DELETED

Island Visual Arts / '89 / PolyGram / THE.
**VHS** . . . . . . . . . . . . . . . . . . . . . . SPC 00092
Spectrum (1) / Oct '89 / PolyGram.

## ONE WOMAN SHOW.
**Tracks:** Warm leatherette / Walking in the rain / Feel up / La vie en rose / Demolition man / Pull up to the bumper / Private life / My Jamaican guy / Living my life.
**VHS** . . . . . . . . . . . . . . . . . . . . . . . 0829943
Polygram Music Video / '92 / PolyGram.

## PARTY GIRL (Special Remix).
**Tracks:** Party girl (special remix) / White collar crime.
■ **12"** . . . . . . . . . . . . . . . . . . . . . .12MT 20
■ **7" P.Disc** . . . . . . . . . . . . . . . . . MTB 20 B
■ **7"** . . . . . . . . . . . . . . . . . . . . . . . MT 20
EMI-Manhattan / Mar '87.

## PORTFOLIO.
**Tracks:** Send in the clowns / What I did for love / Tomorrow / La vie en rose / Sorry / That's the trouble / I need a man.
**MC** . . . . . . . . . . . . . . . . . . . . . . . ICM 9470
■ **LP** . . . . . . . . . . . . . . . . . . . . . .ILPM 9470
Island / Feb '87 / PolyGram.
■ **CD** . . . . . . . . . . . . . . . . . . . . . . CID 9470
Island / May '88.
**CD** . . . . . . . . . . . . . . . . . . . . . . .IMCD 19
Island / Jun '89 / PolyGram.
**MC** . . . . . . . . . . . . . . . . . . . . . . . 842 614 4
Island / '90 / PolyGram.

## PRIVATE LIFE.
**Tracks:** Private life (new "Groucho" remix) / My Jamaican guy / Feel up (vocal) (Available on 12" single only.) / She's lost control (Track available on 12" single only.).
■ **12"** . . . . . . . . . . . . . . . . . . . . .12WIP 6629
■ **7"** . . . . . . . . . . . . . . . . . . . . . . WIP 6629
Island / Jul '80.
■ **12"** . . . . . . . . . . . . . . . . . . . . . .12IS 273
■ **7"** . . . . . . . . . . . . . . . . . . . . . . . IS 273
Island / May '86.

## PULL UP TO THE BUMPER.
**Tracks:** Pull up to the Bumper / La vie en rose / Feel up.
■ **7"** . . . . . . . . . . . . . . . . . . . . . . WIP 6696
Island / Jun '81.
■ **7" P.Disc** . . . . . . . . . . . . . . . . . . ISP 240
■ **12"** . . . . . . . . . . . . . . . . . . . . . .12IS 240
■ **7"** . . . . . . . . . . . . . . . . . . . . . . . IS 240
■ **MC Single**. . . . . . . . . . . . . . . . . . CIS 240
Island / Jan '86.

## ROLLING STONE.
**Tracks:** Rolling stone / Sinning.
■ **12"** . . . . . . . . . . . . . . . . . . . . .12WIP 6591
■ **7"** . . . . . . . . . . . . . . . . . . . . . . WIP 6591
Island / Apr '80.

## SEX DRIVE.
**Tracks:** Sex drive / Sex drive (mixes).
■ **12"** . . . . . . . . . . . . . . . . . . . . . 12 IS 582
■ **CD Single**. . . . . . . . . . . . . . . . . CIDX 582
Island / Nov '93.

## SLAVE TO THE RHYTHM.
**Tracks:** Jones the rhythm / Fashion show / Frog and the princess / Operattack / Slave to the rhythm / Crossing (ooh the action) / Don't cry - it's only the rhythm / Ladies and gentlemen: Miss Grace Jones.
■ **LP** . . . . . . . . . . . . . . . . . . . . . . . GRACE 1
■ **MC** . . . . . . . . . . . . . . . . . . . . . . GRACEC 1
Island / Nov '85.
■ **CD** . . . . . . . . . . . . . . . . . . . . . . CID 4011
Island / Jul '87.
**CD** . . . . . . . . . . . . . . . . . . . . . . .IMCD 65
Island / '89 / PolyGram.
**MC** . . . . . . . . . . . . . . . . . . . . . . . ICM 2032
**MC** . . . . . . . . . . . . . . . . . . . . . . . 842 612 4
Island / '90 / PolyGram.

## SLAVE TO THE RHYTHM.
**Tracks:** Slave to the rhythm.
■ **12" P.Disc**. . . . . . . . . . . . . . . . .12ISP 206
■ **12"** . . . . . . . . . . . . . . . . . . . . . .12IS 206
Island / Oct '85.
■ **7"** . . . . . . . . . . . . . . . . . . . . . . . IS 206
Island / Sep '85.
■ **12"** . . . . . . . . . . . . . . . . . . . . . .ZANG 50T
■ **CD Single** . . . . . . . . . . . . . . . . ZANG 50CD2
■ **CD Single** . . . . . . . . . . . . . . . . ZANG 50CD1
■ **MC Single** . . . . . . . . . . . . . . . . ZANG 50C
ZTT / Apr '94.

## THAT'S THE TROUBLE.
**Tracks:** That's the trouble / Sorry.
■ **7"** . . . . . . . . . . . . . . . . . . . . . . .2058 856
Polydor / Mar '77.

## WALKING IN THE RAIN (Jones, Grace & Compass Point Allstars).
**Tracks:** Walking in the rain / Peanut butter / Pull up to the bumper.
■ **12"** . . . . . . . . . . . . . . . . . . . . .12WIP 6739
■ **7"** . . . . . . . . . . . . . . . . . . . . . . WIP 6739
Island / Oct '81.

## WARM LEATHERETTE.
**Tracks:** Warm leatherette / Private life / Rolling stone / Love is the drug / Hunter gets captured by the game / Bullshit / Breakdown / Pars.
■ **LP** . . . . . . . . . . . . . . . . . . . . . . ILPS 9592
Island / Aug '80.
■ **CD** . . . . . . . . . . . . . . . . . . . . . . CID 9592
■ **LP** . . . . . . . . . . . . . . . . . . . . . .ILPM 9592
■ **MC** . . . . . . . . . . . . . . . . . . . . . . ICM 9592
Island / Sep '86.
**CD** . . . . . . . . . . . . . . . . . . . . . . .IMCD 15
Island / Jun '89 / PolyGram.
**MC** . . . . . . . . . . . . . . . . . . . . . . . 842 611 4
Island / '90 / PolyGram.

## WARM            LEATHERETTE/ NIGHTCLUBBING.
**Tracks:** Not Advised.
**CD Set** . . . . . . . . . . . . . . . . . . . .ITSCD 4
Island / Nov '92 / PolyGram.

# Jones, Jill

## JILL JONES.
**Tracks:** Mia Bocca / G-spot / Violet blue / With you / All day, all night / For love / My man / Baby, you're a trip / Intro (baby you're a trip).
■ **LP** . . . . . . . . . . . . . . . . . . . . . . WX 110
**MC** . . . . . . . . . . . . . . . . . . . . . . WX 110C
Paisley Park / Jul '87 / WEA.
■ **LP** . . . . . . . . . . . . . . . . . . . . . .925575 1
**MC** . . . . . . . . . . . . . . . . . . . . . . .925575 4
Paisley Park / Jun '87 / WEA.
**CD** . . . . . . . . . . . . . . . . . . . . . . .925575 2
Paisley Park / Oct '87 / WEA.

## MIA BOCA.
**Tracks:** Mia boca / Bleaker Street.
■ **12"** . . . . . . . . . . . . . . . . . . . . . . W 8438T
■ **7"** . . . . . . . . . . . . . . . . . . . . . . . W 8438
Paisley Park / Jun '87.

# Jones, Jimmy

## GOOD TIMIN'.
**Tracks:** Not Advised.
■ **LP** . . . . . . . . . . . . . . . . . . . . . . CUB 3847
Cub / Oct '87.

## GOOD TIMIN' (OLD GOLD).
**Tracks:** Good timin' / Handy man.
■ **7"** . . . . . . . . . . . . . . . . . . . . . . .OG 9445
Old Gold / Jul '84.

## HANDY MAN.
**Tracks:** Handy man.
■ **7"** . . . . . . . . . . . . . . . . . . . . . . MGM 1051
MGM (EMI) / Mar '60.

## I JUST GO FOR YOU.
**Tracks:** I just go for you.
■ **7"** . . . . . . . . . . . . . . . . . . . . . . MGM 1091
MGM (EMI) / Aug '60.

## I TOLD YOU SO.
**Tracks:** I told you so.
■ **7"** . . . . . . . . . . . . . . . . . . . . . . MGM 1123
MGM (EMI) / Mar '61.

## IT'S TOO LATE NOW.
**Tracks:** It's too late now / Give me your word.
■ **7"** . . . . . . . . . . . . . . . . . . . . 7N 45371
Pye / Jul '74.

## LET'S TALK ABOUT JESUS.
**Tracks:** Not Advised.
**LP** . . . . . . . . . . . . . . . . . . . . . . SL 14715
Savoy / Apr '90 / Jazz Music / Wellard / Savoy Records / Conifer Records.

## READY FOR LOVE.
**Tracks:** Ready for love.
■ **7"** . . . . . . . . . . . . . . . . . . . . . . MGM 1103
MGM (EMI) / Nov '60.

## STRANDED.
**Tracks:** Stranded / Walking in the door.
■ **7"** . . . . . . . . . . . . . . . . . . . . . . LARK 1
Lark / Feb '83.

## WHEN I GET TO HEAVEN.
**Tracks:** Not Advised.
**LP** . . . . . . . . . . . . . . . . . . . . . . SL 14667

Savoy / Apr '90 / Jazz Music / Wellard / Savoy Records / Conifer Records.

## YOU'LL NEVER KNOW.
**Tracks:** You'll never know / County fair.
■ **7"** . . . . . . . . . . . . . . . . . . . . . . RR 106
Riversdale / Mar '77.

# Jones, Joe

## YOU TALK TOO MUCH.
**Tracks:** You talk too much / Take a little walk / McDonald's daughter / A tisket a tasket / One big mouth (two big ears) / Here's what you gotta do / Where is my baby / To prove my love to you / Big mule / I cried for you / Just write / You talk too much (original) / I'm glad for your sake / One big mouth (original) / I love you still / Every night about eight / Tell me what's happening / Please don't talk about me when I'm gone / I need someone / Always picking on me / California sun / Cause I love you / I've got a uh-uh wife / Oh gee how I cried / Indian love call / Down by the river.
**CD** . . . . . . . . . . . . . . . . . . . . . . .NEMCD 672
Sequel / Jun '94 / Total / BMG.

# Jones, Johnny

## PURPLE HAZE (Jones, Johnny & The King Casuals).
**Tracks:** Purple haze / Horsing around.
■ **7"** . . . . . . . . . . . . . . . . . . . . . .CRM 5004
Cream / Mar '87.

# Jones, Keziah

## BLUFUNK IS A FACT!.
**Tracks:** Not Advised.
**CD** . . . . . . . . . . . . . . . . . . . . . . CDDLB 1
■ **LP** . . . . . . . . . . . . . . . . . . . . . . LPDLB 1
**MC** . . . . . . . . . . . . . . . . . . . . . . MCDLB 1
Delabel / Mar '92 / PolyGram.

## FREE YOUR SOUL.
**Tracks:** Free your soul / Inside out, upside down / Jones convertible (poem) / It's a colourful world.
■ **12"** . . . . . . . . . . . . . . . . . . . . . 12CL 602
■ **MC Single**. . . . . . . . . . . . . . . . . TCCL 602
Capitol / Feb '91.

## LIVE E.P.
**Tracks:** Scream / Hidetheology / Rainy London streets / Blufunk is alive / Secret thoughts / Rhythm is love.
■ **CD Single** . . . . . . . . . . . . . . . . CDDLB 8
■ **MC Single** . . . . . . . . . . . . . . . . MCDLB 8
Delabel / Jun '93.

## RHYTHM IS LOVE.
**Tracks:** Rhythm is love.
■ **12"** . . . . . . . . . . . . . . . . . . . . . DLBT 2
■ **7"** . . . . . . . . . . . . . . . . . . . . . . DLB 2
■ **CD Single** . . . . . . . . . . . . . . . . DLBCD 2
Delabel / Mar '92.

## WHERE'S LIFE.
**Tracks:** Where's life.
■ **CD Single** . . . . . . . . . . . . . . . . DLBCD 4
Delabel / Sep '92.

# Jones, Linda

Highlight of Linda Jones' short career was 1967 U.S. million-seller *Hypnotized*. Hit was sandwiched between early '60s stints with Richard Tee and George Kerr and later solo efforts on Neptune and Turbo labels. After final R&B hit *Your Precious Love*, Jones died of diabetes in 1972.

## 20 GOLDEN CLASSICS.
**Tracks:** Not Advised.
■ **LP** . . . . . . . . . . . . . . . . . . . . . . COL 5120
Collectables (USA) / Jul '88.

## I JUST CAN'T LIVE MY LIFE.
**Tracks:** I just can't live my life / My heart will understand.
■ **7"** . . . . . . . . . . . . . . . . . . . . . . K 16621
Warner / Nov '75.

## YOUR PRECIOUS LOVE.
**Tracks:** Your precious love / I do / I love you (I need you) / I've given you the best years of my life / Don't go (I can't stand to be alone) / Not on the outside / Doggin' me around / Let it be me / Hypnotised / If only we had met sooner / Fugitive from love / I'm so glad I found you / Stay with me forever / Things I've been through / When hurt comes back / I can't make it alone / Behold / Dancing in the street.
**CD** . . . . . . . . . . . . . . . . . . . . . . NEXCD 167
Sequel / Jul '91 / Total / BMG.

## Jones, Oran 'Juice'

### 1.2.1.
Tracks: 1.2.1. / Here I go again / Curiosity.
- ■ 12" . . . . . . . . . . . . . . . . . . . . 6507806
- ■ 7" . . . . . . . . . . . . . . . . . . . . . 6507807

Def Jam / Apr '87.

### COLD SPENDING MY MONEY.
Tracks: Cold spending my money / Cold spending my money (version).
- ■ 12" . . . . . . . . . . . . . . . . . . . 6511216
- ■ 12" . . . . . . . . . . . . . . . . . . . 4406960

Def Jam / Sep '87.

### CURIOSITY.
Tracks: Curiosity / Here I go again.
- ■ 12" . . . . . . . . . . . . . . . . . . 12 OJJ 2
- ■ 7" . . . . . . . . . . . . . . . . . . . . OJJ 2

Def Jam / Jan '87.

### G.T.O. GANGSTERS TAKIN' OVER.
Tracks: Cold spending my money / Not on the outside / You don't miss the rain / How to love again / We were friends / I just can't say goodbye / Rock the night away / Baby don't walk out on me / Your song / U bring it out.
- ■ CD . . . . . . . . . . . . . . . . . . . 4604062
- ■ LP . . . . . . . . . . . . . . . . . . . 4604061
- ■ MC . . . . . . . . . . . . . . . . . . . 4604064

Def Jam / Oct '87.

### JUICE.
Tracks: Rain / You can't hide from love / Here I go again / Curiosity / Your song / Love will find a way / It's yours / 1.2.1. / Two faces.
- ■ LP . . . . . . . . . . . . . . . . . . DEF 26934
- MC . . . . . . . . . . . . . . . . . . . 4026934

Def Jam / Jun '86 / PolyGram.

### ORAN' JUICE JONES.
Tracks: Not Advised.
- ■ CD . . . . . . . . . . . . . . . . . . . CD 26934

CBS / '88.

### RAIN ,THE.
Tracks: Rain / Your song.
- ■ 7" . . . . . . . . . . . . . . . . . . . . .A 7303

Def Jam / Oct '86.

### RAIN, THE (OLD GOLD).
Tracks: Rain / Happy.
- 12" . . . . . . . . . . . . . . . . . . . . .OG 4149

Old Gold / Jan '90 / Pickwick.

### TO BE IMMORTAL.
Tracks: Money, honey / Pipe dreams / Gangster attitude / Never say goodbye / To be immortal / Dollar and a dream / Sacrifices / Shaniqua / Street style / Time.
- CD . . . . . . . . . . . . . . . . . . . .466004 2
- ■ LP . . . . . . . . . . . . . . . . . . .466004 1
- MC . . . . . . . . . . . . . . . . . . . .466004 4

O.B.R. / Jan '90 / Sony.

## Jones, Quincy

Best-known for his Michael Jackson productions, Quincy Jones has had long and largely illustrious career. Forgoing opportunity to tour with friend Ray Charles, 20-year old Jones served apprenticeship with Lionel Hampton Big Band; graduating to, among others, Dizzy Gillespie, Sarah Vaughan and Dinah Washington. In early '60s, he embarked on full-time production career - clients ranging from Brook Benton to Sinatra - and achieved first no. 1 with Lesley Gore's 1963 *It's My Party*. After six years of scoring films, he signed to Mercury to resume previously-intermittent solo recording; heralded by Grammy-winning *Walking In Space*. Jones maintained parallel careers in '70s; including masterminding Brothers Johnson, producing likes of Rufus and Aretha Franklin, and cultivating partnerships with songwriter Rod Temperton and singers James Ingram and Patti Austin. Further buoyed by success of first (and best) Jackson production *Off the Wall*, Jones launched Qwest label in 1980; move which began his highest-profile years. International hit album *The Dude* set pace, spawning three hits and cleaning up at Grammys; and wildly-successful work with George Benson and Jackson made Jones natural producer for star-studded charity single *We Are the World*. *Color Purple* soundtrack and final Jackson collaboration *Bad* filled time before Jones resumed 'solo' career: 1989's *Back On The Block* boasted stellar cast, ranging from Ice T to Barry White and Chaka Khan to Sarah Vaughan. Multi-media pursuits continue today; his TV production company

is responsible for *Fresh Prince Of Bel-Air*. Latterly eclipsed by new breed of swingbeat producers, Jones is nonetheless a giant of soul and remains The Dude.

### AI NO CORRIDA.
Tracks: Ai no corrida.
- ■ 7" . . . . . . . . . . . . . . . . . . . AMS 8109
- ■ 12" . . . . . . . . . . . . . . . . . . AMSX 8109

A&M / Mar '81.

### AT THE BEAULIEU THEATRE LAUSANNE 1960.
Tracks: Cherokee / Chinese checkers / Birth of a band / I remember Clifford / Ghana / Big red / My reverie / Parisian thoroughfare / Moanin' / Soul / Midnight sun will never set / Phantom's blues / Airmail special / Airmail special (Encore).
- CD . . . . . . . . . . . . . . . . . . . TCB 2012

TCB / Jul '94 / New Note.

### BACK ON THE BLOCK.
Tracks: Prologue (2 Q's rap) / Back on the block / I don't go for that / I'll be good to you / Verb to be / Wee b dooinit (aka we been doing it) / Places you find love / Jazz corner of the world / Birdland (instrumental version) / Setembro (Brazilian wedding song) / One man woman / Tomorrow (a better you, better me) / Prelude to the garden / Secret garden.
- CD . . . . . . . . . . . . . . . . . . . .926020 2
- ■ LP . . . . . . . . . . . . . . . . . . . WX 313
- MC . . . . . . . . . . . . . . . . . . . WX 313C

Qwest / Dec '89 / WEA.

### BASIN STREET EAST (see under Eckstine, Billy).

### BEST, THE.
Tracks: Ai no corrida / Stuff like that / I heard that / You have to do it yourself / Love, I never had it so good / Betcha' wouldn't hurt me / Superstition / Razzamatazz / Dude / Is it love that we're missin' / One hundred ways / I'm gonna miss you in the morning / Body heat.
- ■ LP . . . . . . . . . . . . . . . . . . AMLH 68542
- ■ MC . . . . . . . . . . . . . . . . . . CAM 68542

A&M / Feb '82.
- ■ CD . . . . . . . . . . . . . . . . . . . CDA 68542

A&M / Feb '85.

### BETCHA WOULDN'T HURT ME.
Tracks: Betcha wouldn't hurt me.
- ■ 7" . . . . . . . . . . . . . . . . . . . AMS 8157

A&M / Aug '81.

### BILLY ECKSTINE AND QUINCY JONES (see under Eckstine, Billy).

### BIRTH OF A BAND.
Tracks: Not Advised.
- CD . . . . . . . . . . . . . . . . . . . 822 469-2

Emarcy / A.D.A. Distribution / Direct Distribution / Topic Records.

### BOSSA NOVA.
Tracks: Soul bossa nova / Boogie bossa nova / Desafinado / Carnival / Se e tarde me pardoa / On the street where you live / Samba de una nota so / Lalo bossa nova / Serenta / Chega de saudade.

### COMPACT HITS: QUINCY JONES.
Tracks: Razzamatazz / Stuff like that / Ai no corrida / Dude.
- ■ CD Single . . . . . . . . . . . . . . . AMCD 908

A&M / Apr '88.

### DEADEND WALKING IN SPACE.
Tracks: Not Advised.
- ■ LP . . . . . . . . . . . . . . . . . . . . PLP 1
- MC . . . . . . . . . . . . . . . . . . . . PMC 1

Platinum (W.Germany) / Oct '85.

### DUDE, THE.
Tracks: Ai no corrida / Dude / Just one / Betcha wouldnt hurt me / Something special / Razzamatazz / One hundred ways / Valas / Turn on the action.
- ■ CD . . . . . . . . . . . . . . . . . . CDA 63721

A&M / '83.
- ■ MC . . . . . . . . . . . . . . . . . . CKM 63721
- ■ LP . . . . . . . . . . . . . . . . . . AMLK 63721

A&M / Apr '86.
- CD . . . . . . . . . . . . . . . . . . . CDMID 119
- MC . . . . . . . . . . . . . . . . . . . CMID 119

A&M / Oct '92 / PolyGram.

### FREE AND EASY - IN SWEDEN 1960.
Tracks: Not Advised.
- CD . . . . . . . . . . . . . . . . . . . ANC 9500

Ancha / Sep '94 / Jazz Music.

### GO WEST, MAN.
Tracks: Not Advised.
- ■ LP . . . . . . . . . . . . . . . . . . . JASM 1048

Jasmine / '88.

### ■ LP . . . . . . . . . . . . . . . . . . . . FS 73
Fresh Sounds / Feb '88.

### GREAT WIDE WORLD, THE.
Tracks: Lester leaps in / Ghana / Caravan / Everybody's blues / Cherokee / Airmail special / They say it's wonderful / Chant of the weed / I never have seen snow.
- CD . . . . . . . . . . . . . . . . . . . 8224702

Emarcy / Apr '85 / A.D.A. Distribution / Direct Distribution / Topic Records.

### I'LL BE GOOD TO YOU.
Tracks: I'll be good to you / I'll be good to you (good for you soul mix).
- ■ 12" . . . . . . . . . . . . . . . . . . W 2697T
- ■ 7" . . . . . . . . . . . . . . . . . . . W 2697
- ■ CD Single . . . . . . . . . . . . . W 2697CD

WEA / Jan '90.

### JUST ONCE.
Tracks: Just once / Turn on the action.
- ■ 7" . . . . . . . . . . . . . . . . . . . AMS 8178

A&M / Oct '81.

### LISTEN UP - THE LIVES OF QUINCY JONES.
Tracks: Listen up (instrumental version) / Kansas city wrinkles / Killer Joe / Let the good times roll / Air mail special / Perry's theme / Birth of a band / Fly me to the moon / Midnight sun will never set / Rack 'em up / TV medley / Maybe God is tryin' to tell you somethin' / Walking in space / Pop medley / How do you keep the music playing / Back on the block album medley / Somewhere / Listen up (vocal version).
- CD . . . . . . . . . . . . . . . . . . . 7599263222
- ■ LP . . . . . . . . . . . . . . . . . . 7599263221
- MC . . . . . . . . . . . . . . . . . . . 7599263224

Qwest / Sep '90 / WEA.

### LISTEN UP - THE LIVES OF QUINCY JONES.
Tracks: Not Advised.
- VHS . . . . . . . . . . . . . . . . . . . S 012330

Warner Home Video / Mar '92 / WEA / Hollywood Nites / Gold & Sons / THE.

### LIVE LAUSANNE 1960 (Jones, Quincy & His Orchestra).
Tracks: Not Advised.
- CD . . . . . . . . . . . . . . . . . . . TCB 02012

TCB / Jul '94 / New Note.

### LOVE AND PEACE.
Tracks: Not Advised.
- ■ LP . . . . . . . . . . . . . . . . . . .226 2025
- MC . . . . . . . . . . . . . . . . . . . .216 2025

Street Life / May '88.

### LOVE, I NEVER HAD IT SO GOOD.
Tracks: Love, I never had it so good / Body heat / I heard that.
- ■ 7" . . . . . . . . . . . . . . . . . . . AMS 7385

A&M / Sep '78.

### MELLOW MADNESS.
Tracks: Is it love that we're missin' / Paranoid / Mellow madness / Beautiful black girl / Listen (what it is) / Just a little taste of me / My cherie amour / Tryin' to find out about you / Cry baby / Bluesette.
- ■ LP . . . . . . . . . . . . . . . . . . AMLH 64526

A&M / Aug '75.

### MUSIC IN MY LIFE.
Tracks: Superstition / Getaway love theme / Anderson Tapes, Theme from / Cast your fate to the wind / What's going on / Guitar blues odyssey from roots to fruits / Summer in the City / Eye of love / You've got it bad girl / Brown ballad / Manteca / Tribute to Afro day dreaming / First time ever I saw your face.
- ■ LP . . . . . . . . . . . . . . . . . . SHM 3126
- ■ MC . . . . . . . . . . . . . . . . . . HSC 3126

Hallmark / Aug '83.

### ONE HUNDRED WAYS.
Tracks: One hundred ways / Dude.
- ■ 7" . . . . . . . . . . . . . . . . . . . AMS 8207

A&M / Feb '82.

### PLACES YOU FIND LOVE, THE (Jones, Quincy featuring Chaka Khan & Siedah Garrett).
Tracks: Places you find love.
- ■ 12" . . . . . . . . . . . . . . . . . . W 0001T
- ■ 7" . . . . . . . . . . . . . . . . . . . W 0001
- ■ CD Single . . . . . . . . . . . . . W 0001CD

Qwest / Dec '90.

### Q. VS 808.
Tracks: Q. vs 808.
- ■ 12" . . . . . . . . . . . . . . . . . . W 0047T
- ■ 7" . . . . . . . . . . . . . . . . . . . W 0047
- ■ CD Single . . . . . . . . . . . . . W 0047CD

■ MC Single. . . . . . . . . . . . . . . . .W 0047C
Qwest / Jul '91.

## QUINCY JONES.
Tracks: Not Advised.
CD. . . . . . . . . . . . . . . . . . . . . . ONN 46
Object Enterprises / May '89 / Gold & Sons / THE /
Midland Records.

## QUINCY JONES ALL STARS (Jones, Quincy All Stars).
Tracks: Not Advised.
■ LP. . . . . . . . . . . . . . . . . . . . .ESQ 322
Esquire / Jul '86.

## QUINCY JONES AND HIS ORCHESTRA (Jones, Quincy & His Orchestra).
Tracks: Bridge over troubled water / Gula matari / Ironside / Smackwater Jack / Anderson Tapes, Theme from / Oh happy day / Cast your fate to the wind.
■ LP. . . . . . . . . . . . . . . . . . . MFP 50441
MFP / Jan '80.

## QUINTESSENCE, THE.
Tracks: Quintessence / Robot portrait / Little Karen / Straight, no chaser / For Lena and Lennie / Hard sock dance / Invitation / Twitch.
■ MC. . . . . . . . . . . . . . . . . . . . ASC 11
MCA / '85.
■ LP. . . . . . . . . . . . . . . . . . . . JAS 79
Jasmine / Jan '85.
■ LP. . . . . . . . . . . . . . . . . . . . AS 11
Impulse Jazz / Oct '85.
■ CD. . . . . . . . . . . . . . . . . . .MCAD 5728
MCA / '87.

## RAZZAMATAZZ.
Tracks: Razzamatazz / Velas.
■ 12". . . . . . . . . . . . . . . . . . AMSP 8140
■ 7". . . . . . . . . . . . . . . . . . . AMS 8140
A&M / Jun '81.

## SECRET GARDEN, THE.
Tracks: Secret garden.
■ 12". . . . . . . . . . . . . . . . . . . W 9992T
■ 7". . . . . . . . . . . . . . . . . . . . W 9992
■ CD Single. . . . . . . . . . . . . . . W 9992CD
■ MC Single. . . . . . . . . . . . . . . .W 9992C
Qwest / Mar '90.

## SMACKWATER JACK.
Tracks: Smackwater Jack / Cast your fate to the wind / Ironside / What's going on / Anderson tapes, Theme from / Brown ballad / Hikky burr / Guitar blues odyssey from roots to fruits.
■ LP. . . . . . . . . . . . . . . . . . AMLS 63037
A&M / Dec '71.
■ MC. . . . . . . . . . . . . . . . . . CAM 63037
A&M / '74.

## SOUNDS..AND STUFF LIKE THAT.
Tracks: Stuff like that / Love, I never had it so good / Superwoman / I'm gonna miss you in the morning / Love me by my name / Takin' it to the streets.
■ LP. . . . . . . . . . . . . . . . . . AMLH 64685
■ MC. . . . . . . . . . . . . . . . . . CAM 64685
A&M / Jun '78.
■ CD. . . . . . . . . . . . . . . . . . . CDA 3249
A&M / Jul '89.
CD. . . . . . . . . . . . . . . . . . . .CDMID 120
■ MC. . . . . . . . . . . . . . . . . . . CMID 120
A&M / Oct '92 / PolyGram.

## STRIKE UP THE BAND.
Tracks: Baby elephant walk / Pink panther / Dreamsville / Soldier in the rain / Blues in the night / Take five / After hours / Desafinado / Cast your fate to the wind / Jive samba / Strike up the band / Dear old Stockholm / Gentle rain / Bossa nova USA.
CD. . . . . . . . . . . . . . . . . . . . 830 774-2
Verve / Feb '88 / PolyGram.

## STUFF LIKE THAT.
Tracks: Stuff like that.
■ 7". . . . . . . . . . . . . . . . . . . AMS 7367
A&M / Jul '78.

## STUFF LIKE THAT (OLD GOLD).
Tracks: Stuff like that / Ai no corrida.
■ 12". . . . . . . . . . . . . . . . . . .OG 4012
Old Gold / Jan '87.

## TAKE FIVE.
Tracks: Walk on the wild side / Bossa nova USA / Take five / Gravy waltz / Exodus / Back at the chicken shack / Watermelon man / Cast your fate to the wind.
■ LP. . . . . . . . . . . . . . . . . . . . B 90115
MC. . . . . . . . . . . . . . . . . . . MB 990115
Happy Bird (Germany) / Aug '83.

## THIS IS HOW I FEEL.
Tracks: Walkin' / Sleepin' bee / Sermonette / Stockholm sweetenin' / Evening in Paris / Boo's blues.
■ LP. . . . . . . . . . . . . . . . . . . JASM 1035
Jasmine / Feb '84.

## THIS IS HOW I FEEL ABOUT JAZZ.
Tracks: Walkin' / Stockholm sweetnin' / Evening in Paris / Sermonette / Sleepin' bee / Boo's blues / Dancin' pants / Be my guest / Kings road blues / Bright moon / Oom is blues / What's new / We'll be together again / Time on my hands / You got to my head / Laura.
CD. . . . . . . . . . . . . . . . . . . . GRP 11152
Impulse Jazz / Jul '92 / New Note.

## TRAVELLIN' ON THE BAND WAGON (Jones, Quincy Big Band).
Tracks: Hot sake / Strike up the band / Africana / Meadowlands / Under Paris skies / Rico Vacilon / Mack the knife / Manolette de Espana / Baia / Come back to Sorrento / Swedish varmland.
■ LP. . . . . . . . . . . . . . . . . . SML 30003
Mercury / Nov '67.

## WALK ON THE WILD SIDE.
Tracks: Not Advised.
CD. . . . . . . . . . . . . . . . . . . CDCD 1194
Charly / Sep '94 / Charly.

## WALKING IN SPACE.
Tracks: Dead end / Walking in space / Killer Joe / Love and peace / I never told you / Oh happy day.
■ LP. . . . . . . . . . . . . . . . . . . AMLS 961
A&M / Oct '69.
■ LP. . . . . . . . . . . . . . . . . AMLH 68050
A&M / '74.
CD. . . . . . . . . . . . . . . . . . . CDA 0801
A&M / Nov '88 / PolyGram.

## WE HAD A BALL.
Tracks: Birth of a band / Golden boy theme / Soul serenade / Midnight sun will never set / Boy in the tree / Happy faces / Airmail special / Back at the chicken shack / Exodus / Everybody's blues / Eesom / I had a ball.
■ LP. . . . . . . . . . . . . . . . . . . TIME 07
MC. . . . . . . . . . . . . . . . . . . TIMEC 07
Philips (Timeless) / Sep '84 / PolyGram.

## Jones, Samantha

## AND SUDDENLY.
Tracks: And suddenly.
■ 7". . . . . . . . . . . . . . . . . . . . UP 2258
United Artists / '68.

## GIRL NAMED SAM.
Tracks: Feeling that I get / Until tomorrow / Today / Taking the heart out of love / I'll never fall in love again / Feelin' better / Do I still figure in your life / In the morning / Come to me slowly / Put a little love in your heart / I'm sorry but I think I love you / Natural woman.
■ LP. . . . . . . . . . . . . . . . . . . PELS 501
Penny Farthing / Jun '70.

## SURROUNDED BY A RAY OF SUNSHINE.
Tracks: Surrounded by a ray of sunshine.
■ 7". . . . . . . . . . . . . . . . . . . . UP 1185
United Artists / Jun '67.

## THAT SPECIAL WAY.
Tracks: That special way / Somebody else's baby.
■ 7". . . . . . . . . . . . . . . . . . . . UP 1139
United Artists / Jun '66.

## Jones, Shirley

## ALWAYS IN THE MOOD.
Tracks: Do you get enough love / Breaking up / Last night I needed somebody / She knew about me / Always in the mood / I'll do anything for you / Surrender.
■ MC. . . . . . . . . . . . . . . . . . TCPHIL 4000
■ LP. . . . . . . . . . . . . . . . . . . PHIL 4000
Philadelphia Int. / Jul '86.

## DO YOU GET ENOUGH LOVE.
Tracks: Do you get enough love / We can work it out.
■ 12". . . . . . . . . . . . . . . . . . . 12PIR 2
■ 7". . . . . . . . . . . . . . . . . . . . PIR 2
Philadelphia Int. / Jul '86.

## NIGHTS OVER EGYPT.
Tracks: Nights over Egypt.
12". . . . . . . . . . . . . . . . . . . DIVT 03
CD Single. . . . . . . . . . . . . . . . DIVD 03
Diverse / Aug '94 / Jetstar.

## WITH YOU.
Tracks: Gonna get over you / What about me / I've been expecting you / Say / Come closer / Perfect love / Nights over Eygpt / With you / I just can't wait / Dreams do come true / I'm yours tonight / I ain't going nowhere.
CD. . . . . . . . . . . . . . . . . . . .DIVCD 3
LP. . . . . . . . . . . . . . . . . . . .DIVLP 3
MC. . . . . . . . . . . . . . . . . . .DIVMC 3
Diverse / Jul '94 / Jetstar.

## Jones, Tamiko

## CAN'T LIVE WITHOUT YOUR LOVE.
Tracks: Can't live without your love / Let it flow.
■ 12". . . . . . . . . . . . . . . . . . .STEPX 1
■ 7". . . . . . . . . . . . . . . . . . . STEP 1
Polydor / Sep '79.

## CLOUDY.
Tracks: Cloudy / Creepin' / Feel like makin' love / Make love to your mind / Afraid of losing you / Let it flow / Boy you're growing on me / Reachin' out for your love / Woman driver / Let it flow Tamiko.
■ LP. . . . . . . . . . . . . . . . . . .CLP 602
Contempo (1).

## I WANT YOU.
Tracks: I want you.
■ 12". . . . . . . . . . . . . . . . . . 12 DETAIL 2
Hot Melt / Dec '86.

## I'M SPELLBOUND.
Tracks: I'm spellbound / T.J.'s magic.
■ 7". . . . . . . . . . . . . . . . . . . CS 2079
Contempo (1) / Jan '76.

## LET IT FLOW.
Tracks: Let it flow / Reaching out for your love / Creepin' / Feel like makin' love / Boy you're growing on me / Oh how I love you / Let me in your life / Make love to your mind / Cloudy / Afraid of losing you.
■ LP. . . . . . . . . . . . . . . . . . .CLP 537
Contempo (1) / Feb '77.

## TOUCH ME BABY (REACHING OUT FOR YOUR LOVE).
Tracks: Touch me baby (reaching out for your love) / Creepin' (in my dreams).
■ 7". . . . . . . . . . . . . . . . . . . ARISTA 6
Arista / Apr '75.

## Jones, Thelma

## HOUSE THAT JACK BUILT, THE.
Tracks: House that Jack built.
■ 7". . . . . . . . . . . . . . . . . . . SC 110
Soul City (60's) / '69.

## Joneses

## HARD.
Tracks: Not Advised.
■ CD. . . . . . . . . . . . . . . . . . .756782072
■ LP. . . . . . . . . . . . . . . . . . .756782071
■ MC. . . . . . . . . . . . . . . . . . .756782074
Atlantic / Apr '90.

## HEY BABE.
Tracks: Hey babe / Hey babe (part 2).
■ 7". . . . . . . . . . . . . . . . . . . 6052531
Mercury / Jul '74.

## SUGAR PIE GUY.
Tracks: Sugar pie guy / Keep smiling.
■ 12". . . . . . . . . . . . . . . . . . .9198184
■ 7". . . . . . . . . . . . . . . . . . . 6167780
Mercury / Apr '79.
■ 12". . . . . . . . . . . . . . . . . . .MERX 138
■ 7". . . . . . . . . . . . . . . . . . . MER 138
Mercury / Mar '83.

## SUMMER GROOVE.
Tracks: Summer groove.
■ 12". . . . . . . . . . . . . . . . . . .FIZY 507
■ 7". . . . . . . . . . . . . . . . . . . FIZZ 507
Champagne / Oct '81.

## Jonzun Crew

## DOWN TO EARTH.
Tracks: Tonight's the night / We're going all the way / Lovin' / You got the lovin' / Mechanism / Wizard of space / Time is running out / Ugly thing.
■ LP. . . . . . . . . . . . . . . . . . . 825 167
Tommy Boy / May '85.

## LOST IN SPACE.
Tracks: Pac jam / Space is the place / We are the jonzun crew / Space cowboy / Electro boogie encounter / Ground control.

■ DELETED

229

MC. . . . . . . . . . . . . . . . . . . POLDC 5098
■ LP . . . . . . . . . . . . . . . . . POLD 5098
21 / Apr '83.

## LOVIN'.
**Tracks:** Lovin' / Mechanism.
■ 12". . . . . . . . . . . . . . . . . POSPX 725
■ 7". . . . . . . . . . . . . . . . . . POSP 725
Tommy Boy / Feb '85.

## SPACE COWBOY.
**Tracks:** Space cowboy.
■ 12". . . . . . . . . . . . . . . . . POSPX 623
■ 7". . . . . . . . . . . . . . . . . . POSP 623
21 / Jul '83.

## SPACE IS THE PLACE.
**Tracks:** Space is the place / Pac jam.
■ 12". . . . . . . . . . . . . . . . . POSPX 562
■ 7". . . . . . . . . . . . . . . . . . POSP 562
Polydor / Feb '82.

# Jordan, Jeremy

## RIGHT KIND OF LOVE, THE.
**Tracks:** Right kind of love / Right kind of love (mixes).
■ 12". . . . . . . . . . . . . . . . . . . . . .W 0167T
■ 7". . . . . . . . . . . . . . . . . . . . . . W 0167
■ CD Single . . . . . . . . . . . . . .W 0167CD
■ MC Single . . . . . . . . . . . . . .W 0167C
WEA / Mar '93.

# Jordan, Ronny

## ANTIDOTE, THE.
**Tracks:** Get to grips / Blues grinder / After hours / See the new / So what / Nite spice / Summer smile.
CD. . . . . . . . . . . . . . . . . . . . . . CID 9988
■ LP. . . . . . . . . . . . . . . . . . . ILPS 9988
MC. . . . . . . . . . . . . . . . . . . . .ICT 9988
Island / Feb '92 / PolyGram.

## BAD BROTHERS (Jordan, Ronny & DJ Krush).
**Tracks:** Jackal / Shit goes down / Love I never had it so good / So what / Season for a change / Bad brother.
CD . . . . . . . . . . . . . . . . . . IMCD 8024
LP. . . . . . . . . . . . . . . . . . . . IMA 8024
MC. . . . . . . . . . . . . . . . . . . ICM 8024
Island / Aug '94 / PolyGram.

## COME WITH ME.
**Tracks:** Come with me / Shit goes down.
■ 12". . . . . . . . . . . . . . . . 12 IS 584
■ 7". . . . . . . . . . . . . . . . . . . IS 584
■ CD Single . . . . . . . . . . . . . CID 584
■ MC Single . . . . . . . . . . . . . CIS 584
Island / Mar '94.

## GET TO GRIPS.
**Tracks:** Get to grips / Flat out.
■ 12". . . . . . . . . . . . . . . . .12IS 521
■ 7". . . . . . . . . . . . . . . . . . . IS 521
■ MC Single . . . . . . . . . . . . . CIS 521
■ CD Single . . . . . . . . . . . . . CID 521
Island / Mar '92.

## QUIET REVOLUTION, THE.
**Tracks:** Season for change / In full swing / Slam in a jam / Mr Walker / Jackal / Come with me / Morning after / Under your spell / Tinseltown / Vanston place (00 am).
CD. . . . . . . . . . . . . . . . . . . . . CID 8009
LP Set. . . . . . . . . . . . . . . . . ILPSD 8009
MC. . . . . . . . . . . . . . . . . . . .ICT 8009
Island / Sep '93 / PolyGram.

## SO WHAT.
**Tracks:** So what.
■ 12". . . . . . . . . . . . . . . . 12 ANN 14
■ 7". . . . . . . . . . . . . . . . . . ANN 14
■ CD Single . . . . . . . . . . . . ANNCD 14
Antilles/New Directions / Feb '92.

## TINSEL TOWN.
**Tracks:** Tinsel town / My favourite things.
■ 12". . . . . . . . . . . . . . . . 12 IS 566
■ 7". . . . . . . . . . . . . . . . . . . IS 566
■ CD Single . . . . . . . . . . . . . CID 566
■ MC Single . . . . . . . . . . . . . CIS 566
Island / Nov '93.

## UNDER YOUR SPELL.
**Tracks:** Under your spell / In full swing / Under your spell (Radio).
■ 12". . . . . . . . . . . . . . . . .12IS 565
■ 7". . . . . . . . . . . . . . . . . . . IS 565
■ CD Single . . . . . . . . . . . . . CID 565
■ MC Single. . . . . . . . . . . . . CIS 565
Island / Sep '93.

# Joseph, David

## BE A STAR.
**Tracks:** Be a star / Megastar.
■ 12". . . . . . . . . . . . . . . . . .12IS 128
■ 7". . . . . . . . . . . . . . . . . . . IS 128
Island / Sep '83.

## BRITISH HUSTLE - THE BEST OF DAVID JOSEPH & HI-TENSION (Joseph, David & Hi-tension).
**Tracks:** You can't hide (Your love from me) / Hi tension / Joys of love / Funktfied / British hustle / There's a reason / Let's live it up (Nite people) / Latin inspiration / You're my girl / Discover / Expansions '86 / Power and lighting / Peace on earth.
CD. . . . . . . . . . . . . . . . . . IMCD 157
MC. . . . . . . . . . . . . . . . . . ICM 2077
Island / Jul '93 / PolyGram.

## JOYS OF LIFE, THE.
**Tracks:** No time to waste / Joys of life / Guiding star / Baby won't you take my love / Dreaming / Be a star / I'm so in love / Do you feel my love now baby.
MC. . . . . . . . . . . . . . . . . . . .ICT 9739
■ LP. . . . . . . . . . . . . . . . . . ILPS 9739
Island / Nov '83 / PolyGram.

## JOYS OF LIFE, THE.
**Tracks:** Joys of life / Baby won't you take my love.
■ 12". . . . . . . . . . . . . . . . .12IS 135
■ 7". . . . . . . . . . . . . . . . . . . IS 135
Island / Jan '84.

## LET'S LIVE IT UP (NITE PEOPLE).
**Tracks:** Let's live it up (Nite people).
■ 12". . . . . . . . . . . . . . . . 12 IS 116
■ 7". . . . . . . . . . . . . . . . . . . IS 116
Island / May '83.

## NO TURNING BACK.
**Tracks:** No turning back.
■ 12". . . . . . . . . . . . . . . 12 BRW 66
■ 7". . . . . . . . . . . . . . . . . BRW 66
4th & Broadway / Aug '87.

## YOU CAN'T HIDE (YOUR LOVE FROM ME).
**Tracks:** You can't hide (your love from me) / You can't hide (your love from me) (mixes).
■ 12". . . . . . . . . . . . . . . . 12 IS 101
■ 7". . . . . . . . . . . . . . . . . . . IS 101
Island / Feb '83.
■ 12". . . . . . . . . . . . . . . .12 BRW 277
■ 7". . . . . . . . . . . . . . . . . BRW 277
■ CD Single . . . . . . . . . . . .BRCD 277
■ MC Single. . . . . . . . . . . .BRCA 277
Island / May '93.

# Joseph, Margie

## CAN'T MOVE NO MOUNTAIN.
**Tracks:** Can't move no mountain / As soon as the feeling.
7". . . . . . . . . . . . . . . . . . . K 10646
Atlantic / Jul '75 / WEA.

## I'VE GOT TO HAVE YOUR LOVE.
**Tracks:** I've got to have your love / I've got to have your love (version).
■ 12". . . . . . . . . . . . . . . . 12 PO 12
Ichiban / Sep '88.

## IN THE NAME OF LOVE (Best of Margie Joseph).
**Tracks:** Your sweet lovin' / Same thing / Tell it like it is / Never can be / Make me believe you'll stay / Takin' all the love I can / Stop in the name of love / I'm fed up / One more chance / Didn't have to tell me / What's wrong baby / What you gonna do / Sweeter tomorrow / Strungout.
■ LP . . . . . . . . . . . . . . . . . .SX 015
Stax / Oct '88.

## KNOCKOUT.
**Tracks:** Knockout.
■ 12". . . . . . . . . . . . . . . . . JIVET 32
■ 7". . . . . . . . . . . . . . . . . . JIVE 32
Jive / Apr '83.

## MAKES A NEW IMPRESSION.
**Tracks:** Monologue / Women talk / Stop in the name of love / Punish me / Medicine bend / Come tomorrow sweeter tomorrow / Same thing / How beautiful the rain / I'm fed up / Make me believe you'll stay / Temptation's about to take your love.
■ LP . . . . . . . . . . . . . . . . . 2362008
Stax / Oct '71.

## MAKES A NEW IMPRESSION/PHASE II.
**Tracks:** Women talk / Stop in the name of love / Punish me / Medicine bend / Come tomorrow / Sweeter tomorrow / Same thing / How beautiful the

rain / I'm fed up / Make me believe you'll stay / Temptation's about to take your love / That other woman got my man and gone / My world is empty without you / I'll always love you / Strung out / Please don't stop loving me / I love you too much to say goodbye / Didn't have to tell me / Takin' all the love I can.
CD. . . . . . . . . . . . . . . . . . CDSXD 097
Stax / Jul '93 / Pinnacle.

## MIDNIGHT LOVER.
**Tracks:** Midnight lover / Big strong man / I want mo' stuff.
■ 12". . . . . . . . . . . . . . . . . . B 9713 T
■ 7". . . . . . . . . . . . . . . . . .B 9713
Atlantic / Aug '84.

## READY FOR THE NIGHT.
**Tracks:** Not Advised.
■ LP . . . . . . . . . . . . . . . . . 7901581
Cotillion / May '89.

## STAY.
**Tracks:** Not Advised.
■ LP . . . . . . . . . . . . . . . . . ICH 1027
Ichiban / Jul '88.
MC. . . . . . . . . . . . . . . . .ZCICH 1027
Ichiban / Sep '88 / A.D.A. Distribution / Pinnacle / ACD Trading Ltd. / Koch International / Direct Distribution.

## SWEET SURRENDER.
**Tracks:** Sweet surrender / My love.
■ 7". . . . . . . . . . . . . . . . . K 10460
WEA / Jul '74.

## WHAT'S COME OVER ME (Joseph, Margie & Blue Magic).
**Tracks:** What's come over me / You and me.
■ 7". . . . . . . . . . . . . . . . . K 10649
Atlantic / Dec '75.

# Joubert Singers

## STAND ON THE WORD.
**Tracks:** Stand on the word.
■ 7". . . . . . . . . . . . . . . . . . TEN 48
■ 12". . . . . . . . . . . . . . . .TEN 48-12
10 / May '85.

# Joyce, Rosaline

## ARE YOU REALLY GOING.
**Tracks:** Are you really going.
■ 12". . . . . . . . . . . . . . . . . . HAR 01
Hartone / Aug '85.

## FALLING IN LOVE AGAIN.
**Tracks:** Falling in love again / I need all your loving.
■ 12". . . . . . . . . . . . . . . . .12ROS 3
Jam Today / Mar '88.

## FRIENDS NOT LOVERS.
**Tracks:** Friends not lovers / Friends not lovers (doin' fine mix).
■ 7". . . . . . . . . . . . . . . . . DAZZ 57
Elite Records / Sep '86.
■ 12". . . . . . . . . . . . . . . . DAZZ 57 R
Elite Records / Jan '87.

## LOVERS SOUL.
**Tracks:** Not Advised.
■ LP . . . . . . . . . . . . . . . . . ROSLP 1
MC. . . . . . . . . . . . . . . . . ZCROS 1
Jam Today / Oct '87 / Jetstar.

## NO QUESTIONS, NO ANSWERS.
**Tracks:** No questions, no answers / Yankee / Yankee (The London mix) / B-boy mix.
■ 12". . . . . . . . . . . . . . . . .12ROS 1
Jam Today / Nov '87.

# Juicy

## AFTER LOVING YOU.
**Tracks:** After loving you / Private party / Sugar free.
■ 7". . . . . . . . . . . . . . . . 6504316
Epic / Mar '87.

## ALL WORK NO PLAY.
**Tracks:** All work no play / Serious.
■ 7". . . . . . . . . . . . . . . . . .650888
■ 12". . . . . . . . . . . . . . . . .650888 6
Private I (USA) / May '87.

## BAD BOY.
**Tracks:** Bad boy / Bad boy (dub mix).
■ 12". . . . . . . . . . . . . . . . . TA 6470
■ 7". . . . . . . . . . . . . . . . . .A 6470
Private I (USA) / Apr '86.

■ DELETED

## BEATSTREET STRUT.
Tracks: Beatstreet strut.
- 12" . . . . . . . . . . . . . . . . . . . . . A 9665T
- 7" . . . . . . . . . . . . . . . . . . . . .A 9665
Atlantic / Jul '84.

## IT TAKES TWO.
Tracks: Bad boy / It takes two / Love is good enough / Slow dancing / Nobody but you / Sugar free / Stay with me / Forever and ever.
- LP . . . . . . . . . . . . . . . . . . . EPC 26886
- MC. . . . . . . . . . . . . . . . . . . .40 26886
Epic / Mar '86.

## SPREAD THE LOVE.
Tracks: All work, no play / Show and tell / After loving you / Make you mine / Midnight fantasy / Serious / Spread the love / Private party.
- LP . . . . . . . . . . . . . . . . . . . . . 4504801
MC. . . . . . . . . . . . . . . . . . . . . . 4504804
Epic / Apr '87 / Sony.

## SUGAR FREE.
Tracks: Sugar free / Forever and ever / Bad boy* ("Extra track available on 12" version only).
- 12" . . . . . . . . . . . . . . . . . . . .TA 6917
- 7" . . . . . . . . . . . . . . . . . . . . .A 6917
Private I (USA) / Feb '86.

## Julia & Co.

## BREAKIN' DOWN.
Tracks: Breakin' down.
- 12" . . . . . . . . . . . . . . . . . . . . LONX 46
- 7" . . . . . . . . . . . . . . . . . . . . . LON 46
London / Mar '84.

## I'M SO HAPPY.
Tracks: I'm so happy / Breakin' down.
- 12" . . . . . . . . . . . . . . . . . . . . LONX 61
- 7" . . . . . . . . . . . . . . . . . . . . . LON 61
London / Feb '85.

## Jupiter, Duke

## LINE OF YOUR FIRE.
Tracks: Dancing on the ice / We might fall in love / Only you / I want to love you / You're my hero / Line of your fire / Since you've been gone / Turnin' me on / Never say goodbye / Sounds like love.
- LP . . . . . . . . . . . . . . . . . . . ZL 72411
Motown / Dec '85.

## LITTLE LADY.
Tracks: Little lady.
- 12". . . . . . . . . . . . . . . . . . TMGT 1342
- 7" . . . . . . . . . . . . . . . . . . .TMG 1342
Morocco (USA) / Jun '84.

## WHITE KNUCKLE RIDE.
Tracks: She's so hot / Rescue me / Don't turn your back / Top of the bay / Backfire / Little lady / Woman like you / Work it out / Me & Michelle / Little black book.
- LP . . . . . . . . . . . . . . . . . . . ZL 72193
- MC . . . . . . . . . . . . . . . . . . . ZK 72193
Motown / Oct '84.

## Juvet, Patrick

## ANOTHER LONELY MAN.
Tracks: Another lonely man / Where is my woman.
- 7" . . . . . . . . . . . . . . . . . . . .CAN 142
Casablanca / Feb '79.

## GOT A FEELING.
Tracks: Got a feelin'.
- 7" . . . . . . . . . . . . . . . . . . . .CAN 127
Casablanca / Sep '78.

## I LOVE AMERICA.
Tracks: Not Advised.
- LP . . . . . . . . . . . . . . . . . . . . 91003
Barclay (France) / Nov '79.

## I LOVE AMERICA.
Tracks: I love America.
- 7" . . . . . . . . . . . . . . . . . . . .CAN 132
Casablanca / Nov '78.

## I LOVE AMERICA (OLD GOLD).
Tracks: I love America / Got a feelin'.
- 12". . . . . . . . . . . . . . . . . . .OG 4083
Old Gold / Oct '88.

## LADY NIGHT.
Tracks: Lady night / Swiss kiss / Viva California / Gay Paris / French pillow talk.
- LP . . . . . . . . . . . . . . . . . . . CAL 2049
Casablanca / '79.

## OU SONT LES FEMMES.
Tracks: Ou sont les femmes / Les bleu au coeur.
- 7" . . . . . . . . . . . . . . . . . . . .BAR 709
Barclay (France) / Aug '78.

## PARIS BY NIGHT.
Tracks: Not Advised.
- LP . . . . . . . . . . . . . . . . . . . . 90098
Barclay (France) / '79.

## SEX ET DRUGS ET ROCK 'N' ROLL (Juvet, Patrick & His Sweet Perversions).
Tracks: Sex et drugs et rock 'n' roll / Wake up & make love with me.
- 7" . . . . . . . . . . . . . . . . . . MERDE 1
Virgin / '79.

## VIVA CALIFORNIA.
Tracks: Viva California / Gay Paris.
- 12". . . . . . . . . . . . . . . . . .CANL 150
- 7" . . . . . . . . . . . . . . . . . . .CAN 150
Casablanca / Jun '79.

# K

## Kandidate

### CAN'T SAY 'BYE.
Tracks: Can't say 'bye / Never say 'bye.
- 12"..........................POSPX 443
- 7"............................POSP 443
Polydor / May '82.

### DON'T WANNA SAY GOODNIGHT.
Tracks: Don't wanna say goodnight.
- 7"..............................RAK 280
RAK / Aug '78.

### GIRLS GIRLS GIRLS.
Tracks: Girls, girls, girls.
- 7"..............................RAK 295
RAK / Aug '79.

### I DON'T WANNA LOSE YOU.
Tracks: I don't wanna lose you / What are you gonna do.
- 7"..............................RAK 289
RAK / Mar '79.

### I DON'T WANNA LOSE YOU (OLD GOLD).
Tracks: I don't wanna lose you / We do it.
- 7"..............................OG 9684
Old Gold / Mar '87.

### I'M YOUNG.
Tracks: I'm young / Go to work on you.
- 12"..........................12RAK 316
- 7"............................RAK 316
RAK / May '80.

### LET ME ROCK YOU.
Tracks: Let me rock you / Mr. Magic.
- 7"..............................RAK 306
RAK / Mar '80.

## Kashif

### ARE YOU THE WOMAN.
Tracks: Are you the woman / Lover turn me on.
- 12"........................ARIST 12575
- 7"..........................ARIST 575
Arista / Aug '84.

### BABY DON'T BREAK YOUR BABY'S HEART.
Tracks: Baby don't break your baby's heart.
- 12"........................ARIST 12568
- 7"..........................ARIST 568
Arista / May '84.

### BEST OF KASHIF.
Tracks: I just gotta have you (lover turn me on) / Baby don't break your baby's heart / Are you the woman / Reservations for two / Love changes / Fifty ways (to fall in love) / Stone love / Love me all over / Help yourself to my love / Dancing in the dark (heart to heart).
- CD..............................262817
Arista / Jun '92 / BMG.

### CONDITION OF THE HEART.
Tracks: Stay the night / Condition of the heart / I wanna have love with you / Weakness / Say you love me / Movie song / Dancing in the dark / Botha Botha (Apartheid song).
- LP..............................207426
- MC..............................407426
Arista / Nov '85.
- CD..............................257426
Arista / Apr '88.

### I JUST GOTTA HAVE YOU.
Tracks: I just gotta have you.
- 12"........................ARIST 12521
- 7"..........................ARIST 521
Arista / Mar '83.

### KASHIF.
Tracks: Don't stop my love / Stone love / I just gotta have you / Help yourself (to my love) / Rumors / Say something love / Mood / All.
- LP..............................205347
Arista / Mar '83.

### LOVE CHANGES.
Tracks: Reservations for two (with Dionne Warwick) / 50 ways (to fall in love) / Who's getting serious (with Expose) / Love changes (with Melisa Morgan) / Loving you only / It all begins again / Love me all over / Midnight mood / Vacant heart.
- LP..............................208145
- MC..............................408145
Arista / Nov '87.
- CD..............................258145
Arista / '88.

### SEND ME YOUR LOVE.
Tracks: Baby don't break your baby's heart / Ohh love / Are you the woman / Love has no end / Call me tonight / Send me your love / I've been missing you / Edgartown groove / That's how it goes.
- LP..............................206350
Arista / Jun '84.

### STONE LOVE.
Tracks: Stone love / Mood.
- 12"....................... ARIST 12534
- 7"..........................ARIST 534
Arista / Jul '83.

## Kay Gees

### ESSENTIAL DANCEFLOOR ARTISTS VOL. 5 - KAYGEES.
Tracks: You've got to / Keep on bumpin' / Get down / Master plan / Hustle wit every muscle / Waiting at the bus stop / Cheek to cheek / I believe in music / Tango hustle / Killowatt / Killowatt/Invasion / Who's the man (with the master plan).
- CD......................DGPCD 707
Deep Beats / Sep '94 / BMG.

## Kaye, Linda

### I CAN'T STOP THINKING ABOUT YOU.
Tracks: I can't stop thinking about you / When we meet again.
- 7"......................... DB 7915
Columbia / May '66.

## Keisa

### KEISA.
Tracks: Not Advised.
- CD....................... TLCD 673
- LP....................... PPR 1744
Total / Jan '90.

## Keith, Brian

### AIN'T NO WAY TO TREAT A LADY.
Tracks: Ain't no way to treat a lady.
- 7"...................... GO 353
Logo / Jun '79.

### MEMORIES OF YOU (Keith, Brian Creation).
Tracks: Memories of you.
- 7"...................... ALA 1018
Alaska / Feb '76.

### TOUCH ME (LOVE ME TONIGHT).
Tracks: Touch me (love me tonight).
- 12"..................... CBE 1237
- 7"......................CBE 737
City Beat / Feb '89.

## Kelly Brothers

### FALLING IN LOVE AGAIN.
Tracks: Falling in love again / Crying days over again.
- 7"...................... W 14034
Sue / Apr '67.

### SWEET SOUL.
Tracks: That's what you mean to me / You put your touch on me / Hanging in there / Comin' on in / If that will hold you / Got the feeling / Can't stand it no longer / Cryin' days are over / Make me glad / How can true love be this way / Falling in love again / I'd rather have you.
- LP...................... PTL 1019
President / Jul '68.

### YOU PUT YOUR TOUCH ON ME.
Tracks: You put your touch on me / Hanging in there.
- 7"......................PT 143
President / Jun '67.

## Kelly, Frankie

### AIN'T THAT THE TRUTH.
Tracks: Ain't that the truth / Nyeema I love you.
- 12"........................TEN 87-12
- 7"..........................TEN 87
10 / Oct '85.

## Kelly, Paul

One of the great, underrated singer/songwriters, Kelly was born in Miami in 1940 and won a first professional gig when local artist/producer Clarence Reid invited him to join the Del-Mires in '63. Turning solo a couple of years later he cut a series of Reid song's to the decade's end, notably Chills And Fever, later covered by Tom Jones. A year on he enjoyed an even bigger hit with the controversial Stealing In The Name Of The Lord, which took on bogus preachers, leading to a deal with Warner Bros for whom he recorded four albums. The first, Dirt was a repackaging of earlier material, but the next two, Don't Burn Me ('73) and Hooked, Hogtied & Collared ('74), established him as one of the UK's favourite cult soulmen. Stand On The Positive Side ('76) suffered from Gene Page's over-production and interest wained accordingly. Kelly then jumped from singles deals with Epic and A&M to form his own Laurence Records in '83, and dropped occasional 45's right up until '93 when an out-of-the-blue contract with Bullseye Blues saw the emergence of an excellent comeback album, Gonna Stick And Stay. Much loved Kelly compositions over the years have included Personally (Jackie Moore) and You Should Be Here With Me (Annette Snell).

### CHILLS AND FEVER.
Tracks: Chills and fever / Only your love.
- 7"...................... AT 4053
Atlantic / Nov '65.

### DARLING IT HURTS (Kelly, Paul & The Messengers).
Tracks: Darling it hurts / Desdemona, before too long.
- 12"...................... AMY 459
- 7"...................... AM 459
A&M / Sep '88.

### GONNA STICK & STAY.
Tracks: Not Advised.
- CD...................... BB 9523CD
- MC...................... BB 9523C
Bullseye Blues / May '93 / New Note / Topic Records / Direct Distribution.

### GOSSIP (Kelly, Paul & The Coloured Girls).
Tracks: Not Advised.
- Double LP.................. L 45961 2
Mushroom (Australia) / Sep '87.

### HANGIN' ON IN THERE.
Tracks: Stealing in the name of the Lord / 509 / Poor but proud / Hangin' on in there / Come by here / Love me now / Don't burn me / Come lay some lovin' on me / I wanna get next to you / Let your love come down (let it fall on me) / Take it away from him (put it on me) / I'm into somethin' I can't shake loose / I believe I can / Hooked, hogtied and collared.
- LP...................... ED 316
Edsel / Feb '90.

### SO MUCH WATER SO CLOSE TO HOME (Kelly, Paul & The Messengers).
Tracks: You can't take it with you / Sweet guy / Most wanted man in the world / I had forgotten you / She's a melody (stupid song) / South of Germany / Careless / Moon in the bed / No you / Everything's turning to white / Pigeon/Jundamurra / Cities of Texas.
- CD...................... CDA 5266
- LP...................... AMA 5266

232

■ DELETED

■ MC. . . . . . . . . . . . . . . . . . . . . AMC 5266
A&M / Aug '89.

## UNDER THE SUN (Kelly, Paul & The Messengers).
Tracks: Not Advised.
MC. . . . . . . . . . . . . . . . . . . . . . AMC 5207
■ LP . . . . . . . . . . . . . . . . . . . . AMA 5207
■ CD . . . . . . . . . . . . . . . . . . . . CDA 5207
A&M / Sep '88 / PolyGram.

## WANTED MAN.
Tracks: Summer rain / God's hotel / She's rare / Just like animals / Love never runs out on time / Song from thee 16th floor / Maybe this time for sure / Ball and chain / Still picking the same sore / Everybody wants to touch me / We've started a fire / Lately / Nuhkanya.
CD. . . . . . . . . . . . . . . . . . . FIENDCD 758
Demon / Aug '94 / Pinnacle / A.D.A. Distribution.

# Kemp, Johnny

## BIRTHDAY SUIT.
Tracks: Birthday suit / Birthday suit (7" remix) / Birthday suit (extended mix) / Birthday suit (club dub) / Birthday suit (percapella).
■ 12". . . . . . . . . . . . . . . . . . . . 6548387
■ 12". . . . . . . . . . . . . . . . . . . . 6548388
■ 12" Remix. . . . . . . . . . . . . . . . 6548381
■ 7". . . . . . . . . . . . . . . . . . . . . 6548380
■ CD Single. . . . . . . . . . . . . . . . 6548382
CBS / May '89.

## DANCING WITH MYSELF.
Tracks: Dancing with myself / Dancing with myself (ext.) / Dancing with myself (alt. dub mix) (CD single only.) / Dancing with myself (alt. mix) (12" only.) / Just got paid (12" only.).
■ 12". . . . . . . . . . . . . . . . . . . . 6530206
■ 12" Remix. . . . . . . . . . . . . . . . 6530201
■ 7". . . . . . . . . . . . . . . . . . . . . 6530207
■ CD Single. . . . . . . . . . . . . . . . 6530202
CBS / Sep '88.

## JUST GOT PAID.
Tracks: Just got paid / Just got paid (dub mix) / Just got paid (inst) / Penthouse lover (CD single only).
■ 12". . . . . . . . . . . . . . . . . . . . 6514708
■ 12". . . . . . . . . . . . . . . . . . . . 6514709
■ 12" Remix. . . . . . . . . . . . . . . . 6514706
■ 7". . . . . . . . . . . . . . . . . . . . . 6514707
■ CD Single. . . . . . . . . . . . . . . . 6514702
CBS / Jun '88.

## SECRETS OF FLYING.
Tracks: Just got paid / One thing led to another / My only want is you / Dancin' with myself / Urban times / Feeling without touching / Just like flyin'.
■ LP . . . . . . . . . . . . . . . . . . . . BFC 40770
■ CD . . . . . . . . . . . . . . . . . . . . 4609042
■ LP . . . . . . . . . . . . . . . . . . . . 4609041
■ MC. . . . . . . . . . . . . . . . . . . . 4609044
CBS / Jul '88.

# Kemp, Tara

## HOLD YOU TIGHT.
Tracks: Hold you tight.
■ 12". . . . . . . . . . . . . . . . . . . . WOO 20T
■ 7". . . . . . . . . . . . . . . . . . . . . WOO 20
■ CD Single. . . . . . . . . . . . . . . . WOO 20CD
■ MC Single. . . . . . . . . . . . . . . . WOO 20C
Giant / Mar '91.

## PIECE OF MY HEART.
Tracks: Piece of my heart.
■ 12". . . . . . . . . . . . . . . . . . . . W 0048T
Giant / Jul '91.

## TARA KEMP.
Tracks: Prologue / Hold you tight / Be my lover / Too much / One love / Tara by the way / Piece of my heart / Together / Way you make me feel / Something to groove to / Monday love / Epilogue.
CD. . . . . . . . . . . . . . . . . . . . 7599244082
■ LP . . . . . . . . . . . . . . . . . . . 7599244081
MC. . . . . . . . . . . . . . . . . . . . 7599244084
WEA / May '91 / WEA.

# Kendricks, Eddie
Former singer with Ohio group Cavaliers, Kendricks co-founded the Temptations in 1961. Combination of his and David Ruffin's voices provided heart of classics like Can't Get Next to You and Cloud Nine. Acrimoniously quitting after 1971 U.S. chart-topper Just My Imagination (Running Away With Me), Kendricks launched solo career and established following in New York clubs. Groundwork paid off

in '73 when Keep On Truckin' made U.S. No. 1. After second smash with Boogie Down in early '74, Kendricks coasted through remainder of '70s. Having made brief return to Temptations for 1982 Reunion LP, Kendricks was encouraged by blue-eyed soulsters Hall & Oates into further reunions with Ruffin. Among the results were Hall & Oates' excellent Live at the Apollo album, spot at Live Aid, and excellent 1988 Ruffin & Kendricks album, latter including cover of Sly Stone's Family Affair. Sadly, Ruffin died in 1991, and lung cancer took Kendricks' life in '92.

## ALL BY MYSELF.
Tracks: Let's go back to Day One / This used to be the home of Johnnie Mae / I did it all for you / It's so hard for me to say goodbye / Something's burning / Can I / Didn't we.
■ LP . . . . . . . . . . . . . . . . . . . STML 11186
Tamla Motown / Sep '71.

## BOOGIE DOWN.
Tracks: Boogie down.
■ 7". . . . . . . . . . . . . . . . . . . . TMG 888
Tamla Motown / Mar '74.

## GOIN' UP IN SMOKE.
Tracks: Goin' up in smoke / Newness is gone / Sweet tenderoni / Born again / Don't you want light / Music man / Thanks for the memories / To you from me / Don't put off till tomorrow / Skeleton in your closet.
■ LP . . . . . . . . . . . . . . . . . . . STML 12043
Motown / Nov '76.

## GOING UP IN SMOKE.
Tracks: Going up in smoke / Get it while it's hot.
■ 7". . . . . . . . . . . . . . . . . . . . TMG 1061
Motown / Jan '77.

## HE'S A FRIEND.
Tracks: He's a friend / All of my love.
■ 7". . . . . . . . . . . . . . . . . . . . TMG 1021
Tamla Motown / Feb '76.

## HOW'S YOUR LOVE LIFE BABY?.
Tracks: How's your love life baby / Ain't no smoke.
■ 7". . . . . . . . . . . . . . . . . . . . ARIST 182
Arista / Apr '78.

## KEEP ON TRUCKIN'.
Tracks: Keep on truckin'.
■ 7". . . . . . . . . . . . . . . . . . . . TMG 873
Tamla Motown / Nov '73.
■ 7". . . . . . . . . . . . . . . . . . . . TMG 985
Tamla Motown / Aug '75.

## LOVE KEYS.
Tracks: Oh I need your loving / I'm in need of love / I don't need nobody else / Old home town / Bernadette / You can't stop my loving / Never alone / Hot / Looking for love / In love we're one.
■ LP . . . . . . . . . . . . . . . . . . . K 50779
■ MC. . . . . . . . . . . . . . . . . . . K4 50779
Atlantic / Mar '81.

## PEOPLE, HOLD ON.
Tracks: My people..hold on / Date with the rain / Eddie's love / I'm on the sideline / Just memories / If you let me / Let me run into your lonely heart / Day by day / Girl you need a change of my mind / Someday we'll have a better world.
■ LP . . . . . . . . . . . . . . . . . . . STML 11213
Tamla Motown / Feb '73.

## SLICK.
Tracks: Something shady / Baby I want to live / You got it / Intimate friends / Diamond girl / Then came you / I'll have to let you go / California woman.
■ LP . . . . . . . . . . . . . . . . . . . STML 12071
Motown / Dec '77.

## SON OF SAGITTARIUS.
Tracks: Son of Sagittarius / Can't help what I am.
■ 7". . . . . . . . . . . . . . . . . . . . TMG 901
Tamla Motown / Jun '74.

# Kenny G.
Kenny Gorelick was 17 when he enjoyed his first standing ovations, for soloing with Barry White's Love Unlimited Orchestra. However, the former Seattlite and accountancy graduate won more widespread acclaim for his work with Jeff Lorber, prompting Arista to sign him as a solo act. Investment paid off when his tune Songbird joined the largest-selling instrumentals of all time and made him an international star. 1993 album Breathless confirmed his commercial supremacy, and with numerous guest appearances to his credit (Johnny Gill, Four

Tops, President Clinton), Kenny G can probably afford to ignore jibes of critics.

## AGAINST DOCTORS ORDERS.
Tracks: Against doctors orders / Tradewinds / Songbird (live version).
■ 12". . . . . . . . . . . . . . . . . . . . 612293
■ 7". . . . . . . . . . . . . . . . . . . . . 112293
■ CD Single. . . . . . . . . . . . . . . . 662293
Arista / Mar '90.

## BREATHLESS.
Tracks: Joy of life / Forever in love / In the rain / Sentimental / By the time this night is over (With Peabo Bryson.) / End on the night / Morning / Even if my heart would break (With Aaron Neville.) / G-Bop / Sister Rose / Year ago / Homeland / Natural ride / Wedding song / Alone.
CD. . . . . . . . . . . . . . . . . . 07822 18646-2
MC. . . . . . . . . . . . . . . . . 07822 18646-40
Arista / Mar '93 / BMG.

## BY THE TIME THIS NIGHT IS OVER.
Tracks: By the time this night is over / Silhouette (On CD single only) / Homeland (On cassette single only) / Songbird (On CD single only).
■ CD Single. . . . . . . . . . . . . 74321 157152
■ CD Single. . . . . . . . . . . . . 74321 157142
■ MC Single. . . . . . . . . . . . . 74321 151904
Arista / Jun '93.

## CHAMPAGNE.
Tracks: Champagne / What does it take (to win your love) / Hi, how ya doin (Extra track available on 12" version only).
■ 12". . . . . . . . . . . . . . . . . ARIST 12686
■ 7". . . . . . . . . . . . . . . . . . ARIST 686
Arista / Nov '86.

## DON'T MAKE ME WAIT FOR LOVE.
Tracks: Don't make me wait for love / Midnight motion / Virgin Island / Japan.
■ 12". . . . . . . . . . . . . . . . . . RIST 37
■ 7". . . . . . . . . . . . . . . . . . RIS 37
Arista / Sep '87.

## DUOTONES.
Tracks: You make me believe / Slip of the tongue / What does it take (to win your love) / Don't make me wait for love / Sade / Esther / Songbird / Champagne / Midnight / Three of a kind.
CD. . . . . . . . . . . . . . . . . . . . . 257792
■ LP . . . . . . . . . . . . . . . . . . . . 207792
MC. . . . . . . . . . . . . . . . . . . . . 407792
Arista / Sep '86 / BMG.
DCC . . . . . . . . . . . . . . . . 07822184275
Arista / Jan '93 / BMG.

## DYING YOUNG, THEME FROM.
Tracks: Dying young, Theme from / I'll never leave you / Silhouette.
■ 7". . . . . . . . . . . . . . . . . . . . . 114592
■ CD Single. . . . . . . . . . . . . . . . 664592
Arista / Aug '91.

## FOREVER IN LOVE.
Tracks: Forever in love.
■ 7". . . . . . . . . . . . . . . . . 7432114555-7
■ CD Single. . . . . . . . . . . . . 7432114555-2
■ MC Single. . . . . . . . . . . . . 7432114555-4
Arista / Apr '93.

## G FORCE.
Tracks: Hi, how ya doin / I've been missing you / Tribeca / G force / Do me right / I wanna be yours / Sunset at noon / Help yourself to my love.
■ CD . . . . . . . . . . . . . . . . . . . . 256168
■ LP . . . . . . . . . . . . . . . . . . . . 206168
■ MC. . . . . . . . . . . . . . . . . . . . 406168
Arista / Mar '84.
CD. . . . . . . . . . . . . . . . . . . . . 259059
■ LP . . . . . . . . . . . . . . . . . . . . 209059
■ MC. . . . . . . . . . . . . . . . . . . . 409059
Arista / May '88 / BMG.

## GRAVITY.
Tracks: Love on the rise / One man's poison (another man's sweetness) / Where do we take it (from here) / One night stand / Japan / Sax attack / Virgin island / Gravity / Last night of the year.
■ LP . . . . . . . . . . . . . . . . . . . . 207120
■ MC. . . . . . . . . . . . . . . . . . . . 407120
Arista / May '85.
CD. . . . . . . . . . . . . . . . . 7432116164-2
Arista / Feb '94 / BMG.

## HI HOW YA DOIN'.
Tracks: Hi, how ya doin / What does it take (to win your love).
■ 12". . . . . . . . . . . . . . . . . ARIST 12561
■ 7". . . . . . . . . . . . . . . . . . ARIST 561
Arista / Mar '84.

## HI HOW YA DOIN' (OLD GOLD).
Tracks: Hi, how ya doin / What does it take.
■ 12″ . . . . . . . . . . . . . . . . . . . OG 4058
Old Gold / Jul '89.

## HI HOW YA DOIN' (REMIX).
Tracks: Hi, how ya doin.
■ 12″ . . . . . . . . . . . . . . . . ARIST 12574
■ 7″ . . . . . . . . . . . . . . . . . . .ARIST 574
■ 7″ P.Disc . . . . . . . . . . . . . . ARISD 574
Arista / Jun '84.

## KENNY G.
Tracks: Mercy, Mercy, Mercy / Here we are / Stop and go / I can't tell you why / Shuffle / Tell me / Find a way / Crystal mountain / Come close.
CD . . . . . . . . . . . . . . . . . . . . .259337
■ MC . . . . . . . . . . . . . . . . . . . .409337
■ LP . . . . . . . . . . . . . . . . . . . .209337
Arista / Oct '88 / BMG.

## KENNY G LIVE.
Tracks: Sade / Silhouette / Midnight motion / Uncle Al / Brogan / Against doctors orders / Esther / Don't make me wait for love / Going home / Tribeca / Songbird.
VHS . . . . . . . . . . . . . . . . . . . 790 345
BMG Video / Apr '90 / BMG.

## LOVE ON THE RISE (Kenny G. & Kashif).
Tracks: Love on the rise / Virgin island.
■ 12″ . . . . . . . . . . . . . . . . . ARIST 12618
■ 7″ . . . . . . . . . . . . . . . . . . .ARIST 618
Arista / May '85.

## MONTAGE.
Tracks: Songbird / I can't tell you why / Tribeca / Virgin island / I've been missing you / Uncle Al / What does it take (to win your love) / Silhouette / Midnight motion / Against doctors orders / Hi, how ya doin' / Sade / Going home / We've saved the best till last.
CD . . . . . . . . . . . . . . . . . . . . .260621
MC . . . . . . . . . . . . . . . . . . . . .410621
■ LP . . . . . . . . . . . . . . . . . . . .210621
Arista / Apr '90 / BMG.

## SILHOUETTE.
Tracks: Silhouette / We've saved the best for last / Trade winds / I'll be alright / Against doctor's orders / Pastel / All in one night / Let go / Home / Summer song.
CD . . . . . . . . . . . . . . . . . . . . .259284
■ LP . . . . . . . . . . . . . . . . . . . .209284
MC . . . . . . . . . . . . . . . . . . . . .409284
Arista / Nov '88 / BMG.
DCC . . . . . . . . . . . . . . . . 07822184575
Arista / Jan '93 / BMG.

## SILHOUETTE.
Tracks: Silhouette / Home / Looking for a way to let go (Only on 12″).
■ 12″ . . . . . . . . . . . . . . . . . . .611832
■ CD Single . . . . . . . . . . . . . . . .661832
Arista / Nov '88.
■ 7″ . . . . . . . . . . . . . . . . . . . .111832
Arista / Oct '88.

## SONGBIRD.
Tracks: Songbird / Midnight motion / Songbird (ext.).
■ 12″ . . . . . . . . . . . . . . . . . . RIST 18
■ 12″ Remix . . . . . . . . . . . . . . RISTX 18
■ 7″ . . . . . . . . . . . . . . . . . . . .RIS 18
Arista / May '87.

## WHAT DOES IT TAKE.
Tracks: What does it take (to win your love) / Songbird.
■ 7″ . . . . . . . . . . . . . . . . . . .ARIST 672
Arista / Aug '86.
■ 7″ . . . . . . . . . . . . . . . . . . . .109843
Arista / Mar '88.

## Kent, Al

### YOU'VE GOT TO PAY THE PRICE.
Tracks: You've got to pay the price.
■ 7″ . . . . . . . . . . . . . . . . . . . .604016
Track / '67.

## Kerr, George

### LOVE LOVE LOVE.
Tracks: Not Advised.
■ LP . . . . . . . . . . . . . . . . . . . .HB 3000
Harbor Lights / Jul '88.

## Keys, Amy

### GOOD FOR YOU.
Tracks: Good for you (extended remix) / I know what's good for you (dub) / I know what's good for you (accapella).
■ 12″ . . . . . . . . . . . . . . . . . . . 6552008
Epic / Aug '89.

### I KNOW WHAT'S GOOD FOR YOU.
Tracks: I know what's good for you (remix) (On 7″ only.) / Even now / I know what's good for you (extended remix) (On 12″ only.) / I know what's good for you (LP version) (On 12″ only.).
■ 12″ . . . . . . . . . . . . . . . . . . . 6552006
■ 7″ . . . . . . . . . . . . . . . . . . . . 6552007
■ CD Single . . . . . . . . . . . . . . . . 6552002
Epic / Aug '89.

### LOVER'S INTUITION.
Tracks: I know what's good for you / Lover's intuition / Will you respect me (in the morning) / Someone's gonna fall in love / Has it come to this / Even now / Man and a woman / Everytime I close my eyes / Precious / Crazy love.
CD . . . . . . . . . . . . . . . . . . . . . 4633832
Epic / May '89 / Sony.
■ LP . . . . . . . . . . . . . . . . . FE 44100
Epic (import) / May '89.
■ MC . . . . . . . . . . . . . . . . . . . . 4633834
■ LP . . . . . . . . . . . . . . . . . . . . 4633831
Epic / May '89.

### LOVER'S INTUITION.
Tracks: Lover's intuition / Everytime I close my eyes / Precious.
■ 12″ . . . . . . . . . . . . . . . . . . . 6548106
■ 7″ . . . . . . . . . . . . . . . . . . . . 6548107
■ CD Single . . . . . . . . . . . . . . . . 6548102
Epic / Apr '89.

## Khan, Chaka

Yvette Stevens grew up in Chicago, changing to her stage name in the late 60's as she hit the local club circuit. In '71 she joined American Breed, a funk-rock group who also switched names, to Rufus, that same year. Two years later they recorded their first album for ABC Records with Chaka as lead singer. By the mid-'70s, however, Khan was seeking a solo deal and eventually released her debut album in '78: Chaka included the hit I'm Every Woman. Having begun a professional association with Quincy Jones, appearing on his Sounds And Stuff Like That LP, she moved to Los Angeles and cut a pair of albums, Naughty (80) and Whatcha Gonna Do For Me (82), before returning to New York to make Chaka Khan. She also joined Rufus for a farewell live performance, released as the album Stomping At The Savoy, which included four studio tracks. One of these, Ain't Nobody, became a worldwide hit in '84 and shortly thereafter she returned to the top of the charts with a solo single, the Prince penned/produced I Feel For You. An album of the same name followed and produced one further hit, This Is My Night, but her career since the late '80s has reflected her personality: at times wayward and unfulfilled, always fascinating. C.K. ('88) featured both Miles Davis and Prince, while her most recent album, The Woman I Am featured Chaka in the role of executive producer for the first time. She is reportedly working on her first jazz album for Warners.

### AIN'T NOBODY (Rufus & Chaka Khan).
Tracks: Stop on by / Ain't nobody / Don't go to strangers.
■ 12″ . . . . . . . . . . . . . . . . . . . RCKT 1
■ 7″ . . . . . . . . . . . . . . . . . . . . RCK 1
WEA / Mar '84.
■ 12″ . . . . . . . . . . . . . . . . . . . W 2880
■ CD Single . . . . . . . . . . . . . . . W 2880CD
■ MC Single . . . . . . . . . . . . . . .W 2880C
■ 12″ . . . . . . . . . . . . . . . . . . .W 2880T
WEA / Jun '89.

### BEST IN THE WEST.
Tracks: Best in the west / Be bop medley.
■ 12″ . . . . . . . . . . . . . . . . . . W 9753T
■ 7″ . . . . . . . . . . . . . . . . . . . W 9753
WEA / Feb '83.

### CHAKA.
Tracks: I'm every woman / Love has fallen on me / Roll me through the rushes / Sleep on it / Life is a dance / We got the love / Some love / Woman in a man's world / Message in the middle of the bottom / I was made to love him.
■ MC . . . . . . . . . . . . . . . . . . K4 56560

### CHAKA.
■ LP . . . . . . . . . . . . . . . . . K 56560
WEA / Jan '79.

### CHAKA KHAN.
Tracks: Tearin' it up / Best in the west / Got to be there / Twisted / So not to worry / Pass it on, a sure thing / Slow dancing / Hot house / East of Suez / Epistrophy / Yardbird suite / Con Alma / Giant steps.
■ LP . . . . . . . . . . . . . . . . . .923729 1
WEA / Jan '83.

### CK.
Tracks: Signed, sealed, delivered (I'm yours) / Soul talkin' / It's my party / Eternity / Sticky wicked / End of a love affair / Baby me / Make it last / Where are you tonight / I'll be around.
CD . . . . . . . . . . . . . . . . . . . .925707 2
CD . . . . . . . . . . . . . . . . . . WX 124CD
■ LP . . . . . . . . . . . . . . . . . . . WX 124
■ MC . . . . . . . . . . . . . . . . . . . WX 124C
WEA / Nov '88 / WEA.

### CLOUDS.
Tracks: Clouds / What you did.
■ 7″ . . . . . . . . . . . . . . . . . . K 17617
WEA / May '80.

### DESTINY.
Tracks: Love a lifetime / Earth to Mickey / Watching the world / Other side of the world / My destiny / I can't be loved / It's you / So close / Tight fit / Who's it gonna be / Coltrane dreams.
■ CD . . . . . . . . . . . . . . . . . .925425 2
■ LP . . . . . . . . . . . . . . . . . . . .WX 45
■ MC . . . . . . . . . . . . . . . . . . .WX 45 C
WEA / Jul '86.

### DON'T LOOK AT ME THAT WAY.
Tracks: Don't look at me that way (Edit) / I'm every woman (mixes).
■ 12″ . . . . . . . . . . . . . . . . . . .W 0192T
■ 7″ . . . . . . . . . . . . . . . . . . . W 0192
■ CD Single . . . . . . . . . . . . . . .W 0192CD
■ MC Single . . . . . . . . . . . . . . .W 0192C
Warner Bros. / Jul '93.

### EYE TO EYE.
Tracks: Eye to eye / La flamme.
■ 12″ . . . . . . . . . . . . . . . . . . . W 9009T
■ 7″ . . . . . . . . . . . . . . . . . . . W 9009
WEA / Apr '85.

### GOT TO BE THERE.
Tracks: Got to be there / Pass it on.
■ 7″ . . . . . . . . . . . . . . . . . . .929881
WEA / Nov '82.

### HEED THE WARNING.
Tracks: Heed the warning / Night moods.
■ 12″ . . . . . . . . . . . . . . . . . . K 17793T
■ 7″ . . . . . . . . . . . . . . . . . . K 17793
WEA / Apr '81.

### I FEEL FOR YOU.
Tracks: This is my night / Stronger than before / My love is alive / Eye to eye / La flamme / I feel for you / Hold her / Through the fire / Caught in the act / Chinatown.
CD . . . . . . . . . . . . . . . . . . . .925162 2
MC . . . . . . . . . . . . . . . . . . . .925162 4
■ LP . . . . . . . . . . . . . . . . . . .925162 1
WEA / Oct '84 / WEA.

### I FEEL FOR YOU.
Tracks: I feel for you / Chinatown.
■ 12″ . . . . . . . . . . . . . . . . . . .W 9209T
■ 7″ . . . . . . . . . . . . . . . . . . . W 9209
WEA / Oct '85.

### I FEEL FOR YOU (REMIX).
Tracks: I feel for you / I know you live you.
■ 12″ . . . . . . . . . . . . . . . . . . W 2764 T
■ 7″ . . . . . . . . . . . . . . . . . . . W 2764
■ CD Single . . . . . . . . . . . . . . . W 2764 CD
■ MC Single . . . . . . . . . . . . . . . W 2764 C
WEA / Sep '89.

### I KNOW YOU I LOVE YOU.
Tracks: I know you I love you.
■ 12″ . . . . . . . . . . . . . . . . . . .RM 4003
Rock Mo (USA) / Nov '87.

### I'M EVERY WOMAN.
Tracks: I'm every woman / Woman in a man's world.
■ 7″ . . . . . . . . . . . . . . . . . . K 17269
WEA / Dec '78.

### I'M EVERY WOMAN.
Tracks: I'm every woman / Baby me.
■ 12″ . . . . . . . . . . . . . . . . . . .W 2963T
■ 7″ . . . . . . . . . . . . . . . . . . . W 2963
■ CD Single . . . . . . . . . . . . . . .W 2963CD

■ DELETED

■ MC Single. . . . . . . . . . . . . . W 2963MC
WEA / Apr '89.

## IT'S MY PARTY.
Tracks: It's my party / Where are you tonight.
■ 12". . . . . . . . . . . . . . . . . . . W 7678 T
■ 7". . . . . . . . . . . . . . . . . . . W 7678
WEA / Jan '89.

## KRUSH GROOVE (CAN'T STOP THE STREET).
Tracks: Krush groove.
■ 12". . . . . . . . . . . . . . . . . .W 8923T
■ 7". . . . . . . . . . . . . . . . . . W 8923
WEA / Sep '85.

## LIFE IS A DANCE (The Remix Project).
Tracks: Life is a dance / This is my night / Slow dancing / I'm every woman / Ain't nobody / I feel for you / I know you, I live you / Eye to eye / Fate / One million kisses / Clouds / Clouds (classic trax version).
CD. . . . . . . . . . . . . . . . . . . .925946 2
■ LP . . . . . . . . . . . . . . . . . . . WX 268
MC. . . . . . . . . . . . . . . . . . . WX 268C
WEA / May '89 / WEA.

## LIFE IS A DANCE.
Tracks: Life is a dance / Some love.
■ 7". . . . . . . . . . . . . . . . . . . K 17320
WEA / '79.

## LOVE OF A LIFETIME.
Tracks: Love of a lifetime / Coltrane dreams.
■ 12". . . . . . . . . . . . . . . . . .W 8671T
■ 7". . . . . . . . . . . . . . . . . . W 8671
WEA / Jun '86.

## LOVE YOU ALL MY LIFETIME.
Tracks: Love you all my lifetime.
■ 12". . . . . . . . . . . . . . . . . .W 0087T
■ 7". . . . . . . . . . . . . . . . . . W 0087
■ CD Single. . . . . . . . . . . . . .W 0087CD
■ MC Single. . . . . . . . . . . . . .W 0087C
WEA / Mar '92.

## NAUGHTY.
Tracks: Clouds / Get ready get set / Move me no mountain / Nothing's gonna take me away / Do naughty / Too much love / All night's alright / What you did / Papillon / Our love's in danger.
■ LP . . . . . . . . . . . . . . . . . . . K 56713
■ MC. . . . . . . . . . . . . . . . . K4 56713
WEA / Jan '80.

## STAR PORTRAITS: CHAKA KHAN.
Tracks: Not Advised.
VHS . . . . . . . . . . . . . . . . . GEMV 5012
Gemini Vision / Sep '94 / Sony / THE.

## THIS IS MY NIGHT.
Tracks: This is my night / Caught in the act.
■ 12". . . . . . . . . . . . . . . . . .W 9097T
■ 7". . . . . . . . . . . . . . . . . . W 9097
WEA / Jan '85.

## THIS IS MY NIGHT.
Tracks: Not Advised.
VHS . . . . . . . . . . . . . . . . . . . .VVD 066
Virgin Vision / '88 / Gold & Sons / THE.

## THROUGH THE FIRE.
Tracks: Through the fire.
■ 12". . . . . . . . . . . . . . . . . .W 9025T
■ 7". . . . . . . . . . . . . . . . . . W 9025
WEA / Aug '85.

## WATCHING THE WORLD.
Tracks: Watching the world / I can't be loved.
■ 12". . . . . . . . . . . . . . . . . .W 8534 T
■ 7". . . . . . . . . . . . . . . . . . W 8534
WEA / Nov '86.

## WHAT 'CHA GONNA DO FOR ME.
Tracks: What 'cha gonna do for me / We got the love.
■ 7". . . . . . . . . . . . . . . . . . . K 17821
WEA / Jun '81.

## WHAT CHA GONNA DO FOR ME.
Tracks: We can work it out / What cha gonna do for me / I know you, I live you / Any old Sunday / We got each other / Night in Tunisia / Night moods / Heed the warning / Father he said / Fate / I know you, I live you (reprise).
■ LP . . . . . . . . . . . . . . . . . . . K 56888
WEA / Apr '81.

## WOMAN I AM, THE.
Tracks: Woman I am / Give me all.
■ 12". . . . . . . . . . . . . . . . . .W 0120T
■ 7". . . . . . . . . . . . . . . . . . W 0120
■ CD Single. . . . . . . . . . . . . .W 0120CD
East West / Jul '92.

---

## WOMAN I AM, THE.
Tracks: Everything changes / Give me all / Telephone / Keep givin' me lovin' / Facts of love / Love you all my lifetime / I want / You can make the story right / Be my eyes / This time / Woman I am / Don't look at me that way.
CD. . . . . . . . . . . . . . . . . . . .7599262962
MC. . . . . . . . . . . . . . . . . . . .7599262964
Warner Bros. / Apr '92 / WEA.

## Kiara

### CIVILISED ROGUES.
Tracks: You're right about that / Got my eyes on you / Take my time / In the tabloids / My girl / Party intro / Mr. Deejay / Perfect one / Summer day interlude / Always / Every little thing / Slowburn / Always (reprise).
■ CD . . . . . . . . . . . . . . . . . . .261043
■ LP . . . . . . . . . . . . . . . . . . .211043
■ MC. . . . . . . . . . . . . . . . . . .411043
Arista / Oct '90.

### EVERY LITTLE TIME.
Tracks: Every little time (hip hop edit) / Every little time (version) / Every little time (NY mix) (Available on 12" and CD only) / Every little time (Detroit mix) (Available on 12" only) / This time (Available on CD only).
■ MC Single. . . . . . . . . . . . . .410117
■ 12". . . . . . . . . . . . . . . . . .612292
■ 7". . . . . . . . . . . . . . . . . . .112292
■ CD Single. . . . . . . . . . . . . .662292
Arista / Jun '89.

### THIS TIME.
Tracks: This time / Wait so long / Strawberry letter 23.
■ 12". . . . . . . . . . . . . . . . . .612001
■ 12" Remix. . . . . . . . . . . . . .612067
■ 7". . . . . . . . . . . . . . . . . . .112001
■ CD Single. . . . . . . . . . . . . .162001
Arista / Feb '89.

### TO CHANGE AND/OR TO MAKE A DIFFERENCE.
Tracks: Best of me / Wait so long / Strawberry letter 23 / Just like magic / Step by step / Every little time / Candy lips / This time / Quiet guy / Same old story.
■ LP . . . . . . . . . . . . . . . . . . .209248
■ CD . . . . . . . . . . . . . . . . . . .259248
■ MC. . . . . . . . . . . . . . . . . . .409248
Arista / Mar '89.

## Kid Can't Dance

### LOVE, PEACE AND UNDERSTANDING.
Tracks: Love, peace and understanding (Not on 12") / River (On all versions) / Love, peace and understanding (remix) (On CD & 12" only) / Love, peace and understanding (dub) (On 12" only) / Sugar in the backyard (On CD only).
■ 12". . . . . . . . . . . . . . . . . .SRNT 90
■ 7". . . . . . . . . . . . . . . . . . .SRN 90
■ CD Single. . . . . . . . . . . . . .SRNCD 90
Siren / Sep '88.

### UP ON THE ROOFTOP.
Tracks: Up on the rooftop / In your eyes / Up on the rooftop (club) (12" only) / Up on the rooftop (extended) (12" only).
■ 12". . . . . . . . . . . . . . . . . .SRNT 74
■ 7". . . . . . . . . . . . . . . . . . .SRN 74
Siren / May '88.

## Kid Creole

### ANNIE I'M NOT YOUR DADDY (Kid Creole & The Coconuts).
Tracks: Annie I'm not your daddy / You had no intention.
■ 7" P.Disc . . . . . . . . . . . . . .PWIP 6801
■ 7". . . . . . . . . . . . . . . . . . WIP 6801
Island / Oct '82.

### BEST OF KID CREOLE & THE COCONUTS, THE (Kid Creole & The Coconuts).
Tracks: Not Advised.
CD. . . . . . . . . . . . . . . . . . . CID 8011
MC. . . . . . . . . . . . . . . . . . .ICT 8011
Island / Apr '93 / PolyGram.

### CAROLINE WAS A DROPOUT (Kid Creole & The Coconuts).
Tracks: Caroline was a dropout / You can't keep a good man down.
■ 12". . . . . . . . . . . . . . . . . .W 8785T
■ 7". . . . . . . . . . . . . . . . . . W 8785
Sire / Jan '86.

---

### CRE-OLE (Best of Kid Creole & The Coconuts) (Kid Creole & The Coconuts).
Tracks: Lifeboat party / Gina Gina / Me no pop I / Off the coast of me / Don't take my coconuts / Maladie d'amour / There's something wrong in paradise / Stool pigeon / Annie / I'm not your daddy / Latin music / I'm a wonderful thing baby / Imitation / Dear Addy / Back in the field again.
■ LP . . . . . . . . . . . . . . . . . . IMA 13
MC. . . . . . . . . . . . . . . . . . IMC 13
Island / Sep '84 / PolyGram.
CD. . . . . . . . . . . . . . . . . . .IMCD 113
■ LP . . . . . . . . . . . . . . . . . .IMA 113
MC. . . . . . . . . . . . . . . . . . IMC 113
Island / Jun '90 / PolyGram.

### CREOLE MIX.
Tracks: Creole mix.
■ 12". . . . . . . . . . . . . . . . . 12 THN 2
■ 7". . . . . . . . . . . . . . . . . . THN 2
■ CD Single . . . . . . . . . . . . .CDTHN 2
Then / Nov '92.

### DANCIN' AT THE BAINS DOUCHES (Kid Creole & The Coconuts).
Tracks: Dancin' at the Bains Douches / Midsummer madness (The refrain).
■ 12". . . . . . . . . . . . . . . . . .W 8329T
■ 7". . . . . . . . . . . . . . . . . . W 8329
Sire / Jul '87.

### DEAR ADDY (Kid Creole & The Coconuts).
Tracks: Dear Addy / No fish today / Christmas on Riverside Drive / Yolanda (On 12" only).
■ 12". . . . . . . . . . . . . . . . . 12WIP 6840
■ 7". . . . . . . . . . . . . . . . . . WIP 6840
■ 7" P.Disc . . . . . . . . . . . . . PWIP 6840
Island / Dec '82.

### DON'T TAKE MY COCONUTS (Kid Creole & The Coconuts).
Tracks: Don't take my coconuts / Naughty boy / Maladie d'amour / Ticket to the tropics / Indiscreet / Kriminal tango / Did you have to love me like you did / If I only had a brain / Glory that was Eden.
■ LP . . . . . . . . . . . . . . . AML 4001801
EMI-America / Jul '83.

### DON'T TAKE MY COCONUTS (Kid Creole & The Coconuts).
Tracks: Don't take my coconuts / Going places.
■ 12". . . . . . . . . . . . . . . . . .12IS 190
■ 7". . . . . . . . . . . . . . . . . . IS 190
Island / Jul '84.

### DOPPELGANGER (Kid Creole & The Coconuts).
Tracks: Not Advised.
■ LP . . . . . . . . . . . . . . . . . .ILPS 9743
Island / Sep '83.

### ENDICOTT (Kid Creole & The Coconuts).
Tracks: Endicott.
■ 12". . . . . . . . . . . . . . . . . .W 8959T
■ 7". . . . . . . . . . . . . . . . . . W 8959
Sire / May '85.

### FRESH FRUIT IN FOREIGN PLACES (Kid Creole & The Coconuts).
Tracks: Going places / In the jungle / Animal crackers / I stand accused / Latin music / Musicana Americana / I am Schweinerei / Gina Gina / With a girl name Mimi / Table manners / Dear Addy.
■ LP . . . . . . . . . . . . . . . . . .ILPS 7014
■ MC. . . . . . . . . . . . . . . . . .ICT 7014
Island / May '81.
■ LP . . . . . . . . . . . . . . . . . .ILPM 7014
■ MC. . . . . . . . . . . . . . . . . ICM 7014
Island / Apr '87.

### FRESH FRUIT/ TROPICAL GANGSTERS (Kid Creole & The Coconuts).
Tracks: Not Advised.
CD Set . . . . . . . . . . . . . . . . .ITSCD 7
Island / Nov '92 / PolyGram.

### I AM (Kid Creole & The Coconuts).
Tracks: I am / Darrio.
■ 7". . . . . . . . . . . . . . . . . . WIP 6728
Island / Jul '84.

### I LOVE GIRLS (Kid Creole & The Coconuts).
Tracks: I love girls / When Lucy does the boomerang.
■ 12". . . . . . . . . . . . . . . . . .6560736
■ 7". . . . . . . . . . . . . . . . . . .6560737
■ CD Single. . . . . . . . . . . . . .6560732
■ MC Single. . . . . . . . . . . . . .6560734
CBS / Jul '90.

■ DELETED

235

## I'M A WONDERFUL THING BABY (Kid Creole & The Coconuts).

**Tracks:** I'm a wonderful thing baby / I'm a wonderful thing baby (mixes).

| | |
|---|---|
| ■ 12″ | 12IS 551 |
| ■ 7″ | IS 551 |
| ■ CD Single | CID 551 |
| ■ MC Single | CIS 551 |

Island / Mar '93.

## I, TOO, HAVE SEEN THE WOODS (Kid Creole & The Coconuts).

**Tracks:** Beginning / Buttermilk channel / Part of my design / Agony..ecstasy / Dancin' at the Bains Douches / El hijo / Cold wave / End / So far, so good / Midsummer madness / Consider me / Boxed out / Call it a day.

| | |
|---|---|
| CD | 925579 2 |
| ■ LP | WX 112 |
| MC | WX 112C |

Sire / Jul '87 / WEA.

## IN PRAISE OF OLDER WOMEN (Kid Creole & The Coconuts).

**Tracks:** Endicott / Particul'y int'rested / Name it / (Darlin' you can) take me / Luv got me dancen' on my kneez / Caroline was a drop-out / He can have you / Animal cop / Dowopsalsaboprock / You can't keep a good man down / In praise of older women / Other crimes.

| | |
|---|---|
| ■ LP | WX 19 |
| MC | WX 19C |

Sire / Jul '85 / WEA.

## KID CREOLE AND THE COCONUTS (Kid Creole & The Coconuts).

**Tracks:** Stool pigeon / Say hay / I'm a wonderful thing / No fish today / Dear Addy / Don't take my coconuts / Table manners / Mr. Softie / Lifeboat party.

| | |
|---|---|
| CD | OPTMCD 002 |
| MC | OPTMC 002 |

Icon / May '93 / Pinnacle.

## LATIN MUSIC (Kid Creole & The Coconuts).

**Tracks:** Latin music / Musica Americana / Going places.

| | |
|---|---|
| ■ 12″ | 12WIP 6719 |
| ■ 7″ | WIP 6719 |

Island / Oct '81.

## LIFEBOAT PARTY (Kid Creole & The Coconuts).

**Tracks:** Lifeboat party / Gina Gina.

| | |
|---|---|
| ■ 12″ | 12 IS 142 |
| ■ 7″ | IS 142 |

Island / Nov '83.

## LIVE AT HAMMERSMITH (Kid Creole & The Coconuts).

**Tracks:** Not Advised.

| | |
|---|---|
| VHS | VFM 001 |

Videoform / Jan '84 / Gold & Sons.

## LIVE AT THE RITZ (Kid Creole & The Coconuts).

**Tracks:** Going places / In the jungle / Animal crackers / I am / Schweinerei / Gina Gina / Coati Mundi rap / Latin music / Table manners / Dear Addy.

| | |
|---|---|
| VHS | IVA 011 |

Island Visual Arts / Feb '89 / PolyGram / THE.

## MALADIE D'AMOUR (Kid Creole & The Coconuts).

**Tracks:** Maladie d'amour / He's not such a bad guy / There but for the grace of God go I.

| | |
|---|---|
| ■ 12″ | 12WIP 6619 |
| ■ 7″ | WIP 6619 |

Island / Aug '80.

## MY MALE CURIOSITY (Kid Creole & The Coconuts).

**Tracks:** My male curiosity / For love alone.

| | |
|---|---|
| ■ 12″ | VS 690 12 |
| ■ 7″ | VS 690 |

Virgin / Jun '84.

## OFF THE COAST OF ME (Kid Creole & The Coconuts).

**Tracks:** Mister softee / Maladie d'amour / Yolanda / Off the coast of me / Darrio / Lili Marlene / Bogota affair / Calypso pan American.

| | |
|---|---|
| ■ LP | ILPS 7012 |
| ■ MC | ICT 7012 |

Island / Aug '82.

## PRIVATE WATERS IN THE GREAT DIVIDE (Kid Creole & The Coconuts).

**Tracks:** I love girls / No more casual sex / Sex of it / Cory's song / Dr. Paradise / Takin' a holiday /

---

Lambada / Funky Audrey & the coconut rag / When Lucy does the boomerang / He's takin' the rap / Pardon my appearance / Laughing with our backs against the wall / My love.

| | |
|---|---|
| ■ LP | 4662511 |
| MC | 4662514 |
| ■ CD | 4662512 |

CBS / May '90 / Sony.

## SEX OF IT, THE (Kid Creole & The Coconuts).

**Tracks:** Sex of it / He's taking the rap.

| | |
|---|---|
| ■ 12″ | 6556986 |
| ■ 12″ P.Disc. | 6556988 |
| ■ 7″ | 6556987 |
| ■ CD Single | 6556982 |
| ■ MC Single | 6556984 |

CBS / Mar '90.

## STOOL PIGEON (Kid Creole & The Coconuts).

**Tracks:** Stool pigeon.

| | |
|---|---|
| ■ 7″ | WIP 6793 |

Island / Jul '82.

## STOOL PIGEON (Kid Creole & The Coconuts).

**Tracks:** Not Advised.

| | |
|---|---|
| ■ VHS | HEN 2297 |

Hendring Video / Oct '91.

## STOOL PIGEON (Kid Creole & The Coconuts).

**Tracks:** Not Advised.

| | |
|---|---|
| CD | ST 5002 |

Star Collection / Nov '93 / BMG.

## THERE'S SOMETHING WRONG IN PARADISE (Kid Creole & The Coconuts).

**Tracks:** There's something in paradise / Fireside story / Broadway rhythm.

| | |
|---|---|
| ■ 12″ | 12 IS 130 |
| ■ 7″ | IS 130 |

Island / Sep '83.

## TROPICAL GANGSTERS (Kid Creole & The Coconuts).

**Tracks:** Annie (I'm not your daddy) / I'm a wonderful thing baby / Imitation / I'm corrupt / Loving you made a fool out of me / Stool pigeon / Love we have / No fish today.

| | |
|---|---|
| MC | ICT 7016 |
| ■ LP | ILPS 7016 |

Island / May '82 / PolyGram.

| | |
|---|---|
| ■ CD | CID 7016 |

Island / May '88.

| | |
|---|---|
| CD | IMCD 6 |

Island / '89 / PolyGram.

## WONDERFUL THING (Kid Creole & The Coconuts).

**Tracks:** Wonderful thing / Table manners.

| | |
|---|---|
| ■ 12″ | 12WIP 6756 |
| ■ 7″ | WIP 6756 |

Island / May '82.

## YOU SHOULDA TOLD ME YOU WERE.. (Kid Creole & The Coconuts).

**Tracks:** It's automatic / Baby Doc / My soul intention / Oh Marie / Consequently your move / (She's a) party girl / Something incomplete / Madison Avenue / How can I forget you (the benedektion).

| | |
|---|---|
| ■ CD | 4687322 |
| ■ LP | 4687321 |
| ■ MC | 4687324 |

Columbia / Aug '91.

## Kilgore, Theola

### I'LL KEEP TRYING.

**Tracks:** I'll keep trying / He's coming back to me.

| | |
|---|---|
| ■ 7″ | W 14035 |

Sue / Apr '67.

## Kimbrough, Junior

### ALL NIGHT LONG.

**Tracks:** Not Advised.

| | |
|---|---|
| CD | FIENDCD 742 |

Demon / Nov '93 / Pinnacle / A.D.A. Distribution.

## King, Albert

### ALBERT.

**Tracks:** Guitar man / I'm ready / Ain't nothing you can do / I don't care what my baby do / Change of pace / My babe / Running out of steam / Rub my back / (Ain't it) a real good sign.

| | |
|---|---|
| CD | CDCHARLY 103 |
| ■ LP | CRB 1173 |
| MC | TCCRB 1173 |

Charly R&B / Mar '88 / Charly.

---

### ALBERT LIVE.

**Tracks:** Watermelon man / Don't burn down the bridge / Blues at sunrise / That's what the blues is all about / Stormy Monday / Kansas City / I'm gonna call you as soon as the sun goes down (King) / Matchbox holds my clothes / Jam in a flat / As the years go passing by / Overall junction / I'll play the blues for you.

| | |
|---|---|
| CD | CDCHARLY 136 |
| ■ Double LP | CDX 35 |
| ■ MC | TCCDX 35 |

Charly / Nov '88 / Charly.

### AS YEARS GO BY.

**Tracks:** Not Advised.

| | |
|---|---|
| CD | CDSXD 045 |

Stax / Apr '92 / Pinnacle.

### BEST OF ALBERT KING, THE (I'll Play the Blues For You).

**Tracks:** Born under a bad sign / Answer to the laundromatt blues / You threw your love on me too strong / Crosscut saw / I'll play the blues for you (Part 1) / Angel of mercy / Heart fixing business / Killing floor / Sky is crying / Going back to luka / (I think I'm) drowning on dry land (Part 2) / That's what the blues is all about / Left hand woman (get right with me) / Driving wheel / Firing line (Available on CD only) / Don't burn the bridge (cause you might wanna come back.. (Available on CD only) / Can't you see what you're doing to me (Available on CD only).

| | |
|---|---|
| ■ LP | SX 007 |
| MC | SXC 007 |

Stax / Mar '88 / Pinnacle.

| | |
|---|---|
| CD | CDSX 007 |

Stax / Jan '90 / Pinnacle.

| | |
|---|---|
| CD | CDSXD 969 |

Stax / Mar '91 / Pinnacle.

### BIG BLUES, THE.

**Tracks:** Not Advised.

| | |
|---|---|
| CD | KCD 000852 |

King / Sep '92 / New Note / Koch International.

### BLUES AT SUNRISE.

**Tracks:** Don't burn the bridge (cause you might wanna come back.. / For the love of a woman / I'll play the blues for you / Roadhouse blues / I believe to my soul / Blues at sunrise / Little brother (make a way).

| | |
|---|---|
| ■ LP | SX 017 |

Stax / Nov '88.

### BLUES AT SUNRISE.

**Tracks:** Not Advised.

| | |
|---|---|
| CD | CD 52034 |

Blues Encore / May '94 / BMG.

### BLUES DON'T CHANGE, THE.

**Tracks:** Blues don't change / I'm doing fine / Nice to be nice / Oh pretty woman / King of kings / Feel the need / Firing line / Pinch paid off (Part I) / Pinch paid off (Part II) / I can't stand the rain / Ain't it beautiful.

| | |
|---|---|
| CD | CDSXE 085 |

Stax / Feb '93 / Pinnacle.

### BORN UNDER A BAD SIGN.

**Tracks:** Crosscut saw / Kansas City / Oh pretty woman / Down, don't bother me / Hunter / I almost lost my mind / Born under a bad sign / Personal manager / Laundromat blues / As the years go passing by / Very thought of you.

| | |
|---|---|
| ■ LP | 723 |

Stax / Mar '68.

| | |
|---|---|
| ■ LP | SD7723 |

Atlantic / Jun '88.

### BORN UNDER A BAD SIGN.

**Tracks:** Born under a bad sign / Personal manager.

| | |
|---|---|
| ■ 7″ | 601015 |

Stax / Jul '67.

### CHICAGO 1978.

**Tracks:** Not Advised.

| | |
|---|---|
| CD | CDBL 754 |

Charly / Nov '94 / Charly.

### CROSSCUT SAW.

**Tracks:** Crosscut saw / Down don't bother me / Honey bee / Ask me no questions / I'm gonna move to the outskirts of town / They made the Queen welcome / Floodin' in California / I found love in the food stamp line / Match box blues / Why you so mean to me.

| | |
|---|---|
| ■ 7″ | 584099 |

Atlantic / Feb '67.

| | |
|---|---|
| CD | CDSXE 076 |

Stax / Oct '92 / Pinnacle.

### CROSSCUT SAW - ALBERT KING IN SAN FRANCISCO.

**Tracks:** Honey bee / Ask me no questions / I'm gonna move to the outskirts of town / They made the

---

queen welcome / Floodin' in California / I found love in the food stamp line / Match box blues / Crosscut saw / Why you so mean to me.
**CD** . . . . . . . . . . . . . . . . . . . . CDSXE 076
Stax / Oct '92 / Pinnacle.

## DOOR TO DOOR (King, Albert & Otis Rush).
**Tracks:** Not Advised.
■ **LP** . . . . . . . . . . . . . . . . . . . . .515021
Vogue / Oct '88.
■ **CD** . . . . . . . . . . . . . . . . . . CHD 9322
■ **CD** . . . . . . . . . . . . . . . . . . CH 9322
Chess (MCA) / Sep '90.
■ **CD** . . . . . . . . . . . . . . . . .CHLD 19169
Chess (MCA) / Nov '91.

## GREAT KING ALBERT.
**Tracks:** Not Advised.
**CD** . . . . . . . . . . . . . . . . . . . . 2696032
■ **LP** . . . . . . . . . . . . . . . . . . . 2696031
**MC** . . . . . . . . . . . . . . . . . . . . 2696034
Tomato (USA) / May '88 / Vital Distribution.

## I WANNA GET FUNKY.
**Tracks:** I wanna get funky / Playing on me / Walking the back streets and crying / 'Til my back ain't got no bone / Flat tire / I can't haer nothing but the blues / Travelin' man / Crosscut saw / That's what the blues is all about.
**CD** . . . . . . . . . . . . . . . . . . . CDSXE 081
Stax / Jul '93 / Pinnacle.

## I'LL PLAY THE BLUES FOR YOU (King, Albert & John Lee Hooker).
**Tracks:** Born under a bad sign / Very thought of you / I worked hard / When you down / Feel good / Boom boom / Serves me right / One bourbon, one scotch, one beer / King snake.
**CD** . . . . . . . . . . . . . . . . . . . . 2696142
Tomato (1) / Oct '92 / RTM / Pinnacle.

## I'M IN A PHONE BOOTH BABY.
**Tracks:** Phone booth / My broom / Sky is crying / Brother, go ahead and take her / Your bread ain't done / Firing line / Game goes on / Truck load of lovin / You gotta sacrifice.
**CD** . . . . . . . . . . . . . . . . . . . CDSXE 083
Stax / Jul '93 / Pinnacle.

## JAMMED TOGETHER (see under Cropper, Steve).

## JUST PICKIN'.
**Tracks:** Not Advised.
**CD** . . . . . . . . . . . . . . . . MBCD 721
Modern Blues Recordings / Jun '93 / Topic Records / Direct Distribution.

## KING ALBERT.
**Tracks:** Love shock / You upset me baby / Chump chance / Let me rock you easy / Boot lace / Love mechanic / Call my job / Good time Charlie.
**CD** . . . . . . . . . . . . . . . . . CDCRB 1191
■ **LP** . . . . . . . . . . . . . . . . . CRB 1191
**MC** . . . . . . . . . . . . . . . . TCCRB 1191
Charly R&B / Jul '88 / Charly.

## KING DOES THE KING'S THINGS (Blues For Elvis).
**Tracks:** Hound dog / That's all right / All shook up / Jailhouse rock / Heartbreak hotel / Don't be cruel / One night / Blue suede shoes / Love me tender.
■ **LP** . . . . . . . . . . . . . . . . . SXATS 1017
Stax / Nov '69.
**CD** . . . . . . . . . . . . . . . . . . . CDSXE 073
Stax / Sep '92 / Pinnacle.

## KING OF THE BLUES GUITAR.
**Tracks:** Cold feet / You're gonna need me / Born under a bad sign / I love Luzy / Crosscut saw / You sure drive a hard bargain / Oh pretty woman / Overall junction / Funk-shun / Laundromat blues / Personal manager.
■ **LP** . . . . . . . . . . . . . . . . 588 173
Atlantic / Apr '69.
**CD** . . . . . . . . . . . . . . . .756782017-2
Atlantic / Mar '93 / WEA.

## LAST SESSION, THE.
**Tracks:** Won't gimme no livin' / Cold in hand / Stop lying / All the way down / Tell me what true love is / Down the road I go / Sun gone down.
■ **LP** . . . . . . . . . . . . . . . . MPS 8534
Stax / Nov '86.

## LAUNDROMAT BLUES.
**Tracks:** Born under a bad sign / Laundromat blues / I love Lucy / Crosscut saw / You sure drive a hard bargain / You're gonna need me / (When I lost my baby) I almost lost my mind / Overall junction / Oh pretty woman / Funk-shun / Hunter / Personal manager / Cold feet / Kansas City / Down don't bother me / As the years go passing by.

■ **LP** . . . . . . . . . . . . . . . . ED 130
Edsel / Apr '84.

## LET'S HAVE A NATURAL BALL.
**Tracks:** Not Advised.
**CD** . . . . . . . . . . . . . . . . MBCD 723
Modern Blues Recordings / Jun '93 / Topic Records / Direct Distribution.

## LIVE (Charly Blues - Masterworks Vol 18).
**Tracks:** Watermelon man / Don't burn down the bridge / Blues at sunrise / That's what the blues is all about / Stormy Monday / Kansas city / I'm gonna call you as soon as the sun goes down / As the years go passing by / Overall junction / I'll play the blues for you.
**CD** . . . . . . . . . . . . . . . . . CDBM 18
**MC** . . . . . . . . . . . . . . . . . TCBM 18
Charly / Apr '92 / Charly.

## LIVE WIRE/BLUES POWER (VOL. 1).
**Tracks:** Watermelon man / Blues power / Night stomp / Blues at sunrise / Please love me / Lookout.
■ **LP** . . . . . . . . . . . . . . . .SXATS 1002
Stax / Dec '68.
■ **LP** . . . . . . . . . . . . . . . . 2363003
Stax / Jun '71.
**CD** . . . . . . . . . . . . . . . .MFCD 838
Mobile Fidelity Sound Lab(USA) / '86.
**CD** . . . . . . . . . . . . . . . . . CDSXE 022
■ **LP** . . . . . . . . . . . . . . . . SXE 022
Stax / Nov '89 / Pinnacle.

## LIVE WIRE/BLUES POWER (VOL. 2).
**Tracks:** Not Advised.
■ **LP** . . . . . . . . . . . . . . . . STX 4148
Stax / Dec '88.

## LOST SESSION, THE.
**Tracks:** She won't gimme no lovin' / Cold in hand / Stop lying / All the way down / Tell me what true love is / Down the road I go / Money lovin' women / Sun gone down (take 1) / Brand new razor / Sun gone down (take 2).
**CD** . . . . . . . . . . . . . . . . . CDSXE 066
Stax / Nov '92 / Pinnacle.

## LOVEJOY.
**Tracks:** Honky tonk women / Bay area blues / Corina Corina / She caught the Katie and left me a mule to ride / For the love of a woman / Lovejoy III / Everybody wants to go to heaven / Going back to Luka / Like a road leading home.
■ **LP** . . . . . . . . . . . . . . . . 2325042
Stax / Sep '71.

## NEW ORLEANS HEAT.
**Tracks:** Get out of my life woman / Born under a bad sign / Feeling / We all wanna boogie / Very thought of you / I got the blues / I get evil / Angel of Mercy / Flat tire.
■ **LP** . . . . . . . . . . . . . . . . CRB 1066
Charly R&B / '84.
**CD** . . . . . . . . . . . . . . . . CDCHARLY 49
Charly / Jan '87 / Charly.

## RED HOUSE.
**Tracks:** Stop / Bluesman / Don't let me be lonely / When you walk out the door / Problems / Our love is going to win / Trouble / If you got it / Red house.
**CD** . . . . . . . . . . . . . . . . . ESSCD 147
**MC** . . . . . . . . . . . . . . . . . ESSMC 147
■ **LP** . . . . . . . . . . . . . . . . ESSLP 147
Essential / Apr '91 / Total / BMG.

## SAN FRANCISCO 83.
**Tracks:** Not Advised.
■ **LP** . . . . . . . . . . . . . . . . F 9627
Fantasy / Nov '83.
■ **LP** . . . . . . . . . . . . . . . . 68535
Carrere (France) / Apr '84.

## SO MANY ROADS (Charly Blues - Masterworks Volume 2) (King, Albert & Otis Rush).
**Tracks:** Bad luck (blues) / (Be on your) merry way / Murder / Searching for a woman / California blues / Wild woman / Won't be hangin' around no more / Howlin' for my darling / So many roads, so many trains / I'm satisfied / So close / All your love / You know my love / I can't stop baby.
**CD** . . . . . . . . . . . . . . . . CD BM 2
**MC** . . . . . . . . . . . . . . . . TC BM 2
Charly / Apr '92 / Charly.

## THURSDAY NIGHT IN SAN FRANCISCO.
**Tracks:** San-ho-zay / You upset me baby / Stormy Monday blues / Everyday (I have the blues) / Drifting blues / I've made nights by myself / Crosscut saw / I'm gonna move to the outskirts of town / Ooh-ee baby.
**CD** . . . . . . . . . . . . . . . . CDSXE 032

**LP** . . . . . . . . . . . . . . . .SXE 032
Stax / Oct '90 / Pinnacle.

## TOMATO YEARS, THE.
**Tracks:** Not Advised.
**CD** . . . . . . . . . . . . . . . . 598 10962
Tomato (1) / Jul '94 / RTM / Pinnacle.

## TRAVELLIN' TO CALIFORNIA.
**Tracks:** Travellin' to California / What can I do to change your mind / I get evil / Had you told it like it was / This morning / I walked all night long / Let's have a natural ball / I've made nights by myself / This funny feeling / Ooh-ee baby / Dyna flow.
■ **LP** . . . . . . . . . . . . . . . .2343 026
Polydor / Feb '71.
■ **LP** . . . . . . . . . . . . . . . . BID 8016
Bellaphon / Jul '88.

## TRUCKLOAD OF LOVIN'.
**Tracks:** Cold women with warm hearts / Gonna make it somehow / Sensation, communication, together / I'm your mate / Truckload of lovin' / Hold hands with one another / Cadillac assembly line / Nobody wants a loser.
**CD** . . . . . . . . . . . . . . . . CDCHARLY 112
■ **LP** . . . . . . . . . . . . . . . . CRB 1180
**MC** . . . . . . . . . . . . . . . . TCCRB 1180
Charly R&B / Apr '88 / Charly.

## VINTAGE BLUES (King, Albert & Otis Rush).
**Tracks:** Be on your merry way / Bad luck blues / Murder / Searchin' for a woman / California blues / Wild woman / Won't be hangin' around / Howlin' for my darling / So many roads, so many trains / I'm satisfied / So close / All your love / You know my love / I can't stop baby / It must have been the devil / Five spot / I'm leaving you / I'm in love with you baby / Ice cream man / Rattlesnake / Be careful / Tough times / You got me.
■ **CD** . . . . . . . . . . . . . . . . CDRED 9
Charly / May '89.

## WEDNESDAY NIGHT IN SAN FRANCISCO.
**Tracks:** Not Advised.
**CD** . . . . . . . . . . . . . . . . CDSXE 031
■ **LP** . . . . . . . . . . . . . . . . SXE 031
Stax / Sep '90 / Pinnacle.

## YEARS GONE BY.
**Tracks:** Wrapped up in love again / You don't love me / Cockroach / Killing floor / Lonely man / If the washing don't get you / Drowning on dry land / Heart fixing business / You threw your love on me / Sky is crying.
■ **LP** . . . . . . . . . . . . . . . .SXATS 1022
Stax / Oct '69.

## King, Ben E.

Benjamin Earl Nelson's year-long tenure with ever-shifting Drifters yielded handful of classics, notably There Goes My Baby and U.K. No. 1 Save the Last Dance For Me. Having quit in late 1960, he returned to U.S. charts with Spanish Harlem and Stand By Me, both huge hits and both becoming pop standards, yielding covers by acts ranging from Aretha Franklin to John Lennon. Success declined towards close of decade, when King quit Atlantic; consequent obscurity sent him back to label for 1975 U.S. disco hit Supernatural Thing. He teamed up with Average White Band for Benny & Us album and tour in '77, and reunited with Drifters in early '80s. His own fortunes were briefly revived in '87 when use of Stand By Me in Levis commercial sent song to top of U.K. charts.

## AMOR, AMOR.
**Tracks:** Amor, amor.
■ **7"** . . . . . . . . . . . . . . . . HLK 9416
London-American / Oct '61.

## ANTHOLOGY.
**Tracks:** Not Advised.
**CD Set** . . . . . . . . . . . . . . . . 8122712152
Atlantic / Oct '93 / WEA.

## BEN E KING AND THE DRIFTERS (King, Ben E. & The Drifters).
**Tracks:** Not Advised.
**CD** . . . . . . . . . . . . . . . . ONCD 5118
K-Tel / '88.

## BEN E KING STORY, THE.
**Tracks:** Amor / Don't play that song / I (who have nothing) / How can I forget / I could have danced all night / Spanish harlem / That's when it hurts / Auf

■ DELETED

237

wiedersehen, my dear / Around the corner / Young boy blues / What now my love / Stand by me.
■ LP . . . . . . . . . . . . . . . . . . . . . K 50139
Atlantic / Nov '78.

**BENNY AND US (see under Average White Band).**

**CRY NO MORE.**
Tracks: Cry no more / (There's) no place to hide.
■ 7" . . . . . . . . . . . . . . . . . . . . . AT 4043
Atlantic / '66.

**DANCING IN THE NIGHT.**
Tracks: Dancing in the night (version) / Dancing in the night.
■ 12" . . . . . . . . . . . . . . . . . . . . 12 SY 3
■ 7" . . . . . . . . . . . . . . . . . . . . . SY 3
Syncopate / Jun '87.

**DO IT IN THE NAME OF LOVE.**
Tracks: Do it in the name of love / Imagination.
■ 7" . . . . . . . . . . . . . . . . . . . . K 10636
Atlantic / Jul '75.

**DRIFTERS WITH BEN E KING (see under Drifters).**

**FIRST TASTE OF LOVE.**
Tracks: First taste of love.
■ 7" . . . . . . . . . . . . . . . . . . . . HLK 9258
London-American / Feb '61.

**GOODNIGHT MY LOVE, PLEASANT DREAMS.**
Tracks: Goodnight my love, pleasant dreams / Tell daddy.
■ 7" . . . . . . . . . . . . . . . . . . . . AT 4065
Atlantic / Jan '66.

**GREATEST HITS.**
Tracks: That's when it hurts / Auf Wiederseh'n my dear / Around the corner / Young boy blues / What now my love / Stand by me / Amor / Don't play that song / I who have nothing / How can I forget / I could have danced all night / Spanish Harlem.
■ LP . . . . . . . . . . . . . . . . . . . .2464 010
Atlantic / Jun '70.

**GREATEST HITS: BEN E KING & DRIFTERS (King, Ben E. & The Drifters).**
Tracks: Not Advised.
CD . . . . . . . . . . . . . . . . . . . . . 120 111
MCS Look Back / Jan '89.

**GREATEST HITS: BEN E. KING.**
Tracks: Not Advised.
MC . . . . . . . . . . . . . . . . . . . . SD 33165
Atco / Oct '84 / WEA.
CD . . . . . . . . . . . . . . . . . . . CDSGP 045
Prestige / Apr '93 / Total / BMG.

**HERE COMES THE NIGHT.**
Tracks: Brace yourself / Here comes the night / On the horizon / Perfidia / Ecstacy / Yes / Jamaica / Tell Daddy / Gypsy / In the middle of the night / It's all over / Let the water run down / River of tears / Seven letters / Record / Goodnight my love.
■ LP . . . . . . . . . . . . . . . . . . . . ED 131
Edsel / May '84.

**IT'S AMAZING.**
Tracks: It's amazing / Tears, tears, tears.
■ 7" . . . . . . . . . . . . . . . . . . . .209 1100
Atlantic / Jul '71.

**LET ME LIVE IN YOUR LIFE.**
Tracks: Tippin' / Wonder woman / Let me live in your life / I see the light / Fly away / Dark storm on the horizon / Family jewels / Sweet rhapsody / Spoiled / Fifty years.
■ LP . . . . . . . . . . . . . . . . . . . . K 50527
Atlantic / Feb '79.

**LOVER'S QUESTION.**
Tracks: Lover's question / Stand by me (1987 version.) / Because of last night.
■ 12" . . . . . . . . . . . . . . . . . . .12MT 33
■ 7" . . . . . . . . . . . . . . . . . . . . MT 33
EMI-Manhattan / Nov '87.

**MUSIC TRANCE.**
Tracks: Music trance / And this is love / Touched by your love / You've only got one chance to be young / Hired gun / Everyday / Work that body.
■ LP . . . . . . . . . . . . . . . . . . . . K 50713
Atlantic / Aug '80.

**MUSIC TRANCE.**
Tracks: Music trance / This is love.
■ 7" . . . . . . . . . . . . . . . . . . . . K 11407
Atlantic / Nov '79.

**RECORD, THE (BABY I LOVE YOU).**
Tracks: Record, The (baby I love you) / Way you shake it.
■ 7" . . . . . . . . . . . . . . . . . . . . AT 4025
Atlantic / '65.

**SAVE THE LAST DANCE FOR ME.**
Tracks: Wheel of love / Save the last dance for me / Because of last night / Lover's question / Whatever this is (it ain't true love) / Halfway to paradise / Let a man do it for you / I cry for you / Test of time / Two lovers.
■ LP . . . . . . . . . . . . . . . . . . . . MTL 1013
■ MC . . . . . . . . . . . . . . . . . . TCMTL 1013
EMI-Manhattan / Nov '87.
■ CD . . . . . . . . . . . . . . . . . . CDMTL 1013
EMI-Manhattan / Mar '88.

**SAVE THE LAST DANCE FOR ME.**
Tracks: Save the last dance for me.
■ 12" . . . . . . . . . . . . . . . . . . . .12MT 25
■ 7" . . . . . . . . . . . . . . . . . . . . MT 25
EMI-Manhattan / Jun '87.

**SAVE THE LAST DANCE FOR ME.**
Tracks: Save the last dance for me / Stand by me.
7" . . . . . . . . . . . . . . . . . . . . . .584090
Atlantic / Mar '67 / WEA.

**SEVEN LETTERS.**
Tracks: Seven letters / River of tears.
■ 7" . . . . . . . . . . . . . . . . . . . . AT 4018
Atlantic / '65.

**SEVEN LETTERS.**
Tracks: River of tears / I'm standing by / Jamaica / Down home / Si Senor / It's all over / Let the water run down / Seven letters / This is my dream / It's no good for me / In the middle of the night / Don't drive me away.
■ LP . . . . . . . . . . . . . . . . . . . . 588 125
Atlantic / Oct '68.

**SO IMPORTANT TO ME.**
Tracks: So important to me.
■ 12" . . . . . . . . . . . . . . . . . . .ICHST 711
■ 7" . . . . . . . . . . . . . . . . . . . . ICHS 711
Backs / Oct '91.

**SO MUCH LOVE.**
Tracks: So much love / Don't drive me away.
7" . . . . . . . . . . . . . . . . . . . . . .584008
Atlantic / May '66 / WEA.

**SOUL KINGS VOL.3.**
Tracks: Stand by me / Spanish harlem / I who have nothing / Don't play that song for me / Super natural thing / Take me to the pilot / Travellin woman / Love is / Into the mystic / Poison in my mind / She does it right / Beginning of it all / All your tomorrows.
CD . . . . . . . . . . . . . . . . . . . . SMS 058
Pickwick / Oct '92 / Pickwick.

**SPANISH HARLEM.**
Tracks: Not Advised.
■ LP . . . . . . . . . . . . . . . . . . . . 590 001
Atlantic / Jul '67.

**SPANISH HARLEM.**
Tracks: Spanish Harlem / First taste of love.
■ 12" . . . . . . . . . . . . . . . . . . YZ 118 T
■ 7" . . . . . . . . . . . . . . . . . . . .YZ 118
Atlantic / Apr '87.
■ 12" . . . . . . . . . . . . . . . . . . . CRT 97
■ 7" . . . . . . . . . . . . . . . . . . . . CR 97
Creole Classics / Mar '87.

**SPANISH HARLEM (OLD GOLD).**
Tracks: Spanish harlem / Stand by me.
7" . . . . . . . . . . . . . . . . . . . . . .OG 9101
Old Gold / Mar '90 / Pickwick.

**STAND BY ME.**
Tracks: Not Advised.
■ LP . . . . . . . . . . . . . . . . . . . . 34045
MC . . . . . . . . . . . . . . . . . . . . 64045
Flashback / May '88.
CD . . . . . . . . . . . . . . . . . . . . ONN 45
Object Enterprises / May '89 / Gold & Sons / THE / Midland Records.

**STAND BY ME.**
Tracks: Stand By Me / Yakety yak.
■ 7" . . . . . . . . . . . . . . . . . . . .A 9361
■ 12" . . . . . . . . . . . . . . . . . . A 9361 T
Atlantic / Jan '87.

**STAND BY ME (THE ULTIMATE COLLECTION).**
Tracks: Stand by me / Save the last dance for me / I (Who have nothing) / That's when it hurts / I could have danced all night / First taste of love / Dream lover / Moon river / Spanish harlem / Amor / I count the tears / Don't play that song / This magic moment

/ Young boy blues / It's all in the game / Supernatural thing (part 1).
CD . . . . . . . . . . . . . . . . . . . . 7802132
■ LP . . . . . . . . . . . . . . . . . . . . WX 90
■ MC . . . . . . . . . . . . . . . . . . . .WX 90 C
Atlantic / Feb '87 / WEA.
CD . . . . . . . . . . . . . . . . . . . CD 66006
Ce De International / Jul '87 / BMG.

**STREET TOUGH.**
Tracks: Street tough / Made for each other / Staying power / Stay a while with me / Why is the question / You made the difference to my life / Souvenirs of love / Something to be loved.
■ LP . . . . . . . . . . . . . . . . . . . . K 50787
Atlantic / May '81.

**SUPERNATURAL THING.**
Tracks: Supernatural thing (part 1) / Supernatural thing (part 2) / You're lovin' ain't good enough / Drop my heart off (on your way out the door) / Do it in the name of love / Happiness is where you find it / Do you wanna do a thing / Imagination / What do you want me to do.
■ LP . . . . . . . . . . . . . . . . . . . . K 50118
Atlantic / '74.

**TEARS TEARS TEARS.**
Tracks: Tears tears tears / Man without a dream.
■ 7" . . . . . . . . . . . . . . . . . . . .584106
Atlantic / Apr '67.

**WHAT IS SOUL.**
Tracks: What is soul / They don't give medals to yesterday's heroes.
■ 7" . . . . . . . . . . . . . . . . . . . .584069
Atlantic / Jan '67.

**WHAT'S IMPORTANT TO ME.**
Tracks: Not Advised.
■ MC . . . . . . . . . . . . . . . . ICH 1133MC
Ichiban / Jun '92.
CD . . . . . . . . . . . . . . . . . .ICH 1133CD
Ichiban / Jan '94 / A.D.A. Distribution / Pinnacle / ACD Trading Ltd. / Koch International / Direct Distribution.

**WHAT'S IMPORTANT TO ME.**
Tracks: What's important to me / It's your love (that makes me happy).
■ 12" . . . . . . . . . . . . . . . . . . ICH 1211
■ 7" . . . . . . . . . . . . . . . . . . . . ICH 711
Ichiban / Oct '91.

**WHITE MOON.**
Tracks: White moon / All of your sorrows.
■ 7" . . . . . . . . . . . . . . . . . . . CBS 7397
CBS / Jul '71.

**YOU'VE ONLY GOT ONE CHANCE TO BE YOUNG.**
Tracks: You've only got one chance to be young / Music trance.
■ 7" . . . . . . . . . . . . . . . . . . . . K 11495
Atlantic / Jun '80.

# King, Bobby

**BOBBY KING.**
Tracks: Not Advised.
■ LP . . . . . . . . . . . . . . . . . . . . BSK 3568
WEA / Aug '81.

**CLOSE TO ME.**
Tracks: Close to me / Love in the fire.
■ 12" . . . . . . . . . . . . . . . . . . TMGT 1347
■ 7" . . . . . . . . . . . . . . . . . . . TMG 1347
Motown / Aug '84.

**LIVE AND LET LIVE (King, Bobby & Terry Evans).**
Tracks: Not Advised.
■ CD . . . . . . . . . . . . . . . . . . . CD 2089
■ LP . . . . . . . . . . . . . . . . . ROUNDER 2089
■ MC . . . . . . . . . . . . . . . .ROUNDER 2089C
Rounder / '88.
■ LP . . . . . . . . . . . . . . . . . . . SPD 1016
■ MC . . . . . . . . . . . . . . . . . . SPDC 1016
Special Delivery / May '88.
CD . . . . . . . . . . . . . . . . . . . SPCD 1016
Special Delivery / Apr '94 / Vital Distribution / A.D.A. Distribution / Topic Records / Direct Distribution / Jazz Music / C.M. Distribution.

**LOVE IN THE FIRE.**
Tracks: Show me your magic / Somewhere along the way / Close to me / Lovequake / Ain't never met a woman like you / Sweet love / Midnight shine / Fall in love / Love in the fire.
■ LP . . . . . . . . . . . . . . . . . . . ZL 72151
MC . . . . . . . . . . . . . . . . . . . ZK 72151
Motown / Apr '84 / PolyGram.

■ DELETED

**LOVEQUAKE.**
Tracks: Lovequake / Fall in love.
■ 12″. . . . . . . . . . . . . . . . . . . . TMGT 1335
■ 7″. . . . . . . . . . . . . . . . . . . . . TMG 1335
Motown / Mar '84.

**RHYTHM, BLUES, SOUL AND GROOVES**
(King, Bobby & Terry Evans).
Tracks: Not Advised.
■ CD . . . . . . . . . . . . . . . . . . . SPDCD 1036
■ LP . . . . . . . . . . . . . . . . . . . . SPD 1036
■ MC . . . . . . . . . . . . . . . . . . . SPDC 1036
Special Delivery / Sep '90.

**SEEING IS BELIEVING (King, Bobby & Terry Evans).**
Tracks: Seeing is believing.
■ 12″. . . . . . . . . . . . . . . . . . . . . . . CM 12
Zensor (Germany) / Jan '89.

## King Dream Chorus

**KING HOLIDAY (King Dream Chorus & The Holiday Crew).**
Tracks: King holiday / (Martin Luther King Tribute song).
■ 12″. . . . . . . . . . . . . . . . . . . . . JABX 29
■ 7″. . . . . . . . . . . . . . . . . . . . . . JAB 29
Club / Feb '86.

## King, Earl

**GLAZED (King, Earl With Roomful Of Blues).**
Tracks: It all went down the drain / Your love was never there / Everybody's gotta cry sometime / Lone rent / Iron cupid / Somebody's got a tail / I met a stranger / Mardi gras in the city / Those lonely lonely nights / One step beyond love.
■ LP . . . . . . . . . . . . . . . . . . . . FIEND 87
Demon / Jan '87.
CD . . . . . . . . . . . . . . . . . . . . . CD 1035
■ LP . . . . . . . . . . . . . . . . . . . . . BT 1035
MC . . . . . . . . . . . . . . . . . . . . . BT 1035C
Black Top (USA) / '88 / C.M. Distribution / Direct Distribution / Hot Shot / Topic Records.

**HARD RIVER TO CROSS.**
Tracks: Not Advised.
CD . . . . . . . . . . . . . . . . . . . BT 1090CD
MC . . . . . . . . . . . . . . . . . . . . BT 1090C
Black Top (USA) / Jun '93 / C.M. Distribution / Direct Distribution / Hot Shot / Topic Records.

**LET THE GOOD TIMES ROLL.**
Tracks: Is everything alright / Those lonely lonely nights / Little girl / My love is strong / I'll take you back home / It must have been love / You can fly high / Darling honey child / Mother told me not to go / Well o well o well o baby / Those lonely lonely feelings / I'll never get tired / Weary silent night / Everybody's carried away.
■ LP . . . . . . . . . . . . . . . . . . . . . . CH 15
Ace / Aug '87.

**NEW ORLEANS ROCK 'N' ROLL.**
Tracks: Let's make a better world / Trick bag / Do-re-mi / One and one / Time for the sun to rise / Always the first time / Baby sittin' / Mama and papa / Panic's on / Let the good times roll.
■ LP . . . . . . . . . . . . . . . . . . . . SNTF 719
Sonet / Aug '77.

**SEXUAL TELEPATHY.**
Tracks: Old Mr. Bad Luck / I'll take you back home / Weary silent night / Time for the sun to rise / No one more for the road / Going public / Love is the way of life / Sexual telepathy / Happy little nobody's waggy tail dog / Always a first time / Make a better world.
CD . . . . . . . . . . . . . . . . . . . FIEND CD 168
LP . . . . . . . . . . . . . . . . . . . . .FIEND 168
Demon / Aug '90 / Pinnacle / A.D.A. Distribution.
MC . . . . . . . . . . . . . . . . . . . . . BT 1052C
Black Top (USA) / Mar '92 / C.M. Distribution / Direct Distribution / Hot Shot / Topic Records.

**SOUL BAG (The best of Earl King).**
Tracks: Trick bag / You better know / Things that I used to do / Always a first time / Mama and papa / Love me now / Mother's love / Come on (Pt.1) / Come on (Pt.2) / Don't cry my friend / Don't you lose it / We are just good friends / You're more to me than gold / Case of love.
■ LP . . . . . . . . . . . . . . . . . . 2C 068 83299
EMI (France) / '83.
■ MC . . . . . . . . . . . . . . . . . . .TCSSL 6027
■ LP . . . . . . . . . . . . . . . . . . . . SSL 6027
Stateside / Apr '87.

**STREET PARADE.**
Tracks: Street parade (Part 1) / You make me feel good / Some people are / Fallin' / Mother's love /

Mama and papa / Medieval days / This is what I call living / Do the grind / Part of me / Love look out for me / Street parade (Part 2) / All my love / I'm gonna keep on trying / Up on her hill / Am I your dog (Part 1) / Am I your dog (Part 2) / Real McCoy.
■ LP . . . . . . . . . . . . . . . . . . .CRM 2021
Charly / Nov '81.
CD . . . . . . . . . . . . . . . . CDCHARLY 232
Charly / Aug '90 / Charly.

## King, Evelyn

**ACTION (King, Evelyn 'Champagne').**
Tracks: Action / Let's get crazy.
■ 12″. . . . . . . . . . . . . . . . . . . . RCAT 383
RCA / Jan '84.

**BACK TO LOVE (King, Evelyn 'Champagne').**
Tracks: Back to love / I can't stand it.
■ 12″. . . . . . . . . . . . . . . . . . . . RCAT 287
■ 7″. . . . . . . . . . . . . . . . . . . . .RCA 287
RCA / Nov '82.

**BEST OF EVELYN 'CHAMPAGNE' KING, THE (King, Evelyn 'Champagne').**
Tracks: Shame / I'm in love / If you want my lovin' / Just for the night / Betcha she don't love you / I'm so romantic / Back to love (Only on cassette and CD.) / I don't know if it's right / Love come down / Action / High horse / Get loose / Music box / Shake down / I can't stand it / Your personal touch.
CD . . . . . . . . . . . . . . . . . . . ND 74538
■ LP . . . . . . . . . . . . . . . . . . . NL 74538
■ MC . . . . . . . . . . . . . . . . . . NK 74538
RCA / Apr '90 / BMG.

**CHAMPAGNE (King, Evelyn 'Champagne').**
Tracks: Not Advised.
■ LP . . . . . . . . . . . . . . . . . . . PL 84725
MC . . . . . . . . . . . . . . . . . . . . PK 84725
RCA / Dec '83 / BMG.

**DAY TO DAY (King, Evelyn 'Champagne').**
Tracks: Day to day (7″ blazin' edit) (7″ only.) / Kisses don't lie / Day to day (12″ blazin' remix) (Not on 7″.) / Day to day (dance mix) (Not on 7″.).
■ 12″. . . . . . . . . . . . . . . . . . . .12MT 79
■ 7″. . . . . . . . . . . . . . . . . . . . . MT 79
■ CD Single . . . . . . . . . . . . . . . CDMT 79
EMI-Manhattan / Feb '90.

**ESSENTIAL WORKS OF EVELYN 'CHAMPAGNE' KING (King, Evelyn 'Champagne').**
Tracks: Love come down / Back to love / Other side of love / Get loose / Your kind of loving / Till I come off the road / If you want my lovin' / I'm in love / I need your love / Let's start all over again / Till midnight / Show is over / Smooth talk / Out of control / Shame / Shame* '92 remix.
■ Double LP . . . . . . . . . . .74321 10703-1
MC Set . . . . . . . . . . . . . .74321 10703-4
■ CD . . . . . . . . . . . . . . . .74321 10703-2
RCA / Aug '92 / BMG.

**EVELYN KING (4 TRACK CASSETTE EP) (King, Evelyn 'Champagne').**
Tracks: Get loose / Back to love / Shame / I'm in love.
■ MC Single. . . . . . . . . . . . . . .RCXK 009
RCA / May '83.

**FLIRT (King, Evelyn 'Champagne').**
Tracks: Flirt / You can turn me on / Kisses don't lie / Stop it / Hold on to what you've got / When your heart says yes / Before the date / Whenever you touch me.
■ CD . . . . . . . . . . . . . . . . . . CDMTL 1022
■ MC . . . . . . . . . . . . . . . . . TCMTL 1022
■ LP . . . . . . . . . . . . . . . . . . . MTL 1022
EMI-Manhattan / May '88.

**FLIRT (Radio mix) (King, Evelyn 'Champagne').**
Tracks: Flirt / Flirt (flirt to flirt dub) / Flirt (body groove) (12″ only.).
■ 12″. . . . . . . . . . . . . . . . . . . .12MT 37
■ 12″ Remix. . . . . . . . . . . . . . .12MTX 37
■ 7″. . . . . . . . . . . . . . . . . . . . . MT 37
EMI-Manhattan / Apr '88.

**GET LOOSE (King, Evelyn 'Champagne').**
Tracks: Love come down / I can't stand it / Betcha she don't love you / Get loose / Back to love / Stop that / Get up off your love / I'm just warmin' up.

MC . . . . . . . . . . . . . . . . . RCAK 3093
■ LP . . . . . . . . . . . . . . . . . RCALP 3093
RCA / Sep '82 / BMG.

**GET LOOSE (King, Evelyn 'Champagne').**
Tracks: Get loose / I'm in love.
■ 12″. . . . . . . . . . . . . . . . . . . . RCAT 315
■ 7″. . . . . . . . . . . . . . . . . . . . .RCA 315
RCA / Feb '83.

**GIRL NEXT DOOR, THE (King, Evelyn 'Champagne').**
Tracks: Girl next door / Magnet / Day to day / Cross your mind / Footsteps in the dark / Do right / Love man / Serious / This song / Thief in the night.
■ CD . . . . . . . . . . . . . . . . . CDMTL 1050
■ LP . . . . . . . . . . . . . . . . . . . MTL 1050
■ MC . . . . . . . . . . . . . . . . . TCMTL 1050
EMI-Manhattan / Feb '90.

**GIVE IT UP (King, Evelyn 'Champagne').**
Tracks: Give it up / Armies of the night.
■ 12″. . . . . . . . . . . . . . . . . . . . . TA 6671
■ 7″. . . . . . . . . . . . . . . . . . . . . . A 6671
Epic / Apr '86.

**GIVE ME ONE REASON (King, Evelyn 'Champagne').**
Tracks: Give me one reason / Don't it feel good.
■ 12″. . . . . . . . . . . . . . . . . . . . RCAT 474
■ 7″. . . . . . . . . . . . . . . . . . . . .RCA 474
RCA / Feb '85.

**HIGH HORSE (King, Evelyn 'Champagne').**
Tracks: High horse / Take a chance / High horse (remix) (on 12″ only.) / Shame* (*extra track on 12″ version only).
■ 12″. . . . . . . . . . . . . . . . . . . . PT 49892
■ 7″. . . . . . . . . . . . . . . . . . . . . PB 49891
RCA / Mar '86.

**HOLD ON TO WHAT YOU'VE GOT (King, Evelyn 'Champagne').**
Tracks: Hold on to what you've got / Hold on to what you've got (set it off dub) / Hold on to what you've got (ext. version) / Hold on to what you've got (radio mix) / Hold on to what you've got (instrumental).
■ 12″. . . . . . . . . . . . . . . . . . . .12MT 49
■ 12″ Remix. . . . . . . . . . . . . . .12MTX 49
■ 7″. . . . . . . . . . . . . . . . . . . . . MT 49
EMI-Manhattan / Jul '88.

**I DON'T KNOW IF IT'S RIGHT (King, Evelyn 'Champagne').**
Tracks: I don't know if it's right / We're going to a party.
■ 7″. . . . . . . . . . . . . . . . . . . . . PB 1386
RCA / Feb '79.

**I'M IN LOVE (King, Evelyn 'Champagne').**
Tracks: Your personal touch / I'm in love / If you want my lovin' / Don't hide our love / What are you waiting for / Spirit of the dancer / Other side of love / I can't take it / Best is yet to come.
■ LP . . . . . . . . . . . . . . . . . RCALP 5048
MC . . . . . . . . . . . . . . . . . . RCAK 5048
RCA / Jul '81 / BMG.

**I'M IN LOVE (King, Evelyn 'Champagne').**
Tracks: I'm in love / Other side of love.
■ 12″. . . . . . . . . . . . . . . . . . . . . RCAT 95
■ 7″. . . . . . . . . . . . . . . . . . . . . RCA 95
RCA / Jun '81.

**I'M IN LOVE (OLD GOLD) (King, Evelyn 'Champagne').**
Tracks: I'm in love / Your personal touch.
■ 12″. . . . . . . . . . . . . . . . . . . .OG 4035
Old Gold / Nov '87.

**I'M SO ROMANTIC (King, Evelyn 'Champagne').**
Tracks: I'm so romantic / Teenager.
■ 12″. . . . . . . . . . . . . . . . . . . . RCAT 446
■ 7″. . . . . . . . . . . . . . . . . . . . .RCA 446
RCA / Sep '84.

**IF YOU WANT MY LOVIN' (King, Evelyn 'Champagne').**
Tracks: If you want my lovin'.
■ 12″. . . . . . . . . . . . . . . . . . . . RCAT 131
■ 7″. . . . . . . . . . . . . . . . . . . . .RCA 131
RCA / Sep '81.

**LET'S GET FUNKY TONIGHT (King, Evelyn 'Champagne').**
Tracks: Let's get funky tonight / Just a little bit of you.
■ 12″. . . . . . . . . . . . . . . . . . . . . PC 2075

■ 7" . . . . . . . . . . . . . . . . . . . . . . PB 2075
RCA / Nov '80.

**LONG TIME COMING, A (King, Evelyn
'Champagne').**
**Tracks:** Chemistry of love / Change is gonna come /
Spellbound / If you find the time / Slow down / If I let
myself go / Your personal touch / I'm scared / High
horse.
■ LP . . . . . . . . . . . . . . . . . . . . . PL 87015
■ MC . . . . . . . . . . . . . . . . . . . . . PK 87015
RCA / Nov '85.

**LOVE COME DOWN (King, Evelyn
'Champagne').**
**Tracks:** Love come down / Don't hide our love.
■ 7" . . . . . . . . . . . . . . . . . . . . .RCA 249
■ 12" . . . . . . . . . . . . . . . . . . . RCAT 249
RCA / Jul '82.

**LOVE COME DOWN (OLD GOLD) (King,
Evelyn 'Champagne').**
**Tracks:** Love come down / Shame.
■ 7" . . . . . . . . . . . . . . . . . . . . .OG 9705
Old Gold / Apr '87.
■ 12" . . . . . . . . . . . . . . . . . . . . OG 4021
Old Gold / Sep '87.

**LOVE COME DOWN(OLD GOLD) (King,
Evelyn 'Champagne').**
**Tracks:** Love come down / I'm in love / Shame.
■ CD Single . . . . . . . . . . . . . . . . . OG 6525
Pickwick / Oct '92.

**MUSIC    BOX    (King,    Evelyn
'Champagne').**
**Tracks:** Steppin' out / I think my heart is telling /
Let's start all over again / Music box / Make up your
mind / Out there / It's OK / No time for fooling
around.
■ LP . . . . . . . . . . . . . . . . . . . . PL 13033
RCA / '79.

**MUSIC    BOX    (King,    Evelyn
'Champagne').**
**Tracks:** Music box / It's OK.
■ 12" . . . . . . . . . . . . . . . . . . . . PC 1586
■ 7" . . . . . . . . . . . . . . . . . . . . PB 1586
RCA / Jun '79.

**SHAME (King, Evelyn 'Champagne').**
**Tracks:** Not Advised.
■ LP . . . . . . . . . . . . . . . . . . . INTS 5240
■ MC . . . . . . . . . . . . . . . . . . . NK 89420
RCA / '85 / BMG.

**SHAME (King, Evelyn 'Champagne').**
**Tracks:** Shame / Dancin' dancin' dancin'.
■ 12" . . . . . . . . . . . . . . . . . . . . PC 1122
■ 7" . . . . . . . . . . . . . . . . . . . . PB 1122
RCA / '79.
■ 7" . . . . . . . . . . . . . . . . . . . . DDC 001
RCA / Apr '79.
■ 12" . . . . . . . . . . . . . . . . . . . PT 45488
RCA / Jun '92.

**SMOOTH    TALK    (King,    Evelyn
'Champagne').**
**Tracks:** Smooth talk / I don't know if it's right / Till I
come off the road / Dancin' dancin' dancin' / Shame /
Nobody knows / We're going to a party / Show is
over.
■ LP . . . . . . . . . . . . . . . . . . . . PL 12466
■ MC . . . . . . . . . . . . . . . . . . . PK 12466
RCA / Jun '78.

**SO    ROMANTIC    (King,    Evelyn
'Champagne').**
**Tracks:** Show me / Heartbreaker / Till midnight / Just
for the night / Give me one reason / Out of control /
Talking in my sleep / So in love / I'm so romantic.
■ LP . . . . . . . . . . . . . . . . . . . . PL 85308
■ MC . . . . . . . . . . . . . . . . . . . PK 85308
RCA / Sep '84.
■ CD . . . . . . . . . . . . . . . . . . . . PD 85308
RCA / Jan '85.

**SPIRIT OF THE DANCER (King, Evelyn
'Champagne').**
**Tracks:** Spirit of the dancer.
■ 12" . . . . . . . . . . . . . . . . . . . RCAT 179
■ 7" . . . . . . . . . . . . . . . . . . . .RCA 179
RCA / Jan '82.

**YOUR PERSONAL TOUCH (King, Evelyn
'Champagne').**
**Tracks:** Your personal touch / Talking in my sleep.
■ 12" . . . . . . . . . . . . . . . . . . . PT 49916
■ 7" . . . . . . . . . . . . . . . . . . . . PB 49915
RCA / Oct '85.

## King, Will

**BACK UP AGAINST THE WALL.**
**Tracks:** Not Advised.
■ LP . . . . . . . . . . . . . . . . . . . . FL 85710
■ MC . . . . . . . . . . . . . . . . . . . FK 85710
RCA / May '85.

**BACK UP AGAINST THE WALL.**
**Tracks:** Back up against the wall / I'm sorry.
■ 12" . . . . . . . . . . . . . . . . . . . FT 49966
■ 7" . . . . . . . . . . . . . . . . . . . FB 49965
Total Experience / Jun '85.

## Kinney, Fern

**BEAUTIFUL LOVE SONG.**
**Tracks:** Beautiful love song / Pipin' hot.
■ 12" . . . . . . . . . . . . . . . . . . . MAL 12 005
■ 7" . . . . . . . . . . . . . . . . . . . MAL 005
Malaco / Mar '83.

**CHEMISTRY (The Best Of Fern Kinney).**
**Tracks:** Groove me / If tomorrow never comes /
Together we are beautiful / Easy lovin' / Under fire /
Nothing takes the place of you / Boogie box / Don't
make me wait / Angel on the ground / I'm ready for
your love / Sweet music man / Beautiful love song /
Most girls / Sun, moon, rain / Baby let me kiss you /
Pipin' hot / Pillow talk.
CD . . . . . . . . . . . . . . . . . . . . MCCD 167
MC . . . . . . . . . . . . . . . . . . .MCTC 167
Music Collection International / Jul '94 / THE / Jazz
Music.

**FERN.**
**Tracks:** Let the good times roll / Let me entertain you
/ I want you back / Love me tonite / I've been lonely
for so long / It's alright / No one but you / Tonight /
Never be another night like this.
■ LP . . . . . . . . . . . . . . . . . . . . K 99144
■ MC . . . . . . . . . . . . . . . . . . . K4 99144
WEA / Mar '81.

**GROOVE ME.**
**Tracks:** Groove me / Under fire / Angel on the
ground / Pillow talk / Together we're beautiful / Sun,
moon, rain / Baby let me kiss you.
■ LP . . . . . . . . . . . . . . . . . . . . K 99076
MC . . . . . . . . . . . . . . . . . . . K4 99076
WEA / May '80 / WEA.

**I WANT YOU BACK.**
**Tracks:** I want you back / Groove me.
■ 7" . . . . . . . . . . . . . . . . . . . . 79136
WEA / Jun '80.

**I'M READY FOR YOUR LOVE.**
**Tracks:** I'm ready for your love.
■ 12" . . . . . . . . . . . . . . . . . . . MAL 12 006
Malaco / Dec '82.

**I'VE BEEN LONELY FOR SO LONG.**
**Tracks:** I've been lonely for so long / Love me.
■ 12" . . . . . . . . . . . . . . . . . . . K 79203 T
WEA / Mar '81.
■ 7" . . . . . . . . . . . . . . . . . . . K 79203
WEA / May '81.

**MOVIE SHOW.**
**Tracks:** Movie show / Sun, moon, rain.
■ 7" . . . . . . . . . . . . . . . . . . . K 79148
WEA / Aug '80.

**SWEET LIFE.**
**Tracks:** Sweet life / Tonight the night.
■ 7" . . . . . . . . . . . . . . . . . . . CBS 8368
CBS / Apr '80.

**SWEET MUSIC.**
**Tracks:** Not Advised.
■ LP . . . . . . . . . . . . . . . . . . . . MAL 7410
Malaco / '88.

**TOGETHER WE ARE BEAUTIFUL.**
**Tracks:** Together we're beautiful / Baby let me kiss
you.
■ 7" . . . . . . . . . . . . . . . . . . . K 79111
WEA / Jan '80.

**TOGETHER WE ARE BEAUTIFUL (OLD
GOLD).**
**Tracks:** Together we're beautiful.
■ 7" . . . . . . . . . . . . . . . . . . . .OG 9592
Old Gold / Mar '86.

## Kinsman Dazz

**KEEP ON ROCKIN'.**
**Tracks:** Keep on rockin' / I searched around.
■ 12" . . . . . . . . . . . . . . . . . . . TCD 2417
■ 7" . . . . . . . . . . . . . . . . . . . TC 2417
20th Century / Jan '80.

## Kirkland, Bo

**YOU'RE GONNA GET NEXT TO ME (Kirk
land, Bo & Ruth Davis).**
**Tracks:** You're gonna get next to me.
■ 7" . . . . . . . . . . . . . . . . . . . . INT 53
EMI International / Jun '77.

## Kirton, Lew

**DON'T WANNA WAIT.**
**Tracks:** Don't wanna wait / Stuck in the middle
(Between two).
■ 12" . . . . . . . . . . . . . . . . . . . MCAT 107
■ 7" . . . . . . . . . . . . . . . . . . . .MCA 107
MCA / Jul '86.

**JUST CAN'T GET ENOUGH.**
**Tracks:** Just can't get enough / Don't give up on you
dream / Here's my love.
■ 12" . . . . . . . . . . . . . . . . . . . TA 406
■ 7" . . . . . . . . . . . . . . . . . . . .A 406
Epic / Dec '83.

**TALK TO ME.**
**Tracks:** Talk to me / I can't live without you / Don'
give up your dream (hang on in there) / Always will /
Just can't get enough / Hooked on you / Got to fine
somebody to love / Here's my love.
■ LP . . . . . . . . . . . . . . . . . . . . EPC 2562
MC . . . . . . . . . . . . . . . . . . . .40 2562
Epic / Jan '84 / Sony.

**TALK TO ME.**
**Tracks:** Talk to me.
■ 12" . . . . . . . . . . . . . . . . . . . TA 3805
■ 7" . . . . . . . . . . . . . . . . . . . .A 3805
Epic / Oct '83.

## Kissoon, Katie

**I NEED A MAN IN MY LIFE.**
**Tracks:** I need a man in my life.
■ 12" . . . . . . . . . . . . . . . . . . . JIVET 70
■ 7" . . . . . . . . . . . . . . . . . . . JIVE 70
Jive / Jul '84.

**IF NOT FOR YOUR LOVE.**
**Tracks:** If not for your love / This thing.
■ 7" . . . . . . . . . . . . . . . . . . . .STAT 54
State / Jul '77.

**PENNY LOVER.**
**Tracks:** Penny lover / Going back to where we
started.
■ 12" . . . . . . . . . . . . . . . . . . . JIVET 60
■ 7" . . . . . . . . . . . . . . . . . . . JIVE 60
■ 7" P.Disc . . . . . . . . . . . . . . . JIVEP 60
Jive / Jan '84.

**YOU'RE    THE    ONE    (YOU'RE    MY
NUMBER ONE).**
**Tracks:** You're the one.
■ 12" . . . . . . . . . . . . . . . . . . . JIVET 37
■ 7" . . . . . . . . . . . . . . . . . . . JIVE 37
Jive / Jul '83.

## Kissoon, Mac

**LAVENDER BLUE.**
**Tracks:** Lavender blue / I'm on my way again.
■ 7" . . . . . . . . . . . . . . . . . . . .CAR 112
Carrere / '79.

**LAVENDER BLUE.**
**Tracks:** Lavender blue / Black and white.
■ 7" . . . . . . . . . . . . . . . . . . . CV 001
Crazy Viking / Oct '82.

## Kissoon, Mac & Katie

**LIKE A BUTTERFLY (Kissoon, Mac &
Katie).**
**Tracks:** Like a butterfly.
■ 7" . . . . . . . . . . . . . . . . . . . STAT 9
State / Jul '75.

**LOVE AND UNDERSTANDING (Kissoon,
Mac & Family).**
**Tracks:** Love and understanding / Baby you're the
one.
■ 7" . . . . . . . . . . . . . . . . . . . YB 0125
Young Blood / Nov '81.

**LOVE WILL KEEP US TOGETHER (Kis-
soon, Mac & Katie).**
**Tracks:** Love will keep us together / I'm in heaven.
■ 7" . . . . . . . . . . . . . . . . . . . YB 1060
Young Blood / Jan '75.

■ DELETED

## 6 TRACK HITS: MAC & KATIE KISSOON.
Tracks: Sugar candy kisses.
■ EP . . . . . . . . . . . . . . . . . . 7SR 5054
MC. . . . . . . . . . . . . . . . . . . . 7SC 5054
Scoop 33 / Oct '84.

## BEGINNING.
Tracks: Otis, Janis, Jimi and me / I've found my freedom / Do you really love me / Games people play / Chirpy chirpy cheep cheep / Hey diddle diddle / Lead me to paradise / Show me / Swinging on a star / Pigeon / Love came today.
■ LP . . . . . . . . . . . . . . . . . . SSYB 15
Young Blood / Dec '71.

## CHIRPY CHIRPY CHEEP CHEEP.
Tracks: Chirpy chirpy cheep cheep.
■ 7" . . . . . . . . . . . . . . . . . . . YB 1026
Young Blood / Jun '71.

## DON'T DO IT BABY.
Tracks: Don't do it baby.
■ 7" . . . . . . . . . . . . . . . . . . . STAT 4
State / May '75.

## FREEDOM.
Tracks: Not Advised.
CD . . . . . . . . . . . . . . . . . . . FG2 806
Creole / Jun '92 / THE / BMG.

## GREATEST HITS: MAC & KATIE KISSOON.
Tracks: Not Advised.
MC. . . . . . . . . . . . . . . . . . . . ASK 788
Autograph / Apr '85.

## MAC & KATIE KISSOON STORY, THE.
Tracks: Sugar candy kisses / Hold on baby / I'm just dreaming / There's a hurricane comin' / It's a million miles from Harlem / Like a butterfly / Don't do it baby / Walking in the park, together / Two of us / If there's no such thing as a miracle / Where would our love be / Your love.
■ LP . . . . . . . . . . . . . . . . . . ETMP 1
State / Feb '78.

## STAR COLLECTION.
Tracks: Not Advised.
CD . . . . . . . . . . . . . . . . . . . STCD 1003
Disky / Jun '93 / THE.

## SUGAR CANDY KISSES.
Tracks: Sugar candy kisses / Walking in the city / No greater love / Darling I love you / Everybody move / Hold on to me babe / If there's no such thing as a miracle / Like a butterfly / High on dreams / Beautiful day / There's a hurricane comin'.
■ LP . . . . . . . . . . . . . . . . . . ETAT 2
State.

## SUGAR CANDY KISSES.
Tracks: Sugar candy kisses / I'm just dreaming.
■ 7" . . . . . . . . . . . . . . . . . . . STAT 70
State / Feb '78.

## SWINGING SOUL OF MAC AND KATIE KISSOON.
Tracks: Hey you love / Pidgeon / Chirpy chirpy cheep cheep / It's a hang up world / Change it all / (I found my) freedom / True love forgives / It's all over now / Love will keep us together / Vow / Love grows / Bless me / Don't make me cry / Swingin' on a star / Black skinned blue eyed boys / Sing along / Love me baby / Show me / Hey diddle diddle.
CD . . . . . . . . . . . . . . . . . . . C5CD-538
■ LP . . . . . . . . . . . . . . . . . . C5-538
C5 / '89 / Pinnacle.

## TWO OF US, THE.
Tracks: Two of us / I'm just dreaming / Gimme gimme your lovin' / Slave in golden chains / Fly away / Hold on baby / Where would our love be / Walking in the park together / I just can't seem to smile again / Million miles from Harlem / And the Lord said / Your love.
■ LP . . . . . . . . . . . . . . . . . . ETAT 7
State / '76.

## TWO OF US, THE.
Tracks: Two of us.
■ 7" . . . . . . . . . . . . . . . . . . . STAT 21
State / May '76.

## Kleeer

Nine-piece act who released debut album *I Love to Dance* in 1979. *Keep Your Body Working* was minor hit at tail-end of disco; founder member Woody Cunningham also scored dance successes such as *Jingo* with percussionist Candido. As '80s progressed,

New York-based group continued to serve soul market on both sides of Atlantic with negligble crossover success.

## CLOSE TO YOU.
Tracks: Close to you / Tonight's the night / I love to love.
■ 7" . . . . . . . . . . . . . . . . . . . LV 36
Atlantic / Apr '80.

## DE KLEEER TING.
Tracks: De kleeer ting / Running back to you.
■ 12" . . . . . . . . . . . . . . . . . K 11599T
■ 7" . . . . . . . . . . . . . . . . . . K 11599
Atlantic / Jun '81.

## GET READY.
Tracks: Not Advised.
■ LP . . . . . . . . . . . . . . . . . K 7800381
Web / Jun '83.

## GET TOUGH.
Tracks: Get tough / Hypnotised.
■ 12" . . . . . . . . . . . . . . . . K 11560 T
■ 7" . . . . . . . . . . . . . . . . . K 11560
Atlantic / Feb '81.

## I LOVE TO DANCE.
Tracks: Tonight's the night / Keep your body working / Happy me / I love to dance / It's magic / To groove you / Amour / Kleeer sailing.
■ LP . . . . . . . . . . . . . . . . . K 50614
Atlantic / '77.

## INTIMATE CONNECTION.
Tracks: Next time it's for real / Break / Tonight / Do you want to / Ride it / You do it again / Go for it / Intimate connection.
■ LP . . . . . . . . . . . . . . . . . 780 145-1
Atlantic / Mar '84.

## INTIMATE CONNECTION.
Tracks: Intimate connection / Go for it / Open your mind (on 12" only).
■ 12" . . . . . . . . . . . . . . . . . A 9637T
■ 7" . . . . . . . . . . . . . . . . . . A 9637
Atlantic / Aug '84.

## IT'S MAGIC.
Tracks: It's magic / Tonight's the night / Keep your body working (instrumental).
■ 7" . . . . . . . . . . . . . . . . . . . LV 33
WEA / '79.

## KEEP YOUR BODY WORKING.
Tracks: Keep your body working / To groove me.
■ 7" . . . . . . . . . . . . . . . . . . . LV 21
Atlantic / Mar '79.

## KEEP YOUR BODY WORKING (OLD GOLD).
Tracks: Keep yoru body working / Get tough.
12" . . . . . . . . . . . . . . . . . . OG 4214
Old Gold / '92 / Pickwick.

## KLEEER WINNERS.
Tracks: Intimate connection / Take your heart away / Seeekret / Never cry again / Winners / Do kleer ting / Keep your body working / Get tough / Open your mind / Wall to wall.
MC. . . . . . . . . . . . . . . . . . . . WX 42 C
■ LP . . . . . . . . . . . . . . . . . . WX 42
Atlantic / Apr '86 / WEA.

## LICENSED TO DREAM.
Tracks: De Kleeer ting / Running back to you / Sittin' and kissin' / Hypnotised / Licensed to dream / Get tough / Say you love me / Where would I be.
■ LP . . . . . . . . . . . . . . . . . SD 19288
Atlantic / Mar '81.

## NEVER CRY AGAIN.
Tracks: Never cry again / Lay ya down ez.
■ 12" . . . . . . . . . . . . . . . . . A 9505T
■ 7" . . . . . . . . . . . . . . . . . . A 9505
Atlantic / Sep '85.

## NEXT TIME IT'S FOR REAL.
Tracks: Next time it's for real / Break / Keep your body working (on 12" only).
■ 12" . . . . . . . . . . . . . . . . . A 9699T
■ 7" . . . . . . . . . . . . . . . . . . A 9699
Atlantic / May '84.

## SEEEKRET.
Tracks: Take your heart away / You got me rockin' / Lay ya down ez / Seeekret / Do not lie to me / Never cry again / Call my name.
■ LP . . . . . . . . . . . . . . . . . 781 254-1
Atlantic / Jul '85.

## TAKE YOUR HEART AWAY.
Tracks: Take your heart away / Call my name.
■ 12" . . . . . . . . . . . . . . . . . A 9549T

■ 7" . . . . . . . . . . . . . . . . . . A 9549
Atlantic / Jun '85.

## TASTE THE MUSIC.
Tracks: Taste the music / I've had enough / De ting continues / Wall to wall / I shall get over / Fella / Swann / Affirmative mood.
■ LP . . . . . . . . . . . . . . . . . K50873
Atlantic / Mar '82.

## WINNERS (OLD GOLD).
Tracks: Winners.
12" . . . . . . . . . . . . . . . . . . OG 4217
Old Gold / '92 / Pickwick.

## Klemmer, John

## BAREFOOT BALLET.
Tracks: Naked / Barefoot ballet / Forest child / Crystal fingers / Whisper to the wind / Poem painter / At 17 / Talking hands / Rain dancer.
■ CD . . . . . . . . . . . . . . . . MCAD 1583
MCA / Apr '87.

## BLOWIN' GOLD.
Tracks: Excursion [8]X2 / My love has butterfly wings / Hey Jude / Third stone from the sun / Free soul / Children of the earth flames / Summer song / Rose petals / A mon frere africain / Gardens of Uranus / All the children cried / Here comes the child / I whisper a prayer for peace / Pulsations of a green eyed lady / Journey's end / La de dah / Soliloquy for tenor and voice.
■ Double LP . . . . . . . . . . . . . GCH 2-6036
Chess (Charly) / '89.

## FINESSE.
Tracks: Finesse / Man and woman / Sometimes / Greatest love of all / Sun, the moon and the stars / Beloved / But are you beautiful inside.
■ LP . . . . . . . . . . . . . . . . . E 0197
Elektra / Feb '83.
CD . . . . . . . . . . . . . . . . . . 9601972
Elektra / Jul '84 / WEA.

## HUSH.
Tracks: Hush / Let's make love / Taboo / Life is so beautiful / Magic / Hot / I love you madly / Hummingbird bay / Feelin' free.
■ LP . . . . . . . . . . . . . . . . . K 52297
Elektra / Jul '81.

## NEXUS ONE.
Tracks: Mr. P.C. / My one and only love / Softly as in a morning sunrise / Impressions / Nexus.
■ CD . . . . . . . . . . . . . . . . . ND 86577
Bluebird / Jun '88.

## WATERFALLS.
Tracks: Prelude 1 / Waterfall / Utopia: Man's dream, part 1 / Utopia: Man's dream, part 2 / There's some light ahead / Centrifugal force / Prelude 2 / Waterfall 2.
CD . . . . . . . . . . . . . . . . . MCAD 33123
Impulse Jazz / Oct '90 / New Note.

## Klique

## I CAN'T SHAKE THIS FEELING.
Tracks: I can't shake this feeling / Dance like crazy / Pump your rump.
■ 12" . . . . . . . . . . . . . . . . MCAT 789
■ 7" . . . . . . . . . . . . . . . . . MCA 789
MCA / Sep '82.

## LOVE CYCLES.
Tracks: Not Advised.
■ LP . . . . . . . . . . . . . . . . . MCF 3258
MCA / Apr '85.

## PUMP YOUR RUMP.
Tracks: Pump your rump / Dance like crazy.
■ 12" . . . . . . . . . . . . . . . . MCAT 779
MCA / Jul '82.

## STOP DOGGING ME AROUND.
Tracks: Stop dogging me around / Honey.
■ 12" . . . . . . . . . . . . . . . . MCAT 843
■ 7" . . . . . . . . . . . . . . . . . MCA 843
MCA / Oct '83.

## Klugh, Earl

## BALLADS.
Tracks: This time / Waltz for Debby / If you're still in love with me / April fools / Rayna / Natural thing / Waiting for Cathy / Julie / Nature boy / Dream come true / Shadow of your smile / Christina.
CD . . . . . . . . . . . . . . . . . CDP 8273262
Capitol / Feb '94 / EMI.

## BEST OF EARL KLUGH.
**Tracks:** Tropical legs (Wishful thinking) / Amazon (Dream come true) / Magic in your eyes / Calypso getaway / Dr. Macumba / Long ago and far away (Finger paintings) / Angelina / Heart string / Livin' inside your love / Christina (Low ride) / Wishful thinking / I don't want to leave you alone anymore.
```
CD . . . . . . . . . . . . . . . . . . . . . . BNZ 264
■ MC . . . . . . . . . . . . . . . . . . . . B4 46625
```
Blue Note / Mar '91 / EMI.

## BEST OF EARL KLUGH - VOL.2.
**Tracks:** Crazy for you / Night drive / Gootime Charlie's got the blues / Cabo frio / Back in Central Park / Natural thing / Jolanta / Rainmaker / Captain Caribe / Cast your fate to the wind / I'll see you again / Right from the street.
```
CD . . . . . . . . . . . . . . . . . . . . . . . BNZ 307
```
Blue Note / Feb '93 / EMI.

## COLLABORATION (see under Benson, George).

## CRAZY FOR YOU.
**Tracks:** Dance with me / I'm ready for your love / Soft stuff (and other sweet delights) / Twinkle / Broadway ramble / Calypso getaway / Rainmaker / Ballad in A / Crazy for you / Livin' inside your love.
```
■ LP . . . . . . . . . . . . . . . . . . . . . LBG 30329
■ MC . . . . . . . . . . . . . . . . TC LBG 30329
```
Liberty / Oct '81.
```
■ CD . . . . . . . . . . . . . . . . . . . . . . . CZ 59
```
EMI / Jun '88.

## CRY A LITTLE WHILE.
**Tracks:** Cry a little while / Magic in your eyes.
```
■ 7" . . . . . . . . . . . . . . . . . . . . . . UP 36441
```
United Artists / Aug '78.

## DANCE WITH ME.
**Tracks:** Dance with me / Living inside your love.
```
■ 7" . . . . . . . . . . . . . . . . . . . . . . . UP 642
```
United Artists / Aug '81.

## DREAM COME TRUE.
**Tracks:** If it's in your heart (it's in your smile) / Doc / Amazon (dream come true) / I don't want to leave you alone anymore / Spellbound / Sweet rum and starlight / Dream come true / Message to Michael.
```
■ CD . . . . . . . . . . . . . . . . . . . . . . . CZ 60
```
EMI / Jun '88.

## EARL KLUGH.
**Tracks:** Las manos de fuego (hands of fire) / Could it be I'm falling in love / Angelina / Slippin' in the back door / Vonetta / Laughter in the rain / Waltz for Debbie / Wind in the sea.
```
■ CD . . . . . . . . . . . . . . . . . CDP 746 553 2
```
EMI-America / Jul '87.

## EARL KLUGH TRIO, THE.
**Tracks:** Bewitched / Days of wine and roses / Insensatez (how insensitive) / Love theme from "Spartacus" / I'll remember April / What are you doing the rest of your life / I'll say a little prayer / Night and day / Lonely girl / Too marvellous for words / One note samba.
```
CD . . . . . . . . . . . . . . . . . . . . . 7599267502
■ LP . . . . . . . . . . . . . . . . . . . . 7599267501
MC . . . . . . . . . . . . . . . . . . . . . 7599267504
```
WEA / Dec '91 / WEA.

## FINGER PAINTING.
**Tracks:** Dr. Macumba / Long ago and far away / Cabo frio / Keep your eye on the sparrow / Catherine / Dance with me / Jolanta / Summer song / This time.
```
■ LP . . . . . . . . . . . . . . . . . . . . . UAG 20011
```
United Artists / Aug '77.
```
■ CD . . . . . . . . . . . . . . . . . . . . . . . CZ 44
```
EMI / Jun '88.

## HEART STRING.
**Tracks:** Heartstring / I'll see you again / Acoustic lady (Part 1) / Spanish night / Pretty world / Waiting for Cathy / Rayna / Heartstring (reprise) / Acoustic lady (Part 2).
```
■ LP . . . . . . . . . . . . . . . . . . . . . UAG 30233
```
United Artists / Apr '79.
```
■ CD . . . . . . . . . . . . . . . . . CDP 746 552 2
```
EMI-America / Apr '87.

## HEART STRING/LATE NIGHT GUITAR.
**Tracks:** Heartstring / I'll see you again / Acoustic lady (Part 1) / Spanish night / Pretty world / Waiting for Cathy / Rayna / Heart string (reprise) / Smoke gets in your eyes / Nice to be around / Like a lover / Laura / Jamaica farewell / Tenderly / Mona Lisa / Triste / Two for the road / Mirabella / Lisbon Antigua / Time for love / I'll never say goodbye / Acoustic lady (Part 2).
```
■ MC . . . . . . . . . . . . . . . . . TC2X 1834139
```
Liberty / Jun '83.

## I HEARD IT THROUGH THE GRAPEVINE.
**Tracks:** I heard it through the grapevine / Kiko.
```
■ 7" . . . . . . . . . . . . . . . . . . . . . . UP 36251
```
United Artists / May '77.

## LATE NIGHT GUITAR.
**Tracks:** Smoke gets in your eyes / Nice to be around / Like a lover / Laura / Jamaica farewell / Tenderly / Mona Lisa / Triste / Two for the road / Mirabella / Lisbon Antigua / Time for love / I'll never say goodbye.
```
■ LP . . . . . . . . . . . . . . . . . . . . . UAG 30332
```
United Artists / Dec '80.

## LIFE STORIES.
**Tracks:** Traveller / Just for your love / Second chances / For the love of you / Debra Anne / Santiago sunset / Sandman / Return of the rainmaker / Moon and the stars / Traveller, The (part 2).
```
■ CD . . . . . . . . . . . . . . . . . . . . . .925478 2
■ LP . . . . . . . . . . . . . . . . . . . . . .925478 1
■ MC . . . . . . . . . . . . . . . . . . . . . .925478 4
```
WEA / Sep '86.

## LIVING INSIDE YOUR LOVE.
**Tracks:** Captain caribe / I heard it through the grapevine / Felicia / Living inside your love / Another time another place / April fools / Kiko.
```
■ LP . . . . . . . . . . . . . . . . . . . . . UAG 20009
```
United Artists / Jan '77.
```
■ CD . . . . . . . . . . . . . . . . . . . . . . . CZ 40
```
EMI / Jun '88.

## LIVING INSIDE YOUR LOVE/ FINGER PAINTINGS.
**Tracks:** Not Advised.
```
■ MC . . . . . . . . . . . . . . . . . TC 2X 1834119
```
Liberty / Jun '83.

## LOW RIDE.
**Tracks:** Back in Central Park / Be my love / Low ride / Just like yesterday / If you're still in love with me / I never thought I'd leave you / Christina / Night drive.
```
■ LP . . . . . . . . . . . . . . . . . . . . . . EST 12253
■ MC . . . . . . . . . . . . . . . . . . TCEST 12253
```
Capitol / May '83.
```
■ CD . . . . . . . . . . . . . . . . . CDP 746 007 2
```
Capitol / Jan '84.

## MAGIC IN YOUR EYES.
**Tracks:** Magic in your eyes / Alicia / Julie / Lode star / Cast your fate to the wind / Rose hips / Good time Charlie's got the blues / Mayaguez / Cry a little while.
```
■ LP . . . . . . . . . . . . . . . . . . . . . UAG 30171
```
United Artists / May '78.
```
■ CD . . . . . . . . . . . . . . . . . . . . . . . CZ 61
```
EMI / Aug '88.

## MAGIC IN YOUR EYES/ DREAM COME TRUE.
**Tracks:** Not Advised.
```
■ MC . . . . . . . . . . . . . . . . . . TC 2X 1834129
```
Liberty / Jun '83.

## MOVE.
**Tracks:** Across the sand / Move / Far from home / Tiptoein' / Nightwalk / Face in the wind / Big turtle river / Highway song / Winter rain / Doin' it / Across the sand part II.
```
CD . . . . . . . . . . . . . . . . . . . . . .936245596-2
```
Warner Bros. / May '94 / WEA.

## NIGHT SONGS.
**Tracks:** Ain't misbehavin' / Pawnbroker (Theme from) / Look of love / Nature boy / Stay gold (Theme from The Outsiders) / Night song / c.c. rider / Certain smile / Shadow of your smile / Picnic, Theme from.
```
■ MC . . . . . . . . . . . . . . . . . . . EJ 2402284
■ LP . . . . . . . . . . . . . . . . . . . . EJ 2402281
```
Capitol / Oct '84.
```
■ CD . . . . . . . . . . . . . . . . . CDP 746 472 2
```
EMI / May '87.

## SODA FOUNTAIN SHUFFLE.
**Tracks:** Just pretend / Baby cakes / Soda fountain shuffle / Moonlight dancing / Incognito / One night alone with you / Some other time / Rainbow man / Close to your heart / April love.
```
■ LP . . . . . . . . . . . . . . . . . . . . . .925262 1
■ MC . . . . . . . . . . . . . . . . . . . . . .925262 4
```
WEA / May '85.
```
■ CD . . . . . . . . . . . . . . . . . . . . . .925262 2
```
WEA / Feb '87.

## SOLO GUITAR.
**Tracks:** It's only a paper moon / So many stars / I'm confessin' (that I love you) / If I only had a brain / Emily / Love is here to stay (instrumental only) / Someday my Prince will come / Any old time of day / Once upon a summertime / Embraceable you (instrumental only) / I'm all smiles / You make me feel so young / Autumn leaves / Way you look tonight.

```
CD . . . . . . . . . . . . . . . . . . . . . . K 9260182
■ LP . . . . . . . . . . . . . . . . . . . . K 9260181
■ MC . . . . . . . . . . . . . . . . . . . K 9260184
```
WEA / Sep '89 / WEA.

## TRIO.
**Tracks:** Not Advised.
```
CD . . . . . . . . . . . . . . . . . . . . . 759926752
■ LP . . . . . . . . . . . . . . . . . . . . 759926751
MC . . . . . . . . . . . . . . . . . . . . . 759926754
```
WEA / Dec '91 / WEA.

## TWINKLE.
**Tracks:** Twinkle / Broadway ramble / Dance with me (Only on 12" single.).
```
■ 12" . . . . . . . . . . . . . . . . . . . . . 12UP 647
■ 7" . . . . . . . . . . . . . . . . . . . . . . . UP 647
```
United Artists / Nov '81.

## TWO OF A KIND (Klugh, Earl & Bob James).
**Tracks:** Falcon / Whiplash / Sandstorm / Where I wander / Ingenue / Wes.
```
■ LP . . . . . . . . . . . . . . . . . . . . EAST 12244
■ MC . . . . . . . . . . . . . . . . . TCEAST 12244
```
Capitol / Nov '82.
```
CD . . . . . . . . . . . . . . . . . . . CDP 7991912
```
Capitol / Feb '94 / EMI.

## WHISPERS AND PROMISES.
**Tracks:** What love can do / Master of suspence / Water song / Strawberry avenue / Fall in love / Summer nights / Just you and me / Whispers and promises / Frisky biscuits / Tango classico.
```
CD . . . . . . . . . . . . . . . . . . . . . .925902 2
```
WEA / May '89 / WEA.

## WISHFUL THINKING.
**Tracks:** Wishful thinking / Tropical legs / All the time / Natural thing / Once again / Big band / Only one for me / Right from the start.
```
■ MC . . . . . . . . . . . . . . . . . TCEST 2400924
■ CD . . . . . . . . . . . . . . . . . CDP 746 030 2
■ LP . . . . . . . . . . . . . . . . . . . EST 2400921
```
Capitol / Mar '84.

# Klymaxx

## GIRLS IN THE BAND, THE.
**Tracks:** Not Advised.
```
■ LP . . . . . . . . . . . . . . . . . . . . . . 9602821
```
Elektra / Nov '83.

## GIRLS WILL BE GIRLS.
**Tracks:** Girls will be girls / Wild girls / Convince me / Man in my life / Heartbreaker / All turned out / Offer I can't refuse / If you love me / Don't hide your love.
```
■ LP . . . . . . . . . . . . . . . . . . . . . . 9601771
```
Solar / Dec '82.

## GOOD LOVE.
**Tracks:** Good love.
```
■ 12" . . . . . . . . . . . . . . . . . . . . MCAT 1427
■ 7" . . . . . . . . . . . . . . . . . . . . . MCA 1427
■ CD Single . . . . . . . . . . . . . . DMCAT 1427
```
MCA / May '90.

## I MISS YOU.
**Tracks:** I miss you / Video kid.
```
■ 12" . . . . . . . . . . . . . . . . . . . . MCAT 1033
■ 7" . . . . . . . . . . . . . . . . . . . . . MCA 1033
```
MCA / Jan '86.

## KLYMAXX.
**Tracks:** Sexy / Fab attack / Divas need love too / I'd still say yes / Fashion / Danger zone / Long distance love affair / Come back / Man size love.
```
■ LP . . . . . . . . . . . . . . . . . . . . . MCF 3350
■ MC . . . . . . . . . . . . . . . . . . . MCFC 3350
```
MCA / Dec '86.
```
CD . . . . . . . . . . . . . . . . . . . . . MCAD 5832
```
MCA / Oct '87 / BMG.

## MAN IN MY LIFE.
**Tracks:** Man in my life / Heartbreaker.
```
■ 12" . . . . . . . . . . . . . . . . . . . . . E 9910T
■ 7" . . . . . . . . . . . . . . . . . . . . . .E 9910
```
Elektra / Jan '83.

## MAN SIZE LOVE.
**Tracks:** Man size love.
```
■ 12" . . . . . . . . . . . . . . . . . . . . MCAT 1111
■ 7" . . . . . . . . . . . . . . . . . . . . . MCA 1112
```
MCA / Jan '87.

## MAXX IS BACK, THE.
**Tracks:** Maxx is back / Private party / Finishing touch / Don't mess with my man / Don't run away / Good love / When you kiss me / Girls chasing boys / Shame / She's a user.
```
■ CD . . . . . . . . . . . . . . . . . . DMCG 6096
■ LP . . . . . . . . . . . . . . . . . . . MCG 6096
■ MC . . . . . . . . . . . . . . . . . . MCGC 6096
```
MCA / Jul '90.

## MEETING IN THE LADIES ROOM.
Tracks: Men all pause / Lock and key / I miss you / Just our luck / Meeting in the ladies room / Video kid / Ask me no questions / Love bandit / I betcha.
■ LP .................... MCF 3247
MCA / Jan '85.
■ LP .................... MCF 3313
■ MC. .................... MCFC 3313
MCA / Jun '86.
■ CD .................... MCAD 5529
MCA / Jul '87.

## NEVER UNDERESTIMATE THE POWER OF A WOMAN.
Tracks: All fired up / I wish you would / I want to love you tonight / You're the greatest / Never underestimate the power of a woman / Beat of my heart / No words / Can't let love just pass me by.
■ LP .................... K 52304
MC. .................... K4 52304
Solar / Jul '81 / Sony.

## NEVER UNDERESTIMATE THE POWER OF A WOMAN.
Tracks: Never underestimate the power of a woman / No words.
■ 7" .................... K 12641
Solar / Jun '81.

## WILD GIRLS.
Tracks: Wild girls / Let love just pass.
■ 12" .................... K 969955 T
■ 7" .................... K 969955 7
Solar / Nov '82.

# Knight, Curtis

## LIVE IN EUROPE.
Tracks: Not Advised.
■ LP .................... .088816
S.P.V. / Sep '89.
CD .................... .858817
S.P.V. / '90.

# Knight, Frederick

## BETCHA DIDN'T KNOW THAT.
Tracks: I betcha didn't know that / Let's make a deal.
■ 7" .................... STXS 2028
Stax / Jun '75.

## BETCHA DIDN'T KNOW THAT.
Tracks: I betcha didn't know that / I've been lonely or so long.
■ 7" .................... STAX 2008
Stax / Mar '78.

## I'VE BEEN LONELY FOR SO LONG.
Tracks: I've been lonely for so long / This is my song of love to you / Take me on home witcha / Friend / I let my chance go by / Your love's all over me / Pick 'um up, put 'um down / Now that I've found you / Lean on me / Trouble / Someday we'll be together.
CD .................... CDSXE 099
Stax / Nov '93 / Pinnacle.

## I'VE BEEN LONELY SO LONG.
Tracks: I've been lonely for so long.
■ 7" .................... .2025 098
Stax / Jun '72.
■ 7" .................... STAX 811
Stax / Aug '87.

## KNIGHT RAP.
Tracks: River flowing know that / River flowing / Wrapped in your love / Staying power / I love the way you love / You make my life complete / When it ain't right with my baby / Uphill peace of mind.
■ LP .................... TRLP 110
Timeless (Soul) / Aug '87.
■ LP .................... TRPL 110
Timeless (Soul) / Jan '90.

## KNIGHT TIME.
Tracks: Knight time / If tomorrow never comes / Old shop / I'll come back to you / You're the best thing in my life / When will the love need me / Shining star / Even a fool would let go / Bundle of love.
■ LP .................... TRLP 103
Timeless (Soul) / Dec '87.

# Knight, Gladys

Born in Atlanta, Georgia in '44, Gladys Knight, joined by her famous Pips a mere nine years later, has generally been regarded as one of Motown's most successful vocalists, though in fact the majority of her sales occurred after she left the label. Gladys And The Pips - brother Merald and cousins William Guest and Edward Patten

- toured with Jackie Wilson in the late '50s and enjoyed a first hit in '61 with *Every Beat Of My Heart*. One Van McCoy produced single, *Giving Up*, later, the group signed to Motown where their single, *Just Walk In My Shoes* became a 66 hit. From then until '73 the hits flowed freely, the quartet recording the original version of *I Heard It Through The Grapevine* and scoring with *If I Were your Woman*, *It Should Have Been Me*, *Help Me Make It Through The Night* and *Neither One Of Us* amongst others. Dissatisfaction with their Motown contract led to a departure to Buddah and the most lucrative period of the group's career, international hits like *The Way We Were*, *The Best Thing That Ever Happend To Me*, *Part Time Lover*, and *Midnight Train To Georgia* placing them in pop charts the world over. Their last major hit occurred in '77, *Baby Don't Change Your Mind* drawn successfully from the *Still Together* album. The Pips then recorded a couple of albums on their own, while in '80, Gladys made a duet LP with Johnny Mathis. Joining CBS in '83, Gladys and The Pips reunited for two of the best albums, *Visions* and *Life*, both part produced by Sam Dees and Leon Sylvers. A further album two years later, *All Our Love* (MCA), produced a UK top 50 hit, *Love Overboard* after which Gladys decided to go solo. In '89 she sang the theme to the Bond movie *Licence To Kill* and has recorded two albums for MCA since '91, *Good Woman* and *Just For You* the latter including the Babyface written hit single *I Don't Want To Know*.

## 16 GREAT CLASSICS (Knight, Gladys & The Pips).
Tracks: How do you say goodbye / Jungle love / I want that kind of love / Before now, after then / I can't stand by / What shall I do / Every beat of my heart / Room in my heart / Guess who / Running around / Darlin / Letter full of tears / You broke your promise / Operator / Trust in you / Morning, noon and night.
CD .................... XELCD 103
■ LP .................... XELLP 103
MC. .................... XELMC 103
Exel / Mar '88 / Henry Hadaway Organisation / EMI.

## 17 GREATEST HITS: GLADYS KNIGHT.
Tracks: Not Advised.
CD .................... .530043-2
■ MC. .................... .530043-4
Motown / Jan '92 / PolyGram.

## 20 GOLDEN GREATS: GLADYS KNIGHT (Knight, Gladys & The Pips).
Tracks: Help me make it through the night / Take me in your arms and love me / Just walk in my shoes / Look of love / Friendship train / Nitty gritty / You need love like I do / Every beat of my heart / It should have been me / Daddy could swear, I declare / Neither one of us / I heard it through the grapevine / Everybody needs love / If I were your woman / I wish it would rain / I don't want to do wrong / Make me the woman that you come home to / Letter full of tears / Didn't you know (you'd have to cry sometime) / End of our road.
■ LP .................... .STML 12122
■ MC. .................... .CSTML 12122
Motown / Oct '81.

## 30 GREATEST (Knight, Gladys & The Pips).
Tracks: Not Advised.
■ LP .................... NE 1004
K-Tel / Nov '77.

## ABOUT LOVE (Knight, Gladys & The Pips).
Tracks: Landlord / Taste of bitter love / Still such a thing / Get the love / Add it up / Bourgie bourgie / Friendly persuasion / We need hearts.
■ LP .................... CBS 84178
CBS / Aug '80.
■ LP .................... 32543
CBS / Aug '87.

## ALL OUR LOVE (Knight, Gladys & The Pips).
Tracks: Love overboard / Lovin' on next to nothin' / Thief in paradise / You / Let me be the one / Complete recovery / Say what you mean / It's gonna take all our love / Love is fire / Point of view / Overnight success.
■ LP .................... MCF 3409
■ CD .................... DMCF 3409
■ MC. .................... MCFC 3409
MCA / Feb '88.
■ CD .................... DMCL 1895
MCA / Jan '90.

## ALL THE GREATEST HITS (Knight, Gladys & The Pips).
Tracks: Help me make it through the night / Take me in your arms and love me / I heard it through the grapevine / End of our road / Nitty gritty / Friendship train / You need love like I do / Just walk in my shoes / I don't want to do wrong / Look of love / Neither one of us / Daddy could swear, I declare / Make me the woman that you come home to / If I were your woman.
■ LP .................... WL 72373
■ MC. .................... WK 72373
Motown / Apr '85.
■ CD .................... WD 72373
Motown / Mar '89.

## AM I TOO LATE (Knight, Gladys & The Pips).
Tracks: Am I too late / It's the same old song.
■ 7" .................... CBS 7173
CBS / Mar '79.

## ANTHOLOGY - GLADYS KNIGHT (Volumes 1 and 2) (Knight, Gladys & The Pips).
Tracks: Letter full of tears / Giving up / Just walk in my shoes / Do you love me just a little, honey / You don't love me no more / Take me in your arms and love me / Everybody needs love / I heard it through the grapevine / End of our road / I know better / Don't let her take your love from me / It should have been me / I wish it would rain / Valley of the Dolls, Theme from / Didn't you know (you'd have to cry sometime) / Got myself a good man / All I could do was cry / Friendship train / Tracks of my tears / You need love like I do / Every little bit hurts / If I were your woman / I don't want to do wrong / One less bell to answer / Is there a place (in his heart for me) / Master of my mind / No one could love you more / Can't give it up no more / For once in my life / Make me the woman that you come home to / Help me make it through the night / Neither one of us / Daddy could swear, I declare / All I need is time / Don't tell me I'm crazy / Oh what a love I have found / Only time you love me is when you're losing me / Between her goodbye and my hello.
■ Double LP. .................... TMSP 1127
■ MC Set .................... CTMSP 1127
Motown / Oct '81.
■ CD Set. .................... ZD 72535
Motown / Jun '87.
■ CD .................... WD 72535
Motown / Apr '89.
CD .................... .530187-2
Motown / Jan '92 / PolyGram.

## BABY DON'T CHANGE YOUR MIND (Knight, Gladys & The Pips).
Tracks: Baby don't change your mind / I love to feel that feeling.
■ 7" .................... .BDS 458
Buddah / May '77.

## BEFORE NOW AFTER THEN (Knight, Gladys & The Pips).
Tracks: I trust in you / Linda / Happiness / Love call / Room in your heart / Love like mine / Darlin / It hurts so bad / Jungle love / Queen of tears / Bless the one / What shall I do.
■ Double LP. .................... CR 118
■ MC Set .................... CRT 118
Cambra / Apr '84.

## BEST OF GLADYS KNIGHT & THE PIPS (Knight, Gladys & The Pips).
Tracks: Taste of bitter love / Ain't no greater love / I will fight / Save the overtime for me / You're number one in my book / Landlord / Hero / Friend of mine / My time.
■ MC. .................... ZC BDS 5013
Buddah / Feb '76.
■ LP .................... BDLH 5013
Buddah / Mar '76.
CD .................... 4624162
■ LP .................... 4624161
■ MC. .................... 4624164
CBS / Aug '88 / Sony.
CD .................... 9827352
Pickwick/Sony Collector's Choice / Apr '92 / Pickwick / Pinnacle.

## BEST OF GLADYS KNIGHT & THE PIPS (Knight, Gladys & The Pips).
Tracks: Not Advised.
CD .................... MATCD 205
Castle / Dec '92 / BMG.
■ MC. .................... MATMC 205
Castle / May '94.

## BEST OF GLADYS KNIGHT & THE PIPS, THE (1980 - 1985) (Knight, Gladys & The Pips).

**Tracks:** Licence to kill / Taste of bitter love / Bourgie bourgie / Love overboard / I will fight / My time / Landlord / Baby don't change your mind / Come back and finish what you started / Nobody but you / Part time love / One and only / Midnight train to Georgia / Wind beneath my wings / Try to remember/the way we were / Best thing that ever happened to me /

■ CD . . . . . . . . . . . . . . . . . . . . 4674502
■ LP . . . . . . . . . . . . . . . . . . . . 4674501
■ MC . . . . . . . . . . . . . . . . . . . . 4674504
CBS / Oct '90.
CD . . . . . . . . . . . . . . . . . . . . .472038 2
MC . . . . . . . . . . . . . . . . . . . . .472038 4
Sony Music / '93 / Sony.

## BEST THING THAT EVER HAPPENED TO ME (Knight, Gladys & The Pips).

**Tracks:** Best thing that ever happened to me / Midnight train to Georgia / Every beat of my heart.
■ 7" . . . . . . . . . . . . . . . . . . . . .BDS 432
Buddah / Jul '75.
■ 7" . . . . . . . . . . . . . . . . . . . . . CR 213
Creole (Replay) / Jan '83.

## BEST THING THAT EVER HAPPENED TO ME (OLD GOLD) (Knight, Gladys & The Pips).

**Tracks:** Best thing that ever happened to me / Baby don't change your mind.
7" . . . . . . . . . . . . . . . . . . . . .OG 9923
Old Gold / Jan '90 / Pickwick.

## BLESS THIS HOUSE (Knight, Gladys & The Pips).

**Tracks:** Night before Christmas / Do you hear what I hear / Christmas song / Away in a manger / Ava Maria / Silent night / Bless this house / Jesu, joy of man's desiring / Jesus is my kind of people / Jesus is alright with me.
■ LP . . . . . . . . . . . . . . . . . . . BDLP 4050
Buddah / Dec '84.

## BOURGIE BOURGIE (Knight, Gladys & The Pips).

**Tracks:** Bourgie bourgie / Get the love.
■ 7" . . . . . . . . . . . . . . . . . . . CBS 9081
CBS / Nov '80.

## BROKEN PROMISES (Knight, Gladys & The Pips).

**Tracks:** Operator / You broke your promise / Morning, noon and night / Guess who / Love like mine / I really didn't mean it / One more lonely night / Come see about me / I can't stand by / I want that kind of love.
■ LP . . . . . . . . . . . . . . . . . . . . .TOP 169
MC . . . . . . . . . . . . . . . . . . . . KTOP 169
Topline / Mar '87 / Charly.

## CHRISTMAS EVERYDAY (Knight, Gladys & The Pips).

**Tracks:** Christmas everyday / Christmas everyday (inst).
■ 12" . . . . . . . . . . . . . . . . . . . MCAT 1112
■ 7" . . . . . . . . . . . . . . . . . . . .MCA 1104
MCA / Nov '86.

## CLAUDINE/STILL TOGETHER (Knight, Gladys & The Pips).

**Tracks:** Mr. Welfare man / To be invisible / On and on / Makings of you / Claudine theme (instrumental) / Hold on / Make yours a happy home / Love is always on your mind / Home is where the heart is / Little bit of love / Baby don't change your mind / Walk softly / I love to feel that feeling / To make a long story short / You put a new life in my body.
CD . . . . . . . . . . . . . . . . . . . NEXCD 206
Sequel / Jun '92 / Total / BMG.

## COLLECTION: GLADYS KNIGHT.

**Tracks:** Best thing that ever happened to me / I heard it through the grapevine / Heaven sent / Neither one of us / Midnight train to Georgia / Take me in your arms and love me / For once in my life / One and only / Taste of bitter love / Way we were / Try to remember / Help me make it through the night / We don't make each other laugh anymore / Tracks of my tears / Best thing we can do is say goodbye / Look of love / Baby don't change your mind / Goin' out of my head / If that will make you happy / Way it was / Hero.
■ LP . . . . . . . . . . . . . . . . . . . . .NITE 1
■ MC . . . . . . . . . . . . . . . . . . . . KNITE 1
Starblend / Feb '85.

## COLLECTION: GLADYS KNIGHT & THE PIPS (Knight, Gladys & The Pips).

**Tracks:** Make yours a happy home / Best thing that ever happened to me / I feel a song / Midnight train to Georgia / On and on / Where peaceful waters flow / I've got to use my imagination / I can see clearly now / Try to remember / One and only / Come back and finish what you started / It's a better than good time / Sorry doesn't always make it right / Be yourself / So sad the song / Nobody but you / Pipe dreams / Baby don't change your mind / Part time lover / Way we were.
CD . . . . . . . . . . . . . . . . . . . CCSCD 206
■ Double LP . . . . . . . . . . . . . . . CCSLP 206
■ MC . . . . . . . . . . . . . . . . . .CCSMC 206
Castle Collector Series / Oct '88 / BMG / Pinnacle / Castle Communications.

## COLLECTION: GLADYS KNIGHT (BOX SET) (Knight, Gladys & The Pips).

**Tracks:** Not Advised.
■ LP Set . . . . . . . . . . . . . . . . . 11PP 602
Buddah / Sep '78.

## COLUMBIA YEARS, THE (Knight, Gladys & The Pips).

**Tracks:** Not Advised.
■ LP . . . . . . . . . . . . . . . . . . . . FC 40878
CBS / Jul '88.

## COME BACK AND FINISH WHAT YOU STARTED (Knight, Gladys & The Pips).

**Tracks:** Come back and finish what you started / It's up to you.
■ 7" . . . . . . . . . . . . . . . . . . . .BDS 473
Buddah / Jun '78.

## COMPACT COMMAND PERFORMANCES (17 Greatest Hits) (Knight, Gladys & The Pips).

**Tracks:** Everybody needs love / I heard it through the grapevine / End of our road / It should have been me / I wish it would rain / Didn't you know (you'd have to cry sometime) / Nitty gritty / Friendship train / You need love like I do / If I were your woman / I don't want to do wrong / Make me the woman that you come home to / Help me make it through the night / Neither one of us / Daddy could swear, I declare / All I need is time / Between her goodbye and my hello.
■ CD . . . . . . . . . . . . . . . . . . . WD 72299
Motown / '86.

## DO YOU HEAR WHAT I HEAR (Knight, Gladys & The Pips).

**Tracks:** Do you hear what I hear / Gospel medley.
■ 7" . . . . . . . . . . . . . . . . . . . .BDS 480
Buddah / Nov '78.

## EASYRIDING: GLADYS KNIGHT (Knight, Gladys & The Pips).

**Tracks:** Best thing that ever happened to me / Midnight train to Georgia / Baby don't change your mind / Come back and finish what you started / Part time lover / Where peaceful waters flow / I've got to use my imagination / I can see clearly now / We don't make each other laugh any more / Way it was / I feel a song in my heart / Home is where the heart is / I love to feel the feeling.
■ LP . . . . . . . . . . . . . . . . . .KNLP 11003
■ MC . . . . . . . . . . . . . . . . . KNMC 11003
Easyriding / Jul '88.

## EVERY BEAT OF MY HEART.

**Tracks:** Tracks of my tears / Every little bit hurts / Yesterday / It's Summer / You've lost that lovin' feelin' / Look of love.
■ LP . . . . . . . . . . . . . . . . . . . .MS 3506
■ MC . . . . . . . . . . . . . . . . . . .TMC 3506
Motown / '82.
■ LP . . . . . . . . . . . . . . . . . . . RMB 5618
Crusader / Mar '89.

## EVERY BEAT OF MY HEART (Knight, Gladys & The Pips).

**Tracks:** Every beat of my heart / Queen of tears.
■ 7" . . . . . . . . . . . . . . . . . . . . DJS 681
DJM / May '76.

## EVERY BEAT OF MY HEART (Knight, Gladys & The Pips).

**Tracks:** Not Advised.
CD . . . . . . . . . . . . . . . . . . . CDCD 1055
Charly / Mar '93 / Charly.

## EVERY BEAT OF MY HEART (2).

**Tracks:** what shall I do / I can't stand by / Before now after then / Goodnight my love / Love me again / Running around / Room in your heart / Every beat of your heart / Trust in you / Morning, noon and night.
■ LP . . . . . . . . . . . . . . . . . . . BMM 003
Blue Moon (1) / Mar '86.

## EVERYBODY NEEDS LOVE (Knight, Gladys & The Pips).

**Tracks:** Everybody needs love / I'll be standing by / Since I've lost you / I heard it through the grapevine / You don't love me no more / Ain't no sun since you've been gone / Take me in your arms and love me / He's my kind of fellow / Yes I'm ready / My bed of thorns / Do you love me just a little honey / Just walk in my shoes.
■ LP . . . . . . . . . . . . . . . . . .STML 11058
Tamla Motown / Jan '68.
■ LP . . . . . . . . . . . . . . . . . . STMS 5039
■ MC . . . . . . . . . . . . . . . . . CSTMS 5039
Motown / Mar '82.

## FABULOUS (Knight, Gladys & The Pips).

**Tracks:** Take me in your arms & love me / Just walk in my shoes / That's the way love is.
■ LP . . . . . . . . . . . . . . . . . . MFP 50304
MFP / Nov '76.

## FEELIN' BLUESY (Knight, Gladys & The Pips).

**Tracks:** End of our road / That's the way love is / Don't you miss me a little bit baby / Boy from cross town / Ain't you glad you chose love / I know better / Don't let her take your love from me / It should have been me / Don't turn me away / What good am I without you / Your old standby / It's time to go now.
■ LP . . . . . . . . . . . . . . . . . .STML 11080
Tamla Motown / Sep '68.

## FIRST SHOT.

**Tracks:** Every beat of my heart / Room in your heart / Guess who / Jungle love / I want that kind of love / Before now, after then / I can't stand by / What shall I do.
■ LP . . . . . . . . . . . . . . . . . . . MAN 5002
Manhattan Records / Sep '89.

## FLIPHITS (Knight, Gladys & The Pips).

**Tracks:** Help me make it through the night / Just walk in my shoes / Look of love / Take me in your arms.
■ MC Single . . . . . . . . . . . . . . CTME 2036
Motown / Jul '83.

## FUNKY.

**Tracks:** Letter full of tears / Operator / Trust in you / What shall I do / Room in your heart / Guess who / Running around / Darling.
■ LP . . . . . . . . . . . . . . . . . . . MAN 5003
Manhattan Records / Nov '80.

## GLADYS KNIGHT.

**Tracks:** Am I too late / You bring out the best in me / I just want to be with you / If you need somebody / You don't have to say I love you / I / My world / Best thing we can do is say goodbye / It's the same old song / You loved away the pain.
■ LP . . . . . . . . . . . . . . . . . . CBS 83341
CBS / '79.

## GLADYS KNIGHT.

**Tracks:** Not Advised.
CD . . . . . . . . . . . . . . . . . . . LECD 048
Dynamite (2) / May '94 / THE.

## GLADYS KNIGHT & THE PIPS (Knight, Gladys & The Pips).

**Tracks:** Not Advised.
■ CD . . . . . . . . . . . . . . . . . . . 500 060
Intertape / Jul '87.

## GLADYS KNIGHT & THE PIPS (EP) (Knight, Gladys & The Pips).

**Tracks:** Midnight train to Georgia / Baby don't change your mind / Come back and finish what you started / Try to remember / Way we were.
■ CD Single . . . . . . . . . . . . . . . CD3-15
Special Edition / '88.

## GLADYS KNIGHT & THE PIPS - 2ND ANNIVERSARY / PIPE DREAMS (Knight, Gladys & The Pips).

**Tracks:** Money / Street brother / Part time love / At every end there's a beginning / Georgia on my mind / You and me against the world / Where do I put his memory / Summer sun / Feel like makin' love / So sad the song / Alaskan pipeline / Pot of Jazz / I'll miss you / Nobody but you / Pipe dreams / Everybody's got to find a way / I will follow my dream.
CD . . . . . . . . . . . . . . . . . . NEXCD 206
Sequel / Mar '93 / Total / BMG.

## GOLDEN HOUR OF GLADYS KNIGHT AND THE PIPS (Knight, Gladys & The Pips).

**Tracks:** Not Advised.
■ CD . . . . . . . . . . . . . . . . . . KGHCD 147
■ MC . . . . . . . . . . . . . . . . . KGHMC 147
Knight / Apr '91.

■ DELETED

## GOOD WOMAN.
Tracks: Not Advised.
- LP . . . . . . . . . . . . . . . . . MCA 10329
- MC . . . . . . . . . . . . . . . . . MCAC 10329
- CD . . . . . . . . . . . . . . . . . MCAD 10329

MCA / Jul '91.

## GREATEST HITS (Knight, Gladys & The Pips).
Tracks: I wish it would rain / Didn't you know / You need love like I do / Friendship train / Nitty gritty / It should have been me / Take me in your arms and love me / Every beat of my heart / Letter full of tears / Giving up / Everybody needs love / I heard it through the grapevine / End of our road / Just walk in my shoes.
- LP . . . . . . . . . . . . . . . . . STML 11148

Tamla Motown / Jun '70.

## HEART AND SOUL OF GLADYS KNIGHT.
Tracks: Try to remember/The way we were / One and only / I can see clearly now / I've got to use my imagination / Nobody but you / On and on / Midnight train to Georgia / Baby don't change your mind / Come back and finish what you started / So sad the song / Part time love / Where peaceful waters flow / Georgia on my mind / Best thing that ever happened to me.
- LP . . . . . . . . . . . . . . . . . KNLP 12050

Knight / Mar '90.
- CD . . . . . . . . . . . . . . . . . KNCD 12050
- MC . . . . . . . . . . . . . . . . . KNMC 12050

Knight / Jul '91.

## HELP ME MAKE IT THROUGH THE NIGHT (Knight, Gladys & The Pips).
Tracks: Help me make it through the night.
- 7" . . . . . . . . . . . . . . . . . TMG 830

Tamla Motown / Nov '72.

## HELP ME MAKE IT THROUGH THE NIGHT (Knight, Gladys & The Pips).
Tracks: Help me make it through the night / Goin' out of my head / Didn't you know (you'd have to cry sometime) / I wish it would rain / Look of love / Letter full of tears / Tracks of my tears / Ain't you had you chose love / Since I've lost you / You're my everything / Everybody needs love / Ain't no sun since you've been gone / It should have been me / I know better.
- LP . . . . . . . . . . . . . . . . . STML 11226

Tamla Motown / Feb '73.
- LP . . . . . . . . . . . . . . . . . STMS 5096
- MC . . . . . . . . . . . . . . . . . CSTMS 5096

Motown / Jun '83.

## HERO (Knight, Gladys & The Pips).
Tracks: Hero / Seconds.
- 12" . . . . . . . . . . . . . . . . . TA 3763
- 7" . . . . . . . . . . . . . . . . . A 3763

CBS / Sep '83.

## HIT SINGLE COLLECTABLES (Knight, Gladys & The Pips).
Tracks: Not Advised.
- CD . . . . . . . . . . . . . . . . . DISK 4506

Disky / Apr '94 / THE.

## HOME IS WHERE THE HEART IS (Knight, Gladys & The Pips).
Tracks: Home is where the heart is / You put a new life in my body.
- 7" . . . . . . . . . . . . . . . . . BDS 460

Buddah / Sep '77.

## I FEEL A SONG (Knight, Gladys & The Pips).
Tracks: Not Advised.
- LP . . . . . . . . . . . . . . . . . BDLP 4030

Buddah / May '75.

## I HEARD IT THROUGH THE GRAPEVINE (Knight, Gladys & The Pips).
Tracks: I heard it through the grapevine.
- 7" . . . . . . . . . . . . . . . . . TMG 629

Tamla Motown / Dec '67.

## I WILL FIGHT (Knight, Gladys & The Pips).
Tracks: I will fight / Reach high.
- 7" . . . . . . . . . . . . . . . . . A 2075

CBS / Apr '82.

## I'LL TAKE A MELODY.
Tracks: I'll take a melody / Way it was.
- 7" . . . . . . . . . . . . . . . . . BDS 483

Buddah / Feb '81.

## IF I WERE YOUR WOMAN (Knight, Gladys & The Pips).
Tracks: If I were your woman / Only time you love me / Tracks of my tears.

---

- 7" . . . . . . . . . . . . . . . . . TMG 765

Tamla Motown / Mar '71.
- 7" . . . . . . . . . . . . . . . . . TMG 955

Tamla Motown / Jul '75.

## IF I WERE YOUR WOMAN (Knight, Gladys & The Pips).
Tracks: If I were your woman / Feelin' alright / One less bell to answer / Let it be / I don't want to do wrong / One step away / Here I am again / How can you say that ain't love / Is there a place / Everybody is a star / Signed Gladys / Your love's been good for me.
- LP . . . . . . . . . . . . . . . . . STML 11187

Tamla Motown / Sep '71.

## IMAGINATION (Knight, Gladys & The Pips).
Tracks: Midnight train to Georgia / I've got to use my imagination / Storms of troubled times / Best thing that ever happened to me / Once in a lifetime thing / Where peaceful waters flow / I can see clearly now / Perfect love / Window raisin' granny.
- LP . . . . . . . . . . . . . . . . . BDLP 4005

Buddah / Aug '74.

MC . . . . . . . . . . . . . . . . . 252 210-4
- LP . . . . . . . . . . . . . . . . . 252 210-1

Buddah / Jul '85.

## IMAGINATION/I FEEL A SONG (2 LP's on 1 CD) (Knight, Gladys & The Pips).
Tracks: Midnight train to Georgia / I've got to use my imagination / Storms of troubled times / Best thing that ever happened to me / Once in a lifetime thing / Where peaceful waters flow / I can see clearly now / Perfect love / Window raisin' Granny / I feel a song (in my heart) / Love finds it's own way / Seconds / Going ups and coming downs / Way we were / Try to remember / Better go your own way / Dont' burn down the bridge / Need to be / Tenderness is his way.

CD . . . . . . . . . . . . . . . . . NEXCD 192

Sequel / Sep '92 / Total / BMG.

## IT'S A BETTER THAN GOOD TIME (Knight, Gladys & The Pips).
Tracks: It's a better than good time / Saved by the grace of your love.
- 7" . . . . . . . . . . . . . . . . . BDS 478

Buddah / Sep '78.

## JUKE BOX GIANTS (Knight, Gladys & The Pips).
Tracks: Letter full of tears / Linda / Love call / Bless the one / I had a dream last night / Love like mine / Darlin' / How do you say goodbye / Jungle love / Before now, after then / What shall I do / Queen of tears / What will become of me / To whom it may concern / Happiness is the light of love / Walkin' round in circles / It hurts so bad / Every beat of my heart / One more lonely night / Really didn't mean it.
- LP . . . . . . . . . . . . . . . . . AFEMP 1022

Audio Fidelity / May '82.

## JUST FOR YOU.
Tracks: Not Advised.
CD . . . . . . . . . . . . . . . . . MCD 10946
MC . . . . . . . . . . . . . . . . . MCC 10946

MCA / Sep '94 / BMG.

## JUST WALK IN MY SHOES (Knight, Gladys & The Pips).
Tracks: Just walk in my shoes.
- 7" . . . . . . . . . . . . . . . . . TMG 576

Tamla Motown / Sep '66.

## JUST WALK IN MY SHOES (Knight, Gladys & The Pips).
Tracks: Just walk in my shoes.
- 7" . . . . . . . . . . . . . . . . . TMG 813

Tamla Motown / Jun '72.

## LANDLORD.
Tracks: Landlord / We need a heart.
- 7" . . . . . . . . . . . . . . . . . CBS 8542

CBS / May '80.

## LIFE (Knight, Gladys & The Pips).
Tracks: Strivin' / Keep giving me love / Just let me love you / Life / Till i see you again / My time / Forever / Do you wanna have some fun / Straight up / Glitter.
- LP . . . . . . . . . . . . . . . . . CBS 26184

CBS / May '85.

## LIVE IN CONCERT (Knight, Gladys & The Pips).
Tracks: Best thing that ever happened to me / America / Friendship train / Georgia on my mind / How can you say that ain't love / Every beat of my heart / So sad the song / So good I feel / Evergreen / Second hand rose / Way we were / Jesus Christ superstar / Imagination / I heard it through the grapevine /

---

Busted / I can see clearly now / Neither one of us / Hit the road Jack / Neither one of us (reprise).
VHS . . . . . . . . . . . . . . . . . WNR 1062

Wienerworld Video / '88 / VCI Distribution / THE.

## LOOK OF LOVE (Knight, Gladys & The Pips).
Tracks: Not Advised.
- LP . . . . . . . . . . . . . . . . . MFP 50417

MFP / Feb '79.

## LOOK OF LOVE (Knight, Gladys & The Pips).
Tracks: Look of love.
- 7" . . . . . . . . . . . . . . . . . TMG 844

Tamla Motown / Mar '73.

## LOOKING BACK..THE FURY YEARS (Knight, Gladys & The Pips).
Tracks: Guess who / Darlin' / Letter full of tears / You broke your promise / Operator / Every beat of my heart / Come see about me / One more lonely night / Really didn't mean it / How do you say goodbye / Jungle love / Room in your heart.
- LP . . . . . . . . . . . . . . . . . BDL 1040

Bulldog Records / Jul '82.

## LOVE OVERBOARD.
Tracks: Love overboard (women & children first remix).
- 7" . . . . . . . . . . . . . . . . . MCA 1223

MCA / Jan '88.

## LOVIN' ON NEXT TO NOTHIN' (Knight, Gladys & The Pips).
Tracks: Lovin' on next to nothin' (mixes) / Send it to me.
- 12" . . . . . . . . . . . . . . . . . MCAX 1237
- 12" . . . . . . . . . . . . . . . . . MCAT 1237
- 7" . . . . . . . . . . . . . . . . . MCA 1237
- CD Single . . . . . . . . . . . . . . . . . DMCA 1237

MCA / Mar '88.

## LOVING ON BORROWED TIME (Knight, Gladys & The Pips).
Tracks: Loving on borrowed time / Angel of the city.
- 7" . . . . . . . . . . . . . . . . . 6500627

Epic / Aug '86.

## MAKE YOURS A HAPPY HOME (Knight, Gladys & The Pips).
Tracks: Make yours a happy home.
- 7" . . . . . . . . . . . . . . . . . BDS 447

Buddah / Jul '76.

## MEMORIES OF THE WAY WERE.
Tracks: I'll take a melody / With you in mind / I'm coming home again / Part time love / Nobody but you / All the time / Butterfly / One and only / So sad the song / Pipe dream / Don't say no to me tonight / Seconds / Way it was / Perfect love / Try to remember / Way we were.
- Double LP. . . . . . . . . . . . . . . . . BDLD 2004
- MC . . . . . . . . . . . . . . . . . ZCBD 2004

Buddah / Sep '79.

## MIDNIGHT TRAIN TO GEORGIA (Knight, Gladys & The Pips).
Tracks: Not Advised.
- LP . . . . . . . . . . . . . . . . . SHM 3057
- MC . . . . . . . . . . . . . . . . . HSC 3057

Hallmark / Mar '81.

## MIDNIGHT TRAIN TO GEORGIA (Knight, Gladys & The Pips).
Tracks: Midnight train to Georgia.
- 7" . . . . . . . . . . . . . . . . . BDS 444

Buddah / May '76.

## MIDNIGHT TRAIN TO GEORGIA.
Tracks: Not Advised.
CD . . . . . . . . . . . . . . . . . 550 7352
MC . . . . . . . . . . . . . . . . . 550 7354

Spectrum (1) / Sep '94 / PolyGram.

## MIDNIGHT TRAIN TO GEORGIA (OLD GOLD) (Knight, Gladys & The Pips).
Tracks: Midnight train to Georgia / Way we were / Try to remember.
7" . . . . . . . . . . . . . . . . . OG 9920

Old Gold / Jan '90 / Pickwick.

## MISS GLADYS KNIGHT.
Tracks: I'm comin' home again / Sail away / Freedom for the stallion / I'm still caught up with you / It's better than a good time / We don't make each other laugh anymore / Way it was / I'll take a melody / With you in mind / Love gives you the power.
- LP . . . . . . . . . . . . . . . . . BDLP 4056

Buddah / Feb '79.

## MY TIME.
**Tracks:** My time.
■ 12" . . . . . . . . . . . . . . . . . . . . . . TA 6104
■ 7" . . . . . . . . . . . . . . . . . . . . . . .A 6104
CBS / Mar '85.

## NEITHER ONE OF US.
**Tracks:** Neither one of us / It's gotta be that way / For once in my life / This child needs it's father / Who is she (and what is she to you) / And this is love / Daddy could swear, I declare / Can't give it up no more / Don't it make you feel guilty.
■ LP . . . . . . . . . . . . . . . . . . . . STMS 5041
■ MC. . . . . . . . . . . . . . . . . . . . CSTMS 5041
Motown / Mar '82.

## NEITHER ONE OF US (Knight, Gladys & The Pips).
**Tracks:** Neither one of us.
■ 7" . . . . . . . . . . . . . . . . . . . . TMG 855
Tamla Motown / May '73.

## NEITHER ONE OF US/ ALL I NEED IS TIME (2 Classic Albums) (Knight, Gladys & The Pips).
**Tracks:** Neither one of us / It's gotta be that way / For once in my life / This Child needs it's father / Who is she (and what is she to you) / Daddy / Daddy could swear, I declare / Can't give it up no more / Don't it make you feel guilty / I'll be here (when you get home) / All I need is time / Heavy makes you happy / Only time you love me is when you're losing me / Here I am again / There's a lesson to be learned / Oh what a love I have found / Thank you (falletinme be mice elf agin) / It's all over but the shouting / Singer.
■ CD . . . . . . . . . . . . . . . . . . . . ZD 72461
Motown.

## NIGHTFUL.
**Tracks:** Running around / Really didn't mean it / How do you say goodbye / What shall I do / I can't stand it / One more lonely night / Letter full of tears / Operator.
■ LP . . . . . . . . . . . . . . . . . . . . .MAN 5001
Manhattan Records / Feb '80.

## NITTY GRITTY (Knight, Gladys & The Pips).
**Tracks:** Cloud 9 / Runnin out / Didn't you know (you'd have to cry sometime) / (I know), I'm losing you / Nitty gritty / Ain't no sun since you've been gone / All I could do was cry / Keep an eye / Got myself a good man / It's Summer / Stranger / I want him to say it again.
■ LP . . . . . . . . . . . . . . . . . . . . STML 11135
Tamla Motown / Feb '70.
■ LP . . . . . . . . . . . . . . . . . . . . STMS 5040
■ MC. . . . . . . . . . . . . . . . . . . . CSTMS 5040
Motown / Mar '82.

## NOBODY BUT YOU (Knight, Gladys & The Pips).
**Tracks:** Nobody but you / Pipe dreams.
■ 7" . . . . . . . . . . . . . . . . . . . . .BDS 451
Buddah / Jan '77.

## ON AND ON (Knight, Gladys & The Pips).
**Tracks:** Not Advised.
MC. . . . . . . . . . . . . . . . . . . . . . ORC 002
Orchid Music / Feb '82 / Pinnacle.

## ONE AND ONLY, THE (Knight, Gladys & The Pips).
**Tracks:** Not Advised.
■ LP . . . . . . . . . . . . . . . . . . . . BDLP 4051
Buddah / May '78.

## ONE AND ONLY, THE (Knight, Gladys & The Pips).
**Tracks:** One & only.
■ 7" . . . . . . . . . . . . . . . . . . . . .BDS 470
Buddah / May '78.

## ONE AND ONLY/MISS GLADY'S KNIGHT (Knight, Gladys & The Pips).
**Tracks:** One and only / What if I should never need you / Sorry doesn't always make it right / Don't say no to me tonight / Butterfly / Sail away/Freedom for the stallion / It's better than a good time (Disco) / Way it was / With you in mind / Be yourself / All the time / Come back and finish what you started / It's up to you (Do what you do) / I'm coming home again / I'm still caught up with you / We don't make each other laugh anymore / I'll take a melody / Love gives you the power.
CD. . . . . . . . . . . . . . . . . . . . . .NEMCD 645
Sequel / Apr '94 / Total / BMG.

## PART TIME LOVER (Knight, Gladys & The Pips).
**Tracks:** Part time lover.
■ 7" . . . . . . . . . . . . . . . . . . . . .BDS 438
Buddah / Nov '75.

## REPLAY ON GLADYS KNIGHT (Knight, Gladys & The Pips).
**Tracks:** Not Advised.
■ LP . . . . . . . . . . . . . . . . . . . FEDB 5031
MC. . . . . . . . . . . . . . . . . . . . CFEDB 5031
Sierra / May '86.

## SEND IT TO ME (Knight, Gladys & The Pips).
**Tracks:** Send it to me / Send it to me (acapella).
■ 12" . . . . . . . . . . . . . . . . . . . MCAT 1122
■ 7" . . . . . . . . . . . . . . . . . . . . .MCA 1122
MCA / Mar '87.

## SEND THE OVERTIME FOR ME.
**Tracks:** Send the overtime for me / Ain't no greater love.
■ 12" . . . . . . . . . . . . . . . . . . . TA 3314
■ 7" . . . . . . . . . . . . . . . . . . . . .A 3314
CBS / Apr '83.

## SILENT NIGHT (Knight, Gladys & The Pips).
**Tracks:** Silent night / Do you hear what I hear.
■ 7" . . . . . . . . . . . . . . . . . . . . .BDS 441
Buddah / Jan '76.

## SILK 'N' SOUL (Knight, Gladys & The Pips).
**Tracks:** I wish it would rain / Look of love / Goin' out of my head / Yesterday / Groovin' / You've lost that lovin' feelin' / Valley of the dolls / Baby I need your loving / Together / Tracks of my tears / You're my everything / Every little bit hurts.
■ LP . . . . . . . . . . . . . . . . . . . .STML 11100
Tamla Motown / Apr '69.

## SINGLES ALBUM - GLADYS KNIGHT & THE PIPS (Knight, Gladys & The Pips).
**Tracks:** Licence to kill / Help me make it through the night / Best thing that ever happened to me / Baby don't change your mind / Bourgie bourgie / Taste of bitter love / One and only / Just walk in my shoes / Midnight train to Georgia / Try to remember / Look of love / Part time lover / Come back and finish what you started / So sad the song / Take me in your arms and love me / Love overboard / Lovin' on next to nothin' / Neither one of us.
CD. . . . . . . . . . . . . . . . . . . . . 842 003 2
■ LP . . . . . . . . . . . . . . . . . . . . GKTV 1
MC. . . . . . . . . . . . . . . . . . . . GKTVC 1
Polygram T.V. / Oct '89 / PolyGram.

## SO SAD THE SONG (Knight, Gladys & The Pips).
**Tracks:** So sad the song / So sad the song (version).
■ 7" . . . . . . . . . . . . . . . . . . . . .BDS 448
Buddah / Nov '76.

## SOUL QUEENS VOL.2.
**Tracks:** Every beat of my heart / Room in your heart / Runnin around / Trust in you / Letter full of tears / You broke your promise / Operator / Come see about me / Morning, noon and night / Guess who / What shall I do.
CD. . . . . . . . . . . . . . . . . . . . . SMS 060
Pickwick / Oct '92 / Pickwick.

## SPOTLIGHT ON GLADYS KNIGHT & THE PIPS.
**Tracks:** Baby don't change your mind / Make yours a happy home / Little bit of love / I can see clearly now / It's up to you / Everybody's got to find a way / Try to remember / So sad the song / Walk softly / Don't say no to me tonight / Part time lover / I'll miss you / Best thing that ever happened to me / Midnight train to Georgia / Once in a lifetime thing / One and only / To be invisible / You put a new life in my body / Come back and finish what you started / Be yourself / I love to feel the feeling / Nobody but you / Home is where the heart is / It's better than a good time / Way we were.
■ Double LP. . . . . . . . . . . . . . . . SPOT 1006
■ MC Set . . . . . . . . . . . . . . . . .ZCSPT 1006
PRT / '80.

## STANDING OVATION (Knight, Gladys & The Pips).
**Tracks:** Make me the woman that you go home to / Can you give me love with a guarantee / Fire & rain / Master of my mind / He ain't heavy he's my brother / Bridge over troubled water / It takes a whole lotta man for a woman like me / Help me make it through the night / Long & winding road / If You're gonna leave / No one could love you more.

## ■ LP . . . . . . . . . . . . . . . . . . . .STML 112(
Tamla Motown / Jul '72.

## STILL SUCH A THING (Knight, Gladys & The Pips).
**Tracks:** Still such a thing / We have hearts.
■ 7" . . . . . . . . . . . . . . . . . . . . .CBS 94(
CBS / Jan '81.

## STILL TOGETHER (Knight, Gladys & Th Pips).
**Tracks:** Love is always on your mind / Home where the heart is / Little bit of love / Baby dor change your life / Walk softly / I love to feel th feeling / To make a long story short / You put a ne life in my body.
■ LP . . . . . . . . . . . . . . . . . . . . BDLH 50
Buddah / Mar '77.

## TAKE ME BACK (Knight, Gladys & Th Pips).
**Tracks:** How do you say goodbye / Jungle love / want that kind of love / before now after then Goodnight my love / Love me again / Come se about me / One more lonely night.
■ LP . . . . . . . . . . . . . . . . . . . .MAN 50
Manhattan Records / Jul '80.

## TAKE ME IN YOUR ARMS AND LOVE M (Knight, Gladys & The Pips).
**Tracks:** Take me in your arms and love me / Do yc love me just a little honey.
■ 7" . . . . . . . . . . . . . . . . . . . . TMG 6(
Tamla Motown / Jun '67.

## TASTE OF BITTER LOVE (Knight, Glady & The Pips).
**Tracks:** Taste of bitter love / Am I too late / Love wa made for two / You loved the pain / You don't have say I love you / Get the love / Bourgie bourgie / I ju want to be with you / I who have nothing / Baby bat don't waste my time / It's the same old song Landlord.
■ LP . . . . . . . . . . . . . . . . . . . .SHM 313
■ MC. . . . . . . . . . . . . . . . . . . . HSC 313
Hallmark / Nov '83.

## TASTE OF BITTER LOVE (Knight, Glady & The Pips).
**Tracks:** Taste of bitter love / Add it up.
■ 12" . . . . . . . . . . . . . . . . . . . CBS 13 88(
■ 7" . . . . . . . . . . . . . . . . . . . . .CBS 88(
CBS / Aug '80.

## TASTE OF BITTER LOVE (OLD GOLI (Knight, Gladys & The Pips).
**Tracks:** Taste of bitter love / Bourgie bourgie.
7" . . . . . . . . . . . . . . . . . . . . .OG 99(
Old Gold / Oct '90 / Pickwick.

## TASTIEST HITS (Knight, Gladys & Th Pips).
**Tracks:** Giving up / Either way I lose / Another love Lovers always forgive / Daybreak / If ever I shou fall in love / Devil in me / Tell her you're mine / Stc and get a hold of myself / Why don't you love me Maybe maybe baby / Who knows / Go away sta away.
■ LP . . . . . . . . . . . . . . . . . . . .MBLL 1(
Bell / Jul '68.

## TEEN ANGUISH VOL.3 (Early years, The (Knight, Gladys & The Pips).
**Tracks:** If ever I should fall in love / Every beat of m heart / Either way I lose / Baby / Why don you love me / Maybe, Maybe baby / Letter full tears / Giving up / Go away, stay away / What w become of me / Queen of tears / Stop and get a hol of myself / Tell her you're mine / There will never t another love / Lovers always forgive / Who knows just can't trust you any more).
CD. . . . . . . . . . . . . . . . . . . . . TOP CD 5(
Topline / '86 / Charly.
■ LP . . . . . . . . . . . . . . . . . . . .CRM 20
Charly / '86.

## THAT SPECIAL TIME OF YEAR (Knigh Gladys & The Pips).
**Tracks:** That special time of year / Jingle bells / Wh are you doing New Year's Eve / This Christmas Santa Claus is coming to town / It's the happiest tir of the year / I believe / When a child is born / Lord prayer / Let there be peace on earth.
■ LP . . . . . . . . . . . . . . . . . . . .CBS 858(
CBS / Dec '82.
■ LP . . . . . . . . . . . . . . . . . . . .46045(
■ MC. . . . . . . . . . . . . . . . . . . . 46045(
CBS Cameo / Dec '87.

## THAT'LL MAKE YOU HAPPY (Knigh Gladys & The Pips).
**Tracks:** That'll make you happy / Love was made f two.

■ DELETE

■ 7" . . . . . . . . . . . . . . . . . . . . . .A 1534
CBS / Sep '81.

## THEIR VERY BEST BACK TO BACK (see under Wonder, Stevie).

## TOUCH (Knight, Gladys & The Pips).
**Tracks:** I will fight / If that'll make you happy / Baby, baby don't waste my time / Friend of mine / Love was made for two / God is / Changed / Reach high / I will survive.
■ LP . . . . . . . . . . . . . . . . . . CBS 84908
CBS / Nov '81.

## TOUCH OF LOVE, A (Knight, Gladys & The Pips).
**Tracks:** Not Advised.
■ LP . . . . . . . . . . . . . . . . . . NE 1090
K-Tel / Oct '80.

## VERY BEST OF GLADYS KNIGHT & THE PIPS (Knight, Gladys & The Pips).
**Tracks:** Not Advised.
CD. . . . . . . . . . . . . . . . . . . . BRCD 21
■ LP. . . . . . . . . . . . . . . . . . .BRLP 21
MC. . . . . . . . . . . . . . . . . . . . BRMC 21
BR Music/BR Music (Holland) / Dec '88 / BMG.

## VERY BEST OF GLADYS KNIGHT, THE.
**Tracks:** Not Advised.
CD. . . . . . . . . . . . . . . . . . . TRTCD 132
MC. . . . . . . . . . . . . . . . . . . TRTMC 132
True Trax / Oct '94 / THE.

## VISIONS (Knight, Gladys & The Pips).
**Tracks:** When you're far away / Just be my lover / Save the overtime (for me) / Heaven sent / Don't make me run away / Ain't no greater love / Seconds / You're number one (in my book) / Oh la de da / Hero.
MC. . . . . . . . . . . . . . . . . . .40 25096
■ LP . . . . . . . . . . . . . . . . CBS 25096
CBS / Jun '83 / Sony.
CD. . . . . . . . . . . . . . . . . .902119-2
Pickwick / Jul '89 / Pickwick.

## WAY WE WERE, THE (Knight, Gladys & The Pips).
**Tracks:** Way we were / Try to remember (medley).
■ 7" . . . . . . . . . . . . . . . . . . .BDS 428
Buddah / May '75.

## WAY WE WERE, THE (Knight, Gladys & The Pips).
**Tracks:** Midnight train to Georgia / So sad the song / Baby don't change your mind / Home is where the heart is / Nobody but you / I feel a song / Feel like makin' love / Hold on / Little bit of love / Try to remember/The way we were / Come back and finish what we started / Part time love / It's a better than good time / Georgia on my mind / Make yours a happy home / Best thing that ever happened to me / We don't make each other laugh anymore / Sorry doesn't always make it right.
CD. . . . . . . . . . . . . . . . . . . MCCD 005
MC. . . . . . . . . . . . . . . . . . .MCTC 005
Music Club / Feb '91 / Gold & Sons / THE / Video Collection / C.M. Distribution.

## WAY WE WERE, THE (EP) (Knight, Gladys & The Pips).
**Tracks:** Way we were / Best thing that ever happened to me / Midnight train to Georgia / Baby don't change your mind.
■ EP . . . . . . . . . . . . . . . . . . FBEP 108
Flashback / Jul '80.

## WAY WE WERE, THE (OLD GOLD) (Knight, Gladys & The Pips).
**Tracks:** Way we were / Midnight train to Georgia.
■ 7" . . . . . . . . . . . . . . . . . .OG 9290
Old Gold / Apr '83.

## YOU BRING OUT THE BEST IN ME.
**Tracks:** You bring out the best in me / You loved away the pain.
■ 7" . . . . . . . . . . . . . . . . . . CBS 7445
CBS / Jun '79.

## YOU'VE LOST THAT LOVIN' FEELIN' (Knight, Gladys & The Pips).
**Tracks:** Every beat of my heart / Groovin' / Every little bit hurts / Nitty gritty / Your old stand-by / Theme from "Valley Of The Dolls" / Look of love / Just walk in my shoes / Don't let her take your love from me / I wish it would rain / Tracks of my tears / It's summer / You've lost that lovin' feelin' / Yesterday.
CD. . . . . . . . . . . . . . . . . . .550074-2
MC. . . . . . . . . . . . . . . . . . .550074-4
Spectrum (1) / May '93 / PolyGram.

---

## Knight, Jason

### OUR LOVE IS GETTING STRONGER.
**Tracks:** Our love is getting stronger / Standing in my shoes.
■ 7" . . . . . . . . . . . . . . . . . . 7N 17399
Pye / Oct '67.

## Knight, Jean

### MR BIG STUFF.
**Tracks:** Mr. Big Stuff / Little bit of something / Don't talk about Jody / Think it over / Take him (you can have my man) / You city slicker / Why I keep living these memories / Call me your fool if you want to / You six-bit change / Do me / Helping man / Carry on / Save the last kiss for me / Pick up the pieces / You think you're hot stuff.
■ LP . . . . . . . . . . . . . . . . . . SXE 003
Stax / Aug '87.
■ LP . . . . . . . . . . . . . . . . . .SX 003
Stax / Dec '88.
CD. . . . . . . . . . . . . . . . . . .CDSX 003
Stax / Apr '90 / Pinnacle.

### MR BIG STUFF.
**Tracks:** Mr. Big Stuff.
■ 7" . . . . . . . . . . . . . . . . . STAX 2007
Stax / Feb '78.
■ 7" . . . . . . . . . . . . . . . . . STAX 1005
Stax / Mar '82.
■ 7" . . . . . . . . . . . . . . . . . STAX 804
■ 12" . . . . . . . . . . . . . . . . . STAT 804
Stax / Jun '87.

### MR. BIG STUFF.
**Tracks:** Mr. Big Stuff / Do the funky chicken.
■ 7" . . . . . . . . . . . . . . . . . .OG 9534
Old Gold / Jan '87.

### MR. BIG STUFF.
**Tracks:** Mr. Big Stuff / Little bit of something / Don't talk about Jody / Think it over / Take him / You city slicker / Why I keep living these memories / Call me your fool / One-way ticket to nowhere / Your six-bit change.
■ LP . . . . . . . . . . . . . . . . . . 2362022
Stax / '72.

### MR. BIG STUFF.
**Tracks:** Mr. Big Stuff / Why I keep living these memories.
■ 7" . . . . . . . . . . . . . . . . . .2025 049
Stax / Jul '71.

## Knight, Jerry

### I'M DOWN FOR THAT.
**Tracks:** I'm down for that / She's got to be a dancer.
■ 12" . . . . . . . . . . . . . . . . . USAF 1227
Funk America / Feb '83.

### LOVE'S ON OUR SIDE.
**Tracks:** She's got to be (a dancer) / I'm down for that / Nothing can hold us back / Brand new fool / Fire / Do it all for you / Do you really mean it / Beautiful.
■ LP . . . . . . . . . . . . . . . . . AMLH 64877
A&M / Mar '83.

### OVERNIGHT SENSATION.
**Tracks:** Overnight sensation / Freak show.
■ 7" . . . . . . . . . . . . . . . . . .AMS 7521
A&M / Apr '80.

### PERFECT FIT.
**Tracks:** Perfect fit / Higher / Turn it out / Interlude / Play sista' / Easier to run away / Too busy / Rainbow.
■ LP . . . . . . . . . . . . . . . . . AMLH 64843
A&M / '81.

### PERFECT FIT.
**Tracks:** Perfect fit / Let me be the reason.
■ 7" . . . . . . . . . . . . . . . . . .AMS 8112
A&M / Mar '81.

## Knight, Robert

### EVERLASTING LOVE.
**Tracks:** Everlasting love.
■ 7" . . . . . . . . . . . . . . . . . .MON 1008
Monument / Jan '68.
■ 7" . . . . . . . . . . . . . . . . . .MNT 2106
Monument / Mar '74.

### LOVE ON A MOUNTAIN TOP.
**Tracks:** Love on a mountain top.
■ 7" . . . . . . . . . . . . . . . . . .MNT 1875
Monument / Nov '73.

---

### LOVE ON A MOUNTAIN TOP (OLD GOLD).
**Tracks:** Love on a mountain top / Everlasting love.
■ 7" . . . . . . . . . . . . . . . . . .OG 9956
Old Gold / Nov '90 / Pickwick.

### ROBERT KNIGHT.
**Tracks:** Everlasting love / Somewhere my love / Sandy / Somebody's bay / My rainbow valley / Letter / Never my love / Rachel the stranger / It's been worth it / Dance of love / Branded.
■ LP . . . . . . . . . . . . . . . . . .SMO 5015
Monument / Oct '68.

## Koko Pop

### BRAND NEW BEAT.
**Tracks:** Brand new beat.
■ 7" . . . . . . . . . . . . . . . . . . ZB 40401
■ 12" . . . . . . . . . . . . . . . . . ZT 40402
Motown / Oct '85.

### I'M IN LOVE WITH YOU.
**Tracks:** I'm in love with you / On the beach.
■ 12" . . . . . . . . . . . . . . . . . TMGT 1363
■ 7" . . . . . . . . . . . . . . . . . .TMG 1363
Motown / Dec '84.

### KOKO POP.
**Tracks:** Baby sister / Serious side / I'm in love with you / Make you feel better / I wish it would rain / Make up your mind / Baby on the run / On the beach.
■ LP . . . . . . . . . . . . . . . . . . ZL 72191
■ MC . . . . . . . . . . . . . . . . . . ZK 72191
Motown / Apr '85.

### SECRETS OF LONELY BOYS.
**Tracks:** Lonely girl lonely boy / Brand new beat / First impression / Sugar pop baby / Fallin' in love / Tell me that you're mine / No more secrets / He's got ulterior motives / Nasty / Foolish heart.
■ LP . . . . . . . . . . . . . . . . . .ZL72396
Motown / Oct '85.

## Kokomo

### ASIA MINOR.
**Tracks:** Asia minor.
■ 7" . . . . . . . . . . . . . . . . . . HLU 9305
London-American / Apr '61.

### KOKOMO.
**Tracks:** Little bit further away / Part time affair / Follow (the stars will bring you home) / Nowhere to go on Tuesday night / Stuck in a groove / Ain't never heard the boogie / All through the night / Keep on dancing / Let me have it all.
■ LP . . . . . . . . . . . . . . . . . . CBS 85604
CBS / May '82.

### LITTLE BIT FURTHER AWAY, A.
**Tracks:** Little bit further away.
■ 7" . . . . . . . . . . . . . . . . . .A 2064
CBS / May '82.

## Konders, Bobby

### BOBBY KONDERS AND MASSIVE SOUNDS (Konders, Bobby & Massive Sounds).
**Tracks:** Heads / Mack Daddy / Bad boy / Poem '92 / Unity / You don't know / Rising / Blue note groove / Future / I love the way / Under the surveillance / And the road / Mack Daddy (dance hall) / Risen (lovers mix).
■ LP . . . . . . . . . . . . . . . . . .510927-1
■ CD . . . . . . . . . . . . . . . . . .510927-2
■ MC . . . . . . . . . . . . . . . . . .510927-4
Mercury / Apr '92.

### COOL CALM AND COLLECTIVE (Konders, Bobby Project).
**Tracks:** Not Advised.
LP . . . . . . . . . . . . . . . . . .LUVLP 9
Desire / Oct '90 / Pinnacle.

### MACK DADDY (Konders, Bobby & Massive Sounds).
**Tracks:** Mack Daddy (album version) / Mack Daddy (dance hall version) / Heads / Blue Note groove.
■ 12" . . . . . . . . . . . . . . . . .MERX 364
Mercury / Feb '92.

### POEM, THE.
**Tracks:** Poem / Massai women.
■ 12" . . . . . . . . . . . . . . . . . WANTX 29
Desire / May '90.

■ DELETED

# Kool & The Gang

Formed in 1964 by 14-year old Robert 'Kool' Bell, New Jersey's Jazziacs became Kool & the Gang in 1969. Signed to newly-formed De-Lite label, with whom they remained until 1988, Gang debuted with eponymous instrumental. Further, modestly successful JB/Sly-influenced singles paved way for '74's *Wild & Peaceful*. Gold-selling album - seventh in five years - spawned classics *Funky Stuff*, *Jungle Boogie* and *Hollywood Swinging*; all U.S. smashes, later heavily sampled (another song, *Summer Madness* was successfully remodelled by Jazzy Jeff & Fresh Prince). Ironically, group floundered during disco, despite featuring on globe-conquering *Saturday Night Fever* soundtrack. Revival occurred in late '79, with *Ladies' Night* single and album, featuring new vocalist James Taylor and producer Eumir Deodato. Previously wild funk evolved into straightforward dance, epitomised by double-platinum U.S. no. 1 *Celebration*, and infectious U.K. no. 3 *Get Down On It*, while mellow side yielded transatlantic Top 5 ballad *Joanna*. U.K. track record was particularly impressive: 19 consecutive hits between 1979 and '85. JT quit in '88 for disastrous solo career; replaced by vocal trio boasting ex-Dazz Band singer Skip Martin. Although chart success has dwindled away, band remain popular live attraction in Europe. Bell can claim credit for two younger acts: he guided Color Me Badd to stardom and son Hakim leads swing funk POV.

## (JUMP ON THE) RHYTHM & RIDE.
**Tracks:** (Jump on the) Rhythm & ride.
| | |
|---|---|
| ■ 12" | .12JRS 101 |
| ■ 7" | JRS 101 |
| ■ CD Single | CDJRS 101 |
Ammi / Oct '92.

## ANTHOLOGY.
**Tracks:** Kool and the gang / Let the music take your mind / Funky man / Who's gonna take the weight (part 1) / Love the life you live (part 1) / Country junkie / Funky stuff / Jungle boogie / Hollywood swinging / Rhyme tyme people / Spirit of the boogie / Open sesame (part 1) / Jones vs Jones / Take my heart (you can have it if you want it) / Big fun / Tonight / Fresh / Victory / Stone love / Celebration (1988 remix).
| | |
|---|---|
| CD | VSOPCD 168 |
| MC | VSOPMC 168 |
Connoisseur Collection / Nov '91 / Pinnacle.

## AS ONE.
**Tracks:** Street kids / Big fun / As one / Hi de hi, hi de ho / Let's go dancing / Pretty baby / Think it over.
| | |
|---|---|
| ■ LP | DSR 3 |
De-Lite / Oct '82.
| ■ CD | 822 535-2 |
De-Lite / '86.

## AT THEIR BEST.
**Tracks:** Not Advised.
| | |
|---|---|
| CD | 810 877-2 |
Polydor / '88 / PolyGram.

## BALLAD COLLECTION.
**Tracks:** Not Advised.
| | |
|---|---|
| ■ CD | 8425192 |
Mercury / Aug '90.

## BEST OF KOOL & THE GANG.
**Tracks:** Penguin / Let the music take your mind / Kool it / Pneumonia / Chocolate buttermilk / Who's gonna take the weight / Kool & the Gang / Kool's back again / Raw hamburger / Give it up / Funky man.
| | |
|---|---|
| ■ LP | 2347002 |
Mojo / Dec '71.

## BEST OF, 1969-1976.
**Tracks:** Not Advised.
| | |
|---|---|
| CD | 514 822-2 |
| MC | 514 822-4 |
Phonogram / Jun '93 / PolyGram.

## BIG FUN.
**Tracks:** Big fun / Get down on it.
| | |
|---|---|
| ■ 12" | DEX 7 |
| ■ 7" | DE 7 |
De-Lite / Aug '82.

## CELEBRATE.
**Tracks:** Celebration / Jones Vs Jones / Take it to the top / Morning star / Love festival / Just friends / Night people / Love affair.
| | |
|---|---|
| ■ LP | .6359 029 |
De-Lite / Dec '80.

| | |
|---|---|
| ■ LP | PRICE 53 |
| ■ MC | PRICM 53 |
De-Lite / Dec '83.
| ■ CD | 822 538 2 |
De-Lite / '88.

## CELEBRATION.
**Tracks:** Celebration / Morning star.
| | |
|---|---|
| ■ 12" | .KOOL 10 12 |
| ■ 7" | KOOL 10 |
Kool Kat / Oct '80.

## CELEBRATION (OLD GOLD).
**Tracks:** Celebration / Ladies night.
| | |
|---|---|
| ■ 7" | .OG 9766 |
Old Gold / Feb '88.
| 12" | .OG 4167 |
Old Gold / May '90 / Pickwick.

## CELEBRATION (REMIX).
**Tracks:** Celebration (SAW remix) (Remixed by Stock, Aitken & Waterman.) / Rags to riches / Celebration (Original version.)
| | |
|---|---|
| ■ CD Single | .JABCD 78 |
| ■ 12" | .JABX 78 |
| ■ 7" | JAB 78 |
Club / Dec '88.

## CHERISH.
**Tracks:** Cherish / Celebration.
| | |
|---|---|
| ■ 12" | DEX 20 |
| ■ 7" | DE 20 |
De-Lite / Apr '85.

## CHERISH (BOX SET).
**Tracks:** Cherish / Fresh / Joanna.
| | |
|---|---|
| ■ 7" Set | GANG 20 |
De-Lite / Jul '85.

## DANCE COLLECTION.
**Tracks:** Not Advised.
| | |
|---|---|
| CD | 8425202 |
Mercury / Aug '90 / PolyGram.

## DECADE.
**Tracks:** Not Advised.
| | |
|---|---|
| VHS | CFV 07672 |
Channel 5 / '88 / Channel 5 Video / P.R.O. Video / Gold & Sons.
| CD Video | 080 106 1 |
Polygram Music Video / Oct '88 / PolyGram.

## EMERGENCY.
**Tracks:** Emergency / Fresh / Misled / Cherish / Surrender (12" only.) / Bad woman / You are the one.
| | |
|---|---|
| MC | .DCR 6 |
| ■ LP | .DSR 6 |
| ■ CD | 822 943 2 |
De-Lite / Nov '84 / PolyGram.

## EMERGENCY.
**Tracks:** Emergency / Ooh la la / Fresh / Misled / Cherish.
| | |
|---|---|
| ■ 12" | DEX 21 |
| ■ 7" | DE 21 |
De-Lite / Nov '85.

## FRESH.
**Tracks:** Fresh.
| | |
|---|---|
| ■ 12" | DEX 18 |
| ■ 7" | DE 18 |
De-Lite / Nov '84.

## GET DOWN ON IT.
**Tracks:** Get down on it / Summer madness.
| | |
|---|---|
| ■ 7" | .DE 5 |
De-Lite / Dec '81.
| ■ 12" | DEX 5 |
De-Lite / Jan '82.

## GET DOWN ON IT.
**Tracks:** Get down on it / Celebration / Megamix (Only on 12" and CD single).
| | |
|---|---|
| ■ 12" | .MERX 346 |
| ■ 7" | MER 346 |
| ■ CD Single | .MERCD 346 |
Mercury / Jun '91.

## GET DOWN ON IT.
**Tracks:** Get down on it / Steppin' out.
| | |
|---|---|
| 7" | .OG 6517 |
Old Gold / Apr '92 / Pickwick.

## GREAT AND REMIXED '91.
**Tracks:** Not Advised.
| | |
|---|---|
| CD | 848 604-2 |
| MC | 848 604-4 |
| ■ LP | 848 604-1 |
Mercury / Jul '91 / PolyGram.

## GREATEST HITS LIVE.
**Tracks:** Victory / Ladies night / Fresh / Take my heart (You can have it if you want it) / Hollywood swinging / Too hot / Joanna / Cherish / Ooh la la la (Let's go dancin') / Get down on it / Celebration / Tonight / Emergency.
| | |
|---|---|
| CD | FG 2-80 |
Freestyle (2) / Mar '94 / BMG.
| CD | 16225 C |
Success (3) / Sep '94 / Pickwick.

## HANGIN' OUT.
**Tracks:** Hangin' out.
| | |
|---|---|
| ■ 12" | .KOOL 91 |
| ■ 7" | .KOOL |
De-Lite / Jul '80.

## HI DE HI, HI DE HO.
**Tracks:** Hi de hi, hi de ho / No show.
| | |
|---|---|
| ■ 12" | DEX 1 |
| ■ 7" | .DE 1 |
De-Lite / Dec '82.

## HOLLYWOOD SWINGING.
**Tracks:** Hollywood swinging / Dujii.
| | |
|---|---|
| ■ 7" | .200153 |
Polydor / Jul '74.

## IN CONCERT.
**Tracks:** Not Advised.
| | |
|---|---|
| CD | HP 9347 |
Start / Nov '94 / THE / Koch International.

## IN THE HEART.
**Tracks:** In the heart / Joanna / Tonight / Rollin' Place for us / Straight ahead / Home is where the heart is / You can do it / September love.
| | |
|---|---|
| ■ CD | DECD 850 |
De-Lite.
| ■ LP | .DSR |
| ■ MC | .DCR |
De-Lite / Dec '83.
| ■ CD | 814 351 |
| ■ LP | 814 351 |
| ■ MC | 814 351 |
De-Lite / '88.

## JOANNA.
**Tracks:** Joanna / Tonight.
| | |
|---|---|
| ■ 12" | DEX 1 |
| ■ 7" | .DE 1 |
De-Lite / Feb '84.

## JOANNA (OLD GOLD).
**Tracks:** Joanna / Cherish.
| | |
|---|---|
| ■ 7" | .OG 977 |
Old Gold / Feb '88.

## JONES VS JONES.
**Tracks:** Jones vs Jones / Summer madness.
| | |
|---|---|
| ■ 7" | KOOL 1 |
De-Lite / Feb '81.

## KOOL & THE GANG.
**Tracks:** Not Advised.
| | |
|---|---|
| VHS | EMB 45600 |
Not Advised / '88.

## KOOL AND THE GANG.
**Tracks:** Not Advised.
| | |
|---|---|
| CD | .014356 |
| ■ LP | .014402 |
| MC | .014404 |
Arcade / May '90 / Sony / Grapevine Distribution.

## KOOL KUTS.
**Tracks:** Open sesame / Spirit of the boogie / Kool and the gang / Hollywood swinging / Funky stuff More funky stuff / Jungle boogie / Caribbean festival / Love and understanding / Summer madness.
| | |
|---|---|
| ■ LP | .MIP 1931 |
| MC | MIP4 1931 |
De-Lite / Nov '82 / PolyGram.

## KOOL LOVE.
**Tracks:** Not Advised.
| | |
|---|---|
| ■ LP | STAR 243 |
| ■ CD | TCD 243 |
| ■ MC | STAC 243 |
Telstar/Ronco / Oct '90.

## LADIES NIGHT.
**Tracks:** Got you into my life / Hangin' out / If you feel like dancin' / Ladies' night / Tonight's the night / Too hot.
| | |
|---|---|
| ■ LP | 637276 |
Mercury / Nov '79.
| ■ LP | PRICE 53 |
| ■ MC | .PRIMC 5 |
De-Lite / Dec '83.
| ■ CD | 822 537- |
De-Lite / '86.

## LADIES NIGHT.
**Tracks:** Ladies night.
| | |
|---|---|
| ■ 7" | .KOOL |
De-Lite / Oct '79.

■ DELETED

**LADIES NIGHT (OLD GOLD).**
Tracks: Ladies night / Get down on it (Only on 12"
single) / Fresh (Only on CD single) / Big fun (Only on
CD single).
■ 12" . . . . . . . . . . . . . . . . . . . . . . . . OG 4160
Old Gold / Mar '90 / Pickwick.
■ CD Single . . . . . . . . . . . . . . . . . . . OG 6519
Old Gold / Jun '92 / Pickwick.

**LIVE AT P.J.'S.**
Tracks: Penguin / Rick sonata / Sombreo Sam /
Ronnie's grove / Ike's mood / You've lost that loving
feeling / Lucky for me / Dujii.
■ LP . . . . . . . . . . . . . . . . . . . . . . . . 2347001
Mojo / Jun '72.

**LIVE AT THE SEX MACHINE.**
Tracks: What would the world be like without music /
Let the music take your mind / Walk on by / Choco-
ate buttermilk / Try to make a fool of me / Who's
gonna take the weight / Pneumonia / Wichita lineman / I want to take you higher / Funky man / Touch
of you.
■ LP . . . . . . . . . . . . . . . . . . . . . . . . 2347003
Mojo / '72.

**LIVE ON STAGE.**
Tracks: Not Advised.
CD . . . . . . . . . . . . . . . . . . . . . . . . MSCD 7
Music De-Luxe / Nov '94 / MMG Distribution / THE.

**MISLED.**
Tracks: Misled / Rollin'.
■ 12" . . . . . . . . . . . . . . . . . . . . . . DERX 19
■ 7" . . . . . . . . . . . . . . . . . . . . . . . DER 19
De-Lite / Feb '85.

**NIGHT PEOPLE.**
Tracks: Not Advised.
CD . . . . . . . . . . . . . . . . . . . . . . . 550 1982
MC. . . . . . . . . . . . . . . . . . . . . . . 550 1984
Spectrum (1) / Aug '94 / PolyGram.

**NYC COOL.**
Tracks: Not Advised.
CD . . . . . . . . . . . . . . . . . . . . . . . . MDCD 4
MMG / Jan '94 / THE.

**OOH LA LA LA (LET'S GO DANCING).**
Tracks: Ooh la la la (let's go dancing) / Stand up and
sing.
■ 12" . . . . . . . . . . . . . . . . . . . . . . . DEX 9
■ 7" . . . . . . . . . . . . . . . . . . . . . . . . DE 9
De-Lite / Oct '82.

**RAINDROPS.**
Tracks: Raindrops / Amore amore / Raindrops (extended version) (Only on 12" and CD single.) / Raindrops (dub) (Only on 12" single.).
■ 12" . . . . . . . . . . . . . . . . . . . . . MERX 293
■ 7" . . . . . . . . . . . . . . . . . . . . . . MER 293
■ CD Single . . . . . . . . . . . . . . . . . MERCD 293
■ MC Single . . . . . . . . . . . . . . . . MERMC 293
Mercury / Jul '89.

**RHYME TYME PEOPLE.**
Tracks: Rhyme tyme people / Father, father.
■ 7" . . . . . . . . . . . . . . . . . . . . . . 2001958
Polydor / Jan '75.

**SINGLES COLLECTION, THE.**
Tracks: Celebration / Ladies night / Too hot / Get
down on it / Joanna / Jones vs. Jones / Straight
ahead / Fresh / Ooh la la la (let's go dancing) / Big
fun / Cherish / In the heat / Hi de hi, hi de ho / Take it
to the top / Victory / Steppin' out.
CD . . . . . . . . . . . . . . . . . . . . . . 836 636-2
■ LP . . . . . . . . . . . . . . . . . . . . . . . KGTV 1
MC. . . . . . . . . . . . . . . . . . . . . . . KGTVC 1
De-Lite / Oct '88 / PolyGram.

**SOMETHING SPECIAL.**
Tracks: Steppin' out / Good time tonight / Take my
heart / Be my lady / Get down on it / Pass it on /
Stand up and sing / No show.
■ LP . . . . . . . . . . . . . . . . . . . . . . . DSR 001
De-Lite / Nov '81.
■ LP . . . . . . . . . . . . . . . . . . . . . . . PRICE 81
■ MC. . . . . . . . . . . . . . . . . . . . . . . PRIMC 81
De-Lite / Mar '85.
. . . . . . . . . . . . . . . . . . . . . . . . . 822 534-2
De-Lite / '86 / PolyGram.

**STEPPIN OUT.**
Tracks: Steppin' out / Funky stuff / Hollywood swinging / Peace maker / Victory / Rags to riches / Hangin'
out / Big fun / Cherish / Too hot / Just friends / Good
time tonight / Emergency / Stone love / Strong / Let's
go dancin (Ooh la la, la).
CD . . . . . . . . . . . . . . . . . . . . . . PWKS 4109 P

MC. . . . . . . . . . . . . . . . . . . . PWKMC 4109P
Pickwick / Sep '92 / Pickwick.

**STEPPIN' OUT.**
Tracks: Steppin' out.
■ 7" . . . . . . . . . . . . . . . . . . . . . . . DE 4
De-Lite / Oct '81.

**STONE LOVE.**
Tracks: Stone love / Dance champion / Get down on
it (ext mix) (On double pack single only) / Ladies
night (remix) (extra track on double pack single
only).
■ 12" . . . . . . . . . . . . . . . . . . . . . JABX 47
■ 7" . . . . . . . . . . . . . . . . . . . . . . . JAB 47
■ 7" Set . . . . . . . . . . . . . . . . . . . JABXD 47
Club / Feb '87.

**STRAIGHT AHEAD.**
Tracks: Straight ahead / Place for us.
■ 12" . . . . . . . . . . . . . . . . . . . . . DEX 15
■ 7" . . . . . . . . . . . . . . . . . . . . . . . DE 15
De-Lite / Dec '83.

**SWEAT.**
Tracks: I sweat / This is what a love can do / Never
give up / You got my heart on fire / Someday /
Raindrops / In your company / I'll follow you any-
where / All she wants to do is dance / Now can I get
close to you / You are the meaning of friend.
■ CD . . . . . . . . . . . . . . . . . . . . . . 838233 2
■ LP . . . . . . . . . . . . . . . . . . . . . . 838233 1
■ MC. . . . . . . . . . . . . . . . . . . . . . 838233 4
Mercury / Sep '89.

**TAKE IT TO THE TOP.**
Tracks: Take it to the top / Celebremos.
■ 12" . . . . . . . . . . . . . . . . . . . . . . DEX 2
■ 7" . . . . . . . . . . . . . . . . . . . . . . . DE 2
De-Lite / May '81.

**TAKE MY HEART (YOU CAN HAVE IT IF
YOU WANT IT).**
Tracks: Take my heart (you can have it if you want it)
/ Caribbean festival / Winter sadness.
■ 12" . . . . . . . . . . . . . . . . . . . . . . DEX 6
■ 7" . . . . . . . . . . . . . . . . . . . . . . . DE 6
De-Lite / Mar '82.

**THROWDOWN MIX.**
Tracks: Get down on it / Ladies night / Fresh / Big
fun / Celebration / Victory (7" version) / Bad woman.
■ 12" . . . . . . . . . . . . . . . . . . . . JABXR 44
Club / Dec '86.

**TOO HOT.**
Tracks: Too hot / Tonight's the night.
■ 7" . . . . . . . . . . . . . . . . . . . . . . KOOL 8
■ 12" . . . . . . . . . . . . . . . . . . . . . KOOL 812
De-Lite / Jan '80.

**TWICE AS KOOL.**
Tracks: Ladies night / Big fun / Celebration / Take it
to the top / Get down on it / Hi de hi hi de ho / Funky
stuff / Hollywood swinging / Summer madness
(theme from Rocky) / Open sesame / Steppin' out /
Night people / Street kids / Ooh la la la, let's go
dancing / Jones Vs Jones / Too hot / Take my heart /
Hangin' out.
■ Double LP . . . . . . . . . . . . . . . . . PROLP 2
MC Set . . . . . . . . . . . . . . . . . . . . PROMC 2
De-Lite / May '83 / PolyGram.

**UNITE.**
Tracks: (Jump up on the) Rhythm and ride / I think I
love you / Love comes down / Sexy Miss / Better late
than never / Heart / My search is over / Summer /
Brown / Give right now / Weight / Show us the way /
Unite / God will find you.
■ CD . . . . . . . . . . . . . . . . . . . . . JRSCD 1002
BMG / Nov '92.
CD . . . . . . . . . . . . . . . . . . . . . . CDUNITE 1
Charly / Oct '93 / Charly.

**VERY BEST OF KOOL & THE GANG.**
Tracks: Not Advised.
CD . . . . . . . . . . . . . . . . . . . . . . 01440062
Arcade / Sep '90 / Sony / Grapevine Distribution.

**VICTORY.**
Tracks: Victory / I.B.M.C. / Stone love / Forever /
Holiday / Peace maker / Broadway / Special way /
God's country.
■ CD . . . . . . . . . . . . . . . . . . . . . 830 398 2
■ LP . . . . . . . . . . . . . . . . . . . . . . . JABH 23
■ MC. . . . . . . . . . . . . . . . . . . . . . JABHC 23
Club / Dec '86.

**VICTORY.**
Tracks: Victory.
■ 12" . . . . . . . . . . . . . . . . . . . . . . JABX 44

■ 7" . . . . . . . . . . . . . . . . . . . . . . . JAB 44
■ CD Single . . . . . . . . . . . . . . . . . JABCD 44
■ MC Single . . . . . . . . . . . . . . . . . JABM 44
Club / Dec '86.

**WHEN YOU SAY LOVE SOMEBODY
FROM THE HEART.**
Tracks: When you say you love somebody from the
heart.
■ 12" . . . . . . . . . . . . . . . . . . . . . DEX 17
■ 7" . . . . . . . . . . . . . . . . . . . . . . . DE 17
De-Lite / Apr '84.

## Kreamcicle

**NO NEWS IS NEWS.**
Tracks: No news is news.
■ 12" . . . . . . . . . . . . . . . . . . . . . . BRT 25
■ 7" . . . . . . . . . . . . . . . . . . . . . . . BR 25
Blue Bird (2) / Jul '86.

## Kreuz

**NEW GENERATION.**
Tracks: Not Advised.
CD . . . . . . . . . . . . . . . . . . . . . . 530203-2
■ LP . . . . . . . . . . . . . . . . . . . . . . 530203-1
■ MC. . . . . . . . . . . . . . . . . . . . . . 530203-4
Motown / Apr '93 / PolyGram.

**U.K. SWING.**
Tracks: U.K. swing / Sunshine.
■ 12" . . . . . . . . . . . . . . . . . . . . . TMUX 2
■ 7" . . . . . . . . . . . . . . . . . . . . . . TMU 2
■ CD Single . . . . . . . . . . . . . . . . TMUCD 2
Polydor / Jul '93.

## Krush Perspective

**LET'S GET TOGETHER NOW (SO
GROOVY).**
Tracks: Let's get together now (so groovy) / Let's get
together now (so groovy)(mixes).
■ 12" . . . . . . . . . . . . . . . . . . . . PERT 7416
■ 7" . . . . . . . . . . . . . . . . . . . . . PERS 7416
■ CD Single. . . . . . . . . . . . . . . . . PERD 7416
■ MC Single. . . . . . . . . . . . . . . . PERCS 7416
A&M / Jan '93.

## Krystol

**NOBODY'S GONNA GET THIS LOVIN'
BUT YOU.**
Tracks: Nobody's gonna get this lovin' but you /
Nobody's gonna get this lovin' but you version.
■ 7" . . . . . . . . . . . . . . . . . . . . . . A 4405
Epic / Jun '84.

**PASSION FROM A WOMAN.**
Tracks: Passion from a woman / Love attack / Pre-
cious precious / All my love / I might fall in love with
you / He's so jive / Baby make your mind up / Scared
single.
■ LP . . . . . . . . . . . . . . . . . . . . . EPC 26944
■ MC. . . . . . . . . . . . . . . . . . . . . . 40 26944
Epic / Sep '87.

**PASSION FROM A WOMAN.**
Tracks: Passion from a woman.
■ 7" . . . . . . . . . . . . . . . . . . . . . . A 7203
Epic / Aug '87.

**PRECIOUS PRECIOUS.**
Tracks: Precious precious / He's so jive.
■ 12" . . . . . . . . . . . . . . . . . . . . . 6502556
■ 7" . . . . . . . . . . . . . . . . . . . . . . 6502557
Epic / Nov '86.

## Kuban, Bob

**CHEATER, THE (Kuban, Bob & The
In-Men).**
Tracks: Cheater / Try me baby.
■ 7" . . . . . . . . . . . . . . . . . . . . . . SS 488
Stateside / '65.

**TEASER (Kuban, Bob & The In-Men).**
Tracks: Teaser / All I want.
■ 7" . . . . . . . . . . . . . . . . . . . . . . SS 514
Stateside / May '66.

# L

## L.A. Boppers

### BE BOP DANCING.
**Tracks:** Be bop dancing / Saturday.
- **12".** . . . . . . . . . . . . . . . . . MERX 27
- **7".** . . . . . . . . . . . . . . . . . . MER 27

Mercury / Aug '80.

### GIVE ME SOME.
**Tracks:** Give me some.
- **12".** . . . . . . . . . . . . . . . . . . .LA 704

Dance Classics / Feb '89.

### IS THIS THE BEST.
**Tracks:** Is this the best / Watching life.
- **12".** . . . . . . . . . . . . . . . . . MERX 12
- **7".** . . . . . . . . . . . . . . . . . . MER 12

Mercury / Jun '80.

### LA LA MEANS I LOVE YOU.
**Tracks:** La la means i love you / Is this the best / Be bop dancing.
- **12".** . . . . . . . . . . . . . . . . . MERX 71
- **7".** . . . . . . . . . . . . . . . . . . MER 71

Mercury / May '81.

## L.A. Mix

### CHECK THIS OUT.
**Tracks:** Check this out / Check this out (sweaty Cuban mix).
- **12".** . . . . . . . . . . . . . . . . . USAT 629
- **7".** . . . . . . . . . . . . . . . . . .USA 629

Breakout / May '88.

### COMING BACK FOR MORE.
**Tracks:** Not Advised.
- **CD.** . . . . . . . . . . . . . . . . . 3970892
- **LP.** . . . . . . . . . . . . . . . . . 3970891
- **MC.** . . . . . . . . . . . . . . . . . 3970894

A&M / Nov '90.

### COMING BACK FOR MORE.
**Tracks:** Coming back for more.
- **12".** . . . . . . . . . . . . . . . . . AMY 579
- **12" Remix.** . . . . . . . . . . . . . AMX 579
- **7".** . . . . . . . . . . . . . . . . . . AM 579
- **CD Single.** . . . . . . . . . . . . AMCD 579

A&M / Aug '90.

### DON'T STOP (JAMMIN') L.A. MIX.
**Tracks:** Don't stop (Jammin') L.A. Mix / Don't stop (Philly jazz).
- **7".** . . . . . . . . . . . . . . . . . .USA 615

Breakout / Sep '87.

### GET LOOSE (L.A. Mix featuring Jazzi P).
**Tracks:** Get loose / Get loose (atmospheric mix).
- **12".** . . . . . . . . . . . . . . . . . USAT 659
- **12".** . . . . . . . . . . . . . . . . . USAF 659
- **7".** . . . . . . . . . . . . . . . . . .USA 659
- **CD Single.** . . . . . . . . . . . . USACD 659

A&M / Jun '89.

### LOVE TOGETHER.
**Tracks:** Love together / Love together (American lovers edit).
- **12".** . . . . . . . . . . . . . . . . . USAF 662
- **12".** . . . . . . . . . . . . . . . . . USAT 662
- **7".** . . . . . . . . . . . . . . . . . .USA 662
- **CD Single.** . . . . . . . . . . . . USACD 662

A&M / Aug '89.

### MYSTERIES OF LOVE.
**Tracks:** Mysteries of love / Mysteries of love (instrumental).
- **12" Remix.** . . . . . . . . . . . . . AMX 707
- **7".** . . . . . . . . . . . . . . . . . . AM 707
- **12".** . . . . . . . . . . . . . . . . . AMY 707
- **CD Single.** . . . . . . . . . . . . AMCD 707
- **MC Single.** . . . . . . . . . . . . AMMC 707

A&M / Jan '91.

### ON THE SIDE.
**Tracks:** Get loose / You are the one / Breathe deep / Don't turn away / Love together / Just waiting / Mellow mellow / Don't stop / Check this out.
- **CD.** . . . . . . . . . . . . . . . . . CDA 9009
- **LP.** . . . . . . . . . . . . . . . . . AMA 9009
- **MC.** . . . . . . . . . . . . . . . . . AMC 9009

A&M / Sep '89 / PolyGram.

## WE SHOULDN'T HOLD HANDS IN THE DARK.
**Tracks:** We shouldn't hold hands in the dark / Free my mind.
- **12".** . . . . . . . . . . . . . . . . . AMY 755
- **7".** . . . . . . . . . . . . . . . . . . AM 755
- **CD Single.** . . . . . . . . . . . . AMCD 755

A&M / Mar '91.

## L.A.X.

### ALL MY LOVE.
**Tracks:** All my love / Possessed / Thanks but no thanks / Fight back / Like a simple song of love / Love me tonight.
- **LP.** . . . . . . . . . . . . . . . . . EPC 84859

Epic / '81.

### ALL MY LOVE.
**Tracks:** All my love / Thanks but no thanks.
- **7".** . . . . . . . . . . . . . . . . . EPC 9457

Epic / Jan '81.

### DANCIN' AT THE DISCO.
**Tracks:** Dancin' at the disco / Dancin' at the disco (version).
- **12".** . . . . . . . . . . . . . . . . . 12P 5002
- **7".** . . . . . . . . . . . . . . . . . . 7P 5002

PRT / Jun '79.

### POSSESSED.
**Tracks:** Possessed / Fight back.
- **12".** . . . . . . . . . . . . . . . . . EPC 13 1103
- **7".** . . . . . . . . . . . . . . . . . .EPC A 1103

Epic / May '81.

## L.T.D.

### DANCE 'N' SING 'N'.
**Tracks:** Dance 'n' sing 'n' / Give it all.
- **7".** . . . . . . . . . . . . . . . . . . AMS 7458

A&M / Nov '79.

### DEVOTION.
**Tracks:** One by one / Share my love / Stand up to L.T.D. / Say that you'll be mine / Dance 'n' sing 'n' / Sometimes / Promise you'll stay / Stranger / Feel it.
- **LP.** . . . . . . . . . . . . . . . . . AMLH 64771

A&M / '79.

### HOLDING ON (WHEN LOVE IS GONE).
**Tracks:** Holding on (when love is gone) / Back in love again.
- **12".** . . . . . . . . . . . . . . . . . AMSP 7378
- **7".** . . . . . . . . . . . . . . . . . . AMS 7378

A&M / Sep '78.

### LOVE TO THE WORLD.
**Tracks:** Not Advised.
- **LP.** . . . . . . . . . . . . . . . . . AMLH 64589

A&M / Sep '76.

### SHINE ON.
**Tracks:** You gave me love / Where did we go wrong / Getaway / Will love grow / Love is what you need / Shine on / Lovers everywhere / Lady love / Don'tcha know.
- **LP.** . . . . . . . . . . . . . . . . . AMLH 64819

A&M / Nov '80.

### SHINE ON.
**Tracks:** Shine on / Stand up L.T.D.
- **12".** . . . . . . . . . . . . . . . . . AMSP 7555
- **7".** . . . . . . . . . . . . . . . . . . AMS 7555

A&M / Aug '80.

### SOMETHING TO LOVE.
**Tracks:** Not Advised.
- **LP.** . . . . . . . . . . . . . . . . . AMLH 64646

A&M / Nov '77.

### STOP ON BY.
**Tracks:** Stop on by / For you.
- **12".** . . . . . . . . . . . . . . . . . VIBE 5 T
- **7".** . . . . . . . . . . . . . . . . . .VIBE 5

Buzz Int. / Jul '84.

### TOGETHERNESS.
**Tracks:** Not Advised.
- **LP.** . . . . . . . . . . . . . . . . . AMLH 64705

A&M / Jun '78.

## La La

### JOLIE FILLE D'ALGIER.
**Tracks:** Jolie fille d'algier / Adieu Paris.
- **7".** . . . . . . . . . . . . . . . . . . CB 406

Charisma / Jan '83.

### LA LA.
**Tracks:** (If you) love me just a little / I got a thing for you / I don't wanna go / We'll keep striving / Any man will do / My love is on the money / Deal with it / All work, no play / So into love.
- **LP.** . . . . . . . . . . . . . . . . . .208146
- **MC.** . . . . . . . . . . . . . . . . . .408146

Arista / '88.

### LA LA MEANS I LOVE YOU.
**Tracks:** Not Advised.
- **CD.** . . . . . . . . . . . . . . . . . ZD 72753
- **LP.** . . . . . . . . . . . . . . . . . ZL 72753
- **MC.** . . . . . . . . . . . . . . . . . ZK 72753

Motown / Sep '91.

### WE'LL KEEP ON STRIVING.
**Tracks:** We'll keep striving / So in love / Love is on the money.
- **12".** . . . . . . . . . . . . . . . . . RIST 46
- **7".** . . . . . . . . . . . . . . . . . . RIS 46

Arista / Oct '87.

## Labelle

### GET YOU SOMEBODY.
**Tracks:** Get you somebody / Who's watching the watcher.
- **7".** . . . . . . . . . . . . . . . . . EPC 4655

Epic / Oct '76.

### LADY MARMALADE.
**Tracks:** Lady Marmalade / Space children.
- **7".** . . . . . . . . . . . . . . . . . EPC 2852
- **7".** . . . . . . . . . . . . . . . . . .A 4590

Epic / Mar '75.
CBS / Jul '84.

### NIGHTBIRDS.
**Tracks:** Lady Marmalade / Somebody somewhere / Are you lonely / It took a long time / Don't bring me down / What can I do for you / Nightbird / Space children / All girl band / You turn me on.
- **CD.** . . . . . . . . . . . . . . . . . .983382

Pickwick / Feb '94 / Pickwick.

## Labelle, Patti

Born Patricia Holt in Philadelphia in 1944, Pattie LaBelle formed her group Patti and The Bluebelles, with Cindy Birdsong, Nona Hendryx and Sarah Dash, in '61. That year they also enjoyed their first million-seller, *Sold My Heart To The Junkman* becoming an American number one hit. When Cindy left to join the Supremes, the group became simply Labelle, and signed to Warners where they recorded one album before moving to RCA for *Moon Shadow* and *Pressure Cookin'*. Their big break arrived in '75, however, when *Nightbirds*, led by the single *Lady Marmalade*, became a pop crossover hit. Two albums later *Phoeni* ('75) and *Chameleon* ('76) LaBelle went solo, but it took several years before she found a formula suited to her impressive, nasal wail. Albums for CBS, *Patti LaBelle* and *Tasty* passed the public by, but a trio she cut at Philadelphia International, *The Spirit's In It, I'm In Love Again* and *Patti* spawned several hit singles, most notably the R&B number one, *If only you knew*. A spell on Broadway, in the musical *Your Arm's Too Short To Box With God* with Al Green proved successful and in '84 she joined Bobby Womack on three tracks of his *Poet 2*; one, *Love Has Finally Come At Last*, being a hit single. Since '85 she's been signed to MCA Records, scoring with another duet *On My Own* (with Michael McDonald) and releasing *Winner In You, By Yourself, Gems* and a live album.

■ DELETE

## DREAMER (La Belle, Patti & The Blue Belles).
Tracks: Always something there to remind me / I'm still waiting / Take me for a little while / I don't want to go on without you / Tender words / Danny boy / Dreamer / That's how heartaches are made / One phone call / Down the aisle / Where are you.
■ LP . . . . . . . . . . . . . . . . . . . . . . . . . 8147
Atlantic / Mar '68.

# Lace

## MY LOVE IS DEEP.
Tracks: My love is deep (mixes).
■ 12" . . . . . . . . . . . . . . . . . . . WINGX 1
■ 7" . . . . . . . . . . . . . . . . . . . . . WING 1
Wing (USA) / Nov '87.

# Lakeside

## BEST OF LAKESIDE.
Tracks: Shot of love / One minute after midnight / Given in to love / It's all the way live / Rough rider / If you like our music (Get on up & move) / Fantastic voyage / Your love is on the one / We want you (On the floor) / Say yes / Ever ready man / I want to hold your hand / Raid / Outrageous / Bulls eye.
CD . . . . . . . . . . . . . . . . . . . . .NEMCD 681
Sequel / Aug '94 / Total / BMG.

## FANTASTIC JOURNEY.
Tracks: Fantastic journey / I can't get you out of my head.
■ 12". . . . . . . . . . . . . . . . . . . . . SOT 15
■ 7" . . . . . . . . . . . . . . . . . . . . . SO 15
Solar / Feb '81.

## FANTASTIC VOYAGE.
Tracks: Fantastic voyage / Your love is on the one / I need you / Strung out / Say yes / Eveready man / I love everything you do.
LP . . . . . . . . . . . . . . . . . . . . . . SOLA 6
Solar / Dec '80.

## FROM 9 UNTIL ..
Tracks: From 9 until .. / All in my mind.
■ 12". . . . . . . . . . . . . . . . . . . . . SO12-6
■ 6". . . . . . . . . . . . . . . . . . . . . . SO 6
Solar / Apr '80.

## IT'S ALL THE WAY LIVE.
Tracks: It's all the way live / Give in to love.
■ 7" . . . . . . . . . . . . . . . . . . . . FC 1382
RCA / Jan '79.

## KEEP ON MOVING STRAIGHT AHEAD.
Tracks: Keep on moving straight ahead / It's you / Be my lady / It's got to be love / We want you / BAck together again / Anything for you / All for you.
LP . . . . . . . . . . . . . . . . . . . . . . SOLA 11
Solar / Mar '82.
LP . . . . . . . . . . . . . . . . . . . . . . RCA 11
Solar / May '82.

## OUTRAGEOUS.
Tracks: Outrageous / So let's love.
■ 12". . . . . . . . . . . . . . . . . . . .MCAT 952
■ 7". . . . . . . . . . . . . . . . . . . . . MCA 952
RCA / Apr '85.

## RAID.
Tracks: Raid / Urban man / Your wish is my command.
■ 12". . . . . . . . . . . . . . . . . . . E 9836T
■ 7". . . . . . . . . . . . . . . . . . . . .E 9836
Elektra / Mar '83.

## YOUR WISH IS MY COMMAND.
Tracks: Your wish is my command / Songwriter / Urban man / I'll be standing by / I want to hold your hand / Something about that woman.
LP . . . . . . . . . . . . . . . . . . . . . . K 52340
Solar / Feb '82.

# Lance, Major

## AIN'T NO SOUL (LEFT IN THESE OLE SHOES).
Tracks: Ain't no soul (left in these ole shoes) / You'll want me back.
■ 7" . . . . . . . . . . . . . . . . . . . . DB 8122
Columbia / Feb '67.

## GIMME LITTLE SIGN.
Tracks: Gimme little sign / How can you say goodbye.
■ 7" . . . . . . . . . . . . . . . . . . . . CS 2017
Contempo (2) / Jun '74.

## NEVER THOUGHT I'D BE LOSING YOU.
Tracks: I never thought I'd be losing you / Chicago disco.

■ 7" . . . . . . . . . . . . . . . . . . TMG 1109
Motown / May '78.

## LIVE AT HINKLEY.
Tracks: Not Advised.
■ LP . . . . . . . . . . . . . . . . . .TORCHLP 1
Torch / Apr '86.

## LIVE AT THE TORCH.
Tracks: Hey hey / I wanna make up / My girl / Um, um, um, um, um, um / Beat / Ain't no soul / Investigate / Monkey time.
■ LP . . . . . . . . . . . . . . . . . . . . CLP 523
Contempo (1) / '73.

## MONKEY TIME.
Tracks: Not Advised.
■ LP . . . . . . . . . . . . . . . . . . . . . ED 124
Edsel / Jan '84.

## NOW ARRIVING.
Tracks: I never thought / Wild & free / Chicago disco / Do the mess around / How my love goes / Think about the love we had / Troubles / Love pains / It's all over.
■ LP . . . . . . . . . . . . . . . . . .STML 12094
Motown / Oct '78.

## PRIDE AND JOY.
Tracks: Pride and joy / I'm the one.
■ 7" . . . . . . . . . . . . . . . . . . . . DB 7609
Columbia / '63.

## UM UM UM UM UM UM.
Tracks: Um, um, um, um, um, um.
■ 7" . . . . . . . . . . . . . . . . . . . . DB 7205
Columbia / Feb '64.

# Lanier & Co.

## DANCING IN THE NIGHT.
Tracks: Dancing in the night / Strange love affair / You know that I want you / Afraid of losing you / Lies / I don't know / Superlady / Sassy / Lately / Let's go for it.
■ CD . . . . . . . . . . . . . . . CDP 748 608 2
■ LP . . . . . . . . . . . . . . . . . SYLP 6001
■ MC . . . . . . . . . . . . . . . .TCSYLP 6001
Syncopate / Nov '87.

## I DON'T KNOW.
Tracks: I don't know (extended version) / Dancing in the night (remix) / I don't know / Afraid of losing you.
■ 12". . . . . . . . . . . . . . . . . . .12SY 7
■ 7". . . . . . . . . . . . . . . . . . . . SY 7
Syncopate / Oct '87.

## I DON'T KNOW WHAT TO DO ABOUT YOU.
Tracks: I don't know what to do about you.
■ 12". . . . . . . . . . . . . . . . . . .WAY 102T
Threeway / Mar '87.

# Larkins, Percy

## MUSIC OF PASSION.
Tracks: Not Advised.
■ LP . . . . . . . . . . . . . . . . . . . MVLP 3
Move / Jul '85.

## MUSIC OF PASSION.
Tracks: Music of passion / Strangers into lovers.
■ 7" . . . . . . . . . . . . . . . . . . . . MVS 1
Move / Jun '85.

# Larson, Neil

## JUNGLE FEVER.
Tracks: Sudden samba / Promenade / Windsong / Emerald city / Jungle fever / Red desert / Last tango in Paris / From a dream.
■ LP . . . . . . . . . . . . . . . . . . AMLJ 733
Horizon / Jan '79.

## SMOOTH TALK.
Tracks: Not Advised.
■ LP . . . . . . . . . . . . . . . . MCA 42296
■ CD . . . . . . . . . . . . . . . MCAD 42296
■ MC . . . . . . . . . . . . . . . MCAC 42296
MCA / Jun '89.

# Lasalle, Denise

## COME TO BED.
Tracks: Come to bed / I was not the best woman.
■ 12". . . . . . . . . . . . . . . .MAL 12 009
■ 7". . . . . . . . . . . . . . . . . MAL 009
Malaco / May '83.
■ 12". . . . . . . . . . . . . . . . . TA 6513
■ 7". . . . . . . . . . . . . . . . . .A 6513
Epic / Aug '85.

## HERE I AM AGAIN.
Tracks: Here I am again / Married, but not to each other / Share your man with me / I wanna do what's on your mind / Trying to forget / My brand on you / Stay with me awhile / Any time is the right time / Don't nobody live here (by the name of fool) / Hit and run / We've got love / Get up off my mind / Who's the fool / Best thing I ever had.
CD . . . . . . . . . . . . . . . . . . CDSEW 066
Westbound / Sep '93 / Pinnacle.

## HITTIN' WHERE IT HURTS.
Tracks: Not Advised.
■ LP . . . . . . . . . . . . . . . . . MAL 7447
MC. . . . . . . . . . . . . . . . . MALC 7447
Malaco / Mar '89 / C.M. Distribution / Charly / Pinnacle.
CD. . . . . . . . . . . . . . . . . MALCD 7447
Malaco / Mar '93 / C.M. Distribution / Charly / Pinnacle.

## HOLDING HANDS WITH THE BLUES.
Tracks: Not Advised.
■ LP . . . . . . . . . . . . . . . . .MALP 013
Malaco / '88.

## IT'S LYING TIME AGAIN.
Tracks: Not Advised.
■ LP . . . . . . . . . . . . . . . . . MAL 7441
MC. . . . . . . . . . . . . . . . . MALC 7441
Malaco / Mar '89 / C.M. Distribution / Charly / Pinnacle.

## LADY IN THE STREET, A.
Tracks: Not Advised.
■ LP . . . . . . . . . . . . . . . . . MAL 7412
MC. . . . . . . . . . . . . . . . . MALC 7412
Malaco / May '83 / C.M. Distribution / Charly / Pinnacle.

## LET THE FOUR WINDS BLOW.
Tracks: Let the four winds blow.
■ 12". . . . . . . . . . . . . . . .MAL 12 030
■ 7". . . . . . . . . . . . . . . . . MAL 030
Malaco / Feb '86.

## LOVE ME RIGHT.
Tracks: Not Advised.
CD . . . . . . . . . . . . . . . . MALCD 7464
Malaco / Mar '93 / C.M. Distribution / Charly / Pinnacle.

## LOVE TALKIN'.
Tracks: Not Advised.
■ LP . . . . . . . . . . . . . . . . . MAL 7422
MC. . . . . . . . . . . . . . . . . MALC 7422
Malaco / Mar '89 / C.M. Distribution / Charly / Pinnacle.

## MY TOOT TOOT.
Tracks: Talkin' in your sleep / Someone else is steppin' in / Nobody loves me like you do / Give me yo' most strongest whisky / Love is a five letter word / Lady in the street / Love talkin' / Get what you can get / Linger a little longer / Keeps me runnin' back / Too many lovers / My toot toot / Come to bed.
■ LP . . . . . . . . . . . . . . . . . EPC 26603
■ MC . . . . . . . . . . . . . . . .40 26603
Epic / Aug '85.

## MY TOOT TOOT.
Tracks: My toot toot / Give me yo' most strongest whisky.
■ 12". . . . . . . . . . . . . . . . . TX 6334
■ 7". . . . . . . . . . . . . . . . . .A 6334
Epic / Jun '85.

## ON THE LOOSE.
Tracks: Man size job / What it takes to get a good woman / Harper Valley PTA / What am I doing wrong / Breaking up somebody's home / There ain't enough hate around (to make me turn around) / Your man and your best friend / Lean on me / Making a good thing better / I'm over you / I'm satisfied.
CD. . . . . . . . . . . . . . . . . CDSEW 005
■ LP . . . . . . . . . . . . . . . . . SEW 005
MC. . . . . . . . . . . . . . . . . .SEWC 005
Westbound / Jul '89 / Pinnacle.

## RAIN AND FIRE.
Tracks: It be's that way sometimes / I'm sho gonna mess with yo man / What's goin' on in my house / Look what can happen to you. (Look what can happen to you ( if you get caught messin' with my tu tu)) / Shame, shame, shame / Dip, bam, thank you maam / Learnin' how to cheat on you / Rain and fire / It takes you all night / Is he lovin' someone else tonight.
■ LP . . . . . . . . . . . . . . . . . MAL 7434
MC. . . . . . . . . . . . . . . . . MALC 7434
Malaco / Mar '89 / C.M. Distribution / Charly / Pinnacle.

### RIGHT PLACE, RIGHT TIME.
Tracks: Not Advised.
■ LP . . . . . . . . . . . . . . . . . . MAL 7417
MC . . . . . . . . . . . . . . . . . . MALC 7417
Malaco / Mar '89 / C.M. Distribution / Charly /
Pinnacle.

### RIGHT PLACE, RIGHT TIME (Lasalle, Denise & Latimore).
Tracks: Right place, right time / Come to bed / Let's straighten it out.
■ 12" . . . . . . . . . . . . . . . . MAL 12 022
■ 7" . . . . . . . . . . . . . . . . . . MAL 022
Malaco / Jun '84.

### STILL TRAPPED.
Tracks: Not Advised.
CD . . . . . . . . . . . . . . . . . MALCD 7454
Malaco / Mar '93 / C.M. Distribution / Charly /
Pinnacle.

### TRAPPED BY A THING CALLED LOVE.
Tracks: Trapped by a thing called love / Now run and tell that / Heartbreaker of the year / Good goody getter / Catch me if you can / Hung up, strung out / Do me right / Deeper I go (the better it gets) / If you should lose me / It's too late / Keep it coming.
■ LP . . . . . . . . . . . . . . . . . . 6310206
Janus / Jun '72.
CD . . . . . . . . . . . . . . . . . CDSEW 018
LP . . . . . . . . . . . . . . . . . . SEW 018
MC . . . . . . . . . . . . . . . . . . SEWC 018
Westbound / Jan '90 / Pinnacle.

### TRAPPED BY A THING CALLED LOVE/ ON THE LOOSE.
Tracks: Man sized job / What it takes to get a good woman / Harper Valley P.T.A. / What am I doing wrong / Breaking up somebody's home / There ain't enough hate around / Your man and your best friend / Lean on me / Making a good thing better / I'm over you / I'm satisfied / Trapped by a thing called love / Now run and tell that / Heartbreaker of the year / Goody goody getter / Catch me if you can / Hung up, strung up / Do me right / Deeper I go (better it gets) / You'll lose a good thing / Keeping it coming / It's too late.
CD Set . . . . . . . . . . . . . . . CDSEWD 018
Westbound / Feb '92 / Pinnacle.

### WHEN WE'RE MAKING LOVE.
Tracks: When we're making love.
■ 12" . . . . . . . . . . . . . . . . DEBTX 3143
Debut (1) / Nov '92.

## Lasley, David

### SAVED BY LOVE.
Tracks: Saved by love / Oh.
■ 12" . . . . . . . . . . . . . . . . 12EA 184
■ 7" . . . . . . . . . . . . . . . . . . EA 184
EMI-America / Nov '84.

### TREAT WILLIE GOOD.
Tracks: Treat Willie good / There's gotta be somebody.
■ 7" . . . . . . . . . . . . . . . . . . EA 139
EMI-America / Jul '82.

### WHERE DOES THAT BOY HANG OUT.
Tracks: Where does the boy hang out / Next time.
■ 7" . . . . . . . . . . . . . . . . . . EA 179
■ 12" . . . . . . . . . . . . . . . . 12EA 179
EMI-America / Aug '84.

## Laso

### ANOTHER STAR.
Tracks: Another star / Happy smoke.
■ 7" . . . . . . . . . . . . . . . . . . MCA 302
MCA / Jun '77.

## Latimore

Born in Charleston, Tennesse in 1939, Benny Latimore frst came to prominence as an expressive, busy soul singer on the TK distributed Glades Records in early '70s. Along with Betty Wright and Gwen McCrae, Benny provided a soulful contrast in the Miami sound to the likes of KC & The Sunshine Band and George McCrae, albums like *Latimore* ('71), *More, More, Latimore* ('72) and *Latimore III* ('73) paving the way for his most successful album, *Let's Straighten It Out* ('74), from which the title song sprinted to number one on the R&B singles charts. *It Aint' Where You Been* the following year continued his run of success, but by the time of *Dig A Little Deeper* the disco boom was having it's effect. A blank

period ended the mid-eighties when he signed to Malaco Records in Jackson, Mississippi, since he's released several albums of improving quality including *Good Time Man* and *Slow Down* and resumed regular touring.

### EVERY WAY BUT WRONG.
Tracks: Not Advised.
■ LP . . . . . . . . . . . . . . . . . . MALP 007
Malaco / '88.

### GOOD TIME MAN.
Tracks: Not Advised.
■ LP . . . . . . . . . . . . . . . . . . MAL 7423
Malaco / Jun '85.

### I'LL DO ANYTHING FOR YOU.
Tracks: Not Advised.
■ LP . . . . . . . . . . . . . . . . . . MAL 7414
Malaco / '88.

### IT AIN'T WHERE YOU BEEN..IT'S WHERE YOU'RE GOIN'.
Tracks: It ain't where you been / Somethin' 'bout 'cha / All the way lover / Sweet vibrations / Let's do it in slow motion / Let me go / I get lifted.
■ LP . . . . . . . . . . . . . . . . . . XL 14034
TK / '77.

### ONLY WAY IS UP.
Tracks: Not Advised.
CD . . . . . . . . . . . . . . . . . MALCD 7456
Malaco / Apr '93 / C.M. Distribution / Charly /
Pinnacle.

### SINGING IN THE KEY OF LOVE.
Tracks: Not Advised.
■ LP . . . . . . . . . . . . . . . . . . MAL 7409
MC . . . . . . . . . . . . . . . . . . MALC 7409
Malaco / Jul '82 / C.M. Distribution / Charly /
Pinnacle.

### SLOW DOWN.
Tracks: Not Advised.
■ LP . . . . . . . . . . . . . . . . . . MAL 7443
MC . . . . . . . . . . . . . . . . . . MALC 7443
Malaco / Mar '89 / C.M. Distribution / Charly /
Pinnacle.
CD . . . . . . . . . . . . . . . . . MALCD 7443
Malaco / Mar '93 / C.M. Distribution / Charly /
Pinnacle.

### SOMETHIN' 'BOUT 'CHA.
Tracks: Somethin' 'bout 'cha / Sweet vibrations.
■ 7" . . . . . . . . . . . . . . . . . . XB 2151
TK / May '77.

### SWEET VIBRATIONS.
Tracks: (They call it) Stormy Monday / Ain't nothing you can do / Snap your fingers / Let's straighten it out / Keep the home fires burnin' / There's a redneck in the sould band / Qualified man / It ain't where you been / Something 'bout'cha / Sweet vibrations / I get lifted / Dig a little deeper / Long distance love.
CD . . . . . . . . . . . . . . . . . NEXCD 166
Sequel / May '91 / Total / BMG.

### TOO HOT TO HANDLE.
Tracks: Too hot to handle / Let me go.
■ 7" . . . . . . . . . . . . . . . . . . TKR 7524
TK / Feb '79.

## Latter, Gene

### ALWAYS.
Tracks: Always / Woman called sorrow.
■ 7" . . . . . . . . . . . . . . . . . . 202655
CBS / Mar '67.

### AMERICAN GIRL.
Tracks: American girl.
■ 7" . . . . . . . . . . . . . . . . . . 7N 45581
Pye / Mar '76.

### JUST A MINUTE OR TWO.
Tracks: Just a minute or two / Dream lover.
■ 7" . . . . . . . . . . . . . . . . . . F 12364
Decca / Mar '66.

### LITTLE PIECE OF LEATHER.
Tracks: Little piece of leather / Funny face.
■ 7" . . . . . . . . . . . . . . . . . . 2843
CBS / Jul '67.

### LITTLE PIECE OF LEATHER, A.
Tracks: Little piece of leather / Funny face girl.
■ 7" . . . . . . . . . . . . . . . . . . CBS 2843
CBS / Jul '67.

### MOTHER'S LITTLE HELPER.
Tracks: Mother's little helper / Please come back to me again.

■ 7" . . . . . . . . . . . . . . . . . . F 1239
Decca / May '66.

### ROCK BABY ROCK.
Tracks: Rock baby rock / Sweet sugar.
■ 7" . . . . . . . . . . . . . . . . . . MAG 23
Magnet / Jul '82.

### SOMETHING INSIDE ME DIED.
Tracks: Something inside me died / Don't go.
■ 7" . . . . . . . . . . . . . . . . . . 20248
CBS / Dec '66.

## Lattisaw, Stacy

### ATTACK OF THE NAME GAME.
Tracks: Attack of the name game / I could love yc so divine.
■ 7" . . . . . . . . . . . . . . . . . . 799968
Cotillion / Nov '82.

### BABY I LOVE YOU.
Tracks: Baby I love you / With you.
■ 7" . . . . . . . . . . . . . . . . . . K 1168
Atlantic / Oct '81.

### BLOCK PARTY (Lattisaw, Stacy Johnny Gill).
Tracks: Block party / Baby it's you.
■ 12" . . . . . . . . . . . . . . . . B 9719
■ 7" . . . . . . . . . . . . . . . . . . B 97
Cotillion / Aug '84.

### CALL ME.
Tracks: Call me (instrumental) / Call me (extended (12" only.) / Call me ("Track on 12" only.)
■ 12" . . . . . . . . . . . . . . . . ZT 4226
■ 7" . . . . . . . . . . . . . . . . . . ZB 4226
Motown / Oct '88.

### DYNAMITE.
Tracks: Dynamite / Dreaming.
■ 7" . . . . . . . . . . . . . . . . . . K 1155
Atlantic / Aug '80.

### I'M NOT THE SAME GIRL.
Tracks: Can't stop thinking about you / Coming aliv / Now we are starting over again / He's just not you I'm not the same girl / Toughen up / Together / thought it took a little time.
■ LP . . . . . . . . . . . . . . . . . . 790280
Cotillion / Aug '85.

### JUMP INTO MY LIFE.
Tracks: Jump into my life / Long shot.
■ 12" . . . . . . . . . . . . . . . . ZT 4111
■ 7" . . . . . . . . . . . . . . . . . . ZB 4110
Motown / Jan '87.

### JUMP TO THE BEAT.
Tracks: Jump to the beat.
■ 12" . . . . . . . . . . . . . . . . K 11496
■ 7" . . . . . . . . . . . . . . . . . . K 1149
Atlantic / Jun '80.

### JUMP TO THE BEAT (OLD GOLD).
Tracks: Jump to the beat / Dynamite.
■ 7" . . . . . . . . . . . . . . . . . . OG 990
Old Gold / '89.
12" . . . . . . . . . . . . . . . . OG 420
Old Gold / Jun '91 / Pickwick.

### LET ME BE YOUR ANGEL.
Tracks: Jump to the beat / Dynamite / You don't lov me anymore / Dreaming / Let me be your angel Don't you want to feel it / You know I like it / My love
■ LP . . . . . . . . . . . . . . . . . . K 5071
MC . . . . . . . . . . . . . . . . . . K4 5071
Atlantic / Jul '80 / WEA.

### LOVE ON A TWO WAY STREET.
Tracks: Love on a two way street / Young girl.
■ 7" . . . . . . . . . . . . . . . . . . K 1167
Atlantic / Jul '81.

### MILLION DOLLAR BABE.
Tracks: Million dollar babe / Ways of love / Hey ther lonely boy.
■ 12" . . . . . . . . . . . . . . . . B 9819
■ 7" . . . . . . . . . . . . . . . . . . B 981
Cotillion / Jan '84.

### NAIL IT TO THE WALL.
Tracks: Nail it to the wall / Nail it to the wa (instrumental).
■ 7" . . . . . . . . . . . . . . . . . . ZB 4088
Motown / Sep '86.

### PERFECT COMBINATION (Lattisaw Stacy & Johnny Gill).
Tracks: Not Advised.
■ LP . . . . . . . . . . . . . . . . . . 790136
WEA / Apr '84.

■ DELETE

**PERSONAL ATTENTION.**
Tracks: Personal attention / Love town / Let me take you down / Ain't no mountain high enough / He's got hold on me / Find another lover / Changes / Every top of your love / Call me / Electronic eyes.
■ CD . . . . . . . . . . . . . . . . . . . . ZD 72620
■ LP . . . . . . . . . . . . . . . . . . . . ZL 72620
■ MC . . . . . . . . . . . . . . . . . . . . ZK 72620
Motown / Mar '88.

**SNEAKIN' OUT.**
Tracks: Jump to the beat / Sneakin' out / Guys like you.
■ 12" . . . . . . . . . . . . . . . . . . . K 11770T
■ 7" . . . . . . . . . . . . . . . . . . . . K 11770
Motown / Sep '82.

**TAKE ME ALL THE WAY.**
Tracks: Just jump into my life / Hard way / Take me all the way / Little bit of heaven / Long shot / Nail it to the wall / Love me like the first time / You ain't leavin Over the top / One more night.
■ LP . . . . . . . . . . . . . . . . . . . . ZL 72479
■ MC . . . . . . . . . . . . . . . . . . . . ZK 72479
Motown / Nov '86.

**WHAT YOU NEED.**
Tracks: What you need / Dance for you / You touched the woman in me / R U man enuff / Guilty (lock me up) / Falling (in love again) / I don't have the heart / Where do we go from here / Tender love / That's the reason why I love you.
■ CD . . . . . . . . . . . . . . . . . . . . ZD 72685
■ LP . . . . . . . . . . . . . . . . . . . . ZL 72685
■ MC . . . . . . . . . . . . . . . . . . . . ZK 72685
Motown / Mar '90.

**WHERE DO WE GO FROM HERE (Lattimaw, Stacy & Johnny Gill).**
Tracks: Where do we go from here / What you need / What you need (Club version).
■ 7" . . . . . . . . . . . . . . . . . . . ZB 43499
■ 12" . . . . . . . . . . . . . . . . . . . ZT 43500
Motown / Feb '90.

**WITH YOU.**
Tracks: Feel my love tonight / Screamin' off the top / I was so easy / Baby I love you / Love on a two way street / With you / Young girl / Spotlight / You take me to heaven.
■ LP . . . . . . . . . . . . . . . . . . . K 50798
Atlantic / Jun '81.

## Lauren, Jessica

**SIREN SONG.**
Tracks: Leo rises / Fire monkey / Siren song / When you call my name / Serengeti / Just a dream / Dance for Lotte / Dangerous curves / Freefall.
■ CD . . . . . . . . . . . . . . . . . . . SJRCD 020
■ LP . . . . . . . . . . . . . . . . . . . SJRLP 020
Soul Jazz / Sep '94 / New Note.

## Laurence, Paul

**HAVEN'T YOU HEARD.**
Tracks: Strung out / She's not a sleaze (With Lillo Thomas & Freddie Jackson.) / You hooked me / Good and plenty / Racism / Haven't you heard / There ain't nothin' (like your lovin') / I'm sensitive.
■ LP . . . . . . . . . . . . . . . . . . . EST 2005
Capitol / Apr '86.

**SHE'S NOT A SLEAZE.**
Tracks: She's not a sleaze / There ain't nothin' (like your lovin').
■ 7" . . . . . . . . . . . . . . . . . . . . CL 378
■ 12" . . . . . . . . . . . . . . . . . . . 12CL 378
Capitol / Sep '85.

**STRUNG OUT.**
Tracks: Strung out / I'm sensitive.
■ 12" . . . . . . . . . . . . . . . . . . . 12CL 393
■ 7" . . . . . . . . . . . . . . . . . . . . CL 393
Capitol / Feb '86.

**UNDER EXPOSED.**
Tracks: Make my baby happy / I ain't wit it / She's not an ordinary girl / Main course / Cut the crap / Use me / She's gone / I'm a business man (kick it too).
■ CD . . . . . . . . . . . . . . . . . . . CDEST 2090
■ LP . . . . . . . . . . . . . . . . . . . EST 2090
■ MC . . . . . . . . . . . . . . . . . . . TCEST 2090
Capitol / Mar '89.

## Lavell, Miss

**EVERYBODY'S GOT SOMEBODY.**
Tracks: Everybody's got somebody.
■ 7" . . . . . . . . . . . . . . . . . . . VP 9236
Vocalion / Apr '65.

## Lavette, Betty

**DOING THE BEST I CAN.**
Tracks: Doing the best I can / Doing the best I can (version).
■ 7" . . . . . . . . . . . . . . . . . . . . LV 9
Atlantic / Feb '79.

**EASIER TO SAY.**
Tracks: Easier to say than do.
■ 7" . . . . . . . . . . . . . . . . . . . CTD 107
Charly / Jul '80.

**I CAN'T STOP.**
Tracks: I can't stop / Either way we lose.
■ 7" . . . . . . . . . . . . . . . . . . . TMG 1265
Motown / Jul '82.

**I FEEL GOOD ALL OVER.**
Tracks: I feel good (all over) / Only your love can save me.
■ 7" . . . . . . . . . . . . . . . . . . . SS 2015
Stateside / Apr '67.

**I'M IN LOVE.**
Tracks: He made a woman out of me / Do your duty / We got to slip around / Piece of my heart / Easier to say than do / My train's comin' in / At the mercy of a man / Let me down easy / Games people play / Nearer to you / Love's made a fool of me / I'm in love.
■ LP . . . . . . . . . . . . . . . . . . . CRB 1059
Charly R&B / Jan '85.

**NEARER TO YOU.**
Tracks: Not Advised.
CD . . . . . . . . . . . . . . . . . . . CDCHARLY 276
Charly / Jan '91 / Charly.

**NOT GONNA HAPPEN TWICE.**
Tracks: Not Advised.
■ CD . . . . . . . . . . . . . . . . . . . MOTCCD 45
Motor City / Oct '90.

**TELL ME A LIE.**
Tracks: Right in the middle / Either way we lose / Suspicions / You seen one you seen 'em all / I heard it through the grapevine / Tell me a lie / I like it like that / Before I even knew your name / I can't stop / If I were your woman.
■ LP . . . . . . . . . . . . . . . . . . . STML 12166
Motown / Jan '82.

**YOU SEEN ONE YOU SEEN 'EM ALL.**
Tracks: You seen one you seen 'em all.
■ 7" . . . . . . . . . . . . . . . . . . . TMG 1257
Motown / Mar '82.

## Law, Joanna

**FIRST TIME EVER I SAW YOUR FACE.**
Tracks: First time ever I saw your face.
■ 12" . . . . . . . . . . . . . . . . . . . CBE 1252
■ 7" . . . . . . . . . . . . . . . . . . . CBE 752
■ MC Single. . . . . . . . . . . . . . . . CBE 752C
City Beat / Jul '90.

**LOVE IS NOT ENOUGH.**
Tracks: Love is not enough.
■ 12" . . . . . . . . . . . . . . . . . . . EZS 7568
RCA / Nov '90.

**WARM LOVE.**
Tracks: Warm love.
■ 12" . . . . . . . . . . . . . . . . . . . 12LM 2
Law Music/Total / Aug '92.

## Laws, Debra

**ON MY OWN.**
Tracks: On my own / Long as we're together.
■ 12" . . . . . . . . . . . . . . . . . . . K 12529 T
Elektra / May '81.

**VERY SPECIAL.**
Tracks: On my own / Meant for you / Very special / Be yourself / Long as we're together / Your love / How long / All the things I love.
■ LP . . . . . . . . . . . . . . . . . . . K 52281
Elektra / Jun '81.

## Laws, Eloise

**ELOISE LAWS.**
Tracks: Let's find those two people again / Strength of a woman / Almost all the way to love / I'm just warmin' up / You are everything / Moment to moment / Got you into my life / If I don't watch out / Search find.
■ LP . . . . . . . . . . . . . . . . . . . UAG 30331
United Artists / Mar '81.

**LOVE FACTORY (Laws, Eloise & Just Brothers).**
Tracks: Love factory / Sliced tomatoes.
■ 7" . . . . . . . . . . . . . . . . . . . HEAT 15
Inferno (1) / Jul '80.

**LOVE GOES DEEPER THAN THAT.**
Tracks: Love goes deeper than that / Camouflage.
■ 7" . . . . . . . . . . . . . . . . . . . INV 5289
Invictus / Jun '77.

## Laws, Hubert

**LAWS OF JAZZ/FLUTE BY-LAWS, THE.**
Tracks: Not Advised.
CD . . . . . . . . . . . . . . . . . . . 812271636-2
Atlantic / May '94 / WEA.

**REDS, THEME FROM (Laws, Hubert & Cheryl Lynn).**
Tracks: Reds (theme from) / Reds (theme from) (part 2).
■ 7" . . . . . . . . . . . . . . . . . . . A 2052
CBS / Mar '82.

**RITE OF SPRING, THE.**
Tracks: Not Advised.
■ CD . . . . . . . . . . . . . . . . . . . 4505632
CBS / '88.

## Laws, Ronnie

This saxophonist, flautist, singer, songwriter and producer was briefly a member of Earth Wind & Fire during the early '70s, and used that band's jazz influences when launching his solo career in 1975. Ronnie is the younger brother of noted musicians, Hubert and Eloise Laws. His first LP, '75's *Pressure Sensitive*, became the biggest selling debut album in the history of Blue Note Records; a smash on the Billboard jazz charts and No. 73 on the pop list. It included the classic *Always There*, which has been covered by many, most succesfully by Incognito in 1991. This, and Laws' other early albums, were produced by Wayne Henderson of Crusaders. He began producing himself in 1980, releasing well crafted and respectably-selling jazz-funk records.

**ALL DAY RHYTHM.**
Tracks: Smoke house / Dreams I dream / All day rhythm / Rhythm of romance / Still / Junior boy / Nite life / Distant eyes / Arrival / Home dance.
CD . . . . . . . . . . . . . . . . . . . 4605922
■ LP . . . . . . . . . . . . . . . . . . . 4605921
■ MC . . . . . . . . . . . . . . . . . . . 4605924
CBS / Dec '87 / Sony.

**ALL FOR YOU.**
Tracks: All for you / Let's keep it together.
■ 12" . . . . . . . . . . . . . . . . . . . 12UP 36481
■ 7" . . . . . . . . . . . . . . . . . . . UP 36481
United Artists / Feb '79.

**ALWAYS THERE.**
Tracks: Always there / Love is here / Goodtime ride.
■ 7" . . . . . . . . . . . . . . . . . . . BNXW 7004
Blue Note / Jan '76.
■ 7" . . . . . . . . . . . . . . . . . . . UP 36497
United Artists / Mar '80.

**BEST OF RONNIE LAWS.**
Tracks: Always there / Night breeze / Let's keep it together / Karmen / Friends and strangers / New day / Just love / Flame / Solid ground / Just as you are / Living love / Love is here / Saturday evening.
CD . . . . . . . . . . . . . . . . . . . BNZ 287
Blue Note / Feb '92 / EMI.

**BROTHERHOOD.**
Tracks: Still in the band / I feel fine / See the day / Night thing / HAndy man / Brotherhood / Tidal wave / Distant lover / My river / When I fall in love.
CD . . . . . . . . . . . . . . . . . . . 101S 71492
101 South / Aug '94 / New Note.

**CLASSIC MASTERS.**
Tracks: City girl / Always there / Love is here / Every generation / Paradise (you are) / Friends and strangers / In the groove / Stay awake / Saturday evening.
■ CD . . . . . . . . . . . . . . . . . . . BU 6
Capitol / Mar '88.

**DEEP SOUL.**
Tracks: Not Advised.
CD . . . . . . . . . . . . . . . . . . . 101S 8771252
101 South / Aug '94 / New Note.

## EVERY GENERATION.
**Tracks:** Young child / Never get back to Houston / Every generation / Tomorrow / O.T.B.A. law (Outta be a law) / Love's victory / Thoughts and memories / As one.
■ **LP** .................... UAG 30289
United Artists / Feb '80.

## EVERY GENERATION.
**Tracks:** Every generation / O.T.B.A. law.
■ **12"** .................... 12UP 626
■ **7"** .................... UP 626
United Artists / May '80.

## FEVER.
**Tracks:** Let's keep it together / fever / All the time / Stay still (And let me love you) / Strugglin' / Captain Midnight / Karmen / Night breeze / From Ronnie with love.
■ **CD** .................... CDP 7895412
Blue Note / Aug '93.

## FLAME.
**Tracks:** All for you / These days / Flame / Living love / Love is here / Grace / Joy / Live your life away.
■ **LP** .................... UAG 30204
United Artists / Jan '79.

## FRIENDS AND STRANGERS.
**Tracks:** Goodtime ride / Saturday evening / Friends and strangers / Nuthin' 'bout nuthin' / New day / Life in paradise / Same old story / Just love.
**CD** .................... UAG 30079
EMI / Jan '89 / EMI.

## IDENTITY.
**Tracks:** Not Advised.
**CD** .................... 101S 70892
101 South / Aug '94 / New Note.

## MIRROR TOWN.
**Tracks:** Come to me / Misled / Tell me / Mirror town / Like a crazy man / Midnight side / Cold day / You have to be in love / Take a chance.
**MC** .................... 4500684
■ **LP** .................... 4500681
CBS / Oct '86 / Sony.

## MR NICE GUY.
**Tracks:** Can't save tomorrow / Mr. Nice Guy / In the groove / Third hour / You / Big stars / Rollin' / What does it take (to win your love) / Off and on again.
■ **LP** .................... ATAK 67
**MC** .................... TCATAK 67
Capitol / Sep '83 / EMI.

## PRESSURE SENSITIVE (Laws, Ronnie & Pressure).
**Tracks:** Always there / Momma / Never be the same / Tell me something good / Nothing to lose / Tidal wave / Why do you laugh at me / Mis' Mary's place.
■ **CD** .................... CDP 746 554 2
EMI-America / May '87.

## RONNIE LAWS.
**Tracks:** City girl / Always there / Love is here / Every generation / Paradise (you are) / Friends and strangers / In the groove / Stay awake / Saturday evening.

## SOLID GROUND.
**Tracks:** Solid ground / Heavy on easy / Segue / There's a way / Stay awake / Your stuff / Just as you are / Summer fool / Good feelings.
■ **LP** .................... LBG 30336
Liberty / Oct '81.

## STAY AWAKE.
**Tracks:** Stay awake / Heavy on easy.
■ **12"** .................... 12UP 644
United Artists / Sep '81.

## THERE'S A WAY.
**Tracks:** There's a way / Your stuff / Always there.
■ **12"** .................... 12UP 648
■ **7"** .................... UP 648
United Artists / Jan '82.

## TRUE SPIRIT.
**Tracks:** Gotta say goodbye / Love this way again / Virgin winds (before the rainfall) / From a glance / Song for Hiram / Heart station / Favorite love / Imo.
■ **CD** .................... PAR 2003CD
Par / Aug '93.
**CD** .................... ITMP 970053
I.T.M. / Jan '94 / C.M. Distribution / Charly / Koch International / Complete Record Co. Ltd.
**CD** .................... PRCDSP 200
Prestige / Jan '94 / Total / BMG.

## YOUNG CHILD.
**Tracks:** Young child / Tomorrow.
■ **12"** .................... 12UP 619

■ **7"** .................... UP 619
United Artists / Feb '80.

## Leaders

## MUDFOOT.
**Tracks:** Miss Nancy / Elaborations / Midnight train / Freedom swing song / Song of her / Mudfoot / Cupid.
■ **LP** .................... BKH 52001
Blackhawk / Jan '87.
**CD** .................... CDBKH 52001
Blackhawk / Jul '87 / Pinnacle.

## OUT HERE LIKE THIS.
**Tracks:** Zero / Luna / Cool T / Donkey dust / Portraits / Felicite / Loves I once knew.
■ **LP** .................... 120 119
Black Saint / '88.

## Lee, Darrell

## DARRELL LEE.
**Tracks:** Slow dance / Just a little bit / Girl, I'm alone / Sexy / She made me / Lisa / Big city life / Lock these people up.
**CD** .................... CDGEM 4005
■ **LP** .................... GEM 4005
**MC** .................... ZCGEM 4005
Gemc / Jul '89 / Backs Distribution / Ichiban Records (UK).

## SEXY.
**Tracks:** Sexy (dance mix) / Sexy (radio edit & bonus mix).
■ **12"** .................... 12 PO 19
Gemc / May '89.

## Lee, Dee C.

## COME HELL OR WATERS HIGH.
**Tracks:** Come hell or waters high / I don't miss.
■ **12"** .................... TA 6869
■ **7"** .................... A 6869
CBS / Feb '86.

## DON'T DO IT BABY.
**Tracks:** Don't do it baby / Yes.
■ **12"** .................... TA 4838
■ **7"** .................... A 4838
CBS / Nov '84.

## HEY WHAT'D YA SAY.
**Tracks:** Hey what'd ya say / Selina wow wow.
■ **12"** .................... TA 7294
■ **7"** .................... A 7294
CBS / Jul '86.

## HOLD ON.
**Tracks:** Hold on / Welcome.
■ **12"** .................... TA 7179
■ **7"** .................... A 7179
CBS / May '86.

## NEW REALITY VIBE.
**Tracks:** New reality vibe / New reality vibe (dub).
**12"** .................... MW 019
Mo Wax / Apr '94 / Vital Distribution.

## SEE THE DAY.
**Tracks:** See the day / Paris match.
■ **7"** .................... A 6570
CBS / Nov '85.

## SELINA WOW WOW.
**Tracks:** Selina wow wow / Hey what'd ya say.
■ **12"** .................... TA 4192
■ **7"** .................... A 4192
CBS / Feb '84.

## SHRINE.
**Tracks:** Shrine / Hey what'd ya say / That's when something special starts / He's gone / Come hell or waters high / What about me / Still the children cry / Just my type / Hold on / See the day.
■ **LP** .................... CBS 26915
**MC** .................... 40 26915
■ **CD** .................... CD 26915
CBS / Jul '86 / Sony.
**CD** .................... 982999 2
Pickwick/Sony Collector's Choice / Aug '93 / Pickwick / Pinnacle.

## YIPPEE-YI-YAY.
**Tracks:** Yippee-I-ay / Space and time.
■ **12"** .................... TA 4377
■ **7"** .................... A 4377
CBS / May '84.

## Lee, Jackie

## DUCK.
**Tracks:** Duck / Hully gully / Shotgun and the duck / Do the temptation walk / Shotgun / Land of a thousand dances / Dancin' in the street / Bounce / Do you love me / Everybody jerk / Harlem shuffle.
■ **LP** .................... JOYS 192
Joy / Apr '71.

## DUCK, THE.
**Tracks:** Not Advised.
**CD** .................... GSCD 011
Goldmine / Feb '93 / Vital Distribution.

## I KNOW KNOW KNOW.
**Tracks:** I know know know / So love me.
■ **7"** .................... DB 7860
Columbia / Mar '66.

## JOHNNY SAID COME OVER.
**Tracks:** Johnny said come over / End of a rainbow.
■ **7"** .................... 7N 45088
Pye / Aug '71.

## ONE MORE MOUNTAIN.
**Tracks:** One more mountain / What will I do.
■ **7"** .................... 7N 45072
Pye / May '71.

## SHOTGUN AND THE DUCK.
**Tracks:** Shotgun and the duck / Do the temptation walk.
■ **7"** .................... BOY 26
Jay Boy / Apr '71.

## WOULD YOU BELIEVE.
**Tracks:** Would you believe / You're everything.
■ **7"** .................... BOY 28
Jay Boy / Jul '71.

## Lee, Laura

Familiar background of gospel training and independent recording led Lee to Chess, with whom she developed forthright image (*Dirty Man, Wanted: Lover, No Experience Necessary*). Recruited to Hot Wax label by Holland-Dozier-Holland, she continued run of R&B hits and took *Women's Love Rights* into '71 pop chart. Decline began when she abandoned both proto-feminist lyrical stance and H-D-H in mid-70s, although she resurfaced in '83 with Al Green-produced gospel album *Jesus Is The Light Of My Life*.

## LAURA LEE.
**Tracks:** At last / Crumbs off the table / Every little bit hurts / Empty bed blues / Guess who I saw today / If you can beat me rocking / Workin' and lovin' together / Rip off / When a man loves a woman / If I'm good enough to love (I'm good enough to marry) / You've got to save me.
■ **LP** .................... HA 714
Buddah / '72.

## MUSCLE SHOALS SOUL (Lee, Laura & Irma Thomas).
**Tracks:** Not Advised.
**CD** .................... RTS 33033
Provogue / Aug '91 / Pinnacle.

## RIP OFF.
**Tracks:** Rip off / Two lonely pillows.
■ **7"** .................... HDH 45-3
HDH / Jul '84.

## RIP OFF, THE.
**Tracks:** Wedlock is a padlock / Women's love rights / I don't want nothing old (but money) / Love and liberty / Two lonely pillows / (Don't be sorry) be careful if you can't be good / If I'm good enough to love (I'm good enough to marry) / Rip off / If you can hear me rockin' (you can have my chair) / (If you want to try love again) remember me / Workin' and lovin' together / I'll catch you when you fall / I can't hold on much longer / I need it just as bad as you.
■ **LP** .................... HDH LP 003
HDH / Dec '84.

## SOMEONE TO LOVE ME.
**Tracks:** Someone to love me / Look left, look right.
■ **7"** .................... DB 877
Columbia / Mar '71.

## THAT'S HOW IT IS.
**Tracks:** Wanted: Lover no experience necessary / Up tight good man / Another man's woman / He will break your heart / Dirty man / Hang it up / Man with some backbone / It ain't what you do / Meet love halfway.
■ **LP** .................... GCH 8102
Chess (Charly) / '89.

■ CD . . . . . . . . . . . . . . . . . CHD 93005
Chess (MCA) / Sep '90.
CD . . . . . . . . . . . . . . . . . . .CDRED 27
Charly / Sep '91 / Charly.

## WOMEN'S LOVE RIGHTS.
**Tracks:** Women's love rights / Wedlock is a padlock / I don't want nothing old but money / Be careful if you can't be good / Love & Liberty / It's not what you fall for it's what you stand for / Since I fell for you / Two lovely pillows / That's how strong my love is / Her picture matches mine.
■ LP . . . . . . . . . . . . . . . . . SHW 5006
Hot Wax / Sep '72.

## Lee, Little Mr.

### YOUNG LOVER (Lee, Little Mr. & The Cherokees).
**Tracks:** Young lover / I don't want to go.
■ 7" . . . . . . . . . . . . . . . . . . VP 9268
Vocalion / Mar '66.

## Lee, Toney

### LOVE SO DEEP.
**Tracks:** Love so deep.
■ 12" . . . . . . . . . . . . . . . . . . DEST 2
Design Communications / Aug '83.

### REACH OUT.
**Tracks:** Reach out.
■ 12" . . . . . . . . . . . . . . . . . . TMTT 2
■ 7" . . . . . . . . . . . . . . . . . . TMT 2
T.M.T. / Jan '83.

## Legacy

### DON'T WASTE THE NIGHT.
**Tracks:** Don't waste the night.
■ 12" . . . . . . . . . . . . . . . . . . TA 6407
■ 7" . . . . . . . . . . . . . . . . . . .A 6407
Epic / Jun '85.

### GUILTY.
**Tracks:** Guilty / Guilty (inst).
■ 12" . . . . . . . . . . . . . . . .12EMI 5586
■ 7" . . . . . . . . . . . . . . . . EMI 5586
EMI / Mar '87.

### I DON'T MIND.
**Tracks:** I don't mind.
■ 12" . . . . . . . . . . . . . . . .12GLOBE 115
■ 7" . . . . . . . . . . . . . . . . GLOBE 115
■ CD Single . . . . . . . . . . . . CDGLOBE 115
■ MC Single . . . . . . . . . . . . CAGLOBE 115
All Around The World / Aug '92.

## Legend, Tobi

### TIME WILL PASS YOU BY (see under Parrish, Dean).

## Lemon

### FREAK, A.
**Tracks:** Freak A / Inside my heart.
■ 7" . . . . . . . . . . . . . . . . . . CBS 7219
CBS / Apr '79.

### LEMON.
**Tracks:** Freak A / Hot bodies / Freak on / Chance to dance / Inside my heart / Hot hands.
■ LP . . . . . . . . . . . . . . . . . CBS 83623
CBS / '79.

## Leniece

### GIVE MY LOVE TO YOU.
**Tracks:** Give my love to you / Give my love to you (version).
■ 12" . . . . . . . . . . . . . . . . .12JABA 4
■ 7" . . . . . . . . . . . . . . . . . JABA 4
Jaba / Sep '90.

## Lennox

### DON'T GO.
**Tracks:** Don't go / Free.
■ 12" . . . . . . . . . . . . . . . . . CBE 1255
■ 7" . . . . . . . . . . . . . . . . . CBE 755
City Beat / Nov '90.

## Leo's Sunshipp

### GIVE ME THE SUNSHINE.
**Tracks:** Give me the sunshine / I'm back for more.
■ 7" . . . . . . . . . . . . . . . . . . REDC 3
Grape-Vine / Oct '80.
■ 7" . . . . . . . . . . . . . . . . . EXPAND 3
Expansion / Aug '86.

## Leotis

### ON A MISSION.
**Tracks:** On a mission / On a mission (7" remix) / On a mission (12" remix) / On a mission (a cappella).
■ 12" . . . . . . . . . . . . . . . . .MERX 289
■ 7" . . . . . . . . . . . . . . . . MER 289
■ CD Single . . . . . . . . . . . . .MERCD 289
Mercury / May '89.

### ON A MISSION.
**Tracks:** Not Advised.
■ CD . . . . . . . . . . . . . . . . . 838 188-2
■ LP . . . . . . . . . . . . . . . . . 838 188-1
■ MC . . . . . . . . . . . . . . . . . 838 188-4
Mercury / Jun '89.

## Lester, Ketty

### BUT NOT FOR ME.
**Tracks:** But not for me.
■ 7" . . . . . . . . . . . . . . . . . HLN 9574
London-American / Jul '62.

### LOVE LETTERS.
**Tracks:** Love letters.
■ 7" . . . . . . . . . . . . . . . . . HLN 9527
London-American / Apr '62.

### LOVE LETTERS.
**Tracks:** Love letters / Then you can tell me goobye.
■ 7" . . . . . . . . . . . . . . . . . LIG 9012
Lightning / Apr '79.

### LOVE LETTERS (OLD GOLD).
**Tracks:** Love letters.
■ 7" . . . . . . . . . . . . . . . . . .OG 9012
Old Gold / Jul '82.

## Level 42

### ALL OVER YOU.
**Tracks:** All over you.
■ 12" . . . . . . . . . . . . . . 7432120565-1
■ CD Single . . . . . . . . . . . 7432120566-2
■ CD Single . . . . . . . . . . . 7432120565-2
■ MC Single . . . . . . . . . . . 7432120565-4
RCA / Apr '94.

### ARE YOU HEARING (WHAT I HEAR).
**Tracks:** Are you hearing (what I hear) / Return of the handsome rugged man.
■ 12" . . . . . . . . . . . . . . . . . POSPX 396
■ 7" . . . . . . . . . . . . . . . . . POSP 396
Polydor / May '82.

### CHANT HAS BEGUN, THE.
**Tracks:** Chant has begun / Almost there / Ill bread but with jam / Sun goes down (living it up).
■ 12" . . . . . . . . . . . . . . . . . POSPX 710
■ 7" . . . . . . . . . . . . . . . . . POSP 710
Polydor / Nov '84.

### CHILDREN SAY.
**Tracks:** Children say (remix) / Starchild (remix) / Children say (extended remix) (Only on cassette single.) / Something about you (Shep Pettibone remix) (Only on cassette single.) / Family edition megamix)
■ 12" . . . . . . . . . . . . . . . . . POSPX 911
■ 7" . . . . . . . . . . . . . . . . . POSP 911
■ 7" P.Disc . . . . . . . . . . . . . . POSPP 911
■ CD Single . . . . . . . . . . . . . . POCD 911
■ MC Single . . . . . . . . . . . . . . POSPC 911
Polydor / Dec '87.

### CHINESE WAY, THE.
**Tracks:** Chinese way / 88.
■ 12" . . . . . . . . . . . . . . . . . POSPX 538
■ 7" . . . . . . . . . . . . . . . . . POSP 538
Polydor / Jan '83.

### EARLY TAPES, THE (JULY/AUGUST, 1980).
**Tracks:** Sandstorm / Love meeting love / Theme to Margaret / Autumn (paradise is free) / Wings of love / Woman / Mr. Pink / 88.
■ LP . . . . . . . . . . . . . . . . . POLS 1064
Polydor / Apr '82.
■ LP . . . . . . . . . . . . . . . . . SPELP 28
■ MC . . . . . . . . . . . . . . . . . SPEMC 28
Polydor / Aug '83.

## FAIT ACCOMPLI.
**Tracks:** Heaven in my hands / Tracie / Take a look / Two hearts collide / Silence / Over there / I don't know why / Staring at the sun / Man / Gresham blues / Lessons in love / It's over / Running in the family.
■ VHS . . . . . . . . . . . . . . . . . CFV 08182
Polygram Music Video / Oct '94 / PolyGram.

## FAMILY OF FIVE.
**Tracks:** Running in the family / Lessons in love / Children say / It's over / To be with you again.
■ CD Video . . . . . . . . . . . . . . 080 276 9
Polygram Music Video / Oct '88 / PolyGram.
■ VHS . . . . . . . . . . . . . . . . . CFV 04512
Channel 5 / Oct '88 / Channel 5 Video / P.R.O. Video / Gold & Sons.

## FLYING ON THE WINGS OF LOVE.
**Tracks:** Flying on the wings of love / Wings of love.
■ 12" . . . . . . . . . . . . . . . . . POSPX 200
■ 7" . . . . . . . . . . . . . . . . . POSP 200
Polydor / Nov '80.

## FOREVER NOW.
**Tracks:** Forever now / Model friend / Tired of waiting / All over you / Love in a peaceful world / Romance / Billy's gone / One in a million / Sunbed song / Talking in your sleep / Don't bother me.
CD . . . . . . . . . . . . . . .74321 18996-2
MC . . . . . . . . . . . . . . .74321 18996-4
RCA / Mar '94 / BMG.

## FOREVER NOW.
**Tracks:** All over you / All over you (mixes) / Forever now / Forever now (mixes).
■ 12" . . . . . . . . . . . . . . .74321 19027-1
■ CD Single . . . . . . . . . . .74321 19027-2
■ MC Single . . . . . . . . . . .74321 19027-4
Arista / Feb '94.

## GUARANTEED.
**Tracks:** Guaranteed / All she wants.
■ 12" . . . . . . . . . . . . . . . . . PT 44746
■ 7" . . . . . . . . . . . . . . . . . PB 44745
■ CD Single . . . . . . . . . . . . . . PD 44746
■ MC Single . . . . . . . . . . . . . . PK 44745
RCA / Aug '91.

## GUARANTEED.
**Tracks:** Guaranteed / Overtime / Her big day / Seven years / Set me up / Ape / My father's shoes / Kinder eye / She can't help herself / If you were mine / Lasso the moon (Not available on LP) / With a little love (Not available on LP).
■ LP . . . . . . . . . . . . . . . . . PL 75005
MC . . . . . . . . . . . . . . . . . PK 75055
■ CD . . . . . . . . . . . . . . . . . PD 75005
RCA / Sep '91 / BMG.
DCC . . . . . . . . . . . . . . . . 07863621785
RCA / Jan '93 / BMG.

## GUARANTEED (LIVE).
**Tracks:** Hot water / Her big day / Sun goes down / Children say / Spirit is free / Leaving me now / Guaranteed / Heaven in my hands / She can't help herself / If you were mine / To be with you again / Running in the family / Lessons in love / Something about you / Mr. Pink / Love games / Chinese way.
■ VHS . . . . . . . . . . . . . . . . . MVN 4910093
PMI / May '92.

## HEAVEN IN MY HANDS.
**Tracks:** Heaven in my hands / Heaven in my hands (extended remix) (Only on CD single & 12".) / Gresham blues / Heaven in my hands (7" mix) (Only on CD single & 12".).
■ CD Single . . . . . . . . . . . . . . PZCD 14
■ 12" . . . . . . . . . . . . . . . . . PZ 14
■ 12" . . . . . . . . . . . . . . . . . PZX 14
■ 7" . . . . . . . . . . . . . . . . . PO 14
Polydor / Aug '88.

## HEAVEN IN MY HANDS (CD VIDEO).
**Tracks:** Heaven in my hands (single version) / Gresham blues / Heaven in my hands (extended version).
CD Video . . . . . . . . . . . . . . 080 502 2
Polydor / Oct '88 / PolyGram.

## HOT WATER.
**Tracks:** Hot water / Standing in the light.
■ 12" . . . . . . . . . . . . . . . . . POSPX 697
■ 7" . . . . . . . . . . . . . . . . . POSP 697
Polydor / Aug '84.

## IT'S OVER.
**Tracks:** It's over / Physical presence.
■ 12" . . . . . . . . . . . . . . . . . POSPX 900
■ 7" . . . . . . . . . . . . . . . . . POSP 900
■ MC Single . . . . . . . . . . . . . . POSPC 900
Polydor / Aug '87.

## IT'S OVER (CD VIDEO).
**Tracks:** It's over (extended remix) / Running in the family (Dave 'O' remix) / Physical presence. A (live).

CD Video . . . . . . . . . . . . . . . . . . . 080 156 2
Polydor / '89 / PolyGram.

## LEAVING ME NOW.
**Tracks:** Leaving me now / I sleep on my heart (remix).
- 12" . . . . . . . . . . . . . . . . . . . POSX 776
- 10" . . . . . . . . . . . . . . . . . . . POSPT 776
- 7" . . . . . . . . . . . . . . . . . . . POSP 776
Polydor / Nov '85.

## LEAVING ME NOW (CD VIDEO).
**Tracks:** Leaving me now.
CD Video . . . . . . . . . . . . . . . . . . . 080 218 2
Polygram Music Video / Oct '88 / PolyGram.

## LESSONS IN LOVE.
**Tracks:** Hot water (live) / World machine (Extra track on 12" version only) / Lessons in love.
- 12" . . . . . . . . . . . . . . . . . . . POSPX 790
- 7" . . . . . . . . . . . . . . . . . . . POSP 790
Polydor / Apr '86.

## LESSONS IN LOVE (CD VIDEO).
**Tracks:** Lessons in love.
CD Video . . . . . . . . . . . . . . . . . . . 080 004 2
Polygram Music Video / Oct '88 / PolyGram.

## LEVEL 42.
**Tracks:** Turn it on / 43 / Why are you leaving / Almost there / Heathrow / Love games / Dune tune / Starchild.
- LP . . . . . . . . . . . . . . . . . . . POLS 1036
MC. . . . . . . . . . . . . . . . . . . POLSC 1036
Polydor / Aug '81 / PolyGram.
CD. . . . . . . . . . . . . . . . . . . 821 935-2
Polydor / Jul '84 / PolyGram.

## LEVEL 42: CD BOX SET.
**Tracks:** Not Advised.
CD Set . . . . . . . . . . . . . . . . . . . 839 877-2
Polydor / Dec '89 / PolyGram.

## LEVEL 42: INTERVIEW PICTURE DISC.
**Tracks:** Not Advised.
- LP P.Disc . . . . . . . . . . . . . . . BAK 2043
Baktabak / May '87.

## LEVEL 42: VIDEO SINGLE.
**Tracks:** Not Advised.
VHS . . . . . . . . . . . . . . . . . .041 3932
Polygram Music Video / Jul '86 / PolyGram.

## LEVEL BEST.
**Tracks:** Running in the family / Sun goes down / Something about you / Tracie / Starchild / It's over / Hot water / Take care of yourself / Heaven in my hands / Children say / Love games / Chinese way / Leaving me now / Lessons in love / Micro kid (Only on CD and cassette.) / Take a look (Only on CD and cassette.) / To be with you again (Only on CD and cassette.) / Chant has begun (Only on CD and cassette.).
CD. . . . . . . . . . . . . . . . . . . 841 399-2
- LP . . . . . . . . . . . . . . . . . . .LEVTC 1
MC. . . . . . . . . . . . . . . . . . . LEVT 1
Polydor / Nov '89 / PolyGram.
DCC . . . . . . . . . . . . . . . . . . 841 399-5
Polydor / Jan '93 / PolyGram.

## LEVEL BEST.
**Tracks:** Running in the family / Hot water / Sun goes down (living it up) / Lessons in love / Chinese way / Children say / Heaven in my hands / To be with you again / Love games / It's over / Leaving me now / Take a look / Tracie / Micro kid / Starchild / Take care of yourself / Chant has begun / Something about you.
VHS . . . . . . . . . . . . . . . . . . CFV 10032
Channel 5 / Nov '89 / Channel 5 Video / P.R.O. Video / Gold & Sons.
VHS . . . . . . . . . . . . . . . . . . LED 80182
4 Front / May '91 / PolyGram Video.

## LIVE AT WEMBLEY.
**Tracks:** Fashion fever / World machine / Children say / Chinese way / Love games / Leaving me now / Chant has begun / Lessons in love / Sun goes down (living it up) / Something about you / Hot water / Running in the family (video).
VHS . . . . . . . . . . . . . . . . . . CFV 07042
Channel 5 / '87 / Channel 5 Video / P.R.O. Video / Gold & Sons.
CD Video . . . . . . . . . . . . . . . . . . . 080 036 1
Polygram Music Video / Oct '88 / PolyGram.

## LOVE GAMES.
**Tracks:** Love games.
- 12" . . . . . . . . . . . . . . . . . . . POSPX 234
- 7" . . . . . . . . . . . . . . . . . . . POSP 234
Polydor / Apr '81.

## LOVE IN A PEACEFUL WORLD.
**Tracks:** Love in a peaceful world (mixes) / The Bends (12", cassette single & CD(1) only) / Heart On The Line (12" & CD(1) only) / Leaving Me Now (CD(2) only) / It's Over (CD(2) only) / Take A Look (CD(2) only).
- 12" . . . . . . . . . . . . . . . . . . . 7432122032-1
- CD Single . . . . . . . . . . . . . . . 7432122033-2
- CD Single . . . . . . . . . . . . . . . 7432122032-2
- MC Single . . . . . . . . . . . . . . . 7432122032-4
Arista / Jul '94.

## LOVE MEETING LOVE.
**Tracks:** Love meeting love / Love meeting love (part 2).
- 12" . . . . . . . . . . . . . . . . . . . POSPX 170
- 7" . . . . . . . . . . . . . . . . . . . POSP 170
Polydor / Aug '80.

## MICRO KID.
**Tracks:** Micro kid / Turn it on (live).
- 12" . . . . . . . . . . . . . . . . . . . POSPX 643
- 7" . . . . . . . . . . . . . . . . . . . POSP 643
Polydor / Oct '83.

## MY FATHER'S SHOES.
**Tracks:** My father's shoes / As years go by / Her big day (Only on CD single) / Sun goes down (Only on CD single).
- CD Single . . . . . . . . . . . . . . . PD 45274
- 7" . . . . . . . . . . . . . . . . . . . PB 45271
- MC Single . . . . . . . . . . . . . . . PK 45271
RCA / Apr '92.

## ON A LEVEL.
**Tracks:** Running in the family / Physical presence / Take care of yourself / Love games / Two hearts collide / Love meeting love / True believers / Children say / Two solitudes / Turn it on / Chinese way / Almost there / (Flying on the) wings of love / Coup d'etat.
CD . . . . . . . . . . . . . . . . . .550 0102
MC . . . . . . . . . . . . . . . . . .550 0104
Spectrum (1) / May '93 / PolyGram.

## ON THE LEVEL.
**Tracks:** Heaven in my hands / Two hearts collide / Staring at the sun / Almost there / Wings of love / Tracie / Man / Take a look / Weave your spell / World machine / I don't know why / I sleep on my heart / Dream crazy / Standing in the light / Last chance / Are you hearing (what I hear).
CD . . . . . . . . . . . . . . . . . . PWKS 4078P
MC . . . . . . . . . . . . . . . . . . PWKMC 4078P
Pickwick / Oct '91 / Pickwick.

## OUT OF SIGHT, OUT OF MIND.
**Tracks:** Out of sight out of mind / You can't blame Louis.
- 12" . . . . . . . . . . . . . . . . . . . POSPX 570
- 7" . . . . . . . . . . . . . . . . . . . POSP 570
- 7" P.Disc . . . . . . . . . . . . . . . POSPP 570
Polydor / Apr '83.

## OVERTIME.
**Tracks:** Overtime / At this great distance / Overtime (instrumental).
- 12" . . . . . . . . . . . . . . . . . . . PT 44998
- 7" . . . . . . . . . . . . . . . . . . . PB 44997
- CD Single . . . . . . . . . . . . . . . PD 44998
RCA / Oct '91.

## PHYSICAL PRESENCE EP - FOLLOW ME.
**Tracks:** Physical presence / Follow me.
- 12" . . . . . . . . . . . . . . . . . . . POSPX 746
- EP . . . . . . . . . . . . . . . . . . . POSP 746
Polydor / Jun '85.

## PHYSICAL PRESENCE, A.
**Tracks:** Almost there / Turn it on / Mr. Pink / Eyes waterfalling / Kansas city milkman / Follow me / Foundation and empire / Chant has begun / Chinese way / Sun goes down (living it up) / Hot water / Love games / 88 (Available on LP and cassette only).
CD . . . . . . . . . . . . . . . . . . 825 677-2
- LP . . . . . . . . . . . . . . . . . . . POLH 23
MC . . . . . . . . . . . . . . . . . .POLHC 23
Polydor / Jun '85 / PolyGram.

## PURSUIT OF ACCIDENTS, THE.
**Tracks:** Weave your spell / Pursuit of accidents / Last chance / Are you hearing (what I hear) / You can't blame Louis / Shapeshifter / Chinese way / Chinese way, The (extended version) (on CD only) / You can't blame Louis (extended version) (on CD only).
- LP . . . . . . . . . . . . . . . . . . . POLD 5067
MC . . . . . . . . . . . . . . . . . . POLDC 5067
Polydor / Sep '82 / PolyGram.
CD . . . . . . . . . . . . . . . . . . 810 015-2
- LP . . . . . . . . . . . . . . . . . . . 810 015-1

MC . . . . . . . . . . . . . . . . . . 810 015-4
Polydor / Jun '90 / PolyGram.

## RUNNING IN THE FAMILY.
**Tracks:** Lessons in love / Children say / Running in the family / It's over / To be with you again / Two solitudes / Fashion fever / Sleepwalkers / Freedom someday.
CD . . . . . . . . . . . . . . . . . . 831 593-2
- LP . . . . . . . . . . . . . . . . . . . POLH 42
- LP . . . . . . . . . . . . . . . . . . .POLHA 42
- MC . . . . . . . . . . . . . . . . . . .POLHC 42
Polydor / Mar '87 / PolyGram.

## RUNNING IN THE FAMILY.
**Tracks:** Running in the family / Dream crazy.
- 7" . . . . . . . . . . . . . . . . . . . POSP 842
- 12" . . . . . . . . . . . . . . . . . . . POSPX 842
Polydor / Jan '87.

## RUNNING IN THE FAMILY (CD VIDEO SINGLE).
**Tracks:** Running in the family / Dream crazy / Hot water (live).
CD Video . . . . . . . . . . . . . . . . . . . 080 000 2
Polygram Music Video / Oct '88 / PolyGram.

## RUNNING IN THE FAMILY (OLD GOLD).
**Tracks:** Running in the family / Something about you.
- 12" . . . . . . . . . . . . . . . . . . .OG 4239
Pickwick / Oct '92.

## RUNNING IN THE FAMILY - PLATINUM EDITION.
**Tracks:** Children say / Running in the family (Dave 'O' remix) / It's over (remix) / Freedom someday / To be with you again / Two solitudes / Fashion fever / Sleepwalkers / Something about you (Shep Pettibone remix) / World machine (Shep Pettibone remix).
CD. . . . . . . . . . . . . . . . . . . 833 689-2
MC. . . . . . . . . . . . . . . . . . . 833 689-4
Polydor / Oct '87 / PolyGram.

## SOMETHING ABOUT YOU.
**Tracks:** Something about you / Coup d'etat.
- 12" . . . . . . . . . . . . . . . . . . . POSPX 759
- 7" . . . . . . . . . . . . . . . . . . . POSP 759
Polydor / Sep '85.

## STANDING IN THE LIGHT.
**Tracks:** Micro-kid / Sun goes down (living it up) / Out of sight out of mind / Dance on heavy weather / Pharaoh's dream of endless time / Standing in the light / I want eyes / People / Machine stops.
- LP . . . . . . . . . . . . . . . . . . . POLD 5110
MC. . . . . . . . . . . . . . . . . . . POLDC 5110
Polydor / Aug '83 / PolyGram.
CD. . . . . . . . . . . . . . . . . . . 813 865-2
- LP . . . . . . . . . . . . . . . . . . . 813 865-1
MC. . . . . . . . . . . . . . . . . . . 813 865-4
Polydor / Jun '90 / PolyGram.

## STARCHILD.
**Tracks:** Starchild / Foundation & empire.
- 7" . . . . . . . . . . . . . . . . . . .POSP 343
Polydor / Nov '81.

## STARING AT THE SUN.
**Tracks:** Heaven in my hands / I don't know why / Take a look / Over there / Silence / Tracie / Staring at the sun / Two hearts collide / Man / Gresham blues.
CD. . . . . . . . . . . . . . . . . . . 837 247-2
- LP . . . . . . . . . . . . . . . . . . . POLH 50
- MC. . . . . . . . . . . . . . . . . . .POLHC 50
Polydor / Sep '88 / PolyGram.

## STRATEGY.
**Tracks:** Not Advised.
- LP . . . . . . . . . . . . . . . . . . .LEVLP 1
Elite Records / Dec '81.

## SUN GOES DOWN (LIVING IT UP), THE.
**Tracks:** Sun goes down (living it up) / Can't walk you home.
- 12" . . . . . . . . . . . . . . . . . . . POSPX 622
- 7" . . . . . . . . . . . . . . . . . . . POSP 622
Polydor / Jul '83.

## TAKE A LOOK.
**Tracks:** Take a look (remix) / Man / Take a look (extended mix) (Only on 12" version and CD single.).
- 12" . . . . . . . . . . . . . . . . . . . PZY 14
- 12" . . . . . . . . . . . . . . . . . . . PZ 24
- 7" . . . . . . . . . . . . . . . . . . . POG 24
- 7" . . . . . . . . . . . . . . . . . . . PO 24
- CD Single . . . . . . . . . . . . . . . PZCD 24
Polydor / Oct '88.

## TAKE A LOOK (CD VIDEO).
**Tracks:** Take a look (extended version) / Man / Take a look (single version).

CD Video . . . . . . . . . . . . . . . . . 080 576 2
Polygram Music Video / Sep '89 / PolyGram.

## TAKE CARE OF YOURSELF.
Tracks: Take care of yourself / Silence (live) / Man (live) (Available on 12" and CD single only) / Take care of yourself (extended version) (Available on 12" only).
■ MC Single. . . . . . . . . . . . . . . POCS 58
■ 12" . . . . . . . . . . . . . . . . . . . . PZR 58
■ 12" . . . . . . . . . . . . . . . . . . . . PZ 58
■ 7" . . . . . . . . . . . . . . . . . . . . . PO 58
■ CD Single . . . . . . . . . . . . . . PZCD 58
Polydor / Oct '89.

## TO BE WITH YOU AGAIN.
Tracks: To be with you again / Micro kid (live).
■ 7" . . . . . . . . . . . . . . . . . . . . POSP 855
■ 7" P.Disc . . . . . . . . . . . . . POSPP 855
■ 12" . . . . . . . . . . . . . . . . . POSPX 855
Polydor / Apr '87.

## TRACIE.
Tracks: Tracie (extended mix) (Only on 12" & CD single) / Three words / Tracie (U.S. remix) (Only on 12"(PZX 34.) / Tracie.
■ 12" Remix . . . . . . . . . . . . . . . PZX 34
■ 12" . . . . . . . . . . . . . . . . . . . . PZ 34
■ 7" . . . . . . . . . . . . . . . . . . . . . PO 34
■ 7" . . . . . . . . . . . . . . . . . . . . POG 34
■ CD Single . . . . . . . . . . . . . . PZCD 34
Polydor / Jan '89.

## TRUE COLOURS.
Tracks: Chant has begun / Kansas City milkman / Seven days / Hot water / Floating life / True believers / Kouyate / Hours by the window.
■ LP . . . . . . . . . . . . . . . . . . . . POLH 10
MC . . . . . . . . . . . . . . . . . . . . POLHC 10
Polydor / Sep '84 / PolyGram.
CD . . . . . . . . . . . . . . . . . . . 823 545-2
Polydor / '88 / PolyGram.

## TURN IT ON.
Tracks: Turn it on / Beezer one.
■ 12" . . . . . . . . . . . . . . . . . POSPX 286
■ 7" . . . . . . . . . . . . . . . . . . POSP 286
Polydor / Aug '81.

## WEAVE YOUR SPELL.
Tracks: Weave your spell.
■ 12" . . . . . . . . . . . . . . . . . POSPX 500
■ 7" . . . . . . . . . . . . . . . . . . POSP 500
Polydor / Oct '82.

## WORLD MACHINE.
Tracks: World machine / Physical presence / Something about you / Leaving me now / I sleep on my heart / It's not the same for us / Good man in a storm / Coup d'etat / Lying still / Dream crazy / Love games (US remix) (Extra track on limited cassette) / Hot water (12" mix) (Extra track on limited cassette) / Sun goes down (living it up) (up front mix) (Extra track on limited cassette) / Chinese way, The (US mix) (Extra track on limited cassette) / I sleep on my heart (remix) (Extra track on limited cassette) / Something about you (sisa mix).
CD . . . . . . . . . . . . . . . . . . . 827 487-2
■ LP . . . . . . . . . . . . . . . . . . . . POLH 25
Polydor / Oct '85 / PolyGram.
MC . . . . . . . . . . . . . . . . . . . POLHX 25
Polydor / May '86 / PolyGram.

## WORLD MACHINE (U.S. EDITION).
Tracks: Something about you / World machine / Physical presence / Leaving me now / Hot water / It's not the same for us / Good man in a storm / Chant has begun.
CD . . . . . . . . . . . . . . . . . . . 829 627-2
Polydor / '86 / PolyGram.
■ LP . . . . . . . . . . . . . . . . . . 827 487-1
Polydor / May '86.

## Levert

In late 1980s, Eddie Levert had reasons to be cheerful. His group O'Jays were emerging from commercial doldrums, and sons Gerald and Eddie had returned family name to charts. After one independent album and single in '85, brothers signed to Atlantic and scored R&B hit with *(Pop Pop Pop Pop) Goes My Mind*. Escalating U.S. success was briefly matched in U.K., when *Casanova* became Levert's sole hit in '87. Successful albums and outside production continued into '90s; they also appeared on *New Jack City* soundtrack. In '94, Gerald toured with Boyz II Men, released solo album and produced Barry White's latest.

## BIG THROWDOWN, THE.
Tracks: Casanova / Good stuff / Don't u think it's time / My forever love / Love the way U love me / Sweet sensation / In 'n' out / Temptation / Throwdown.
CD . . . . . . . . . . . . . . . . . . . 781 773-2
■ LP . . . . . . . . . . . . . . . . . . . . WX 131
■ MC . . . . . . . . . . . . . . . . . . WX 131C
Atlantic / Sep '87 / WEA.

## CASANOVA.
Tracks: Casanova.
■ 7" . . . . . . . . . . . . . . . . . . . . .A 9217
■ 12" . . . . . . . . . . . . . . . . . . A 9217 T
Atlantic / Aug '87.

## CASANOVA (OLD GOLD).
Tracks: Casanova.
12" . . . . . . . . . . . . . . . . . . . .OG 4215
Old Gold / '92 / Pickwick.

## FOR REAL THO'.
Tracks: Me 'n' you / Clap your hands / Tribute song / Good ol' days / She's all that (I've been looking for) / For real tho' / Quiet storm / Do the thangs / My place (your place) / Say you will / ABC 123.
CD . . . . . . . . . . . . . . . . . .756782462-2
LP . . . . . . . . . . . . . . . . . . .756782462-1
MC . . . . . . . . . . . . . . . . . . .756782462-4
East West / Mar '93 / WEA.

## JUST COOLIN'.
Tracks: Pull over / Just coolin' / Gotta get the money / Take your time / Join in the fun / Let's get romantic / Feel real / Smilin' / Start me up again / Loveable.
■ CD . . . . . . . . . . . . . . . . . . 781 926-2
■ LP . . . . . . . . . . . . . . . . . . 781 926-1
■ MC . . . . . . . . . . . . . . . . . . 781 926-4
Atlantic / Oct '88.

## POP POP POP GOES MY MIND.
Tracks: Pop pop pop goes my mind / Looking for love.
■ 7" . . . . . . . . . . . . . . . . . . . .A 9389
■ 12" . . . . . . . . . . . . . . . . . . A 9389 T
Atlantic / Oct '87.

## ROPE A DOPE STYLE.
Tracks: Now you know / Rope a dope style / Absolutely positive / All season / Rain / Nobody does it better / I've been waiting / Baby I'm ready / Hey girl / Give a little love.
CD . . . . . . . . . . . . . . . . . . 7567821642
MC . . . . . . . . . . . . . . . . . . 7567821644
East West / Nov '90 / WEA.

## RUB A DUB STYLE.
Tracks: Not Advised.
CD . . . . . . . . . . . . . . . . . . .756821642
■ LP . . . . . . . . . . . . . . . . . .756821641
MC . . . . . . . . . . . . . . . . . . .756821644
Atlantic / Nov '90 / WEA.

## Levert, Gerald

## GROOVE ON.
Tracks: Not Advised.
CD . . . . . . . . . . . . . . . . . .756792416-2
LP . . . . . . . . . . . . . . . . . . .756792416-1
MC . . . . . . . . . . . . . . . . . . .756792416-4
Warner Bros. / Sep '94 / WEA.

## I'D GIVE ANYTHING.
Tracks: I'd give anything (Mixes).
12" . . . . . . . . . . . . . . . . . . . A 8228T
CD Single . . . . . . . . . . . . . . A 8228CD
MC Single . . . . . . . . . . . . . . . A 8228C
Atlantic / Oct '94 / WEA.

## Lewis, Barbara

## BABY I'M YOURS.
Tracks: Baby I'm yours / Hello stranger.
■ 7" . . . . . . . . . . . . . . . . . . . CS 8004
Contempo (1) / Mar '78.

## BABY I'M YOURS.
Tracks: Baby I'm yours / My heart went do dat da / Come home / Think a little sugar / If you love her / Stop that girl / Puppy love / Hello stranger / Someday we're gonna love again / Snap your fingers / How can I say goodbye / Straighten up your heart.
■ LP . . . . . . . . . . . . . . . . . . ATL 5042
Atlantic / Feb '66.

## DON'T FORGET ABOUT ME.
Tracks: Don't forget about me / It's magic.
■ 7" . . . . . . . . . . . . . . . . . . . AT 4068
Atlantic / Feb '66.

## HELLO STRANGER.
Tracks: Hello stranger.
■ 7" . . . . . . . . . . . . . . . . . . HLK 9724
London / '63.

## HELLO STRANGER - THE BEST OF BARBARA LEWIS.
Tracks: Not Advised.
CD . . . . . . . . . . . . . . . . . .812271619-2
Atlantic / Aug '94 / WEA.

## MAKE ME YOUR BABY.
Tracks: Make me your baby / Love to be loved.
■ 7" . . . . . . . . . . . . . . . . . . . AT 4041
Atlantic / Sep '65.

## MANY GROOVES OF BARBARA LEWIS, THE.
Tracks: Baby that's a no no / Windmills of your mind / Slip away / How can I tell / I can't break away from your love / Oh be my love / Just the way you are today / Anyway / But you know I love you / You made me a woman / Stars / Do I deserve it baby / Ask the lonely (Not on LP) / Why did it take you so long (Not on LP) / That's the way I like it (Not on LP).
■ LP . . . . . . . . . . . . . . . . . .SXATS 1035
Stax / Jul '70.
CD . . . . . . . . . . . . . . . . . . CDSXE 077
Stax / Jul '93 / Pinnacle.

## Lewis, Dave

## COLLECTION OF SHORT DREAMS.
Tracks: Stay right here forever / Late show / Go all out to get it / Papa boy / Whole lotta something goin' on / Lucy took a ride / Beautiful woman / Open up your heart / Woman like you.
■ LP . . . . . . . . . . . . . . . . . . . 2383522
Polydor / Jan '79.

## GOOD TO BE HOME AGAIN.
Tracks: Good to be home again / Lucky took a ride.
■ 7" . . . . . . . . . . . . . . . . . . . 2058974
Polydor / Feb '78.

## LUCY TOOK A RIDE.
Tracks: Lucy took a ride / Wholelot of somethin' going on.
■ 7" . . . . . . . . . . . . . . . . . . . 2059075
Polydor / Nov '78.

## TRAVELLING MAN.
Tracks: Travelling man / Easy come, easy go.
■ 7" . . . . . . . . . . . . . . . . . . . 2058645
Polydor / Oct '75.

## Lewis, Dee

## BEST OF MY LOVE, THE.
Tracks: Best of my love.
■ 12" . . . . . . . . . . . . . . . . . . .DEE 312
■ 7" . . . . . . . . . . . . . . . . . . . . DEE 3
■ CD Single . . . . . . . . . . . . . DEECD 3
Mercury / May '88.

## DON'T MAKE ME WAIT.
Tracks: Don't make me wait / This love.
■ 12" . . . . . . . . . . . . . . . . . . .DEE 212
■ 7" . . . . . . . . . . . . . . . . . . . . DEE 2
Mercury / Jan '88.

## DOUBLE STANDARD.
Tracks: Double standard / Double standard (version).
■ 12" . . . . . . . . . . . . . . . . . . . DEEX 5
■ 12" Remix . . . . . . . . . . . . . . DEEXR 5
■ 7" . . . . . . . . . . . . . . . . . . . . DEE 5
■ CD Single . . . . . . . . . . . . . DEECD 5
■ MC Single . . . . . . . . . . . . . DEEMC 5
Mercury / Oct '89.

## STUCK ON LOVE.
Tracks: Stuck on love.
■ 12" . . . . . . . . . . . . . . . . . . .DEE 412
■ 7" . . . . . . . . . . . . . . . . . . . . DEE 4
Mercury / Aug '87.

## Lewis, Jimmy

## TOTALLY INVOLVED.
Tracks: It ain't what's on the woman / There ain't no man that can't be caught / Is that any way to treat a lady / How long is a heartache suppose to last / Thank you / Go on live your life / That won't stop me from loving you / Help me understand you.
■ LP . . . . . . . . . . . . . . . . . . HA 50000
Hot Atlanta / '74.

## Lewis, Linda

## (REMEMBER THE DAYS OF) THE OLD SCHOOL YARD.
Tracks: (Remember the days of) the old school yard / Cordon blues.
■ 7" . . . . . . . . . . . . . . . . . . BELL 1405
Bell / Feb '75.

■ DELETED

## BABY I'M YOURS.
**Tracks:** Baby I'm yours.
■ 7" . . . . . . . . . . . . . . . . . . . . . . . ARIST 43
Arista / Apr '76.

## CAN'T WE JUST SIT DOWN & TALK IT OVER.
**Tracks:** Can't we just sit down and talk it over / Light years away.
■ 7" . . . . . . . . . . . . . . . . . . . . . . .ARIST 170
Arista / Mar '78.

## CLASS STYLE.
**Tracks:** Class style / You turn my bitter into sweet.
■ 12" . . . . . . . . . . . . . . . . . . . . . . TRICT 5
■ 12" Remix. . . . . . . . . . . . . . . . . . RTRIC 5
■ 7" . . . . . . . . . . . . . . . . . . . . . . . TRIC 5
■ 7" P.Disc . . . . . . . . . . . . . . . . . . PTRIC 5
Electricity / May '84.

## CLOSE THE DOOR TAKE YOUR HEART.
**Tracks:** Close the door, take your heart.
■ 7" . . . . . . . . . . . . . . . . . . . . . . . .A 3337
Epic / Apr '85.

## HACIENDA VIEW.
**Tracks:** Data love / Rolling for a while / Best days of my life / 109 Jamaica highway / Beggars and kings / I'd be surprisingly good for you / It seemed like a good idea at the time / Save the last dance for me / Sleeping like a baby now.
■ LP . . . . . . . . . . . . . . . . . . . . . . . ARL 5033
Ariola / Dec '79.

## I'D BE SURPRISINGLY GOOD FOR YOU.
**Tracks:** I'd be surprisingly good for you / Best days of my life.
■ 7" . . . . . . . . . . . . . . . . . . . . . . .ARIST 246
Arista / Mar '79.

## I'D BE SURPRISINGLY GOOD FOR YOU.
**Tracks:** I'd be surprisingly good for you / Best days of my life.
■ 7" . . . . . . . . . . . . . . . . . . . . . . . ARO 166
Ariola / Jun '79.

## IT'S IN HIS KISS.
**Tracks:** It's in his kiss.
■ 7" . . . . . . . . . . . . . . . . . . . . . . . ARIST 17
Arista / Jul '75.

## IT'S IN HIS KISS (OLD GOLD).
**Tracks:** It's in his kiss / Remember the days of the old schoolyard.
■ 7" . . . . . . . . . . . . . . . . . . . . . . .OG 9852
Old Gold / Jan '89.

## LARK.
**Tracks:** Spring song / Reach for the truth / It's the frame / Feeling feeling / What are you asking me for / Old Smokey / Gladly give my hand / More than a fool / Been my best / Water baby / Little Indians.
■ LP . . . . . . . . . . . . . . . . . . . . . . . K 44208
Reprise / Nov '72.

## MOON AND I.
**Tracks:** Moon and I / Flipped over your love.
■ 7" . . . . . . . . . . . . . . . . . . . . . . .ARIST 100
Arista / May '77.

## NOT A LITTLE GIRL ANYMORE.
**Tracks:** Not Advised.
■ LP . . . . . . . . . . . . . . . . . . . . . . . ARTY 109
Arista / Aug '75.

## PLAY AROUND.
**Tracks:** Play around / On the stage.
■ 7" . . . . . . . . . . . . . . . . . . . . . . . RA 18505
Raft / '73.

## ROCK A DOODLE DOO.
**Tracks:** Rock a doodle doo.
■ 7" . . . . . . . . . . . . . . . . . . . . . . . RA 18502
Raft / Jun '75.

## SIDEWAY SHUFFLE.
**Tracks:** Sideway shuffle / Safe and sound.
■ 7" . . . . . . . . . . . . . . . . . . . . . . . RA 18507
Raft / '74.

## SLEEPING LIKE A BABY.
**Tracks:** Sleeping like a baby / Rolling for a while.
■ 7" . . . . . . . . . . . . . . . . . . . . . . . ARO 207
Ariola / Feb '80.

## SLEEPING LIKE A BABY (ORIGINAL).
**Tracks:** Sleeping like a baby / Beggars and kings.
■ 7" . . . . . . . . . . . . . . . . . . . . . . . ARO 181
Ariola / Aug '79.

## TAKE YOUR HEART.
**Tracks:** Take your heart / I am what I am.
■ 7" . . . . . . . . . . . . . . . . . . . . . . . EPCA 3337
Epic / Apr '83.

## TEAR AND A SMILE, A.
**Tracks:** This boy / Desination love / Close the door, take your heart / Don't let it go / I am what I am / Take me for a little while / You don't know what you're missing / Why can't I be the other woman / Sweet heartache / I can't get enough.
■ LP . . . . . . . . . . . . . . . . . . . . . . . EPC 25478
MC. . . . . . . . . . . . . . . . . . . . . . . .40 25478
Epic / Sep '83 / Sony.

## THAT'S LOVE.
**Tracks:** That's love / My aphrodisiac is you.
■ 7" . . . . . . . . . . . . . . . . . . . . . . . ARO 231
Ariola / Jun '80.

## THIS BOY.
**Tracks:** This boy / I can take it.
■ 7" . . . . . . . . . . . . . . . . . . . . . . . .A 3518
Epic / Jul '83.

## WE CAN WIN.
**Tracks:** We can win / Hampstead way.
■ 7" . . . . . . . . . . . . . . . . . . . . . . . K 14096
Kinney / Aug '71.

## WHY CAN'T I BE THE OTHER WOMAN?.
**Tracks:** Why can't I be the other woman / Come on back.
■ 7" . . . . . . . . . . . . . . . . . . . . . . . KRL A2860
Kaleidoscope / Oct '82.

## WINTER WONDERLAND.
**Tracks:** Winter wonderland / All comes back to love.
■ 7" . . . . . . . . . . . . . . . . . . . . . . . ARIST 82
Arista / Dec '76.

## WOMAN OVERBOARD.
**Tracks:** Not Advised.
■ LP . . . . . . . . . . . . . . . . . . . . . . .SPARTY 1003
Arista / Apr '77.

## YOU TURNED MY BITTER INTO SWEET.
**Tracks:** You turned my bitter into sweet.
■ 7" . . . . . . . . . . . . . . . . . . . . . . . 56173
Polydor / '67.

---

## Lewis, Pat

### SEPARATION.
**Tracks:** Separation.
■ 12" . . . . . . . . . . . . . . . . . . . . . . . DEBTX 3131
Debut (2) / Oct '91.

---

## Lewis, Ramsey

After an impressive childhood and adolescence, during which his playing won scholarships and plaudits galore, Chicago-born pianist formed jazz-orientated group in 1956. Slow but steady rise of Ramsey Lewis Trio climaxed with 1965 cover of *The In Crowd* (A perennial dancefloor favourite and theme tune for Jimmy Saville's *Old Record Club*), a hit earlier that year for vocalist Dobie Gray. Lewis' instrumental rendition shot to No. 5, the formula was milked with *Hang On Sloopy*, *Hard Day's Night* and *Wade In The Water* (latter was rare and belated U.K. hit in 1972). Concentrating on albums from late '60s, some produced by Earth Wind & Fire alumni (Maurice White was drummer in final incarnation of trio), Lewis continued to enjoy commercial success by reworking both well-known and unfamiliar numbers. He was still going strong in '90s; recording, hosting syndicated U.S. radio show and directing jazz festivals. 1994 MCA charity album *Red Hot And Cool* saw him teamed with Carleen Anderson.

## 16 GREATEST HITS.
**Tracks:** Not Advised.
CD. . . . . . . . . . . . . . . . . . . . . . . CD 8024
16 / May '94 / BMG.

## BEST OF RAMSEY LEWIS.
**Tracks:** Sun goddess / Skippin' / Caring for you / Spring high / All the way live / Tequila mockingbird / Hot dawgit / Funky serenity / Love notes / Brazilica.
■ LP . . . . . . . . . . . . . . . . . . . . . . . CBS 84911
CBS / Jan '82.

## CHANCE ENCOUNTER.
**Tracks:** What's going on / Chance encounter / Up where we belong / Intimacy / Special place / Paradise / I can't wait / Just a little ditty.
■ LP . . . . . . . . . . . . . . . . . . . . . . . CBS 25057
CBS / Jan '83.

## CLASSIC ENCOUNTER.
**Tracks:** Not Advised.
■ CD. . . . . . . . . . . . . . . . . . . . . . . 4608182

■ LP . . . . . . . . . . . . . . . . . . . . . . . 4608181
■ MC . . . . . . . . . . . . . . . . . . . . . . . 4608184
CBS.

## DANCING IN THE STREET (Lewis, Ramsey Trio).
**Tracks:** Mood for Mendes / Struttin' lightly / You don't know me / Django / What now my love / Dancing in the street / Quiet nights / Black Orpheus medley.
■ LP . . . . . . . . . . . . . . . . . . . . . . . CRS 4533
Chess / Mar '68.

## DOWN TO EARTH (Lewis, Ramsey Trio).
**Tracks:** Dark eyes / Sorrento / Soul mist / John Henry / Greensleeves / We blue it / Billy boy / Motherless child / Suzanne / Decisions.
■ LP . . . . . . . . . . . . . . . . . . . . . . . SFJL 962
Fontana / Nov '68.

## ELECTRIC COLLECTION.
**Tracks:** Not Advised.
CD. . . . . . . . . . . . . . . . . . . . . . . 4679032
MC. . . . . . . . . . . . . . . . . . . . . . . 4679034
Sony (Import) / Jun '91 / Sony.

## FANTASY.
**Tracks:** This ain't no fantasy / Ram jam / It's gonna change / Les ciefs de mon coeur / Victim of a broken heart / Slow dancing / Never give up / Part of me / Quest.
■ LP . . . . . . . . . . . . . . . . . . . . . . . CBS 26688
CBS / '86.

## FUNCTION AT THE JUNCTION.
**Tracks:** Function at the junction / Hey Missus Jones.
■ 7" . . . . . . . . . . . . . . . . . . . . . . . CRS 8050
Chess / Jun '67.

## HANG ON RAMSEY (Lewis, Ramsey Trio).
**Tracks:** Not Advised.
■ LP . . . . . . . . . . . . . . . . . . . . . . . CRL 4520
Chess / May '66.

## HIS GREATEST SIDES VOL.1.
**Tracks:** High heel sneakers / Hang on sloopy / Dancing in the street / Hard day's night / Something you've got / In crowd / Wade in the water / Soul man / Since you've been gone / One two three / Les fleurs / Uptight.
■ LP . . . . . . . . . . . . . . . . . . . . . . . CXMP 2051
Chess (PRT) / Jun '84.
■ LP . . . . . . . . . . . . . . . . . . . . . . . GCH 8003
MC. . . . . . . . . . . . . . . . . . . . . . . GCHK 78003
Chess (Charly) / Aug '86 / Charly.

## HOT DOGGIT (Lewis, Ramsey with Earth, Wind & Fire).
**Tracks:** Hot doggit / Tambura.
■ 7" . . . . . . . . . . . . . . . . . . . . . . . CBS 3033
CBS / Feb '75.

## IN CONCERT - 1965 (Lewis, Ramsey Trio).
**Tracks:** Satin doll / And I love her / Come Sunday / Hard day's night / "In" crowd.
CD. . . . . . . . . . . . . . . . . . . . . . . CD 53108
Giants Of Jazz / May '92 / Wellard / Swift / Target / Jazz Music / BMG.

## IN CROWD.
**Tracks:** In crowd / Hang on Sloopy / Wade in the water / Hard day's night.
■ 7" . . . . . . . . . . . . . . . . . . . . . . . CHES 4006
Chess (PRT) / Jul '85.

## IN CROWD, THE.
**Tracks:** In crowd / Hang on sloopy / Wade in the water / Hard day's night / Soul man / Up tight / Something you got / One, two, three / Hi hell sneakers / Day tripper / Dancing in the street / Since you've been gone / Les fleurs / Since I fell for you / Tennessee waltz / You been talkin' 'bout me baby / Spartacus (love theme) / Felicidade / Come Sunday.
CD. . . . . . . . . . . . . . . . . . . . . . . CDGRF 019
Tring / '93 / Prism Leisure PLC / Midland Records.

## IN CROWD, THE - GREATEST HITS.
**Tracks:** Hang on sloopy / 'In' crowd / Dancing in the street / High heel sneakers / Something you've got / Soul man / One two three / Since I fell for you / Wade in the water / Hard day's night / Upright / You been talking 'bout me baby / Since you've been gone / Les fleurs / Tennessee waltz / Felicidade / Love theme Spartacus / Come Sunday.
CD. . . . . . . . . . . . . . . . . . . . . . . 2636462
MC. . . . . . . . . . . . . . . . . . . . . . . 2636464
Black Tulip / Oct '89.
■ CD . . . . . . . . . . . . . . . . . . . . . . . MCLD 19062
■ MC . . . . . . . . . . . . . . . . . . . . . . . MCLC 19062
MCA / Oct '92.
CD. . . . . . . . . . . . . . . . . . . . . . . CDCD 1103
Charly / Jul '93 / Charly.

■ DELETED

## INSTRUMENTAL SOUL HITS (Lewis, Ramsey & King Curtis).
Tracks: Not Advised.
CD . . . . . . . . . . . . . . . . . . RMB 75047
MC . . . . . . . . . . . . . . . . . . RMB 45047
Remember / Nov '93 / Midland Records / BMG.

## IVORY PYRAMID.
Tracks: Bazillica / People make the world go round / Ivory pyramid / Sarah Jane / Tequila mockingbird / Night in Bahia / Malachi (The messenger) / Pavanne / Love's gotta hold / Jackson park.
CD . . . . . . . . . . . . . . . . . . GRP 96882
GRP / Nov '92 / BMG / New Note.

## KEYS TO THE CITY.
Tracks: Keys to the city / You're falling in love / 7-11 / Strangers / My love will lead you home / Melody of life / Shamballa / Love and understanding.
■ LP . . . . . . . . . . . . . . . . . . 4508701
MC . . . . . . . . . . . . . . . . . . 4508704
CBS / May '87 / Sony.

## LEGACY.
Tracks: Toccata / Adagio / Fugue / All the way love / I love to please you / Well, well, well / Moogin' on / Don't look back.
■ LP . . . . . . . . . . . . . . . . . . CBS 82964
CBS / Jan '79.

## LES FLEURS.
Tracks: Super woman / House is not a home / Essence of love / Les fleurs / Physical / With a gentle touch / Reasons.
■ LP . . . . . . . . . . . . . . . . . . CBS 25524
CBS / Sep '83.

## LIVE (Lewis, Ramsey Trio).
Tracks: Not Advised.
CD . . . . . . . . . . . . . . . . . . JHR 73524
Jazz Hour / May '93 / Target / Jazz Music.

## LIVE AT THE SAVOY.
Tracks: Close your eyes and remember / Sassy stew / Callin' fallin' / Baby what you want me to do / You never know / Lynn / It's just called love / Wade in the water / Hang on Sloopy / In crowd.
■ LP . . . . . . . . . . . . . . . . . . CBS 85502
CBS / Apr '82.

## MAIDEN VOYAGE.
Tracks: Maiden voyage / Mighty Quinn / Sweet rain / Lady Madonna / Way to San Jose / Fleur / Since you've been gone / Heat of the night / African boogaloo / Only when I'm dreaming / Eternal journey.
■ LP . . . . . . . . . . . . . . . . . . CRLS 4539
Chess / Nov '68.

## MAIDEN VOYAGE (AND MORE).
Tracks: Maiden voyage / Mighty Quin / Sweet rain / Lady Madonna / Do you know the way to San Jose / Ode / Les fleur / Since you've been gone / Only when I'm dreaming / Eternal journey / Mother nature's son / Julia / Good night / Dear prudence.
CD . . . . . . . . . . . . . . . . . . GRP 18042
GRP / Jun '94 / BMG / New Note.

## MOTHER NATURE'S SON.
Tracks: Mother nature's son / Rocky Raccoon / Julie / Back in the USSR / Prologue / Cry baby cry / Good night / Everybody's got something to hide except me and my monkey / Sexy Sadie / Blackbird.
■ LP . . . . . . . . . . . . . . . . . . CRLS 4545
Chess / May '69.

## RAMSEY LEWIS.
Tracks: Aquarius / Let the sun shine in / Wearin' it out / I just can't give you up / Every chance I get / Dancin' / I'll always dream about you / Intermezzo / Spanoletts / Don't cry for me Argentina.
■ LP . . . . . . . . . . . . . . . . . . CBS 83584
CBS / '79.

## REUNION.
Tracks: In crowd / (Song of) Delilah / Hello cello / Hang on sloopy / Wind / Carmen / Horizon.
■ LP . . . . . . . . . . . . . . . . . . CBS 25804
MC . . . . . . . . . . . . . . . . . . .40 25804
CBS / Jan '84 / Sony.

## ROUTES.
Tracks: Whisper zone / High point / Tondelayo / Caribbean blue / Looking glass / Come back Jack / Colors in space / Crystals in sequence / You are the reason / Hell on wheels.
■ LP . . . . . . . . . . . . . . . . . . CBS 84243
CBS / Oct '80.

## SKY ISLANDS.
Tracks: Julia / Aprez vous / Who are you / Suavecito / Tonight / Sky islands / Song for you / Medley / Love will find a way / Come back to me / Tonight (instrumental version).

## CD . . . . . . . . . . . . . . . . . . GRP 97452
GRP / Oct '93 / BMG / New Note.

## SOLID IVORY (Ramsey Lewis's Greatest Hits).
Tracks: Ain't that peculiar / Cry baby cry / Day tripper / Felicidade / Les fleurs / Function at the junction / Hang on sloopy / Hard day's night / Hurt so bad / In crowd / Jade East / Julia / Maiden voyage / Since I fell for you / Soul man / Tennessee waltz / Uptight / Wade in the water / What now my love.
■ LP . . . . . . . . . . . . . . . . . . 6641328
■ MC . . . . . . . . . . . . . . . . . . 7559103
Chess / Jan '77.

## SOUND OF CHRISTMAS, THE (Lewis, Ramsey Trio).
Tracks: Merry Christmas baby / Winter wonderland / Santa Claus is coming to town / Christmas blues / Here comes Santa Claus / Sound of Christmas / Christmas song / God rest ye merry gentlemen / Sleigh ride / What are you doing New Year's Eve.
■ LP . . . . . . . . . . . . . . . . . . GCH 8016
MC . . . . . . . . . . . . . . . . . . GCHK 8016
Chess (Charly) / Jan '87 / Charly.

## SPRING HIGH.
Tracks: Spring high / Tequila mockingbird / All the way.
■ 7" . . . . . . . . . . . . . . . . . . CBS 8007
CBS / Nov '79.

## SUN GODDESS.
Tracks: Sun goddess / Jungle strut.
■ 7" . . . . . . . . . . . . . . . . . . CBS 3319
CBS / Jun '75.

## THREE PIECE SUITE.
Tracks: Lakeshore cowboy / Romance me / Will you / Love is / Michelle / Don't ever go away / So much more / Can't wait till summer / She's out of my life / Expansions.
■ LP . . . . . . . . . . . . . . . . . . CBS 84980
CBS / Jul '81.

## TOBACCO ROAD.
Tracks: Them changes / Tobacco road / Mi compasion / Hurt so bad / Unsilent majority / Do whatever sets you free / Something / Oh happy day.
■ LP . . . . . . . . . . . . . . . . . . 6310124
Chess / Nov '72.

## UP POPS RAMSEY LEWIS.
Tracks: Soul man / Look of love / Respect / Goin' out of my head / Party time / Bearmash / I was made to love her / Alfie / Why am I treated so bad / Jade east.
■ LP . . . . . . . . . . . . . . . . . . CRLS 4535
Chess / May '68.

## UP WHERE WE BELONG.
Tracks: Up where we belong / Chance encounter.
■ 7" . . . . . . . . . . . . . . . . . . A 2946
CBS / Dec '82.

## WADE IN THE WATER.
Tracks: In crowd / Wade in the water.
■ 7" . . . . . . . . . . . . . . . . . . 6145 004
Chess / Apr '72.
■ 12" . . . . . . . . . . . . . . . . . . CHESL 101
■ 7" . . . . . . . . . . . . . . . . . . CHES 101
Chess (PRT) / Jun '81.

## WADE IN THE WATER (OLD GOLD) (Lewis, Ramsey Trio).
Tracks: Wade in the water / In crowd.
■ 7" . . . . . . . . . . . . . . . . . . OG 9848
Old Gold / Jan '89.

# Lewis, Shirley

## DON'T SAY A WORD.
Tracks: Don't say a word.
■ 12" . . . . . . . . . . . . . . . . . . ELCT 1
Electricity / Jan '84.

## HEARTBREAKER.
Tracks: Heartbreaker / Waiting for the dawn.
■ 12" . . . . . . . . . . . . . . . . . . USAT 661
■ 7" . . . . . . . . . . . . . . . . . . USA 661
Breakout / Aug '89.

## LOVE'S WARMING UP.
Tracks: Love's warming up.
■ 12" . . . . . . . . . . . . . . . . . . HET 101
■ 7" . . . . . . . . . . . . . . . . . . HE 101
CBS / Jul '83.

## PASSION IN THE HEART.
Tracks: Not Advised.
■ CD . . . . . . . . . . . . . . . . . . CDA 5270

## LP . . . . . . . . . . . . . . . . . . AMA 5270
■ MC . . . . . . . . . . . . . . . . . . AMC 5270
A&M / Sep '89.

## REALISTIC.
Tracks: Realistic / Realistic (R&B version).
■ 12" . . . . . . . . . . . . . . . . . . USAT 660
■ 7" . . . . . . . . . . . . . . . . . . USA 660
■ CD Single . . . . . . . . . . . . . . . . . . USACD 660
A&M / Jul '89.

## ROMANTIC.
Tracks: Romantic (Some like it hot mix) / Romantic (romancing the street mix).
■ 12" . . . . . . . . . . . . . . . . . . USAT 635
■ 12" Remix . . . . . . . . . . . . . . . . . . USAF 635
■ 7" . . . . . . . . . . . . . . . . . . USA 635
Breakout / Jun '88.

# Lewis Sisters

## YOU NEED ME.
Tracks: You need me.
■ 7" . . . . . . . . . . . . . . . . . . TMG 536
Tamla Motown / Oct '65.

# Lewis, Tamala

## YOU WON'T SAY NOTHING.
Tracks: You won't say nothing / If you can stand me.
■ 7" . . . . . . . . . . . . . . . . . . DS 1010
Destiny (Northern Soul) / Dec '79.

# Lewis, Webster

## 8 FOR THE 80'S.
Tracks: You deserve to dance / Give me some emotion / Love you give to me / I want to blow / Fire / Go for it / Heavenly / Mild wind.
■ LP . . . . . . . . . . . . . . . . . . EPC 84283
Epic / Jul '80.

## GIMME SOME EMOTION.
Tracks: Gimme some emotion / I want to blow my horn.
■ 7" . . . . . . . . . . . . . . . . . . EPC 8510
Epic / Apr '80.

## LET ME BE THE ONE.
Tracks: Not Advised.
■ LP . . . . . . . . . . . . . . . . . . EPC 36878
Epic / Sep '89.

# Liggins, Joe

## DARKTOWN STRUTTERS' BALL, THE (Liggins, Joe & His Honey Drippers).
Tracks: Miss Betty's blues / Got your love in my heart / Caravan / I know my love is true / Got a right to cry / Walkin' / Tanya / Sugar lump / at the darktown strutter's ball / Downhome blues / Breaking my heart / Sweet Georgia Brown / Blues / Loosiana / Spooks holiday / Daddy on my mind.
■ LP . . . . . . . . . . . . . . . . . . JB 601
Jukebox Lil (Sweden) / Aug '81.
CD . . . . . . . . . . . . . . . . . . RBD 601
RBD / Oct '93 / Jazz Music.

## DRIPPER'S BOOGIE VOL.2 (Liggins, Joe & His Honey Drippers).
Tracks: Sentimental lover / Little Joe's boogie / Daddy on my mind / Little Joe's boogie AKA Guitar boogie / Bob is my guy / That's the one for me / Little black town / So alone / Oh how I miss you / Boogie woogie Lou / Cryin' over you / Dripper's boogie / My heart cried / Farewell blues / Deep feeling kind of love / Hey, Betty Martin / Everyone's down on me / Make love to me / Tenderly / Tears on my pillow.
■ CD . . . . . . . . . . . . . . . . . . CDCHD 436
Ace / Jan '93.

## GREAT RHYTHM AND BLUES VOL.6.
Tracks: Honeydripper (part 1) / Honeydripper (part 2) / Pink champagne / Boom-chick-a-boogie / Goin' back to L.A. / I've got a right to cry / Tanya / Stinky / Brown angel.
■ LP . . . . . . . . . . . . . . . . . . BDL 1005
Bulldog Records / Jul '82.

## HONEYDRIPPER, THE (1945-49) (Liggins, Joe & His Honey Drippers).
Tracks: Not Advised.
■ LP . . . . . . . . . . . . . . . . . . JB 622
Jukebox Lil (Sweden) / Nov '88.

## JOE & JIMMY LIGGINS (Liggins, Joe & Jimmy).
Tracks: Honey dripper / Pink champagne / I've got a right to cry / Rhythm in the barnyard / Little Joe's boogie / So alone / Dripper's boogie / Saturday night boogie woogie man / Drunk / Homecoming blue /

■ DELETED

Nite life boogie / Tear drop blues / Cadillac boogie /
Washboard special.
■ LP . . . . . . . . . . . . . . . . . . . . . . SNTF 5020
Sonet / '74.

## JOE LIGGINS AND THE HONEYDRIP-PERS (Liggins, Joe & His Honey Drippers).

**Tracks:** Pink champagne / Ramblin' blues / Rag mop
/ Rhythm in the barnyard / Going back to New
Orleans / I've got a right to cry / Honeydripper / I just
can't help myself / Don't miss that train / Frankie Lee
/ Brand new deal in mobile / Little Joe's boogie /
One sweet letter / Whiskey, gin and wine / Louisiana
woman / Trying to lose the blues / Shuffle boogie
blues / Rain, rain, rain / Flying Dutchman / Tanya /
Blues for Tanya / Freight train blues / Whiskey,
women and loaded dice / Big dipper / Do you love
me pretty baby.
CD . . . . . . . . . . . . . . . . . . . .CDCHD 307
Ace / Oct '90 / Pinnacle / Complete Record Co. Ltd.

## Light Of The World

### BEST OF LIGHT OF THE WORLD.
**Tracks:** London town '85 / Visualise yourself (and
your mind) / Pete's crusade / I'm so happy / Boys in
blue / Swingin' / I shot the Sheriff / Time.
■ LP . . . . . . . . . . . . . . . . . . . . . ENGY 1
MC. . . . . . . . . . . . . . . . . . . . . . ENGC 1
Ensign / Nov '85 / EMI.
■ LP . . . . . . . . . . . . . . . . . . . CHEN 29
■ MC. . . . . . . . . . . . . . . . . TCCHEN 29
■ CD . . . . . . . . . . . . . . . . .CDCHEN 29
Ensign / Oct '92.

### BEST OF LIGHT OF THE WORLD, THE.
**Tracks:** Not Advised.
CD. . . . . . . . . . . . . . . . . . . . . . MCCD 189
MC. . . . . . . . . . . . . . . . . . . . . MCTC 189
Music Club / Nov '94 / Gold & Sons / THE / Video
Collection / C.M. Distribution.

### BOYS IN BLUE.
**Tracks:** Boys in blue / This is this.
■ 12" . . . . . . . . . . . . . . . . . . .ENY 36-12
■ 7" . . . . . . . . . . . . . . . . . . . ENY 36
Ensign / Feb '80.

### CHECK US OUT.
**Tracks:** Check us out / Famous faces / I can't stop /
Don't run / Tubbs in the caribbean / Soho / Number
one girl / Everybody move / Easy things to say.
■ LP . . . . . . . . . . . . . . . . . . . EMC 3410
EMI / Jun '82.

### CHECK US OUT.
**Tracks:** Check us out / I can't stop.
■ 12" . . . . . . . . . . . . . . . . . .12EMI 5294
■ 7" . . . . . . . . . . . . . . . . . . EMI 5294
EMI / May '82.

### FAMOUS FACES.
**Tracks:** Famous faces / Get on board.
■ 12" . . . . . . . . . . . . . . . . . .12EMI 5324
■ 7" . . . . . . . . . . . . . . . . . . EMI 5324
EMI / Sep '82.

### I SHOT THE SHERIFF.
**Tracks:** I shot the sheriff / New soft song.
■ 12" . . . . . . . . . . . . . . . . . . ENY 4612
Ensign / Nov '80.
■ 7" . . . . . . . . . . . . . . . . . . ENY 46
Ensign / Jan '81.

### JEALOUS LOVER.
**Tracks:** Jealous lover / Stranger.
■ 12" . . . . . . . . . . . . . . . . . .12EMI 5403
■ 7" . . . . . . . . . . . . . . . . . . EMI 5403
EMI / Jul '83.

### KEEP THE DREAM ALIVE.
**Tracks:** Keep the dream alive / Keep the dream alive
(part 2) (12" & CD single only) / Keep the dream alive
(groove buster) (12" only) / Keep the dream alive
(full version) (7" & cassingle only) / Keep the dream
alive (12" version) (12" & CD single only).
■ 12" . . . . . . . . . . . . . . . . . .COOLX 232
■ 7" . . . . . . . . . . . . . . . . . .COOL 232
■ CD Single . . . . . . . . . . . . . .COOLCD 232
■ MC Single. . . . . . . . . . . . . .COOLMC 232
Cool Tempo / Apr '91.

### LIGHT OF THE WORLD.
**Tracks:** Aspects / Dreams / Liv togevver / Midnight
groovin' / Mirror of my soul / Swingin' / Who are you.
■ LP . . . . . . . . . . . . . . . . . . . ENVY 7
Ensign / '79.

### LONDON TOWN.
**Tracks:** London town / Pete's crusade.
■ 7" . . . . . . . . . . . . . . . . . . . ENY 43
Ensign / Oct '80.

### LONDON TOWN '85.
**Tracks:** London Town '85.
■ 7" . . . . . . . . . . . . . . . . . . .ENY 518
■ 12" . . . . . . . . . . . . . . . . . 12ENY 518
Ensign / Jun '85.

### LONDON TOWN (OLD GOLD).
**Tracks:** London town / Time.
■ 12" . . . . . . . . . . . . . . . . . . .OG 4095
Old Gold / Jan '89.

### MIDNIGHT GROOVIN'.
**Tracks:** Midnight groovin'.
■ 12" . . . . . . . . . . . . . . . . . ENY 2912
■ 7" . . . . . . . . . . . . . . . . . . ENY 29
Ensign / Jul '79.

### NO.1 GIRL.
**Tracks:** No.1 girl / Don't run.
■ 12" . . . . . . . . . . . . . . . . . .12EMI 5319
■ 7" . . . . . . . . . . . . . . . . . . EMI 5319
EMI / Jul '82.

### ONE DESTINATION.
**Tracks:** One destination.
■ 12" . . . . . . . . . . . . . . . . . .COOLX 209
■ 7" . . . . . . . . . . . . . . . . . .COOL 209
■ CD Single . . . . . . . . . . . . . .COOLCD 209
■ MC Single . . . . . . . . . . . . . .COOLMC 209
Cool Tempo / Jun '90.

### REMIXED..
**Tracks:** Not Advised.
■ LP . . . . . . . . . . . . . . . . . . . .6359 062
Mercury / Jun '81.

### RIDE THE LOVE TRAIN.
**Tracks:** Ride the love train / Get on board.
■ 12" . . . . . . . . . . . . . . . . . .12EMI 5242
■ 7" . . . . . . . . . . . . . . . . . . EMI 5242
EMI / Nov '81.

### ROUND TRIP.
**Tracks:** Time / London Town / I shot the sherriff / I'm
so happy / More of myself / Visualise yourself / I
Painted lady / I walk the streets alone / Pete's
crusade / Something for nothing.
■ LP . . . . . . . . . . . . . . . . . . .ENVY 14
Ensign / Jan '81.

### SWINGIN'.
**Tracks:** Swingin' / World is out.
■ 12" . . . . . . . . . . . . . . . . . ENY 2212
■ 7" . . . . . . . . . . . . . . . . . . ENY 22
Ensign / Apr '79.

### TIME.
**Tracks:** Time / I'm so happy.
■ 12" . . . . . . . . . . . . . . . . . . MERX 64
■ 7" . . . . . . . . . . . . . . . . . . MER 64
Mercury / Mar '81.

## Limit

### PLEASE PLEASE ME.
**Tracks:** Please please me / My world at night.
■ 7" . . . . . . . . . . . . . . . . . .PVT 156
Private Stock / Jul '78.

### SAY YEAH!.
**Tracks:** Say yeah.
■ 12" . . . . . . . . . . . . . . . . . . TA 4808
■ 7" . . . . . . . . . . . . . . . . . .A 4808
Portrait / Dec '84.

### SHE'S SO DIVINE.
**Tracks:** She's so divine.
■ 12" . . . . . . . . . . . . . . . . . .AROD 285
■ 7" . . . . . . . . . . . . . . . . . . ARO 285
Ariola / Feb '85.

### SHOCK WAVES.
**Tracks:** Shockwaves / OK go.
■ 7" . . . . . . . . . . . . . . . . . .SUR 002
Survival (1) / Jul '81.

### TAKE IT.
**Tracks:** Take it.
■ 7" . . . . . . . . . . . . . . . . . .SUR 004
Survival (1) / Nov '81.

## Limmie & Family Cooking

### DREAMBOAT.
**Tracks:** Dreamboat.
■ 7" . . . . . . . . . . . . . . . . . . .6105 025
Avco-Embassy / Apr '74.

### HOLD ME, THRILL ME, KISS ME.
**Tracks:** Hold me, thrill me, kiss me / My baby will
never go.
■ 7" . . . . . . . . . . . . . . . . . . 6105901
Philips / Nov '75.

### I CAN STOP ANY TIME I WANT TO.
**Tracks:** I can stop any time I want to / Only a movie.
■ 7" . . . . . . . . . . . . . . . . . .EMBS 354
Ember / Nov '77.

### LOLLYPOP.
**Tracks:** Lollypop / When you told me were through.
■ 7" . . . . . . . . . . . . . . . . . . 6105900
United Artists / Jun '75.

### YOU CAN DO MAGIC.
**Tracks:** You can do magic / Walkin' miracle.
■ 7" . . . . . . . . . . . . . . . . . . .6105 019
Avco-Embassy / Jul '73.
■ 7" . . . . . . . . . . . . . . . . . .CUT 110
Classic Cuts / Oct '80.

### YOU CAN DO MAGIC (OLD GOLD).
**Tracks:** You can do magic / Walking miracle.
■ 7" . . . . . . . . . . . . . . . . . .OG 9477
Old Gold / Jan '85.

## Linsey

### PERFECT LOVE.
**Tracks:** More outta life / Courtney's festival / Sear-
chin' / Smooth talk / Bring it back / Perfect love /
Battery acid / It's not a waste of time / U R Loved.
MC. . . . . . . . . . . . . . . . . . .VUSMC 138
■ CD . . . . . . . . . . . . . . . . . .CDVUS 38
■ LP . . . . . . . . . . . . . . . . . . .VUSLP 38
Virgin / Jun '91 / EMI.

## Linx

### CAN'T HELP MYSELF.
**Tracks:** Can't help myself / I'm not joking.
■ 12" . . . . . . . . . . . . . . . . .CHS 122565
■ 7" . . . . . . . . . . . . . . . . . .CHS 2565
Chrysalis / Nov '81.

### DON'T HIT ME WITH LOVE.
**Tracks:** Don't hit me with love / It's my life.
■ 7" . . . . . . . . . . . . . . . . . .CHS 2650
■ 12" . . . . . . . . . . . . . . . . .CHS 122650
Chrysalis / '83.

### GO AHEAD.
**Tracks:** So this is romance / I don't want to learn / I
wanna be with you / Urban refugee / I won't play the
game / Can't help myself / All my yesterdays / Know
what it is to be lonely / Tinsel Town (you don't fool
me).
MC. . . . . . . . . . . . . . . . . . .ZCHR 1358
■ LP . . . . . . . . . . . . . . . . . . .CHR 1358
Chrysalis / Oct '81 / EMI.

### INTUITION.
**Tracks:** Wonder what you're doing now / I Won't
forget / Intuition / There's love / Rise and shine /
Throw away the key / Together we can shine / Count
on me / Don't get in my way.
■ LP . . . . . . . . . . . . . . . . . .CHR 1332
Chrysalis / '83.
■ LP . . . . . . . . . . . . . . . . . FA 41 3088 1
MC. . . . . . . . . . . . . . . . . .TCFA 41 30884
Fame / Nov '83 / EMI.
■ LP . . . . . . . . . . . . . . . . . .MFP 5756
MFP / Oct '86.

### INTUITION.
**Tracks:** Intuition / Together we can shine.
■ 12" . . . . . . . . . . . . . . . . .CHS 122500
■ 7" . . . . . . . . . . . . . . . . . .CHS 2500
Chrysalis / Mar '81.

### LAST LINX.
**Tracks:** Together we can shine / Throw away the key
/ You're lying / Wonder what you're doing now /
Intuition / So this is romance / Urban refugee.
■ LP . . . . . . . . . . . . . . . . . .CHR 1409
■ MC . . . . . . . . . . . . . . . . .ZCHR 1409
Chrysalis / '83.

### PLAYTHING.
**Tracks:** Plaything / I won't play the game (remix) /
Plaything (extended version) (Only on 12" version).
■ 12" . . . . . . . . . . . . . . . . .CHS 122621
Chrysalis / '82.

■ 7" . . . . . . . . . . . . . . . . . . . . . . CHS 2621
Chrysalis / Jul '82.

## RISE AND SHINE.
Tracks: Rise and shine / I won't forget (instrumental).
■ 7" . . . . . . . . . . . . . . . . . . . . . . CHS 2480
Chrysalis / Dec '80.
■ 12" . . . . . . . . . . . . . . . . . . . . CHS 122480
Chrysalis / '82.

## SO THIS IS ROMANCE.
Tracks: So this is romance / So this is romance (Rio mix).
■ 12" . . . . . . . . . . . . . . . . . . . . CHS 122546
■ 7" . . . . . . . . . . . . . . . . . . . . . . CHS 2546
Chrysalis / '82.

## THROW AWAY THE KEY.
Tracks: Throw away the key / Ice is melting / Together we can shine (version) (Only on 12" version).
■ 12" . . . . . . . . . . . . . . . . . . . . CHS 122519
■ 7" . . . . . . . . . . . . . . . . . . . . . . CHS 2519
Chrysalis / '82.

## YOU'RE LYING.
Tracks: You're lying / You're lying (instrumental).
■ 12" . . . . . . . . . . . . . . . . . . . . CHS 122461
■ 7" . . . . . . . . . . . . . . . . . . . . . . CHS 2461
Chrysalis / Sep '80.

## YOU'RE LYING (OLD GOLD).
Tracks: You're lying / Throw away the key / Intuition / So this is romance.
■ 12" . . . . . . . . . . . . . . . . . . . . . . OG 4018
■ 7" . . . . . . . . . . . . . . . . . . . . . . OG 9694
Old Gold / Jan '87.

## Lipps Inc.

## FUNKY TOWN.
Tracks: Funky town / All night dancing.
■ 12" . . . . . . . . . . . . . . . . . . . . . . CANL 194
■ 7" . . . . . . . . . . . . . . . . . . . . . . CAN 194
Casablanca / May '80.

## FUNKY TOWN (OLD GOLD).
Tracks: Never knew love like this before / Funky town.
■ 7" . . . . . . . . . . . . . . . . . . . . . . OG 9489
Old Gold / Jan '85.
12" . . . . . . . . . . . . . . . . . . . . . . OG 4174
Old Gold / May '90 / Pickwick.

## HOW LONG.
Tracks: How long / There they are.
■ 7" . . . . . . . . . . . . . . . . . . . . . . CAN 212
Casablanca / Oct '80.

## MOUTH TO MOUTH.
Tracks: Funkytown / All night dancing / Rock it / Power.
■ LP . . . . . . . . . . . . . . . . . . . . . . NBLP 7197
Casablanca / Jul '80.

## PUCKER UP.
Tracks: How long / Tight pair / Always lookin' / Gossip song / There they are / Jazzy.
■ LP . . . . . . . . . . . . . . . . . . . . . . NBLP 7242
Casablanca / Nov '80.

## ROCK IT.
Tracks: Rock it.
■ 7" . . . . . . . . . . . . . . . . . . . . . . CAN 172
Casablanca / Aug '80.

## Little Benny

## BUGGIN' OUT (Little Benny & The Masters).
Tracks: Buggin' out / Buggin' out (inst) / Who comes to boogie.
■ 12" . . . . . . . . . . . . . . . . . . . . . . BRT 37
■ 7" . . . . . . . . . . . . . . . . . . . . . . BR 37
Blue Bird (2) / Aug '87.

## WHO COMES TO BOOGIE (Little Benny & The Masters).
Tracks: Who comes to boogie.
■ 12" . . . . . . . . . . . . . . . . . . . . . . BRT 13
■ 7" . . . . . . . . . . . . . . . . . . . . . . BR 13
Blue Bird (2) / Jan '85.

## Little Eva

## KEEP YOUR HANDS OFF MY BABY.
Tracks: Keep your hands off my baby.
■ 7" . . . . . . . . . . . . . . . . . . . . . . HLU 9633
London-American / Jan '63.

## LET'S TURKEY TROT.
Tracks: Let's turkey trot.
■ 7" . . . . . . . . . . . . . . . . . . . . . . HLU 9687
London-American / Mar '63.

## LIL'LOCO-MOTION.
Tracks: Locomotion / Some kind-a wonderful / I have a love / Down home / Breaking up is hard to do / Run to her / He is the boy / Will you love me tomorrow / Keep your hands off my baby / Let's turkey trot / Old smokey locomotion / Locomotion (extended version).
MC. . . . . . . . . . . . . . . . . . . . . . KTBC 44
■ LP . . . . . . . . . . . . . . . . . . . . . . TAB 44
Rock Echoes / Apr '82 / PolyGram.
CD. . . . . . . . . . . . . . . . . . . . . . 8206152
London / Nov '88 / PolyGram.

## LILLILOCO-MOTION.
Tracks: Loco-motion / Some kind of wonderful / I have a love / Down home / Breaking up is hard to do / Run to her / Uptown / Where do I go / Up on the roof / Sharing you / He is the boy / Will you love me tomorrow.
■ LP . . . . . . . . . . . . . . . . . . . . . . SHU 8437
London / Nov '72.

## LOCO-MOTION, THE.
Tracks: Loco-motion / Let's turkey trot / He is the boy / Keep your hands off my baby (Extra track available on 12" version only).
■ 7" . . . . . . . . . . . . . . . . . . . . . . HL 9581
London-American / Mar '80.
■ 12" . . . . . . . . . . . . . . . . . . . . . . LOCOX 1
■ 7" . . . . . . . . . . . . . . . . . . . . . . LOCO 1
London / Sep '86.
■ 7" . . . . . . . . . . . . . . . . . . . . . . .H 9581
London / '88.

## LOCOMOTION (OLD GOLD).
Tracks: Locomotion / Keep your hands off my baby.
■ 7" . . . . . . . . . . . . . . . . . . . . . . OG 9328
Old Gold / Jun '88.

## STAND BY ME.
Tracks: Stand by me.
■ 7" . . . . . . . . . . . . . . . . . . . . . . SS 477
Stateside / '64.

## Little Foxes

## CROSSED LINE.
Tracks: Crossed line.
■ 7" . . . . . . . . . . . . . . . . . . . . . . CD 2
C&D / Feb '83.

## GOLDEN BODIES.
Tracks: Golden bodies / Behind the rain.
■ 7" . . . . . . . . . . . . . . . . . . . . . . CD 4
C&D / Jul '83.

## Little Mac

## IN THE MIDNIGHT HOUR (Little Mac & The Boss Sounds).
Tracks: In the midnight hour / You can't love me in the midnight hour.
■ 7" . . . . . . . . . . . . . . . . . . . . . . K 11448
Atlantic / Mar '80.

## Little Milton

## ANNIE MAE'S CAFE.
Tracks: Annie Mae's cafe.
■ 7" . . . . . . . . . . . . . . . . . . . . . . MAL 008
Malaco / Dec '86.

## BACK TO BACK.
Tracks: Not Advised.
■ LP . . . . . . . . . . . . . . . . . . . . . . MALP 7448
Malaco / '89.
CD. . . . . . . . . . . . . . . . . . . . . . MALCD 7448
Malaco / Mar '93 / C.M. Distribution / Charly / Pinnacle.

## BLUES 'N' SOUL/WAITING FOR LITTLE MILTON.
Tracks: It's amazing / Who can handle me is you / Woman, you don't have to be so cold / Thrill is gone / Monologue 1 / That's how strong my love is / What it is / Little bluebird / Woman across the river / Behind closed doors / Sweet woman of mine / Worried dream / How could you do it to me / You're no good / Tain't nobody's biz-ness if I do / Hard luck blues.
CD. . . . . . . . . . . . . . . . . . . . . . CDSXD 052
Stax / Jun '92 / Pinnacle.

## BLUES IN THE NIGHT.
Tracks: We're gonna make it / Grits ain't groceries / Who's cheating who / Can't hold me back the tears / If walls could talk / Blues in the night / I play dirty / More and more / Blind man.
CD. . . . . . . . . . . . . . . . . . . . . . 26 10 072
MC. . . . . . . . . . . . . . . . . . . . . . 26 10 074
Dillion / '92 / Sound Solutions.

## BLUES IS ALRIGHT, THE.
Tracks: Blues is alright / How could you do it to me / Bad luck is falling / Chains and things / Walking the back streets and crying / I'd rather drink muddy water / I'm digging you / Things have got to change.
CD. . . . . . . . . . . . . . . . . . . . . . ECD 26026-2
Evidence / Feb '93 / Harmonia Mundi (UK).

## CHICAGO GOLDEN YEARS.
Tracks: Not Advised.
■ Double LP. . . . . . . . . . . . . . . . . . .427013
Vogue / Oct '88.

## GOLDEN DECADE.
Tracks: If walls could talk / I play dirty / Blind man / Just a little bit / Baby I love you / Sweet sixteen / Grits ain't groceries / Did you ever love a woman / We're gonna make it / Who's cheatin' who / Stormy Monday / I feel so bad.
■ LP . . . . . . . . . . . . . . . . . . . . . . 5310120
Chess / Sep '72.

## HIS GREATEST HITS.
Tracks: Grits ain't groceries / I play dirty / Just a little bit / Who's cheating who / Losing hand / Blind man / More and more / If walls could talk / We're gonna make it / Baby I love you / Man loves two / So mean to me / Without my sweet baby / Feel so bad.
■ LP . . . . . . . . . . . . . . . . . . . . . . GCH 8011
MC. . . . . . . . . . . . . . . . . . . . . . GCHK 78011
Chess (Charly) / Jan '87 / Charly.

## HIS GREATEST SIDES VOL 1.
Tracks: Grits ain't groceries / I play dirty / Just a little bit / Who's cheating who / Losing hand / Blind man / More and more / If walls could talk / We're gonna make it / Baby I love you / Man loves two / So mean to me / Without my sweet baby / Feel so bad.
■ LP . . . . . . . . . . . . . . . . . . . . . . CXMP 2053
Chess (PRT) / Jul '84.

## HITTIN' THE BOOGIE (Memphis days 1953-54).
Tracks: Not Advised.
■ LP . . . . . . . . . . . . . . . . . . . . . . Z 2007
Zu Zazz / '88.

## I WILL SURVIVE.
Tracks: Not Advised.
■ LP . . . . . . . . . . . . . . . . . . . . . . MAL 7427
Malaco / '88.

## IF WALLS COULD TALK.
Tracks: If walls could talk / Baby I love you / Let's get together / Things I used to do / Kansas City / Poor man's song / Blues get off my shoulder / I play dirty / Good to me as I am to you / Your precious love / I don't know.
■ LP . . . . . . . . . . . . . . . . . . . . . . 515014
Vogue / Oct '88.
■ CD . . . . . . . . . . . . . . . . . . . . . . CHD 9289
■ CD . . . . . . . . . . . . . . . . . . . . . . CH 9289
Chess (MCA) / Jul '90.
■ CD . . . . . . . . . . . . . . . . . . . . . . CHLD 19100
Chess (MCA) / Sep '92.

## LITTLE MILTON SINGS BIG BLUES.
Tracks: Feel so bad / Reconsider / Stormy monday / Woke up this morning / Hard luck blues / Please,please / Sweet sixteen / Fever / Sneakin' around / Don't decieve me / Have mercy baby / Part time love.
■ LP . . . . . . . . . . . . . . . . . . . . . . GCH 8037
MC. . . . . . . . . . . . . . . . . . . . . . GCHK 78037
Chess (Charly) / Oct '87 / Charly.

## MOVIN' TO THE COUNTRY.
Tracks: Not Advised.
■ LP . . . . . . . . . . . . . . . . . . . . . . MAL 7445
Malaco / Dec '87.
MC. . . . . . . . . . . . . . . . . . . . . . MALC 7445
Malaco / Mar '89 / C.M. Distribution / Charly / Pinnacle.
CD. . . . . . . . . . . . . . . . . . . . . . MALCD 7445
Malaco / Mar '93 / C.M. Distribution / Charly / Pinnacle.

## PLAYING FOR KEEPS.
Tracks: Not Advised.
■ LP . . . . . . . . . . . . . . . . . . . . . . MAL 7419
Malaco / Dec '84.

## RAISE A LITTLE SAND.
Tracks: Homesick for my baby / Somebody told me / Lonesome for my baby / If you love me / Begging my baby / Let's boogie baby / Love at first sight / Hold me tight / I'm trying / Dead love / I found me a new love / Long distance operator / That will never do / My baby pleases me / Same old blues / I'm a lonely man.
■ LP . . . . . . . . . . . . . . . . . . . . . . RL 011
Red Lightnin' / Sep '82.

## REALITY.
**Tracks:** Not Advised.
CD. . . . . . . . . . . . . . . . . . . . . MALCD 7462
Malaco / Mar '93 / C.M. Distribution / Charly /
Pinnacle.

## SAM'S BLUES.
**Tracks:** Not Advised.
■ LP . . . . . . . . . . . . . . . . . . . . . CR 30102
Charly / Jun '76.

## STRUGGLIN' BABY.
**Tracks:** Not Advised.
CD. . . . . . . . . . . . . . . . . . . . . MALCD 7465
Malaco / Mar '93 / C.M. Distribution / Charly /
Pinnacle.

## TK SESSIONS.
**Tracks:** Not Advised.
CD. . . . . . . . . . . . . . . . . . . . . NEXCD 168
Sequel / May '91 / Total / BMG.

## TOO MUCH PAIN.
**Tracks:** Not Advised.
CD. . . . . . . . . . . . . . . . . . . . . MALCD 7453
Malaco / Mar '93 / C.M. Distribution / Charly /
Pinnacle.

## WE'RE GONNA MAKE IT.
**Tracks:** Losing hand / Believe in me / Ain't no big
deal on you / Life is like that / Blind man / Stand by
me / We're gonna make it / Who's cheating who /
You're welcome to the club / I'm gonna move to the
outskirts of town / Can't hold back the tears / Grits
ain't groceries / Just a little bit / Poor man / Baby I
love you / Let's get together / Your precious love /
Kansas City / Good to me as I am to you / I play dirty
/ Things I used to do / I don't know / Blues get off my
shoulder / If walls could talk.
■ LP . . . . . . . . . . . . . . . . . . . . . GCH 8028
MC. . . . . . . . . . . . . . . . . . . . . GCHK 78028
Chess (Charly) / Apr '87 / Charly.
CD. . . . . . . . . . . . . . . . . . . . . CDRED 18
Charly / Jun '90 / Charly.

## WE'RE GONNA MAKE IT (2).
**Tracks:** Ain't no big deal on you / Believe in me /
Blues in the night / Can't hold back the tears / I'm
gonna move to the outskirts of town / We're gonna
make it / You're welcome to the club / Fever / Have
mercy baby / Part time love / Life is like that / Blind
man / Stand by me / Country style / Man loves two /
Who's cheating who / Feel so bad / Hard luck blues /
More and more / Please please please.
CD. . . . . . . . . . . . . . . . . . . . . RTS 43012
CD. . . . . . . . . . . . . . . . . . . . . RTS 33012
Roots / May '93 / Pinnacle / Target.

## Little Sister

### BOYS COMPANY.
**Tracks:** Boys company.
CD Single. . . . . . . . . . . . . . . . .MEMOCD 003
CD Single. . . . . . . . . . . . . . . . .MEMOCD 003P
MC Single . . . . . . . . . . . . . . . . MEMOMC 003
Station 2 Station / Nov '94 / Pinnacle.

## Little Sonny

### BLACK & BLUE.
**Tracks:** Hung up / Sonny's fever (instrumental) / You
got a good thing / Woman named trouble / Honest I
do / Wade in the water (instrumental) / Paying
through the nose / Memphis B-K (instrumental) /
Going home where women got meat on their bones /
I found love / They want money.
CD. . . . . . . . . . . . . . . . . . . . . CDSXE 057
Stax / Jul '93 / Pinnacle.

### NEW KING OF THE BLUES HARMONICA.
**Tracks:** Baby what you want me to do / Eli's pork
chop / Hey little girl / Hot potato / Don't ask me no
questions / Tomorrow's blues today / Back down
yonder / Sad funk / Creeper return.
■ LP . . . . . . . . . . . . . . . . . . . . . 2363005
Stax / Jul '71.
■ LP . . . . . . . . . . . . . . . . . . . . . MPS 8533
MC. . . . . . . . . . . . . . . . . . . . . MPS 58533
Stax / Nov '86 / Pinnacle.

### NEW KING OF THE BLUES HARMONI-
CA/HARD GOIN' UP.
**Tracks:** Baby, what you want me to do / Eli's pork
chop / Hey little girl / Hot potato / Don't ask me no
questions / Tomorrow's blues today / Back down
yonder / Sad funk / Creeper returns / It's hard going
up (but twice as hard coming down) / My woman is
good to me / You're spreading yourself a little too
thin / Day you left me / You can be replaced / Do it
right now / You made me strong / Sure is good / I
want you.

---

CD. . . . . . . . . . . . . . . . . . . . . CDSXD 968
Stax / Jul '91 / Pinnacle.

## NEW ORLEANS RHYTHM & BLUES.
**Tracks:** Not Advised.
CD. . . . . . . . . . . . . . . . . . . . . .BM 9023
Black Magic (1) / Feb '94 / Hot Shot / Swift / Projec-
tion / Duncans / Topic Records / Direct Distribution /
C.M. Distribution.

## Little Willie John

### FEVER.
**Tracks:** Fever / I'm stickin' with you baby / Do
something for me / Love, life and money / Suffering
with the blues / Dinner date / All around the world /
Need your love so bad / Young girl / Letter from my
darling / I've got to go cry / My nerves.
■ LP . . . . . . . . . . . . . . . . . . . . . SING 564
Sing / '88.
■ CD. . . . . . . . . . . . . . . . . . . . CDCHARLY 246
Charly / Oct '90.

### FREE AT LAST.
**Tracks:** Not Advised.
■ LP . . . . . . . . . . . . . . . . . . . . . BID 8017
Bellaphon / Jul '88.
MC. . . . . . . . . . . . . . . . . . . . . GD 5034
Gusto (USA) / Mar '88.

### GRITS AND SOUL.
**Tracks:** All around the world / Need your love so bad
/ Fever / Do something for me / Suffering with the
blues / I've been around / Person to person / Talk to
me, talk to me / Let's rock while the rockin's good /
Let them talk / Leave my kitten alone / Walk slow /
My baby's in love with another guy / You hurt me /
Big blue diamonds / Come back to me.
■ LP . . . . . . . . . . . . . . . . . . . . . CRB 1098
MC. . . . . . . . . . . . . . . . . . . . . TCCRB 1098
Charly R&B / Jul '85 / Charly.
CD. . . . . . . . . . . . . . . . . . . . . CDCHARLY 46
Charly R&B / '87 / Charly.

### MISTER LITTLE WILLIE JOHN.
**Tracks:** You're a sweetheart / Let's rock while the
rockin's good / Look what you've done to me / Home
at last / Are you ever coming back / Don't leave me
dear / All my love belongs to you / Spasms / Will the
sun shine tomorrow / You got to get up early in the
morning / Little bit of lovin' / Why don't you haul off
and love me.
■ LP . . . . . . . . . . . . . . . . . . . . . SING 603
Sing / Dec '87.
■ MC. . . . . . . . . . . . . . . . . . . . ZCLG 015
Calligraph / Dec '87.
■ LP . . . . . . . . . . . . . . . . . . . . . BID 8004
Bellaphon / Jul '88.
CD. . . . . . . . . . . . . . . . . . . . . .KCD 603
King / Mar '90 / New Note / Koch International.

### SURE THINGS.
**Tracks:** Not Advised.
CD. . . . . . . . . . . . . . . . . . . . . .KCD 739
King / Mar '90 / New Note / Koch International.
CD. . . . . . . . . . . . . . . . . . . . . .KCD 000739
King / Dec '92 / New Note / Koch International.

### TALK TO ME, TALK TO ME.
**Tracks:** Talk to me, talk to me / I've been around /
Drive me home / I'll carry your love wherever I go /
No more in life / Uh uh baby / Person to person /
Until you go / Tell it like it is / Don't be ashamed to
call my name / If I thought you needed me / There is
someone in this world for me.
■ LP . . . . . . . . . . . . . . . . . . . . . SING 596
Sing / Jul '88.

## Littles, Hattie

### BORDERLINE.
**Tracks:** Not Advised.
■ CD. . . . . . . . . . . . . . . . . . . . MOTCCD 79
Motor City / Mar '92.

## Living Proof

### LIVING PROOF.
**Tracks:** Hold on to your dreams / Something I like /
Stay forever / Fell in love too late / Where did I go
wrong / Apple of my eye / Special invitation / I'll
always know.
CD. . . . . . . . . . . . . . . . . . . . . CDGEM 4002
■ LP . . . . . . . . . . . . . . . . . . . . . GEM 4002
MC. . . . . . . . . . . . . . . . . . . . . ZCGEM 4002
Gemc / Jul '89 / Backs Distribution / Ichiban Records
(UK).

### WHERE DID I GO WRONG.
**Tracks:** Where did I go wrong.
■ 12″ . . . . . . . . . . . . . . . . . . . . 12 PO 29
Gemc / Sep '89.

---

## YOU'RE THE APPLE OF MY EYE.
**Tracks:** You're the apple of my eye (radio edit) /
You're the apple of my eye (full length).
■ 12″ . . . . . . . . . . . . . . . . . . . . 12 PO 18
Gemc / May '89.

## Lloyd, Carol

### CAROL LLOYD.
**Tracks:** Come see about me / I just want to love you /
Tonight / Mr. ladies man / Baby baby i'm yours / Oh
baby baby / Score.
■ LP . . . . . . . . . . . . . . . . . . . . . PWLP 1004
Philly World (USA) / May '83.

### COME SEE ABOUT ME.
**Tracks:** Come see about me / I just want to love you.
■ 12″ . . . . . . . . . . . . . . . . . . . . .PWSL 104
■ 7″ . . . . . . . . . . . . . . . . . . . . . PWS 104
Philly World (USA) / Oct '82.

## Locksmith

### UNLOCK THE FUNK.
**Tracks:** Unlock the funk / Far beyond / Black Jack.
■ 12″ . . . . . . . . . . . . . . . . . . . . ARIST 12364
■ 7″ . . . . . . . . . . . . . . . . . . . . .ARIST 364
Arista / Aug '80.

### UNLOCK THE FUNK (OLD GOLD) (see
under G.Q.).

## Lollipops

### LONELY LOVE.
**Tracks:** Lonely love / Bella mia.
■ 7″ . . . . . . . . . . . . . . . . . . . . . EMI 2548
EMI / Dec '76.

## London Beat

### 9 AM (THE COMFORT ZONE).
**Tracks:** 9 a.m. (the comfort zone) / Talent on the
make / There's an acid house going on (Track on 12″
only & cassette single.) / Falling in love again (Track
on CD single only.) / Up all night (Track on CD single
only.) / 9 a.m. (the comfort zone) (version) (Only on
cassette single.)
■ MC Single. . . . . . . . . . . . . . . ANX 008 V
Anxious / Dec '88.
■ 12″ . . . . . . . . . . . . . . . . . . . . ANXT 008
■ 7″ . . . . . . . . . . . . . . . . . . . . . ANX 008
■ CD Single. . . . . . . . . . . . . . . ANX 008 CD
Anxious / Nov '88.

### BETTER LOVE, A.
**Tracks:** Better love / K.I.S.S.
■ 7″ . . . . . . . . . . . . . . . . . . . . . ANX 22
■ MC Single. . . . . . . . . . . . . . . ANXK 21
Anxious / Dec '90.
■ CD Single. . . . . . . . . . . . . . . .ANXCD 21
■ MC Single. . . . . . . . . . . . . . . ANXC 21
■ 12″ . . . . . . . . . . . . . . . . . . . . ANXT 21
■ 7″ . . . . . . . . . . . . . . . . . . . . . ANX 21
Anxious / Oct '90.

### BETTER LOVE, A.
**Tracks:** Better love / I've been thinking about you.
■ 12″ . . . . . . . . . . . . . . . . . . . . .ANXT 32
■ 7″ . . . . . . . . . . . . . . . . . . . . . ANX 32
■ CD Single. . . . . . . . . . . . . . . .ANXCD 32
■ MC Single. . . . . . . . . . . . . . . ANXK 32
RCA / Jul '91.

### FAILING IN LOVE AGAIN.
**Tracks:** Failing in love again / Failing in love again
(album version) / Jerk / Over the speed limit (Available on 12″single and CD only.)
■ CD Single. . . . . . . . . . . . . . . ANX 007 CD
■ 12″ . . . . . . . . . . . . . . . . . . . . ANXT 007
■ 7″ . . . . . . . . . . . . . . . . . . . . . .ANX 007
Anxious / Jan '89.

### HARMONY.
**Tracks:** You bring the sun / Lover you send me
colours / That's how I feel about you / Some lucky
guy / Secret garden / Give a gift to yourself / Har-
mony / All born equal / Rainbow ride / Keeping the
memories alive / Sea of tranquility.
■ LP . . . . . . . . . . . . . . . . . . . . .74321 11060-16
■ MC. . . . . . . . . . . . . . . . . . . . 74321 11060-47
Anxious / Nov '92.
DCC . . . . . . . . . . . . . . . . . . . . . 74321110605
RCA / Jan '93 / BMG.
CD. . . . . . . . . . . . . . . . . . . . . .74321 11060-2
RCA / Apr '94 / BMG.

### HARMONY.
**Tracks:** Not Advised.
VHS . . . . . . . . . . . . . . . . . . . . .432 1120953
BMG / Nov '92 / BMG.

---

■ DELETED

### I'VE BEEN THINKING ABOUT YOU.
**Tracks:** I've been thinking about you / 9 a.m. (live at Moles).
- 12"...........................ANXT 14
- MC Single...................ANXC 14
- 7"...........................ANX 14
- CD Single..................ANXCD 14

Anxious / Aug '90.

### IN THE BLOOD.
**Tracks:** It's in the blood / Getcha ya ya / She broke my heart (in 36 places) / She said she loves me / No woman, no cry / This is your life / I've been thinking about you / Better love / In an I love you mood / You love and learn / Crying in the rain / Step inside my shoes (Only on CD).
- CD.......................... ZD 74810
- MC.......................... ZK 74810
- LP.......................... ZL 74810

Anxious / Sep '90 / BMG / Pinnacle.
- DCC.....................74321100105

RCA / Jan '93 / BMG.

### NO WOMAN NO CRY.
**Tracks:** No woman, no cry / Step inside my shoes.
- 12".........................ANXT 25
- 7"...........................ANX 25
- CD Single..................ANXCD 25
- 12" Remix...................ANXT 26
- MC Single..................ANXK 25

Anxious / Feb '91.

### ONE BLINK.
**Tracks:** One blink / Beat patrol / Killer drop (Only on 12".) / 9 a.m. (the comfort zone) (Only on CD single.) / Failing in love (Only on CD single.).
- 12".........................ANXT 011
- 7"...........................ANX 011
- CD Single..................ANXCD 011

RCA / May '89.

### ROAD TO HARMONY, THE.
**Tracks:** I've been thinking about you / There's a beat going on / Failing in love again / Crying in the rain / 9 a.m. (the comfort zone) / Better love / It's in the blood / No woman, no cry / Harmony / You bring on the sun / Lover you send me colours / That's how I feel about you.
- VHS ...................... 74321 12085-36

BMG Video / Nov '92.

### SPEAK.
**Tracks:** There's a beat going on / Beat patrol / Failing in love again / 9 a.m. (the comfort zone) / Drop / Nice here when it's nice / Get wet / One blink / Talent on the make / Please baby (can I have my heart back please) / Jerk (CD/cassette only) / Katey / Bribe the bride (CD only) / There's a deep house going on (CD only).
- LP.......................... ZL 71857
- CD.......................... ZD 71857
- MC.......................... ZK 71857

Anxious / Oct '87.

### THAT'S HOW I FEEL ABOUT YOU.
**Tracks:** That's how I feel about you / Sea of tranquility.
- 7".........................74321116877
- CD Single.................74321116872
- 12".........................74321116871
- MC Single.................74321116874

Anxious / Oct '92.

### THERE'S A BEAT GOING ON.
**Tracks:** There's a beat going on / Bribe the bride.
- 12".........................ANXT 004
- 7"...........................ANX 004

Anxious / Jun '88.

### YOU BRING ON THE SUN.
**Tracks:** You bring on the sun / Dreaming of you.
- 12".........................ANXT 37
- CD Single...................ANCD 37
- 7"...........................ANX 37
- MC Single..................ANXK 37

Anxious / Jun '92.

## Long, Shorty

### CHANTILLY LACE.
**Tracks:** Chantilly lace / Your love is amazing.
- 7"...........................TMG 600

Tamla Motown / Mar '67.

### FUNCTION AT THE JUNCTION.
**Tracks:** Function at the junction.
- 7"...........................TMG 573

Tamla Motown / '66.

### HERE COMES THE JUDGE.
**Tracks:** Here comes the judge / Function at the junction.
- 7"...........................TMG 663

---

Tamla Motown / Jul '68.
- 7"........................... ZB 41915

Motown / Apr '88.

### HERE COMES THE JUDGE.
**Tracks:** Here comes the judge / Night fo' last / Function at the junction / Don't mess with my weekend / Devil in the blue dress / Stranded in the jungle / Here comes fat Albert / Sing what you wanna / Another hurt like this / People sure act funny.
- LP...................STML 11086

Tamla Motown / Dec '68.

### OUT TO GET YOU.
**Tracks:** Out to get you.
- 7"........................... TMG 512

Tamla Motown / '65.

### PRIME OF SHORTY LONG.
**Tracks:** I had a dream / Whiter shade of pale / Memories are made of this / I'm walkin' / I cross my heart / Lillie of the valley / Blue Monday / Baby come home to me / I wish you were here / When you are available / Give me some air / Deacon work.
- LP...................STML 11144

Tamla Motown / May '70.

## Longmire, Wilbert

### BLACK IS THE COLOUR.
**Tracks:** Black is the colour.
- 12"......................... SWAVE 8

Streetwave / May '86.

### CHAMPAGNE.
**Tracks:** Diane's dilemma / Love's holiday / Ragtown / Pleasure island / Funshine.
- LP...................... CBS 83257

CBS / '79.

### WITH ALL MY LOVE.
**Tracks:** But I love you / Hawkeye / Crystal clear / Music speaks louder than words / Take your time / Just as long as we have love / Strawberry sunset.
- LP...................... CBS 84155

CBS / Jun '80.

## Loose Ends

Hailing from South London's glamorous Peckham, Loose Ends were at forefront of UK soul scene in mid-'80s. Bid for authenti-city saw band recording first albums in U.S. with Philadelphia-based producer Nick Martinelli; scheme which paid off when '85's *So Where Are You?* spawned two U.K. hits - *Hangin' On A String* and *Magic Touch*. Former album topped U.S. R&B charts; first single by UK group to do so. Group continued to place singles in lower reaches of charts, but disappeared from view in early '90s. Hits collection and apparent epitaph, *Tighten Up* (1992), including remixes by likes of Frankie Knuckles and PM Dawn, yielded successful reworking of *Hangin' On A String*; paving way for comeback in '93. In meantime, group had worked with variety of acts, including Juliet Roberts, Cheryl Lynn and Caron Wheeler.

### CHEAP TALK.
**Tracks:** Cheap talk / Let the vibes flow through / Love's got me.
- MC Single................. TENC 344
- 12"......................... TENX 344
- 12" Remix................. TENR 344
- 7".......................... TEN 344
- CD Single................. TENCD 344

10 / Mar '91.

### CHOOSE ME (RESCUE ME).
**Tracks:** Choose me (rescue me).
- 7"...........................VS 697

Virgin / Jul '84.

### DON'T BE A FOOL.
**Tracks:** Don't be a fool / Let's wax a fatty.
- 12"......................... TENX 312
- 12" Remix................. TENR 312
- 7".......................... TEN 312
- CD Single................. TENCD 312
- MC Single................. TENC 312

10 / Aug '90.

### DON'T HOLD BACK YOUR LOVE.
**Tracks:** Don't hold back your love / No stranger to darkness.
- 12"......................... VS 588 12
- 7"...........................VS 588

Virgin / Apr '83.

---

### EMERGENCY (DIAL 999).
**Tracks:** Emergency (dial 999)-extended remix / Emergency (dial 999)-dub mix.
- 12"......................... VS 677-12
- 7"...........................VS 677

Virgin / '84.

### GOLDEN YEARS.
**Tracks:** Golden years / Let's rock.
- 7"...........................VS 795
- 12"......................... VS 795-12

Virgin / Jul '85.

### HANGIN' ON A STRING.
**Tracks:** Hangin' on a string (7" only) / Little spice (On all versions) / Hangin' on a string (contemplating)-extended dance mix (CD & 12" only) / Emergency (dial 999)-extended remix (CD only).
- 7"...........................VS 748
- 12"......................... VS 748-12

Virgin / '85.
- CD Single................. CDT 39

Virgin / '88.

### HANGIN' ON A STRING (OLD GOLD).
**Tracks:** Hangin' on a string / Emergency (dial 999).
- 12"......................... OG 4098

Old Gold / Feb '89.

### HANGIN' ON A STRING (REMIX).
**Tracks:** Hangin' on a string / Johnny Broadhead (part 2).
- 12"......................... TENX 406
- 7".......................... TEN 406
- CD Single................. TENCD 406
- MC Single................. TENC 406

10 / Jun '92.

### IN THE SKY.
**Tracks:** In the sky.
- 12"......................... VS 497-12
- 7"...........................VS 497

Virgin / May '82.

### LITTLE SPICE, A.
**Tracks:** Tell me what you want / Feels so right now / Let's rock / Dial 999 / Music makes me higher / Choose me (rescue me) / Little spice / So much in love.
- LP.......................... V 2381

Virgin / Apr '84.
- MC.......................... OVEDC 159
- LP.......................... OVED 159

Virgin / Apr '86.
- CD.......................... CDV 2301

Virgin / Jun '88 / EMI.

### LOOK HOW LONG.
**Tracks:** Look how long / Don't you ever (try to change me) / Time is ticking / Love's got me / Don't be a fool / Cheap talk / Love controversy / Try my love / Hold tight / I don't need to love / Symptons of love.
- CD.......................... DIXCD 94
- MC.......................... CDIX 94
- LP.......................... DIX 94

10 / Sep '90 / EMI.

### LOOSE ENDS.
**Tracks:** Not Advised.
- VHS .......................VVC 165

Virgin Vision / Sep '86 / Gold & Sons / THE.

### LOVE'S GOT ME.
**Tracks:** Love's got me / Feel the vibe.
- 12"......................... TENX 330
- 12" Remix................. TENR 330
- 7".......................... TEN 330
- CD Single................. TENCD 330
- MC Single................. TENC 330

10 / Nov '90.

### MAGIC TOUCH.
**Tracks:** Magic touch / Magic touch (instrumental).
- 12"......................... VS 761-12
- 7"...........................VS 761

Virgin / Apr '85.

### MAGIC TOUCH (OLD GOLD).
**Tracks:** Magic touch / Slow down.
- 12"......................... OG 4108

Old Gold / Mar '89.

### MAGIC TOUCH, THE.
**Tracks:** Magic touch.
- 12"......................... TENX 409
- 7".......................... TEN 409
- CD Single................. TENCD 409
- MC Single................. TENC 409

10 / Jul '92.

■ DELETED

## MASTERMIND MEGA MIX, THE.
**Tracks:** Mastermind mega mix.
- ■ 12″. . . . . . . . . . . . . . . . . . . . . . . . VS 88413
Virgin / '89.

## MR. BACHELOR.
**Tracks:** Mr. Bachelor / Too much / Mr. Bachelor (mix) / Johnny Broadhead ([8]X2).
- ■ 7″. . . . . . . . . . . . . . . . . . . . . . . . . VS 1080
- ■ 12″. . . . . . . . . . . . . . . . . . . . . . . VST 1080
- ■ 12″. . . . . . . . . . . . . . . . . . . . . . VSTG 1080
- ■ CD Single. . . . . . . . . . . . . . . . . VSCD 1080
Virgin / Aug '88.

## NIGHTS OF PLEASURE.
**Tracks:** Nights of pleasure (7″ only) / Let's rock (7″ only) / Nights of pleasure (12″ full length version) (On VS 919-12 only) / Let's rock (full length version) (On 12″ only) / Nights of pleasure (dub version) (On VS 919-12 only) / Nights of pleasure (12″ mix by Dancing Danny Dee) (On VS 919-13 only) / Johnny Broadhead (On VS 919-13 only).
- ■ 12″. . . . . . . . . . . . . . . . . . . . . . . VS 919-12
- ■ 7″. . . . . . . . . . . . . . . . . . . . . . . . . VS 919
- ■ 12″ Remix. . . . . . . . . . . . . . . . . VS 919-13
Virgin / Nov '86.

## OOH, YOU MAKE ME FEEL.
**Tracks:** Ooh, you make me feel / Ooh, you make me feel (extended mix) (On cassette & 12″ only) / Gonna make you mine (On 12″ only) / Ooh, you make me feel (percussapella mix) (On cassette only) / Ooh, you make me feel (dub mix) (On cassette only).
- ■ 12″. . . . . . . . . . . . . . . . . . . . . . . . VS 991-12
- ■ 7″. . . . . . . . . . . . . . . . . . . . . . . . . . VS 991
- ■ MC Single. . . . . . . . . . . . . . . VSC 991-12
Virgin / Aug '87.

## REAL CHUCKEEBOO, THE.
**Tracks:** Watching you / (There's no) gratitude / Tomorrow (part 1 of the real chuckeeboo) / Mr. Bachelor (Part 2 of The Real Chuckeeboo.) / You've just got to have it all / Life / What goes around / Easier said than done / Hungry / Is it ever too late / Remote control / Too much (CD & cassette only) / Johnny broadhead (part 2) (CD & cassette only).
- CD. . . . . . . . . . . . . . . . . . . . . . . . . CDV 2528
- ■ LP. . . . . . . . . . . . . . . . . . . . . . . . . . V 2528
- ■ MC. . . . . . . . . . . . . . . . . . . . . . . TCV 2528
Virgin / Jun '88 / EMI.

## SLOWDOWN.
**Tracks:** Slowdown / Slow down (instrumental) / Gonna make you mine / Slowdown (12″ remix) (12″ only) / Slowdown (slowjam) (12″ only).
- ■ 12″ Remix. . . . . . . . . . . . . . . . VSD 884-12
- ■ 7″. . . . . . . . . . . . . . . . . . . . . . . . . . VS 884
- ■ 12″. . . . . . . . . . . . . . . . . . . . . . . VS 884-12
Virgin / Sep '86.

## SO WHERE ARE YOU.
**Tracks:** Magic touch / New horizon / If my lovin' makes you hot / So where are you / Golden years / Hangin' on a string (contemplating) / Give it all you got / Sweetest pain / You can't stop the rain / Silent talking.
- ■ LP. . . . . . . . . . . . . . . . . . . . . . . . . . V 2340
- ■ MC. . . . . . . . . . . . . . . . . . . . . . . TCV 2340
Virgin / Mar '85.
- ■ CD. . . . . . . . . . . . . . . . . . . . . . . . CDV 2340
Virgin / '87.

## STAY A LITTLE WHILE CHILD.
**Tracks:** Stay a little while child (7″ only) / Gonna make you mine / Stay a little while child (extended version) (12″ only) / Ooh, you make me feel (dub version) (12″ only).
- ■ 12″. . . . . . . . . . . . . . . . . . . . . . . VS 819-12
- ■ 7″. . . . . . . . . . . . . . . . . . . . . . . . . . VS 819
Virgin / May '86.

## TELL ME WHAT YOU WANT.
**Tracks:** Tell me what you want / Tell me what you want (version).
- ■ 12″. . . . . . . . . . . . . . . . . . . . . . . VS 658-12
- ■ 7″. . . . . . . . . . . . . . . . . . . . . . . . . . VS 658
Virgin / Feb '84.

## TIGHTEN UP VOL. 1.
**Tracks:** Magic touch / Gonna make you mine / Hangin' on a string / Choose me / Little spice / Slow down / Don't worry / Love's got me / Don't be a fool / Watching you / Tell me what you want / Ooh you make me feel / Hangin' on a string (original).
- CD. . . . . . . . . . . . . . . . . . . . . . . . DIXCD 112
- ■ LP. . . . . . . . . . . . . . . . . . . . . . . . . DIX 112
- MC. . . . . . . . . . . . . . . . . . . . . . . . CDIX 112
10 / Jul '92 / EMI.

## TIME IS TICKING EP.
**Tracks:** Time is ticking.
- ■ 12″. . . . . . . . . . . . . . . . . . . . . . . TENX 376
10 / Oct '91.

## WATCHING YOU.
**Tracks:** Watching you (7″ mix on all versions) / Life (7″ only) / Watching you (US 12″ remix) (On 12″ & CD only) / Life (the complete version) (On 12″ only) / Watching you (Kevin Saunderson remix) (On CD only) / Life (the complete rebirth) (On CD only).
- ■ 12″ Remix. . . . . . . . . . . . . . . . . VSR 1101
- ■ 7″. . . . . . . . . . . . . . . . . . . . . . . . . VS 1101
- ■ CD Single. . . . . . . . . . . . . . . . . VSCD 1101
- ■ 12″. . . . . . . . . . . . . . . . . . . . . . . VST 1101
Virgin / Aug '88.

## WE'RE ARRIVED.
**Tracks:** We're arrived / In the sky.
- ■ 12″. . . . . . . . . . . . . . . . . . . . . . VS 542 12
- ■ 7″. . . . . . . . . . . . . . . . . . . . . . . . .VS 542
Virgin / Oct '82.

## ZAGORA.
**Tracks:** Stay a little while child / Be thankful (Mama's song) / Slow down / Ooh, you make me feel / Just a minute / Who are you / I can't wait / Nights of pleasure / Let's get back to love / Rainbow / Take the 'A' train.
- CD. . . . . . . . . . . . . . . . . . . . . . . . CDV 2384
- ■ LP. . . . . . . . . . . . . . . . . . . . . . . . . V 2384
- ■ MC. . . . . . . . . . . . . . . . . . . . . . . TCV 2384
Virgin / Jun '86 / EMI.
- ■ LP. . . . . . . . . . . . . . . . . . . . . . . OVED 296
MC. . . . . . . . . . . . . . . . . . . . . . . OVEDC 296
Virgin / Apr '90 / EMI.

# Lorber, Jeff

## BEST PART OF THE NIGHT.
**Tracks:** Best part of the night / Step by step.
- ■ 12″. . . . . . . . . . . . . . . . . . . . . . .JABX 13
- ■ 7″. . . . . . . . . . . . . . . . . . . . . . . . JAB 13
Club / May '85.

## EVERY WOMAN NEEDS IT.
**Tracks:** Every woman needs it / Best part of the night.
- ■ 12″. . . . . . . . . . . . . . . . . . . . . . .JABX 23
- ■ 7″. . . . . . . . . . . . . . . . . . . . . . . . JAB 23
Club / Sep '85.

## FACTS OF LOVE.
**Tracks:** Facts of love / Sand castles / Every woman needs it.
- ■ 12″. . . . . . . . . . . . . . . . . . . . . . .JABX 48
- ■ 7″. . . . . . . . . . . . . . . . . . . . . . . . JAB 48
- ■ 7″ Set. . . . . . . . . . . . . . . . . . . JABXD 48
Club / Mar '87.

## FUSION JUICE (EP) (Lorber, Jeff Fusion).
**Tracks:** Fusion juice / Disco nights / Say you love me / Afterglow.
- ■ 12″. . . . . . . . . . . . . . . . . . . ARIST 12368
Arista / Oct '80.

## MONSTER MAN (Lorber, Jeff Fusion).
**Tracks:** Monster man / Magic Mady.
- ■ 12″. . . . . . . . . . . . . . . . . . . ARIST 12410
Arista / Apr '81.

## PRIVATE PASSION.
**Tracks:** Facts of love / True confessions / Jamaica / Back in love / Kristen / Private passion / Sand castles / Keep on lovin' her / Midnight snack.
- ■ LP. . . . . . . . . . . . . . . . . . . . . . . .JABH 21
- ■ MC. . . . . . . . . . . . . . . . . . . . . . .JABHC 21
Club / Nov '86.

## STEP BY STEP.
**Tracks:** Step by step / Best part of the night / Groovacious / Every woman needs it / On the wild side / This is the night / Pacific Coast highway / It takes a woman / When you gonna come back home.
- ■ LP. . . . . . . . . . . . . . . . . . . . . . . .JABH 9
- ■ CD. . . . . . . . . . . . . . . . . . . . . 824 684 2
Club / May '85.

## WATER SIGN (Lorber, Jeff Fusion).
**Tracks:** Toad's place / Country / Tune 88 / Sparkle / Water sign / Rain dance / Right here / Lights out.
- ■ CD. . . . . . . . . . . . . . . . . . . . . . .259338
- ■ LP. . . . . . . . . . . . . . . . . . . . . . . .209338
- ■ MC. . . . . . . . . . . . . . . . . . . . . . .409338
Arista / Oct '88.

# Lord Finesse

## RETURN OF THE FUNKY MAN.
**Tracks:** Lord Fitness intro / Return of the funky man / I like my girls with a boom / Hey look at shorty / Praise the lord / Save that shit / Show 'em how we do things / Isn't he something / Fat for the 90's / Stop sweating the next man / Funky on the fast tip / That's how smooth I am / Party over here / Kicking flavour with my man / Hands in the air-mouth shut / Yes you may.
- ■ CD. . . . . . . . . . . . . . . . . . . . 7599242372
- ■ LP. . . . . . . . . . . . . . . . . . . . 7599244371
- ■ MC. . . . . . . . . . . . . . . . . . . . 7599244374
WEA / Oct '91.

# Loren, Brian

## BRIAN LOREN.
**Tracks:** Not Advised.
- ■ LP. . . . . . . . . . . . . . . . . . . . . . . . . . V2322
Virgin / Sep '84.

## EASIER SAID THAN DONE.
**Tracks:** Easier said than done / Do you really love me.
- ■ 12″. . . . . . . . . . . . . . . . . . . . . . . VS 706-12
- ■ 7″. . . . . . . . . . . . . . . . . . . . . . . . .VS 706
Virgin / Aug '84.

## LOLLIPOP LUV.
**Tracks:** Lollipop luv / Lollipop luv (version).
- ■ 12″. . . . . . . . . . . . . . . . . . . . . . . VS 653-12
- ■ 7″. . . . . . . . . . . . . . . . . . . . . . . . .VS 653
Virgin / Feb '84.

# Lorenz, Trey

## PHOTOGRAPH OF MARY.
**Tracks:** Photograph of Mary (Album version) / Photograph of Mary mixes.
- ■ 12″. . . . . . . . . . . . . . . . . . . . . . .658954 6
- ■ 7″. . . . . . . . . . . . . . . . . . . . . . . .658954 7
- ■ CD Single. . . . . . . . . . . . . . . . .658954 2
Epic / Jan '93.

## SOMEONE TO HOLD.
**Tracks:** Someone to hold / Find a way / Wanna girl (On CDs only).
- ■ 7″. . . . . . . . . . . . . . . . . . . . . . . .658785-7
- ■ CD Single. . . . . . . . . . . . . . . . .658785-2
- ■ MC Single. . . . . . . . . . . . . . . . .658785-4
Epic / Nov '92.

## TREY LORENZ.
**Tracks:** Someone to hold / Photograph of Mary / Just to be to you / Run back to me / Always in love / Wipe all my tears away / Baby I'm in heaven / It only hurts when it's love / How can I say goodbye / Find a way / When troubles come.
- CD. . . . . . . . . . . . . . . . . . . . . . . .472172-2
- ■ LP. . . . . . . . . . . . . . . . . . . . . . . .472172-1
- MC. . . . . . . . . . . . . . . . . . . . . . . .472172-4
Epic / Dec '92 / Sony.

# Lorenzo

## KING POSER.
**Tracks:** King poser / Chat up line.
- ■ 7″. . . . . . . . . . . . . . . . . . . . . . . . . . NJ 1
Direct (1) / Jun '85.

## TIK TOK.
**Tracks:** Tik tok / I can't stand the pain.
- ■ 12″. . . . . . . . . . . . . . . . . . . . . . EXPAND 35
Expansion / Jul '93.

# Loring, Gloria

## FRIENDS AND LOVERS (Loring, Gloria & Carl Anderson).
**Tracks:** Friends and lovers / You always knew.
- ■ 12″. . . . . . . . . . . . . . . . . . . . . . . CART 400
- ■ 7″. . . . . . . . . . . . . . . . . . . . . . . . .CAR 400
Carrere / Sep '86.

# Lost Generation

## MIDNIGHT MEAT TRAIN.
**Tracks:** Not Advised.
- ■ CD. . . . . . . . . . . . . . . . . . . . . . .HMAXD 156
- ■ LP. . . . . . . . . . . . . . . . . . . . . . .HMUSA 156
- ■ MC. . . . . . . . . . . . . . . . . . . . . . HMAMC 156
Heavy Metal America / Dec '90.

# Louistine

## TAKE ME ON.
**Tracks:** Take me on / Now and forever / Dancing / Self serve woman / Love me / Trying to win your love / I don't wanna love nobody like you.
- ■ CD. . . . . . . . . . . . . . . . . . . . . . .TLCD 355
- ■ LP. . . . . . . . . . . . . . . . . . . . . . . TRPL 109
Timeless (Soul) / Jan '90.

■ DELETED

## Love Committee

### AW AND ORDER.
racks: Law and order / Where will it end.
■ 7" . . . . . . . . . . . . . . . . . . . . . . . SSOL 109
alsoul / Jun '78.

### AW AND ORDER.
racks: Law & order / Tired of being your fool / If you hange your mind / Cheaters never win / Pass the uck / Put it in the back of your mind / Give her love / ust as long as I got you.
■ LP . . . . . . . . . . . . . . . . . . . . . SSLP 1506
alsoul / Sep '78.

### NE DAY OF PEACE.
racks: One day of peace / One dozen roses.
■ 7" . . . . . . . . . . . . . . . . . . . . . PIR 3035
hiladelphia / Jan '75.

## Love, Mary

### AY THIS BURDEN DOWN.
acks: Lay this burden down / Think it over baby.
■ 7" . . . . . . . . . . . . . . . . . . . . . SS 2009
ateside / Mar '67.

### HEN AND NOW.
acks: I'm in your hands / Let me know / Because of ou / I woke up / Hey stoney face / Lay this burden own / Satisfied feeling / I can't wait / Come out of e sandbox / Price / Baby I'll come / Move a little oser / More than enough love / Grace / I've gotta et you back / Talkin' about my man / Mr Man / B aby / Caught up / You turned my bitter into sweet / m so glad) He uses me.
D . . . . . . . . . . . . . . . . . . . . . CDKEND 109
ent / May '94 / Pinnacle.

### OU TURNED MY BITTER INTO SWEET.
acks: You turned my bitter into sweet / I can't get ough / This couldn't be me.
7" . . . . . . . . . . . . . . . . . . . . . TOWN 501
ent / Nov '82.

## Love, Ronnie

### ET'S MAKE LOVE.
acks: Let's make love / Nothing to it.
7" . . . . . . . . . . . . . . . . . . . . . GRP 108
apevine (Northern Soul) / '78.

## Love Unlimited Orchestra

### LWAYS THINKING OF YOU.
acks: Always thinking of you / Satin soul.
7" . . . . . . . . . . . . . . . . . . . . . BTC 2168
th Century / Apr '75.

### ON'T YOU KNOW HOW MUCH I LOVE OU?.
acks: Don't you know how much I love you / Hey ok at me, I'm in love.
7" . . . . . . . . . . . . . . . . . . . . . BTC 2367
th Century / Apr '78.

### E'S ALL I'VE GOT.
acks: I did it for love / Never, never say goodbye / hisper you love me / He's mine (No you can't have m) / I guess I'm just another girl in love / He's all e got.
. . . . . . . . . . . . . . . . . . . . . CDSEWM 077
uth Bound / Feb '94 / Pinnacle.

### IGH STEPPIN' FELLA.
acks: High steppin' fella.
7" . . . . . . . . . . . . . . . . . . . . . ULG 8161
limited Gold(USA) / Jan '80.

### MAY BE WINTER OUTSIDE.
acks: It may be Winter outside.
7" . . . . . . . . . . . . . . . . . . . . . BTC 2149
h Century / Jan '75.

### T 'EM DANCE.
acks: Bayou / Jamaican girl / I wanna boogie and ogie with you / Vieni qua bella mi / Freeway flyer m in the mood / Young America.
. . . . . . . . . . . . . . . . . . . . . CDSEWM 079
uth Bound / Feb '94 / Pinnacle.

### FT YOUR VOICE AND SAY.
acks: Lift your voice and say / My fantasies.
12" . . . . . . . . . . . . . . . . . . . ULGA 13 1496
7" . . . . . . . . . . . . . . . . . . . ULGA 1496
limited Gold(USA) / Aug '81.

### VE IS BACK.
acks: I'm so glad that I'm a woman / High steppin', dressin' fella (You got it together) / When I'm in ur arms, everything's okay / If you want me say it /

I'm giving you a love (every man is searching for) / Gotta be where you are / I'm his woman.
■ LP . . . . . . . . . . . . . . . . . . . . . ULG 83790
Unlimited Gold(USA) / Apr '80.
■ LP . . . . . . . . . . . . . . . . . . . . . JA 36130
Columbia / Jan '89.
CD . . . . . . . . . . . . . . . . . . . . .CDSEWM 078
South Bound / Aug '93 / Pinnacle.

### LOVE UNLIMITED.
Tracks: I should have known / Are you sure / Is it really true boy / If this world were mine / Another chance / Fragile - handle with care / I'll be yours forever more / Walking in the rain with the one I love.
■ LP . . . . . . . . . . . . . . . . . . . . .MCL 1877
■ CD . . . . . . . . . . . . . . . . . . . . .DMCL 1877
■ MC . . . . . . . . . . . . . . . . . . . . . MCLC 1877
MCA / Oct '88.

### LOVE'S THEME.
Tracks: Love's theme / It may be Winter outside.
■ 7" . . . . . . . . . . . . . . . . . . . . . 7N 25635
Pye International / '74.
■ 7" . . . . . . . . . . . . . . . . . . . . .GOLD 529
RCA Golden Grooves / Aug '81.

### LOVE'S THEME (OLD GOLD).
Tracks: Love's theme / Walking in the rain with the one I love.
■ 7" . . . . . . . . . . . . . . . . . . . . .OG 9769
Old Gold / Feb '88.

### RISE.
Tracks: Take a good look (and what do you see) / My laboratory (Is ready for you) / After five / Do it to the music ..please / In Brazil / Anna Lisa / Goodbye concerto.
CD . . . . . . . . . . . . . . . . . . . . .CDSEWM 080
South Bound / Feb '94 / Pinnacle.

### WALKIN' IN THE RAIN WITH THE ONE I LOVE.
Tracks: Walking in the rain with the one I love.
■ 7" . . . . . . . . . . . . . . . . . . . . . UN 539
UNI / Jun '72.

### WALKING IN THE RAIN WITH THE ONE I LOVE.
Tracks: Walking in the rain with the one I love / Is it really true, boy.
■ 7" . . . . . . . . . . . . . . . . . . . . . MCA 145
MCA / Jun '74.

## Lovelites

### GET IT OFF MY CONSCIENCE.
Tracks: Get it off my conscience / Oh what a day.
■ 7" . . . . . . . . . . . . . . . . . . . . .GRP 107
Grapevine (Northern Soul) / '78.

## Lovesmith, Michael

### AIN'T NOTHIN' LIKE IT.
Tracks: Ain't nothing like it / Fast girls.
■ 12" . . . . . . . . . . . . . . . . . . . . . ZT 40370
■ 7" . . . . . . . . . . . . . . . . . . . . . ZB 40369
Motown / Sep '85.

### BABY I WILL.
Tracks: Baby I will / What's the bottom line.
■ 12" . . . . . . . . . . . . . . . . . . . . . TMGT 1311
■ 7" . . . . . . . . . . . . . . . . . . . . . TMG 1311
Motown / Jul '83.

### BREAK THE ICE.
Tracks: Break the ice / Luck in love.
■ 12" . . . . . . . . . . . . . . . . . . . . . ZT 40274
■ 7" . . . . . . . . . . . . . . . . . . . . . ZB 40273
Motown / Jul '85.

### I CAN MAKE IT HAPPEN.
Tracks: He only looks the part / Sorry won't get it / She's trouble / Promise is a promise / What's the bottom line / I can make it happen for you / Baby i will / Even as we speak / Just say the word.
■ LP . . . . . . . . . . . . . . . . . . . . .STML 12192
■ MC . . . . . . . . . . . . . . . . . . . . .CSTML 12192
Motown / Sep '83.

### RHYMES OF PASSION.
Tracks: I'm good at it / Cover girl / Break the ice / You ain't been loved yet / Love in the combat zone / Temporary insanity / Haunted heart / Ain't nothin' like it / We both will have to bend / Raider of the heart.
■ LP . . . . . . . . . . . . . . . . . . . . . ZL 72376
■ MC . . . . . . . . . . . . . . . . . . . . . ZK 72376
Motown / Aug '85.

## Lovetones

### TURN THIS HEART AROUND.
Tracks: Not Advised.
■ CD . . . . . . . . . . . . . . . . . . . . . MOTCCD 72
Motor City / Oct '92.

## Low Key

### TRY ME BABY.
Tracks: Try me baby.
■ 12" . . . . . . . . . . . . . . . . . . . . . SGT 2
Network / Dec '93.

## Lowrell

### LOWRELL.
Tracks: Out of breath / You're playing dirty / Overdose / Mellow mellow right on / Smooth and wild.
■ LP . . . . . . . . . . . . . . . . . . . . . AVLP 504
AVI (USA) / Jan '80.

### MELLOW MELLOW RIGHT ON.
Tracks: Mellow mellow right on.
■ 7" . . . . . . . . . . . . . . . . . . . . . AVIS 108
AVI (USA) / Nov '79.

### MELLOW MELLOW RIGHT ON (OLD GOLD).
Tracks: Mellow mellow right on / Overdose of love.
12" . . . . . . . . . . . . . . . . . . . . .OG 4183
Old Gold / Jul '90 / Pickwick.

## Lucas, Carrie

### DANCE WITH YOU.
Tracks: Dance with you / Simpler days.
■ 7" . . . . . . . . . . . . . . . . . . . . .FB 1482
Solar / Jun '79.

### IN DANCELAND.
Tracks: Danceland / Sometimes a love goes wrong / Are you dancing / Dance with you / I'm gonna make you happy / Southern star.
■ LP . . . . . . . . . . . . . . . . . . . . . FL 13219
Solar / '79.

### IT'S NOT WHAT YOU'VE GOT.
Tracks: It's not what you've got / Keep smiling.
■ 12" . . . . . . . . . . . . . . . . . . . . . SOT 13
■ 7" . . . . . . . . . . . . . . . . . . . . . SO 13
Solar / Oct '80.

### KEEP SMILING.
Tracks: Keep smiling / I'm gonna make you happy.
■ 12" . . . . . . . . . . . . . . . . . . . . .SO 12 9
■ 7" . . . . . . . . . . . . . . . . . . . . .SO 9
Solar / Aug '80.

### PORTRAIT OF CARRIE.
Tracks: It's not what you've got / Lovin' is on my mind / Career girl / Use it or lose it / Fashion / Just a memory / Keep smiling.
■ LP . . . . . . . . . . . . . . . . . . . . . SOLA 5
Solar / Oct '80.

### SHOW ME WHERE YOU'RE COMING FROM.
Tracks: Show me where you're coming from / Still in love.
■ 7" . . . . . . . . . . . . . . . . . . . . . K 13175
Solar / May '82.

### STILL IN LOVE.
Tracks: Show me where your coming from / Sweet love / Men / Is it a dream / Rockin' for your love / Dreamer / I just can't do without your love / Still in love.
■ LP . . . . . . . . . . . . . . . . . . . . . K 52400
Solar / Jun '82.

### STREET CORNER SYMPHONY.
Tracks: Street corner symphony / Stand by me / Duke of Earl / Raindrops / Licking stick / Dancing in the street / My girl / Way you do the things you do / Sherry / My guy / But my heart says no / Tic toc / Depths of my soul / Edge of night / Questions / Simpler days / Reflections.
■ LP . . . . . . . . . . . . . . . . . . . . . FL 12773
■ MC . . . . . . . . . . . . . . . . . . . . . FK 12773
Solar / Jul '78.

### STREET CORNER SYMPHONY.
Tracks: Street corner symphony / Tic toc.
■ 7" . . . . . . . . . . . . . . . . . . . . . PB 1310
RCA / Sep '78.

## Lucas, Tammy

### HEY BOY.
Tracks: Hey Boy (touch remix).
■ 12"..................... LICT 019
■ 7"...................... LIC 019
Republic / Mar '89.

## Luciana

### GET IT UP FOR LOVE.
Tracks: Get it up for love / Sister sister (Not available on 12).
■ 12"..................... 12CHS 5008
■ 7"...................... CHS 5008
■ CD Single.............. CDCHS 5008
■ MC Single............. TCCHS 5008
Chrysalis / Apr '94.

### IF YOU WANT.
Tracks: If you want (Mixes) / Think (Does not feature on 12CHS 5009.).
12" Remix................ 12CHSX 5009
Chrysalis / Aug '94 / EMI.
12"...................... 12CHS 5009
7"....................... CHS 5009
CD Single................ CDCHS 5009
MC Single............... TCCHS 5009
Chrysalis / Jul '94 / EMI.

### WHAT GOES AROUND.
Tracks: What goes around (mixes) / One more river.
12"...................... 12 CHS 5015
7"....................... CHS 5015
CD Single................ CDCHS 5015
MC Single............... TCCHS 5015
Chrysalis / Oct '94 / EMI.

## LW 5

### GET TO KNOW YOU.
Tracks: Not Advised.
■ LP..................... V 2363
■ MC..................... TCV 2363
Virgin / Nov '85.

### KILL OR BE KILLED.
Tracks: Kill or be killed / Naturally.
■ 12".................... VS 809-12
■ 7"..................... VS 809
Virgin / Oct '84.

### RIPE FOR THE PICKING.
Tracks: Ripe for the picking / Last lie / Ripe for the picking (extended Hardcastle mix-April 85) (On VS 747-14 only).
■ 12".................... VS 767-14
■ 7"..................... VS 767
■ 12".................... VS 767-12
Virgin / Jun '85.

## Lyle, Bobby

### BEST OF BOBBY LYLE, THE.
Tracks: Pisces / Night breeze / Mother Nile / I didn't know what time it was / New warrior / Star traveller / What is this thing called love / For love / Blues for Scott Joplin.
■ CD..................... CDP 7892842
Blue Note / Jun '93.

### IVORY DREAMS.
Tracks: Ivory dreams / Save it for a rainy day / 88 ways / Tropical / Been so long / Locomotion / Nova.
CD....................... K 781 938 2
■ LP..................... K 781 938 1
■ MC..................... K 781 938 4
Atlantic / Mar '89 / WEA.

### NEW WARRIOR.
Tracks: Prelude / New warrior / Good inside / Believe / Interlude / Groove / Inner space / Missing your love / Star traveller / What is this thing called love.
■ LP..................... EAST 11809
Capitol / Sep '78.

### NIGHT FIRE.
Tracks: Stop running away from love / Da ya ance / Gettin' into love / Dream lady / Space place / Blues for Scott Joplin / For love / Rhap-so-dee / Just one of those things.
■ LP..................... EST 11956
Capitol / Oct '79.

## Lynn, Barbara

### SO GOOD.
Tracks: Not Advised.
CD....................... BB 9540CD
MC....................... BB 9540C
Bullseye Blues / Feb '94 / New Note / Topic Records / Direct Distribution.

### YOU DON'T HAVE TO GO.
Tracks: You make me so hot / Misty blue / Trying to love two / You're losing me / You don't have to go / We got a good thing going / Sugar coated love / You'll lose a good thing.
■ LP..................... ICH 1024
MC....................... ZCICH 1024
Ichiban / Jul '88 / A.D.A. Distribution / Pinnacle / ACD Trading Ltd. / Koch International / Direct Distribution.

### YOU LOSE A GOOD THING.
Tracks: You lose a good thing / Lonely heartaches.
■ 7"..................... WI 4038
Sue / Apr '67.

### YOU MAKE ME SO HOT.
Tracks: You make me so hot / Sugar coated love.
■ 12".................... ICHT 704
Ichiban / Jul '88.

### YOU'LL LOSE A GOOD THING.
Tracks: You'll lose a good thing.
■ 7"..................... OVAL 1006
Oval / May '82.

## Lynn, Bobbi

### EARTHQUAKE.
Tracks: Earthquake / Opportunity street.
■ 7"..................... SS 2088
Stateside / '68.

## Lynn, Cheryl

### AT LAST YOU'RE MINE.
Tracks: At last you're mine / Look what you've done to me.
■ 7"..................... A 6132
Epic / Apr '85.

### CHERYL LYNN.
Tracks: Got to be real / All my lovin' / Star love / Come in from the rain / You saved my day / Give my love to you / Nothing you say / You're the one / Daybreak.
■ LP..................... CBS 83145
CBS / Apr '79.

### ENCORE.
Tracks: Encore.
■ 7"..................... KHAN 23
Streetwave / Sep '84.

### ENCORE (OLD GOLD) (see under Nicole (1)).

### FEEL IT.
Tracks: Feel it / Chances.
■ 7"..................... CBS 8242
CBS / Feb '80.

### FIDELITY.
Tracks: Fidelity / Free.
■ 12".................... TX 6373
■ 7"..................... A 6373
CBS / Jul '85.

### GOT TO BE REAL.
Tracks: Got to be real / Come in from the rain.
■ 7"..................... CBS 6967
CBS / Feb '79.

### GOT TO BE REAL (OLD GOLD).
Tracks: Got to be real / Shake it up tonight.
12"...................... OG 4193
Old Gold / Oct '90 / Pickwick.

### IF THIS WORLD WAS MINE (Lynn, Cheryl & Luther Vandross).
Tracks: If this world was mine / I just want to be your fantasy.
■ 7"..................... A 2952
■ 12".................... A 13 2952
CBS / Jan '83.

### IN LOVE.
Tracks: I've got faith in you / Hide it away / Feel it / Keep it hot / I've got just what you need / Love bomb / Chances / Don't let it fade away.
■ LP..................... CBS 83829
CBS / Jun '80.

### INSTANT LOVE.
Tracks: Instant love / Sleep walkin' / Day after day / Look before you leap / Say you'll be mine / I just wanna be your fantasy / Believe in me / If this world was mine.
■ LP..................... CBS 85849
CBS / Nov '82.

### IT'S GONNA BE RIGHT.
Tracks: It's gonna be right / Fidelity / Fade to black / Love's been here before / Let me love you / Fin somebody new / Loafin' / Slipped me a mickey / Tu o' war.
■ LP..................... CBS 2649
■ MC..................... .40 2649
CBS / Aug '85.

### PREPPIE.
Tracks: Encore / Fix it / Fool a fool / This time Change the channel / Preppie / Love rush / No on else will do / Free / Life's too short.
MC....................... .40 2571
CBS / Dec '83 / Sony.
■ LP..................... 2571
CBS / Apr '84.

### SHAKE IT UP TONIGHT.
Tracks: Shake it up tonight / Baby.
■ 12".................... A 13 143
■ 7"..................... A 13 143
CBS / Aug '81.

### STAR LOVE.
Tracks: Star love / You're the one.
■ 7"..................... CBS 731
CBS / Jun '79.

## Lynn, Judy

### MARRIED TO A MEMORY.
Tracks: Married to a memory / So natural is my love
■ 7"..................... SS 218
Stateside / May '71.

## Lynn, Tammi

### I'M GONNA RUN AWAY FROM YOU.
Tracks: I'm gonna run away from you / Boy ne. door.
■ 7"..................... AT 407
Atlantic / '66.
■ 7"..................... 2092 00
Mojo / May '71.
■ 7"..................... CS 902
Mojo / May '75.

### LOVE IS HERE AND NOW YOU'R GONE.
Tracks: Introduction to a love affair / Wings upc your horns / Hoping / Love is here and now you'll gone / Final attempt / Can't last much longer / Nex time / That's understanding / I'm gonna run awa from you / Ain't no soul / World you left behind you Never no more.
■ LP..................... 291600
Mojo / Dec '71.

## Lynn, Trudy

### 24 HOUR WOMAN.
Tracks: Not Advised.
CD....................... ICH 1172C
MC....................... ICH 1172M
Ichiban / Jun '94 / A.D.A. Distribution / Pinnacle ACD Trading Ltd. / Koch International / Dire Distribution.

### COME TO MAMA.
Tracks: Right back in the water / When something wrong with my baby / Come to Mama / When yo took your love from me / One woman man / Wo man's gotta have it / Do I need you (too) / Fish gi blues / Making love to me.
LP....................... ICHA 106
MC....................... ICHA 1063 M
Ichiban / Sep '90 / A.D.A. Distribution / Pinnacle ACD Trading Ltd. / Koch International / Dire Distribution.
CD....................... CDICH 106
Ichiban / Oct '93 / A.D.A. Distribution / Pinnacle ACD Trading Ltd. / Koch International / Dire Distribution.

### TRUDY SINGS THE BLUES.
Tracks: Sittin' and drinkin' / Just a little bit / I can te / Trudy sings the blues / Dr. Feelgood / Do I nee you / Bring the beef home to me / Ball and chain.
MC....................... ZCICH 104
■ LP..................... ICH 104
Ichiban / Sep '89 / A.D.A. Distribution / Pinnacle ACD Trading Ltd. / Koch International / Dire Distribution.
CD....................... CDICH 104
Ichiban / Oct '93 / A.D.A. Distribution / Pinnacle ACD Trading Ltd. / Koch International / Dire Distribution.

### WOMAN IN ME, THE.
Tracks: Woman in me / My baby can / Speak now o forever hold your peace / You owe it to yourself

■ DELETE

Can't nothin' keep me from you / Still on my mind / I've been thinkin' / Feel you, feel me / Spare the rod (love the child).

■ **LP** . . . . . . . . . . . . . . . . . . **ICH 1125**
■ **MC**. . . . . . . . . . . . . . . . . **ICH 1125 MC**
Ichiban / Nov '91.
**CD**. . . . . . . . . . . . . . . . . .**CDICH 1125**

Ichiban / Oct '93 / A.D.A. Distribution / Pinnacle / ACD Trading Ltd. / Koch International / Direct Distribution.

# M

## M.L.

**I'LL BE THERE FOR YOU.**
Tracks: I'll be there for you (Mixes).
■ 12"................. 12JUJA 2
Skratch (1) / Mar '94.

**I'LL BE THERE FOR YOU.**
Tracks: Not Advised.
CD...................... KIK 4176CD
MC...................... KIK 4176MC
Ichiban / Feb '94 / A.D.A. Distribution / Pinnacle / ACD Trading Ltd. / Koch International / Direct Distribution.

**WAITING FOR YOU.**
Tracks: Waiting for you.
12"....................... 12PO 185
Ichiban / Mar '94 / A.D.A. Distribution / Pinnacle / ACD Trading Ltd. / Koch International / Direct Distribution.

## Mac Band

**JEALOUS.**
Tracks: Jealous (Only on the 7" version.) / Jealous (instrumental) (Only on the 12" version.)
■ CD Single.............. DMCA 1292
■ 12"..................... MCAT 1292
■ 7"..................... MCA 1292
MCA / Nov '88.

**MAC BAND LP, THE.**
Tracks: Not Advised.
■ LP ................. MCA 42090
MCA / Jul '88.

**MAC BAND, THE.**
Tracks: Not Advised.
■ LP ..................... MCG 6032
■ CD ..................... DMCG 6032
■ MC ..................... MCGC 6032
MCA / Aug '88.

**ROSES ARE RED.**
Tracks: Roses are red / Roses are red (instrumental) / Roses are red (extended version) (12" version only.) / Roses are red (instrumental dub) (12" version only.).
■ 12"..................... MCAT 1264
■ 7"..................... MCA 1264
■ 7"..................... MCA 23791
MCA / Jun '88.

**STALEMATE (Mac Band featuring McCampbell Brothers).**
Tracks: Stalemate / Stalemate (instrumental) / Stalemate (accapella) (12" only).
■ 12"..................... MCAT 1271
■ CD Single.............. DMCA 1271
■ 7"..................... MCA 1271
MCA / Aug '88.

## McBride, Jeff

**DO YOU STILL REMEMBER LOVE?.**
Tracks: You go to my head / No sweeter love / Do you still remember love / Just an American girl / Good old days / Gotta good thing / Love is gonna get you / Doesn't that mean something / I just laugh.
■ CD ..................... 261008
■ LP ..................... 211008
■ MC ..................... 411008
Arista / Sep '90.

## McCall, Toussaint

**NOTHING TAKES THE PLACE OF YOU.**
Tracks: Nothing takes the place of you / Foot stompin' / Duke of Earl (Avaliable on 12" only.).
■ 12"..................... CYZ 127
■ 7"..................... CYZ 7127
Charly / Oct '88.

**NOTHING TAKES THE PLACE OF YOU**
(see under Giles, Eddie).

## McClain, Alton

**CRAZY LOVE (McClain, Alton & Destiny).**
Tracks: Crazy love / God said love ye one another.
■ 7"..................... 2095092
Polydor / Aug '79.

**IT MUST BE LOVE (McClain, Alton & Destiny).**
Tracks: It must be love / Taking my love for granted.
■ 7"..................... 209 502 6
Polydor / Apr '79.

**IT MUST BE LOVE (McClain, Alton & Mahogany Rush).**
Tracks: It must be love / Crazy love / Sweet temptation / Taking my love for granted / My empty room / Power of love / Push and pull / God said 'Love ye one another'.
■ LP ..................... 2391370
Polydor / '79.

**MORE OF YOU (McClain, Alton & Destiny).**
Tracks: Love waves / I don't want to be with nobody else / Hang on in there baby / More of you / Thank heaven for you / Stares and whispers / Ninety nine and a half (won't do) / You bring to me my morning light.
■ LP ..................... 2391 452
Polydor / Jun '80.

## McClain, Janice

**JANICE MCCLAIN.**
Tracks: Passion and pain / When love calls / Second chance on love / Let's spend the night / Give a little bit of love / It's gonna come back to you / Hideaway / Rhythm of our love / Last goodbye.
■ LP ..................... MCF 3323
■ MC..................... MCFC 3323
MCA / Feb '87.

**PASSION AND PAIN.**
Tracks: Passion and pain / Passion and pain (Inst).
■ 12"..................... MCAT 1109
■ 7"..................... MCA 1109
MCA / Mar '87.

## McClain, Marlon

**CHANGES.**
Tracks: Shake it up / Star of my life / Together in the afternoon / Close to you / Pastel / Can we still be friends / Don't run away from love / Changes / Why / Do you miss that feelin'.
■ LP ..................... F 9606
Fantasy / Aug '81.

**SHAKE IT UP.**
Tracks: Shake it up / Pastel.
■ 12"..................... FTCT 198
■ 7"..................... FTC 198
Fantasy / Aug '81.

## McClary, Thomas

**THIN WALLS.**
Tracks: Thin walls / Love will find a way.
■ 12"..................... TMGT 1366
■ 7"..................... TMG 1366
Motown / Jan '85.

## McClure, Bobby

**BOBBY MCCLURE & WILLIE CLAYTON (McClure, Bobby & Willie Clayton).**
Tracks: Not Advised.
CD..................... HIUKCD 134
Demon / Aug '92 / Pinnacle / A.D.A. Distribution.

**CHERRY, THE.**
Tracks: Today you started leaving him (and loving me) / Cherry pie / When the flavour's gone / I can't get enough / Do do do doop / I need a job / Please don't put me out the band / I write another love song / I brought it back / Younger man blues.
CD..................... SDE 4008CD
■ LP ..................... SDE 4008

MC..................... SDE 4008MC
S.D.E.G. / Oct '89 / RTM / Pinnacle / ACD Trading Ltd.

**IT FEELS SO GOOD (TO BE BACK HOME).**
Tracks: It feels so good (to be back home) / You never miss your water / It feels so good (radio version).
■ 12"..................... DEBTX 3021
Debut (1) / Apr '87.

## McCoy, Van

Washington-born keyboardist, songwriter, arranger, producer and orchestra leader was successful behind-the-scenes figure in '60s and '70s. His first break came in '61, when as A&R executive and producer at Scepter Records, he wrote Shirelles' hit Stop the Music. In '62 he was taken under wing of famous songwriting/production team, Jerry Leiber and Mike Stoller and later became a staff writer for Blackwood Music. By close of '60s, his tally of hits included classics like When You're Young And In Love (Ruby & the Romantics/Marvelettes) and I Get the Sweetest Feeling (Jackie Wilson). Success continued into '70s with likes of Stylistics, David Ruffin and Melba Moore. His own The Shuffle also reached U.K. Top 10. Although his U.S. success had dimmed, American industry was nonetheless shocked when heart attack killed him in 1979, aged 39.

**CHANGE WITH THE TIMES.**
Tracks: Change with the times.
■ 7"..................... 6105 042
Avco-Embassy / Nov '75.

**DISCO BABY (McCoy, Van & Soul City Symphony).**
Tracks: Not Advised.
■ LP ..................... 9109 004
Avco-Embassy / Jul '75.

**HUSTLE TO THE BEST OF VAN MCCOY.**
Tracks: Not Advised.
■ LP ..................... 9109 013
H & L (USA) / Feb '77.

**HUSTLE, THE.**
Tracks: Hustle / Shuffle.
■ 7"..................... 6105 037
Avco-Embassy / May '75.

**HUSTLE, THE (OLD GOLD).**
Tracks: Hustle.
■ 7"..................... OG 9246
Old Gold / Jul '82.

**MY FAVOURITE FANTASY.**
Tracks: My favourite fantasy / You're so right for me.
■ 7"..................... MCA 37
MCA / Jun '78.

**MY FAVOURITE FANTASY.**
Tracks: That's the story of my life / That's why I lov you so much / Two points / Right now / You're s right for me / My favourite fantasy / Before and afte / Trying to make the best of it / I choose love as m weapon / Wings of love.
■ LP ..................... MCF 2840
MCA / Jul '78.

**PARTY.**
Tracks: Party / Love is the anwser.
■ 7"..................... 610506
H & L (USA) / Jul '76.

**SHUFFLE, THE.**
Tracks: Shuffle / That's the joint.
■ 7"..................... 6105 079
Avco-Embassy / Apr '77.

**SOUL CHA CHA.**
Tracks: Soul cha cha / African symphony.
■ 7"..................... 610506
H & L (USA) / Jan '77.

■ DELETE

## SOUL IMPROVISATIONS.
Tracks: Soul improvisations.
7" . . . . . . . . . . . . . . . . . . . . .BDS 418
uddah / Jan '75.

## SPANISH BOOGIE.
Tracks: Spanish boogie / Love child.
7" . . . . . . . . . . . . . . . . . .6105 083
& L (USA) / Jul '77.

## SWEET RHYTHM.
Tracks: Change with the times / Disco baby / Hustle /
eep on hustlin' / Jet setting / Love at first sight /
ight walk / Pick up the pieces / Roll with the
unches / Shaky ground / Shuffle / Soul cha cha /
weet sweet rhythm / That's my philosophy.
LP . . . . . . . . . . . . . . . . . . . . 6467651
& L (USA) / Dec '79.

## McCracklin, Jimmy

### LAST 'EM DEAD.
Tracks: She's gone / My days are limited / She felt
o good / End / Cheater / Share and share alike /
ear my story / Every time / Pleasin' papa / We
ould make a go I know / Blues and trouble / I don't
ant no woman / Hello baby / Night and day / You
ok so fine -take 1 / Keep trying / Swinging thing.
Double LP . . . . . . . . . . . . . . . .CHD 219
ce / Dec '88.

### LASTING THE BLUES.
Tracks: Story of Jimmy McCracklin / If I won't talk I
ave a copyright on your love / I wanna make love to
ou / Mama mama / Reconsider baby / I just got to
now / Hop, skip and jump / You're the one.
LP . . . . . . . . . . . . . . . . . . . JSP 1057
SP / Jun '83.

### BLUES AND SOUL.
Tracks: Walk / Looking for a woman / That's the way
goes / Every night every day / I did wrong / I had to
et with it / Just got to know / Think / Get back / R M
ues / I don't care / I'll see it through / Pretty little
weet thing / What's going on / Stinger / You ain't
thing but a devil.
MC. . . . . . . . . . . . . . . .TCSSL 6007
LP . . . . . . . . . . . . . . . . . SSL 6007
ateside / Oct '86.

### EVERYBODY ROCK! (Best of Jimmy
McCracklin).
Tracks: Walk / I'm to blame / Later on / I'm through /
innie Lee / Take care of yourself / Suffer / Get
ugh / Everybody rock / Hurt me / Country baby /
obble / I'll take the blame / He knows the rules / I
ow / Come on.
D. . . . . . . . . . . . . . . . . . . . CD RED 10
LP . . . . . . . . . . . . . . . . . RED LP 10
. . . . . . . . . . . . . . . . . .TCRED 10
harly / Feb '89 / Charly.

### HIGH ON THE BLUES.
Tracks: Not Advised.
D. . . . . . . . . . . . . . . . . . CDSXE 072
ax / Jul '93 / Pinnacle.

### I'M GONNA HAVE MY FUN (McCracklin,
immy & His Blues Blasters).
Tracks: I'm gonna have my fun / True love blues /
hat's your phone number / Your heart ain't right / I
und that woman / Cheater / Beer tavern girl / She's
ne / My days are limited / I cried / End / Take a
ance / I'm the one / Blues blasters boogie / Fare
u well.
LP . . . . . . . . . . . . . . . . . . KIX 29
oute 66 (Sweden) / May '86.

### JIMMY MCCRACKLIN & HIS BLUESB-
LASTERS (McCracklin, Jimmy & His
lues Blasters).
Tracks: reelin' and rockin' / Love when it rains /
eer drinking woman / I think my time is here / I'll
et a break someday / Just won't let her go / Ragged
a mop / My life depends on you / Gonna find
other woman / Up and down blues.
LP . . . . . . . . . . . . . . . . . . 10 CH 28
nnacle / '81.

### MERCURY RECORDINGS, THE.
Tracks: Wobble / Georgia slop / Hitched / No one to
ve me / (I'll be glad when you're dead) you rascal
u / By myself / Doomed lover / With your love /
t's do it / Bridge / What's that (part 1) / What's that
art 2) / Folsom prison blues.
D. . . . . . . . . . . . . . . . . . BCD 15558
ear Family / Mar '92 / Rollercoaster Records / Swift
Direct Distribution / Topic Records.

### MY STORY.
Tracks: Tomorrow / Real love / Arkansas / Keep it
e it is / It's got to be love / In the alley / After hours

/ Stuck with loneliness / Mama and papa / Join the
club / My story / Just a matter of time.
CD . . . . . . . . . . . . . . . . . . NETCD 9508
Bullseye Blues / Jul '91.

### PIECE OF JIMMY MCCRACKLIN.
Tracks: Get together / How you like your love / Pay
before you get / Believe in me / Walk / Advise / Walk
right in / Dog / Pretty little sweet thing / You're the
one / Just got to know / A and I.
LP . . . . . . . . . . . . . . . . . . . MLS 40003
Minit / Aug '68.

### ROCKIN' MAN.
Tracks: Miss Mattie left me / Rock and bye / Miss
Minnie Lee blues / Bad condition blues / Gotta cut
out / Rockin' man / Looking for a woman / She felt
too good / I wanna make love to you / I can't
understand love / Just won't let her go / Movin' on
down the line / That's life / Share and share alike /
Hear my story / You're the one.
LP . . . . . . . . . . . . . . . . . . . KIX 12
Route 66 (Sweden) / Jun '80.

### SAME LOVIN'.
Tracks: All shucks / Games to strong / Outside help /
Just gotta know / Same lovin' / Do it together / My
answer / Think.
CD. . . . . . . . . . . . . . . . . . EJRCD 4013
LP . . . . . . . . . . . . . . . . . . EJR 4013
MC. . . . . . . . . . . . . . . . . . EJRMC 4013
Evejim / Sep '89 / Ichiban Records (UK) / Backs
Distribution.

### TASTE OF THE BLUES, A.
Tracks: Not Advised.
CD . . . . . . . . . . . . . . . . . . BB 9535CD
MC. . . . . . . . . . . . . . . . . . BB 9535MC
Bullseye Blues / Aug '94 / New Note / Topic Records
/ Direct Distribution.

### WALK, THE.
Tracks: Walk / I'm to blame / He knows the rules /
Everybody rock.
CD Single. . . . . . . . . . . . . . . . CDS 13
Charly / Apr '89.
12" . . . . . . . . . . . . . . . . .REDZ 100
7" . . . . . . . . . . . . . . . . . REDZ 7100
Charly / Feb '89.

### YOU DECEIVED ME.
Tracks: Mean mistreated lover / Baby don't you want
to go / Special for you / Highway 101 / You had your
chance / You deceived me / Rock and rye part 1 /
Rock and rye part 2 / Bad luck and trouble / I am
tired / Railroad blues / Blues blaster shuffle /
Jimmy's blues / South side road / Deceiving blues /
Panics on.
LP . . . . . . . . . . . . . . . . . . . IG 405
Crown Prince (Sweden) / May '86.

## McCrae, George

### BEST OF GEORGE MCCRAE.
Tracks: Not Advised.
LP . . . . . . . . . . . . . . . . . . .JSB 100
Jay Boy / Nov '76.

### DIAMOND TOUCH.
Tracks: Nothing but love / Love in motion / I'm gonna
stay with my baby / Givin' back the feeling / Cut the
rug / Dance in a circle / Dancin' through the storm /
Loved and lost.
LP . . . . . . . . . . . . . . . . . . XL 14042
TK / Jul '77.

### DON'T YOU FEEL MY LOVE.
Tracks: Don't you feel my love / You've got me going
crazy.
7" . . . . . . . . . . . . . . . . . TKR 7554
TK / Oct '79.

### GEORGE MCCRAE.
Tracks: Let's dance / Hey sexy dancer / Kiss me /
Sitting in limbo / Never never girl / Over my head / I
got love / Let George do it.
LP . . . . . . . . . . . . . . . . . .JSL 10
Jay Boy / Sep '75.
LP . . . . . . . . . . . . . . . . . TKR 82509
TK / Jun '78.

### GIRLS DON'T LIE.
Tracks: Girls don't lie / I have a heart / That's love
(Extra track on 12" version).
12" . . . . . . . . . . . . . . . . .FED 43T
7" . . . . . . . . . . . . . . . . . FED 43
Sierra / Feb '88.

### HONEY I.
Tracks: Honey I.
7" . . . . . . . . . . . . . . . . . .BOY 107
Jay Boy / Jan '76.

### I AIN'T LYIN'.
Tracks: I ain't lyin'.
7" . . . . . . . . . . . . . . . . . .BOY 105
Jay Boy / Oct '75.

### I CAN'T LEAVE YOU ALONE.
Tracks: I can't leave you alone.
7" . . . . . . . . . . . . . . . . BOY 90
Jay Boy / Oct '74.

### I'LL DO THE ROCKIN' (McCrae, George
& Gwen).
Tracks: I'll do the rockin' / I'm comin' at you.
7" . . . . . . . . . . . . . . . . . .PT 447
President / Dec '75.

### IT'S BEEN SO LONG.
Tracks: It's been so long.
7" . . . . . . . . . . . . . . . . . .BOY 100
Jay Boy / Oct '75.

### KISS ME THE WAY I LIKE IT.
Tracks: Kiss me the way I like it.
7" . . . . . . . . . . . . . . . . TKR 6005
TK / Nov '77.

### LET'S DANCE.
Tracks: Let's dance / Never forget your eyes.
12" . . . . . . . . . . . . . . . . . PT 12-542
7" . . . . . . . . . . . . . . . . . PT 542
President / Jan '86.

### LISTEN TO YOUR HEART.
Tracks: Listen to your heart / Now that I have you.
12" . . . . . . . . . . . . . . . . . PT 12 528
7" . . . . . . . . . . . . . . . . . .PT 528
President / Jun '84.

### LOVE'S BEEN GOOD TO ME.
Tracks: Love's been good to me / Out of knowhere
(into my life).
12" . . . . . . . . . . . . . . . . . PT 12 549
7" . . . . . . . . . . . . . . . . . .PT 549
President / Sep '86.

### LOVE'S BEEN GOOD TO ME.
Tracks: Love's been good to me / Every time you say
goodbye / If it wasn't for you / Now that I have you /
One step closer (to love) / Listen to your heart / Just
another fool / Let's dance / I never forgot your eyes /
Own the night / I'm still believin' / Fire in the night /
Out of nowhere (into my life) / It was always you /
Never too late / Own the night (12" dance mix).
CD . . . . . . . . . . . . . . . . . .PCOM 1135
President / May '94 / Grapevine Distribution / Target
/ Jazz Music / BMG.

### ONE STEP CLOSER TO LOVE.
Tracks: Just another fool / If it wasn't for you / Never
too late / Now that I have you / One step closer (to
love) / Every time I say goodbye / Fire in the night / It
was always you / I'm still believing / Listen to your
heart.
LP . . . . . . . . . . . . . . . . . PTLS 1075
MC. . . . . . . . . . . . . . . . . PTLC 1075
President / Mar '84 / Grapevine Distribution / Target
/ Jazz Music / BMG.

### ONE STEP CLOSER TO LOVE.
Tracks: One step closer (to love) / If it wasn't for you.
12" . . . . . . . . . . . . . . . . . PT 12 522
7" . . . . . . . . . . . . . . . . . .PT 522
President / Feb '84.

### OWN THE NIGHT.
Tracks: Own the night / Every time you say goodbye.
12" . . . . . . . . . . . . . . . . . PT 12 530
7" . . . . . . . . . . . . . . . . . PT 530
President / Sep '84.

### ROCK YOUR BABY.
Tracks: Ooh baby / Rock your baby / You go my
heart / Don't you feel my love / I got love / You can
have it all / Let's dance / Kiss me / Look at you / I
can't leave you alone.
LP . . . . . . . . . . . . . . . . . JSL 3
Jay Boy / Aug '74.
LP . . . . . . . . . . . . . . . . SHM 3050
MC . . . . . . . . . . . . . . . . HSC 3050
Hallmark / Apr '81.
CD . . . . . . . . . . . . . . . . .MUSCD 503
MC. . . . . . . . . . . . . . . . . MUSMC 503
Music Collection International / Sep '94 / THE / Jazz
Music.

### ROCK YOUR BABY.
Tracks: Rock your baby / Rock your baby (part 2).
7" . . . . . . . . . . . . . . . . . .BOY 85
Jay Boy / Jun '74.
12" . . . . . . . . . . . . . . . . .650312 6
7" . . . . . . . . . . . . . . . . . .650312 7
Portrait / Feb '87.

### ROCK YOUR BABY.
**Tracks:** Rock your baby / I can't leave you alone / You got my heart / You can have it all / Look at you / Make it right / I need somebody like you / I get lifted.
■ **LP** . . . . . . . . . . . . . . . . . . . **TKR 82512**
TK / Apr '78.

### ROCK YOUR BABY (OLD GOLD).
**Tracks:** Rock your baby / It's been so long.
7" . . . . . . . . . . . . . . . . . . . . . . **OG 9999**
Old Gold / '92 / Pickwick.

### ROCK YOUR BABY - THE BEST OF GEORGE & GWEN MCCRAE (McCrae, George & Gwen).
**Tracks:** Rock your baby / I can't leave you alone / You can't have it all / Sing a happy song / It's been so long / I ain't lyin' / Honey (I'll rev my life for you) / I get lifted / He keeps something / 90% of me is you / All this love I'm giving / Let's straighten it out / Love insurance / Rocking chair / Love without sex / I'll do the rockin'.
■ **CD** . . . . . . . . . . . . . . . . . . **CDEMS 1493**
■ **LP** . . . . . . . . . . . . . . . . . . . **EMS 1493**
■ **MC** . . . . . . . . . . . . . . . . . **TCEMS 1493**
EMI / Apr '93.

### SING A HAPPY SONG.
**Tracks:** Sing a happy song.
■ **7"** . . . . . . . . . . . . . . . . . . . **BOY 95**
Jay Boy / Mar '75.

### TOGETHER (McCrae, George & Gwen).
**Tracks:** Not Advised.
■ **LP** . . . . . . . . . . . . . . . . . . **PTLS 1070**
President / Dec '85.

### YOU CAN HAVE IT ALL.
**Tracks:** You can have it all.
■ **7"** . . . . . . . . . . . . . . . . . . . **BOY 92**
Jay Boy / Dec '74.

## McCrae, Gwen

### ALL THIS LOVE THAT I'M GIVING.
**Tracks:** All this love that I'm giving.
■ **12"** . . . . . . . . . . . . . . . . . . **MELT 7T**
■ **7"** . . . . . . . . . . . . . . . . . . . **MELT 7**
Rhythm King / Mar '88.

### BEST OF GWEN MCCRAE.
**Tracks:** Rockin' chair / For your love / It's worth the hurt / 90% of me is you / It keeps on raining / He don't ever lose his groove / Winners together or losers apart / Let your love do the talkin' / You and I were made for each other / Damn right it's good / Love without sex / Starting all over again / Tonights the night / Let's straighten it out / Love insurance / Cradle of love / Maybe I'll find somebody new / Melody of life / All this love I'm giving.
CD. . . . . . . . . . . . . . . . . . . **NEXCD 189**
Sequel / May '92 / Total / BMG.

### CRADLE OF LOVE.
**Tracks:** Cradle of love / Easy rock.
■ **7"** . . . . . . . . . . . . . . . . . . . **PT 452**
President / May '76.

### DO YOU KNOW WHAT I MEAN.
**Tracks:** Do you know what I mean.
■ **12"** . . . . . . . . . . . . . . . . . . **FED 3T**
■ **7"** . . . . . . . . . . . . . . . . . . . **FED 3**
Sierra / Nov '84.

### DOIN' IT.
**Tracks:** Doin' it / Hey world.
■ **12"** . . . . . . . . . . . . . . . . . **A 9901 T**
■ **7"** . . . . . . . . . . . . . . . . . . .**A 9901**
Atlantic / Feb '83.

### EIGHTIES LADY.
**Tracks:** Eighties lady.
■ **12"** . . . . . . . . . . . . . . . . . . **YARD T1**
■ **7"** . . . . . . . . . . . . . . . . . . . **YARD 1**
Danceyard / Jul '88.

### FUNKY SENSATION.
**Tracks:** Funky sensation / Funky sensation (off Broadway mix).
■ **12"** . . . . . . . . . . . . . . . . . . **LEFT 15T**
■ **7"** . . . . . . . . . . . . . . . . . . . **LEFT 15**
Rhythm King / Sep '87.

### I CAN ONLY THINK OF YOU.
**Tracks:** I can only think of you.
■ **12"** . . . . . . . . . . . . . . . . . **EXPAND 36**
Expansion / Feb '93.

### IT'S WORTH THE HURT.
**Tracks:** It's worth the hurt / 90% of me is you.
■ **7"** . . . . . . . . . . . . . . . . . . . **PT 416**
President / Jun '74.

---

### KEEP THE FIRE BURNING.
**Tracks:** Keep the fire burning / Funky..
■ **12"** . . . . . . . . . . . . . . . . . **FLAM 1 T**
■ **7"** . . . . . . . . . . . . . . . . . . . **FLAM 1**
Atlantic / Oct '82.

### KEEP THE FIRE BURNING 94.
**Tracks:** Keep the fire burning (mixes).
**12"** . . . . . . . . . . . . . . . . . . **CLUBA 017**
**12"** . . . . . . . . . . . . . . . . . **CLUBAX 017**
**CD Single** . . . . . . . . . . . . . . **CLUBAD 017**
Club Vision / Nov '94 / Vital Distribution.

### LOVE INSURANCE.
**Tracks:** Love insurance / She keeps something groovy goin' on.
■ **7"** . . . . . . . . . . . . . . . . . . . **PT 444**
President / Nov '75.

## McCrarys

### LOVE ON A SUMMER NIGHT.
**Tracks:** Love on a summer night / Miles above.
■ **12"** . . . . . . . . . . . . . . . . . **12CL 251**
■ **7"** . . . . . . . . . . . . . . . . . . .**CL 251**
Capitol / Jul '82.

## McDaniels, Gene

### ANOTHER TEAR FALLS.
**Tracks:** Hundred pounds of clay / Spanish Harlem / Walk with a winner / Point of no return / Chip chip / Hang on (just a little bit longer) / Tear / Tower of strength / Another tear falls / Raindrops / Forgotten man / It's a lonely town / Spanish lace / I don't want to cry / Cry baby cry / You can have her.
■ **LP** . . . . . . . . . . . . . . . . . . **CRB 1136**
Charly R&B / Aug '86.

### HEADLESS HEROES OF THE APOCALYPSE.
**Tracks:** Lord is back / Jagger the dagger / Lovin' man / Headless heroes / Susan Jane / Freedom death dance / Supermarket blues / Parasite.
■ **LP** . . . . . . . . . . . . . . . . . . **2400163**
Atlantic / Oct '71.

### OUTLAW.
**Tracks:** Outlaw / Sagittarius red / Welfare city / Silent majority / Love letter to America / Unspoken dreams of light / Cherrystones / Reverend Lee / Black boy.
■ **LP** . . . . . . . . . . . . . . . . . . .**2465 022**
Atlantic / Apr '71.

### TOWER OF STRENGTH.
**Tracks:** Tower of strength.
■ **7"** . . . . . . . . . . . . . . . . . . . **HLG 9448**
London-American / Nov '61.

### WALK WITH A WINNER.
**Tracks:** Walk with a winner.
■ **7"** . . . . . . . . . . . . . . . . . . . **LIB 55805**
Liberty / '65.

## MacDonald, Ralph

### COUNTERPOINT.
**Tracks:** I need someone / You are in love / Tell the truth / Discolypso / Always something missing / East dry river.
■ **LP** . . . . . . . . . . . . . . . . . . **TKR 83373**
TK / Nov '79.

### IN THE NAME OF LOVE.
**Tracks:** In the name of love / Universal rhythm.
■ **12"** . . . . . . . . . . . . . . . . . . **LONX 57**
■ **7"** . . . . . . . . . . . . . . . . . . . **LON 57**
London / Oct '84.

### UNIVERSAL RHYTHM.
**Tracks:** In the name of love / Outcasts (another time, another place), Theme from / Universal rhythm / Trade winds / Playpen / It's the game / Park Plaza.
■ **LP** . . . . . . . . . . . . . . . . . **LONLP 3**
**MC** . . . . . . . . . . . . . . . . . . . **LONC 3**
London / Sep '84 / PolyGram.

### UNIVERSAL RHYTHM.
**Tracks:** Universal rhythm / Outcasts.
■ **12"** . . . . . . . . . . . . . . . . . . **LONX 55**
■ **7"** . . . . . . . . . . . . . . . . . . . **LON 55**
London / Sep '85.

### YOU NEED MORE CALYPSO.
**Tracks:** You need more calypso / In the name of love.
■ **12"** . . . . . . . . . . . . . . . . . . **LONX 91**
■ **7"** . . . . . . . . . . . . . . . . . . . **LON 91**
London / Mar '86.

---

## McDonald, Michael

### ALL WE GOT.
**Tracks:** All we got / Take it to heart.
■ **12"** . . . . . . . . . . . . . . . . . **W 9489 T**
Reprise / Dec '90.
■ **7"** . . . . . . . . . . . . . . . . . . . **W 9489**
Reprise / Nov '90.

### BLINK OF AN EYE.
**Tracks:** I stand for you / East of Eden / More to us than that / I want you / No more prayin' / Matters of the heart / Hey girl / What makes a man hold on / Blink of an eye / Everlasting / For a child.
CD. . . . . . . . . . . . . . . . . . **9362452932**
MC. . . . . . . . . . . . . . . . . . **9362452934**
Reprise / Aug '93 / WEA.

### I GOTTA TRY.
**Tracks:** I gotta try.
■ **7"** . . . . . . . . . . . . . . . . . . . **W 9862**
WEA / Jan '83.

### I KEEP FORGETTING.
**Tracks:** I keep forgettin' / Losin' end.
■ **12"** . . . . . . . . . . . . . . . . . **K 17992 T**
■ **7"** . . . . . . . . . . . . . . . . . . . **K 17992**
WEA / Jun '86.

### I STAND FOR YOU.
**Tracks:** I stand for you (Edit) / I stand for you (LP version).
■ **7"** . . . . . . . . . . . . . . . . . . . **WD 208**
■ **CD Single** . . . . . . . . . . . . . . **WD 208CD**
■ **MC Single** . . . . . . . . . . . . . . **WD 208C**
WEA / Sep '93.

### IF THAT'S WHAT IT TAKES.
**Tracks:** Playin' by the rules / I keep forgettin' / Love lies / Gotta try / I can let go now / That's why / If that's what it takes / No such luck / Losin' end / Believe in it.
■ **CD** . . . . . . . . . . . . . . . . . . **257 018**
■ **LP** . . . . . . . . . . . . . . . . . . **K 57018**
■ **MC** . . . . . . . . . . . . . . . . . . **K4 57018**
WEA / Aug '82.
■ **CD** . . . . . . . . . . . . . . . . . .**923703 2**
WEA / Jul '88.

### LONELY TALK.
**Tracks:** Not Advised.
■ **CD** . . . . . . . . . . . . . . . . . .**925979 2**
WEA / '89.

### NO LOOKING BACK.
**Tracks:** No looking back / By heart / Bad times / (I'll be your) Angel / Any foolish thing / Our love / (I hang) On your every word / Lost in the parade / Don't let me down.
■ **LP** . . . . . . . . . . . . . . . . . .**925291 1**
■ **MC** . . . . . . . . . . . . . . . . . .**925291 4**
WEA / Aug '85.
■ **CD** . . . . . . . . . . . . . . . . . .**925291 2**
WEA / Feb '87.

### NO LOOKING BACK.
**Tracks:** No looking back (Extra track on 12" version only.) / Don't let me down.
■ **12"** . . . . . . . . . . . . . . . . . **W 8960T**
■ **7"** . . . . . . . . . . . . . . . . . . . **W 8960**
WEA / Oct '86.

### SWEET FREEDOM.
**Tracks:** Sweet freedom / Freedom lights.
■ **7"** . . . . . . . . . . . . . . . . . . .**MCA 1073**
MCA / Aug '86.

### SWEET FREEDOM: BEST OF MICHAEL MCDONALD.
**Tracks:** Sweet freedom / I'll be your angel / Yah mo b there / I gotta try / I keep forgettin' / Our love / On my own / No lookin back / Any foolish thing / That's why / What a fool believes / I can let go now.
CD. . . . . . . . . . . . . . . . . . **2410492**
■ **LP** . . . . . . . . . . . . . . . . . . **WX 67**
**MC**. . . . . . . . . . . . . . . . . . . **WX 67C**
WEA / Nov '86 / WEA.

### TAKE IT TO HEART.
**Tracks:** All we got / Get the word started / Love can break your heart / Take it to heart / Tear it up Lonely talk / Searchin' for understanding / Homeboy / No amount of reason / One step away / You show me.
■ **CD**. . . . . . . . . . . . . . . . . . **WX 285CD**
CD. . . . . . . . . . . . . . . . . **7599259792**
■ **LP** . . . . . . . . . . . . . . . . . . **WX 285**
■ **MC** . . . . . . . . . . . . . . . . . . **WX 285C**
WEA / May '90 / WEA.

### TEAR IT UP.
**Tracks:** Tear it up / Plain of jars.
■ **12"** . . . . . . . . . . . . . . . . . **W 9769**
■ **7"** . . . . . . . . . . . . . . . . . . . **W 9769**

■ DELETED

■ CD Single. . . . . . . . . . . . . . . W 9769 CD
■ MC Single. . . . . . . . . . . . . . . W 9769 C
WEA / Jul '90.

**YAH MO BE THERE (see under Ingram, James).**

## McDowell, Carrie

### CARRIE MCDOWELL.
Tracks: Uh, uh, no, no casual sex (part 1) / Secret fire / When a woman loves a man / Just dance / It's the power of your love (growing on me) / Fly (white bird fly) / Tracks of my tears / I'm here for you / Up the down side of love.
■ LP . . . . . . . . . . . . . . . . . . . ZL 72590
■ MC. . . . . . . . . . . . . . . . . . . ZK 72590
Motown / Nov '87.

### UH UH NO NO CASUAL SEX.
Tracks: Uh, uh, no, no casual sex / Uh, uh, no, no casual sex (part 2) / Uh, uh, no, no casual sex (dub) / Uh, uh, no, no casual sex (sunrise mix).
■ 12". . . . . . . . . . . . . . . . . . . ZT 41502
■ 7". . . . . . . . . . . . . . . . . . . ZB 41501
Motown / Sep '87.

### WHEN A WOMAN LOVES A MAN.
Tracks: When a woman loves a man.
■ 7". . . . . . . . . . . . . . . . . . . ZB 41651
Motown / Jul '87.

## McDuff, Jack

### ANOTHER REAL GOOD 'UN.
Tracks: Another real good 'un / Summertime / Off the beaten path / Long day blues / Rock candy / I can't get started / I cover the waterfront.
LP. . . . . . . . . . . . . . . . . . . . . MR 5374
MC. . . . . . . . . . . . . . . . . . . . . MC 5374
Muse / Sep '92 / New Note / Jazz Horizons / C.M. Distribution.
CD. . . . . . . . . . . . . . . . . . . . . MCD 5374
Muse / Sep '92 / New Note / Jazz Horizons / C.M. Distribution.

### BRONX TALE (McDuff, Jack & Friends).
Tracks: C Jam blues / Streets of the Bronx / Time after time / Pepper & salt / Cry me a river / Ice candy / Old folks / Martino / Loverman.
CD. . . . . . . . . . . . . . . . . . . . . KICJ 204
Paddlewheel / Aug '94 / New Note.

### COLOUR ME BLUE (McDuff, Jack & Friends).
Tracks: Not Advised.
CD. . . . . . . . . . . . . . . . . . . . . CCD 4516
Concord / Aug '92 / New Note.

### GEORGE BENSON AND JACK MCDUFF (see under Benson, George).

### HONEYDRIPPER,THE.
Tracks: Not Advised.
■ LP . . . . . . . . . . . . . . . . . . . OJC 222
Original Jazz Classics / Apr '86.

### HOT BARBEQUE (McDuff, Brother Jack).
Tracks: Not Advised.
LP. . . . . . . . . . . . . . . . . . . . . BGPD 1054
BGP / Apr '93 / Pinnacle.

### HOT BARBEQUE.
Tracks: Not Advised.
CD. . . . . . . . . . . . . . . . . . . . . CDBGP 053
BGP / May '93 / Pinnacle.

### HOT BARBEQUE/LIVE (AT THE FRONT ROOM) (McDuff, Brother Jack).
Tracks: Hot barbeque / Party's over / Briar patch / Hippy dip / 601 1 No.poplar / Cry me a river / Three day thang / Rock candy / It ain't necessarily so / Santified samba / Whistle while you work / Real good'n / Undecided.
CD. . . . . . . . . . . . . . . . . . . . . CDBGPD 053
BGP / Apr '93 / Pinnacle.

### WRITE ON CAP'N.
Tracks: Spec-tator / From the pulpit / Killer Joe / Room / Night in Tunisia / Captain's quarters / Billy-ack / Out of my head / Goin' to the wall / Havin' a good time.
CD. . . . . . . . . . . . . . . . . . . . . CCD 4568
Concord / Sep '93 / New Note.

## McElroy, Foster

### FM SQUARED.
Tracks: Not Advised.
CD. . . . . . . . . . . . . . . . . . . . . 781 994-2
■ LP . . . . . . . . . . . . . . . . . . . 781 994-1
MC. . . . . . . . . . . . . . . . . . . . . 781 994-4
Atlantic / Feb '90 / WEA.

## McFadden & Whitehead

### AIN'T NO STOPPIN' US NOW.
Tracks: Ain't no stoppin' us now / I got the love.
■ 7". . . . . . . . . . . . . . . . . . . PIR 7365
Philadelphia Int. / May '79.

### AIN'T NO STOPPIN' US NOW.
Tracks: Ain't no stoppin' us now / Bring the family back.
■ 7". . . . . . . . . . . . . . . . . . . PIR 8871
Philadelphia Int. / May '82.
■ 12". . . . . . . . . . . . . . . . . . . BDSL 504
■ 7". . . . . . . . . . . . . . . . . . . BDS 504
Buddah / May '84.
■ 12". . . . . . . . . . . . . . . . . . . SWAVE 2
Streetwave / Sep '85.
■ 12". . . . . . . . . . . . . . . . 4 ZH 06923
Philadelphia Int. / Nov '87.

### AIN'T NO STOPPIN' US NOW (OLD GOLD).
Tracks: Ain't no stoppin' us now / I got the love.
■ 7". . . . . . . . . . . . . . . . . . . OG 9400
Old Gold / Jul '84.
■ 12". . . . . . . . . . . . . . . . . . . OG 4072
Old Gold / Jul '88.

### AIN'T NO STOPPING US NOW.
Tracks: Not Advised.
CD. . . . . . . . . . . . . . . . . . . . . KWEST 5406
Disky / May '93 / THE.

### DO YOU WANT TO DANCE.
Tracks: Do you want to dance / I've been pushed aside.
■ 7". . . . . . . . . . . . . . . . . . . PIR 7744
Philadelphia Int. / Nov '79.

### I HEARD IT IN A LOVE SONG.
Tracks: I heard it in a love song / That lets me know I'm love / I know what I'm gonna do / Always room for one more / Why oh why / Don't feel bad / This is my song / Love song no.690.
■ LP . . . . . . . . . . . . . . . . . . . PIR 84616
MC. . . . . . . . . . . . . . . . . . . . . 40 84616
Philadelphia Int. / Dec '80 / EMI.

### I HEARD IT IN A LOVE SONG.
Tracks: I heard it in a love song / Always room for one more.
■ 7". . . . . . . . . . . . . . . . . . . PIR 8964
Philadelphia Int. / Sep '80.

### MCFADDEN & WHITEHEAD.
Tracks: Ain't no stoppin' us now / I've been pushed aside / Mr. Music / Just wanna love you baby / Got to change / You're my someone to love / I got the love / Do you want to dance.
■ LP . . . . . . . . . . . . . . . . . . . PIR 83613
Philadelphia Int. / '79.

## McFerrin, Bobby

### BOBBY MCFERRIN.
Tracks: Dance with me / Feline / You really got a hold on me / All feets can dance / Sightless bird / Peace / Jubilee / Hallucinations / Chicken.
■ LP . . . . . . . . . . . . . . . . . . . K 52387
Elektra / Jun '82.
CD. . . . . . . . . . . . . . . . . . . . . 9600232
Elektra / '89 / WEA.

### DON'T WORRY BE HAPPY.
Tracks: Don't worry be happy (LP version) / Simple pleasures / From me to you (CD single only.) / Don't worry be happy (7" version).
■ 12". . . . . . . . . . . . . . . . . . . 12MT 56
■ CD Single. . . . . . . . . . . . . . . CDMT 56
■ 7". . . . . . . . . . . . . . . . . . . MT 56
EMI-Manhattan / Sep '88.

### GARDEN, THE.
Tracks: Garden / Soma so de la de sase / Don't worry, be happy (Not on 7".) / Drive my car (CD single only.)
■ 12". . . . . . . . . . . . . . . . . . . 12MT 92
■ 7". . . . . . . . . . . . . . . . . . . MT 92
■ CD Single. . . . . . . . . . . . . . . CDMT 92
EMI-Manhattan / Oct '90.

### GOOD LOVIN'.
Tracks: Good lovin' / There ya go.
■ 12". . . . . . . . . . . . . . . . . . . 12MT 42

■ 7". . . . . . . . . . . . . . . . . . . MT 42
■ CD Single. . . . . . . . . . . . . . . CDMT 42
EMI-Manhattan / Jun '88.

### MEDICINE MUSIC.
Tracks: Medicine man / Baby / Yes, you / Garden / Common threads / Sweet in the mornin' (Featuring voicestra.) / Discipline (Featuring Robert McFerrin Sr. and voicestra.) / He ran all the way / Angry (Gima) / Train / Soma so de la de sase / 23rd Psalm.
■ LP . . . . . . . . . . . . . . . . . . . MTL 1059
■ MC . . . . . . . . . . . . . . . . . . TCMTL 1059
■ CD . . . . . . . . . . . . . . . . . . CDMTL 1059
EMI-Manhattan / Oct '90.

### PLAY (McFerrin, Bobby & Chick Corea).
Tracks: Spain / Even for me / Autumn leaves / Blues connotation / 'Round midnight / Blue bossa.
■ CD . . . . . . . . . . . . . . . . . . CDP 7954772
Blue Note / Jan '92.

### SIMPLE PLEASURES.
Tracks: Don't worry, be happy / All I want / Drive my car / Simple pleasures / Good lovin' / Come to me / Suzie Q / Drive / Them changes / Sunshine of your love.
CD. . . . . . . . . . . . . . . . . . . . . CDMTL 1018
■ LP . . . . . . . . . . . . . . . . . . . MTL 1018
■ MC . . . . . . . . . . . . . . . . . . TCMTL 1018
EMI-Manhattan / Apr '88 / EMI.
■ LP . . . . . . . . . . . . . . . . . . . ATAK 170
MC. . . . . . . . . . . . . . . . . . . . . TCATAK 170
■ CD . . . . . . . . . . . . . . . . . . CDP 748 059 2
EMI-Manhattan / Mar '91 / EMI.

### SPONTANEOUS INVENTIONS.
Tracks: Thinkin' about your body / Turtle shoes / From me to you / There ya go / Cara mia / Another night in Tunisia / Opportunity / Walkin' / I hear music / Beverly Hills blues / Manana Iguana.
■ CD . . . . . . . . . . . . . . . . . . BNZ 57
Blue Note / Dec '86.
■ LP . . . . . . . . . . . . . . . . . . . BT 85110
■ MC. . . . . . . . . . . . . . . . . . TCBT 85110
Blue Note / Jan '89.

### SPONTANEOUS INVENTIONS.
Tracks: Scrapple from the apple / Honeysuckle rose / Bwee Dop / Cara mia / Fascinating Rhythm / Itsy bitsy spider / Thinkin' about your body / Drive / Opportunity / I got the feelin' / Walkin' / Blackbird / Manna Iguana.
■ VHS . . . . . . . . . . . . . . . . MVP 99 1145 2
PMI / Nov '86.
Laser Disc . . . . . . . . . . . . . . PLMJA 00321
Pioneer LDCE / Jun '92 / Video Collection / THE.

### THINKIN' ABOUT YOUR BODY (For Debs).
Tracks: Thinkin' about your body / From me to you.
■ 7". . . . . . . . . . . . . . . . . . . BLUE 4
EMI / Dec '86.

### THINKIN' ABOUT YOUR BODY.
Tracks: Thinkin' about your body / Don't worry be happy / From me to you (Not on 7".) / Come to me (Only available on CD single.)
■ 12". . . . . . . . . . . . . . . . . . . 12BLUE 6
■ 7". . . . . . . . . . . . . . . . . . . BLUE 6
■ CD Single. . . . . . . . . . . . . . . CDBLUE 6
EMI-Manhattan / Dec '88.

### VOICE, THE.
Tracks: Blackbird / El brujo / I feel good / I'm my own walkman / Music box.
■ LP . . . . . . . . . . . . . . . . . . . 960661
Elektra / Aug '84.
■ CD . . . . . . . . . . . . . . . . . . 9603662
Elektra / '88.

## McGee, Francine

### DELIRIUM.
Tracks: Delirium.
■ 12". . . . . . . . . . . . . . . . . . . BRT 5
Blue Bird (2) / Nov '83.

### FEELIN' GOOD.
Tracks: Feeling good / Delirium.
■ 7". . . . . . . . . . . . . . . . . . . PC 9216
RCA / Mar '78.

## McGee, Jay W

### WHEN WE PARTY (UPTOWN DOWNTOWN).
Tracks: When we party (uptown downtown) / I've been checking out.
■ 7". . . . . . . . . . . . . . . . . . . ENY 231
■ 12". . . . . . . . . . . . . . . . . . . ENYT 231
Ensign / Sep '82.

## McGloiry, Michael

**WON'T YOU LET ME BE THE ONE.**
Tracks: Won't you let me be the one.
■ 12" . . . . . . . . . . . . . . . . . . . 12 SHACK 2
■ 7" . . . . . . . . . . . . . . . . . . . . . . SHACK 2
Record Shack / Jun '81.

## McGriff, Jimmy

**ALL ABOUT MY GIRL.**
Tracks: All about my girl.
■ 7" . . . . . . . . . . . . . . . . . . 2C 008 83376
EMI / Apr '83.

**BLUES FOR MR.JIMMY.**
Tracks: Bump de bump de bump / Discotheque U.S.A
/ Cash box / Blues for Joe / Blues for Mr.Jimmy /
Dog (you dog) / Sho' nuff / Turn blue / Party's over.
■ MC. . . . . . . . . . . . . . . . . . . . TCSSL 6005
■ LP . . . . . . . . . . . . . . . . . . . . . SSL 6005
Stateside / Apr '86.

**COUNTDOWN.**
Tracks: Countdown.
■ LP . . . . . . . . . . . . . . . . . . . . . . M 9116
Milestone / Nov '83.

**ELECTRIC FUNK.**
Tracks: Back on the track / Chris cross / Miss Poopie
/ Bird wave / Spear for moon dog - Part 2 / Tight
times / Spinning wheel / Funky junk.
■ LP . . . . . . . . . . . . . . . . . . . . . B1 84350
Blue Note / Sep '93.

**FLY DUDE.**
Tracks: Not Advised.
■ LP . . . . . . . . . . . . . . . . . . . . . . PLEO 14
Not Advised / '87.

**FUNKIEST LITTLE BAND ON THE
WORLD.**
Tracks: Groove fly / Shuckin & Jivin / Dig on it / Bug
out / Fat cakes / Super funk / Plain brown bag /
Jumpin' the blues / Tiki / Cotton boy blues / These
foolish things / Worm turns / Sermon.
■ CD . . . . . . . . . . . . . . . . . . . . CDC 9046
LRC / Nov '92.

**GEORGIA ON MY MIND.**
Tracks: Let's stay together / Shaft / Theme from /
What's going on / Georgia on my mind / April in
Paris / Everyday I have the blues / Yardbird suite /
It's you I adore / Lonesome road / Mack the knife /
There will never be another you / Canadian sunset /
Mr. Lucky / Moonglow / Red sails in the sunset /
Secret love.
CD. . . . . . . . . . . . . . . . . . . . . CDC-8513
MC. . . . . . . . . . . . . . . . . . . . . MC 8513
LRC Jazz / Nov '90 / Harmonia Mundi (UK).

**GROOVE GREASE.**
Tracks: Groove grease / Bird / Plain brown bag /
There will never be another you / Canadian sunset /
Mr. Lucky / Moonglow / Red sails in the sunset /
Secret love.
■ LP . . . . . . . . . . . . . . . . . . . . . GM 503
Groove Merchant / Jul '72.

**I GOT A WOMAN.**
Tracks: I got a woman / All about my girl / Shimmy
shimmy walk / Stick shift.
■ EP . . . . . . . . . . . . . . . . . . . . . . ENS 6
Ensign / Oct '83.

**I GOT A WOMAN.**
Tracks: I got a woman / All about my girl / Watermelon man.
■ 7" . . . . . . . . . . . . . . . . . . . . . UP 613
United Artists / Nov '79.

**JIMMY MCGRIFF FEATURING HANK
CRAWFORD (McGriff, Jimmy & Hank
Crawford).**
Tracks: Not Advised.
CD. . . . . . . . . . . . . . . . . . . . . CDC 9001
MC. . . . . . . . . . . . . . . . . . . . . MC 9001
LRC Jazz / Oct '90 / Harmonia Mundi (UK).

**LAST MINUTE, THE.**
Tracks: Not Advised.
■ EP . . . . . . . . . . . . . . . . . . . . ENSUE 2
Sue / Dec '83.

**PLAYS THE WORM.**
Tracks: Worm / Keep loose / Heavyweight / Think /
Lock it up / Girl talk / Blue juice / Take the A train.
■ LP . . . . . . . . . . . . . . . . . . . UAS 29004
United Artists / May '69.

**PULLIN' OUT THE STOPS - BEST OF
JIMMY MCGRIFF.**
Tracks: All about my girl / I've got a woman (parts 1
& 2) / Discotheque / Kiko / See see rider / Cash box /
Gospel time / Where it's at / Last minute / Blue juice
/ Step one / Chris cross / South Wes / Black pearl /
Worm / Ain't it funky now / Fat cakes.
CD. . . . . . . . . . . . . . . . . . . . CDP 8307242
Blue Note / Sep '94 / EMI.

**SONNY LESTER COLLECTION.**
Tracks: Not Advised.
CD. . . . . . . . . . . . . . . . . . . . . . CDC 9070
LRC / Nov '93 / New Note.

**SOUL BROTHERS (see under Crawford,
Hank).**

**SOUL SURVIVORS (McGriff, Jimmy &
Hank Crawford).**
Tracks: Because of you / Frim fram sauce / Peeper /
One mint julep / Second time around / After supper.
■ LP . . . . . . . . . . . . . . . . . . . . . M 9142
MC. . . . . . . . . . . . . . . . . . . . . . 5M 9142
Milestone / Oct '86 / Jazz Music / Pinnacle / Cadillac.

**STARTING FIVE, THE.**
Tracks: Not Advised.
■ LP . . . . . . . . . . . . . . . . . . . . . MX 9148
Milestone / Oct '87.

**STATE OF THE ART.**
Tracks: Headbender / Stormy weather / Cheesesteak
/ Don't ever doubt me / New wave blues / Slow
gindin' / Hip hop be bop.
■ LP . . . . . . . . . . . . . . . . . . . . . M 9135
Milestone / Feb '86.

**TRIBUTE TO BASIE (McGriff, Jimmy Big
Band).**
Tracks: Not Advised.
CD. . . . . . . . . . . . . . . . . . . . . . CDC 9027
MC. . . . . . . . . . . . . . . . . . . . . . MC 9027
LRC Jazz / Mar '91 / Harmonia Mundi (UK).

## Macho

**I'M A MAN.**
Tracks: I'm a man / Cose there's music in the air.
■ 7" . . . . . . . . . . . . . . . . . . . . EMI 2882
EMI / Oct '78.

## McKnight, Brian

**BRIAN MCKNIGHT.**
Tracks: Yours / Way love goes / Goodbye my love /
Love me, hold me / After the love / One last cry /
Never felt this way / I couldn't say / Stay the night / Is
the feeling gone / Love is / I can go for that / Oh Lord
/ My prayer.
■ CD . . . . . . . . . . . . . . . . . . . .514899-2
■ LP . . . . . . . . . . . . . . . . . . . .514899-1
■ MC . . . . . . . . . . . . . . . . . . . .514899-4
Mercury / Nov '93.

## McKone, Vivienne

**HEADING RIGHT BACK TO YOU.**
Tracks: Not Advised.
■ 12" . . . . . . . . . . . . . . . . . . . .FX 233
■ CD Single . . . . . . . . . . . . . . . .FCD 233
FFRR / Nov '93.

**SING.**
Tracks: Sing / Sing (Mix) / Fly.
■ 12" . . . . . . . . . . . . . . . . . . . .FX 183
■ 7" . . . . . . . . . . . . . . . . . . . . . F 183
■ CD Single . . . . . . . . . . . . . . . .FCD 183
■ MC Single. . . . . . . . . . . . . . . .FCS 183
FFRR / Jul '92.

**VIVIENNE MCKONE.**
Tracks: Sing / Beware / He's not here anymore /
Move on / Heading right back to you / Self control /
Don't push me to my limit / No turning back / Why /
Fly / Reaching your goals / Get to know you / Zero.
LP . . . . . . . . . . . . . . . . . . . . . 8283761
■ CD . . . . . . . . . . . . . . . . . . . . 8283762
■ MC. . . . . . . . . . . . . . . . . . . . 8283764
FFRR / Jan '93 / PolyGram.

## McKoy

**FAMILY.**
Tracks: Family.
■ 12" . . . . . . . . . . . . . . . . . . . RTKOY 1
■ 7" . . . . . . . . . . . . . . . . . . . 7 RTKOY
■ CD Single . . . . . . . . . . . . . CDRTKOY 1
Right Track / Jan '92.
MC Single . . . . . . . . . . . . . . . CATUM 8

■ 12" . . . . . . . . . . . . . . . . . . . 12TUM 8
■ 12" Remix. . . . . . . . . . . . . . .12TUMX 8
■ CD Single . . . . . . . . . . . . . . . CDTUM 8
Gut Reaction / Mar '94 / Total.

**FIGHT.**
Tracks: Fight.
■ 12" . . . . . . . . . . . . . . . . . . . 12TUM 1
■ 7" . . . . . . . . . . . . . . . . . . . . TUM 1
■ CD Single . . . . . . . . . . . . . . . CDTUM 1
■ MC Single. . . . . . . . . . . . . . . CATUM 1
Right Track Records / Jan '93.

**FULL CIRCLE.**
Tracks: Not Advised.
CD. . . . . . . . . . . . . . . . . . . . . TUMCD 1
LP . . . . . . . . . . . . . . . . . . . . . TUMLP 1
MC. . . . . . . . . . . . . . . . . . . . TUMMC 1
Right Track / Apr '94 / Jetstar.

**ON THE STREETS.**
Tracks: On the streets.
■ 12" . . . . . . . . . . . . . . . . . . . 12 TUM 7
■ CD Single . . . . . . . . . . . . . . . CDTUM 7
Gut Reaction / Nov '93.

## McLean, Andy

**ANDY'S THEME.**
Tracks: Two hearts / Funny / Saliya / Take 5 & 6 /
Please stay / Andy's theme / Is this for real / Make it
last / Summer song / Early bird.
CD . . . . . . . . . . . . . . . . . . . CALLCD 001
Callisto / Sep '94 / Timewarp.

## McNair, Barbara

**YOU'RE GONNA LOVE MY BABY.**
Tracks: You're gonna love my baby.
■ 7" . . . . . . . . . . . . . . . . . . . TMG 544
Tamla Motown / '66.

## McNeely, Big Jay

**BEST OF BIG JAY MCNEELY.**
Tracks: Not Advised.
■ LP . . . . . . . . . . . . . . . . . . . . BP 1300
Saxophonograph (Sweden) / Jan '86.

**BIG 'J' IN 3-D.**
Tracks: Not Advised.
CD. . . . . . . . . . . . . . . . . . . .KCD 000650
King / Dec '92 / New Note / Koch International.

**BIG J IN 3-D.**
Tracks: Goof / Ice water / Big Jay shuffle / Rock
candy / Whipped cream / Hot cinders - 3-D / Hardtack / Nervous man / Mule milk / Let's work /
Beachcomber.
■ LP . . . . . . . . . . . . . . . . . . . . SING 650
Sing / Aug '88.
CD. . . . . . . . . . . . . . . . . . . . .KCD 650
King / Mar '90 / New Note / Koch International.

**BIG JAY MCNEELY MEETS THE PENGUINS (McNeely, Big Jay & The
Penguins).**
Tracks: Honky tonk / Night train / Harlem nocturne /
Watch out, Big Jay's loose / Money honey / Hey
senorita / Love will make your mind go wild / Ooky
ook / Only you / Saturday night at the movies /
Memories of El Monte / Earth angel.
■ LP . . . . . . . . . . . . . . . . . . . . CH 191
Ace / Aug '87.

**BLUES AT DAYBREAK (McNeel, Big Jay
& C. Rannenberg).**
Tracks: Not Advised.
CD. . . . . . . . . . . . . . . . . . .BEST 1018CD
Acoustic Music Records / Nov '93 / A.D.A.
Distribution.

**DEACON RIDES AGAIN.**
Tracks: Not Advised.
■ LP . . . . . . . . . . . . . . . . . . .PM 1546691
Pathe Marconi (France) / Sep '84.

**FROM HARLEM TO CAMDEN.**
Tracks: Harlem nocturne / Camden bounce / Some
kinda boogie / Just because / Jumpin' with Jay /
Strollin' sax / Pembridge court / Catalina swing /
Rockin' the reeds.
■ LP . . . . . . . . . . . . . . . . . . . . CH 111
Ace / Aug '87.

**LIVE AND RARE.**
Tracks: Blues in G minor / Deacon's hop / There is
something on your mind / Back..shack..track / Honky
tonk / My darling dear Texas turkey / Big Jay's
Count.
LP . . . . . . . . . . . . . . . . . . . . . .JD 908

■ DELETED

Earth Angel (Sweden) / Jan '91 / Swift / Wellard / C.M. Distribution.

## ROADHOUSE BOOGIE.

Tracks: Blow big Jay / Road house boogie / Willie the cool cat / Midnight dreams / Hoppin' the hunter / Junie Flip / Real crazy cool / Let's split / Penthouse serenade.

■ LP . . . . . . . . . . . . . . . . . . . . . . BP 505
Saxophonograph (Sweden) / May '85.
CD . . . . . . . . . . . . . . . . . . . . . .RBD 505
Saxophonograph (Sweden) / Apr '91 / C.M. Distribution / Swift / Wellard.

## McNeir, Ronnie

### COME BE WITH ME.

Tracks: Come be with me / Light my fire / Is this what happens to a love / Keep giving me love.
■ 12" . . . . . . . . . . . . . . . . . . . 12CL 329
Capitol / Apr '84.

### FOLLOW YOUR HEART.

Tracks: Follow your heart / Everybody's in a hurry / Love's under suspect.
■ 7" . . . . . . . . . . . . . . . . . . . EXPAND 6
Expansion / Nov '86.

### I'M SO IN LOVE WITH YOU BABY.

Tracks: I'm so in love with you / Serve it up.
■ 12" . . . . . . . . . . . . . . . . . . EXPAND 11
Expansion / Oct '87.

### LIFE AND LOVE.

Tracks: Not Advised.
LP . . . . . . . . . . . . . . . . . . . . .EXELP 2
■ CD . . . . . . . . . . . . . . . . . . . EXCDP 2
Debut (1) / Jul '92 / Pinnacle.

### LOVE SUSPECT.

Tracks: Love suspect / Lately / Summertime medley / Sexy mama / Everybody's in a hurry / I'll be loving you / Follow your heart / Tying to keep my heart / Please come and be with me.
■ LP . . . . . . . . . . . . . . . . . . . . EXLP 1
Expansion / Apr '87.
CD . . . . . . . . . . . . . . . . . . . . EXCDP 1
Passion/Debut/Scratch Music / Jun '93 / Pinnacle / 3MV.

### LOVE'S COMIN' DOWN.

Tracks: You're all I need to survive / Selling my heart to the junkman / My love is comin' down / Say you will / 2 - 1 = Loneliness / Have you ever seen them / Shake shake it baby / Funky situation / It won't be long / Goodbye after Sunday / Mama and Daddy.
■ LP . . . . . . . . . . . . . . . . . . .STML 12041
Motown / Nov '76.

### TAKE THE FIRST STEP.

Tracks: Take the first step / Whole heartedly.
■ 12" . . . . . . . . . . . . . . . . . 12MOTC 81
Motor City / Nov '91.

### WENDY IS GONE.

Tracks: Wendy is gone / Give me a sign.
■ 7" . . . . . . . . . . . . . . . . . . HLA 10494
London / Jul '75.

## McPhatter, Clyde

### 18 ORIGINAL HITS: CLYDE MCPHATTER/BILLY WARD (McPhatter, Clyde & Billy Ward).

Tracks: Not Advised.
■ LP . . . . . . . . . . . . . . . . . . . .K 5006
King (USA) / Mar '88.

### BEST OF CLYDE MCPHATTER, THE.

Tracks: Not Advised.
CD . . . . . . . . . . . . . . . . . RSACD 812
Sequel / Oct '94 / Total / BMG.

### BIP BAM.

Tracks: Money honey / Let the boogie woogie roll / Don't dog me / Gone / Such a night / Lucille / Warm your heart / Way I feel / Bip bam / Honey love / Whatcha gonna do / If I didn't love you like I do / There you go / Try try baby / Everyone's laughing / Three thirty three.
■ LP . . . . . . . . . . . . . . . . . . . . ED 132
Edsel / May '84.

### CLYDE MCPHATTER.

Tracks: Not Advised.
■ LP . . . . . . . . . . . . . . . . . . . BID 8006
Bellaphon / Jul '88.

### GOOD GRAVY (McPhatter, Clyde & Drifters).

Tracks: Without love / Someday you'll want me / Treasure of love / I'm not worthy of you / Bells of St. Mary's / White Christmas / I make believe / Seven

days / Warm your heart / Money honey / Whatcha gonna do / Such a night / Honey love / 30 days.
■ LP . . . . . . . . . . . . . . . . . . . 587 144
Atlantic / Feb '69.

### LAVENDER LACE.

Tracks: Lavender lace / Sweet and innocent.
■ 7" . . . . . . . . . . . . . . . . . . . .SS 592
Stateside / Feb '67.

### LOVER PLEASE.

Tracks: Not Advised.
■ LP . . . . . . . . . . . . . . . . . CLYDE 1000
Not Advised / Jul '88.

### RHYTHM 'N' SOUL.

Tracks: Not Advised.
■ LP Set . . . . . . . . . . . . . . . BFX 15271/9
Bear Family / Dec '87.

### ROCK AND CRY.

Tracks: Seven days / Treasure of love / Thirty days / Without love / Rock and cry / You'll be there / Just hold my hand / Long lonely nights / No love like her love / Come what may / Deep sea ball / Lover's question / I can't stand up alone / Lovey dovey / Since you've been gone / You went back on your word.
■ LP . . . . . . . . . . . . . . . . . . CRB 1073
■ MC . . . . . . . . . . . . . . . . TCCRB 1073
Charly R&B / Apr '84.

### TREASURE OF LOVE.

Tracks: Treasure of love.
■ 7" . . . . . . . . . . . . . . . . . HLE 8293
London-American / Aug '56.

### TRIBUTE TO CLYDE MCPHATTER.

Tracks: Treasure of love / Lover's question / Money honey / Seven days / Honey love / White Christmas / Long lonely nights / Without love / Warm your heart / Such a night / Just to hold my hand / Someday you'll want me to want you / What'cha gonna do / Bells of St. Marys.
■ LP . . . . . . . . . . . . . . . . . . . K 30033
Atlantic / Apr '73.

### WELCOME HOME.

Tracks: I'll belong to you / Why can't we get together / Anyone can tell / Book of memories / Please give me one more chance / If you only knew / Mixed up cup / Our day will come / Someone to believe in / Mr. Heartache / Ties that bind / Mother's love.
■ LP . . . . . . . . . . . . . . . . . .MUPS 418
MCA / Mar '71.

## McWilliams, Brigette

### I GET THE JOB DONE.

Tracks: I get the job done (mixes).
12" . . . . . . . . . . . . . . . . . . .VUST 85
CD Single . . . . . . . . . . . . . . .VUSCD 85
MC Single . . . . . . . . . . . . . . . VUSC 85
Virgin / Oct '94 / EMI.

### TAKE ADVANTAGE OF ME.

Tracks: Set up / Cherish this love / Baby don't play me / Take advantage of me / No groove sweating (A funky space reincarnation) / Gotta be down / It's on / I get the job done / That's on me / Blankets of playboys / You got someth'n I want / (Don't let me catch you) slippin' / I'm ready.
LP . . . . . . . . . . . . . . . . . . VUSLP 77
Virgin / Aug '94 / EMI.
CD . . . . . . . . . . . . . . . . . .CDVUS 77
MC . . . . . . . . . . . . . . . . . VUSMC 77
Virgin / Jul '94 / EMI.

## Mad Lads

### DON'T HAVE TO SHOP AROUND.

Tracks: Don't have to shop around / Tear-maker.
■ 7" . . . . . . . . . . . . . . . . . AT 4051
Atlantic / Nov '65.

### I WANT SOMEONE.

Tracks: I want someone / Nothing can break through.
■ 7" . . . . . . . . . . . . . . . . . AT 4083
Atlantic / Mar '66.

### MAD, MAD, MAD, MAD, MAD LADS, THE/NEW BEGINNING, A.

Tracks: So nice / Cry baby / I just can't forget / These old memories / By the time I get to Phoenix / No strings attached / It's loving time / Love is here today and gone tomorrow / Make this young lady mine / I've never found a girl / Monkey time / Pass the word (love's the word) / I'm so glad I fell in love with you / Seeing is believing / I'll still be loving you / Gone, the promises of yesterday / I forgot to be your lover / I'm afraid (of losing you) / Destination / Make room.
CD . . . . . . . . . . . . . . . . . .CDSXD 958
Stax / Oct '90 / Pinnacle.

## Madden, Danny

### FACT OF LIFE, THE.

Tracks: Facts of life.
■ 12" . . . . . . . . . . . . . . . . . YZ 576T
Eternal / May '91.

### FACTS OF LIFE, THE.

Tracks: Facts of life.
■ 12" . . . . . . . . . . . . . . . . . YZ 473 T
■ 7" . . . . . . . . . . . . . . . . . .YZ 473
■ CD Single . . . . . . . . . . . . . . YZ 473 C
Eternal / Jul '90.

### THESE ARE THE FACTS OF LIFE.

Tracks: Not Advised.
CD . . . . . . . . . . . . . . . . . 9031744512
■ LP . . . . . . . . . . . . . . . . . . WX 367
MC. . . . . . . . . . . . . . . . . . WX 367 C
Eternal / May '91 / WEA.

## Magic Lady

### BETCHA CAN'T LOSE (WITH MY LOVE).

Tracks: Betcha can't lose.
■ 12" . . . . . . . . . . . . . . . . ZT 42004
■ 7" . . . . . . . . . . . . . . . . . ZB 42003
Motown / May '88.

### MAGIC LADY.

Tracks: Betcha can't lose / Love overdrive / Misty eyed / Yes I'm ready / Hit and run / Cupid / Wait a minute / Paradise / Summer love.
■ LP . . . . . . . . . . . . . . . . . NL 72637
■ CD . . . . . . . . . . . . . . . . . ND 72637
■ MC. . . . . . . . . . . . . . . . . NK 72637
Bluebird / Jun '88.

### SEXY BODY.

Tracks: Sexy body / Get off.
■ 7" . . . . . . . . . . . . . . . . USAF 1222
A&M / Aug '82.

## Magnum Force

### SHARE MY LOVE.

Tracks: Not Advised.
■ LP . . . . . . . . . . . . . . . . . BRLP 1002
Blue Bird (2) / Nov '84.
■ LP . . . . . . . . . . . . . . . . LPBR 1002
Blue Bird (2) / Jan '85.

## Mahoney, Skip

### LAND OF LOVE (Mahoney, Skip & The Casuals).

Tracks: Land of love / This is my last time / Bless my soul / It's love / Wherever you go / Running away from love / I love you / Happily ever after.
■ LP . . . . . . . . . . . . . . . . . .CLP 539
Contempo (1) / Feb '77.

## Mai Tai

### AM I LOSING YOU FOREVER.

Tracks: Am I losing you forever / Rules of love.
■ 12" . . . . . . . . . . . . . . . . .VS 822-12
■ 7" . . . . . . . . . . . . . . . . . .VS 822
Virgin / Oct '85.

### BET THAT'S WHAT YOU SAY.

Tracks: Bet that's what you say / Too much of nothing.
■ 12" . . . . . . . . . . . . . . . . . DJIT 1
■ 7" . . . . . . . . . . . . . . . . . .DJI 1
Injection Disco Dance / Aug '87.

### BODY AND SOUL.

Tracks: Body & soul / What goes on / Body and soul (extended remix) (12" only).
■ 12" . . . . . . . . . . . . . . . . . VS 801-12
■ 7" . . . . . . . . . . . . . . . . . .VS 801
Virgin / Jul '85.

### FEMALE INTUITION.

Tracks: Female intuition / Female intuition (inst).
■ 12" . . . . . . . . . . . . . . . . . VS 844-12
■ 7" . . . . . . . . . . . . . . . . . .VS 844
Virgin / Feb '86.

### HISTORY.

Tracks: History / Body & soul / Chemistry / Rhythm of the street / What, where, when, who / What goes on / You control me / Rules of love / Am I losing you forever.
■ LP . . . . . . . . . . . . . . . . . .V 2359
■ MC. . . . . . . . . . . . . . . . . TCV 2359
Virgin / Jun '85.
■ LP . . . . . . . . . . . . . . . . . OVED 192
■ MC. . . . . . . . . . . . . . . . . OVEDC 192
Virgin / '88.

## HISTORY.
**Tracks:** History (special dance mix) / Female intuition (compressed dance mix) / Rules of love, The (groove side) / Am I losing you forever(smooth side edit).
■ CD Single . . . . . . . . . . . . . . . . CDT 38
Virgin / '88.

## HISTORY.
**Tracks:** History (7" only) / History (special dance mix) (12" only) / History (club version) (12" only) / History (instrumental version) (12" only).
■ 12" . . . . . . . . . . . . . . . . . . . . . VS 773-12
■ 7" . . . . . . . . . . . . . . . . . . . . . .VS 773
Virgin / May '85.

## HISTORY (OLD GOLD).
**Tracks:** History / Body & soul.
■ 12" . . . . . . . . . . . . . . . . . . . .OG 4104
Old Gold / Feb '89.

## WHAT GOES ON.
**Tracks:** What goes on.
■ 12" . . . . . . . . . . . . . . . . . . . TRICT 11
■ 7" . . . . . . . . . . . . . . . . . . . . . TRIC 11
Electricity / Sep '84.

# Main Ingredient

## DO ME RIGHT.
**Tracks:** Do me right / Do me right (Inst).
■ 12" . . . . . . . . . . . . . . . . . . .COOLX 126
■ 7" . . . . . . . . . . . . . . . . . . . . .COOL 126
Cool Tempo / Jun '86.

## HAPPINESS IS JUST AROUND THE BEND (OLD GOLD).
**Tracks:** Happiness is just around the bend / Have you ever tried it / Just don't want to be lonely.
■ 12" . . . . . . . . . . . . . . . . . . . . .OG 4513
Old Gold / Apr '89.

## I JUST WANNA LOVE YOU.
**Tracks:** Not Advised.
CD . . . . . . . . . . . . . . . . . . . . . 841 249-2
■ LP . . . . . . . . . . . . . . . . . . . . 841 249-1
■ MC . . . . . . . . . . . . . . . . . . . . 841 249-4
Polydor / Mar '90 / PolyGram.

## JUST DON'T WANT TO BE LONELY.
**Tracks:** Just don't want to be lonely.
■ 7" . . . . . . . . . . . . . . . . . . . APBO 0205
RCA / Jun '74.

## JUST DON'T WANT TO BE LONELY (OLD GOLD).
**Tracks:** Just don't want to be lonely / Snake.
■ 7" . . . . . . . . . . . . . . . . . . . .OG 9851
Old Gold / Jan '89.

## TASTEFUL SOUL.
**Tracks:** I'm better off without you / Magic shoes / I'm so proud / Somebody's been sleeping / Make it with you / Spinning around / Need her love / That's what fate will do / Look at me / Searching.
■ LP . . . . . . . . . . . . . . . . . . . . LSA 3020
RCA / Jan '71.

# Mainstreet

## HOLDING ON.
**Tracks:** Holding on / You got everything.
■ 7" . . . . . . . . . . . . . . . . . . . . .STAT 56
State / '77.

## NO APPOINTMENT NECESSARY.
**Tracks:** No appointment necessary / Hanging on to love.
■ 7" . . . . . . . . . . . . . . . . . . . . .STAT 74
State / Feb '78.

# Majestics

## FEEL THE MUSIC.
**Tracks:** Feel the music / Price of fame.
■ 7" . . . . . . . . . . . . . . . . . . . . .2058 911
Polydor / '77.

## I LOVE HER SO MUCH (IT HURTS).
**Tracks:** I love her so much (it hurts).
■ 7" . . . . . . . . . . . . . . . . . . . . .7SS 106
Soul Supply / May '85.

## SHAZAM.
**Tracks:** Shazam / I'd love to hate you.
■ 7" . . . . . . . . . . . . . . . . . . . . BUG 46
Cube / Jul '74.

# Majors

## IT ONLY HAPPENS.
**Tracks:** It only happens / One sided love affair.
■ 7" . . . . . . . . . . . . . . . . . . . . MAG 79
Magnet / Jan '77.

## STOOKY STOP.
**Tracks:** Stooky stop / Dance, dance, dance.
■ 7" . . . . . . . . . . . . . . . . . . . . .P 2601
Psycho (2) / Apr '78.

# Malemen

## FIRST CLASS MALE.
**Tracks:** Not Advised.
LP . . . . . . . . . . . . . . . . . . . . MSS 2207
MC. . . . . . . . . . . . . . . . . . . . . MSSC 2207
Malaco / Dec '90 / C.M. Distribution / Charly / Pinnacle.

# Mancha, Steve

## HOPELESSLY.
**Tracks:** Hopelessly / Hopelessly (version).
■ 12" . . . . . . . . . . . . . . . . . . . MARE 50
■ 7" . . . . . . . . . . . . . . . . . . . MARES 50
Nightmare / May '88.

## IT'S ALL OVER THE GRAPEVINE.
**Tracks:** It's all over the grapevine / It's all over the grapevine (instrumental).
■ 12" . . . . . . . . . . . . . . . . . . . 12DB 9138
■ 7" . . . . . . . . . . . . . . . . . . . . DB 9138
Columbia / Aug '86.

## RARE STAMPS (see under Barnes, J.J.).

## STANDING IN LINE.
**Tracks:** Standing in line / Standing in line (instrumental).
■ 12" . . . . . . . . . . . . . . . . . . . MARE 13
■ 7" . . . . . . . . . . . . . . . . . . . MARES 13
Nightmare / Mar '87.

# Mandell, Mike

## PEG.
**Tracks:** Peg / Jupiter finger.
■ 7" . . . . . . . . . . . . . . . . . . . VS 5010
Vanguard (1) / Mar '79.

## SKY MUSIC.
**Tracks:** Pyramids / Just the way you are / Elephant and castle / Peg / As fine as you are / Jupiter finger / Another kind of spring.
■ LP . . . . . . . . . . . . . . . . . . . VSD 79409
Vanguard (1) / Jan '79.

# Mandrill

## FUNKY MONKEY.
**Tracks:** Funky monkey / Can you get it.
■ 7" . . . . . . . . . . . . . . . . . . . .ARIST 164
Arista / Jul '79.

## MANDRILL.
**Tracks:** Mandrill / Warning blues / Symphonic revolution / Rollin' on / Peace and love / Movement - Birth, Now, Time, Encounter, Beginning / Chutney.
■ LP . . . . . . . . . . . . . . . . . . . .2489 028
Polydor / Aug '71.

## MANDRILL IS.
**Tracks:** Ape is high / Cohelo / Git it all / Children of the sun / I refuse to smile / Universal rhythms / Lord of the Golden Baboon / Central Park / Kofijahm / Here today gone tomorrow / Sun must go down.
■ LP . . . . . . . . . . . . . . . . . . . 2391030
Polydor / '72.

## NEW WORLDS.
**Tracks:** Too late / It's so easy lovin' you / Third world girl / Mean streets / When you smile.
■ LP . . . . . . . . . . . . . . . . . . . .ARTY 162
Arista / Mar '79.

## WHEN YOU SMILE.
**Tracks:** When you smile / Holiday.
■ 7" . . . . . . . . . . . . . . . . . . . .ARIST 231
Arista / Dec '78.

# Mangione, Chuck

## ALIVE.
**Tracks:** Hi-heel sneakers / Legend of the one-eyed sailor / St. Thomas / Sixty miles young.
■ LP . . . . . . . . . . . . . . . . . . . . 6338132
Mercury / Feb '73.

## BELLA VIA.
**Tracks:** Bella via / Lullaby.
■ 7" . . . . . . . . . . . . . . . . . . .AMS 7417
A&M / '79.

## CHILDREN OF SANCHEZ.
**Tracks:** Children of Sanchez / Doin' everything with you.
■ 7" . . . . . . . . . . . . . . . . . . .AMS 7389
A&M / Nov '78.

## CLASSICS:CHUCK MANGIONE.
**Tracks:** Not Advised.
■ CD . . . . . . . . . . . . . . . . . . . CDA 2502
A&M.

## COMPACT JAZZ: CHUCK MANGIONE.
**Tracks:** Hill where the Lord hides / Lullaby for Nancy Carol / And in the beginning / Land of make believe / Legend of the one eyed sailor / As long as we're together / Freddie's walkin' / Friends and love theme.
■ MC . . . . . . . . . . . . . . . . . . . 830 696-4
■ CD . . . . . . . . . . . . . . . . . . . 830 696-2
Mercury / '87.

## EVENING OF MAGIC, AN.
**Tracks:** Feels so good / XIth commandment / Chase the clouds away / Hill where the Lord hides / Doin' everything with you / Love the feelin' / I get crazy / Land of make believe / Hide and seek / Day after / Children of Sanchez / B'bye.
■ Double LP . . . . . . . . . . . . . . AMLM 66701
A&M / '79.

## EYE OF THE VEILED TEMPTRESS.
**Tracks:** That's nice / Eyes of the veiled temptress / Do you ever think about me / Open their eyes / Long hour soulful / Sweet butterfly / Freedom song.
■ CD . . . . . . . . . . . . . . . . . . . 4611622
■ LP . . . . . . . . . . . . . . . . . . . 4611621
■ MC . . . . . . . . . . . . . . . . . . . 4611624
CBS / Jul '88.

## FEELS SO GOOD.
**Tracks:** Feels so good / Maui waui / Side Street, Theme from / Hide and seek / Last dance / XIth commandment.
■ LP . . . . . . . . . . . . . . . . . . . AMLH 64658
A&M / Apr '78.

## FEELS SO GOOD.
**Tracks:** Feels so good / Maui waui.
■ 7" . . . . . . . . . . . . . . . . . . .AMS 7357
A&M / Jun '78.

## FUN AND GAMES.
**Tracks:** Fun and games / Give it all you've got / Feels so good.
■ 12" . . . . . . . . . . . . . . . . . . .AMSP 7522
A&M / May '80.

## GIVE IT ALL YOU'VE GOT.
**Tracks:** Give it all you've got / B'bye.
■ 7" . . . . . . . . . . . . . . . . . . .AMS 7508
A&M / Feb '80.

## JAZZ BROTHER.
**Tracks:** Hey baby / Bag's groove / Night has a thousand eyes / Givin' the business / Wha's happ'-nin' / Just you, just me / Old folks / Bassett sound / Recuerdo / Big foot / I had the craziest dream / Solar / Blues for Saandar / If ever I should leave you / Little prince.
■ Double LP . . . . . . . . . . . . . . M 47042
Milestone / Jul '80.

## JOURNEY TO A RAINBOW.
**Tracks:** Not Advised.
■ LP . . . . . . . . . . . . . . . . . . . CBS 25435
MC . . . . . . . . . . . . . . . . . . . .40 25435
CBS / Jul '83 / Sony.

## LOVE NOTES.
**Tracks:** Steppin' out / No problem / Memories of Scirocco / To the 80's / Love notes.
■ LP . . . . . . . . . . . . . . . . . . . CBS 85879
CBS / Sep '82.

## QUARTET.
**Tracks:** Land of make believe / Self portrait / Little sunflower / Floating / Manha de carnival.
■ LP . . . . . . . . . . . . . . . . . . . .6338 109
Mercury / Sep '72.

## SAVE TONIGHT FOR ME.
**Tracks:** Not Advised.
■ CD . . . . . . . . . . . . . . . . . . . CD 26890
CBS / May '87.
■ LP . . . . . . . . . . . . . . . . . . . 26890
CBS / '90.

## TARANTELLA.
Tracks: Tarantella / Neopolitan tarantella / XIth Commandment suite / Legend of the one eyed sailor / Bellavia / Hill where the Lord hides / Lake Placid fanfare / Things to come / Round midnight / Manteca / My one and only love / All blues.
■ **Double LP**.............. **AMLM 66703**
A&M / Jun '81.

## TIME OF THE SEASON.
Tracks: Time of the season / Mellow out / You can't cry for help.
■ **7"**.................... **AMS 7377**
A&M / Aug '78.

## Manhattans

The Manhattans were formed in Jersey in 1962; gaining first break at '64 Apollo Theatre talent contest. *I Wanna Be (Your Everything)* was first and last pop hit for 10 years, but they regularly featured on soul chart and impressed Otis Redding enough for him to engage them as support act on several tours. Lead singer George Smith died in 1970 and was replaced by Gerald Alston. New line-up signed to Columbia, cut million-selling *There's No Me Without You* and crossed back over to pop charts, finally surging to No. 1 in '76 with *Kiss and Say Goodbye*. In U.K. where group were previously unknown, both this and *Hurt* reached No. 4. From '77, Manhattans continued in time-honoured fashion, but returned to U.S. Top 40 only with million-selling *Shining Star* in 1980. In '85 they returned to soul chart with Sam Cooke's *You Send Me*, song cited by many as first soul record. Alston went solo in '88.

## 6 TRACK HITS.
Tracks: Kiss and say goodbye / There's no me without you / Don't take your love / Wonderful world of love / We never danced to a love song / La la la wish upon a star.
■ **LP**...................... **7SR 5027**
MC....................... **7SC 5027**
Scoop 33 / Sep '83.

## AFTER MIDNIGHT.
Tracks: Shining star / It's not the same / Girl of my dream / Cloudy, with a chance of tears / Closer you are / If my heart could speak / One life to love / Just as long as I have you / It couldn't hurt / Tired of the single life / I'll never run away from love again.
■ **LP**...................... **CBS 84223**
CBS / Aug '80.

## AM I LOSING YOU?.
Tracks: Am I losing you / Movin'.
■ **7"**...................... **CBS 6162**
CBS / Mar '78.

## BABY COME BACK TO ME.
Tracks: Baby come back to me / That's the way it goes.
■ **7"**......................**A 9594**
Atlantic / Feb '85.

## BACK TO BASICS.
Tracks: Change of heart / Where did we go wrong / All I need / I'm through trying to prove my love to you / Mr. D.J. / Back into the night / Just like you / Maybe tomorrow / Don't look in my eyes / Neither one of us.
■ **LP**...................... **4500631**
MC....................... **4500634**
■ **CD**...................... **4500632**
CBS / Dec '86 / Sony.

## BEST OF THE MANHATTANS.
Tracks: Hurt / We never danced to a love song / Reasons / Am I losing you / Fever / There's no me without you / La la la wish upon a star / Kiss & say goodbye / Don't take your love / Soul train / Summertime in the city / Tomorrow / It's you.
MC.......................**40 31806**
■ **LP**...................... **CBS 31806**
CBS / '84 / Sony.

## BEST OF THE MANHATTANS, THE.
Tracks: I'll never find another / Shining star / Hurt / We never danced to a love song / Reasons / Am I losing you / Fever / There's no me without you / Kiss and say goodbye / Don't take your love from me / Soul train / Summertime in the city / It's you / Crazy / I kinda miss you / It feels good to be loved so bad.
CD....................... **9827282**
Pickwick/Sony Collector's Choice / Apr '92 / Pickwick / Pinnacle.

## COLLECTION: MANHATTANS.
Tracks: Not Advised.
■ **CD**.................... **CCSCD 341**

■ **MC**....................**CCSMC 341**
Castle Collector Series / Jun '92.

## CRAZY.
Tracks: Crazy / Love is gonna find you / Kiss and say goodbye / Shining star.
■ **12"**.................... **TA 3578**
■ **7"**......................**A 3578**
CBS / Aug '83.

## CRAZY (OLD GOLD).
Tracks: Crazy / You send me.
■ **12"**....................**OG 4029**
Old Gold / Nov '87.

## DEDICATED TO YOU/ FOR YOU AND YOURS.
Tracks: Follow your heart / That new girl / Can I / Boston monkey / I've got everything but you / Manhattan stomp / Searchin' for my baby / Our love will never die / I'm the one love forgot / What's it gonna be / Teach me (the Philly dog) / Baby I need you / I call it love / I bet'cha / Sweet little girl / There goes a fool / Alone on New Year's Eve / All I need is your love / I wanna be / When we're made as one / Call somebody please / For the very first time / It's that time of year / Baby I'm sorry.
CD....................... **CDKEND 103**
Ace / Jun '93 / Pinnacle / Complete Record Co. Ltd.

## FOREVER BY YOUR SIDE.
Tracks: Crazy / Start all over again / Forever by your side / Just the lonely talking again / Locked up in your love / Lover's paradise / Love is gonna find you / I'm ready to love you again.
■ **LP**...................... **CBS 25353**
MC.......................**40 25353**
CBS / Sep '83 / Sony.

## HEART AND SOUL OF THE MANHATTANS.
Tracks: Kiss and say goodbye / Hurt / It's you / Shining star / Crazy / There's no me without you / Don't take your love / I kinda miss you / It feels so good to be loved so bad / We never danced to a love song / Am I losing you / You send me / Where did we go wrong / Forever by your side.
■ **CD**.................... **KNCD 12057**
■ **MC**.................... **KNMC 12057**
Knight / Nov '90.

## HERE COMES THE HURT AGAIN.
Tracks: Here comes the hurt again / Don't say goodbye.
■ **7"**...................... **CBS 7360**
CBS / Jun '79.

## HURT.
Tracks: Hurt.
■ **7"**...................... **CBS 4562**
CBS / Oct '76.

## I KINDA MISS YOU.
Tracks: I kinda miss you / Gipsy man.
■ **7"**...................... **CBS 4831**
CBS / Jan '77.

## I WANNA BE YOUR EVERYTHING.
Tracks: Sweet little girl / Follow your heart / I betcha / Baby I need you / I wanna be your everything / Searchin' for my baby / Baby I'm sorry / Can I call somebody please / Teach me.
■ **LP**...................... **DJB 20684**
DJM / Nov '76.

## IT'S YOU.
Tracks: It's you / Mind your business.
■ **7"**...................... **CBS 5093**
CBS / Apr '77.

## KISS AND SAY GOODBYE.
Tracks: Kiss and say goodbye.
■ **7"**...................... **CBS 4317**
CBS / Jun '76.

## KISS AND SAY GOODBYE.
Tracks: I'm not a run around / You'd better believe it / Falling apart at the seams / We'll have forever to love / Take it or leave it / Hurt / If you're ever gonna love me / Shining star / Crazy / I'll never find another / Where did we go wrong / Am I losing you / Way we were/Memories / Here comes the hurt again / How can anything so good be so bad for you / Kiss and say goodbye.
CD.................... **PWKS 4172**
MC.................... **PWKMC 4172**
Pickwick / Sep '93 / Pickwick.

## KISS AND SAY GOODBYE (OLD GOLD).
Tracks: Kiss and say goodbye / Hurt.
■ **7"**......................**OG 9303**
Old Gold / Apr '83.

## LOCKED UP IN YOUR LOVE.
Tracks: Locked up in your love / I'm ready to love you again.
■ **7"**......................**A 3762**
CBS / Sep '83.

## LOVE SONGS: MANHATTANS.
Tracks: Not Advised.
■ **CD**.................... **ADEHCD 818**
Arcade / May '88.

## LOVE TALK.
Tracks: After you / Love talk / Right feeling / At the wrong time / Devil in the dark / Here comes the hurt again / I just wanna be the one in your life / That's not part of the show / Way we were / Memories / We tried.
■ **LP**.................... **CBS 83342**
CBS / '79.

## MANHATTANS.
Tracks: Not Advised.
■ **LP**.................... **CBS 81513**
CBS / Jul '76.

## SHINING STAR.
Tracks: Shining star.
■ **7"**.................... **CBS 8624**
CBS / Jul '80.

## THERE IS NO GOOD IN GOODBYE.
Tracks: There is no good in goodbye / Then you can tell me goodbye / Tomorrow / Share my life / Am I losing you / Happiness / You're my life / Goodbye is the saddest word / Movin' / Everybody has a dream.
■ **LP**.................... **CBS 82567**
CBS / Apr '78.

## TOMORROW.
Tracks: Tomorrow / Happiness.
■ **7"**.................... **CBS 6386**
CBS / May '78.

## TOO HOT TO STOP IT.
Tracks: Don't say no / You send me / Angel of the night / When we are made as one / C'est la vie / Dreamin' / You're gonna love being loved by me / Too hot to stop it.
■ **LP**.................... **CBS 26162**
CBS / Jun '85.
■ **CD**.................... **CDCBS 261 62**
CBS / '88.

## WE NEVER DANCE TO A LOVE SONG.
Tracks: We never danced to a love song / Let's start it all over again.
■ **7"**.................... **CBS 5375**
CBS / Jul '77.

## YOU SEND ME.
Tracks: You send me / You're gonna love being loved by me.
■ **12"**.................... **TA 6046**
■ **7"**......................**A 6046**
CBS / Apr '85.

## Mar-Keys

## DAMIFIKNOW.
Tracks: Mustang Sally / I never loved a man / Knock on wood / Day dream / Double or nothing / Coffee cup / One with sugar / Jive man / Soul man / Heads or tails / Black.
■ **LP**....................**SXATS 1021**
Stax / Nov '69.
■ **LP**.................... **2363008**
Stax / Aug '71.

## DAMIFIKNOW/MEMPHIS EXPERIENCE (2 Albums on 1 CD).
Tracks: Mustang Sally / Knock on wood / Double or nothing / Black / Soul man / Never loved a man (the way I love you) / Day dream / Coffee cup / One with sugar / Heads or tails / Cloud 9 / After the affair / Reach out I'll be there / Angel dust / Hummingbird / Let it be / Creeper's funkatrations / Jive man.
CD.................... **CDSXD 959**
Stax / Nov '90 / Pinnacle.

## GREAT MEMPHIS SOUND, THE.
Tracks: Not Advised.
CD.................... **7567823392**
Atlantic / Jul '93 / WEA.

## LAST NIGHT.
Tracks: Last night / Night before.
■ **7"**....................**584074**
Atlantic / Feb '67.

## MELLOW JELLY.
Tracks: Morning after / Diana / Alright OK you win / Sticks and stones / Misty / Night before / About noon

■ DELETED

/ One degree north / Sack o' woe / Hold it / Ebbtide / Last night.
■ **LP** .................... **587 135**
Atlantic / Feb '69.

### PHILLY DOG.
Tracks: Philly dog / Honeypot.
■ **7"** .................... **AT 4079**
Atlantic / '66.

## Marchan, Bobby

### FIFTIES IN NEW ORLEANS, THE.
Tracks: Just a little walk / Have mercy / You made a fool of me / Just a little ol' wine / Give a helping hand / Pity poor me / Chickee wah-wah / Don't take your love from me / I can't stop loving you / I'll never let you go / Hush your mouth / Well I'll be John Brown / You can't stop her / Rockin' behind the iron curtain / Quit my job / Havin' a good time.
■ **LP** .................... **OFF 6034**
Official.

### GOLDEN CLASSICS.
Tracks: Not Advised.
■ **LP** .................... **COL 5113**
Collectables (USA) / Jul '88.

### I WANNA BUMP.
Tracks: I wanna bump (with the big fat woman) / Disco rabbit.
■ **7"** .................... **.6167 522**
Mercury / '77.

## Mardin, Arif

### GLASS ONION.
Tracks: Glass onion / Proud Mary / Sympathy for the devil / Walk on by / Strange brew / How can I be sure / Dock of the bay / Listen here / Mary Ann / Ain't no way / Midnight walk.
■ **LP** .................... **588 197**
Atlantic / Sep '69.

## Maria, Tania

### BELA VISTA.
Tracks: 210 West / I can't get no satisfaction / Marguerita / Ca c'est bon / I can't give you anything but love / Bela vista / Match box / Encanto meu / Waiting for me.
CD .................... **CDP 793 871 2**
World Pacific / Aug '90 / EMI.

### BEST OF TANIA MARIE.
Tracks: I don't go / Made in New York / I do I love you / Valeu / Bronx / Tanoca Vignette / Chuleta / Please don't stay / O bom e / Ca c'est bon / Marguerita / 210 West.
CD .................... **CDP 7986342**
World Pacific / Jun '93 / EMI.

### BRAZIL WITH MY SOUL.
Tracks: Not Advised.
■ **LP** .................... **90169**
Barclay (France) / May '78.

### COME WITH ME.
Tracks: Sangria / Embraceable you / Lost in Amazonia / Come with me / Sementes, graines and seeds / Nega / Euzinha / Its all over now.
MC .................... **CJPC 200**
■ **LP** .................... **CJP 200**
Concord Picante / Mar '83 / Pinnacle.
CD .................... **CCD 4200**
Concord Picante / Jul '87 / Pinnacle.

### DON'T GO.
Tracks: Don't go / Made in New York.
■ **12"** .................... **12MT 2**
■ **7"** .................... **MT 2**
EMI-Manhattan / May '85.

### LADY FROM BRAZIL, THE.
Tracks: Lady from Brazil / I should not call you / Tanoca vignette / Bronx / Just get up / Valeu / All gone love / It hurts so much.
■ **CD** .................... **CDP 746 425 2**
EMI / Feb '87.

### LIVE: TANIA MARIA.
Tracks: Mr. & Mrs. Gatoamante / Pingas da vida / Seu dia vai chegar / O que e amar / Carona.
■ **LP** .................... **ACV 13005**
MC .................... **130 189**
Musidisc / Aug '83 / Vital Distribution / Discovery / A.D.A. Distribution / Harmonia Mundi (UK).

### LOVE EXPLOSION.
Tracks: Funky tambourine / It's all in my hands / You've got me feeling your love / Love explosion / Bela la bela / Rainbow of your love / Deep cove view / Pour toi.

■ **LP** .................... **CJP 230**
MC .................... **CJPC 230**
Concord Picante / Jan '84 / Pinnacle.
CD .................... **CCD 4230**
Concord Jazz / Dec '86 / New Note.

### MADE IN NEW YORK.
Tracks: Don't go / E carnival / My space / I do love you / Made in New York / Together / Forock / Walking in the rain.
■ **LP** .................... **EJ 2403211**
MC .................... **EJ 2403214**
EMI-Manhattan / Apr '85.

### OUTRAGEOUS.
Tracks: Dear Dee Vee / Confusion / She's outrageous / Bom bom bom / Happiness / Amei demais / Ta tudo cetto / I can do it / Minha Moe / Happiness (2) / Granada.
CD .................... **CCD 4563**
Concord Picante / Aug '93 / Pinnacle.

### PIQUANT.
Tracks: Not Advised.
■ **LP** .................... **CJP 151**
Concord Picante / May '81.
CD .................... **CCD 4151**
Concord Jazz / Jul '88 / New Note.

### REAL TANIA MARIA-WILD, THE.
Tracks: Yatra - ta / A cama na varanda / Vem pra roda / Come with me / Funy tamborine / 2 a.m. / Sangria.
■ **LP** .................... **CJP 264**
MC .................... **CJPC 264**
Concord Picante / Feb '85 / Pinnacle.
CD .................... **CCD 4264**
Concord Jazz / Nov '86 / New Note.

### TAURUS.
Tracks: Not Advised.
■ **LP** .................... **CJP 175**
MC .................... **CJPC 175**
Concord Picante / Mar '82 / Pinnacle.
CD .................... **CCD 4175**
Concord Picante / Oct '87 / Pinnacle.

### VIA BRAZIL (VOLUME 1).
Tracks: Not Advised.
■ **LP** .................... **80550**
Barclay (France) / Jul '87.

## Marie, Teena

California-born Mary Brocker was discovered in late '70s by Motown chief Berry Gordy and nurtured by company's rising star Rick James. Latter duetted with her on '79's I'm A Sucker For Your Love and encouraged her to compose and produce own records. Marie broke through briefly in U.K. with Top Ten smash Behind The Groove, but her career stalled in early '80s. Domestic success resumed with switch from Motown to Epic; '85 LP Starchild yielded pop smash Lovergirl and much-loved tribute Dear Mr Gaye. Success continued in lower-key, although she left Epic in '91.

### BEHIND THE GROOVE.
Tracks: Behind the groove / You're all the boogie.
■ **12"** .................... **TMGT 1185**
■ **7"** .................... **TMG 1185**
Motown / Oct '81.
■ **12"** .................... **TMGT 1385**
■ **7"** .................... **TMG 1385**
Motown / Apr '85.

### CAN IT BE LOVE.
Tracks: Can it be love / Too many colours.
■ **7"** .................... **TMG 1178**
Motown / Oct '81.

### COMPACT COMMAND PERFORMANCES: TEENA MARIE.
Tracks: I'm a sucker for your love / Don't look back / Behind the groove / I need your lovin' / Square biz / It must be magic / Ballad of Cradle Rob and me / Portuguese love / Aladdin's lamp / Irons in the fire / I'm gonna have my cake (and eat it too) / Yes indeed / Deja vu (I've been here before) / Opus III (does anyone care).
■ **CD** .................... **WD 72527**
Motown / Apr '91.

### DON'T LOOK BACK.
Tracks: Don't look back / I'm gonna have my cake (and eat it too).
■ **12"** .................... **12 TMG 1158**
■ **7"** .................... **TMG 1158**
Motown / Sep '79.

### EMERALD CITY.
Tracks: Emerald city / Once is not enough / Lips to find you / You so heavy / Shangri-la / Batucada suite / Love me down easy / Sunny skies.
■ **LP** .................... **EPC 26935**
■ **MC** .................... **.40 26935**
Epic / Jul '86.

### FIX IT.
Tracks: Fix it.
■ **12"** .................... **TA 3820**
■ **7"** .................... **.A 3820**
Epic / Nov '83.

### GREATEST HITS.
Tracks: Lovergirl / Work it / Ooo la la la / If I were a bell / Dear lover / Here's looking at you / Call me (I got yo number) / Cassanova Brown / My dear Mr Gaye / Out on a limb.
MC .................... **4690554**
■ **CD** .................... **4690552**
■ **LP** .................... **4690551**
Epic / Nov '91 / Sony.

### GREATEST HITS: TEENA MARIE (..and more).
Tracks: Behind the groove / It must be magic / I'm a sucker for your love / Square biz / Why can't I get next to you / Lonely desire / Revolution / Co-pilot to pilot / I need your lovin' / 365 / Portuguese love / Love just wouldn't be right / Where's California / Don't look back / Every little bit hurts.
■ **MC** .................... **WK 72428**
■ **LP** .................... **WL 72428**
Motown / Oct '86.
■ **CD** .................... **WD 72428**
Motown / Jan '89.

### I NEED YOUR LOVIN'.
Tracks: I need your lovin'.
■ **12"** .................... **TMGT 1203**
■ **7"** .................... **TMG 1203**
Motown / Oct '81.

### I'M A SUCKER FOR YOUR LOVE.
Tracks: I'm a sucker for your love / Deja vu.
■ **12"** .................... **TMGT 1146**
■ **7"** .................... **TMG 1146**
Motown / Oct '81.

### IRONS IN THE FIRE.
Tracks: I need your lovin' / Young love / First class love / Irons in the fire / Chains / You make love like springtime / Tune in tomorrow / You make love like springtime (reprise).
■ **LP** .................... **.STML 12143**
■ **MC** .................... **.CSTML 12143**
Motown / Oct '81.

### IT MUST BE MAGIC.
Tracks: It must be magic / Revolution / Where's California / 365 / Opus 111 (does anybody care) / Square biz / Ballad of Cradle Rob and me / Portuguese love / Yes indeed.
■ **LP** .................... **.STML 12154**
■ **MC** .................... **.CSTML 12154**
Motown / Oct '81.
CD .................... **MOTD 5355**
Motown / '86 / PolyGram.

### IT MUST BE MAGIC.
Tracks: It must be magic / Yes indeed.
■ **12"** .................... **TMGT 1246**
■ **7"** .................... **TMG 1246**
Motown / Nov '81.

### IVORY.
Tracks: Here's looking at you / Sugar shack / If I were a bell / Just us two / Ivory (a tone poem) / Mr. Icecream / Cupid is a real straight shooter / How can you resist it / Since day one / Miracles need wings to fly.
■ **LP** .................... **4658781**
■ **CD** .................... **4658782**
■ **MC** .................... **4658784**
Epic / Sep '90.

### JAMMIN'.
Tracks: Jamming.
■ **12"** .................... **TA 6226**
■ **7"** .................... **.A 6226**
Epic / May '85.

### LADY T.
Tracks: Behind the groove / Now that I have you / Lonely desire / Aladdin's lamp / You're all the boogie / Can it be love / Young girl in love / Why did I fall in love with you / Too many colors.
■ **LP** .................... **.STML 12130**
Motown / Oct '81.

### LIPS TO FIND YOU.
Tracks: Lips to find you.
■ **12"** .................... **TA 7270**

■ DELETED

7″ . . . . . . . . . . . . . . . . . . . . . . . .A 7270
pic / Jun '86.

ONELY DESIRE.
racks: Lonely desire.
12″. . . . . . . . . . . . . . . . . . . 12TMG 1196
7″ . . . . . . . . . . . . . . . . . . . . TMG 1196
otown / Oct '81.

OVE ME DOWN EASY.
racks: Love me down easy / Love me down easy
nstrumental).
12″ . . . . . . . . . . . . . . . . . . . . .650126 6
7″ . . . . . . . . . . . . . . . . . . . . .650126 7
pic / Oct '86.

OVERGIRL.
racks: Lovergirl.
12″. . . . . . . . . . . . . . . . . . . . . TA 4965
7″ . . . . . . . . . . . . . . . . . . . . . .A 4965
pic / Mar '85.

NAKED TO THE WORLD.
racks: Trick bag / Call me (I got yo number) / Ooo la
la / Crocodile tears / Opus III - the second move-
ent / Surrealistic pillow / Once and future dream /
ork it / Ball / Naked to the world.
LP . . . . . . . . . . . . . . . . . . . . . 4600941
CD . . . . . . . . . . . . . . . . . . . . . 4600942
MC. . . . . . . . . . . . . . . . . . . . . 4600944
pic / Mar '88.

OO LA LA LA.
racks: Ooo la la la / Sing one to your love / Ooo la
la (ext. mix) / Ooo la la la (slightly shorter
ersion).
12″. . . . . . . . . . . . . . . . . . . . 6514236
pic / Feb '88.
12″. . . . . . . . . . . . . . . . . . . . 6514238
12″. . . . . . . . . . . . . . . . . . . . 6514230
7″ . . . . . . . . . . . . . . . . . . . . 6514237
pic / Mar '88.

ORTUGUESE LOVE.
racks: Portuguese love / Ballad of Cradle Rob and
e.
12″ . . . . . . . . . . . . . . . . . . . TMGT 1251
7″ . . . . . . . . . . . . . . . . . . . . TMG 1251
otown / Jan '82.

OBBERY.
racks: Robbery / Playboy / Shadow boxing / Mid-
ght magnet / Fit it / Ask your momma / Dear lover /
op the world (and let me off) / Casanova brown.
LP . . . . . . . . . . . . . . . . . . . EPC 25655
C. . . . . . . . . . . . . . . . . . . . .40 25655
pic / Nov '83 / Sony.

INCE DAY ONE.
acks: Since day one / Since day one (instrumental)
Ooo la la la / Batucada suite.
12″ . . . . . . . . . . . . . . . . . . . 6564298
12″ . . . . . . . . . . . . . . . . . . . 6564296
7″ . . . . . . . . . . . . . . . . . . . . 6564297
CD Single. . . . . . . . . . . . . . . . . 6564292
MC Single. . . . . . . . . . . . . . . . . 6564294
pic / Nov '90.

QUARE BIZ.
acks: Square biz / Opus III (Does anybody care).
12″ . . . . . . . . . . . . . . . . . . TMGT 1236
7″ . . . . . . . . . . . . . . . . . . . . TMG 1236
otown / Oct '81.

TAR CHILD.
acks: Lovergirl / Help youngblood get to the freaky
arty / Out on a limb / Alibi / Star child /
e've got to stop (meeting like this) / My Dear
r Gaye / Light.
) . . . . . . . . . . . . . . . . . 7464 39528-2
LP . . . . . . . . . . . . . . . . . EPC 26315
MC. . . . . . . . . . . . . . . . . .40 26315
pic / Feb '85 / Sony.

EENA MARIE: 14 GREATEST HITS.
acks: Not Advised.
CD . . . . . . . . . . . . . . . . . . .530042-2
MC. . . . . . . . . . . . . . . . . . . .530042-4
otown / Jan '92.

ILD AND PEACEFUL.
acks: I'm a sucker for your love / Turnin' me on /
n't look back / Deja vu / I'm gonna have my cake /
an't love anymore.
LP . . . . . . . . . . . . . . . . . .STML 12109
MC. . . . . . . . . . . . . . . . . .CSTML 12109
otown / Oct '81.

## Markham, Pigmeat

HERE COMES THE JUDGE.
Tracks: Here comes the judge.
■ 7″ . . . . . . . . . . . . . . . . . . . CRS 8077
Chess / Jul '68.

## Marshall, Joy

MORE I SEE YOU, THE.
Tracks: More I see you / Taste of honey.
■ 7″ . . . . . . . . . . . . . . . . . . . F 12422
Decca / Jun '66.

MY LOVE COME HOME.
Tracks: My love come home / When a girl really
loves you.
■ 7″ . . . . . . . . . . . . . . . . . . . F 12222
Decca / Sep '65.

## Marshall, Wayne

90 DEGREES AND RISING.
Tracks: Not Advised.
CD . . . . . . . . . . . . . . . . SOULCD 003
LP . . . . . . . . . . . . . . . . . SOULLP 31
MC. . . . . . . . . . . . . . . . . SOULLC 31
Soultown / Jun '94 / Pinnacle / Jetstar.

GIVE ME THE FIX.
Tracks: Give me the fix / Mike in the hand.
■ 12″ . . . . . . . . . . . . . . . . . . JT 013
Jah Tubbys / Dec '85.

I LOVE (Wayne Marshall).
Tracks: I love / Fear of Jah Jah.
■ 7″ . . . . . . . . . . . . . . . . . . . . QP1
Greensleeves / Oct '86.

MENAGE A TROIS.
Tracks: Menage a trois.
■ 12″ . . . . . . . . . . . . . . . . SOUL 0030
Soultown / Dec '93.

PON A LEVEL.
Tracks: Pon a level / Dance baby dance / Pon a level
(version).
■ 12″ . . . . . . . . . . . . . . . . . . QP 2
Quadro Pack / Jul '87.

RAVE (BOGUL TIME).
Tracks: Rave (bogul time).
■ 12″ . . . . . . . . . . . . . . . . . CRT 098
Charm / May '92.

WILD GILBERT (Marshall, Wayne &
Pinky Lou).
Tracks: Wild Gilbert.
■ 7″ . . . . . . . . . . . . . . . . . . . JDP 12
John Dread Production / Oct '88.

## Martin, Shane

I NEED YOU.
Tracks: I need you / You're so young.
■ 7″ . . . . . . . . . . . . . . . . . . .510384
Columbia (USA) / Mar '83.

## Marvelettes

23 GREATEST HITS: MARVELETTES.
Tracks: Not Advised.
CD . . . . . . . . . . . . . . . . . .530041-2
■ MC. . . . . . . . . . . . . . . . . .530041-4
Motown / Jan '92 / PolyGram.

ANTHOLOGY - MARVELETTES.
Tracks: Please Mr. Postman / Locking up my heart /
Too many fish in the sea / Don't mess with Bill /
When you're young and in love / Reachin' for some-
thing I can't have / Breathtaking guy.
■ LP . . . . . . . . . . . . . . . . STMR 9018
■ MC. . . . . . . . . . . . . . . . CSTMR 9018
Motown / Sep '82.

BEECHWOOD 4-5789.
Tracks: Beechwood 4-5789.
■ 7″ . . . . . . . . . . . . . . . . . . CBA 1764
Oriole / '62.

COMPACT COMMAND PERFORM-
ANCES (23 Greatest Hits).
Tracks: Please Mr. Postman / Twistin' postman /
Playboy / Beechwood 4-5789 / Someday, someway /
Strange I know / Locking up my heart / Forever / My
daddy knows best / As long as I know he's mine /
He's a good guy (yes he is) / You're my remedy / Too
many fish in the sea / I'll keep holding on / Danger
heartbreak dead ahead / Don't mess with Bill /
You're the one / Hunter gets captured by the game /
When you're young and in love / Day you take me on

(you have to take the other) / My baby must be a
magician / Here I am baby / Destination anywhere.
■ CD . . . . . . . . . . . . . . . . . WD 72446
Motown / Mar '87.

DANGER HEARTBREAK DEAD AHEAD.
Tracks: Danger heartbreak dead ahead.
■ 7″ . . . . . . . . . . . . . . . . . . TMG 535
Tamla Motown / Oct '65.

DON'T MESS WITH BILL.
Tracks: Don't mess with Bill.
■ 7″ . . . . . . . . . . . . . . . . . . TMG 546
Tamla Motown / '66.

HUNTER GETS CAPTURED BY THE
GAME.
Tracks: Hunter gets captured by the game / I think I
can change you.
■ 7″ . . . . . . . . . . . . . . . . . . TMG 594
Tamla Motown / Feb '67.

I'LL KEEP HOLDING ON.
Tracks: I'll keep holding on.
■ 7″ . . . . . . . . . . . . . . . . . . TMG 518
Tamla Motown / '65.

IN FULL BLOOM.
Tracks: Seeing is believing / Sunshine days / That's
how heartaches are made / Truth's outside my door
/ I have someone / Uptown / At last I see love as it
really is / Now is the time for love / Too many tears,
too many times / Rainy mourning / Everybody knows
/ Love silent, love deep.
■ LP . . . . . . . . . . . . . . . . .STML 11145
Tamla Motown / May '70.

SOPHISTICATED SOUL.
Tracks: My baby must be a magician / Destination /
Anywhere / I'm gonna hold on as long as I can / Here
I am baby / You're the one for me Bobby / Your love
can save me / Reachin' for something I can't have /
You're the one / Don't make hurting me a habit /
Stranger / What's easy for two is so hard for one.
■ LP . . . . . . . . . . . . . . . . .STML 11090
Tamla Motown / Jan '69.

TOO MANY FISH IN THE SEA.
Tracks: Too many fish in the sea / Please Mr.
Postman.
■ 7″ . . . . . . . . . . . . . . . . . . .SS 369
Stateside / Feb '64.
■ 7″ . . . . . . . . . . . . . . . . . ZB 41917
Motown / Apr '88.

WHEN YOU'RE YOUNG AND IN LOVE.
Tracks: When you're young and in love / Day you
take one (you have to take the other).
■ 7″ . . . . . . . . . . . . . . . . . . TMG 609
Tamla Motown / Jun '67.
■ 7″ . . . . . . . . . . . . . . . . . . TMG 939
Tamla Motown / Jun '75.

YOU'RE THE ONE.
Tracks: You're the one / Paper boy.
■ 7″ . . . . . . . . . . . . . . . . . . TMG 562
Tamla Motown / '66.

## Mary Jane Girls

ALL NIGHT LONG.
Tracks: All night long / Musical love.
■ 12″ . . . . . . . . . . . . . . . . TMGT 1309
■ 7″ . . . . . . . . . . . . . . . . . TMG 1309
Motown / Jun '83.

BOYS.
Tracks: Boys / You are my heaven / All night long
(on 12″ only) / Candy man (on 12″ only).
■ 12″ . . . . . . . . . . . . . . . . TMGT 1315
■ 7″ . . . . . . . . . . . . . . . . . TMG 1315
Motown / Sep '83.

CANDY MAN.
Tracks: Candy man.
■ 12″ . . . . . . . . . . . . . . . . TMGT 1301
■ 7″ . . . . . . . . . . . . . . . . . TMG 1301
Motown / Apr '83.

IN MY HOUSE.
Tracks: In my house.
■ 7″ . . . . . . . . . . . . . . . . . TMG 1377
■ 12″ . . . . . . . . . . . . . . . . TMGT 1377
Motown / Feb '85.

MARY JANE GIRLS.
Tracks: Candy man / Boys / Prove it / Jealousy / You
are my heaven / On the inside / All night long /
Musical love.
■ LP . . . . . . . . . . . . . . . . .STML 12189
■ MC. . . . . . . . . . . . . . . . .CSTML 12189
Motown / Jun '83.
■ CD . . . . . . . . . . . . . . . . . WD 72626
■ LP . . . . . . . . . . . . . . . . . WL 72626

■ MC. . . . . . . . . . . . . . . . . . . . WK 72626
Motown / Sep '88.
■ LP . . . . . . . . . . . . . . . . . . . . ZL 72055
Motown / '89.

### ONLY FOR YOU.
**Tracks:** In my house / Break it up / Shadow lover / Lonely for you / Wild and crazy love / Girlfriend / I betcha / Leather queen.
■ LP . . . . . . . . . . . . . . . . . . . . ZL 72341
■ MC. . . . . . . . . . . . . . . . . . . . ZK 72341
Motown / Apr '85.
■ CD . . . . . . . . . . . . . . . . . . . . ZD 72341
Motown / '86.

### WALK LIKE A MAN.
**Tracks:** Walk Like a Man / All night Long.
■ 12". . . . . . . . . . . . . . . . . . . . ZT 40796
■ 7". . . . . . . . . . . . . . . . . . . . ZB 40795
Motown / Jul '86.

### WILD AND CRAZY LOVE.
**Tracks:** Wild and crazy love / All night long.
■ 12". . . . . . . . . . . . . . . . . . . . ZT 40271
■ 7". . . . . . . . . . . . . . . . . . . . ZB 40271
Motown / Aug '85.

## Mason

### DOUBLE-X-POSURE.
**Tracks:** Double-x-posure / Pour it on.
■ 12". . . . . . . . . . . . . . . . . . . . EKR 56 T
■ 7". . . . . . . . . . . . . . . . . . . . EKR 56
Elektra / Apr '87.

### LIVING ON THE EDGE.
**Tracks:** Livin' on the edge / Pour it on / Double-x-posure / Forever yours / Crazy life / Breathless / Somethin-x-tra / Stay in love.
■ LP . . . . . . . . . . . . . . . . . . . . K 960472 1
MC. . . . . . . . . . . . . . . . . . . . . K 960472 4
Elektra / Feb '87 / WEA.

## Mason, Barbara

### ANOTHER MAN.
**Tracks:** Another man.
■ 12". . . . . . . . . . . . . . . . . . . . MKHAN 3
■ 7". . . . . . . . . . . . . . . . . . . . KHAN 3
Streetwave / Jan '84.

### DON'T I EVER CROSS YOUR MIND SOMETIMES.
**Tracks:** Don't I ever cross your mind sometimes.
■ 12". . . . . . . . . . . . . . . . . . . . MKHAN 15
■ 7". . . . . . . . . . . . . . . . . . . . KHAN 15
Streetwave / Jun '84.

### I'LL NEVER LOVE THE SAME WAY TWICE.
**Tracks:** On and off / Playing with my feelings / I'll never love the same way twice.
■ 12". . . . . . . . . . . . . . . . . . . . BRT 41
■ 7". . . . . . . . . . . . . . . . . . . . BR 41
Blue Bird (2) / Aug '87.

### ON AND OFF.
**Tracks:** On and off / Yes I'm ready.
■ 12". . . . . . . . . . . . . . . . . . . . WMTL 103
■ 7". . . . . . . . . . . . . . . . . . . . WMT 103
W.M.O.T.(USA) / Mar '81.

### PHILADELPHIA'S LADY LOVE (Best of Barbara Mason).
**Tracks:** Give me your love / Bed and board / Shackin' up / Caught in the middle / One two three (you her or me) / There's one man between us / You can be with the one you don't love / So he's yours now / Yes I'm ready / From his woman to you / Me and Mrs. Jones / Your old flame / What am I gonna do / Let me in your life / (He wants) the two of us / I miss your Gordon.
CD. . . . . . . . . . . . . . . . . . . . NEXCD 115
Sequel / May '90 / Total / BMG.

### PIECE OF MY LIFE, A.
**Tracks:** Let me give you love / I'll never love the same / Oh and off / Playing with my feelings / So in love with you / Yes I'm ready / Love having you around / You know who I love / All inside of me / You did not stay last night.
■ LP . . . . . . . . . . . . . . . . . . . . WMLP 5002
W.M.O.T.(USA) / May '81.
■ LP . . . . . . . . . . . . . . . . . . . . LPBR 1004
MC. . . . . . . . . . . . . . . . . . . . . MCBR 1004
Blue Bird (2) / Apr '85 / Jetstar.

### TIED UP.
**Tracks:** Not Advised.
■ LP . . . . . . . . . . . . . . . . . . . . OEBM 1
Other End / Jun '84.

## Mason, Harvey

### GROOVIN' YOU.
**Tracks:** Groovin' you / Never give you up.
■ 7". . . . . . . . . . . . . . . . . . . . ARIST 270
Arista / Nov '79.

### HOW DOES IT FEEL.
**Tracks:** How does it feel / On and on / Till you take my love.
■ 12". . . . . . . . . . . . . . . . . . . . ARIST 12399
Arista / May '81.

### M.V.P.
**Tracks:** How does it feel / We can start tonight / Flesh / Universal rhyme / Spell / On and on / Going through the motions / You and me / Don't doubt my love.
■ LP . . . . . . . . . . . . . . . . . . . . AB 4283
Arista / Jun '81.

### MAZE.
**Tracks:** Maze / Sho' nuff groove.
■ 7". . . . . . . . . . . . . . . . . . . . ARIST 80
Arista / Dec '76.

### PACK UP YOUR BAGS.
**Tracks:** Pack up your bags / Funk in a mason jar.
■ 7". . . . . . . . . . . . . . . . . . . . ARIST 208
Arista / Sep '78.

### TILL YOU TAKE MY LOVE.
**Tracks:** Till you take my love / What's going on.
■ 7". . . . . . . . . . . . . . . . . . . . ARIST 188
Arista / May '78.

## Mason, Laverna

### DO YOU BELIEVE.
**Tracks:** Do you believe / Deliverance / Reach out your hand / Perfect love.
■ 12". . . . . . . . . . . . . . . . . . . . AT 12-06
About Time / Mar '92.

### SERENITY.
**Tracks:** Deliverance / Do you believe / Reach out your hand / Keep the faith / God watching you / Simple / Always and forever / Can't let him win / Serenity / Jesus is the one / Perfect love / Deliverance (instrumental).
■ LP . . . . . . . . . . . . . . . . . . . . ATLP 009
About Time / Jul '92.

## Masqueraders

### EVERYBODY WANNA LIVE ON.
**Tracks:** Everybody wanna live on / Please don't try / (Call me) The traveling man / Listen / Baby it's you / Sweet sweetning / (My love for you is) Honest and true / Your sweet love is a blessing.
■ LP . . . . . . . . . . . . . . . . . . . . ABCD 921
ABC Records / '75.

### HOW.
**Tracks:** How / This won't change.
■ 7". . . . . . . . . . . . . . . . . . . . GRP 138
Grapevine (Northern Soul) / Apr '80.

### LOVE ANONYMOUS.
**Tracks:** Modern day woman / Love between a woman and a man / Can't nobody love me like you do / Love anonymous / Bicentennial / Be for real / It's a terrible thing to waste your love / Runaway slave.
■ LP . . . . . . . . . . . . . . . . . . . . ABCL 5222
ABC Records / Jun '77.

## Mass Production

### BELIEVE.
**Tracks:** Free and happy / I believe in music / Being here / We love you / Keep my heart together / Cosmic lust / Superlative / People get up.
■ LP . . . . . . . . . . . . . . . . . . . . K 50400
Cotillion.

### CAN'T YOU SEE I'M FIRED UP.
**Tracks:** Can't you see I'm fired up / Eyeballin'.
■ 7". . . . . . . . . . . . . . . . . . . . K 11284
WEA / '79.

### DIAMOND CHIP.
**Tracks:** Diamond chip / Bopp.
■ 12". . . . . . . . . . . . . . . . . . . . K 11598T
■ 7". . . . . . . . . . . . . . . . . . . . K 11598
Cotillion / Jun '81.

### GONNA MAKE YOU LOVE ME.
**Tracks:** Gonna make you love me / Cosmic lust.
■ 7". . . . . . . . . . . . . . . . . . . . K 11601
Cotillion / Aug '80.

### IN A CITY GROOVE.
**Tracks:** Maybe maybe / Never ever / One more chance / Should have known better / Rock / Inner city / Solid love / Weird.
■ LP . . . . . . . . . . . . . . . . . . . . K 5087
Cotillion / May '82.

### IN THE PUREST FORM.
**Tracks:** Firecracker / Love you / With pleasure / Our thought (purity) / Can't you see I'm fired up / New year / Strollin'.
■ LP . . . . . . . . . . . . . . . . . . . . K 5060
Cotillion / '77.

### SHANTE.
**Tracks:** Shante / You love.
■ 7". . . . . . . . . . . . . . . . , . K 1147
Cotillion / May '80.

### SHE'S GOT TO HAVE IT.
**Tracks:** She's got to have it / We bite.
■ 12". . . . . . . . . . . . . . . . . . . . NINE
Nine O Nine / May '87.

### THREE MILES HIGH.
**Tracks:** Watch me do it / Sky high / I don't want to know / Groove me / Our thought / Just wanna make a dream come true / Scarey love / Slow bump, mush & love.
■ LP . . . . . . . . . . . . . . . . . . . . K 5051
Atlantic / Sep '78.

### TURN UP THE MUSIC.
**Tracks:** Our thought / Turn up the music / I can't believe you're going away / Sunshine / Bopp / Saucey / I got to have your love / Diamond chips / Clinch quencher.
■ LP . . . . . . . . . . . . . . . . . . . . K 5078
Cotillion / May '81.

### WELCOME TO OUR WORLD.
**Tracks:** Welcome to our world / Wine flow / Disco / like to dance / Our thought / Magic / Galaxy / Just song / Fun in the sun.
■ LP . . . . . . . . . . . . . . . . . . . . K 5033
Atlantic.

### WELCOME TO OUR WORLD (OF MERRY MUSIC).
**Tracks:** Welcome to our world / Magic.
■ 7". . . . . . . . . . . . . . . . . . . . K 1089
Cotillion / Mar '77.

### WELCOME TO THE WORLD.
**Tracks:** Welcome to our world / Cosmic lusting / Strolling.
■ 12". . . . . . . . . . . . . . . . . . . . LV 3
Atlantic / Nov '79.

### WINE FLOW DISCO.
**Tracks:** Wine flow disco / Fun in the sun.
■ 7". . . . . . . . . . . . . . . . . . . . K 1096
Cotillion / Jun '77.

## Masser, Michael

### ALI BOM-BA-YE (Masser, Michael & Mandrill).
**Tracks:** Ali bom-ba-ye (2 tracks, (I & II)).
■ 7". . . . . . . . . . . . . . . . . . . . ARIST 12
■ 7". . . . . . . . . . . . . . . . . . . . AS 025
Arista / Jul '77.

## Matthews, Al

### FOOL.
**Tracks:** Fool.
■ 7". . . . . . . . . . . . . . . . . . . . CBS 342
CBS / Aug '75.

### I CAN'T FACE THE MUSIC.
**Tracks:** I can't face the music / You without me.
■ 12". . . . . . . . . . . . . . . . . . . . LWOT
■ 7". . . . . . . . . . . . . . . . . . . . WOT 3
Electric / Jun '79.

### IT'S ONLY LOVE.
**Tracks:** It's only love / Stormy days and lonely nights.
■ 7". . . . . . . . . . . . . . . . . . . . 6007 15
Mercury / Sep '77.

### PEOPLE ARE PEOPLE.
**Tracks:** People are people / Run to you.
■ 7". . . . . . . . . . . . . . . . . . . . WOT 2
Electric / Jun '78.

■ DELETE

## Matthews, Milt

**ALL THESE CHANGES.**
**Tracks:** All these changes.
■ 7" . . . . . . . . . . . . . . . . . . .HLF 10479
ondon-American / Feb '75.

## Mayfield, Curtis

Born in Chicago in 1942, the young Curtis ormed the Impressions in the mid-fifties, nstalling friend Jerry Butler as lead singer. For Your Precious Love was an instant hit nd had the effect of launching Butler as a solo artist, Curtis then stepping forward as he group's lead singer on a number of hart riding singles, most notably You've Been Cheating, Choice Of Colours and People Get Ready. In '68, inspired by Berry Gordy and Motown, Mayfield set up Curtom Records, and in '70 went solo himself, beginning his most artistically creative spell. During the early and middle seventies Mayeld was one of black music's most groundbreaking acts, albums like Curtis, Roots, Back To The World and There's No Place like America Today eclipsed only by a magnificent soundtrack to the Superfly movie. Other soundtracks featuring the Staple singers (Do It Again) and Gladys Knight (Claudine) were almost as commercially successful, and a pair of albums by Aretha Franklin - Sparkle (which featured the 45 Giving Him Something He Can Feel) and Almighty Fire - enhanced his producer's reputation. Having exhausted himself temporarily of socially conscious thought, Mayeld saw out the decade with a string of love' albums; returning from semi-retirement in '82 on Boardwalk Records, for whom he recorded Honesty. Label boss Neil Bogart then died suddenly, and Curtis switched to the smaller CRC outfit, to cut one more album, We Come In Peace With A Message Of Love. Sadly, in '90, Mayfield's active life was cut short when a lighting rig fell on top of him at a concert in New York, paralysing him from the neck down - a condition in which he remains. Fortunately, his albums have been re-released to a new generation of listeners by Ichiban Records and the proceeds from a recent tribute album by a mixture of rock and soul stars are helping with rising medical bills.

**BABY IT'S YOU.**
**Tracks:** Baby it's you / Breakin' in the streets.
■ 12" . . . . . . . . . . . . . . . . . CURT 1T
■ 7" . . . . . . . . . . . . . . . . . . CURT 1
3-6 / Nov '86.

**BACK TO THE WORLD.**
**Tracks:** Back to the world / Future shock / Right on for the darkness / Future song (love a good woman, love a good man) / If I were a child again / Can't say nothin' / Keep on trippin'.
■ LP . . . . . . . . . . . . . . . . . .2318 085
Buddah / Sep '73.
CD . . . . . . . . . . . . . . . . . MPG 74029
MC. . . . . . . . . . . . . . . . . MPG 474029
Movieplay Gold / Jan '94 / Target / BMG.
CD . . . . . . . . . . . . . . . . . CPCD 8040
Charly / Jun '94 / Charly.

**BACK TO THE WORLD.**
**Tracks:** Back to the world / Other side of town.
■ 7" . . . . . . . . . . . . . . . . . .2011 187
Buddah / Oct '73.

**BBC RADIO 1 LIVE IN CONCERT.**
**Tracks:** Superfly / It's alright / I'm so proud of you / Billy Jack / Freddie's dead / People get ready / We've gotta have peace / Homeless / Move on up / Invisible / Don't worry.
CD . . . . . . . . . . . . . . . . . WINDCD 052
Windsong / Jan '94 / Pinnacle / A.D.A. Distribution.

**BETWEEN YOU BABY AND ME.**
**Tracks:** Between you baby and me / You're so good to me.
■ 7" . . . . . . . . . . . . . . . . . . RSO 43
RSO / Sep '79.

**CURTIS.**
**Tracks:** (Don't worry) If there's a hell below we're all gonna go / Other side of town / Wild and free / Makings of you / Miss Black America / Move on up / The people who are darker than blue / Give it up.
■ LP . . . . . . . . . . . . . . . . . .2318 015
Buddah / Feb '71.
■ LP . . . . . . . . . . . . . . . . . K 56252
WEA / '76.
CD. . . . . . . . . . . . . . . . . . MPG 74026
MC. . . . . . . . . . . . . . . . . MPG 474026

Movieplay Gold / Jan '94 / Target / BMG.
CD. . . . . . . . . . . . . . . . . . CPCD 8036
Charly / Jun '94 / Charly.
CD . . . . . . . . . . . . . . . . . CUR 2012CD
MC. . . . . . . . . . . . . . . . . CUR 2012MC
Curtom / Mar '94 / ACD Trading Ltd. / Pinnacle / Koch International.

**CURTIS IN CHICAGO.**
**Tracks:** Superfly / For your precious love / I'm so proud for once in my life / Preacher man / If I were a child again / Duke of Earl / Love oh love / Amen.
■ LP . . . . . . . . . . . . . . . . . K 56250
WEA.
■ LP . . . . . . . . . . . . . . . . . .2318 091
Buddah / Mar '74.
CD . . . . . . . . . . . . . . . . . CPCD 8046
Charly Groove / Sep '94 / Charly.

**CURTIS LIVE.**
**Tracks:** Mighty mighty / I plan to stay a believer / We've only just begun / People get ready / Star and stare / Check out your mind / Gypsy woman / Makings of you / We, the people who are darker than blue / Don't worry if there's a hell below we're all / Stone junkie / We're a winner.
■ Double LP . . . . . . . . . . . . . . . K 66047
WEA.
■ LP Set. . . . . . . . . . . . . . . .2659 004
Buddah / Aug '71.
CD Set . . . . . . . . . . . . . . . MPG 74176
Movieplay Gold / Mar '94 / Target / BMG.

**CURTIS MAYFIELD.**
**Tracks:** Move on up / Soul music / In your arms again (shake it) / Do do wap is strong in here / Hard times / So in love / You are, you are / Pusherman / Never stop loving me / Tripping out / Ain't no love lust / Superfly / Freddie's dead / This year / Give me your love / (Don't worry) If there's a hell below, we're all going to go.
CD. . . . . . . . . . . . . . . . . . . 12364
MC. . . . . . . . . . . . . . . . . . . 72364
Laserlight / May '94 / THE / BMG / Target.

**CURTIS MAYFIELD AT RONNIE SCOTT'S.**
**Tracks:** Not Advised.
■ VHS . . . . . . . . . . . . . . . . HEN 2151
Hendring Video / Dec '88.

**CURTIS MAYFIELD LIVE.**
**Tracks:** Not Advised.
CD . . . . . . . . . . . . . . . . . CPCD 8038
LP Set. . . . . . . . . . . . . . . . CPLP 8038 2
Charly / Jun '94 / Charly.

**DIRTY LAUNDRY.**
**Tracks:** Dirty laundry / We gotta have peace / Superfly / Who was that lady.
■ 12" . . . . . . . . . . . . . . . . . 12CUR 108
Ichiban / Nov '90.

**DO BE DOWN.**
**Tracks:** Do be down / Got to be real / Do be down (long version) (Only on 12" single.) / Do be down (radio version) (Only on 12" single.).
■ 7" . . . . . . . . . . . . . . . . . 7 CUR 108
■ 12" . . . . . . . . . . . . . . . . .12 CUR 107
Curtom / Jun '90.

**DO IT ALL NIGHT.**
**Tracks:** Do it all night / No goodbyes / Party, party / Keeps me loving you / In love, in love, in love / You are, you are.
CD. . . . . . . . . . . . . . . . . . CPCD 8050
Charly Groove / Sep '94 / Charly.

**FREDDIE'S DEAD.**
**Tracks:** Freddie's dead / Underground.
■ 7" . . . . . . . . . . . . . . . . . .2011 141
Buddah / Sep '72.

**GET DOWN TO THE FUNKY GROOVE.**
**Tracks:** Get down / Superfly / Freddie's dead / Move on up / Wild and free / (Don't worry) If there's a hell below we're all gonna go / Little child runnin' wild / Pusherman / If I were only a child again / Beautiful brother of mine / Now you're gone / Keep on trippin' / Right on for the darkness.
CD. . . . . . . . . . . . . . . . . . CPCD 8034
Charly / Feb '94 / Charly.

**GIVE GET TAKE AND HAVE.**
**Tracks:** Not Advised.
■ LP . . . . . . . . . . . . . . . . . BDLP 4042
Buddah / Jul '76.
CD. . . . . . . . . . . . . . . . . . CUR 2011CD
MC. . . . . . . . . . . . . . . . . CUR 2011MC
Curtom / Mar '94 / ACD Trading Ltd. / Pinnacle / Koch International.

**GOT TO FIND A WAY.**
**Tracks:** Love me (right in the pocket) / So you don't love me / Prayer / Mother's son / Cannot find a way / Ain't no love lost.
■ LP . . . . . . . . . . . . . . . . . BDLP 4029
Buddah / Jan '75.
CD. . . . . . . . . . . . . . . . . . CPCD 8048
Charly Groove / Sep '94 / Charly.

**GROOVE ON UP.**
**Tracks:** Not Advised.
CD. . . . . . . . . . . . . . . . . . CPCD 8043
Charly / Jun '94 / Charly.

**HARD TIMES.**
**Tracks:** Not Advised.
CD. . . . . . . . . . . . . . . . . . .TL 001333
Traditional Line / Sep '93 / Charly / A.D.A. Distribution / Koch International.

**HEARTBEAT.**
**Tracks:** Tell me, tell me / What is my woman for / Between you baby and me / Victory / Over the hump / You better stop / You're so good to me / Heartbeat.
■ LP . . . . . . . . . . . . . . . . . RSS 4
RSO / Sep '78.

**HOMELESS.**
**Tracks:** Homeless / People never give up.
■ 12" . . . . . . . . . . . . . . . . . 12CUR 106
■ 7" . . . . . . . . . . . . . . . . . .CUR 106
Curtom / Feb '90.

**HONESTY.**
**Tracks:** Hey baby, give it all to me / Still within your heart / If you need me / Dirty laundry / Nobody but you / What you gawn do / Summer hot.
■ LP . . . . . . . . . . . . . . . . . EPC 25317
MC. . . . . . . . . . . . . . . . . .40 25317
Epic / Mar '83 / Sony.

**IF THERE'S A HELL BELOW, WE'RE ALL GOING TO GO.**
**Tracks:** (Don't worry) If there's a hell below, we're all going to go / Makings of you.
■ 7" . . . . . . . . . . . . . . . . . .2011 055
Buddah / Nov '70.

**IMO GIT U SUCKA.**
**Tracks:** Imo git u sucker / He's a fly guy.
■ 7" . . . . . . . . . . . . . . . . . .7CUR 102
■ CD Single . . . . . . . . . . . . . .CDCUR 102
■ 12" . . . . . . . . . . . . . . . . . 12CUR 102
Curtom / May '89.

**IT'S ALRIGHT.**
**Tracks:** It's alright / Superfly.
■ 7" . . . . . . . . . . . . . . . . . RSO 68
RSO / Oct '80.

**KEEP ON KEEPING ON.**
**Tracks:** Keep on keeping on / Stone junkie.
■ 7" . . . . . . . . . . . . . . . . . .2011 119
Buddah / May '72.

**KUNG FU.**
**Tracks:** Kung fu / Right on for the darkness.
■ 7" . . . . . . . . . . . . . . . . . .BDS 402
Buddah / Aug '74.

**LIVE IN EUROPE.**
**Tracks:** Intro / Freddie's dead / We gotta have peace / People get ready / Move on up / Back to the world / Gypsy woman / Pusher man / We've only just begun / When seasons change / If there's a hell below.
■ Double LP. . . . . . . . . . . . . . CUR2 2901
Ichiban / Jun '88.
CD. . . . . . . . . . . . . . . . . . CUR2 2901CD
MC. . . . . . . . . . . . . . . . . CUR2 2901C
Ichiban / Mar '94 / A.D.A. Distribution / Pinnacle / ACD Trading Ltd. / Koch International / Direct Distribution.

**MAN LIKE CURTIS, A.**
**Tracks:** Move on up / Superfly / (Don't worry) If there's a hell below we're all gonna go / You are, you are / Give me your love / Never stop loving me / Tripping out / Soul music / This year / Ain't no love lost / Pusherman / Freddie's dead / Do do wap is strong in here / Hard times / In your arms again (Shake it) / So in love.
CD. . . . . . . . . . . . . . . . . . MUSCD 007
Music Collection International / Nov '92 / THE / Jazz Music.

**MOTHER'S SON.**
**Tracks:** Mother's son / Love me right in the pocket.
■ 7" . . . . . . . . . . . . . . . . . .BDS 426
Buddah / Mar '75.

**MOVE ON UP.**
**Tracks:** Move on up / Little child runnin' wild (Curtom only) / Give it up (Buddah releases only).
■ 7" . . . . . . . . . . . . . . . . . .2011 080

Buddah / Jul '71.
■ 7" . . . . . . . . . . . . . . . . . . . . . . . . BDS 410
Buddah / Nov '74.
■ 12" . . . . . . . . . . . . . . . . . . . . 12CUR 101
■ 7" . . . . . . . . . . . . . . . . . . . . . 7CUR 101
Ichiban / Jun '88.

## MOVE ON UP (The Best Of Curtis Mayfield).
**Tracks:** Not Advised.
■ LP . . . . . . . . . . . . . . . . . . . . . BDLP 4015
Buddah / Nov '74.

## NEVER SAY YOU CAN'T SURVIVE.
**Tracks:** Show me / Just want to be with you / When we're alone / Never say you can't survive / I'm gonna win your love / All night long / When you used to be mine / Sparkle.
■ LP . . . . . . . . . . . . . . . . . . . . . K 56352
Curtom / Mar '77.
CD . . . . . . . . . . . . . . . . . . . . CUR 2010CD
MC . . . . . . . . . . . . . . . . . . . . CUR 2010MC
Curtom / Mar '94 / ACD Trading Ltd. / Pinnacle / Koch International.
CD . . . . . . . . . . . . . . . . . . . . CPCD 8049
Charly Groove / Sep '94 / Charly.

## NO GOODBYES.
**Tracks:** No goodbyes / Party party.
■ 7" . . . . . . . . . . . . . . . . . . . . . . . LV 1
Curtom / Dec '78.

## OF ALL TIME - CLASSIC COLLECTION.
**Tracks:** If there's a hell below / Dirty laundry / Move on up / Only you babe / Doo doo wap is strong here / She don't let nobody (but me) / So in love / Tripping out / Do be down / You are, you are / This year / Between you baby and me / Ain't no love lost / Hard times / Tomorrow night for sure / We people who are darker than blue.
CD . . . . . . . . . . . . . . . . . . CUR 22902CD
■ Double LP . . . . . . . . . . . . . . CUR 22902
MC . . . . . . . . . . . . . . . . . . CUR 22902MC
Curtom / Nov '90 / ACD Trading Ltd. / Pinnacle / Koch International.

## PEOPLE GET READY (Live At Ronnie Scott's).
**Tracks:** Little child runnin' wild / It's all right / People get ready / Freddie's dead / Pusherman / I'm so proud / We've gotta have peace / Billy Jack / Move on up / To be invisible.
■ MC . . . . . . . . . . . . . . . . . . . ESMMC 003
■ CD . . . . . . . . . . . . . . . . . . . ESMCD 003
Essential / Feb '90.

## RIGHT COMBINATION (see under Clifford, Linda).

## ROOTS.
**Tracks:** Get down / Keep on keeping on / Underground / We got to have peace / Beautiful brother of mine / Now you're gone / Love to keep you in my mind.
■ LP . . . . . . . . . . . . . . . . . . . . . K 56249
WEA.
■ LP . . . . . . . . . . . . . . . . . . . . . 2318045
Buddah / Jan '72.
CD . . . . . . . . . . . . . . . . . . . . MPG 74027
MC . . . . . . . . . . . . . . . . . . . . MPG 474027
Movieplay Gold / Jan '94 / Target / BMG.
CD . . . . . . . . . . . . . . . . . . . . CPCD 8037
Charly / Jun '94 / Charly.

## SOMETHING TO BELIEVE IN.
**Tracks:** Love me, love me now / Never let me go / Tripping out / People never give up / It's alright / Something to believe in / Never stop loving me.
■ LP . . . . . . . . . . . . . . . . . . . . . 2394271
RSO / Oct '80.
■ LP . . . . . . . . . . . . . . . . . . . . RS 13077
RSO / May '89.
MC . . . . . . . . . . . . . . . . . . . CURMC 2005
■ LP . . . . . . . . . . . . . . . . . . . . CUR 2005
Curtom / Oct '89 / ACD Trading Ltd. / Pinnacle / Koch International.
CD . . . . . . . . . . . . . . . . . . . . CURCD 2005
Curtom / Oct '94 / ACD Trading Ltd. / Pinnacle / Koch International.

## SUPERFLY.
**Tracks:** Superfly / Give me your love.
■ 7" . . . . . . . . . . . . . . . . . . . . . . 2011 156
Buddah / Feb '73.

## SUPERFLY 1990 (Mayfield, Curtis & Ice-T).
**Tracks:** Superfly 1990 (Mixes).
■ 12" . . . . . . . . . . . . . . . . . . . 12CL 586
■ 7" . . . . . . . . . . . . . . . . . . . . . .CL 586
■ CD Single . . . . . . . . . . . . . . . CDCL 586
■ MC Single . . . . . . . . . . . . . . . TCCL 586
Capitol / Aug '90.

---

## SWEET EXORCIST.
**Tracks:** Not Advised.
■ LP . . . . . . . . . . . . . . . . . . . . .2318 099
Buddah / Aug '74.
CD . . . . . . . . . . . . . . . . . . . . CPCD 8047
Charly Groove / Sep '94 / Charly.

## TAKE IT TO THE STREET.
**Tracks:** Homeless / Got to be real / Do be down / Who was that lady / On and on / He's a fly guy / Don't push / I mo git U sucka.
LP . . . . . . . . . . . . . . . . . . . . . CUR 2008
Curtom / Mar '90 / ACD Trading Ltd. / Pinnacle / Koch International.
CD . . . . . . . . . . . . . . . . . . . . CUR 2008CD
MC . . . . . . . . . . . . . . . . . . . . CUR 2008C
Curtom / Mar '94 / ACD Trading Ltd. / Pinnacle / Koch International.

## THERE'S NO PLACE LIKE AMERICA TODAY.
**Tracks:** Billy Jack / When seasons change / So in love / Jesus / Blue monday people / Hard times / Love to the people.
■ LP . . . . . . . . . . . . . . . . . . . . BDLP 4033
Buddah / Aug '75.
■ LP . . . . . . . . . . . . . . . . . . . . CUR 2003
Ichiban / Jan '89.
CD . . . . . . . . . . . . . . . . . . . . CUR 2003CD
MC . . . . . . . . . . . . . . . . . . . . CUR 2003MC
Ichiban / Mar '94 / A.D.A. Distribution / Pinnacle / ACD Trading Ltd. / Koch International / Direct Distribution.

## THIS YEAR.
**Tracks:** This year (pt 1) / This year (pt 2).
■ 7" . . . . . . . . . . . . . . . . . . . . . . RSO 28
RSO / Mar '79.

## TRIPPING OUT.
**Tracks:** Not Advised.
CD . . . . . . . . . . . . . . . . . . . . CPCD 8065
Charly / Nov '94 / Charly.

## WE COME IN PEACE.
**Tracks:** Not Advised.
■ LP . . . . . . . . . . . . . . . . . . . . . CRC 2001
■ MC . . . . . . . . . . . . . . . . . . CRC 2001 MC
Curtom / Feb '91.

## WE GOT TO HAVE PEACE.
**Tracks:** We got to have peace / People get ready.
■ 7" . . . . . . . . . . . . . . . . . . . . . .2011 101
Buddah / Nov '71.

---

## Mayfield, Percy

## HIT THE ROAD AGAIN.
**Tracks:** Not Advised.
■ LP . . . . . . . . . . . . . . . . . . . . . SJP 170
Timeless (Jazz) / Nov '85.

## INCREDIBLE PERCY MAYFIELD, THE.
**Tracks:** Please send me someone to love / Lost mind / Memory plain / Louisiana / Cry baby / Strange things happening / What a fool I was / Nightless lover / Prayin' for your return / Loose lips / Lost love / River's invitation.
■ LP . . . . . . . . . . . . . . . . . . . . SNTF 5010
Specialty / '72.

## MEMORY PAIN.
**Tracks:** Please send me someone to love / Strange things happen / Two hearts are greater than one / Big question / My blues / Nightless lover / How deep is the well / Ruthie May / My heart / Lonesome highway / Lonely one / I ain't gonna cry no more / Memory pain / You are my future / Kiss tomorrow goodbye / Advice (For men only) / I need love so bad / Does anyone care for me / It's good to see you baby / Sugar mama - Peachy papa / You were lyin' to me / Voice within / Please believe me / Diggin' the moonglow / Hit the road, Jack.
CD . . . . . . . . . . . . . . . . . . . . CDCHD 438
Ace / Jan '93 / Pinnacle / Complete Record Co. Ltd.

## MY HEART IS ALWAYS SINGING SAD SONGS.
**Tracks:** I need love so bad / It's good to see you baby / Nightmare / Hunt is on / My heart / Lonesome highway / You don't exist no more / Bachelor blues / Proposal / Come home / One room country shack / Ain't gonna cry no more / Does anyone care for me / I dare you baby / Wasted dream / Big question.
■ LP . . . . . . . . . . . . . . . . . . . . .CHD 153
Ace / Nov '85.

## PERCY MAYFIELD.
**Tracks:** Life is suicide / Hunt is on / Hopeless / My heart is crying / Baby, you're rich / My blues / I dare you, baby / Memory pain / You are my future / Get

---

way back / Advice (for men only) / Lonesome high way / Kiss tomorrow goodbye / Strange things hap pening / Ruthie Mae / Pease send me someone t love / Hit the road, Jack / Prayin' for your return What a fool I was / Lost love / Nightless lover / Cr baby / Lost mind / River's invitation / Big question Wasted dream / Louisiana / Bachelor blues / Loos lips / You don't exist no more / Nightmare.
■ LP . . . . . . . . . . . . . . . . . . . . .CHD 28
Ace / Oct '89.

## POET OF THE BLUES.
**Tracks:** Please send me someone to love / Prayir for your return / Strange things happening / Life i suicide / What a fool I was / Lost love / Nightles lover / Advice (for men only) / Cry baby / Lost mind I dare you baby / Hopeless / Hunt is on / River invitation / Big question / Wasted dream / Louisian / Bachelor blues / Get way back / Memory pain Loose ups / You don't exist anymore / Nightmare Baby, you're rich / My heart is cryin'.
CD . . . . . . . . . . . . . . . . . . . . CDCHD 28
Ace / Oct '90 / Pinnacle / Complete Record Co. Ltc.

## VOICE WITHIN, THE.
**Tracks:** How wrong can a good man be / Leary blue / Hunt is on / Hopeless / Two hearts are greater tha one / Lonesome highway / I dare you, baby / Ho deep is the well / Lonely one / Bachelor blues Sugar mama - peachy papa / Voice within / My hea / Are you out there / Bluest blues / Blues blues.
■ LP . . . . . . . . . . . . . . . . . . . . . KIX 2
Route 66 (Sweden) / Aug '87.

---

## Mazarati

## MAZARATI.
**Tracks:** Players ball / Lonely girl on Bourbon Street 100 m.p.h. / Stroke / Suzy / Strawberry lover / guess it's all over.
■ MC . . . . . . . . . . . . . . . . . . . .925368
■ LP . . . . . . . . . . . . . . . . . . . .925368
WEA / Apr '86.

---

## Maze

## BACK IN STRIDE.
**Tracks:** Back in stride / Joy and pain.
■ 7" . . . . . . . . . . . . . . . . . . . . . .CL 35
■ 12" . . . . . . . . . . . . . . . . . . . 12CL 35
Capitol / Feb '85.

## BACK TO BASICS.
**Tracks:** Nobody knows what you feel inside / Love i / Morning after / Laid-back girl / What goes up / I time / All night long / Don't wanna lose your love Twilight.
CD . . . . . . . . . . . . . . . . . . . 936245297
Warner Bros. / Sep '93 / WEA.

## BEFORE I LET GO (Maze Featurin Frankie Beverly).
**Tracks:** Before I let go / Golden time of day.
■ 12" . . . . . . . . . . . . . . . . . . . 12CL 24
■ 7" . . . . . . . . . . . . . . . . . . . . . .CL 24
Capitol / Apr '82.

## CAN'T GET OVER YOU (Maze Featuring Frankie Beverly).
**Tracks:** Can't get over you / Africa.
■ 12" . . . . . . . . . . . . . . . . . . . W 2895
■ 7" . . . . . . . . . . . . . . . . . . . . W 289
■ CD Single . . . . . . . . . . . . . . . W 2895 CC
Capitol / Apr '82.

## CAN'T STOP THE LOVE (Maze Featuring Frankie Beverly).
**Tracks:** Back in stride / Can't stop the love / Reach ing down inside / Too many games / I want to fee I'm wanted / Magic / Place in my heart.
■ LP . . . . . . . . . . . . . . . . . . . . MAZE
MC . . . . . . . . . . . . . . . . . . . TC MAZE
Capitol / Mar '85 / EMI.
CD . . . . . . . . . . . . . . . . . . . MUSCD 502
MC . . . . . . . . . . . . . . . . . . . MUSMC 502
Music Collection International / Sep '94 / THE / Jazz Music.

## COLOUR BLIND.
**Tracks:** Colour blind / While I'm alone.
■ 7" . . . . . . . . . . . . . . . . . . . . CL 1592
Capitol / May '77.

## GOLDEN TIME OF DAY (Maze Featuring Frankie Beverly).
**Tracks:** Travelling man / Song for my mother You're not the same / Working together / Golde time of day / I wish you well / I need you.
■ LP . . . . . . . . . . . . . . . . . . . . .EST 1171
Capitol / Mar '78.
■ LP . . . . . . . . . . . . . . . . . . . CAPS 104
Capitol / May '82.

**MC.** . . . . . . . . . . . . . . . TC2GO 1866849
apitol / Jun '83.

**WANNA BE WITH YOU (Maze Featuring rankie Beverly).**
acks: I wanna be with you / I wanna be with you nstrumental).
■ 12″. . . . . . . . . . . . . . . . . . . . 12CL 421
■ 7″ . . . . . . . . . . . . . . . . . . . . .CL 421
apitol / Aug '86.

**NSPIRATION.**
racks: Lovely inspiration / Feel that you're feelin' / all on me / Timin' / Welcome home / Woman is a onder / Ain't it strange.
■ LP . . . . . . . . . . . . . . . . . . . .EST 11912
apitol.

**OY AND PAIN.**
racks: Joy and pain / Happy feelin's / Golden time day (Only on 12″ single.).
■ 7″ . . . . . . . . . . . . . . . . . . . . .CL 211
■ 12″. . . . . . . . . . . . . . . . . . . . 12CL 211
apitol / Mar '82.

**OY AND PAIN (Maze Featuring Frankie everly).**
racks: Changing times / Look in your eyes / Family Roots / Joy and pain / Southern girl / Happiness.
■ LP . . . . . . . . . . . . . . . . . . .EST 12087
■ MC. . . . . . . . . . . . . . . TCEST 12087
apitol / Mar '82.

**OY AND PAIN.**
racks: Too many games / I wanna be with you / Joy id pain.
■ CD Single. . . . . . . . . . . . . .OG 6523
ckwick / Sep '92.

**OY AND PAIN (SINGLE) (2).**
racks: Joy and pain / Twilight (12″ only.) / We are e.
■ CD Single. . . . . . . . . . . . . CDCL 531
apitol / Jun '89.
■ 12″. . . . . . . . . . . . . . . . . . . . 12CL 531
■ 7″ . . . . . . . . . . . . . . . . . . . . .CL 531
apitol / May '89.

**ADY OF MAGIC.**
acks: Lady of magic / Time is on my side.
■ 7″ . . . . . . . . . . . . . . . . . . . CL 15939
apitol / Sep '77.

**FELINES VOL. 1 (Maze Featuring Fran-e Beverly).**
acks: Joy and pain (Featuring Kurtis Blow.) / gol-n time of day / Happy feelin's / Back in stride / efore I let go (Featuring Woody Wood.) / Running way / While I'm alone / Southern girl / Joy and pain riginal LP version) / Before I let go (original LP rsion).
■ . . . . . . . . . . . . . . . . . . . CDEST 2111
■ LP . . . . . . . . . . . . . . . . EST 2111
■ MC. . . . . . . . . . . . . . .TCEST 2111
apitol / Nov '89 / EMI.

**VE IN LOS ANGELES (Maze Featuring ankie Beverly).**
acks: Running away / Too many games / I wanna ank you / You / Happy feelin's / Feel that you're elin' / Joy and pain / Before I let go / Back in stride wanna be with you / Freedom / Dee's song / When u love someone.
C Set . . . . . . . . . . . TC2 ESTSP 24
Double LP. . . . . . . . . . . . . ESTSP 24
apitol / Sep '86 / EMI.
CD. . . . . . . . . . . . CDP 746 369 2
apitol / Jul '87.

**VE IN NEW ORLEANS (Maze Featuring ankie Beverly).**
acks: Changing times / Joy and pain / Southern 1 / Look at California / Feel that you're feelin' / ok in your eyes / Running away / Before I let go / e need love to live / Reason / You (Not on CD.) / appy feelin's (Not on CD.).
Double LP. . . . . . . . . . . . . ESTSP 22
pitol / Jun '81.
MC Set . . . . . . . . . . . TC2 ESTSP 22
pitol / Mar '82.
CD. . . . . . . . . . . . CDP 746 659 2
pitol / Nov '87.

**VE IN NEW ORLEANS (Maze Featuring ankie Beverly).**
acks: Not Advised.
VHS . . . . . . . . . . . . . . MVP 99 1021 2
MI / Jun '86.
S . . . . . . . . . . . . . . . . . .PM 0013
deo Collection / May '87 / Gold & Sons / Video llection / THE.

**LOVE IS THE KEY.**
Tracks: Love is the key / Lady of magic.
■ 12″. . . . . . . . . . . . . . . . . . . . 12CL 290
■ 7″ . . . . . . . . . . . . . . . . . . . . .CL 290
Capitol / Apr '83.

**MAZE (Maze Featuring Frankie Beverly).**
Tracks: Time is on my side / Happy feelin's / Color blind / Lady of magic / While I'm alone / You / Look at California.
■ LP . . . . . . . . . . . . . . . . . . . .EST 11607
Capitol / May '77.
■ LP . . . . . . . . . . . . . . . . . . . CAPS 1039
Capitol / May '82.
■ LP . . . . . . . . . . . . . . . . . . . FA 3202
■ MC. . . . . . . . . . . . . . . TCFA 3202
Fame / Jun '88.

**SILKY SOUL.**
Tracks: Not Advised.
■ LP . . . . . . . . . . . . . . . . . . . . WX 301
■ MC. . . . . . . . . . . . . . . WX 301C
WEA / Sep '89.
CD. . . . . . . . . . . . . . . . . .K 9258022
WEA / Mar '94 / WEA.

**SILKY SOUL.**
Tracks: Silky soul / Can't get over you / Just us / Somebody else's arms / You're on the run / Change our ways / Songs of love / Mandela / Midnight (Available on CD only) / Africa (Available on CD only).
■ 7″ . . . . . . . . . . . . . . . . . . . . W 2738
WEA / Jan '90.

**TOO MANY GAMES.**
Tracks: Too many games / Twilight.
■ 12″. . . . . . . . . . . . . . . . . . . . 12CLX 363
Capitol / Jul '85.

**TRAVELIN' MAN.**
Tracks: Traveli' man / Workin' together.
■ 7″ . . . . . . . . . . . . . . . . . . . CL 15978
Capitol / Apr '78.

**WE ARE ONE.**
Tracks: We are one / Right on time.
■ 12″. . . . . . . . . . . . . . . . . . . . 12CL 295
■ 7″ . . . . . . . . . . . . . . . . . . . . .CL 295
Capitol / Jun '83.

**WE ARE ONE (Maze Featuring Frankie Beverly).**
Tracks: Love is the key / Right on time / Your kind of way / I want to thank you / We are one / Never let you down / I love you so much / Metropolis.
■ LP . . . . . . . . . . . . . . . . . . . .EST 12262
■ MC. . . . . . . . . . . . . . . TC EST 12262
Capitol / Apr '83.

## Mazelle, Kym

**BRILLIANT.**
Tracks: No one can love you more than me (Boiler-house version) / Useless (I don't need you now) / Don't scandalise my name (U.S. remix) / Skin I'm in / Love strain / Missing you (soul to soul remix) / Never in a million years (Doc & James remix) / Crazy 'bout the man (Frankie knuckles mix) / Was that all it was (David Morales mix).
■ CD. . . . . . . . . . . . . . . CDPCS 7354
■ LP . . . . . . . . . . . . . . . . . . . PCS 7354
■ MC. . . . . . . . . . . . . . . TCPCS 7354
Parlophone / May '91.

**CRAZY.**
Tracks: Love strain / No one can love you more than me / This love will never die / Don't scandalize my name / Wait (short) / Just what it takes / Was that all it was / Don't make me over / Got to get you back / Crazy 'bout the man / Never in a million years / Useless (I don't need you now) / Can't make nobody love you.
CD. . . . . . . . . . . . . . .CDSYLP 6004
■ LP . . . . . . . . . . . . . . . . . . . SYLP 6004
■ MC. . . . . . . . . . . . . . . TCSYLP 6004
Syncopate / Oct '89 / EMI.

**GIMME ALL YOUR LOVIN' (Mazelle, Kym & Jocelyn Brown).**
Tracks: Gimme all your lovin' (Mixes) / Somebody else's guy (mixes) (Not on 74321 231312) / Love me the right way (mixes) (Not on 74321 231322).
12″. . . . . . . . . . . . . . . . . . . .74321 23131-1
CD Single . . . . . . . . . . 7432123131-2
CD Single . . . . . . . . . . 7432123132-2
MC Single . . . . . . . . . . 7432123131-4
RCA / Sep '94 / BMG.

**GOT TO GET YOU BACK.**
Tracks: Got to get you back (radio mix) (Not on 12″.) / Got to get you back (groovy piano mix) (CD single &

12 SY only.) / Got to get you back (amazella mix) (CD single & 12 SY only.) / Got to get you back (groovy instrumental mix) (7″ & 12″ only.) / Got to get you back (gettin' back mix) (12SYX only.) / Got to get you back (Saturday night special) (12SYX only.) / Got to get you back (club dub) (12SYX only.)
■ 12″. . . . . . . . . . . . . . . . . . . . 12SYX 25
■ 12″. . . . . . . . . . . . . . . . . . . . .12SY 25
■ 7″ . . . . . . . . . . . . . . . . . . . . SY 25
■ CD Single . . . . . . . . . . . . . CDSY 25
Syncopate / Mar '89.

**I'M A LOVER.**
Tracks: I'm a lover.
■ 12″. . . . . . . . . . . . . . . . . . . . LICT 013
■ 12″ Remix. . . . . . . . . . . . . LIC 013R
■ 7″ . . . . . . . . . . . . . . . . . . . . LIC 013
Republic / Nov '88.

**LOVE STRAIN.**
Tracks: Love strain (radio version) (Not on 12″.) / Love strain (sax strain) / Love strain (dub strain) (12″ only.) / Love strain (Slam City club version) (CD single & 12″ remix only.) / Love strain (Frankie foncett remix) (12″ remix only.) / Love strain (deep dub) (12″ remix only.)
■ 12″. . . . . . . . . . . . . . . . . . . . 12SYX 30
■ 12″. . . . . . . . . . . . . . . . . . . . .12SY 30
■ 12″ Remix . . . . . . . . . . . . SYP 30
■ 7″ . . . . . . . . . . . . . . . . . . . . SY 30
■ CD Single . . . . . . . . . . . . . CDSY 30
■ MC Single . . . . . . . . . . . . .TCSY 30
Syncopate / Sep '89.

**NO MORE TEARS (Mazelle, Kym & Joce-lyn Brown).**
Tracks: No more tears.
■ 12″. . . . . . . . . . . . . . . . . . . . 7432120903-1
■ 7″ . . . . . . . . . . . . . . . . . . . . 7432120903-7
■ CD . . . . . . . . . . . . . . . . . . . 7432120903-2
■ MC Single . . . . . . . . . . . . . 7432120903-4
RCA / May '94.

**NO ONE CAN LOVE YOU MORE THAN ME.**
Tracks: Never in a million years (Not on 12″.) / No one can love you more than me.
■ 12″. . . . . . . . . . . . . . . . . . . . 12R 6287
■ 12″ Remix. . . . . . . . . . . . . .12RX 6287
■ 7″ . . . . . . . . . . . . . . . . . . . . .R 6287
■ CD Single . . . . . . . . . . . . . CDR 6287
■ MC Single . . . . . . . . . . . . . TCR 6287
Parlophone / Mar '91.

**USELESS (I DON'T NEED YOU NOW).**
Tracks: Useless - I don't need you now (radio mix) (7″ & CD single only.) / Useless - I don't need you now (California mix) (7″ only.) / Useless - I don't need you now (12″ mix) (12″ & CD single only.) / Useless - I don't need you now (deep house) (12″ only.) / Useless - I don't need you now (ad lib dub) (12″ only.) / Useless - I don't need you now (long club version) (12″ special only.) / Useless - I don't need you now (after hours club) (12″ special and CD single only.) / Useless - I don't need you now (dub mix) (12″ special only.).
■ 12″. . . . . . . . . . . . . . . . . . . . .12SY 18
■ 12″. . . . . . . . . . . . . . . . . . . . 12SYX 18
■ 7″ . . . . . . . . . . . . . . . . . . . . SY 18
■ CD Single . . . . . . . . . . . . . CDSY 18
Syncopate / Oct '88.

**USELESS, I DON'T NEED YOU NOW (REMIX).**
Tracks: Useless (I don't need you now) (mixes).
■ 12″. . . . . . . . . . . . . . . . . . . . 12SYX 36
■ 12″. . . . . . . . . . . . . . . . . . . . .12SY 36
■ 7″ . . . . . . . . . . . . . . . . . . . . SY 36
■ CD Single . . . . . . . . . . . . . CDSY 36
■ MC Single . . . . . . . . . . . . .TCSY 36
Syncopate / May '90.

**WAS THAT ALL IT WAS.**
Tracks: Was that all it was (def mix) (12″ only.) / Was that all it was (def mix edit) / Was that all it was (def mix dub) / Was that all it was (Classic Philly mix) (12SYX only.) / Was that all it was (South Philly dub) (12SYX only.) / Was that all it was (Center City dub) (12SYX only.) / Was that all it was (Orbital mix) (12SYX only.) / Was that all it was (Jungle mix) (12SYXX only.) / Was that all it was (Red Zone mix) (12SYXX only.).
■ 12″. . . . . . . . . . . . . . . . . . . . 12SYX 32
■ 12″ Remix. . . . . . . . . . . . . 12SYXX 32
Syncopate / Dec '89.
■ 12″. . . . . . . . . . . . . . . . . . . . .12SY 32
■ 7″ . . . . . . . . . . . . . . . . . . . . SY 32
■ CD Single . . . . . . . . . . . . . CDSY 32
■ MC Single . . . . . . . . . . . . .TCSY 32
Syncopate / Nov '89.

**WOMAN OF THE WORLD (Mazelle, Kym & Simon May).**
Tracks: Woman of the world / Woman of the world (instrumental) (Not on 12″ single) / No one can love you more than me (Only on 12″ single) / Was that all it was (Only on 12″ single) / Can't make nobody love you (Only on 12″ single) / Intuition (Only on CD single).

■ 12″ . . . . . . . . . . . . . . . . . . . . . . . 12EM 209
■ 7″ . . . . . . . . . . . . . . . . . . . . . . . . . EM 209
■ CD Single . . . . . . . . . . . . . . . . . .CDEM 209
■ MC Single . . . . . . . . . . . . . . . . . .TCEM 209
EMI / Oct '91.

## Meadows, Marion

**FOR LOVERS ONLY.**
Tracks: I found a new love / Forbidden love / Sleepless nights / For lovers only / Real thing / Personal touch / Paradise / Wonderland / Dear world / Just before dawn.
CD . . . . . . . . . . . . . . . . . . . . . . . PD 83097
■ LP . . . . . . . . . . . . . . . . . . . . . . . PL 83097
■ MC. . . . . . . . . . . . . . . . . . . . . . . PK 83097
RCA / Dec '90 / BMG.

**FORBIDDEN FRUIT, THE.**
Tracks: Red lights / Always on my mind / Asha / Forbidden fruit / Whenever your heart wants to song / You will never know what you're missing / Back-2back / Save the best for last / Somewhere island / Comin' home to you / Nocturnal serenade.
CD . . . . . . . . . . . . . . . . . . . .01241 63167-2
Novus / Mar '94 / BMG.

**KEEP IT RIGHT THERE.**
Tracks: Wishing / In effect / Love was never / Morocco / Come back to me / Color of love / Keep it right there / Oh yes / Heaven / Good lovin' / When will I know / Passion.
CD . . . . . . . . . . . . . . . . . . . . . . . PD 90623
Novus / Apr '92 / BMG.

## Mel & Tim

**BACKFIELD IN MOTION (OLD GOLD).**
Tracks: Backfield in motion / I feel love comin' on.
■ 7″ . . . . . . . . . . . . . . . . . . . . . . .OG 9784
Old Gold / Jun '88.

**STARTING ALL OVER AGAIN.**
Tracks: Starting all over again / It hurts to want it so bad.
■ 7″ . . . . . . . . . . . . . . . . . . . . . STAX 1006
Stax / Mar '82.
■ 7″ . . . . . . . . . . . . . . . . . . . . . . STAX 816
Stax / Sep '87.

**STARTING ALL OVER AGAIN.**
Tracks: Don't mess with my money, my honey or my woman / Starting all over again / I may not be what you want / Carry me / Free for all / Heaven knows / Wrap it up / What's your name / I'm your puppet / Too much wheelin' and dealin' / Forever and a day / It's those little things that count / Same folk / Yes we can-can.
CD . . . . . . . . . . . . . . . . . . . . . CDSXE 078
Stax / Jan '93 / Pinnacle.

## Mella & Co

**BE FREE.**
Tracks: Be free.
■ 12″ . . . . . . . . . . . . . . . . . . . . . . DF 1209
Dancefloor (USA) / Nov '87.

## Melvin, Harold

A Philadelphia native, Melvin formed Harold Melvin & The Blue Notes in the mid-'50s. *If You Love Me* was a local hit on Josie Records, and throughout the '60s their reputation as a live draw in the Pennsylvania state area gradually grew. The group's big break, however, came on signing to Gamble/Huff's Philadelphia International Records. The ballads *I Miss You* and *If You Don't Know Me By Now*, featuring Teddy Pendergrass on lead vocals, kicked them in to the '70s as national, then international stars. Riding the Philly gravy train throughout most of the decade, the group hit further with *The Love I Lost, Satisfaction Guaranteed, Wake Up Everybody* and *Don't Leave Me This Way* before the inevitable happened and Pendergrass went solo. There was no place for Melvin's remaining Bluenotes at PIR, so he replaced Pendergrass with the similar-sounding David Ebo and signed his group to ABC, with whom they enjoyed a moderate amount of success. A

single, *Reaching For The World*, made the U.K. Top 50. Thereafter, the group slipped into soul's second division, releasing the odd cult single - *Prayin'* (Source Records), *Hang On In There* (MCA) and *Today's Your Lucky Day* (Philly World).

**6 TRACK HITS (Melvin, Harold & The Bluenotes).**
Tracks: Love I lost / Wake up everybody / If you don't know me by now / Don't leave me this way / Satisfaction guaranteed / I miss you.
MC. . . . . . . . . . . . . . . . . . . . . . . 7SC 5028
■ Mini LP . . . . . . . . . . . . . . . . . . 7SR 5028
Scoop 33 / Sep '83.

**BLUE ALBUM (Melvin, Harold & The Bluenotes).**
Tracks: Tonight's the night / Prayin' / Baby I'm back / I should be your lover / If you're looking for somebody to love / Your love is taking me on a journey.
■ LP . . . . . . . . . . . . . . . . . . . . . SOR 5000
Source / May '80.

**DON'T GIVE ME UP (Melvin, Harold & The Bluenotes).**
Tracks: Don't give me up.
■ 12″ . . . . . . . . . . . . . . . . . . . . . LONX 47
■ 7″ . . . . . . . . . . . . . . . . . . . . . . LON 47
London / Apr '84.

**DON'T LEAVE ME THIS WAY (Melvin, Harold & The Bluenotes).**
Tracks: Don't leave me this way.
■ 7″ . . . . . . . . . . . . . . . . . . . . . PIR 4909
Philadelphia Int. / Jan '77.
■ 7″ . . . . . . . . . . . . . . . . . . . . . PIR 8867
Philadelphia Int. / May '79.

**DON'T LEAVE ME THIS WAY (Melvin, Harold & The Bluenotes).**
Tracks: Don't leave me this way / Concentrate on me / Where are all my friends / Nobody could take your place / Keep on lovin' you / Satisfaction guaranteed / You know how to make me feel so good / To be true / It all depends on you / Let it be you.
■ LP . . . . . . . . . . . . . . . . . . . . . . 31600
Embassy (1) / Dec '77.

**DON'T LEAVE ME THIS WAY (OLD GOLD 2) (Melvin, Harold & The Bluenotes).**
Tracks: Don't leave me this way / If you don't know me by now (On 7″ only.) / Wake up everybody (Not on 7″.).
■ 12″ . . . . . . . . . . . . . . . . . . . . .OG 4027
Old Gold / '88.
7″ . . . . . . . . . . . . . . . . . . . . . .OG 9306
Old Gold / Mar '90 / Pickwick.

**DON'T LEAVE ME THIS WAY (OLD GOLD).**
Tracks: Don't leave me this way / Wake up everybody / Love I lost.
CD Single . . . . . . . . . . . . . . . . . .OG 6507
Old Gold / Jul '90 / Pickwick.

**GET OUT (AND LET ME CRY).**
Tracks: Get out (and let me cry) / You may not love me.
■ 7″ . . . . . . . . . . . . . . . . . . . . . . RT 06
Route / May '75.

**GREATEST HITS: HAROLD MELVIN & THE BLUE NOTES (Melvin, Harold & The Bluenotes).**
Tracks: Love I lost / Bad luck / If you don't know me by now / I miss you / Wake up everybody / Hope that we can be together soon / Where are all my friends / Be for real / Satisfaction guaranteed.
■ LP . . . . . . . . . . . . . . . . . . . . . PIR 32569
Philadelphia Int. / Feb '85.

**I SHOULD BE YOUR LOVER (Melvin, Harold & The Bluenotes).**
Tracks: I should be your lover / Prayin'.
■ 12″ . . . . . . . . . . . . . . . . . . . . 12SRC 104
■ 7″ . . . . . . . . . . . . . . . . . . . . . .SRC 104
Source / May '80.

**I'M COMIN' HOME TOMORROW (Melvin, Harold & The Bluenotes).**
Tracks: I'm comin' home tomorrow.
■ 7″ . . . . . . . . . . . . . . . . . . . . . PIR 2441
Philadelphia / Jun '74.

**IF YOU DON'T KNOW ME BY NOW (Melvin, Harold & The Bluenotes).**
Tracks: If you don't know me by now.
■ 7″ . . . . . . . . . . . . . . . . . . . . . CBS 8496
CBS / Jan '73.

**LOVE I LOST, THE (Melvin, Harold & The Bluenotes).**
Tracks: Love I lost / Love I lost (part 2).
■ 7″ . . . . . . . . . . . . . . . . . . . . . PIR 1879
Philadelphia Int. / Jan '74.

**NOW IS THE TIME.**
Tracks: Where's the concern for the people / Baby you got my nose open / Let's talk it over / Feels like magic / Now's the time / Power of love / Today tomorrow, forever / Try to live a day.
■ LP . . . . . . . . . . . . . . . . . . . . . ABCL 5237
ABC Records / Feb '78.

**PRAYIN' (Melvin, Harold & The Bluenotes).**
Tracks: Prayin' (1986 remix) / Prayin' (instrumental) Gospel (acappela mix) (Extra track on 12″ version only.) / Your love is taking me on a journey.
■ 12″ . . . . . . . . . . . . . . . . . . . . 12 SRC 103
■ 7″ . . . . . . . . . . . . . . . . . . . . .SRC 103
Source / Jan '80.
■ 12″ . . . . . . . . . . . . . . . . . . . .12 SOURCE 2
■ 7″ . . . . . . . . . . . . . . . . . . . . . SOURCE 1
Source / May '86.

**REACHING FOR THE WORLD (Melvin, Harold & The Bluenotes).**
Tracks: Reaching for the world.
■ 7″ . . . . . . . . . . . . . . . . . . . . . ABC 4165
ABC Records / Apr '77.

**SATISFACTION GUARANTEED (Melvin, Harold & Teddy Pendergrass).**
Tracks: Not Advised.
■ CD . . . . . . . . . . . . . . . . . . . . . NCD 344
■ LP . . . . . . . . . . . . . . . . . . . . . NE 144
■ MC. . . . . . . . . . . . . . . . . . . . . CE 244
K-Tel / Oct '89.

**SATISFACTION GUARANTEED (The Best of Harold Melvin & The Blue Notes (Melvin, Harold & The Bluenotes).**
Tracks: Don't leave me this way / Satisfaction guaranteed (or take your love) / Love I lost / Wake u everybody / Hope that we can be together soon / Yo know how to make me feel so good / Be for real Nobody could take your place / Bad luck / Where ar all my friends / Keep on loving you / Tell the worl about how I feel about cha baby / To be true / I'r searching for a love / To be free to be who we are / you don't know me by now.
■ CD . . . . . . . . . . . . . . . . . . . . . 472039
■ MC. . . . . . . . . . . . . . . . . . . . . 472039
Philadelphia / Jul '92.

**SATISFACTION GUARANTEED (OR TAKE YOUR LOVE BACK) (Melvin, Harold & The Bluenotes).**
Tracks: Satisfaction guaranteed.
■ 7″ . . . . . . . . . . . . . . . . . . . . . PIR 2186
Philadelphia Int. / Apr '74.

**TO BE TRUE (Featuring Theodore Pendergrass) (Melvin, Harold & The Bluenotes).**
Tracks: Where are all my friends / To be true / Prett flower / Hope that we can get together soon / No body could take your place / Somewhere down th line / Bad luck / All because of a woman.
■ LP . . . . . . . . . . . . . . . . . . . . . PIR 8039
Philadelphia / '75.

**TODAY'S YOUR LUCKY DAY (Melvin Harold & The Bluenotes).**
Tracks: Today's your lucky day.
■ 7″ . . . . . . . . . . . . . . . . . . . . . LON 5
London / Aug '84.

**WAKE UP EVERYBODY (Melvin, Harol & The Bluenotes).**
Tracks: Wake up everybody.
■ 7″ . . . . . . . . . . . . . . . . . . . . . PIR 386
Philadelphia Int. / Feb '76.

**WHERE ARE ALL MY FRIENDS? (Melvi Harold & The Bluenotes).**
Tracks: Where are all my friends / Let it be you.
■ 7″ . . . . . . . . . . . . . . . . . . . . . PIR 51
Philadelphia Int. / Mar '77.

■ DELETE

## Memphis Horns

### ET UP AND DANCE.
**Tracks:** Get up and dance / Just for your love / aitin' for the flood / Love is happiness / Memphis ghts / What the funk / Country soul / No go be- eens / Don't abuse it / Keep on smilin'.
LP ......................... **PL 12198**
CA / '79.

### ET UP AND DANCE.
**Tracks:** Get up and dance / Don't abuse it.
7" ......................... **PB 0836**
SA / Jul '77.

### IST FOR YOUR LOVE.
**Tracks:** Just for your love / Keep on smilin'.
7" ......................... **PB 1064**
SA / '79.

### EMPHIS HORNS.
**Tracks:** I can't turn you loose / Soul bowl / Wooly lly / One mile high / To Sam & Dave with love / ckson / You don't know like I know / Soul man / nitation man / Share your love with me / Cry like a by / Cherry tree / Fa fa fa fa fa / Time.
LP ......................... **2466010**
ojo / Jul '71.

## Mendes, Sergio

### LEGRIA.
**Tracks:** Fato consumado / To voltando / Ultima batu- da / Aquelas coisas todas / Adeus America / lagre / Horizonte aberto / O mar e meu chao / senredo.
LP ......................... **K 99096**
EA / Sep '80.

### LIBIS.
**Tracks:** Alibis / Olympia.
7" ......................... **AM 205**
M / Aug '84.

### RASILEIRO.
**Tracks:** Fanfarra / Magalenha / Indiado / What is this ua soberana / Sambadouro / Senhoras do amazo- s / Kalimba / Barabare / Esconjuros / Pipoca / agano / Chorado.
. ......................... **7559613152**
LP ......................... **7559613151**
. ......................... **7559613154**
ektra / May '92 / WEA.

### RAZIL 86'.
**Tracks:** Daylight / Take this love / What do we mean each other / Your smile / River (o rio) / Nonstop / It 't's a whole lot more / Flower of Bahia / No place hide / Here where I belong.
LP ......................... **AMA 5135**
MC. ......................... **AMC 5135**
CD ......................... **CDA 5135**
M / Aug '86.
M / Jan '86.

### ONFETTI.
**Tracks:** Olympia / Say it with your body / Let's give a e more this time / Sound of one song / Alibis / nce attack / Kisses / Real life / To die of love.
LP ......................... **AMLX 64984**
M / Aug '84.
CD ......................... **CDA 4984**
M / Apr '87.

### REATEST HITS: SERGIO MENDES.
**Tracks:** Mas que nada / Scarborough Fair / With a e help from my friends / Like a lover / Look of e / Night and day / Masquerade / Fool on the hill / in' out of my head / Look around / So many stars / /tripper / Pretty world / What the world needs now ove.
CD ......................... **CDA 3258**
M / '88.
......................... **CDMID 123**
M / Oct '92 / PolyGram.

### AS QUE NADA.
**Tracks:** Mas qeu nada.
12" ......................... **USAT 672**
7" ......................... **USA 672**
eakout / Aug '89.

### SUMMER LOVE.
**Tracks:** My summer love / Life in the movies.
7" ......................... **AMS 8249**
M / Aug '82.

### VER GONNA LET YOU GO.
**Tracks:** Never gonna let you go.
7" ......................... **AM 118**
M / Jul '83.

---

### NON STOP.
**Tracks:** Non-stop / Flower of Bahia / Never gonna let you go (Extra track on 12" version only.).
12" ......................... **AMY 341**
7" ......................... **AM 341**
A&M / Aug '86.

### PRIMAL ROOTS.
**Tracks:** Promise of a fisherman / After sunrise / Canto de Ubirantan / Lemanja / Pomba gira / Circle game.
LP ......................... **AMLS 64353**
A&M / Sep '72.

### RAINBOWS END.
**Tracks:** Rainbows end / Si signor.
7" ......................... **AM 142**
A&M.

### REAL THING.
**Tracks:** Real thing / Home cooking.
7" ......................... **K 12244**
Elektra / Feb '77.

### SERGIO MENDES & THE NEW BRAZIL 77 (Mendes, Sergio & New Brazil 77).
**Tracks:** Love me tomorrow / Love city / Mozambique / If you leave me now / Peninsula / Why / Real thing / P-ka-boo / Life.
LP ......................... **K 52056**
Elektra / Jan '77.
LP ......................... **MFP 50434**
MFP / '79.

### SERGIO MENDES (1).
**Tracks:** Voo doo / Never gonna let you go / My summer love / Carnival / Rainbow's end / Love is waiting / Dream hunter / Life in the movies / Si senor.
LP ......................... **AMHL 64937**
MC. ......................... **CAM 64937**
A&M / Jul '83.

### SERGIO MENDES (2).
**Tracks:** Davy / I believe / All in love is fair / Let them work it out / Here comes the sun / If I ever lose this heaven / Looking for another pure love / Someday we'll all be free / You been away too long / Trouble is hello is goodbye.
LP ......................... **K 52014**
Elektra.

### VERY BEST OF SERGIO MENDES (Mendes, Sergio & Brazil 66).
**Tracks:** Not Advised.
LP ......................... **SHM 3144**
MC. ......................... **HSC 3144**
Hallmark / May '84 / Pickwick.

## Merc & Monk

### BABY FACE.
**Tracks:** Baby face.
12" ......................... **12MT 3**
7" ......................... **MT 3**
EMI-Manhattan / May '85.

## Mercury, Eric

### GIMME A CALL SOMETIME.
**Tracks:** Gimme me a call sometime / Include me out.
7" ......................... **CL 216**
Capitol / Oct '81.

## Meters

Meters first took flight as Hawkettes, then evolved into Art Neville Sound and the backbone of New Orleans funk. Recruited by producer Allen Toussaint and partner Marshall Sehorn for the Sansu label, Sounds backed acts like Irma Thomas, Art's brother Aaron and, notably, Lee Dorsey. In '68, quartet signed to Jubilee subsidiary Josie, scoring crossover hits with *Sophisti- cated Cissy* and *Cissy Strut*. Although their pop profile declined in '70s, their stock rose as sessioneers for acts ranging from Robert Palmer and Paul McCartney to Labelle and Dr John. Support slots with likes of Rolling Stones won rock audience and they were later cited as influence by Aerosmith, but acrimonious dispute with Toussaint and Se- horn presaged band's demise in late '70s. Art and 1975 recruit Cyril Neville united with siblings Aaron and Charles in the Neville Brothers.

### BEST OF THE METERS.
**Tracks:** Jungle man / Hey pocky away / Can you do without / Just kissed my baby / Love slip upon you / People say / Africa / Fire on the Bayou.

---

LP ......................... **K 54076**
Reprise.

### CHICKEN STRUT.
**Tracks:** Chicken strut / Tippi toes.
7" ......................... **USA 005**
Island / Jan '75.

### CRESCENT CITY GROOVE MERCHANTS.
**Tracks:** Not Advised.
CD ......................... **CPCD 8066**
Charly / Nov '94 / Charly.

### FUNDAMENTALLY FUNKY.
**Tracks:** Not Advised.
CD ......................... **CPCD 8044**
Charly / Jun '94 / Charly.

### FUNKY MIRACLE.
**Tracks:** Not Advised.
CD ......................... **CDNEV 2**
Charly / Mar '91 / Charly.

### GOOD OLD FUNKY MUSIC.
**Tracks:** Look-ka-py-py / Seahorn's farm / Art / Ease back / Cissy strut / Message from the Meters / Thinking / Good old funky music / Live wire / Stretch your rubber band / Doodle-opp / Tippi-toes / Rigor mortis / 9 'til 5 / Sophisticated Cissy / Chicken strut / Here comes the meter man / Darling darling / Dry spell / Ride your pony.
LP ......................... **PKL 5578**
Pye / May '79.
LP ......................... **SPD 1039**
CD ......................... **SPDCD 1039**
MC. ......................... **SPDC 1039**
Special Delivery / Sep '90 / Vital Distribution / A.D.A. Distribution / Topic Records / Direct Distribution / Jazz Music / C.M. Distribution.

### HERE COME THE METERMEN.
**Tracks:** Sophisticated cissy / Here come the Meter- men / Mob / Funky miracle / Ride your pony / Art / Dry spell / Thinking / Handclapping song / Britches / Liver splash / Same old thing / 6V6 LA / Sehorns farm / Sing a simple song.
LP ......................... **CRB 1112**
Charly R&B / Apr '86.

### LOOK KA PY PY.
**Tracks:** Look ka py py / Tippi toes.
7" ......................... **CTD 113**
Charly / Jul '80.

### METERS JAM, THE.
**Tracks:** People get ready / Bo Diddley / Stretch your rubber band / Come together / Meters jam / It's too late.
CD ......................... **SPDCD 1041**
MC. ......................... **SPDC 1041**
Special Delivery / Apr '92.

### NEW DIRECTIONS.
**Tracks:** No more okey doke / I'm gone / Be my lady / My name up in lights / Funkify your life / Stop that train / We got the kind of love / Give it what you can.
LP ......................... **K 56378**
WEA / Jul '77.

### SECOND LINE STRUT.
**Tracks:** Look-ka py py / Nine til five / Cissy strut / I need more time / Pungee / Ease back / Cardova / Yeah, you're right / Tippi-toes / Chicken strut / Sassy lady / Little money maker / Rigor mortis / Live wire / Message from the Meters / Hey last minute.
LP ......................... **CRB 1009**
Charly R&B / '88.

### STRUTTIN.
**Tracks:** Tippi toes / Sophisticated cissy / Rigor mor- tis / Little old money maker / Look ka py py / Cissy strut / Ease back / Chicken strut / Message from the meters / Ride your pony / Dry spell / Handclapping song / Liver splash / Same old thing / Sehorns Farm / Yeah your right / 9 'til 5 / Pungee.
CD ......................... **CDCHARLY 63**
Charly / Feb '87 / Charly.

### UPTOWN RULERS (Live on the Queen Mary 1975).
**Tracks:** Fire on the bayou / Africa / It ain't no use / Make it with you / Cissy strut / Cardova / It's your thing / Love the one you're with / Rockin' pneumonia / I know / Everybody loves a lover / Liar / Mardi gras mambo / Hey pocky a-way.
CD ......................... **NEXCD 220**
Sequel / Sep '92 / Total / BMG.

## Metropolis

### GREATEST SHOW ON EARTH.
**Tracks:** Greatest show on Earth / New York is my kind of town.
■ 7″ . . . . . . . . . . . . . . . . . . . . SSOL 112
Salsoul / Oct '78.

### GREATEST SHOW ON EARTH.
**Tracks:** Greatest show that all / Go get it / I love New York / New York is my kind of town / Here's to you / Every time I see him / Thunder and lightning.
■ LP . . . . . . . . . . . . . . . . . . . SSLP 1510
Salsoul / Dec '78.

### I LOVE NEW YORK.
**Tracks:** I love New York / I love New York (version).
■ 7″ . . . . . . . . . . . . . . . . . . . . SSOL 107
Salsoul / Apr '78.

## MFSB

MFSB (officially Mother Father Sister Brother; unofficially, Motherfuckin' son of a bitch) were racially intergrated band on most Philadelphia International hits. Label was founded in 1971 by writing/production team Kenny Gamble and Leon Huff, whose 'Philly' sound overtook Motown as prominent force in soul. Like vintage Motown, Philly's artists were predominantly vocalists; in-house band was most economic way of providing music on records. In '73, MFSB released own album, featuring soul, jazz and MOR. Following year, ensemble scored U.S. smash with single *TSOP (The Sound of Philadelphia)*; formerly *Soul Train* TV theme, now anthem for Philly label itself. Record climaxed with chants by Three Degrees, whose career received considerable boost as result. MFSB issued series of moderately successful, mostly disco/funk albums during rest of '70s, but folded along with Philadelphia International Records in 1983.

### END OF PHASE 1 - A COLLECTION OF THEIR GREATEST HITS.
**Tracks:** Philadelphia freedom / Love is the message / Love has no time or place / Freddie's dead / Sunnin' and funnin' / TSOP / Let's go disco / My one and only love / TLC / Back stabbers.
■ LP . . . . . . . . . . . . . . . . . . . . PIR 81889
Philadelphia / Feb '78.

### GAMBLE-HUFF ORCHESTRA, THE.
**Tracks:** Dance with me tonight / To be in love / Let's party down / Wishing on a star / Use ta be my guy / Is it something I said / Redwood Beach.
■ LP . . . . . . . . . . . . . . . . . . . . PIR 83010
Philadelphia Int. / Jan '79.

### K-JEE.
**Tracks:** K-jee / My mood.
■ 7″ . . . . . . . . . . . . . . . . . . . . PIR 6287
Philadelphia Int. / May '78.

### MYSTERIES OF THE WORLD.
**Tracks:** Manhattan skyline / Mysteries of the world / Tell me why / Metamorphosis / Fortune teller / Old San Juan / Thank you Miss Scott / In the shadow.
■ LP . . . . . . . . . . . . . . . . . . . . PIR 84521
Philadelphia Int. / Feb '81.

### MYSTERIES OF THE WORLD.
**Tracks:** Mysteries of the world / Manhattan skyline.
■ 12″ . . . . . . . . . . . . . . . . . . . . 13-9501
■ 7″ . . . . . . . . . . . . . . . . . . . . PIR 9501
Philadelphia Int. / Jan '81.

### MYSTERIES OF THE WORLD (OLD GOLD).
**Tracks:** Mysteries of the world / TSOP / Sexy.
12″ . . . . . . . . . . . . . . . . . . . . OG 4150
Old Gold / Jan '90 / Pickwick.

### SEXY.
**Tracks:** Sexy.
■ 7″ . . . . . . . . . . . . . . . . . . . . PIR 3381
Philadelphia Int. / Jul '75.

### SOUND OF PHILADELPHIA.
**Tracks:** Sound of Philadelphia / Love is the message.
■ 12″ . . . . . . . . . . . . . . . . . . 4ZHA 06924
Philadelphia Int. / Oct '87.

### T.S.O.P.
**Tracks:** T.S.O.P.
■ 7″ . . . . . . . . . . . . . . . . . . . . PIR 2289
Philadelphia Int. / Apr '74.

### T.S.O.P. (OLD GOLD).
**Tracks:** T.S.O.P. / Live is the message.
■ 7″ . . . . . . . . . . . . . . . . . . . . OG 9869
Old Gold / Apr '89.

## Miami

### YOU ARE TEMPTATION.
**Tracks:** You are temptation / You are temptation (instrumental).
■ 12″ . . . . . . . . . . . . . . . . . . GRANAT 001
■ 7″ . . . . . . . . . . . . . . . . . . GRANA 001
Grana / Feb '86.

## Michaels, Cody

### SEVEN DAYS 52 WEEKS.
**Tracks:** Seven days 52 weeks / Don't look back.
■ 7″ . . . . . . . . . . . . . . . . . . . . GRP 121
Grapevine (Northern Soul) / Sep '79.

## Middleton, Tony

### DON'T EVER LEAVE ME.
**Tracks:** Don't ever leave me / To the ends of the earth.
■ 7″ . . . . . . . . . . . . . . . . . . BM 56704
Polydor / Mar '66.

### PARIS BLUES.
**Tracks:** Paris blues.
■ 7″ . . . . . . . . . . . . . . . . . . . . GRP 115
Grapevine (Northern Soul) / Nov '78.

## Midnight Express

### BIEN BENIDOS.
**Tracks:** Not Advised.
■ LP . . . . . . . . . . . . . . . . . . . . BGC 308
Country House / Jun '82.

## Midnight Star

### BEGINNING.
**Tracks:** Two in love / Follow the path / You're the star / Searching for love / Set me on fire / Keep the spirit high / Make it last.
■ LP . . . . . . . . . . . . . . . . . . . . SOLA 2
Solar / Jul '80.

### BEST OF MIDNIGHT STAR, THE.
**Tracks:** Midas touch / Headlines / Curious / Follow the path / Slow jam / Move me / Electricity / Freak-A-Zoid / Luv-U-Up / Wet my whistle / Engine No.9 / Money can't buy you love / Feels so good / Can't give you up / Midas touch (Extended version).
■ MC . . . . . . . . . . . . . . . . . . . . 468920
Solar / Oct '92.

### BEST OF MIDNIGHT STAR, THE.
**Tracks:** I've been watching you / Hot spot / Feels so good / Playmates / Scientific love / Headlines / Don't rock the boat / I won't let you be lonely / Wet my whistle / Curious / Let's celebrate / Operator / Midas touch.
CD . . . . . . . . . . . . . . . . . . NEMCD 682
Sequel / Oct '94 / Total / BMG.

### CURIOUS.
**Tracks:** Curious / Body snatchers.
■ 12″ . . . . . . . . . . . . . . . . . . MCAT 961
■ 7″ . . . . . . . . . . . . . . . . . . . MCA 961
MCA / Mar '85.

### ENGINE NO.9.
**Tracks:** Engine no.9 / (US mix).
■ 12″ . . . . . . . . . . . . . . . . . MCAT 1117
■ 12″ Remix . . . . . . . . . . . . . . MCAX 1117
■ 7″ . . . . . . . . . . . . . . . . . . MCA 1117
MCA / Jan '87.

### FEELS SO GOOD.
**Tracks:** Feels so good / Slow jam.
■ 7″ . . . . . . . . . . . . . . . . . . . . E 9775
Elektra / Mar '84.

### HEADLINES.
**Tracks:** Searching for love / Headlines / Get dressed / Stay here by my side / Midas touch / Close encounter / Engine no.9 / Dead end / Headlines (extra extra mix) / Operator / Curious.
■ CD . . . . . . . . . . . . . . . . . . DMCF 3322
MCA / '86.
■ LP . . . . . . . . . . . . . . . . . . . MCF 3322
■ MC . . . . . . . . . . . . . . . . . . MCFC 3322
MCA / Jul '86.

### HEADLINES.
**Tracks:** Headlines.
■ 12″ . . . . . . . . . . . . . . . . . MCAX 1065

. . . . . . . . . . . . . . . . . . . . MCA 10
MCA / Jul '86.

### I'VE BEEN WATCHING YOU.
**Tracks:** I've been watching you / Open up to love.
■ 7″ . . . . . . . . . . . . . . . . . . . . K 125
Solar / Jul '81.

### MAKE IT LAST.
**Tracks:** Make it last / Follow the path.
■ 12″ . . . . . . . . . . . . . . . . . . . . SO 12
Solar / Mar '80.

### MIDAS TOUCH.
**Tracks:** Midas touch (extended remix) / Midas tou (acappella).
■ 12″ . . . . . . . . . . . . . . . . . . MCAT 10
■ 7″ . . . . . . . . . . . . . . . . . . . MCA 10
MCA / Sep '86.

### MIDAS TOUCH (OLD GOLD).
**Tracks:** Midas touch / Operator.
■ 12″ . . . . . . . . . . . . . . . . . . . . OG 41
Old Gold / May '89.

### MIDNIGHT STAR.
**Tracks:** Don't rock my boat / Heartbeat / Snake in th grass / Love song / 90 days / I don't wanna be lone / Request line / Pamper me.
■ LP . . . . . . . . . . . . . . . . . . . . DI 725
Solar / Feb '89.
■ LP . . . . . . . . . . . . . . . . . . . MCG 60
■ CD . . . . . . . . . . . . . . . . . . DMCG 60
■ MC . . . . . . . . . . . . . . . . . . MCGC 60
MCA / Mar '89.

### NO PARKING ON THE DANCE FLOOR.
**Tracks:** Electricity / Night rider / Feels so good / W my whistle / No parking (on the dance floor) / Frea a-zoid / Slow jam / Play mates.
■ MC . . . . . . . . . . . . . . . . . . MCLC 18
■ LP . . . . . . . . . . . . . . . . . . . MCL 18
MCA / Mar '87.

### OPERATOR.
**Tracks:** Operator / Playmates.
■ 12″ . . . . . . . . . . . . . . . . . . MCAT 9
■ 7″ . . . . . . . . . . . . . . . . . . . MCA 9
MCA / Feb '85.

### PLANETARY INVASION.
**Tracks:** Operator / Body snatchers / Can you sta with / Scientific love / Planetary invasion / Today n love / Let's celebrate / Curious.
■ LP . . . . . . . . . . . . . . . . . . . MCF 32
MCA / Feb '85.
■ LP . . . . . . . . . . . . . . . . . . . MCL 18
■ MC . . . . . . . . . . . . . . . . . . MCLC 18
MCA / Dec '86.

### STANDING TOGETHER.
**Tracks:** Standing together / Tuff / Can't give you up Hold out / I've been watching you / I won't let you b lonely / I've got what you need / Open up to love.
■ LP . . . . . . . . . . . . . . . . . . . . K 523
MC. . . . . . . . . . . . . . . . . . . . K4 523
Solar / Jul '81 / Sony.

### VICTORY.
**Tracks:** Victory / Strike a match / Move me / Mak time / Hot spot / You can't stop me / Be with you Love is alive.
■ LP . . . . . . . . . . . . . . . . . . . . K 523
Solar / Oct '82.

### WET MY WHISTLE.
**Tracks:** Wet my whistle / Curious / Freak-a-zoid Headlines (extra extra mix).
■ 12″ . . . . . . . . . . . . . . . . . . MCAT 112
■ 7″ . . . . . . . . . . . . . . . . . . MCA 112
MCA / Apr '87.

### WORK IT OUT.
**Tracks:** Do it (one more time) / Work it out / All I wa / Money can't buy you love / Love of my life / Luv-up / Red roses / One life to live / If walls could talk Take your shoes off.
■ LP . . . . . . . . . . . . . . . . . . . . Z 753
Solar / Jun '90.
■ LP . . . . . . . . . . . . . . . . . . . 46607
■ MC . . . . . . . . . . . . . . . . . . 46607
Epic / Sep '90.
CD. . . . . . . . . . . . . . . . . . . . .983252
Pickwick/Sony Collector's Choice / Aug '93 / Pic wick / Pinnacle.

## Midnite Express

### LOVE GETS STRONGER EVERY DAY.
**Tracks:** Love gets stronger every day / Many a hear
■ 7″ . . . . . . . . . . . . . . . . . . . . GT 2
GTO / Aug '80.

■ DELETE

## Mighty Fire

**NO TIME FOR MASQUERADING.**
Tracks: Sweet fire / One good love is worth two in the bush / I could write a love song / Love fantasy / Look what you made me do / Missing you / Love attack / Love fuzz.
■ LP . . . . . . . . . . . . . . . . . . . . . K 52294
Elektra / Jul '81.

**PORTRAITS.**
Tracks: Not Advised.
■ LP . . . . . . . . . . . . . . . . . . . . . K 52294
Asylum / May '81.

## Mighty Truth

**HEAVY KNOWLEDGE/WIZARD.**
Tracks: Heavy knowledge (Song mix) / Heavy knowledge (Spoken mix) / Wizard.
12" . . . . . . . . . . . . . . . . . .12 TNG 12011
Tongue 'N' Groove / Jun '94 / Vital Distribution.

## Miles, Arthur

**HELPING HAND.**
Tracks: Helping hand (12" & cassingle only.) / Trippin' on your love (Cassingle & CD single only.) / Trippin' on your love (edit) (7" only.) / Trippin' on your love (club remix) (12" only.) / Helping hand (incisive remix) (CD single only.).
■ 12" . . . . . . . . . . . . . . . . . . . . .FX 148
■ 7" . . . . . . . . . . . . . . . . . . . . . . F 148
■ CD Single . . . . . . . . . . . . . . . . .FCD 148
■ MC Single . . . . . . . . . . . . . . . . .FCS 148
FFRR / Dec '90.

**VICTIMS OF OUR LOVE.**
Tracks: Victims of our love.
■ 12" . . . . . . . . . . . . . . . . . . . . NMX 570
New Music / May '91.

## Miles, Buddy

**HELL AND BACK (Miles, Buddy Express).**
Tracks: Born under a bad sign / Change / All along the watchtower / Let it be me / Come back home / Be kind to your girlfriend / Decision / Nothing left to lose.
CD . . . . . . . . . . . . . . . . . . . . . RCD 10305
Black Arc / Jun '94 / Vital Distribution.

**LIVE: BUDDY MILES (Miles, Buddy & Carlos Santana).**
Tracks: Not Advised.
■ LP . . . . . . . . . . . . . . . . . . . . CBS 32271
■ MC . . . . . . . . . . . . . . . . . . . .40 32271
CBS / Sep '84.

**SNEAK ATTACK (Miles, Buddy Regiment).**
Tracks: Latin rock fusion / Can you hold me / Sunshine of your love / I've made up my mind / Working hard every day / Colossus / Let's make it together / Jazz fusion / Buddy Miles, live at CIM, Chino, Ca / Hold her tight / Dust in the wind / For your precious love.
■ LP . . . . . . . . . . . . . . . . . . . . K 60156
Atlantic / Oct '81.

**THEM CHANGES.**
Tracks: Not Advised.
CD . . . . . . . . . . . . . . . . . . . .LMCD 951170
Line / Sep '92 / C.M. Distribution / Grapevine Distribution / A.D.A. Distribution / Conifer Records.

**WHOLESALE LOVE.**
Tracks: Wholesale love / That's the way life is.
■ 7" . . . . . . . . . . . . . . . . . . . . 6052077
Mercury / May '71.

## Miles, Floyd

**CRAZY MAN (Miles, Floyd & Friends).**
Tracks: Not Advised.
■ CD . . . . . . . . . . . . . . . . . . ICH 9022 CD
■ MC . . . . . . . . . . . . . . . . . . ICH 9022 MC
Ichiban / Dec '92.

**GOIN' BACK TO DAYTONA.**
Tracks: Same thing / Goin' back to Daytona / Mean heartbreaker / No life at all / Oh, Mary / Two against them all / All the love I can / Samson & Delilah / That's why I'm here tonight / Love on the rocks.
CD . . . . . . . . . . . . . . . . . . . . . .FCD 752
Demon / Jun '94 / Pinnacle / A.D.A. Distribution.

## Milestones

**JOKER, THE.**
Tracks: Joker.
■ 7" . . . . . . . . . . . . . . . . . . . . . BM 111
Black Magic (2) / Jan '76.

## Milira

**MERCY MERCY ME.**
Tracks: Mercy mercy me.
■ 12" . . . . . . . . . . . . . . . . . . . ZT 43680
■ 7" . . . . . . . . . . . . . . . . . . . ZB 43679
■ CD Single . . . . . . . . . . . . . . . ZD 43680
Motown / May '90.

**MILIRA.**
Tracks: Mercy mercy me / Go inside the rain / Waiting here for you / That man in my life / Good times are back again / I want to be to you (What you are to me) / Let me have a chance / Treat me right / Home / That four letter word (Only on CD) / Mercy mercy me(The ecology)(Vocal mix) (Only on CD).
■ CD . . . . . . . . . . . . . . . . . . . ZD 72714
■ LP . . . . . . . . . . . . . . . . . . . ZL 72714
■ MC . . . . . . . . . . . . . . . . . . . ZK 72714
Motown / Jun '90.

**MILIRA BACK AGAIN.**
Tracks: Not Advised.
■ CD . . . . . . . . . . . . . . . . . . . .530081-2
Motown / Jan '93.

## Miller, Byron

**GIT WIT ME.**
Tracks: Not Advised.
CD . . . . . . . . . . . . . . . . . . . NOVA 9029
Nova / Jan '93 / Jazzizit Organisation.

## Miller, Cat

**READY OR NOT.**
Tracks: Ready or not.
■ 12" . . . . . . . . . . . . . . . . . . . CRT 67
■ 7" . . . . . . . . . . . . . . . . . . . . CR 67
Creole / Sep '84.
■ 12" . . . . . . . . . . . . . . . . . . . CRT 87
Street Level / Mar '85.

## Miller, Marcus

**LOVIN' YOU.**
Tracks: Loving you / Suddenly.
■ 12" . . . . . . . . . . . . . . . . . . . W 0101T
WEA / Apr '83.

**SUDDENLY.**
Tracks: Not Advised.
■ LP . . . . . . . . . . . . . . . . . . . K 123806
Asylum / Mar '83.

**SUN DON'T LIE, THE.**
Tracks: Panther / Steveland / Rampage / Sun don't lie / Scoop / Mr. Pastorius / Funny (all she needs is love) / Moons / Teen town / Ju Ju / King is gone (for miles).
CD . . . . . . . . . . . . . . . . . . . FDM 365602
Dreyfus / Aug '93 / Topic Records / A.D.A. Distribution / Direct Distribution / New Note.
MC . . . . . . . . . . . . . . . . . . . FDM 365604
Dreyfus / Feb '94 / Topic Records / A.D.A. Distribution / Direct Distribution / New Note.

## Milli Vanilli

**ALL OR NOTHING.**
Tracks: Not Advised.
■ LP . . . . . . . . . . . . . . . . . . . .CTLP 11
■ CD . . . . . . . . . . . . . . . . . . . CCD 1696
■ MC . . . . . . . . . . . . . . . . . . . ZCTLP 11
Cool Tempo / Dec '88.

**ALL OR NOTHING.**
Tracks: All or nothing.
■ 7" . . . . . . . . . . . . . . . . . . . COOL 199
■ 12" . . . . . . . . . . . . . . . . . . . COOLX 199
■ CD Single . . . . . . . . . . . . . . . COOLCD 199
Cool Tempo / Feb '90.

**BABY, DON'T FORGET MY NUMBER.**
Tracks: Too much monkey business / Baby don't forget my number (radio mix) (Only available on 12" version).
■ 12" . . . . . . . . . . . . . . . . . . . COOLX 178
■ 7" . . . . . . . . . . . . . . . . . . . COOL 178
Cool Tempo / Dec '88.
■ 12" Remix . . . . . . . . . . . . . . . COOLXR 178
■ CD Single . . . . . . . . . . . . . . . COOLCD 178
Cool Tempo / Dec '88.

**BLAME IT ON THE RAIN.**
Tracks: Blame it on the rain / Money.
■ 7" . . . . . . . . . . . . . . . . . . . COOL 180
■ MC Single . . . . . . . . . . . . . . . COOLMC 180
■ 12" . . . . . . . . . . . . . . . . . . . COOLX 180
■ CD Single . . . . . . . . . . . . . . . COOLCD 180
Cool Tempo / Jun '89.

**GIRL I'M GONNA MISS YOU.**
Tracks: Girl I'm gonna miss you / Can't you feel my love.
■ 12" . . . . . . . . . . . . . . . . . . . COOLX 191
■ 7" . . . . . . . . . . . . . . . . . . . COOL 191
■ CD Single . . . . . . . . . . . . . . . COOLCD 191
■ MC Single . . . . . . . . . . . . . . . COOLMC 191
Cool Tempo / Sep '89.

**GIRL YOU KNOW IT'S TRUE.**
Tracks: Girl you know it's true (DJ edit) / Magic touch.
■ 12" . . . . . . . . . . . . . . . . . . . COOLX 170
■ 7" . . . . . . . . . . . . . . . . . . . COOL 170
■ 12" Remix . . . . . . . . . . . . . . . COOLXR 170
Cool Tempo / Dec '88.

**KEEP ON RUNNING.**
Tracks: Keep on running (7" & cassingle only) / End of good times / Keep on running (Running man mix) (12" & CD single only.) / Keep on running (Radio version) (12" & CD single only.) / Keep on running (Club mix) (12" & CD single only.).
■ 12" . . . . . . . . . . . . . . . . . . .CHS 123614
■ 7" . . . . . . . . . . . . . . . . . . . CHS 3614
■ CD Single . . . . . . . . . . . . . . . CHSCD 3614
■ MC Single . . . . . . . . . . . . . . . CHSMC 3614
Chrysalis / Dec '90.

**MILLI VANILLI.**
Tracks: All or nothing / Girl you know it's true / Baby don't forget my number / Girl I'm gonna miss you / Blame it on the rain.
VHS . . . . . . . . . . . . . . . . . . . CVHS 5031
Chrysalis Music Video / Dec '89 / EMI.

**TOO LATE.**
Tracks: Too late (7" & cassingle only) / Too late (club mix) (12" & CD single only) / Too late (radio mix) (12" & CD single only) / Too late (Saka/Wonder) (12" & CD single only) / Dance with the devil.
■ 12" . . . . . . . . . . . . . . . . . . .CHS 123686
■ 7" . . . . . . . . . . . . . . . . . . . CHS 3686
■ CD Single . . . . . . . . . . . . . . . CHSCD 3686
■ MC Single . . . . . . . . . . . . . . . CHSMC 3686
Chrysalis / Apr '91.

**TWO X TWO.**
Tracks: Can't you feel my love / Boy in the tree / Money / Dance with the devil / I'm gonna miss you / All or nothing / Baby don't forget my number / Dreams to remember / Is it love / Ma Baker / Girl you know it's true / Blame it on the rain (Club mix long version) / More than you'll ever know / Take it as it comes / It's your thing / Dreams to remember (Remix) / All or nothing (club mix) / Baby don't forget my number (Remix) / I'm gonna miss you (Remix) / Girl you know it's true (N.Y.Subway mix).
CD . . . . . . . . . . . . . . . . . . . CCD 1724
■ LP . . . . . . . . . . . . . . . . . . .CTLPD 1724
■ MC . . . . . . . . . . . . . . . . . . . ZTLP 1724
Cool Tempo / Oct '89 / EMI.

## Millionaires

**DON'T MESS WITH MY LOVE.**
Tracks: Don't mess with my love / This is love.
■ 7" . . . . . . . . . . . . . . . . . . . ADS 9003
Ardent / Aug '89.

## Mills, Barbara

**QUEEN OF FOOLS.**
Tracks: Queen of fools / Run baby run.
■ 7" . . . . . . . . . . . . . . . . . . . HEAT 9
Inferno (1) / Aug '82.

## Mills, Eleonore

**MR. RIGHT.**
Tracks: Mr. Right / Mr. Right (mix).
■ 12" . . . . . . . . . . . . . . . . . . . DEBTX 3020
■ 7" . . . . . . . . . . . . . . . . . . . DEBT 3020
Debut (1) / Apr '87.

**YOU CAN'T HAVE MY DREAMS.**
Tracks: You can't have my dreams (dub) / You can't have my dreams / You can't have my dreams (club mix) (Featured on 12" version only.) / You can't have my dreams (radio mix) (Featured on 12" version only.) / You can't have my dreams (sax dub) (Featured on 12" version only.) / You can't have my dreams (bonus beats) (Featured on 12" version only.).

■ 12″ . . . . . . . . . . . . . . . . . DEBTX 3043
■ 7″ . . . . . . . . . . . . . . . . . DEBT 3043
Debut (1) / Mar '88.

## Mills, Stephanie

A New Yorker born in 1957, Mills first won acclaim when she triumphed in the legendary Harlem Apollo amateur talent contests six weeks running; her reward being a tour spot in support of the Isley Brothers. She returned home, aged 17, to a Broadway role in *The Wiz*, a musical based on *The Wizard Of Oz*, and a deal with Paramount Records that produced a first 45, *I Knew It Was Love*. One album for Motown sparked little interest, but three more for 20th Century, produced by the Mtume/Lucas team, established her on the charts. *What'cha Gonna Do With My Lovin'* and *Put Your Body In It* were both fair-sized club hits, but were surpassed by the international success of *Never Knew Love Like This Before* in '80. She also married Jeffrey Daniel, of Shalamar fame, but they stayed together only just over a year. The early '80s saw Stephanie on Casablanca records, her biggest hit being *The Medicine Song* from the '84 album *I've Got The Cure*. Around this time she also returned to *The Wiz*, enjoying a Broadway revival. From '85 Mills signed to MCA, and a series of albums installed her among the top-selling and most artistically-respected of female vocalists. *If I Were Your Woman* in '87, featuring *I Feel Good All Over* and *(You're Puttin') A Rush On Me*, is generally regarded as her finest work, though *Home* ('89) runs it close. She also recorded a couple of duets with Robert Brookins, including a version of Flack/Hathaway's *Where Is The Love*. Recently she released a gospel album, *Personal Inspirations*, and her final album for MCA before being dropped in '94 was *Something Real*.

### ALL DAY, ALL NIGHT.
**Tracks:** All day, all night.
■ 12″ . . . . . . . . . . . . . . . MCST 1778
■ CD Single . . . . . . . . . . . . . MCSTD 1778
■ MC Single . . . . . . . . . . . . . MCSC 1778
MCA / Jun '93.

### BIT BIT BIT.
**Tracks:** Bit by bit / Exotic states.
■ 12″ . . . . . . . . . . . . . . . .MCAT 990
■ 7″ . . . . . . . . . . . . . . . . MCA 990
MCA / Aug '85.

### COLLECTION: STEPHANIE MILLS.
**Tracks:** Not Advised.
■ CD . . . . . . . . . . . . . . . . CCSCD 337
■ MC . . . . . . . . . . . . . . . .CCSMC 337
Castle Collector Series / Jun '92.

### D-A-N-C-I-N-G.
**Tracks:** D-A-N-C-I-N-G / Better than ever.
■ 12″ . . . . . . . . . . . . . . . . TCD 2464
20th Century / Aug '80.

### FOR THE FIRST TIME.
**Tracks:** I took my strength from you / Living on plastic / No one remembers my name / If you can learn how to cry / Loneliness remembers (what happiness forgets) / This empty place / Way I feel about you / I see you for the first time / All the way to Paradise / Please let go.
■ LP . . . . . . . . . . . . . . . . STMS 5069
■ MC . . . . . . . . . . . . . . . CSTMS 5069
Motown / Jul '82.

### HEART AND SOUL OF STEPHANIE MILLS.
**Tracks:** Not Advised.
■ CD . . . . . . . . . . . . . . . . KNCD 12064
■ MC . . . . . . . . . . . . . . . .KNMC 12064
Knight / Jul '91.

### HOME.
**Tracks:** Not Advised.
■ LP . . . . . . . . . . . . . . . .MCA 6312
■ CD . . . . . . . . . . . . . . . .MCAD 6312
■ MC . . . . . . . . . . . . . . . .MCAC 6312
MCA / Jul '89.

### I FEEL GOOD ALL OVER.
**Tracks:** I feel good all over / Secret lady.
■ 12″ . . . . . . . . . . . . . . . MCAT 1213
MCA / Nov '87.
■ 7″ . . . . . . . . . . . . . . . .MCA 1213
MCA / Nov '87.

---

### I'VE GOT THE CURE.
**Tracks:** Medicine song / Edge of the razor / In my life / Give it half a chance / You just might need a friend / Everlasting love / Rough trade / Undercover.
■ CD . . . . . . . . . . . . . . . . 822 421-2
Club / Dec '84.
■ LP . . . . . . . . . . . . . . . . JABL 5
Club / Dec '84.

### IF I WERE YOUR WOMAN.
**Tracks:** I feel good all over / If I were your woman / Rush on me, A (You're puttin') / Jesse / Secret lady / Touch me now / Running for your love / Can't change my ways.
■ CD . . . . . . . . . . . . . . . . DMCF 3385
■ LP . . . . . . . . . . . . . . . . MCF 3385
■ MC . . . . . . . . . . . . . . . . MCFC 3385
MCA / Aug '87.

### IN MY LIFE.
**Tracks:** Not Advised.
■ CD . . . . . . . . . . . . . . . . 832 519-2
■ LP . . . . . . . . . . . . . . . .JABB 25
■ MC . . . . . . . . . . . . . . . .JABBC 25
Mercury / Apr '88.

### IN MY LIFE.
**Tracks:** In my life / Everlasting love / Never knew love like this before (Only on 12″ single.) / Watcha gonna do with my lovin' (Only on 12″ single.)
■ 12″ . . . . . . . . . . . . . . . . JABX 9
■ 7″ . . . . . . . . . . . . . . . . JAB 9
Club / Nov '84.

### MEDICINE SONG.
**Tracks:** Medicine song.
■ 12″ . . . . . . . . . . . . . . . . JABX 8
■ 7″ . . . . . . . . . . . . . . . . JAB 8
Club / Aug '84.

### MEDICINE SONG (OLD GOLD).
**Tracks:** Medicine song / I never knew love like this before.
12″ . . . . . . . . . . . . . . . . .OG 4162
Old Gold / Mar '90 / Pickwick.

### MERCILESS.
**Tracks:** How come you don't call me anymore / Never get enough of you / Eternal love / His name is Michael / Here I am / My body / Do you love him / Pilot error / Since we've been together.
■ LP . . . . . . . . . . . . . . . . 811 364 1
Casablanca / Nov '83.

### MOVIN' IN THE RIGHT DIRECTION.
**Tracks:** Movin' in the right direction / You do it to me.
■ 7″ . . . . . . . . . . . . . . . . ABC 4227
ABC Records / Aug '78.

### NEVER DO YOU WRONG.
**Tracks:** Not Advised.
■ CD Single . . . . . . . . . . . . . MCSTD 1767
■ MC Single . . . . . . . . . . . . . MCSC 1767
MCA / Feb '93.

### NEVER KNEW LOVE LIKE THIS BEFORE.
**Tracks:** Never knew love like this before / Still mine.
■ 12″ . . . . . . . . . . . . . . . . TCD 2460
■ 7″ . . . . . . . . . . . . . . . . TC 2460
20th Century / Oct '80.

### NEVER KNEW LOVE LIKE THIS BEFORE (OLD GOLD) (see under Lipps Inc.).

### SOMETHING IN THE WAY YOU MAKE ME FEEL.
**Tracks:** Something in the way you make me feel.
■ 12″ . . . . . . . . . . . . . . . . MCAT 1375
■ 7″ . . . . . . . . . . . . . . . . MCA 1375
MCA / Nov '89.

### SOMETHING REAL.
**Tracks:** Never do you wrong / All day, all night / Somewhere in this broken heart / Stone cold woman / Love the hurt away / Heartache / Policy of love / I found a new love / All in how much we give / 24-hour woman / Never gonna give you up / I just want love.
CD . . . . . . . . . . . . . . . . . MCD 10690
LP . . . . . . . . . . . . . . . . . MCA 10690
■ MC . . . . . . . . . . . . . . . . MCC 10690
MCA / May '93 / BMG.

### STEPHANIE MILLS.
**Tracks:** Not Advised.
■ LP . . . . . . . . . . . . . . . . T 700
MC. . . . . . . . . . . . . . . . . . C 700
20th Century / May '81.
CD . . . . . . . . . . . . . . . . . MCAD 5669
MCA / Apr '87 / BMG.

---

### SWEET SENSATION.
**Tracks:** Sweet sensation / Wish that you were mine
■ 12″ . . . . . . . . . . . . . . . . TCD 244?
20th Century / May '80.

### SWEET SENSATION.
**Tracks:** Sweet sensation / Try my love / I just wanna say / Wish that you were mine / D-a-n-c-i-n / Still mine / Never knew love like this before / Mixture of love.
■ LP . . . . . . . . . . . . . . . . T 60.
20th Century / Dec '80.

### TANTALIZINGLY HOT.
**Tracks:** Last night / Still lovin' you / Keep away girl / You can't run from my love / True love don't come easy / Ole love / Your love is always new / I can give back the love I feel.
■ LP . . . . . . . . . . . . . . . . CANS ?
MC. . . . . . . . . . . . . . . . . . CANSC
Casablanca / Jul '82.

### THIS EMPTY PLACE.
**Tracks:** This empty place / I see you for the first time
■ 7″ . . . . . . . . . . . . . . . .TMG 102?
Tamla Motown / Feb '76.

### TOP OF MY LIST.
**Tracks:** Top of my list / Magic.
■ 12″ . . . . . . . . . . . . . . . . TCD 250?
■ 7″ . . . . . . . . . . . . . . . . TC 250?
20th Century / Jul '81.

### TWO HEARTS.
**Tracks:** Two hearts / Just wanna say.
■ 12″ . . . . . . . . . . . . . . . . TCD 249?
■ 7″ . . . . . . . . . . . . . . . . TC 249?
20th Century / May '81.

### YOU CAN GET OVER.
**Tracks:** You can get over / Deeper inside your love
■ 7″ . . . . . . . . . . . . . . . . TC 243?
20th Century / Dec '79.

### YOU CAN'T RUN FROM MY LOVE.
**Tracks:** You can't run from my love.
■ 12″ . . . . . . . . . . . . . . . . CANX 101
■ 7″ . . . . . . . . . . . . . . . . CAN 101
20th Century / Jul '82.

### YOU'RE PUTTIN' A RUSH ON ME.
**Tracks:** Rush on me, A (You're puttin') / Rush on me, A (You're puttin') (Inst).
■ 12″ . . . . . . . . . . . . . . . . MCAT 118?
■ 7″ . . . . . . . . . . . . . . . . MCA 118?
MCA / Aug '87.

## Mimms, Garnet

### ALL ABOUT LOVE.
**Tracks:** All about love / Truth hurts.
■ 7″ . . . . . . . . . . . . . . . . UP 117?
United Artists / Feb '67.

### AS LONG AS I HAVE YOU.
**Tracks:** As long as I have you / Yesterday.
■ 7″ . . . . . . . . . . . . . . . . UP 118?
United Artists / Jul '67.

### CRY BABY.
**Tracks:** Cry baby / Don't change your heart.
■ 7″ . . . . . . . . . . . . . . . . UP 103?
United Artists / Oct '63.

### I'LL TAKE GOOD CARE OF YOU.
**Tracks:** I'll take good care of you / Looking for you
■ 7″ . . . . . . . . . . . . . . . . UP 113?
United Artists / '66.

### IT WAS EASIER TO HURT HER.
**Tracks:** It was easier to hurt her.
■ 7″ . . . . . . . . . . . . . . . . UP 109?
United Artists / May '65.

### ROLL WITH THE PUNCHES.
**Tracks:** All about love / One woman man / Don't change your heart / Prove it to me / Truth hurts / There is something on my mind / Looking for you / Roll with the punches / (It won't hurt) half as much / Please send me someone to love / Only your love / keep wanting you / Until you were gone / Anytime you want me / I'll make it up to you / Welcome home.
■ LP . . . . . . . . . . . . . . . . CRB 112?
Charly R&B / Apr '86.

### WARM AND SOULFUL: THE BEST OF GARNET MIMMS.
**Tracks:** Cry baby / For your precious love / Baby don't you weep / Tell me baby / Quiet place / One girl / Look away / Little bit of soap / It was easier to hurt her / That goes to show you / I'll take good care of you / More than a miracle / As long as I have you

---

■ DELETE

It's just a matter of time / It's been such a long way home / My baby.
- ■ MC . . . . . . . . . . . . . . . . . . EG 2602924
- ■ LP . . . . . . . . . . . . . . . . . . EG 2602921
Liberty / Oct '84.

**WHAT IT IS.**
Tracks: What it is / What it is (instrumental).
- ■ 7" . . . . . . . . . . . . . . . . . . . . . . .109
Arista / Jun '77.

## Mint Condition

**BREAKIN' MY HEART (PRETTY BROWN EYES).**
Tracks: Breakin' my heart (pretty brown eyes).
- ■ 12" . . . . . . . . . . . . . . . . . . PERT 664
- ■ 7" . . . . . . . . . . . . . . . . . . PERSS 664
- ■ CD Single . . . . . . . . . . . . . . PERD 664
- ■ MC Single . . . . . . . . . . . . . PERCS 664
Perspective / Mar '92.

## Miracles

**LOVE MACHINE.**
Tracks: 25 miles / Love machine.
- ■ 7" . . . . . . . . . . . . . . . . . . TMG 1015
Tamla Motown / Nov '75.

**LOVE MACHINE (PART 1).**
Tracks: Love machine (part 1).
- ■ 7" . . . . . . . . . . . . . . . . . . ZB 41919
Motown / Apr '88.

**POWER OF MUSIC.**
Tracks: Power of music / Love to make love / Can I pretend / Gossip / Let the children play / Street of love / You need a miracle.
- ■ LP . . . . . . . . . . . . . . . . . STML 12038
Motown / Nov '76.

**WHERE ARE YOU GOING TO MY LOVE.**
Tracks: Where are you going to my love / Up again.
- ■ 7" . . . . . . . . . . . . . . . . . . TMG 940
Tamla Motown / Jan '75.

**WOMEN (MAKE THE WORLD GO ROUND).**
Tracks: Women (make the world go round) / I can touch the sky.
- ■ 7" . . . . . . . . . . . . . . . . . . CBS 5200
CBS / May '77.

## Mirage

**AS FROM NOW.**
Tracks: As from now / Luckiest people.
- ■ 12" . . . . . . . . . . . . . . . . . COPD 156
Solid Gold (1) / Dec '81.
- ■ 12" . . . . . . . . . . . . . . . . . COPDIS 006
- ■ 7" . . . . . . . . . . . . . . . . . . COP 006
Copasetic / Jun '82.

**SUMMER GROOVES.**
Tracks: Summer grooves / Love and devotion.
- ■ 12" . . . . . . . . . . . . . . . . . . FM 12 7
- ■ 7" . . . . . . . . . . . . . . . . . . . FM 7
Flamingo / Aug '88.

## Mirettes

**HE'S ALRIGHT WITH ME.**
Tracks: He's alright with me / Your kind ain't no good.
- ■ 7" . . . . . . . . . . . . . . . . . . CS 9039
Contempo (1) / Feb '76.

**IN THE MIDNIGHT HOUR.**
Tracks: In the midnight hour / Real thing / First love / Tweedle dee / To love somebody / Whole new thing / Somewhere (and 3 others).
- ■ LP . . . . . . . . . . . . . . . . . MUPS 344
MCA / Nov '68.

## Mistura

**COAST TO COAST.**
Tracks: Coast to coast (mixes).
- ■ 12" . . . . . . . . . . . . . . . . . MW 007
Mo Wax / Aug '93.

**FLASHER, THE.**
Tracks: Flasher / Life is a song worth singing.
- ■ 7" . . . . . . . . . . . . . . . . . . RT 30
Route / May '76.

## Mitchell, Barbara

**HIGH ON LOVE.**
Tracks: Ace of my heart / High on love / Never had a love like this before / Can't help the way I feel / I need some loving / Take your time / Don't look me over.
- ■ LP . . . . . . . . . . . . . . . . . 826 887-1
- ■ MC . . . . . . . . . . . . . . . . . 826 887-4
Club / Jun '86.

## Mitchell, Billy

**FACES.**
Tracks: Not Advised.
- ■ LP . . . . . . . . . . . . . . . . . VR 2501
Optimism / Oct '87.

**IN FOCUS.**
Tracks: Not Advised.
- ■ CD . . . . . . . . . . . . . . . . . OPCD 2502
- ■ LP . . . . . . . . . . . . . . . . . OP 2502
Optimism / Apr '89.

**VINTAGE PIANO VOL.3 (Mitchell, Billy & Paul Lingle).**
Tracks: Not Advised.
- ■ LP . . . . . . . . . . . . . . . . . ESR 1203
Euphonic / Apr '79.

## Mitchell, Prince Phillip

Another of the great cult soulmen, Phillip Mitchell hails from Louisville, Kentucky and, now in his 49th year, is still intermittently a songwriter. He began as an artist, however, recording for numerous labels in the '60s: sides on Shout, Smash and Lollipop Records each became Northern Soul favourites. His songs for Millie Jackson gave him a higher profile in the '70s - Mitchell contributing *I'm Tired Of Hiding* to the *Caught Up* era - and he wrote Mel & Tim's huge soul chart hit *Starting All Over Again*. Indeed, he profited from the era's penchant for 'slippin' around' songs, even cutting his own single on the subject for Event in '75, *There's Another In My Life/If We Get Caught I Don't Know You*. After a brief appearance with Norman Connors on his own tune *Once I've Been There* in '77, he signed a solo deal with Atlantic; cutting one memorable album, *Make It Good*, featuring the original version of the Ben E. King/AWB hit *Star In The Ghetto* (and one not so memorable, *Top Of The Line*). The disco period quietened him considerably, but he returned in the late '80s to record a couple of albums from Ichiban, including the excellent *Devastation*.

**DEVASTATION.**
Tracks: Body shop / I taught her everything she knows / Show must go on / In her own way / This is our song / I can't get used to sleeping by myself / You're gonna come back to love / She was my lady.
- ■ LP . . . . . . . . . . . . . . . . . ICH 1004
- MC . . . . . . . . . . . . . . . . . ZCICH 1004
Ichiban / Aug '87 / A.D.A. Distribution / Pinnacle / ACD Trading Ltd. / Koch International / Direct Distribution.

**LONER.**
Tracks: While the cat's away / Starting from scratch / Come to bed / Can't nobody love you better than me / Never let her down / Nothing hurts like love / You did what you had to do / Loner / She's a party animal.
- LP . . . . . . . . . . . . . . . . . ICH 1110
- MC . . . . . . . . . . . . . . . . . ICH 1110MC
Ichiban / Jun '91 / A.D.A. Distribution / Pinnacle / ACD Trading Ltd. / Koch International / Direct Distribution.
- CD . . . . . . . . . . . . . . . . . CDICH 1110
Ichiban / Oct '93 / A.D.A. Distribution / Pinnacle / ACD Trading Ltd. / Koch International / Direct Distribution.

**MAKE IT GOOD.**
Tracks: Star in the ghetto / You're all I got in the world / One on one / Falling from heaven / You'll throw bricks at him / Make it good / If I can't be your man / Only smoke remains.
- ■ LP . . . . . . . . . . . . . . . . . SD 19160
Atlantic / '78.

## Mitchell, Vernessa

**BE FOR REAL.**
Tracks: Be for real.
- ■ 12" . . . . . . . . . . . . . . . . . EXPAND 30
Expansion / Jul '92.

## Mitchell, Willie

Cornerstone of '60s/'70s soul and R&B. Born in Mississippi, Mitchell was raised in Memphis, whose Hi label he joined in early '60s; his driving instrumentals became fixtures on U.S. soul chart. Although Hi was overshadowed by Stax/Volt, two Mitchell singles crossed over to Top 40: *20-75* in '64 and *Soul Serenade* in '68. Team enjoyed greatest success in early '70s with new singers, Al Green and Ann Peebles. Former chalked up eight million-sellers between '71-'74, mostly co-written by Mitchell, Green and ex-MG Al Jackson. By '75, Mitchell's 'Memphis Sound' was wearing thin and - bar instrumental hit *The Champion* - his creative career tailed off. However, he resumed production in '80s for new label Waylo, notably Green's Grammy-winning *Going Away* in '87.

**BAD EYE.**
Tracks: Bad eye / Sugar-T.
- ■ 7" . . . . . . . . . . . . . . . . . HLU 10039
London-American / May '66.

**CHAMPION, THE.**
Tracks: Champion.
- ■ 7" . . . . . . . . . . . . . . . . . HLU 10545
London-American / Jan '76.

**EVERYTHING IS GONNA BE ALRIGHT.**
Tracks: Everything is gonna be alright / That driving beat.
- ■ 7" . . . . . . . . . . . . . . . . . HLU 10004
London-American / '65.

**LIVE.**
Tracks: 20-75 / My girl / Mustang Sally / Mercy mercy mercy / Smokie / Late date / Tequila / Rum daddy / Bootleg / Honky tonk / I'll be in trouble / Pin head.
- ■ LP . . . . . . . . . . . . . . . . . SHU 8368
London / Oct '68.

**MERCY.**
Tracks: Mercy / Sticks and stones.
- ■ 7" . . . . . . . . . . . . . . . . . HLU 10085
London / Oct '66.

**ON TOP.**
Tracks: Take five / Poppin' / Canadian sunset / Ain't too proud to beg / Louie Louie / Big power house / 30-6-90 / Who's making love / I say a little prayer / Come see about me / I wish it would rain / Sunshine of your love.
- ■ LP . . . . . . . . . . . . . . . . . SHU 8388
London / May '69.

**OOH BABY YOU TURN ME ON.**
Tracks: Not Advised.
- CD . . . . . . . . . . . . . . . . . HIUKCD 132
Demon / Jun '93 / Pinnacle / A.D.A. Distribution.

**SOLID SOUL.**
Tracks: Prayer meetin' / Grazing in the grass / Windy / Sunrise serenade / Horse / Groovin' / San Ho-Zay / Uphard / Monkey jump / Strawberry soul / Hideaway / Willie-wam.
- ■ LP . . . . . . . . . . . . . . . . . SHU 6372
London / Mar '69.
- CD . . . . . . . . . . . . . . . . . HIUKCD 120
Demon / Jul '91 / Pinnacle / A.D.A. Distribution.

**SOUL BAG.**
Tracks: Apollo X / One mint julep / I'm a midnight mover / Cherry tree / Young people / Blue blue light / Everyday people / Knock on wood / Grand slam / Honey pot / Hawaii five-o / Set free.
- ■ LP . . . . . . . . . . . . . . . . . SHU 8408
London / Mar '70.

**SOUL SERENADE.**
Tracks: Soul serenade.
- ■ 7" . . . . . . . . . . . . . . . . . HLU 10186
London-American / Apr '68.

**SOUL SERENADE.**
Tracks: Ooh baby you turn me on / Soul finger / Cleo's mood / Slippin' and slidin' / Have you ever had the blues / Soul serenade / Willie's mood / Sunny / Pearl time / Papa's got a brand new bag / Respect / Toddlin'.
- ■ LP . . . . . . . . . . . . . . . . . SHU 8365
London / Sep '68.

**SPARKLE.**
Tracks: Sparkle / Reaching out / Honey bear / Midnight rhapsody / Give the world more love / Sugar candy / Expressions / Happy hour.
- CD . . . . . . . . . . . . . . . . . CSCD-517
- ■ LP . . . . . . . . . . . . . . . . . C5-517

**MC.** . . . . . . . . . . . . . . . . . . .**C5K-517**
C5 / Jun '88 / Pinnacle.

**THAT DRIVING BEAT.**
Tracks: That driving beat / 20-75 / Percolatin' / Champion / Ooh baby you turn me on / Mercy / 30-60-90 / Young people / Everything is gonna be alright / Bad eye / Buster Browne / Soul serenade / At the woodchopper's ball / Up-hard / Bum daddy / Crawl.
■ **LP** . . . . . . . . . . . . . . . . . . .**HIUKLP 408**
Hi / Nov '86.

**THAT DRIVING BEAT.**
Tracks: That driving beat.
■ **7"** . . . . . . . . . . . . . . . . . . .**.HCS 104**
Hi-Cream / Jun '80.

**WALKIN' WITH WILLIE.**
Tracks: Not Advised.
**CD** . . . . . . . . . . . . . . . . . . . **RCCD 3009**
Rollercoaster / Jun '94 / Rollercoaster Records / Swift / Topic Records.

### Mizelle, Cyndi

**THIS COULD BE THE NIGHT.**
Tracks: This could be the night.
■ **12"** . . . . . . . . . . . . . . . . . . . **A 9635 T**
■ **7"** . . . . . . . . . . . . . . . . . . .**.A 9635**
Atlantic / Mar '85.

### Mo & Beev

**COMIN' ON TO ME.**
Tracks: Comin' on to me.
■ **12"** . . . . . . . . . . . . . . . . . . . **RUMAT 63**
Rumour / Feb '93.

### Mob

**GIVE IT TO ME.**
Tracks: Give it to me / I'd like to see more of you.
■ **7"** . . . . . . . . . . . . . . . . . . . **2001169**
Polydor / Apr '71.

**MOB.**
Tracks: I'd like to see more of you / Once a man, twice a child / Give it to me / Maybe I'll find a way / Good time baby / I dig everything about you / For a little while / Love's got a hold on me / Lost / Back on the road again.
■ **LP** . . . . . . . . . . . . . . . . . . .**.2344 001**
Polydor / Mar '71.

**MONEY.**
Tracks: Money / Once a man, twice a child.
■ **7"** . . . . . . . . . . . . . . . . . . .**.2001 200**
Polydor / Jun '71.

**ROCK & ROLLER.**
Tracks: Rock & roller / Just one good woman.
■ **7"** . . . . . . . . . . . . . . . . . . . **PVT 18**
Private Stock / May '75.

### Modern Rocketry

**CUBA LIBRE.**
Tracks: Cuba libre / Homosexuality.
■ **12"** . . . . . . . . . . . . . . . . . . .**.GRY 003**
Greyhound / Jan '87.

**HOMOSEXUALITY.**
Tracks: Not Advised.
■ **LP** . . . . . . . . . . . . . . . . . . . **20052**
ZYX / Feb '86.

**HOMOSEXUALITY.**
Tracks: Homosexuality.
■ **12"** . . . . . . . . . . . . . . . . . . . **ZYX 5311**
ZYX / Nov '85.

### Modernique

**LOVE'S GONNA GET YOU.**
Tracks: Love's gonna get you / Love's gonna get you (instrumental).
■ **7"** . . . . . . . . . . . . . . . . . . . **TEN 123**
■ **12"** . . . . . . . . . . . . . . . . . . . **TENT 123**
10 / Sep '86.

**MODERNIQUE.**
Tracks: Tossin' 'n turnin' / One hot ticket / I believe in love / Call it what you want / Linda, my love / Take a risk on love / Falling in love / From friends to lovers / You can call on me.
■ **LP** . . . . . . . . . . . . . . . . . . . **K 925633 1**
**MC.** . . . . . . . . . . . . . . . . . . . **K 925633 4**
Sire / Dec '87 / WEA.

### Modulations

**ROUGH OUT HERE.**
Tracks: Rough out here / Head on collision with heartbreak / Love at last / I'll always love you / I'm hopelessly in love / I can't fight your love / Worth your weight in gold / Those were the best days of my life / Share what you got, keep what you need / What good am I / Your love has me locked up.
**CD** . . . . . . . . . . . . . . . . . . .**NEMCD 628**
Sequel / Nov '92 / Total / BMG.

### Mohawks

**CHAMP, THE.**
Tracks: Champ.
■ **12"** . . . . . . . . . . . . . . . . . . . **PMT 1**
■ **7"** . . . . . . . . . . . . . . . . . . .**.PM 1**
Pama / Jan '87.

### Moment Of Truth

**MOMENT OF TRUTH.**
Tracks: Chained to your love / Lovin' you is killing me / At long last / You got me hummin' / Helplessly / You're all I want to be / Come on in / So much for love.
■ **LP** . . . . . . . . . . . . . . . . . . . **SZS 5509**
Salsoul / Sep '77.

### Moments

Sweet soul vocal trio who first attracted attention in late 1960s with singles like *Sunday*. 1970 brought them U.S. million-seller with *Love On A Two Way Street*. Signed to Sylvia Robinson's All Platinum organisation (forerunner of Sugarhill Records). Moments were chart regulars in early '70s, scoring crossover hit in '74 with *Sexy Mama*. Following year, with All Platinum gaining momentum in Britain, trio zoomed to No. 3 with *Girls*; first of three Top 10 hits. Shortly afterwards, Harry Ray, Al Goodman and Billy Brown abandoned Moments billing to record as Ray, Goodman and Brown. Trio continued into '80s, harmonies intact.

**BEST OF THE MOMENTS.**
Tracks: Dolly my love / Don't cry out loud / Girls / I don't wanna go / It doesn't rain in my backyard / Jack in the box / Look at me, I'm in love / Nine times / Sexy Mama / Sweet, sweet lady / Two way street / With you / You beat me to the punch.
■ **LP** . . . . . . . . . . . . . . . . . . . **9109407**
All Platinum / Oct '77.

**DOLLY MY LOVE.**
Tracks: Dolly my love.
■ **7"** . . . . . . . . . . . . . . . . . . .**.6146 306**
All Platinum / Jul '75.

**GIRLS.**
Tracks: Girls / Dolly my love.
■ **7"** . . . . . . . . . . . . . . . . . . .**.6146 302**
All Platinum / Mar '75.
■ **7"** . . . . . . . . . . . . . . . . . . . **FBS 16**
Flashback / Jan '83.

**GIRLS (OLD GOLD) (Moments & Whatnauts).**
Tracks: Girls / Dolly my love / Jack in the box.
**12"** . . . . . . . . . . . . . . . . . . .**.OG 4153**
Old Gold / Jan '90 / Pickwick.

**GREATEST HITS: MOMENTS.**
Tracks: Lovely way she loves / My thing / If I didn't care / Nine times / To you with love / Girls / Jack in the box / Gotta find a way / All I have / Sexy Mama / Love on a two way street / With you / Life and breath / I do / Not on the outside / Lucky me / What's your name / Dolly my love / Look at me (I'm in love) / Girls (french lyrics).
**CD** . . . . . . . . . . . . . . . . . . .**NEMCD 614**
Sequel / May '91 / Total / BMG.

**GREATEST HITS: MOMENTS.**
Tracks: Not Advised.
■ **LP** . . . . . . . . . . . . . . . . . . . **DET 202**
Chess (Charly) / '87.

**IT DON'T RAIN IN MY BACKYARD.**
Tracks: It don't rain in my backyard / Next time I see you.
■ **7"** . . . . . . . . . . . . . . . . . . .**.6146 322**
All Platinum / Jun '77.

**JACK IN THE BOX.**
Tracks: Jack in the box / Love on a two way street.
■ **7"** . . . . . . . . . . . . . . . . . . .**.6146 318**
All Platinum / Jan '77.

### Monk, T.S.

**BON BON VIE.**
Tracks: Bon bon vie / Stay free of his love.
■ **7"** . . . . . . . . . . . . . . . . . . . **K 11653**
Mirage (USA) / Mar '81.

**CANDIDATE FOR LOVE.**
Tracks: Candidate for love / Last of the wicked romancers.
■ **7"** . . . . . . . . . . . . . . . . . . . **K 11648**
Mirage (USA) / Apr '81.

**HOUSE OF MUSIC.**
Tracks: Bon bon vie / Candidate for love / Hot night in the city / Last of the wicked romancers / Can't keep my hands to myself / Stay free of his love / House of music.
■ **LP** . . . . . . . . . . . . . . . . . . . **K 50773**
Atlantic / Feb '81.

**MORE OF THE GOOD LIFE.**
Tracks: Everybody get on up and dance / Too much too soon / Falling in love with you / You / Oh Oh Oh speedo / First lady of love / More to love / You're asking me, I'm askin' you.
■ **LP** . . . . . . . . . . . . . . . . . . . **K 50844**
Mirage (USA) / Feb '82.

**TAKE ONE.**
Tracks: Monaco / Skippy / Infra-rae / Waiting / Boa / Round midnight / Jodi / Bear cat / Capetown ambush / Shoutin' / Minor's holiday / Think of one.
■ **CD** . . . . . . . . . . . . . . . . . . . **CDP 7996142**
Blue Note / Sep '92.

**TOO MUCH TOO SOON.**
Tracks: Too much too soon / First lady of love.
■ **7"** . . . . . . . . . . . . . . . . . . . **K 11693**
Mirage (USA) / Jan '82.

### Monkey Business

**AIN'T NO FUN.**
Tracks: Ain't no fun.
■ **12"** . . . . . . . . . . . . . . . . . . . **DOR 001**
Dorado / Feb '92.

### Montgomery, Jack

**DEARLY BELOVED.**
Tracks: Dearly beloved / That's no way to treat a girl.
■ **7"** . . . . . . . . . . . . . . . . . . . **TOWN 102**
Kent / Apr '85.

### Moonglows

**LOOK, IT'S THE MOONGLOWS.**
Tracks: Love is is a river / Blue velvet / This is love / When I'm with you / I'll stop wanting you / Don't say goodbye / Ten commandments of love / Kiss me baby / Penny arcade / Mean old blues / Sweeter than words / Cold feet.
■ **LP** . . . . . . . . . . . . . . . . . . . **GCH 8045**
**MC.** . . . . . . . . . . . . . . . . . . . **GCHK 78045**
Chess (Charly) / Oct '87 / Charly.

### Moonliters

**OH WHAT A NIGHT.**
Tracks: Oh what a night / Miss you / Open the door to your heart (Available on 12" only.) / Lonely boy (Available on CD single only.).
■ **12"** . . . . . . . . . . . . . . . . . . . **YZ 327T**
■ **7"** . . . . . . . . . . . . . . . . . . . **YZ 327**
■ **CD Single** . . . . . . . . . . . . . . . . . . . **YZ 327CD**
WEA / Nov '88.

### LATE NIGHT SOUL.
Tracks: Best thing for me / This old house / Don't let it get you down / Mama I miss you / Where / Girl I'm gonna miss you / Girl don't go / Baby I'm a want you / Look what you've done / How can I love you / Meeting you was no mistake / Patty / Look at me / I feel so good again / Beautiful woman / I could have loved you / I'll be around / Just because he wants to make love.
**CD** . . . . . . . . . . . . . . . . . . .**NEMCD 626**
Sequel / Jun '92 / Total / BMG.

**LOOK AT ME (I'M IN LOVE).**
Tracks: Look at me (I'm in love).
■ **7"** . . . . . . . . . . . . . . . . . . .**.6146 309**
All Platinum / Oct '75.

■ DELETED

## Moore, Ben

### PURIFIED.
Tracks: I've got a winner in you / Slipping away / Got to see if I can get mommy (to come back home) / Love music / I ain't got to love nobody else / Slow dancing / Get closer / Keeping in touch / Easy as pie.
■ LP . . . . . . . . . . . . . . . . . . . . . . . . . DJF 20552
DJM / Jan '79.

### SLIPPIN' AWAY.
Tracks: Slippin' away / Love music.
■ 7" . . . . . . . . . . . . . . . . . . . . . . . . . DJS 10882
DJM / Feb '79.

## Moore, Chante

### LOVE'S TAKEN OVER.
Tracks: Love's taken over.
■ 12" . . . . . . . . . . . . . . . . . . . . . . . . MCST 1744
■ CD Single . . . . . . . . . . . . . . . . MCSTD 1744
■ MC Single . . . . . . . . . . . . . . . . . MCSC 1744
MCA / Mar '93.

### PRECIOUS.
Tracks: Loves taken over (The quiet storm mix) (Extra track on CD only).
■ MC. . . . . . . . . . . . . . . . . . . . . . MCAC 10605
■ CD . . . . . . . . . . . . . . . . . . . . . . MCAD 10605
■ LP . . . . . . . . . . . . . . . . . . . . . . . MCA 10605
MCA / Oct '92.

## Moore, Dorothy

Orignally based at Mississippi's Milaco Records, Moore shot to fame in 1976 with Transatlantic Top Five ballad *Misty Blue*. Album of same name, another U.S. hit, yielded second U.K. hit with Willie Nelson's *Funny How Time Slips Away*. After successful cover of Addrisi Brothers' *I Believe You*, Moore's lacklustre material failed to match earlier hits and she disappeared from limelight.

### DOROTHY MOORE.
Tracks: Let the music play / I believe you / Love me / Make it soon / With pen in hand / 1-2-3 (you and me) / Loving you is just an old habit / Daddy's eyes / For old time's sake / Too blind to see.
■ LP . . . . . . . . . . . . . . . . . . . . . . . EPC 82356
Epic / Nov '77.

### DOROTHY MOORE ALBUM, THE.
Tracks: Misty blue / I dont want to be with nobody but you / Too much love / Laugh it off / Only time you ever say you love me / I believe you / Funny how time slips away / Dark end of the street / Ain't that mother's luck / Enough woman left / It's so good / With pen in hand.
■ LP . . . . . . . . . . . . . . . . . . . . . . . CBS 31776
■ MC. . . . . . . . . . . . . . . . . . . . . . . .40 31776
CBS / Feb '80.

### FEEL THE LOVE.
Tracks: Not Advised.
LP . . . . . . . . . . . . . . . . . . . . . . . . . MAL 7455
MC. . . . . . . . . . . . . . . . . . . . . . . . MALC 7455
Malaco / Jan '91 / C.M. Distribution / Charly / Pinnacle.
CD . . . . . . . . . . . . . . . . . . . . . . . MALCD 7455
Malaco / Mar '93 / C.M. Distribution / Charly / Pinnacle.

### FOR OLD TIME SAKE.
Tracks: For old time sake / Daddy's eyes.
■ 7" . . . . . . . . . . . . . . . . . . . . . . . . . CS 2107
Contempo (1) / Jan '77.

### FUNNY HOW TIME SLIPS AWAY.
Tracks: Funny how time slips away.
■ 7" . . . . . . . . . . . . . . . . . . . . . . . . . CS 2092
Contempo (1) / Oct '76.

### I BELIEVE YOU.
Tracks: I believe you / Love me.
■ 7" . . . . . . . . . . . . . . . . . . . . . . . EPC 5573
Epic / Oct '77.

### LAUGH IT OFF.
Tracks: Laugh it off / 1,2,3, you and me.
■ 7" . . . . . . . . . . . . . . . . . . . . . . . . MAL 003
Malaco / Feb '83.

### LET THE MUSIC PLAY.
Tracks: Let the music play / Too blind to see.
■ 7" . . . . . . . . . . . . . . . . . . . . . . . EPC 6366
Epic / Jun '78.

### LOVING TIME.
Tracks: Loving time / Write a little prayer.
■ 7" . . . . . . . . . . . . . . . . . . . . . . . EPC 7034
Epic / Feb '79.

### LOVING YOU IS JUST AN OLD HABIT.
Tracks: Loving you is just an old habit / Too blind to see.
■ 7" . . . . . . . . . . . . . . . . . . . . . . . EPC 6172
Epic / Mar.

### MISTY BLUE.
Tracks: Misty blue.
■ 7" . . . . . . . . . . . . . . . . . . . . . . . . CS 2087
Contempo (1) / Nov '76.
■ 7" . . . . . . . . . . . . . . . . . . . . . . MAL 1029
Malaco / Jul '82.

### MISTY BLUE.
Tracks: Not Advised.
■ LP . . . . . . . . . . . . . . . . . . . . . . . MAL 6351
MC. . . . . . . . . . . . . . . . . . . . . . . MALC 6351
Malaco / Mar '89 / C.M. Distribution / Charly / Pinnacle.
CD . . . . . . . . . . . . . . . . . . . . . . MALCD 6351
Malaco / Mar '93 / C.M. Distribution / Charly / Pinnacle.

### MISTY BLUE (OLD GOLD).
Tracks: Misty blue / Funny how time slips away.
■ 7" . . . . . . . . . . . . . . . . . . . . . . . OG 9362
Old Gold / Oct '83.

### ONCE MOORE WITH FEELING.
Tracks: Special occasion / What am I to do / Girl overboard / Write a little prayer / Going ups and coming downs / We need more loving time / Being alone / If I could find my way back to you / He knows just where to touch me.
■ LP . . . . . . . . . . . . . . . . . . . . . . EPC 83450
Epic / Apr '79.

### STAY CLOSE TO HOME.
Tracks: Not Advised.
CD . . . . . . . . . . . . . . . . . . . . . . MALCD 7466
Malaco / Mar '93 / C.M. Distribution / Charly / Pinnacle.

### TALK TO ME.
Tracks: Talk to me / Every beat of my heart / Crazy in love / Angel of the morning / It's all in the game / If I could feel that old feeling again / There'll never be another night like this / Something / Lonely.
■ LP . . . . . . . . . . . . . . . . . . . . . . EPC 84255
Epic / Jun '80.

### TALK TO ME.
Tracks: Talk to me / Every beat of my heart / Lonely.
■ 7" . . . . . . . . . . . . . . . . . . . . . . . EPC 8343
Epic / Mar '80.

### THERE'LL NEVER BE ANOTHER NIGHT LIKE THIS.
Tracks: There'll never be another night like this / Crazy in love.
■ 7" . . . . . . . . . . . . . . . . . . . . . . . EPC 8836
Epic / Aug '80.

### TIME OUT FOR ME.
Tracks: Time out for me / Endless Summer nights / He may not be mine / I still get turned on / Can't get over you / Don't hold your breath / Whatever you can do / Walk through this pain.
■ LP . . . . . . . . . . . . . . . . . . . . . . . VOLT 401
Volt (USA) / Jan '89.

### WITH PEN IN HAND.
Tracks: With pen in hand / Daddy's eyes.
■ 7" . . . . . . . . . . . . . . . . . . . . . . . EPC 5892
Epic / Jan '78.

## Moore, Jackie

### DEAR JOHN.
Tracks: Dear John / Here am I.
■ 7" . . . . . . . . . . . . . . . . . . . . . . . . BOY 35
Jay Boy / Aug '71.

### HOLDING BACK.
Tracks: Holding back.
■ 12" . . . . . . . . . . . . . . . . . . . . . 12SAT 506
■ 7" . . . . . . . . . . . . . . . . . . . . . . . SAT 506
Satriil / Apr '83.

### HOW'S YOUR LOVE LIFE BABY.
Tracks: How's you love life baby / Do ya, got what it takes.
■ 7" . . . . . . . . . . . . . . . . . . . . . . . CBS 8032
CBS / Nov '79.

### I WISH IT WOULD RAIN DOWN.
Tracks: I wish it would rain down.
■ 12" . . . . . . . . . . . . . . . . . . . . . . UPFX 2
■ 7" . . . . . . . . . . . . . . . . . . . . . . . UPF 72
Upfront / Aug '90.

### I'M ON MY WAY.
Tracks: This time baby / Joe can you tell me why / Let's go somewhere and make love / I'm on my way / How's your love life baby / Wrapped up in your lovin' / Do ya got what it takes.
■ LP . . . . . . . . . . . . . . . . . . . . . . CBS 83786
CBS / Oct '79.

### SOMETIMES, IT'S GOT TO RAIN (Moore, Jackie & The Dixie Flyers).
Tracks: Sometimes it's got to rain / Wonderful, marvellous.
■ 7" . . . . . . . . . . . . . . . . . . . . . . . 2091095
Atlantic / Jun '71.

### THIS TIME BABY.
Tracks: This time baby / Let's go somewhere and make love.
■ 7" . . . . . . . . . . . . . . . . . . . . . . . CBS 7722
CBS / Sep '79.
■ 7" . . . . . . . . . . . . . . . . . . . . . . . A 4694
CBS / Aug '84.

### THIS TIME BABY (OLD GOLD).
Tracks: This time baby / Pick me up I'll dance.
■ 12" . . . . . . . . . . . . . . . . . . . . . . OG 4143
Old Gold / Nov '89.

### WHY.
Tracks: Why.
■ 12" . . . . . . . . . . . . . . . . . . . . ZYX 679412
■ 7" . . . . . . . . . . . . . . . . . . . . . ZYX 67947
■ CD Single . . . . . . . . . . . . . . . . ZYX 67948
■ MC Single. . . . . . . . . . . . . . . . ZYX 67944
ZYX (MCA) / Sep '92.

## Moore, Lee

### REACHIN' OUT (FOR YOUR LOVE).
Tracks: Reachin' out (for your love) (2 pts).
■ 12" . . . . . . . . . . . . . . . . . . . . 12SRC 100
■ 7" . . . . . . . . . . . . . . . . . . . . . .SRC 100
Source / Oct '79.

## Moore, Melba

Featured vocalist on original Broadway cast recording of *Hair*, Moore did not capitalise on LP's success as quickly as fellow cast member Ronnie Dyson. Her breakthrough followed 1976 collaboration with writer/producer Van McCoy: *This Is It* reached No. 9 in U.K. chart, to which she returned at three-yearly intervals. In '79 she teamed with McFadden & Whitehead for *Pick Me Up, I'll Dance* and cruised into 1982 Top 20 with *Love's Comin' At Ya*, mastermined by Paul Lawrence Jones III (enjoying simultaneous success with Evelyn King's *Love Come Down*). She continued to make soul charts on both sides of Atlantic, but achieved greater recognition as early champion of Freddie Jackson.

### BURN.
Tracks: Burn / Hot and tasty / If you believe in love / Night people / I don't wanna lose your love / Can't give it up / Miss thing / Need love.
■ LP . . . . . . . . . . . . . . . . . . . . . . EPC 83788
Epic / Dec '79.

### DANCIN' WITH MELBA MOORE.
Tracks: Standing right here / Free / Play boy scout / Promises land / Make me believe in you.
■ LP . . . . . . . . . . . . . . . . . . . . . . BDLP 4059
Buddah / Oct '79.

### DO YOU REALLY WANT MY LOVE?.
Tracks: Do really want my love / Do really want my love? (instrumental).
■ 12" . . . . . . . . . . . . . . . . . . . . . 12CL 592
■ 7" . . . . . . . . . . . . . . . . . . . . . . .CL 592
Capitol / Sep '90.

### I CAN'T BELIEVE IT (IT'S OVER).
Tracks: I can't believe it (it's over) / King of my heart / When you love me like this.
■ 12" . . . . . . . . . . . . . . . . . . . . . 12CL 381
■ 7" . . . . . . . . . . . . . . . . . . . . . . .CL 381
Capitol / Oct '85.

### I'M IN LOVE.
Tracks: Love and kisses / I'm in love / Love always finds a way / I can't complain / I don't know no one else to turn to / I'll never find another you / Keeps me runnin' back / First love / This time / Test of time.
■ CD . . . . . . . . . . . . . . . . . . . . . CDEST 2058
■ LP . . . . . . . . . . . . . . . . . . . . . . EST 2058
■ MC. . . . . . . . . . . . . . . . . . . . . TCEST 2058
Capitol / May '88.

■ DELETED

289

### KEEPIN' MY LOVER SATISFIED.
Tracks: Keepin' my lover satisfied.
- ◼ 12″ ............................ 12CL 317
- ◼ 7″ .............................. .CL 317

Capitol / Nov '83.

### LET'S STAND TOGETHER.
Tracks: Let's stand together / Each second.
- ◼ 12″ ............................ 12EA 137
- ◼ 7″ .............................. EA 137

EMI-America / Mar '82.

### LITTLE BIT MORE, A (see under Jackson, Freddie).

### LOT OF LOVE, A.
Tracks: There I go falling in love again / Falling / It's been so long / I'm not gonna let you go / Love the one I'm with (A lot of love) / You trip me out / Little bit more / Stay / When we touch (it's like fire) / Don't go away.
- ◼ MC. ............................ .TCEST 2017
- ◼ LP ............................. EST 2017

Capitol / Aug '86.
- ◼ CD ............................ CDEST 2017

EMI / Feb '87.

### LOVE'S COMIN' AT YA.
Tracks: Love's comin' at ya / Let's go back to lovin'.
- ◼ 12″ ............................ 12EA 146
- ◼ 7″ .............................. EA 146

EMI-America / Oct '82.

### MAGIC TOUCH, THE.
Tracks: Magic touch / Pretty part of you.
- ◼ 7″ .............................. .HRH 001

Horaces / Jun '88.

### MELBA.
Tracks: There's no other like you / You stepped into my life / It's hard not to like you / Together forever / Pick me up / I'll never dance / Happy / I promise to love you / Where did you ever go.
- ◼ LP ............................. EPC 83269

Epic / Feb '79.

### MIND UP TONIGHT.
Tracks: Mind up tonight / Other side of the rainbow.
- ◼ 12″ ............................ 12CL 272

Capitol / Oct '82.
- ◼ 7″ .............................. .CL 272

Capitol / Oct '82.

### NEVER SAY NEVER.
Tracks: Love me right / Keepin my lover satisfied / Got to have your love / Living for your love / It's really love / Never say never / Lovin' touch / Lean on me.
- ◼ LP ............................. EST 7123051
MC. ................................ TCEST 712305 4

Capitol / Nov '83 / EMI.

### OTHER SIDE OF THE RAINBOW.
Tracks: Love's comin' at ya / Underlove / Mind up tonight / Knack for me / How's love been treatin' you / Don't go away / I can't help myself / Other side of the rainbow.
- ◼ LP .............................. .EST 12243

Capitol / Dec '82.

### PICK ME UP I'LL DANCE (OLD GOLD) (see under Moore, Jackie).

### PICK ME UP, I'LL DANCE.
Tracks: Pick me up, I'll dance / Where did you ever go.
- ◼ 7″ .............................. EPC 7234

Epic / May '79.

### PORTRAIT OF MELBA, A.
Tracks: You are my river / Promised land / I don't know no one else to turn to / Standing right here / Just another link / Living free / Is this the end / Love and I.
- ◼ LP ............................. BDLP 4049

Buddah / May '78.

### READ MY LIPS.
Tracks: Love of a lifetime / I can't believe it (it's over) / Read my lips / Dreams / When you love me like this / Winner / King of my heart / To those who wait / Mind over matter.
- ◼ LP .............................. MEL 1
MC. ................................ TC MEL 1

Capitol / Apr '85 / EMI.

### SOUL EXPOSED.
Tracks: Do you really want my love / Hold me / New love / I love being in love / Lift every voice and sing / Face to face / Crying in the night / Don't you want to be my lover / Too many lovers / Stormy weather / Lift every voice and sing (long version) (Not on LP.).
- ◼ CD. ............................ CDP 792 355 2

---

- ◼ LP .............................. EST 2122
- ◼ MC. ............................ .TCEST 2122

Capitol / May '90.

### STANDING RIGHT HERE.
Tracks: Standing right here / Living free.
- ◼ 7″ .............................. .BDS 464

Buddah / Feb '78.

### THIS IS IT.
Tracks: This is it / Stay awhile.
- ◼ 7″ .............................. .BDS 443

Buddah / May '76.

### THIS IS IT/ MELBA.
Tracks: This is it / Free / One less morning / Make me believe in you / Lean on me / Stay awhile / Playboy scout / Blood red roses / Brand new / Way you make me feel / Good love makes everything all right / Long and winding road / Ain't no love lost / Greatest feeling / Mighty clouds of joy / I need someone / So many mountains.
- ◼ CD ............................ NEXCD 195

Sequel / Mar '92.

### UNDERLOVE.
Tracks: Underlove / Don't go away.
- ◼ 12″ ............................ 12CL 281
- ◼ 7″ .............................. .CL 281

Capitol / Feb '83.

### WHAT A WOMAN NEEDS.
Tracks: Let's stand together / Your sweet lovin' / What a woman needs / Take my love / Overnight sensation / Each second / Piece of the rock / Let's go back to lovin'.
- ◼ LP ............................. AML 3019

EMI-America / Jan '82.

### WHEN YOU LOVE ME LIKE THIS.
Tracks: When you love me like this / Winner.
- ◼ 12″ ............................ 12CL 360
- ◼ 7″ .............................. .CL 360

Capitol / Jul '85.

### YOU STEPPED INTO MY LIFE.
Tracks: You stepped into my life / There's no other like you.
- ◼ 7″ .............................. EPC 6811

Epic / Nov '78.

### YOU STEPPED INTO MY LIFE (OLD GOLD).
Tracks: You stepped into my life / Hard not to like you.
- ◼ 12″ ............................ .OG 4504

Old Gold / Sep '88.

## Morgan, Denroy

### HAPPY FEELING.
Tracks: Happy feeling / Happy feeling (instrumental).
- ◼ 12″ ............................ BKSL 6
- ◼ 7″ .............................. BKS 6

Beckett / Nov '82.

## Morgan, Meli'sa

### DO ME BABY.
Tracks: Fool's paradise / Heart breaking decision / Do you still love me / I'll give it when I want it / Do me baby / Getting to know you / Now or never / Lies.
- ◼ MC. ............................ .TCEST 2008

Capitol / Apr '86.
- ◼ LP .............................. ATAK 118

Capitol / Mar '86.
- ◼ LP .............................. EST 2008

Capitol / Apr '86.
- ◼ CD ............................ CZ 119

Capitol / Jun '87.

### DO ME BABY.
Tracks: Do me baby.
- ◼ 12″ ............................ 12CL 385
- ◼ 7″ .............................. .CL 385

Capitol / Nov '85.

### FOOLS' PARADISE.
Tracks: Fools' paradise / Getting to know you.
- ◼ 12″ ............................ 12CL 415
- ◼ 7″ .............................. .CL 415

Capitol / Jul '86.

### GOOD LOVE.
Tracks: If you can do it I can too / Here comes the night / Just for your touch / Good love / Love changes / Think it over / Ill love no more / I still think about you / You're all I got.
- ◼ LP .............................. EST 2051
- ◼ MC. ............................ .TCEST 2051

Capitol / Nov '87.
- ◼ CD ............................ CDEST 2051

Capitol / Feb '88.

---

### GOOD LOVE.
Tracks: Good love / Here comes the night / Good love (album version) (on 12″ only.) / Good love (extended version) (on CD single only.) / Fool's paradise**.
- ◼ 12″ ............................ 12CL 483
- ◼ 7″ .............................. .CL 483
- ◼ CD Single. .................... .CDCL 483

Capitol / Jun '88.

### IF YOU CAN DO IT I CAN TOO.
Tracks: If you can do it I can too / Fools paradise / Feeling lucky lately (This track is available on 12″ single only.).
- ◼ 7″ .............................. .CL 475
- ◼ 12″ ............................ 12CL 475

Capitol / Nov '87.

### LADY IN ME, THE.
Tracks: Can you give me what I want / Stop, love and listen / You belong to me / Situations / Dancing into love / Don't you know / Wrong lane / Lady in me / I'm better now / So long, goodbye.
- ◼ CD ............................ CDEST 2124
- ◼ LP .............................. EST 2124
- ◼ MC. ............................ .TCEST 2124

Capitol / Jun '90.

### STILL IN LOVE WITH YOU.
Tracks: Still in love with you.
- ◼ 12″ ............................ .EKR 155T
- ◼ 7″ .............................. .EKR 155
- ◼ CD Single. .................... .EKR 155CD
- ◼ MC Single. ................... .EKR 155C

Elektra / Jul '92.

### STILL IN LOVE WITH YOU.
Tracks: Still in love with you / Bring you joy / Never had a love like this / Can't wait / Through the tears / I'm gonna be your lover (tonight) / Let's be real / Release me / Now I have someone / What change have you made lately.
CD. ................................ 3360612732
- ◼ LP .............................. 3360612731
MC. ................................ 3360612734

Pendulum / May '92 / EMI.

### WANTING YOU (Morgan, Meli'sa & Coffee Tea or Me).
Tracks: Wanting you / Wanting you (radio version) / Wanting you (dub version).
- ◼ 12″ ............................ 12 CHE 8413

Master Mix / Jun '87.

## Morning, Noon & Night

### BITE YOUR GRANNY.
Tracks: Bite your granny / Feeling strong.
- ◼ 7″ .............................. UP 36292

United Artists / Aug '77.

### MORNING NOON AND NIGHT.
Tracks: Bite your granny / Feeling strong.
- ◼ LP .............................. UAS 30114

United Artists / '77.

## Morris, Gee

### NATURAL THING.
Tracks: Natural thing.
- ◼ 12″ ............................ CIR 12003
- ◼ 7″ .............................. CIR 7003

Collision / Sep '89.

## Morris, Teeroy

### I HEARD IT THROUGH THE GRAPEVINE.
Tracks: I heard it through the grapevine / Hold on tight.
- ◼ 12″ ............................ POSPX 633
- ◼ 7″ .............................. .POSP 633

Polydor / Aug '83.

## Morrison, Roger

### PICTURES IN MY MIND.
Tracks: Not Advised.
LP ................................ . CHILLP 8

Jam Today / May '90 / Jetstar.

## Morrissey-Mullen

### BADNESS.
Tracks: Do like you / Dragonfly / Blue tears / Stay awhile / Badness / Pass the music on / Slipstream.
- ◼ LP .............................. BEGA 27

Beggars Banquet / Jul '81.
- ◼ CD ............................ BEGA 27 CD

Beggars Banquet / Oct '84.
CD. ................................ .CODA 24CD

---

◼ DELETED

■ **LP** . . . . . . . . . . . . . . . . . . . . . **CODA 24**
Coda / Jun '88 / Roots Records / Pinnacle / C.M.
Distribution / Zodiac Records.

### BLADE RUNNER.
**Tracks:** Bladerunner / I pull the strings.
■ **12″** . . . . . . . . . . . . . . . . . . . . **BEG 87T**
■ **7″** . . . . . . . . . . . . . . . . . . . . . **BEG 87**
Beggars Banquet / Nov '82.

### BRISTOL BOOGIE.
**Tracks:** Bristol boogie / Night song.
■ **7″** . . . . . . . . . . . . . . . . . . **HAR 5193**
Harvest / Nov '79.

### CAPE WRATH.
**Tracks:** Lovely day / Cape Wrath / Bristol boogie /
Return to Tooting Broadway / Soul eyes / Song for
Carla / Dreams so real / Night song.
■ **LP** . . . . . . . . . . . . . . . . . . **SHSP 4098**
Harvest / Apr '79.

### COME AND GET ME.
**Tracks:** Come and get me.
■ **12″** . . . . . . . . . . . . . . . . . . . . **BEG 73T**
■ **7″** . . . . . . . . . . . . . . . . . . . . . **BEG 73**
Beggars Banquet / Feb '82.

### DO LIKE YOU.
**Tracks:** Do like you / Badness.
■ **7″** . . . . . . . . . . . . . . . . . . . . . **BEG 60**
Beggars Banquet / Jul '81.

### HAPPY HOUR.
**Tracks:** Not Advised.
**CD** . . . . . . . . . . . . . . . . . . . **CODA 29 CD**
■ **Double LP** . . . . . . . . . . . . . . . **CODA 29**
**MC** . . . . . . . . . . . . . . . . . . . . . **COCA 29**
Coda / Dec '88 / Roots Records / Pinnacle / C.M.
Distribution / Zodiac Records.

### IT'S ABOUT TIME.
**Tracks:** Stop and look around / It's about time /
Ounce of bounce / So so fine / Ol' sax and Captain
Axe / Bladerunner / Why does it always happen to
me / Do I do / Above the clouds.
■ **LP** . . . . . . . . . . . . . . . . . . . . . **BEGA 44**
Beggars Banquet / Mar '83.
■ **CD** . . . . . . . . . . . . . . . . . . **BEGA 44 CD**
Beggars Banquet / Oct '84.

### LIFE ON THE WIRE.
**Tracks:** Life on the wire / Takin' time / Face of a child
/ Come and get me / Brazil nut / Ships that pass in
the night / Making waves / Running out of time.
■ **LP** . . . . . . . . . . . . . . . . . . . . . **BEGA 33**
Beggars Banquet / Mar '82.
■ **CD** . . . . . . . . . . . . . . . . . . **BEGA 33 CD**
Beggars Banquet / Oct '84.
**CD** . . . . . . . . . . . . . . . . . . . **CODA 27 CD**
Coda / '88 / Roots Records / Pinnacle / C.M. Distribu-
tion / Zodiac Records.

### LIFE ON THE WIRE.
**Tracks:** Life on the wire / Brazil nut.
■ **7″** . . . . . . . . . . . . . . . . . . . . . **BEG 75**
Beggars Banquet / Apr '82.

### LOVE DON'T LIVE HERE ANYMORE.
**Tracks:** Love don't live here anymore / Don't you
worry.
■ **12″** . . . . . . . . . . . . . . . . . . **12 DIG 1001**
Harvest / Jun '79.

### OLD SAX AND CAPTAIN AXE.
**Tracks:** Ol' sax and Captain Axe / It's about time.
■ **12″** . . . . . . . . . . . . . . . . . . . . **BEG 97T**
■ **7″** . . . . . . . . . . . . . . . . . . . . . **BEG 97**
Beggars Banquet / Jul '83.

### ONE STEP.
**Tracks:** One step.
■ **12″** . . . . . . . . . . . . . . . . . . . . **CODS 7T**
■ **7″** . . . . . . . . . . . . . . . . . . . . . **CODS 7**
Coda / Jul '84.

### SO, SO FINE.
**Tracks:** So, so fine / Ol' facts and Captain Aye.
■ **7″** . . . . . . . . . . . . . . . . . . . . . **BEG 94**
Beggars Banquet / Apr '85.

### STAY AWHILE.
**Tracks:** Stay awhile.
■ **12″** . . . . . . . . . . . . . . . . . . . . **BEG 63T**
■ **7″** . . . . . . . . . . . . . . . . . . . . . **BEG 63**
Beggars Banquet / Sep '81.

### THIS MUST BE THE PLACE.
**Tracks:** Tear for crystal / Mean time / This must be
the place / With you / Southend Pier / Visions / All I
want to do.
■ **LP** . . . . . . . . . . . . . . . . . . . . . **CODA 15**
**MC** . . . . . . . . . . . . . . . . . . . . . **COCA 15**

---

Coda / May '84 / Roots Records / Pinnacle / C.M.
Distribution / Zodiac Records.

### UP.
**Tracks:** Footloose / Sing me softly of the blues /
Everything must change / Philip Phuling / What a
way to go / You'll know what I mean / Busted fender.
■ **LP** . . . . . . . . . . . . . . . . . . . . . **K 50835**
Atlantic / Nov '81.

### WITH YOU.
**Tracks:** With you / Meantime.
■ **12″** . . . . . . . . . . . . . . . . . . . **CODS 11T**
■ **7″** . . . . . . . . . . . . . . . . . . . . **CODS 11**
Coda / Mar '85.

## Moten, Wendy

### COME IN OUT OF THE RAIN.
**Tracks:** Come in out of the rain / Magic touch / Step
by step (Available on CDS only).
■ **CD Single** . . . . . . . . . . . . . . . **CDMT 105**
■ **7″** . . . . . . . . . . . . . . . . . . . . . **MT 105**
■ **MC Single** . . . . . . . . . . . . . . . **TCMT 105**
EMI / Jan '94.

### SO CLOSE TO LOVE.
**Tracks:** So close to you / Step by step (Features only
on MCS & 7″.) / Areatha Franklin Medley: Think/
Natural woman/Respect (Features on CDS only).
■ **7″** . . . . . . . . . . . . . . . . . . . . . **MT 106**
■ **CD Single** . . . . . . . . . . . . . . . **CDMT 106**
■ **MC Single** . . . . . . . . . . . . . . . **TCMT 106**
EMI / Apr '94.
■ **CD Single** . . . . . . . . . . . . . . . **CDMTS 106**
EMI / Apr '94.

### WENDY MOTEN.
**Tracks:** Matter of fact / Nobody but you / Step by step
/ So close to love / Forever yours / Whatever it takes
/ Come in out of the rain / Make this love last / Magic
touch / Wonderin' / Once upon a time.
**CD** . . . . . . . . . . . . . . . . . . . **CDMTL 1073**
**MC** . . . . . . . . . . . . . . . . . . . **TCMTL 1073**
EMI-America / Mar '94 / EMI.

## Mother Freedom Band

### BEAUTIFUL SUMMER DAY.
**Tracks:** Beautiful summer day / Flick of the wrist.
■ **7″** . . . . . . . . . . . . . . . . . . . **.6146 326**
All Platinum / '77.

## Mother's Finest

### FIRE.
**Tracks:** Give you all the love / Niggizz can't sing
rock'n'roll / My baby / Fly with me / Dontcha wanna
love me / Rain.
■ **LP** . . . . . . . . . . . . . . . . . . . . **EPC 81595**
Epic / Feb '77.

### IRON AGE.
**Tracks:** Movin' on / Luv drug / Rock'n'roll 2 nite / U
turn me on / All the way / Evolution / Illusion / Time /
Gone with the rain / Earthling.
■ **LP** . . . . . . . . . . . . . . . . . . . . **EPC 84924**
Epic / Jul '81.

### LOOKS COULD KILL.
**Tracks:** For your love / I'm 'n danger / Legs and
lipstick / Dream come true / Still over each other / I'll
never be the same / Brave and strong / Your wish is
my command / Cherish your lover / Heartbreaker /
Call me Mister (CD only.) / Too serious (CD only.).
■ **CD** . . . . . . . . . . . . . . . . . . . **CDEST 2114**
■ **LP** . . . . . . . . . . . . . . . . . . . . **EST 2114**
■ **MC** . . . . . . . . . . . . . . . . . . . **TCEST 2114**
Capitol / Oct '89.

### MOTHER FACTOR.
**Tracks:** Can't fight the feelin' / Tell me / Watch my
stylin' / Love changes / Don't wanna come back /
Give it up / Mr. Goodbar / I can't believe / More and
more.
■ **LP** . . . . . . . . . . . . . . . . . . . . **EPC 83011**
Epic / '79.

### ONE MOTHER TO ANOTHER.
**Tracks:** Secret service / What kind of fool / Victory /
Love me too / Everybody needs somebody / Big shot
Romeo / What you do to me / In my baby's arms /
Some kind of madness / Take me to the middle of
your luv).
■ **LP** . . . . . . . . . . . . . . . . . . . . **EPC 25363**
**MC** . . . . . . . . . . . . . . . . . . . **.40 25363**
Epic / Aug '83 / Sony.
■ **LP** . . . . . . . . . . . . . . . . . . . . **EPC 25263**
Epic / Aug '83.

---

## Motivation

### DON'T PLAY THAT SONG.
**Tracks:** Don't play that song / Love games.
■ **12″** . . . . . . . . . . . . . . . . . . . . **RCRT 3**
■ **7″** . . . . . . . . . . . . . . . . . . . . . **RCR 3**
Rock City / Oct '84.

### GIVE THE GIFT OF MUSIC.
**Tracks:** Give the gift of music / Color blind.
■ **12″** . . . . . . . . . . . . . . . . . . . . **DEX 12**
■ **7″** . . . . . . . . . . . . . . . . . . . . . **DE 12**
De-Lite / Sep '83.

### SO LONELY.
**Tracks:** So lonely / Let me get back to my lonliness.
■ **7″** . . . . . . . . . . . . . . . . . . . . . **RCR 1**
Rock City / Jul '84.

## Motown Sounds

### SPACE DANCE.
**Tracks:** Groove time / Space dance / Easy to love /
You don't like to party / Bad mouthin' / Rich love,
poor love.
■ **LP** . . . . . . . . . . . . . . . . . . . **STML 12105**
Motown / Mar '79.

### SPACE DANCE.
**Tracks:** Space dance / Bad mouthin'.
■ **12″** . . . . . . . . . . . . . . . . . . **12TMG 1143**
■ **7″** . . . . . . . . . . . . . . . . . . . **TMG 1143**
Motown / May '79.

## Mouzon, Alphonse

### BABY COME BACK.
**Tracks:** Not Advised.
■ **LP** . . . . . . . . . . . . . . . . . . . **MPS 60 229**
MPS Jazz / May '81.

### BACK TO JAZZ (Mouzon, Alphonse band).
**Tracks:** Not Advised.
■ **LP** . . . . . . . . . . . . . . . . . . . **LR 45.001**
L&R / Dec '86.

### BACK TOGETHER (see under Coryell, Larry).

### BEST OF ALPHONSE MOUZON.
**Tracks:** Not Advised.
**CD** . . . . . . . . . . . . . . . . . . . **CD 15005-2**
Black Sun / Nov '89 / A.D.A. Distribution.

### BY ALL MEANS (see under Hancock, Herbie).

### DON'T WANT TO LOSE THIS FEELING.
**Tracks:** Don't want to lose this feeling / Don't want to
lose this feeling (part 2).
■ **12″** . . . . . . . . . . . . . . . . . . . **LONX 003**
■ **7″** . . . . . . . . . . . . . . . . . . . . **LON 003**
London / Mar '82.

### I'M GLAD THAT YOU'RE HERE.
**Tracks:** I'm glad that you're here.
■ **12″** . . . . . . . . . . . . . . . . . . . **HLX 10581**
■ **7″** . . . . . . . . . . . . . . . . . . . **HL 10581**
London / Nov '81.

### IN SEARCH OF A DREAM.
**Tracks:** Not Advised.
■ **LP** . . . . . . . . . . . . . . . . . . . **MPS 68 192**
MPS Jazz / Nov '81.

### MIND TRANSPLANT.
**Tracks:** Mind transplant / Snowbound / Carbon diox-
ide / Ascorbic acid / Happiness is loving you / Some
of the things people do / Golden rainbows / Nitrogly-
cerin / Real thing.
**CD** . . . . . . . . . . . . . . . . . . . **RPM 116**
RPM / Sep '93 / Pinnacle.

### MORNING SUN.
**Tracks:** Not Advised.
■ **LP** . . . . . . . . . . . . . . . . . . . **SH 8547**
London / Nov '81.

### SKY IS THE LIMIT, THE.
**Tracks:** Not Advised.
**CD** . . . . . . . . . . . . . . . . . . . **835 948-2**
Polydor / '88 / PolyGram.

## Mr. Dynamite

### SH'MON.
**Tracks:** Sh'mon part 1 / Sh'mon part 2.
■ **7″** . . . . . . . . . . . . . . . . . . . . **WI 4027**
Sue / Feb '67.

---

## Mr. Fingers

### AMMNESIA.
Tracks: Not Advised.
- LP . . . . . . . . . . . . . . . . . . . . . . .FING 2
Jack Trax / Mar '89.

### CLOSER.
Tracks: Closer.
- 12" . . . . . . . . . . . . . . . . . . MCST 1601
- 7" . . . . . . . . . . . . . . . . . . . MCS 1601
- CD Single . . . . . . . . . . . . . . MCSTD 1601
- MC Single . . . . . . . . . . . . . . MCSC 1601
MCA / Feb '92.

### INTRODUCTION.
Tracks: Closer / On a corner called jazz / On my way / Empty / Survivor / We can work it out / Dead end alley / Waves against the shore / Alright / What about the love / U.S.S.R. / Uniform variations / Children at play.
- LP . . . . . . . . . . . . . . . . . . . MCA 10571
- CD . . . . . . . . . . . . . . . . . . MCAD 10571
- MC . . . . . . . . . . . . . . . . . . MCAC 10571
MCA / Apr '92.

### ON A CORNER CALLED JAZZ.
Tracks: On a corner called jazz.
- MC Single . . . . . . . . . . . . . MCSC 1668
- 12" . . . . . . . . . . . . . . . . . . MCSX 1668
- 12" . . . . . . . . . . . . . . . . . . MCST 1668
- 7" . . . . . . . . . . . . . . . . . . . MCS 1668
- CD Single . . . . . . . . . . . . . MCSTD 1668
MCA / Sep '92.

### ON MY WAY.
Tracks: On my way.
- 12" . . . . . . . . . . . . . . . . . . MCST 1630
- 7" . . . . . . . . . . . . . . . . . . . MCS 1630
- CD Single . . . . . . . . . . . . . MCSTD 1630
MCA / May '92.

### SLAM DANCE (EP).
Tracks: Slam dance / Acid attacks / Stars / Waterfalls / I'm strong / For so long.
- 12" . . . . . . . . . . . . . . . . . .12JTRAX 10
Jack Trax / Jan '88.

### WHAT ABOUT THIS LOVE.
Tracks: What about this love / What about this love (version).
- 12" . . . . . . . . . . . . . . . . . . . . .FX 131
- 7" . . . . . . . . . . . . . . . . . . . . . F 131
- CD Single . . . . . . . . . . . . . . . FCD 131
- MC Single . . . . . . . . . . . . . . . FCS 131
London / Feb '90.

## Mtume

### BREATHLESS.
Tracks: Breathless / Theatre of the mind, Theme from.
- 12" . . . . . . . . . . . . . . . . . . . TA 7159
- 7" . . . . . . . . . . . . . . . . . . . . A 7159
Epic / May '86.

### C.O.D. (I'LL DELIVER).
Tracks: C.O.D. (I'll deliver).
- 12" . . . . . . . . . . . . . . . . . . . TA 4887
- 7" . . . . . . . . . . . . . . . . . . . . A 4887
Epic / Nov '84.

### GREEN LIGHT.
Tracks: Green light / Hip dip skipped a beat.
- 12" . . . . . . . . . . . . . . . . . . . TA 3263
- 7" . . . . . . . . . . . . . . . . . . . . A 3263
Epic / Aug '83.

### IN SEARCH OF THE RAINBOW SEEKERS.
Tracks: Give it on up (if you want to) / You can't wait for love / She's a rainbow dancer / We're gonna make it this time / Dance around my naval / Doesn't have to make sense, just cents / So you wanna be a star / Spirit of the dance / Everything good to me / Anticipatin'.
- LP . . . . . . . . . . . . . . . . . . EPC 84629
Epic / Jan '81.

### JUICY FRUIT.
Tracks: Green light / Juicy fruit / Hips / Would you like to / Your love's too good / Hip dip skipped a beat / Ready for your love / After 6 mix.
- LP . . . . . . . . . . . . . . . . . . EPC 25399
- MC . . . . . . . . . . . . . . . . . . .40 25399
Epic / Jul '83 / Sony.

### JUICY FRUIT (OLD GOLD).
Tracks: Juicy fruit / Prime time / Just be good to me / Weekend girl.
- 12" . . . . . . . . . . . . . . . . . . . .OG 4002
Old Gold / Jan '89.

### JUICY FRUIT (PART 1).
Tracks: Juicy fruit (part 1).
- 12" . . . . . . . . . . . . . . . . . . . TA 3424
- 7" . . . . . . . . . . . . . . . . . . . .A 3424
Epic / May '83.

### MTUME.
Tracks: Not Advised.
- CD . . . . . . . . . . . . . . . . . . . CD 26923
Epic / May '87.

### PRIME TIME.
Tracks: Prime time / Juicy fruit / You, me and he (on 12" only).
- 12" . . . . . . . . . . . . . . . . . . . TA 4720
- 7" . . . . . . . . . . . . . . . . . . . .A 4720
Epic / Sep '84.

### PRIME TIME (OLD GOLD).
Tracks: Prime time / Juicy fruit / Sugar free.
- CD Single . . . . . . . . . . . . . . . .OG 6503
Old Gold / Jul '90 / Pickwick.

### SO YOU WANT TO BE A STAR.
Tracks: So you want to be a star / Mrs. Sippi.
- 12" . . . . . . . . . . . . . . . . EPC 12 9337
- 7" . . . . . . . . . . . . . . . . . . EPC 9337
Epic / Dec '80.

### THEATER OF THE MIND.
Tracks: Theater of the mind, Theme from / P.O.P. generation / Breathless / I don't believe you heard me / Body & soul (Take me) / New face Deli / I'd rather be with you / Deep freez (rap-a-song) / Deep freez (tree's thing).
- LP . . . . . . . . . . . . . . . . . . EPC 26923
- MC . . . . . . . . . . . . . . . . . . .40 26923
Epic / Jun '86 / Sony.

### YOU CAN'T WAIT FOR LOVE.
Tracks: You can't wait for love / Everything good to me.
- 7" . . . . . . . . . . . . . . . . . . EPCA 1025
Epic / Jun '81.

### YOU, ME AND HE.
Tracks: C.O.D. (I'll deliver) / You are my sunshine / You, me and he / I simply like / Prime time / Tie me up / Sweet for you and me / To be or not to bop.
- LP . . . . . . . . . . . . . . . . . . EPC 26077
- MC . . . . . . . . . . . . . . . . . . .40 26077
Epic / Sep '84.
- CD . . . . . . . . . . . . . . . . .983302 2
Pickwick/Sony Collector's Choice / Oct '93 / Pickwick / Pinnacle.

## Muhammad, Idris

New Orleans percussionist and occasional singer, Idris Muhammad released series of albums between 1972-'80, having previously worked with Sam Cooke, Curtis Mayfield and others. *Turn This Mutha Out* ('77) yielded one-off U.K. chart entry with club hit *Could Heaven Ever Be Like This?*. However, Muhammad's talents have been better deployed as sideman than performer in his own right. Among artists with whom he worked during '70s were Merry Clayton, Roberta Flack, Bob James and Grover Washington Jr. Like fellow percussionist Ralph McDonald, he varied his schedule by working with both jazz and soul performers.

### BLACK RHYTHM REVOLUTION.
Tracks: Express yourself / Soulful drums / Super bad / Wander / By the red sea.
- LP . . . . . . . . . . . . . . . . . BGPD 1068
BGP / Oct '92 / Pinnacle.

### BLACK RHYTHM REVOLUTION/PEACE AND RHYTHM.
Tracks: Express yourself / Soulful drums / Super bad / Wander / By the red sea / Peace / Rhythm / Brother you know you're doing wrong / Don't knock my love-Part 1 / I'm a believer.
- CD . . . . . . . . . . . . . . . . . CDBPGD 046
BGP / Oct '92 / Pinnacle.

### BOOGIE TO THE TOP.
Tracks: Boogie to the top / Bread / One with a star / Stick it in your face.
- LP . . . . . . . . . . . . . . . . . . . KU 38
CTI (1) / May '78.

### BOOGIE TO THE TOP.
Tracks: Boogie to the top / Boogie to the top (version).
- 7" . . . . . . . . . . . . . . . . . .KUDU 943
Kudu / Jun '78.

### COULD HEAVEN EVER BE LIKE THIS.
Tracks: Could heaven ever be like this / Turn this mutha out.
- 7" . . . . . . . . . . . . . . . . . .KUDU 935
Kudu / Sep '77.

### FOR YOUR LOVE.
Tracks: Fot your love / New Orleans.
- 7" . . . . . . . . . . . . . . . . . . .FTC 191
Fantasy / Nov '80.
- 12" . . . . . . . . . . . . . . . . . . FTCT 191
Fantasy / Nov '80.

### FOXHUNTIN'.
Tracks: Boogie boots / Foxhuntin' / Work your body / Love New Orleans / Are we doin' it / Dancing in the land of lovely ladies.
- LP . . . . . . . . . . . . . . . . . . .FT 562
Fantasy / '79.

### FOXHUNTIN'.
Tracks: Foxhuntin'.
- 12" . . . . . . . . . . . . . . . . .12FTC 181
- 7" . . . . . . . . . . . . . . . . . . .FTC 181
Fantasy / Aug '79.

### KABSHA.
Tracks: Kabsha / I want to talk to you / Little feet / GCCCG Blues / Soulful drums / St. M / Kabsha (Alternate take) / GCCG Blues.
- CD . . . . . . . . . . . . . . . . ECD 22096-2
Evidence / Jul '94 / Harmonia Mundi (UK).

### MAKE IT COUNT.
Tracks: For your love / I'm so glad / Love in the tub / I believe in you / Don't fight the feeling / New Orleans.
- LP . . . . . . . . . . . . . . . . . . .F 9598
Fantasy / Nov '80.

### MY TURN.
Tracks: Piece o' cake / Free / There is a girl / Dark road / Dracula / This love / Happenstance / Stranger / Where did we go wrong.
- CD . . . . . . . . . . . . . . . . . .890022
- LP . . . . . . . . . . . . . . . . . . .890021
- MC . . . . . . . . . . . . . . . . . . .890024
Lipstick / Feb '91 / New Note.

### YOU AIN'T NO FRIEND OF MINE.
Tracks: Disco man / See saw / Doc / You ain't no friend of mine / Tell me, where did we go wrong / Big foo.
- LP . . . . . . . . . . . . . . . . . . .FT 552
Fantasy / Dec '78.

## Murdock, Shirley

### AS WE LAY.
Tracks: As we lay (remix) (Side A) / Danger zone (Side B).
- 12" . . . . . . . . . . . . . . . . . . EKR 53 T
- 7" . . . . . . . . . . . . . . . . . . . EKR 53
Elektra / Mar '87.

### LET THERE BE LOVE.
Tracks: In your eyes / Stay with me tonight / Let there be love / Say it / Mean it / Last hurrah / We should be together / Anywhere, everywhere / Heavenly / Save the children.
- CD . . . . . . . . . . . . . . . . . 7559609512
- LP . . . . . . . . . . . . . . . . . . . EKT 90
- MC . . . . . . . . . . . . . . . . . .EKT 90C
WEA / Jul '91 / WEA.

### NO MORE.
Tracks: No more / One I need / Truth or dare (Extra track on 12" version only).
- 12" . . . . . . . . . . . . . . . . . . EKR 43 T
- 7" . . . . . . . . . . . . . . . . . . . EKR 43
Elektra / Aug '86.

### SHIRLEY MURDOCK.
Tracks: Be free / No more / Go on without you / Truth or dare / Danger zone / Teaser / As we lay / One I need / Tribute.
- LP . . . . . . . . . . . . . . . . . . . EKT 32
Elektra / Mar '86.

### TRUTH OR DARE.
Tracks: Truth or dare / Go on without you.
- 12" . . . . . . . . . . . . . . . . . . EKR 36 T
- 7" . . . . . . . . . . . . . . . . . . . EKR 36
Elektra / Feb '86.

### WOMANS POINT OF VIEW, A.
Tracks: Husband / Found my way / (Everybody wants) something for nothing / If I know / Spend my whole life / Oh what a feeling / I still love you / Woman's point of view / And I am telling you I'm not going / Modern girls / Instrument of praise.
- CD . . . . . . . . . . . . . . . . . . 9607912
- MC . . . . . . . . . . . . . . . . . . 9607914

- DELETED

■ LP . . . . . . . . . . . . . . . . . . . . 9607911
Elektra / Jul '88 / WEA.

## Muscle Shoals Horns

### BORN TO GET DOWN.
**Tracks:** Born to get down / Breakdown / Bump de bump yo boodie / Get it up / Give it to me / Hustle to the music / Open up your heart / Where I'm coming from / Who's gonna love you.
■ LP . . . . . . . . . . . . . . . . . . . SHOT 001
Bang / Feb '77.

## Music & Mystery

### ALL THIS LOVE I'M GIVING.
**Tracks:** All this love I'm giving.
■ 12" . . . . . . . . . . . . . . . . . . 12KTDA 2
■ 7" . . . . . . . . . . . . . . . . . . . KTDA 2
■ CD Single . . . . . . . . . . . . . . CDKTDA 2
■ MC Single . . . . . . . . . . . . . . CAKTDA 2
KTDA / Nov '92.

### ANYTHING U WANT.
**Tracks:** Anything you want / Does it matter / Anything you want (mixes).
■ 12" . . . . . . . . . . . . . . . . . . . KIDA 3TX
■ 12" . . . . . . . . . . . . . . . . . . . KIDA 3T
■ CD Single . . . . . . . . . . . . . . KIDA 3CD
■ MC Single . . . . . . . . . . . . . . KIDA 3C
WEA / Apr '93.

### FALLING LIKE DOMINOES.
**Tracks:** Falling like dominoes.
■ 12" . . . . . . . . . . . . . . . . . . . KTDA 01
KTDA / Apr '92.

### FUNKY SENSATION EP (Music & Mystery Feat. Gwen McCrae).
**Tracks:** Funky sensation.
■ MC Single . . . . . . . . . . . . . . CAKTDA 5
■ 12" . . . . . . . . . . . . . . . . . . 12KTDA 5

### LITTLE BIT O'SOUL.
**Tracks:** Little bit o' soul / I see the light.
■ 7" . . . . . . . . . . . . . . . . . . . SS 2028
Stateside / Jun '67.
■ 7" . . . . . . . . . . . . . . . . . . . USA 9
UK / Apr '75.

### LITTLE BIT O'SOUL.
**Tracks:** I see the light / Everybody / Love love love love / Good time feeling / 96 tears / Can't stop now / Let yourself go / Patches drawn / Little bit o'soul / One potato two / What did I do to deserve such a fate / La la la.
■ LP . . . . . . . . . . . . . . . . . . . SHP 8352
London / May '68.

### LITTLE BLACK EGG.
**Tracks:** Little black egg / Stay by my side.
■ 7" . . . . . . . . . . . . . . . . . . . BF 1547
Philips / Feb '67.

### SUNSHINE GAMES.
**Tracks:** Sunshine games / Can't stop now.
■ 7" . . . . . . . . . . . . . . . . . . . SS 2054
Stateside / Oct '67.

## Musique

### IN THE BUSH.
**Tracks:** In the bush.
■ 7" . . . . . . . . . . . . . . . . . . . CBS 6791
CBS / Nov '78.

### IN THE BUSH (C.C.N. REMIX).
**Tracks:** In the bush (C.C.N. Remix).
■ 12" . . . . . . . . . . . . . . . . . . 12 WGAF 106
■ CD Single . . . . . . . . . . . . . . CDWGAF 106

■ CD Single . . . . . . . . . . . . . . CDKTDA 5
KTDA / Sep '93.

## Music Explosion

### LITTLE BIT O'SOUL.

■ MC Single . . . . . . . . . . . . . . CAWGAF 106
WGAF / Feb '94.

### KEEP ON JUMPIN'.
**Tracks:** Keep on jumpin' / Summer love / In the bush / Summer love theme.
■ LP . . . . . . . . . . . . . . . . . . . CBS 83173
CBS / Nov '78.

### SUMMER LOVE.
**Tracks:** Summer love / Summer love theme.
■ 7" . . . . . . . . . . . . . . . . . . . CBS 6579
CBS / Sep '78.

## Mystic Merlin

### 60 THRILLS A MINUTE.
**Tracks:** 60 thrills a minute / Got to make it better.
■ 12" . . . . . . . . . . . . . . . . . . 12CL 16190
■ 7" . . . . . . . . . . . . . . . . . . . CL 16190
Capitol / Mar '81.

### JUST CAN'T GIVE YOU UP.
**Tracks:** Just can't give you up / Burned to learn / Got to make the best of a love situation / Mr. Magician.
■ 12" . . . . . . . . . . . . . . . . . . 12CL 16133
Capitol / Mar '80.
■ 7" . . . . . . . . . . . . . . . . . . . CL 16133
Capitol / Mar '80.
■ 12" . . . . . . . . . . . . . . . . . . OG 4238
Pickwick / Sep '92.

### MYSTIC MERLIN.
**Tracks:** Burned to learn / Don't you want to be a star / Dreams / Can't stop dancing / Dark side / Got to make the best of a love situation / Just can't give you up.
■ LP . . . . . . . . . . . . . . . . . . . EST 12047
Capitol / Jun '80.

# N

## Najee

### DAY BY DAY.
Tracks: Personality / Day by day / So hard to let go / He's armed 'n' dangerous / Gina / That's the way of the world / Tonight I'm yours / Najee's nasty groove / Sweet sensation / Stand up.
■ CD . . . . . . . . . . . . . . . . . . . . . CDMTL 1026
■ LP . . . . . . . . . . . . . . . . . . . . . . MTL 1026
■ MC . . . . . . . . . . . . . . . . . . . . . TCMTL 1026
EMI-Manhattan / Jul '88.

### JUST AN ILLUSION.
Tracks: Touch of heaven / I adore mi amor / Just an illusion / Breezy / All I ever ask / Noah's Ark / Loving every moment / Burn it up / Skyline / Deep inside your love / Here we go / Until we meet again / Whenever we're together.
■ CD . . . . . . . . . . . . . . . . . . . . . CDMTL 1074
■ MC . . . . . . . . . . . . . . . . . . . . . TCMTL 1074
EMI-America / Jul '93.

### NAJEE'S THEME.
Tracks: Feel so good to me / Najee's theme / For the love of you / Can't hide love / We're still family / Sweet love / Betcha don't know / What you do to me / Mysterious.
■ MC . . . . . . . . . . . . . . . . . . . . . TCAML 3115
■ LP . . . . . . . . . . . . . . . . . . . . . . AML 3115
EMI-America / Jan '87.
■ CD . . . . . . . . . . . . . . . . . . . CDP 746 587 2
EMI-America / Mar '87.

### PERSONALITY.
Tracks: Personality / Sweet love.
■ 12" . . . . . . . . . . . . . . . . . . . . . .12MT 47
■ 7" . . . . . . . . . . . . . . . . . . . . . . . MT 47
EMI-Manhattan / Aug '88.

## Naked Funk

### HIGHER LOVE.
Tracks: Not Advised.
■ 12" . . . . . . . . . . . . . . . . . . . . . .BBR 004
Boogie Back Records / Oct '92.

### MIDNIGHT CALLING.
Tracks: Midnight calling / Stay healthy / Forbidden zone.
12" . . . . . . . . . . . . . . . . . . . . . . .BBR 010
Boogie Back Records / Jan '94 / Vital Distribution.

## Nash, Kevin

### LOVE YA NINE TIMEZ.
Tracks: Without you / Sugar love / Love man / Call me / His girl / I'll do anything / She's an old fashioned girl / Let's make love tonight / Come / Old fashioned girl / I like it / More.
CD . . . . . . . . . . . . . . . . . . . . . ATCD 021
LP . . . . . . . . . . . . . . . . . . . . . . ATLP 021
About Time / May '94 / BMG.

## Natural Four

### LOVE SO WONDERFUL.
Tracks: Love so wonderful / What's happening here.
■ 7" . . . . . . . . . . . . . . . . . . . . . . K 16583
Warner / Jul '75.

## Natural Hii

### BRIDGING THE GAP.
Tracks: Not Advised.
LP . . . . . . . . . . . . . . . . . . . . . RMM 1151
Jetstar / Mar '89 / Jetstar.

## Nayobe

### PROMISE ME.
Tracks: I love the way you love me / I'll be around / Can't let go / You are you / You are everything / Who do I call / Some kind of emotion / Promise me / Main squeeze / Have I said I love you lately.
■ CD . . . . . . . . . . . . . . . . . . . . . 4671212
■ LP . . . . . . . . . . . . . . . . . . . . . 4671211
■ MC . . . . . . . . . . . . . . . . . . . . . 4671214
CBS / Sep '90.

## Nazlyn

### YOUR LOVE MY LOVE.
Tracks: Not Advised.
■ 12" . . . . . . . . . . . . . . . . . . . . . ESTL 011
Eastside / May '93.

## Ndegeocello, Me'shell

### CALL ME.
Tracks: Call me (Mixes).
■ 12" . . . . . . . . . . . . . . . . . . . . . W 0244T
■ 7" . . . . . . . . . . . . . . . . . . . . . . W 0244
■ CD Single . . . . . . . . . . . . . . . . . W 0244CD
■ MC Single . . . . . . . . . . . . . . . . . .W 0244C
East West / May '94.

### IF THAT'S YOUR BOYFRIEND (HE WASN'T LAST NIGHT).
Tracks: If that's your boyfriend (He wasn't last night).
■ 12" . . . . . . . . . . . . . . . . . . . . .W 0223T
■ 7" . . . . . . . . . . . . . . . . . . . . . . W 0223
■ CD Single . . . . . . . . . . . . . . . . W 0223CD2
■ CD Single . . . . . . . . . . . . . . . . W 0223CD1
Maverick / Jan '94.

### PLANTATION LULLABIES.
Tracks: Plantation lullabies / I'm diggin' you (like an old soul record) / If that's your boyfriend (he wasn't last night) / Shoot'n up and gett'n high / Dred loc / Untitled / Step into the projects / Soul on ice / Call me / Outside your door / Picture show / Sweet love / Two lonely hearts (on the subway).
■ CD . . . . . . . . . . . . . . . . . . .936245333-2
■ MC . . . . . . . . . . . . . . . . . . .936245333-4
Maverick / Oct '93.
CD . . . . . . . . . . . . . . . . . . . .936245754-2
LP . . . . . . . . . . . . . . . . . . . .936245754-1
MC . . . . . . . . . . . . . . . . . . . .936245754-4
Maverick / Jul '94 / WEA.

## Ndugu

### SHADOW DANCING.
Tracks: Shadow dancing / Love anew.
■ 12" . . . . . . . . . . . . . . . . . . . . . 13-8371
■ 7" . . . . . . . . . . . . . . . . . . . . . EPC 8371
Epic / May '80.

## Nelson, Phyllis

### CHEMICAL REACTION.
Tracks: Stop don't do this to me / Chemical reaction.
■ 12" . . . . . . . . . . . . . . . . . . . . .CART 401
■ 7" . . . . . . . . . . . . . . . . . . . . . .CAR 401
Carrere / Oct '86.

### I LIKE YOU.
Tracks: I like you / Reachin'.
■ 12" . . . . . . . . . . . . . . . . . . . . .CART 365
■ 7" . . . . . . . . . . . . . . . . . . . . . .CAR 365
Carrere / Jul '86.

### MOVE CLOSER.
Tracks: Not Advised.
■ LP . . . . . . . . . . . . . . . . . . . . . .CAL 203
MC . . . . . . . . . . . . . . . . . . . . . .CAC 203
Carrere / Feb '85 / WEA.
CD . . . . . . . . . . . . . . . . . . . . 827 008 2
Carrere / '88 / WEA.

### MOVE CLOSER.
Tracks: Move closer / Somewhere in the city.
■ 12" . . . . . . . . . . . . . . . . . . . . .CART 337
■ 7" . . . . . . . . . . . . . . . . . . . . . .CAR 337
Carrere / Feb '85.

### MOVE CLOSER.
Tracks: Move closer (mixes).
■ 12" . . . . . . . . . . . . . . . . . . . .12EMCT 9
■ 7" . . . . . . . . . . . . . . . . . . . . . EMCT 9
■ CD Single . . . . . . . . . . . . . . . . CDEMCT 9
■ MC Single . . . . . . . . . . . . . . . . TCEMCT 9
EMI / May '94.

### STOP DON'T DO THIS TO ME.
Tracks: Stop don't do this to me / In a Cadillac.
■ 12" . . . . . . . . . . . . . . . . . . . . .CART 286
Carrere / Jul '83.

## Nelson, Shara

### DOWN THAT ROAD.
Tracks: Down that road.
■ 12" . . . . . . . . . . . . . . . . . . . 12COOL 275
■ 7" . . . . . . . . . . . . . . . . . . . . .COOL 275
■ CD Single . . . . . . . . . . . . . . . . CDCOOL 275
■ MC Single . . . . . . . . . . . . . . . . TCCOOL 275
Chrysalis / Jul '93.

### INSIDE OUT.
Tracks: Inside out / Down that road (MCS/CDS1 only) / One goodbye in ten (MCS/CD1 only) / Uptight (CD1 only) / Inside out (Mixes) (On CD2/MCS only) / Down that road (Mixes) (12" only).
■ 12" . . . . . . . . . . . . . . . . . . . 12COOL 284
■ 7" . . . . . . . . . . . . . . . . . . . . .COOL 284
■ CD Single . . . . . . . . . . . . . . . . CDCOOL 284
■ MC Single . . . . . . . . . . . . . . . . TCCOOL 284
Cool Tempo / Dec '93.
12" . . . . . . . . . . . . . . . . . . . . 12COOL 295
CD Single . . . . . . . . . . . . . . . . CDCOOLR 295
CD Single . . . . . . . . . . . . . . . . CDCOOLX 295
CD Single . . . . . . . . . . . . . . . . CDCOOL 295
MC Single . . . . . . . . . . . . . . . . TCCOOL 295
Cool Tempo / Aug '94 / EMI.

### LOVE HITS YOU.
Tracks: Love hits you / Dub hit you.
■ 12" . . . . . . . . . . . . . . . . . . . . . . .DT 4
Disco Tex / Oct '82.

### NOBODY.
Tracks: Nobody / Nobody (Mixes).
■ 12" . . . . . . . . . . . . . . . . . . . 12COOL 290
■ 7" . . . . . . . . . . . . . . . . . . . . .COOL 290
■ CD Single . . . . . . . . . . . . . . . . CDCOOL 290
■ MC Single . . . . . . . . . . . . . . . . TCCOOL 290
Chrysalis / May '94.

### ONE GOODBYE IN TEN.
Tracks: One goodbye in ten / One goodbye in ten (mixes).
■ 12" . . . . . . . . . . . . . . . . . . . 12COOL 279
■ 7" . . . . . . . . . . . . . . . . . . . . .COOL 279
■ CD Single . . . . . . . . . . . . . . . . CDCOOL 279
■ MC Single . . . . . . . . . . . . . . . . TCCOOL 279
EMI / Aug '93.

### UPTIGHT.
Tracks: Uptight / Uptight (mixes) / What silence knows (Not available on 12).
■ 12" . . . . . . . . . . . . . . . . . . . 12COOL 286
■ 7" . . . . . . . . . . . . . . . . . . . . .COOL 286
■ CD Single . . . . . . . . . . . . . . . . CDCOOL 286
■ MC Single . . . . . . . . . . . . . . . . TCCOOL 286
Chrysalis / Jan '94.

### WHAT SILENCE KNOWS.
Tracks: Nobody / Pain revisited / One goodbye in ten / Inside out / Chance / Uptight / Down that road / Thoughts of you / How close / What silence knows.
CD . . . . . . . . . . . . . . . . . . . . . CTCD 35
LP . . . . . . . . . . . . . . . . . . . . . CTLP 35
MC . . . . . . . . . . . . . . . . . . . . . CTTC 35
Cool Tempo / Sep '93 / EMI.

## Nelson, Tyka

### MARC ANTHONY'S TUNE.
Tracks: Marc Anthony's tune / Be good to me / This girl is gonna fall in love (On 12" only).
■ 7" . . . . . . . . . . . . . . . . . . . . .COOL 166
■ CD Single . . . . . . . . . . . . . . . . COOLCD 166
■ 12" . . . . . . . . . . . . . . . . . . . . COOLX 166
Cool Tempo / Jun '88.

### ROYAL BLUE.
Tracks: No promise / Paris / Marc Antony / Try my passion / My friend / Love / Be good to me / Royal blue / This girl is gonna fall in love.
MC . . . . . . . . . . . . . . . . . . . . . . ZCT 7
CD . . . . . . . . . . . . . . . . . . . . . CCD 1643
■ LP . . . . . . . . . . . . . . . . . . . . . CTLP 7
Cool Tempo / Jun '88 / EMI.

## Nero, Frances

### FOOTSTEPS FOLLOWING ME.
Tracks: Footsteps following me.
■ 12" . . . . . . . . . . . . . . . . . . . . MOTC 24
■ 7" . . . . . . . . . . . . . . . . . . . .7MOTC 24
Motor City / Dec '90.

■ DELETED

## FOOTSTEPS FOLLOWING ME (2).
Tracks: Footsteps following me.
- ■ 12". . . . . . . . . . . . . . . . . . DEBTX 3109
- ■ 7". . . . . . . . . . . . . . . . . . . . DEBT 3109
- ■ CD Single. . . . . . . . . . . . . DEBCD 3109
- ■ MC Single. . . . . . . . . . . . . DEBMC 3109

Debut (2) / Apr '91.

## MAKING MY DAYDREAMS REAL.
Tracks: Making my daydreams real.
- ■ 12". . . . . . . . . . . . . . . . . . . . . MOTC 80

Motor City / Aug '91.

## OUT ON THE FLOOR.
Tracks: Not Advised.
- ■ LP . . . . . . . . . . . . . . . . . . . .MOTCLP 44
- ■ CD . . . . . . . . . . . . . . . . . CDMOTCLP 44

Motor City / Dec '90.

## Neville Brothers

Art, Aaron and Charles Neville have been synonymous with New Orleans R&B for four decades. As Hawkettes, they backed Fats Domino in mid-50's, then began recording collectively and solo, achieving hits on Specialty, Chess, Minit etc. Brothers added musicians to line-up for Neville Sounds in early '60s, but band split when Art and rhythm section were recruited by legendary New Orleans producer, Allen Toussaint, for house band in '68; in which capacity they backed Lee Dorsey, Betty Harris, Irma Thomas and Toussaint himself. As the Meters, they enjoyed several hits in late '60s and early '70s, but were equally well-known as backing band for acts ranging from Patti Labelle to Dr. John. Nevilles reunited in mid-'70s, with youngest brother, Cyril, and resumed vocal career. Their acclaimed releases sold poorly until Yellow Moon and Brother's Keeper ('89 and '90, respectively).

## BIRD ON A WIRE.
Tracks: Bird on a wire.
- ■ 12". . . . . . . . . . . . . . . . . . . . . AMY 568
- ■ 7". . . . . . . . . . . . . . . . . . . . . . AM 568
- ■ CD Single. . . . . . . . . . . . . . AMCD 568

A&M / Jun '90.

## BROTHERS KEEPER.
Tracks: Brother blood / Steer me right / Sons and daughters / Jah love / Witness / Sons and daughters (reprise) / Bird on a wire / Brother Jake / Fearless / Fallin' rain / River of life / My brother's keeper / Mystery train.
- CD. . . . . . . . . . . . . . . . . . . . . . .395 3122
- MC. . . . . . . . . . . . . . . . . . . . . . .395 3124
- ■ LP . . . . . . . . . . . . . . . . . . . . . .395 3121

A&M / Aug '90 / PolyGram.
- DCC . . . . . . . . . . . . . . . . . . . . 395 312-5

A&M / Jan '93 / PolyGram.

## CHANGE IS GONNA COME, A.
Tracks: Change is gonna come / Sister Rosa.
- ■ 7". . . . . . . . . . . . . . . . . . . . . . .USA 656
- ■ 12". . . . . . . . . . . . . . . . . . . . . USAT 656

A&M / Apr '89.

## CHANGE IS GONNA COME, A (RE-RELEASE).
Tracks: Change is gonna come / Wake up (live) / Sister Rosa (live).
- ■ 12". . . . . . . . . . . . . . . . . . . . . AMY 548
- ■ 7". . . . . . . . . . . . . . . . . . . . . . AM 548
- ■ CD Single. . . . . . . . . . . . . . CDEE 548

A&M / Jan '90.

## FAMILY GROOVE.
Tracks: Fly like an eagle / One more day / I can see it in your eyes / Day to day thing / Line of fire / Take me to heart / It takes more / Family groove / True love / On the other side of paradise / Let my people go / Saxafunk / Maori chant / Good song.
- CD . . . . . . . . . . . . . . . . . . . . . . . 3971802

A&M / Apr '92 / PolyGram.

## FEARLESS.
Tracks: Fearless / Shake your tambourine (live) / Change is gonna come (Only on 12" and CD single.).
- ■ 12". . . . . . . . . . . . . . . . . . . . . AMY 600
- ■ 7". . . . . . . . . . . . . . . . . . . . . . . AM 600
- ■ CD Single. . . . . . . . . . . . . . AMCD 600

A&M / Sep '90.

## FIYO ON THE BAYOU.
Tracks: Hey pocky away / Sweet honey dripper / Fire on the Bayou / Ten commandments / Sitting in limbo / Brother John / Iko iko / Mona lisa / Run Joe.
- CD. . . . . . . . . . . . . . . . . . . . . FIENDCD 65
- ■ LP . . . . . . . . . . . . . . . . . . . . . FIEND 65
- MC. . . . . . . . . . . . . . . . . . . FIENDCASS 65

Demon / Jul '86 / Pinnacle / A.D.A. Distribution.

## FLY LIKE AN EAGLE.
Tracks: Fly like an eagle / Fly like an eagle (instrumental).
- ■ 7". . . . . . . . . . . . . . . . . . . . . . . AM 872
- ■ MC Single. . . . . . . . . . . . . . AMMC 872
- ■ 12". . . . . . . . . . . . . . . . . . . . . . AMY 872
- ■ CD . . . . . . . . . . . . . . . . . . . . AMCD 872

A&M / Oct '92.

## GOD ON YOUR SIDE.
Tracks: God on your side / Voodoo.
- ■ 12". . . . . . . . . . . . . . . . . . . . . AMY 545
- ■ 7". . . . . . . . . . . . . . . . . . . . . . . AM 545
- ■ CD Single. . . . . . . . . . . . . . AMCD 545

A&M / Nov '89.

## LEGACY (A History Of The Nevilles).
Tracks: Mardi Gras mambo / Over you / Funky miracle / Little girl from the candy store / Show me the way / Sophisticated Cissy / I'm waiting at the station / My baby don't love me anymore / 6v6 LA / Ride your pony / Wrong number / Cardova / I need someone / How could I help but love you / Cissy strut / Humdinger / That rock'n'roll beat / Chicken strut / Don't cry / All these things / Britches / Even though (reality) / Get out of my life / Darling, don't leave me this way / Live wire / House on the hill (rock'n'roll hootenanny) / Tippi toes / Hook line and sinker / For every boy there's a girl / Art / Same old thing / You won't do right / Everyday / Sweet little mama / Pains in my heart / Joog / Tell it like it is / Hercules / I'm gonna put some hurt on you / Make me strong / Look ka py py / Ease back / Bo Diddley / Speak to me / Cry me a river / Heartaches / Been so wrong / Message from the Meters / Going home.
- CD Set . . . . . . . . . . . . . . . . . CDNEV 1
- MC Set . . . . . . . . . . . . . . . . . TCNEV 1

Charly R&B / Apr '90 / Charly.

## LIVE AT TIPITINA'S.
Tracks: Not Advised.
- CD. . . . . . . . . . . . . . . . . . . . . . . TL 1328

Traditional Line / Apr '94 / Charly / A.D.A. Distribution / Koch International.

## LIVE AT TIPITINA'S VOL.2.
Tracks: Wishin' / Rock and roll medley / All over again / Everybody's got to wake up / Dance your blues away / Little Liza Jane / Wildflower / My girl / Riverside / Saib's groove / Pocky way / Doo wop medley / Rocking pneumonia and the boogie woogie flu / Something you got / I know / Everybody loves a lover.
- ■ LP . . . . . . . . . . . . . . . . . . . . .FIEND 120

Demon / Jun '88.
- ■ LP . . . . . . . . . . . . . . . . . . . . . ESSLP 130
- ■ CD . . . . . . . . . . . . . . . . . . . . ESSCD 130
- ■ MC. . . . . . . . . . . . . . . . . . . ESSMC 130

Essential / Aug '90.
- CD . . . . . . . . . . . . . . . . . . . . CLACD 347

Castle / Jun '94 / BMG.

## LIVE ON PLANET EARTH.
Tracks: Shake your tambourine / Voodoo / Dealer / Junk man / Brother Jake / Sister Rosa / Yellow moon / Her African eyes / Sands of time / Congo Square / Love the one you're with/You can't always get what you want / Let my people go/Get up stand up / Amazing Grace / One love/People get ready/Sermon.
- CD . . . . . . . . . . . . . . . . . . . . .540225-2
- MC. . . . . . . . . . . . . . . . . . . . .540225-4

A&M / Apr '94 / PolyGram.

## NEVILLE BROTHERS.
Tracks: Dancing Jones / Washable ink / All night's alright / Audience for my pain / Breakaway / If it takes all night / I'll take my chances / Vieux carre rouge / Arianne / Speed of light.
- ■ LP . . . . . . . . . . . . . . . . . . . . .EST 11865

Capitol / '79.

## NEVILLE-IZATION.
Tracks: Fever / Woman's gotta have it / Mojo Hannah / Tell it like it is / Why you wanna hurt my heart / Fear, hate, envy, jealousy / Caravan / Big chief / Africa.
- ■ LP . . . . . . . . . . . . . . . . . . . . . FIEND 31

Demon / Sep '84.
- CD . . . . . . . . . . . . . . . . . . . . FIENDCD 31

Demon / Nov '86 / Pinnacle / A.D.A. Distribution.
- ■ LP . . . . . . . . . . . . . . . . . . . . . BT 1031

MC. . . . . . . . . . . . . . . . . . . . . BT 1031C

Black Top (USA) / '88 / C.M. Distribution / Direct Distribution / Hot Shot / Topic Records.
- MC. . . . . . . . . . . . . . . . . . FIENDCASS 31

Demon / Oct '91 / Pinnacle / A.D.A. Distribution.

## RIVER OF LIFE.
Tracks: River of life / Tell it like it is (live).
- ■ 12". . . . . . . . . . . . . . . . . . . . . AMY 586
- ■ 7". . . . . . . . . . . . . . . . . . . . . . . AM 586

## CD Single. . . . . . . . . . . . . . . . AMCD 586
A&M / Aug '90.

## TELL IT LIKE IT IS.
Tracks: Tell it like it is / Over you / That rock 'n' roll beat / For every boy there's a girl / I'm waiting at the station / House on the hill (rock 'n' roll hootenanny) / How many times / How could I help but love you / All these things / Cry me a river / Speak to me / Hook, line and sinker / Mardi Gras mambo / Cardova / Funky miracle / Ride your pony / Struttin' on Sunday / Make me strong / Heartaches / Show me the way / Wrong number / You won't do right / Get out of my life / Hercules.
- CD . . . . . . . . . . . . . . . . . . . . . MCCD 022
- MC. . . . . . . . . . . . . . . . . . . . .MCTC 022

Music Club / May '91 / Gold & Sons / THE / Video Collection / C.M. Distribution.

## TELL IT LIKE IT IS.
Tracks: 30N X 90W / Yellow moon / Falling out of love / Closer to you / Midnight rider / Tell it like it is / My blood / Sixty minute man / Sister Rosa / Fire and brimstone / Middle of the night / Ya, ya / Brother John / Iko iko / Fire on the Bayou.
- ■ VHS . . . . . . . . . . . . . . . . . . . 790 365

BMG Video / Jul '90.

## TREACHEROUS-A HISTORY OF THE NEVILLE BROTHERS (1955-1985).
Tracks: Mardis gras mambo / Cha dooky-doo / Zing, zing / Over you / Let's live / Waiting at the station / All these things / Wrong number / Tell it like it is / Where is my baby / Hercules / Brother John / Meet de boys on de battlefront / Greatest love / Dancing Jones / Arianne / Washable ink / I love her too / Her pocky way / Sitting in limbo / Fire on the Bayou / Fever / Fear, hate, envy, jealousy / Amazing grace / Down by the riverside / Amen.
- ■ Double LP. . . . . . . . . . . . . . .RNFP 71494
- MC. . . . . . . . . . . . . . . . . . . . .RNFC 71494

Rhino (USA) / Feb '88 / WEA.

## UPTOWN.
Tracks: Whatever it takes / Forever..for tonight / You're the one / Money back guarantee (my love is guaranteed) / Drift away / Shek-a-na-na / Old habits die hard / I never need no one / Midnight key / Spirits of the world.
- CD . . . . . . . . . . . . . . . . . . . . CDFA 3255
- ■ LP . . . . . . . . . . . . . . . . . . . . . FA 3255
- MC. . . . . . . . . . . . . . . . . . . . . TCFA 3255

Fame / Apr '91 / EMI.

## YELLOW MOON.
Tracks: My blood / Yellow moon / Fire and brimstone / Change is gonna come / Sister Rosa / With God on our side / Wake up / Voodoo / Ballad of Hollis Brown / Will the circle be unbroken / Healing chant / Wild injuns.
- CD . . . . . . . . . . . . . . . . . . . . . CDA 5240
- ■ LP . . . . . . . . . . . . . . . . . . . . . AMA 5240
- MC. . . . . . . . . . . . . . . . . . . . . .AMC 5240

A&M / Mar '89 / PolyGram.

## YELLOW MOON.
Tracks: Yellow moon / With God on our side.
- ■ 12". . . . . . . . . . . . . . . . . . . . . USAT 657
- ■ 7". . . . . . . . . . . . . . . . . . . . . . .USA 657

A&M / Jun '89.
- ■ CD Single. . . . . . . . . . . . . . . USACD 657

A&M / Oct '89.

## Neville, Aaron

## CLOSE YOUR EYES.
Tracks: Close your eyes.
- ■ 12". . . . . . . . . . . . . . . . . . . . . AMY 835
- ■ 7". . . . . . . . . . . . . . . . . . . . . . . AM 835
- ■ CD Single. . . . . . . . . . . . . . AMCD 835
- ■ MC Single. . . . . . . . . . . . . . AMMC 835

A&M / Oct '91.

## EVERYBODY PLAYS THE FOOL.
Tracks: Everybody plays the fool.
- ■ 12". . . . . . . . . . . . . . . . . . . . . AMY 793
- ■ 7". . . . . . . . . . . . . . . . . . . . . . . AM 793
- ■ CD Single. . . . . . . . . . . . . . AMCD 793
- ■ MC Single. . . . . . . . . . . . . . AMMC 793

A&M / Aug '91.

## GET A LITTLE FREAKY.
Tracks: Get a little freaky.
- ■ 12". . . . . . . . . . . . . . . . . . . . . MCST 1936
- ■ CD Single. . . . . . . . . . . . . . MCSTD 1936
- ■ MC Single. . . . . . . . . . . . . . MCSC 1936

MCA / Oct '93.

## HERCULES.
Tracks: Over you / Show me the way / How could I help but love you / Get out of my life / Wrong number

/ I'm waiting at the station / I found another love / How many times / Hey little Alice / Let's live / Tell it like it is / Struttin' on Sunday / Make me strong / Hercules / Been so wrong / Cry me a river / Greatest love / One fine day / All these things / Performance.
CD . . . . . . . . . . . . . . . . . . . . . . . . . CPCD 8016
Charly / Feb '94 / Charly.

### HUMDINGER.
**Tracks:** Over you / I'm waitin' at the station / Everyday / Sweet little mama / Let's live / Humdinger / Wrong number / Reality / How many times / Don't cry / Get out of my life / I found another love / How could I help but love you / Show me the way.
■ MC. . . . . . . . . . . . . . . . . . . . . TCSSL 6011
Stateside / Sep '86.
■ LP . . . . . . . . . . . . . . . . . . . . . . SSL 6011
Stateside / Sep '86.

### I FALL TO PIECES.
**Tracks:** I fall to pieces.
■ CD Single . . . . . . . . . . . . . . MCSTD 1975
■ MC Single. . . . . . . . . . . . . . . MCSC 1975
MCA / Jun '94.

### MAKE ME STRONG.
**Tracks:** Struttin' on Sunday / Hercules / Make me strong / All these things / Baby I'm a want you / Performance / Mojo Hannah / Greatest love / One fine day / Tell it like it is / Cry me a river / Been so wrong / Speak to me / Wild flower / Feelings / Nadie / For the good times / She's on my mind.
MC. . . . . . . . . . . . . . . . . . . . . TCCRB 1111
Charly R&B / Sep '86 / Charly.
■ LP . . . . . . . . . . . . . . . . . . . . . CRB 1111
Charly R&B / Sep '86.
CD . . . . . . . . . . . . . . . . . . . CDCHARLY 64
Charly R&B / Feb '87 / Charly.

### ORCHID IN THE STORM.
**Tracks:** Pledging my love / For your precious love / Ten commandments of love / This is my story / We belong together / Earth angel.
■ LP . . . . . . . . . . . . . . . . . . . . . . . VEX 6
Demon / Apr '86.

### RULER OF HEARTS/SHOW ME THE WAY (see under Thomas, Irma).

### SHOW ME THE WAY.
**Tracks:** How could I help but love you / Over you / Even though (reality) / Show me the way / I found another love / How many times / Everyday / Hey little Alice / Sweet little mama / Don't cry / Ticks of the clock / For every boy there's a girl / I'm waiting at the station / Wrong number / I've done it again / Let's live / Get out of my life.
CD . . . . . . . . . . . . . . . . . . . . CDCHARLY 162
■ LP . . . . . . . . . . . . . . . . . . . . . CRB 1217
MC. . . . . . . . . . . . . . . . . . . . . TCCRB 1217
Charly R&B / Aug '89 / Charly.

### SOMEWHERE SOMEBODY.
**Tracks:** Somewhere somebody.
■ 12" . . . . . . . . . . . . . . . . . . . . . . AMY 798
■ 7" . . . . . . . . . . . . . . . . . . . . . . . AM 798
■ CD Single. . . . . . . . . . . . . . . . AMCD 798
■ MC Single. . . . . . . . . . . . . . . . AMMC 798
A&M / Aug '91.

### TELL IT LIKE IT IS.
**Tracks:** Fever / Iko Iko / Fortune teller.
■ 12" . . . . . . . . . . . . . . . . . . . . . . CYZ 124
■ 7" . . . . . . . . . . . . . . . . . . . . . CYZ 7 124
Charly Groove / Jun '88.

### TELL IT LIKE IT IS.
**Tracks:** Tell it like it is / Why worry / She took you for a ride / Hard nut to crack / You think you're so smart / Jailhouse / Bet you're surprised / Love, love, love / Since you're gone / Space man / Hold on, help is on the way / Those three words.
CD . . . . . . . . . . . . . . . . . . . . . . . CDCH 301
LP . . . . . . . . . . . . . . . . . . . . . . . . CH 301
Ace / Aug '90 / Pinnacle / Complete Record Co. Ltd.

### TELL IT LIKE IT IS.
**Tracks:** Not Advised.
■ CD . . . . . . . . . . . . . . . . . . . . CDCHM 301
Ace / Sep '90.

### WARM YOUR HEART.
**Tracks:** Louisiana 1927 / Everybody plays the fool / It feels like rain / Somewhere somebody / Don't go please stay / With you in mind / That's the ways she loves / Angola bound / Close your eyes / La vie dansante / Warm your heart / I bid you goodnight / Ave Maria / House on a hill.
CD . . . . . . . . . . . . . . . . . . . . . . . 3971482
■ LP . . . . . . . . . . . . . . . . . . . . . . 3971481
MC. . . . . . . . . . . . . . . . . . . . . . . 3971484
A&M / Jul '91 / PolyGram.
DCC . . . . . . . . . . . . . . . . . . . . 397 148-5
A&M / Jan '93 / PolyGram.

## Neville, Art

### HIS SPECIALTY RECORDINGS 1956-58.
**Tracks:** Please believe me / Standing on the highway / Please don't go / When my baby went away / Please listen to my song / Lover's song / Oooh-baby / Whiffenpoof song / Oooh-wee baby / Let's rock / Back home to me / Zing zing / Cha dooky doo / That old time Rock 'N' Roll / Arabian love call / Rockin' pneumonia / What's going on / Belle amie / Dummy / I'm a fool to care.
CD . . . . . . . . . . . . . . . . . . . . . CDCHD 434
Ace / Jan '93 / Pinnacle / Complete Record Co. Ltd.

### KEYS TO THE CRESCENT (Neville, Art, Eddie Bo, Charles Brown & Willie Tee).
**Tracks:** Not Advised.
CD . . . . . . . . . . . . . . . . . . . . . CDROU 2087
Rounder / Sep '91 / Roots Records / C.M. Distribution / Topic Records / A.D.A. Distribution / Direct Distribution.

### MARDI GRAS ROCK 'N' ROLL.
**Tracks:** Zing zing / Bella Mae / Cha dooky-doo / a fool to care / Cha dooky-doo / Back home to me / What's going on / Old time Rock 'n' roll / Rockin' pneumonia and the boogie woogie flu / Bring it on home to me / Dummy / Let's rock / Arabian love call / Please listen to my song / Whiffenpoof song.
■ LP . . . . . . . . . . . . . . . . . . . . . .CHD 188
Ace / Nov '86.
CD . . . . . . . . . . . . . . . . . . . . . CDCHD 188
Ace / Oct '90 / Pinnacle / Complete Record Co. Ltd.

### ROCK 'N' SOUL HOOTENANNY.
**Tracks:** House on the hill / Skeet scat / Little girl from the candy store / Humdinger / All these things / My baby don't love me no more / Darling, don't leave me this way / Come back love / Hook, line and sinker / Too much / Pain in my heart / Heartaches / I need somebody / You won't do right / That rock 'n' roll beat / Bo Diddley.
■ LP . . . . . . . . . . . . . . . . . . . . . CRB 1177
Charly R&B / Sep '88.

## New Birth

### DREAM MERCHANT.
**Tracks:** Dream merchant / Why did I.
■ 7" . . . . . . . . . . . . . . . . . . . . . .BDS 434
Buddah / Aug '75.

## New Edition

Remembered in U.K. for 1983 chart-topper *Candy Girl*, New Edition were far more important in U.S. soul scene. Moulded by writer/producer Maurice Starr into recreation of vintage Jackson Five, they inspired new generation of black teen groups, notably Boyz II Men (Starr avenged his dismissal from New Edition camp by conceiving New Kids on the Block). In 1985, they achieved million-seller with *Cool It Now*; followed by Ray Parker Jr production *Mr.Telephone Man*, which restored New Edition to U.K. Top 20 and was another Stateside smash. 1988's *Heartbreak* album, their first without Bobby Brown (who quit for solo career), spawned four US Top 10 hits. In 1989, group undertook tour with Guy; inter-band rivalry climaxed with killing of New Edition's stage manager. Shortly afterwords, band disintegrated: Johnny Gill (Brown's replacement) and Ralph Tresvant went solo, while Ricky Bell, Michael Bivins and Ronnie DeVoe formed Bell Biv Devoe.

### ALL FOR LOVE.
**Tracks:** Count me in / Little bit of love / Sweet thing / With you all the way / Let's be friends / Kick back / Tonight's your night / Whispers in bed / Who do you trust / School / All for love.
■ LP . . . . . . . . . . . . . . . . . . . . . MCF 3305
■ MC. . . . . . . . . . . . . . . . . . . . MCFC 3305
MCA / Jun '86.

### CANDY GIRL.
**Tracks:** Gimme your love / She gives me a bang / Is this the end / Pass the beat / Popcorn love / Candy girl / Ooh baby / Should have never told me / Gotta have your lovin' / Jealous girl.
MC. . . . . . . . . . . . . . . . . . . . . . KSAC 8553
■ LP . . . . . . . . . . . . . . . . . . . . . SH 8553
Streetwave / Aug '83.

### CANDY GIRL.
**Tracks:** Candy girl.
■ 12" . . . . . . . . . . . . . . . . . . . . LONX 21
■ 7" . . . . . . . . . . . . . . . . . . . . . LON 21
London / Apr '83.

### COOL IT NOW.
**Tracks:** Cool it now.
■ 12" . . . . . . . . . . . . . . . . . . . . MCAT 922
■ 7" . . . . . . . . . . . . . . . . . . . . MCA 922
MCA / Oct '84.
■ 12" . . . . . . . . . . . . . . . . . . . . MCAT 963
■ 7" . . . . . . . . . . . . . . . . . . . . MCA 963
MCA / Apr '85.

### CRUCIAL.
**Tracks:** Crucial.
■ 12" . . . . . . . . . . . . . . . . . . MCA 23934
■ 12" . . . . . . . . . . . . . . . . . MCAT 1333
■ 7" . . . . . . . . . . . . . . . . . . MCA 1333
MCA / Apr '89.

### EARTH ANGEL.
**Tracks:** Million to one / Duke of Earl / Hey there lonely girl / Thousand miles away / What's your name / Tears on my pillow / Blue moon / Since I don't have you / Bring back the memories.
■ LP . . . . . . . . . . . . . . . . . . . . . MCF 3356
■ MC. . . . . . . . . . . . . . . . . . . . MCFC 3356
MCA / Feb '87.

### EARTH ANGEL.
**Tracks:** Earth angel / With you all the way.
■ 12" . . . . . . . . . . . . . . . . . . MCAT 1103
■ 7" . . . . . . . . . . . . . . . . . . .MCA 1103
MCA / Nov '86.

### GREATEST HITS: NEW EDITION.
**Tracks:** Not Advised.
■ CD . . . . . . . . . . . . . . . . . MCAD 10434
■ LP . . . . . . . . . . . . . . . . . . MCA 10434
■ MC . . . . . . . . . . . . . . . . . MCAC 10434
MCA / Oct '91.

### HEART BREAK.
**Tracks:** Not Advised.
■ LP . . . . . . . . . . . . . . . . . . MCA 42207
MCA / Aug '88.

### HEARTBEAT.
**Tracks:** Not Advised.
■ CD . . . . . . . . . . . . . . . . . . DMCF 3422
■ LP . . . . . . . . . . . . . . . . . . MCF 3422
■ MC. . . . . . . . . . . . . . . . . . MCFC 3422
MCA / Sep '88.

### IF IT ISN'T LOVE.
**Tracks:** If it isn't love / If it isn't love (instrumental) / If it isn't love (dubapella) (on 12" only).
■ 12" . . . . . . . . . . . . . . . . . . MCAT 1269
■ 7" . . . . . . . . . . . . . . . . . . . MCA 1269
MCA / Aug '88.

### IS THIS THE END.
**Tracks:** Is this the end / She gives me a bang.
■ 12" . . . . . . . . . . . . . . . . . . LONX 35
■ 7" . . . . . . . . . . . . . . . . . . . LON 35
London / Oct '83.

### LITTLE BIT OF LOVE, A (IS ALL IT TAKES).
**Tracks:** Little bit of love / Sneakin' around / Little bit of love, A (Inst).
■ 12" . . . . . . . . . . . . . . . . . . MCAT 1032
■ 7" . . . . . . . . . . . . . . . . . . .MCA 1032
MCA / Feb '86.

### MR TELEPHONE MAN.
**Tracks:** Mr. Telephone man.
■ 12" . . . . . . . . . . . . . . . . . . MCAT 938
■ 7" . . . . . . . . . . . . . . . . . . . MCA 938
MCA / Feb '85.

### NEW EDITION.
**Tracks:** Cool it now / Mr. Telephone man / I'm leaving you again / Baby love / Delicious / My secret (didja gitit yet) / Hide and seek / Lost in love / Kinda girl we like / Amryann.
■ CD . . . . . . . . . . . . . . . . . . . DIDX 328
MCA.
■ LP . . . . . . . . . . . . . . . . . . MCF 3238
■ MC. . . . . . . . . . . . . . . . . . MCFC 3238
MCA / Nov '84.

### NEW EDITION: VIDEO EP.
**Tracks:** Not Advised.
■ VHS . . . . . . . . . . . . . . . . . HEN 2178
Hendring Video / '88.

### POPCORN LOVE.
**Tracks:** Popcorn love / Pass the beat.
■ 12" . . . . . . . . . . . . . . . . . . LONX 31
■ 7" . . . . . . . . . . . . . . . . . . . LON 31
London / Aug '83.

## New Experience

**ROVE IT TO ME.**
racks: Prove it to me.
■ 12″ . . . . . . . . . . . . . . . . . . . POSPX 736
■ 7″ . . . . . . . . . . . . . . . . . . . . POSP 736
oiling Point / Jul '85.

## New Jersey Connection

**OVE DON'T COME EASY.**
racks: Love don't come easy.
■ 7″ . . . . . . . . . . . . . . . . . . . . . . LIFE 1
■ 12″ . . . . . . . . . . . . . . . . . . . LIFE 112
ite Life / Nov '82.

## New Version Of Soul

**IRTH OF SOULADELIC.**
racks: Mr. Skater / Intro / Swang da funk / Gappy
eaver (Interlude) / Uponit / Cherry tree / When I
was 16 / Pump up the sound / Skatter's theme /
riginal / 66 Mello / Heaven prelude / Heaven / Mr.
katter's souldelic nursery rhymes (Interlude) / Cur-
ous creem / Git I away / Souldelic mindz / Mr.
katter conclusion / Let the vibes flow through.
■ CD . . . . . . . . . . . . . . . . . . CDEST 2200
■ LP . . . . . . . . . . . . . . . . . . . . EST 2200
■ MC . . . . . . . . . . . . . . . . . . .TCEST 2200
apitol / May '93.

## New Wanderers

**THIS MAN IN LOVE.**
acks: This man in love / Adam and Eve.
■ 7″ . . . . . . . . . . . . . . . . . . . . .GRP 144
rapevine (Northern Soul) / Dec '79.

## New York City

**'M DOIN' FINE NOW.**
racks: Not Advised.
■ CD . . . . . . . . . . . . . . . . . . CHELD 1001
■ LP . . . . . . . . . . . . . . . . . . CHELV 1001
MC . . . . . . . . . . . . . . . . . . CHELC 1001
tart / Jun '89 / THE / Koch International.

**'M DOIN' FINE NOW.**
racks: I'm doin' fine now.
■ 7″ . . . . . . . . . . . . . . . . . . . RCA 2351
CA / Jul '73.

## New York Port Authority

**GOT IT.**
racks: I got it / I got it (version).
■ 7″ . . . . . . . . . . . . . . . . . . . INV 5312
nvictus / Jul '77.

**THREE THOUSAND MILES FROM HOME.**
racks: I got it / I used to hate it ('til I ate it) / I don't
want to work today / Rainbow / Three thousand
iles from home / Guess I'm gonna cry / Twilight
one / Home on a rainy day.
■ LP . . . . . . . . . . . . . . . . . . . INV 81951
nvictus / Sep '77.

## New York Skyy

**BAD BOY.**
racks: Bad boy / Swing it.
■ 12″ . . . . . . . . . . . . . . . . . . . . TA 3751
■ 7″ . . . . . . . . . . . . . . . . . . . EPCA 3571
pic / Jul '83.

**CALL ME.**
racks: Call me / Jam the box.
■ 12″ . . . . . . . . . . . . . . . . . EPCA 132151
■ 7″ . . . . . . . . . . . . . . . . . . EPCA 2151
pic / Mar '82.

**DESPERATE FOR YOUR LOVE.**
Tracks: Desperate for your love / Great balloon race.
■ 7″ . . . . . . . . . . . . . . . . . . . .A 6124
pic / Mar '85.

**FIRST TIME AROUND.**
Tracks: First time around / Disco dancin'.
■ 7″ . . . . . . . . . . . . . . . . . . . SSOL 119
alsoul / Jul '79.

**FROM THE LEFT SIDE.**
racks: Givin' it (to you) / Love attack / Non-stop /
ong song / Big fun / Love illogical / Tell her you
are / Jealousitis / Rock it.
■ LP . . . . . . . . . . . . . . . . . . . EST 2014
■ MC . . . . . . . . . . . . . . . . . .TCEST 2014
apitol / May '86.

## GIVIN' IT (TO YOU).

Tracks: Givin' it (to you) / Givin' it (to you) (Dub remix).
■ 7″ . . . . . . . . . . . . . . . . . . .CL 401
Capitol / Jun '86.
■ 12″ . . . . . . . . . . . . . . . . . 12CL 401
Capitol / May '86.

## GREATEST HITS: NEW YORK SKYY.

Tracks: Not Advised.
CD . . . . . . . . . . . . . . . . . . . CDNYS 1
■ LP . . . . . . . . . . . . . . . . . . . . NYS 1
MC . . . . . . . . . . . . . . . . . . ZCNYS 1
Street Sounds / Jan '87 / BMG / Total.

## HERE'S TO YOU.

Tracks: Here's to you / No music.
■ 12″ . . . . . . . . . . . . . . . . . EXCL 504
Excaliber / Feb '81.

## HIGH.

Tracks: High / First time around.
■ 12″ . . . . . . . . . . . . . . . . . . SAL 12-1
Salsoul / May '80.

## INNER CITY.

Tracks: Because of you / Two hearts / Dancin' to be
dancin' / Pay up / Passion in the night / I got your
number / Love is blind / Slow motion / It's my life.
■ LP . . . . . . . . . . . . . . . . . . FL 84161
Salsoul / Jan '85.

## LET LOVE SHINE.

Tracks: Let love shine / Won't you be mine.
■ 12″ . . . . . . . . . . . . . . . EPCA 132975
■ 7″ . . . . . . . . . . . . . . . . . EPCA 2975
Epic / Nov '82.

## LET'S CELEBRATE.

Tracks: Let's celebrate / Call me.
■ 7″ . . . . . . . . . . . . . . . . . EPCA 1898
Epic / Jan '82.

## NON-STOP.

Tracks: Non-stop / Tell her you care.
■ 12″ . . . . . . . . . . . . . . . . . 12CL 434
■ 7″ . . . . . . . . . . . . . . . . . . .CL 434
Capitol / Sep '86.

## SHOW ME THE WAY.

Tracks: Show me the way / Now that we've found
love.
■ 12″ . . . . . . . . . . . . . . . . . . TA 3691
■ 7″ . . . . . . . . . . . . . . . . . . . A 3691
Epic / Aug '83.

## SKYY.

Tracks: This groove is bad / First time around / Let's
turn it out / Fallin' in love again / Stand by me / Disco
dancin' / Let's get up.
■ LP . . . . . . . . . . . . . . . . . . SSLP 1516
Salsoul / '79.

## SKYYJAMMERS.

Tracks: Movin' violation / Won't you be mine / This
song is for you / Miracle / Skyyjammers / Let love
shine / Together / Freak outta.
■ LP . . . . . . . . . . . . . . . . . . EPC 25110
Epic / '83.

## SKYYLIGHT.

Tracks: Bad boy / Married man / Questions no
answers / Now that we've found love / Hey girl /
Show me the way / She's gone / Swing it.
■ LP . . . . . . . . . . . . . . . . . . EPC 25632
MC . . . . . . . . . . . . . . . . . . .40 25632
Epic / Aug '83 / Sony.

## SKYYLINE.

Tracks: Let's celebrate / Call me / Girl in blue / Jam
the box / When you touch me / Gonna get it on / Get
into the beat.
■ LP . . . . . . . . . . . . . . . . . . EPC 85494
Epic / Mar '82.

## SKYYPORT.

Tracks: Here's to you / I can't get enough / Super-
lover / No music / Take it easy / Sun won't shine /
For the first time / Arrival.
■ LP . . . . . . . . . . . . . . . . .EXCLP 5002
Excaliber / Feb '81.

## START OF A ROMANCE.

Tracks: Start of a romance / Sendin' a message /
Feeling it now / Let's touch / Love all the way / Sexy
minded / Real love / Sunshine.
CD . . . . . . . . . . . . . . . . . . K 781 853 2
■ LP . . . . . . . . . . . . . . . . . K 781 853 1
■ MC . . . . . . . . . . . . . . . . . K 781 853 4
Atlantic / Mar '89 / WEA.

## SUPER LOVE.

Tracks: Super love / I can't get enough / Take it easy
(on 12″ only).

■ 12″ . . . . . . . . . . . . . . . . . EXCL 507
■ 7″ . . . . . . . . . . . . . . . . . . EXC 507
Excaliber / Mar '81.

## Newberry, Booker III

**I GET ROMANTIC.**
Tracks: I get romantic.
■ 12″ . . . . . . . . . . . . . . . . . . VIBE 6T
Buzz Int. / Sep '85.

**LOVE TOWN.**
Tracks: Love town / Attitude / Shadows / Love drums
/ Teddy bear / Morning after the night before /
Shower of love / Never gonna let you go.
■ LP . . . . . . . . . . . . . . . . . .MALP 001
MC . . . . . . . . . . . . . . . . . . ZCMAL 1
Malaco / Nov '84 / C.M. Distribution / Charly /
Pinnacle.
■ LP . . . . . . . . . . . . . . . . 815 012-1
Polydor (Germany) / Sep '84.

**LOVE TOWN.**
Tracks: Love town / Doin' what comes naturally.
■ 12″ . . . . . . . . . . . . . . . . . POSPX 613
■ 7″ . . . . . . . . . . . . . . . . . . POSP 613
Polydor / May '83.

**LOVE TOWN.**
Tracks: Love town.
■ 12″ . . . . . . . . . . . . . . . . . 12SCR 007
■ CD Single . . . . . . . . . . . . . C7SCR 007
Scratch / Jun '93.

**SHADOWS.**
Tracks: Shadows.
■ 12″ . . . . . . . . . . . . . . . . .MAL 12 028
■ 7″ . . . . . . . . . . . . . . . . . MAL 028
Malaco / Oct '84.

**TAKE A PIECE OF ME.**
Tracks: Take a piece of me.
■ 12″ . . . . . . . . . . . . . . . . .12 OMN 1
■ 7″ . . . . . . . . . . . . . . . . . . .OMN 1
Omni (USA) / Apr '86.

**TEDDYBEAR.**
Tracks: Teddybear.
■ 12″ . . . . . . . . . . . . . . . . . POSPX 637
■ 7″ . . . . . . . . . . . . . . . . . . POSP 637
Polydor / Oct '83.

## Next Generation

**IN MY BABY'S ARMS.**
Tracks: In my baby's arms.
■ 12″ . . . . . . . . . . . . . . . . .MAR 1032
Mass Media / Sep '89.

## Nicci

**CAN'T GET CLOSE TO YOU.**
Tracks: Can't get close to you / Close to who.
■ 7″ . . . . . . . . . . . . . . . . . DEBT 3002
Debut (1) / Feb '86.

**RESPECT.**
Tracks: Respect.
■ 12″ . . . . . . . . . . . . . . . . . EDITL 3321
■ 7″ . . . . . . . . . . . . . . . . . EDIT 3321
Sedition / May '87.

**SO IN LOVE.**
Tracks: So in love.
■ 12″ . . . . . . . . . . . . . . . . . DEBT 07(12)
■ 7″ . . . . . . . . . . . . . . . . . .DEBT 07
Debut (1) / Aug '85.
■ 12″ . . . . . . . . . . . . . . . . . POSPX 774
■ 7″ . . . . . . . . . . . . . . . . . . POSP 774
Boiling Point / Oct '85.

## Nicole

**DON'T YOU WANT MY LOVE.**
Tracks: Don't you want my love / Shy boy.
■ 12″ . . . . . . . . . . . . . . . . . . TA 6933
■ 7″ . . . . . . . . . . . . . . . . . . .A 6933
Portrait / Feb '86.

**HORSE CALLS.**
Tracks: Horse calls / It happens every night.
■ 7″ . . . . . . . . . . . . . . . . . .650129 7
Portrait / Oct '86.

**JAM PACKED (AT THE WALL).**
Tracks: Jam packed (at the wall) / Don't you want my
love / Jam packed (at the wall) (club mix) (Available

on 12" only) / Jam packed (at the wall) (house mix)(12" only) (Available on 12" only).
- **■ 12"** . . . . . . . . . . . . . . . . . . . . .652822 6
- **■ 7"** . . . . . . . . . . . . . . . . . . . . .652822 7

Portrait / Jun '88.

## JAMPACKED.
**Tracks:** Jam packed (at the wall) / Desire / Let's talk about love / So lost without your love / Rock the house / Two hearts are better than one / Everlasting love / Throwdown / He's so romeo.
- **■ LP** . . . . . . . . . . . . . . . . . . . BFE 40575
- **■ LP** . . . . . . . . . . . . . . . . . . . 4600431
- **■ CD** . . . . . . . . . . . . . . . . . . . 4600432
- **■ MC** . . . . . . . . . . . . . . . . . . . 4600434

Epic / Jun '88.

## NEW YORK EYES (Nicole & Timmy Thomas).
**Tracks:** New York eyes / New York eyes (remix)(12" only).
- **■ 12"** . . . . . . . . . . . . . . . . . . . QTA 6805
- **■ 7"** . . . . . . . . . . . . . . . . . . . .A 6805

Portrait / Dec '85.

## NEW YORK EYES (Thomas, Timmy & Nicole).
**Tracks:** New York eyes / Ordinary girl / New York eyes (remix).
MC Set . . . . . . . . . . . . . . . . . . . CC/026
Cover To Cover / Sep '86 / THE.

## NEW YORK EYES (OLD GOLD) (Nicole & Timmy Thomas).
**Tracks:** New York eyes / Encore.
- **■ 12"** . . . . . . . . . . . . . . . . . . . .OG 4145

Old Gold / Nov '89.

## WHAT ABOUT ME.
**Tracks:** Don't want my love / New York eyes / Housecalls / What about me / Always and forever / Why you take my love / Ordinary girl / Shy boy / It happens every night / New York eyes (remix).
- **■ LP** . . . . . . . . . . . . . . . . . . . PRT 26844
- **■ MC** . . . . . . . . . . . . . . . . . . . .40 26844

Portrait / Feb '86.

## WHAT ABOUT ME.
**Tracks:** What about me.
- **■ 12"** . . . . . . . . . . . . . . . . . . . TA 7266
- **■ 7"** . . . . . . . . . . . . . . . . . . . .A 7266

Portrait / Jun '86.

# Nightingale, Maxine

## BITTERSWEET.
**Tracks:** Take your heart / I'm givin' it all to you / Work on it / Just because / All night with me / Never enough / Tight spot / Why did you turn me on.
- **■ LP** . . . . . . . . . . . . . . . . . . . LBG 30323

Liberty / Feb '81.

## BRING OUT THE GIRL IN ME.
**Tracks:** Bring out the girl in me / Most important person.
- **■ 7"** . . . . . . . . . . . . . . . . . . . UP 36395

United Artists / May '78.

## LEAD ME ON.
**Tracks:** Lead me on / No one like my baby.
- **■ 7"** . . . . . . . . . . . . . . . . . . . UP 36447

United Artists / Aug '78.

## LEAD ME ON.
**Tracks:** Lead me on / Love me like you meant it.
- **■ 7"** . . . . . . . . . . . . . . . . . . . BP 337

Liberty / Feb '80.

## LOVE HIT ME.
**Tracks:** Love hit me / Will you be my lover / I wonder who's waiting up for you tonight / How much love / Get it up for love / You / Right now / Ain't nothin' but a maybe / Eternal bridge / Love or let me be lonely.
- **■ LP** . . . . . . . . . . . . . . . . . . . UAS 30076
- **■ MC** . . . . . . . . . . . . . . . . . . . CK 30076

United Artists / May '77.

## LOVE HIT ME.
**Tracks:** Love hit me / Life has just begun.
- **■ 7"** . . . . . . . . . . . . . . . . . . . UP 36215

United Artists / Mar '77.

## LOVE ON BORROWED TIME.
**Tracks:** Love on borrowed time / It's that hurtin' thing.
- **■ 7"** . . . . . . . . . . . . . . . . . . . 7N 45046

Pye / May '71.

## LOVELINES.
**Tracks:** You are the most important person in your life / You got to me / Your love is too strong / Bringing out the girl in me / Love me like you meant it / Lead me on / Darlin' dear / Ask Billy / No one like

my baby / Someone like me / You made my life beautiful.
- **■ LP** . . . . . . . . . . . . . . . . . . . UAG 30179

United Artists / Sep '78.

## NIGHT LIFE.
**Tracks:** Will you be my lover / You are everything / Love hit me / You / Get it up for love / Didn't I / Love or let me be lonely / I wonder who's waiting up for you tonight / How much love / Right now.
- **■ LP** . . . . . . . . . . . . . . . . . . . UAS 30105

United Artists / Sep '77.

## RIGHT BACK WHERE WE STARTED FROM.
**Tracks:** Right back where we started from (single).
- **■ 7"** . . . . . . . . . . . . . . . . . . . UP 36015

United Artists / Nov '75.

## RIGHT BACK WHERE WE STARTED FROM.
**Tracks:** Love hit me / Think I want to possess you / Bless you / Right back where we started from / In love we grow / Gotta be the one / One last ride / Reasons / If I ever lose this Heaven / Love enough / You got the love / Life has just begun / Every time I see a butterfly / Goodbye again.
- **■ LP** . . . . . . . . . . . . . . . . . . . UAG 29953

United Artists / May '76.

## RIGHT BACK WHERE WE STARTED FROM (OLD GOLD).
**Tracks:** Right back where we started from.
- **■ 7"** . . . . . . . . . . . . . . . . . . . .OG 9656

Old Gold / Mar '87.

## TAKE YOUR HEART.
**Tracks:** Take your heart / I'm givin' it all to you.
- **■ 7"** . . . . . . . . . . . . . . . . . . . BP 384

Liberty / Jan '81.

## WILL YOU BE MY LOVER.
**Tracks:** Will you be my lover / How much love.
- **■ 7"** . . . . . . . . . . . . . . . . . . . UP 36283

United Artists / Jul '77.

## WORK ON IT.
**Tracks:** Work on it / All night with me.
- **■ 7"** . . . . . . . . . . . . . . . . . . . BP 375

Liberty / Oct '80.

# Nightwriters

## LET THE MUSIC USE YOU.
**Tracks:** Let the music use you.
- **■ 12" Remix.** . . . . . . . . . . . . . DANCT 003

Danceteria / Jan '92.

## OVER YOU.
**Tracks:** Over you.
- **■ 12"** . . . . . . . . . . . . . . . . . . .12JTRAX 24

Jack Trax / Apr '89.

# Niteflyte

## DON'T CHA KNOW.
**Tracks:** Don't cha know.
- **■ 12"** . . . . . . . . . . . . . . . . . . . WANTX 45

Desire / Jul '91.

## IF YOU WANT IT.
**Tracks:** If you want it / I wonder if I'm falling in love.
- **■ 7"** . . . . . . . . . . . . . . . . . . . ARO 220

Ariola / Feb '80.

# Noble, Ike

## IKE NOBLE.
**Tracks:** Lonely people / I promise you / Angie / I'm gonna miss your love / Your love / Keep me cryin' / Best years of my life / Shake it loose.
- **■ LP** . . . . . . . . . . . . . . . . . . . TRLP 100
- **■ LP** . . . . . . . . . . . . . . . . . . . TRPL 100

Timeless (Soul) / Dec '87.
Timeless (Soul) / Jan '90.

## LONELY PEOPLE.
**Tracks:** Not Advised.
- **■ CD** . . . . . . . . . . . . . . . . . . . TLCD 353

Timeless (Soul) / Jan '90.

# Nobles, Cliff

## HORSE, THE.
**Tracks:** Horse / Love is alright.
- **■ 7"** . . . . . . . . . . . . . . . . . . . CBS 3518

CBS / Jan '76.

# Nolen & Crossley

## READY OR NOT.
**Tracks:** Ready or not / Place in my heart.
- **■ 12"** . . . . . . . . . . . . . . . . . . . TMGT 12
- **■ 7"** . . . . . . . . . . . . . . . . . . . .TMG 12

Motown / Apr '82.

# North, Freddie

## CUSS THE WIND.
**Tracks:** Cuss the wind / My whole world has ende Love to hate / Sun comes up / Gotta go get yo mommy / I loved another woman / Oh Lord, what a you doing / Rainy night in Georgia.
- **■ LP** . . . . . . . . . . . . . . . . . . . .CLP 5

Contempo (1) / Feb '77.

## FRIEND.
**Tracks:** She's all I got / Raining on a sunny day Sweeter than sweetness / Sidewalks, fences & wa / I did the woman wrong / Yours love / Laid back easy / You and me togetnher forever / Ain't nothi in the news / Did I come back too soon.
- **■ LP** . . . . . . . . . . . . . . . . . . . 29160

Mojo / Aug '72.

## I'M YOUR MAN.
**Tracks:** Do me baby / I'm your man / If this is the la time / Love has it's price / Differently / Don't ma me cry / If you're even gonna love me / Everlastin love / (You're killing me) slowly but surely / It's n the spotlight / Someday she'll come along.
- **■ LP** . . . . . . . . . . . . . . . . . . . .CRB 12

Charly R&B / Mar '89.

# Norwood

## I CAN'T LET YOU GO.
**Tracks:** I can't let you go / Don't let love / Shou have been us together / Lady in love / I can't liv without you / Give it up / Feels so good / Glad I foun you / Come back my lover.
- **■ LP** . . . . . . . . . . . . . . . . . . . MCF 337
- **■ MC** . . . . . . . . . . . . . . . . . . . MCFC 337

MCA / May '87.

## I CAN'T LET YOU GO.
**Tracks:** I can't let you go.
- **■ 12"** . . . . . . . . . . . . . . . . . . . MCAT 111
- **■ 7"** . . . . . . . . . . . . . . . . . . . MCA 111

MCA / Apr '87.

## SHOULD HAVE BEEN US TOGETHER.
**Tracks:** Should have been us together / Come bac my lover.
- **■ 7"** . . . . . . . . . . . . . . . . . . . .MCA 118

MCA / Aug '87.

# Notations

## THINK BEFORE YOU STOP.
**Tracks:** Think before you stop / I'm losing.
- **■ 7"** . . . . . . . . . . . . . . . . . . . K 166

Curtom / Feb '76.

# Nu Colours

## POWER.
**Tracks:** Power / Power (mixes).
- **■ 12"** . . . . . . . . . . . . . . . . . . . CARDX
- **■ 7"** . . . . . . . . . . . . . . . . . . . CARD
- **■ MC Single.** . . . . . . . . . . . . . . CARDC
- **■ CD Single.** . . . . . . . . . . . . . . CARDD

Wild Card / Nov '93.

## TEARS.
**Tracks:** Tears.
- **■ 12"** . . . . . . . . . . . . . . . . . . . CARDX
- **■ CD Single.** . . . . . . . . . . . . . . CARDD
- **■ MC Single.** . . . . . . . . . . . . . . CARDC

Wild Card / Jun '92.

## UNLIMITED.
**Tracks:** Not Advised.
CD . . . . . . . . . . . . . . . . . . . .511160-
- **■ MC** . . . . . . . . . . . . . . . . . . . .511160-

Wild Card / Jun '93 / PolyGram.

# Nu Visions

## ISSUES OF LIFE.
**Tracks:** Not Advised.
- **■ 12"** . . . . . . . . . . . . . . . . . . . SRT 92 L

Vision Sound / Oct '92.

## WHAT YOU WON'T DO FOR LOVE.
**Tracks:** What you won't do for love.
- **■ 12"** . . . . . . . . . . . . . . . . . . . VZS 4
- **■ CD Single** . . . . . . . . . . . . . . VZS 4CD

Vizion Sound / Jan '93.

■ DELETED

## Nunn, Bobby

**ON'T KNOCK IT.**
racks: Don't knock it / Private party.
■ 12"................... TMGT 1323
■ 7"................... TMG 1323
otown / Jan '84.

**RIVATE PARTY.**
racks: Private party / Do you look that good in the
orning / Sex maniac / Ladykiller / Don't knock it /
angin' out at the mall / Because of you / Too young.
■ LP................... STML 12199
■ MC................... CSTML 12199
otown / Jul '84.

## Nunnally, Keith

**REEDOM.**
racks: Freedom.
■ 12"................... W 0079T
'EA / Jan '92.

**SEASONS OF LOVE.**
Tracks: Seasons of love.
■ MC Single................. W 0034C
■ 12"................... W 0034T
■ 7"................... W 0034
WEA / May '91.

## Nutmegs

**NUTMEGS GREATEST HITS, THE.**
Tracks: Not Advised.
■ LP................... HERALD 5011
Herald / Aug '87.

**NUTMEGS, THE (Feat. Leroy Griffin).**
Tracks: Not Advised.
■ LP................... RELIC 5002
Relic (USA) / Aug '87.

## Nuttin' Nyce

**IN MY NATURE.**
Tracks: In my nature.
■ CD Single.............. JIVECD 338
■ CD Single.............. JIVERCD 338
■ MC Single.............. JIVEC 338
■ 12"................... JIVET 338
■ 12" Remix.............. JIVER 338
Jive / Jan '94.

# O

## O'Bryan

### I'M FREAKY.
Tracks: I'm freaky / Doin' alright.
- 12"............................12CL 286
- 7".................................CL 286

Capitol / Apr '83.

### STILL WATER.
Tracks: Still water / Can't live without your love.
- 12"............................12CL 240
- 7".................................CL 240

Capitol / Apr '82.

## Obsession

### IF I CAN'T HAVE YOU.
Tracks: If I can't have you.
- 12".............................ALMY 008

Almighty / Jan '93 / Total / BMG.

### LOVE INSURANCE.
Tracks: Love insurance.
- 12".............................ALMY 002

Almighty / Jan '93 / Total / BMG.

### NEVER ENDING STORY.
Tracks: Never ending story (mixes).
- 12"..............................LBAY 9

Loading Bay / Mar '90.

### SUSPICIOUS MINDS.
Tracks: Suspicious minds.
- 12".............................ALMY 018

Almighty / Jan '93 / Total / BMG.

### WITHOUT YOU.
Tracks: Without you.
- 12".........................12 ALMY 53
- CD Single..................CDALMY 53

Almighty / Mar '94.

## Ocean

### LIFE IS GOOD.
Tracks: Life is good.
- 7".............................BRIGHT 1

New Stars / Dec '84.

### OCEAN.
Tracks: Not Advised.
- LP...............................1200 182

IMS / Sep '81.

### SILVER.
Tracks: Not Advised.
- CD.................................DHR 1
- MC..............................DHR 1MC

Doll's House Records / Mar '94 / Pinnacle.

### YOU ARE.
Tracks: You are.
- 12"...............................001088

Ocean (1) / Aug '88.

### YOU ARE TO BE MINE.
Tracks: You are to be mine.
- 12"...............................GPS 001

Ocean (1) / Jul '88.

## Ocean, Billy

Despite being born in Trinidad, Billy Ocean has been acclaimed as Britain's most successful international soul artist. Having grown up in London, he first scored in '76 with *Love Really Hurts Without You*. Further U.K. pop and U.S. R&B hits maintained his profile into the '80s, before his popularity exploded in '84. *Caribbean Queen* topped the U.S. pop chart: the first of a series of transatlantic hits that peaked with *When The Going Gets Tough (The Tough Get Going)* in '88. He also scored four, long-running U.K. Top 10 albums. However, no sooner had he persuaded an unspecified belle to get out of his dreams and into his car than his career got out of the limelight and into the dumpster; not helped by a wrongful arrest for drug supplying in 1991.

### 6 TRACK HITS.
Tracks: Love really hurts without you / Who's gonna rock you / Are you ready / American hearts / Stop me / red light spells danger.
- EP...............................7SR 5024
- MC..............................7SC 5024

Scoop 33 / Sep '83.

### AMERICAN HEARTS.
Tracks: American hearts.
- 7"...................................GT 244

GTO / Jan '79.

### ARE YOU READY.
Tracks: Are you ready / Maybe tonight.
- 7"...................................GT 259

GTO / Jan '80.

### BILLY OCEAN.
Tracks: Tell him to move over / Stop me (if you've heard it all before) / Let's put our emotions in motion / Let's do it all again / Love really hurts without you / Whose little girl are you / Soul rock / One kiss away / Hungry for love / Eye of a storm / L.O.D. (Love on delivery).
- LP.................................GTLP 15

GTO / Nov '76.
- LP...............................EPC 32561
- MC................................40 32561

Epic / Jan '85 / Sony.

### BILLY OCEAN - RED LIGHT.
Tracks: Not Advised.
- CD.................................BRCD 95
- LP.................................BRLP 95
- MC................................BRMC 95

BR Music/BR Music (Holland) / Oct '88 / BMG.

### BILLY OCEAN IN LONDON.
Tracks: Not Advised.
- VHS................................VVD 240

Virgin Vision / '87 / Gold & Sons / THE.

### BITTERSWEET.
Tracks: Bittersweet / Bittersweet (inst.).
- 12"...............................JIVET 133
- 7".................................JIVE 133

Jive / Oct '86.

### CALYPSO CRAZY.
Tracks: Calypso crazy / Let's get back together.
- 12"................................BOST 2
- 7"..................................BOS 2

Jive / Apr '88.
- CD Single......................BOSCD 2

Jive / Apr '88.

### CARIBBEAN QUEEN.
Tracks: Caribbean queen (no more love on the run) / European queen.
- MC Single......................JIVEK 77
- 12"................................JIVET 77
- 7".................................JIVE 77

Jive / Sep '84.

### CITY LIMIT.
Tracks: American hearts / Are you ready / Stay the night.
- LP................................GTLP 038

GTO / Jun '80.

### COLLECTION: BILLY OCEAN.
Tracks: Love really hurts without you / red light spells danger / Are you ready / Don't say stop / Inner feelings / City limit / Calypso funkin' / Soul rock / Mind games / Nights (feel like getting down) / One kiss away / Eye of a storm / Another day won't matter / Stop me / Let's put our emotions in motion / L.O.D. (Love on delivery) / American hearts / Hungry for love / Taking chances / Stay the night / Dance with me / Whose little girl are you.
- Double LP.....................CCSLP 205
- MC.............................CCSMC 205

Castle Collector Series / Nov '88.
- CD............................CCSCD 205

Castle Collector Series / Jan '94.

### COLOUR OF LOVE.
Tracks: Colour of love.
- 12"................................BOST 3
- 7"..................................BOS 3
- CD Single......................BOSCD 3

Jive / Jul '88.

### EUROPEAN QUEEN (NO MORE LOVE ON THE RUN).
Tracks: European queen (no more love on the run)
- 12"...............................JIVET
- 7"................................JIVE 5

Jive / May '84.
- MC Single......................JIVEC

Jive / May '84.

### EVERYTHING'S CHANGED.
Tracks: Everything's changed / Tell him to move over.
- 7"...................................GT 2

GTO / Mar '78.

### GET OUTTA MY DREAMS, GET INTO MY CAR.
Tracks: Get outta my dreams, get into my car / Showdown.
- 12"...............................BOST
- 12" Remix......................BOSR
- 7".................................BOS

Jive / Jan '88.

### GREATEST HITS.
Tracks: When the going gets tough the tough get going / Caribbean queen (no more love on the run) / Suddenly / Licence to chill / There'll be sad songs ( make you cry) / Loverboy / Get outta my dreams, get into my car / Love zone / Here's to you / I sleep much better (in someone else's bed) / Colour of love.
- CD.................................BOCD
- LP.................................BOTV
- MC.................................BOTC

Jive / Sep '89 / BMG.

### GREATEST HITS: BILLY OCEAN.
Tracks: When the going gets tough, the tough get going / Get outta my dreams get into my car / Caribbean queen (no more love on the run) / There'll be sad songs ( to make you cry) / Loverboy / Suddenly / Licence to chill / Love zone / Tear down these walls / Colour of love.
- VHS.................................ZV 00

Zomba (Video) / Dec '89.

### I CAN'T STOP.
Tracks: I can't stop / Inner feelings.
- 7"................................EPCA 245

Epic / Jun '82.

### IN MOTION.
Tracks: On the run / What's gonna happen / Light up the world with sunshine / On the run (hold on brother) / Let's put our emotions in motion / Love really hurts without you / Whose little girl are you / Black as he's painted / Wild beautiful women / On the run (extended remix long).
- LP................................MFP 576
- MC.............................TCMFP 576

MFP / Oct '86.
- CD................................OR 000

Music Collection International / Apr '87 / THE / Jazz Music.

### INNER FEELINGS.
Tracks: Calypso funkin / Rockabye baby / No matter what / Dance with me / I can't stop / Tryin' to get through / Mind games / Was it you / Inner feelings.
- LP...............................EPC 8556

Epic / Aug '82.
- LP...............................EPC 3279
- MC................................40 3279

Epic / Jun '86.

### L.O.D. (LOVE ON DELIVERY).
Tracks: L.O.D. (love on delivery).
- 7"...................................GT 6

GTO / Jul '76.

### LICENCE TO CHILL.
Tracks: Licence to chill.
- 12"................................BOST
- 7"..................................BOS
- CD Single.......................BOSCD

Jive / Sep '89.

### LOVE IS FOREVER.
Tracks: Love is forever / Suddenly / Loverboy (Extra track on 12" version only).
- 12"...............................JIVET 13
- 7".................................JIVE 13

Jive / Dec '86.

300

■ DELETE

## LOVE REALLY HURTS WITHOUT YOU.
Tracks: What's gonna happen to our love / On the run / Let's put our emotions in motion / Eye of a storm / Wild beautiful woman / Can you feel it / Light up the world with sunshine / Whose little girl are you / On the run (The battle is over).

| | |
|---|---|
| CD . . . . . . . . . . . . . . . . . | .100415.8 |

Magnum Music / Apr '88 / Magnum Music Group / THE.

| | |
|---|---|
| MC. . . . . . . . . . . . . . . . . . | .500107 |

Magnum Music / '89 / Magnum Music Group / THE.

## LOVE REALLY HURTS WITHOUT YOU.
Tracks: Love really hurts without you (mixes) / Red light spells danger.

| | |
|---|---|
| ■ 7" . . . . . . . . . . . . . . . . . . | GT 52 |

GTO / Feb '76.

| | |
|---|---|
| ■ 12" . . . . . . . . . . . . . . . . | SUPET 110 |
| ■ 12" Remix. . . . . . . . . . . | SUPETX 010 |
| ■ 7" . . . . . . . . . . . . . . . . . | SUPE 110 |

Supreme / Nov '86.

## LOVE REALLY HURTS WITHOUT YOU (OLD GOLD).
Tracks: Love really hurts without you / red light spells danger.

| | |
|---|---|
| ■ 7" . . . . . . . . . . . . . . . . . | .OG 9197 |

Old Gold / Jul '82.

## LOVE ZONE.
Tracks: When the going gets tough (the tough get going) / Love zone / Without you / There'll be sad songs (to make you cry) / Bittersweet / It's never too late to try / Showdown / Promise me / Love is forever / Love zone (Instrumental mix).

| | |
|---|---|
| ■ CD . . . . . . . . . . . . . . . . | CHIP 35 |

Jive / Aug '86.

| | |
|---|---|
| ■ LP . . . . . . . . . . . . . . . . . | HIP 35 |
| ■ MC. . . . . . . . . . . . . . . . . | HIPC 35 |

Jive / Jun '86.

## LOVE ZONE.
Tracks: Love zone.

| | |
|---|---|
| ■ 7" . . . . . . . . . . . . . . . . . | .JIVE 124 |
| ■ 12" . . . . . . . . . . . . . . . . | .JIVET 124 |

Jive / Jul '86.

## LOVER BOY.
Tracks: Loverboy.

| | |
|---|---|
| ■ 12" . . . . . . . . . . . . . . . . | JIVET 80 |
| ■ 7" . . . . . . . . . . . . . . . . . | JIVE 80 |
| ■ 7" P.Disc . . . . . . . . . . . . | JIVES 80 |

Jive / Jan '85.

## LOVER BOY.
Tracks: Lover boy / Let's get back together / Promise me / Without you / Long and winding road / It's never too late to try / Here's to you / Caribbean queen (no more love on the run) / Stand and deliver / Colour of love / There'll be sad songs (To make you cry) / If I should lose you / Showdown / Because of you.

| | |
|---|---|
| CD . . . . . . . . . . . . . . . . . . | 5501182 |
| MC. . . . . . . . . . . . . . . . . . | 5501184 |

Spectrum (1) / Oct '93 / PolyGram.

## MYSTERY LADY.
Tracks: Mystery lady / Suddenly.

| | |
|---|---|
| ■ 12" . . . . . . . . . . . . . . . . | JIVET 98 |
| ■ MC Single. . . . . . . . . . . . | JIVEK 98 |

Jive / Aug '85.

| | |
|---|---|
| ■ 7" . . . . . . . . . . . . . . . . . | JIVE 98 |

Jive / Aug '85.

## NIGHTS.
Tracks: Nights / Everlasting love.

| | |
|---|---|
| ■ 12" . . . . . . . . . . . . . . . . | GT13 286 |
| ■ 7" . . . . . . . . . . . . . . . . . | GT 286 |

GTO / Oct '80.

## NIGHTS (FEEL LIKE GETTING DOWN).
Tracks: Are you ready / Don't say stop / Whatever turns you on / Another day won't matter / nights (feel like getting down) / Who's gonna rock you / Stay the night / Everlasting love / Taking chances.

| | |
|---|---|
| ■ LP . . . . . . . . . . . . . . . . . | EPC 32716 |
| MC. . . . . . . . . . . . . . . . . . | .40 32716 |

Epic / Apr '86 / Sony.

## NIGHTS (FEEL LIKE GETTING DOWN).
Tracks: Nights (feel like getting down) / Nights (feel like getting down) (pt 2).

| | |
|---|---|
| ■ 7" . . . . . . . . . . . . . . . . . | GT 13 303 |

GTO / Sep '81.

## PEARLS FROM THE PAST - BILLY OCEAN.
Tracks: Not Advised.

| | |
|---|---|
| CD . . . . . . . . . . . . . . . . . . | KLMCD 001 |

Scratch / Nov '93 / Scratch Records / BMG / Grape-vine Distribution.

---

## PICK UP THE PIECES.
Tracks: Pick up the pieces.

| | |
|---|---|
| ■ 12" . . . . . . . . . . . . . . . . | BOST 7 |
| ■ 7" . . . . . . . . . . . . . . . . . | BOS 7 |
| ■ CD Single . . . . . . . . . . . . | BOSCD 7 |
| ■ MC Single. . . . . . . . . . . . | BOSC 7 |

Jive / May '93.

## PRESSURE.
Tracks: Pressure.

| | |
|---|---|
| ■ 12" . . . . . . . . . . . . . . . . | BOST 6 |
| ■ 7" . . . . . . . . . . . . . . . . . | BOS 6 |
| ■ CD Single . . . . . . . . . . . . | BOSCD 6 |
| ■ MC Single. . . . . . . . . . . . | BOSC 6 |

Jive / Jan '93.

## RED LIGHT.
Tracks: Not Advised.

| | |
|---|---|
| CD . . . . . . . . . . . . . . . . . . | 266 226 2 |
| MC. . . . . . . . . . . . . . . . . . | 266 226 4 |

Street Life / May '88.

## RED LIGHT SPELLS DANGER.
Tracks: red light spells danger.

| | |
|---|---|
| ■ 7" . . . . . . . . . . . . . . . . . | GT 85 |

GTO / Mar '77.

## STAND AND DELIVER.
Tracks: Stand and deliver / Pleasure.

| | |
|---|---|
| ■ 12" . . . . . . . . . . . . . . . . | BOST 4 |
| ■ 7" . . . . . . . . . . . . . . . . . | BOS 4 |
| ■ CD Single . . . . . . . . . . . . | BOSCD 4 |

Jive / Oct '88.

## STAY THE NIGHT.
Tracks: Stay the night / What you doing to me.

| | |
|---|---|
| ■ 7" . . . . . . . . . . . . . . . . . | GT 271 |

GTO / Apr '80.

## STOP ME (IF YOU'VE HEARD IT ALL BEFORE).
Tracks: Stop me (if you've heard it all before).

| | |
|---|---|
| ■ 7" . . . . . . . . . . . . . . . . . | GT 72 |

GTO / Nov '76.

## SUDDENLY.
Tracks: Caribbean queen (no more love on the run) / Mystery lady / Syncopation / Long and winding road / Loverboy / Lucky man / Dance floor / If I should lose you / Suddenly.

| | |
|---|---|
| CD . . . . . . . . . . . . . . . . . . | CHIP 12 |
| ■ LP . . . . . . . . . . . . . . . . . | HIP 12 |
| MC. . . . . . . . . . . . . . . . . . | HIPC 12 |

Jive / Aug '84 / BMG.

| | |
|---|---|
| ■ LP . . . . . . . . . . . . . . . . . | JIP 12 |

Jive / Nov '84.

## SUDDENLY.
Tracks: Suddenly / Lover boy / Caribbean queen (no more love on the run) / Stay the night / Are you ready / Lucky man.

| | |
|---|---|
| ■ 12" . . . . . . . . . . . . . . . . | JIVET 90 |
| ■ 7" . . . . . . . . . . . . . . . . . | JIVE 90 |

Jive / May '85.

## TEAR DOWN THESE HITS.
Tracks: Not Advised.

| | |
|---|---|
| VHS . . . . . . . . . . . . . . . . . | .VVD 313 |

Virgin Vision / Mar '88 / Gold & Sons / THE.

## TEAR DOWN THESE WALLS.
Tracks: Tear down these walls / Soon as you're ready / Because of you / Gun for hire / Colour of love / Get outta my dreams, get into my car / Pleasure / Here's to you / Stand and deliver / Calypso crazy.

| | |
|---|---|
| ■ CD . . . . . . . . . . . . . . . . | CHIP 57 |
| ■ LP . . . . . . . . . . . . . . . . . | HIP 57 |
| ■ MC. . . . . . . . . . . . . . . . . | HIPC 57 |

Jive / Mar '88.

| | |
|---|---|
| ■ CD . . . . . . . . . . . . . . . . | CHIPX 57 |

Jive / Jan '90.

## THERE'LL BE SAD SONGS (TO MAKE YOU CRY).
Tracks: There'll be sad songs (to make you cry) / If I should lose you.

| | |
|---|---|
| ■ 12" . . . . . . . . . . . . . . . . | JIVET 117 |
| ■ 7" . . . . . . . . . . . . . . . . . | JIVE 117 |

Jive / Apr '86.

## TIME TO MOVE ON.
Tracks: Not Advised.

| | |
|---|---|
| ■ CD . . . . . . . . . . . . . . . . | CHIP 132 |
| ■ LP . . . . . . . . . . . . . . . . . | HIP 132 |
| ■ MC. . . . . . . . . . . . . . . . . | HIPC 132 |

Jive / Jun '93.

## WHEN THE GOING GETS TOUGH (THE TOUGH GET GOING).
Tracks: When the going gets tough (the tough get going).

| | |
|---|---|
| ■ 12" Remix. . . . . . . . . . . | JIVER 114 |
| ■ 12" . . . . . . . . . . . . . . . . | JIVET 114 |

---

| | |
|---|---|
| ■ 7" P.Disc . . . . . . . . . . . . | JIVES 114 |
| ■ 7" . . . . . . . . . . . . . . . . . | JIVE 114 |
| ■ 7" Set . . . . . . . . . . . . . . | JIVED 114 |

Jive / Jan '86.

# Octavia

## 2 THE LIMIT.
Tracks: 2 the limit.

| | |
|---|---|
| ■ 7" . . . . . . . . . . . . . . . . . | .COOL 131 |
| ■ 12" . . . . . . . . . . . . . . . . | COOLX 131 |

Cool Tempo / Sep '86.

| | |
|---|---|
| ■ 12" . . . . . . . . . . . . . . . . | PW 415 |

Pow Wow (USA) / Sep '87.

# Odetta

## CHRISTMAS SPIRITUALS.
Tracks: Rise up shepherd and follow / What month was Jesus born in / Mary had a baby / Somebody talking 'bout Jesus / Virgin Mary had one son / Go tell it on the mountain / Shout for joy / Poor little Jesus / O Jerusalem / Ain't that a-rockin' / If anybody asks you / Beautiful star / Children go where I send thee.

| | |
|---|---|
| CD. . . . . . . . . . . . . . . . . . | VBR 20382 |
| MC. . . . . . . . . . . . . . . . . . | VBR 20384 |

Vera Bra / Nov '90 / Pinnacle / New Note.

## ESSENTIAL, THE.
Tracks: Not Advised.

| | |
|---|---|
| CD Set . . . . . . . . . . . . . | CDVCD 43/44 |
| ■ Double LP. . . . . . . . . . . . | .VSD 43/44 |
| MC Set . . . . . . . . . . . . . | CVSD 43/44 |

Start / Sep '89 / THE / Koch International.

## IT'S IMPOSSIBLE.
Tracks: Not Advised.

| | |
|---|---|
| ■ LP . . . . . . . . . . . . . . . . . | FLC 5007 |

Four Leaf Clover / '78.

## ODETTA AND THE BLUES.
Tracks: Hard, oh Lord / Believe I'll go / Oh papa / How long blues / Hogan's alley / Leavin' this morning / Oh, my babe / Yonder come the blues / Make me a pallet on the floor / Weeping willow blues / Go down sunshine / Nobody knows you (when you're down and out).

| | |
|---|---|
| ■ LP . . . . . . . . . . . . . . . . . | OBC 509 |

Original Blues Classics / Jun '84.

| | |
|---|---|
| CD. . . . . . . . . . . . . . . . . | .OBCCD 509 |

Original Blues Classics / Nov '92 / Pinnacle.

## SINGS.
Tracks: Take me to the pilot / Mama told me not to come / Every night / Hit or miss / Give a damn / My God and I / Lo and behold / Bless the children / No expectations / Movin' it on.

| | |
|---|---|
| ■ LP . . . . . . . . . . . . . . . . . | .2489 012 |

Polydor / Apr '71.

# Odyssey

## BEST OF ODYSSEY.
Tracks: Use it up and wear it out / Easy come, easy go / Hold de mota down / Follow me / If you're looking for a way out / Lucky star / Native New Yorker / Going back to my roots / Hang together / I got the melody / Ever lovin' Sam / It will be alright / Don't tell me, tell her.

| | |
|---|---|
| ■ LP . . . . . . . . . . . . . . . . . | RCALP 6023 |
| MC. . . . . . . . . . . . . . . . . . | RCAK 6023 |

RCA / Dec '81 / BMG.

| | |
|---|---|
| ■ LP . . . . . . . . . . . . . . . . . | PL 89541 |

RCA / '86.

## EASY COME, EASY GO.
Tracks: Easy come, easy go / Golden hands.

| | |
|---|---|
| ■ 7" . . . . . . . . . . . . . . . . . | .PB 9252 |

RCA / '79.

## EASY COME, EASY GO.
Tracks: Easy come, easy go.

| | |
|---|---|
| ■ 12" . . . . . . . . . . . . . . . . | .RCAT 295 |
| ■ 7" . . . . . . . . . . . . . . . . . | .RCA 295 |

RCA / Oct '82.

## GOING BACK TO MY ROOTS.
Tracks: Going back to my roots / Bawa awa / Roots suite (on 12" only).

| | |
|---|---|
| ■ 12" . . . . . . . . . . . . . . . . | RCAT 85 |
| ■ 7" . . . . . . . . . . . . . . . . . | .RCA 85 |

RCA / May '81.

## GOING BACK TO MY ROOTS (OLD GOLD).
Tracks: Going back to my roots / Inside out.

| | |
|---|---|
| 12" . . . . . . . . . . . . . . . . . | .OG 4210 |

Old Gold / Jun '91 / Pickwick.

## GREATEST HITS.
Tracks: Going back to my roots / Inside out / Magic touch / Oh no not my baby / Weekend lover / Don't

---

tell me tell her / Native New Yorker / Use it up and wear it out / Hang together / It will be alright / Follow me (play follow the leader) / Easy come, easy go / When you love somebody / If you're looking for a way out / Native New Yorker (Brooklyn club mix) (CD only).

| | |
|---|---|
| **CD** | **ND 90436** |
| ■ **LP** | **NL 90436** |
| **MC.** | **NK 90436** |

RCA / Mar '90 / BMG.

## HANG TOGETHER.
**Tracks:** Hang together / Never had it all / Don't tell me, tell her / Down boy / Follow me / Use it up and wear it out / If you're looking for a way out / Rooster loose in the barnyard.

| | |
|---|---|
| ■ **LP** | **PL 13526** |

RCA / Aug '80.

| | |
|---|---|
| ■ **LP** | **RCALP 3045** |
| **MC.** | **RCAK 3045** |

RCA / Sep '81 / BMG.

## HANG TOGETHER.
**Tracks:** Hang together / Down boy.

| | |
|---|---|
| ■ **7"** | **RCA 23** |

RCA / Jan '81.

## HAPPY TOGETHER.
**Tracks:** Together / Happy people / Inside out / Happy together / When you love somebody / Love's alright / Magic touch.

| | |
|---|---|
| ■ **LP** | **RCALP 6036** |

RCA / Jun '82.

## HOLLYWOOD PARTY NIGHT.
**Tracks:** Single again / What time does the balloon go up / Pride / You wouldn't know a real live true love.. (Full title: You wouldn't know a real live true love if it walked right u) / Hey Bill / Lilly and Harvey, late to the party again / Lucky star / Comin' back for more / I dare ya / I got the melody / Roots suite / Ajomara / Going back to my roots / Baba awa / Holding back my love / Baby that's all I want / It will be alright / Oh no not my baby / Hold on to love.

| | |
|---|---|
| ■ **LP** | **PL 13031** |

RCA / Nov '78.

## I GOT THE MELODY.
**Tracks:** Not Advised.

| | |
|---|---|
| ■ **LP** | **RCALP 5028** |
| **MC.** | **RCAK 5028** |

RCA / May '81 / BMG.

## I KNOW IT.
**Tracks:** I know it / Laughter and smiling.

| | |
|---|---|
| ■ **12"** | **BUTCH 12** |
| ■ **7"** | **BUTCH 1** |

Mirror / Jul '85.

## IF YOU'RE LOOKIN' FOR A WAY OUT.
**Tracks:** If you're looking for a way out / Never had it all.

| | |
|---|---|
| ■ **7"** | **RCA 5** |

RCA / Sep '80.

## INSIDE OUT.
**Tracks:** Native New Yorker (Manhattan flute mix) / Inside out.

| | |
|---|---|
| ■ **12"** | **RCAT 226** |
| ■ **7"** | **RCA 226** |

RCA / Jun '82.

| | |
|---|---|
| ■ **12"** | **PT 49624** |
| ■ **7"** | **PB 49623** |

RCA / Sep '87.

## IT WILL BE ALRIGHT.
**Tracks:** It will be alright / Oh no not my baby.

| | |
|---|---|
| ■ **12"** | **RCAT 128** |
| ■ **7"** | **RCA 128** |

RCA / Sep '81.

## LUCKY STAR.
**Tracks:** Lucky star / You wouldn't know a real true love if it ..

| | |
|---|---|
| ■ **7"** | **PB 1444** |

RCA / Jan '79.

## MAGIC MOMENTS WITH ODYSSEY.
**Tracks:** Native New Yorker / If you're looking for a way out / Follow me / Oh no not my baby / Roots suite / Don't tell me, tell her / Magic touch / Hang together / Use it up and wear it out / It will be alright / Easy come, easy go / Happy together / Weekend lover / Ever lovin' Sam / Inside out / When you love somebody.

| | |
|---|---|
| ■ **MC.** | **NK 89405** |

RCA / Jun '84.

## MAGIC TOUCH (REMIX).
**Tracks:** Magic touch / Happy people.

| | |
|---|---|
| ■ **12"** | **RCAT 275** |
| ■ **7"** | **RCA 275** |

RCA / Aug '82.

## MAGIC TOUCH OF ODYSSEY.
**Tracks:** Use it up and wear it out / Going back to my roots / Inside out / Native New Yorker / When you love somebody / If you're looking for a way out / Easy come, easy go / Hold de mota down.

| | |
|---|---|
| ■ **LP** | **STAR 2223** |
| **MC.** | **STAC 2223** |

Telstar/Ronco / Nov '82 / BMG.

## NATIVE NEW YORKER.
**Tracks:** Native New Yorker / Ever lovin' Sam.

| | |
|---|---|
| ■ **12"** | **PC 1129** |
| ■ **7"** | **PB 1129** |

RCA / '79.

| | |
|---|---|
| ■ **7"** | **DDC 002** |

RCA / Apr '79.

## NATIVE NEW YORKER.
**Tracks:** Native New Yorker.

| | |
|---|---|
| ■ **7"** | **GOLD 517** |

RCA Golden Grooves / Jul '81.

## ODYSSEY.
**Tracks:** Going back to my roots / Use it up and wear it out / If you're looking for a way out / Native New Yorker.

| | |
|---|---|
| ■ **MC Single.** | **RCXK 003** |

RCA / May '83.

## ODYSSEY.
**Tracks:** Native New Yorker / Ever lovin' Sam / Weekend lover / You keep me dancin' / Woman behind the man / Easy come, easy go / Hold de mota down / Golden hands / Thank you, God, for one more day.

| | |
|---|---|
| ■ **LP** | **PL 12204** |

RCA / '79.

## ODYSSEY - GREATEST HITS.
**Tracks:** Native New Yorker / Weekend lover / When you love somebody / Inside out / It will be alright / Ever lovin' Sam / If you're looking for a way out / Use it up and wear it out / Don't tell me, tell her / Easy come, easy go / Hold de mota down / Going back to my roots / Magic touch / Follow me (Play follow the leader) / Hang together.

| | |
|---|---|
| ■ **LP** | **SMR 735** |

Stylus / Aug '87.

## PIPING JOURNEY, A.
**Tracks:** Not Advised.

| | |
|---|---|
| ■ **LP** | **MMC 001** |

Mannick Music / Aug '87.

## ROOTS.
**Tracks:** Use it up and wear it out / Going back to my roots / Easy come, easy go / Hang together / It will be alright / Lucky star / Magic touch / Don't tell me / Oh no not my baby / Happy together / You keep me dancin' / Comin' back for more / Ever had it all / I can't keep holding bakc my love / Down boy / Happy people.

| | |
|---|---|
| **CD** | **PWKS 4123** |
| **MC.** | **PWKMC 4123** |

Pickwick / Nov '92 / Pickwick.

## USE IT UP AND WEAR IT OUT.
**Tracks:** Use it up and wear it out.

| | |
|---|---|
| ■ **7"** | **PB 1962** |

RCA / Jun '80.

| | |
|---|---|
| ■ **CD Single.** | **PD 49457** |

RCA / Jun '89.

## USE IT UP AND WEAR IT OUT (OLD GOLD).
**Tracks:** Use it up and wear it out / Native New Yorker (On 4208) / Inside out (On 9835).

| | |
|---|---|
| ■ **7"** | **OG 9835** |

Old Gold / Nov '88.

| | |
|---|---|
| **12"** | **OG 4208** |

Old Gold / Jun '91 / Pickwick.

# Offitt, Lillian

1957 - 1961 (see under Everett, Betty).

# Ohio Players

As Ohio Untouchables, seven-strong group were R&B backing musicians in '60s but achieved success in own right with new name and U.S. hit *Funky Worm* in '73. Subsequently much-imitated and sampled, song initiated series of million-sellers in freaky funk mould; including pair of U.S. No. 1's: *Fire* in '75 and *Love Rollercoaster* in '76 (band also became notorious for soft-porn album sleeves). They burned out during disco, but scored sole U.K. hit with *Who'd She Coo?* in '76, and periodically reformed in 1980s.

## ANGEL.
**Tracks:** Angel / Merry go round / Glad to know you're mine / Don't fight my love / Body vibes / Can you still love me / O.H.I.O.

| | |
|---|---|
| ■ **LP** | **9100037** |

Mercury / Jun '77.

## BEST OF THE WESTBOUND YEARS, THE.
**Tracks:** Never had a dream / Pride and vanity / Varee is love / Funky worm / Ecstasy / You and me (I wanna know) do you feel it / Black cat / Sleep talk / Players balling (players doin' their own thing) / Reds.

| | |
|---|---|
| **CD** | **CDSEWD 039** |

Westbound / Apr '91.

## ECSTASY.
**Tracks:** Ecstasy / You and me / (Not so) sad and lonely / (I wanna know) do you feel it / Black cat / Food stamps y'all / Spinning / Sleep talk / Silly Billy / Short change.

| | |
|---|---|
| **CD** | **CDSEW 026** |
| **LP** | **SEW 026** |
| ■ **MC.** | **SEWC 026** |

Westbound / Feb '90 / Pinnacle.

## EVERYBODY UP.
**Tracks:** Everybody up / Take de funk off, fly.

| | |
|---|---|
| ■ **7"** | **ARIST 268** |

Arista / '79.

## EVERYBODY UP.
**Tracks:** Everybody up / Don't say goodbye / Make me feel / Say it / Take de funk off / Fly / Something special.

| | |
|---|---|
| **CD** | **7432114773-2** |

Arista / Jul '93 / BMG.

## FIRE.
**Tracks:** Fire / I want to be free / It's all over / Runnin from the devil / Smoke / Together / What the hell.

| | |
|---|---|
| ■ **LP** | **9100 009** |

Mercury / Jan '75.

## FIRE.
**Tracks:** Fire / Together.

| | |
|---|---|
| ■ **7"** | **6167058** |

Mercury / Jan '75.

## FOLLOW ME.
**Tracks:** Follow me / Fast track.

| | |
|---|---|
| ■ **12"** | **AIR 3700 12** |
| ■ **7"** | **AIR 3700 7** |

Air City / Mar '85.

## FUNKY WORM.
**Tracks:** Funky worm / Paint me.

| | |
|---|---|
| ■ **7"** | **6146100** |

Westbound / Jul '74.

## GOLD.
**Tracks:** Fire / Skin tight / Who'd she coo / Love rollercoaster / Sweet sticky thing / Angel / Far east / Mississippi / Feel the beat / Fopp / I want to be free / Jive turkey / Only a child can love.

| | |
|---|---|
| ■ **LP** | **9100 030** |

Mercury / Feb '77.

| | |
|---|---|
| ■ **MC.** | **JABBC 28** |
| ■ **LP** | **JABB 28** |

Club / Nov '87.

## GRADUATION.
**Tracks:** Not Advised.

| | |
|---|---|
| ■ **LP** | **AIR 7601** |
| **MC.** | **AIRZC 7601** |

Air City / Mar '85.

## LOVE ROLLER COASTER.
**Tracks:** Love roller coaster.

| | |
|---|---|
| ■ **7"** | **6167225** |

Mercury / Nov '75.

## ORGASM.
**Tracks:** Pain / Pleasure / Ecstasy / Climax / Funky worm / Player's balling (players doin' their own thing) / Varee is love / Sleep talk / Walt's first trip / Laid it / What's going on / Singing in the morning / Food stamps y'all / I want to hear / Ain't that lovin you (for more reasons than one).

| | |
|---|---|
| **CD** | **CDSEWD 062** |

Ace / Jun '93 / Pinnacle / Complete Record Co. Ltd

## OUCH!.
**Tracks:** Do your thing / Star of the party / Sweet lil lady / Everybody dance / My baby gets the best of my love / Just me / Thinkin'bout you / Devoted / I'd better take a coffee break.

| | |
|---|---|
| ■ **LP** | **EPC 85562** |

Epic / Mar '82.

■ **DELETED**

## AIN.
racks: Pain / Never had a dream / Players balling layers doin' their own thing) / I wanna hear it from ou / Reds / Singing in the morning.

D .................................. CDSEW 004
LP .................................. SEW 004
C ................................... SEWC 004
estbound / Aug '89 / Pinnacle.

## LEASURE.
racks: Pleasure / Laid it / Pride and vanity / Walt's st trip / Varee is love / Walked away from you / aint me / Funky worm / Our love has died.

D .................................. CDSEWM 014
LP .................................. SEW 014
MC. ................................. SEWC 014
estbound / Oct '89 / Pinnacle.

## ENDERNESS.
racks: Try a little tenderness / Sometimes I cry xinny / Try to be a man / Board walkin' / Call me / Sittin' on) The dock of the bay / It takes a while / ard to love your brother.

LP ................................... EPC 85041
pic / May '81.

## WHO'D SHE COO.
racks: Who'd she coo.

7" .................................. PLAY 001
ercury / Jul '76.

# Ohlson, Curtis

## ETTER THAN EVER.
racks: Not Advised.

D .................................... CDENV 518
LP ................................... ENVLP 518
C. ................................... TCENV 518
nigma (EMI) / Dec '88 / EMI.

## O FAST.
racks: Half nelson / Love's school / I'm dreaming of ou (As I sing.) / Johnson family / Verbal abuse / ou / So fast / Village chant.

LP .................................. 3274 1
nigma (EMI) / Dec '87.

# O'Jays

he O'Jays started life in the early '60s as he Mascots, a quintet of Eddie Levert, Valter Williams, Bobby Massey, Bill Powell nd Bill Isles. They changed their name when Cleveland DJ Eddie O'Jay helped get hem a deal with Imperial Records. Though hey enjoyed several small scale soul hits during the late '60s, the real step up oc-ured in 1970 when they began a associa-on with Philadelphia writer/producers Gamble & Huff, then owners of Neptune Records and later founders of Philadelphia nternational. Indeed, the O'Jays' Backstab-ers virtually launched the PIR label on its wn in '72, establishing that funky, orches-ral sound and impassioned vocals as a widely-recognised trademark. Lighter hits such as Darlin' Darlin' Baby, Used Ta Be My Girl and Brandy could not disguise the eal soul power in albums like Ship Ahoy, Survival, Message In The Music and Family Reunion; ensuring that the group - now re-uced to a trio - maintained its popularity with all sides of the marketplace. When PIR witched its distribution from CBS to EMI in he late '80s, only the O'Jays stayed on the abel, probably suffering as a consequence of their loyalty. But by the end of the de-cade, they reasserted their profitability, signing directly to EMI and taking on the writing and production of their own material.

## 5 TRACK HITS: O'JAYS.
racks: Not Advised.

EP .................................. 7SR 5053
C. ................................... 7SC 5053
Scoop 33 / Mar '84.

## BACK STABBERS.
racks: Back stabbers.

7" .................................. CBS 8270
CBS / Sep '72.

## BACK STABBERS.
racks: When the world's at peace / Back stabbers / Who am I / Mr. Lucky / Time to get down / 992 arguments / Listen to the clock on the wall / Shift-ess, shady, jealous kind of people / Sunshine / Lovetrain.

LP .................................. CBS 65257
CBS / Dec '72.

---

## BRANDY.
Tracks: Brandy / Take me to the stars.

■ 7" .................................. PIR 6658
Philadelphia Int. / Sep '78.

## CHRISTMAS AIN'T CHRISTMAS, NEW YEARS AIN'T NEW YEARS.
Tracks: Christmas ain't christmas, New Years ain't New Years / Just can't get enough.

■ 7" .................................. PIR 3743
Philadelphia / Dec '75.

## COLLECTION: O'JAYS.
Tracks: Not Advised.

■ CD .................................. CCSCD 342
■ MC. ................................. CCSMC 342
Castle Collector Series / Jun '92.

## COLLECTOR'S ITEMS.
Tracks: Family reunion / Survival / Give the people what they want / Let me make love to you / I love music / Stairway to heaven / Back stabbers / For the love of money / Sunshine / You got your hooks in me / Love train / Livin' for the weekend / Wildflower / Darling, darling baby (sweet tender love).

MC. ................................. 4689224
■ CD .................................. 4689222
Epic / Oct '91 / Sony.

## COLLECTOR'S ITEMS.
Tracks: Love train / 992 arguments / Message in our music / Give the people what they want / Livin' for the weekend / I love music (part 1) / For the love of money / Put your hands together / Darlin' darlin' baby (sweet tender love).

■ LP .................................. PIR 32189
MC. ................................. 40 32189
Philadelphia Int. / Nov '82 / EMI.

## DARLING DARLING BABY (SWEET TENDER LOVE).
Tracks: Darlin' darlin' baby (sweet tender love) / Prayer.

■ 7" .................................. PIR 4834
Philadelphia Int. / Jan '77.

## DON'T TAKE YOUR LOVE AWAY.
Tracks: Don't take your love away / I just want somebody to love me.

■ 12" .................................. 12PIR 5
■ 7" .................................. PIR 5
Philadelphia Int. / Sep '87.

## EMOTIONALLY YOURS.
Tracks: Don't let me down / Sosmething for nothing / Emotionally yours (R & B version) / Respect / Keep on lovin' me / Love and trust / Don't you know true love / Emotionally yours (Gospel version) / That's how love is / Closer to you / If I find love again / Keep on pleasing me / Lies / Make it feel good.

■ CD .................................. CDMTL 1060
■ LP .................................. MTL 1060
■ MC. ................................. TCMTL 1060
EMI-Manhattan / Apr '91.

## EMOTIONALLY YOURS.
Tracks: Emotionally yours (Gospel version) / Emotio-nally yours (R & B version) / Have you had your love today (12" & CD single only.)

■ 12" .................................. 12MT 96
■ 7" .................................. MT 96
■ CD Single. ........................... CDMT 96
■ MC Single. ........................... TCMT 96
EMI-Manhattan / May '91.

## EXTRAORDINARY GIRL.
Tracks: Not Advised.

■ LP .................................. CXMB 7200
Chess (PRT) / Oct '84.

## EXTRAORDINARY GIRL.
Tracks: Extraordinary girl / I really need you now.

■ 12" .................................. TA 4387
■ 7" .................................. A 4387
Philadelphia Int. / Apr '84.

## FROM THE BEGINNING.
Tracks: One night affair / You're the best thing since candy / Branded bad / Losing touch / I should be your lover / Deeper in love with you / Let me in your world / I can't get enough / I've got the groove / There's someone waiting / It's too strong.

■ LP .................................. GCH 8087
Chess (Charly) / Jun '88.

## FULL OF SOUL.
Tracks: Lipstick traces / Think it over baby / I'm gonna make it / Oh how you hurt me / Stand tall / Hold on it won't hurt / Lonely drifter / Blowing wind / Working on your case.

■ LP .................................. SLS 50038
Sunset (France) / Dec '68.

---

## GIRL DON'T LET IT GET YOU DOWN.
Tracks: Girl don't let it get you down / You're the girl of my dreams.

■ 7" .................................. PIR 8928
Philadelphia Int. / Aug '80.

## GREATEST HITS: O'JAYS.
Tracks: For the love of money / Back stabbers / Forever mine / Stairway to heaven / Love train / Sunshine / Let me make love to you / Used to be my girl / Darlin' darlin' baby / I love music.

■ LP .................................. PIR 32189
Philadelphia Int. / Dec '82.

■ LP .................................. PIR 32441
MC. ................................. 40 32441
Philadelphia Int. / Jun '84 / EMI.

## HEART AND SOUL OF THE O'JAYS.
Tracks: Love train / Sing a happy song / Put our heads together / Time to get down / 992 arguments / Work on me / Used ta be my girl / I love music / Darlin' darlin' baby / Message in our music / Girl don't let it get you down / I just want to satisfy / Livin' for the weekend / Brandy.

■ LP .................................. KNLP 12052
■ CD .................................. KNCD 12052
■ MC. ................................. KNMC 12052
Knight / Mar '90.

## HEARTBREAKER.
Tracks: Cryin' the blues / One wonderful girl / Some-body else will / Show me the right way / Trouble / Can't let you go / Decisions / No can do / Heart-breaker / He loves you.

■ CD .................................. CDMTL 1077
■ LP .................................. MTL 1077
■ MC. ................................. TCMTL 1077
EMI-America / Jul '93.

## HOME FOR CHRISTMAS.
Tracks: I can hardly wait 'til Christmas / Merry Christmas baby / White Christmas / Christmas song / Wanna be home for Christmas / Christmas time in the city / (Tell 'em) Santa's on his way / Have yourself a merry little Christmas / What are you doing on New Year's eve / Carol of the bells.

CD .................................. CDMTL 1063
MC. ................................. TCMTL 1063
EMI-Manhattan / Nov '91 / EMI.

## I DIG YOUR ACT.
Tracks: I dig your act.

■ 7" .................................. SS 2073
Stateside / '67.

## I JUST WANT TO SATISFY.
Tracks: I just want to satisfy / Don't walk away mad.

■ 7" .................................. PIRA 2247
Philadelphia Int. / May '82.

## I LOVE MUSIC.
Tracks: I love music / Used to be my girl.

■ 7" .................................. PIR 3879
Philadelphia Int. / Jan '76.

■ 7" .................................. PIR 6093
Philadelphia Int. / Feb '78.

■ 7" .................................. PIR 8869
Philadelphia Int. / Apr '82.

## I LOVE MUSIC (OLD GOLD).
Tracks: I love music.

■ 7" .................................. OG 9728
Old Gold / Nov '87.

## IDENTIFY.
Tracks: Identify / Hurry up and come back.

■ 7" .................................. PIR 8054
Philadelphia Int. / Nov '79.

## IDENTIFY YOURSELF.
Tracks: Sing a happy song / Get on out and party / Identify yourself / So nice I tried it twice / Hurry up and come back / Forever mine / I want you here with me / One in a million.

■ LP .................................. PIR 83666
■ MC. ................................. 40 83666
Philadelphia Int. / Sep '79.

## JUST ANOTHER LONELY NIGHT.
Tracks: Just another lonely night / What good are these arms of mine.

■ 12" .................................. 12PIR 1
■ 7" .................................. PIR 1
Philadelphia Int. / Sep '85.

## LET ME TOUCH YOU.
Tracks: Don't take your love away / Loving you / True love never dies / Still missing / I just want somebody to love me / Let me touch you / Under-cover lover / No lies to cloud my eyes / Don't let the dream get away / 'Cause I want you back again.

■ CD .................................. CDMTL 1014
■ LP .................................. MTL 1014

---

■ DELETED

■ MC. . . . . . . . . . . . . . . TCMTL 1014
EMI-Manhattan / Jul '87.

## LIPSTICK TRACES (ON A CIGARETTE).
**Tracks:** Lipstick traces.
■ 7" . . . . . . . . . . . . . . . . LIB 66102
Liberty / Jun '65.

## LOVE AND MORE.
**Tracks:** Not Advised.
MC. . . . . . . . . . . . . . . . . .40 25998
■ LP . . . . . . . . . . . . . . . . PIR 25998
Philadelphia Int. / Jul '84 / EMI.

## LOVE TRAIN.
**Tracks:** Love train / I love music.
■ 7" . . . . . . . . . . . . . . . . . .A 7235
Philadelphia Int. / May '86.

## LOVE TRAIN (OLD GOLD).
**Tracks:** Love train / Back stabbers.
■ 7" . . . . . . . . . . . . . . . . .OG 9310
Old Gold / Apr '83.

## LOVIN' YOU.
**Tracks:** Loving you / Don't take your love away (ext. remix) / Don't let the dream get away.
■ 12" . . . . . . . . . . . . . . . 12PIR 6
■ 7" . . . . . . . . . . . . . . . . . PIR 6
Philadelphia Int. / Feb '88.

## MESSAGE IN THE MUSIC.
**Tracks:** Message in our music / Prayer / Make a joyful noise / Desire me / Darlin' darlin' baby / I swear / I love no one but you / Let life flow.
■ LP . . . . . . . . . . . . . . . . PIR 81460
Philadelphia Int. / Sep '76.

## MY FAVOURITE PERSON.
**Tracks:** Summer fling / My favourite person.
■ 12" . . . . . . . . . . . . . . . OJAY T 1
■ 7" . . . . . . . . . . . . . . . . OJAY 1
Epic / Aug '87.

## MY FAVOURITE PERSON.
**Tracks:** I just want to satisfy you / Your body's here with me / My favourite person / One on one / I like to see us get down / Your true heart / Out in the real world / Don't walk away / Mad.
■ LP . . . . . . . . . . . . . . . . PIR 85712
Philadelphia Int. / Jul '82.

## O'JAYS (4 Track Cassette EP).
**Tracks:** Love train / I love music / Used to be my girl / Darlin' darlin' baby.
MC. . . . . . . . . . . . . . . . PIRA 402628
Philadelphia Int. / Aug '82 / EMI.

## O'JAYS: GREATEST HITS.
**Tracks:** Love train / 992 arguements / Message in our music / Give the people what they want / Livin' for the weekend / I love music / Back stabbers / Time to get down / Sunshine / For the love of money / Put your hands together / Darlin' darlin'.
■ LP . . . . . . . . . . . . . . . . PIR 86058
Philadelphia Int. / May '78.

## PEACE.
**Tracks:** Now he's home / Little brother / Crossroads of life / La de dah / Peace / Shattered man / Your turn this time / Just to be with you / Gotta get my broom out / Never can say goodbye / Year 2000 / To prove I love you / You'll never know / You're the girl of my dreams / You won't feel / Girl don't let it get you down / Answer's in you / Once is not enough.
■ LP . . . . . . . . . . . . . . . . PHX 1001
Phoenix (2) / Jul '81.

## PUT OUR HEADS TOGETHER.
**Tracks:** Put our heads together / Letter to my friends.
■ 12" . . . . . . . . . . . . . . . TA 3642
■ 7" . . . . . . . . . . . . . . . . .A 3642
Philadelphia Int. / Jul '83.

## PUT OUR HEADS TOGETHER (OLD GOLD).
**Tracks:** Put our heads together / Crazy / Weekend girl.
CD Single. . . . . . . . . . . . . . .OG 6508
Old Gold / Jul '90 / Pickwick.

## PUT YOUR HANDS TOGETHER (OLD GOLD).
**Tracks:** Put your hands together / I love music.
■ 12" . . . . . . . . . . . . . . . .OG 4023
Old Gold / Sep '87.

## REFLECTIONS IN GOLD (1973-1982).
**Tracks:** Ship ahoy / Now that we found love / Don't call me brother / Survival / How time flies / You and me / She is only a woman / Cry together / This time baby / Brandy / Help somebody please / Hurry up and come back / Your body's here with me.
CD. . . . . . . . . . . . . . . . CDCHARLY 109

■ Double LP. . . . . . . . . . . . . . CDX 28
MC. . . . . . . . . . . . . . . . .TCCDX 28
Charly / Jun '88 / Charly.

## SERIOUS.
**Tracks:** Out of my mind / Leave it alone / Have you had your love today / Serious hold on me / Friend of a friend / Never been better / Rainbow / Fading / Pot can't call the kettle black.
■ LP . . . . . . . . . . . . . . . . MTL 1041
EMI-Manhattan / May '89.
■ MC. . . . . . . . . . . . . . . TCMTL 1041
EMI-America / May '89.
■ CD . . . . . . . . . . . . . . CDMTL 1041
EMI-Manhattan / May '89.

## SHIP AHOY.
**Tracks:** Put your hands together / Ship ahoy / This air I breathe / You got your hooks in me / For the love of money / Now that we found love / Don't call me brother / People keep tellin' me.
CD. . . . . . . . . . . . . . . . . 32408
CBS / '88 / Sony.

## SING A HAPPY SONG.
**Tracks:** Sing a happy song.
■ 7" . . . . . . . . . . . . . . . . PIR 7825
Philadelphia Int. / Sep '79.

## SO FULL OF LOVE.
**Tracks:** Sing my heart out / Use ta be my girl / Cry together / This time baby / Brandy / Take me to the stars / Help / Strokety stroke.
■ LP . . . . . . . . . . . . . . . . PIR 86066
Philadelphia Int. / Aug '78.

## SO GLAD I GOT YOU GAL.
**Tracks:** So glad I got you gal / Let's spend some time together.
■ 7" . . . . . . . . . . . . . . . . PIR 5337
Philadelphia Int. / Jun '77.

## SUMMER FLING.
**Tracks:** Summer fling / Give my love to the ladies.
■ 12" . . . . . . . . . . . . . . . TA 4613
■ 7" . . . . . . . . . . . . . . . . .A 4613
Philadelphia Int. / Jul '84.

## SUMMER FLING (OLD GOLD).
**Tracks:** Summer fling / Extraordinary girl.
■ 12" . . . . . . . . . . . . . . . .OG 4073
Old Gold / Jul '88.

## SUNSHINE.
**Tracks:** Sunshine.
■ 7" . . . . . . . . . . . . . . . . PIR 2950
Philadelphia Int. / Jan '75.

## TRAVELLIN' AT THE SPEED OF THOUGHT.
**Tracks:** Travellin' at the speed of thought / We're all in this thing together / So glad I got you girl / Stand up / Those lies / Feelings / Work on me / Let's spend some time together.
■ LP . . . . . . . . . . . . . . . . PIR 81977
Philadelphia Int. / Jul '77.

## USED TA BE MY GIRL.
**Tracks:** Used ta be my girl / This time baby.
■ 7" . . . . . . . . . . . . . . . . PIR 6332
Philadelphia Int. / Jun '78.

## WE'RE ALL IN THIS THING TOGETHER.
**Tracks:** We're all in this togther / Feelings.
■ 7" . . . . . . . . . . . . . . . . PIR 5582
Philadelphia Int. / Aug '77.

## WHEN WILL I SEE YOU AGAIN.
**Tracks:** I can't stand the pain / Betcha don't know / When will I see you again / House of fire / Letter to my friends / Put our heads together / Ain't nothin' wrong with good lovin' / Nice and easy.
■ LP . . . . . . . . . . . . . . . . PIR 25290
MC. . . . . . . . . . . . . . . . . .40 25290
Philadelphia Int. / Sep '83 / EMI.

## WORKING ON YOUR CASE.
**Tracks:** Lipstick traces / How does it feel / You're the one / Rented tuxedo / Let it all out / You're on top / No time for you / My dearest beloved / Working on your case / Hold on / Lonely drifter / Today and tomorrow / Storm is over / Stand in for love / Dotted line / Stand tall.
■ MC. . . . . . . . . . . . . . EG 2604824
■ LP . . . . . . . . . . . . . . EG 2604821
Stateside / Mar '85.

## YEAR 2000, THE.
**Tracks:** Year 2000 / To prove I love you / You'll never know / You're the girl of my dreams / You won't fail / Girl don't let it get you down / Answer's in you / Once is not enough.
■ LP . . . . . . . . . . . . . . . . PIR 84221

MC. . . . . . . . . . . . . . . . .40 84221
Philadelphia Int. / Oct '80 / EMI.

# Okaysions

## GIRL WATCHER.
**Tracks:** Girl watcher.
■ 7" . . . . . . . . . . . . . . . . SS 2126
Stateside / '68.

# Oldland Montano

## JUST A GAME.
**Tracks:** Just a game (On all versions) / Old man (On all versions) / Just a game (extended version) (CD & 12" only) / Whatever happened to (me & you boy) (CD only).
■ 12" . . . . . . . . . . . . . . . SRNT 79
■ 7" . . . . . . . . . . . . . . . . SRN 79
■ CD Single . . . . . . . . . . . SRNCD 79
Siren / Jul '88.

## LOVE DIMENSION.
**Tracks:** Love dimension / Secrets.
■ 7" . . . . . . . . . . . . . . . . SRN 67
■ 12" . . . . . . . . . . . . . . . SRNT 67
Siren / Nov '87.

## SOMETIMES BLACK, SOMETIMES WHITE.
**Tracks:** Sometimes black, sometimes white (7" & CD only) / You're losing me (7" & CD only) / Dance in the dark (12" & CD only) / I've got to use my imagination (CD only) / Sometimes black, sometimes white (extended) (12" only) / You're losing me (extended) (12" only).
■ 12" . . . . . . . . . . . . . . . SRNT 94
■ 7" . . . . . . . . . . . . . . . . SRN 94
■ CD Single . . . . . . . . . . . SRNCD 94
Siren / Oct '88.

## SUGAR MONEY.
**Tracks:** Sugar money / Whatever happened to (me & you boy) / Imagination (12" only).
■ 12" . . . . . . . . . . . . . . . SRN 63-12
■ 7" . . . . . . . . . . . . . . . . SRN 63
Siren / Sep '87.

## TIME HAS COME, THE.
**Tracks:** My world / Ocean of emotion / Just a game / Sometimes black, sometimes white / Skin deep / Time has come / Sugar mummy / Am I hooked / Love dimension / Sunken love / Problems / Forbidden fruit.
■ LP . . . . . . . . . . . . . . . . SRNLP 17
Siren / '88.
■ MC. . . . . . . . . . . . . . . SRNMC 17
Siren / Aug '88.
CD. . . . . . . . . . . . . . . . .CDSRN 17
Siren / Nov '88 / EMI.

# Oldland, Misty

## FAIR AFFAIR (JE T'AIME), A.
**Tracks:** Fair affair (je t'aime) / Fair affair (je t'aime) (mixes) / Caroline (Not available on 12).
■ 12" . . . . . . . . . . . . . . .660161 6
■ MC Single. . . . . . . . . . . .660161 4
■ CD Single. . . . . . . . . . . .660161 2
Columbia / Feb '94.

## GOT ME A FEELING.
**Tracks:** Got me a feeling / Still my heart.
■ 12" . . . . . . . . . . . . . . .BBR 007
Boogie Back Records / Dec '92.
■ 12" . . . . . . . . . . . . . . .659787 6
■ CD Single. . . . . . . . . . . .659787 2
■ MC Single. . . . . . . . . . . .659787 4
Columbia / Sep '93.

## I WROTE YOU A SONG.
**Tracks:** I wrote you a song (mixes) / Like I need (On CD only).
12". . . . . . . . . . . . . . . .660373 6
CD Single . . . . . . . . . . . .660373 2
MC Single . . . . . . . . . . . .660373 4
Columbia / Jun '94 / Sony.

## SUPERNATURAL.
**Tracks:** I wrote you a song / Fair affair (Je T'Aime) / Got me a feeling / Imprison me / Why do I trust you (Only on cassette and cd.) / Caroline / Kissing the planet / One world / You are the one / Like I need / I often wonder / Groove eternity.
CD. . . . . . . . . . . . . . . . .4759585 2
LP . . . . . . . . . . . . . . . . .475958 1
MC. . . . . . . . . . . . . . . . .475958 4
Columbia / Apr '94 / Sony.

## Oliver, David

### BONSOIR FRANCOISE.
**Tracks:** Bonsoir Francoise.
■ 7″ .......................DJS 10609
DJM / Sep '75.

## Oliver, Mondee

### STAY CLOSE.
**Tracks:** Stay close.
■ 12″...................12 BRW 162
■ 7″ ....................... BRW 162
■ CD Single.............. .BRCD 162
4th & Broadway / Jan '90.

## Ollie & Jerry

### BREAKIN' THERE'S NO STOPPIN' US (OLD GOLD).
**Tracks:** Breakin' there's no stoppin' us / You can dance if you want to.
■ 7″ ........................OG 4131
Old Gold / Aug '89.

### BREAKIN' THERE'S NO STOPPING US.
**Tracks:** Breakin' there's no stopping us / Breakin' here's no stopping us (instr.).
■ 7″ ......................POSP 690
Polydor / Jun '84.

### ELECTRIC BOOGALOO.
**Tracks:** Electric boogaloo / Physical clash.
■ 12″.....................POSPX 730
■ 7″ ......................POSP 730
Polydor / Mar '85.

## Ollie & The Nightingales

### OLLIE & THE NIGHTINGALES.
**Tracks:** You'll never do wrong / Don't make the good suffer / Don't do what I did / I've got a feeling / You're leaving me / Broke in love / ABCD / Mellow way you treat your man / Girl you make my heart sing / I've never found a girl / Showered with love.
■ CD .....................CDSXE 068
Stax / Nov '92 / Pinnacle.

## Olu

### FORGOTTEN MAN.
**Tracks:** Forgotten man / Another broken heart / Entertainment inc.
■ 12″.......................TENX 407
■ 7″ ........................TEN 407
■ CD Single................ TENCD 407
10 / Jul '92.

### LIVING FREE.
**Tracks:** Living free (Joie de vivre mix) (On 12″ and CD single only.) / Living free(flute mix) (On 12″ and CD single onlu.) / Living free (album version) (On 12″ only.) / Forgotten man (Tee's pella [8]X1) (On 12″ only.) / Living free (7″ mix) (On 7″ and CD single only.) / Sophia aids.
■ 7″ ........................TEN 411
■ 12″.......................TENX 411
■ CD Single................ TENCD 411
10 / Oct '92.

### REACHING OUT.
**Tracks:** Forgotten man / Rhythm & Soul / Reaching out / Living in the shadow / Destiny / Don't let it die / One nation / Love affair / Living free / People searching.
■ CD ......................DIXCD 115
■ LP .......................DIX 115
■ MC.......................CDIX 115
10 / Nov '92 / EMI.

## Olympic Runners

### BITCH, THE.
**Tracks:** Bitch / Energy beam.
■ 12″.....................POSPX 63
■ 7″ ......................POSP 63
Polydor / Jul '79.

### DRAG IT OVER HERE.
**Tracks:** Drag it over here / Mac B. Coolie.
■ 7″ ......................HLU 10488
London / May '75.

### GET IT WHILE YOU CAN.
**Tracks:** Get it while you can / Onya.
■ 12″ ......................RUN 12 7
■ 7″ ........................RUN 7
Polydor / Oct '78.

---

### HOT TO TROT.
**Tracks:** Say what you wanna but it sure is funky / Just enough / One step at a time / Just funkin' around / Straight St. strut / Personal thang / World record / Just a little lick / Bahama mama / Love on my mind.
■ LP ....................... NORT 1
Chipping Norton / Jan '77.

### IT'S A BITCH.
**Tracks:** Bitch / 130 beats a minute / Crazy talk / Make it happen / Closer to paradise / Betcha can't dance / Making it better / Disco smash.
■ LP ...................... 2383549
Polydor / Nov '79.

### KEEP IT UP.
**Tracks:** Keep it up / Whatever it takes.
■ 12″ ....................... PC 5048
■ 7″ .......................DDC 004
RCA / Apr '79.

### KEEPIN' IT UP.
**Tracks:** Solar heat / Down to the bone / Guacamole getdown / Interference free / Hash browns / Keep it up / Swamp lizard / Boogie line.
■ LP ...................... PL 25124
■ MC ...................... PK 25124
RCA / Mar '78.

### LOVE ON MY MIND.
**Tracks:** Love on my mind / In the can.
■ 7″ .......................CHIP 4
Chipping Norton / Feb '77.

### OUT OF THE GROUND.
**Tracks:** Whatever it takes / Back on the track / Out of the ground / Don't let up / Party time is here to stay / In the can / Pacapaco-wa-wa / Kool gent.
■ LP ...................... PL 25195
RCA / '79.

### PERSONAL THANG.
**Tracks:** Personal thang / Don't let up.
■ 7″ .......................CHIP 3
Chipping Norton / Jan '77.

### PUTTING IT ON YA.
**Tracks:** Sir Dancealot / Wooden head / When you're dancing / God bless you / Energy beam / Get it while you can / Breakout / Onya.
■ LP ...................... POLD 5015
Polydor / '78.

### SIR DANCEALOT.
**Tracks:** Sir Dancealot / Crossword.
■ 7″ ...................... POSP 17
Polydor / Jan '79.

### WHATEVER IT TAKES.
**Tracks:** Whatever it takes / Solar heat.
■ 12″ ...................... PC 5078
■ 7″ ...................... PB 5078
RCA / May '78.

## Olympics

### DOIN' THE HULLY GULLY.
**Tracks:** Big boy Pete / Little Pedro / Stay away from Joe / Big Chief, Little Puss / Stay where you are / What'd I say / Private eye / Baby it's hot / Dooley / Baby hully gully / Dodge City / I'll never fall in love again / Working hard.
■ LP ...................... CH 56
Ace / Aug '82.
■ CD .......................CDCHD 324
Ace / Jul '91 / Pinnacle / Complete Record Co. Ltd.

### HULLY GULLY.
**Tracks:** Hully gully / Big boy Pete.
■ 7″ ...................... BOY 27
Jay Boy / Jul '71.

### I WISH I COULD SHIMMY LIKE MY SISTER KATE.
**Tracks:** I wish I could shimmy like my sister Kate.
■ 7″ ...................... V 9174
Vogue / Jan '61.

### OLYMPICS MEET THE MARATHONS, THE.
**Tracks:** C. Percy Mercy of Scotland Yard / Oink Jones / Chicken spaceman / Nothing in the world / Gee / Tight sweater / Talkin' trash / Peanut butter / Shimmy like Kate / Slop / Party popper / Scotch / Mash them taters / Stomp / Boo-dee green / Dance by the light of the moon.
■ LP ...................... CH 123
Ace / Jan '85.

---

### WE GO TOGETHER.
**Tracks:** We go together / Secret agents.
■ 7″ .......................TF 678
Fontana / Mar '66.

### WESTERN MOVIES.
**Tracks:** Western movies.
■ 7″ .......................POP 528
H.M.V. / Oct '58.

### WESTERN MOVIES.
**Tracks:** Western movies / Private eye / Everybody needs love / Well.
■ 12″ ...................... EMI 2924
EMI / '79.

## Omar

Kent's great soul hope. Born in Canterbury in '69, Omar Lye Fook attended Cheatham Music School in Manchester and spent a period as a percussionist in the Kent Youth Orchestra, before a tape of his song *Mr Postman* found its way to Radio London DJ Dave Pearce in the mid-'80s. Consequent appearances on the now-legendary Radio London Nights Out led to his signing to Harlesden-based Kongo Records, for who he recorded *There's Nothing Like This* in 1990. The debut album sold almost 50,000 copies and became an underground smash. Talkin' Loud, Phonogram's trendy funk-jazz off-shoot, won the race to sign him and, after re-releasing (and slightly revising) *There's Nothing Like This*, they launched Omar nationally with the *Music* LP in '92. It failed to improve on his first album's sales and he was subsequently dropped. Currently on RCA, his '94 album *For Pleasure* looked destined for similar under-achievement.

### DON'T MEAN A THING.
**Tracks:** Don't mean a thing / Use me (acapella) / Walk in the park (Only on 12″ and CD Single).
■ 12″.......................TLKX 13
■ 7″ ........................TLK 13
■ CD Single................TLKCD 13
■ MC Single................ .TLKC 13
Talkin' Loud / Aug '91.

### FOR PLEASURE.
**Tracks:** My baby says / I'm still standing / Saturday / Keep steppin' / Magical mystery interlude / Outside / Little boy / Need you bad / Can't get nowhere / Confection / Magic mystical way / Making sense of it / Pleasure.
■ CD...................... 7432120853-2
■ MC...................... 7432120853-4
■ LP ...................... 7432120853-1
RCA / Jun '94 / BMG.

### KEEP STEPPIN'.
**Tracks:** Keep steppin' (mixes) / There's nothing like this (On 74321 23368 2 only) / Who chooses the seasons (duet with Carleen Anderson) (On 74321 23368 2 only).
■ 12″...................... 74321 23367 1
■ CD Single................ 74321 23368 2
■ CD Single................ 74321 23367 2
■ MC Single................ 74321 23367 4
Arista / Sep '94 / BMG.

### MUSIC.
**Tracks:** Not Advised.
■ CD...................... 512 401-2
■ LP ...................... 512 401-1
■ MC...................... 512 401-4
Phonogram / Nov '92 / PolyGram.

### OUTSIDE.
**Tracks:** Outside (Mixes) / Saturday (Foncett's gangster club ride).
■ 12″...................... 74321 213971
■ CD Single................ 74321 213972
■ CD Single................ 74321 213982
■ MC Single................ 74321 213974
RCA / Jul '94.

### THERE'S NOTHING LIKE THIS.
**Tracks:** There's nothing like this / Don't mean a thing / You and me / Positive / I'm in love / Meaning of life / Stop messing around / Serious style / I don't mind the waiting / Fine (acapella).
■ CD...................... KDCD 2
■ LP ...................... KDLP 2
Kongo Dance / Jul '90 / Total / BMG.
■ MC...................... KDMC 2
Kongo Dance / Jun '90 / Total / BMG.
■ LP ...................... .510021-1
■ CD...................... .510021-2
■ MC...................... .510021-4
Talkin' Loud / Jul '91.

---

■ DELETED

## THERE'S NOTHING LIKE THIS.
**Tracks:** There's nothing like this (7" & 12" only) / I don't mind the waiting (12" only).
- 12" . . . . . . . . . . . . . . . . . . . .12 DPST 7
- 7" . . . . . . . . . . . . . . . . . . . . . DPST 7

Kongo Dance / Sep '90.
- 12" . . . . . . . . . . . . . . . . . . . TLKX 9
- 7" . . . . . . . . . . . . . . . . . . . . TLK 9
- CD Single. . . . . . . . . . . . . . . TLKCD 9
- MC Single. . . . . . . . . . . . . . TLKMC 9

Talkin' Loud / Jun '91.

## YOUR LOSS, MY GAIN.
**Tracks:** Your loss, my gain / Get to know you better / Reality (Available on 12" and CD single formats only.).
- 12" . . . . . . . . . . . . . . . . . . .TLKX 22
- 7" . . . . . . . . . . . . . . . . . . . TLK 22
- CD Single. . . . . . . . . . . . . . TLKCD 22
- MC Single. . . . . . . . . . . . . .TLKMC 22

Talkin' Loud / May '92.

## Omari

### AFTER LOVING YOU.
**Tracks:** After loving you.
- 12" . . . . . . . . . . . . . . . . . 12 BJ 1001

Beau-Jolly / Feb '84.
- 12" . . . . . . . . . . . . . . . . 12 RFR 001

Recent Future / Nov '85.
- 12" . . . . . . . . . . . . . . . . . . SILHT 001
- 7" . . . . . . . . . . . . . . . . . SILH 001

Silhouette / Nov '88.

## One Family

### ALL AROUND THE WORLD.
**Tracks:** All around the world.
12" . . . . . . . . . . . . . . . . . . . . . . PPDT 4
CD Single. . . . . . . . . . . . . . . . PPDCD 4
MC Single . . . . . . . . . . . . . . . PPDMC 4

Warner Bros. / Sep '94 / WEA.

### GOOD LOVE (One Family Featuring Sylvia Tella).
**Tracks:** Good love.
- 12" . . . . . . . . . . . . . . . . . . . . PRIM 006

One Family / Apr '93.

## One Hand One Heart

### MIRACLE HEART.
**Tracks:** Miracle heart / Too close for comfort.
- 12" . . . . . . . . . . . . . . . . . . . . WUNT 1
- 7" . . . . . . . . . . . . . . . . . . . . WUN Q1
- 7" . . . . . . . . . . . . . . . . . . . . .WUN 1
- CD Single. . . . . . . . . . . . . . . CDWUN 1

Epic / Aug '88.

### ONE STEP CLOSER.
**Tracks:** One step closer.
- 12" . . . . . . . . . . . . . . . . . . . WUN T2
- 7" . . . . . . . . . . . . . . . . . . . WUN G2
- 7" . . . . . . . . . . . . . . . . . . . .WUN 2
- CD Single. . . . . . . . . . . . . . . CDWUN 2

Epic / Dec '88.

### ONE STEP CLOSER (BOXED SINGLES SET).
**Tracks:** Not Advised.
- 7" Set . . . . . . . . . . . . . . . . . WUN B2

Epic / Jan '89.

## One Way

### LADY.
**Tracks:** Not Advised.
- LP . . . . . . . . . . . . . . . . . . MCF 3219

MCA / Jul '84.

### PUSH.
**Tracks:** Push / All over again.
- 12" . . . . . . . . . . . . . . . . . MCAT 738
- 7" . . . . . . . . . . . . . . . . . . MCA 738

MCA / '81.

### SHINE ON ME.
**Tracks:** Shine on me / Didn't you know it / Together forever.
- 12" . . . . . . . . . . . . . . . . . MCAT 832
- 7" . . . . . . . . . . . . . . . . . . MCA 832

MCA / Sep '83.

### WHO'S FOOLING WHO.
**Tracks:** Who's fooling who / Sweet lady.
- 12" . . . . . . . . . . . . . . . . . MCAT 768
- 7" . . . . . . . . . . . . . . . . . . MCA 768

MCA / May '82.

---

## WILD NIGHT (One Way Featuring Al Hudson).
**Tracks:** Not Advised.
- LP . . . . . . . . . . . . . . . . . . MCF 3153

MCA / Nov '82.

## One World

### COME INTO MY HEART.
**Tracks:** Come into my heart (7" only) / Come into my heart (prophet mix) (12" only) / Come into my heart (extended club mix) (12" only) / Come into my heart (loved up mix) (12" only) / Come into my heart (viva mix) (12" remix only) / Come into my heart (m40 mix) (12" remix only) / Come into my heart (nude dub mix) (12" remix only).
- 12" . . . . . . . . . . . . . . . . . . . . .FX 154
- 12" Remix . . . . . . . . . . . . . .FXR 154
- 7" . . . . . . . . . . . . . . . . . . . . F 154

FFRR / Mar '91.

### DOWN ON LOVE.
**Tracks:** Down on love (Assertive edit) / Down on love (Instrumental) / Blissful shorts (12" only) / Down on love (Mix) (CD only).
- 12" . . . . . . . . . . . . . . . . . . . . .FX 129
- 7" . . . . . . . . . . . . . . . . . . . . F 129
- CD Single. . . . . . . . . . . . . . . .FCD 129

FFRR / Feb '90.

## O'Neal, Alexander

Mississippi-born singer who sang with small-time outfits before hooking into emergent Minneapolis funk scene. Tenure with Flyte Tyme outfit ended when Prince formed The Time instead and brought Morris Day instead. However, project initiated association with producers Jam & Lewis, who took him to Tabu label for hit-making career. By '87, even before release of chartbusting Hearsay album, O'Neal could boast Top 20 placing for solo debut, sold-out Wembley Arena gigs, and clutch of hits, including classic 1985 duet with Cherelle, Saturday Love. Hearsay itself, in original and remixed incarnations, remained on chart for two years; success which O'Neal could not realistically hope to repeat. Although All True Man and Greatest Hits albums sold well, his career floundered when he split from Jam & Lewis for '93's Love Makes No Sense.

### (WHAT CAN I SAY) TO MAKE YOU LOVE ME.
**Tracks:** (What can I say) to make you love me / Broken heart can mend / You were mean't to be my lady (not my girl)*.
- 12" . . . . . . . . . . . . . . . . . . . .652652 8
- 12" . . . . . . . . . . . . . . . . . . . .652852 6
- 7" . . . . . . . . . . . . . . . . . . . .652852 7
- CD Single. . . . . . . . . . . . . . . .652852 2

Tabu / Jul '88.

### ALEXANDER O'NEAL.
**Tracks:** Broken heart can mend / If you were here tonight / Do you wanna like I do / Look at us now / Innocent / You were meant to be my lady (not my girl) / Alex 99 / What's missing.
- LP . . . . . . . . . . . . . . . . . TBU 26485
MC. . . . . . . . . . . . . . . . . . .40 26485

Tabu / Nov '86 / Sony.
- CD . . . . . . . . . . . . . . . . . .460187 2
- LP . . . . . . . . . . . . . . . . . .460187 1
- MC . . . . . . . . . . . . . . . . . .460187 4

Tabu / Mar '90.

### ALEXANDER O'NEAL - THE 12" TAPE.
**Tracks:** Hersay '89 / Critcize / Whats missing / You were meant to be my lady (not my girl) / If you were here tonight.
- MC. . . . . . . . . . . . . . . . . . . 4689874

Tabu / Sep '91.

### ALL TRUE MAN.
**Tracks:** Time is running out / Yoke (G.U.O.T.R.) / Every time I get up / Somebody changed your mind / Midnight run / Used / All true man / Sentimental / What is this thing called love / Morning after / Hang on / Shame on me.
- LP . . . . . . . . . . . . . . . . . . 4658821
- CD . . . . . . . . . . . . . . . . . . 4658822
- MC. . . . . . . . . . . . . . . . . . 4658824

Tabu / Nov '90.

### ALL TRUE MAN.
**Tracks:** All true man / Hang on / Official bootleg mega-mix, The (12" version) / (What can I say) to make you love me / Never knew love like this / Fake / Hearsay / Criticize / Innocent.
- 12" . . . . . . . . . . . . . . . . . . . .6565716
- 12" . . . . . . . . . . . . . . . . . . . .6565718

---

- 7" . . . . . . . . . . . . . . . . . . . .656571
- CD Single . . . . . . . . . . . . . . .656571
- MC Single . . . . . . . . . . . . . . .656571

Tabu / Dec '90.

### BROKEN HEART CAN'T MEND.
**Tracks:** Broken heart can mend / If you were here tonight.
- 12" . . . . . . . . . . . . . . . . . . . QTA 624
- 7" . . . . . . . . . . . . . . . . . . . .QA 624
- 7" . . . . . . . . . . . . . . . . . . . .A 624

Tabu / Mar '86.

### CHRISTMAS SONG, THE.
**Tracks:** Christmas song / Thank you for a good year / Sleigh ride (*Not on 7" version).
- 12" . . . . . . . . . . . . . . . . . . .653182
- 7" . . . . . . . . . . . . . . . . . . . .653182
- 7" . . . . . . . . . . . . . . . . . . . .653182
- CD Single. . . . . . . . . . . . . . . .653182

Tabu / Nov '88.

### CRITICIZE.
**Tracks:** Criticize / Criticize (critical edit) / Criticize (nag mix) / Criticize (remix) (On 12" version only.) / Criticize (critical mix) (On 12" version only.) / Criticize (critical dub) (On 12" version only.) / Criticize (acapella).
- 12" . . . . . . . . . . . . . . . . . . . .6512110
- 10" . . . . . . . . . . . . . . . . . . . .6512118

Tabu / Nov '87.
- 12" . . . . . . . . . . . . . . . . . . . .6512110
- 7" . . . . . . . . . . . . . . . . . . . .6512117

Tabu / Oct '87.

### FAKE.
**Tracks:** Fake / Look at us now / Fake (extended version).
- 12" . . . . . . . . . . . . . . . . . . . .650891
- MC Single. . . . . . . . . . . . . . .650891
- 7" . . . . . . . . . . . . . . . . . . . .650891

Tabu / May '87.

### FAKE '88.
**Tracks:** Fake '88 / Innocent / Fake '88 (short house mix) (652949 0 only.).
- 12" . . . . . . . . . . . . . . . . . . . .652949
- 7" . . . . . . . . . . . . . . . . . . . .652949
- 7" . . . . . . . . . . . . . . . . . . . .652949
- CD Single . . . . . . . . . . . . . . .652949

Tabu / Sep '88.

### FAKE (ORIGINAL EXTENDED VERSION).
**Tracks:** Fake (original extended version) / Fake 88 (hop mix) / Fake 88 (acapella) / Innocent.
- 12" . . . . . . . . . . . . . . . . . . . .652949

Tabu / Sep '88.

### GREATEST HITS, THE/ALL MIXED UP.
**Tracks:** Not Advised.
CD Set . . . . . . . . . . . . . . . .4717142 D

Epic / Feb '93 / Sony.

### HEARSAY.
**Tracks:** To make you love me (what can I say) / Hearsay / Lovers / Fake / Criticize / Never knew love like this / Sunshine / Crying overtime / When the party's over.
- LP . . . . . . . . . . . . . . . . . . .450936 1
- MC . . . . . . . . . . . . . . . . . . .450936 4
- CD . . . . . . . . . . . . . . . . . . .450936 2

Tabu / Jul '87.
MiniDisc. . . . . . . . . . . . . . . . . .450936-8

Tabu / Aug '93 / Sony.

### HEARSAY 89.
**Tracks:** Hearsay / You were meant to be my lady / Hearsay 89 (Extended remix) / Hearsay 89 (Club instrumental).
- 12" . . . . . . . . . . . . . . . . . . . .654 667-6
- 12" . . . . . . . . . . . . . . . . . . . .654 667-8
- 7" . . . . . . . . . . . . . . . . . . . .654 667-7
- CD Single . . . . . . . . . . . . . . .654 667-2

Tabu / Feb '89.

### HEARSAY ALL MIXED UP.
**Tracks:** Fake 88 (house mix) / (What can I say) to make you love me (Hateful club mix) / Never knew love like this (extended version) / Criticize (Ben Liebrand remix) / Lovers, The (extended version) / Criticize (remix) / (What can I say) to make you love me (Ben Liebrand remix) / Fake (extended version) / You were meant to be my lady (88 Keith Cohen extended remix) / Innocent (88 Keith Cohen House mix) (Only on CD.).
CD . . . . . . . . . . . . . . . . . . . .MIXUP 2
- LP . . . . . . . . . . . . . . . . . . .MIXUP 1
MC. . . . . . . . . . . . . . . . . . . .MIXUP 4

Tabu / Nov '88 / Sony.
CD . . . . . . . . . . . . . . . . . . . . 4634962
- MC . . . . . . . . . . . . . . . . . . 4631964

Tabu / May '91 / Sony.

■ DELETED

## HEARSAY/ALL MIXED UP.
**Tracks:** What can I say to make you love me / Hearsay / Lovers / Fake / Criticize / Never knew love like this / Crying overtime / When the party's over / Fake 88 (House mix) / What can I say to make you love me (Hateful club mix) / Never knew love like this (ext. version) / Criticize (Ben Liebrand remix) / Lovers, The (ext. version) / Criticize (remix) / Fake (ext. version).

| | | |
|---|---|---|
| ■ CD | | 466 123 2 |
| ■ LP | | 466 123 1 |
| ■ MC | | 466 123 4 |

Tabu / Dec '89 / Sony.

## HITMIX (THE OFFICIAL BOOTLEG MEGA-MIX).
**Tracks:** Hitmix (the official bootleg mega-mix) / Sleigh ride / Hitmix (the official bootleg mega-mix) 12" version).

| | | |
|---|---|---|
| ■ 12" | | 655 504 6 |
| ■ 7" | | 655 504 7 |
| ■ CD Single | | 655 504 2 |
| ■ MC Single | | 655 504 4 |
| ■ MC Single | | 655 504 8 |

Tabu / Nov '89.

## IF YOU WERE HERE TONIGHT.
**Tracks:** If you were here tonight / If you were here tonight (remix) / Soft version.

| | | |
|---|---|---|
| ■ 12" | | QTA 6391 |
| ■ 7" | | A 6391 |

Tabu / Feb '86.

## IN THE MIDDLE.
**Tracks:** In the middle / In the middle (mixes).

| | | |
|---|---|---|
| ■ 12" | | 587714-1 |
| ■ 7" | | 587714-7 |
| ■ CD Single | | 587714-2 |
| ■ MC Single | | 587714-4 |

A&M / Jun '93.

## LIVE IN LONDON.
**Tracks:** Alex 9000 / Time is running out / Broken heart can mend / What can I say (to make you love me) / Crying overtime / Criticize / If you were here tonight / Fake / Sunshine.

| | | |
|---|---|---|
| ■ VHS | | MVN 99 1212 3 |

PMI / Mar '90.

## LOVE MAKES NO SENSE.
**Tracks:** Love makes no sense / Love makes no sense (mixes).

| | | |
|---|---|---|
| ■ 12" | | AMY 7708 |
| ■ 7" | | AM 7708 |
| ■ CD Single | | AMCD 7708 |

Tabu / Jan '93.

## LOVE MAKES NO SENSE.
**Tracks:** In the middle / If you let it / Aphrodisia / Love makes no sense / Home is where the heart is / Change of heart / Lady / All that matters to me / Since I've been lovin' you / What a wonderful world.

| | | |
|---|---|---|
| ■ CD | | 549502 |
| ■ LP | | 549501 |
| ■ MC | | 549504 |

A&M / Feb '93 / PolyGram.

## LOVERS, THE.
**Tracks:** Lovers / Lovers, The (inst.) / Lovers, The (extended version) (track on 12".) / Lovers, The (acapella) (track on 12".) / Lovers, The (bonus beats).

| | | |
|---|---|---|
| ■ 12" | | 651595 6 |
| ■ 7" | | 651595 7 |
| ■ CD Single | | 651595 2 |

Tabu / May '88.

## MY GIFT TO YOU.
**Tracks:** My gift to you / Sleigh ride / Our first Christmas / Remember (why it's Christmas) / Little drummer boy / Christmas song / This Christmas / Winter wonderland / Thank you for a good year / Remember why it's Christmas (reprise).

| | | |
|---|---|---|
| ■ LP | | 463152 1 |
| ■ MC | | 463152 4 |
| ■ CD | | 463152 2 |

Tabu / Dec '88 / Sony.

## NEVER KNEW LOVE LIKE THIS (O'Neal, Alexander & Cherrelle).
**Tracks:** Never knew love like this (ext. version) / Never knew love like this (inst.) / Never knew love like this (reprise).

| | | |
|---|---|---|
| ■ 10" | | 651382 0 |
| ■ 12" | | 651382 6 |
| ■ 7" | | 651382 7 |
| ■ 7" | | 651382 9 |
| ■ CD Single | | 651382 2 |

Tabu / Jan '88.

## SENTIMENTAL.
**Tracks:** Sentimental / Yoke, The (G.U.O.T.R.).

| | | |
|---|---|---|
| ■ 12" | | 6580146 |

## 

| | | |
|---|---|---|
| ■ 7" | | 6580147 |
| ■ CD Single | | 6580142 |

Epic / Apr '92.

| | | |
|---|---|---|
| ■ MC | | 6580144 |

Tabu / Apr '92.

## SHAME ON ME.
**Tracks:** Shame on me.

| | | |
|---|---|---|
| ■ 12" | | 6568736 |
| ■ 7" | | 6568737 |
| ■ CD Single | | 6568732 |
| ■ MC Single | | 6568734 |

Tabu / May '91.

## SUNSHINE.
**Tracks:** Sunshine (edit) / Do you wanna like I do / Crying overtime (On 12" & CD single.) / Broken heart can mend (On 12" & CD single.).

| | | |
|---|---|---|
| ■ 12" | | 655191 6 |
| ■ 7" | | 655191 7 |
| ■ CD Single | | 655191 2 |

Tabu / Aug '89.

## THANK YOU FOR A GOOD YEAR.
**Tracks:** Thank you for a good year / Sleigh ride / Christmas song.

| | | |
|---|---|---|
| ■ 12" | | 653 182-8 |
| ■ 7" | | 653 182-9 |
| ■ CD Single | | 654 533-2 |

Tabu / Jan '89.

## THIS THING CALLED LOVE-GREATEST HITS OF ALEXANDER O'NEAL.
**Tracks:** Criticize / Fake 88 (remix) / Broken heart can mend / Hearsay 89 (remix) / (What can I say) to make you love me / Sunshine / What's missing / If you were here tonight (remix) / Never knew love like this / All true man / Lovers / Crying overtime / What is this thing called love / Innocent / Sentimental.

| | | |
|---|---|---|
| ■ CD | | 4717142 |
| ■ LP | | 4717141 |
| ■ MC | | 4717144 |

Tabu / May '92.

| | | |
|---|---|---|
| MiniDisc | | 4717143 |

Tabu / Feb '93 / Sony.

## TWELVE INCH MIXES.
**Tracks:** Hearsay 89 (extended remix) / Criticize (remix) / What's missing (extended remix) / You were meant to be my baby (remix) / If you were here tonight (soft version).

| | | |
|---|---|---|
| CD | | 468987-2 |

Tabu / Nov '92 / Sony.

| | | |
|---|---|---|
| MC | | 468987-4 |

Epic / Nov '92 / Sony.

## VOICE ON VIDEO.
**Tracks:** Innocent / If you were here tonight / Broken heart can mend / Fake / Criticize / Never knew love like this.

| | | |
|---|---|---|
| VHS | | 5394 50 |

CBS-Fox / Feb '88 / Sony / THE.

| | | |
|---|---|---|
| VHS | | 498142 |

CMV Enterprises (Video) / May '89 / Sony.

## WHAT IS THIS THING CALLED LOVE?.
**Tracks:** What is this thing called love? (edit) (Not on 12" single) / Crying overtime (Not on 12" single) / What is this thing called love (album version) (Only on 12" & CD single) / Lovers, The (extended version) (Only on 12" & CD single) / If you were here tonight (Only on 12" & CD single).

| | | |
|---|---|---|
| ■ 12" | | 6567316 |
| ■ 12" Remix | | 6567318 |
| ■ 7" | | 6567317 |
| ■ CD Single | | 6567312 |
| ■ MC Single | | 6567314 |

Tabu / Mar '91.

## WHAT'S MISSING.
**Tracks:** What's missing / Do you wanna.

| | | |
|---|---|---|
| ■ 12" | | TA 7191 |
| ■ 7" | | A 7191 |

Tabu / May '86.

## YOU WERE MEANT TO BE MY LADY.
**Tracks:** You were meant to be my lady.

| | | |
|---|---|---|
| ■ 12" | | 6500486 |
| ■ 7" | | 6500487 |

Tabu / Aug '86.

## Oneness Of Ju Ju

### ELECTRIC JUJU NATION.
**Tracks:** Not Advised.

| | | |
|---|---|---|
| ■ LP | | MVLP 14 |

Move / Apr '86.

### EVERYWAY BUT LOOSE.
**Tracks:** Every way but loose / Higher / Always have to say goodbye / Make a change / Run away bay / Love's wonderland.

| | | |
|---|---|---|
| ■ 12" | | BDSL 497 |

## 

| | | |
|---|---|---|
| ■ 7" | | BDS 497 |

Buddah / Apr '82.

## Opaz

### ACTION SPEAKS LOUDER THAN WORDS.
**Tracks:** Action speaks louder than words / I admit it.

| | | |
|---|---|---|
| ■ 12" | | AMY 852 |
| ■ 7" | | AM 852 |
| ■ CD Single | | AMCD 852 |
| ■ MC Single | | AMMC 852 |

A&M / Feb '92.

### OH MY GOODNESS.
**Tracks:** Oh my goodness.

| | | |
|---|---|---|
| 12" | | OPH 002 |
| CD Single | | OPH 002CD |

Opaz Records / Jul '94 / Pinnacle.

## Originals

### ANOTHER TIME, ANOTHER PLACE.
**Tracks:** Fantasy interlude / Don't put me on / I've loved, I've lost, I've learned / Temporarily out of order / Ladies / Take this love / It's alright / Thanks for your love.

| | | |
|---|---|---|
| ■ LP | | FT 542 |

Fantasy / Jun '78.

### ANOTHER TIME, ANOTHER PLACE/ COME AWAY WITH ME.
**Tracks:** Fantasy interlude / Don't put me on / I've loved, I've lost, I've learned / Temporarily out of order / Ladies (we need you) / Take this love / It's alright / Jezebel / J.E.A.L.O.U.S. means I love you / While the cat's away / Come away with me / Stay with me / Blue moon / Thanks for your love (Happiness is you).

| | | |
|---|---|---|
| CD | | CDSEWD 084 |

South Bound / Jul '93 / Pinnacle.

### GOODNIGHT IRENE.
**Tracks:** Goodnight Irene / Need your lovin'.

| | | |
|---|---|---|
| ■ 7" | | TMG 592 |

Tamla Motown / Jan '67.

### GREEN GROW THE LILACS.
**Tracks:** We've got a way out love / Green grow the lilacs / Baby, I'm for real / I've never begged before / Red sails in the sunset / One life we live / Moment of truth / Why when love is gone / When will we learn / You're the one / Love is a wonder / You, mysterious you.

| | | |
|---|---|---|
| ■ LP | | STML 11116 |

Tamla Motown / Nov '69.

## Orlons

### DON'T HANG UP.
**Tracks:** Don't hang up.

| | | |
|---|---|---|
| ■ 7" | | C 231 |

Cameo Parkway / Dec '62.

### SPINNIN' TOP.
**Tracks:** Spinnin' top.

| | | |
|---|---|---|
| ■ 7" | | PLF 117 |

Planet (2) / '66.

## Osborne, Jeffrey

Former mainman of mid-70's disco act LTD (who scored U.S. hits with *Love Ballad* and *Back In Love Again*), Osborne launched solo career in 1982: both *Stay With Me Tonight* and *On The Wings Of Love* were transatlantic hits. After series of George Duke-produced albums, Osborne retreated from limelight, and has latterly found more success as songwriter and producer; clients including Whitney Houston and Johnny Gill.

### BORDERLINE.
**Tracks:** Borderline / Crazy 'bout you.

| | | |
|---|---|---|
| ■ 12" | | AMY 230 |
| ■ 7" | | AM 230 |

A&M / Jan '85.

### DON'T STOP.
**Tracks:** Don't stop / Let me know / Border lines / Power / Is it right / You can't be serious / Crazy 'bout cha / Hot coals / Live for today.

| | | |
|---|---|---|
| ■ CD | | CDA 5017 |
| ■ LP | | AMA 5017 |
| ■ MC | | AMC 5017 |

A&M / Oct '84.

### DON'T STOP.
**Tracks:** Don't stop.

| | | |
|---|---|---|
| ■ 12" | | AMX 222 |
| ■ 7" | | AM 222 |

A&M / Oct '84.

## DON'T YOU GET SO MAD.
**Tracks:** Don't you get so mad / So much love.
- 12" . . . . . . . . . . . . . . . . . . . . AMX 140
- 7" . . . . . . . . . . . . . . . . . . . . . AM 140

A&M / Sep '83.

## EENIE MEENIE.
**Tracks:** Eenie meenie / You were made to love.
- 7" . . . . . . . . . . . . . . . . . . . . USAF 1223

A&M / Aug '82.

## EMOTIONAL.
**Tracks:** We belong to love / You should be mine / Soweto / In your eyes / Room with a view / Emotional / Second chance / Love's not ready / Who would have guessed / Come midnight.
- CD . . . . . . . . . . . . . . . . . . . . . CDA 5103
- LP . . . . . . . . . . . . . . . . . . . . . AMA 5103
- MC . . . . . . . . . . . . . . . . . . . . . AMC 5103

A&M / Jun '86.

## I REALLY DON'T NEED NO LIGHT.
**Tracks:** I really don't need no light / One million kisses.
- 12" . . . . . . . . . . . . . . . . . . . AMS 128234
- 7" . . . . . . . . . . . . . . . . . . . . AMS 8234

A&M / Jul '82.

## IF MY BROTHER'S IN TROUBLE.
**Tracks:** If my brother's in trouble (Radio edit) (Only on 7" and CD Single) / If my brother's in trouble (R&B Single version) (Only on 7" single) / If my brother's in trouble (Club mix) (Only on 12" and CD Single) / If my brother's in trouble (Extended Hip Hop) (Only on 12" single) / If my brother's in trouble (Double mix) (Only on 12" single).
- 12" . . . . . . . . . . . . . . . . . . . . 613 992
- 7" . . . . . . . . . . . . . . . . . . . . . 113 992
- CD Single . . . . . . . . . . . . . . . . . 663 992

Arista / May '91.

## JEFFREY OSBORNE.
**Tracks:** New love / Eeny meeny / I really don't need no light / On the wings of love / Ready for your love / Who you talkin' to / You were made to love / Ain't nothin' missin' baby / Congratulations.
- LP . . . . . . . . . . . . . . . . . . . . AMLH 64896
- MC . . . . . . . . . . . . . . . . . . . . CAM 64896

A&M / Nov '85.
- CD . . . . . . . . . . . . . . . . . . . . . CDA 3272

A&M / '88.
- CD . . . . . . . . . . . . . . . . . . . . CDMID 125

A&M / Oct '92 / PolyGram.

## ON THE WINGS OF LOVE.
**Tracks:** On the wings of love / I'm begging.
- 12" . . . . . . . . . . . . . . . . . . . . USAF 1225
- 7" . . . . . . . . . . . . . . . . . . . . . USA 1225

Funk America / Jan '83.
- 12" . . . . . . . . . . . . . . . . . . . . AMX 198
- 7" P.Disc . . . . . . . . . . . . . . . . . AMSP 198
- 7" . . . . . . . . . . . . . . . . . . . . . AM 198

A&M / Jun '84.

## ON THE WINGS OF LOVE (OLD GOLD).
**Tracks:** On the wings of love / Stay with me tonight.
- 12" . . . . . . . . . . . . . . . . . . . . OG 4088

Old Gold / Nov '84.

## ONE LOVE ONE DREAM.
**Tracks:** She's on the left / Can't go back on a promise / True believers / One love one dream / All because of you / La cuenta, por favor / Family / My heart can wait forever / You can't wait forever / Cindy ([8]X).
- CD . . . . . . . . . . . . . . . . . . . . . CDA 5205
- LP . . . . . . . . . . . . . . . . . . . . . AMA 5205
- MC . . . . . . . . . . . . . . . . . . . . . AMC 5205

A&M / Aug '88.

## ONLY HUMAN.
**Tracks:** If my brother's in trouble / Only human / Good things come to those who wait / Morning after / Lay your head / Baby wait a minute / Sending you a love / Feel like makin' love / Back in your arms / Nightime (Only on cassette and CD.) / Getting better all the time.
- LP . . . . . . . . . . . . . . . . . . . . . 210920
- MC . . . . . . . . . . . . . . . . . . . . . 410920
- CD . . . . . . . . . . . . . . . . . . . . . 260920

Arista / Feb '91.

## ROOM WITH A VIEW.
**Tracks:** Room with a view / Power.
- 12" . . . . . . . . . . . . . . . . . . . . AMY 352
- 7" . . . . . . . . . . . . . . . . . . . . . AM 352

A&M / Sep '86.

## SHE'S ON THE LEFT.
**Tracks:** She's on the left / Plane love.
- 7" . . . . . . . . . . . . . . . . . . . . . USA 643
- 12" . . . . . . . . . . . . . . . . . . . . USAT 643

Breakout / Oct '88.

## SOWETO.
**Tracks:** Soweto / Plain love.
- 12" . . . . . . . . . . . . . . . . . . . . AMY 334
- 7" . . . . . . . . . . . . . . . . . . . . . AM 334

A&M / Jul '86.

## STAY WITH ME TONIGHT.
**Tracks:** Don't you get so mad / We're going all the way / Stay with me tonight / Greatest love affair / Plane love / Other side of the coin / I'll make believe / When are you coming back / Two wrongs don't make a right.
- CD . . . . . . . . . . . . . . . . . . . . . CDA 64940
- MC . . . . . . . . . . . . . . . . . . . . . CXM 64940
- LP . . . . . . . . . . . . . . . . . . . . AMLX 64940

A&M / Aug '83 / PolyGram.

## STAY WITH ME TONIGHT.
**Tracks:** Stay with me tonight / Ready for your love.
- 12" . . . . . . . . . . . . . . . . . . . . AMX 157
- 7" . . . . . . . . . . . . . . . . . . . . . AM 157

A&M / Oct '83.
- 7" . . . . . . . . . . . . . . . . . . . . . AM 188

A&M / Apr '84.

## TAKE GOOD CARE OF YOU AND ME
(see under Warwick, Dionne).

## YOU SHOULD BE MINE.
**Tracks:** You should be mine / Eenie / Stay with me tonight (* Extra tack on 12" version only).
- 12" . . . . . . . . . . . . . . . . . . . . AMY 311
- 7" . . . . . . . . . . . . . . . . . . . . . AM 311

A&M / May '86.

## Osibisa

## BEST OF OSIBISA.
**Tracks:** Beautiful seven / Music for gong gong / Y sharp / Akwaaba / Wango wango / Dawn / Phallus C / Kokoroko / Woyaya.
- LP . . . . . . . . . . . . . . . . . . . . . MCL 1693
- MC . . . . . . . . . . . . . . . . . . . . . MCLC 1693

MCA / Jul '82.

## BEST OF OSIBISA (2).
**Tracks:** Welcome home / Odensu / Seaside meditation / Do it / Kolomashie / Warrior / Cherry field / Ohah awake / Hamattan / Time is right / Gumbe / Jumbo / Kyrie Eleison / Lost fisherman / Sunshine day / Choboi / Right now / Uhuru / Coffee song / Flying bird / Dance the body music / Keep on trying / Sakaba / Get up / Soldier / Abele / Africa we go go / Sakura.
- LP Set . . . . . . . . . . . . . . . . . . . REF 776

BBC / Aug '90 / Pinnacle / Bond Street Music / THE.
- MC Set . . . . . . . . . . . . . . . . . . . ZCD 776

BBC / Jul '92 / Pinnacle / Bond Street Music / THE.
- CD Set . . . . . . . . . . . . . . . . . . BBCCD 2009

BBC / Oct '92 / Pinnacle / Bond Street Music / THE.

## BEST OF OSIBISA (KWEST).
**Tracks:** Not Advised.
- CD . . . . . . . . . . . . . . . . . . . . KWEST 5226
- MC . . . . . . . . . . . . . . . . . . . . KWEST 4226

Kwest / Jul '92 / THE.

## BLACK ANT.
**Tracks:** Black ant / Kotoko.
- 7" . . . . . . . . . . . . . . . . . . . . . SS 1001

Smoke / Jul '71.

## BLACK MAGIC NIGHT.
**Tracks:** Introduction / Welcome home / Living loving feeling / Spirits up above / Fire / Beautiful seven / Encore / Dawn / Ayiko bia / Woyaya / Ke le le / Music for gong gong / Sunshine day / Survival.
- CD . . . . . . . . . . . . . . . . . . . . BBCCD 777
- MC . . . . . . . . . . . . . . . . . . . . . ZCF 777

BBC / Jul '92 / Pinnacle / Bond Street Music / THE.

## CELEBRATION.
**Tracks:** Celebration / Moving on.
- 12" . . . . . . . . . . . . . . . . . . . . CABL 104
- 7" . . . . . . . . . . . . . . . . . . . . . CAB 104

Calibre / Aug '80.

## CELEBRATION - THE BEST OF OSIBISA.
**Tracks:** Not Advised.
- CD . . . . . . . . . . . . . . . . . . . . AIM 1036CD
- MC . . . . . . . . . . . . . . . . . . . . . AIM 1036C

Aim (2) / Oct '93 / Topic Records / Direct Distribution / A.D.A. Distribution.

## CRISS CROSS RHYTHMS.
**Tracks:** Introduction / Dawn / Ayiko bia / Living, loving, feeling / Woyaya / Spirit up above / Ke le le / Fire / Music for gong gong / Survival / Kyrie Eleison.
- CD . . . . . . . . . . . . . . . . . . . . . 26 20 042
- MC . . . . . . . . . . . . . . . . . . . . . 26 20 044

Point (2) / '92 / Sound Solutions.

## DANCE THE BODY MUSIC.
**Tracks:** Dance the body music.
- 7" . . . . . . . . . . . . . . . . . . . . . BRO 2#

Bronze / Jun '76.

## HAPPY CHILDREN.
**Tracks:** Happy children / We want to know / Kotuku Adwoa / Bassa-Bassa / Somaja / Fire.
- LP . . . . . . . . . . . . . . . . . . . . . K 5602#

WEA / Jul '77.

## HEADS.
**Tracks:** Kokorokoo / Wango wango / So so mi la so / Sweet America / Ye tie wo / Che che Kule / Mentum / Sweet sounds / Do you know.
- LP . . . . . . . . . . . . . . . . . . . . MDKS 8007

MCA / Nov '72.

## LIVE AT THE MARQUEE, 1983.
**Tracks:** Fire / Life / Ayiko / Who's got the paper . Woyaya (end s1) / Music for Gong gong / Too much going on / Happy children / Warrior / Sunshine day
- LP . . . . . . . . . . . . . . . . . . . . . CBR 1035
- MC . . . . . . . . . . . . . . . . . . . . . KCBR 1035

Premier (Sony) / '84 / Sony / Pinnacle.

## LIVING LOVING FEELING.
**Tracks:** Living loving feeling / Welcome home.
- 7" . . . . . . . . . . . . . . . . . . . . . BRO 49

Bronze / Jan '78.

## MOVE YOUR BODY.
**Tracks:** Move your body / Sunshine day.
- 12" . . . . . . . . . . . . . . . . . . . 12MAG 235
- 7" . . . . . . . . . . . . . . . . . . . . MAG 235

Magnet / Aug '82.

## MYSTIC ENERGY.
**Tracks:** Meeting point / Celebration / Africa we go go / Orebo (magic people) / Moving on / Mama (I will be back) / (I feel) pata pata / Fatima / Obinkabimame.
- LP . . . . . . . . . . . . . . . . . . . . CABLP 1002
- MC . . . . . . . . . . . . . . . . . . . . ZCCZB 1002

Calibre / Jan '81.
- CD . . . . . . . . . . . . . . . . . . . . MAUCD 614

Mau Mau / Feb '92 / Pinnacle.

## OJAH AWAKE.
**Tracks:** Not Advised.
- LP . . . . . . . . . . . . . . . . . . . . . ILPS 9411

Island / Nov '76.

## OREBA (Magic People).
**Tracks:** Oreba / Moving on.
- 12" . . . . . . . . . . . . . . . . . . . . CABL 106
- 7" . . . . . . . . . . . . . . . . . . . . . CAB 106

Calibre / Nov '80.

## OSIBISA.
**Tracks:** Dawn / Music for Gong Gong / Ayiko Bia / Akwaaba / Oranges / Phallus C / Think about the people.
- LP . . . . . . . . . . . . . . . . . . . . MDKS 8001

MCA / May '71.

## OSIBISA UNLEASHED.
**Tracks:** Raghupati raghava ragaram / Time is right / Kelele / We bring you love / Happy children / Move your body / Why / Get up and dance / Beautiful India.
- LP . . . . . . . . . . . . . . . . . . . . . MAGL 5053
- MC . . . . . . . . . . . . . . . . . . . . ZCMAG 5053

Magnet / Jul '83 / WEA.

## OSIBISA'S FIRST.
**Tracks:** Not Advised.
- CD . . . . . . . . . . . . . . . . . . . . LCCD 901266

Line / Sep '94 / C.M. Distribution / Grapevine Distribution / A.D.A. Distribution / Conifer Records.

## OSIBROCK.
**Tracks:** Who's got the paper / Why / Osibrock / Celele / Atinga bells / African jive / We belong / Komfo (High Priest) / Kangaroo / Home affairs.
- LP . . . . . . . . . . . . . . . . . . . . . K 56048

WEA.

## PATA-PATA.
**Tracks:** Pata-pata / Jumbo.
- 12" . . . . . . . . . . . . . . . . . . . . 12P 5013
- 7" . . . . . . . . . . . . . . . . . . . . . 7P 5013

PRT / Jan '80.

## RAGHUPATI RAGHAVA RAGARAM.
**Tracks:** Raghupati raghava ragaram.
- 7" . . . . . . . . . . . . . . . . . . . . AVM 1003

AVM / Mar '83.

## SUNSHINE DAY.
**Tracks:** Sunshine day / Welcome home / Densu / Choboi / Do it / Right now / Seaside meditation / Kolomashie / Ko ko rio ko / Pata pata / Lion's walk / Inkosi sikeeli Africa / Movements.
- CD . . . . . . . . . . . . . . . . . . . . . 26 20 062

■ DELETED

**IC.** . . . . . . . . . . . . . . . . 26 20 064
pint (2) / '92 / Sound Solutions.

**UNSHINE DAY.**
▪acks: Sunshine day.
▪ 7″ . . . . . . . . . . . . . . . . . BRO 20
/onze / Jan '76.
▪ 12″ . . . . . . . . . . . . . . 12 RSL 246
▪ 7″ . . . . . . . . . . . . . . . . RESL 246
BC / May '90.

**WARRIOR.**
▪acks: Warrior / Saxabo.
▪ 7″ . . . . . . . . . . . . . . . . . BRO 16
ronze / Jul '75.
▪ 7″ . . . . . . . . . . . . . . . . . BRO 41
ronze / Jun '77.

**WARRIOR.**
▪acks: Not Advised.
▪ VHS . . . . . . . . . . . . . . . HEN 2197
endring Video / Mar '90.

**WARRIOR, THE.**
▪ld: Coffee song / Warrior / Flying bird / Cherry
▪ld / Dance the body music / Ojah awake / Keep on
▪ying / Sakabo / Time is right / Get up / Soldier /
▪umbo / Abele / Africa we go go.
▪) . . . . . . . . . . . . . . . . . 26 20 052
▪C. . . . . . . . . . . . . . . . . 26 20 054
pint (2) / '92 / Sound Solutions.

**WOOLY BULLY.**
▪acks: Wooly bully / Lions walk.
▪ 12″ . . . . . . . . . . . . . . . .FED 14T
▪ 7″ . . . . . . . . . . . . . . . . FED 14
erra / Aug '85.

**OYAYA.**
▪acks: Beautiful seven / Y sharp / Spirits up above /
▪rvival / Move on / Rabiatu / Woyaya.
▪ LP . . . . . . . . . . . . . . . MDKS 8005
CA / May '72.

## Oskar, Lee

**AN FRANCISCO BAY.**
▪acks: San Francisco Bay / Haunted house.
▪ 7″ . . . . . . . . . . . . . . . . MCA 524
CA / Oct '79.

## Otis, Byron

**RING BACK MY BABY.**
▪acks: Bring back my baby.
▪ 12″ . . . . . . . . . . . . . . . . ITD 005
al / Mar '82.

**ISSING YOUR LOVE.**
▪acks: Not Advised.
▪ LP . . . . . . . . . . . . . . . . CSLP 003
arendon Sounds / Jun '85.

**O YOU SAY.**
▪acks: So you say / So you dub.
▪ 12″ . . . . . . . . . . . . . . . SHA 0010
▪ashanane / '82.

## Otis, Johnny

**ARRELHOUSE STOMP.**
▪acks: Omaha flash / Jeff-hi stomp / Miss Mitchell /
▪tra-violet / Sgt. Barksdale / Love's nocturne /
▪arrelhouse stomp / Pay day blues / Hog jaws / Jelly
▪ll / Happy new year baby / That's your last boogie /
▪ligator meat / Stardust / One nighter blues.
▪ LP . . . . . . . . . . . . . . . . .JB 611
▪kebox Lil (Sweden) / Aug '87.
▪C. . . . . . . . . . . . . . . . . .JBC 611
▪kebox Lil (Sweden) / Aug '87 / Swift / Wellard.

**YE BYE BABY (Otis, Johnny Show).**
▪acks: Bye bye baby.
▪ 7″ . . . . . . . . . . . . . . . CL 14817
▪apitol / Jan '58.

**ORMIDABLE.**
▪acks: Shake it Lucy baby / Romance in the dark /
▪op de loop / Lonely river / Story untold / Can't you
▪ear me calling / Theme & Good golly / Stay with me
▪t's too soon to know / Hum ding a ling / Livin' in
▪sery / Ma he's making eyes at me / Tell me so.
▪ LP . . . . . . . . . . . . . . . SPE 6604
▪mber / May '69.

**EE BABY (Otis, Johnny & Co.).**
▪acks: Gee baby / Alimony boogie / My heart tells
▪ / Crazy 'bout your cousin / Square dance / New
▪ve / Baby baby blues / Voodoo / Call operator /
▪oomp blues / What's your name / Gypsy blues /
▪hittlin' switch / Brown skin butterball / Why don't
▪u believe me / Wishing well.

---

■ LP . . . . . . . . . . . . . . . . .JB 617
Jukebox Lil (Sweden) / Aug '87.

**GOOD LOVIN' BLUES (Otis, Johnny Show).**
Tracks: Ida Mae / Ice water in your veins / Your last boogie / Pop and sons boogie / In the driver's seat / Loving you is all I know / Listen women / Time to say 'bye bye' / Open house at my house / Good good lovin' blues / Come on over baby / Hey, Mr Bartender / Rock me baby.
CD. . . . . . . . . . . . . . . .CDCH 299
■ LP . . . . . . . . . . . . . . . . CH 299
Ace / Jul '91 / Pinnacle / Complete Record Co. Ltd.

**GREAT RHYTHM AND BLUES VOL.3.**
Tracks: Willie and the hand jive / Barrelhouse blues / Please don't leave me / Bad luck shadow / Fannie Mae / Signifying monkey / Harlem nocturne / Stack-a-lee / Don't start me to talkin' / Baby, I've got news for you / Country girl / Bye bye baby.
■ LP . . . . . . . . . . . . . . . . BDL 1002
Bulldog Records / Jul '82.

**INTO THE EIGHTIES.**
Tracks: Rock 'n' roll wedding / Stand by me / Love (makes me do foolish things) / Hit that jive, jack rollin' / Do it again, baby / In the still of the night / Hide away / Will you love me tomorrow / Soothe me baby / When something is wrong with my baby / I found you / Fine and mellow / I'm gonna leave these women alone.
■ LP . . . . . . . . . . . . . . . . CRB 1110
Charly R&B / May '86.

**JOHNNY OTIS.**
Tracks: Shake it / I won't be your fool no more / Butterball / Sandy's boogie.
■ EP . . . . . . . . . . . . . . . VEP 170162
Vocalion / '65.

**JOHNNY OTIS SHOW/CREEPING WITH THE CATS (Otis, Johnny Show).**
Tracks: Midnight creeper (part 1) / Driftin' blues / Ali Baba's boogie / Let the sunshine in my life (once more) / Hey hey hey hey / Dog face (part 1) / Dog face (part 2) / Show me the way to go home / Sleepy shines butt shuffle / Organ grinder swing / Someday / Sadie / Butterball / Wa wa (part 1) / My eyes are full of tears / Turtle dove / Groove juice / Trouble on my mind / Number 69/ number 21 / Creeper returns / Stop, look and love me / Night is young (and you're so fine).
CD. . . . . . . . . . . . . . . .CDCHD 325
Ace / Jul '91 / Pinnacle / Complete Record Co. Ltd.

**LET'S LIVE IT UP.**
Tracks: Let's rock (let's surf awhile) / Hand jive one more time / It must be love / I say I love you / She's alright / Baby I got news for you / California mash (the hash) / Darling / I'll be true / Let's live it up / That's the chance you've got to take / Hey, hey song / Somebody call the station / Early in the morning blues / You better love me / Queen of the twist / Oh my soul / Wilted rose buds / I know my love is true / Cold, cold heart / Bye bye baby (I'm leaving you) / Yes / In the evening.
CD. . . . . . . . . . . . . . .CDCHARLY 269
Charly / Nov '92 / Charly.

**LIVE AT MONTEREY (Otis, Johnny Show).**
Tracks: Willie and the hand jive / Cry me a river / Cleanhead's blues / I got a gal / Baby you don't know / Preacher's blues / Good rockin' tonight / Time machine / Margie's boogie / Little Esther's blues / Blowtop blues / T-Bone blues / Jelly, jelly / Kidney stew / Things I used to do / R.M. blues / Shuggies blues / You better look out / Goin' back to L.A. / Plastic man / Boogie woogie bye bye.
CD. . . . . . . . . . . . . . . . ED CD 266
■ Double LP. . . . . . . . . . . . .DED 266
Edsel / May '88 / Pinnacle.

**MA, HE'S MAKING EYES AT ME (Otis, Johnny Show/Marie Adams/Three Tons Of Joy).**
Tracks: Ma, he's making eyes at me.
■ 7″ . . . . . . . . . . . . . . . CL 14794
Capitol / Nov '57.

**MA, HE'S MAKING EYES AT ME (OLD GOLD) (Otis, Johnny Show).**
Tracks: Ma, he's making eyes at me / Fever.
■ 7″ . . . . . . . . . . . . . . . .OG 9720
Old Gold / Apr '87.

**NEW JOHNNY OTIS SHOW, THE.**
Tracks: Drinkin' wine spo-dee-o-dee / Every beat of my heart / Jonella and Jack / What else can I do / Half steppin' woman / Why don't you do right / Big time scoop / I never felt this way before / Don't deceive me / So fine.

---

LP . . . . . . . . . . . . . . . SNTF 878
MC. . . . . . . . . . . . . . . . AC 4726
Alligator / Jun '91 / Topic Records / Direct Distribution / C.M. Distribution / A.D.A. Distribution / Jazz Music.
CD. . . . . . . . . . . . . . . . ALCD 4726
Alligator / May '93 / Topic Records / Direct Distribution / C.M. Distribution / A.D.A. Distribution / Jazz Music.

**ORIGINAL JOHNNY OTIS SHOW, THE.**
Tracks: Not Advised.
■ LP . . . . . . . . . . . . . . . SJL 2230
Savoy Jazz (USA) / Mar '85.

**ORIGINAL JOHNNY OTIS VOL 2, THE.**
Tracks: Not Advised.
■ LP . . . . . . . . . . . . . . . SJL 2252
Savoy Jazz (USA) / Mar '85.

**REASON WHY.**
Tracks: Reason why / Secret agent.
■ 7″ . . . . . . . . . . . . . . . SON 2253
Sonet / Jun '83.

**ROCK 'N' ROLL REVUE.**
Tracks: Shake it Lucy baby / Willie and the hand jive / Ring-a-ling-a-ling / Bye bye baby / Light still shines / Tell me so / Telephone baby / Mumblin' moise / Good golly / Ma, he's making eyes at me / Crazy country hop / Hum ding a ling / You just kissed me goodbye / In the dark / Can't you hear me callin' / Castin' my spell.
■ LP . . . . . . . . . . . . . . . CRB 1041
Charly R&B / Mar '82.

**ROCK AND ROLL HIT PARADE.**
Tracks: Not Advised.
■ LP . . . . . . . . . . . . . . . FLY 550
Flyright / Oct '79.

**SPIRIT OF THE BLACK TERRITORY BANDS.**
Tracks: Not Advised.
CD. . . . . . . . . . . . . . . ARHCD 384
Arhoolie (USA) / Mar '93 / Pinnacle / Cadillac / Swift / Projection / Hot Shot / A.D.A. Distribution / Jazz Music.

**WILLIE AND THE HAND JIVE.**
Tracks: Willie and the hand jive / Harlem nocturne.
■ 7″ . . . . . . . . . . . . . . . .BD 2
Bulldog Records / Feb '75.

## Outside

**ALMOST IN.**
Tracks: Not Advised.
CD. . . . . . . . . . . . . . . .DORO 18CD
LP . . . . . . . . . . . . . . . .DORO 18LP
Dorado / Dec '93 / RTM / Pinnacle.

**BIG CITY.**
Tracks: Big city / Ruffneck radio.
■ 12″ . . . . . . . . . . . . . . DOR 013
■ CD Single . . . . . . . . . . .DOR 013CD
Dorado / Jul '93.

**KALEIDOSCOPIC SUMMER.**
Tracks: Kaleidoscopic summer.
12″ . . . . . . . . . . . . . . . DOR 19
CD Single . . . . . . . . . . . . DOR 19CD
Dorado / Apr '94 / RTM / Pinnacle.

**MOVIN' ON.**
Tracks: Movin' on.
■ 12″ . . . . . . . . . . . . . . DOR 17
■ CD Single . . . . . . . . . . . DOR 17CD
Dorado / Dec '93.

**NO TIME FOR CHANGE.**
Tracks: No time for change / No time for change (mix).
■ 12″ . . . . . . . . . . . . . . DOR 009
Dorado / Feb '93.

## Ozone

**DO WHAT'CHA WANNA DO.**
Tracks: Do what'cha wanna do / Come on in.
■ 12″ . . . . . . . . . . . . . . TMGT 1259
■ 7″ . . . . . . . . . . . . . . . TMG 1259
Motown / Apr '82.

**GIGOLETTE.**
Tracks: Gigolette.
■ 12″ . . . . . . . . . . . . . . TMGT 1249
■ 7″ . . . . . . . . . . . . . . . TMG 1249
Motown / Nov '81.

**WALK ON.**
Tracks: Walk on / This is funkin insane.
■ 7″ . . . . . . . . . . . . . . . TMG 1192
Motown / Oct '81.

# P

## P-Funk All Stars

### HYDRAULIC PUMP.
Tracks: Hydraulic pump / Hydraulic pump (part 2).
- 12" . . . . . . . . . . . . . . . . . . . . . . VS 48712
- 7" . . . . . . . . . . . . . . . . . . . . . . . . VS 487
Virgin / Mar '82.

### P. FUNK ALL-STARS LIVE.
Tracks: Audience chant: P funk / Introduction of the band: do that stuff / Cosmic slop / Let's take it to the stage / Mothership connection / I call my baby pussycat / Give up the funk / (Not just) knee deep / Maggot brain / Atomic dog / Flash light / One nation under a groove (On CD only).
- CD Set . . . . . . . . . . . . . . . . . CDSEW2 031
- CD Set. . . . . . . . . . . . . . . . PDSEW2 031
- Double LP. . . . . . . . . . . . . . . . SEW2 031
- MC Set . . . . . . . . . . . . . . . SEWC2 031
Westbound / Oct '90 / Pinnacle.

## P.U.R.E. Blax

### IS IT THE X.
Tracks: Not Advised.
- 12" . . . . . . . . . . . . . . . . . . . . . . TFT 007
Time Flyte / May '93.

## Pacific Eardrum

### LOVE ON A MERRY-GO-ROUND.
Tracks: Love on a merry-go-round / Nothing you can do about that.
- 7" . . . . . . . . . . . . . . . . . . . . . . . CB 317
Charisma / '78.

### PACIFIC EARDRUM.
Tracks: Active factor / All around us / Sitting on a daisy / Sun, sea & samba / Smoke signal / Desert dance / In search of a dream / Crossin' wires.
- LP . . . . . . . . . . . . . . . . . . . . . . CAS 1133
Charisma / Nov '77.

### SITTING ON A DAISY.
Tracks: Sitting on a daisy / Cross lines.
- 7" . . . . . . . . . . . . . . . . . . . . . . . CB 314
Charisma / Jun '78.

## Page, Gene

### ALL OUR DREAMS ARE COMING TRUE.
Tracks: All our dreams are coming true / Don't play that song.
- 7" . . . . . . . . . . . . . . . . . . . . . . K 10591
Atlantic / Jun '75.

## Pagoda

### FINDERS KEEPERS.
Tracks: Finders keepers / We're alright tonight / Go back (Only on 12" version.).
- 12" . . . . . . . . . . . . . . . . . . . . CHS 122714
Chrysalis / '83.
- 7" . . . . . . . . . . . . . . . . . . . . . CHS 2714
Chrysalis / Jun '83.

## Paige, Sharon

### TONIGHT'S THE NIGHT.
Tracks: Tonight's the night.
- 12" . . . . . . . . . . . . . . . . . . 12SRC 103
- 7" . . . . . . . . . . . . . . . . . . . . . SRC 103
Source / Mar '80.

## Pandy, Darryl

### ANIMAL MAGNETISM.
Tracks: Animal magnetism (inst) / Tearing up the house (Remix) (Available on 12" version only.) / Animal magnetism.
- 12" . . . . . . . . . . . . . . . . . . . . . . MARE 2
- 7" . . . . . . . . . . . . . . . . . . . . . . MARES 2
Nightmare / Oct '86.

### FREE MAN (Pandy, Darryl & Farley Jackmaster Funk).
Tracks: Free man.
- 12" . . . . . . . . . . . . . . . . . . . . . . DJ 955
DJ International / Oct '87.

## I LOVE MUSIC.
Tracks: I love music.
- 12" . . . . . . . . . . . . . . . . . . . . . . YZ 478T
- 7" . . . . . . . . . . . . . . . . . . . . . . . YZ 478
Eternal / Jul '90.

## I PUT MY LOVE ON THE LINE.
Tracks: I put my love on the line.
- 7" . . . . . . . . . . . . . . . . . . . . . . MARES 27
Nightmare / May '87.

## Paradise

### DESIGNED IN HEAVEN.
Tracks: Not Advised.
- LP . . . . . . . . . . . . . . . . . . . . . BBSLP 004
Blue Beat / Oct '89.

### GUARDIAN ANGEL.
Tracks: Guardian angel.
- 12" . . . . . . . . . . . . . . . . . . . . . BBLS 003
- 7" . . . . . . . . . . . . . . . . . . . . . BBSP 003
Spirtual House / Aug '89.

### HEARTSTRINGS.
Tracks: Heartstrings.
- 12" . . . . . . . . . . . . . . . . . . . . . . PX 12
- 7" . . . . . . . . . . . . . . . . . . . . . . . P 12
Priority / Jul '85.

### LOVE IS THE ANSWER.
Tracks: Love is the answer / One mind two hearts / Back together / Just can't stop.
- LP . . . . . . . . . . . . . . . . . . . . . . PLP 1
- MC . . . . . . . . . . . . . . . . . . . . . PCAS 1
Priority / Nov '83.

### LOVE IS THE ANSWER.
Tracks: Love is the answer / Just can't stop / One mind, two hearts.
- 12" . . . . . . . . . . . . . . . . . . . . . . PX 6
- 7" . . . . . . . . . . . . . . . . . . . . . . . P 6
Priority / Nov '83.

### ONE MIND TWO HEARTS.
Tracks: One mind two hearts / Back together.
- 12" . . . . . . . . . . . . . . . . . . . . . . PX 1
- 7" . . . . . . . . . . . . . . . . . . . . . . . P 1
Priority / Aug '83.

### OVER THE RAINBOW (Paradise Featuring Jahneen).
Tracks: Over the rainbow / Show some emotion.
12" . . . . . . . . . . . . . . . . . . . . . . LBAY 17
Loading Bay / Jan '93 / Loading Bay Records.

### WE CAN WORK IT OUT.
Tracks: We can work it out / With you.
- 12" . . . . . . . . . . . . . . . . . . . . . . PX 8
- 7" . . . . . . . . . . . . . . . . . . . . . . . P 8
Priority / Mar '84.

## Paris

### ANOTHER SAD AFFAIR.
Tracks: Another sad affair / America.
- 7" . . . . . . . . . . . . . . . . . . . . . RCA 351
RCA / Jul '83.

### BREAK THE GRIP OF SHAME.
Tracks: Break the grip of shame.
- 12" . . . . . . . . . . . . . . . . . . . . . . TB 950
Tommy Boy / Apr '90.

### CENSORED.
Tracks: Censored.
- 12" . . . . . . . . . . . . . . . . . . . . . RCAT 288
- 7" . . . . . . . . . . . . . . . . . . . . . . RCA 288
RCA / Jan '83.

### HAVE YOU EVER BEEN IN LOVE.
Tracks: Have you ever been in love / One touch.
- 7" . . . . . . . . . . . . . . . . . . . . . . HANSA7
Ariola Hansa / Feb '82.
- 7" . . . . . . . . . . . . . . . . . . . . . RCA 210
RCA / Mar '82.

### I CHOOSE YOU.
Tracks: I choose you / Punkin' funkin'.
- 12" . . . . . . . . . . . . . . . . . . . . . . BRT 9
- 7" . . . . . . . . . . . . . . . . . . . . . . . BR 9
Blue Bird (2) / Oct '84.

## I WALKED AWAY.
- 12" . . . . . . . . . . . . . . . . . . . . . . BRT 38
- 7" . . . . . . . . . . . . . . . . . . . . . . . BR 38
Blue Bird (2) / Jun '87.

### LEARN TO LOVE.
Tracks: Learn to love.
- 12" . . . . . . . . . . . . . . . . . . . . . . DJINT 9
DJ International / May '89.

### NO GETTING OVER YOU.
Tracks: No getting over you / Fighting for the country.
- 7" . . . . . . . . . . . . . . . . . . . . . . RCA 222
RCA / Apr '82.

## Paris, Bobby

### I WALKED AWAY.
Tracks: I walked away / Heartbreaker.
- 7" . . . . . . . . . . . . . . . . . . . . . . CL 1606
Capitol / Feb '79.

### PER-SO-NAL-LY.
Tracks: Per-so-nal-ly / Tragedy.
- 7" . . . . . . . . . . . . . . . . . . . . . . 56747
Polydor / '68.

## Paris, Hari

### MY FAVOURITE THING (Paris, Hari & Calvin Brooks).
Tracks: My favourite thing.
- 12" . . . . . . . . . . . . . . . . . . . . EXPAND 2
Expansion / Mar '92.

## Paris, Mica

A South Londoner born in 1970, Michelle Warren honed her vocal skills as lead singer of Spirit Of Watts gospel quintet - before a chance meeting with Mark Roger - from the pop group Hollywood Beyond led to a first taste of rock and roll life as a support vocalist. Picked up by 4th & Broad way in '88, Mica Paris - as she had become - launched herself as Britain's leading soul diva with the So Good album and U.K. Top Ten hit My One Temptation. A duet the following year with Will Downing - a new version of Flack/Hathaway's Where Is The Love - also hit, but a second album directed at a younger, hip-hop/soul audience (Contribution) failed massively. London street soulers preferred her b-sides, notably the Omar-produced I Should've Known Better, but 4th & Broadway's response was to wheel in Narada Michael Walden and Rod Temperton for a disastrous third album. Whisper A Prayer's appalling sales cost Paris her deal. Now close both professionally and personally to percussionist/vibes man Max Beesley, Paris is gathering material for an as-yet unsigned fourth album.

### BREATHE LIFE INTO ME.
Tracks: Breathe life into me (Radio mix Only on 12" / In the city.
- 12" . . . . . . . . . . . . . . . . . . . 12 BRW 11
- 7" . . . . . . . . . . . . . . . . . . . . . BRW 11
- CD Single . . . . . . . . . . . . . . . BRCDP 11
4th & Broadway / Sep '88.

### CONTRIBUTION.
Tracks: Contribution / South of the river / If I love u nite / Just to be with you / Take me away / Truth an honesty / Deep Afrika / More love / You can make wish / Just make me the one / I've been watchin you / Who can we blame / One world.
- CD . . . . . . . . . . . . . . . . . . . . . BRCD 55
- LP . . . . . . . . . . . . . . . . . . . . . BRLP 55
- MC . . . . . . . . . . . . . . . . . . . . . BRCA 55
4th & Broadway / Oct '90.
- CD . . . . . . . . . . . . . . . . . . . . . IMCD 18
- MC . . . . . . . . . . . . . . . . . . . . . ICM 208
Island / Mar '94 / PolyGram.

### CONTRIBUTION.
Tracks: Showers of love / Contribution (Available on 12BRW 188 & BRCD 188 only).
- 12" . . . . . . . . . . . . . . . . . . . . 12 BRW 18
- 12" Remix. . . . . . . . . . . . . . . . 12 BRX 18

■ DELETE

■ 7″ . . . . . . . . . . . . . . . . . . . . BRW 188
■ CD Single. . . . . . . . . . . . . . . .BRCD 188
■ MC Single. . . . . . . . . . . . . . . .BRCA 188
4th & Broadway / Sep '90.

## I NEVER FELT LIKE THIS BEFORE.
Tracks: I never felt like this before / Call me by my / I
never felt like this before mixes.
■ 12″. . . . . . . . . . . . . . . . . . .12BRW 263
■ 7″. . . . . . . . . . . . . . . . . . . . . BRW 263
■ CD Single. . . . . . . . . . . . . . . . BRCD 263
■ MC Single. . . . . . . . . . . . . . . .BRCA 263
4th & Broadway / Mar '93.

## I WANNA HOLD ON TO YOU.
Tracks: I wanna hold on to you (Mixes) / Say you will
/ Old school (Features on CDS only.)
■ 12″. . . . . . . . . . . . . . . . . .12 BRW 275
■ 7″. . . . . . . . . . . . . . . . . . . . . BRW 275
■ CD Single. . . . . . . . . . . . . . . . BRCD 275
■ MC Single. . . . . . . . . . . . . . . .BRCA 275
4th & Broadway / Apr '93.

## IF I LOVE U 2 NITE.
Tracks: If I love U 2 nite.
■ 12″. . . . . . . . . . . . . . . . . .12 BRW 207
■ 7″. . . . . . . . . . . . . . . . . . . . . BRW 207
■ CD Single. . . . . . . . . . . . . . . . BRCD 207
■ MC Single. . . . . . . . . . . . . . . .BRCA 207
4th & Broadway / Feb '91.

## LIKE DREAMERS DO (Featuring Court-ney Pine).
Tracks: Like dreamers do / Wicked.
■ 12″. . . . . . . . . . . . . . . . . .12 BRW 108
■ 12″ P.Disc. . . . . . . . . . . . . . .12 BRP 108
■ 7″ . . . . . . . . . . . . . . . . . . . . BRW 108
■ 7″ . . . . . . . . . . . . . . . . . . . BRWG 108
■ CD Single . . . . . . . . . . . . . . . BRCDP 108
4th & Broadway / Jun '88.

## MICA PARIS.
Tracks: Not Advised.
VHS . . . . . . . . . . . . . . . . . . . . IVA 058
Island Visual Arts / Jan '91 / PolyGram / THE.

## MY ONE TEMPTATION.
Tracks: My one temptation / Rock together.
■ 12″ . . . . . . . . . . . . . . . . . . 12 BRW 85
■ 12″ Remix. . . . . . . . . . . . . . .12BRX 85
■ 7″ . . . . . . . . . . . . . . . . . . . . BRW 85
■ EP . . . . . . . . . . . . . . . . . . BRWEP 85
4th & Broadway / Apr '88.

## SO GOOD.
Tracks: Where is the love / My one temptation / Like
dreamers do / Breathe life into me.
CD. . . . . . . . . . . . . . . . . . . .BRCDX 525
■ CD . . . . . . . . . . . . . . . . . . . BRCD 525
■ LP . . . . . . . . . . . . . . . . . . . BRLP 525
■ MC . . . . . . . . . . . . . . . . . . .BRCA 525
4th & Broadway / Aug '88 / PolyGram.

## SO GOOD/ CONTRIBUTION.
Tracks: Not Advised.
CD Set . . . . . . . . . . . . . . . . . . .ITSCD 5
Island / Nov '92 / PolyGram.

## SOUTH OF THE RIVER.
Tracks: South of the river / I should have known
better / Where are the children.
■ 12″. . . . . . . . . . . . . . . . . .12 BRW 199
■ 7″ . . . . . . . . . . . . . . . . . . . . BRW 199
■ CD Single. . . . . . . . . . . . . . . . BRCD 199
■ MC Single. . . . . . . . . . . . . . . .BRCA 199
4th & Broadway / Nov '90.

## TWO IN A MILLION.
Tracks: Two in a million / Love bizarre / Two in a
million (mixes).
■ 12″ . . . . . . . . . . . . . . . . . 12BRW 285
■ 7″ . . . . . . . . . . . . . . . . . . . . BRW 285
■ CD Single. . . . . . . . . . . . . . . .BRCD 285
■ MC Single. . . . . . . . . . . . . . . .BRCA 285
4th & Broadway / Jul '93.

## WHISPER A PRAYER.
Tracks: I never felt like this before / I wanna hold
on to you / You put a move on my heart / We were made
for love / Whisper a prayer / Too far apart / I bless
the day / Two in a million / Positivity / Can't seem to
make up my mind / You got a special way / Love
keeps coming back.
CD. . . . . . . . . . . . . . . . . . . . . 5147762
CD . . . . . . . . . . . . . . . . . . . . . 5147761
CD. . . . . . . . . . . . . . . . . . . . . 5147764
4th & Broadway / Apr '93 / PolyGram.
CD. . . . . . . . . . . . . . . . . . . . .BRCD 591
LP . . . . . . . . . . . . . . . . . . . . .BRLP 591
MC. . . . . . . . . . . . . . . . . . . . .BRCA 591
Island / Jun '93 / PolyGram.

---

## WHISPER A PRAYER.
Tracks: Whisper a prayer / You / I bless the day
(Available on CDS only) / South of the river (Avail-
able on CDS only) / My one temptation (Available on
CDS 2 only) / Where is the love (Available on CDS 2
only) / Breathe life into me (Available on CDS 2
only).
■ 7″ . . . . . . . . . . . . . . . . . . . . BRW 287
■ CD Single . . . . . . . . . . . . . . . .BRCD 287
■ CD Single . . . . . . . . . . . . . . . BRCDX 287
■ MC Single. . . . . . . . . . . . . . . .BRCA 287
4th & Broadway / Nov '93.

## YOUNG SOUL REBELS.
Tracks: Young soul rebels.
■ 12″ . . . . . . . . . . . . . . . . . . . . .BLRT 57
■ CD Single . . . . . . . . . . . . . . . .BLRCD 57
Big Life / Aug '91.

## Parker, Bobby

### BENT OUT OF SHAPE.
Tracks: Not Advised.
CD. . . . . . . . . . . . . . . . . . . . BT 1086CD
MC. . . . . . . . . . . . . . . . . . . .BT 1086MC
Black Top (USA) / May '93 / C.M. Distribution / Direct
Distribution / Hot Shot / Topic Records.

## Parker, Eddie

### LOVE YOU BABY.
Tracks: Love you baby / Love you baby (inst.).
■ 7″ . . . . . . . . . . . . . . . . . . . .GRP 119
Grapevine (Northern Soul) / May '79.

## Parker, Junior

### BAREFOOT ROCK (see under Bland, Bobby).

### BLUE SHADOWS FALLING.
Tracks: Five long years / Tin pan alley / Blue shadows falling / That's alright / Way back home / Need
your love so bad / Look on yonder wall / Man or
mouse / Sweet home Chicago / I like your style.
■ LP . . . . . . . . . . . . . . . . . . . . GM 502
Groove Merchant / Jul '72.

### I WANNA RAMBLE (Parker, Junior & the Blue Flames).
Tracks: I wanna ramble / Please baby blues / Dirty
friend blues / Can't understand / Sittin', drinkin' and
thinkin' / Driving me mad / I'm tender / Pretty baby /
Sweet home Chicago / Long years / Can you tell me,
baby / Backtracking / There better be no feet /
Mother-in-law blues / That's alright.
■ LP . . . . . . . . . . . . . . . . . . . . CH 42
Ace / Feb '82.

### JUNIOR PARKER EP.
Tracks: Love my baby / Mystery train / Feeling good
/ Fussin' and fightin' blues.
■ EP . . . . . . . . . . . . . . . . . . . .CEP 104
Charly / Feb '77.

### LEGENDARY SUN PERFORMERS (Parker, Junior & Billy 'Red' Love).
Tracks: Feeling good / Mystery train / Love my baby
/ Fussin' and fightin' blues / Sittin' at the window /
Sittin' at the bar / Sittin', drinkin' and thinkin' / Feel
so bad / Gee I wish / Hearts bread boogie / News is
all around town / Blues leave me alone / If you want
to make me happy / There's no use / Early in the
morning / Dream.
■ LP . . . . . . . . . . . . . . . . . . . . CR 30135
Charly / '77.

### LITTLE JUNIOR PARKER (Parker, Little Jr.).
Tracks: Not Advised.
CD. . . . . . . . . . . . . . . . . . . . CDC 9002
MC. . . . . . . . . . . . . . . . . . . . .MC 9002
LRC Jazz / Oct '90 / Harmonia Mundi (UK).

### MEMPHIS BLUES BROTHERS (Parker, Junior & Bobby Bland).
Tracks: Good lovin' / Drifting from town to town takes
1 & 2 / Dry up baby / Crying all night long / Love me
baby / You're my angel / Bad women, bad whiskey /
Whole heap of mama / I wronged to a woman / I
can't forgive you / Sad and lonely / Rumpus romp /
Trouble and me / I cried / Midnight hours journey.
■ LP . . . . . . . . . . . . . . . . . . .CHAD 265
Ace / Jul '89.

### THESE KIND OF BLUES.
Tracks: These kind of blues / These kind of blues
(part 2).
■ 7″ . . . . . . . . . . . . . . . . . . . . VP 9256
Vocalion / Jan '66.

## Parker, Maceo

James Brown's saxophonist in early '70s
established own name with 1974 Us album
and '75 cut Across The Tracks (copies of
latter commanded huge sums in Northern
Soul scene before its reissue in '87). Shortly
afterwards, Parker, trombonist Fred Wesley
and bassist Bootsy Collins quit court of King
James for George Clinton's P-Funk dynasty,
teaming up in Bootsy's Rubber Band.
Signed to Atlantic at behest of Maggot Over-
lord, Wesley and Parker cut two LPs as
Horny Horns in '77 and '79. Duo continue to
record and tour to this day with All The
King's Men, occasionally accompanied by
other ex-JBs like Collins and Bobby Byrd.
1993 album Southern Exposure included
Wesley, Pee Wee Ellis and two ex-Meters.

### CROSS THE TRACK (WE BETTER GO BACK) (Parker, Maceo & The Macks).
Tracks: Cross the track (we better go back ext ver-
sion) / Parrty (part 1) / Soul power*.
■ 7″ . . . . . . . . . . . . . . . . . . . .URB 1
■ 12″ . . . . . . . . . . . . . . . . . . .URBX 1
Urban / Apr '87.

### DOING THEIR OWN THING (Parker, Ma-ceo & The Kings Men).
Tracks: Maceo / Got to getcha / Southwick / Funky
women / Shake it baby / Better half / Don't waste this
world away / (I remember) Mr. Banks / Thank you for
letting me be myself again (On CD only).
■ LP . . . . . . . . . . . . . . . . . . . CRB 1176
■ MC. . . . . . . . . . . . . . . . . TCCRB 1176
Charly R&B / Apr '88.
CD. . . . . . . . . . . . . . . . . . . . CPCD 8041
Charly / Jun '94 / Charly.

### FUNKY MUSIC MACHINE (Parker, Ma-ceo & The Kings Men).
Tracks: Funky music machine / I want to sing /
Dreams / Feeling alright / Something / Born to
wander / T.S.U / For no one / Make it with you /
Funky tale to tell.
■ LP . . . . . . . . . . . . . . . . . . . 2916017
Mojo / '72.
CD. . . . . . . . . . . . . . . . . . .CDSEWM 087
South Bound / Nov '93 / Pinnacle.

### LET 'EM OUT.
Tracks: Let 'em out / Fax machine / Tell the world.
■ 12″ . . . . . . . . . . . . . . . . . .12 BRW 203
4th & Broadway / Nov '90.

### LIFE ON PLANET GROOVE.
Tracks: Shake everything you've got / Pass the peas
/ I got you (I feel good) / Got to get U / Addicted love /
Children's world / Georgia on my mind / Soul power
'92.
CD. . . . . . . . . . . . . . . . . . . . MM 801023
Double CD . . . . . . . . . . . . . . . MM 1023
Minor / Sep '92 / Impetus Records / Charly / New
Note.

### ROOTS REVISITED.
Tracks: Them that got / Children's world / Better git it
in your soul / People get ready / Up and down east
street / Over the rainbow / Jumpin the blues / In
time.
■ LP . . . . . . . . . . . . . . . . . . . 843 751-1
■ CD . . . . . . . . . . . . . . . . . . . 843 751-2
■ MC. . . . . . . . . . . . . . . . . . . 843 751-4
Polydor / Jan '91.

### SOUTHERN EXPOSURE.
Tracks: Blues for Shorty Bill / Keep on marching /
Mercy, Mercy, Mercy / Every Saturday night / Way
you look tonight / Splashin' / Walking home together
/ Sister sanctified / Run in the sun.
CD. . . . . . . . . . . . . . . . . . . . MM 801033
LP . . . . . . . . . . . . . . . . . . . . MM 1033
Minor / Nov '93 / Impetus Records / Charly / New
Note.

### US.
Tracks: Not Advised.
■ LP . . . . . . . . . . . . . . . . . . . URBLP 8
■ MC. . . . . . . . . . . . . . . . . . URBMC 8
Urban / Mar '88.

### WHAT GOES AROUND COMES AROUND (see under Byrd, Bobby).

## Parker, Ray Jnr.

### AFTER DARK.
Tracks: I don't think that man should sleep / Over
you / Loving you / You shoulda kept a spare / Past /
You make my nature a spare / Perfect lovers / After
midnite / I love your daughter.
■ CD. . . . . . . . . . . . . . . . . . .924124 2

■ **LP** . . . . . . . . . . . . . . . . . . **WX 122**
■ **MC.** . . . . . . . . . . . . . . . . . . **WX 122C**
WEA / Sep '87.

### BEST OF RAY PARKER JNR (Parker, Ray Jnr.& Raydio).
**Tracks:** Ghostbusters / You can't change that / Woman needs love (just like you do) / More than one way to love a woman / Stay the night / Let me go / Betcha can't love me just once / Jack & Jill / Other woman / Two places at the same time / (I still can't get over) loving you / Girls are more fun / Is this a love thing / For those who like to groove.
**CD.** . . . . . . . . . . . . . . . . . . **260.365**
■ **MC.** . . . . . . . . . . . . . . . . . **410.365**
Ariola / Dec '89 / BMG.

### CHARTBUSTERS.
**Tracks:** Not Advised.
■ **CD** . . . . . . . . . . . . . . . . . . **32RD 14**
Arista / '88.

### COLLECTION, THE.
**Tracks:** Jack & Jill (back up the hill) / You can't change that / Girls are more fun / Other woman / Is this a love thing / Still in the groove / (I still can't get over) Loving you / Bad boy / It's time to party now / Honey I'm rich / Two places at the same time / That old song / Let me go / Jamie / People next door / Ghostbusters.
**CD.** . . . . . . . . . . . . . . . . **7432113986-26**
Arista / Jul '93 / BMG.

### GHOSTBUSTERS.
**Tracks:** Ghostbusters / Ghostbusters (version).
■ **12"** . . . . . . . . . . . . . . **ARIST 12580**
■ **7" P.Disc** . . . . . . . . . . . **ARISD 580**
■ **12" P.Disc** . . . . . . . . . . **ARIPD 12580**
■ **7"** . . . . . . . . . . . . . . . . **ARIST 580**
Arista / Nov '84.

### GHOSTBUSTERS (OLD GOLD).
**Tracks:** Ghostbusters / Jack & Jill / You can't change that.
■ **12"** . . . . . . . . . . . . . . . . **OG 4041**
Old Gold / Jan '88.

### GIRLS ARE MORE FUN.
**Tracks:** Girls are more fun / I'm in love / Ghostbusters.
■ **12"** . . . . . . . . . . . . . . **ARIST 12641**
Arista / Dec '85.
■ **7"** . . . . . . . . . . . . . . . . **ARIST 641**
Arista / Nov '85.

### I DON'T THINK THAT MAN SHOULD SLEEP ALONE.
**Tracks:** I don't think that man should sleep alone / After midnite.
■ **12"** . . . . . . . . . . . . . . . . **GEF 27T**
■ **12" P.Disc** . . . . . . . . . . . **GEF 27TP**
■ **7"** . . . . . . . . . . . . . . . . . **GEF 27**
Geffen / Sep '87.

### LOSING YOU.
**Tracks:** Losing you / She still feels the need / Invasion.
■ **12"** . . . . . . . . . . . . . . **ARIST 12550**
■ **7"** . . . . . . . . . . . . . . . . **ARIST 550**
Arista / Nov '84.

### OTHER WOMAN, THE.
**Tracks:** Other woman / Streetlove / Stay the night / It's our own affair / Let me go / Let's get off / Stop, look before you love / Just having fun.
■ **LP** . . . . . . . . . . . . . . . **SPART 1190**
■ **MC.** . . . . . . . . . . . . . . **TCART 1190**
Arista / May '82.

### OTHER WOMAN, THE.
**Tracks:** Other woman / Stay the night.
■ **12"** . . . . . . . . . . . . . **ARIST 12466**
■ **7"** . . . . . . . . . . . . . . . **ARIST 466**
Arista / '82.

### OVER YOU (Parker, Ray Jnr. & Natalie Cole).
**Tracks:** Over you / Loving you.
■ **12"** . . . . . . . . . . . . . . . **GEF 33T**
■ **7"** . . . . . . . . . . . . . . . . **GEF 33**
Geffen / Jan '88.

### SEX AND THE SINGLE MAN.
**Tracks:** Not Advised.
■ **LP** . . . . . . . . . . . . . . . . **207252**
■ **MC.** . . . . . . . . . . . . . . . **407252**
Arista / Oct '85.

### THAT OLD SONG.
**Tracks:** That old song / All in the way you get down.
■ **7"** . . . . . . . . . . . . . . . **ARIST 417**
Arista / '81.

### VERY BEST OF RAY PARKER JNR.
**Tracks:** Other woman / You can't change that / Is this a love thing / Woman needs love / Jack & Jill / Bad boy / Two places at the same time / For those who like to groove / That old song / People next door.
■ **MC.** . . . . . . . . . . . . . . . . **405078**
■ **LP** . . . . . . . . . . . . . . . . . **205078**
Arista / Dec '82.

### WOMAN NEEDS LOVE, A (Parker, Ray Jnr.& Raydio).
**Tracks:** Woman needs love / It's your night / That old song / All in the way you get down / You can't fight what you feel / Old pro / Still in the groove / So into you.
■ **LP** . . . . . . . . . . . . . . . **SPART 1152**
Arista / Apr '81.

### WOMAN NEEDS LOVE, A (Parker, Ray Jnr.& Raydio).
**Tracks:** Woman needs love / So into you / Still in the groove.
■ **12"** . . . . . . . . . . . . . . **ARIST 12392**
Arista / Jul '81.

### WOMAN OUT OF CONTROL.
**Tracks:** Woman out of control / I still can't get over loving you / Electronic lover / In the heat of the night / I don't wanna know / She still feels the need / Invasion / N2U2.
■ **LP** . . . . . . . . . . . . . . . . **205752**
■ **MC.** . . . . . . . . . . . . . . . **405752**
Arista / Nov '83.

### YOU CAN'T CHANGE THAT.
**Tracks:** You can't change that / Bad boy.
■ **7"** . . . . . . . . . . . . . . . **ARIST 249**
Arista / Apr '79.
■ **12"** . . . . . . . . . . . . . . **ARIST 12512**
■ **7"** . . . . . . . . . . . . . . . **ARIST 512**
Arista / Feb '83.

### YOU SHOULDA KEPT A SPARE.
**Tracks:** You shoulda kept a spare / I love your daughter.
■ **12"** . . . . . . . . . . . . . . . **GEF 36T**
■ **7"** . . . . . . . . . . . . . . . . **GEF 36**
Geffen / Apr '88.

## Parker, Robert

### BAREFOOTIN'.
**Tracks:** Let the good times roll / Barefootin' / Stay (just a little while).
■ **7"** . . . . . . . . . . . . . . . . **CR 218**
Creole (Replay) / Aug '84.

### BAREFOOTIN'.
**Tracks:** Barefootin' / Duke of earl / Let's go baby (where the action is) / Hiccup (on 12" only.).
■ **LP Set.** . . . . . . . . . . . . . . **CS 9010**
Contempo (1) / Jan '77.
■ **7"** . . . . . . . . . . . . . . . . **TAN 12**
Important / Aug '86.
■ **12"** . . . . . . . . . . . . . . . **CYZ 121**
■ **7"** . . . . . . . . . . . . . . . **CYZ 7121**
Charly / Jul '87.

### BAREFOOTIN'.
**Tracks:** Barefootin'.
■ **7"** . . . . . . . . . . . . . . . . **WI 286**
Island / Aug '66.

### BAREFOOTIN'.
**Tracks:** Barefootin' / Let's go baby (where the action is) / Little bit of something / Sneaking Sally through the alley / Better luck in the summertime / You see me / Give me the country side of life / Get right down / Get ta' steppin' / Hiccup / Hot 'n' cold / Skinny dippin' / I like what you do to me / Disco doctor.
**CD.** . . . . . . . . . . . . . . . **CPCD 8013**
Charly / Feb '94 / Charly.

### GET TA STEPPIN'.
**Tracks:** Barefootin' / Let's go baby (where the action is) / Little bit of something / Sneaking Sally thru the alley / Better luck in the summertime / You see me / Give me the country side of life / Get right down / Get ta steppin / Hiccup / Hot and cold / Skinny dippin' / I like what you do to me / Disco doctor.
■ **LP** . . . . . . . . . . . . . . . **CRB 1174**
**MC.** . . . . . . . . . . . . . . . **TCCRB 1174**
Charly R&B / Sep '87 / Charly.

## Parlet

### BEST OF PARLET, THE.
**Tracks:** Pleasure principle / No rump to bump / Help from my friends / Wolf tickets / Love amnesia / Misunderstanding / Play me or trade me / Huff-n-puff / Funk until the edge of time / Ridin' high / Cookie jar.

**CD** . . . . . . . . . . . . . . . . . **522455 2**
Casablanca / Jun '94.

### INVASION OF THE BODY SNATCHERS.
**Tracks:** Riding high / No rump to bump / Don't ever stop / Booty snatchers / You're leaving / Huff'n'puff.
■ **LP** . . . . . . . . . . . . . . . **CAL 2052**
Casablanca / '79.

## Parliament

Parliament evolved from George Clinton's doo-wop outfit the Parliaments, making their debut with 1970's *Osmium* (revamped and reissued as *Rhenium*). Project was put on ice for four years while personnel recorded as Funkadelic; then revived in triumphant bid for commercial success. *Up For The Down Stroke* opened string of hits which peaked with all-time funk anthems *Tear The Roof Off The Sucker* (1976) and *Flash Light* (1978). Key to group's success was combination of Clinton's vision, Bernie Worrell's keyboard vamps and Bootsy Collins' bass-playing; whose legacy lives on in innumerable hip-hop samples. Parliament's albums have stood the test of time better than their Funkadelic counterparts; the cream can be found on hits compilations *Uncut Funk.. The Bomb* and *Tear The Roof Off The Sucker.*

### ACQUA BOOGIE.
**Tracks:** Acqua boogie / Acqua boogie (version).
■ **7"** . . . . . . . . . . . . . . . . **CAN 136**
Casablanca / Dec '78.

### AGONY OF DEFEAT.
**Tracks:** Agony of defeat / Freeze.
■ **12"** . . . . . . . . . . . . . . **CANL 223**
■ **7"** . . . . . . . . . . . . . . . **CAN 223**
Casablanca / Apr '81.

### BOP GUN.
**Tracks:** Bop gun / I've been watching you.
■ **7"** . . . . . . . . . . . . . . . . **CAN 115**
Casablanca / Jan '78.

### CLONES OF DR. FUNKENSTEIN, THE.
**Tracks:** Prelude / Gamin' on ya / Dr. Funkenstein / Children of productions / Gettin' to know you / Do that stuff / Everybody is on the one / I've been watching you / Funkin' for fun.
■ **LP** . . . . . . . . . . . . . . . **CAL 2003**
Casablanca / Jun '77.
**CD** . . . . . . . . . . . . . . . . **8426202**
Casablanca / Feb '91.

### DEEP.
**Tracks:** Deep / Flashlight.
■ **12"** . . . . . . . . . . . . . . **CANL 154**
■ **7"** . . . . . . . . . . . . . . . **CAN 154**
Casablanca / '79.

### FLASHLIGHT.
**Tracks:** Flashlight / Swing low, sweet chariot.
■ **7"** . . . . . . . . . . . . . . . **CAN 123**
Casablanca / Aug '78.

### FUNKENTELECHY VS. THE PLACEBO SYNDROME.
**Tracks:** Bop fun / Sir Nose D'Voidoffunk / Wizard of finance / Funkentelechy / Flash light / Placebo syndrome.
■ **LP** . . . . . . . . . . . . . . . **CALH 2021**
Casablanca / Jan '78.

### GLORYHALLASTOOPID.
**Tracks:** Gloryhallastoopid / Party people / Big bang theory / Freeze / Colour me funky / Theme from The Black Hole / May we bang you.
■ **LP** . . . . . . . . . . . . . . . **NBLP 7195**
Casablanca / Jan '80.

### I CALL MY BABY PUSSYCAT.
**Tracks:** I call my baby pussycat.
■ **7"** . . . . . . . . . . . . . . . . **HDH 45**
HDH / Dec '84.

### I WANNA TESTIFY.
**Tracks:** (I wanna) testify / Time / Good ole music / I can feel the ice melting / Don't be sore at me / All your goodies are gone / Little man / Goose that laid the golden egg / What you been growing / Look at what I almost missed / New day beings / Fellow let's make it last / All your goodies are gone (inst) / Baby I owe you something (inst) / I'll wait / I'll wait (inst).
**CD.** . . . . . . . . . . . . . . . **GSCD 05**
Goldmine / Oct '94 / Vital Distribution.

■ DELETED

## MOTHERSHIP CONNECTION.
Tracks: P. Funk / Mothership connection / Unfunky UFO / Supergroovalisticprosifunkstication / Handcuffs / Give up the funk / Night of the Thumpasorus peoples.
- LP . . . . . . . . . . . . . . . . . . . . . . . . CBC 4009
Casablanca / '75.
- LP . . . . . . . . . . . . . . . . . . . . . . 824 502-1
MC. . . . . . . . . . . . . . . . . . . . . . . . 824 502-4
Casablanca / Aug '87.

## MOTOR BOOTY AFFAIR.
Tracks: Mr. Wiggles / Rumpopsteelskin / Water sign / Aqua boogie / One of those funky things / Liquid sunshine / Motor booty affair / Deep.
- LP . . . . . . . . . . . . . . . . . . . . . . . CALH 2043
Casablanca / Jan '79.
- CD . . . . . . . . . . . . . . . . . . . . . . . 8426212
Casablanca / Feb '91.

## OSMIUM.
Tracks: I call my baby Pussycat / Put love in your life / Little ole country boy / Moonshine Heather / Oh Lord, why Lord/Prayer / My automobile / Nothing before me but thang / Funky women / Livin' the life / Silent boatman.
- LP . . . . . . . . . . . . . . . . . . . . . . . SVT 1004
Invictus / Jul '71.

## PARLIAMENT LIVE.
Tracks: Dr. Funkentein's supergroovalisticprosifunkstication / Let's take it to the stage / Take your dead ass home / Do that stuff / Landing / Undisco kid / Tear off the production / Mothership connection / Swing down, sweet chariot / This is the way we funk with you / Gamin' on ya / Tear the roof of the sucker / Give up the funk / Get off your ass and jam / Night of the thumpasorus people / Fantasy is reality.
- LP Set. . . . . . . . . . . . . . . . . . . . . CALD 5002
Casablanca / Jul '77.

## PARTY PEOPLE.
Tracks: Party people / Tear the roof off the sucker / Flashlight.
- 12" . . . . . . . . . . . . . . . . . . . . . . . NBL 2222
- 7" . . . . . . . . . . . . . . . . . . . . . . . NR 2222
Casablanca / Jan '80.

## THENIUM.
Tracks: Breakdown / Call my baby pussycat / Little ole country boy / Moonshine Heather / Oh Lord, why Lord - prayer / Red hot mama / My automobile / Nothing before me but thang / Funky woman / Come out of the rain / Silent boatman.
- CD . . . . . . . . . . . . . . . . . . . . . . HDH CD 008
- LP . . . . . . . . . . . . . . . . . . . . . . .HDH LP 008
- MC. . . . . . . . . . . . . . . . . . . . . . HDH MC 008
HDH / Feb '90 / Pinnacle.

## SILENT BOATMAN.
Tracks: Silent boatman / Livin' the life.
- 7" . . . . . . . . . . . . . . . . . . . . . . . INV 513
Invictus / Jun '71.

## TEAR THE ROOF OFF THE SUCKER.
Tracks: Not Advised.
- CD Set . . . . . . . . . . . . . . . . . . . .514417 2
Chronogram / Jun '93 / PolyGram.

## TROMBIPULATION.
Tracks: Trombipulation / Crush it / Long way round / Agony of defeat / New doo review / Let's play house / Body language / Peek-a-groove.
- LP . . . . . . . . . . . . . . . . . . . . . . . NBLP 7249
Casablanca / Apr '81.
- CD. . . . . . . . . . . . . . . . . . . . . . . 8426232
Casablanca / Feb '91.

## UNCUT FUNK-THE BOMB (The Best Of Parliament).
Tracks: P-funk (wants to get funked) / Give up the funk / Up for the down stroke / Chocolate city / Big footin theory / Flashlight / Gloryhallastoopid (Pin the tail on the Funk) / Aqua boogie.
- LP . . . . . . . . . . . . . . . . . . . . . . .JABB 18
- MC. . . . . . . . . . . . . . . . . . . . . . .JABBC 18
Club / Sep '86.

## UP FOR THE DOWN STROKE.
Tracks: Up for the down stroke / Presence of a brain.
- 7" . . . . . . . . . . . . . . . . . . . . . . .CBX 505
Casablanca / Jan '75.

# Parrish, Dean

## DETERMINATION.
Tracks: Determination.
- 7" . . . . . . . . . . . . . . . . . . . . . . .SS 550
Stateside / '66.

## I ON MY WAY.
Tracks: I'm on my way.
- 7" . . . . . . . . . . . . . . . . . . . . . . . USA 2
? / Feb '75.

## I'M ON MY WAY.
Tracks: I'm on my way / Time will pass you by / Long after tonight is all over.
- 7" . . . . . . . . . . . . . . . . . . . . . . . RK 1004
RK / Feb '78.

## SKAKE (PARTS 1 & 2).
Tracks: Skake.
- 7" . . . . . . . . . . . . . . . . . . . . . . .SS 580
Stateside / Jan '67.

## TELL HER.
Tracks: Tell her / Fall on me.
- 7" . . . . . . . . . . . . . . . . . . . . . . .SS 531
Stateside / '66.

# Pasadenas

## ANOTHER LOVER.
Tracks: Another lover / Love to dance (house mix) / Another lover (Pasadenas mix) (Only on 12" single) / Tribute (right on) (Only on 12" single) / Riding on a train (Only on 12" single).
- 12" . . . . . . . . . . . . . . . . . . . . . . . 6568456
- 7" . . . . . . . . . . . . . . . . . . . . . . . 6568457
- MC Single. . . . . . . . . . . . . . . . . . . 6568454
Columbia / Apr '91.

## ELEVATE.
Tracks: Reeling / South Africa / Love thing / I'd die for you / Bridge over troubled water / Another lover / I'd die for you (reprise) / Strong enough / Cry my tears (posthumously yours) / I want to be / More time / For love / Base is slipping / Love changes / I want to be (uk mix) (Only on MC and CD).
- LP . . . . . . . . . . . . . . . . . . . . . . . 4670231
- CD. . . . . . . . . . . . . . . . . . . . . . . 4670232
- MC. . . . . . . . . . . . . . . . . . . . . . . 4670234
CBS / May '90.

## ENCHANTED LADY.
Tracks: Enchanted lady / New love (original version) / New love (instrumental) (Only on 12" version.) / Tribute (right on) (Only on CD single.) / Riding on a train (segue mix) (Only on CD single.).
- 12" . . . . . . . . . . . . . . . . . . . . . . PASAT 3
- 12" . . . . . . . . . . . . . . . . . . . . . . PASA Q3
- 7" . . . . . . . . . . . . . . . . . . . . . . . PASA B3
- 7" . . . . . . . . . . . . . . . . . . . . . . . PASA 3
- CD Single . . . . . . . . . . . . . . . . . . CDPASA 3
CBS / Nov '88.

## I BELIEVE IN MIRACLES.
Tracks: I believe in miracles / Base is slipping.
- 12" . . . . . . . . . . . . . . . . . . . . . . . 6580566
- 7" . . . . . . . . . . . . . . . . . . . . . . . 6580567
- CD Single. . . . . . . . . . . . . . . . . . . 6580562
- MC Single. . . . . . . . . . . . . . . . . . . 6580564
Columbia / May '92.

## I'M DOING FINE NOW.
Tracks: I'm doing fine now / Cry my tears (posthumously yours).
- 12" . . . . . . . . . . . . . . . . . . . . . . . 6577186
- 7" . . . . . . . . . . . . . . . . . . . . . . . 6577187
- CD Single . . . . . . . . . . . . . . . . . . . 6577182
- MC Single . . . . . . . . . . . . . . . . . . . 6577184
Columbia / Jan '92.

## LET'S STAY TOGETHER.
Tracks: Let's stay together / More time for love / Medley (Feat.Moving in the right direction/I believe in miracles/Tribute (Right on)/Riding on a train/Make it with you/I'm doing fine now) (On CDs/12" only).
- 12" . . . . . . . . . . . . . . . . . . . . . .658774-6
- 7" . . . . . . . . . . . . . . . . . . . . . . .658774-7
- CD Single. . . . . . . . . . . . . . . . . . . 658774-2
- MC Single. . . . . . . . . . . . . . . . . . . 658774-4
Columbia / Nov '92.

## LONGING FOR SOMEONE.
Tracks: Longing for someone.
CD Single . . . . . . . . . . . . . . . . . CDSOLOR 1
Solor / Nov '94 / Total / BMG.

## LOVE THING.
Tracks: Love thing / He'll give you all / Love thing (mix).
- 12" . . . . . . . . . . . . . . . . . . . . . . PASA T4
- 7" . . . . . . . . . . . . . . . . . . . . . . . PASA 4
- CD Single . . . . . . . . . . . . . . . . . . CDPASA 4
- MC Single. . . . . . . . . . . . . . . . . . . PASA M4
CBS / Apr '90.
- 12" Remix . . . . . . . . . . . . . . . . . . PASAQT 4
CBS / Apr '90.

## MAKE IT WITH YOU.
Tracks: Make it with you / I want to be.
- 12" . . . . . . . . . . . . . . . . . . . . . . . 6579256
- 7" . . . . . . . . . . . . . . . . . . . . . . . 6579257
- MC Single. . . . . . . . . . . . . . . . . . . 6579254
- CD Single. . . . . . . . . . . . . . . . . . . 6579252
Columbia / Mar '92.

## MOVING IN THE RIGHT DIRECTION.
Tracks: Moving in the right direction / I really miss you.
- 12" . . . . . . . . . . . . . . . . . . . . . . . 6584316
- 7" . . . . . . . . . . . . . . . . . . . . . . . 6584317
- CD Single . . . . . . . . . . . . . . . . . . . 6584312
- MC Single. . . . . . . . . . . . . . . . . . . 6584314
Columbia / Sep '92.

## REELING.
Tracks: Reeling / State of shock.
- 12" . . . . . . . . . . . . . . . . . . . . . . . PASA T5
- 7" . . . . . . . . . . . . . . . . . . . . . . . PASA 5
- CD Single . . . . . . . . . . . . . . . . . . . PASA C5
- MC Single . . . . . . . . . . . . . . . . . . . PASA M5
CBS / Jul '90.

## RIDING ON A TRAIN.
Tracks: Riding on a train (7" only) / My baby don't love me no more / Riding on a train (ext. version) (12" only) / Riding on a train (Clapham Jct. demo mix) (12" and CD only) / Riding on a train (full version) / Riding on a train (dub version) / Little love.
- 12" . . . . . . . . . . . . . . . . . . . . . .PASAT PT2
- 12" . . . . . . . . . . . . . . . . . . . . . . PASA QT2
- 7" . . . . . . . . . . . . . . . . . . . . . . . PASA Q2
- 7" . . . . . . . . . . . . . . . . . . . . . . . PASA 2
- CD Single . . . . . . . . . . . . . . . . . . CDPASA 2
CBS / Aug '88.
- 12" . . . . . . . . . . . . . . . . . . . . . . . PASAT 2
CBS / Aug '88.

## TO WHOM IT MAY CONCERN.
Tracks: Funny feeling / Living in the footsteps of another man / Enchanted lady / New love / Riding on a train / Give a little peace / Tribute (right on) / I really miss you / Justice for the world / Something else.
- LP . . . . . . . . . . . . . . . . . . . . . . . 4628771
CBS / Oct '88.
- CD. . . . . . . . . . . . . . . . . . . . . . . 4628772
- MC. . . . . . . . . . . . . . . . . . . . . . . 4628774
Columbia / Oct '91 / Sony.

## TRIBUTE (RIGHT ON).
Tracks: Tribute - Right on (mixes) / I believe / All night long (live) (On 12" and CD single only.) / Enchanted lady (Acappella version) (On 12" only.).
- 7" . . . . . . . . . . . . . . . . . . . . . . . PASA S1
- 12" . . . . . . . . . . . . . . . . . . . . . . PASA T1
- 12" . . . . . . . . . . . . . . . . . . . . . . PASA QT1
- 7" . . . . . . . . . . . . . . . . . . . . . . . PASA 1
- 7" P.Disc . . . . . . . . . . . . . . . . . . . PASAB 1
- 7" P.Disc . . . . . . . . . . . . . . . . . . . PASAP 1
- CD Single . . . . . . . . . . . . . . . . . . PASAC 1
CBS / May '88.

## TRIBUTE (RIGHT ON) (OLD GOLD).
Tracks: Tribute (right ong) / Enchanted lady.
12" . . . . . . . . . . . . . . . . . . . . . . .OG 4227
Old Gold / Jun '92 / Pickwick.

## YOURS SINCERELY.
Tracks: I'm doing fine now / Moving in the right direction / Make it with you / Let's get it on / Lucy in the sky with diamonds / Everybody's singing love songs / Waiting in vain / I believe in miracles / Come on down (get your head out of the clouds) / Weak at the knees.
- LP . . . . . . . . . . . . . . . . . . . . . . . 4712641
- CD . . . . . . . . . . . . . . . . . . . . . . . 4712642
- MC. . . . . . . . . . . . . . . . . . . . . . . 4712644
Columbia / Feb '92.
- MiniDisc. . . . . . . . . . . . . . . . . . . .471264-3
Columbia / Apr '93 / Sony.

# Passion

## DON'T STOP MY LOVE.
Tracks: Don't stop my love / Don't stop my love (part 2).
- 12" . . . . . . . . . . . . . . . . . . . . . . PRLA 13-27
- 7" . . . . . . . . . . . . . . . . . . . . . . . PRLA 2704
Prelude / Sep '82.

# Patillo, Leon

## BRAND NEW.
Tracks: Not Advised.
- LP . . . . . . . . . . . . . . . . . . . . . . . BIRD R 191
- MC. . . . . . . . . . . . . . . . . . . . . . . BIRD C 191
Sparrow / Nov '87 / Word Records (UK) / Sony.

## DANCE, CHILDREN, DANCE.
Tracks: Dance, children, dance / High on You / These signs / Born again / Temple to the sky / Trinity / He is comin' / Come.
- LP . . . . . . . . . . . . . . . . . . . . . . . MM 0049
- MC. . . . . . . . . . . . . . . . . . . . . . . TC MM 0049
Maranatha / May '82 / Word Records (UK) / Sony.

## DON'T GIVE IN.
**Tracks:** Blessed is / Have faith / Flesh of My flesh / We must believe / Your love is lifting me higher and higher / Star of the morning / Don't give in / How can I begin / My sweet Lord / Go.
■ LP . . . . . . . . . . . . . . . . . . . . . . . MYR 1091
MC. . . . . . . . . . . . . . . . . . . . . . . . . MC 1091
Myrrh / May '82 / Word Records (UK) / Sony.

## LIVE EXPERIENCE.
**Tracks:** Not Advised.
■ LP . . . . . . . . . . . . . . . . . . . . . . . MYR 1136
Myrrh / '91.

## LOVE AROUND THE WORLD.
**Tracks:** Not Advised.
■ LP . . . . . . . . . . . . . . . . . . . . MYR R 1184
MC. . . . . . . . . . . . . . . . . . . . . . MYR C 1184
Myrrh / Feb '86 / Word Records (UK) / Sony.

## SKY'S THE LIMIT, THE.
**Tracks:** Not Advised.
■ LP . . . . . . . . . . . . . . . . . . . . . . . MYR 1167
MC. . . . . . . . . . . . . . . . . . . . . . . . . MC 1167
Myrrh / Jun '84 / Word Records (UK) / Sony.

## Patrick, Chris

### SLOW JAM.
**Tracks:** Slow jam (Mixes).
12" . . . . . . . . . . . . . . . . . . . . . . . . DA 001
Il Da Gz's / May '94 / Jetstar.

### STAND FOR.
**Tracks:** Stand for.
■ 7" . . . . . . . . . . . . . . . . . . . . . . UNKNOWN
Collision / Jul '89.

### SWEET LOVE.
**Tracks:** Not Advised.
■ 12" . . . . . . . . . . . . . . . . . . . . . . . THP 001
THP production / Oct '92.

## Patrick, Keith

### KEITH PATRICK.
**Tracks:** Be my girl / How far / All my love / Sail away / Heaven / Reach for the sky / You're the one / Love U now / Night to remember.
CD . . . . . . . . . . . . . . . . . . . . . K 781 815 2
■ LP . . . . . . . . . . . . . . . . . . . . . K 781 815 1
MC. . . . . . . . . . . . . . . . . . . . . . K 781 815 4
Atlantic / Apr '88 / WEA.

### NIGHT TO REMEMBER, A.
**Tracks:** Night to remember,A / Night to remember, A ( Instrumental).
■ 12" . . . . . . . . . . . . . . . . . . . . . . .INRT 2
■ 7" . . . . . . . . . . . . . . . . . . . . . . . INR 2
In Recordings / Nov '86.

## Patrick, Rikki

### BREAKPOINT.
**Tracks:** I never thought it would come to this / Night moves / So much in love / Take a raincheck / Save us / Breakpoint / Clear the way / Don't you wanna / You've got it all / Never too late.
■ LP . . . . . . . . . . . . . . . . . . . . . CBS 25924
CBS / Apr '85.

### CLEAR THE WAY.
**Tracks:** Clear the way / Take a raincheck.
■ 12" . . . . . . . . . . . . . . . . . . . . . . TX 5039
■ 7" . . . . . . . . . . . . . . . . . . . . . . A 5039
CBS / Feb '85.

### I NEVER THOUGHT IT WOULD COME TO THIS.
**Tracks:** I never thought it would come to this / Take a raincheck.
■ 7" . . . . . . . . . . . . . . . . . . . . . . A 4414
CBS / Jun '84.

### NEVER TOO LATE.
**Tracks:** Never too late / So much in love.
■ 12" . . . . . . . . . . . . . . . . . . . . . . TX 6180
■ 7" . . . . . . . . . . . . . . . . . . . . . . A 6180
CBS / Apr '85.

### NIGHT MOVES.
**Tracks:** Night moves / Night moves (remix) / Breakpoint.
■ 12" . . . . . . . . . . . . . . . . . . . . . . TA 4144
■ 7" . . . . . . . . . . . . . . . . . . . . . . A 4144
CBS / Mar '84.
■ 12" . . . . . . . . . . . . . . . . . . . DECKS 125
■ 12" . . . . . . . . . . . . . . . . . . . . DECK 125
■ 7" . . . . . . . . . . . . . . . . . . . . . DECK 5
DMC / Mar '87.

## Patterson, Bobby

### BOBBY PATTERSON.
**Tracks:** Not Advised.
■ MC. . . . . . . . . . . . . . . . . . . . . .BLP 101
Bullseye / Jan '79.

### TAKING CARE OF BUSINESS.
**Tracks:** Till you give in / You just got to understand / What's your problem baby / If I didn't have you / Long ago / Soul is our music / Let them talk / Sock some lovin' at me / I'm Leroy, I'll take her / Broadway ain't funky no more / I met my match / Don't be so mean / Good ol' days / Busy, busy bee / Sweet taste of love / T.C.B. or T.Y.A. / What a wonderful night for love / My thing is your thing / Keeping it in the family / My baby's coming back to me / Guess who / Knock out power of love / Trial of Mary McGuire / If a man ever loved a woman / You taught me how to love / I'm in love with you / Married lady / If I didn't know better / Who wants to fall in love.
CD . . . . . . . . . . . . . . . . . . . . CDKEND 098
Kent / Apr '91 / Pinnacle.

## Patterson, Colin

### CAN'T RUSH LOVE.
**Tracks:** Not Advised.
■ 12" . . . . . . . . . . . . . . . . . . . . . STD 10
White / Jul '89.

## Patto, Michael

### (I'VE GOT) LOVE ENOUGH FOR TWO.
**Tracks:** (I've got) love enough for two / What can I do.
■ 12" . . . . . . . . . . . . . . . . . . . . . ZT 44530
■ 7" . . . . . . . . . . . . . . . . . . . . ZB 44529
■ CD Single . . . . . . . . . . . . . . . . . . ZD 44529
■ MC Single. . . . . . . . . . . . . . . . . . ZK 44529
Imagine / Apr '91.

### SO MUCH FOR THE LOVIN'.
**Tracks:** So much for the lovin' / So much for the lovin' (radical mix).
■ MC Single . . . . . . . . . . . . . . . . . . ZK 44781
■ 12" . . . . . . . . . . . . . . . . . . . . . ZT 44782
■ 7" . . . . . . . . . . . . . . . . . . . . ZB 44781
■ CD Single . . . . . . . . . . . . . . . . . . ZD 44782
Imagine / Jul '91.

### TIME TO BE RIGHT.
**Tracks:** So much for the lovin' / Calling / Few good moments / Hold on / Paradise has gone / (I've got) love enough for two / Time to be right / Very thought of you / What can I do / Don't say a word.
CD . . . . . . . . . . . . . . . . . . . . . ZD 74976
■ LP . . . . . . . . . . . . . . . . . . . . . ZL 74976
■ MC. . . . . . . . . . . . . . . . . . . . . ZK 74976
Imagine / Aug '91.

## Patton, Alexander

### LIL LOVIN' SOMETIMES, A.
**Tracks:** Lill lovin' sometimes.
■ 7" . . . . . . . . . . . . . . . . . . . . . CL 15461
Capitol / '66.

## Paul, Billy

Although he began career at 11, Paul was 38 before he enjoyed first hit. Born Paul Williams in Philadelphia, 1934, he formed own trio and released first record, *Why Am I*, in 1955. After stint in army, he struggled through '60s, but forged useful links with Harold Melvin and Gamble & Huff. Signed to latter's Philadelphia International, Paul finally hit with '72 U.S. chart-topper *Me And Mrs Jones*. Although this remained his biggest hit, association with Philly yielded further memorable songs, including BBC-banned *Let's Make A Baby*. In 1977 he successfully reworked Paul McCartney's *Let 'Em In* (featuring excerpts of speeches by Martin Luther King) and Elton John's *Your Song*. After self-imposed break, he made disappointing comeback attempt in 1985 with *Sexual Therapy* (carbon copy of Marvin Gaye's *Sexual Healing*), but withdrew again at close of decade.

### 360 DEGREES OF BILLY PAUL.
**Tracks:** Brown baby / I'm just a prisoner / It's too late / Me and Mrs Jones / Am I black enough for you / Let's stay together / Your song / I'm gonna make it this time.
CD . . . . . . . . . . . . . . . . . . . . .983378 2
Pickwick / Feb '94 / Pickwick.

### 6 TRACK HITS.
**Tracks:** Me & Mrs. Jones / Let's make a baby / Thanks for saving my life / Let 'em in / Don't give on us / Brown baby.
MC. . . . . . . . . . . . . . . . . . . . . . 7SC 50
Scoop 33 / Sep '83.

### BEST OF.
**Tracks:** Let 'em in / Only the strong survive / Do give up on us / July july july / Without you / Bring the family back / Me and Mrs. Jones / Let's make a baby / You're my sweetness / Thanks for saving my life / trust you / Your song.
■ LP . . . . . . . . . . . . . . . . . . . . . PIR 841
Philadelphia Int. / May '80.

### BILLY PAUL'S GREATEST HITS.
**Tracks:** Not Advised.
MC. . . . . . . . . . . . . . . . . . . . . .40 323
■ LP . . . . . . . . . . . . . . . . . . . . . PIR 323
Philadelphia Int. / Jul '83 / EMI.

### BRING THE FAMILY BACK.
**Tracks:** Bring the family back.
■ 12" . . . . . . . . . . . . . . . . . . . . PIR 1374
■ 7" . . . . . . . . . . . . . . . . . . . . PIR 74
Philadelphia Int. / Jul '79.

### EVERYBODY'S BREAKIN' UP.
**Tracks:** Everybody's breakin' up / One man's junk
■ 7" . . . . . . . . . . . . . . . . . . . . PIR 59
Philadelphia Int. / Jan '78.

### FIRST CLASS.
**Tracks:** False faces / Bring the family back / Game life / It's critical / Thank you / What a way to love / glad to see you again / Treasure of my life / I go put this life down.
■ LP . . . . . . . . . . . . . . . . . . . . . PIR 834
Philadelphia Int. / '79.

### FIRST CLASS.
**Tracks:** Not Advised.
CD . . . . . . . . . . . . . . . . . . . . . KWEST 54
Disky / Mar '93 / THE.

### JULY JULY JULY.
**Tracks:** July July July / Be truthful to me.
■ 7" . . . . . . . . . . . . . . . . . . . . PIR 32
Philadelphia Int. / Jun '75.

### LATELY.
**Tracks:** Fire in her love / Sexual therapy / Lately search no more / I only have eyes for you / Hot dat Get down to lovin' / Let me in / Me and you / On clear day.
CD . . . . . . . . . . . . . . . . . . . . . FL 857
■ LP . . . . . . . . . . . . . . . . . . . . . PL 857
MC. . . . . . . . . . . . . . . . . . . . . . PK 857
Total Experience / Sep '85 / PolyGram.

### LATELY.
**Tracks:** Lately / I search no more.
■ 7" . . . . . . . . . . . . . . . . . . . . FB 498
Total Experience / Jan '86.

### LET 'EM IN.
**Tracks:** Let 'em in / We all got a mission / How go is your game / Love won't come easy / Without yo Word sure gets around / I trust you / I think I'll s home today.
■ LP . . . . . . . . . . . . . . . . . . . . . PIR 816
Philadelphia Int. / Feb '77.

### LET 'EM IN.
**Tracks:** Let 'em in.
■ 7" . . . . . . . . . . . . . . . . . . . . PIR 5
Philadelphia Int. / Apr '77.

### LET'S MAKE A BABY.
**Tracks:** Let's make a baby.
■ 7" . . . . . . . . . . . . . . . . . . . . PIR 41
Philadelphia Int. / May '76.

### LET'S MAKE A BABY (OLD GOLD).
**Tracks:** Let's make a baby / America (we need t light) / Malorie.
■ 12" . . . . . . . . . . . . . . . . . . . . .OG 40
Old Gold / Aug '88.

### ME AND MRS JONES.
**Tracks:** Me & Mrs. Jones.
■ 7" . . . . . . . . . . . . . . . . . . . . EPC 10
Epic / Jan '73.

### ME AND MRS JONES (OLD GOLD).
**Tracks:** Me & Mrs. Jones / Let's make a baby.
■ 7" . . . . . . . . . . . . . . . . . . . . .OG 93
Old Gold / Apr '83.

■ DELET

**NLY THE STRONG SURVIVE.**
acks: Only the strong survive / Takin' it to the
eets / Sooner or later / One man's junk / Every-
dy's breakin' up / Times of our lives / Don't give
on us / Where I belong.
■ LP . . . . . . . . . . . . . . . . . . . . . **PIR 82236**
iladelphia Int. / Dec '77.

**NLY THE STRONG SURVIVE.**
acks: Only the strong survive / Where I belong.
■ 7" . . . . . . . . . . . . . . . . . . . . . **PIR 5699**
iladelphia Int. / Nov '77.

**EOPLE POWER.**
acks: People power / I want cha baby.
■ 7" . . . . . . . . . . . . . . . . . . . . . **PIR 4461**
iladelphia Int. / Jul '76.

**EXUAL THERAPY.**
acks: Sexual therapy / I only have eyes for you.
■ 12" . . . . . . . . . . . . . . . . . . . . . **PT 49934**
■ 7" . . . . . . . . . . . . . . . . . . . . . **PB 49933**
tal Experience / Sep '85.

**OUND OF SOUL, THE.**
acks: Not Advised.
■ . . . . . . . . . . . . . . . . . . . . . **BLATCD 14**
■ . . . . . . . . . . . . . . . . . . . . . **BLATMC 14**
■ LP . . . . . . . . . . . . . . . . . . . . **BLATLP 14**
atant / Apr '89 / Roots Records.

**HANKS FOR SAVING MY LIFE.**
acks: Thanks for saving my life.
■ 7" . . . . . . . . . . . . . . . . . . . . . **PIR 1928**
iladelphia Int. / Jan '74.

**E COULD HAVE BEEN.**
acks: We could have been / Wide open / Dirty
undry (12" only).
■ 12" . . . . . . . . . . . . . . . . . . . . . **ICHT 705**
■ 7" . . . . . . . . . . . . . . . . . . . . . **ICHS 705**
riban / May '89.

**HEN LOVE IS NEW.**
acks: People power / America (we need the light) /
the dollar circulate / Malorie / When love is new /
antcha baby / Let's make a baby.
■ LP . . . . . . . . . . . . . . . . . . . . . **PIR 69207**
iladelphia Int. / Jan '76.

**IDE OPEN.**
acks: Not Advised.
■ . . . . . . . . . . . . . . . . . . . . . **CDICH 1025**
■ . . . . . . . . . . . . . . . . . . . . . **ZCICH 1025**
riban / Sep '88 / A.D.A. Distribution / Pinnacle /
D Trading Ltd. / Koch International / Direct
stribution.
■ LP . . . . . . . . . . . . . . . . . . . . . **ICH 1025**
riban / Sep '88.

**OU'RE MY SWEETNESS.**
acks: You're my sweetness / Me and Mrs. Jones.
■ 7" . . . . . . . . . . . . . . . . . . . . . **EPC 8202**
c / Feb '80.

**OUR SONG.**
acks: Your song.
■ 7" . . . . . . . . . . . . . . . . . . . . . **PIR 5391**
iladelphia Int. / Jul '77.

## Paul, Chris

**ACK IN MY ARMS.**
acks: Back in my arms (radio edit) / City nights.
■ 12" . . . . . . . . . . . . . . . . . . . . . **12 SY 5**
■ 7" . . . . . . . . . . . . . . . . . . . . . **SY 5**
ncopate / Oct '87.
■ 12" Remix . . . . . . . . . . . . . . . **12SYX 5**
ncopate / Oct '87.

**XPANSIONS '86 (EXPAND YOUR**
**IND).**
acks: Expansions '86 (expand your mind)(remix) /
pansions '86 / Broadway boulevard.
■ 12" . . . . . . . . . . . . . . . . . . . **12 BRWX 48**
■ 12" Remix . . . . . . . . . . . . . . . **12 BRW 48**
■ 7" . . . . . . . . . . . . . . . . . . . . . **BRW 48**
& Broadway / May '86.

**URN THE MUSIC UP.**
acks: Turn the music up / House on the move /
rn the music up (acidic dub) (Available on 12"
ly).
■ 12" . . . . . . . . . . . . . . . . . . . . . **12SY 13**
■ 12" Remix . . . . . . . . . . . . . . . **12SYX 13**
■ 7" . . . . . . . . . . . . . . . . . . . . . **SY 13**
ncopate / Aug '88.

## Paul, Darlene

**ACT LIKE NOTHING HAPPENED.**
Tracks: Act like nothing happened / Little bit of
heaven.
■ 7" . . . . . . . . . . . . . . . . . . . . . **CL 15344**
Capitol / May '64.

## Payne, Freda

**BAND OF GOLD.**
Tracks: Band of gold / Easiest way to fall.
■ 12" . . . . . . . . . . . . . . . . . . . . . **VATS 301**
■ 7" . . . . . . . . . . . . . . . . . . . . . **VAT 301**
Champagne / Jan '81.
■ 7" . . . . . . . . . . . . . . . . . . . . . **HGH 451**
HDH / Jun '89.

**BAND OF GOLD.**
Tracks: Band of gold.
■ 7" . . . . . . . . . . . . . . . . . . . . . **INV 502**
Invictus / Sep '70.

**BAND OF GOLD.**
Tracks: Band of gold / I left some dreams back there
/ Deeper and deeper / Rock me in the cradle /
Unhooked generation / Love on borrowed time /
Through the memory of my mind / This girl is a
woman now / World don't owe you a thing / Now is
the time to say goodbye / Happy hurt / Easiest way to
fall.
■ LP . . . . . . . . . . . . . . . . . . . . . **SVT 1001**
Invictus / Nov '70.

**BANDS OF GOLD.**
Tracks: Band of gold / Easiest way to fall / Unhooked
generation / Deeper and deeper / Rock me in the
cradle / Love on borrowed time / Cherish what is
dear to you (while it's near to you) / I shall not be
moved / Suddenly it's yesterday / You brought the
joy / Odds and ends / Come on.
■ LP . . . . . . . . . . . . . . . . . . . . . **HDH LP 002**
HDH / Apr '84.

**BEST OF FREDA PAYNE.**
Tracks: Band of gold / Deeper & deeper / How can I
live without my life / Just a woman / Come back /
He's in my life / Unhooked generation / Cherish what
is dear to you / You brought the joy / Now is the time
to say goodbye / Road we didn't take / You're the
only bargain I've got / Through the memory of my
mind / Bring the boys home.
■ LP . . . . . . . . . . . . . . . . . . . . . **SVT 1007**
Invictus / '72.

**BRINGS THE BOYS HOME.**
Tracks: Brings the boys home / Odds and ends.
■ 7" . . . . . . . . . . . . . . . . . . . . . **INV 515**
Invictus / Jul '71.

**CHERISH WHAT IS DEAR TO YOU.**
Tracks: Cherish what is dear to you / World don't
owe you a living.
■ 7" . . . . . . . . . . . . . . . . . . . . . **INV 509**
Invictus / Mar '71.

**CONTACT.**
Tracks: I'm not getting any better / Suddenly it's
yesterday / You brought the joy / Bring the boys
home / You've got to love somebody / Prelude /
Road we didn't take / Odds and ends / Cherish what
is dear to you / I shall not be moved / Mama's gone.
■ LP . . . . . . . . . . . . . . . . . . . . . **SVT 1005**
Invictus / Aug '71.

**DEEPER AND DEEPER.**
Tracks: Deeper and deeper.
■ 7" . . . . . . . . . . . . . . . . . . . . . **INV 505**
Invictus / Nov '70.

**DEEPER AND DEEPER - THE BEST OF**
**FREDA PAYNE.**
Tracks: Unhooked generation / I left some dreams
back there / Rock me in the cradle of love / Cherish
what is dear to you / Mama's gone / Bring the boys
home / You brought the joy / I'm not getting any
better / You've got to love somebody / Road we
didn't take / He's my life / Band of gold / Deeper and
deeper / Easiest way to fall / Now is the time to say
goodbye / Just a woman / Through the memory of
my mind / World don't owe you a thing / Suddenly
it's yesterday / How can I live without my life / Odds
and ends / You're the only bargain I've got.
CD . . . . . . . . . . . . . . . . . . . . . **HDH CD 005**
HDH / Aug '89 / Pinnacle.
■ LP . . . . . . . . . . . . . . . . . . . . . **HDH LP 005**
HDH / Aug '89.

**GREATEST HITS: FREDA PAYNE.**
Tracks: Not Advised.
■ LP . . . . . . . . . . . . . . . . . . . . . **BRLP 62**
MC . . . . . . . . . . . . . . . . . . . . . **BRMC 62**
BR Music/BR Music (Holland) / Oct '88 / BMG.

**HAPPY DAYS ARE HERE AGAIN.**
Tracks: Happy days are here again / Happy music /
I'd do anything for you.
■ 7" . . . . . . . . . . . . . . . . . . . . . **CL 16030**
Capitol / Nov '78.

**I GET HIGH ON YOUR MEMORY.**
Tracks: I get high on your memory / I can't live on a
memory.
■ 7" . . . . . . . . . . . . . . . . . . . . . **CL 15919**
Capitol / Apr '77.

**IN MOTION.**
Tracks: In motion.
■ 7" . . . . . . . . . . . . . . . . . . . . . **BDS 498**
Buddah / Nov '82.

**IT'S YOURS TO HAVE.**
Tracks: It's yours to have / Run for your life.
■ 7" . . . . . . . . . . . . . . . . . . . . . **ABC 4027**
ABC Records / Jan '75.

**LOVE MAGNET.**
Tracks: Love magnet / Bring back the joy.
■ 7" . . . . . . . . . . . . . . . . . . . . . **CL 15959**
Capitol / Jan '78.

**ROCK ME IN THE CRADLE.**
Tracks: Rock me in the cradle / Now is the time to
say goodbye.
■ 7" . . . . . . . . . . . . . . . . . . . . . **INV 512**
Invictus / May '71.

**STARES & WHISPERS.**
Tracks: Master of love / Love magnet / Stares &
whispers / Feed me your love / I get high / Loving
you means so much to me / Bring back the joy.
■ LP . . . . . . . . . . . . . . . . . . . . . **EST 11700**
Capitol / Feb '78.

**SUPERNATURAL HIGH.**
Tracks: Happy days are here again / Happy music /
Pullin' back / Tell me please / Just the thought of you
/ Livin' for the best / Falling in love / I'll do anything
for you / Storybook romance.
■ LP . . . . . . . . . . . . . . . . . . . . . **EST 11864**
Capitol / Dec '78.

## Payne, Scherrie

**CHASING ME INTO SOMEONE ELSE'S**
**ARMS.**
Tracks: Chasing me into someone else's arms.
■ 12" . . . . . . . . . . . . . . . . . . . . . **NGR 8**
Nightmare Gold / Feb '87.

**I'M NOT IN LOVE.**
Tracks: I'm not in love / Girl you're in love.
■ 7" . . . . . . . . . . . . . . . . . . . . . **SOHO 1**
Record Shack / Dec '82.

**ONE NIGHT ONLY.**
Tracks: One night only.
■ 12" . . . . . . . . . . . . . . . . . . . **12EMI 5491**
EMI / Aug '84.

## Payne, Tammy

**DO YOU FEEL IT (LIKE I DO).**
Tracks: Do you feel it (Like I do)(Mixes).
■ 12" . . . . . . . . . . . . . . . . . . . . . **TLKX 19**
■ CD Single . . . . . . . . . . . . . . . **TLKCD 19**
Talkin' Loud / Sep '92.

**FREE.**
Tracks: Free / Push 'em.
■ 12" . . . . . . . . . . . . . . . . . . . . . **YZ 510 T**
■ 7" . . . . . . . . . . . . . . . . . . . . . **YZ 510**
■ CD Single . . . . . . . . . . . . . . . **YZ 510 CD**
■ MC Single. . . . . . . . . . . . . . . **YZ 510 C**
East West / Jun '90.

**TAKE ME NOW.**
Tracks: Take me now / In heart and mind (Not on 12"
remix).
■ 12" . . . . . . . . . . . . . . . . . . . . . **TLKX 12**
■ 12" Remix . . . . . . . . . . . . . . . **TLKXR 12**
■ 7" . . . . . . . . . . . . . . . . . . . . . **TLK 12**
■ CD Single . . . . . . . . . . . . . . . **TLKCD 12**
Talkin' Loud / Jul '91.

## Peaches & Herb

**CLOSE YOUR EYES.**
Tracks: Close your eyes / I will watch over you.
■ 7" . . . . . . . . . . . . . . . . . . . . . **2711**
CBS / Apr '67.

**FOR YOUR LOVE.**
Tracks: For your love / I need your love so
desperately.

## PEACHES & HERB (continued)

■ 7" . . . . . . . . . . . . . . . . . . . . CBS 2866
CBS / Jul '67.

### FREEWAY.
**Tracks:** Freeway / Picking up the pieces.
■ 7" . . . . . . . . . . . . . . . . . . . . POSP 330
Polydor / Sep '81.

### GOLDEN DUETS.
**Tracks:** Two little kids / Rockin' good way / Let it be me / What's the matter with you baby / Something you got / Somethin' stupid / Love is strange / Baby / Mockingbird / We belong together / I want to stay here / I do.
■ LP . . . . . . . . . . . . . . . . . . . . 8 63263
Direction / Apr '68.

### I PLEDGE MY LOVE.
**Tracks:** I pledge my love / Roller skatin' mate.
■ 12" . . . . . . . . . . . . . . . . . . . . POSPX 86
Polydor / Dec '79.

### LET'S FALL IN LOVE.
**Tracks:** Let's fall in love / We're in this thing together.
■ 7" . . . . . . . . . . . . . . . . . . . . .202509
CBS / Jan '67.

### ONE CHILD OF LOVE.
**Tracks:** One child of love / Fun time.
■ 12" . . . . . . . . . . . . . . . . . . . . POSPX 198
■ 7" . . . . . . . . . . . . . . . . . . . . POSP 198
Polydor / Nov '80.

### PEACHES & HERB.
**Tracks:** We're still together / Love is here beside us / I'm counting on you / Just remind me / Our love will never change / That's the way I love you / We've got a lot to be thankful for / Good good times / It will never be the same again.
■ LP . . . . . . . . . . . . . . . . . . . . MCF 2802
MCA / Jun '77.

### REUNITED.
**Tracks:** Reunited / Easy as pie.
■ 7" . . . . . . . . . . . . . . . . . . . . POSP 43
Polydor / Apr '79.
■ 12" . . . . . . . . . . . . . . . . . . . . POSPX 604
Polydor / Nov '82.

### REUNITED (OLD GOLD).
**Tracks:** Reunited / Shake your groovy thing.
■ 7" . . . . . . . . . . . . . . . . . . . . OG 9441
Old Gold / Jul '84.

### SHAKE YOUR GROOVE THING.
**Tracks:** Shake your groove thing.
■ 7" . . . . . . . . . . . . . . . . . . . . .2066 992
Polydor / Jan '79.

### SHAKE YOUR GROOVE THING.
**Tracks:** Shake your groove thing (mixes).
12" . . . . . . . . . . . . . . . . . . . . 12MUM 61
7" . . . . . . . . . . . . . . . . . . . . MUM 61
CD Single . . . . . . . . . . . . . . . . . MUMCD 61
MC Single . . . . . . . . . . . . . . . . . MUMSC 61
Mother / Oct '94 / PolyGram.

### SOOTHE ME WITH YOUR LOVE.
**Tracks:** Soothe me with your love / We're so much in love.
■ 7" . . . . . . . . . . . . . . . . . . . . CBS 5249
CBS / May '71.

### TWICE THE FIRE.
**Tracks:** Roller skatin' mate / I pledge my love / Gypsy lady / Howzabout some love / Gettin' down, gettin' down / Put it there / Back together / Love lift.
■ LP . . . . . . . . . . . . . . . . . . . . 2391433
Polydor / Dec '79.

### TWO HOT.
**Tracks:** We've got love / Shake your groove thing / Reunited / All your love / Love it up tonight / Four's a traffic jam / Star of my life / Easy as pie.
■ LP . . . . . . . . . . . . . . . . . . . . 239 237 8
Polydor / Apr '79.

### WE ARE STILL TOGETHER.
**Tracks:** We are still together / Love is here beside us.
■ 7" . . . . . . . . . . . . . . . . . . . . MCA 297
MCA / May '77.

### WE'VE GOT LOVE.
**Tracks:** We've got love / Four's a traffic jam.
■ 7" . . . . . . . . . . . . . . . . . . . . POSP 65
Polydor / Jul '79.

### WELL WORTH THE WAIT.
**Tracks:** Not Advised.
■ LP . . . . . . . . . . . . . . . . . . . . .2391 484
Polydor / Sep '80.

## Pearce, Bob

### HEY HEY THE BLUES IS ALRIGHT (Pearce, Bob & His Blues Band).
**Tracks:** '65 Chevy / We're gonna ball tonight / What is this here / Reconsider baby / Poison ivy / Hoodoo man / Strange blues / I ain't no Eddie Kirkland / This ain't the way (love's supposed to be) / Blues is alright / Some things never change / Key to the highway.
LP . . . . . . . . . . . . . . . . . . . . BLUH 012
Blue Horizon / Mar '91 / Pinnacle / Hot Shot.

### KEEP ON KEEPIN' ON.
**Tracks:** Not Advised.
CD . . . . . . . . . . . . . . . . . . . . TRCD 9913
Tramp / Apr '93 / Direct Distribution / A.D.A. Distribution / C.M. Distribution / Topic Records.

## Peaston, David

### CAN I.
**Tracks:** Can I.
■ 7" . . . . . . . . . . . . . . . . . . . . GEF 67
Geffen / Oct '89.

### INTRODUCING DAVID PEASTON.
**Tracks:** Two wrongs / Take me now / We're all in this together / Eyes of love / Thank you for the moment / God bless the child / Tonight / Can I / Don't say no.
CD . . . . . . . . . . . . . . . . . . . . K 9242282
LP . . . . . . . . . . . . . . . . . . . . K 9242281
MC . . . . . . . . . . . . . . . . . . . . K 9242284
Elektra / Jun '89 / WEA.

### MIXED EMOTIONS.
**Tracks:** Not Advised.
■ CD . . . . . . . . . . . . . . . . . . . . MCAD 10383
■ LP . . . . . . . . . . . . . . . . . . . . MCA 10383
■ MC . . . . . . . . . . . . . . . . . . . . MCAC 10383
MCA / Oct '91.

### TWO WRONGS DON'T MAKE A RIGHT.
**Tracks:** Two wrongs don't make a right / Thank you for the moment.
■ 12" . . . . . . . . . . . . . . . . . . . . GEF 58T
■ 7" . . . . . . . . . . . . . . . . . . . . GEF 58
Geffen / Jul '89.

### WE'RE ALL IN THIS TOGETHER.
**Tracks:** We're all in this together / Don't say no.
■ 12" . . . . . . . . . . . . . . . . . . . . GEF 70T
■ 7" . . . . . . . . . . . . . . . . . . . . GEF 70
■ CD Single . . . . . . . . . . . . . . . . . GEF 70CD
■ MC Single . . . . . . . . . . . . . . . . . GEF 70C
Geffen / Feb '90.

## Pebbles

### ALWAYS.
**Tracks:** Not Advised.
■ CD . . . . . . . . . . . . . . . . . . . . DMCG 6108
■ LP . . . . . . . . . . . . . . . . . . . . MCG 6108
■ MC . . . . . . . . . . . . . . . . . . . . MCGC 6108
MCA / Oct '90.

### BACKYARD.
**Tracks:** Backyard.
■ 12" . . . . . . . . . . . . . . . . . . . . MCST 1522
■ 7" . . . . . . . . . . . . . . . . . . . . MCS 1522
■ CD Single . . . . . . . . . . . . . . . . . MCSTD 1522
MCA / May '91.

### DO IT.
**Tracks:** Do it.
■ 12" . . . . . . . . . . . . . . . . . . . . SAP 0011
Sapphire / Feb '84.

### DO ME RIGHT.
**Tracks:** Not Advised.
■ LP . . . . . . . . . . . . . . . . . . . . MCA 8040
MCA / Jan '89.

### GIRLFRIEND.
**Tracks:** Girlfriend (mixes) / Love - Hate (Radio edit).
■ 12" . . . . . . . . . . . . . . . . . . . . MCAT 1233
■ 12" Remix . . . . . . . . . . . . . . . . . MCAX 1223
■ CD Single . . . . . . . . . . . . . . . . . DMCA 1233
■ 7" . . . . . . . . . . . . . . . . . . . . MCA 1233
MCA / Mar '88.

### GIVING YOU THE BENEFIT.
**Tracks:** Giving you the benefit / Giving you the benefit (version).
■ 12" . . . . . . . . . . . . . . . . . . . . MCAT 1448
■ 7" . . . . . . . . . . . . . . . . . . . . MCA 1448
■ CD Single . . . . . . . . . . . . . . . . . DMCAT 1448
MCA / Sep '90.
■ 12" Remix . . . . . . . . . . . . . . . . . MCATR 1448
MCA / Sep '90.

### MERCEDES BOY.
**Tracks:** Mercedes boy / Love hate / Mercedes b (extended version) / Love hate (extended version
■ 12" . . . . . . . . . . . . . . . . . . . . MCAT 12
■ 7" . . . . . . . . . . . . . . . . . . . . MCA 12
■ CD Single . . . . . . . . . . . . . . . . . DMCA 12
MCA / May '88.

### PEBBLES.
**Tracks:** Not Advised.
■ CD . . . . . . . . . . . . . . . . . . . . DMCF 34
■ LP . . . . . . . . . . . . . . . . . . . . MCF 34
■ MC . . . . . . . . . . . . . . . . . . . . MCFC 34
MCA / Apr '88.

## Peddle, Wendy

### GONNA GET OVER YOU.
**Tracks:** Gonna get over you.
■ 12" . . . . . . . . . . . . . . . . . . . . BLUECHIP 2
■ 7" . . . . . . . . . . . . . . . . . . . . BLUECHIP
Blue Chip / Jul '88.

## Peebles, Ann

Raised on gospel, Peebles' big break can in 1969 when, aged 22, she signed to label. Alliance with producer Willie Mitche yielded run of U.S. soul hits in first half '70s; although her style was earthier tha label mate Al Green and thus did not enje similar crossover success. However, h two best-known tracks became pe smashes for other artists: *I Can't Stand T Rain* was transatlantic 1978 hit for Eruptie and later included on Tina Turner's 19 album *Private Dancer*; while *I'm Goni Tear Your Playhouse Down* took Paul Youi into U.S. Top 20 and U.K. Top 10. Peeble herself faded into obscurity, although sh was still recording in '80s.

### 99 LBS.
**Tracks:** 99 lbs / Walk away / Give me some credi Heartaches / Somebody's on your case / I still lo you / Part time love / I'll get along / Generation g between us / Slipped, tripped and fell in love Trouble / Heartaches and sadness / I feel like brea ing up somebody's home / I pity the fool / Do I ne you / I can't let you go / One way street.
■ LP . . . . . . . . . . . . . . . . . . . . HIUKLP 4
Hi / Apr '87.

### CALL ME.
**Tracks:** Not Advised.
LP . . . . . . . . . . . . . . . . . . . . 269 509
MC . . . . . . . . . . . . . . . . . . . . 269 509
Waylo / Jan '90 / Charly.
CD . . . . . . . . . . . . . . . . . . . . 269 509
Waylo / Apr '94 / Charly.

### DO I NEED YOU.
**Tracks:** Do I need you / Love vibration.
■ 7" . . . . . . . . . . . . . . . . . . . . HLU 104
London / Jun '74.

### FLIPSIDE.
**Tracks:** Not Advised.
CD . . . . . . . . . . . . . . . . . . . . HIUKCD 1
Demon / Aug '93 / Pinnacle / A.D.A. Distribution.

### FULL TIME LOVE.
**Tracks:** Not Advised.
■ CD . . . . . . . . . . . . . . . . . . . . NETCD 95
Bullseye Blues / Jul '92.

### GREATEST HITS.
**Tracks:** 99 lbs / Walk away / Give me some credi Heartaches, heartaches / Somebody's on your case I still love you / Part time love / Generation g between us / Slipped, tripped and fell in love Trouble heartaches and sadness / I feel like brea ing up somebody's home / I pity the fool / Do I ne you / One way street / I can't stand the rain / Bewa / Love vibration / Dr. Love Power / It was jealous Being here with you / I'm gonna tear your playhou down / When in your arms / Good day for lovin Come to Mama / Old man with young ideas / If this heaven.
CD . . . . . . . . . . . . . . . . . . . . HIUKCD
Hi / Apr '88 / Pinnacle.

### I CAN'T STAND THE RAIN.
**Tracks:** I can't stand the rain / Do I need you / Un you came into my life / Hangin' on / Run, run, run we can't trust each other / Love vibration / You got feed the fire / I'm gonna tear your playhouse dow One way street.
■ LP . . . . . . . . . . . . . . . . . . . . SHU 84
London-American / '74.
CD . . . . . . . . . . . . . . . . . . . . HIUKCD 1
Demon / Sep '92 / Pinnacle / A.D.A. Distribution.

## CAN'T STAND THE RAIN.
Tracks: I can't stand the rain / Love vibration.
■ 7".................................HL 10428
London-American / Apr '74.
■ 12"...............................HIUK 45 7002 T
■ 7"................................HIUK 45 7002
i / Mar '85.

## PITY THE FOOL.
Tracks: I pity the fool / Heartaches heartaches.
■ 7"................................HLU 10328
London / Mar '71.

## I'M GONNA TEAR YOUR PLAYHOUSE DOWN.
Tracks: I can't stand the rain / Beware / Love vibration / Dr. Love Power / Love played a game / It was jealousy / What you laid on me / Being here with you / I'm gonna tear your playhouse down / When I'm in your arms / Good day for lovin' / Come to Mama / Old man with young ideas / I needed somebody / This is heaven.
■ LP................................HIUKLP 422
■C................................HIUKCASS 422
i / '87 / Pinnacle.

## LOOKIN' FOR A LOVIN'.
Tracks: Respect / Have you / It's your thing / Won't you try me / My man (mon homme) / I'll get along / What you laid on me / (You keep me) hangin' in / Love played a game / I needed somebody / You're gonna make me cry / Bip, bam, Thank you ham / Handwriting is on the wall / Livin' in lovin' out Lookin' for a lovin' / You've got the papers (I've got the man) / I didn't take your man / Heartaches / Be or me / Mon belle amour / I'd rather leave while I'm in love.
■D................................HIUKCD 105
i / Aug '90 / Pinnacle.

## STRAIGHT FROM THE HEART.
Tracks: Slipped, tripped & fell in love / Trouble, heartache & sadness / What you laid on me / How wrong is a woman / Somebody's on your case / Give me some credit / I'll get along / I feel like breaking up somebody's home tonight / I've been there before / I pity the fool / 99 lbs / I take what I want / Solid foundation / Generation gap between us.
■ LP................................SHU 8434
London / Aug '72.

## STRAIGHT FROM THE HEART/I CAN'T STAND THE RAIN.
Tracks: Slipped, tripped and fell in love / Trouble, heartaches and sadness / What you laid on me / How wrong is a woman / Somebody's on your case / I feel like breaking up somebody's home / I've been there before / I pity the fool / 99 Pounds / I take what I want / (You keep me) Hangin' on / Run, run, run / If we can't trust each other / Love vibration / You got to feed the fire / I'm gonna tear your playhouse down / One way street.
■D................................HIUKCD 107
emon / Jan '93 / Pinnacle / A.D.A. Distribution.

## TELLIN' IT/IF THIS IS HEAVEN.
Tracks: Come to Mama / I don't lend my man / I needed somebody / Stand by woman / It was jealousy / Dr. Love Power / You can't hold a man / Beware / Put yourself in my place / Love played a game / If this is heaven / Good day for lovin' / I'm so thankful / Being here with you / Boy I gotta have you / When I'm in your arms / You're gonna make me cry / Games / Lovin' you wihtout love / It must be love.
■D................................HIUKCD 138
emon / Jan '93 / Pinnacle / A.D.A. Distribution.

## THIS IS ANN PEEBLES.
Tracks: Not Advised.
■D................................HIUKCD 139
emon / Jun '93 / Pinnacle / A.D.A. Distribution.

## Peech Boys

## DON'T MAKE ME WAIT.
Tracks: Don't make me wait / Don't make me wait (It. version).
■ 12"...............................TMMT 7001
■ 7"................................TMT 7001
M.T. / Oct '82.

## LIFE IS SOMETHING SPECIAL.
Tracks: Not Advised.
■ LP................................ILPS 9761
■ MC................................ICT 9761
and / Sep '83.

## LIFE IS SOMETHING SPECIAL.
Tracks: Life is something special.
■ 12"...............................12 WIP 6846
■ 7"................................WIP 6846
and / Feb '83.

---

## ON A JOURNEY.
Tracks: On a journey.
■ 12"...............................12 IS 119
■ 7"................................IS 119
Island / Sep '83.

## Peels

## JUANITA BANANA.
Tracks: Juanita banana / Fun.
■ 7"................................SS 513
Stateside / May '66.

## SCROOEY MOOEY.
Tracks: Scrooey mooey / Time marches on.
■ 7"................................ASSP 527
Audio Fidelity / Jun '66.

## TIME MARCHES ON.
Tracks: Time marches on / Scrooey mooey.
■ 7"................................AFSP 527
Audio Fidelity / '66.

## Peeples, Nia

## KISSING THE WIND.
Tracks: Kissing the wind.
■ 12"...............................CUST 7
■ 7"................................CUSS 7
■ CD Single............................CUSCD 7
■ MC Single............................CUSC 7
Charisma / Apr '92.

## NIA PEEPLES.
Tracks: Kissing the wind / Street of dreams / Faces of love / You make me wanna / Hurricane / Entity (sex) / Heaven help me / With every word / King of cool / Shut up and fix it.
■ CD................................CDCUS 10
■ LP................................CUSLP 10
■ MC................................CUSMC 10
Charisma / May '92.

## STREET OF DREAMS.
Tracks: Street of dreams.
■ 12"...............................CUST 6
■ 7"................................CUSS 6
■ CD Single............................CUSDG 6
■ MC Single............................CUSC 6
Charisma / Nov '91.

## Pendergrass, Teddy

From ordained priest as a teenager to sex symbol to paraplegic, Pendergrass has at least had an eventful life. To watch their son become lead singer in Harold Melvin & The Bluenotes was probably a big enough surprise for his deeply committed Christian family, but to see women the world over hurling underwear at and generally disporting themselves before him must have had them praying for divine intervention. Perhaps that's the way they viewed the car accident which in '87 put Teddy in a wheelchair for the rest of his life. Whatever, between '76, when he left the Bluenotes, and the moment he ended up in the bottom of a New Jersey ditch, Pendergrass had become the biggest sex 'n' soul star on the circuit, even to the point of stealing Marvin Gaye's girlfriend. At times on *Teddy Pendergrass*, *Life Is A Song Worth Singing*, *It's Time For Love*, and most of all, *T.P.*, he was simply as good as the genre ever gets. Sadly his post-accident work, though often well assembled, ultimately suffers from the artist's lack of lung power, though his career maintenance is something to admire. *Joy* ('88) and *Truly Blessed* ('91) are the best of this period.

## 2 A.M.
Tracks: 2 a.m.
■ 12"...............................EKR 83T
■ 7"................................EKR 83
Elektra / Nov '88.

## CLOSE THE DOOR.
Tracks: Close the door / Get up, get down, get funky, get loose.
■ 7"................................PIR 6417
Philadelphia Int. / Jun '78.

## CLOSE THE DOOR.
Tracks: Close the door / Only you.
■ 7"................................PIR 6713
Philadelphia Int. / Oct '78.

---

## GREATEST HITS: TEDDY PENDERGRASS.
Tracks: Turn off the lights / Love TKO / I don't love you anymore / More I get the more I want / Only you / Close the door / When somebody loves you back / You can't hide from yourself / Come go with me.
■ LP................................PIR 32442
MC................................40 32442
Philadelphia Int. / Jun '84 / EMI.

## HEAVEN ONLY KNOWS.
Tracks: Crazy about your love / Judge for yourself / I want my baby back / Life is for living / You and me for right now / Just because you're mine / Heaven only knows / Don't ever stop.
■ LP................................PIR 25691
MC................................40 25691
Philadelphia Int. / Dec '83 / EMI.

## HOLD ME (see under Houston, Whitney).

## I DON'T LOVE YOU ANY MORE.
Tracks: I don't love you anymore / Easy easy got to take it easy.
■ 7"................................PIR 5444
Philadelphia Int. / Jul '77.

## I JUST CALLED TO SAY.
Tracks: I just called to say / Reach out and touch.
■ 7"................................PIRA 2047
Philadelphia Int. / Feb '82.

## IT'S TIME FOR LOVE.
Tracks: I can't live without your love / You're my latest greatest inspiration / Nine times out of ten / keep on lovin' me / It's time for love / She's over me / I can't leave your love alone / You must live on.
■ LP................................PIR 85220
Philadelphia Int. / Oct '81.

## JOY.
Tracks: Joy / 2 a.m. / Good to you / I'm ready / Love is the power / This is the last time / Through the falling rain / Can we be lovers.
CD................................9607752
■ LP................................EKT 48
MC................................EKT 48C
Elektra / Jul '88 / WEA.
CD................................7559607752
Pickwick/Warner / Oct '94 / Pinnacle.

## JOY.
Tracks: Joy / Let me be closer.
■ 12"...............................EKT 75T
■ 7"................................EKT 75
Elektra / May '88.

## LIFE IS A SONG WORTH SINGING.
Tracks: Life is a song worth singing / Only you / Cold, cold world / Get up, get down, get funky, get loose / Close the door / It don't hurt now / When somebody loves you back.
■ LP................................PIR 82555
Philadelphia Int. / Aug '78.
■ LP................................PIR 32309
Philadelphia Int. / Apr '83.

## LIFE IS A SONG WORTH SINGING.
Tracks: Life is a song worth singing / Cold cold world.
■ 7"................................PIR 7151
Philadelphia Int. / '79.

## LITTLE MORE MAGIC, A.
Tracks: Believe in love / Slip away / I'm always thinking about you / I choose you / Voodoo / Tender / Can't help nobody / Little more magic, A / My father's child / Say it / No one like you / Reprise - my father's child.
CD................................7559614972
MC................................7559614974
WEA / Oct '93 / WEA.

## LIVE COAST TO COAST.
Tracks: Life is a song worth singing / Only you / If you don't know me by now / Love I lost / Bad luck / Wake up everybody / When somebody loves you back / Ger up get down get funky get loose / LA Rep / Come go with me / Close the door / Turn off the lights / Do me / Where did all the lovin' go / It's you I love / Shout & scream.
■ Double LP..........................PIR 88474
Philadelphia Int. / Apr '80.

## LOVE LANGUAGE.
Tracks: In my time / So sad the song / Hot love / Stay with me / Hold me / You're my choice tonight / Love / This time is yours.
MC................................960 317-4
■ CD................................960 317-2
■ LP................................960 317-1
Asylum / Jul '86 / WEA.

## READY FOR TEDDY.
**Tracks:** Whole town's laughing at me / Turn off the lights / Love TKO / Somebody told me / I just called to say / Close the door / You can't hide from yourself / More I get the more I want / Only you / Life is a song worth singing / Be sure / Take me in your arms tonight.
■ **LP** . . . . . . . . . . . . . . . . . . . . . . **PIR 84903**
**MC**. . . . . . . . . . . . . . . . . . . . . **.40 84903**
Philadelphia Int. / Apr '81 / EMI.

## SHOUT AND SCREAM.
**Tracks:** Shout and scream / Close the door.
■ **7"** . . . . . . . . . . . . . . . . . . . . . **PIR 8183**
Philadelphia Int. / Feb '80.

## SOUND OF SOUL.
**Tracks:** Not Advised.
**CD**. . . . . . . . . . . . . . . . . . . . **BLATCD 12**
■ **LP** . . . . . . . . . . . . . . . . . . . . **BLATLP 12**
**MC**. . . . . . . . . . . . . . . . . . . . **BLATMC 12**
Blatant / Apr '89 / Roots Records.

## STAR COLLECTION.
**Tracks:** Not Advised.
**CD**. . . . . . . . . . . . . . . . . . . . **STCD 1004**
Disky / Jun '93 / THE.

## T.P.
**Tracks:** Is it still good to ya / Take me in your arms tonight / I just called to say / Can't we try / Feel the fire / Girl you know / Love TKO / Let me love you.
■ **LP** . . . . . . . . . . . . . . . . . . . . **PIR 84542**
Philadelphia Int. / Oct '80.
**CD**. . . . . . . . . . . . . . . . . . . . . **T 266691**
Philadelphia Int. / '93 / EMI.

## TEDDY.
**Tracks:** Come go with me / Turn off the lights / I'll never see heaven again / All I need is you / If you know like I know / Do me / Set me free / Life is a circle.
■ **MC**. . . . . . . . . . . . . . . . . . . . **.40 83656**
Philadelphia Int. / Aug '79.
■ **LP** . . . . . . . . . . . . . . . . . . . . **PIR 83656**
Philadelphia Int. / Aug '79.

## TEDDY PENDERGRASS.
**Tracks:** Not Advised.
■ **LP** . . . . . . . . . . . . . . . . . . . **PIR 32127**
Philadelphia Int. / Mar '82.

## TEDDY PENDERGRASS LIVE.
**Tracks:** Not Advised.
**VHS** . . . . . . . . . . . . . . . . . . . . . **.713550**
CBS-Fox / '88 / Sony / THE.

## TRULY BLESSED.
**Tracks:** She knocks me off my feet / It should've been you / Don't you ever stop / It's over / Glad to be alive / How can you mend a broken heart / I find everything in you / Spend the night, with you / We can't keep going on (like this) / Truly blessed.
**CD**. . . . . . . . . . . . . . . . . . . **7559608912**
■ **LP** . . . . . . . . . . . . . . . . . . . . . **EKT 82**
■ **MC**. . . . . . . . . . . . . . . . . . . . . **.EKT 82C**
Elektra / Mar '91 / WEA.

## TURN OFF THE LIGHTS.
**Tracks:** Turn off the ligts / If you know like I know.
■ **7"** . . . . . . . . . . . . . . . . . . . . **PIR 7749**
Philadelphia Int. / Nov '79.

## WHOLE TOWN'S LAUGHING AT ME.
**Tracks:** Whole town's laughing at me / Love t.k.o.
■ **7"** . . . . . . . . . . . . . . . . . . . . **PIR 5116**
Philadelphia Int. / May '77.
■ **7"** . . . . . . . . . . . . . . . . . . . **.PIRA 1089**
Philadelphia Int. / Apr '81.

## WORKING IT BACK.
**Tracks:** Love 4/2 / One of us fell in love / Never felt like dancing / Closer / Lovely colour blue / Want you back in my life / Working it back / Reach out and touch.
■ **LP** . . . . . . . . . . . . . . . . . . . . . **EKT 26**
**MC**. . . . . . . . . . . . . . . . . . . . . **.EKT 26C**
Elektra / Nov '85 / WEA.
■ **CD** . . . . . . . . . . . . . . . . . . . . **9604472**
Elektra / Jul '86.

## YOU'RE MY CHOICE TONIGHT.
**Tracks:** You're my choice tonight / So sad the song.
■ **12"**. . . . . . . . . . . . . . . . . . . **E 9696T**
■ **7"** . . . . . . . . . . . . . . . . . . . . **E 9696**
Elektra / Apr '85.

318

---

## CRAZY LOVE.
**Tracks:** Crazy love.
■ **12"**. . . . . . . . . . . . . . . . . . **AMY 0600**
■ **7"** . . . . . . . . . . . . . . . . . . . **AM 0600**
■ **CD Single**. . . . . . . . . . . . . . **AMCD 0600**
■ **MC Single**. . . . . . . . . . . . . . **AMMC 0600**
A&M / Sep '92.

## FINALLY.
**Tracks:** Finally.
■ **12"**. . . . . . . . . . . . . . . . . . . **AMY 822**
■ **7"** . . . . . . . . . . . . . . . . . . . **AM 822**
■ **CD Single**. . . . . . . . . . . . . . **AMCD 822**
■ **MC Single**. . . . . . . . . . . . . . **AMMC 822**
A&M / Oct '91.

## FINALLY.
**Tracks:** We got a love thang / Finally / Inside that I cried / Lifeline / It should have been you / Keep on walkin / Crazy love / I see love / You win I win we lose / Virtue / Finally (Somedub mix).
**CD**. . . . . . . . . . . . . . . . . . . . **3971822**
■ **LP** . . . . . . . . . . . . . . . . . . . **3971821**
**MC**. . . . . . . . . . . . . . . . . . . . **3971824**
A&M / Apr '92 / PolyGram.

## FINALLY.
**Tracks:** Finally.
■ **12"**. . . . . . . . . . . . . . . . . . . **AMY 858**
■ **7"** . . . . . . . . . . . . . . . . . . . **AM 858**
■ **CD Single**. . . . . . . . . . . . . . **AMCD 858**
■ **MC Single**. . . . . . . . . . . . . . **AMMC 858**
A&M / Mar '92.

## I'M IN THE MOOD.
**Tracks:** I'm in the mood / I'm in the mood (mixes).
■ **12"**. . . . . . . . . . . . . . . . . . . **AMX 455**
■ **7"** . . . . . . . . . . . . . . . . . . . **AM 455**
■ **CD Single**. . . . . . . . . . . . . . **AMCD 455**
■ **MC Single**. . . . . . . . . . . . . . **AMMC 455**
A&M / Jan '94.

## INSIDE THAT I CRIED.
**Tracks:** Inside that I cried / Hitmix (Features Finally, We Got A Love Thang & Keep On Walkin') (7", MC & CD only) / Hitmix (Extended) (Features Finally, We Got A Love Thang, Keep On Walkin', Lifeline, & It Should Have Been You) (12" & CD only) / It should have been you (12" & CD only).
■ **12"**. . . . . . . . . . . . . . . . . . **AMY 0121**
■ **7"** . . . . . . . . . . . . . . . . . . . **AM 0121**
■ **CD Single**. . . . . . . . . . . . . . **AMCD 0121**
■ **MC Single**. . . . . . . . . . . . . . **AMMC 0121**
A&M / Nov '92.

## KEEP GIVIN' ME YOUR LOVE.
**Tracks:** Keep givin' me your love (Mixes).
■ **12"**. . . . . . . . . . . . . . . . . . **580549-1**
■ **7"** . . . . . . . . . . . . . . . . . . . **580548-7**
■ **CD Single**. . . . . . . . . . . . . . **580548-2**
■ **MC Single**. . . . . . . . . . . . . . **580548-4**
A&M / Feb '94.

## KEEP ON WALKIN'.
**Tracks:** Keep on walkin'.
■ **12"**. . . . . . . . . . . . . . . . . . . **AMY 878**
■ **7"** . . . . . . . . . . . . . . . . . . . **AM 878**
■ **CD Single**. . . . . . . . . . . . . . **AMCD 878**
A&M / May '92.

## THOUGHT 'YA KNEW.
**Tracks:** Searchin' / I'm in the mood / Hit by love / Whatever it is / Forever in my heart / I'm not over you / Any way you wanna go / Give what I'm givin' / Through those doors / Let my love surround you / Keep givin' me your love / If you love me, I will love you / Maybe it's the way.
**CD**. . . . . . . . . . . . . . . . . . **540 138-2**
**LP** . . . . . . . . . . . . . . . . . . . . **.540138-1**
**MC**. . . . . . . . . . . . . . . . . . . . **.540138-4**
A&M / Jan '94 / PolyGram.
**DCC**. . . . . . . . . . . . . . . . . . . **.540201-5**
A&M / May '94 / PolyGram.

## WE GOT A LOVE THANG.
**Tracks:** We got a love thang.
■ **12"**. . . . . . . . . . . . . . . . . . . **AMY 846**
■ **7"** . . . . . . . . . . . . . . . . . . . **AM 846**
■ **CD Single**. . . . . . . . . . . . . . **AMCD 846**
■ **MC Single**. . . . . . . . . . . . . . **AMMC 846**
A&M / Jan '92.

## DO RIGHT MAN.
**Tracks:** Not Advised.
**CD**. . . . . . . . . . . . . . . . **.936245519-2**
Warner Bros. / Oct '94 / WEA.

---

## 24 HOURS A DAY.
**Tracks:** 24 hours a day / I can't erase the thoughs o you.
■ **7"** . . . . . . . . . . . . . . . . . . . . **UP 3617**
United Artists / Oct '76.

## ALL AMERICAN BOY.
**Tracks:** All American boy / Sorry, wrong number Skiing in the snow.
■ **12"**. . . . . . . . . . . . . . . . . . . **.SOHOT 2**
■ **7"** . . . . . . . . . . . . . . . . . . . **SOHO 2**
Record Shack / Sep '84.
■ **12"**. . . . . . . . . . . . . . . . . . . **.SOHOB**
Record Shack / Feb '88.

## ALL TIME LOSER.
**Tracks:** All time loser / It's so hard getting over.
■ **7"** . . . . . . . . . . . . . . . . . . . . **UP 3642**
United Artists / Aug '78.

## DON'T STOP THE WORLD.
**Tracks:** Don't stop the world.
■ **7"** . . . . . . . . . . . . . . . . . . . **MARES**
Nightmare / Feb '87.
■ **12"**. . . . . . . . . . . . . . . . . . . **. MARE**
Nightmare / Feb '87.

## MIDNIGHT RIDE.
**Tracks:** Midnight ride / All time loser / Trusted frien / Spend a little time with me / Can't help being guilt / Twenty four hours a day / It's so hard getting over You are the music within me.
■ **LP** . . . . . . . . . . . . . . . . . . . **UAS 3014**
United Artists / Mar '78.

## MIDNIGHT RIDE.
**Tracks:** Midnight ride / I can't keep my heart still.
■ **7"** . . . . . . . . . . . . . . . . . . . . **UP 3637**
United Artists / Apr '78.

## ON A CROWDED STREET.
**Tracks:** On a crowded street.
■ **12"**. . . . . . . . . . . . . . . . . . . **.SOHOT 4**
■ **7"** . . . . . . . . . . . . . . . . . . . **SOHO 4**
Record Shack / Aug '85.

## ON A CROWDED STREET (OLD GOLD).
**Tracks:** On a crowded street / Fan the flame.
■ **12"**. . . . . . . . . . . . . . . . . . . **.OG 413**
Old Gold / '89.

## OUT OF THE DARKEST NIGHT.
**Tracks:** Not Advised.
■ **LP** . . . . . . . . . . . . . . . . . . . **SOHOLP**
**MC**. . . . . . . . . . . . . . . . . . . . **SOHOTC**
Record Shack / Aug '85.

## SPEND A LITTLE TIME WITH ME.
**Tracks:** Spend a little time with me / Can't help bein guilty.
■ **7"** . . . . . . . . . . . . . . . . . . . . **UP 3634**
United Artists / Jan '78.

## THERE ARE BRIGHTER DAYS.
**Tracks:** There are brighter days / There are brighte days (version).
■ **12"**. . . . . . . . . . . . . . . . . . . **MARE 4**
■ **7"** . . . . . . . . . . . . . . . . . . . **MARES 4**
Nightmare / Apr '88.

## WAYDOWN DEEP IN MY SOUL.
**Tracks:** Waydown deep in my soul / All America boy.
■ **12"**. . . . . . . . . . . . . . . . . . . **.SOHOT 3**
■ **7"** . . . . . . . . . . . . . . . . . . . **SOHO 3**
Record Shack / Jan '85.

## YOU ARE THE MUSIC WITHIN ME.
**Tracks:** You are the music within me / Running i another direction.
■ **7"** . . . . . . . . . . . . . . . . . . . . **UP 3623**
United Artists / Apr '77.

## DO IT (ANYWAY YOU WANNA).
**Tracks:** Do it anyway you wanna.
■ **7"** . . . . . . . . . . . . . . . . . . . **PIR 350**
Philadelphia Int. / Sep '75.

## DO IT (ANYWAY YOU WANNA) (OL GOLD).
**Tracks:** Do it (anyway you wanna).
■ **7"** . . . . . . . . . . . . . . . . . . . **.OG 950**
Old Gold / Sep '85.

## IF YOU GONNA DO IT.
**Tracks:** If you gonna do it / If you gonna do (version).
■ **7"** . . . . . . . . . . . . . . . . . . . **PIR 523**
Philadelphia Int. / Jun '77.

### JAM JAM JAM.
**Tracks:** Jam jam jam / Cold blooded and downright funky.
■ 7" . . . . . . . . . . . . . . . . . . . . . PIR 5891
Philadelphia Int. / Jan '78.

### WE GOT THE RHYTHM.
**Tracks:** Here we go again / Jam, jam, jam / All night long / We got the rhythm / Cold-blooded and downright funky / Movin' all directions / Opus de funk / Mellow mood.
■ LP . . . . . . . . . . . . . . . . . . . . . PIR 81370
Philadelphia Int. / Jul '76.

## Perception

### OUT AND ABOUT EP (Perception & K-Creative).
**Tracks:** Feed the feeling (edit) (7" only.) / Three times a maybe / Feed the feeling (Pal Joey remix) (Not on 7".) / K spells knowledge (Not on 7".).
■ 12" . . . . . . . . . . . . . . . . . . . . TLKX 17
Talkin' Loud / Feb '92.
■ CD Single . . . . . . . . . . . . . . . . . TLKCD 17
Talkin' Loud / Feb '92.
■ 12" Remix . . . . . . . . . . . . . . . . . TLKXR 17
Talkin' Loud / Feb '92.

### TAKE U HIGHER.
**Tracks:** Not Advised.
■ 12" . . . . . . . . . . . . . . . . . . . . TLKX 33
■ 7" . . . . . . . . . . . . . . . . . . . . . TLK 33
■ CD Single . . . . . . . . . . . . . . . . . TLKCD 33
■ MC Single . . . . . . . . . . . . . . . . . TLKMC 33
Talkin' Loud / Feb '93.

## Perfect Fit

### IF YOU ONLY KNEW.
**Tracks:** If you only knew / Heartbreaking.
■ 12" . . . . . . . . . . . . . . . . . . . . . MS 16
Move / Sep '86.

## Perri

### CELEBRATE.
**Tracks:** Not Advised.
■ LP . . . . . . . . . . . . . . . . . . . . . MCF 3325
■ MC . . . . . . . . . . . . . . . . . . . . MCFC 3325
MCA / Nov '86.

### FALL IN LOVE.
**Tracks:** Fall in love.
■ 12" . . . . . . . . . . . . . . . . . . . . MCA T1293
■ CD Single . . . . . . . . . . . . . . . . . DMCA 1293
■ 7" . . . . . . . . . . . . . . . . . . . . . MCA 1293
MCA / Oct '88.

### FEEL SO GOOD.
**Tracks:** Feel so good / Feel so good (instrumental) / Feel so good (extended).
■ 12" . . . . . . . . . . . . . . . . . . . . AT 43084
■ 7" . . . . . . . . . . . . . . . . . . . . . ZB 43083
■ CD Single . . . . . . . . . . . . . . . . . ZD 43084
Motown / Oct '89.

### I'M THE ONE.
**Tracks:** I'm the one.
■ CD Single . . . . . . . . . . . . . . . . . DMCAT 1311
■ 12" . . . . . . . . . . . . . . . . . . . . MCAT 1311
■ 7" . . . . . . . . . . . . . . . . . . . . . MCA 1311
MCA / Apr '89.

### INFLIGHT.
**Tracks:** I'm the one / No place to go / Flight / Secret weapon / Caves of Altmira / Upside down / Fall in love / I don't wanna lose your love / Travels / Eternal life.
■ CD . . . . . . . . . . . . . . . . . . . . DMCF 3434
■ LP . . . . . . . . . . . . . . . . . . . . . MCF 3434
■ MC . . . . . . . . . . . . . . . . . . . . MCFC 3434
MCA / Oct '88.

### TRADE WINDS.
**Tracks:** Someone like you / You taught me how / Talk to me / Crazy / No way to treat a lady / It's been you / Tradewinds / You're the one / Mary Mary / Say you will.
■ MC . . . . . . . . . . . . . . . . . . . . MCGC 6104
■ CD . . . . . . . . . . . . . . . . . . . . DMCG 6104
■ LP . . . . . . . . . . . . . . . . . . . . . MCG 6104
MCA / Aug '90.

## Perry, Greg

### BOOGIE MAN.
**Tracks:** Boogie man (part 1) / Will she meet the train in the rain.
■ 7" . . . . . . . . . . . . . . . . . . . . . CBX 511
Casablanca / Jul '75.

## Perry, Phil

### AMAZING LOVE.
**Tracks:** Amazing love / Amazing love (instrumental).
■ 12" . . . . . . . . . . . . . . . . . . . . 12CL 615
■ 7" . . . . . . . . . . . . . . . . . . . . . CL 615
■ CD Single . . . . . . . . . . . . . . . . . CDCL 615
■ MC Single . . . . . . . . . . . . . . . . . TCCL 615
Capitol / Jun '91.

### HEART OF THE MAN.
**Tracks:** Amazing love / Say anything / Forever / Woman / More nights / Call me / (Forever in the) arms of love / Best of me / God's gift to the world / Good-bye / Who do you love (CD & cassette only).
■ MC . . . . . . . . . . . . . . . . . . . . C4 92115
■ CD . . . . . . . . . . . . . . . . . . . . C2 92115
■ LP . . . . . . . . . . . . . . . . . . . . . C1 92115
Capitol / May '91 / EMI.

### PURE PLEASURE.
**Tracks:** One touch / Way that I want U / After the love has gone / If only you knew / I love it, I love it / When it comes to love / Heaven / You say, I say / Angel of the night / Love don't love nobody.
■ CD . . . . . . . . . . . . . . . . . . . . GRM 40272
GRP / Oct '94 / BMG / New Note.

## Person, Houston

### ALWAYS ON MY MIND.
**Tracks:** Not Advised.
■ LP . . . . . . . . . . . . . . . . . . . . . MR 5289
Muse / Sep '92 / New Note / Jazz Horizons / C.M. Distribution.

### BASICS.
**Tracks:** Not Advised.
■ LP . . . . . . . . . . . . . . . . . . . . . MR 5344
■ CD . . . . . . . . . . . . . . . . . . . . MCD 5344
Muse / Sep '92 / New Note / Jazz Horizons / C.M. Distribution.

### BIG HORN, THE.
**Tracks:** Not Advised.
■ LP . . . . . . . . . . . . . . . . . . . . . MR 5136
Muse / Apr '81.

### HEAVY JUICE.
**Tracks:** Heavy juice / Summertime / Loveboat theme / Never let me go / Let the feeling flow / Please send me someone to love / Texas shuffle / Blue hue.
■ LP . . . . . . . . . . . . . . . . . . . . . MR 5260
Muse / Nov '82.

### IN COMMON (Person, Houston & Ron Carter).
**Tracks:** Not Advised.
■ LP . . . . . . . . . . . . . . . . . . . . . MR 5376
Muse / Sep '92 / New Note / Jazz Horizons / C.M. Distribution.

### JIVE SAMBA.
**Tracks:** Jive samba / Pain.
■ 12" . . . . . . . . . . . . . . . . . . . . BASL2T
Baseline / Mar '90.

### NEARNESS OF YOU, THE.
**Tracks:** Not Advised.
■ LP . . . . . . . . . . . . . . . . . . . . . MR 5178
Muse / Apr '81.

### NOW'S THE TIME (Person, Houston & Ron Carter).
**Tracks:** Bermsha swing / Spring can really hang you up / Einbahnstrasse / Memories of you / Quiet nights / If you could see me now / Now's the time / Since I fell for you / Little waltz.
■ CD . . . . . . . . . . . . . . . . . . . . MCD 5421
Muse / Aug '93 / New Note / Jazz Horizons / C.M. Distribution.

### PARTY, THE.
**Tracks:** Not Advised.
■ CD . . . . . . . . . . . . . . . . . . . . MCD 5451
■ MC . . . . . . . . . . . . . . . . . . . . MC 5451
Muse / Nov '91 / New Note / Jazz Horizons / C.M. Distribution.

### PERSONALITY.
**Tracks:** Kittitian carnival / Funky sunday afternoon / Pain / Shotgun / Touch of the bad stuff / He'll fight my battles / All in love is fair / Mayola / Until it's time for you to go / You are the sunshine of my life / Don't go to strangers / Easy walker.
■ CD . . . . . . . . . . . . . . . . . . . . CDBGPD 070
BGP / Mar '93 / Pinnacle.

### SOMETHING IN COMMON (Person, Houston & Ron Carter).
**Tracks:** Blue seven / It thought about you / Mack the knife / Joy Spring / Good morning heartache / Anthropology / Once in a while / Blues for two.

■ LP . . . . . . . . . . . . . . . . . . . . . 600633
Muse / Apr '91 / New Note / Jazz Horizons / C.M. Distribution.
■ CD . . . . . . . . . . . . . . . . . . . . MCD 5376
Muse / Apr '91 / New Note / Jazz Horizons / C.M. Distribution.

### STOLEN SWEETS.
**Tracks:** Not Advised.
■ LP . . . . . . . . . . . . . . . . . . . . . MR 5110
Muse / Apr '81.

### SUSPICIONS.
**Tracks:** Not Advised.
■ LP . . . . . . . . . . . . . . . . . . . . . MR 5199
Muse / '81.

### TALK OF THE TOWN.
**Tracks:** Not Advised.
■ CD . . . . . . . . . . . . . . . . . . . . MCD 5331
■ LP . . . . . . . . . . . . . . . . . . . . . MR 5331
Muse / Sep '92 / New Note / Jazz Horizons / C.M. Distribution.

### VERY PERSONAL.
**Tracks:** Not Advised.
■ LP . . . . . . . . . . . . . . . . . . . . . MR 5231
Muse / Sep '92 / New Note / Jazz Horizons / C.M. Distribution.

### WHY NOT?.
**Tracks:** Why not / As time goes by / Namely you / Joey's blues / Blue gardenia / Deed I do.
■ CD . . . . . . . . . . . . . . . . . . . . MCD 5433
■ MC . . . . . . . . . . . . . . . . . . . . MR 5433
Muse / Jan '92 / New Note / Jazz Horizons / C.M. Distribution.

### WILDFLOWER.
**Tracks:** Not Advised.
■ LP . . . . . . . . . . . . . . . . . . . . . MR 5161
Muse / Sep '92 / New Note / Jazz Horizons / C.M. Distribution.

## Persuaders

### THIN LINE BETWEEN LOVE AND HATE.
**Tracks:** Thin line between love and hate / Let's go down together / Blood brothers / You musta put something in your love / Thanks for loving me / Love gonna pack up / If this is what you call love / Mr. Sunshine / Thigh spy / Can't go no further & do no better.
■ LP . . . . . . . . . . . . . . . . . . . . . K 40370
Atlantic / Sep '72.

## Persuasions

### ACAPPELLA.
**Tracks:** Introduction / Searchin' for my baby / I just can't work no longer / Old man river / Monologue introduction / Don't look back / Whole world is a stage / Up on the roof / Bounce / Since I fell for you / Too late / It's all right.
■ LP . . . . . . . . . . . . . . . . . . . . . STS 1062
Straight / Jun '70.
■ LP . . . . . . . . . . . . . . . . . . . . . ED 296
Edsel / Oct '89.

### CHIRPIN.
**Tracks:** Not Advised.
■ LP . . . . . . . . . . . . . . . . . . . . . K 52057
Elektra / May '77.

### COMIN' AT YA.
**Tracks:** Not Advised.
■ LP . . . . . . . . . . . . . . . . . . . . . FF 093
Flying Fish / Sep '79.

### FREE NELSON.
**Tracks:** Not Advised.
■ MC . . . . . . . . . . . . . . . . . . . . BFC 08
Bruce's Fingers / Oct '93 / Cadillac.

### GOOD NEWS.
**Tracks:** Not Advised.
■ LP . . . . . . . . . . . . . . . . . . . . . ROUNDER 3053
■ MC . . . . . . . . . . . . . . . . . . . . ROUNDER 3053C
Rounder / Aug '88 / Roots Records / C.M. Distribution / Topic Records / A.D.A. Distribution / Direct Distribution.

### LA LA LA LA LA.
**Tracks:** La la la la la / Opportunity.
■ 7" . . . . . . . . . . . . . . . . . . . . . DB 7859
Columbia / Mar '66.

### NO FRILLS.
**Tracks:** You can have her / Under the boardwalk / Sand in my shoes / I was wrong / I woke up in love this morning / I wonder do you love the Lord like I do / Still ain't got no band / Victim / Treasure of love /

Sweet was the wine / What are you doing New Year's Eve / Slip slidin' away.
■ LP . . . . . . . . . . . . . . . . . . . . . ROUNDER 3083
Rounder / Jul '84.
■ LP . . . . . . . . . . . . . . . . . . . . . . . FIEND 46
Demon / Apr '85.
CD . . . . . . . . . . . . . . . . . . . . . . . . CD 3083
MC. . . . . . . . . . . . . . . . . . . . .ROUNDER 3083C
Rounder / Aug '88 / Roots Records / C.M. Distribution / Topic Records / A.D.A. Distribution / Direct Distribution.

### RIGHT AROUND THE CORNER.
Tracks: Not Advised.
CD . . . . . . . . . . . . . . . . . . . . . . . BBCD 9556
MC. . . . . . . . . . . . . . . . . . . . . . . BBMC 9556
Bullseye Blues / Oct '94 / New Note / Topic Records / Direct Distribution.

### STARDUST.
Tracks: Not Advised.
■ LP . . . . . . . . . . . . . . . . . . . . . . CATA 905
Catamount / Aug '87.

### TIME IS RIGHT, THE.
Tracks: Time is right.
■ 12" . . . . . . . . . . . . . . . . . . . . . JTYG 0121
Zoo Experience / Apr '89.

## Peters, Cyndee

### BLACK IS THE COLOUR.
Tracks: Not Advised.
LP . . . . . . . . . . . . . . . . . . . . . . . . OP 7706
Opus 3 / Sep '91 / Quantum Audio Ltd.

## Pettus, Giorge

### GIORGE PETTUS.
Tracks: My night for love / Can you wait / I'm good for you / One track mind / Trouble in paradise / You're perfect / Make it right / I can fix-U-up / One time affair.
■ LP . . . . . . . . . . . . . . . . . . . . . . MCF 3406
■ MC. . . . . . . . . . . . . . . . . . . . . . MCFC 3406
MCA / Nov '87.
■ CD . . . . . . . . . . . . . . . . . . . . . DMCF 3406
MCA / Apr '88.

### MY NIGHT FOR LOVE.
Tracks: My night for love.
■ 12" . . . . . . . . . . . . . . . . . . . . . MCAT 1251
■ 7" . . . . . . . . . . . . . . . . . . . . . . MCA 1251
MCA / Apr '88.

## Phalon

### RISING TO THE TOP.
Tracks: Rising to the top / Don't cha wanna / Ready or not / Dance floor of life / Fall in the groove / Just 'n' time / Jazze's thing / "Go pinto".
CD . . . . . . . . . . . . . . . . . . . . . 7559609662
■ LP . . . . . . . . . . . . . . . . . . . . 7559609661
MC. . . . . . . . . . . . . . . . . . . . . 7559609664
Elektra / Nov '90 / WEA.

## Phase 2

### MYSTERY.
Tracks: Mystery.
■ 12" . . . . . . . . . . . . . . . . . . . . . . QK 007
Quark (USA) / Nov '87.

### REACHIN'.
Tracks: Reachin' / It's a mystery.
■ 12" . . . . . . . . . . . . . . . . . . . . LICT 006 X
■ 12" . . . . . . . . . . . . . . . . . . . . . LICT 006
■ 7" . . . . . . . . . . . . . . . . . . . . . . LIC 006
Republic / Jan '89.

### ROXY.
Tracks: Roxy.
■ 12" . . . . . . . . . . . . . . . . . . . . . CYZ 102
Celluloid (USA) / May '83.

## Philadelphia Five

### BUMP.
Tracks: Bump.
■ 12" . . . . . . . . . . . . . . . . . . . . . . KK 002
K K / Apr '88.

### I AM SHARED.
Tracks: I am shared.
■ 12" . . . . . . . . . . . . . . . . . . . . . . KK 007
K K / Oct '88.

### WATCH OUT (REMIX & ACID RETURN).
Tracks: Watch out (remix & acid return).
■ 12" Remix . . . . . . . . . . . . . . . . . . KK 014
K K / '89.

## Phillinganes, Greg

### BEHIND THE MASK.
Tracks: Behind the mask / Only you.
■ 12" . . . . . . . . . . . . . . . . . . . . . RPST 110
■ 7" . . . . . . . . . . . . . . . . . . . . . . RPS 110
Planet (1) / Mar '85.

### PULSE.
Tracks: Behind the mask / Won't be long now / Playin' with fire / I have dreamed / Come as you are / Lazy Nina / Signals / Countdown to love / Shake it.
■ LP . . . . . . . . . . . . . . . . . . . . . FL 84698
■ MC. . . . . . . . . . . . . . . . . . . . . FK 84698
Planet (1) / Mar '85.
■ LP . . . . . . . . . . . . . . . . . . . . . PL 84698
■ MC. . . . . . . . . . . . . . . . . . . . . PK 84698
RCA / Jan '87.
■ MC. . . . . . . . . . . . . . . . . . . . . NK 90554
■ CD . . . . . . . . . . . . . . . . . . . . . ND 90554
RCA / Jun '91.

### SIGNIFICANT GAINS.
Tracks: Girl talk / Baby I do love you / Takin' it up all night / Forever now / Big man / I don't want to be the one / Maxxed out / Do it all for love / Call.
■ LP . . . . . . . . . . . . . . . . . . . . . K 52299
Asylum / Jul '81.

## Phillips, Esther

### AND I LOVE HIM.
Tracks: And I love him / Shangri-la.
■ 7" . . . . . . . . . . . . . . . . . . . . . AT 4028
Atlantic / '66.

### BAD BAD GIRL.
Tracks: Ring-a-ding doo / I'm a bad bad girl / Deacon moves in / Looking for a man / Hound dog / Cherry wine / Turn the lamps down low / Flesh blood and bones / Last laugh blues / You took my love too fast / Saturday night daddy / Mainliner / Hollerin' and screamin' / Storm / Ramblin' blues / Aged and mellow blues.
■ LP . . . . . . . . . . . . . . . . . . . . . CRB 1100
MC. . . . . . . . . . . . . . . . . . . . . . TCCRB 1100
Charly R&B / Jul '85 / Charly.
CD . . . . . . . . . . . . . . . . . . . . CDCHARLY 47
Charly R&B / Jan '87 / Charly.

### BETTER BEWARE.
Tracks: Looking for a man / Other lips / Other arms / Deacon moves in / I'm a bad, bad girl / Crying and singing the blues / Ring-a-ding doo / Hold me / Better beware / Aged and mellow blues / Ramblin' blues / Storm / Hollerin' and screamin' / Saturday night daddy / Mainliner / You took my love too fast / Last laugh blues / Flesh, blood and bones / Turn the lamps down low / Cherry wine / Hound dog.
■ CD . . . . . . . . . . . . . . . . . CDCHARLY 248
Charly / Oct '90.

### CAPRICORN PRINCESS.
Tracks: Magic's in the air / I haven't got anything better to do / Boy I really tried one on / Candy / Beautiful friendship / Higher and higher / All the way down / Dream.
■ LP . . . . . . . . . . . . . . . . . . . . . . KU 31
Kudu / Feb '77.

### COMPLETE SAVOY RECORDINGS.
Tracks: Not Advised.
■ Double LP . . . . . . . . . . . . . . . . SJL 2258
Savoy Jazz (USA) / Jan '87.

### CONFESSIN' THE BLUES.
Tracks: I'm gettin' 'long alright / I wonder / Confessin' the blues / Romance in the dark / C.C. rider / Cherry red / In the evening / I love Paris / It could happen to you / Bye bye blackbird / Blow top blues / Jelly jelly blues / Long John blues.
■ LP . . . . . . . . . . . . . . . . . . . . . K 50521
Atlantic / Feb '79.
CD . . . . . . . . . . . . . . . . . . . . . 7567906702
Atlantic / Jul '93 / WEA.

### CONFESSIN' THE BLUES.
Tracks: Not Advised.
CD . . . . . . . . . . . . . . . . . . . . . RSACD 807
Sequel / Oct '94 / Total / BMG.

### ESTHER PHILLIPS.
Tracks: What a difference a day made / Home is where the hatred is / I feel the same / I've never found a man (to love me like you do) / Boy I really tried one on / One night affair / From a whisper to a scream / Justified / Living alone / Candy.
■ LP . . . . . . . . . . . . . . . . . . . . . SKU 001
Kudu / Apr '78.

### ESTHER PHILLIPS SINGS.
Tracks: It's alright with me / Shadow of your smile / Crazy he calls me / He touched me / Taste of honey / Let there be love / You can't go home again / Just say goodbye / I could have told you so / Everytime we say goodbye / As tears go by / Party's over.
■ LP . . . . . . . . . . . . . . . . . . . . . 587 010
Atlanta / Aug '66.

### FOR ALL WE KNOW.
Tracks: For all we know / Fever.
■ 7" . . . . . . . . . . . . . . . . . . . . . .KUDU 929
Kudu / Feb '76.

### FROM A WHISPER TO A SCREAM.
Tracks: Home is where the hatred is / From a whisper to a scream / To lay down beside you / That's alright with me / Til my back ain't got no bone / Sweet touch of love / Baby, I'm for real / Your love is so doggone good / Scarred knees.
■ LP . . . . . . . . . . . . . . . . . . . . . KUL 2
Creed Taylor / Jul '72.

### GOOD BLACK IS HARD TO CRACK.
Tracks: Not Advised.
■ LP . . . . . . . . . . . . . . . . . . . . . SRM 14005
Mercury / Apr '81.

### HERE'S ESTHER-ARE YOU READY.
Tracks: Mr. Melody / Philadelphia freedom / I hope you'll be very unhappy without me / Love makes a woman / Our day will come / Bedtime stories / Ooo oop oo oop / I'll close my eyes.
■ LP . . . . . . . . . . . . . . . . . . . . . .9100 065
Mercury / Sep '79.

### I COULD HAVE TOLD YOU.
Tracks: I could have told you / Just say goodbye.
■ 7" . . . . . . . . . . . . . . . . . . . . . AT 4077
Atlantic / '65.

### I PAID MY DUES.
Tracks: Better beware / Hold me / Somebody new / Bring my lovin' back to me / I paid my dues / Sweet lips / Love oh love / I'll be there (at your beck and call) / Street lights / Heart to heart / Tell him that I need him / Summertime / Cryin' blues / Other lips, other arms / Don't make a fool out of me / Cryin' & singin' the blues.
CD . . . . . . . . . . . . . . . . . . . . . SING 81156
■ LP . . . . . . . . . . . . . . . . . . . .SING 1156
MC. . . . . . . . . . . . . . . . . . . . . SING 41156
Sing / May '88 / Charly / Cadillac.

### I'M SORRY.
Tracks: I'm sorry / Cheater man.
7" . . . . . . . . . . . . . . . . . . . . . .584126
Atlantic / Aug '67 / WEA.

### LET ME KNOW WHEN IT'S OVER.
Tracks: Let me know when it's over / I saw me.
■ 7" . . . . . . . . . . . . . . . . . . . . . AT 4048
Atlantic / Oct '65.

### WAY TO SAY GOODBYE, A.
Tracks: It's all in the game / Mama said / Going in circles / Nowhere to run / We are through / Fa fa fa fa fa (sad song) / Mr. Bojangles / Shake this off / Way to say goodbye.
CD . . . . . . . . . . . . . . . . . . . . . .MCD 5302
MC. . . . . . . . . . . . . . . . . . . . . .MRC 5302
Muse / Feb '87 / New Note / Jazz Horizons / C.M. Distribution.
LP . . . . . . . . . . . . . . . . . . . . . .MR 5302
Muse / Sep '92 / New Note / Jazz Horizons / C.M. Distribution.

### WHAT A DIFFERENCE A DAY MADE.
Tracks: One night affair / What a difference a day made / Hurtin' house / Oh papa / Turn around, look at me.
■ LP . . . . . . . . . . . . . . . . . . . . . .CTI 9023
MC. . . . . . . . . . . . . . . . . . . . . . CTK 9523
CTI (Musidisc France) / Jul '85.
■ CD . . . . . . . . . . . . . . . . . . . . . 4504652
CBS / '88.

### WHAT A DIFFERENCE A DAY MADE.
Tracks: What a difference a day made.
■ 7" . . . . . . . . . . . . . . . . . . . . . KUDU 925
Kudu / Oct '75.

## Phillips, Steve

### CRYIN' OVER YOU.
Tracks: Cryin' over you.
■ 12" . . . . . . . . . . . . . . . . . . . . . 12ZAM 007
■ 7" . . . . . . . . . . . . . . . . . . . . . .7ZAM 007
RMO / Mar '91.

## Phillips, West

### COMFORT ZONE.
Tracks: Comfort zone.
■ 12″. . . . . . . . . . . . . . . . . . . . . GWT 01
Genial Wave / Oct '92.

### I'M JUST A SUCKER FOR A PRETTY FACE.
Tracks: I'm just a sucker for a pretty face.
■ 12″. . . . . . . . . . . . . . . . . . . . BUBT 401
Trans Q / Mar '84.

### LOOKING FOR THE SAME THING.
Tracks: Looking for the same thing / Another pretty face.
■ 12″. . . . . . . . . . . . . . . . . . . . 12 PO 5
Ichiban / Nov '87.

### TELL ME.
Tracks: Tell me.
■ 12″. . . . . . . . . . . . . . . . . . . . KOOLT 7
Kool Kat / Aug '87.

## Philly Cream

### COWBOYS TO GIRLS.
Tracks: Cowboys to girls / No time like now.
■ 12″. . . . . . . . . . . . . . . . . . WMTL 101
■ 7″. . . . . . . . . . . . . . . . . . . WMT 101
W.M.O.T.(USA) / Feb '81.

### JAMMIN' AT THE DISCO.
Tracks: Jammin' at the disco / Soul man.
■ 12″. . . . . . . . . . . . . . . . . . XFTC 173
■ 7″. . . . . . . . . . . . . . . . . . . FTC 173
Fantasy / Apr '79.

### MOTOWN REVUE.
Tracks: Motown revue / Join the army.
■ 12″. . . . . . . . . . . . . . . . . . .12FTC 180
Fantasy / Jul '79.

### NO TIME LIKE NOW.
Tracks: No time like now / What cha puttin' down / Slow down / Cowboys to girls / Fun fun fun / Devil / So much to talk about / Who do you do.
■ LP. . . . . . . . . . . . . . . . . . WMLP 5001
W.M.O.T.(USA) / Dec '80.

### NO TIME LIKE NOW.
Tracks: No time like now / Who do.
■ 12″. . . . . . . . . . . . . . . . . . .CABL 504
■ 7″. . . . . . . . . . . . . . . . . . . .CAB 504
Calibre / Jul '80.

### PHILLY CREAM.
Tracks: Sly hi / Motown review / Doin' it to death / Jammin' at the disco / Soul man / Join the army.
■ LP. . . . . . . . . . . . . . . . . . . . FT 559
Fantasy / '79.

## Philly Devotions

### I JUST CAN'T SAY GOODBYE.
Tracks: I just can't say goodbye (2 pts).
■ 7″. . . . . . . . . . . . . . . . . . . CBS 3042
CBS / Feb '75.

## Pic & Bill

### GIVIN' IT TO YOU.
Tracks: Don't leave me / Moments like these / Soul of a man / You walk so fine / Just a tear / How many times / Talk about love / Yesterday / Talking 'bout nobody but my baby / When something is wrong with my baby / It's not you / This is my story / Sad world without you / Gonna give it to you / All I want is you / Love is a many splendoured thing.
■ LP. . . . . . . . . . . . . . . . . . . CRB 1172
Charly R&B / Feb '88.

### TAKING UP THE SLACK.
Tracks: Not Advised.
CD. . . . . . . . . . . . . . . . . . . BAN 4109CD
LP. . . . . . . . . . . . . . . . . . . . BAN 4109
MC. . . . . . . . . . . . . . . . . . . BAN 4109MC
Backs / Sep '91 / RTM / Pinnacle.

## Pickett, Lenny

### LENNY PICKETT & THE BORNEO HORNS (Pickett, Lenny & The Borneo Horns).
Tracks: Dance music for Borneo Horns (1-5) / Solo for saxaphone / Septer / Dance suite / Landscape.
■ LP. . . . . . . . . . . . . . . . . . . HNBL 1321
Hannibal / Jul '87.
CD. . . . . . . . . . . . . . . . . . . HNCD 1321
MC. . . . . . . . . . . . . . . . . . . HNBC 1321

Hannibal / May '89 / Vital Distribution / A.D.A. Distribution / Topic Records / Direct Distribution.

## Pickett, Wilson

The Wicked Pickett served period as leader of Detroit's Falcons, before launching solo career in 1963. Breakthrough came when he teamed up with Stax's Steve Cropper; resultant *In The Midnight Hour* paved way for several years of hits, including *634-5789* and a typical cover of *Hey Jude*. Despite recording for RCA, Motown and EMI in ensuing years, Pickett never reclaimed limelight. Increasingly bitter and self-destructive, he began 12-month sentence for drunk driving in January '94.

### 634-5789.
Tracks: 634-5789 / That's a man's way.
■ 7″. . . . . . . . . . . . . . . . . . . . AT 4072
Atlantic / Mar '66.

### AMERICAN SOUL MAN.
Tracks: Thing called love / When your heart speaks / Love never let me down / Man of value / (I wanna) make love to you / In the midnight hour / Don't turn away / Just let her know / Can't stop now.
■ LP. . . . . . . . . . . . . . . . . . . ZL 72615
■ MC. . . . . . . . . . . . . . . . . . . ZK 72615
Motown / Oct '87.

### AMERICAN SOUL MAN.
Tracks: Thing called love / When your heart speaks / Love never let me down / Man of value / (I wanna) make love to you / In the midnight hour / Don't turn away / Just let her know / Can't stop now.
CD. . . . . . . . . . . . . . . . . . . .550178-2
MC. . . . . . . . . . . . . . . . . . . .550178-4
Spectrum (1) / Mar '94 / PolyGram.

### BEST OF WILSON PICKETT.
Tracks: In the midnight hour / 634 5789 / I found a love / Mustang Sally / ninety nine and a half (won't do) / Everybody needs somebody to love / Don't fight it / I'm a midnight mover / Funky Broadway / Soul dance number three / I'm in love / Land of a thousand dances.
■ LP. . . . . . . . . . . . . . . . . . . .588092
Atlantic / Nov '69.
■ LP. . . . . . . . . . . . . . . . . . 780 170-1
■ MC. . . . . . . . . . . . . . . . . . 780 170-4
Atlantic / Apr '82.
CD. . . . . . . . . . . . . . . . . . . 781 737-2
Atlantic / Jul '87 / WEA.
CD. . . . . . . . . . . . . . . . . . .756781737-2
WEA / Mar '93 / WEA.

### BILLY THE KID.
Tracks: Billy the kid / I don't want no part-time love.
■ 7″. . . . . . . . . . . . . . . . . . . HLU 10146
London-American / Jul '67.

### COLLECTION: WILSON PICKETT.
Tracks: Not Advised.
■ CD. . . . . . . . . . . . . . . . . . CCSCD 338
■ MC. . . . . . . . . . . . . . . . . . CCSMC 338
Castle Collector Series / Jun '92.

### DON'T FIGHT IT.
Tracks: Don't fight it / It's all over.
■ 7″. . . . . . . . . . . . . . . . . . . . AT 4052
Atlantic / Nov '65.

### DON'T KNOW MY LOVE.
Tracks: Fire and water / Mighty long way / Covering the same old ground / Don't knock my love / Call my name, I'll be there / Hot love / Not enough to satisfy / You can't judge a book by its cover / Pledging my love / Mama told me not to come / Woman let me down home.
■ LP. . . . . . . . . . . . . . . . . . . K 40319
Atlantic / Apr '72.

### DON'T KNOW MY LOVE.
Tracks: Don't know my love.
■ 7″. . . . . . . . . . . . . . . . . . . .2091 124
Atlantic / Jul '71.

### DON'T UNDERESTIMATE THE POWER OF LOVE.
Tracks: Don't underestimate the power of love / Ain't gonna give you no more / I want you (On 12″ only).
■ 12″. . . . . . . . . . . . . . . . . . 12EA 120
■ 7″. . . . . . . . . . . . . . . . . . . . EA 120
EMI-America / Feb '81.

### ENGINE NUMBER 9.
Tracks: Run Joey run / Help the needy / Come right here / Bumble bee / Don't let the green grass fool you / Get me back on time / Engine number 9 / Days go by / International playboy / Ain't no doubt about it.
■ LP. . . . . . . . . . . . . . . . . . . .2400 026
Atlantic / Apr '71.

### EVERYBODY NEEDS SOMEBODY TO LOVE.
Tracks: Everybody needs somebody to love / Nothing you can do.
■ 7″. . . . . . . . . . . . . . . . . . . .584101
Atlantic / Feb '67.

### EXCITING WILSON PICKETT, THE.
Tracks: Not Advised.
■ LP. . . . . . . . . . . . . . . . . . . SD8129
Atlantic / Jun '88.

### FIRE AND WATER.
Tracks: Fire and water / Don't let the green grass fool you.
■ 7″. . . . . . . . . . . . . . . . . . . 2091086
Atlantic / Apr '71.

### FUNKY BROADWAY.
Tracks: Funky broadway.
■ 7″. . . . . . . . . . . . . . . . . . . 584 130
Atlantic / Sep '67.

### GREATEST HITS: WILSON PICKETT.
Tracks: In the midnight hour / I found a love / 634-5789 / If you need me / Everybody needs somebody to love / It's too late / Ninety nine and a half (won't do) / Funky broadway / Soul dance number three / Land of a thousand dances / Don't let the green grass fool you / Sugar sugar / Get me back on time / I'm a midnight mover / Man and a half / Mama told me not to come / She's looking good / I'm in love / Don't knock my love - part 1 / Hey Jude / I found a true love / Mustang Sally / You keep me hangin' on.
■ LP. . . . . . . . . . . . . . . . . . . K 60038
Atlantic.

### GROOVE CITY.
Tracks: Groove city / Love of my life.
■ 7″. . . . . . . . . . . . . . . . . . . EA 12104
EMI-America / Dec '79.

### HEART AND SOUL.
Tracks: Not Advised.
■ CD. . . . . . . . . . . . . . . . . . KNCD 12062
■ MC. . . . . . . . . . . . . . . . . . KNMC 12062
Knight / Jul '91.

### HEY JUDE.
Tracks: Hey Jude.
■ 7″. . . . . . . . . . . . . . . . . . . 584 236
Atlantic / Jan '69.

### HEY JUDE.
Tracks: Save me / Hey Jude / Back in your arms / Toe hold / Night owl / My own style of loving / Man and a half / Sit down and talk this over / Search your heart / Born to be wild / People make the world.
■ LP. . . . . . . . . . . . . . . . . . . 588 170
Atlantic / Apr '69.

### I WANT YOU.
Tracks: Groove city / You are the love of my life.
■ LP. . . . . . . . . . . . . . . . . . . AML 3007
EMI-America / Jan '80.

### I'M A MIDNIGHT MOVER.
Tracks: I'm a midnight mover.
■ 7″. . . . . . . . . . . . . . . . . . . 584 203
Atlantic / Sep '68.

### I'M IN LOVE.
Tracks: Jealous love / Stagger Lee / That kind of love / I'm in love / Hello sunshine / Don't cry no more / We've got to have love / Bring it on home / She is looking good / I've come a long way.
■ LP. . . . . . . . . . . . . . . . . . . 588 107
Atlantic / Apr '68.

### IF YOU NEED ME.
Tracks: If you need me / I'm gonna love you.
■ 7″. . . . . . . . . . . . . . . . . . . .PT 319
President / Apr '71.

### IN THE MIDNIGHT HOUR.
Tracks: In the midnight hour / I'm not tired.
■ 7″. . . . . . . . . . . . . . . . . . . AT 4036
Atlantic / Sep '65.

### IN THE MIDNIGHT HOUR.
Tracks: In the midnight hour / In the midnight hour (dub) (on 12″ only).
■ 7″. . . . . . . . . . . . . . . . . . . .YZ 169
WEA / '87.
■ 12″. . . . . . . . . . . . . . . . . . ZT 41584
■ 7″. . . . . . . . . . . . . . . . . . . ZB 41583
Motown / Nov '87.

### IN THE MIDNIGHT HOUR (OLD GOLD).
Tracks: In the midnight hour / 634-5789.
■ 7″. . . . . . . . . . . . . . . . . . .OG 9497
Old Gold / Feb '85.

## LAND OF 1000 DANCES.
Tracks: Land of a thousand dances.
■ 7" . . . . . . . . . . . . . . . . . . . . . . 584 039
Atlantic / Sep '66.

## LAND OF 1000 DANCES (Wilson Pickett/ Sam & Dave).
Tracks: Land of a thousand dances / In the midnight hour / You don't know like I know / Soul man.
■ 7" . . . . . . . . . . . . . . . . . . . . . . ATM 7
Atlantic / Apr '80.

## MAN AND A HALF, A.
Tracks: Not Advised.
CD . . . . . . . . . . . . . . . . . . . . . 8122702872
WEA / Jul '93 / WEA.

## MIDNIGHT MOVER.
Tracks: It's a groove / Remember I been good to you / I'm gonna cry / Deborah / I found a true love / Down by the sea / Trust me / Midnight mover / Let's get an understanding / For better or worse.
■ LP . . . . . . . . . . . . . . . . . . . . . 588 111
Atlantic / Oct '68.

## MUSTANG SALLY.
Tracks: Mustang Sally.
■ 7" . . . . . . . . . . . . . . . . . . . . . . 584 066
Atlantic / Dec '66.

## MY HEART BELONGS TO YOU.
Tracks: My heart belongs to you / Let me be your boy.
■ 7" . . . . . . . . . . . . . . . . . . MGM 1286
MGM (EMI) / '64.

## NEW ORLEANS.
Tracks: New Orleans / Soul dance.
■ 7" . . . . . . . . . . . . . . . . . . . . . 584107
Atlantic / May '67.

## RIGHT ON.
Tracks: Groovy little woman / Funky way / Sugar, sugar / Sweet inspiration / This old town / You keep me hangin' on / Lord pity us all / It's still good / Woman likes to hear that / She said yes / Hey Joe / Steal away.
■ LP . . . . . . . . . . . . . . . . . . . . . 2465 002
Atlantic / Jul '70.

## RIGHT TRACK, THE.
Tracks: Back on the right track / If you can't beat em' join em' / Help me be without / I ain't gonna give you no more / Maybe this time / Don't underestimate the power of love / It's you.
■ LP . . . . . . . . . . . . . . . . . . . . . AML 3016
EMI-America / Mar '81.

## SECONDS (Pickett, Wilson & Jackie Moore).
Tracks: Second / Second (inst).
■ 12" . . . . . . . . . . . . . . . . . . . . . NYT 101
■ 7" . . . . . . . . . . . . . . . . . . . . . NY 101
New York 42 / Feb '88.

## SHAMELESS.
Tracks: Shameless / Superstar.
■ 7" . . . . . . . . . . . . . . . . . . . . . EA 107
EMI-America / Apr '80.

## SOUND OF WILSON PICKETT.
Tracks: Soul dance no. 3 / Funky Broadway / I need a lot of love / I found a love / You can't stand alone / Mojo mamma / I found the one / Something within me / I'm sorry about that / Love is a beautiful thing.
■ LP . . . . . . . . . . . . . . . . . . . . . 588 080
Atlantic / Nov '67.

## VERY BEST OF WILSON PICKETT, THE.
Tracks: Not Advised.
CD . . . . . . . . . . . . . . . . . . . . . .812271212-2
Atlantic / Jun '93 / WEA.

## WHO TURNED YOU ON.
Tracks: Who turned you on / Dance you down.
■ 7" . . . . . . . . . . . . . . . . . . . . . K 11180
Atlantic / Aug '78.

### Pieces Of A Dream

## 'BOUT DAT TIME.
Tracks: 'Bout dat time / What can I do / Can't be alone / For you / Pick up the pieces / Lonely hearts of love / Take me tonight / Kicking / Surrender.
■ MC . . . . . . . . . . . . . . . . . . . TCMTL 1048
■ LP . . . . . . . . . . . . . . . . . . . . MTL 1048
EMI-Manhattan / Aug '89.

## JOYRIDE.
Tracks: Save some time for me / Say la la / I can give you want you want / Joy ride / Love of my life / Careless whisper / Outside in / Winning streak / Sunshine.

## MAKES YOU WANNA.
Tracks: Ain't my love enough / We belong to each other / Makes you wanna / Rising to the top / Round midnight / Mellow magic / Feeling for you / Holding back the years.
■ MC . . . . . . . . . . . . . . . . . . . TCMTL 1030
■ CD . . . . . . . . . . . . . . . . . . CDMTL 1030
■ LP . . . . . . . . . . . . . . . . . . . . MTL 1030
EMI-Manhattan / Jul '88.

## PIECES OF A DREAM.
Tracks: All about love / Easy road home / Lovers / Body magic / Warm weather / Steady glide / Touch me in the spring / Pieces of a dream.
■ LP . . . . . . . . . . . . . . . . . . . . . K 52320
Elektra / Dec '81.
CD . . . . . . . . . . . . . . . . . . . . . 71020
Discovery (USA) / Nov '94 / New Note.

## RISING TO THE TOP.
Tracks: Rising to the top / Ain't my love enough / Rising to the top (U.K. remix) (12" only.) / Rising to the top (radio version) (12" only.) / Ain't my love enough (12" version) (12" only.).
■ 12" . . . . . . . . . . . . . . . . . . .12MT 54
■ 7" . . . . . . . . . . . . . . . . . . . . . MT 54
EMI-Manhattan / Sep '88.

## SAY LA LA.
Tracks: Say la la / Outside in.
■ 12" . . . . . . . . . . . . . . . . . . .12MT 12
■ 7" . . . . . . . . . . . . . . . . . . . . . MT 12
EMI-Manhattan / Jul '86.

## WARM WEATHER.
Tracks: Warm weather / Body magic.
■ 7" . . . . . . . . . . . . . . . . . . . . . K 12569
Elektra / Nov '81.

## WARM WEATHER.
Tracks: Warm weather / Mount Airey groove.
■ 12" . . . . . . . . . . . . . . . . . . . K 13201T
■ 7" . . . . . . . . . . . . . . . . . . . . . K 13201
Elektra / Sep '82.

## WE ARE ONE.
Tracks: Don't be sad / Please don't do this to me / For Ramsey / You know I want you / Mt airy groove / We are one / When you are here with me / Pop rock / Yo frat.
CD . . . . . . . . . . . . . . . . . . . . . 71021
Discovery (USA) / Nov '94 / New Note.

### Pinky

## LOOKING FOR A LOVE.
Tracks: Looking for a love.
■ 12" . . . . . . . . . . . . . . . . . . . .RUFF 12
1st Bass / Sep '91.

## LOOKING FOR LOVE.
Tracks: Looking for love.
■ 12" . . . . . . . . . . . . . . . . . . . .RUF 012
Big One Records / Aug '91.

### Pinnock, Delroy

## I DON'T KNOW WHY.
Tracks: I don't know why / No dub.
■ 7" . . . . . . . . . . . . . . . . . . . . . SG 7
Solid Groove / Nov '81.

### Pips

## AT LAST MY SEARCH IS OVER.
Tracks: At last my search is over / Tomorrow child.
■ 7" . . . . . . . . . . . . . . . . . . . .CAN 118
Casablanca / Apr '78.

## AT LAST..THE PIPS.
Tracks: At last my search is over / If I could bring back yesterday / Midnight flight to your love / Happiness / Uncle James / Tomorrow child.
■ LP . . . . . . . . . . . . . . . . . . . . CAL 2022
Casablanca / Jan '78.

## BABY I'M YOUR FOOL.
Tracks: Baby I'm your fool / Uncle James.
■ 7" . . . . . . . . . . . . . . . . . . . .CAN 130
Casablanca / Sep '78.

## CALLIN'.
Tracks: Baby I'm your fool / Callin' / Mr. Blue / Lights of the city / Anything / I don't have the heart / Don't stop / I think ought to.
■ LP . . . . . . . . . . . . . . . . . . . . CAL 2031
Casablanca / Oct '78.

## Platinum Hook

## GOTTA FIND A WOMAN.
Tracks: Gotta find a woman / Hooked for life.
■ 7" . . . . . . . . . . . . . . . . . . .TMG 1128
Motown / Nov '78.

## IT'S TIME.
Tracks: Give me time to say / Time / Be not a long time / Play with you / One more day / It's for you / Love makes me feel good.
■ LP . . . . . . . . . . . . . . . . . . .STML 12110
Motown / '79.

## STANDING ON THE VERGE OF GETTING IT ON.
Tracks: Standing on the verge of getting it on.
■ 7" . . . . . . . . . . . . . . . . . . .TMG 1115
Motown / Sep '78.

## Platters

## 10TH ANNIVERSARY ALBUM.
Tracks: Little things mean a lot / Love me tender / Volare / Twist / Don't be cruel / Anniversary song / Great pretender / Tammy / Moulin Rouge / Rock around the clock.
■ LP . . . . . . . . . . . . . . . . . . . .WL 1174
Wing / Feb '68.

## 16 GREATEST HITS.
Tracks: Not Advised.
CD . . . . . . . . . . . . . . . . . . . . .CD 1011
Gusto (USA) / '88.

## 18 ORIGINAL HITS: PLATTERS.
Tracks: Not Advised.
■ LP . . . . . . . . . . . . . . . . . . . .K 5002
King (USA) / Mar '88.

## 20 CLASSIC HITS: PLATTERS.
Tracks: Not Advised.
■ LP . . . . . . . . . . . . . . . . . . . .9100 049
Mercury / Apr '78.

## 20 GOLDEN PIECES: PLATTERS.
Tracks: Only you / Hey now / I need you all the time / Maggie doesn't work here anymore / You made me cry / Tell the world / Voo vee ah vee / Give thanks / Shake it up mambo / Love all night / I believe / World is not my home / Crying in the chapel / My prayer / Put your hand in the hand / How great Thou art / Loving you / He's my friend / Heading home / Sweet inspiration.
■ LP . . . . . . . . . . . . . . . . . . . . BDL 2037
Bulldog Records / Feb '84.

## 20 GREATEST HITS: PLATTERS.
Tracks: Not Advised.
CD . . . . . . . . . . . . . . . . . . . .SPEC 85014
Spectrum (CD) / Dec '88 / M.S.D.
■ LP . . . . . . . . . . . . . . . . . . MA 101285
■ MC . . . . . . . . . . . . . . . . . MAMC 101285
Masters (Holland) / Dec '88.

## 20 GREATEST HITS: PLATTERS.
Tracks: My prayer / Smoke gets in your eyes / Great pretender / Twilight time / (You've got) the magic touch / Only you / Harbour lights / I'm sorry / If I had you / How beautiful our love is / With this ring / I love you a thousand times / Red sails in the sunset / Washed ashore (on a lonely island in the sun) / Sweet sweet lovin' / Doesn't it ring a bell / Unchained melody / Devri / One in million / Pledging my love.
CD . . . . . . . . . . . . . . . . . . . . . CD 35
Bescol / May '87 / C.M. Distribution.

## 6 TRACK HITS.
Tracks: Great pretender / Only you / Smoke gets in your eyes / I'm sorry / Twilight time / My prayer.
■ EP . . . . . . . . . . . . . . . . . . . . 7SR 5006
■ MC . . . . . . . . . . . . . . . . . . . 7SC 5006
Scoop 33 / Sep '83.

## AUDIO ARCHIVE.
Tracks: Great pretender / Smoke gets in your eyes / Magic touch / Only you / Twilight time / Wonder of you / I get the sweetest feeling / I'm sorry / I love you 1000 times / Red sails in the sunset / Sweet sweet lovin' / Delilah / Harbour lights / My prayer / Washed ashore / Heaven on earth / I love you yes I do / All my love belongs to you / More I see you / Sayonara.
CD . . . . . . . . . . . . . . . . . . . . .CDAA 007
MC . . . . . . . . . . . . . . . . . . . . .MCAA 007
Tring / Jan '92 / Prism Leisure PLC / Midland Records.

## BEST OF THE PLATTERS.
Tracks: My prayer / Smoke gets in your eyes / Sweet sweet love / Red sails in the sunset / Only you / Harbour lights / Unchained melody / Magic touch.
■ CD . . . . . . . . . . . . . . . . . . . .NCD 5147

■ DELETED

■ LP . . . . . . . . . . . . . . . . . . . . . NE 1380
■ MC. . . . . . . . . . . . . . . . . . . . . . CE 2380
K-Tel / Oct '87.

## DANCING TO THE MUSIC OF LOVE.
**Tracks:** Dancing to the music of love / Full heart and empty arms.
■ 7" . . . . . . . . . . . . . . . . . . . . . 6006 488
Philips / Oct '75.

## EARLY YEARS, THE.
**Tracks:** Only you / Hey now / I need you all the time / Maggie doesn't work here anymore / You made me cry / Tell the world / Voo vee ah vee / Give thanks / Shake it up mambo / Love all night.
■ LP . . . . . . . . . . . . . . . . . . . . . BDL 1036
Bulldog Records / Jul '82.

## ENCHANTED.
**Tracks:** Great pretender / Enchanted / You'll never never know / Little things mean a lot / I'll never smile again / (You got) The magic touch / Sixteen tons / I'm sorry / September song / Where / You're making a mistake / My dream / Trees / Winner takes all.
CD. . . . . . . . . . . . . . . . . . . . . . . 5500922
MC. . . . . . . . . . . . . . . . . . . . . . . 5500924
Spectrum (1) / Oct '93 / PolyGram.

## ENCORE OF GOLDEN HITS.
**Tracks:** Great pretender / Twilight time / Smoke gets in your eyes / Magic touch / Enchanted / My prayer / Only you / Remember when / Heaven on earth / I'm sorry / You'll never never know / It isn't right.
■ LP . . . . . . . . . . . . . . . . . . . . . 6463 062
MC. . . . . . . . . . . . . . . . . . . . . . . 7145 062
Mercury / Oct '80 / PolyGram.

## FOUR PLATTERS AND ONE LOVELY DISH.
**Tracks:** Bark, battle and ball / I wanna / Why should I / Only you (and you alone) / Great pretender / I'm just a dancing partner / Winner take all / (You've got) the magic touch / My prayer / Someone to watch over me / I'm sorry / At your beck and call / Heaven on earth / Bewitched, bothered and bewildered / On my word of honor / Glory of love / Have mercy / Remember when / You'll never, never know / One in a million / I give you my word / It isn't right / You've changed / He's mine / I'll get by / I don't know why / Heart of stone / I'd climb the highest mountain / Temptation / In the still of the night / September in the rain / Wagon wheels / You can depend on me / Take me in your arms / You're making a mistake / My dream / Lie low / Darktown strutter's ball / Mean to me / You are too beautiful / No power on earth / I'm gonna sit right down and write myself a letter / Time and tide / Love you, funny thing / In the middle of nowhere / When you return / Let's start all over again / Oh promise me / Don't forget / Only because / Sweet sixteen / Mystery of you / Indif'rent / Sixteen tons / Goodnight sweetheart, it's time to go / My serenade / Try a little tenderness / My old flame / Sleepy time gal / Don't blame me / Wish me love / Helpless / I wish / No matter what you are / Twilight time (1) / Twilight time (2) / That old feeling / I'll take you home again Kathleen / It's raining outside / For the first time / Whispering wind / But not like you / Out of my mind / Don't let go / You don't say / Are you sincere / If I didn't care / Smoke gets in your eyes / Thanks for the memory / I can't get started / Somebody loves me / My blue heaven / Love in bloom / Prisoner of love / Until the real thing comes along / I'll never smile again / Tisket, a tasket / Hula hop / Wish it were me / Enchanted / Where / Love of a lifetime / Sound and the fury / To each his own / Harbor lights / (By the) sleepy lagoon / By the river Saintie Marie / Rainbow on the river / Sad river / Ebb tide / Reflections in the water / My secret / What does it matter / Whispering grass / I'll be with you in apple blossom time / Lullaby of the leaves / Jeannine / Tumbling tumbleweeds / Trees / Orchids in the moonlight / Little white gardenia / Honeysuckle rose / Life is just a bowl of cherries / When you wore a tulip (& I wore a big red rose) / Roses of picardy / Movin' in / One love / Immortal love / Love, your magic spell is everywhere / Love is just around the corner / Love me or leave me / It's love, love, love / Let's fall in love / Advertise it / Who wouldn't love you / Masquerade is over / Nearness of you / You'll never know / It's magic / I love you truly / Love is / Love is the sweetest thing / Love is a many splendoured thing / Don't let me fall in love / True lover / Rear view mirror / I miss you so / I just got rid of a heartache / Reaching for a star / All the things you are / Song for the lonely / Say a prayer / How will I know / Keep me in love / If only you knew / Summertime / Embraceable you / People will say we're in love / Poor butterfly / Stormy weather / Every little movement / More than you know / September song / That old black magic / My heart belongs to daddy / Sometimes I'm happy / But not for me / Heartbreak / Memories / Moon over Miami / On the top of my mind / In a little Spanish town / Shine on harvest moon / Oh, how I miss you tonight / I'll see you in my dreams / Moonlight memories / Moonlight and roses / My reverie / Full moon and empty arms / Once in a while / Sentimental journey / It might as well be spring / But beautiful / I only have eyes for you / Pennies from heaven / Singin' in the rain / Blues in the night / As time goes by / My romance / Moonlight and shadows / Sweet Leilani / Stay as sweet as you are / Here comes heaven again / Viva jujuy / Cuando calienta el sol / Maria Elena / Solamente tu / Siboney / Amor / Aquellos ojos verdes / Aquarela do Brazil / Tu dolce voz / La hora del crepusculo / Besame mucho / Malaguena salerosa / Strangers / Winter wonderland / White Christmas / Silent night / Santa Claus is comin' to town / I'll be home for Christmas / For Auld Lang Syne / Rudolph, the red nosed reindeer / All I want for Christmas is my two front teeth / Come home for Christmas / Jingle bell rock / Jingle bells jingle / Blue Christmas / Christmas time / Sincerely / P.S. I love you / Hut sut song / Day-o / Mississippi mud / False hearted lover / Michael, row the boat ashore / Crying in the chapel / Java jive / Three coins in the fountain / Way down yonder in New Orleans / Three bells / Song from Moulin Rouge / Little things mean a lot / Rock around the clock / Don't be cruel / Tammy / Volare / Mack the knife / Theme from A Summer Place / Exodus song / Twist / Love me tender / Anniversary song / Gypsy / When I fall in love / Big forget / Soothe me / Easy street / It could happen to you / Blues serenade / These foolish things / Somewhere along the way / Lover / House of the rising sun / Hard hearted Hannah (the vamp of Savannah).
CD. . . . . . . . . . . . . . . . . . . . . . . BCD 15741
Bear Family / Jan '94 / Rollercoaster Records / Swift / Direct Distribution / Topic Records.

## GOLDEN HIT COLLECTION.
**Tracks:** Washed ashore (on a lonely island in the sun) / Lovely / If I had a love / I'll be home / I'm sorry / Harbour lights / Twilight time / I love you because / Heaven on earth / Great pretender / If I had you / I love you a thousand times.
MC Set . . . . . . . . . . . . . . . . . . . DTO 10003
Ditto / Jul '82 / Pickwick.

## GOLDEN HITS COLLECTION.
**Tracks:** Not Advised.
CD. . . . . . . . . . . . . . . . . . . . . . . PWK 071
Pickwick / Sep '88 / Pickwick.
MC. . . . . . . . . . . . . . . . . . . . . . . HSC 3405
Hallmark / Sep '88 / Pickwick.

## GOLDEN HITS: PLATTERS.
**Tracks:** Great pretender / Only you / I love you a thousand times / With this ring / My prayer / You've got the magic touch / Harbour lights / Smoke gets in your eyes / I'm sorry / Twilight time.
■ LP . . . . . . . . . . . . . . . . . . . . . PHX 1014
Phoenix (2) / Oct '82.

## GOLDENS HITS, THE.
**Tracks:** Not Advised.
CD. . . . . . . . . . . . . . . . . . . . . . . 826 447-2
Mercury / '86 / PolyGram.

## GRAFFITI COLLECTION.
**Tracks:** Not Advised.
CD. . . . . . . . . . . . . . . . . . . . . . . GRCD 08
MC. . . . . . . . . . . . . . . . . . . . . . . GRMC 08
Graffiti Collection / Aug '90 / THE.

## GREAT PRETENDER.
**Tracks:** Great pretender / Only you.
■ 78 rpm. . . . . . . . . . . . . . . . . . . MT 117
Mercury (Pye) / '56.

## GREAT PRETENDER, THE.
**Tracks:** One in a million / Great pretender / With this ring / Pledging my love / Washed ashore (on a lonely island in the sun) / Twilight time / I'm sorry / You've got the magic touch.
■ LP . . . . . . . . . . . . . . . . . . . . . MFM 025
Magnum Force / Apr '87.

## GREAT PRETENDER, THE (2).
**Tracks:** Not Advised.
■ LP . . . . . . . . . . . . . . . . . . . . . RMB 5614
Crusader / Mar '89.

## GREATEST HITS.
**Tracks:** Not Advised.
CD. . . . . . . . . . . . . . . . . . . . . . . GRF 215
MC. . . . . . . . . . . . . . . . . . . . . . . MCGRF 215
Tring / Mar '93 / Prism Leisure PLC / Midland Records.

## GREATEST HITS: PLATTERS.
**Tracks:** Not Advised.
CD. . . . . . . . . . . . . . . . . . . . . . . ENTCD 274
MC. . . . . . . . . . . . . . . . . . . . . . . ENT MC 13047
Entertainers / Mar '92 / BMG.

## GREATEST HITS: PLATTERS.
**Tracks:** Not Advised.
CD. . . . . . . . . . . . . . . . . . . . . . . 2636752
MC. . . . . . . . . . . . . . . . . . . . . . . 2636754
Black Tulip / May '88.

## GREATEST HITS: THE PLATTERS.
**Tracks:** Not Advised.
CD. . . . . . . . . . . . . . . . . . . . . . . FUNCD 9041
■ LP . . . . . . . . . . . . . . . . . . . . . FUN 9041
MC. . . . . . . . . . . . . . . . . . . . . . . FUNC 9041
Fun (Holland) / Oct '88 / Pinnacle.

## HARBOUR LIGHTS.
**Tracks:** Harbour lights.
■ 7" . . . . . . . . . . . . . . . . . . . . . AMT 1081
Mercury (EMI) / Jan '60.

## I LOVE YOU 1000 TIMES.
**Tracks:** I love you 1000 times / Hear no evil, speak no evil, see no evil.
■ 7" . . . . . . . . . . . . . . . . . . . . . SS 511
Stateside / '66.

## I'M SORRY.
**Tracks:** I'm sorry.
■ 78 rpm. . . . . . . . . . . . . . . . . . . MT 145
Mercury (Pye) / '57.

## JUKE BOX GIANTS.
**Tracks:** Great pretender / Harbour lights / Only you / One in a million / Pledging my love / Love letter / Washed ashore (on a lonely island in the sea) / With this ring / I love you a thousand times / Smoke gets in your eyes / Twilight time / You've got the magic touch / Heaven on earth / If I had you / I'll be home / Sweet sweet lovin' / How beautiful our love is / Red sails in the sunset / I'm sorry.
■ LP . . . . . . . . . . . . . . . . . . . . . AFEMP 1007
Audio Fidelity / May '82.

## MORE GOLDEN HITS.
**Tracks:** If I didn't care / I wish / Enchanted / Remember when / To each his own / Only because / My dream / Heaven on earth / You'll never never know / One in a million / I'm sorry / Trees / I'll never smile again / Helpless / It's raining outside / It isn't right.
CD. . . . . . . . . . . . . . . . . . . . . . . 830 773 2
Mercury / '88 / PolyGram.

## MORE I SEE YOU, THE.
**Tracks:** Wonder of you / One in a million / All my love belongs to you / On the top of my mind / I can't get used to sharing you / What name shall I give you, my love / I love you, yes I do / Love letters / Going back to Detroit / Love must go on / Wish it were me.
■ LP . . . . . . . . . . . . . . . . . . . . . SPR 8500
MC. . . . . . . . . . . . . . . . . . . . . . . SPC 8500
Spot / Feb '83.

## MUSIC FOR THE MILLIONS.
**Tracks:** Only you / She's mine / My prayer / Remember when / Red sails in the sunset / You've got the magic touch / Thanks for the memory / You'll never know / Sincerely / One in a million / Stormy weather / Mack the knife / Love me tender / Sentimental journey / September song / Great pretender / Smoke gets in your eyes / Twilight time / I'm sorry / It's magic / Ebb tide / Trees / Song for the lonely / Summertime / Heaven on earth / Moonlight beach / My dream / Harbour lights / I'll never smile again / My blue Heaven.
■ Double LP. . . . . . . . . . . . . . . . . 818 412 1
MC Set . . . . . . . . . . . . . . . . . . . 818 412 4
Philips / Sep '84 / PolyGram.

## MUSICOR YEARS, THE.
**Tracks:** With this ring / I love you 1,000 / I can't get used to sharing you / Don't hear, speak, see no evil / Washed ashore / Doesn't it ring a bell / Devri / Why do you wanna make me blue / Think before you walk / So many tears / Alone in the night / How beautiful our love is / Hard to get thing called love / Sweet, sweet lovin' / Going back to Detroit / Run while it's dark / Fear of losing you / Not my girl / Get a hold of yourself / Shing-a-ling-a-loo / Baby, baby / Love must go on / I'll be home / If I had a love / What name shall I give you my love / (You've got) The magic touch / Sonata / Why.
CD. . . . . . . . . . . . . . . . . . . . . . . CDKEND 116
Kent / Jul '94 / Pinnacle.

## MY PRAYER.
**Tracks:** My prayer.
■ 78 rpm. . . . . . . . . . . . . . . . . . . MT 120
Mercury (Pye) / '56.

## NEW GOLDEN HITS.
**Tracks:** I love you 1000 times / With this ring / Washed ashore / Great pretender / My prayer / Only you / Magic touch / Harbour lights / Smoke gets in your eyes / I'm sorry / Twilight time / Heaven on earth.

■ LP . . . . . . . . . . . . . . . . . . . . . SSL 10227
Stateside / Mar '68.

## ONLY YOU.
Tracks: Only you / Smoke gets in your eyes.
■ 7" . . . . . . . . . . . . . . . . . . . . . . . . 6052253
Mercury / May '78.

## ONLY YOU.
Tracks: Only you / Here comes the boogie man.
■ 7" . . . . . . . . . . . . . . . . . . . . . 7N 25760
Pye International / Apr '78.

## ONLY YOU.
Tracks: Only you / I'm sorry / Harbour lights / Remember when / Smoke gets in your eyes / You'll never know / Red sails in the sunset / Enchanted / It's magic / Ebb tide / On a slow boat to China / Thanks for the memory.
■ LP . . . . . . . . . . . . . . . . . . . . . .2878 246
MC . . . . . . . . . . . . . . . . . . . . . . .3472 246
Karussell (Germany) / Apr '82.
CD . . . . . . . . . . . . . . . . . . . . . . . . .U 4029
Karussell (Germany) / Jun '88.

## ONLY YOU.
Tracks: Not Advised.
CD . . . . . . . . . . . . . . . . . . . . . . CDCD 1045
Charly / Mar '93 / Charly.

## ONLY YOU.
Tracks: I need you all the time / Hey now / Tell the world / You made me cry / Only you / I'll cry when you're gone / Maggie dosen't work here anymore / Voo vee ah bee / Love all night / Give thanks / Shake it up mambo / Roses of Picardy.
■ LP . . . . . . . . . . . . . . . . . . . . . . . 236 223
Polydor / Apr '68.

## ONLY YOU.
Tracks: Not Advised.
CD . . . . . . . . . . . . . . . . . . . . . . . .15 077
MC . . . . . . . . . . . . . . . . . . . . . . . .79 257
Laserlight / Aug '92 / THE / BMG / Target.

## ONLY YOU.
Tracks: Not Advised.
CD . . . . . . . . . . . . . . . . . . . . . DRIVE 3017
In-Market / Dec '87.

## ONLY YOU.
Tracks: Not Advised.
■ MC . . . . . . . . . . . . . . . . . . . . . BRC 2527
Bravo / Feb '80.

## ONLY YOU (OLD GOLD).
Tracks: Only you / Great pretender.
■ 7" . . . . . . . . . . . . . . . . . . . . . .OG 9485
Old Gold / Jun '88.

## PERFECT HARMONY.
Tracks: Not Advised.
CD . . . . . . . . . . . . . . . . . . . . . CDCD 1112
Charly / Jul '93 / Charly.

## PLATTERAMA.
Tracks: Platterama medley / Red sails in the sunset / Twilight time / You've got the magic touch / Only you / Great pretender / My prayer / Harbour lights / Enchanted / Smoke gets in your eyes.
MC . . . . . . . . . . . . . . . . . . . . . MCR 414050
Mercury / Sep '82 / PolyGram.
■ LP . . . . . . . . . . . . . . . . . . . . . SRM 14050
Mercury / Sep '82.

## PLATTERAMA MEDLEY.
Tracks: Platterama medley.
■ 7" . . . . . . . . . . . . . . . . . . . . . MER 111
Mercury / Jul '82.

## PLATTERS.
Tracks: Great pretender / Only you / Smoke gets in your eyes / Red sails in the sunset / Harbour lights / I'll be home / My prayer / Twilight time / I'm sorry / Pledging my love / With this ring / Washed ashore (on a lonely island in the sea).
■ LP . . . . . . . . . . . . . . . . . . . . . COUNT 3
■ MC . . . . . . . . . . . . . . . . . . . . ZC CNT 3
Dakota (Countdown Series) / Oct '82.

## PLATTERS.
Tracks: Not Advised.
CD . . . . . . . . . . . . . . . . . . . . . . . LECD 040
Dynamite (2) / May '94 / THE.

## PLATTERS COLLECTION (20 Golden Greats).
Tracks: Only you / Smoke gets in your eyes / Great pretender / My prayer / Red sails in the sunset / I love you because / Twilight time / Sweet sweet lovin' / Harbour lights / My way / I'm sorry / With this ring / Unchained melody / Heaven on earth / I love you a thousand times / Magic touch / Why / Doesn't ring a bell / Alone in the night / If I had love.

■ LP . . . . . . . . . . . . . . . . . . . . . . DVLP 2055
MC . . . . . . . . . . . . . . . . . . . . . . DVMC 2055
Deja Vu / '86 / Jazz Music / Music Collection International.
CD . . . . . . . . . . . . . . . . . . . . . . DVCD 2055
Deja Vu / Jun '88 / Jazz Music / Music Collection International.

## PLATTERS COLLECTION, THE.
Tracks: Not Advised.
■ Double LP . . . . . . . . . . . . . . . . . . PDA 003
Pickwick / Mar '76.
MC Set . . . . . . . . . . . . . . . . . . . . PDC 003
Pickwick / Feb '80 / Pickwick.

## PLATTERS GREATEST HITS.
Tracks: Not Advised.
CD . . . . . . . . . . . . . . . . . . . . . CDSGP 014
MC . . . . . . . . . . . . . . . . . . . . CASSGP 014
Total / Oct '92 / Total / BMG.

## PLATTERS MEET THE DRIFTERS, THE (Platters, The & The Drifters).
Tracks: Not Advised.
CD . . . . . . . . . . . . . . . . . . . . . . K 3014-2
MC . . . . . . . . . . . . . . . . . . . . . U 3014-2
Spectrum (CD) / Jun '89 / M.S.D.

## PLATTERS, THE.
Tracks: Not Advised.
■ LP . . . . . . . . . . . . . . . . . . . . . BID 8002
Bellaphon / Jul '88.

## PLATTERS, THE.
Tracks: Only you / Hey now / I need you all the time / Maggie dosen't work here anymore / You made me cry / Tell the world / Voo vee ah vee / Give thanks shake it up mambo / Love all night / I believe / Work is not my home / Crying in the chapel / My prayer / Put your hand in the hand / How great thou art / Loving you / He's my friend / Heading home / Sweet inspiration.
MC . . . . . . . . . . . . . . . . . . . . . LEMC 008
Legends In Music / Jul '94 / Conifer Records.

## PLATTERS, THE.
Tracks: Not Advised.
CD . . . . . . . . . . . . . . . . . . . . . . . KCD 651
King / Mar '90 / New Note / Koch International.

## PLATTERS, THE.
Tracks: Not Advised.
■ LP . . . . . . . . . . . . . . . . . . . . . SM 3886
MC . . . . . . . . . . . . . . . . . . . . . MC 3886
Joker (USA) / '88 / C.M. Distribution / Jazz Horizons / Jazz Music.

## PLATTERS, THE.
Tracks: Not Advised.
MC . . . . . . . . . . . . . . . . . . . . . ZCGAS 718
Audio Fidelity / Oct '84 / Telstar/Ronco.

## REMEMBER WHEN.
Tracks: Not Advised.
CD . . . . . . . . . . . . . . . . . . . . . . . .U 4056
Spectrum (1) / Jun '88 / PolyGram.

## REMEMBER WHEN.
Tracks: Remember when.
■ 7" . . . . . . . . . . . . . . . . . . . . . AMT 1053
Mercury (EMI) / Aug '59.

## REMEMBER WHEN.
Tracks: Not Advised.
CD . . . . . . . . . . . . . . . . . . . . AIM 1026CD
Aim (2) / Oct '93 / Topic Records / Direct Distribution / A.D.A. Distribution.

## SINCERELY.
Tracks: Only you (And you alone) / Smoke gets in your eyes / Thanks for the memory / Red sails in teh sunset / I wish / I wanna / I only have eyes for you / On a slow boat to China / To each his own / Heaven on earth / I wish it were me / Glory of love / Lazy river / Sincerely.
CD . . . . . . . . . . . . . . . . . . . . . . .550 0522
MC . . . . . . . . . . . . . . . . . . . . . . .550 0524
Spectrum (1) / May '93 / PolyGram.

## SING LATINO.
Tracks: To dolce voz / Siboney / Amor / Solo tu / Viva ju juy / La hora del crepusculo / Malaguana salerosa / Besame mucho / Maria Elena / Cuando caliente el sol / Aquellos ojos verdes / Acquarela do Brazil.
■ LP . . . . . . . . . . . . . . . . . . . . . SFL 13040
Fontana / Jul '68.

## SMOKE GETS IN YOUR EYES.
Tracks: Smoke gets in your eyes.
■ 7" . . . . . . . . . . . . . . . . . . . . . AMT 1016
Mercury (EMI) / Jan '59.

## SMOKE GETS IN YOUR EYES.
Tracks: Great pretender / Only you / Harbour lights / Pledging my love / With this ring / My prayer / Smoke gets in your eyes / Twilight time / I'm sorry / If I had you / Red sails in the sunset / I'll be home / I love you 1,000 times / Sweet, sweet lovin' / Delilah / Washed ashore / (You've got) the magic touch / Heaven on earth / I love you, yes I do / All my love belongs to you.
CD . . . . . . . . . . . . . . . . . . . . . CDINS 5045
Charly / Sep '91 / Charly.

## SMOKE GETS IN YOUR EYES.
Tracks: Smoke gets in your eyes / Red sails in the sunset / Full moon and empty arms / To each his own / Harbour lights / Stormy weather / Mack the knife / Magic touch / Heaven on earth / Moonlight beach / Temptation / Sincerely.
■ LP . . . . . . . . . . . . . . . . . . . . . SMWL 21012
Mercury / Dec '68.

## SMOKE GETS IN YOUR EYES (OLD GOLD).
Tracks: Smoke gets in your eyes / My prayer.
■ 7" . . . . . . . . . . . . . . . . . . . . . OG 9486
Old Gold / Jan '85.

## SWEET SWEET LOVIN'.
Tracks: Sweet sweet lovin' / Sonata.
■ 7" . . . . . . . . . . . . . . . . . . . . . SS 2067
Stateside / '67.
■ 7" . . . . . . . . . . . . . . . . . . . . . 7N 25559
Pye / Jul '71.

## TWENTY CLASSIC HITS.
Tracks: Only you / Great pretender / You've got the magic touch / My prayer / Heaven on earth / You'll never never know / One in a million / I'm sorry / My dream / Twilight time / I wish / Smoke gets in your eyes / Enchanted / Remember when / Harbour lights / Sleepy lagoon / Ebb tide / Red sails in the sunset / To each his own.
■ LP . . . . . . . . . . . . . . . . . . . . . PRICE 56
■ MC . . . . . . . . . . . . . . . . . . . . PRIMC 56
Mercury / Jan '84.

## TWILIGHT TIME.
Tracks: Twilight time.
■ 78 rpm. . . . . . . . . . . . . . . . . . . MT 214
Mercury (Pye) / '58.

## YOU'LL NEVER NEVER KNOW.
Tracks: You'll never never know / It isn't right.
■ 78 rpm. . . . . . . . . . . . . . . . . . . MT 130
Mercury (Pye) / '57.

# Players

## CHRISTMAS.
Tracks: Not Advised.
CD . . . . . . . . . . . . . . . . . . . . . EXPALCD 6
LP . . . . . . . . . . . . . . . . . . . . . . EXPAL 6
MC . . . . . . . . . . . . . . . . . . . . . EXPALMC 6
Expression / Nov '91 / Pinnacle.

# Players Association

## DISCO INFERNO.
Tracks: Disco inferno / I like it.
■ 7" . . . . . . . . . . . . . . . . . . . . . VS 5006
Vanguard (1) / Mar '78.

## GET DOWN MELLOW MELLOW SOUND.
Tracks: Get down mellow mellow sound / More than a little bit.
■ 12" . . . . . . . . . . . . . . . . . . . . . VSL 5017
■ 7" . . . . . . . . . . . . . . . . . . . . . VS 5017
Vanguard (1) / Mar '80.

## GET ON UP NOW.
Tracks: Get on up now / Let your body go.
■ 12" . . . . . . . . . . . . . . . . . . . . . VSL 5020
Vanguard (1) / May '81.

## LET YOUR BODY GO.
Tracks: Get on up now / Groovin' on home / Let your body go / R & R bop-bop / Things you get me to do / Life is just a song.
■ LP . . . . . . . . . . . . . . . . . . . . . VSD 79434
Vanguard (1) / Jul '81.

## PLAYERS ASOCIATION.
Tracks: Born to dance / Goin' to the disco / Make it last all night / Disco inferno / We were born to dance / Everything's gonna be OK / Footsteps / How do you like it.
■ LP . . . . . . . . . . . . . . . . . . . . . VSD 79398
Vanguard (1) / Apr '78.

## RIDE THE GROOVE.
Tracks: Ride the groove.
■ 12" . . . . . . . . . . . . . . . . . . . . . VSL 5012

■ **7"** . . . . . . . . . . . . . . . . . . . . . **VS 5012**
Vanguard (1) / May '79.

## TURN THE MUSIC UP.
**Tracks:** Turn the music up / Closer I get to you / Everybody dance / I wish / More than a little bit / Ride the groove.
■ **LP** . . . . . . . . . . . . . . . . . . . **VSD 79421**
Vanguard (1) / Mar '79.

## TURN THE MUSIC UP.
**Tracks:** Turn the music up / Goin' to the disco.
■ **12"** . . . . . . . . . . . . . . . . . . . . **VSL 5011**
■ **7"** . . . . . . . . . . . . . . . . . . . . . **VS 5011**
Vanguard (1) / Mar '79.

## TURN THE MUSIC UP (OLD GOLD).
**Tracks:** Turn the music up / Ride the groove / Get down mellow sound.
■ **12"** . . . . . . . . . . . . . . . . . . . . .**OG 4130**
Old Gold / Aug '89.

## WE GOT THE GROOVE.
**Tracks:** We got the groove / I like it.
■ **7"** . . . . . . . . . . . . . . . . . . . . . **VS 5016**
Vanguard (1) / Feb '80.

## Pleasure Bombs

### DAYS OF HEAVEN.
**Tracks:** Tumblin' down / Love takes a walk / Heat comes down / Love machine / Summer's over / Cash / Pushin' up / Come this may / Out with the boys / Fade to black.
**CD** . . . . . . . . . . . . . . . . . . . 7567917792
■ **LP** . . . . . . . . . . . . . . . . . . . 7567917791
**MC** . . . . . . . . . . . . . . . . . . . 7567917794
East West / Aug '91 / WEA.

## Plum, Jean

### LOOK AT THE BOY.
**Tracks:** Look at the boy / Back to you.
■ **7"** . . . . . . . . . . . . . . . . . . . **HLU 10514**
London-American / Jan '76.

## Plunky Branch

### TROPICAL CHILL.
**Tracks:** Not Advised.
■ **LP** . . . . . . . . . . . . . . . . . . . **NB 19881**
Branch / Jul '88.

## Plus One

### IT'S HAPPENIN'.
**Tracks:** It's happening / It's happenin' (Instrumental).
■ **12"** . . . . . . . . . . . . . . . . . . . **DJV 001**
White / Oct '89.
■ **12"** . . . . . . . . . . . . . . . . . . **MCAT 1405**
■ **12" Remix.** . . . . . . . . . . . . . **MCAX 1405**
■ **7"** . . . . . . . . . . . . . . . . . . . **MCA 1405**
■ **CD Single.** . . . . . . . . . . . . . **DMCAT 1405**
■ **MC Single.** . . . . . . . . . . . . . **MCAC 1405**
MCA / May '90.

## SONG WILL ALWAYS BE THE SAME, THE.
**Tracks:** Song will always be the same.
■ **12"** . . . . . . . . . . . . . . . . . . **MCST 1535**
■ **7"** . . . . . . . . . . . . . . . . . . . **MCS 1535**
■ **CD Single.** . . . . . . . . . . . . . **MCSTD 1535**
MCA / May '91.

## Plush

### FREE AND EASY.
**Tracks:** Free and easy.
■ **12"** . . . . . . . . . . . . . . . . . . . .**PL 703**
Not Advised / Feb '89.

## Pockets

### COME GO WITH ME.
**Tracks:** Come go with me / Wizzard wuzzit.
■ **7"** . . . . . . . . . . . . . . . . . . . **CBS 5780**
CBS / Nov '77.

### IN THE POCKET.
**Tracks:** In the pocket / Doin' the do.
■ **7"** . . . . . . . . . . . . . . . . . . . **CBS 6120**
CBS / Mar '78.

## Poindexter Brothers

### GIT YOUR BACKFIELD IN MOTION.
**Tracks:** Git your backfield in motion / Give that girl some slack.
**7"** . . . . . . . . . . . . . . . . . . . . .**VS 550**
Verve / Jan '67 / PolyGram.

■ **DELETED**

## Pointer Sisters

From West Oakland Church of God to Crunchie commercials, the Pointer Sisters have lived up to their father's prediction, "You surely have a gift from God and should prosper with it." Gospel-trained quartet established reputation as back-up singers with variety of rock acts, before pursuing group career in 1973. Jazzy style carried them through to mid-'70s, giving way to tougher direction when group signed to Richard Perry's Planet label in '78. Acclaimed *Energy* album yielded version of Bruce Springsteen's *Fire*; No. 2 in U.S. and Sisters' first U.K. hit. Pointers' popularity peaked in '84: *Automatic*, *Jump (For My Love)* and *I'm So Excited* were transatlantic smashes (latter was revived in '90s as soundtrack to bizarre chocolately activities). Despite two further hits in '85, the original sisters with voices were eclipsed by new breed.

### ALL YOUR LOVE.
**Tracks:** All your love / Shape I'm in.
■ **7"** . . . . . . . . . . . . . . . . . . . **K 12395**
Planet (1) / Mar '76.

### AMERICAN MUSIC.
**Tracks:** American music / I want to do it with you.
■ **7"** . . . . . . . . . . . . . . . . . . . .**RPS 101**
Planet (1) / Sep '82.

### AUTOMATIC.
**Tracks:** Automatic.
■ **CD Single.** . . . . . . . . . . . . . **PD 49469**
RCA / Jun '89.

### AUTOMATIC.
**Tracks:** Automatic / Nightline.
■ **12"** . . . . . . . . . . . . . . . . . . . **RPST 105**
■ **7"** . . . . . . . . . . . . . . . . . . . .**RPS 105**
Planet (1) / Apr '84.

### AUTOMATIC (OLD GOLD).
**Tracks:** Automatic / Jump.
■ **12"** . . . . . . . . . . . . . . . . . . . .**OG 4028**
Old Gold / Nov '87.

### AUTOMATIC(OLD GOLD).
**Tracks:** Automatic / Jump / I'm so excited.
■ **CD Single.** . . . . . . . . . . . . . .**OG 6526**
Pickwick / Oct '92.

### AUTOMATIC.
**Tracks:** Not Advised.
■ **7"** . . . . . . . . . . . . . . . . . . **PB 43035**
■ **CD Single.** . . . . . . . . . . . . . **PD 43036**
■ **12"** . . . . . . . . . . . . . . . . . . **PT 43036**
RCA / Aug '89.

### BABY COME AND GET IT.
**Tracks:** Baby come and get it / Operator.
■ **12"** . . . . . . . . . . . . . . . . . . **FT 49983**
■ **7"** . . . . . . . . . . . . . . . . . . **RB 49982**
Planet (1) / Apr '85.

### BACK IN MY ARMS AGAIN.
**Tracks:** Back in my arms again / Dance electric / Dare me (remix) (Track on 12" version only).
■ **12"** . . . . . . . . . . . . . . . . . . **PT 49866**
■ **7"** . . . . . . . . . . . . . . . . . . **PB 49865**
RCA / May '86.

### BE THERE.
**Tracks:** Be there / Be there (acappella) / Be there (ext. Version).
■ **12"** . . . . . . . . . . . . . . . . . . **MCAT 1181**
■ **7"** . . . . . . . . . . . . . . . . . . .**MCA 1181**
MCA / Jun '87.

### BEST OF POINTER SISTERS.
**Tracks:** You gotta believe / Black coffee / Wang dang doodle / Salt peanuts / Steam heat / Cloudburst / Easy days / Ja da / That's a plenty / Little pony / Sugar / Yes we can-can / Sleeping alone / Fairtales / Shakey flat / Going down slowly / How long.
■ **Double LP.** . . . . . . . . . . . . . .**ABCD 611**
ABC Records / Jan '77.

### BLACK AND WHITE.
**Tracks:** Sweet lover man / Someday we'll be together / Take my heart, take my soul / Slow hand / We're gonna make it / What a surprise / Got to find love / Fall in love again / Should I do it.
■ **LP** . . . . . . . . . . . . . . . . . . . **K 52300**
Planet (1) / Aug '81.
■ **LP** . . . . . . . . . . . . . . . . . . . **NL 89378**
■ **MC** . . . . . . . . . . . . . . . . . . . **NK 89378**
Planet (1) / Jul '84.
**CD** . . . . . . . . . . . . . . . . . . . **ND 89378**
RCA / Feb '90 / BMG.

### BREAK OUT.
**Tracks:** Jump (for my love) / Automatic / I'm so excited / I need you / Dance electric / Neutron dance / Easy persuasion / Baby come and get it / Telegraph your love / Operator.
■ **CD** . . . . . . . . . . . . . . . . . . . **FD 89450**
■ **LP** . . . . . . . . . . . . . . . . . . . **FL 89450**
■ **MC** . . . . . . . . . . . . . . . . . . . **FK 89450**
Planet (1) / Oct '84.
■ **LP** . . . . . . . . . . . . . . . . . . . **NL 90206**
■ **MC** . . . . . . . . . . . . . . . . . . . **NK 90206**
RCA / Aug '88.
**CD** . . . . . . . . . . . . . . . . . . . **ND 90206**
RCA / Aug '88 / BMG.

### COLLECTION, THE.
**Tracks:** Yes we can-can / Fairytale / Fire / Happiness / He's so shy / Slow hand / I'm so excited / American music / Should I do it / If you wanna get back / Your lady / I need you / Jump (for my love) / Automatic / Neutron dance / Baby come and get it / Dare me / Twist my arm / Goldmine.
**CD** . . . . . . . . . . . . . . . . .**74321 13957-2**
RCA / Jul '93 / BMG.

### COLLECTION: POINTER SISTERS.
**Tracks:** Cloudburst / Lonely girl / Sugar / Chainy do / Wang dang doodle / Salt peanuts / Bring your sweet stuff home to me / Grinning in your face / Save the bones for Henry Jones.. / Shakey flat blues / Naked foot / I need a man / Sleeping alone / Pains and tears / Yes we can / Fairytale / How long / Black coffee / Going down / Little pony.
■ **Double LP.** . . . . . . . . . . . . . . **CCSLP 175**
■ **MC** . . . . . . . . . . . . . . . . . . .**CCSMC 175**
Castle Collector Series / '87.

### CONTACT.
**Tracks:** Twist my arm / Hey you / Pound, pound, pound / Back in my arms / Burn down the night / Bodies and souls / Contact / Dare me / Freedom.
■ **LP** . . . . . . . . . . . . . . . . . . . **PL 85457**
Planet (1) / Jul '85.
■ **CD** . . . . . . . . . . . . . . . . . . . **ND 90089**
■ **LP** . . . . . . . . . . . . . . . . . . . **NL 90089**
■ **MC** . . . . . . . . . . . . . . . . . . . **NK 90089**
RCA / May '88.

### COULD I BE DREAMIN'.
**Tracks:** Could I be dreamin' / Evie.
■ **7"** . . . . . . . . . . . . . . . . . . . **K 12505**
Planet (1) / Feb '81.

### DARE ME.
**Tracks:** Dare me / I'll be there.
■ **12"** . . . . . . . . . . . . . . . . . . **PT 49958**
■ **7"** . . . . . . . . . . . . . . . . . . **PB 49957**
RCA / Jul '85.

### ENERGY.
**Tracks:** Happiness / Fire / Angry eyes / Echoes of love / Everybody is a star / Lay it on the line / Dirty work / Hypnotised / As I come of age / Come and get your love.
■ **LP** . . . . . . . . . . . . . . . . . . . **K 52107**
Planet (1) / Mar '79.
■ **LP** . . . . . . . . . . . . . . . . . . . **NL 85091**
■ **MC** . . . . . . . . . . . . . . . . . . . **NK 85091**
RCA / Nov '84.
**CD** . . . . . . . . . . . . . . . . .**74321 13591-2**
**MC** . . . . . . . . . . . . . . . . .**74321 13591-4**
Ariola Express / Feb '94 / BMG.

### EVERYBODY IS A STAR.
**Tracks:** Everybody is a star / Lay it on the line.
■ **7"** . . . . . . . . . . . . . . . . . . . **K 12324**
Planet (1) / Feb '79.

### FIRE.
**Tracks:** Fire / Should I do it.
■ **7"** . . . . . . . . . . . . . . . . . . . **K 12339**
Planet (1) / Mar '79.

### FREEDOM.
**Tracks:** Freedom.
■ **12"** . . . . . . . . . . . . . . . . . . **PT 49914**
■ **7"** . . . . . . . . . . . . . . . . . . **PB 49913**
RCA / Nov '85.

### FRIENDS ADVICE (DON'T TAKE IT).
**Tracks:** Friends advice (Don't take it).
■ **12"** . . . . . . . . . . . . . . . . . . **ZT 43678**
■ **7"** . . . . . . . . . . . . . . . . . . **ZB 43677**
■ **CD Single.** . . . . . . . . . . . . . **ZD 43678**
Motown / Jul '90.

### FROM THE POINTER SISTERS WITH LOVE.
**Tracks:** Slow hand / I'm in love / All I know is the way I feel / Moonlight dancing / Easy persuasion / Someday we will be together / He's so shy / Fire / I feel for you / Dirty work / See how the love goes / Got to find love / I will be there / I need you.

■ CD. . . . . . . . . . . . . . . . . . ND 90541
■ MC. . . . . . . . . . . . . . . . . . NK 90541
RCA / Mar '91.

## FRUIT TO THE ROOT.
Tracks: Hands up / Wang dang doodle (all night long) / Steam heat / Salt peanuts / Yes we can.
■ VHS . . . . . . . . . . . . . . . . . 791 011
BMG Video / Feb '91.

## GOLDMINE.
Tracks: Sexual power / Goldmine.
■ 12". . . . . . . . . . . . . . . . . . PB 40988
■ 7" . . . . . . . . . . . . . . . . . . PB 40987
Planet (1) / Nov '86.

## GREATEST HITS: POINTER SISTERS.
Tracks: He's so shy / Fire / Should I do it / Someday we'll be together / Happiness / Slow hand / Could I be dreamin' / Love too good to last / Take my heart, take my soul / Special things.
■ LP . . . . . . . . . . . . . . . . . . 9602031
Planet (1) / Nov '82.

## HAPPINESS.
Tracks: Happiness / Lay it on the line.
■ 7" . . . . . . . . . . . . . . . . . . K 12350
Planet (1) / '79.

## HAVING A PARTY.
Tracks: Having a party / Don't it drive you crazy / I need a man / Waiting on you / I'll get by without you / Bring your sweet stuff home to me / Lonely gal.
■ LP . . . . . . . . . . . . . . . . . . ABCL 5163
ABC Records / Feb '78.

## HE'S SO SHY.
Tracks: He's so shy / Happiness.
■ 7" . . . . . . . . . . . . . . . . . . K 12470
Asylum / Aug '80.
■ 7" . . . . . . . . . . . . . . . . . . E 9924
Planet (1) / Nov '82.

## HEART TO HEART.
Tracks: Heart to heart / If you wanna get back your lady.
■ 12". . . . . . . . . . . . . . . . . . RPST 102
■ 7" . . . . . . . . . . . . . . . . . . RPS 102
Planet (1) / Sep '82.

## HOT TOGETHER.
Tracks: My life / Mercury rising / Goldmine / Say the word / Hot together / Sexual power / Set me free / Tast / Eyes don't lie.
■ CD . . . . . . . . . . . . . . . . . . PD 85609
■ LP . . . . . . . . . . . . . . . . . . PL 85609
■ MC. . . . . . . . . . . . . . . . . . PK 85609
RCA / Jan '87.

## HOW LONG.
Tracks: How long / Easy days.
■ 7" . . . . . . . . . . . . . . . . . . ABC 4069
Anchor (3) / Jul '75.

## I NEED YOU.
Tracks: I need you / So excited / Slow hand.
■ 7" . . . . . . . . . . . . . . . . . . RST 104
Planet (1) / Nov '83.
■ 12". . . . . . . . . . . . . . . . . . RPST 107
■ 7" . . . . . . . . . . . . . . . . . . RPS 107
Planet (1) / Aug '84.

## I'M SO EXCITED.
Tracks: I'm so excited.
■ 12". . . . . . . . . . . . . . . . . . RPST 108
■ 7" . . . . . . . . . . . . . . . . . . RPS 108
Planet (1) / Oct '84.

## JUMP (for my love).
Tracks: Jump / Heartbeat.
■ 12". . . . . . . . . . . . . . . . . . RPST 106
■ 7" . . . . . . . . . . . . . . . . . . RPS 106
Planet (1) / Jun '84.

## JUMP (Best Of The Pointer Sisters).
Tracks: Jump (for my love) / Someday we'll be together / Automatic / He's so shy / Should I do it / Slow hand / Heart to heart / Telegraph your love / I'm so excited / Goldmine / Back in my arms / I need you / Neutron dance / Dare me / See how the love goes / Overnight success (Only on cassette and CD.) / I'm ready for love (Only on cassette and CD.) / Fire (Only on CD.).
CD . . . . . . . . . . . . . . . . . . PD 90319
MC. . . . . . . . . . . . . . . . . . PK 90319
■ LP . . . . . . . . . . . . . . . . . . PL 90319
RCA / Jul '89 / BMG.

## LIVE YOUR LIFE BEFORE YOU DIE.
Tracks: Live your life before you die / Shaky flat blues.
■ 7" . . . . . . . . . . . . . . . . . . ABC 4048
Anchor (1) / Apr '75.

## NEUTRON DANCE.
Tracks: Neutron dance / Telegraph for your love / I feel for you.
■ 12". . . . . . . . . . . . . . . . . . RPST109
■ 7" . . . . . . . . . . . . . . . . . . RPS 109
Planet (1) / Dec '84.

## ONLY SISTERS CAN DO THAT.
Tracks: It ain't a man's world / I want fireworks / Don't walk away / Eyes like a child / Only sisters can do that / Feel for the physical / Tell it to my heart / Vibetime / Lose myself to find myself / Sex, love or money.
LP . . . . . . . . . . . . . . . . . . SBKLP 26
MC. . . . . . . . . . . . . . . . . . SBKTC 26
■ CD . . . . . . . . . . . . . . . . . . SBKCD 26
SBK / Nov '93 / EMI.

## POINTER SISTERS.
Tracks: Twist my arm / Hey you / Pound pound pound / Back in my arms / Burn down the night / Bodies and souls / Contact / Dare me / Freedom.
CD . . . . . . . . . . . . . . . . . . PD 85487
Planet (1) / Nov '85 / Grapevine Distribution / A.D.A. Distribution / C.M. Distribution / SRD.

## POINTER SISTERS EP.
Tracks: How long / Going down slowly / Yes we can can / You've gotta believe.
■ EP . . . . . . . . . . . . . . . . . . ABE 12012
ABC Records / Dec '77.

## PRIORITY.
Tracks: Who do you love / All you love / Dreaming as one / Turned up too late / Happy / Blind faith / Don't let a thief steal into your heart / She's got the fever / Shape I'm in.
■ LP . . . . . . . . . . . . . . . . . . K 52161
Planet (1) / Oct '79.

## RETROSPECT.
Tracks: Yes, we can can / Sleeping alone / Fairytale / Easy days / Chainey do / That's a plenty / Surfeit USA / Old songs / Salt peanuts / Cloudburst / Ain't got nothing but the blues / Rocks in my bed / Creole love song / Satin doll / I got it bad (and that ain't good) / Mood indigo.
■ LP . . . . . . . . . . . . . . . . . . MCL 1636
■ MC. . . . . . . . . . . . . . . . . . MCLC 1636
MCA / Dec '81.

## RIGHT RHYTHM.
Tracks: Friend's advice (don't take it) / Man with the right rhythm / Real life / After you / You knocked the love (right outta my heart) / Billy said Yes / Insanity / What a woman wants / Where have you been / (We just wanna)Thank you (Not on Album).
■ CD . . . . . . . . . . . . . . . . . . ZD 72704
■ LP . . . . . . . . . . . . . . . . . . ZL 72704
■ MC. . . . . . . . . . . . . . . . . . ZK 72704
Motown / Jul '90.

## SAVE THIS NIGHT FOR LOVE.
Tracks: Save this night for love / Special things.
■ 7" . . . . . . . . . . . . . . . . . . K 12484
Planet (1) / Nov '80.

## SERIOUS SLAMMIN'.
Tracks: Serious slammin' / Shut up and dance / Moonlight dancing / He turned me out / Flirtations / My life / I'm in love / Pride / Uh uh / I will be there.
■ CD . . . . . . . . . . . . . . . . . . PD 86562
■ LP . . . . . . . . . . . . . . . . . . PL 86562
■ MC. . . . . . . . . . . . . . . . . . PK 86562
RCA / Mar '88.

## SHOULD I DO IT.
Tracks: Should I do it / Sweet lover man.
■ 7" . . . . . . . . . . . . . . . . . . K 12578
Reprise / Dec '81.

## SLOW HAND.
Tracks: Slow hand / Holdin' out for love.
■ 7" . . . . . . . . . . . . . . . . . . K 12530
Planet (1) / '81.

## SLOW HAND (OLD GOLD).
Tracks: Slow hand / Fire / Everybody is a star.
■ 12". . . . . . . . . . . . . . . . . . OG 4034
Old Gold / Nov '87.

## SO EXCITED.
Tracks: I'm so excited / See how the love goes / All of you / Heart beat / If you wanna get back your lady / I feel for you / Heart to heart / American music.
■ LP . . . . . . . . . . . . . . . . . . NL 90255
■ MC. . . . . . . . . . . . . . . . . . NK 90255
■ CD . . . . . . . . . . . . . . . . . . ND 90255
RCA / Oct '88.

## SO EXCITED.
Tracks: Not Advised.
VHS . . . . . . . . . . . . . . . . . . RVT 10929

RCA/Columbia (Video) / '88 / Gold & Sons / THE / Sony.

## SOMEDAY WE WILL BE TOGETHER.
Tracks: Someday we will be together / Special things.
■ 7" . . . . . . . . . . . . . . . . . . K12591
WEA / Feb '82.

## SPECIAL THINGS.
Tracks: Could I be dreamin' / He's so shy / Love too good to last / Evil / Save this night for love / We've got the power / Where did the time go / Special things / Here is where your love belongs.
■ LP . . . . . . . . . . . . . . . . . . K52242
■ MC. . . . . . . . . . . . . . . . . . K4 52242
Planet (1) / Sep '80.
■ LP . . . . . . . . . . . . . . . . . . NL 85088
■ MC. . . . . . . . . . . . . . . . . . NK 85088
RCA / Oct '85.

## WHO DO YOU LOVE.
Tracks: Who do you love / We turned up.
■ 7" . . . . . . . . . . . . . . . . . . K 12406
Planet (1) / Jan '80.

## YOU'VE GOT TO BELIEVE.
Tracks: You've got to believe / Shakey flat blues.
■ 7" . . . . . . . . . . . . . . . . . . ABC 4157
ABC Records / Dec '76.

# Pointer, Bonnie

## BEAST IN ME.
Tracks: Beast in me / There's nobody quite like you.
■ 12". . . . . . . . . . . . . . . . . . TA 6082
■ 7" . . . . . . . . . . . . . . . . . . A 6082
Epic / Mar '85.

## BONNIE POINTER.
Tracks: When I'm gone / Free me from my freedom / Tie me to a tree / Heaven must have sent you / More and more / I love to sing to you / I wanna make it / My everything.
■ LP . . . . . . . . . . . . . . . . . . STML 12101
Motown / Jan '79.

## BONNIE POINTER II.
Tracks: I can't help myself / Jimmy Mack / Heaven must have sent you / When the lovelight starts shining through his eyes / Deep inside my soul / Come see about me / Nowhere to run.
■ LP . . . . . . . . . . . . . . . . . . STML 12129
Motown / Oct '81.

## DEEP INSIDE MY SOUL.
Tracks: Deep inside my soul / I love to sing to you.
■ 7" . . . . . . . . . . . . . . . . . . TMG 1184
Motown / Apr '80.

## HEAVEN MUST HAVE.
Tracks: Heaven must have / Deep inside my soul.
■ 12". . . . . . . . . . . . . . . . . . TMGT 1383
■ 7" . . . . . . . . . . . . . . . . . . TMG 1383
Motown / Apr '85.

## HEAVEN MUST HAVE SENT YOU.
Tracks: Heaven must have sent you / My everything.
■ 7" . . . . . . . . . . . . . . . . . . TMG 1145
Motown / Jul '79.

## HEAVEN MUST HAVE SENT YOU.
Tracks: Heaven must have sent you / I wanna make it.
■ 7" . . . . . . . . . . . . . . . . . . TMG 1134
Motown / Jan '79.

## I CAN'T HELP MYSELF.
Tracks: I can't help myself / When I'm gone.
■ 7" . . . . . . . . . . . . . . . . . . TMG 1171
Motown / Oct '81.

## IF THE PRICE IS RIGHT.
Tracks: Premonition / Johnny / Come softly to me / Under the influence of love / Your touch / Tight blue jeans / There's nobody quite like you / If the price is right.
MC. . . . . . . . . . . . . . . . . . 40 26128
■ LP . . . . . . . . . . . . . . . . . . EPC 26128
Epic / Oct '84 / Sony.

## YOUR TOUCH.
Tracks: Your touch / There's nobody quite like you.
■ 12". . . . . . . . . . . . . . . . . . TA 4418
■ 7" . . . . . . . . . . . . . . . . . . A 4418
Epic / Sep '84.

■ DELETED

## Pointer, Noel

### ALL MY REASONS.
**Tracks:** Classy lady / East St. Louis melody / All the reasons why / Brookline / Savin' it up / Virgie / I feel your soul / Oh what a beautiful city / Land of make believe.
■ LP . . . . . . . . . . . . . . . . . . . . LBG 30340
Liberty / Nov '81.

### CLASSY LADY.
**Tracks:** Classy lady / There's a feeling.
■ 7" . . . . . . . . . . . . . . . . . . . . . UP 645
United Artists / Oct '81.

### FEEL IT.
**Tracks:** Not Advised.
■ LP . . . . . . . . . . . . . . . . . . UAG 30278
United Artists / Dec '79.

### NEVER LOSE YOUR HEART.
**Tracks:** Not Advised.
CD. . . . . . . . . . . . . . . . . . . . . SHCD 5007
MC. . . . . . . . . . . . . . . . . . . . . SHMC 5007
Shanachie / Dec '93 / A.D.A. Distribution / Jazz Music / C.M. Distribution / Koch International.

### STARDUST LADY.
**Tracks:** Stardust lady / Movin' in.
■ 7" . . . . . . . . . . . . . . . . . . . . UP 36398
United Artists / May '78.

## Politicians

### POLITICIANS.
**Tracks:** Psycha-soula-funkadelic / World we live in / Church / Free your mind / Everything good is bad / Song for you / Speak on it / Funky toes / Politicians theme / Close your big mouth.
■ LP . . . . . . . . . . . . . . . . . . . . SHW 5007
Hot Wax / '72.

## Pollard, Ray

### DRIFTER, THE.
**Tracks:** Drifter / Let him go (and let me love you).
■ 7" . . . . . . . . . . . . . . . . . . . . UP 1111
United Artists / '65.

### IT'S A SAD THING.
**Tracks:** It's a sad thing / All the things you are.
■ 7" . . . . . . . . . . . . . . . . . . . . UP 1133
United Artists / '66.

### THIS TIME.
**Tracks:** This time.
■ 7" . . . . . . . . . . . . . . . . . . . .HRH 005
Horaces / Jun '90.

## Polo, Jimi

### EXPRESS YOURSELF.
**Tracks:** Express yourself.
■ CD Single . . . . . . . . . . . . . . 74321101822
■ 12" . . . . . . . . . . . . . . . . . 74321101821
■ 7" . . . . . . . . . . . . . . . . . 74321101827
Perfecto (BMG) / Aug '92.

### FREE YOURSELF.
**Tracks:** Free yourself / Better days.
■ 7" . . . . . . . . . . . . . . . . . . . . URB 36
■ 12" . . . . . . . . . . . . . . . . . . . URBX 36
Urban / Apr '89.

## Ponsar, Serge

### BACK TO THE LIGHT.
**Tracks:** Out in the night / I want money / Gotta get outside / Back to the light / Keep it hot / Life time / V.I.D.E.O.
■ LP . . . . . . . . . . . . . . . . . . . . 9239141
WEA / Sep '83.

### I WANT MONEY.
**Tracks:** I want money.
■ 12" . . . . . . . . . . . . . . . . . . U 9756 T
■ 7" . . . . . . . . . . . . . . . . . . .U 9756
WEA / Nov '83.

### OUT IN THE NIGHT.
**Tracks:** Out in the night / Gotta get outside.
■ 12" . . . . . . . . . . . . . . . . . . U 9852 T
■ 7" . . . . . . . . . . . . . . . . . . .U 9852
WEA / Jul '83.

## Porter, David

### GRITTY, GROOVY AND GETTIN' IT.
**Tracks:** I only have eyes for you / Guess who / I'm tellin' you / Just be true / Way you do the things you do / Can't see you when I want you / One part - two parts / Don't know why I love you.
■ LP . . . . . . . . . . . . . . . . . . .SXATS 1034
Stax / Aug '70.

### INTO THE REAL THING.
**Tracks:** Hang on Sloopy / Ooo-wee girl / Too real to live a lie / Grocery man / I don't want to cry / Thirty days.
■ LP . . . . . . . . . . . . . . . . . . . . 2362006
Stax / Mar '71.

## Porter, Nolan

### NOLAN.
**Tracks:** I like waht you give / Groovin' / Somebody's gone / Work it out in the morning / Oh baby / If I could only be sure / Crazy love / Singer man / Burn down the cornfield / Keep on keepin' on.
■ LP . . . . . . . . . . . . . . . . . . . . SPB 1067
Probe / Feb '73.

## Portrait

### BE THANKFUL FOR WHAT YOU'VE GOT.
**Tracks:** Be thankful for what you've got.
■ 12" . . . . . . . . . . . . . . . . . . . PZ 310
■ CD Single . . . . . . . . . . . . . . . PZCD 310
■ MC Single . . . . . . . . . . . . . . . POCS 310
Polydor / Feb '94.

### HERE WE GO AGAIN.
**Tracks:** Here we go again (mixes) / Here we go again (instrumental).
■ 12" . . . . . . . . . . . . . . . . . . 12CL 683
■ 7" . . . . . . . . . . . . . . . . . . . CL 683
■ CD Single . . . . . . . . . . . . . . . CDCL 683
■ MC Single . . . . . . . . . . . . . . . TCCL 683
EMI / Mar '93.

## Positive Force

### WE GOT THE FUNK.
**Tracks:** We got the funk / Tell me what you see.
■ 12" . . . . . . . . . . . . . . . . . .SHL 102
■ 7" . . . . . . . . . . . . . . . . . . SH 102
Sugarhill / Nov '79.

### WE GOT THE FUNK.
**Tracks:** We got the funk / Rappers delight.
■ 12" . . . . . . . . . . . . . . . . . . SWAVE 6
Streetwave / Dec '85.

### WE GOT THE FUNK (OLD GOLD).
**Tracks:** We got the funk / Give you my love.
■ 12" . . . . . . . . . . . . . . . . . .OG 4146
Old Gold / Nov '89.

## POV

### ALL THRU THE NITE (POV & Jade).
**Tracks:** All thru the nite / Anutha luv / All thru the nite (mixes).
■ 12" . . . . . . . . . . . . . . . .74321 18755-1
■ 7" . . . . . . . . . . . . . . . .74321 18755-7
■ CD Single . . . . . . . . . . . . .74321 18755-2
■ MC Single . . . . . . . . . . . . .74321 18755-4
Arista / Jan '94.

### HANDIN' OUT BEATDOWNS.
**Tracks:** Nuff of the ruff stuff / U got what I want / Anutha luv / Good lovin / Tell me / Summer nights / Never believe / Let me do u / U R the only 1 / Sitting here waiting / Settle down / All thru the nite / Ball ya fist.
CD. . . . . . . . . . . . . . . . . . . 7432115946-2
MC. . . . . . . . . . . . . . . . . . . 7432115946-4
Giant / Feb '94 / BMG.

## Powell, Bryan

### I THINK OF YOU.
**Tracks:** I think of you / Friends / I think of you (mixes).
■ 12" . . . . . . . . . . . . . . . . . . .TLKX 38
■ 7" . . . . . . . . . . . . . . . . . . . TLK 38
■ CD Single . . . . . . . . . . . . . . .TLKCD 38
■ MC Single . . . . . . . . . . . . . . .TLKMC 38
Talkin' Loud / May '93.

### I.T.O.Y.
**Tracks:** I think of you / I commit / It's alright / Friends / All my love / Hurtin' / Natural / Night and day / Lady in my life / Smile / Faith / Like U do.
CD . . . . . . . . . . . . . . . . . . . .518065-2

MC. . . . . . . . . . . . . . . . . . . .518065-4
■ LP . . . . . . . . . . . . . . . . . .518065-1
Talkin' Loud / Nov '93 / PolyGram.

### IT'S ALRIGHT.
**Tracks:** Not Advised.
■ 12" . . . . . . . . . . . . . . . . . . .TLKX 34
■ 7" . . . . . . . . . . . . . . . . . . . TLK 34
■ CD Single . . . . . . . . . . . . . . .TLKCD 34
■ MC Single . . . . . . . . . . . . . . .TLKMC 34
Talkin' Loud / Mar '93.

### NATURAL.
**Tracks:** Natural.
■ 12" . . . . . . . . . . . . . . . . . . .TLKX 41
■ 7" . . . . . . . . . . . . . . . . . . . TLK 41
■ CD Single . . . . . . . . . . . . . . .TLKCD 41
■ MC Single . . . . . . . . . . . . . . .TLKMC 41
Talkin' Loud / Aug '93.

## Powell, Doc

### GIVE IT UP.
**Tracks:** Give it up / What I like.
■ 12" . . . . . . . . . . . . . . . . . .JABX 61
■ 7" . . . . . . . . . . . . . . . . . . JAB 61
Club / Nov '87.

### LOVE IS WHERE IT'S AT.
**Tracks:** Not Advised.
■ CD . . . . . . . . . . . . . . . . . . 832 720 2
■ LP . . . . . . . . . . . . . . . . . .JABH 28
■ MC. . . . . . . . . . . . . . . . . .JABHC 28
Club / Dec '87.

## Powell, Keith

### VICTORY.
**Tracks:** Victory / Some people only.
■ 7" . . . . . . . . . . . . . . . . . . 7N 35300
Piccadilly / Mar '66.

### WHEN YOU MOVE YOU LOSE (Powell, Keith & Billie Davis).
**Tracks:** When you move you lose / Tastes sour don't it.
■ 7" . . . . . . . . . . . . . . . . . . 7N 35288
Piccadilly / Jan '66.

## Precisions

### SUCH MISERY.
**Tracks:** Such misery / Lover's plea.
■ 7" . . . . . . . . . . . . . . . . . . .GRP 129
Grapevine (Northern Soul) / Sep '79.

### TRAIN KEEP MOVING.
**Tracks:** Train keep moving / Country fool.
■ 7" . . . . . . . . . . . . . . . . . . . SUE 4
Suemi / '74.

## Pressure

### CAN YOU FEEL IT.
**Tracks:** Can you feel it / That's the thing to do.
■ 7" . . . . . . . . . . . . . . . . . . MCA 574
MCA / Apr '80.

### PRESSURE.
**Tracks:** Pressure.
■ 12" . . . . . . . . . . . . . . . . . 12 ANA 06
Anagram / May '83.

### PRESSURE.
**Tracks:** Not Advised.
■ LP . . . . . . . . . . . . . . . . . .MCF 3055
MCA / Apr '80.

### SLIDE.
**Tracks:** Slide / Real thing.
■ 12" . . . . . . . . . . . . . . . . . FTCT 196
Fantasy / Jul '81.

### YOU TALK WE TALK.
**Tracks:** You talk we talk.
■ 12" . . . . . . . . . . . . . . . . . 12 ANA 02
Anagram / Nov '82.

## Pressure Point

### DREAMING.
**Tracks:** Dreaming / Coming back / Gave me up / Maybe / Leave right now / Everything to me / Stay with me / Do you love me.
CD. . . . . . . . . . . . . . . . . . . . VICECD 1
■ LP . . . . . . . . . . . . . . . . . . VICELP 1
MC. . . . . . . . . . . . . . . . . . . VICEMC 1
Viceroy / Jul '89.

## DREAMING (Pressure Point & P P Arnold).
**Tracks:** Dreaming.
- 12" . . . . . . . . . . . . . . . . . 12VICE 2
- 7" . . . . . . . . . . . . . . . . . . VICE 2

Viceroy / May '89.

## MELLOW MOODS.
**Tracks:** Mellow moods / I need your love.
- 12" . . . . . . . . . . . . . . . 12VICE 001
- 7" . . . . . . . . . . . . . . . . 7VICE 001

Viceroy / Aug '85.
- 12" . . . . . . . . . . . . . . . . . BOSS 1
- 7" . . . . . . . . . . . . . . . . 7 BOSS 1

Hardback / Nov '86.

## STAY (Pressure Point & P P Arnold).
**Tracks:** Stay.
- 12" . . . . . . . . . . . . . 12VICE 0004PP

Viceroy / Jan '91.

## THIS IS LONDON.
**Tracks:** Not Advised.
- LP . . . . . . . . . . . . . . . . . VICELP 1
- MC . . . . . . . . . . . . . . . . VICEMC 1

Total / Jun '89 / Total / BMG.

---

## Preston, Billy

Preston's impressive CV dates from 1956, when aged 10, he appeared with Mahalia Jackson and starred in film *St. Louis Blues*. Early solo recordings in '60s were overshadowed by sessions for Sam Cooke, Little Richard and Ray Charles; latter brought him to attention of Beatles, for whose Apple label he cut two LPs. Association with George Harrison continued into early '70s, when Preston began scoring solo hits on A&M (including *Outa Space* and *Nothing From Nothing*), and became first pop artist to play New York's Radio City Music Hall. Mid-'70s saw him writing Joe Cocker's *You Are So Beautiful*, working with Sly Stone and Rolling Stones, and signing to Motown. Last major hit was Syreeta duet *With You I'm Born Again* in '79, although Preston continued working through '80s. Bad habits (no doubt encouraged by his Stones association) have curtailed his recording activities in recent years.

## AND DANCE.
**Tracks:** And dance / Kick in.
- 12" . . . . . . . . . . . . . . . . . ERCL 116
- 7" . . . . . . . . . . . . . . . . . .ERC 116

ERC / Jun '84.

## APPLE OF THEIR EYE.
**Tracks:** You've lost that lovin' feeling / Eight days a week / Downtown / Ferry 'cross the Mersey / My girl / Go now / Goldfinger / Stop in the name of love / King of the road / Birds and the bees / Can't you hear my heartbeat.
- LP . . . . . . . . . . . . . . . . . PTLS 1034

President / Oct '69.

## BEHOLD.
**Tracks:** I'm giving my life to christ / Heavenly / Born again / All to Jesus I surrender / He will see you through / He brought me out / Motherless child / Yes my God is real / Behold / For you my lord.
- LP . . . . . . . . . . . . . . . . . MYR 1070
- MC. . . . . . . . . . . . . . . . . .MC 1070

Myrrh / May '82 / Word Records (UK) / Sony.

## BEST OF BILLY PRESTON.
**Tracks:** Outa space / Will it go round in circles / That's the way God planned it / Struttin / You are so beautiful / Nothing from nothing / Get back / I'm really gonna miss you / Space race / I wrote a simple song.
- CD. . . . . . . . . . . . . . . . . 393 205-2

A&M / '88 / PolyGram.

## BILLY PRESTON.
**Tracks:** Not Advised.
- MC Set . . . . . . . . . . . . . . DTO 10096

Ditto / Jan '85 / Pickwick.

## BILLY PRESTON & SYREETA (Preston, Billy & Syreeta).
**Tracks:** Someone special / Searchin' / Just for love / It's so easy / Long and lasting love / Love / One more try / Hey you / New way to say I love you / What we did for love.
- LP . . . . . . . . . . . . . . . . . .STML 12155
- MC . . . . . . . . . . . . . . . . .CSTML 12155

Motown / Oct '81.

## BILLY'S BAG.
**Tracks:** Billy's bag / Steady gettin' it / Let me know / Soul meeting / Octopus / Slippin' & slidin' / Lowdown

---

/ I am coming through / My girl / Shotgun / Stop in the name of love / Can't you hear my heartbeat / Downtown / Eight days a week / King of the road / If I had a hammer.
- CD. . . . . . . . . . . . . . . . . TOP CD 514
- LP . . . . . . . . . . . . . . . . . .TOP 164
- MC. . . . . . . . . . . . . . . . . KTOP 164

Topline / Feb '87 / Charly.

## CHANGE IS GONNA COME, A.
**Tracks:** Change is gonna come / You.
- 7" . . . . . . . . . . . . . . . . .TMG 1231

Motown / Oct '81.

## COLLECTION: BILLY PRESTON.
**Tracks:** Bus / How long has the train been gone / It's alright ma (I'm only bleeding) / Blackbird / Let's make love / Will it go round in circles / Outa space / Let it be / I can't stand it (live) / You are so beautiful / Should've known better / You got me buzzin' / Billy's bag / Listen to the wind (Live) / I'm so tired / Struttin' / Space race / It's my pleasure / Nothing from nothing / Disco dancin' / Get back.
- MC . . . . . . . . . . . . . . . . .CCSMC 210
- Double LP . . . . . . . . . . . . . CCSLP 210
- CD . . . . . . . . . . . . . . . . . CCSCD 210

Castle Collector Series / Mar '89.

## ENCOURAGING WORDS.
**Tracks:** Right now / Little girl / Use what you got / My sweet Lord / Let the music play / Same thing again / I've got a feeling / Sing one for the Lord / When you are mine / I don't want you to pretend / Encouraging words / All things (Must pass) / You've been acting strange / As long as I got my baby (Not on LP) / All that I've got (I'm gonna give to you) (Not on LP).
- LP . . . . . . . . . . . . . . . . . SAPCOR 14

Apple / Oct '70.
- CD. . . . . . . . . . . . . . . . . CDP 7812792

Apple / Mar '93 / EMI.

## GET BACK.
**Tracks:** Get back / Space race.
- 7" . . . . . . . . . . . . . . . . . AMS 7418

A&M / '79.

## GO FOR IT (Preston, Billy & Syreeta).
**Tracks:** Go for it.
- 7" . . . . . . . . . . . . . . . . .TMG 1139

Motown / Oct '81.

## GOSPEL IN MY SOUL.
**Tracks:** Lay my burdens down / Just a closer walk with thee / Do Lord / How great thou art / Angels keep watching over me / Praise God from whom all blessings flow / Pass me not / Gospel interlude / Only hope we have / His eye is on the sparrow / May the good Lord bless and keep you.
- LP . . . . . . . . . . . . . . . . . JOYS 174

Joy / Oct '70.

## HEROES.
**Tracks:** Heroes.
- 7" . . . . . . . . . . . . . . . . . OUTER 1
- 12" . . . . . . . . . . . . . . . . 12OUTER 1

Outerspace / May '91.

## HOPE.
**Tracks:** Hope / Give it up, hot.
- 12" . . . . . . . . . . . . . . . . .TMGT 1224
- 7" . . . . . . . . . . . . . . . . .TMG 1224

Motown / Oct '81.

## I'M NEVER GONNA SAY GOODBYE.
**Tracks:** I'm never gonna say goodbye.
- 7" . . . . . . . . . . . . . . . . .TMG 1283

Motown / Oct '82.

## IT WILL COME IN TIME (Preston, Billy & Syreeta).
**Tracks:** It will come in time / All i wanted was you.
- 7" . . . . . . . . . . . . . . . . .TMG 1175

Motown / Oct '81.

## LATE AT NIGHT.
**Tracks:** Give it up / Hot / Late at night / All I wanted was you / You / I come to rest in you / It will come in time / Lovely lady / With you I'm born again / Sock it rocket.
- LP . . . . . . . . . . . . . . . . . .STML 12116
- MC . . . . . . . . . . . . . . . . .CSTML 12116

Motown / Oct '81.

## MOST EXCITING ORGAN EVER.
**Tracks:** If I had a hammer / Low down / Slippin' and slidin' / Drown in my own tears / I am coming through / Octopus / Don't let the sun catch you crying / Soul meeting / Let me know / Billy's bag / Masquerade is over / Steady gettin' it.
- LP . . . . . . . . . . . . . . . . . .JOY 112

Joy / Oct '68.

---

## MUSIC IS MY LIFE.
**Tracks:** We're gonna make it / God loves you / Make the devil mad / One time or another / Blackbird / wonder why / Will it go round in circles.
- LP . . . . . . . . . . . . . . . . AMLS 63510

A&M / Feb '73.

## NEW WAY TO SAY I LOVE YOU (Preston, Billy & Syreeta).
**Tracks:** New way to say I love you / Hey you.
- 12" . . . . . . . . . . . . . . . . TMGT 1290
- 7" . . . . . . . . . . . . . . . . TMG 1290

Motown / Feb '82.

## ONE MORE TIME FOR LOVE (Preston, Billy & Syreeta).
**Tracks:** One more time for love / Dance for me children.
- 7" . . . . . . . . . . . . . . . . .TMG 1181

Motown / Oct '81.

## OUTA SPACE.
**Tracks:** Outa space.
- 7" . . . . . . . . . . . . . . . . . AMS 7007

A&M / Sep '72.

## PLEASE STAY (Preston, Billy & Syreeta).
**Tracks:** Please stay / Signed, sealed and delivered I'm yours.
- 7" . . . . . . . . . . . . . . . . .TMG 1217

Motown / Oct '81.

## PRESSIN' ON.
**Tracks:** Pressing on / I'd like to go back home again / Lovin' you is easy / Turn it out / I'm never gonna say goodbye / Thanks but no thanks / Don't try to fight it / I love you so.
- LP . . . . . . . . . . . . . . . . . SRML 1217
- MC . . . . . . . . . . . . . . . . .CSTML 1217

Motown / Nov '82.

## THAT'S THE WAY GOD PLANNED IT.
**Tracks:** That's the way God planned it.
- 7" . . . . . . . . . . . . . . . . . APPLE 12

Apple / Jul '69.

## THAT'S THE WAY GOD PLANNED IT.
**Tracks:** Do what you want / I want to thank you / Everything's alright / She belongs to me / It doesn't matter / Morning star / Hey brother / What about you / Let us all get together right now / This is it / Keep to yourself / That's the way God planned it / Through all times (Not on original LP) / As I get older (Not on original LP) / That's the way God planned it (alternate) (Not on original LP).
- LP . . . . . . . . . . . . . . . . . SAPCOR 9

Apple / Sep '69.
- CD. . . . . . . . . . . . . . . . . CDP 7975802
- Double LP . . . . . . . . . . . . .SAPCOR 9
- MC . . . . . . . . . . . . . . . . .TCSAPCOR 9

Apple / Oct '91 / EMI.

## WAY I AM, THE.
**Tracks:** Hope / Good life boogie / Keep on truckin' / Change is gonna come / Let your feeling on me / won't mistreat your love / Baby I'm yours / Until the / Way I am.
- LP . . . . . . . . . . . . . . . . . .STML 12148
- MC . . . . . . . . . . . . . . . . .CSTML 12148

Motown / Oct '81.

## WHOLE NEW THING.
**Tracks:** Whole new thing / Disco dancin' / Complicated sayings / Attitudes / I'm really gonna miss you / Wide stride / You got me buzzin' / Sweet Marie Happy / Touch me love / You don't have to go.
- LP . . . . . . . . . . . . . . . . . AMLH 64656

A&M / Mar '78.

## WIDE STRIDE.
**Tracks:** Wide stride / Whole new thing.
- 7" . . . . . . . . . . . . . . . . . AMS 7340

A&M / Mar '78.

## WILDEST ORGAN IN TOWN.
**Tracks:** Uptight / I got you / Hard day's night / It's got to happen / Satisfaction (and seven others).
- LP . . . . . . . . . . . . . . . . . ST 2532

Capitol / Sep '69.

## WITH YOU I'M BORN AGAIN (Preston, Billy & Syreeta).
**Tracks:** With you I'm born again / Sock it, rocket.
- 7" . . . . . . . . . . . . . . . . .TMG 1159

Motown / Mar '83.

---

■ DELETED

## Price, Lloyd

### HEAVY DREAMS.
Tracks: Chee-koo baby / Coo-ee baby / Oooh-oooh-
ooooh / Restless heart / Tell me pretty baby / They
say / I'm too young / Ain't it a shame / Jimmie Lee /
Baby, don't turn your back on me / Old echo song /
Too late for tears / Carry me home / Little Bea /
Night and day / Oh love / Woe ho ho / Breaking my
heart (All over again) / Iyi yi gomen-a-sai (I'm sorry)
/ Country boy rock / Heavy dreams / Why / I'm goin
back.
■ LP . . . . . . . . . . . . . . . . . . . . . . . CDCHD 512
Ace / Jan '94 / Pinnacle / Complete Record Co. Ltd.

### HOOKED ON A FEELING.
Tracks: Hooked on a feeling / If you really love him.
■ 7" . . . . . . . . . . . . . . . . . . . . . . . . . . WN 17
Wand / May '71.

### I'M GONNA GET MARRIED.
Tracks: I'm gonna get married.
■ 7" . . . . . . . . . . . . . . . . . . . . . . . . . POP 650
H.M.V. / Sep '59.

### JUKE BOX GIANTS.
Tracks: Stagger Lee / Just because / Lawdy Miss
Clawdy / I'm gonna get married / I'll be a fool for you
/ Try a little tenderness / Hooked on a feeling / Me
and a dog named Poo / Personality / Question /
Imagination / Misty / Mr. & Mrs. Untrue / You're
nobody 'til somebody loves you / Ready for Betty /
Where were you (on our wedding day).
■ LP . . . . . . . . . . . . . . . . . . . . . . AFEMP 1009
Audio Fidelity / May '82.

### LADY LUCK.
Tracks: Lady luck.
■ 7" . . . . . . . . . . . . . . . . . . . . . . . . . POP 712
H.M.V. / Apr '60.

### LAWDY.
Tracks: Lawdy Miss Clawdy / Mailman blues / Chee
koo baby / Oo-ee baby / So long / Operator / Laur-
elle / What's the matter now / If crying was murder /
Walkin' the track / Where you at / Lord, lord, amen /
Carry me home / Froglegs / I wish your picture was
you / Let me come home baby / Tryin' to find
someone to love / Night and day blues / All alone /
What a fire / Rock 'n' roll dance / I'm glad, glad /
Baby please come home / Forgive me Clawdy.
■ CD . . . . . . . . . . . . . . . . . . . . . . . CDCHD 360
Ace / Nov '91 / Pinnacle / Complete Record Co. Ltd.

### LAWDY MISS CLAWDY.
Tracks: Lawdy Miss Clawdy / Mailman blues / Ain't it
a shame / Restless heart / What's the matter now /
Baby don't turn your back on me / SS Heart / Lord
lord amen / Walkin' the track / Woe ho ho / L yi yi
gomen a sai / Trying to find some one to love / Frog
legs / Oo wee baby / Baby please come home /
Breaking my heart / Rock 'n' roll dance.
■ LP . . . . . . . . . . . . . . . . . . . . . . . . . . CH 127
Ace / Jan '85.

### LLOYD AT ANY PRICE.
Tracks: Not Advised.
■ LP . . . . . . . . . . . . . . . . . . . . . . . . . JOY 179
Joy / '88.

### LLOYD PRICE.
Tracks: Hooked on a feeling / I'm gonna get married
/ Lawdy Miss Clawdy / Misty / Mr. & Mrs. Untrue /
Personality / Just because / Stagger Lee / Try a little
tenderness / Where were you on our wedding day /
You're nobody 'til somebody loves you / I'll be a fool
for you / Me and you and a dog named Boo / Ready
for Betty.
■ CD . . . . . . . . . . . . . . . . . . . . . . . . . OR 0019
Music Collection International / Aug '87 / THE / Jazz
Music.

### LLOYD PRICE.
Tracks: stagger lee / Personality / Just because /
Where were you on our wedding day.
■ LP . . . . . . . . . . . . . . . . . . . . . . . ABE 12015
ABC Records / Feb '78.

### MR. PERSONALITY REVISITED.
Tracks: Stagger Lee / Mailman blues / Have you
ever had the blues / Question / You need love / What
do you do to my heart / Come into my heart / I'm
gonna get married / Where were you (on our wedding day) / Oh, oh, oh, why / I wish your picture was
you / Lady Luck / Just because / Lawdy Miss Clawdy
/ Personality.
■ LP . . . . . . . . . . . . . . . . . . . . . . . . CRB 1052
Charly R&B / Jun '83.

### NOW.
Tracks: Bad conditions / Light my fire / Grass will
sing / Feeling good / Fire / For once in my life /
Understand / By the time I get to Phoenix / Don't do
me / Little green apples.

■ LP . . . . . . . . . . . . . . . . . . . . . . . . SMLP 57
Major Minor / Jul '69.

### PERSONALITY.
Tracks: Personality.
■ 7" . . . . . . . . . . . . . . . . . . . . . . . . . POP 626
H.M.V. / Jun '59.

### STAGGER LEE & ALL HIS OTHER GREATEST HITS.
Tracks: Not Advised.
CD . . . . . . . . . . . . . . . . . . . . . . . . CD 66126
Ce De International / Jul '93 / BMG.

### STAGGERLEE.
Tracks: stagger lee / Personality.
■ 7" . . . . . . . . . . . . . . . . . . . . . . . . . POP 580
H.M.V. / Feb '59.
■ 7" . . . . . . . . . . . . . . . . . . . . . . . . . BAK 11
Dakota / Aug '82.

### STAGGERLEE.
Tracks: stagger lee / Personality / Where were you.
■ 7" . . . . . . . . . . . . . . . . . . . . . . . . . CR 211
Creole (Replay) / Nov '80.

### WALKIN' THE TRACK.
Tracks: Not Advised.
■ LP . . . . . . . . . . . . . . . . . . . . . . . . SP 2163
Specialty / Sep '87.

### WHERE WERE YOU.
Tracks: Where were you.
■ 7" . . . . . . . . . . . . . . . . . . . . . . . . . POP 598
H.M.V. / May '59.

## Price, Louis

### LOUIS PRICE.
Tracks: Distant lover / Play it by heart / Heart's
devotion / Flesh and blood / What becomes of the
broken hearted / Nobody but you / Just one thing /
How can I make you love me / Try it baby / I believe
in you (Cassette & CD only).
■ CD . . . . . . . . . . . . . . . . . . . . . . . ZD 72746
■ LP . . . . . . . . . . . . . . . . . . . . . . . ZL 72746
■ MC . . . . . . . . . . . . . . . . . . . . . . . ZK 72746
Motown / Jun '91.

## Pride, Lou

### GONE BAD AGAIN.
Tracks: Gone bad again / So far away / Been so long
/ I didn't take your woman / I found a love / We're
only fooling ourselves / Very special / I'm not
through loving you.
■ LP . . . . . . . . . . . . . . . . . . . . . . . CUR 2009
Curtom / Mar '90.
CD . . . . . . . . . . . . . . . . . . . . . . CUR 2009CD
MC. . . . . . . . . . . . . . . . . . . . . . . CUR 2009C
Curtom / Mar '94 / ACD Trading Ltd. / Pinnacle /
Koch International.

### I WAS BORN TO LOVE YOU.
Tracks: Not Advised.
■ MC . . . . . . . . . . . . . . . . . . . . . . . SPAR 003
Spar / '76.

## Prime Number

### NEVER LEAVE ME.
Tracks: Never leave me.
■ 12" . . . . . . . . . . . . . . . . . . . . . . . MRBIG 5
Big Tuff / Jan '93.

## Prime Time

### BABY CONFESS IT.
Tracks: Guilty / What's that you slipped into my wine
/ I bet 'cha / Sex-o-logical / Confess it baby / Baby
don't break my back / Come into my love life / Give
me a chance / Remote control.
■ LP . . . . . . . . . . . . . . . . . . . . . . . FL 85712
■ MC. . . . . . . . . . . . . . . . . . . . . . . FK 85712
RCA / Nov '85.

## Prince

Although his reputation now far exceeds his
sales, Prince is among the most commercially and critically successful musicians of
our time. Initially regarded as ersatz Stevie
Wonder, his albums took a turn for the
individual with 1980's Dirty Mind, although
widespread public acclaim was delayed until '81's Controversy. Even more success
was enjoyed by his proteges The Time:
their eponymous debut was an early product of Prince's funk empire, latterly known
as Paisley Park. Worldwide success began

with 1999, which introduced the highly-in-
fluential 'Minneapolis sound', and exploded
with the multi-million selling Purple Rain.
1984 saw one triumph after another: When
Doves Cry topped U.S. charts, becoming the
year's best-selling single; album spent
months at No. 1; film and tour did record-
breaking business. Subsequently, Prince
did - in Rolling Stone's words - "pretty much
whatever the fuck he wanted". The peaks of
the ensuing decade include musical
triumphs Sign O' The Times and Symbol,
and successful bids to recapture sales com-
mensurate with fame, notably the Batman
and Diamonds and Pearls albums, and Most
Beautiful Girl in the World single. Demon-
strably influenced by George Clinton and
Sly Stone, Prince fully deserves equal rank-
ing and is likely to be an enduring
superstar.

### 1999.
Tracks: 1999 / Little red corvette / Delirious / Let's
pretend we're married / D.M.S.R. / Automatic / So-
mething in the water / Free / Lady cab driver / All the
critics love you in New York / International lover.
■ LP . . . . . . . . . . . . . . . . . . . . . . . . W 3809
WEA / Apr '83.
CD Set . . . . . . . . . . . . . . . . . . . . .923720 2
■ Double LP . . . . . . . . . . . . . . . . . . .923720 1
MC Set . . . . . . . . . . . . . . . . . . . . .923720 4
WEA / Nov '84 / WEA.

### 1999.
Tracks: 1999 / Uptown (On cassingle only) / Controversy (On cassingle only) / Dirty mind (On cassingle
only) / Sexuality (On cassingle only) / How come U
don't call me anymore (Not on cassingle) / D.M.S.R.
(On 12" only).
■ 12" . . . . . . . . . . . . . . . . . . . . . . . W 9896 T
■ 7" . . . . . . . . . . . . . . . . . . . . . . . . W 9896
■ MC Single. . . . . . . . . . . . . . . . . . W 9896 C
WEA / Feb '83.

### 1999/LITTLE RED CORVETTE (Prince & The Revolution).
Tracks: 1999 / Little red corvette / Uptown (On cassingle only) / Controversy (On cassingle only) / Sexy
dancer (On cassingle only).
■ MC Single. . . . . . . . . . . . . . . . . . W 1999 C
■ 12" . . . . . . . . . . . . . . . . . . . . . . . W 1999 T
■ 7" . . . . . . . . . . . . . . . . . . . . . . . . W 1999
WEA / Jan '85.

### 3 CHAINS O' GOLD.
Tracks: My name is Prince / Sexy M.F. / Love 2 the
9s / Blue light / I wanna melt with U / 7 / 3 chains o'
gold / Continental / Max.
VHS . . . . . . . . . . . . . . . . . . . .759938399-3
Warner Music Video / Aug '94 / WEA.

### 7.
Tracks: 7 (album edit) / 7 (album version) / 7 (acous-
tic version).
■ 12" . . . . . . . . . . . . . . . . . . . . . . . W 0147T
■ 7" . . . . . . . . . . . . . . . . . . . . . . . . W 0147
■ CD Single. . . . . . . . . . . . . . . . . . .W 0147CD
■ MC Single. . . . . . . . . . . . . . . . . . .W 0147C
Paisley Park / Nov '92.

### ALPHABET STREET.
Tracks: Alphabet Street / Alphabet Street (version) /
This is not music, this is a trip (On 12"/CD only).
■ 7" . . . . . . . . . . . . . . . . . . . . . . . . W 7900
■ CD Single. . . . . . . . . . . . . . . . . . .W 7900CD
■ MC Single. . . . . . . . . . . . . . . . . . .W 7900C
■ 12" . . . . . . . . . . . . . . . . . . . . . . . W 7900T
Paisley Park / Apr '88.

### ANOTHERLOVERHOLENYOHEAD (Prince & The Revolution).
Tracks: Anotherloverholenyohead / I wanna be your
lover / Mountains (On 7" double pack only) / Alexa
de Paris (edit) (On 7" double pack only).
■ 7" . . . . . . . . . . . . . . . . . . . . . . . . W 8521
■ 7" . . . . . . . . . . . . . . . . . . . . . . . . W 8521W
■ 7" Set . . . . . . . . . . . . . . . . . . . . . W 8521F
■ 12" . . . . . . . . . . . . . . . . . . . . . . .W 8521T
Paisley Park / Oct '86.

### ARMS OF ORION, THE.
Tracks: Arms of Orion / I love U in me.
■ 12" P.Disc. . . . . . . . . . . . . . . . . . W 2757 TP
WEA / Nov '89.
■ 12" . . . . . . . . . . . . . . . . . . . . . . . W 2757 T
■ 7" . . . . . . . . . . . . . . . . . . . . . . . . W 2757
■ CD Single . . . . . . . . . . . . . . . . . W 2757 CD
■ CD Single . . . . . . . . . . . . . . . . . W 2757 CDX
■ MC Single. . . . . . . . . . . . . . . . . . W 2757 C
WEA / Oct '89.

## AROUND THE WORLD IN A DAY.
**Tracks:** Around the world in a day / Paisley Park / Condition of the heart / Raspberry beret / Tambourine / America / Pop life / Ladder / Temptation.

■ LP . . . . . . . . . . . . . . . . . . . .925286 1
MC . . . . . . . . . . . . . . . . . . . .925286 4
Paisley Park / '85 / WEA.
CD . . . . . . . . . . . . . . . . . . . .925286 2
WEA / May '85 / WEA.

## BATDANCE.
**Tracks:** Batdance / 200 balloons / Batdance (mixes) (On W 2924TX 12" only).

■ 12" P.Disc. . . . . . . . . . . . . . . W 2924TP
■ CD Single . . . . . . . . . . . . . W 2924CDX
WEA / Jul '89.
■ 12" . . . . . . . . . . . . . . . . . . W 2924TX
■ 12" . . . . . . . . . . . . . . . . . . W 2924 T
■ 7" . . . . . . . . . . . . . . . . . . . W 2924
■ CD Single . . . . . . . . . . . . . . W 2924CD
■ MC Single. . . . . . . . . . . . . . . W 2924 C
WEA / Jun '89.

## BEAUTIFUL EXPERIENCE.
**Tracks:** Most beautiful girl in the world (mixes).

12" . . . . . . . . . . . . . . . . . . . NPG 60211
CD Single. . . . . . . . . . . . . . . . NPG 60212
MC Single . . . . . . . . . . . . . . . NPG 60214
New Power Generation / May '94 / Grapevine Distribution / THE.

## COME.
**Tracks:** Come / Space / Pheromone / Loose / Papa / Race / Dark / Solo / Letigo / Orgasm.

CD . . . . . . . . . . . . . . . . . . .936245700-2
LP . . . . . . . . . . . . . . . . . . .936245700-1
MC . . . . . . . . . . . . . . . . . . .936245700-4
Paisley Park / Aug '94 / WEA.

## CONTROVERSY.
**Tracks:** Private joy / Ronnie talk to Russia / Let's work / Annie Christian / Jack u off / Sexuality / Controversy / Do me baby.

■ LP . . . . . . . . . . . . . . . . . . . K 56950
WEA / Dec '81.
MC. . . . . . . . . . . . . . . . . . . K 456 950
WEA / Nov '81 / WEA.
CD . . . . . . . . . . . . . . . . . . . K 256 950
WEA / '84 / WEA.

## CONTROVERSY.
**Tracks:** Controversy / When you were mine.

■ 12" . . . . . . . . . . . . . . . . . . K 17866T
■ 7" . . . . . . . . . . . . . . . . . . . K 17866
WEA / Oct '81.

## CONTROVERSY.
**Tracks:** Controversy.

■ 12" . . . . . . . . . . . . . . . . . .W 0215P
■ CD Single . . . . . . . . . . . . W 0125CD2
■ CD Single . . . . . . . . . . . . W 0125CD1
■ MC Single. . . . . . . . . . . . . . .W 0215C
Paisley Park / Dec '93.

## CREAM (Prince & The New Power Generation).
**Tracks:** Cream / Horny pony / Gangster glam (On 12"/CD only).

■ 12" . . . . . . . . . . . . . . . . . . W 0061 T
■ 7" . . . . . . . . . . . . . . . . . . . W 0061
■ CD Single . . . . . . . . . . . . . W 0061 CD
■ MC Single. . . . . . . . . . . . . . W 0061 C
Paisley Park / Sep '91.

## DIAMONDS AND PEARLS (Prince & The New Power Generation).
**Tracks:** Thunder / Daddy pop / Diamonds and pearls / Cream / Strollin' / Willing and able / Gett off / Walk don't walk / Jughead / Money don't matter 2 night / Push / Insatiable / Live 4 love.

CD . . . . . . . . . . . . . . . . . . . 7599253792
■ LP . . . . . . . . . . . . . . . . . . . WX 432
MC . . . . . . . . . . . . . . . . . . . WX 432C
Paisley Park / Oct '91 / WEA.
DCC . . . . . . . . . . . . . . . . . .7599 253795
WEA / Jan '93 / WEA.

## DIAMONDS AND PEARLS (Prince & The New Power Generation).
**Tracks:** Diamonds and pearls / Q in doubt (instrumental) (On 7"/MC only) / Housebangers (On 12" only) / Cream (N.P.G. mix) (On 12" only) / 2 the wire (Creamy instrumental) (On CD only) / Things have gotta change (Tony M. rap) (On 12" only) / Do your dance (KC's remix) (On CD only).

■ 12" . . . . . . . . . . . . . . . . . . W 0075T
■ 7" . . . . . . . . . . . . . . . . . . . W 0075
■ CD Single . . . . . . . . . . . . . W 0075CDX
■ MC Single. . . . . . . . . . . . . . . W 0075C
WEA / Nov '91.

## DIAMONDS AND PEARLS.
**Tracks:** Gett off / Cream / Diamonds and pearls / Call the law / Insatiable / Thunder / Dr Feelgood / Jughead / Live 4 love.

VHS . . . . . . . . . . . . . . . . . 7599382916
WEA / Nov '92 / WEA.

## DIRTY MIND.
**Tracks:** Dirty mind / When you were mine / Do it all night / Gotta broken heart again / Uptown / Head / Sister / Party up.

CD . . . . . . . . . . . . . . . . . . . K 256 862
WEA / Jan '86 / WEA.
■ LP . . . . . . . . . . . . . . . . . . . K 56862
MC. . . . . . . . . . . . . . . . . . . K4 56862
WEA / '89 / WEA.

## DO IT ALL NIGHT.
**Tracks:** Do it all night / Head.

■ 12" . . . . . . . . . . . . . . . . . K 17768T
■ 7" . . . . . . . . . . . . . . . . . . . K 17768
WEA / Mar '81.

## FOR YOU.
**Tracks:** For you / In love / Soft and wet / Crazy you / Just as long as we're together / Baby / My love is forever / So blue / I'm yours.

■ LP . . . . . . . . . . . . . . . . . . . K 56989
MC. . . . . . . . . . . . . . . . . . . K4 56989
WEA / Sep '86 / WEA.
CD . . . . . . . . . . . . . . . . . . . K2 56989
WEA / Oct '87 / WEA.

## GETT OFF.
**Tracks:** Gett off / Violet the organ grinder / Gangster glam / Clockin' the jizz.

VHS . . . . . . . . . . . . . . . . . 7599382593
Warner Music Video / Nov '91 / WEA.

## GETT OFF (Prince & The New Power Generation).
**Tracks:** Not Advised.

CD . . . . . . . . . . . . . . . . . . . 9401380
■ LP . . . . . . . . . . . . . . . . . . . 9401382
Paisley Park / Aug '91 / WEA.

## GETT OFF (Prince & The New Power Generation).
**Tracks:** Gett off (mixes) / Horny pony.

■ 12" . . . . . . . . . . . . . . . . . . W 0056 T
■ 7" . . . . . . . . . . . . . . . . . . . W 0056
CD Single . . . . . . . . . . . . . W 0056 CD
■ MC Single. . . . . . . . . . . . . . W 0056 C
Paisley Park / Aug '91 / WEA.

## GIRLS AND BOYS (Prince & The Revolution).
**Tracks:** Girls and Boys / Under the cherry moon / She's always in my hair (edit) (On 7" double pack only) / 17 days (On 7" double pack only) / Erotic city (On 12" only).

■ 12" . . . . . . . . . . . . . . . . . .W 8586T
■ 7" . . . . . . . . . . . . . . . . . . . W 8586
■ 7" P.Disc . . . . . . . . . . . . . . .W 8586P
■ 7" Set . . . . . . . . . . . . . . . . W 8586F
Paisley Park / Aug '86.

## GLAM SLAM.
**Tracks:** Glam slam / Escape.

■ 12" . . . . . . . . . . . . . . . . . .W 7806T
■ 7" . . . . . . . . . . . . . . . . . . . W 7806
■ CD Single . . . . . . . . . . . . .W 7806CD
Paisley Park / Jul '88.

## GOTTA STOP (MESSIN' ABOUT).
**Tracks:** Gotta stop (messin' about) / I wanna be your lover (On second 7"/12" only) / Uptown (On first 7"/ 12" only) / Head (On 12"s only).

■ 12" . . . . . . . . . . . . . . . . . K 17819T
■ 7" . . . . . . . . . . . . . . . . . . . K 17819
WEA / Jun '81.
■ 12" . . . . . . . . . . . . . . . . . K 17819T
■ 7" . . . . . . . . . . . . . . . . . . . K 17819
WEA / May '81.

## HITS & B-SIDES, THE.
**Tracks:** When doves cry / Pop life / Soft and wet / I feel for you / Why you wanna treat me so bad / When you were mine / Uptown / Let's go crazy / 1999 / I could never take the place of your man / Nothing compares 2 U / Adore / Pink cashmere / Alphabet St. / Sign 'o' the times / Thieves in the temple / Diamonds and pearls / 7 / Controversy / Dirty mind / I wanna be your lover / Head / Do me, baby / Delirious / Little red corvette / I would die 4 U / Raspberry beret / If I was your girlfriend / Kiss / Peach / U got the look / Sexy M.F. / Gett off / Cream / Pope / Purple rain / Hello / 200 Balloons / Escape / Gotta stop (messin' about) / Horny toad / Feel U up / Girl / I love U in me / Erotic city / Shockadelica / Irresistible bitch

/ Scarlet pussy / La la la he he hee / She's always my hair / 17 Days / How come U don't call m anymore / Another lonely Christmas / God / 4 Th tears in your eyes / Power fantastic.

CD Set . . . . . . . . . . . . . . . 93624544
MC Set . . . . . . . . . . . . . . . 93624544
Paisley Park / Sep '93 / WEA.

## HITS 1, THE.
**Tracks:** When doves cry / Pop life / Soft and wet feel for you / Why you wanna treat me so bad / Whe you were mine / Uptown / Let's go crazy / 1999 could never take the place of your man / Nothin compares 2 U / Adore / Pink cashmere / Alphabet S / Sign 'o' the times / Thieves in the temple / Di monds and pearls / 7.

CD . . . . . . . . . . . . . . . . . . . 93624543
LP . . . . . . . . . . . . . . . . . . . 93624543
MC. . . . . . . . . . . . . . . . . . . 93624543
Paisley Park / Sep '93 / WEA.

## HITS 2, THE.
**Tracks:** Controversy / Dirty mind / I wanna be yo lover / Head / Do me, baby / Delirious / Little re corvette / I would die 4 U / Raspberry beret / If I w your girlfriend / Kiss / Peach / U got the look / Se M.F. / Gett off / Cream / Pope / Purple rain.

CD . . . . . . . . . . . . . . . . . . . 93624543
LP . . . . . . . . . . . . . . . . . . . 93624543
MC. . . . . . . . . . . . . . . . . . . 93624543
Paisley Park / Sep '93 / WEA.

## HITS COLLECTION, THE.
**Tracks:** Peach / Uptown / 1999 / Dirty mind / I wanr be your lover / Little red corvette / Kiss / Cream / 7 Sign 'o' the times / Raspberry beret / Diamonds ar pearls / I would die 4 U / Alphabet St. / Controvers

VHS . . . . . . . . . . . . . . . . . 7599 38371
Warner Music Video / Sep '93 / WEA.

## I COULD NEVER TAKE THE PLACE O YOUR MAN.
**Tracks:** I could never take the place of your man Hot thing (edit) / Hot thing (extended remix) (On 12 only).

■ 12" . . . . . . . . . . . . . . . . . . W 8288
■ 12" P.Disc. . . . . . . . . . . . . . W 8288 1
■ 7" . . . . . . . . . . . . . . . . . . . W 828
■ MC Single. . . . . . . . . . . . . .W 8288
Paisley Park / Nov '87.

## I WANNA BE YOUR LOVER.
**Tracks:** I wanna be your lover (edit) (Not on 12") Just as long as we're together / I wanna be yo lover (On 12" only).

■ 12" . . . . . . . . . . . . . . . . . .K 17537
■ 7" . . . . . . . . . . . . . . . . . . . K 1753
Warner Bros. / Dec '79.
■ 7" . . . . . . . . . . . . . . . . . . . K 1752
WEA / Jan '80.

## I WISH U HEAVEN.
**Tracks:** I wish U heaven / Scarlet pussy.

■ 12" . . . . . . . . . . . . . . . . . .W 7745
■ CD Single. . . . . . . . . . . . . .W 7745C
■ 7" . . . . . . . . . . . . . . . . . . . W 774
■ 7" . . . . . . . . . . . . . . . . . . .W 7745
Paisley Park / Oct '88.

## I WOULD DIE 4 U (Prince & Th Revolution).
**Tracks:** I would die 4 U / Another lonely Christmas Free (On W 9121T only).

■ 12" . . . . . . . . . . . . . . . . . . W 9121
■ 12" . . . . . . . . . . . . . . . . . . W 912
■ 7" . . . . . . . . . . . . . . . . . . . W 912
WEA / Dec '84.

## IF I WAS YOUR GIRLFRIEND.
**Tracks:** If I was your girlfriend / Shockadelica.

■ 12" P.Disc. . . . . . . . . . . . . . W 8334
■ 7" . . . . . . . . . . . . . . . . . . . W 8334
■ 7" P.Disc . . . . . . . . . . . . . . .W 8334
■ 7" . . . . . . . . . . . . . . . . . . . W 833
■ MC Single. . . . . . . . . . . . . .W 8334
■ 12" . . . . . . . . . . . . . . . . . . W 8334
Paisley Park / Jun '87.

## KISS (Prince & The Revolution).
**Tracks:** Kiss / Love or money.

■ 12" . . . . . . . . . . . . . . . . . .W 8751
■ 7" P.Disc . . . . . . . . . . . . . . .W 8751
■ 7" . . . . . . . . . . . . . . . . . . . W 875
Paisley Park / Feb '86.

## KISSES 4 U.
**Tracks:** Not Advised.

MC. . . . . . . . . . . . . . . . . . .MBAK 601
Baktabak / Oct '90 / Arabesque Ltd.

■ DELETE

**LET'S GO CRAZY (Prince & The Revolution).**
Tracks: Let's go crazy (edit) (On 7" only) / Take me with U / Let's go crazy (extended) (On 12" only) / Erotic City (On 12" only).
■ 12" . . . . . . . . . . . . . . . . . . . . . . W 2000T
■ 7" . . . . . . . . . . . . . . . . . . . . . . W 2000
WEA / Feb '85.

**LET'S WORK.**
Tracks: Let's work / Ronnie talk to Russia / Let's work (remix) (On 12" only).
■ 12" . . . . . . . . . . . . . . . . . . . . . K 17922T
■ 7" . . . . . . . . . . . . . . . . . . . . . K 17922
WEA / Apr '82.

**LETITGO.**
Tracks: Letitgo / Solo.
12" . . . . . . . . . . . . . . . . . . . . . .W 0260T
. . . . . . . . . . . . . . . . . . . . . . W 0260P
D Single . . . . . . . . . . . . . . . .W 0260CD
C Single . . . . . . . . . . . . . . . .W 0260C
Paisley Park / Aug '94 / WEA.

**LITTLE RED CORVETTE.**
Tracks: Little red corvette / Lady cab driver (edit) (On W 9688 only) / Horny toad (On W 9436 & W 9436T only) / Automatic (On W 9688T only) / International lover (On W 9688T only).
■ 12" . . . . . . . . . . . . . . . . . . . W 9688T
■ 7" . . . . . . . . . . . . . . . . . . . . W 9688
WEA / Apr '83.
■ 12" . . . . . . . . . . . . . . . . . . . W 9436T
■ 7" . . . . . . . . . . . . . . . . . . . . W 9436
WEA / Nov '83.

**LOVESEXY.**
Tracks: I no / Alphabet Street / Glam slam / Anna Stesia / Dance on / Lovesexy / When 2 r in love / I wish U heaven / Positivity.
■ LP . . . . . . . . . . . . . . . . . . . . . . WX 164
C. . . . . . . . . . . . . . . . . . . . . . . WX 164C
Paisley Park / May '88 / WEA.
D . . . . . . . . . . . . . . . . . . . . .925720 2
Paisley Park / May '88 / WEA.

**LOVESEXY (PART 1).**
Tracks: I know / Lovesexy / Glam slam / Cross / I wish you heaven / Kiss / Let's go crazy / When doves cry / Purple rain / 1999 / Alphabet street / When 2 R in love / Starfish and coffee / Raspberry beret / Condition of the heart / Strange relationship.
HS . . . . . . . . . . . . . . . . . . . PVC 3017 M
Palace Video / Apr '89 / Palace Video.

**LOVESEXY (PART 2).**
Tracks: Erotic city / Housequake / Slow love / Adore / Delirious / Jack U off / Sister / Adore (2) / I wanna be your lover / Head / When you were mine / Blues in C / Little red corvette / Controversy / Dirty mind / Superfunkycalifragisexy / Bob George / Anna Stesia.
HS . . . . . . . . . . . . . . . . . . . PVC 3018 M
Palace Video / Apr '89 / Palace Video.

**LOVESEXY (PARTS 1 & 2) (CD VIDEO).**
Tracks: Erotic city / Housequake / Slow love / Adore / Delirious / Jack U off / Sister / I wanna be your lover / Head / When we're mine / Blues in C (If I had a harem) / Little red corvette / Controversy / Dirty mind / Superfunkacalifragisexy / Bob George / Anna stesia / Lovesexy / Glam slam / Cross / I wish heaven / Kiss / Whe 2 R (are) in love / Starfish and coffee / Raspberry beret / Condition of the heart / Strange relationship / Let's go crazy / When doves cry / Purple rain / 1999 / Alphabet street.
D Video . . . . . . . . . . . . . . . . . . 080 844 1
Polygram Music Video / Nov '89 / PolyGram.

**MONEY DON'T MATTER 2 NIGHT.**
Tracks: Money don't matter 2 night / Call the law / wish (On 12"/CD only).
12" P.Disc. . . . . . . . . . . . . . . W 0091TP
7" . . . . . . . . . . . . . . . . . . . . . W 0091
CD Single . . . . . . . . . . . . . . W 0091CDX
MC Single. . . . . . . . . . . . . . . W 0091C
Paisley Park / Mar '92.

**MORNING PAPERS, THE.**
Tracks: Morning papers / Live 4 love.
7" . . . . . . . . . . . . . . . . . . . . . . W 0162
CD Single . . . . . . . . . . . . . . .W 0162CD
MC Single. . . . . . . . . . . . . . . .W 0162C
Paisley Park / Mar '93.

**MOST BEAUTIFUL GIRL IN THE WORLD, THE.**
Tracks: Most beautiful girl in the world, The.
2" . . . . . . . . . . . . . . . . . . . . . NPG 60150
. . . . . . . . . . . . . . . . . . . . . NPG 60157
D Single . . . . . . . . . . . . . . . NPG 60155
C Single . . . . . . . . . . . . . . . NPG 60159
New Power Generation / Mar '94 / Grapevine Distribution / THE.

---

**MOUNTAINS (Prince & The Revolution).**
Tracks: Mountains / Alexa de Paris.
■ 10" . . . . . . . . . . . . . . . . . . W 8711 TW
■ 12" P.Disc. . . . . . . . . . . . . . W 8711 TP
■ 7" . . . . . . . . . . . . . . . . . . . . W 8711
■ 12" . . . . . . . . . . . . . . . . . . . W 8711 T
WEA / May '86.

**MUSIC AND MEDIA INTERVIEW PICTURE DISC.**
Tracks: Not Advised.
■ LP P.Disc. . . . . . . . . . . . . PRINCE 1001
Music & Media / Feb '88.

**MY NAME IS PRINCE.**
Tracks: My name is prince.
■ 12" . . . . . . . . . . . . . . . . . . .W 0132T
■ 12" P.Disc. . . . . . . . . . . . . W 0132TP
■ 7" . . . . . . . . . . . . . . . . . . . W 0132
■ CD Single . . . . . . . . . . . . .W 0132CD
■ MC Single. . . . . . . . . . . . . .W 0132C
Paisley Park / Sep '92.

**NEW POWER GENERATION.**
Tracks: New power generation / New power generation pt. II / Melody cool (extended remix) (On 12"/CD only).
■ 12" . . . . . . . . . . . . . . . . . . .W 9525T
■ 12" P.Disc. . . . . . . . . . . . . W 9525TP
■ 7" . . . . . . . . . . . . . . . . . . . W 9525
■ CD Single . . . . . . . . . . . . .W 9525CD
■ MC Single. . . . . . . . . . . . . .W 9525C
Paisley Park / Nov '90.

**PAISLEY PARK.**
Tracks: Paisley Park / She's always in my hair / Paisley Park (remix) (On 12" only).
■ 7" P.Disc. . . . . . . . . . . . . . W 9052 P
■ 12" . . . . . . . . . . . . . . . . . . W 9052 T
■ 7" . . . . . . . . . . . . . . . . . . . W 9052
WEA / May '85.

**PARTYMAN.**
Tracks: Partyman (mixes) / Feel u up.
■ 12" . . . . . . . . . . . . . . . . . . .W 2814T
■ 12" P.Disc. . . . . . . . . . . . . .W 2814TP
■ 7" . . . . . . . . . . . . . . . . . . . W 2814
■ CD Single . . . . . . . . . . . . W 2814CDX
■ CD Single . . . . . . . . . . . . .W 2814CD
■ MC Single. . . . . . . . . . . . . .W 2814C
WEA / Aug '89.

**PEACH.**
Tracks: Peach (LP Version) / My name is Prince (On CD2 only) / I wish heaven (On CD2 only) / I wish heaven (On CD2 only) / Money Don't Matter 2 Nite (On CD1 only) / Partyman (On CD1 only) / Girls and boys (On CD2 only).
■ 7" . . . . . . . . . . . . . . . . . . . W 0210
■ CD Single . . . . . . . . . . . W 0210CD1
■ CD Single . . . . . . . . . . . W 0210CD2
MC. . . . . . . . . . . . . . . . . . . . W 0210C
Warner Bros. / Oct '93 / WEA.

**POP LIFE (Prince & The Revolution).**
Tracks: Pop life / Girl.
■ 12" . . . . . . . . . . . . . . . . . . . W 8858 T
■ 7" . . . . . . . . . . . . . . . . . . . W 8858
Paisley Park / Oct '85.

**PRINCE.**
Tracks: I wanna be your lover / Why you wanna treat me so bad / Sexy dancer / When we're dancing close and slow / With you / Bambi / Still waiting / I feel for you / It's gonna be lonely.
■ LP . . . . . . . . . . . . . . . . . . . . K 56772
MC. . . . . . . . . . . . . . . . . . . . . K4 56772
WEA / Jan '80 / WEA.
CD. . . . . . . . . . . . . . . . . . . . .K256772
WEA / '86 / WEA.

**PRINCE & THE REVOLUTION: LIVE (Prince & The Revolution).**
Tracks: Let's go crazy / Delirious / 1999 / Little red corvette / Take me with U / Do me, baby / Irresistible bitch / Possessed / How come U don't call me anymore / Let's pretend we're married / International lover / God / Computer blue / Darling Nikki / Beautiful ones / When doves cry / I would die 4 U / Baby I'm a star / Purple rain.
VHS . . . . . . . . . . . . . . . . . . . . 0413082
Polygram T.V. / Jan '86 / PolyGram.
VHS . . . . . . . . . . . . . . . . . . . CFV 01292
Channel 5 / Nov '87 / Channel 5 Video / P.R.O. Video / Gold & Sons.

**PRINCE INTERVIEW 86.**
Tracks: Not Advised.
■ 12" . . . . . . . . . . . . . . . . . . .PRINCE 212

---

■ 7" . . . . . . . . . . . . . . . . . . . PRINCE 2
■ 7" P.Disc . . . . . . . . . . . . . . PRINCE 2P
Wax / '89.

**PRINCE: INTERVIEW COMPACT DISC.**
Tracks: Not Advised.
CD P.Disc. . . . . . . . . . . . . . . CBAK 4018
Baktabak / Nov '89 / Arabesque Ltd.

**PRINCE: INTERVIEW PICTURE DISC.**
Tracks: Not Advised.
■ LP P.Disc . . . . . . . . . . . . . . . BAK 2056
Baktabak / Oct '87.

**PRINCE: INTERVIEW PICTURE DISC (COLLECTION).**
Tracks: Not Advised.
■ 7" Set . . . . . . . . . . . . . . . . BAKPAK 1014
Baktabak / Dec '88.

**PURPLE PARTY MIX, THE.**
Tracks: Purple party mix / Partyman (mixes) / Feel U up (short stroke).
■ 12" . . . . . . . . . . . . . . . . . . . W 2814TX
■ CD Single . . . . . . . . . . . . . W 2814CDT
WEA / Aug '89.

**PURPLE RAIN (Prince & The Revolution).**
Tracks: Purple rain / God.
■ 12" . . . . . . . . . . . . . . . . . . .W 9216T
■ 7" . . . . . . . . . . . . . . . . . . . W 9174
■ 7" . . . . . . . . . . . . . . . . . . . W 9216
WEA / Sep '84.

**RASPBERRY BERET.**
Tracks: Raspberry beret / Hello.
■ 12" . . . . . . . . . . . . . . . . . . W 8929 T
■ 7" . . . . . . . . . . . . . . . . . . . W 8929
Paisley Park / Jul '85.

**SEXY DANCER.**
Tracks: Sexy dancer / Bambi.
■ 12" . . . . . . . . . . . . . . . . . . K 17590T
■ 7" . . . . . . . . . . . . . . . . . . . K 17590
WEA / Apr '80.

**SEXY M.F.**
Tracks: Sexy M.F. / Strollin' / Daddy pop (On 12"/CD only).
■ 12" . . . . . . . . . . . . . . . . . . W 0123 T
■ 7" . . . . . . . . . . . . . . . . . . . W 0123
■ CD Single . . . . . . . . . . . . W 0123 CD
■ MC Single. . . . . . . . . . . . . W 0123 C
Paisley Park / Jun '92.

**SEXY M.F. (Prince & The New Power Generation).**
Tracks: Sexy M.F.
VHS . . . . . . . . . . . . . . . . . 7599383143
Warner Music Video / Aug '92 / WEA.

**SIGN O' THE TIMES.**
Tracks: Sign o' the times / Play in the sunshine / Little red corvette / Housequake / Slow love / I could never take the place of your man / Hot thing / Now's the time / U got the look / If I was your girlfriend / Forever in my life / It's gonna be a beautiful night / Cross.
VHS . . . . . . . . . . . . . . . . . PVC 3016 M
Palace Video / Sep '88 / Palace Video.
VHS . . . . . . . . . . . . . . . . . . .083863
4 Front / May '92 / PolyGram Video.

**SIGN OF THE TIMES.**
Tracks: Play in the sunshine / Housequake / Ballad of Dorothy Parker / It / Starfish and coffee / Slow love / Hot thing / Forever in my life / U got the look / If I was your girlfriend / Strange relationship / I could never take the place of your man / Cross / It's gonna be a beautiful night / Adore / Sign of the times.
CD Set . . . . . . . . . . . . . . . . 925 577 2
■ Double LP. . . . . . . . . . . . . . . WX 88
MC Set . . . . . . . . . . . . . . . . . WX 88C
Paisley Park / Apr '87 / WEA.

**SIGN OF THE TIMES.**
Tracks: Sign of the times / La la la, he he hee.
■ 12" . . . . . . . . . . . . . . . . . . .W 8399T
■ 7" . . . . . . . . . . . . . . . . . . . W 8399
Paisley Park / Feb '87.
■ 12" P.Disc. . . . . . . . . . . . . . W 8399TP
Paisley Park / Nov '87.

**SYMBOL.**
Tracks: My name is Prince / Sexy M.F. / Love 2 the 9s / Morning papers / Max / Segue / Blue light / I wanna melt with u / Sweet baby / Continental / Damn U / Arrogance / Flow / 7 / And God created woman / 3 chains o' gold / Sacrifice of Victor.
CD. . . . . . . . . . . . . . . . . . . 9362450372
■ LP . . . . . . . . . . . . . . . . . . . WX 490
MC. . . . . . . . . . . . . . . . . . . . WX 490C
Paisley Park / Oct '92 / WEA.

## THIEVES IN THE TEMPLE.
**Tracks:** Thieves in the temple (mixes).
- ■ 12" . . . . . . . . . . . . . . . . . . . . . W 9751 T
- ■ 12" P.Disc. . . . . . . . . . . . . . . . W 9751 TP
- ■ 7" . . . . . . . . . . . . . . . . . . . . . . W 9751
- ■ CD Single. . . . . . . . . . . . . . . W 9751 CD
- ■ MC Single. . . . . . . . . . . . . . . . W 9751 C

WEA / Aug '90.

## THUNDER.
**Tracks:** Thunder / Violet the organ grinder / Gett off (thrust dub).
- ■ 12" . . . . . . . . . . . . . . . . . . . . . W 0113 T
- ■ 12" P.Disc. . . . . . . . . . . . . . . . W 0113 TP

Paisley Park / Jun '92.

## U GOT THE LOOK.
**Tracks:** U got the look / Housequake / 7 minutes moquake (On 12"s only).
- ■ 12" . . . . . . . . . . . . . . . . . . . . . W 8289 T

WEA / Aug '87.
- ■ 12" P.Disc. . . . . . . . . . . . . . . . W 8289 TP

Paisley Park / Aug '87.
- ■ 7" . . . . . . . . . . . . . . . . . . . . . . W 8289

WEA / Aug '87.
- ■ MC Single. . . . . . . . . . . . . . . . W 8289 C

Paisley Park / Aug '87.

## WHEN DOVES CRY.
**Tracks:** When doves cry / 17 days / 1999 (Cassingle only) / DMSR (Cassingle only).
- ■ MC Single. . . . . . . . . . . . . . . . W 9286C
- ■ 12" . . . . . . . . . . . . . . . . . . . . . W 9286T
- ■ 7" . . . . . . . . . . . . . . . . . . . . . . W 9286

WEA / Jun '84.

## Prince Charles

### BEAT THE BUSH.
**Tracks:** Beat the bush / Mixers delight / Bonus beat.
- ■ 12" . . . . . . . . . . . . . . . . . . . . VS 610-12
- ■ 7" . . . . . . . . . . . . . . . . . . . . . . .VS 610

Virgin / Sep '83.

### CASH (Prince Charles & The City Beat Band).
**Tracks:** Cash / Jungle stomp.
- ■ 12" . . . . . . . . . . . . . . . . . . . . VS 596 12
- ■ 7" . . . . . . . . . . . . . . . . . . . . . . .VS 596

Virgin / Apr '83.

### COMBAT ZONE (Prince Charles & The City Beat Band).
**Tracks:** Stone cold killers / More money / Jailhouse rock / I need you / Skintight Tina / I want (to satisfy you) / City life / Combat zone.
- ■ LP . . . . . . . . . . . . . . . . . . . . . OVED 145
- ■ MC . . . . . . . . . . . . . . . . . . . . OVEDC 145

Virgin / Aug '88.

### I CAN'T STOP LOVING YOU (Prince Charles & The City Beat Band).
**Tracks:** I can't stop loving you.
- ■ 12" . . . . . . . . . . . . . . . . . . . . . CART 411

Carrere / Apr '87.

### IN THE STREET (Prince Charles & The City Beat Band).
**Tracks:** In the street.
- ■ 12" . . . . . . . . . . . . . . . . . . . . . GRPT 103
- ■ 7" . . . . . . . . . . . . . . . . . . . . . . .GRP 103

Greyhound / Apr '83.

### MORE MONEY.
**Tracks:** More money / Don't take the funk.
- ■ 12" . . . . . . . . . . . . . . . . . . . . VS 669 12
- ■ 7" . . . . . . . . . . . . . . . . . . . . . . .VS 669

Virgin / Mar '84.

### STONE KILLERS (Prince Charles & The City Beat Band).
**Tracks:** Don't take the funk / Cash (cash money) / Big chested girls / Cold as ice (NYC blues) / I'm a fool for love / Jungle stomp / Bush beat / Video freak (defend it).
- ■ LP . . . . . . . . . . . . . . . . . . . . . . . V 2271

Virgin / Apr '83.
- ■ MC . . . . . . . . . . . . . . . . . . . . OVEDC 128
- ■ LP . . . . . . . . . . . . . . . . . . . . . OVED 128

Virgin / Aug '88.

### WE CAN MAKE IT HAPPEN (Prince Charles & The City Beat Band).
**Tracks:** We can make it happen / Chaka beat / We can make it happen (vocal mix) (Track on Picture disc only) / Radio live (Track on Picture disc only) / Saxxy licks (Track on Picture disc only).
- ■ 12" . . . . . . . . . . . . . . . . . . . . . 12P 348
- ■ 12" P.Disc. . . . . . . . . . . . . . . . 12PD 348
- ■ 7" . . . . . . . . . . . . . . . . . . . . . . .7P 348

PRT / Mar '86.

---

## Prince, Steve

### SHOULD HAVE BEEN YOU.
**Tracks:** Should have been you.
- ■ 12" . . . . . . . . . . . . . . . . . . . . . .PAD 001

Pyramid / Nov '83.

---

## Princess

### AFTER THE LOVE HAS GONE.
**Tracks:** After the love has gone / After the dub has gone.
- ■ 12" . . . . . . . . . . . . . . . . . . . . . SUPET 103
- ■ 7" . . . . . . . . . . . . . . . . . . . . . . SUPE 103
- ■ 7" Set . . . . . . . . . . . . . . . . . . SUPETD 103
- ■ MC Single. . . . . . . . . . . . . . . SUPETX 103

Supreme / Oct '85.
- ■ 7" . . . . . . . . . . . . . . . . . . . . . SUPETG 103

Supreme / Oct '85.

### ALL FOR LOVE.
**Tracks:** Red hot / Shoot the moon / Risky business / Where are the stars / I cannot carry on / Programmed to love you (CD & Cassette only) / All for love / Jammin' with your love / I wish you love.
- ■ CD . . . . . . . . . . . . . . . . . . . . . 835 114-2
- ■ LP . . . . . . . . . . . . . . . . . . . . . POLH 35
- ■ MC . . . . . . . . . . . . . . . . . . . . .POLHC 35

Polydor / Jan '88.

### I CANNOT CARRY ON.
**Tracks:** I cannot carry on / I can't say goodbye.
- ■ 12" . . . . . . . . . . . . . . . . . . . . POSPX 893
- ■ 7" . . . . . . . . . . . . . . . . . . . . . POSP 893

Polydor / Oct '87.

### I'LL KEEP ON LOVING YOU.
**Tracks:** I'll keep on loving you / I'll keep on loving you (instrumental) / Say it / Keep on scratching (mix) / Chad's scratch mix.
- ■ 12" . . . . . . . . . . . . . . . . . . . . SUPET 105
- ■ 12" Remix. . . . . . . . . . . . . . . SUPETX 105
- ■ 7" . . . . . . . . . . . . . . . . . . . . . . SUPE 105
- ■ 7" Set . . . . . . . . . . . . . . . . . . SUPED 105

Supreme / Apr '86.
- ■ 12" P.Disc. . . . . . . . . . . . . . . . SUPETP 105

Supreme / Apr '86.

### IN THE HEAT OF A PASSIONATE MOMENT.
**Tracks:** In the heat of a passionate moment / I'll keep loving you (Extra track available on 12" version only.).
- ■ 12" . . . . . . . . . . . . . . . . . . . . SUPET 108
- ■ 7" . . . . . . . . . . . . . . . . . . . . . . SUPE 108

Supreme / Sep '86.

### LOVER DON'T GO.
**Tracks:** Lover don't go.
- ■ 12" . . . . . . . . . . . . . . . . . . . . . OUCT 1
- ■ 12" Remix. . . . . . . . . . . . . . . . OUCTR 1
- ■ 7" . . . . . . . . . . . . . . . . . . . . . . . OUC 1

Touch Tone / Jul '89.

### PRINCESS.
**Tracks:** In the heat of a passionate moment / I'll keep on loving you / After the love has gone / Say I'm your number one / If it makes you feel good / Tell me tomorrow / Anytimes the right time / Just a tease.
- CD . . . . . . . . . . . . . . . . . . . . . . . CDSU 1
- ■ LP . . . . . . . . . . . . . . . . . . . . . . . SU 1
- MC . . . . . . . . . . . . . . . . . . . . . . ZCSU 1

Supreme / Jul '86 / Pinnacle.

### RED HOT.
**Tracks:** Red hot / Programmed to love you / Red hot (ext. mix) (Track on 12" only.) / Red hot (dub mix) (Track on 12" only.) / Red hot (inferno mix) (Track on 12" remix version only.).
- ■ 12" . . . . . . . . . . . . . . . . . . . . POSPX 868
- ■ 12" Remix. . . . . . . . . . . . . . . POSPA 868
- ■ 7" . . . . . . . . . . . . . . . . . . . . . POSP 868

Polydor / May '87.

### SAY I'M YOUR NUMBER ONE.
**Tracks:** Say I'm your number one / Senza voce version / Funky sisters (Remix).
- ■ 12" . . . . . . . . . . . . . . . . . . . . SUPET 101
- ■ 12" . . . . . . . . . . . . . . . . . . . . SUPETZ 101
- ■ 12" Remix. . . . . . . . . . . . . . . SUPETX 101
- ■ 7" . . . . . . . . . . . . . . . . . . . . . . SUPE 101

Supreme / Jul '85.

### SAY I'M YOUR NUMBER ONE (OLD GOLD).
**Tracks:** Say I'm your number one / After the love has gone.
- 12" . . . . . . . . . . . . . . . . . . . . . .OG 4203

Old Gold / Jun '91 / Pickwick.

### TELL ME TOMORROW.
**Tracks:** Tell me tomorrow.
- ■ 12" . . . . . . . . . . . . . . . . . . . . . SUPET 106

---

- ■ 7" . . . . . . . . . . . . . . . . . . . . . . SUPE 106

Supreme / Jun '86.

## Principle, Jamie

### BABY WANTS TO RIDE.
**Tracks:** Baby wants to ride / Baby wants to ride(dub).
- ■ 12" . . . . . . . . . . . . . . . . . . . . . .DJ 903

DJ International / Nov '87.
- ■ 12" . . . . . . . . . . . . . . . . . . . . . FFRX 1
- ■ 7" . . . . . . . . . . . . . . . . . . . . . . FFR 1

FFRR / Feb '88.

### DATE WITH THE RAIN.
**Tracks:** Date with the rain.
- ■ 12" . . . . . . . . . . . . . . . . . . . . . A 7965 T
- ■ 7" . . . . . . . . . . . . . . . . . . . . . . .A 7965

East West / Jun '90.

### I'M GONNA MAKE YOU SCREAM.
**Tracks:** I'm gonna make you scream.
- ■ 7" . . . . . . . . . . . . . . . . . . . . . .DJW 102

DJ World Records (USA) / Oct '88.

### REBELS (GET RIGHTEOUS).
**Tracks:** Rebels (get righteous) / Baby wants to ride / Rebels (get righteous) - (acid mix) / Rebels (get righteous) - (house of trix mix).
- ■ 12" . . . . . . . . . . . . . . . . . . . . .FFRX 10
- ■ 12" Remix . . . . . . . . . . . . . . .FFRXR 10
- ■ 7" . . . . . . . . . . . . . . . . . . . . . . FFR 10

FFRR / Sep '88.

### WAITING ON MY ANGEL.
**Tracks:** Waiting on my angel.
- ■ 12" . . . . . . . . . . . . . . . . . . . . ZYX 5303

ZYX / Dec '85.

### YOU'RE ALL I'VE WAITED 4.
**Tracks:** You're all I've waited 4.
- ■ 12" . . . . . . . . . . . . . . . . . . . . . URBX 85

Urban / Jan '92.

## Project One

### PLAY PLAY GIRL.
**Tracks:** Play play girl / Strong love.
- ■ 12" . . . . . . . . . . . . . . . . . . . . . SVR 09

Sea View / Aug '85.

### RUB YOU THE RIGHT WAY.
**Tracks:** Rub you the right way.
- ■ 12" . . . . . . . . . . . . . . . . . . . . ZT 43702
- ■ 7" . . . . . . . . . . . . . . . . . . . . . ZB 43701
- ■ CD Single . . . . . . . . . . . . . . . ZD 43702

Motown / Jul '90.

### WRAP MY BODY TIGHT.
**Tracks:** Wrap my body tight (radio edit) / Wrap my body tight (funk radio) (Only on 7" single.) / Wrap my body tight (12" remake version) (Only on 12" and CD single.) / My my (live version) (extended mix) (Only on 12" single) / Wrap my body tight (soul mix) (Only on CD single) / Wrap my body tight (instrumental) (Only on CD single).
- ■ 12" . . . . . . . . . . . . . . . . . . . . ZT 44272
- ■ 7" . . . . . . . . . . . . . . . . . . . . . ZB 44271
- ■ CD Single . . . . . . . . . . . . . . . ZD 44272

Motown / Feb '91.

## Projection

### DON'T FAKE MY LOVE.
**Tracks:** Don't fake my love.
- ■ 7" . . . . . . . . . . . . . . . . . . . . . DAZZ 58

Elite Records / Sep '86.

### HEART AND SOUL.
**Tracks:** Heart and soul / Heart and soul (version).
- ■ 12" . . . . . . . . . . . . . . . . . . . .12CHIL 1?

Jam Today / Dec '89.

### LOVE STRUCK.
**Tracks:** Lovestruck / Turn your love (right around).
- ■ 12" . . . . . . . . . . . . . . . . . . . .12CHIL 1?

Jam Today / May '89.

### LOVESTRUCK.
**Tracks:** Lovestruck (wireless mix) / Dumbstruck.
- ■ 12" . . . . . . . . . . . . . . . . . . . . DAZZ 6?

Elite Records / Dec '86.

### TURN YOUR LOVE (RIGHT AROUND).
**Tracks:** Turn your love (right around) / Hardrock soul remix / Allstars (remix).
- ■ 12" . . . . . . . . . . . . . . . . . . . . DAZZ 4?

Elite Records / Mar '86.

### WHAT'S YOUR PROBLEM.
**Tracks:** What's your problem / What's your problem (version).
- ■ 12" . . . . . . . . . . . . . . . . . . . . 12CHIL

■ 7″ . . . . . . . . . . . . . . . . . . . . . .CHIL 8
Jam Today / Sep '88.

## Prysock, Arthur

**ALL MY LIFE.**
Tracks: All my life / This is what you mean to me.
■ 7″ . . . . . . . . . . . . . . . . . . . .2121 323
Polydor / Jun '77.

**ALL MY LIFE.**
Tracks: I wantcha baby / All my life / I love makin'
love to you / Baby I'm the one / When love is new /
One broken heart / All I need is you tonight / This is
what you mean to me.
■ LP . . . . . . . . . . . . . . . . . . . . . 2383441
Polydor / May '77.

**DOES IT AGAIN.**
Tracks: You can do it / Between hello and goodbye /
Shady lady / Love is what you make it / Born to be in
love with you again / Never gonna let you go again /
You're the best of all ladies / Since I fell for you.
■ LP . . . . . . . . . . . . . . . . . . . . . 2383481
Polydor / Jan '78.

**ROCK 'N' ROLL.**
Tracks: Jump, Red jump / Happy feet / Blow your
horn / Little Jamie / Zonked / Rock 'n' roll / Zip /
Fat's place / Alright, okay you win / That's the groovy
thing / Jumbo / Hand clappin'.
■ LP . . . . . . . . . . . . . . . . . . . OFF 6017
Official / '88.

**ROCKIN' GOOD WAY, A.**
Tracks: Baby (you've got what it takes) / I want to
thank you, girl / Bloodshot eyes / Teach me tonight /
Every morning baby / Passing strangers / Next time
you see me / Rockin' good way.
■ LP . . . . . . . . . . . . . . . . . . . . M 9139
Milestone / Feb '86.

**WHEN LOVE IS NEW.**
Tracks: When love is new / All I need is you tonight.
■ 7″ . . . . . . . . . . . . . . . . . . . . . 2058842
Polydor / Feb '77.

## Purdie, Bernard

**PURDIE GOOD.**
Tracks: Cold sweat / Montego Bay / Purdie good /
Wasteland / Everybody's talkin'. / You turn me on.
LP . . . . . . . . . . . . . . . . . . . . BGPD 1051
BGP / Mar '93 / Pinnacle.

**PURDIE GOOD/SHAFT.**
Tracks: Cold sweat / Montego bay / Purdie good /
Wasteland / Everybody's talkin' / You turn me on /
Theme from shaft / Way back home / Attica / Them
changes / Summer melody / Butterfingers.
CD . . . . . . . . . . . . . . . . . . . . CDBGPD 050
BGP / Mar '93 / Pinnacle.

**SHAFT.**
Tracks: Theme from Shaft / Way back home / Attica /
Them changes / Summer melody / Butterfingers.

LP . . . . . . . . . . . . . . . . . . . . . BGPD 1052
BGP / Mar '93 / Pinnacle.

## Purify, James

**I'M YOUR PUPPET.**
Tracks: I'm your puppet.
■ 7″ . . . . . . . . . . . . . . . . . . . . .6167 324
Mercury / Apr '76.

**MORNING GLORY.**
Tracks: Morning glory / Turning back the pages.
■ 7″ . . . . . . . . . . . . . . . . . . . . .6167 380
Mercury / Aug '76.

## Purify, James & Bobby

**100% PURIFIED SOUL.**
Tracks: I take what I want / Untie me / I've got
everything I need (I've got you) / Wish you didn't
have to go / Do unto me / You left the water running /
I don't want to have to wait / I'm your puppet / Shake
a tailfeather / So many reasons / I've been loving
you too long / Sixteen tons / Change is gonna come /
Let love come between us / Blame me (don't blame
my heart) / You can't keep a good man down.
■ LP . . . . . . . . . . . . . . . . . . . . CRB 1182
MC. . . . . . . . . . . . . . . . . . . TCCRB 1182
Charly R&B / Jun '88 / Charly.

**DO UNTO ME.**
Tracks: Do unto me / Everybody needs somebody to
love.
■ 7″ . . . . . . . . . . . . . . . . . . . . SS 2093
Stateside / '68.

**DO YOUR THING.**
Tracks: Do your thing / Why love.
■ 7″ . . . . . . . . . . . . . . . . . . . .CBX 520
Casablanca / Jul '76.

**GET CLOSER.**
Tracks: Get closer / What's better than love.
■ 7″ . . . . . . . . . . . . . . . . . . . 6167500
Mercury / Mar '77.

**GONNA GIVE HER ALL THE LOVE I'VE
GOT.**
Tracks: Gonna give her all the love I've got / You talk
too much.
■ 7″ . . . . . . . . . . . . . . . . . . . .CAN 119
Casablanca / Feb '78.

**I TAKE WHAT I WANT.**
Tracks: I take what I want / Sixteen tons.
■ 7″ . . . . . . . . . . . . . . . . . . . . SS 2039
Stateside / Jul '67.

**I'M YOUR PUPPET.**
Tracks: I'm your puppet / So many reasons.
■ 7″ . . . . . . . . . . . . . . . . . . . .SS 547
Stateside / Jun '66.

**JAMES & BOBBY PURIFY.**
Tracks: Everything must change / Fire's burning /
Get closer / Hope that we can be together soon / I

ain't got to love nobody else / I'm your puppet / Lay
me down easy / Morning glory / Starting all over
again / Turning back the pages / What's better than
love / When a man loves a woman.
■ LP . . . . . . . . . . . . . . . . . . . . 9100028
Mercury / Jun '77.

**LET LOVE COME BETWEEN US.**
Tracks: Let love come between us / I don't want to
have to wait.
■ 7″ . . . . . . . . . . . . . . . . . . . SS 2049
Stateside / Sep '67.

**PURE SOUNDS.**
Tracks: I take what I want / Hello there / 16 tons / I
don't want to have to wait / When something is
wrong / Let love come between us / Shake a tail
feather / Soothe me / Goodness gracious / I love you
/ You don't love me.
■ LP . . . . . . . . . . . . . . . . . . . SBLL 101
Bell / Mar '68.

**SHAKE A TAIL FEATHER.**
Tracks: Shake a tailfeather / Goodness gracious.
■ 7″ . . . . . . . . . . . . . . . . . . . SS 2016
Stateside / Apr '67.

**SLOW DANCING (Purify Brothers).**
Tracks: Slow dancing / Fire's burning.
■ 7″ . . . . . . . . . . . . . . . . . . . .6167 535
Mercury / Jun '77.

**WISH YOU DIDN'T HAVE TO GO.**
Tracks: Wish you didn't have to go / You can't keep a
good man down.
■ 7″ . . . . . . . . . . . . . . . . . . . .SS 595
Stateside / '67.

**YOU AND ME TOGETHER FOREVER.**
Tracks: I can't stop / All the love I've got / Man can't
be a man without a woman / You talk too much / Do
your thing / Silly little girl / I need love / Still thinkin'
bout you / Why you / You and me together forever.
■ LP . . . . . . . . . . . . . . . . . . . CAN 2025
Casablanca / Apr '78.

## Push

**MIDNIGHT.**
Tracks: Midnight / Who's gonna.
■ 12″ . . . . . . . . . . . . . . . . . . . EXCL 532
■ 7″ . . . . . . . . . . . . . . . . . . . .EXC 532
Excaliber / May '83.

**MY HEART.**
Tracks: My heart.
■ 12″ . . . . . . . . . . . . . . . . . . . EXCL 524
■ 7″ . . . . . . . . . . . . . . . . . . . .EXC 524
Excaliber / Oct '82.

# Q

## Q-Feel

**DANCING IN HEAVEN.**
**Tracks:** Dancing in heaven / At the top.
■ 12"........................JIVET 7
■ 7"..........................JIVE 7
Jive / Apr '82.

**DOCTOR ON THE RADIO.**
**Tracks:** Doctor on the radio.
■ 7"........................JIVE 001
Jive / Jul '81.

**HEROES NEVER DIE.**
**Tracks:** Heroes never die.
■ 12".......................JIVET 52
■ 7".........................JIVE 52
Jive / Feb '84.

## Quadraphonics

**BETCHA IF YOU CHECK IT OUT.**
**Tracks:** Betcha if you check it out.
■ 7".......................CS 2045
Contempo (1) / May '75.

## Quaite, Christine

**LONG AFTER TONIGHT IS ALL OVER.**
**Tracks:** Long after tonight is all over / I'm hoping.
■ 7"........................SS 482
Stateside / Jan '66.

## Quazar

**FUNK 'N' ROLL.**
**Tracks:** Funk 'n' roll / Savin' my love for a rainy day.
■ 7".......................ARIST 224
Arista / Nov '78.

**QUAZAR.**
**Tracks:** Funk with a big foot / Funk with a capital G / Funk and roll / Workin' on the buildin' / Your lovin' is easy / Love me baby / Savin' my love for a rainy day / Starlight circus / Shades of quaze.
■ LP......................ARTY 157
Arista / Dec '78.

## Que

**GOOD LOVE (Que featuring Ruby Turner).**
**Tracks:** Not Advised.
■ 12"......................BCQ 1001
CD........................BCQCD 1001
MC........................BCQMC 1001
Black Current / Oct '92 / Grapevine Distribution.

## Quiet Boys

**CAN'T HOLD THE VIBE.**
**Tracks:** Inside your mind / Let it go / Give it all u got / Make me say it again girl / Roaring fast / Long way from me / Sim ting / Att etude / Modal / Can't hold the vibe / Mellow blow.
CD....................JAZIDCD 045

LP....................JAZIDLP 045
Acid Jazz / Mar '92 / Vital Distribution.

**LET THE GOOD TIMES ROLL.**
**Tracks:** Let the good times roll.
■ 12"....................JAZID 10 T
Acid Jazz / Feb '89.

**MAKE ME SAY IT AGAIN GIRL (Quiet Boys & Camelle Hinds).**
**Tracks:** Make me say it again girl.
■ 12"....................JAZID 44T
Acid Jazz / Nov '91.

**MODAL.**
**Tracks:** Modal.
■ 12"....................JAZID 34T
Acid Jazz / Jul '91.

## Quiet Elegance

**YOU GOT MY MIND MESSED UP.**
**Tracks:** After you / Mama said / Do you love me / Something you got / I'm afraid of losing you / You brought the sun back into my life / I need love / Tired of being alone / Will you be my man (in the morning) / You got my mind messed up / Your love is strange / Roots of love / Love will make you feel better / Have you been making out OK / Set the record straight / How's your love life baby.
CD....................HIUKCD 109
Hi / Dec '89 / Pinnacle.

## R. Kelly

Among the biggest sensations of recent years, Chicago's R. Kelly snatched reins from Bobby Brown, mixing swing and bedroom soul. Signed after his group MGM won talent contest, Kelly scored U.S. success with debut *Born Into the '90s*. Stardom escalated with *12 Play*, from which *Bump N' Grind* topped charts for four weeks. Kelly has enjoyed lower profile in U.K., where his releases tended to enjoy lengthy periods in lower reaches of charts; among his early non-hits was 1993 cover of Stevie Wonder's 1966 hit *Hey Love*. Nonetheless, he sold out four nights at prestigious Hammersmith Apollo in early '94. He has also guided teenage protege Aaliyah into charts, written for Changing Faces, and remixed Whitney and Janet. Kelly's own tunes, including rerelease of his first, minor chart entry *She's Got That Vibe*, finally took him into Top 40 in latter half of '94.

### 12 PLAY.
Tracks: Not Advised.
- **CD**...................**CHIP 144**
- **LP**....................**HIP 144**
- **MC**....................**HIPC 144**
Jive / Nov '93.

### BORN INTO THE 90'S (R. Kelly & Public Announcement).
Tracks: Not Advised.
CD........................**CHIP 123**
- **LP**....................**HIP 123**
MC.........................**HIPC 123**
Jive / Feb '92 / BMG.

### BUMP 'N' GRIND.
Tracks: Bump 'n' grind (Mixes).
- **12"**....................**JIVET 350**
- **CD Single**.............**JIVECD 350**
Jive / Feb '94.

### SEX ME.
Tracks: Sex me.
- **7"**.....................**JIVE 346**
- **12"**....................**JIVET 346**
- **CD Single**.............**JIVECD 346**
Jive / Oct '93.

### SHE'S GOT THAT VIBE (R. Kelly & Public Announcement).
Tracks: She's got that vibe (Mixes).
- **7"**.....................**JIVE 292**
- **CD Single**.............**JIVECD 292**
- **MC Single**.............**JIVEC 292**
- **12"**....................**JIVET 292**
Jive / May '92.
- **12"**....................**JIVET 364**
- **CD Single**.............**JIVECD 364**
- **MC Single**.............**JIVEC 364**
Jive / Oct '94 / BMG.

### SUMMER BUNNIES.
Tracks: Summer bunnies (Mixes).
12"........................**JIVET 358**
CD Single..................**JIVERCD 358**
CD Single..................**JIVECD 358**
MC Single..................**JIVEC 358**
Jive / Aug '94 / BMG.

### YOUR BODY'S CALLING.
Tracks: Your body's calling (Mixes).
- **12"**....................**JIVET 353**
- **CD Single**.............**JIVECD 353**
- **CD Single**.............**JIVERCD 353**
- **MC Single**.............**JIVEC 353**
Jive / May '94.

## Radcliffe, Jimmy

### LONG AFTER TONIGHT IS ALL OVER.
Tracks: Not Advised.
- **7"**.......................**SS 374**
Stateside / Feb '65.

## Rae, Fonda

### HEOBAH.
Tracks: Heobah.
- **7"**.......................**TMT 6**
T.M.T. / Sep '83.

### OVER LIKE A FAT RAT.
Tracks: Over like a fat rat.
- **12"**...................**VSL 5023**
- **7"**.....................**VS 5023**
Vanguard (1) / Jul '82.

### TOUCH ME.
Tracks: Touch me / Who do you love.
12"........................**OG 4205**
Old Gold / Jun '91 / Pickwick.

### TOUCH ME.
Tracks: Touch me.
- **12"**..................**MKHAN 28**
- **7"**....................**KHAN 28**
Streetwave / Oct '84.

## Raelettes

### BAD WATER.
Tracks: Bad water / That goes to show you.
- **7"**......................**6121002**
Tangerine / Jul '71.

## Ragland, Lou

### I TRAVEL ALONE.
Tracks: Travel alone / Didn't I tell you / Since you said you'd be mine.
- **7"**.....................**BURN 4**
Inferno (1) / Dec '83.

## Rah Band

### ACROSS THE BAY.
Tracks: Jammin' on the byte / Take some thyme.
- **12"**...................**PT 41100**
- **7"**....................**PB 41099**
RCA / Jan '87.

### ARE YOU SATISFIED (FUNKA NOVA).
Tracks: Are you satisfied / Shadow of your love.
- **12"**...................**RCAT 470**
- **7"**....................**RCA 470**
RCA / Dec '84.

### CLOUDS ACROSS THE MOON.
Tracks: Clouds across the moon.
- **12"**...................**PT 40025**
- **7"**....................**PB 40025**
RCA / Mar '85.

### CRUNCH AND BEYOND, THE.
Tracks: Crunch / Electric fling / Concrete / Is anybody there / Beyond / Spacerace / Turkey roll / Vampire vamp / Woogie boogie / Crunch, The (reprise).
- **LP**....................**EBY 1001**
- **MC**...................**EBK 1001**
Ebony (1) / '79.

### CRUNCH, THE.
Tracks: Crunch / Crunch, The (part 2).
- **7"**......................**GD 7**
Good Earth / Jul '77.
- **12"**...................**PT 40482**
- **7"**....................**PB 40481**
RCA / Nov '85.

### DOWNSIDE UP.
Tracks: Downside up / Dream on.
- **12"**..................**DJR 10967**
- **7"**...................**DJS 10967**
DJM / '82.

### FALCON.
Tracks: Falcon / Falcon 2 / Toyko flyer.
- **12"**..................**DJR 18014**
D.E.M. / Sep '80.
- **7"**...................**DJS 10954**
DJM / '82.

### IS ANYBODY THERE.
Tracks: Is anybody there / Vampire vamp.
- **7"**......................**EYE 9**
Ebony (2) / '79.

### JIGGERY POKERY.
Tracks: Jiggery pokery / Porridge.
- **7"**......................**EYE 4**
Ebony (2) / '79.

### MESSAGES FROM THE STARS.
Tracks: Messages from the stars.
- **12"**....................**TMTT 5**
- **7"**.....................**TMT 5**
T.M.T. / Jul '83.

### MYSTERY.
Tracks: Clouds across the moon / Night wind / Sorry doesn't make it anymore / Float / Mystery boy / Are you satisfied / Shadow of your love / Out on the edge.
- **LP**....................**PL 70640**
RCA / Mar '85.

### PAST PRESENT AND FUTURE.
Tracks: What'll become of the children / Star dance / Perfumed garden / Rock me down to Rio / Are you satisfied / Clouds across the moon / Messages from the stars / Falcon / Sam the samba man / Crunch.
- **LP**....................**PL 70888**
- **MC**...................**PK 70888**
RCA / Oct '85.

### PERFUMED GARDEN.
Tracks: Perfumed garden / Funk me down.
- **12"**....................**KRT 5**
- **7"**.....................**KR 5**
KR / Apr '82.

### QUESTIONS (WHAT YOU GONNA DO).
Tracks: Questions / Falcon 2 (on 12" only).
- **12"**...................**SNDS 1**
- **7"**....................**SND 1**
S.O.U.N.D Recordings / Nov '83.

### RAH BAND.
Tracks: Falcon / Downside up / Dream on / Slide / Blue horizon drifter / Dancing on the moon / Ride.
- **LP**...................**DJF 20573**
MC.......................**DJH 40573**
DJM / '82 / PolyGram.

### RIDING ON A FANTASY.
Tracks: Riding on a fantasy / Rock me down to Rio.
- **12"**..................**DJR 10973**
- **7"**...................**DJS 10973**
DJM / Jul '81.

### RUN FOR THE SUN.
Tracks: Run for the sun / Life after love.
- **12"**...................**PT 41413**
- **7"**....................**PB 41413**
RCA / Jul '87.

### SAM THE SAMBA MAN.
Tracks: Sam the samba man.
- **12"**....................**TMTT 3**
- **7"**.....................**TMT 3**
T.M.T. / Apr '83.
- **12"**..................**RAHXL 901**
- **7"**...................**RAHS 901**
S.O.U.N.D Recordings / Jun '84.

### SILVERBIRD.
Tracks: Silverbird.
- **7"**....................**EAGLE 12**
I'll Call You (I.C.Y.) Records / Aug '89.

### SLIDE.
Tracks: Slide / Drat that cat.
- **12"**..................**DJR 10964**
- **7"**...................**DJS 10964**
DJM / '82.

### SOMETHING ABOUT THE MUSIC.
Tracks: Run 4 the sun / Something about the music / Take some thyme / Nothing in the world / Woman's life / Adventures of E man / Life after love / Jammin' on the byte / Across the bay / Road of no return.
- **LP**...................**PL 71560**
RCA / '87.

## SORRY DOESN'T MAKE IT ANYMORE.
Tracks: Sorry doesn't make it anymore / Nightwinds.
■ 12" . . . . . . . . . . . . . . . . . . . . PT 40192
■ 7" . . . . . . . . . . . . . . . . . . . . PB 40191
RCA / Jun '85.

## SWEET FORBIDDEN.
Tracks: Sweet forbidden / Perfect stranger.
■ 12" . . . . . . . . . . . . . . . . . . . . PT 40780
■ 7" . . . . . . . . . . . . . . . . . . . . PB 40779
RCA / Jun '86.

## TEARS AND RAIN.
Tracks: Tears and rain / Hungry for your jungle love /
Party games.
■ 12" . . . . . . . . . . . . . . . . . . . . KRT 10
■ 7" . . . . . . . . . . . . . . . . . . . . KR 10
KR / Jul '82.

## TIME KEEPS TEARING US APART.
Tracks: Time keeps tearing us apart / Adventures of
E-man / Aliens are coming (inst.mix).
■ 12" . . . . . . . . . . . . . . . . . . . . NINE 21
■ 7" . . . . . . . . . . . . . . . . . . . . NINE 721
Nine O Nine / Oct '88.

## TOKYO FLYER.
Tracks: Tokyo flyer / Tokyo flyer (instrumental).
■ 7" . . . . . . . . . . . . . . . . . . . . DJS 10930
DJM / '82.

## UPPER CUTS.
Tracks: Not Advised.
■ LP . . . . . . . . . . . . . . . . . . . . SNDLP 601
S.O.U.N.D Recordings / Apr '84.

## WHAT'LL BECOME OF THE CHILDREN.
Tracks: What'll become of the children / Out on the
edge / Float.
■ 12" . . . . . . . . . . . . . . . . . . . . PT 40374
■ 7" . . . . . . . . . . . . . . . . . . . . PB 40373
RCA / Sep '85.

## Rainbow People

## LIVING IN A DREAM WORLD.
Tracks: Living in a dreamworld / Nobody knows
what's going on.
■ 7" . . . . . . . . . . . . . . . . . . . . CC 14
Casino Classics / Nov '79.

## Rallo, Tony

## BURNIN' ALIVE (Rallo, Tony & The Mid-
night Band).
Tracks: Holdin' on / Burnin' alive / Fais l'amour /
Travelin' flights of m mind / Say you believe.
■ LP . . . . . . . . . . . . . . . . . . . . CABLP 5001
Calibre / Apr '80.

## HOLDIN' ON (Rallo, Tony & The Midnight
Band).
Tracks: Holdin' on / Burnin' alive.
■ 7" . . . . . . . . . . . . . . . . . . . . CAB 150
Calibre / Feb '80.

## LIFE.
Tracks: Not Advised.
■ LP . . . . . . . . . . . . . . . . . . . . LD 5003
MC. . . . . . . . . . . . . . . . . . . . . LDC 5003
Daylight / '86 / Daylight Records.

## Randolph, Barbara

## BREAKING INTO MY HEART.
Tracks: Not Advised.
■ CD . . . . . . . . . . . . . . . . . . . . MOTCCD 86
Motor City / Oct '92.

## I GOT A FEELING.
Tracks: I got a feeling / Can I get a witness (On 1981
issue only.) / You got me hurtin' all over.
■ 7" . . . . . . . . . . . . . . . . . . . . TMG 628
Tamla Motown / Nov '67.
■ 7" . . . . . . . . . . . . . . . . . . . . TMG 788
Tamla Motown / Sep '71.
■ 7" . . . . . . . . . . . . . . . . . . . . TMG 1133
Motown / Oct '81.

## Rare Earth

## BAND TOGETHER.
Tracks: Warm ride / You / Love is what you get /
Love do me right / Dreamer / Maybe the magic /
Love music / Rock 'n' roll man / Mota molata.
■ LP . . . . . . . . . . . . . . . . . . . . PDL 2088
Prodigal / Jul '78.

## DIFFERENT WORLD.
Tracks: Not Advised.
CD. . . . . . . . . . . . . . . . . . . . . .341002

## MC. . . . . . . . . . . . . . . . . . . . . .241004
Koch International / Feb '93 / Koch International.

## ECOLOGY.
Tracks: Born to wander / Long time leavin' / I know
I'm losing you / Satisfaction guaranteed / Nice place
to visit / No. 1 man / Eleanor Rigby.
■ LP . . . . . . . . . . . . . . . . . . . . STML 11180
Tamla Motown / Mar '71.

## GET READY.
Tracks: Magic key / Tobacco road / Feelin' alright /
In bed / Train to nowhere / Get ready.
■ LP . . . . . . . . . . . . . . . . . . . . STML 11165
Motown / Nov '70.

## GRAND SLAM.
Tracks: My eyes only / Save me, save me / When a
man loves a woman / I heard it through the grapevine / You got my love / I wish it would rain / I can
feel my love risin' / Stop her on sight / Mighty good
love.
■ LP . . . . . . . . . . . . . . . . . . . . PDL 2009
Prodigal / Nov '78.

## GREATEST HITS AND RARE CLASSICS.
Tracks: Get ready / Generation (light up the sky) / (I
know) I'm losing you / When Joanie smiles / Born to
wander / Here comes the night / I just want to
celebrate / Love shines down / Good time Sally / Hey
big brother / We're gonna have a good time / Big
John is my name / Chained / Warm ride / I can feel
my love risin' / Keepin' me outof the storm / It makes
you happy (but it ain't gonna last!) / Midnightlady /
Hum along and dance / Fresh from the can.
■ CD . . . . . . . . . . . . . . . . . . . . WD 72740
Motown / Dec '91.

## MADE IN SWITZERLAND.
Tracks: Not Advised.
CD. . . . . . . . . . . . . . . . . . . . . LICD9.00865
Line / Nov '89 / C.M. Distribution / Grapevine Distri-
bution / A.D.A. Distribution / Conifer Records.

## WARM RIDE.
Tracks: Warm ride / Would you like to come along.
■ 7" . . . . . . . . . . . . . . . . . . . . PROD 9
Prodigal / May '78.

## Rare Essence

## LOVE TALKING.
Tracks: Love talking / Love talking (version).
■ 7" . . . . . . . . . . . . . . . . . . . . PVT 149
Private Stock / Apr '78.

## Rare Moods

## DANCIN' THRO THE NIGHT.
Tracks: Dancin' thro the night / Dancin' thro the night
(dub).
■ 12" . . . . . . . . . . . . . . . . . . . . CRT 89
■ 7" . . . . . . . . . . . . . . . . . . . . CR 89
Creole / Mar '86.

## I'VE GOT LOVE.
Tracks: I've got love.
■ 12" . . . . . . . . . . . . . . . . . . . . 12 AGR 5
■ 7" . . . . . . . . . . . . . . . . . . . . AGR 5
AGR / Sep '86.

## Raw Silk

## DO IT TO THE MUSIC.
Tracks: Do it to the music.
■ 12" . . . . . . . . . . . . . . . . . . . . KRT 14
■ 7" . . . . . . . . . . . . . . . . . . . . KR 14
KR / Sep '82.

## JUST IN TIME.
Tracks: Just in time.
■ 12" . . . . . . . . . . . . . . . . . . . . WEND 122
■ 7" . . . . . . . . . . . . . . . . . . . . WEND 2
West End / Sep '83.

## Raw Stylus

## MANY WAYS.
Tracks: Not Advised.
■ 12" . . . . . . . . . . . . . . . . . . . . MW 002
Mo Wax / Nov '92.

## USE ME.
Tracks: Use me (mixes) / Boom.
■ 12" . . . . . . . . . . . . . . . . . . . . JAZID 069T
■ CD Single. . . . . . . . . . . . . . . . . . JAZID 069CD
Acid Jazz / Apr '93.

## Raw To The Core

## DON'T ASK MY NEIGHBOUR (Raw To
The Core & Samantha Scott).
Tracks: Don't ask my neighbour.
12" . . . . . . . . . . . . . . . . . . . . KGR 12003
KGR / Jan '94 / Jetstar.

## IF YOU WERE HERE TONIGHT (Raw To
The Core & Mark Kelsor).
Tracks: If you were here tonight.
12" . . . . . . . . . . . . . . . . . . . . FJ 12004
FJ / Jun '94 / Jetstar.

## IN THE MOOD.
Tracks: Not Advised.
LP . . . . . . . . . . . . . . . . . . . . KGRLP 001
KGR / Oct '94 / Jetstar.

## Rawls, Lou

As singer with Pilgrim Travelers Quartet,
Rawls supported Sam Cooke on 1958 tour.
Three years and one coma later (latter the
result of car crash on same tour), he sang
on Cooke's Bring It On Home To Me, then
launched solo career on Capitol. He finally
scored R&B chart-topper with Love Is A
Hurtin' Thing, and by '67 warranted name-
check alongside Otis Redding, James
Brown, Sam & Dave and Wilson Pickett on
Arthur Conley's Sweet Soul Music. Further
recordings brought him crossover success
and two Grammies, but fortunes slumped in
early '70s. Salvation came in form of mighty
Philadelphia International, with whom
Rawls recorded international smash You'll
Never Find Another Love Like Mine in '76.
Renewed R&B success carried him into
'80s, when he switched to Epic for albums
boasting illustrious names like Mtume/Lu-
cas, Thom Bell, Dexter Wansel and Garfield
the Cat (Here Comes Garfield, '86). After
one-album reunion with Gamble & Huff in
'87, he signed to jazz label Blue Note, continuing penchant for big-name collaborators
and modest sales.

## ALL THINGS IN TIME.
Tracks: You're the one / Need you forever / This
song will last forever / Let's fall in love all over again
/ From now on / Pure imagination / You'll never find
another love like mine / Time / Groovy people.
■ LP . . . . . . . . . . . . . . . . . . . . PIR 81368
Philadelphia Int. / Jun '76.

## ALL TIME LOVE.
Tracks: All time love / When we were young.
■ 7" . . . . . . . . . . . . . . . . . . . . A 4578
Epic / Oct '84.

## ARE YOU WITH ME?.
Tracks: Are you with me / Are you with me
(Instrumental).
■ 12" . . . . . . . . . . . . . . . . . . . . TA 6966
■ 7" . . . . . . . . . . . . . . . . . . . . A 6966
Epic / Mar '86.

## AT LAST.
Tracks: At last / Two years of torture / Fine brown
frame / Good intentions / That's where it's at / If I
were a magician / You can't go home / Room with a
view / After the lights go down low / She's no lady /
Oh what a night.
■ LP . . . . . . . . . . . . . . . . . . . . B1 91937
■ MC. . . . . . . . . . . . . . . . . . . . TCB1 91937
■ CD . . . . . . . . . . . . . . . . . . . . CDB1 91937
Blue Note / Jun '89.

## AT LAST.
Tracks: At last / Room with a view / They call it
Stormy Monday (12" & CD single only.) / She's no
lady (CD single only.).
■ 12" . . . . . . . . . . . . . . . . . . . . 12BLUE 7
■ 7" . . . . . . . . . . . . . . . . . . . . BLUE 7
■ CD Single. . . . . . . . . . . . . . . . . . CDBLUE 7
■ MC Single. . . . . . . . . . . . . . . . . . TCBLUE 7
Blue Note / Feb '90.

## BEST OF LOU RAWLS.
Tracks: Dead end street / Tobacco Road / Soul
serenade / Trouble down here below / Down here on
the ground / It was a very good year / Trouble in
mind / Beautiful friendship / Love is a hurtin' thing /
World of trouble / Nobody by me / One for my baby /
Stormy weather / God bless the child / Three o'clock
in the morning / Your good thing.
■ LP . . . . . . . . . . . . . . . . . . . . CAPS 1027
Capitol / Apr '79.

## CLASSIC SOUL.
Tracks: Sad song / Trying as hard as I can / I love
you yes I do / Season of the witch / I wonder / I want

336                                                           ■ DELETED

to be loved / Your good thing is about to end / When a man loves a woman / Gentle on my mind.
■ **LP** . . . . . . . . . . . . . . . . . . . . **BMM 005**
Blue Moon (1) / Apr '86.

## CLOSE COMPANY.
**Tracks:** All time lover / In the middle of the night / Close company / Pretty eyes / When we were young / Ready or not / Forever i do / Lady in my life / ay it again / Sunshine.
■ **LP** . . . . . . . . . . . . . . . . . . . **EPC 26127**
Epic / Dec '84.

## DEAD END STREET.
**Tracks:** Dead end street / Yes it hurts doesn't it.
■ **7"** . . . . . . . . . . . . . . . . . . . **CL 15499**
Capitol / Apr '67.

## FEELIN' GOOD.
**Tracks:** Letter / My ancestors / For what it's worth / Even when you cry / Hangups / Evil woman / My son / Feeling good / Encore / I'm gonna use what I got / Gotta find a way.
■ **LP** . . . . . . . . . . . . . . . . . . . . **ST 2864**
Capitol / May '68.

## FOR YOU MY LOVE.
**Tracks:** For you my love / If I had my life to live over / Nobody but me / Whispering grass / Gee baby, ain't I good to you / If it's the last thing I do / Blues for the weepers / That's your red wagon / Just squeeze me (but don't tease me) / It's you / I love you yes I do / I wonder / Wee baby blues / I wonder where our love has gone.
**CD** . . . . . . . . . . . . . . . . . . **CDP 8289792**
Capitol Jazz / Oct '94 / EMI.

## HEART AND SOUL OF LOU RAWLS.
**Tracks:** You'll never find another love like mine / Way you look tonight / Let me be good to you / It never entered my mind / Sit down and talk to me / Love all your blues away / Wind beneath my wings / Lady love / You're my blessing / Willow weep for me / One life to live / We'll be together again / See you when I get there / Groovy people.
■ **LP** . . . . . . . . . . . . . . . . . **KNLP 12053**
Knight / Mar '90.
■ **CD** . . . . . . . . . . . . . . . . . **KNCD 12053**
Knight / Mar '90.
■ **MC** . . . . . . . . . . . . . . . . . **KNMC 12053**
Knight / Jul '91.

## IT'S SUPPOSED TO BE FUN.
**Tracks:** It's supposed to be fun / Don't let me be misunderstood / All around the world / Good morning blues / Moonglows / Any day now / This bitter earth / If you gotta make a fool of somebody (CD only.) / One more time / You're the one / I wonder where our love has gone / But I do (CD only.) / Good night my love / Last night of the world.
**MC.** . . . . . . . . . . . . . . . . . . . . **B4 93841**
■ **CD** . . . . . . . . . . . . . . . . . . **CDB1 93841**
■ **LP** . . . . . . . . . . . . . . . . . . . **B1 93841**
Blue Note / Oct '90 / EMI.

## LADY LOVE.
**Tracks:** Lady love / Not the staying kind.
■ **7"** . . . . . . . . . . . . . . . . . . . **PIR 5911**
Philadelphia Int. / Jan '78.

## LEGENDARY LOU RAWLS, THE.
**Tracks:** I'd rather drink muddy water / World of trouble / Tobacco Road / Willow weep for me / They call it stormy Monday / God bless the child / For you my love / Dead end street / Your good thing (is about to end) / Love is a hurtin' thing / You can't go home no more / At last / Fine brown frame / Room with a view / Don't let me be misunderstood / All around the world / Good morning blues.
■ **MC.** . . . . . . . . . . . . . . . . . . . **B4 98306**
■ **CD** . . . . . . . . . . . . . . . . . **CDP 7983062**
Blue Note / Jan '92.

## LET ME BE GOOD TO YOU.
**Tracks:** Time will take care of everything / What's the matter with the world / Tomorrow / We keep getting closer / Bark, bite / Let me be good to you / Lover's holiday / Sweet tender nights.
■ **LP** . . . . . . . . . . . . . . . . . . . **PIR 83658**
Philadelphia Int. / Jul '79.

## LOU RAWLS (LIVE).
**Tracks:** Lady love / I wish it were yesterday / One life to live / Dollar green / Trade winds / There will be love / Unforgettable / That would do it for me / If I coulda, woulda, shoulda / Not the staying kind / This song will last forever / 'Tribute' medley / See you when I git there / We understand each other / Early morning love / When you say Budweiser, you've said it all / Send in the clowns / You'll never find another ove like mine / Lovely way to spend an evening.
■ **Double LP.** . . . . . . . . . . . . . . . **PIR 88316**
Philadelphia Int. / Jan '79.

## LOU RAWLS IN THE HEART.
**Tracks:** Not Advised.
**CD** . . . . . . . . . . . . . . . . . . . . **847 948-2**
Polydor / May '91 / PolyGram.

## LOVE ALL YOUR BLUES AWAY.
**Tracks:** Change your mind / Are you with me / Love all your blues away / Stop me from starting this feeling / Learn to love again / Willow weep for me / We'll be together again / Way you look tonight / It never entered my mind.
■ **LP** . . . . . . . . . . . . . . . . . . . **EPC 26809**
**MC** . . . . . . . . . . . . . . . . . . . .**40 26809**
Epic / Apr '86 / Sony.

## LOVE SONGS: LOU RAWLS.
**Tracks:** Not Advised.
**MC** . . . . . . . . . . . . . . . . . . . . **4XL 9040**
Capitol (Specials) / Dec '88.

## MERRY CHRISTMAS HO HO HO.
**Tracks:** Little drummer boy / Good time Christmas / Little boy dear / Christmas is / Have yourself a merry little Christmas / Santa Claus is coming to town / Merry Christmas baby / Christmas song / Christmas will really be Christmas / What are you doing New Year's Eve / Child with a toy.
■ **CD** . . . . . . . . . . . . . . . . . . . **C2 94703**
■ **MC.** . . . . . . . . . . . . . . . . . . . **C4 94703**
Capitol / Nov '90.

## NATURAL MAN.
**Tracks:** Natural man / Everywhere I go / I'm a king bee / What a beautiful mornin' / Got to get you into my life / You can't hold on / When I fall in love / How thoughtless I've become / Till love touches your life / Got a lotta love.
■ **LP** . . . . . . . . . . . . . . . . . . . .**2315 054**
MGM (Polydor) / Dec '71.

## NOW IS THE TIME.
**Tracks:** Kiss me one more time / Let me show you how / Ain't that love / Baby / While the rain comes down / Now is the time for love / Watch your back / It's too late / Back to you / This love.
■ **LP** . . . . . . . . . . . . . . . . . . . **PRT 85193**
Portrait / Nov '82.

## PORTRAIT OF THE BLUES.
**Tracks:** I just wanna make love to you / Lover's question / Person to person / Since I met you baby / I'm still in love with you / Snap your fingers / Baby what you want me to do / Suffering with the blues / Hide nor hair / Chains of love / My babe / I ain't got nothin' but the blues / Save your love for me / Saturday night fish fry / Sweet slumber.
**CD** . . . . . . . . . . . . . . . . . . **CDP 7995482**
■ **MC** . . . . . . . . . . . . . . . . . . **B4 99548**
Manhattan Records / Mar '93 / EMI.

## SHADES OF BLUE.
**Tracks:** Did you ever love a woman / Cottage for sale / Be anything / You've lost that lovin' feelin' / I go crazy / Think / Hoochie coochie man / Baby watcha want me to do.
■ **LP** . . . . . . . . . . . . . . . . . . . **PIR 84572**
**MC.** . . . . . . . . . . . . . . . . . . . .**40 84572**
Philadelphia Int. / Apr '81 / EMI.

## SHOW BUSINESS.
**Tracks:** Show business / When love goes wrong.
■ **7"** . . . . . . . . . . . . . . . . . . . **CL 15507**
Capitol / Jul '67.

## SIT DOWN AND TALK TO ME.
**Tracks:** One day soon you'll need me / Heartaches / Ain't that loving you baby / When you get home / Sit down and talk to me / You're my blessing / Old times / You are.
■ **LP** . . . . . . . . . . . . . . . . . . . **PIR 84024**
Philadelphia Int. / Jun '80.

## SIT DOWN AND TALK TO ME.
**Tracks:** Sit down and talk to me / When you get home.
■ **7"** . . . . . . . . . . . . . . . . . . . **PIR 8201**
Philadelphia Int. / Feb '80.

## SOME FOLKS NEVER LEARN.
**Tracks:** Some folks never learn / Early morning love.
■ **7"** . . . . . . . . . . . . . . . . . . . **PIR 5232**
Philadelphia Int. / May '77.

## SOUL MEN (Rawls, Lou & Al Jarreau).
**Tracks:** Not Advised.
■ **CD** . . . . . . . . . . . . . . . . . . . **NCD 5160**
K-Tel / Feb '88.

## SOUL SERENADE.
**Tracks:** Dead end street / Down here on the ground / I'd rather drink muddy water / Love is a hurtin' thing / Your good thing is about to end / Wade in the water / Chained and bound / For what it's worth / Stormy Monday / Tobacco Road / They don't give medals /

Please send me someone to love / My ancestors / Evil woman / I'm gonna use what I got (to get what I need) / Hard to get / Thing called love.
■ **LP** . . . . . . . . . . . . . . . . . **EG 2606681**
■ **CD** . . . . . . . . . . . . . . . . . **EG 2606684**
Stateside / Aug '85.

## STAR COLLECTION.
**Tracks:** Not Advised.
**CD** . . . . . . . . . . . . . . . . . . . **STCD 1002**
Disky / Jun '93 / THE.

## STAR PORTRAITS: LOU RAWLS.
**Tracks:** Not Advised.
**VHS** . . . . . . . . . . . . . . . . . . **GEMV 5013**
Gemini Vision / Sep '94 / Sony / THE.

## STOP ME FROM STARTING THIS FEELING.
**Tracks:** Stop me from starting this feeling / Love all your blues away / See you when I get there (Extra track on 12" version only.) / Natural man (Extra track on 12" version only).
■ **12"** . . . . . . . . . . . . . . . . . . . **TA 7263**
■ **7"** . . . . . . . . . . . . . . . . . . .**A 7263**
Epic / Jun '86.

## STORMY MONDAY (Rawls, Lou & Les McCann Limited).
**Tracks:** Stormy Monday / God bless the child / c.c. rider / Willow weep for me / I'm gonna move to the outskirts of town / In the evening / T'aint nobody's business if I do / Lost and lookin' / I'd rather drink muddy water / Sweet lover / Blues is a woman (CD only.) / Little Les of Lou's blues (CD only.) / Stormy Monday (alternate) (CD only.).
■ **LP** . . . . . . . . . . . . . . . . . . . . **SEE 51**
See For Miles / Jun '85.
■ **LP** . . . . . . . . . . . . . . . . . . **B1 91441**
■ **CD** . . . . . . . . . . . . . . . . . . .**BNZ 237**
Blue Note / Mar '90.

## THAT'S YOU.
**Tracks:** When love goes wrong / Problems / What are you doing about today / Street of dreams / Love I give / etc.
■ **LP** . . . . . . . . . . . . . . . . . . . . **T 2756**
Capitol / Dec '67.

## TIME WILL TAKE CARE OF EVERYTHING.
**Tracks:** Time will take care of everything / Lovers holiday.
■ **7"** . . . . . . . . . . . . . . . . . . . **PIR 7500**
Philadelphia Int. / Nov '79.

## TRADE WINDS.
**Tracks:** Trade winds / If I coulda, woulda, shoulda.
■ **7"** . . . . . . . . . . . . . . . . . . . **PIR 6354**
Philadelphia Int. / May '78.

## UNMISTAKABLY LOU.
**Tracks:** See you when I get there / Spring again / Early morning love / Somefolks never learn / Someday you'll be old / Secret tears / We understand each other / It's our anniversary today / All the way.
■ **LP** . . . . . . . . . . . . . . . . . . **PIR 81873**
Philadelphia Int. / May '77.

## WAY IT WAS, THE WAY IT IS, THE.
**Tracks:** Fa fa fa fa fa / Trying just as hard as I can / Your good thing / I love you, yes I do / When a man loves a woman / Season of the witch / Gentle on my mind / I wonder / I want to be loved / It's you.
■ **LP** . . . . . . . . . . . . . . . . . . . **EST 215**
Capitol / Feb '70.

## WHAT'S THE MATTER WITH THE WORLD.
**Tracks:** What's the matter with the world / Tomorrow.
■ **7"** . . . . . . . . . . . . . . . . . . . **PIR 7901**
Philadelphia Int. / Oct '79.

## WHEN THE NIGHT COMES.
**Tracks:** Upside down / Wind beneath my wings / If your gonna love me / Couple more years / One I sing my songs to / You can't take it with you / When the night comes / Midnight sunshine / That's when the magic begins / I been him.
■ **LP** . . . . . . . . . . . . . . . . . . **EPC 25305**
Epic / Jul '83.

## WHEN YOU HEAR LOU, YOU'VE HEARD IT ALL.
**Tracks:** Lady love / I wish it were yesterday / One life to live / Dollar green / Trade winds / There will be love / Unforgettable / That would do it for me / If I coulda, woulda, shoulda / Not the staying kind.
■ **LP** . . . . . . . . . . . . . . . . . . **PIR 82402**
Philadelphia Int. / Feb '78.

## YOU CAN BRING ME ALL YOUR HEARTACHES.
**Tracks:** You can bring me all your heartaches / Woman who's a woman.
■ 7" . . . . . . . . . . . . . . . . . . . . . CL 15488
Capitol / Jan '67.

## YOU'LL NEVER FIND.
**Tracks:** Not Advised.
CD . . . . . . . . . . . . . . . . . . . . .WMCD 5700
Disky / Oct '94 / THE.

## YOU'LL NEVER FIND ANOTHER LOVE LIKE MINE.
**Tracks:** You'll never find another love like mine.
■ 7" . . . . . . . . . . . . . . . . . . . . PIR 7372
Philadelphia Int. / Jul '76.

## YOU'LL NEVER FIND ANOTHER LOVE LIKE MINE (OLD GOLD).
**Tracks:** You'll never find another love like mine / Lady love.
■ 7" . . . . . . . . . . . . . . . . . . . . .OG 9560
Old Gold / Sep '85.

## YOU'RE GOOD FOR ME.
**Tracks:** Down here on the ground / I want to hear it from you / Beautiful friendship / Baby I could be so good at lovin' you / Soul serenade / Life time / You're good for me / Ol' man river / One for my baby / I'm satisfied.
■ LP . . . . . . . . . . . . . . . . . . . . ST 2927
Capitol / Dec '68.

## YOU'VE MADE ME SO VERY HAPPY.
**Tracks:** All God's children got soul / Let's burn down the cornfield / You've made me so very happy / When someone comes along / Whole lotta sunlight / Feelin' alright / Mama told me not to come / Hurtin' / Yesterday's dreams / How can that be / Will someone carry the ball.
■ LP . . . . . . . . . . . . . . . . . . . . EST 427
Capitol / Jun '70.

## Ray & Goodman

### MOOD FOR LOVIN' (Ray,Goodman & Brown).
**Tracks:** Where did you get that body..baby / Mood for lovin' / Where are you now / Say it / Electrified / Next time I'll know / Never stop lovin' you / Don't make me wait.
■ CD . . . . . . . . . . . . . . . . . . . . CDMTL 1038
■ LP . . . . . . . . . . . . . . . . . . . . MTL 1038
■ MC . . . . . . . . . . . . . . . . . . . TCMTL 1038
EMI-Manhattan / Nov '88.

### RAY, GOODMAN & BROWN (Ray,Goodman & Brown).
**Tracks:** Inside of you / Special lady / Slipped away / Way it should be / Treat her right / Thrill/friends / Deja vu / Another day.
■ LP . . . . . . . . . . . . . . . . . . . . 9109800
Mercury / May '80.

### SPECIAL LADY (Ray,Goodman & Brown).
**Tracks:** Special lady / Deja vu.
■ 7" . . . . . . . . . . . . . . . . . . . . 6008800
Mercury / Mar '80.

### TAKE IT TO THE LIMIT (Ray,Goodman & Brown).
**Tracks:** Take it to the limit / Baby, let's make love tonight / Good love / Celebrate your love / Why must I wait / Waiting for Dawn / We've got tonight / Someone's missing your love.
■ MC . . . . . . . . . . . . . . . . . . . TCAML 3113
■ LP . . . . . . . . . . . . . . . . . . . . AML 3113
EMI-America / Dec '86.
■ CD . . . . . . . . . . . . . . . . . . . .BU 9
EMI-America / Mar '88.

## Ray, Cecilia

### CECILIA RAY.
**Tracks:** Not Advised.
CD . . . . . . . . . . . . . . . . . . . . . RIPEXD 195
LP . . . . . . . . . . . . . . . . . . . . . . RIPELP 195
MC . . . . . . . . . . . . . . . . . . . . . RIPEMC 195
FM Records / Mar '93 / FM Revolver / Sony.

### ROUND 'N' ROUND.
**Tracks:** round and 'round.
■ 12" . . . . . . . . . . . . . . . . . . . 12 FMD 185
■ CD Single . . . . . . . . . . . . . . . FMJXD 185
FM Dance / Oct '92.

## Ray, Harry

### IT'S GOOD TO BE HOME.
**Tracks:** It's good to be home / You ain't been loved / Love is a game / Sweet baby / I'm willin' / You're killing me / Lost affair / I will love you anyway.
■ LP . . . . . . . . . . . . . . . . . . . . SHLP 1008
MC . . . . . . . . . . . . . . . . . . . . . ZCSH 1008
Sugarhill / Apr '83 / Roots Records / C.M. Distribution / A.D.A. Distribution / Direct Distribution.

### LOVE IS A GAME.
**Tracks:** Love is a game / Sweet baby.
■ 12" . . . . . . . . . . . . . . . . . . . .SHL 122
■ 7" . . . . . . . . . . . . . . . . . . . . SH 122
Sugarhill / Feb '83.

## Ray, James

### ITTY BITTY PIECES.
**Tracks:** One by one / Marie / Come rain or come shine / Old man & the mule / Lazybones / Guilty / On that day / If you gotta make a fool of somebody / Itty bitty pieces / It's been a drag / St. James Infirmary / Put me in your diary / You remember the face / Things are gonna be different / We got a thing going on / I'm gonna keep on trying.
■ LP . . . . . . . . . . . . . . . . . . . . CRB 1065
Charly R&B / May '84.

## Raydio

### BETCHA CAN'T LOVE ME JUST ONCE.
**Tracks:** Betcha can't love me just once / You need this.
■ 7" . . . . . . . . . . . . . . . . . . . .ARIST 227
Arista / Dec '78.

### HONEY I'M RICH.
**Tracks:** Honey I'm rich / Me.
■ 7" . . . . . . . . . . . . . . . . . . . .ARIST 183
Arista / May '78.

### IS THIS A LOVE THING.
**Tracks:** Is this a love thing.
■ 7" . . . . . . . . . . . . . . . . . . . .ARIST 193
Arista / Jul '78.

### JACK AND JILL.
**Tracks:** Jack & Jill / Get down.
■ 7" . . . . . . . . . . . . . . . . . . . .ARIST 161
Arista / Feb '78.

### JACK AND JILL (OLD GOLD).
**Tracks:** You can't change that / Jack & Jill.
■ 7" . . . . . . . . . . . . . . . . . . . .OG 9782
Old Gold / Jun '88.

### RAYDIO.
**Tracks:** Is this a love thing / You need this to satisfy that / Betcha can't love me just once / Honey I'm rich / Jack & Jill / Me / Let's go all the way / Get down.
■ LP . . . . . . . . . . . . . . . . . . . . SPART 1041
Arista / '82.

### ROCK ON.
**Tracks:** What you waiting for / Hot stuff / You can't change that / Rock on / More than one way to love / Woman / When you're in the need of love / Goin' thru school and love / Honey I'm a star.
■ LP . . . . . . . . . . . . . . . . . . . . SPART 1087
Arista / Aug '79.

### TWO PLACES AT THE SAME TIME.
**Tracks:** Not Advised.
■ LP . . . . . . . . . . . . . . . . . . . . SPART 1121
Arista / May '80.

### TWO PLACES AT THE SAME TIME.
**Tracks:** Two places at the same time / For those who like to groove.
■ 7" . . . . . . . . . . . . . . . . . . . .ARIST 334
Arista / Mar '80.

### WOMAN NEEDS LOVE, A.
**Tracks:** Woman needs love.
■ 7" . . . . . . . . . . . . . . . . . . . .ARIST 392
Arista / '82.

## Raye, Michael

### NO LOVE INTENDED (Raye, Michael Featuring Wayne Cobham).
**Tracks:** No love intended / Black and white.
■ 12" . . . . . . . . . . . . . . . . . . . MENUT 6
■ 7" . . . . . . . . . . . . . . . . . . . . MENU 6
Menu / Jan '90.

## Ready For The World

### LONG TIME COMING.
**Tracks:** Not Advised.
■ LP . . . . . . . . . . . . . . . . . . . . MCF 3352
■ MC . . . . . . . . . . . . . . . . . . . MCFC 3352
MCA / Dec '86.

### LOVE YOU DOWN.
**Tracks:** Human toy / Love you down.
■ 12" . . . . . . . . . . . . . . . . . . . MCAT 1110
■ 7" . . . . . . . . . . . . . . . . . . . .MCA 1110
MCA / Feb '87.

### MARY GOES ROUND.
**Tracks:** Mary goes round / It's all a game.
■ 7" . . . . . . . . . . . . . . . . . . . .MCA 1144
MCA / May '87.

### OH SHEILA.
**Tracks:** Oh Sheila / I'm the one who loves you (Extra track in double pack.) / Side over.
■ 12" . . . . . . . . . . . . . . . . . . . MCAT 1005
■ 7" . . . . . . . . . . . . . . . . . . . .MCA 1005
MCA / Sep '85.
■ 12" . . . . . . . . . . . . . . . . . . . RFT WX 1
■ 7" . . . . . . . . . . . . . . . . . . . .RFT WD 1
MCA / May '86.

## Real Thing

### 100 MINUTES OF THE REAL THING.
**Tracks:** Not Advised.
■ MC . . . . . . . . . . . . . . . . . . . ZCTON 109
PRT / Jun '82.

### 4 FROM 8.
**Tracks:** Love's such a wonderful thing / Lovin' you is like a dream / Kathy / Down to the way you feel / Plastic man / Lightning strikes again / I wish you well / Liverpool 8 / Children of the ghetto / Stanhope Street.
■ LP . . . . . . . . . . . . . . . . . . . . NSPH 20
Pye / '77.

### BEST OF THE REAL THING.
**Tracks:** You to me are everything (remix) / Rainin' through my sunshine / She's got a groovy freak / (We've gotta take it to the) second stage / You'll never know what you're missing / Can you feel the force / Can't get by without you (remix) / Won't you step into our world / Love takes tears / Whenever you want my love / Children of the ghetto / Whatcha say watcha do.
■ CD . . . . . . . . . . . . . . . . . . . . CDNRT 1
■ MC . . . . . . . . . . . . . . . . . . . ZCNRT 1
■ LP . . . . . . . . . . . . . . . . . . . . NRT 1
West 5 / Aug '86.

### BOOGIE DOWN (GET FUNKY NOW).
**Tracks:** Boogie down.
■ 12" . . . . . . . . . . . . . . . . . . . 12P 109
■ 7" . . . . . . . . . . . . . . . . . . . .7P 109
PRT / Jul '79.

### CAN YOU FEEL THE FORCE.
**Tracks:** Can you feel the force / Children of the ghetto / You to me are everything / Can't get by without you.
■ 7" . . . . . . . . . . . . . . . . . . . . 7N 46147
Pye / Feb '79.
■ CD Single . . . . . . . . . . . . . . . .OG 6186
Pickwick / Nov '92.
■ CD Single . . . . . . . . . . . . . . . CDWGAF 102
■ 12" . . . . . . . . . . . . . . . . . . . 12WGAF 102
WGAF / Jul '93.

### CAN YOU FEEL THE FORCE.
**Tracks:** Watcha say, watcha do / We gonna take it to the second stage / Can you feel the force / Lady, I love you all the time / Rainin' through my sunshine / Give me the chance / Won't you step into my world / Whenever you want my love / You gotta keep holding on / Love me right.
■ LP . . . . . . . . . . . . . . . . . . . .NSPH 18601
Pye / Apr '79.

### CAN YOU FEEL THE FORCE (OLD GOLD).
**Tracks:** Can you feel the force / Whenever you want my love / You to me are everything.
■ 12" . . . . . . . . . . . . . . . . . . . .OG 4090
■ 7" . . . . . . . . . . . . . . . . . . . .OG 9837
Old Gold / Jan '89.

### CAN YOU FEEL THE FORCE (REISSUES).
**Tracks:** Can you feel the force(1986 Mix) / Love's such a wonderful thing / Lightning strikes (Extra track on 12" version only.).
■ 12" . . . . . . . . . . . . . . . . . . . 12P 105
PRT / May '79.
■ 12" . . . . . . . . . . . . . . . . . . . 12P 358

■ DELETED

■ 7" . . . . . . . . . . . . . . . . . . . . . . . . .7P 358
PRT / Aug '86.
■ 12" . . . . . . . . . . . . . . . . . . . . . . . . PYT 26
■ 7" . . . . . . . . . . . . . . . . . . . . . . . . PYS 26
PRT / May '89.

## CAN'T GET BY WITHOUT YOU.
**Tracks:** Can't get by without you / Can't get by without you (The 2nd decade remix) / She's a groovy freak / You'll never know what you're missing.
■ 7" . . . . . . . . . . . . . . . . . . . . 7N 45618
Pye / Sep '76.
■ 12" . . . . . . . . . . . . . . . . . . . . 12P 352
■ 7" . . . . . . . . . . . . . . . . . . . . . .7P 352
PRT / May '86.

## CRIME OF LOVE.
**Tracks:** Crime of love / Baby don't go.
■ 12" . . . . . . . . . . . . . . . . . . . PT 42848
■ 7" . . . . . . . . . . . . . . . . . . . PB 42847
■ CD Single . . . . . . . . . . . . . . . PD 42848
RCA / Jul '89.

## FOOT TAPPIN'.
**Tracks:** Foot tappin'.
■ 12" . . . . . . . . . . . . . . . . . . CABL 110
■ 7" . . . . . . . . . . . . . . . . . . .CAB 110
Calibre / Nov '81.

## GOLDEN HOUR OF THE REAL THING, A.
**Tracks:** Not Advised.
■ CD . . . . . . . . . . . . . . . . . . .KGHCD 153
■ MC . . . . . . . . . . . . . . . . . . .KGHMC 153
Knight / Jul '91.

## GREATEST HITS: REAL THING.
**Tracks:** Not Advised.
■ LP . . . . . . . . . . . . . . . . . . . . NE 1073
K-Tel / May '80.

## HARD TIMES.
**Tracks:** Children of the ghetto / Mystique (Only on 12" version.).
■ 12" . . . . . . . . . . . . . . . . . . .JIVET 137
■ 7" . . . . . . . . . . . . . . . . . . . .JIVE 137
Jive / Feb '87.

## HEART AND SOUL OF THE REAL THING.
**Tracks:** You to me are everything / You'll never know what you're missing / Raining through my sunshine / Love's such a groovy thing / Hard times / Can you feel the force / I can't help myself / I can't get by without you / Mystique / Let's go disco / Children of the ghetto / Boogie down / Straight to the heart.
■ LP . . . . . . . . . . . . . . . . . . .KNLP 12051
■ CD . . . . . . . . . . . . . . . . . . .KNCD 12051
■ MC . . . . . . . . . . . . . . . . . . .KNMC 12051
Knight / Mar '90.

## I BELIEVE IN YOU.
**Tracks:** I believe in you / You're my number one.
■ 12" . . . . . . . . . . . . . . . . . . CABL 109
■ 7" . . . . . . . . . . . . . . . . . . .CAB 109
Calibre / Jun '81.

## I CAN'T HELP MYSELF.
**Tracks:** I can't help myself / Hard times.
■ 7" . . . . . . . . . . . . . . . . . . .JIVE 147
■ 12" . . . . . . . . . . . . . . . . . . .JIVET 147
Jive / Aug '87.

## LET'S GO DISCO.
**Tracks:** Let's go disco / Plastic man.
■ 7" . . . . . . . . . . . . . . . . . . 7N 46078
Pye / Jun '78.

## LOVE TAKES TWO.
**Tracks:** Love takes tears / Goin' for the big one.
■ 12" . . . . . . . . . . . . . . . . . . CABL 112
■ 7" . . . . . . . . . . . . . . . . . . .CAB 112
Calibre / Jan '82.

## LOVE'S SUCH A WONDERFUL THING.
**Tracks:** Love's such a wonderful thing / Topsy turvy.
■ 7" . . . . . . . . . . . . . . . . . . 7N 45701
Pye / Jul '77.

## RAININ' THROUGH MY SUNSHINE.
**Tracks:** Rainin' through my sunshine.
■ 7" . . . . . . . . . . . . . . . . . . 7N 46113
Pye / Aug '78.

## RAINING THROUGH MY SUNSHINE.
**Tracks:** Raining through my sunshine / Can you feel the force / You to me are everything / Can't get by without you.
■ 7" . . . . . . . . . . . . . . . . . . .7P 178
PRT / May '80.

## REAL THING, THE.
**Tracks:** Hallelujah man / You to me are everything / Topsy turvy / He's just a moneymaker / Young and foolish / Flash / Can't get by without you / Why oh

why / Keep an eye (on your best friend) / You'll never know what you're missing.
■ LP . . . . . . . . . . . . . . . . . . .NSPL 18507
Pye / Oct '76.
■ CD . . . . . . . . . . . . . . . . . . .GHCD 8
■ MC . . . . . . . . . . . . . . . . . . .C 908
PRT / May '89.

## SAINT ON SINNER.
**Tracks:** Saint on sinner / We gotta take it to the second stage.
■ 12" . . . . . . . . . . . . . . . . . . .12P 161
■ 7" . . . . . . . . . . . . . . . . . . .7P 161
PRT / Feb '80.

## SAINTS OR SINNERS.
**Tracks:** Boogie down / Saints or sinners / Story of my life / Thank you for loving me / You can't force the funk / Give me your love / One girl in my life.
■ LP . . . . . . . . . . . . . . . . . . CABLP 100
Calibre / Jul '81.

## SEEN TO SMILE.
**Tracks:** Seen to smile / Look up to the sky.
■ 12" . . . . . . . . . . . . . . . . . . 12EMI 5337
■ 7" . . . . . . . . . . . . . . . . . . . EMI 5337
EMI / Aug '82.

## SHE'S A GROOVY FREAK.
**Tracks:** She's a groovy freak / It's the real thing.
■ 12" . . . . . . . . . . . . . . . . . . CABL 105
■ 7" . . . . . . . . . . . . . . . . . . .CAB 105
Calibre / Nov '80.

## STEP INTO OUR WORLD.
**Tracks:** Whatcha say, whatcha do / Lady, I love you all the time / Rainin' through my sunshine / Can you feel the force / Give me the chance / Second stage / Won't you step into my world / Whenever you want my love / You gotta keep holding on / Love me right.
■ LP . . . . . . . . . . . . . . . . . . .NSPL 18587
Pye / Nov '78.

## STONE COLD LOVE AFFAIR.
**Tracks:** Stone cold love affair / Love that's real.
■ 7" . . . . . . . . . . . . . . . . . . 7N 25681
Pye / May '75.

## STRAIGHT TO THE HEART.
**Tracks:** Straight to the heart / Mystique.
■ 12" . . . . . . . . . . . . . . . . . . .JIVET 129
■ 7" . . . . . . . . . . . . . . . . . . .JIVE 129
Jive / Oct '86.

## WE GOT LOVE.
**Tracks:** We got love / Street scene.
■ 12" . . . . . . . . . . . . . . . . . . RCAT 445
■ 7" . . . . . . . . . . . . . . . . . . .RCA 445
RCA / Oct '84.

## WHENEVER YOU WANT MY LOVE.
**Tracks:** Whenever you want my love / Stanhope Street.
■ 7" . . . . . . . . . . . . . . . . . . 7N 46045
Pye / Mar '78.

## YOU TO ME ARE EVERYTHING.
**Tracks:** You to me are everything / You to me are everything(decade remix '76-78) / Foot tappin / Children of the Ghetto (original '78 vintage version).
■ 7" . . . . . . . . . . . . . . . . . . 7N 25709
Pye International / Jul '76.
■ 12" . . . . . . . . . . . . . . . . . . .12P 349
■ 7" . . . . . . . . . . . . . . . . . . .7P 349
PRT / Feb '86.

## YOU TO ME ARE EVERYTHING.
**Tracks:** Not Advised.
CD . . . . . . . . . . . . . . . . . . .550 7402
MC . . . . . . . . . . . . . . . . . . .550 7404
Spectrum (1) / Sep '94 / PolyGram.

## YOU TO ME ARE EVERYTHING (DECADE MIX).
**Tracks:** You to me are everything (decade mix) / Can't get by without you (2nd decade mix) / Can you feel the force (Remix).
■ CD Single . . . . . . . . . . . . . . OG 6524
Pickwick / Oct '92.

## YOU TO ME ARE EVERYTHING (OLD GOLD).
**Tracks:** You to me are everything / Can't get by without you.
■ 7" . . . . . . . . . . . . . . . . . . OG 9294
Old Gold / Jun '88.

## YOU'LL NEVER KNOW WHAT YOU'RE MISSING.
**Tracks:** You'll never know what you're missing.
■ 7" . . . . . . . . . . . . . . . . . . 7N 45662
Pye / Feb '77.

# Real To Reel

## BLUE.
**Tracks:** Blue / Wind up man.
■ 7" . . . . . . . . . . . . . . . . . . . REDS 006
R.E.D. / Sep '80.

## LOVE ME LIKE THIS.
**Tracks:** Love me like this / Taking the long way home.
■ 12" . . . . . . . . . . . . . . . . . . ARIST 12565
■ 7" . . . . . . . . . . . . . . . . . . .ARIST 565
Arista / Apr '84.

## LOVE ME LIKE THIS (OLD GOLD).
**Tracks:** Love me like this / I just gotta have you.
12" . . . . . . . . . . . . . . . . . . .OG 4164
Old Gold / Mar '90 / Pickwick.

## MR & MRS.
**Tracks:** Mr. & Mrs. / Not the one.
■ 7" . . . . . . . . . . . . . . . . . . REDS 101
Red Shadow / Feb '81.

## WHITE MAN REGGAE.
**Tracks:** White man reggae / One of these days.
■ 7" . . . . . . . . . . . . . . . . . . REDS 001
R.E.D. / Mar '80.

# Reason

## HEARTACHE (Reason & Leanne Golding).
**Tracks:** Heartache.
■ 12" . . . . . . . . . . . . . . . . . . RATT 12 001
Room At The Top / Jan '93.

# Record, Eugene

## MAGNETISM.
**Tracks:** Magnetism / I don't mind, take everything.
■ 7" . . . . . . . . . . . . . . . . . . . LV 25
Laser / '79.

# Redd, Jeff

## COME AND GET YOUR LOVIN'.
**Tracks:** Come and get your lovin' / Come and get your lovin' (instrumental).
■ 12" . . . . . . . . . . . . . . . . . . MCAT 1413
■ 7" . . . . . . . . . . . . . . . . . . MCA 1413
MCA / May '90.

## DOWN LOW.
**Tracks:** Show you / You called and told me / Dreamer / I still do care / Sex ain't the only thing / Why (my guilt) / Hard soft, slow fast / Down low / Let's spend the night / Take it off.
CD . . . . . . . . . . . . . . . . . . . CDMTL 1080
LP . . . . . . . . . . . . . . . . . . . MTL 1080
MC . . . . . . . . . . . . . . . . . . . TCMTL 1080
EMI / Apr '94 / EMI.

## QUIET STORM, A.
**Tracks:** Not Advised.
■ CD . . . . . . . . . . . . . . . . . . .DMCG 6086
■ LP . . . . . . . . . . . . . . . . . . .MCG 6086
■ MC . . . . . . . . . . . . . . . . . . .MCGC 6086
MCA / Apr '90.

# Redd, Sharon

## BEAT THE STREET.
**Tracks:** Can you handle it / Never give you up / Love how you feel / You're a winner / In the name of love / Beat the street / Somebody save the night / You got my love.
■ LP . . . . . . . . . . . . . . . . . . .PRSLP 6002
■ MC . . . . . . . . . . . . . . . . . . PRSK 6002
Prelude / Oct '84.

## CAN YOU HANDLE IT?.
**Tracks:** Can you handle it / Leaving you is easier said than done.
■ 12" . . . . . . . . . . . . . . . . . . EPC 13-9572
■ 7" . . . . . . . . . . . . . . . . . . . EPC 9572
Epic / Feb '81.

## ESSENTIAL DANCEFLOOR.
**Tracks:** Not Advised.
CD . . . . . . . . . . . . . . . . . . . DGPCD 698
LP . . . . . . . . . . . . . . . . . . . DGPLP 698
Deep Beats / Jun '94 / BMG.

## IN THE NAME OF LOVE.
**Tracks:** In the name of love / Send your love / Can you handle it.
■ 7" . . . . . . . . . . . . . . . . . . PRLA 2905
Prelude / Jan '83.

■ DELETED

### LOVE HOW YOU FEEL.
**Tracks:** Love how you feel.
- 12" . . . . . . . . . . . . . . . . . . . TA 3868
- 7" . . . . . . . . . . . . . . . . . . . .A 3868
Prelude / Oct '83.

### LOVE HOW YOU FEEL.
**Tracks:** Activate / You're a winner / Got ya where I want ya / Liar on the wire / Sweet sensation / Somebody save the night / Love how you feel.
- LP . . . . . . . . . . . . . . . . . . . PRL 25776
Prelude / Apr '84.

### LOVE IS GOING TO GET YOU.
**Tracks:** Love is going to get you / It's a lie.
- 7" . . . . . . . . . . . . . . . . . . . EPC A 1210
Epic / May '81.

### NEVER GIVE YOU UP.
**Tracks:** Never give you up / Send your love.
- 7" . . . . . . . . . . . . . . . . . . . PRLA 2755
Prelude / Oct '82.

### REDD HOTT.
**Tracks:** Never give you up / You're the one / Send your love / Beat the street / In the name of love / Takin' a chance on love / We're friewnds again.
- LP . . . . . . . . . . . . . . . . . . . PRL 25056
Prelude / Oct '82.

### SHARON REDD.
**Tracks:** You got my love / Can you handle it / It's a lie / Try my love on for size / Leaving you is easier said than over / Love is gonna get ya / You stayed on my mind / Never give you up / Love how you feel / You're a winner / In the name of love / Beat the street / Somebody save the night.
- LP . . . . . . . . . . . . . . . . . . . EPC 84894
MC. . . . . . . . . . . . . . . . . . . .40 84894
Epic / Apr '81 / Sony.

### SHARON REDD COLLECTION.
**Tracks:** Not Advised.
CD. . . . . . . . . . . . . . . . . . . . CCSCD 388
MC. . . . . . . . . . . . . . . . . . . CCSMC 388
Castle / Oct '93 / BMG.

### TAKING A CHANCE ON LOVE.
**Tracks:** Taking a chance on love / You're the..
- 12" . . . . . . . . . . . . . . . . . . . PRLA 13 3197
- 7" . . . . . . . . . . . . . . . . . . . PRLA 3197
Prelude / Mar '83.

### THAT'S FUNK.
**Tracks:** Not Advised.
- LP . . . . . . . . . . . . . . . . . . . 6 25470
Teldec (1) / Apr '84.

### YOU'RE A WINNER.
**Tracks:** You're a winner / Activate.
- 12" . . . . . . . . . . . . . . . . . . . TA 4127
- 7" . . . . . . . . . . . . . . . . . . . .A 4127
Prelude / Jan '84.

## Redding, Otis

Revisionists argue that Redding is over-rated, his gargling style of limited artistic worth, his better songs in the minority. There's little doubt, however, that the gentle giant's rasping blend of blues and gospel defined soul music not only for a generation of urban American black people, but for almost a planet's worth of sixties hipsters. All this from a country boy from Dawson, Georgia. He recorded his first disc *These Arms Of Mine* in someone else's spare studio time, saw it snapped up by Volt/Stax in '62, and followed it two years later with a debut album, *Pain In My Heart*. From there on it's a hit list familiar to all: *Respect, I've Been Loving You Too Long, That's How Strong My Love Is, Security, Try A Little Tenderness, Dock Of The Bay.*. When Otis's private jet crashed into a Wisconsin lake in '67, killing its owner and several members of The Bar-Kays, he was already the number one soulman and set fair for a blissful period in the early '70s when soul music shook its creative shackles. He'd have been right there with Stevie, Marvin, Sly and the rest.

### (SITTIN' ON THE) DOCK OF THE BAY.
**Tracks:** (Sittin' on) the dock of the bay.
- 7" . . . . . . . . . . . . . . . . . . . 601 031
Stax / Feb '68.

### (SITTIN' ON THE) DOCK OF THE BAY.
**Tracks:** (Sittin' on) The dock of the bay.
- 7" . . . . . . . . . . . . . . . . . . . .A 9607
Atlantic / Oct '84.

### (SITTIN' ON THE) DOCK OF THE BAY (OLD GOLD).
**Tracks:** (Sittin' on) the dock of the bay / You don't miss your water.
- 7" . . . . . . . . . . . . . . . . . . . .OG 9500
Old Gold / Jan '85.

### (SITTIN' ON) THE DOCK OF THE BAY.
**Tracks:** (Sittin' on) the dock of the bay / Respect / Mr. Pitiful.
- 7" . . . . . . . . . . . . . . . . . . . K 10126
Atlantic / '74.

### BEST OF OTIS REDDING.
**Tracks:** Mr. Pitiful / My girl / Respect / I've been loving you too long / Love man / Cigarettes and coffee / I can't get no satisfaction / Try a little tenderness / I can't turn you loose / Hard to handle / Fa fa fa fa fa (sad song) / (Sittin' on) the dock of the bay / Shake / Ole man trouble / Good to me / Tell the truth / Down in the valley / These arms of mine / Tramp / Just one more day / Pain in my heart / My lover's prayer / Chain gang / You don't miss your water / Rock me baby / That's how strong my love is / Change is gonna come.
- MC. . . . . . . . . . . . . . . . . . . K4 60016
Atlantic / '74.
- LP . . . . . . . . . . . . . . . . . . . 780 171-1
MC . . . . . . . . . . . . . . . . . . . 780 171-4
Atlantic / Jul '84 / WEA.
- Double LP. . . . . . . . . . . . . . . . K 60016
Atlantic / Mar '87.
- CD . . . . . . . . . . . . . . . . . . . K2 60016
Atlantic / Mar '87.

### COLLECTION: OTIS REDDING.
**Tracks:** Not Advised.
- CD . . . . . . . . . . . . . . . . . . . CCSCD 339
- MC. . . . . . . . . . . . . . . . . . . CCSMC 339
Castle Collector Series / Jun '92.

### COME TO ME.
**Tracks:** These arms of mine / Hey hey baby / That's what my heart needs / Mary's little lamb / Pain in my heart / Something is worrying me / Security / Lucille / Come to me / Don't leave me this way / I want to thank you / Chained and bound / Your one & only man / I'm depending on you.
- LP . . . . . . . . . . . . . . . . . . . CRB 1077
- MC . . . . . . . . . . . . . . . . . . . TCCRB 1077
Charly R&B / Apr '84.

### CONCERTHOUSE, STOCKHOLM.
**Tracks:** Not Advised.
CD . . . . . . . . . . . . . . . . . . . K880 801
Koine / Feb '89.

### DAY TRIPPER.
**Tracks:** Day tripper / Shake.
- 7" . . . . . . . . . . . . . . . . . . . 601 005
Stax / Mar '67.

### DOCK OF THE BAY (The Definitive Collection).
**Tracks:** Shake / Mr. Pitiful / Respect / Love man / I can't get no satisfaction / I can't turn you loose / Hard to handle / Fa fa fa fa fa (sad song) / My girl / I've been loving you too long / Try a little tenderness / My lover's prayer / That's how strong my love is / Pain in my heart / Change is gonna come / (Sittin' on) the dock of the bay / Cigarettes and coffee (Extra track available on C.D. only) / These arms of mine (Extra track available on C.D. only) / Tramp (Extra track available on C.D. only) / Sweet lorene.
CD . . . . . . . . . . . . . . . . . . . 241 118-2
- LP . . . . . . . . . . . . . . . . . . . 241 118-1
MC. . . . . . . . . . . . . . . . . . . 241 118-4
Atlantic / May '87 / WEA.
CD . . . . . . . . . . . . . . . . . . . 9548317092
MC. . . . . . . . . . . . . . . . . . . 9548317084
WEA / Nov '92 / WEA.

### DOCK OF THE BAY.
**Tracks:** (Sittin' on) The dock of the bay (Single).
- 12" . . . . . . . . . . . . . . . . . . . A 4432 T
- 7" . . . . . . . . . . . . . . . . . . . .A 4432
- CD Single . . . . . . . . . . . . . . . A 4432 CD
- MC Single. . . . . . . . . . . . . . . . A 4432 C
WEA / Nov '92.

### DOCK OF THE BAY.
**Tracks:** Dock of the bay / I love you more than words can say / Let me come on home / Open the door / Don't mess with Cupid / Glory of love / I'm coming home / Tramp / Huckle-buck / Nobody knows you / Ole man trouble.
- LP . . . . . . . . . . . . . . . . . . . 231 001
Stax / Jun '68.
- LP . . . . . . . . . . . . . . . . . . . 228 022
Atco / Jun '69.

### FA FA FA FA FA (SAD SONG).
**Tracks:** Fa fa fa fa fa (sad song).
- 7" . . . . . . . . . . . . . . . . . . . 584 049
Atlantic / Nov '66.

### GOOD TO ME (Recorded Live at the Whiskey a Go Go Vol.2).
**Tracks:** Introduction / I'm depending on you / Your one & only man / Good to me / Chained and bound / Ol' man trouble / Pain in my heart / These arms of mine / I can't turn you loose / I've been loving you too long / Security / Hard day's night.
CD . . . . . . . . . . . . . . . . . . . CDSX 089
LP . . . . . . . . . . . . . . . . . . . SXD 089
Stax / Apr '93 / Pinnacle.

### GREAT OTIS REDDING SINGS SOUL BALLADS, THE.
**Tracks:** Not Advised.
- LP . . . . . . . . . . . . . . . . . . . SD 33248
Atco / Jun '88.

### HAPPY SONG.
**Tracks:** Happy song.
- 7" . . . . . . . . . . . . . . . . . . . 601 040
Stax / May '68.

### HARD TO HANDLE.
**Tracks:** Hard to handle.
- 7" . . . . . . . . . . . . . . . . . . . 584 199
Atlantic / Jul '68.

### HEART AND SOUL.
**Tracks:** Not Advised.
- CD . . . . . . . . . . . . . . . . . . . KNCD 12060
- MC . . . . . . . . . . . . . . . . . . . KNMC 12060
Knight / Jul '91.

### HISTORY OF OTIS REDDING.
**Tracks:** I've been loving you too long / Try a little tenderness / These arms of mine / Pain in my heart / My lover's prayer / Fa fa fa fa fa (sad song) / Respect / Satisfaction / Mr. Pitiful / Security / I can't turn you loose / Shake.
- LP . . . . . . . . . . . . . . . . . . . S 418
Atlantic / Feb '68.
- LP . . . . . . . . . . . . . . . . . . . 228 001
Atco / Apr '69.
- LP . . . . . . . . . . . . . . . . . . . K 40066
- MC . . . . . . . . . . . . . . . . . . . K4 40066
Atlantic / '74.

### I CAN'T TURN YOU LOOSE.
**Tracks:** I can't turn you loose.
- 7" . . . . . . . . . . . . . . . . . . . 584 061
Atlantic / Aug '66.

### I CAN'T TURN YOU LOOSE (EP).
**Tracks:** I can't turn you loose / (Sittin' on) The dock of the bay / Respect / Think.
- EP . . . . . . . . . . . . . . . . . . . .ATM 2
Atlantic / Apr '80.

### I'VE BEEN LOVIN' YOU TOO LONG.
**Tracks:** Not Advised.
CD . . . . . . . . . . . . . . . . . . . .TS 022
That's Soul / Mar '94 / BMG.

### IMMORTAL OTIS REDDING.
**Tracks:** I've got dreams to remember / You made a man out of me / Nobody's fault but mine / Thousand miles away / Happy song / Think about it / Waste of time / Champagne and wine / Fool for you / Amen.
- LP . . . . . . . . . . . . . . . . . . . 588 113
Atlantic / Oct '68.

### IMMORTAL, THE.
**Tracks:** Not Advised.
CD . . . . . . . . . . . . . . . . . . . .756780270-2
Atlantic / Jun '93 / WEA.

### IT'S NOT JUST SENTIMENTAL.
**Tracks:** Trick or treat / Loving by the pound 1 / There goes my baby / Remember me / Send me some lovin' / She's all right / Cupid / Boston monkey / Don't be afraid of love / Little ol me / Loving by the pound 2 / You got good lovin' / Gone again / I'm coming home / (Sittin' on the) Dock of the bay (Not on LP) / Respect (Not on LP) / Open the door (Not on LP) / I've got dreams to remember (Not on LP) / Come to me (Not on LP) / Try a little tenderness (Not on LP) / Stay in school (Not on LP).
CD . . . . . . . . . . . . . . . . . . . CDSXD 041
LP . . . . . . . . . . . . . . . . . . . .SXD 041
MC. . . . . . . . . . . . . . . . . . . .SXDC 041
Stax / Jan '92 / Pinnacle.

### KING AND QUEEN (Redding, Otis & Carla Thomas).
**Tracks:** Not Advised.
- LP . . . . . . . . . . . . . . . . . . . 589-007
Atlantic / Jun '67.
- LP . . . . . . . . . . . . . . . . . . . SD 7716

■ DELETED

atlantic / Jun '88.
CD. . . . . . . . . . . . . . . . . . . . . . 7567822562
MC. . . . . . . . . . . . . . . . . . . . . . 7567822564
WEA / Nov '92 / WEA.

## KNOCK ON WOOD.
Tracks: Knock on wood.
■ 7" . . . . . . . . . . . . . . . . . . . . . 601 021
Stax / Oct '67.

## LET ME COME ON HOME.
Tracks: Let me come on home.
■ 7" . . . . . . . . . . . . . . . . . . . . . 601 007
Stax / Mar '67.

## LIVE IN EUROPE.
Tracks: Not Advised.
CD. . . . . . . . . . . . . . . . . . . . . . 7567903952
Atlantic / Jul '93 / WEA.

## LIVE: OTIS REDDING.
Tracks: Destiny / Good to me / Chained and bound /
Ol' man trouble / I can't turn you loose / I've been
loving you too long / Security / Hard day's night.
■ LP . . . . . . . . . . . . . . . . . . . . K50881
Atlantic / May '82.

## LOVE MAN.
Tracks: I'm a changed man / (Your love has lifted
me) higher and higher / That's a good idea / I'll let
nothing separate us / Direct me / Love man / Groo-
vin' time / Your feeling is mine / Got to get myself
together / Free me / Lover's question / Look at that
girl.
■ LP . . . . . . . . . . . . . . . . . . . . 228 025
Atco / Sep '69.
■ LP . . . . . . . . . . . . . . . . . . . . K 40078
Atlantic / '74.
CD. . . . . . . . . . . . . . . . . . . . . . 8122702942
MC. . . . . . . . . . . . . . . . . . . . . . 8122702944
WEA / Nov '92 / WEA.

## LOVE MAN.
Tracks: Love man.
■ 7" . . . . . . . . . . . . . . . . . . . . . 226 001
Atco / Jul '69.

## LOVING YOU TOO LONG.
Tracks: Loving you too long / Try a little tenderness.
■ 7" . . . . . . . . . . . . . . . . . . . . .2091 062
Atlantic / Mar '71.

## MY GIRL.
Tracks: My girl / Down in the valley.
■ 7" . . . . . . . . . . . . . . . . . . . . AT 4050
Atlantic / Nov '65.

## MY GIRL.
Tracks: Mr. Pitiful.
■ 7" . . . . . . . . . . . . . . . . . . . . .584092
Atlantic / Feb '68.

## MY GIRL (REISSUES).
Tracks: My girl / Hard to handle / Down in the valley.
■ 7" . . . . . . . . . . . . . . . . . . . . K 10601
Atlantic / '79.

## MY LOVER'S PRAYER.
Tracks: My lover's prayer.
■ 7" . . . . . . . . . . . . . . . . . . . . 584 019
Atlantic / Jul '66.

## OTIS.
Tracks: Not Advised.
CD Set . . . . . . . . . . . . . . . . . . . 8122714392
Atlantic / Oct '93 / WEA.

## OTIS BLUE.
Tracks: Ole man trouble / Respect / Change gonna
come / Down in the valley / I've been loving you too
long / Shake / My girl / Wonderful world / Rock me
baby / Satisfaction / You don't miss your water.
■ LP . . . . . . . . . . . . . . . . . . . . ATL 5041
Atlantic / Feb '66.
■ LP . . . . . . . . . . . . . . . . . . . . 587 036
Atlantic / Jan '67.
■ LP . . . . . . . . . . . . . . . . . . . . K 40003
MC. . . . . . . . . . . . . . . . . . . . . . K 440 003
Atco / Dec '83.
CD. . . . . . . . . . . . . . . . . . . . . . 7567803182
LP . . . . . . . . . . . . . . . . . . . . . 7567803181
C. . . . . . . . . . . . . . . . . . . . . . 7567803184
WEA / Nov '92 / WEA.

## OTIS REDDING & LITTLE JOE CURTIS
(Redding, Otis & Little Joe Curtis).
Tracks: Gettin' hip / She's alright / Your mini-skirt /
Have mercy on me / Let me make it up to you / Tuff
nuff / Guilty of being poor / Bring back my love /
Don't bother my baby / Gama Lama.

■ LP . . . . . . . . . . . . . . . . . . . . MAL 772
Marble Arch / Feb '68.

## OTIS REDDING DICTIONARY OF SOUL.
Tracks: Fa fa fa fa fa (sad song) / I'm sick y'all /
Tennessee waltz / My sweet Lorene / Try a little
tenderness / Day tripper / My lover's prayer / She
put the hurt on me / Ton of joy / You're still my baby /
Hawg for you / Love have mercy.
■ LP . . . . . . . . . . . . . . . . . . . . 588-050
Atlantic / Jan '67.
■ LP . . . . . . . . . . . . . . . . . . . . SD 33249
Atco / Jun '88.
CD. . . . . . . . . . . . . . . . . . . . . . 7567917072
MC. . . . . . . . . . . . . . . . . . . . . . 7567917074
WEA / Nov '92 / WEA.

## OTIS REDDING IN EUROPE.
Tracks: Respect / I can't turn you loose / I've been
loving you too long / My girl / Shake / I can't get no
satisfaction / Fa fa fa fa fa / These arms of mine /
Day tripper / Try a little tenderness.
■ LP . . . . . . . . . . . . . . . . . . . . 589-016
Stax / Mar '68.
■ LP . . . . . . . . . . . . . . . . . . . . 228 017
Atco / Aug '69.

## OTIS REDDING IN PERSON AT THE
WHISKY A GO GO.
Tracks: I can't turn you loose / Pain in my heart / Just
one more day / Mr. Pitiful / (I can't get no) satisfac-
tion / I'm depending on you / Any ole way / These
arms of mine / Papa's got a brand new bag /
Respect.
■ LP . . . . . . . . . . . . . . . . . . . . 588 148
Atlantic / Dec '68.
MC. . . . . . . . . . . . . . . . . . . . . . 8122703804
WEA / Nov '92 / WEA.
CD. . . . . . . . . . . . . . . . . . . . . . 8122703802
Pickwick / Oct '94 / Pickwick.

## OTIS REDDING LIVE.
Tracks: Not Advised.
CD. . . . . . . . . . . . . . . . . . . . . . TL 1032
Traditional Line / Jan '91 / Charly / A.D.A. Distribu-
tion / Koch International.

## OTIS REDDING STORY, THE.
Tracks: These arms of mine / That's what my heart
needs / Mary's little lamb / Pain in my heart /
Something is worrying me / Security / Come to me /
I've been loving you too long / Change is gonna
come / Shake / Rock me baby / Respect / You don't
miss your water / Satisfaction / Chain gang / My
lover's prayer / It's growing / Fa fa fa fa (sad song)
/ I'm sick y'all / Sweet Lorene / Try a little tenderness / Day tripper / Stay in school / You left the
water running / Happy song / Hard to handle / Amen
/ I've got dreams to remember / Champagne and
wine / Direct me / Your one & only man / Chained
and bound / That's how strong my love is / Mr. Pitiful
/ Keep your arms around me / For your precious
love / Woman, a lover, a friend / Home in your heart
/ Ole man trouble / Down in the valley / I can't turn
you loose / Just one more day / Papa's got a brand
new bag / Good to me / Cigarettes and coffee / Ton
of joy / Hawg for you / Tramp / Knock on wood /
Lovey dovey / New year's resolution / Ooh Carla ooh
Otis / Merry Christmas baby / White Christmas /
Love man / Free me / Look at that girl / Match game
/ Tell the truth / (Sittin' on) The dock of the bay.
CD Set . . . . . . . . . . . . . . . . . . . K 781 762 2
■ LP Set . . . . . . . . . . . . . . . . . . K 781 762 1
MC Set . . . . . . . . . . . . . . . . . . . K 781 762 4
Atlantic / Dec '88 / WEA.
CD. . . . . . . . . . . . . . . . . . . . . .756781762-2
Atlantic / Mar '93 / WEA.

## OTIS REDDING STORY, VOL 1.
Tracks: Not Advised.
■ Double LP. . . . . . . . . . . . . . . . . SD 2807
Atco / Jun '88.

## OTIS REDDING STORY, VOL 2.
Tracks: Not Advised.
■ Double LP. . . . . . . . . . . . . . . . . SD 2808
Atco / Jun '88.

## PAIN IN MY HEART.
Tracks: Not Advised.
■ LP . . . . . . . . . . . . . . . . . . . . 587 042
Atlantic / Apr '67.
CD. . . . . . . . . . . . . . . . . . . . . .756780253-2
Atlantic / Jun '93 / WEA.

## PURE OTIS.
Tracks: Respect / Down in the valley / I've been
loving you too long / Shake / My girl / Wonderful
world / (I can't get no) satisfaction / Try a little
tenderness / That's how strong my love is / Love
man / Mr. Pitiful / Higher and higher / Stand by me /

Louie Louie / Hard to handle / These arms of mine /
Fa fa fa fa (sad song) / (Sittin' on) The dock of the
bay / Big blue eyes / You send me.
■ LP . . . . . . . . . . . . . . . . . . . . K 50564
Atlantic / Jul '79.

## READY STEADY GO SPECIAL.
Tracks: Satisfaction / My girl / Respect / This is a
man's world / Shake / Land of a thousand dances.
■ VHS . . . . . . . . . . . . . . . . . . . MVR 99 0016 2
PMI / Oct '84.

## REMEMBERING.
Tracks: Mr Pitiful / It's growing / Don't mess with
Cupid / 634-5789 / My girl / Try a little tenderness /
Fa-fa-fa-fa-fa / That's how strong my love is / She put
the hurt on me / Wonderful world / I've been loving
you too long / Day tripper.
■ LP . . . . . . . . . . . . . . . . . . . .2464 003
Atlantic / Jun '70.

## REMEMBERING OTIS.
Tracks: Not Advised.
VHS . . . . . . . . . . . . . . . . . . . . .VVD 650
Virgin Vision / Sep '91 / Gold & Sons / THE.

## RESPECT.
Tracks: Respect / I've been loving you too long.
■ 7" . . . . . . . . . . . . . . . . . . . . AT 4039
Atlantic / Aug '65.

## RESPECT.
Tracks: Respect / These arms of mine.
■ 7" . . . . . . . . . . . . . . . . . . . . .584091
Atlantic / Mar '67.

## SATISFACTION.
Tracks: Satisfaction / Any ole way.
■ 7" . . . . . . . . . . . . . . . . . . . . AT 4080
Atlantic / Apr '66.

## SHAKE.
Tracks: Shake / 634-5789.
■ 7" . . . . . . . . . . . . . . . . . . . . 601 011
Stax / Jun '67.

## SOUL ALBUM, THE.
Tracks: Just one more day / It's growing / Cigarettes
and coffee / Chain gang / Nobody knows you (when
you're down and out) / Good to me / Scratch my back
/ Treat her right / Everybody makes a mistake / Any
ole way / 634 5789.
■ LP . . . . . . . . . . . . . . . . . . . . 587-011
Atlantic / Jul '66.
CD. . . . . . . . . . . . . . . . . . . . . . 7567917052
MC. . . . . . . . . . . . . . . . . . . . . . 7567917054
WEA / Nov '92 / WEA.

## SOUL BALLADS.
Tracks: That's how strong my love is / Chained and
bound / Woman, a lover, a friend / Your one & only
man / Nothing can change this love / It's too late for
your precious love / I want to thank you / Come to
me / Home in your heart / Keep your arms around
me / Mr. Pitiful.
■ LP . . . . . . . . . . . . . . . . . . . . ATL 5029
Atlantic / Apr '66.
CD. . . . . . . . . . . . . . . . . . . . . . 7567917062
MC. . . . . . . . . . . . . . . . . . . . . . 7567917064
WEA / Nov '92 / WEA.

## TELL THE TRUTH.
Tracks: Demonstration / Tell the truth / Out of sight /
Give away none of my love / Wholesale love / I got
the will / Johnny's heartbreak / Snatch a little piece /
Slippin' & slidin' / Match game / Little time / Swingin'
on a string.
■ LP . . . . . . . . . . . . . . . . . . . .2400 013
Atco / Nov '70.
CD. . . . . . . . . . . . . . . . . . . . . . 8122702952
MC. . . . . . . . . . . . . . . . . . . . . . 8122702954
WEA / Nov '92 / WEA.

## TRAMP (Redding, Otis & Carla Thomas).
Tracks: Tramp / Ooh Otis ooh Carla.
■ 7" . . . . . . . . . . . . . . . . . . . . 601 012
Stax / Jul '67.

## TRAMP (OLD GOLD) (Redding, Otis &
Carla Thomas).
Tracks: Tramp / Knock on wood.
■ 7" . . . . . . . . . . . . . . . . . . . . .OG 9910
Old Gold / '89.

## TRY A LITTLE TENDERNESS.
Tracks: Try a little tenderness.
■ 12" . . . . . . . . . . . . . . . . . . . . MCST 1577
■ 7" . . . . . . . . . . . . . . . . . . . . MCS 1577

■ CD Single. . . . . . . . . . . . . . . MCSTD 1577
■ MC Single. . . . . . . . . . . . . . . MCSC 1577
MCA / Aug '91.

## TRY A LITTLE TENDERNESS.
Tracks: Try a little tenderness / Sick y'all.
■ 7" . . . . . . . . . . . . . . . . . . . . . . . .584070
Atlantic / Jan '67.

### Reddings

## AWAKENING, THE.
Tracks: Remote control / Funkin' on the one / Come in out of the rain / It's Friday night / Awakening, The (part 1) / I want it / Doin' it / Lady be my lovesong / Awakening, The (part 2).
■ LP . . . . . . . . . . . . . . . . . . EPC 84767
Epic / Mar '81.

## IF LOOKS COULD KILL.
Tracks: In my pants / Where did our love go / Didn't want to fall in love / Parasite / I don't understand it / Talk's all over town / If looks could kill / Third party.
■ LP . . . . . . . . . . . . . . . . . . . 823 324-1
Polydor / Nov '85.

## PARASITE.
Tracks: Parasite / In my pants.
■ 12" . . . . . . . . . . . . . . . . . . . POSPX 738
■ 7" . . . . . . . . . . . . . . . . . . . . POSP 738
Boiling Point / Jul '85.

## REMOTE CONTROL.
Tracks: Remote control / Awakening.
■ 7" . . . . . . . . . . . . . . . . . . . . EPC 9360
Epic / Jan '81.

## STEAMIN' HOT.
Tracks: I know you got another / (Sittin' on) The dock of the bay / You bring me joy / Follow me / Steamin' hot / For you / You can be a star / Time won't wait.
■ LP . . . . . . . . . . . . . . . . . . . EPC 85725
Epic / Dec '82.

### Reed, Dalton

## LOUISIANA SOUL MAN.
Tracks: Read me my rights / Blues of the month club / Keep on loving me / Last to understand / Heavy love / Full moon / Keep the spirit / I'm only guilty of loving you / Party on the farm / Chained and bound.
CD. . . . . . . . . . . . . . . . . . . . CDBB 9517
Bullseye Blues / Sep '92 / New Note / Topic Records / Direct Distribution.

## WILLING AND ABLE.
Tracks: Not Advised.
CD. . . . . . . . . . . . . . . . . . . . . BB 9547
Bullseye Blues / Apr '94 / New Note / Topic Records / Direct Distribution.

### Reed, Herb

## CAN'T HELP FALLING IN LOVE (Reed, Herb & The Original Platters).
Tracks: Can't help falling in love / Showman.
■ 7" . . . . . . . . . . . . . . . . . . . .PVK 003
PVK / May '77.

## EVERYBODY GET TOGETHER (Reed, Herb Group).
Tracks: Everybody get together / Ruby let me down.
■ 7" . . . . . . . . . . . . . . . . . . . . . PV 34
PVK / Feb '80.

## HUNG UP OVER YOU (Reed, Herb & Sweet River).
Tracks: Hung up over you / Time is on my side.
■ 7" . . . . . . . . . . . . . . . . . . . . PV 23
PVK / Jun '79.

## JUKE BOX GIRL (Reed, Herb & Sweet River).
Tracks: Juke box girl / Time is on my side.
■ 7" . . . . . . . . . . . . . . . . . . . .PVK 009
PVK / Nov '77.

## NEXT BEST THING (Reed, Herb & Sweet River).
Tracks: Next best thing / Nobody got so much soul.
■ 7" . . . . . . . . . . . . . . . . . . . . PVO 14
PVK / Apr '78.

## ONE MORE MINUTE (Reed, Herb & Sweet River).
Tracks: One more minute / Bubbling under.
■ 12" . . . . . . . . . . . . . . . . . . . PV 12-20
■ 7" . . . . . . . . . . . . . . . . . . . . PV 20
PVK / Feb '79.

---

## SWEET RIVER.
Tracks: What's your name, what's your number / It's the funny way / Ruby let me down / Little juke box girl / Showman / Nobody got so much soul / Next best thing / Reasons / Bubbling under / Time is on my side.
■ LP . . . . . . . . . . . . . . . . . . . SPVK 002
PVK / Nov '77.

### Reegan, Vala

## FIREMAN (Reegan, Vala & The Valarons).
Tracks: Fireman.
■ 7" . . . . . . . . . . . . . . . . . . . .584009
Atlantic / '66.

### Reese, Della

## BEST OF DELLA REESE.
Tracks: Stormy weather / Pennies from heaven / Happiness is a thing called Joe / I'm nobody's baby / What do you know about love / I've got my love to keep me warm / All alone / All of me / In the still of the night / Nobody knows the trouble I've seen / Melancholy baby / Party's over.
■ LP . . . . . . . . . . . . . . . . . . .SSL 10230
Stateside / Aug '94.

## BLACK IS BEAUTIFUL.
Tracks: Games people play / Compared to what / Choice of colours / Get together / With pen in hand / Comment / Proud Mary / You know how love is / Cycles / If everybody in the world loved everybody in the world.
■ LP . . . . . . . . . . . . . . . . . . .6466 004
Avada / Nov '70.

## CLASSIC DELLA.
Tracks: Story of a starry night / These are the things I love / If you are but a dream / My reverie / Take my heart / Stranger in Paradise / Gone / Serenade / Moon love / Softly my love / Til the end of time / Don't you know.
■ LP . . . . . . . . . . . . . . . . . . .INTS 5046
■ MC. . . . . . . . . . . . . . . . . . .INTK 5046
RCA / Oct '80.

## DELLA.
Tracks: Lady is a tramp / If I could be with you one hour tonight / Let's get away from it all / Thou swell / You're driving me crazy / Goody goody / And the angels sing / Baby won't you please come home / I'm beginning to see the light / I'll get by / Blue skies / Someday.
■ LP . . . . . . . . . . . . . . . . . . . NL 89054
■ MC. . . . . . . . . . . . . . . . . . . NK 89054
RCA / Oct '83.

## DELLA BY STARLIGHT.
Tracks: Touch of your lips / He was too good to me / That old feeling / I had the craziest dream / I wish I knew / Lamplight / How did he look / More than you know / These follish things / Deep in a dream / Embraceable you / Two sleeepy people.
■ LP . . . . . . . . . . . . . . . . . . .INTS 5194
RCA / Sep '82.

## DELLA DELLA CHA-CHA-CHA.
Tracks: Diamonds are a girl's best friend / Come on..a my house / Why don't you do right / My heart belongs to daddy / Let's do it / Whatever Lola wants (Lola gets) / Daddy / Tea for two / Always true to you in my fashion / It's so nice to have a man around the house / There's a small hotel / Love for sale.
■ LP . . . . . . . . . . . . . . . . . . . NL 90039
■ MC. . . . . . . . . . . . . . . . . . . NK 90039
RCA / Jun '87.

## I GOTTA BE ME.
Tracks: I gotta be me / Low, go / Drinkin' again / Never my love / I got the blues / Pop goes the world / Every evenin' blues (and 6 others).
■ LP . . . . . . . . . . . . . . . . . . .SSL 10261
Stateside / Nov '68.

## I LIKE IT LIKE DAT.
Tracks: Travellin' light / If it's the last thing I do / T'aint nobody's business if I do / Ev'ry evening blues / Stranger on earth / I ain't ready for that / Fool that I am / If I ever get to heaven / Drinking again / Man with a horn / In the dark / Nobody knows the way I feel this morning.
■ LP . . . . . . . . . . . . . . . . . . . JASM 1504
Jasmine / Mar '84.

## IT WAS A VERY GOOD YEAR.
Tracks: It was a very good year / Solitary woman.
■ 7" . . . . . . . . . . . . . . . . . . . POP 1553
H.M.V. / Jun '66.

---

## ON STRINGS OF BLUE.
Tracks: South side of Chicago / I had to know my way around / Mean to me / I heard you cried last night / Something cool / Walking by the river / I don't know enough about you / House is not a home / Do I worry / Show must go on / Some of my best friends are blues / I'm coming home Los Angeles.
■ LP . . . . . . . . . . . . . . . . . . . CSD 3653
H.M.V. / Nov '67.

## RIGHT NOW.
Tracks: Billy my love / Simple song of freedom / Love story / Brand new day / Something / Daydream city / Leftover wine / Why not now / Skip a rope / What are you doing the rest of your life.
■ LP . . . . . . . . . . . . . . . . . . .6466 005
Avco-Embassy / Mar '71.

## SURE LIKE LOVIN' YOU.
Tracks: When I fall in love / That's all / Come rain or come shine / Love me tender / Touch me again / Morning comes too soon / Air that I breathe / Wrapped up in the comfort of you / Two together / Sure like lovin' you / It's over now.
■ LP . . . . . . . . . . . . . . . . . . .PRCV 126
President / May '85.

## THREE GREAT GIRLS (Reese, Della/Ann Margret/Kitty Kallen).
Tracks: How lovely to be a woman / I'm in the mood for love / Begin the beguine / Misty / What is there to say / When a woman loves a man / Best is yet to come / I really don't want to know / It amazes me / True / I hadn't anyone 'til you / I get the blues when i rains.
■ LP . . . . . . . . . . . . . . . . . . . NL 89455
MC. . . . . . . . . . . . . . . . . . . NK 89455
RCA / Aug '88 / BMG.

## TROUBLE MAKER.
Tracks: Trouble maker / Love I've been lookin' for.
■ 7" . . . . . . . . . . . . . . . . . . . 610500
Avco-Embassy / May '71.

### Reeves, Dianne

## BETTER DAYS.
Tracks: Better days (Exta track on 12" version only. / Better days (re-mix) / That's all.
■ 12" . . . . . . . . . . . . . . . . . .12BLUE 5
■ 7" . . . . . . . . . . . . . . . . . . . BLUE 5
Blue Note / May '88.

## DIANNE REEVES.
Tracks: Sky islands / I'm OK / Better days / Harvest time / Chan's song / Yesterdays / I got it bad (and that ain't good) / That's all.
■ MC. . . . . . . . . . . . . . . . . TCBLJ 46901
■ LP . . . . . . . . . . . . . . . . . .BLJ 46901
Blue Note / Dec '87.
■ CD. . . . . . . . . . . . . . . . . CDBLJ 46901
Blue Note / Aug '88.

## FOR EVERY HEART.
Tracks: Not Advised.
■ LP . . . . . . . . . . . . . . . . . . . PA 20
Palo Alto / Jan '85.

## I REMEMBER.
Tracks: Afro blue / Nearness of you, The/Misty / remember / Love for sale / Softly as in the mornin sunrise / Like a lover / How high the moon / Yo taught my heart to sing / For all we know.
■ LP . . . . . . . . . . . . . . . . . . . B1 9026
■ CD. . . . . . . . . . . . . . . . . CDP 790264
Blue Note / Apr '91.

## NEVER TOO FAR.
Tracks: Hello, haven't I seen you before / Never to far / Come in / How long / Eyes on the prize / Brin me joy / Fumilayo / More to love (than making love) / We belong together / Company.
■ LP . . . . . . . . . . . . . . . . . . . DIANNE
■ MC. . . . . . . . . . . . . . . . . TCDIANNE
■ CD. . . . . . . . . . . . . . . . . CDDIANNE
EMI-America / Jan '90.

## NEVER TOO FAR.
Tracks: Never too far (Not on 12".) / Never too far (L version) (Not on 7".) / Eyes on the prize (Not on CE single.) / Eyes on the prize (LP version) (CD single only.) / Sky islands (12" only.) / Sky islands (L version) (CD single only.).
■ 12" . . . . . . . . . . . . . . . . . . 203 847
■ 12" . . . . . . . . . . . . . . . . . .12MT 8
■ 7" . . . . . . . . . . . . . . . . . . . MT 8
■ 7" . . . . . . . . . . . . . . . . . . 203 847
■ CD Single. . . . . . . . . . . . . . . CDMT 8
EMI-Manhattan / May '90.

## WELCOME TO MY LOVE.
Tracks: Not Advised.
■ LP . . . . . . . . . . . . . . . . . . . PA 802

■ DELETE

Palo Alto / Jan '84.
**MC.** . . . . . . . . . . . . . . . . . . **PAC 8026**
Palo Alto / Jul '86.

## Reeves, Martha

Martha Reeves is nothing if not assertive. Determined to obtain a Motown recording contract, in '61 she took an office job within the company, and when Mary Wells twice failed to show for sessions she sung in her place. Thus was born Martha Reeves and The Vandellas, a group whose eight year history with Gordy's outfit provided some of the company's most soulfully sung dance hits as well as some of the best internal rows: Berry Gordy and Martha were often at loggerheads. The hits are amongst the era's most memorable: *Heatwave* ('63), *Dancing In The Street* ('64), *Nowhere To Run* ('65) and *Jimmy Mack* ('67) for example. Reeves left for MCA in '70, cutting further albums for RCA and Fantasy, but it's only the Motown hits she sings on the "golden oldie" circuit.

**24 GREATEST HITS: MARTHA & THE VANDELLAS (Reeves, Martha & The Vandellas).**
**Tracks:** Not Advised.
**CD.** . . . . . . . . . . . . . . . . . . . .530040-2
**MC.** . . . . . . . . . . . . . . . . . . . .530040-4
Motown / Jan '92 / PolyGram.

**4 TRACK CASSETTE EP (Reeves, Martha & The Vandellas).**
**Tracks:** Not Advised.
**MC Single.** . . . . . . . . . . . . **CTME 2028**
Motown / May '83.

**ANTHOLOGY - MARTHA REEVES (Reeves, Martha & The Vandellas).**
**Tracks:** Come and get these memories / Heatwave / Quicksand / In my lonely room / Dancing in the street / Nowhere to run / You've been in love too long / My baby loves me / I'm ready for love / Jimmy Mack / Love bug leave my heart alone / Honey love / I can't dance to that music you're playing / (We've got) honey love / Forget me not / I gotta let you go / Bless you / In and out of my life.
**LP** . . . . . . . . . . . . . . . . . **STMR 9017**
**MC** . . . . . . . . . . . . . . . . . **CSTMR 9017**
Motown / Sep '82.
**MC** . . . . . . . . . . . . . . . . . . . **ZK 72166**
**LP** . . . . . . . . . . . . . . . . . . . **ZL 72166**
Motown / '86.

**BLACK MAGIC (Reeves, Martha & The Vandellas).**
**Tracks:** Not Advised.
**LP** . . . . . . . . . . . . . . . . . .**STML 11204**
Motown / May '72.

**BLESS YOU (Reeves, Martha & The Vandellas).**
**Tracks:** Bless you.
**7"** . . . . . . . . . . . . . . . . . . **TMG 794**
Tamla Motown / Jan '72.

**COME AND GET THESE MEMORIES (Reeves, Martha & The Vandellas).**
**Tracks:** Come and get these memories.
**7"** . . . . . . . . . . . . . . . . . . **CBA 1819**
Oriole / '63.

**COMPACT COMMAND PERFORMANCES (24 Greatest Hits) (Reeves, Martha & The Vandellas).**
**Tracks:** Come and get these memories / Heatwave / Quicksand / In my lonely room / Dancing in the street / Nowhere to run / You've been in love too long / My baby loves me / I'm ready for love / Jimmy Mack / Love bug leave my heart alone / Honey chile / I can't dance to that music you're playing / Honey love / I gotta let you go / Bless you / Love like yours / Live wire / Wild one / Motoring / Love (makes me do foolish things) / Third finger, left hand / I promise to wait my love / Sweet darlin'.
**CD** . . . . . . . . . . . . . . . . . . **WD 72447**
Motown / Mar '87.

**DANCING IN THE STREET (Reeves, Martha & The Vandellas).**
**Tracks:** Dancing in the street / Heatwave.
**7"** . . . . . . . . . . . . . . . . . . . . **SS 345**
Stateside / Oct '64.
**7"** . . . . . . . . . . . . . . . . . . **TMG 684**
Tamla Motown / Jan '69.
**7"** . . . . . . . . . . . . . . . . . .**TMG 1176**
Motown / Jun '83.

**DANCING IN THE STREET.**
**Tracks:** Dancing in the street / I can't dance that music you're playing.
**MC Single.** . . . . . . . . . . . . **TMGCS 1418**
**7"** . . . . . . . . . . . . . . . . . .**TMG 1418**
**CD Single.** . . . . . . . . . . . . **TMGCD 1418**
Motown / Jul '93.

**DANCING IN THE STREET (Reeves, Martha & The Vandellas).**
**Tracks:** Dancing in the street / Heatwave / Jimmy Mack / In the midnight hour / I want you back / Come see about me / Gotta see Jane / Nowhere to run / Spooky / It's the same old song / I say a little prayer / Get ready / I heard it through the grapevine.
**CD** . . . . . . . . . . . . . . . . . **CDCD 1140**
Charly / Nov '93 / Charly.

**DANCING IN THE STREET (Reeves, Martha & The Vandellas).**
**Tracks:** Dancing in the street / Heatwave / Jimmy Mack / I'm ready for love / Nowhere to run / Forget me not / Love bug leave my heart alone / Love like yours / Without you / Happiness is guaranteed / Wild one / Quicksand.
**LP** . . . . . . . . . . . . . . . . . .**STML 11099**
Tamla Motown / Apr '69.

**DANCING IN THE STREETS (Reeves, Martha & The Vandellas).**
**Tracks:** Dancing in the street / Nowhere to run / (Love is like a ) Heat wave / I'm ready for love / Third finger left hand / Jimmy Mack / Motoring / You've been in love too long / My baby loves me / I gotta love yours (Don't come knocking everyday) / Forget me not / Quicksand.
**CD** . . . . . . . . . . . . . . . . . .530230-2
**MC** . . . . . . . . . . . . . . . . . .530230-4
Motown / Jan '92 / PolyGram.

**FORGET ME NOT (Reeves, Martha & The Vandellas).**
**Tracks:** Forget me not / I'm ready.
**7"** . . . . . . . . . . . . . . . . . . **TMG 762**
Tamla Motown / Feb '71.
**7"** . . . . . . . . . . . . . . . . . . **TMG 983**
Tamla Motown / Aug '75.

**GREATEST HITS, VOL. 2.**
**Tracks:** Jimmy Mack / Honey chile / I gotta let you go / Love bug let my heart alone / Third finger, left hand / I should be proud / Your love makes it all worthwhile / I promise to wait my love / I can't dance to that music you're playin' / Sweet darlin' / Honey love / Bless you / I tried / In & out of my life / Forget me not / What am I going to do without your love.
**LP** . . . . . . . . . . . . . . . . . .**STML 11223**
Tamla Motown / Feb '73.

**GREATEST HITS: MARTHA & THE VANDELLAS (Reeves, Martha & The Vandellas).**
**Tracks:** My baby loves me / Come and get these memories / Heatwave / Dancing in the street / Quicksand / Live wire / You've been in love too long / In my lonely room / Love (makes me do foolish things) / Love like yours / Nowhere to run / Wild one.
**LP** . . . . . . . . . . . . . . . . . . **STMS 5042**
Motown / Jul '82.
**MC** . . . . . . . . . . . . . . . . . . **WK 72089**
**LP** . . . . . . . . . . . . . . . . . . **WL 72089**
Motown / Mar '82.
**CD** . . . . . . . . . . . . . . . . . . **WD 72089**
Motown / Aug '88.

**HEATWAVE (Reeves, Martha & The Vandellas).**
**Tracks:** Heatwave / Then he kissed me / Hey there, lonely boy / More / Danke schon / If I had a hammer / Hello stranger / Just one look / Wait till my Bobby gets home / My boyfriend's back / Mockingbird / Quicksand.
**LP** . . . . . . . . . . . . . . . . . . **STMS 5009**
**MC** . . . . . . . . . . . . . . . . . **CSTMS 5009**
Motown / Oct '81.
**LP** . . . . . . . . . . . . . . . . . . **WL 72070**
Motown / '86.

**HONEY CHILE (Reeves, Martha & The Vandellas).**
**Tracks:** Honey chile.
**7"** . . . . . . . . . . . . . . . . . . **TMG 636**
Tamla Motown / Jan '68.

**I'M READY FOR LOVE (Reeves, Martha & The Vandellas).**
**Tracks:** I'm ready for love.
**7"** . . . . . . . . . . . . . . . . . . **TMG 582**
Tamla Motown / Dec '66.

**JIMMY MACK (Reeves, Martha & The Vandellas).**
**Tracks:** Jimmy Mack / Third finger left hand.
**7"** . . . . . . . . . . . . . . . . . . **TMG 599**
Tamla Motown / '67.

**JIMMY MACK (Reeves, Martha & The Vandellas).**
**Tracks:** Jimmy Mack / Dancing in the street (Extra track on 12" version) / Medley (Extra track on 12" version) / My guy.
**12"** . . . . . . . . . . . . . . . . . . . **CRT 99**
**7"** . . . . . . . . . . . . . . . . . . . **CR 99**
Creole Classics / Mar '87.

**LOVE BUG LEAVE MY HEART ALONE (Reeves, Martha & The Vandellas).**
**Tracks:** Love bug leave my heart alone / One way out.
**7"** . . . . . . . . . . . . . . . . . . **TMG 621**
Tamla Motown / Sep '67.

**MARTHA REEVES.**
**Tracks:** Jimmy Mack / Quick sand / Heatwave / Dancing in the street / Nowhere to run / Spooky / In the midnight hour / It's the same old song / I want you back / I say a little prayer / Come see about me / Get ready / I heard it through the grapevine / Gotta see Jane.
**CD** . . . . . . . . . . . . . . . . . . **OR 0009**
Music Collection International / Apr '87 / THE / Jazz Music.

**MY BABY LOVES ME (Reeves, Martha & The Vandellas).**
**Tracks:** My baby loves me.
**7"** . . . . . . . . . . . . . . . . . . **TMG 549**
Tamla Motown / '66.

**NATURAL RESOURCES (Reeves, Martha & The Vandellas).**
**Tracks:** Something / Easily persuaded / Didn't we / I'm in love / Love, guess who / Everybody's talking / Put a little love in your heart / Hunt is over / Take a look / Won't it be so wonderful / I should be proud / People got to be free.
**LP** . . . . . . . . . . . . . . . . . .**STML 11166**
Tamla Motown / Nov '70.

**NOWHERE TO RUN (Reeves, Martha & The Vandellas).**
**Tracks:** Nowhere to run / Forget me not.
**7"** . . . . . . . . . . . . . . . . . . **TMG 502**
Tamla Motown / Apr '65.
**7"** . . . . . . . . . . . . . . . . . . **TMG 694**
Motown / Apr '69.
**7"** . . . . . . . . . . . . . . . . . **ZB 41921**
Motown / Apr '88.

**RIDIN' HIGH (Reeves, Martha & The Vandellas).**
**Tracks:** I promise to wait my love / Honey chile / Always something there to remind me / Leave it in the hands of love / Love bug leave my heart alone / I'm in love / To Sir with love / Forget me not / Honey love / I say a little prayer / Without you / Show me the way.
**LP** . . . . . . . . . . . . . . . . . .**STML 11078**
Motown / Aug '68.

**SUGAR N' SPICE (Reeves, Martha & The Vandellas).**
**Tracks:** Taking my love / Shoe leather expressway / You're the loser now / I'm a winner / What now my love / Soul appeal / Loneliness is a lovely feelin' / I love the man / It ain't like that / I can't get along without you / Heartless / I hope that you have better luck than I did.
**LP** . . . . . . . . . . . . . . . . . .**STML 11134**
Tamla Motown / Feb '70.

**WE MEET AGAIN/GOTTA KEEP MOVING.**
**Tracks:** Free again / You're like sunshine / I feel like magic / One line from every love song / Love don't come no stranger / What are you doing the rest of your life / Dedicated to be your woman / Special to me / Skating in the streets / That's what I want / Really like your rap / Gotta keep moving / Then you came / If it wasn't for my baby.
**CD** . . . . . . . . . . . . . . . . . **CDSEWD 083**
South Bound / Jul '93 / Pinnacle.

**WHAT AM I GOING TO DO WITHOUT YOUR LOVE (Reeves, Martha & The Vandellas).**
**Tracks:** What am I going to do without your love.
**7"** . . . . . . . . . . . . . . . . . . **TMG 567**
Tamla Motown / '66.

**WILD ONE (Reeves, Martha & The Vandellas).**
Tracks: Wild one.
■ 7" . . . . . . . . . . . . . . . . . . . . . . . .SS 383
Stateside / '64.

**YOU'VE BEEN IN LOVE TOO LONG (Reeves, Martha & The Vandellas).**
Tracks: You've been in love too long.
■ 7" . . . . . . . . . . . . . . . . . . . . . TMG 530
Tamla Motown / '66.

**YOUR LOVE KEEPS LIFTING ME HIGHER AND HIGHER.**
Tracks: Your love keeps lifting me higher and higher / Now that I've found love.
■ 7" . . . . . . . . . . . . . . . . . . . . . ARIST 36
Arista / Jan '76.

## Reflections

**(JUST LIKE) ROMEO & JULIET.**
Tracks: (Just like) Romeo & Juliet / Can't you tell me the look in my eyes.
■ 7" . . . . . . . . . . . . . . . . . . . . . .SS 294
Stateside / May '64.

**JUST LIKE ROMEO AND JULIET.**
Tracks: Just like Romeo and Juliet / Can't you tell me the look in my eyes.
■ 7" . . . . . . . . . . . . . . . . . . . . TMG 907
Tamla Motown / Jun '74.

## Regan, Joan

**DON'T TALK TO ME ABOUT LOVE.**
Tracks: Don't talk to me about love.
■ 7" . . . . . . . . . . . . . . . . . . .CBS 202100
CBS / '81.

**HAPPY ANNIVERSARY.**
Tracks: Happy anniversary.
■ 7" . . . . . . . . . . . . . . . . . . . . 7N 15238
Pye / Feb '60.

**IF I GIVE MY HEART TO YOU.**
Tracks: If I give my heart to you.
■ 7" . . . . . . . . . . . . . . . . . . . . F 10373
Decca / Oct '54.

**JOAN REGAN COLLECTION, THE.**
Tracks: Not Advised.
CD. . . . . . . . . . . . . . . . . . . . . .NRCD 102
■ LP . . . . . . . . . . . . . . . . . . . . .NRP 102
MC. . . . . . . . . . . . . . . . . . . . . .NRTC 102
Nectar / Nov '89 / Pinnacle.

**MAY YOU ALWAYS.**
Tracks: May you always.
■ 7" . . . . . . . . . . . . . . . . . . . . .POP 593
H.M.V. / May '59.

**MUST BE SANTA.**
Tracks: Must be Santa.
■ 7" . . . . . . . . . . . . . . . . . . . . 7N 15303
Pye / Jan '61.

**NO ONE BESIDE ME.**
Tracks: No one beside me / Love so fine.
■ 7" . . . . . . . . . . . . . . . . . . . . .202657
CBS / Mar '67.

**ONE OF THE LUCKY ONES.**
Tracks: One of the lucky ones.
■ 7" . . . . . . . . . . . . . . . . . . . . 7N 15310
Pye / Nov '60.

**OPEN UP YOUR HEART.**
Tracks: Open up your heart.
■ 7" . . . . . . . . . . . . . . . . . . . . F 10474
Decca / May '55.

**PAPA LOVES MAMA.**
Tracks: Papa loves mama.
■ 7" . . . . . . . . . . . . . . . . . . . . 7N 15278
Pye / Jul '60.

**PRIZE OF GOLD.**
Tracks: Prize of gold.
■ 7" . . . . . . . . . . . . . . . . . . . . F 10432
Decca / Mar '55.

**RICOCHET.**
Tracks: Ricochet.
■ 7" . . . . . . . . . . . . . . . . . . . . F 10193
Decca / Dec '53.

**SOMEONE ELSE'S ROSES.**
Tracks: Someone else's roses.
■ 7" . . . . . . . . . . . . . . . . . . . . F 10257
Decca / May '54.

**WAIT FOR ME (Regan, Joan & The Johnston Brothers).**
Tracks: Wait for me.
■ 7" . . . . . . . . . . . . . . . . . . . . F 10362
Decca / Nov '54.

**YOU NEEDED ME.**
Tracks: You needed me / Together again.
■ 7" . . . . . . . . . . . . . . . . . . . . JOAN 1
Nectar / Jun '89.

## Reid

**GOOD TIMES.**
Tracks: Good times (Santa Monica mix) (Not on remix.) / Good times (radio version) (Not on remix.) / Good times (worlds end dub) (Not on remix.) / Good times (red shiny mix) (Remix only.) / Good times (red shiny transformer dub) (Remix only.).
■ 12". . . . . . . . . . . . . . . . . . . .12SY 27
■ 12" Remix. . . . . . . . . . . . . . .12SYX 27
■ 7" . . . . . . . . . . . . . . . . . . . . SY 27
■ CD Single. . . . . . . . . . . . . . . CDSY 27
Syncopate / Apr '89.

**LOVIN' ON THE SIDE.**
Tracks: Lovin' on the side (flute version) (Not on 12".) / Lovin' on the side (sky king version) (12" & CD single only.) / Lovin' on the side (12" version) (12" only.) / Lovin' on the side (Full length flute version) (12" only.).
■ 12". . . . . . . . . . . . . . . . . . . .12REID 1
■ 12" Remix. . . . . . . . . . . . . . .12REIDX 1
■ 7" . . . . . . . . . . . . . . . . . . . . REID 1
■ 7" . . . . . . . . . . . . . . . . . . . . REIDP 1
■ CD Single. . . . . . . . . . . . . . . CDREID 1
■ MC Single. . . . . . . . . . . . . . . TCREID 1
Syncopate / Oct '89.

**ONE WAY OUT.**
Tracks: One way out (12" only.) / One way out (radio edit) / One way out (dub) / One way out (The U-turn mix) (12" special only.) / One way out (The U-turn dub) (12" special only.).
■ 12". . . . . . . . . . . . . . . . . . . .12SY 16
■ 12" Remix. . . . . . . . . . . . . . .12SYX 16
■ 7" . . . . . . . . . . . . . . . . . . . . SY 16
■ 7" . . . . . . . . . . . . . . . . . . . . SYP 16
■ CD Single. . . . . . . . . . . . . . . CDSY 16
■ MC Single. . . . . . . . . . . . . . . TCSY 16
Syncopate / Sep '88.

**REAL EMOTION.**
Tracks: Real emotion (7" only.) / Real emotion (workout version) (Not on 7") / Real emotion (Flat Top House version) (Not on 7") / Real emotion (Flat Top House edit) (7" only.) / Real emotion (radio version) (CD single only.) / Real emotion (Motortown meltdown) / Real emotion (Detroit meets Bedford).
■ 7" . . . . . . . . . . . . . . . . . . . . SY 24
■ 12". . . . . . . . . . . . . . . . . . . .12SY 24
■ 12" Remix. . . . . . . . . . . . . . .12SYX 24
■ CD Single. . . . . . . . . . . . . . . CDSY 24
Syncopate / Jan '89.

**REBREG EXTRACT.**
Tracks: Rebreg extract.
7" . . . . . . . . . . . . . . . . . . . . CROAK 7
Frog / Oct '94 / SRD.

## Reid, Clarence

**FUNKY PARTY.**
Tracks: Funky party / Winterman.
■ 7" . . . . . . . . . . . . . . . . . . . . K 10456
WEA / Jul '74.

## Relford, Sammie

**LOVE YOU ALL OVER (Relford, Sammie & Kim Yvette).**
Tracks: Lover you all over / Lover you all over (instrumental).
■ 12". . . . . . . . . . . . . . . . . . . .12 PO 25
Evejim / Sep '89.

## Rene & Angela

**BANGING THE BOOGIE.**
Tracks: Bangin' the boogie / Secret rendezvous.
■ 12". . . . . . . . . . . . . . . . . . . .12CL 293
■ 7" . . . . . . . . . . . . . . . . . . . . .CL 293
Capitol / May '83.

**DO YOU REALLY LOVE ME.**
Tracks: Do you really love me / Hotel California.
■ 7" . . . . . . . . . . . . . . . . . . . . CL 16145
Capitol / May '80.

**FREE AND EASY.**
Tracks: Free and easy / I don't know where love comes from / Hotel California.
■ 7" . . . . . . . . . . . . . . . . . . . . CL 16155
Capitol / Jun '80.

**I'LL BE GOOD.**
Tracks: I'll be good / You don't have to cry.
■ 12". . . . . . . . . . . . . . . . . . . .JABX 18
■ 7" . . . . . . . . . . . . . . . . . . . . JAB 18
Club / Sep '85.

**I'LL BE GOOD (OLD GOLD).**
Tracks: I'll be good / Save your love (for number 1).
■ 12". . . . . . . . . . . . . . . . . . . .OG 4087
Old Gold / Nov '88.

**SAVE YOUR LOVE (FOR NUMBER 1).**
Tracks: Save your love (for number 1).
■ 12". . . . . . . . . . . . . . . . . . . .JABX 14
■ 7" . . . . . . . . . . . . . . . . . . . . JAB 14
Club / Jun '85.

**SECRET RENDEZVOUS.**
Tracks: Secret rendezvous / Bangin' the boogie.
■ 7" . . . . . . . . . . . . . . . . . . . . CHAMP 5
■ 12". . . . . . . . . . . . . . . . . . . .CHAMP 125
Champion / Oct '85.

**STREET CALLED DESIRE.**
Tracks: Save your love (for number 1) / I'll be good / No how-no way / You don't have to cry / Street called desire / Your smile / Who's foolin' who / Drive my love.
■ LP . . . . . . . . . . . . . . . . . . . . .JABH 12
MC. . . . . . . . . . . . . . . . . . . . . .JABHC 12
■ CD . . . . . . . . . . . . . . . . . . . . 824 607 2
Club / '85 / PolyGram.

**WALL TO WALL.**
Tracks: Wall to wall / Just friends / Secret rendezvous / Wanna be close to you / I love you more / Love's alright / Imaginary playmates / Come my way.
■ LP . . . . . . . . . . . . . . . . . . . . .EMS 1118
■ MC . . . . . . . . . . . . . . . . . . . . TCEMS 1118
Capitol / '85.

**YOUR SMILE.**
Tracks: Your smile / Your smile (Inst.) / Secret rendezvous '86 (Available on 12" version only.)
■ 12". . . . . . . . . . . . . . . . . . . .JABX 24
■ 7" . . . . . . . . . . . . . . . . . . . . JAB 24
Club / '86.

## Rene, Googie

**CHICA-BOO (Rene, Googie Combo).**
Tracks: Chica-boo / Mercy mercy.
7" . . . . . . . . . . . . . . . . . . . . .584015
Atlantic / Jun '66 / WEA.

**SMOKEY JOE'S LA LA (Rene, Googie Combo).**
Tracks: Smokey Joe's la la / Needing you.
■ 7" . . . . . . . . . . . . . . . . . . . . AT 4076
Atlantic / Mar '66.

## Reynolds, L.J.

**LOVIN' MAN.**
Tracks: Lovin' man / Don't give up on us / Don't let nobody hold you down / Don't worry / Touch down / Love take 2 / Weigh all the facts / Love me all over.
■ LP . . . . . . . . . . . . . . . . . . . . .JABL 4
Club / Sep '84.

**SPECIAL EFFECTS.**
Tracks: Special effects / Key to the world.
■ 12". . . . . . . . . . . . . . . . . . . .12CL 260
■ 7" . . . . . . . . . . . . . . . . . . . . .CL 260
Capitol / Aug '82.

**TELL ME YOU WILL.**
Tracks: Not Advised.
■ LP . . . . . . . . . . . . . . . . . . . . .FAX 508
Fantasy / Aug '87.

**WEIGH ALL THE FACTS.**
Tracks: Weigh all the facts / Don't let nobody hold you down / Love me all over / Don't worry.
■ 12". . . . . . . . . . . . . . . . . . . .JABX 5
■ 7" . . . . . . . . . . . . . . . . . . . . JAB 5
Club / Jun '84.

## Rhythm Heritage

**ROCKY, THEME FROM.**
Tracks: Rocky, Theme from / Last night on earth.
■ 7" . . . . . . . . . . . . . . . . . . . . ABC 4164
ABC Records / Feb '77.

■ DELETED

## Rhythm Within

**RHYTHM AIN'T PLAYING.**
Tracks: Rhythm ain't playing.
■ 12″ . . . . . . . . . . . . . . . . . . . .12 MISH 1
Passion/Debut/Scratch Music / Dec '92.

**YOU MAKE ME FEEL.**
Tracks: You make me feel.
12″ . . . . . . . . . . . . . . . . . . . . 12MISH 6
Mission / Jan '94 / Pinnacle.

## Rhyze

**JUST HOW SWEET IS YOUR LOVE.**
Tracks: Just how sweet is your love / I found love in you.
■ 12″ . . . . . . . . . . . . . . . . . EPC 13 8794
■ 7″ . . . . . . . . . . . . . . . . . . . EPC 8794
Epic / Aug '80.

## Rice, Daryle

**FROM NOW ON.**
Tracks: Not Advised.
CD . . . . . . . . . . . . . . . . . . . . AP 100CD
Appaloosa / Jun '94 / A.D.A. Distribution.

**WALK WITH MUSIC (Rice, Daryle & The Loonis McGlohon Quartet).**
Tracks: Not Advised.
■ LP . . . . . . . . . . . . . . . . . . . . AP 141
Audiophile (USA) / Aug '88.

## Rice, Gene

**JUST FOR YOU.**
Tracks: Love is calling you / You're gonna get served / No one can love you like I love you / Let's do it again / Let's get away / You're a victim / I believe / It's too late / So far away / I'll be right here waiting on you.
CD . . . . . . . . . . . . . . . . . . . . PD 83159
■ LP . . . . . . . . . . . . . . . . . . . . PL 83159
■ MC . . . . . . . . . . . . . . . . . . . . PK 83159
RCA / Aug '91 / BMG.

## Rice, Sir Mack

**IT TAKES ONE TO KNOW ONE.**
Tracks: It takes one to know one / It takes one to know one (part 2).
■ 7″ . . . . . . . . . . . . . . . . . . . . CS 2086
Contempo (1) / May '76.

## Rich, Denise

**SWEET PAIN OF LOVE.**
Tracks: Do you wanna dance / Sweet pain of love / Frankie / Too good for you / Show her / We walked away from a love affair / Do ya wanna dance / Silent majority / Years go by so quickly / Talking love / Wind in my soul.
■ LP . . . . . . . . . . . . . . . . . . . MCG 6008
■ MC . . . . . . . . . . . . . . . . . . . MCGC 6008
MCA / Jun '86.

**SWEET PAIN OF LOVE.**
Tracks: Sweet pain of love.
■ 12″ . . . . . . . . . . . . . . . . . . FOUND 412
■ 7″ . . . . . . . . . . . . . . . . . . . FOUND 4
Foundry / Feb '87.

**WE WALKED AWAY FROM A LOVE AFFAIR.**
Tracks: We walked away from a love affair / Win in my soul.
■ 12″ . . . . . . . . . . . . . . . . . . MCAT 1039
■ 7″ . . . . . . . . . . . . . . . . . . . MCA 1039
MCA / May '86.

## Richie, Lionel

Former Commodore who split for solo career (although he remained on band's label Motown) in 1981. Multi-million selling Can't Slow Down and Dancin' on the Ceiling albums spawned string of hits, including Hello and Say You, Say Me. Richie's other successes include duet with Diana Ross, Endless Love, and We Are the World, which he co-wrote with Michael Jackson. He bid farewell to Motown - for whom he was biggest act of '80s - with Back to Front hits compilation; and signed to Mercury in '92.

**ALL NIGHT LONG.**
Tracks: All night long / Wandering stranger.
■ 12″ . . . . . . . . . . . . . . . . . . TMGT 1319

■ 7″ . . . . . . . . . . . . . . . . . . . TMG 1319
Motown / Sep '83.

**ALL NIGHT LONG.**
Tracks: Not Advised.
■ VHS . . . . . . . . . . . . . . . . . RVT 1055 2
RCA/Columbia (Video) / Jan '86.

**BACK TO FRONT.**
Tracks: Do it to me / My destiny / Love oh love / All night long (all night) / Easy / Still / Endless love / Running with the night / Dancing on the ceiling / Sail on / Hello / Truly / Penny lover / Stuck on you / Say you, say me / Three times a lady.
CD . . . . . . . . . . . . . . . . . . . . 5300182
MC . . . . . . . . . . . . . . . . . . . . 5300184
■ LP . . . . . . . . . . . . . . . . . . . . 5300181
Motown / May '92 / PolyGram.
DCC . . . . . . . . . . . . . . . . . . 530 018-5
Motown / Jan '93 / PolyGram.

**BACK TO FRONT.**
Tracks: Not Advised.
VHS . . . . . . . . . . . . . . . . . . 086 112 3
Polygram Music Video / Nov '92 / PolyGram.

**BALLERINA GIRL.**
Tracks: Deep river woman / Dancing on the ceiling*.
■ 12″ . . . . . . . . . . . . . . . . . . . LIOT 3
■ 7″ . . . . . . . . . . . . . . . . . . . . LIO 3
Motown / Dec '86.

**CAN'T SLOW DOWN.**
Tracks: All night long / Stuck on you / Penny lover / Hello / Love will find a way / Running with the night / Only one / Can't slow down.
■ CD . . . . . . . . . . . . . .MCD 06059 MD
■ LP . . . . . . . . . . . . . . . . . STMA 8041
■ MC . . . . . . . . . . . . . . . . CSTMA 8041
Motown / Oct '83.
■ CD . . . . . . . . . . . . . . . . . ZD 72020
Motown / '86.
CD . . . . . . . . . . . . . . . . . . . .530023-2
■ MC . . . . . . . . . . . . . . . . . . .530023-4
Motown / Jan '92 / PolyGram.

**DANCING ON THE CEILING.**
Tracks: Sela / Ballerina girl / Don't stop / Deep river woman / Love will conquer all / Tonight will be alright / Say you, say me / Night train (Smooth alligator) (Cassette and Compact Disc only.) / Dancing on the ceiling / Love will find a way.
■ CD . . . . . . . . . . . . . . . . . ZD 72412
■ LP . . . . . . . . . . . . . . . . . ZL 72412
■ MC . . . . . . . . . . . . . . . . . ZK 72412
Motown / Jan '87.
CD . . . . . . . . . . . . . . . . . . . .530024-2
MC . . . . . . . . . . . . . . . . . . . .530024-4
Motown / Jan '92 / PolyGram.

**DANCING ON THE CEILING.**
Tracks: Dancing on the ceiling.
■ 12″ . . . . . . . . . . . . . . . . . . . LIOT 1
■ 7″ . . . . . . . . . . . . . . . . . . . . LIO 1
Motown / Jul '86.

**DANCING ON THE CEILING.**
Tracks: Not Advised.
■ VHS . . . . . . . . . . . . . . . . . HEN 2046
Hendring Video / '88.

**DO IT TO ME.**
Tracks: Do it to me.
■ 12″ . . . . . . . . . . . . . . . . . . TMGX 1407
■ 7″ . . . . . . . . . . . . . . . . . . . TMG 1407
■ CD Single . . . . . . . . . . . . . TMGCD 1407
■ MC Single . . . . . . . . . . . . . TMGCS 1407
Motown / May '92.

**ENDLESS LOVE (see under Ross, Diana).**

**HELLO.**
Tracks: Hello / All night long / Running with the night.
■ 12″ . . . . . . . . . . . . . . . . . . TMGT 1330
■ 7″ . . . . . . . . . . . . . . . . . . . TMG 1330
Motown / Mar '84.

**LIONEL RICHIE.**
Tracks: Serves you right / Wandering stranger / Tell me / My love / round and 'round / Truly / You are / You mean more to me / Just put some love in your heart.
■ CD . . . . . . . . . . . . . .MCD 06007 MD
■ LP . . . . . . . . . . . . . . . . . STMA 8037
■ MC . . . . . . . . . . . . . . . . CSTMA 8037
Motown / Nov '82.
■ CD . . . . . . . . . . . . . . . . . ZD 72017
Motown / '86.
CD . . . . . . . . . . . . . . . . . . . .530026-2
MC . . . . . . . . . . . . . . . . . . . .530026-4
Motown / Jan '92 / PolyGram.

**LOVE WILL CONQUER ALL.**
Tracks: Love will conquer all / Only one / Love will conquer all (remix) / Love will conquer all (ext remix) / Love will conquer all (radio edit) / Love will conquer all (inst).
■ 12″ . . . . . . . . . . . . . . . . . . . LIOT 2
■ 7″ . . . . . . . . . . . . . . . . . . . . LIO 2
Motown / Sep '86.
■ 12″ Remix. . . . . . . . . . . . . . . LIOT 2R
Motown / Sep '86.

**LOVE, OH LOVE.**
Tracks: Love, oh love.
■ 12″ . . . . . . . . . . . . . . . . . . TMGX 1413
■ 7″ . . . . . . . . . . . . . . . . . . . TMG 1413
■ CD Single . . . . . . . . . . . . . TMGCD 1413
■ MC Single . . . . . . . . . . . . . TMGCS 1413
Motown / Nov '92.

**MY DESTINY.**
Tracks: My destiny.
■ 12″ . . . . . . . . . . . . . . . . . . TMGX 1408
■ 7″ . . . . . . . . . . . . . . . . . . . TMG 1408
■ CD Single . . . . . . . . . . . . . TMGCD 1408
■ MC Single . . . . . . . . . . . . . TMGCS 1408
Motown / Aug '92.

**MY LOVE.**
Tracks: My love / round and 'round.
■ 12″ . . . . . . . . . . . . . . . . . . TMGT 1300
■ 7″ . . . . . . . . . . . . . . . . . . . TMG 1300
Motown / Apr '83.

**OUTRAGEOUS TOUR, THE.**
Tracks: Not Advised.
■ VHS . . . . . . . . . . . . . . . . . VC 4041
Video Collection / '88.
VHS . . . . . . . . . . . . . . . . . .MC 2034
Music Club Video / Aug '89 / Video Collection / Gold & Sons / THE.

**PENNY LOVER.**
Tracks: Penny lover / You are.
■ 7″ . . . . . . . . . . . . . . . . . . . TMG 1356
■ 12″ . . . . . . . . . . . . . . . . . . TMGT 1356
Motown / Oct '84.

**RUNNING WITH THE NIGHT.**
Tracks: Running with the night / All night long.
■ 7″ . . . . . . . . . . . . . . . . . . . TMG 1324
■ 12″ . . . . . . . . . . . . . . . . . . TMGT 1324
Motown / Nov '83.

**SAY YOU SAY ME.**
Tracks: Say you, say me.
■ 12″ . . . . . . . . . . . . . . . . . . . ZT 40421
■ 7″ . . . . . . . . . . . . . . . . . . . ZB 40421
Motown / Nov '85.

**SELA.**
Tracks: Sela / Serves you right.
■ 12″ . . . . . . . . . . . . . . . . . . . LIOT 4
■ 7″ . . . . . . . . . . . . . . . . . . . . LIO 4
Motown / Mar '87.
■ CD Single . . . . . . . . . . . . . . LIOCD 4
Motown / Jun '89.

**STUCK ON YOU.**
Tracks: Stuck on you / round and 'round / Tell me.
■ 12″ . . . . . . . . . . . . . . . . . . TMGT 1341
■ 7″ . . . . . . . . . . . . . . . . . . . TMG 1341
Motown / Jun '84.

**TRULY.**
Tracks: Truly / Just put some love in your heart.
■ 12″ . . . . . . . . . . . . . . . . . . TMGT 1290
■ 7″ . . . . . . . . . . . . . . . . . . . TMG 1290
Motown / Jan '83.

## Ricochet

**RICOCHET.**
Tracks: Ricochet.
12″ . . . . . . . . . . . . . . . . . . . . MJR 5
MJR / Jul '94 / Jetstar.

## Ridley, Sharon

**I'M IN YOUR CORNER.**
Tracks: I'm in your corner / To make a long story short.
■ 7″ . . . . . . . . . . . . . . . . . . . .PT 446
President / Feb '76.

■ DELETED

345

## Riggan, Tracey

### FRIENDS.
**Tracks:** Amazing grace / Challenge / Arms of the Father / Special friend / Never gonna look back / Security / Free / Dance of fire / Hide no more / Celebration.
CD. . . . . . . . . . . . . . . . . . . . MYRCD 1283
MC. . . . . . . . . . . . . . . . . . . . MYRC 1283
Myrrh / Jan '92 / Word Records (UK) / Sony.

## Right Choice

### RIGHT CHOICE, THE.
**Tracks:** Not Advised.
■ LP . . . . . . . . . . . . . . . . . . MOT 6257
Motown / Mar '89.

## Righteous Brothers

### (YOU'RE MY) SOUL AND INSPIRATION.
**Tracks:** (You're my) soul and inspiration.
■ 7" . . . . . . . . . . . . . . . . . . . .VS 535
Verve / Apr '66.

### 21ST ANNIVERSARY CELEBRATION.
**Tracks:** Not Advised.
VHS . . . . . . . . . . . . . . . . . . OGV 0004
Old Gold / May '90 / Pickwick.

### BEST OF RIGHTEOUS BROTHERS.
**Tracks:** You've lost that lovin' feelin' / That lucky old sun / So many lonely nights ahead / Go ahead and cry / Soul and inspiration / Hold on I'm coming / Unchained melody / Drown in my own tears / In the midnight hour / Hung on you / Harlem shuffle / I just want to make love to you / Mine all mine / He / Angels listened in / What'd I say.
■ LP . . . . . . . . . . . . . . . . . . 831 996-1
MC. . . . . . . . . . . . . . . . . . . . 831 996-4
Verve / Oct '87 / PolyGram.

### CHANGE IS GONNA COME, A.
**Tracks:** Not Advised.
CD. . . . . . . . . . . . . . . . . . . . . RC 83117
MC. . . . . . . . . . . . . . . . . . . . . . 82117
Royal Collection / Mar '93 / BMG.

### DREAM ON.
**Tracks:** Dream on.
■ 7" . . . . . . . . . . . . . . . . . . CL 15803
Capitol / Jan '75.

### EBB TIDE.
**Tracks:** Ebb tide / For sentimental reasons.
■ 7" . . . . . . . . . . . . . . . . . . HL 10011
London-American / Jan '66.

### GREATEST HITS, THE.
**Tracks:** Not Advised.
CD. . . . . . . . . . . . . . . . . . . . .JHD 024
MC. . . . . . . . . . . . . . . . . . . MCJHD 024
IMD / Jun '92 / BMG.

### GREATEST HITS: RIGHTEOUS BROTHERS.
**Tracks:** You've lost that lovin' feelin' / White cliffs of Dover / For sentimental reasons / Georgia on my mind / You'll never walk alone / Just once in my life / Unchained Melody / See that girl / Ebb tide / Guess who / Hung on you / Great pretender.
■ LP . . . . . . . . . . . . . . . . . . SPELP 47
MC. . . . . . . . . . . . . . . . . . . SPEMC 47
■ CD . . . . . . . . . . . . . . . . . . 823 119-2
MGM (Polydor) / Nov '83.

### INSPIRATIONS.
**Tracks:** (You're my) soul and inspiration / What now my love / Ebb tide / White cliffs of Dover / Go ahead and cry / Just once in my life / Stranded in the middle of no place / Great pretender / He will break your heart / Island in the sun / (I love you) for sentimental reasons / That lucky old sun / My darling Clementine / Georgia on my mind.
CD. . . . . . . . . . . . . . . . . . . .550197-2
MC. . . . . . . . . . . . . . . . . . . .550197-4
Spectrum (1) / Mar '94 / PolyGram.

### ISLAND IN THE SUN.
**Tracks:** Island in the sun.
■ 7" . . . . . . . . . . . . . . . . . . . .VS 547
Verve / Dec '66.

### JUST ONCE IN MY LIFE.
**Tracks:** Just once in my life.
■ 12" . . . . . . . . . . . . . . . . . . .PZ 128
■ 7" . . . . . . . . . . . . . . . . . . . PO 128
■ CD Single . . . . . . . . . . . . . . PZCD 128
■ MC Single. . . . . . . . . . . . . . POCS 128
Polydor / Feb '91.

### ONE FOR THE ROAD.
**Tracks:** Soul and inspiration / My babe / Oldies but goodies medley / Gospel medley / Unchained / Ooh poo pah doo (and 5 others).
■ LP . . . . . . . . . . . . . . . . . . SVLP 9228
Verve / Nov '68.

### ORIGINAL ALBUMS.
**Tracks:** Not Advised.
CD. . . . . . . . . . . . . . . . . . . . DCD 5285
Disky / Dec '93 / THE.

### REUNION.
**Tracks:** Unchained melody / Just once in my life / Rock and roll heaven / (You're my) soul and inspiration / You've lost that lovin' feelin' / Hung on you / Try to find another woman / Little Latin lupe lu / Ebb tide / My babe / Unchained melody (timeless love extended).
CD. . . . . . . . . . . . . . . . . . . . 467 957 2
■ LP . . . . . . . . . . . . . . . . . . 467 957 1
■ MC. . . . . . . . . . . . . . . . . . 467 957 4
Curb / Feb '91 / PolyGram.

### RIGHTEOUS BROTHERS: 21ST ANNIVERSARY.
**Tracks:** Not Advised.
VHS . . . . . . . . . . . . . . . . . . SVM 804
Start (Video) / Nov '92 / Sony Video Software.

### SOULED OUT.
**Tracks:** Been so nice / Stranded in the middle of no place / It's up to you / So many lonely nights ahead / I don't believe in losing / Love keeps callin' my name / Someone like you / You bent my mind / Without you I'd be lost.
■ LP . . . . . . . . . . . . . . . . . . SVLP 9190
Verve / Feb '68.

### STANDARDS.
**Tracks:** That lucky old sun / That's all / My darling Clementine / All the way / Country boy / Without a song / Since I fell for you / Come rain or come shine / Secret love / If I ruled the world / Somewhere.
■ LP . . . . . . . . . . . . . . . . . . SVLP 9204
Verve / Jun '68.

### THEIR TOP HITS (Righteous Brothers & Bill Medley).
**Tracks:** Not Advised.
MC. . . . . . . . . . . . . . . . . . . . . . .821
Timeless Treasures / Nov '87 / THE.

### UNCHAINED MELODY.
**Tracks:** Unchained melody.
■ 7" . . . . . . . . . . . . . . . . . . HL 9975
London-American / Aug '65.

### UNCHAINED MELODY.
**Tracks:** Unchained melody / You're my soul and inspiration / You've lost that lovin' feelin' (Available on 12" format only.) / White cliffs of Dover (Available on CD single format only.)
■ 12" . . . . . . . . . . . . . . . . . .PZ 101
■ CD Single . . . . . . . . . . . . . . PXCD 101
■ MC Single. . . . . . . . . . . . . . POCS 101
■ 7" . . . . . . . . . . . . . . . . . . PO 101
Polydor / Oct '90.

### UNCHAINED MELODY.
**Tracks:** Not Advised.
CD. . . . . . . . . . . . . . . . . . . . .AVC 513
MC. . . . . . . . . . . . . . . . . . . . AVM 513
Avid / Dec '92 / ACD Trading Ltd. / BMG.

### UNCHAINED MELODY - THE VERY BEST OF THE RIGHTEOUS BROTHERS.
**Tracks:** You've lost that lovin' feeling / Unchained melody / You're my soul and inspiration / Ebb tide / Just once in my life / White cliffs of Dover / He / Hung on you / Little Latin lupe lu (Lupelu) / Go ahead and cry / See that girl / On this side of goodbye.
CD. . . . . . . . . . . . . . . . . . . . 847 248-2
MC. . . . . . . . . . . . . . . . . . . . 847 248-4
■ LP . . . . . . . . . . . . . . . . . . 847 248-1
Verve / Nov '90 / PolyGram.
DCC . . . . . . . . . . . . . . . . . . 847 248-5
Verve / Jan '93 / PolyGram.

### WHITE CLIFFS OF DOVER.
**Tracks:** White cliffs of Dover.
■ 7" . . . . . . . . . . . . . . . . . . HL 10086
London-American / Nov '66.

### YOU'VE LOST THAT LOVIN' FEELING.
**Tracks:** You've lost that lovin' feelin'.
■ 7" . . . . . . . . . . . . . . . . . . HLU 9943
London-American / Jan '65.

### YOU'VE LOST THAT LOVIN' FEELING (OLD GOLD).
**Tracks:** You've lost that lovin' feelin' / Unchained melody.

■ 7" . . . . . . . . . . . . . . . . . . .OG 945
Old Gold / Jun '88.

### YOU'VE LOST THAT LOVIN' FEELING (REISSUES).
**Tracks:** You've lost that lovin' feelin' / Ebb tide Georgia on my mind.
■ 7" . . . . . . . . . . . . . . . . . . HL 1024
London-American / Feb '69.
■ 7" . . . . . . . . . . . . . . . . . . 201002
Phil Spector Int. / Nov '77.
■ 12" . . . . . . . . . . . . . . . . . .PZ 11
■ 7" . . . . . . . . . . . . . . . . . . PO 11
■ CD Single . . . . . . . . . . . . . . POCD 11
■ MC Single. . . . . . . . . . . . . . POCS 11
Polydor / Nov '90.

## Riley, Teddy

Founder member and co-producer of arche typal new jack trio Guy, Riley is now world swingbeat supremo. Reputation sealed b production credit on Michael Jackson' *Dangerous*, although work is best sample on '94 collection *Classic New Jack Swing Mastercuts vol. 3*, which boasts Riley re mixes of, among others, TLC, S.W.V. an Wreckx N Effect (latter were first signings t Riley's own label). Riley's most recer creation, Blackstreet, has continued his hit making career.

### IS IT GOOD TO YOU.
**Tracks:** Is it good to you.
■ 12" . . . . . . . . . . . . . . . . . . MCST 161
■ 7" . . . . . . . . . . . . . . . . . . MCS 161
■ CD Single . . . . . . . . . . . . . . MCSTD 161
MCA / Mar '92.

### MY FANTASY (see under Guy).

## Rimshots

### 7654321 (BLOW YOUR WHISTLE).
**Tracks:** 7654321 (blow your whistle).
■ 7" . . . . . . . . . . . . . . . . . . .6146 30
All Platinum / Jul '75.

### AT NIGHT.
**Tracks:** At night.
■ 7" . . . . . . . . . . . . . . . . . . SPEC 10
Spectro / Oct '81.

### I WAS WRONG.
**Tracks:** I was wrong / Stuck in a boat.
■ 7" . . . . . . . . . . . . . . . . . . SRP 000
Shoc-Wave / Jul '80.

### SWEET TALK.
**Tracks:** Sweet talk / What's the matter baby.
■ 7" . . . . . . . . . . . . . . . . . . RESP
Respond / Mar '82.

### WHO'S GOT THE MONSTER (Rimshots & Whatnauts Band).
**Tracks:** Who's got the monster / Soul walkin'.
■ 7" . . . . . . . . . . . . . . . . . . 614630
All Platinum / Apr '75.

## Rio

### RIO.
**Tracks:** Not Advised.
CD. . . . . . . . . . . . . . . . . . . . BLIPCD 10
Urban London / Mar '94 / Jetstar.

## Riperton, Minnie

Abandoning hoped-for career in opera, Ri perton joined vocal group Gems, with whom she sang backing on Chess label hits to likes of Fontella Bass, Dells and Ramse Lewis. After less illustrious role as Ches receptionist, she joined Rotary Connection whose commercial obscurity was echoed b her early solo efforts. Breakthrough finall came when Epic signed her in '74; sub sequent, Stevie Wonder-produced *Perfec Angel* spawned U.S. No. 1 *Loving You* (als her only international hit). Successful re cording career ran parallel to role as hea of American Cancer Society, Riperton hav ing been diagnosed with breast cancer from which she died in July '79. Posthu mous album *Love Lives Forever* feature tributes from Wonder, George Benson, Pea bo Bryson, Michael Jackson, Roberta Flac and Patrice Rushen.

### BEST OF MINNIE RIPERTON, THE.
**Tracks:** Perfect angel / Memory lane / Loving you Can you feel what I'm saying / Here we go / Inside

■ DELETED

y love / Lover and friend / Woman of heart and
ind / Young, willing and able / You take my breath
way / Adventures in paradise
MC. . . . . . . . . . . . . . . . . TC EST 12189
LP . . . . . . . . . . . . . . . . . .EST 12189
apitol / Nov '81.

**APITOL GOLD: THE BEST OF MINNIE
IPPERTON.**
racks: Perfect angel / Lover and friend (Single
ersion) / Memory lane (Single version) / Woman of
eart and mind / Loving you / Young willing and able
Can you feel what I'm saying / Stick together /
ouldn't matter where you are / Stay in love / Inside
y love / Here we go / Give me time (Single version)
You take my breath away / Adventures in paradise
Simple things / Light my fire.
D. . . . . . . . . . . . . . . . . CDP 7805162
apitol / Aug '93 / EMI.

**SLAND IN THE SUN.**
racks: Island in the sun / Light my fire / Lover and
iend (12" only).
12". . . . . . . . . . . . . . . .12CL 16165
7". . . . . . . . . . . . . . . . CL 16165
apitol / Apr '81.

**OVE LIVES FOREVER.**
racks: Here we go / I'm in love again / Strange
fair / Island in the sun / Give me time / You take my
reath away / Song of life.
LP . . . . . . . . . . . . . . . . .EST 12097
apitol / Oct '80.

**OVIN' YOU (OLD GOLD).**
racks: Not Advised.
7" . . . . . . . . . . . . . . . . .OG 9996
ld Gold / Feb '92.

**OVING YOU.**
racks: Loving you / Inside my love.
7" . . . . . . . . . . . . . . . EPC 3121
pic / Apr '75.

**OVING YOU (OLD GOLD).**
racks: Loving you.
7" . . . . . . . . . . . . . . . .OG 9725
ld Gold / Jun '88.

**MEMORY LANE.**
racks: Memory lane / I'm a woman.
7" . . . . . . . . . . . . . . . CL 16082
apitol / May '79.

**MINNIE.**
racks: Memory lane / Lover and friend / Return to
rever / Love hurts / Dancin' and actin' crazy /
ever existed before / I'm a woman / Light my fire.
LP . . . . . . . . . . . . . . . . .EST 11936
apitol / '79.
LP . . . . . . . . . . . . . . . . . FA 3027
MC. . . . . . . . . . . . . . . . . TCFA 3027
ame / May '82.

**NLY WHEN I'M DREAMING.**
racks: Les fleurs / Completeness / Come to my
arden / Memory lane / Rainy day in Centreville /
ose your eyes and remember / Oh by the way /
xpecting / Only when I'm dreaming.
D. . . . . . . . . . . . . . . . . CDBM 080
ue Moon (1) / Sep '90 / Roots Records / Jazz Music
Swift / Projection / THE / Hot Shot.

**ERFECT ANGEL.**
racks: Not Advised.
LP . . . . . . . . . . . . . . . . . EPC 80426
pic / May '75.

**EEING YOU THIS WAY.**
acks: Seeing you this way / Edge of a dream.
7" . . . . . . . . . . . . . . . CBS 2660
BS / Jan '75.

**TAY IN LOVE.**
racks: Not Advised.
LP . . . . . . . . . . . . . . . . . EPC 81457
pic / Mar '77.

**WHEN IT COMES DOWN TO IT.**
acks: When it comes down to it / Love and it's
ory.
7" . . . . . . . . . . . . . . . EPC 3796
pic / Jan '76.

---

## Ripple

**BEAT GOES ON AND ON.**
Tracks: Beat goes on and on / Facts of life.
■ 7" . . . . . . . . . . . . . . . SSOL 105
Salsoul / Mar '78.

**BEAT GOES ON/GOT MY MIND MADE
UP (Ripple/Instant Funk).**
Tracks: Beat goes on / Got my mind made up.
■ 12" . . . . . . . . . . . . . . 12SALSA 4
Salsoul / Apr '93.

---

## Ritchie Family

**AMERICAN GENERATION.**
Tracks: American generation / Big spender / Good in
love / I feel disco good / Musicman.
■ LP . . . . . . . . . . . . . . . .9109 618
Mercury / Mar '79.

**AMERICAN GENERATION.**
Tracks: American generation / Music man.
■ 7" . . . . . . . . . . . . . . . .6007 199
Mercury / Feb '79.

**BEST DISCO IN TOWN (OLD GOLD).**
Tracks: Best disco in town / Brazil.
■ 12" . . . . . . . . . . . . . . . .OG 4092
Old Gold / Jan '89.

**BEST DISCO IN TOWN, THE.**
Tracks: Best disco in town.
■ 7" . . . . . . . . . . . . . . . .2058 777
Polydor / Sep '76.

**BRAZIL.**
Tracks: Brazil.
■ 7" . . . . . . . . . . . . . . . .2058 625
Polydor / Aug '75.

**BRAZIL (OLD GOLD).**
Tracks: Brazil / Best disco in town / American
generation.
CD Single. . . . . . . . . . . . . .OG 6505
Old Gold / Jul '90 / Pickwick.

**GIVE ME A BREAK.**
Tracks: Give me a break / Bad reputation.
■ 7" . . . . . . . . . . . . . . . MER 17
Mercury / '80.

**I WANT TO DANCE WITH YOU.**
Tracks: I want to dance with you / Lady Champagne.
■ 7" . . . . . . . . . . . . . . . .2058 681
Polydor / Feb '76.

**IT'S A MAN'S WORLD.**
Tracks: It's a man's world / Bad reputation.
■ 7" . . . . . . . . . . . . . . . 6007228
Mercury / Aug '79.

**PUT YOUR FEET TO THE BEAT.**
Tracks: Put your feet to the beat / Where are the
men
■ 12". . . . . . . . . . . . . . . 9198524
■ 7" . . . . . . . . . . . . . . . .6007239
Mercury / Nov '79.

**QUIET VILLAGE.**
Tracks: Quiet village / Voodoo.
■ 7" . . . . . . . . . . . . . . . .2058 912
Polydor / Aug '77.

**RITCHIE FAMILY.**
Tracks: Put your feet to the beat / Bad reputation /
It's a man's world / Where are the men / Sexy man.
■ LP . . . . . . . . . . . . . . . .9109 627
Mercury / Sep '79.
■ LP . . . . . . . . . . . . . . . QUAMP 1
MC. . . . . . . . . . . . . . . . QUAMPC 1
Quazar / Nov '87 / Pinnacle.

---

## RJ's Latest Arrival

**TRULY YOURS.**
Tracks: What becomes of the broken hearted / Off
the hook / Truly yours / Could have been you / I'll
always love you / Miracles / Time 4 love / Nights /
Water pump / Terri's place.
■ CD . . . . . . . . . . . . . . CDP 748 090 2
■ LP . . . . . . . . . . . . . . . MTL 1035
■ MC. . . . . . . . . . . . . . . TCMTL 1035
EMI-Manhattan / Aug '88.

---

## Robbins, Rockie

**ARE YOU READY.**
Tracks: Are you ready.
■ 12" . . . . . . . . . . . . . . DEBTX 3133
Debut (1) / Feb '92.

**I'VE GOT YOUR NUMBER.**
Tracks: I've got your number / Work for love.
■ 12". . . . . . . . . . . . . . .MCAT 975
■ 7" . . . . . . . . . . . . . . . MCA 975
MCA / Jul '85.

**SERIOUS.**
Tracks: Serious.
■ 12". . . . . . . . . . . . . . . PECT 1
■ 7" . . . . . . . . . . . . . . . PEC 1
Respect / Aug '89.

**WE BELONG TOGETHER.**
Tracks: Not Advised.
■ LP . . . . . . . . . . . . . . . MCF 3259
MCA / Apr '85.

**WE BELONG TOGETHER.**
Tracks: We belong together.
■ 12". . . . . . . . . . . . . . .MCAT 950
■ 7" . . . . . . . . . . . . . . . MCA 950
MCA / Apr '85.

---

## Robert & Johnny

**WE BELONG TOGETHER.**
Tracks: We belong together / Broken hearted man / I
don't stand a ghost of a chance / Baby come home /
You're mine / Eternity with you / Dream girl / Oh my
love / Million dollar bills / I got you / Give me the key
to your heart / Wear this ring / Gosh oh gee / Don't
do it / I believe in you / God knows / Bad Dan / Indian
marriage / Your kisses / Baby baby / I hear my
heartbeat / Togetherness / I'm truly truly yours /
Please me please / Try me pretty baby / Baby girl of
mine / Train to paradise.
■ LP . . . . . . . . . . . . . . . . CH 172
Ace / Apr '86.
CD. . . . . . . . . . . . . . . .CDCHD 384
Ace / Apr '93 / Pinnacle / Complete Record Co. Ltd.

---

## Roberts, Juliet

Juliet Roberts' first taste of success came
with Funkmasters' international hit *It's
Over*, a U.K. No. 8 in 1983. In 1993, she
released acclaimed solo debut, *Caught In
The Middle*, followed by *Natural Thing* album in '94. Intervening decade saw Roberts
co-hosting Channel 4 TV's *Solid Soul* and
singing with mildly successful jazz-funk outfit Working Week, before embarking on own
career. Pivotal figures in breakthrough
were Courtney Pine, with whom Roberts
sang, and D-Mob supremo Danny D, to
whose Slam Jam label she signed; both
appeared on *Natural Thing*, as did Atlantic
Starr.

**AGAIN.**
Tracks: Again / Again (mixes) / I want you / I want
you (mixes).
■ 12". . . . . . . . . . . . . . .12COOLS 285
■ 7". . . . . . . . . . . . . . . . COOL 285
■ CD Single. . . . . . . . . . . CDCOOL 285
■ MC Single. . . . . . . . . . . TCCOOL 285
Cool Tempo / Feb '94.

**ANOTHER PLACE, ANOTHER DAY,
ANOTHER TIME.**
Tracks: Another place, another day, another time.
■ 12". . . . . . . . . . . . . . . YZ 606 T
Eternal / Sep '91.

**CAUGHT IN THE MIDDLE.**
Tracks: Caught in the middle / Caught in the middle
(Mixes).
■ 12". . . . . . . . . . . . . . 12COOL 272
■ CD Single. . . . . . . . . . CDCOOL 272
■ 12". . . . . . . . . . . . . . .12COOLR 272
■ MC Single. . . . . . . . . . TCCOOL 272
Cool Tempo / Jul '93.

**CAUGHT IN THE MIDDLE.**
Tracks: Caught in the middle (Mixes) / Stop to love.
12". . . . . . . . . . . . . . . 12 COOL 291
12". . . . . . . . . . . . . . . 12 COOLR 291
CD Single . . . . . . . . . . . COOLCD 291
MC Single . . . . . . . . . . .COOLMC 291
Cool Tempo / Jun '94 / EMI.

**CLOSER THAN CLOSE.**
Tracks: Closer than close.
■ 12" . . . . . . . . . . . . . . . SLAM 2T
■ 7" . . . . . . . . . . . . . . . SLAM 2
■ CD Single. . . . . . . . . . . . SLAM 2CD

**■ MC Single. . . . . . . . . . . . . . . SLAM 2C**
Slam Jam / Mar '92.

## FREE LOVE.
**Tracks:** Free love.
■ 12". . . . . . . . . . . . . . . . . 12COOL 281
■ 7". . . . . . . . . . . . . . . . . . COOL 281
■ CD Single. . . . . . . . . . . . . CDCOOL 281
■ MC Single. . . . . . . . . . . . . TCCOOL 281
Cool Tempo / Jun '92.

## I WANT YOU.
**Tracks:** I want you (mixes).
12". . . . . . . . . . . . . . . . . 12 COOL297
12". . . . . . . . . . . . . . . . .12COOLX 297
CD Single. . . . . . . . . . . . . . CDCOOL 297
MC Single. . . . . . . . . . . . . . TCCOOL 297
Cool Tempo / Sep '94 / EMI.

## JULIET ROBERTS.
**Tracks:** Not Advised.
CD. . . . . . . . . . . . . . . . . . . 4509907042
■ LP. . . . . . . . . . . . . . . . . . . . WX 486
MC. . . . . . . . . . . . . . . . . . . . WX 486 C
WEA / Nov '92 / WEA.

## NATURAL THING.
**Tracks:** Caught in the middle / Free love / Tell me / Life goes around / Someone like you / Force of nature / Save it / Again / I want you / September / Eyes of a child / Natural thing.
CD. . . . . . . . . . . . . . . . . . . . CTCD 39
LP. . . . . . . . . . . . . . . . . . . . CTLP 39
MC. . . . . . . . . . . . . . . . . . . . CTTC 39
Cool Tempo / Mar '94 / EMI.

## Roberts, Lee

### SOULIN' (Roberts, Lee & The Sweaters).
**Tracks:** Not Advised.
■ LP. . . . . . . . . . . . . . . . . . . . BS 4703
Blue Shadow / '88.

## Robins, Jimmy

### I CAN'T PLEASE YOU.
**Tracks:** I can't please you.
■ 7". . . . . . . . . . . . . . . . . . . .PT 118
President / '66.

## Robinson, David

### NEVER STOP LOVIN'.
**Tracks:** Not Advised.
CD. . . . . . . . . . . . . . . . . . . RYTCD 4188
MC. . . . . . . . . . . . . . . . . . . RYTMC 4188
Ichiban / Jun '94 / A.D.A. Distribution / Pinnacle / ACD Trading Ltd. / Koch International / Direct Distribution.

## Robinson, Dutch

### HAPPY.
**Tracks:** Happy.
■ 7". . . . . . . . . . . . . . . . . . . .A 5021
Epic / Feb '85.

### LOWDOWN.
**Tracks:** Lowdown.
■ 12". . . . . . . . . . . . . . . . . .NYT 103
■ 7". . . . . . . . . . . . . . . . . . . NY 103
New York 42 / Jun '88.

## Robinson, Freddie

### AT THE DRIVE IN.
**Tracks:** It's the real thing / Sweet Clara / Miss black America / Creepin' lightly / I found my soul last night / At the drive-in / Wonder what it is / Bluesology.
■ LP. . . . . . . . . . . . . . . . . . . . 2325085
Stax / Nov '72.

## Robinson, James

### CAN WE DO IT AGAIN.
**Tracks:** Can we do it again / You're the one I've been dreaming of.
■ 12". . . . . . . . . . . . . . . . . .650902 6
■ 7". . . . . . . . . . . . . . . . . . .650902 7
Tabu / Jul '87.

### GUILTY.
**Tracks:** Can we do it again / Guilty / Pretend / Feel like going on / Seems so long / Lord's prayer / Kind of love / Just what I've been missing / When you'll be mine / You're the one I've been dreaming of.
■ LP. . . . . . . . . . . . . . . . . . .460091 1
MC. . . . . . . . . . . . . . . . . . . .460091 4
Tabu / Sep '87 / Sony.

## Robinson, Robin

### LOVE SMOKEY.
**Tracks:** Love is the light / (It's the) same old love / Love 'n life / I can't find / Take me through the night / Everything you touch / Don't wanna be just physical / Come to me soon / You made me feel love / Jasmin / Easy / Just another kiss (Only on CD) / Unless you do it again (Only on CD).
■ CD . . . . . . . . . . . . . . . . . . ZD 72666
■ LP . . . . . . . . . . . . . . . . . . ZL 72666
■ MC . . . . . . . . . . . . . . . . . . ZK 72666
Motown / Feb '90.

## Robinson, Roscoe

### HIGH ON JESUS.
**Tracks:** Not Advised.
LP . . . . . . . . . . . . . . . . . . . . SL 14733
Savoy / Apr '90 / Jazz Music / Wellard / Savoy Records / Conifer Records.

### WHY MUST IT END?.
**Tracks:** Let me know / Why are you afraid / Fox hunting on a weekend / You don't move me no more / Darling please tell me / I'm burning and yearning / Why must it end / How many times must I knock / We got a good thing going / Standing in the safety zone / Prove it / You and me / You qualify / Trust me / Yesterday is gone tomorrow is too late.
■ LP . . . . . . . . . . . . . . . . . . . CRB 1154
Charly R&B / May '87.

## Robinson, Smokey

Born in Detroit in '40, William "Smokey" Robinson became fast friends with local songwriter/entrepreneur Berry Gordy in the late '50s, persuading him to open his own record company at the decade's end. Though heading his own group, The Miracles, Smokey's most significant role at Motown was as songwriter/producer: most of the company's biggest acts took Robinson songs up the charts during the '60s, including The Temptations (*My Girl*), Marvin Gaye (*Ain't That Peculiar*) and Mary Wells (*My Guy*). The Miracles' own hits lacked nothing in terms of weight either, the likes of *Tracks Of My Tears*, *Tears Of A Clown* and *You Really Got A Hold On Me* endearing Smokey to almost as many musical peers as ordinary fans. Oddly enough, Smokey's subsequent solo career throughout the '70s and '80s is generally regarded in less complimentary terms, though the truth is he wrote some of the finest material during this period: *Just My Soul Responding* ('73), for example, is Robinson's response to Marvin Gaye's socially conscious *What's Going On* style, while singles like *Cruisin'* ('79) and albums as strong as *One Heartbeat* ('87) reveal the durability of the man's talent. Though once Vice-President at Motown, Smokey left the label for Capitol Records in the early '90s and has yet to recapture his form.

### (COME 'ROUND HERE) I'M THE ONE YOU NEED (Robinson, Smokey & The Miracles).
**Tracks:** (Come 'round here) I'm the one you need.
■ 7" . . . . . . . . . . . . . . . . . . TMG 584
Tamla Motown / Dec '66.

### (COME ROUND HERE) I'M THE ONE YOU NEED (Robinson, Smokey & The Miracles).
**Tracks:** (Come round here) I'm the one you need / I second that emotion.
■ 7" . . . . . . . . . . . . . . . . . . TMG 761
Tamla Motown / Jan '71.
■ 7" . . . . . . . . . . . . . . . . . . TMG 957
Tamla Motown / Feb '75.

### AND I DON'T LOVE YOU.
**Tracks:** And I don't love you / Dynamite.
■ 12" . . . . . . . . . . . . . . . . . TMGT 1344
■ 7" . . . . . . . . . . . . . . . . . . .TMG 1344
Motown / Jun '84.

### ANTHOLOGY - SMOKEY ROBINSON (Robinson, Smokey & The Miracles).
**Tracks:** Got a job / Bad girl / Way over there / You can depend on me / Shop around / Who's loving you / What's so good about goodbye / I'll try something new / I've been good to you / You've really got a hold on me / Love she can count on / Mickey's monkey / I gotta dance to keep from crying / I like it like that / That's what love is made of / Come on do the jerk / Ooo baby baby / Tracks of my tears / My girl has gone / Choosey beggar / Going to a go go / I'm the

one you need / Save me / Love I saw in you was just a mirage / More love / I second that emotion / If you can want / Yester-love / Special occasion / Baby baby don't cry / Doggone right / Here I go again / Abraham, Martin and John / Darling dear / Point it out / Who's gonna take the blame / Tears of a clown / I don't blame you at all / Satisfaction / We've come too far to end it now / I can't stand to see you cry / Crazy about the la la la / Do it baby / Don't cha love it / Love machine.
■ Double LP. . . . . . . . . . . . . . TMSP 6014
■ MC Set . . . . . . . . . . . . . . CTMSP 6014
Motown / Sep '82.
■ Double LP. . . . . . . . . . . . . . . ZL 72134
Motown / '86.
■ CD Set. . . . . . . . . . . . . . . . ZD 72531
Motown / Jun '87.
■ CD Set. . . . . . . . . . . . . . . . WD 72531
Motown / Apr '89.

### BABY THAT'S BACKATCHA.
**Tracks:** Baby that's backatcha / Just passing through.
■ 7" . . . . . . . . . . . . . . . . . . TMG 949
Tamla Motown / Jun '75.

### BEING WITH YOU.
**Tracks:** Being with you / Food for thought / If you wanna make love / Who's sad / Can't fight love / You are forever / As you do / I hear the children singing.
■ LP . . . . . . . . . . . . . . . . . .STML 1215
Motown / Jun '81.
■ LP . . . . . . . . . . . . . . . . . . WL 72256
■ MC . . . . . . . . . . . . . . . . . . WK 72256
Motown / Apr '85.
CD . . . . . . . . . . . . . . . . . . 530 219-2
Motown / Sep '93 / PolyGram.

### BEING WITH YOU.
**Tracks:** Being with you / What's in your life for me.
■ 7" . . . . . . . . . . . . . . . . . . .TMG 1223
Tamla Motown / May '81.

### BIG TIME, THEME FROM.
**Tracks:** Big time, Theme from.
■ 7" . . . . . . . . . . . . . . . . . . .TMG 1085
Motown / Aug '77.

### BLAME IT ON LOVE (Greatest hits).
**Tracks:** Blame it on love / Being with you / Cruisin' / Just my soul responding.
■ LP . . . . . . . . . . . . . . . . . .STML 12193
■ MC . . . . . . . . . . . . . . . . . .CSTML 12193
Motown / Oct '83.

### BLAME IT ON LOVE (Robinson, Smokey & Barbara Mitchell).
**Tracks:** Blame it on love / Even tho'.
■ 7" . . . . . . . . . . . . . . . . . . .TMG 1313
Motown / Aug '83.

### BLAME IT ON LOVE AND ALL THE GREAT HITS.
**Tracks:** Blame it on love / Just like you / Don't play another love song / Tell me tomorrow / Being with you / Cruisin' / If you wanna make love (come 'round here) / Just a touch away / Baby come close / Let me see the clock.
■ MC . . . . . . . . . . . . . . . . . . WK 72542
■ CD . . . . . . . . . . . . . . . . . . WD 72542
Motown / Feb '91.

### CHRISTMAS WITH THE MIRACLES (Robinson, Smokey & The Miracles).
**Tracks:** Not Advised.
CD . . . . . . . . . . . . . . . . . . . .550 4052
MC . . . . . . . . . . . . . . . . . . . .550 4054
Spectrum (1) / Nov '94 / PolyGram.

### COMPACT COMMAND PERFORMANCES (18 Greatest Hits) (Robinson Smokey & The Miracles).
**Tracks:** Shop around / You've really got a hold on me / I'll try something new / You can depend on me / Mickey's monkey / Tracks of my tears / Going to a go go / I second that emotion / If you can want / Baby baby, don't cry / Doggone right / Tears of a clown / I don't blame you at all / Baby come close / Baby that's backatcha / Quiet storm / Cruisin' / Being with you.
■ CD . . . . . . . . . . . . . . . . . TCD 06071 TC
Motown / May '84.
■ CD . . . . . . . . . . . . . . . . . WD 72419
Motown / Oct '87.

### COMPACT COMMAND PERFORMANCES VOL. 2 (Robinson, Smokey & The Miracles).
**Tracks:** Bad girl / What's so good about goodbye Way over there / Love you can count on / I gotta dance to keep from crying / I like it like that / That's what love is made of / Come on do the jerk / Ooo baby baby / Choosey beggar / My girl has gone

■ DELETED

Love I saw in you was just a mirage / More love / I'm the one you need / Yester-love / Special occasion / Here I go again / Abraham, Martin and John / Point it out / We've come too far to end it now / Do it baby / Love machine.
■ CD . . . . . . . . . . . . . . . . . . . . . . . ZD 72510
Motown / Mar '87.
■ CD . . . . . . . . . . . . . . . . . . . . . . . WD 72510
Motown / Aug '89.

## CRUISIN'.
Tracks: Cruisin' / Human song.
■ 7" . . . . . . . . . . . . . . . . . . . . . . . .TMG 1164
Motown / Oct '81.

## DAYLIGHT AND DARKNESS.
Tracks: Daylight and darkness / Why you wanna see my bad side.
■ 7" . . . . . . . . . . . . . . . . . . . . . . . .TMG 1114
Motown / Jul '78.

## DOUBLE GOOD EVERYTHING.
Tracks: Why / Double good everything / Rewind / Be who you are / I love your face / Can't get enough / Rack me back / When a woman cries / You take me away / Skid row.
CD . . . . . . . . . . . . . . . . . . . . . . . .SBKCD 17
■ LP . . . . . . . . . . . . . . . . . . . . . . . .SBKLP 17
MC. . . . . . . . . . . . . . . . . . . . . . . . SBKTC 17
SBK / Feb '92 / EMI.

## DOUBLE GOOD EVERYTHING.
Tracks: Double good everything / Guess what I got for you.
■ 12" . . . . . . . . . . . . . . . . . . . . . . .12SBK 33
■ 7" . . . . . . . . . . . . . . . . . . . . . . . . SBK 33
■ CD Single . . . . . . . . . . . . . . . . . .CDSBK 33
■ MC Single . . . . . . . . . . . . . . . . . .TCSBK 33
SBK / Feb '92.

## ESSAR.
Tracks: And I don't love you / Train of thought / I can't find / Why are you running from my love / Gone forever / Close encounters of the first kind / Little girl, little girl / Girl I'm standing there / Driving thru life in the fast lane.
■ LP . . . . . . . . . . . . . . . . . . . . . . . . ZL 72152
■ MC. . . . . . . . . . . . . . . . . . . . . . . . ZK 72152
Motown / Jul '84.

## FOUR IN BLUE (Robinson, Smokey & The Miracles).
Tracks: You send me / Dreams, dreams / Tomorrow is another day / Hey Jude / California soul / Legend in its own time / You've lost that lovin' feelin' / We can make it we can / When nobody cares / Don't say you love me / Wish I knew / My world is empty without you.
■ LP . . . . . . . . . . . . . . . . . . . . . . . .STML 11151
Tamla Motown / Jul '70.

## GET READY.
Tracks: Get ready / Ever had a dream.
■ 7" . . . . . . . . . . . . . . . . . . . . . . . .TMG 1152
Motown / Nov '79.

## GOING TO A GO GO (Robinson, Smokey & The Miracles).
Tracks: Going to a go go / Whole lot of shaking in my heart / Yester-love.
■ 7" . . . . . . . . . . . . . . . . . . . . . . . . TMG 853
Tamla Motown / Jul '73.

## GOING TO A GO-GO (Robinson, Smokey & The Miracles).
Tracks: Going to a go go / Choosey beggar.
■ 7" . . . . . . . . . . . . . . . . . . . . . . . . TMG 547
Tamla Motown / Feb '66.

## GOING TO A GO-GO (Robinson, Smokey & The Miracles).
Tracks: Tracks of my tears / Going to a go go / Ooh baby baby / My girl has gone / In case you need to love / Choosey beggar / Since you won my heart / From head to toe / All that's good / My baby changes like the weather / Let me have some / Fork in the road.
■ LP . . . . . . . . . . . . . . . . . . . . . . . . TML 11024
Tamla Motown / Feb '66.

## GOING TO A GO-GO/ THE TEARS OF A CLOWN (Robinson, Smokey & The Miracles).
Tracks: Tracks of my tears / Going to a go go / Ooo baby baby / My girl has gone / In case you need to love / Choosey beggar / Since you won my heart / From head to toe / All that's good / My baby changes like the weather / Let me have some / Fork in the road / Soulful shack / Love I saw in you was just a mirage / My love for you / I'm on the outside looking in / Don't think it's me / My love is your love (forever) / More love / After you put back the pieces (Full title: After you put back the pieces (I'll still have a broken Hear)

It's a good feeling / You must be love / Dancing's alright / Tears of a clown.
■ CD. . . . . . . . . . . . . . . . . . . . . . . ZD 72458
Motown / Oct '86.

## GREATEST HITS (Robinson, Smokey & The Miracles).
Tracks: Going to a go-go / Beauty is only skin deep / From head to toe / My girl has gone / You really got a hold on me / More love / Shop around / Ooo baby baby / I second that emotion / Come on, do the Jerk / Love I saw in you was just a mirage / Tracks of my tears / What's so good about goodbye / Mickey's monkey / I'm the one you need.
■ LP . . . . . . . . . . . . . . . . . . . . . . . .STML 11072
Tamla Motown / Jun '68.

## GREATEST HITS LIVE.
Tracks: More love / Tears of a clown / Being with you / Shop around / I second that emotion / Really got a hold on me / Ooo baby baby / I want a love I can see / Medley (Inc: The way you do the things you do, It's growing, Since I lost my baby, Don't look back, Get ready and My girl.) / Save the best for last / More than you know / Double good everything / I love your face / Rewind / Tracks of my tears / Just to see her / Going to a go go.
VHS . . . . . . . . . . . . . . . . . . . . MVN 4910483
PMI / Nov '92 / EMI / Gold & Sons / THE.

## GREATEST HITS, THE (Robinson, Smokey & The Miracles).
Tracks: Being with you / Tracks of my tears / I second that emotion / (Come round here) I'm the one you need / Mickey's monkey / Going to a go go / I don't blame you at all / if you can want / Just to see her / More love / Just my soul responding (On MC/ CD only) / Tears of a clown / Abraham, Martin and John / You've really got a hold on me / Shop around / What's so good about goodbye / Ooo baby baby / Love I saw in you was just a mirage / Quiet storm / One heartbeat / Baby baby don't cry / Cruisin' (On MC/CD only).
CD. . . . . . . . . . . . . . . . . . . . 530 121-2
■ LP . . . . . . . . . . . . . . . . . . . . 530 121-1
MC. . . . . . . . . . . . . . . . . . . . 530 121-4
Polygram T.V. / Nov '92 / PolyGram.

## HEAVY ON THE PRIDE(LIGHT OF LOVE).
Tracks: Heavy on the pride (light of love).
■ 12" . . . . . . . . . . . . . . . . . . . TMGT 1191
Motown / Oct '81.

## HOLD ON TO YOUR LOVE.
Tracks: Hold on to your love / Train of thought.
■ 12" . . . . . . . . . . . . . . . . . . . ZT 40554
■ 7" . . . . . . . . . . . . . . . . . . . . ZB 40553
Motown / Jan '86.

## HOT SMOKEY.
Tracks: Just my soul responding / Responding / Let me be the clock / Vitamin U / Heavy on the pride (light of love) / What's in your life for me / I love the nearness of you.
■ LP . . . . . . . . . . . . . . . . . . . . TMS 3510
■ MC. . . . . . . . . . . . . . . . . . . . TMC 3510
Motown / Jan '82.

## I DON'T BLAME YOU AT ALL (Robinson, Smokey & The Miracles).
Tracks: I don't blame you at all / Ooo baby baby.
■ 7" . . . . . . . . . . . . . . . . . . . . TMG 774
Tamla Motown / Jun '71.
■ 7" . . . . . . . . . . . . . . . . . . . . TMG 980
Tamla Motown / Jun '75.

## I MADE LOVE TO YOU A THOUSAND TIMES.
Tracks: I made love to you a thousand times.
■ 7" . . . . . . . . . . . . . . . . . . . .TMG 1295
Motown / Feb '83.

## I SECOND THAT EMOTION (Robinson, Smokey & The Miracles).
Tracks: I second that emotion.
■ 7" . . . . . . . . . . . . . . . . . . . . TMG 631
Tamla Motown / Dec '67.

## I'VE MADE LOVE TO YOU A THOUSAND TIMES.
Tracks: I've made love to you a thousand times / Greatest hits medley.
■ 12" . . . . . . . . . . . . . . . . . . . TMGT 1295
Motown / Mar '83.

## IF YOU CAN WANT (Robinson, Smokey & The Miracles).
Tracks: If you can want.
■ 7" . . . . . . . . . . . . . . . . . . . . TMG 648
Tamla Motown / Apr '68.

## JUST MY SOUL RESPONDING.
Tracks: Just my soul responding.
■ 7" . . . . . . . . . . . . . . . . . . . . TMG 883
Tamla Motown / Feb '74.

## JUST TO SEE HER.
Tracks: Just to see her / I'm gonna love you like there's no tomorrow / You've really got a hold on me (Only available on 12" version.) / That's what love is made of (Only available on 12" version.) / Ooo baby baby (Only available on 12" version.).
■ 12" . . . . . . . . . . . . . . . . . . . ZT 41148
■ 7" . . . . . . . . . . . . . . . . . . . . ZB 41147
Motown / Feb '87.
■ 12" . . . . . . . . . . . . . . . . . . . ZBA 41148
Motown / Feb '87.

## LET ME BE THE CLOCK.
Tracks: Let me be the clock / Travellin' through.
■ 7" . . . . . . . . . . . . . . . . . . . .TMG 1182
Motown / Oct '81.

## LIVE (Robinson, Smokey & The Miracles).
Tracks: Once in a lifetime / You and the night and the music / I second that emotion / Tracks of my tears / Poinciana / Up, up and away / Valley of the dolls / If you can want / Mickey's monkey / Coo baby baby / Going to a go-go.
■ LP . . . . . . . . . . . . . . . . . . . .STML 11107
Tamla Motown / May '69.

## LOVE BREEZE.
Tracks: Why you wanna see my badside / Love so fine / Feeling you, feeling me / Madam X / Shoe soul / Trying it again / Daylight and darkness / I'm loving you softly.
■ LP . . . . . . . . . . . . . . . . . . . .STML 12081
Motown / Jun '78.

## LOVE DON'T GIVE NO REASON.
Tracks: Love don't give no reason (mixes) / Going to a go go (Extra track available on CD Single only) / You've really got a hold on me (Extra track available on CD Single only).
■ 12" . . . . . . . . . . . . . . . . . . . ZT 41784
■ 7" . . . . . . . . . . . . . . . . . . . . ZB 41783
■ CD Single . . . . . . . . . . . . . . . ZD 41784
Motown / Mar '88.

## LOVE I SAW IN YOU WAS JUST A MIRAGE (Robinson, Smokey & The Miracles).
Tracks: Love I saw in you was just a mirage.
■ 7" . . . . . . . . . . . . . . . . . . . . TMG 598
Tamla Motown / '67.

## LOVE SONGS: MARVIN GAYE & SMOKEY ROBINSON (see under Gaye, Marvin).

## MADAM X.
Tracks: Madam X / Agony and the ecstasy.
■ 7" . . . . . . . . . . . . . . . . . . . .TMG 1106
Motown / Apr '78.

## MAKE IT HAPPEN (Robinson, Smokey & The Miracles).
Tracks: Soulful shack / Love I saw in you / My love for you / On the outside looking in / Don't think it's me / My love is your love / More love / After you put back the pieces / It's a good feeling / You must be love / Dancing's alright / Tears of a clown.
■ LP . . . . . . . . . . . . . . . . . . . .STML 11067
Tamla Motown / Feb '68.

## MARVIN GAYE (see under Gaye, Marvin).

## MORE LOVE (Robinson, Smokey & The Miracles).
Tracks: More love / Swept for you baby.
■ 7" . . . . . . . . . . . . . . . . . . . .TNG 614
Tamla Motown / Jul '67.

## MY GIRL HAS GONE (Robinson, Smokey & The Miracles).
Tracks: My girl has gone.
■ 7" . . . . . . . . . . . . . . . . . . . . TMG 540
Tamla Motown / '66.

## OLD FASHIONED LOVE.
Tracks: Old fashioned love / Destiny.
■ 12" . . . . . . . . . . . . . . . . . . . TMGT 1262
■ 7" . . . . . . . . . . . . . . . . . . . .TMG 1262
Motown / May '82.

## ONE HEARTBEAT.
Tracks: It's time to stop shoppin' around / Why do happy memories hurt so bad / You don't know what it's like / What's too much / Love bought us here

tonight / Love don't give no reason / Keep me / One heartbeat / Just to see her.
- ■ CD . . . . . . . . . . . . . . . . . ZD 72580
- ■ LP . . . . . . . . . . . . . . . . . ZL 72580
- ■ MC . . . . . . . . . . . . . . . . . ZK 72580

Motown / Jan '87.

## ONE HEARTBEAT.
Tracks: One heartbeat.
- ■ 12" . . . . . . . . . . . . . . . . ZT 41526
- ■ 7" . . . . . . . . . . . . . . . . . ZB 41525

Motown / Jul '87.

## OOH BABY BABY (Robinson, Smokey & The Miracles).
Tracks: Ooo baby baby.
- ■ 7" . . . . . . . . . . . . . . . . . TMG 503

Tamla Motown / '65.

## POPS, WE LOVE YOU (see under Ross, Diana).

## PURE SMOKEY.
Tracks: It's her turn to live / Love between me and my kids / Asleep on my love / I am, I am / Just passing through / Virgin man / She's only a baby herself / Fulfil your need / Tattoo.
- ■ LP . . . . . . . . . . . . . . . . STMS 5043
- ■ MC . . . . . . . . . . . . . . . CSTMS 5043

Motown / Mar '82.

## QUIET STORM, A.
Tracks: Quiet storm / Agony and the ecstasy / Baby that's backatcha / Wedding song / Happy love letters / Coincidentally.
- ■ LP . . . . . . . . . . . . . . . . STMS 5044
- ■ MC . . . . . . . . . . . . . . . CSTMS 5044

Motown / Mar '82.

## SLEEPLESS NIGHTS.
Tracks: Sleepless nights / Close encounters of the first kind / Mickey's monkey (Extra track on 12" version only.) / I got a dance to keep from crying (Extra track on 12" version only.) / Some people (will do anything for love).
- ■ 7" . . . . . . . . . . . . . . . . . ZB 40717
- ■ 12" . . . . . . . . . . . . . . . . ZT 40718

Motown / May '86.

## SMOKE SIGNALS.
Tracks: Some people (will do anything for love) / Sleepless nights / Because of you (it's the best it's ever been) / Be kind to the growing mind / Te quiero como si no hubiera un manana / Hold on to your love / Photograph in my mind / No time to stop believing / Wishful thinking / Hanging on by a thread.
- ■ CD . . . . . . . . . . . . . . . . . ZD 72394

Motown / Jan '86.
- ■ LP . . . . . . . . . . . . . . . . . ZL 72394
- ■ MC . . . . . . . . . . . . . . . . . ZK 72394

Motown / Mar '86.

## SMOKEY.
Tracks: Holly / Never my love / Never can say goodbye / Silent partner in a three-way love affair / Just my soul responding / Sweet harmony / Will you love me tomorrow / Wanna know my mind / Family song / Baby come close.
- ■ LP . . . . . . . . . . . . . . . . STMS 5011
- ■ MC . . . . . . . . . . . . . . . CSTMS 5011

Motown / Oct '81.

## SMOKEY ROBINSON & THE MIRACLES (Robinson, Smokey & The Miracles).
Tracks: Flower girl / Who's gonna take the blame / Darling dear / You've got the love I need / Get ready / Bridge over troubled water / Tears of a clown / I'm the one you need / Something / Something you got / Point it out / Don't take it so hard / Backfire / Reel of time / Wishful thinking.
- ■ LP . . . . . . . . . . . . . . . .STML 11172

Tamla Motown / Feb '71.

## SMOKEY ROBINSON AND THE MIRACLES (Robinson, Smokey & The Miracles).
Tracks: Not Advised.
- ■ MC Single. . . . . . . . . . . . . . CTME 2027

Motown / May '83.

## SMOKEY ROBINSON STORY THE.
Tracks: Not Advised.
- ■ LP . . . . . . . . . . . . . . . . . NE 1175
- ■ MC . . . . . . . . . . . . . . . . . CE 2175

K-Tel / Nov '83.

## SMOKEY'S WORLD.
Tracks: Big time / Baby that's backatcha / Quiet storm / There will come a day / Sweet harmony / It's her turn to live / I am I am / Old fashioned man / Vitamin U / Just my soul responding / Silent partner in a three way love affair / Virgin man / Agony and the ecstasy / baby come close / Open.

- ■ LP . . . . . . . . . . . . . . . . .STML 12076

Motown / Mar '78.

## SPECIAL OCCASION (Robinson, Smokey & The Miracles).
Tracks: Yester love / If you can want / Your mother's only daughter / Special occasion / Everybody needs love / Just losing you / Give her up / I heard it through the grapevine / Yesterday / Much better off / You only build me up to tear me down.
- ■ LP . . . . . . . . . . . . . . . .STML 11089

Tamla Motown / Jan '69.

## TEARS OF A CLOWN.
Tracks: Tears of a clown / Tracks of my tears.
- ■ 7" . . . . . . . . . . . . . . . .TMG 1048

Motown / Jul '76.

## TEARS OF A CLOWN (Robinson, Smokey & The Miracles).
Tracks: My girl / Composer / It will be alright / You must be love / We had a love so strong / Something / Something you got / More, more, more of your love / I can't stand to see you cry / I'm the one you need / Hunter gets captured by the game / You ain't livin' until you're lovin'.
- ■ LP . . . . . . . . . . . . . . . . STMS 5010

Motown / Jul '81.
- ■ MC . . . . . . . . . . . . . . . TMC 3501

Motown / Jun '82.
- ■ CD . . . . . . . . . . . . . . . WD 72071
- ■ LP . . . . . . . . . . . . . . . WL 72071

Motown / Aug '88.

## TEARS OF A CLOWN (Robinson, Smokey & The Miracles).
Tracks: Tears of a clown.
- ■ 7" . . . . . . . . . . . . . . . TMG 745

Tamla Motown / Aug '70.

## TEARS OF A CLOWN (Robinson, Smokey & The Miracles).
Tracks: Tears of a clown / You ain't livin' till you're lovin' / Save me / Medley: Something / We had a love so strong / You've lost that lovin' feelin' / My girl / Hunter gets captured by the game / More, more, of your love / (Come round here) I'm the one you need / You must be love / I can't stand to see you cry / It will be alright / Composer.
- CD . . . . . . . . . . . . . . . . .550 0732
- MC . . . . . . . . . . . . . . . . .550 0734

Spectrum (1) / May '93 / PolyGram.

## TEARS OF A CLOWN (MFP) (Robinson, Smokey & The Miracles).
Tracks: Not Advised.
- ■ LP . . . . . . . . . . . . . . . MFP 50422

MFP / Feb '79.

## TELL ME TOMORROW.
Tracks: Tell me tomorrow / Tell me tomorrow (part 2) / Being with you / Aqui con tigo.
- ■ 12" . . . . . . . . . . . . . . . TMGT 1255
- ■ 7" . . . . . . . . . . . . . . . TMG 1255

Motown / Feb '82

## THAT'S WHAT LOVE IS MADE OF (Robinson, Smokey & The Miracles).
Tracks: That's what love is.
- ■ 7" . . . . . . . . . . . . . . . .SS 353

Stateside / '64.

## THERE WILL COME A DAY.
Tracks: There will come a day / Old fashioned man, An.
- ■ 7" . . . . . . . . . . . . . . . .TMG 1065

Motown / Mar '77.

## TIME OUT (Robinson, Smokey & The Miracles).
Tracks: Doggone right / Baby, baby don't cry / My girl / Hurt is over / You neglect me / Abraham, Martin and John / For once in my life / Once I got to know you / Wichita lineman / Composer / Here I go again / I'll take you any way that you come.
- ■ LP . . . . . . . . . . . . . . . .STML 11129

Tamla Motown / Feb '70.

## TOUCH THE SKY.
Tracks: Touch the sky / Gimme what you want / Even tho' / Gone again / All my life's a lie / Sad time / Dynamite / I've made love to you a thousand times.
- ■ LP . . . . . . . . . . . . . . . .STML 12175
- ■ MC . . . . . . . . . . . . . . .CSTML 12175

Motown / Mar '83.

## TOUCH THE SKY.
Tracks: Touch the sky / All my life's a lie.
- ■ 7" . . . . . . . . . . . . . . . .TMG 1307

Motown / May '83.

## TRACKS OF MY TEARS (Robinson, Smokey & The Miracles).
Tracks: Tracks of my tears.
- ■ 7" . . . . . . . . . . . . . . . TMG 696

Tamla Motown / May '69.

## TRACKS OF MY TEARS (Robinson, Smokey & The Miracles).
Tracks: Tracks of my tears / I second that emotion / Going to a go go / Shop around*.
- ■ 12" . . . . . . . . . . . . . . . ZT 41374
- ■ 7" . . . . . . . . . . . . . . . ZB 41373

Motown / May '87.

## TRACKS OF MY TEARS - THE VERY BEST OF SMOKEY ROBINSON (LIVE).
Tracks: Not Advised.
- CD . . . . . . . . . . . . . . . . DINCD 17
- MC . . . . . . . . . . . . . . . .DINMC 17

Dino / '93 / Pinnacle.

## TRACKS OF MY TEARS, THE (Robinson, Smokey & The Miracles).
Tracks: Tracks of my tears / Fork in the road.
- ■ 7" . . . . . . . . . . . . . . . TMG 522

Tamla Motown / '65.

## VITAMIN U.
Tracks: Vitamin U / Holly.
- ■ 7" . . . . . . . . . . . . . . . .TMG 1076

Motown / Jun '77.

## WARM THOUGHTS.
Tracks: Let me be the clock / Heavy on the pride (light of love) / Into each life some rain must fall / Wine, women and song / Melody man / What's in your life for me / I want to be your love / Travellin' through.
- ■ LP . . . . . . . . . . . . . . . .STML 12134

Motown / Oct '81.

## WHAT EVER MAKES YOU HAPPY (More Best Of Smokey Robinson & The Miracles 1961-71) (Robinson, Smokey & The Miracles).
Tracks: Money / Won't you take me back / Mighty good lovin' / I need a change / From head to toe / More, more, more of your love / Swept for you baby / Beauty is only skin deep / Don't think it's me / Dancing's alright / You only build me up to tear me down / I'll take you any way that you come / My world is empty without you / Dreams, dreams / Backfire / Flower girl / Faces.
- CD . . . . . . . . . . . . . . . . .812271181-2
- MC . . . . . . . . . . . . . . . . .812271181-4

WEA / Jun '93 / WEA.

## WHAT'S SO GOOD ABOUT GOODBYE (Robinson, Smokey & The Miracles).
Tracks: What's so good about goodbye.
- ■ 7" . . . . . . . . . . . . . . . H 384

Fontana / '62.

## WHERE THERE'S SMOKE.
Tracks: Smoke / It's a good night / I love the near ness of you / Hurt in you / Ever had a dream / Fire / get ready / Share it / Cruisin'.
- ■ LP . . . . . . . . . . . . . . . .STML 12115
- ■ MC . . . . . . . . . . . . . . .CSTML 12115

Motown / Oct '81.

## WHOLE LOTTA SHAKIN' IN MY HEART (Robinson, Smokey & The Miracles).
Tracks: Whole lotta shakin' in my heart.
- ■ 7" . . . . . . . . . . . . . . . TMG 569

Tamla Motown / Jul '66.

## YES IT'S YOU, LADY.
Tracks: Tell me tomorrow / Yes it's you, lady / Old fashioned love / Are you still there / Only game in town / International baby / Merry-go-ride / I'll try something new / Destiny.
- ■ LP . . . . . . . . . . . . . . . .STML 12165
- ■ MC . . . . . . . . . . . . . . .CSTML 12165

Motown / Mar '82.

## YOU ARE FOREVER.
Tracks: You are forever / I hear the children singing
- ■ 7" . . . . . . . . . . . . . . . .TMG 1232

Motown / Oct '81.

# Robinson, Vickie Sue

## BABY, NOW THAT I'VE FOUND YOU.
Tracks: Baby, now that I've found you / Thanks a million.
- ■ 7" . . . . . . . . . . . . . . . . RCA 2573

RCA / Jul '75.

## HALF AND HALF.
Tracks: Feels so good it must be wrong / Jealousy / Freeway song / Don't try to win me back again

■ DELETED

Trust in me / Hold tight / We found each other / Half and half.
- ■ **LP** .................. **PL 12294**
- ■ **MC**................... **PK 12294**

RCA / '79.

### HOLD TIGHT.
Tracks: Hold tight / Turn the beat around.
- ■ **12"**.................... **PC 1029**
- ■ **7"** ..................... **PB 1029**

RCA / '79.

### MOVIN' ON.
Tracks: Can't accept the fact / Never stop loving me / Hope your feelings are like mine / What's happening in my life / Shine your love on me / High on your love / More complete in the night time / Movin on.
- ■ **LP** .................... **PL 13080**

RCA / Oct '79.

### NEVER GONNA LET YOU GO.
Tracks: Turn the beat around / Common thief / Never gonna let you go / Wonderland of love / We can do almost anything / Lack of respect / When you're lovin' me / Act of mercy.
- ■ **LP** ..................... **RS 1051**

RCA / Jul '76.

### NEVER GONNA LET YOU GO.
Tracks: Never gonna let you go.
- ■ **7"** ..................... **RCA 2651**

RCA / Feb '76.

### NIGHT TIME FANTASY.
Tracks: Night time fantasy / Feels so good it must be wrong.
- ■ **12"** .................... **PC 1441**
- ■ **7"** ..................... **PB 1441**

RCA / '79.

### SHOULD I STAY - I WOULDN'T LET YOU GO.
Tracks: Should I stay - I wouldn't let you go (medley) / When you're lovin' me.
- ■ **7"** ..................... **PB 0863**

RCA / Jan '77.

### TURN THE BEAT AROUND (OLD GOLD).
Tracks: Turn the beat around / Rock the boat.
- ■ **7"** ..................... **OG 9657**

Old Gold / Nov '86.

## Robyn

### SEARCHING.
Tracks: Searching.
- ■ ...................... **12SOUL 4**

Total / Jan '90.
- ■ **12"** .................... **EZY 1207**

E-Zee / Feb '94.

## Rocca, John

### EXTRA EXTRA.
Tracks: Not Advised.
- ■ **CD**.................... **CBCD 001**
- ■ **LP** ................... **CBLP 001**
- ■ **MC**.................... **CBMC 001**

City Beat / Jul '87 / WEA.

### EXTRA EXTRA.
Tracks: Extra extra / Move (rude boy mix).
- ■ **12"** .................... **CBS 1214**
- ■ **7"** ..................... **CBS 714**

City Beat / Nov '87.

### I WANT IT TO BE REAL.
Tracks: I want it to be real (12" version only.) / Club vocal mix (12" version only) / I want it to be real (club vocal) / Basement beats / Farley's hot house piano mix (12" version only.) / I want it to be real (Alternate dance mix) (12" version only.).
- ■ **12"** .................... **BEG 105T**

Beggars Banquet / '83.
- ■ **7"** ..................... **CBE 710**
- ■ **12"** .................... **CBE 1210**

City Beat / Mar '87.

### I WANT YOU.
Tracks: I want you / Come to me.
- ■ **12"** .................... **BEG 138T**
- ■ **7"** ..................... **BEG 138**

Beggars Banquet / Jun '85.

### MY WORLD IS EMPTY WITHOUT YOU.
Tracks: My world is empty without you.
- ■ **12"** .................... **BEG 126 T**
- ■ **7"** ..................... **BEG 126**

Beggars Banquet / Jun '85.

### ONCE UPON A TIME.
Tracks: Not Advised.
- ■ **LP** .................... **BEGA 52**

---

- ■ **MC**..................... **BEGC 52**

Beggars Banquet / Nov '84.

### ONCE UPON A TIME.
Tracks: Once upon a time / Once upon a dub / Once upon a beatbox.
- ■ **12"** .................... **BEG 113T**
- ■ **7"** .....................**BEG 113**

Beggars Banquet / Jul '84.

### RIVER MUST FLOW, THE.
Tracks: River must flow / River must flow, The (Zulu dub).
- ■ **12"** .................... **COBRA 1 T**

Cobra / Mar '89.

### SOUTHERN FREEEZ PART II.
Tracks: Southern freeze part II / Rocca's revenge.
- ■ **12"** .................... **COBRA 2 T**

Cobra / Mar '89.

### TE QUIERO MI AMOUR.
Tracks: Te quiero mi amour.
- ■ **12"** ..................... **WSC 2T**

Who'd She Coo / Oct '88.

### X.Y.Z.
Tracks: X.Y.Z / Eezy dub / Groovin.
- ■ **12"** .................... **COBRA 3T**

Cobra / Jul '89.

## Rochelle

### HOW DO I KNOW.
Tracks: How do I know.
- ■ **12"** ..................... **RV 003**

Right Vibes / Dec '89.

### MY MAGIC MAN.
Tracks: My magic man / Machine gun dub.
- ■ **12"** ..................... **W 8838 T**
- ■ **7"** ...................... **W 8838**

WEA / Jan '86.

## Rodgers, Michael

### I GOT LOVE.
Tracks: I got love.
- ■ **12"** ..................... **416 886 7**

WTG / Sep '89.

## Rodgers, Nile

### ADVENTURES IN THE LAND OF THE GOOD GROOVE.
Tracks: It's all in your hands / My love song for you / Rock bottom / Most down / Kand of the good groove / Yum yum / Beet / Get her crazy.
- ■ **LP** ......................**B 0073**

Mirage (USA) / Apr '83.

### B MOVIE MATINEE.
Tracks: Groove master / Let's go out tonight / Stay out of the light / Same wavelength / Plan number 9 / State your mind / Face in the window / Doll squad.
- ■ **LP** .................... **925290 1**

WEA / Jul '85.
- ■ **CD**.................... **925290 2**

WEA / '88.

### LAND OF THE GOOD GROOVE.
Tracks: Land of the good groove / My love song for you.
- ■ **12"** .................... **B 9911T**
- ■ **7"** ..................... **B 6911**

Mirage (USA) / Apr '83.

### LET'S GO OUT TONIGHT.
Tracks: Let's go out tonight / Doll squad.
- ■ **12"** .................... **W 9049T**
- ■ **7"** ..................... **W 9049**

WEA / Jun '85.

### STATE OF MIND.
Tracks: State of mind / Stayed out of light.
- ■ **12"** .................... **W 8921 T**

WEA / Jan '86.

### YUM YUM.
Tracks: Yum yum / Get her crazy.
- ■ **12"** .................... **B 9918T**
- ■ **7"** ..................... **B 9918**

Mirage (USA) / May '83.

## Rogers, D.J.

### LOVE BROUGHT ME BACK.
Tracks: Love brought me back.
- ■ **7"** ..................... **CBS 6664**

CBS / Sep '78.

### LOVE, MUSIC AND LIFE.
Tracks: Love will make it better / Hold out for love / Love is on the way / She has eyes for me / Saved by love / Beauty and the beast / No need to say good-bye / No price / Love is all I need / You against you.
- ■ **LP** .................... **PL 12218**

RCA / '79.

### ON THE ROAD AGAIN.
Tracks: On the road again / One more day / Love can be found / Let my life shine / Secret lady / Holding on to love / Girl I love you / Only while it lasts / Say you love me one more time.
- ■ **LP** .................... **PL 42021**

RCA / Jan '77.

### ON THE ROAD AGAIN.
Tracks: On the road again / Let my life shine.
- ■ **7"** ..................... **RCA 2755**

RCA / Feb '77.

## Rogers, Evan

### LOVE GAMES.
Tracks: Hold on / Private joy / Full time lover / Sweet 16 / Don't jump to conclusions / One track mind / I'll break the rules for you / Be mine tonight.
- ■ **LP** .................... **PL 89573**

RCA / Sep '85.

### PRIVATE JOY.
Tracks: Private joy / Hold on.
- ■ **12"** .................... **PT 49937**
- ■ **7"** ..................... **PB 49937**

RCA / Jul '85.

### SECRET LOVE.
Tracks: Secret love.
- ■ **12"** .................... **RCAT 392**

RCA / Jul '84.

### STAY HERE WITH ME.
Tracks: Stay here with me.
- ■ **12"** .................... **RCAT 416**
- ■ **7"** .....................**RCA 416**

RCA / May '84.

## Rogers, Richard

### CAN'T STOP.
Tracks: Spread a little love / Can't stop loving you / Sweet essence / Bed of roses / Anything you want / (I'll be your) dream lover / Take care of you / Crazy in love.
- **CD**...................... **BCM 460 CD**
- **LP** ...................... **BCM 460 LP**
- **MC**...................... **BCM 460 MC**

BCM / Jun '90 / Pinnacle.

### CAN'T STOP LOVING YOU.
Tracks: Can't stop loving you.
- ■ **12"** .................... **BCMX 450**
- ■ **7"** ..................... **BCM 450**
- ■ **CD Single**............. **BCMCD 450**

BCM / May '90.

### SPREAD A LITTLE LOVE.
Tracks: Spread a little love.
- ■ **12"** .................... **BCM 12 489**
- ■ **7"** ..................... **BCM 07 489**
- ■ **CD Single**............. **BCM 20 489**

BCM / Feb '91.

## Rogers, Wanda

### PROVE YOUR LOVE.
Tracks: Prove your love / Prove your love (mixes).
**12"** ................................... **INT 004**

Interstate / May '94 / Vital Distribution.

## Rokotto

### BOOGIE ON UP.
Tracks: Boogie on up.
- ■ **7"** .....................**STAT 62**

State / Oct '77.

### FOR THE BROKEN HEARTED.
Tracks: For the broken hearted / You and I.
- ■ **7"** .....................**STAT 68**

State / Jan '78.

## FUNK THEORY.
**Tracks:** Funk theory / Get on down.
■ 7″ .....................STAT 80
State / Jun '78.

## GET UP AND DANCE NOW.
**Tracks:** Get up and dance now / Are you ready.
■ 7″ .....................STAT 51
State / Jun '77.

## IF I HAD YOU.
**Tracks:** If I had you / Six million dollar baby.
■ 7″ .....................STAT 107
State / Sep '81.

## ROKOTTO.
**Tracks:** Boogie on up / Tell me / Jungle fever / Shack up / Moonlight / Dancin' / For the broken hearted / Get on down / Six million dollar baby / You better / Brick house.
■ LP .....................ETAT 15
State / '77.

### Roman, Lyn

## I WANT YOU.
**Tracks:** I want you / Born to live.
■ 12″ .....................ICHT 703
■ 7″ .....................ICHS 703
Ichiban / Jun '88.

## LOVE SLAVE.
**Tracks:** Love slave.
■ 12″ .....................12 PO 4
Ichiban / Nov '87.

## WANTED.
**Tracks:** Faith / Billy the kid / Love slave / Different kind of sweet / Born to live / We belong together / Don't look back.
■ LP .....................ICH 1015
Ichiban / Jan '88.

### Romeos

## JULIET.
**Tracks:** Juliet / Lucky in love.
■ 7″ .....................PB 5119
RCA / Jan '79.

### Ronettes

## BABY I LOVE YOU.
**Tracks:** Baby I love you.
■ 7″ .....................HLU 9826
London-American / Jan '64.

## BE MY BABY.
**Tracks:** Be my baby / I love you.
■ 7″ .....................HLU 9793
London-American / Oct '63.
■ 7″ .....................2010003
Phil Spector Int. / Jul '75.

## BEST OF THE RONETTES.
**Tracks:** Be my baby / Why don't they let us fall in love / Baby I love you / (The best part of) Breakin' up / So young / When I saw you / Do I love you / You baby / How does it feel / Born to together / Is this what I get for loving you / Paradise / Here I sit / I wish I never saw the sunshine / Everything under the sun / You came, you saw, you conquered.
CD.....................PSCD 1006
MC.....................PSTC 1006
Phil Spector Int. / Oct '92 / EMI.

## COLPIX YEARS 1961-63, THE.
**Tracks:** Not Advised.
■ LP .....................000156
Murray Hill / Aug '87.

## COMPLETE COLPIX & BUDDAH SESSIONS, THE.
**Tracks:** He did it / Silhouettes / Good girls / Memory / You bet I would / I'm gonna quit while I'm ahead / I'm on the wagon / Recipe for love / My guiding angel / I want a boy / Sweet sixteen / Getting nearer / Lover lover / Go out and get it / I wish I never saw the sunshine / I wonder what he's doing / Silhouettes (Overdub session).
CD.....................NEMCD 620
Sequel / Jul '92 / Total / BMG.

## DO I LOVE YOU.
**Tracks:** Do I love you / Breaking up.
■ 7″ .....................HLU 9922
London-American / Oct '64.
■ 7″ .....................POSP 377
Polydor / Oct '81.

## RONETTES SING THEIR GREATEST HITS.
**Tracks:** Not Advised.
■ LP .....................2307 003
Phil Spector Int. / Sep '75.

### Roots

## AFRICAN IMAGE.
**Tracks:** Fly machine / War cry / Way I feel / Uneasy playboy / From the roots / African beer.
■ LP .....................GR 8306
MC.....................GRC 8306
Gramavision / Jun '84 / New Note.

## FROM THE GROUND UP.
**Tracks:** It's comin' / Distortion to static / Mellow my man / Dat scat / Worldwide (London groove) / Do you want more.
CD.....................5189412
LP .....................5189411
Talkin' Loud / Jun '94 / PolyGram.

## RUNCOME.
**Tracks:** Not Advised.
■ 12″ .....................ZEN 1202
Ninja Tune / Sep '92.

## SALUTES THE SAX.
**Tracks:** Not Advised.
CD.....................IOR 70162
In & Out / Jun '92 / Cadillac / New Note.

## STABLEMATES.
**Tracks:** Stolen moments / Linden Boulevard / Requim for a rabbit / Night train / I remember Eric Dolphy / Stablemates / Ah, George, we hardly knew ya / Walkin' / Party's over.
CD.....................IOR 70212
In & Out / Jun '93 / Cadillac / New Note.

### Rose, J.B

## TIME 4 LOVE.
**Tracks:** Not Advised.
■ 12″ .....................SIAM 1
Total / Nov '92.

### Rose, Mary

## DEVOTION.
**Tracks:** Not Advised.
■ LP .....................ADTLP 001
Abstract Dance / Oct '91.

## ENDLESS LOVE (Rose, Mary & Chris Ballin).
**Tracks:** Endless love / Concept.
■ 7″ .....................JABA 3
■ 12″ .....................12JABA 3
Jaba / Aug '90.

## ONE STEP (AT A TIME).
**Tracks:** Not Advised.
■ 12″ .....................AMA 004
Ama Productions / May '93.

### Rose Royce

## ANGEL IN THE SKY.
**Tracks:** Angel in the sky / Help.
■ 7″ .....................K 17347
Whitfield (USA) / Apr '79.

## BEST LOVE.
**Tracks:** Best love / Talk to me.
■ 7″ .....................EPCA 2238
Epic / Apr '82.

## CAR WASH.
**Tracks:** Car wash / Water.
■ 7″ .....................MCA 267
MCA / Dec '76.

## CAR WASH.
**Tracks:** Car wash / Is it love you're after.
■ 7″ .....................MCA 1253
■ 12″ .....................MCAT 1253
MCA / May '88.

## CARWASH (OLD GOLD).
**Tracks:** Car wash / I wanna get next to you / Which way is up, Theme from.
■ 7″ .....................OG 9322
Old Gold / Apr '83.
■ 12″ .....................OG 4117
Old Gold / May '89.

## CHIC & ROSE ROYCE GREATEST HITS (see under Chic).

## DO YOUR DANCE.
**Tracks:** Do your dance.
■ 7″ .....................K 17006
Whitfield (USA) / Sep '77.

## FRESH CUT.
**Tracks:** Doesn't have to be this way / Lonely road / Mask doll / I found someone / Listen up / If walls could talk / Just my imagination / For my peace of mind / Fighting chance / I know I'm in the mood.
■ LP .....................CAL 227
MC.....................CAC 227
Carrere / Oct '87 / WEA.

## GOLDEN TOUCH.
**Tracks:** And you wish for yesterday / I wanna make it with you / Funkin' around / Golden touch / Love is in the air / You're a winner / Would you please be mine / Help yourself.
■ LP .....................K 56881
■ MC.....................K4 56881
WEA / Jan '81.

## GOLDEN TOUCH.
**Tracks:** Golden touch / Help yourself.
■ 12″ .....................K 17747T
■ 7″ .....................K 17747
Whitfield (USA) / Feb '81.

## GREATEST HITS: ROSE ROYCE.
**Tracks:** Love don't live here anymore / Wishing on a star / I wanna get next to you / Angel in the sky / I'm in love (and I love the feeling) / I wonder where you are tonight / You're on my mind / Is it love you're after / Car wash / It makes you feel like dancin' / Do your dance / First come, first served / Put your money where your mouth is / Ooh boy.
■ LP .....................RRTV 1
■ MC.....................RRTV 41
Whitfield (USA) / Feb '80.
CD.....................923 457-2
Atlantic / Jan '89 / WEA.

## HITS OF ROSE ROYCE.
**Tracks:** Not Advised.
CD.....................KLMCD 023
Knight / Apr '94 / Castle Communications / BMG.

## I WANNA GET NEXT TO YOU.
**Tracks:** I wanna get next to you / Put your money where your mouth is / Car wash 88 mix (on 12″ only.).
■ 7″ .....................MCA 278
MCA / Mar '77.
■ 12″ .....................MCAT 1274
■ 7″ .....................MCA 1274
■ CD Single.....................DMCA 1274
MCA / Jul '88.

## I WONDER WHERE YOU ARE TONIGHT?.
**Tracks:** I wonder where you are tonight.
■ 7″ .....................K 17463
Whitfield (USA) / Aug '79.

## I'M GOING DOWN.
**Tracks:** I'm going down / Yo yo.
■ 7″ .....................MCA 301
MCA / Jun '77.

## I'M IN LOVE.
**Tracks:** I'm in love / Get up off your fat.
■ 7″ .....................K 17291
WEA / Jun '80.

## IN CONCERT.
**Tracks:** Is it love you're after / I'm in love / Wishing on a star / Magic touch / Do you dance / I wanna get next to you / Love don't live here anymore / Car wash.
VHS .....................MMGV 065
MMG / Mar '94 / THE.

## IN FULL BLOOM.
**Tracks:** Wishing on a star / You can't please everybody / Ooh boy / Do your dance / You're my world girl.
■ LP .....................K 56394
■ MC.....................K 456394
Whitfield (USA) / Aug '77.

## IS IT LOVE YOU'RE AFTER.
**Tracks:** Car wash / Is it love you're after / Wishing on a star / Love don't live here anymore / Magic touch / Do your dance / It makes you feel like dancin' / I wanna get next to you / Put your mouth where your mouth is / I'm going down.
CD.....................BLATCD 9
■ LP .....................BLATLP 9
MC.....................BLATMC 9
Blatant / Jul '88 / Roots Records.

## IS IT LOVE YOU'RE AFTER.
**Tracks:** Is it love you're after / You can't run from yourself.

**7"** . . . . . . . . . . . . . . . . . K 17456
Whitfield (USA) / Nov '79.

### IT MAKES YOU FEEL LIKE DANCIN'.
**Tracks:** It makes you feel like dancin'.
■ **7"** . . . . . . . . . . . . . . . . . K 17148
WEA / May '78.

### JUMP STREET.
**Tracks:** Jump street / Illusions / R.R. express / Famous last words / Tell me that I'm dreaming / Please return your love to me / Fight it.
■ **LP** . . . . . . . . . . . . . . . . . K 56958
WEA / Nov '81.

### JUST MY IMAGINATION.
**Tracks:** Just my imagination / You're my piece of mind.
■ **12"** . . . . . . . . . . . . . . . . . CART 423
■ **7"** . . . . . . . . . . . . . . . . . CAR 423
Carrere / Feb '88.

### LONELY ROAD.
**Tracks:** Lonely road / Doesn't have to be this way.
■ **12"** . . . . . . . . . . . . . . . . . CART 417
■ **7"** . . . . . . . . . . . . . . . . . CAR 417
Carrere / Aug '87.

### LOVE DON'T LIVE HERE ANYMORE.
**Tracks:** Love don't live here anymore / Do it do it.
■ **7"** . . . . . . . . . . . . . . . . . K 17236
Whitfield (USA) / Sep '78.

### LOVE ME RIGHT NOW.
**Tracks:** Love me right now.
■ **12"** . . . . . . . . . . . . . . . . . MKHAN 39
■ **7"** . . . . . . . . . . . . . . . . . KHAN 39
Streetwave / Apr '85.

### MAGIC TOUCH.
**Tracks:** Magic touch / Safe and warm.
■ **12"** . . . . . . . . . . . . . . . . . MKHAN 21
■ **7"** . . . . . . . . . . . . . . . . . KHAN 21
Streetwave / Sep '84.

### MUSIC MAGIC.
**Tracks:** Not Advised.
■ **LP** . . . . . . . . . . . . . . . . . MKL 2
Streetwave / Oct '84.

### NEW LOVE.
**Tracks:** New love.
■ **12"** . . . . . . . . . . . . . . . . . MKHAN 31
■ **7"** . . . . . . . . . . . . . . . . . KHAN 31
Streetwave / Oct '84.

### OOH BOY.
**Tracks:** Ooh boy / What you been waitin' for.
■ **7"** . . . . . . . . . . . . . . . . . K 17575
Whitfield (USA) / Feb '80.

### PERFECT LOVER.
**Tracks:** Perfect lover.
■ **LP** . . . . . . . . . . . . . . . . . 781 944-1
Atlantic / Mar '89.

### PERFECT LOVER.
**Tracks:** Perfect lover (single).
■ **7"** . . . . . . . . . . . . . . . . . 086 452
Omni (USA) / Mar '89.

### POP YOU FINGERS.
**Tracks:** Pop you fingers / I wonder where you are tonight.
■ **12"** . . . . . . . . . . . . . . . . . K 17674T
■ **7"** . . . . . . . . . . . . . . . . . K 17674
WEA / Aug '80.

### PUT YOUR MONEY WHERE YOUR MOUTH IS.
**Tracks:** Put your money where your mouth is / Zig zag.
■ **7"** . . . . . . . . . . . . . . . . . MCA 259
MCA / Oct '76.

### RAINBOW CONNECTION IV.
**Tracks:** I wonder where you are tonight / Is it love you're after / Shine your light / What are you waiting for / Bad mother funker / You can't run from yourself / Lock it down / Pazzaz.
■ **LP** . . . . . . . . . . . . . . . . . K 56714
■ **MC** . . . . . . . . . . . . . . . . . K4 56714
Whitfield (USA) / Aug '79.

### ROSE ROYCE.
**Tracks:** Not Advised.
**CD** . . . . . . . . . . . . . . . . . JHD 103
**MC** . . . . . . . . . . . . . . . . . MCJHD 103
Tring / Aug '93 / Prism Leisure PLC / Midland Records.

### ROSE ROYCE EXPRESS.
**Tracks:** Rose Royce express.
■ **12"** . . . . . . . . . . . . . . . . . K 17875T

**7"** . . . . . . . . . . . . . . . . . K 17875
WEA / Nov '81.

### SHOW MUST GO ON, THE.
**Tracks:** Not Advised.
■ **LP** . . . . . . . . . . . . . . . . . MKLH H5
**MC.** . . . . . . . . . . . . . . . . . ZCMK 5
Streetwave / May '85.
**CD** . . . . . . . . . . . . . . . . . CDMK 005
Streetwave / '88.

### STILL IN LOVE.
**Tracks:** Still in love / Somehow we made it through the rain.
■ **7"** . . . . . . . . . . . . . . . . . EPCA 2615
Epic / '82.

### STRIKES AGAIN.
**Tracks:** Get up off your fat / Do it, do it / I'm in love (and I love the feeling) / First come, first served / Love don't live here anymore / Angel in the sky / Help / Let me be the first to know / That's what's wrong with me.
■ **LP** . . . . . . . . . . . . . . . . . K 56557
Whitfield (USA) / Sep '78.

### STRONGER THAN EVER.
**Tracks:** Dance with me / Sometimes lady / Best love / Still in love / You blew it / Somehow we made it through the rain / Fire in the funk / Talk to me.
■ **LP** . . . . . . . . . . . . . . . . . EPC 85634
**MC.** . . . . . . . . . . . . . . . . . 40 85634
Epic / Apr '82 / Sony.

### THEIR GREATEST HITS (Side By Side) (Rose Royce & Chic).
**Tracks:** Not Advised.
**CD** . . . . . . . . . . . . . . . . . DINCD 23
**LP** . . . . . . . . . . . . . . . . . DINTV 23
**MC.** . . . . . . . . . . . . . . . . . DINMC 23
Dino / Apr '91 / Pinnacle.

### WISHING ON A STAR.
**Tracks:** Wishing on a star / Funky factory.
■ **7"** . . . . . . . . . . . . . . . . . K 17060
WEA / Jan '78.

### WISHING ON A STAR.
**Tracks:** Not Advised.
**CD** . . . . . . . . . . . . . . . . . 9548 317242
**MC.** . . . . . . . . . . . . . . . . . 9548 317244
Pickwick / Jan '93 / Pickwick.

### WISHING ON A STAR (OLD GOLD).
**Tracks:** Wishing on a star / Love don't live here anymore.
■ **7"** . . . . . . . . . . . . . . . . . OG 9517
Old Gold / Sep '85.

## Ross, Anna

### WHERE LOVE LIVES.
**Tracks:** Where love lives / Where love lives (mixes).
■ **12"** . . . . . . . . . . . . . . . . . SJR 0009
■ **CD Single** . . . . . . . . . . . . . SJRCD 0009
Soul Jazz / Aug '93.

## Ross, Diana

Diana Ross has spent more weeks on the U.K. singles chart than any other woman, having scored hits every year since 1970 (in the album stakes she is second only to Madonna). A discographical quirk has Ross' popularity generally soaring at the start of each decade: her first solo chart-topper was *I'm Still Waiting* in '71; *Upside Down* and *My Old Piano* both made the Top Five in 1980; and *When You Tell Me That You Love Me* reached No. 2 in '91. Other career highlights include hit duets with the likes of Marvin Gaye and Ross 'discovery' Michael Jackson, an acclaimed performance in the Billie Holliday bio-pic *Lady Sings the Blues*, and a fascinating feud with her former Supremes cohorts. With no sign of her popularity fading, Ross can boast the greatest longevity and success of any soul star. The cream of her career appears on *Motown's Greatest Hits*, although 1993's *Forever Diana* box-set repays heftier investment. As an appropriate tribute to her 30th anniversary in the music business, the triple-platinum *One Woman* became her biggest-selling U.K. album.

### 14 GREATEST HITS.
**Tracks:** Reach out and touch / Somebody's hand / Ain't no mountain high enough / Remember me / Reach out I'll be there / Good morning heartache / Touch me in the morning / Last time I saw him / Do you know where you're going to / Love hangover /

I'm coming out / Upside down / It's my turn / Endless love.
■ **CD** . . . . . . . . . . . . . . . . . MCD 06072 MD
Motown / May '86.

### 2 CLASSIC ALBUMS : GREATEST HITS (see under Gaye, Marvin).

### 20 GOLDEN GREATS: DIANA ROSS.
**Tracks:** Do you know where you're going to / Touch me in the morning / Stop, look, listen (to your heart) / No one gets the prize / Ain't no mountain high enough / Love hangover / All of my life / I'm still waiting / Lovin', livin' and givin' / Boss / Remember me / Surrender / Reach out and touch / Gettin' ready for love / Doobedood'ndoobe, doobedood'ndoobe / I thought it took a little time (but today I fell in love).
■ **LP** . . . . . . . . . . . . . . . . . EMTV 21
■ **MC** . . . . . . . . . . . . . . . . . CMTV 21
Motown / Oct '81.
■ **LP** . . . . . . . . . . . . . . . . . ZL 72008
■ **MC** . . . . . . . . . . . . . . . . . ZK 72008
Motown / '86.

### 20 GOLDEN GREATS: DIANA ROSS & SUPREMES.
**Tracks:** Where did our love go / Baby love / Come see about me / Stop in the name of love / Back in my arms again / I hear a symphony / My world is empty without you / Love is like an itching in my heart / You can't hurry love / You keep me hangin' on / Love is here and now you're gone / Happening / Reflections / In and out of love / Forever came today / Some things you never get used to / Love child / I'm livin' in shame / No matter what sign you are / Someday we'll be together.
■ **LP** . . . . . . . . . . . . . . . . . EMTV 5
Motown / Sep '77.
■ **LP** . . . . . . . . . . . . . . . . . ZL 72009
■ **MC** . . . . . . . . . . . . . . . . . ZK 72009
Motown / '86.

### 20 GREATEST HITS: DIANA ROSS & THE SUPREMES (Ross, Diana & The Supremes).
**Tracks:** When the lovelight starts shining through his eyes / Where did our love go / Baby love / Come see about me / My world is empty without you / Stop in the name of love / Back in my arms again / I hear a symphony / You can't hurry love / Love is like an itching in my heart / You keep me hangin on / Love is here now you're gone / Reflections / Love child / I'll try something new / I'm gonna make you love me / Someday we'll be together / Ladder to the roof / Stoned love / Nathan Jones.
■ **CD** . . . . . . . . . . . . . . . . . MCD 06073 MD
Motown / May '86.

### 25TH ANNIVERSARY: DIANA ROSS (Ross, Diana & The Supremes).
**Tracks:** Where did our love go / Come see about me / Stop in the name of love / Back in my arms again / You can't hurry love / Love is here and now you're gone / Happening / Someday we'll be together / I'm gonna make you love me / When the lovelight starts shining through his eyes / Nothing but heartaches / My world is empty without you / Love is like an itching in my heart / I'm livin' in shame / Forever came today / Some things you never get used to / Composer / No matter what sign you are / Blue room / Manhattan / Who can I turn to / Some day my prince will come / Sleepwalk / Treat me nice John Henry / Come on and see me / It's all your fault / Ooh wee baby / Come on boy / Heigh ho / Those D.J. shows / Sincerely / Surfer boy / Beach ball / Heaven must have sent you / Just a little misunderstanding / Coca cola commercial (1) (Special lyrics to 'When the lovelight starts shining through his eyes') / Coca cola commercial (2) (Special lyrics to 'Baby love') / Supremes - interview / Baby love / I hear a symphony - Reflections / You keep me hangin on / Love child / In and out of love / If I ruled the world / When you wish upon a star / Are you sure love is the name of this game / Penny pincher / Send me no flowers / We couldn't get along without you.
■ **Double LP.** . . . . . . . . . . . . . WL 72436
■ **MC Set** . . . . . . . . . . . . . . . WK 72436
Tamla Motown / Jul '86.
■ **CD Set.** . . . . . . . . . . . . . . . ZD 72512
Motown / Mar '87.

### AIN'T NO MOUNTAIN HIGH ENOUGH.
**Tracks:** Reach out and touch / Now that there's you / You're all I need to get by / These things will keep me loving you / Ain't no mountain high enough / Something on my mind / I wouldn't change the man he is / Keep an eye / Where there was darkness / Can't it wait until tomorrow / Dark side of the world.
■ **CD** . . . . . . . . . . . . . . . . . WD 72733
■ **MC** . . . . . . . . . . . . . . . . . WK 72733
Motown / Mar '91.

**AIN'T NO MOUNTAIN HIGH ENOUGH.**
**Tracks:** Ain't no mountain high enough / It's my house / Boss (Available on 12" single only) / Remember me (Available on 12" single only.).
■ 7" . . . . . . . . . . . . . . . . . . . . TMG 751
Tamla Motown / Sep '70.
■ 7" . . . . . . . . . . . . . . . . . . . . AB 40803
■ 12" . . . . . . . . . . . . . . . . . . . . ZT 40804
Motown / Jul '86.

**AIN'T NO MOUNTAIN HIGH ENOUGH/ SURRENDER (2 Classic albums).**
**Tracks:** Reach out and touch / Now that there's you / Ain't no mountain high enough / Something on my mind / I wouldn't change the man he is / Keep an eye / Where there was darkness / Can't wait until tomorrow / Dark side of the world / Surrender / I can't give back the love I feel for you / Remember me / And if you see him / Reach out I'll be there / Didn't you know (you'd have to cry sometime) / Simple thing like cry / Did you read the morning paper / I'll settle for you / I'm a winner / All the befores.
■ CD . . . . . . . . . . . . . . . . . . . . ZD 72549
Motown / Jul '87.

**ALL OF MY LIFE.**
**Tracks:** All of my life / Simple thing like love.
■ 7" . . . . . . . . . . . . . . . . . . . . TMG 880
Tamla Motown / Nov '73.

**ALL OF YOU (Ross, Diana & Julio Iglesias).**
**Tracks:** All of you.
■ 7" . . . . . . . . . . . . . . . . . . . . A 4522
CBS / Jun '84.

**ALL THE GREAT HITS.**
**Tracks:** It's my turn / Mahogany, Theme from / Reach out and touch / Touch me in the morning / I'm still waiting / All of my life / Surrender / Remember me / Upside down / I'm coming out / Tenderness / My old piano / Boss / It's my house / Love hangover / Ain't no mountain high enough.
■ LP . . . . . . . . . . . . . . . . . . . . ZL 72016
■ MC . . . . . . . . . . . . . . . . . . . . ZK 72016
Motown / '89.

**ALL THE GREAT LOVE SONGS.**
**Tracks:** I'm still waiting / My man (mon homme) / All of my life / Love me / After you / All night lover / Sparkle / It's my turn / Cryin in my heart out for you / Endless love.
■ CD . . . . . . . . . . . . . . . . . . . . ZD 72221
Motown / Oct '86.
CD . . . . . . . . . . . . . . . . . . . . 530056-2
MC . . . . . . . . . . . . . . . . . . . . 530056-4
Motown / Jan '93 / PolyGram.

**ALL THE GREATEST HITS: DIANA ROSS.**
**Tracks:** It's my turn / Do you know where you're going to / Reach out and touch / Touch me in the morning / I'm still waiting / All of my life / Surrender / Remember me / Upside down / I'm coming out / Tenderness / My old piano / Boss / It's my house / Love hangover / Ain't no mountain high enough.
■ LP . . . . . . . . . . . . . . . . . . . . STMA 8036
MC . . . . . . . . . . . . . . . . . . . . CSTMA 8036
Motown / Dec '81 / PolyGram.

**ANTHOLOGY - DIANA ROSS (Volumes 1 & 2).**
**Tracks:** Reach out and touch / Ain't no mountain high enough / Remember me / Reach out I'll be there / Surrender / I'm still waiting / Good morning heartache / touch me in the morning / You're a special part of me / Last time I saw him / My mistake (was to love you) / Sleepin' / Sorry doesn't always make it right / Do you know where you're going to / I thought it took a little time (but today I / One love in my lifetime / Baby, I love your way / Young mothers / Brown baby/Save the children / Love hangover / Gettin' ready for love / Your love is so good for me / You got it / Top of the world / Lovin', livin' and givin' / What you gave me / Boss / It's my house / Upside down / I'm coming out / It's my turn / One more chance / Cryin' my heart out for you / My old piano / My man (mon homme) / Endless love / Imagine / Too shy to say.
■ CD Set . . . . . . . . . . . . . . . . . . . . ZD 72532
Motown / Jun '87.
■ CD Set . . . . . . . . . . . . . . . . . . . . WD 72532
Motown / Apr '89.
CD Set . . . . . . . . . . . . . . . . . . . . 530199-2
Motown / Jan '93 / PolyGram.

**ANTHOLOGY - DIANA ROSS & THE SUPREMES (Ross, Diana & The Supremes).**
**Tracks:** Let me go the right way / Breath-taking guy / When the lovelight starts shining thru' his eyes / Standing at the crossroads of love / Run, run, run / Where did our love go / Baby love / Ask any girl / I'm livin' in shame / Composer / No matter what sign you are / Someday we'll be together / Come see about me / Stop in the name of love / Back in my arms again / Nothing but heartaches / I hear a symphony / My world is empty without you / Love is like an itching in my heart / You can't hurry love / You keep me hangin' on / Love is here and now you're gone / Happening / Reflections / In and out of love / Forever came today / Some things you never get used to / Love child / I'm gonna make you love me / I'll try something new / Uptight (everything's alright) / I second that emotion.
■ Double LP . . . . . . . . . . . . . . . . . . . . ZL 72130
Motown / '86.

**ANTHOLOGY - DIANA ROSS & THE SUPREMES (Volume 1 & 2) (Ross, Diana & The Supremes).**
**Tracks:** Your heart belongs to me / Let me go the right way / Breathtaking guy / When the lovelight starts shining through his eyes / Standing at the crossroads of love / Where did our love go / Come see about me / Back in my arms again / Nothing but heartaches / My world is empty without you / Love is like an itching in my heart / You can't hurry love / Love is here and now you're gone / Happening / Hard day's night / Funny how time slips away / Falling in love with love / Forever came today / Some things you never get used to / I'm gonna make you love me / I'm livin' in shame / Composer / I'll try anything new / No matter what sign you are / Someday we'll be together / Up the ladder to the roof / Everybody's got the right to love / Automatically sunshine / Your wonderful sweet, sweet love / I guess I'll miss the man / Bad weather / It's all been said before / I'm gonna let my heart do the walking / Reflections / In and out of love / Love child / Composer, The (2) / Young folks / Stoned love / Nathan Jones / Floy joy / Touch / Run, run, run / Baby love / Ask any girl / Stop in the name of love / I hear a symphony / You keep me hangin' on / You send me / I'm the greatest star.
■ CD Set . . . . . . . . . . . . . . . . . . . . ZD 72533
Motown / Jun '87.
■ CD Set . . . . . . . . . . . . . . . . . . . . WD 72533
Motown / Apr '89.
CD Set . . . . . . . . . . . . . . . . . . . . 530196-2
Motown / Jan '93 / PolyGram.

**BABY IT'S ME.**
**Tracks:** Gettin' ready for love / You got it / Baby it's me / Too shy to say / Your love is so good for me / Top of the world / All night lover / Confide in me / Same love that made me laugh / Come in from the rain.
■ LP . . . . . . . . . . . . . . . . . . . . STMS 5097
■ MC . . . . . . . . . . . . . . . . . . . . CSTMS 5097
Motown / Jun '83.

**BEST YEARS OF MY LIFE/UPSIDE DOWN, THE.**
**Tracks:** Upside down / Upside down (mixes) (Not available on 7 or MCS) / Best years of my life / You can't hurry love (Not available on 12).
■ 12" . . . . . . . . . . . . . . . . . . . . 12EM 305
■ 7" . . . . . . . . . . . . . . . . . . . . EM 305
■ CD Single . . . . . . . . . . . . . . . . . . . . CDEM 305
■ MC Single . . . . . . . . . . . . . . . . . . . . TCEM 305
EMI / Mar '94.

**BOSS, THE.**
**Tracks:** No one gets the prize / I ain't been licked / All for one / Boss / Once in the morning / It's my house / Sparkle / I'm in the world.
■ LP . . . . . . . . . . . . . . . . . . . . STML 12118
Motown / Aug '79.
■ LP . . . . . . . . . . . . . . . . . . . . STMS 5049
■ MC . . . . . . . . . . . . . . . . . . . . CSTMS 5049
Motown / Mar '82.
■ LP . . . . . . . . . . . . . . . . . . . . WL 72095
■ CD . . . . . . . . . . . . . . . . . . . . WD 72095
Motown / Aug '88.

**BOSS, THE.**
**Tracks:** Boss.
■ 7" . . . . . . . . . . . . . . . . . . . . TMG 1150
Motown / Oct '81.

**CAPTURED LIVE ON STAGE (Ross, Diana & The Supremes).**
**Tracks:** T.C.B. / Medley (1) (Stop! in the name of love/Come see about me/My world is empty without yo) / Medley (2) (The lady is a tramp/Let's get away from it all.) / Monologue - Diana Ross (1) / Love is here and now you're gone / I'm gonna make you love me / Monologue - Mary Wilson / Can't take my eyes off you / Monologue - Diana Ross & Mary Wilson / Reflections / My man (mon homme) / Didn't we / It's alright with me / Big spender / Falling in love with love / Love child / Dialogue - Diana Ross / Aquarius / Monologue - Diana Ross (2) / Impossible dream / Monologue - Diana Ross (3) / Someday we'll be together / Closing dialogue - Diana Ross & the Supremes.
■ Double LP . . . . . . . . . . . . . . . . . . . . WL 72438
■ MC . . . . . . . . . . . . . . . . . . . . WK 72438
Motown / Feb '87.

**CHAIN REACTION.**
**Tracks:** Chain reaction / Chain reaction (mixes).
■ 12" . . . . . . . . . . . . . . . . . . . . 12CL 386
■ 7" . . . . . . . . . . . . . . . . . . . . CL 386
Capitol / Jan '86.
■ 12" . . . . . . . . . . . . . . . . . . . . 12EM 290
■ 7" . . . . . . . . . . . . . . . . . . . . EM 290
■ CD Single . . . . . . . . . . . . . . . . . . . . CDEM 290
■ MC Single . . . . . . . . . . . . . . . . . . . . TCEM 290
EMI / Nov '93.

**COMPACT COMMAND PERFORMANCES (14 Greatest Hits).**
**Tracks:** Reach out and touch / Remember me / Good morning heartache / Last time I saw him / Love hangover / I'm coming out / It's my turn / Ain't no mountain high enough / Reach out I'll be there / Touch me in the morning / Do you know where you're going to / Boss / Upside down.
■ CD . . . . . . . . . . . . . . . . . . . . ZD 72336
Motown / '86.
■ CD . . . . . . . . . . . . . . . . . . . . WD 72336
Motown / Apr '89.

**COMPACT COMMAND PERFORMANCES (20 Greatest Hits) (Ross, Diana & The Supremes).**
**Tracks:** When the lovelight starts shining through his eyes / Where did our love go / Baby love / Come see about me / My world is empty without you / Stop in the name of love / Back in my arms again / I hear a symphony / You can't hurry love / Love is like an itching in my heart / You keep me hangin on / Love is here now your gone / Reflections / Love child / I'll try something new / I'm gonna make you love me / Someday we'll be together / Up to the ladder to the roof / Stoned love / Nathan Jones.
■ CD . . . . . . . . . . . . . . . . . . . . ZD 72423
Motown / Oct '86.
■ CD . . . . . . . . . . . . . . . . . . . . WD 72423
Motown / Apr '89.

**COMPOSER.**
**Tracks:** Composer / Take me where you go.
■ 7" . . . . . . . . . . . . . . . . . . . . TMG 999
Tamla Motown / Nov '75.

**CREAM OF THE CROP (Ross, Diana & The Supremes).**
**Tracks:** Someday we'll be together / Can't you see it's me / You gave me love / Hey Jude / Young folks / Shadows of society / Loving you is better than ever / When it's to the top / Till Johnny comes / Blowin' in the wind / Beginning of the end.
■ LP . . . . . . . . . . . . . . . . . . . . STML 11137
Tamla Motown / Feb '70.

**CRYIN' MY HEART OUT FOR YOU.**
**Tracks:** Crying my heart out for you / To love again.
■ 7" . . . . . . . . . . . . . . . . . . . . TMG 1233
Motown / Oct '81.

**DIANA.**
**Tracks:** Upside down / Tenderness / Friend to friend / I'm coming out / Have fun (again) / My old piano / Now that you're gone / Give up.
■ LP . . . . . . . . . . . . . . . . . . . . STMA 8033
MC . . . . . . . . . . . . . . . . . . . . CSTMA 8033
Motown / Oct '81 / PolyGram.
■ CD . . . . . . . . . . . . . . . . . . . . WD 72430
■ LP . . . . . . . . . . . . . . . . . . . . WL 72430
■ MC . . . . . . . . . . . . . . . . . . . . WK 72430
Motown / Aug '88.

**DIANA & MARVIN (see under Gaye, Marvin).**

**DIANA / THE BOSS (2 Classic albums).**
**Tracks:** Upside down / Tenderness / Friend to friend / I'm coming out / Have fun (again) / My old piano / Now that you're gone / Give up / No one gets the prize / I ain't been licked / All for one / Boss / Once in the morning / It's my house / Sparkle / I'm in the world.
■ CD . . . . . . . . . . . . . . . . . . . . ZD 72470
Motown / Oct '86.

**DIANA EXTENDED - THE REMIXES.**
**Tracks:** Boss / Love hangover / Upside down / Someday we'll be together / I'm coming out / Chain reaction (Not available on LP) / You're gonna love it (Not available on LP) / Love hangover (mixes) (Available on LP only) / Boss (mixes) (Available on LP only) / I'm coming out (mixes) (Available on LP only) / Someday we'll be together (mixes) (Available on LP only) / Upside down (mixes) (Available on LP only).
CD . . . . . . . . . . . . . . . . . . . . CDDREX 1
LP Set . . . . . . . . . . . . . . . . . . . . DREX 1

354 ■ DELETED

**MC. . . . . . . . . . . . . . . . . . . . . . . . .TCDREX 1**
EMI / Apr '94 / EMI.

## DIANA ROSS.
**Tracks:** Lovin', livin' and givin' / What you gave me / Never say I don't love you / You were the one / Reach out, I'll be there / Sorry, doesn't make it right / Where did we go wrong / To love / Together.
■ **LP . . . . . . . . . . . . . . . . . . . . . . . .STML 12093**
Motown / Nov '78.

## DIANA ROSS & THE SUPREMES JOIN THE TEMPTATIONS (Ross, Diana & The Supremes).
**Tracks:** Try it baby / I second that emotion / Ain't no mountain high enough / I'm gonna make you love me / This guy's in love with you / Funky Broadway / I'll try something new / Place in the sun / Sweet inspiration / Then / Impossible dream.
■ **LP . . . . . . . . . . . . . . . . . . . . . . . .STML 11096**
Tamla Motown / Jan '69.

## DIANA ROSS & THE SUPREMES WITH THE TEMPTATIONS (Ross, Diana & The Supremes & The Temptations).
**Tracks:** I'm gonna make you love me / My guy / My girl / Uptight / Sweet inspiration / I'll try something new / Ain't no mountain high enough / I second that emotion / Why must we fall in love / For better or worse / Weight / I'll be doggone / Stubborn kind of fellow.
■ **LP . . . . . . . . . . . . . . . . . . . . . . STMS 5015**
Motown / Jul '81.
■ **LP . . . . . . . . . . . . . . . . . . . . . . . TMS 3513**
■ **MC. . . . . . . . . . . . . . . . . . . . . . . TMC 3513**
Motown / Oct '82.

## DIANA ROSS & THE SUPREMES: 20 GOLDEN GREATS (Ross, Diana & The Supremes).
**Tracks:** Where did our love go / Baby love / Come see about me / Stop, in the name of love / Back in my arms again / I hear a symphony / My world is empty without you / Love is like an itching in my heart / You can't hurry love / You keep me hangin' on / Love is here and now you're gone / Happening / Reflections / In and out of love / Forever came today / Some things you never get used to / Love child / I'm livin' in shame / No matter what sign you are / Someday we'll be together.
■ **LP . . . . . . . . . . . . . . . . . . . . . . . . MTV 5**
**MC. . . . . . . . . . . . . . . . . . . . . . . CMTV 5**
Motown / Oct '81 / PolyGram.

## DIANA ROSS (2).
**Tracks:** Do you know where you're going to / I thought it took a little time (but today I feel in love) / You're good my child / One love in my lifetime / Ain't nothin' but a maybe / After you / Smile / Love hangover / Kiss me now.
■ **LP . . . . . . . . . . . . . . . . . . . . . . . WL 72375**
■ **MC. . . . . . . . . . . . . . . . . . . . . . WK 72375**
Motown / Oct '81.
■ **CD . . . . . . . . . . . . . . . . . . . . . . WD 72375**
Motown / Feb '90.

## DIANA ROSS (3).
**Tracks:** Not Advised.
■ **LP . . . . . . . . . . . . . . . . . . . . . . . .STML 12022**
Tamla Motown / Mar '76.

## DIANA ROSS JOINS THE TEMP-TATIONS/TOGETHER (Ross, Diana & The Supremes With The Temptations).
**Tracks:** Try it baby / I second that emotion / Ain't no mountain high enough / I'm gonna make you love me / This guy's in love with you / Funky Broadway / I'll try something new / Place in the sun / Sweet inspiration / Then / Impossible dream / Stubborn kind of fellow / I'll be doggone / Weight / Ain't nothing like the real thing / Uptight / Sing a simple song / My guy, my girl / For better or worse / Can't take my eyes off you / Why (must we fall in love).
■ **CD . . . . . . . . . . . . . . . . . . . . . ZD 72502**
Motown / Dec '86.

## DIANA ROSS.
**Tracks:** Reach out and touch / Now that there's you / You're all I need to get by / These things will keep me loving you / Ain't no mountain high enough / Something on my mind / I wouldn't change the man he is / Keep an eye / Where there was darkness / Can't it wait until tomorrow / Dark side of the world.
■ **LP . . . . . . . . . . . . . . . . . . . . . . .STML 11159**
Tamla Motown / Oct '70.
■ **LP . . . . . . . . . . . . . . . . . . . . . STMS 5017**
■ **MC. . . . . . . . . . . . . . . . . . . . . CSTMS 5017**
Motown / Oct '81.

## DIANA'S DUETS (Ross, Diana & various artists).
**Tracks:** Endless love / I'm gonna make you love me / My mistake (was to love you) / I'll something new

/ You're a special part of me / I second that emotion / I'll keep my light in my window / Try it, baby / Stop, look and listen / Pops, we love you / Uptight / You are everything / Stubborn kind of fellow / Ain't nothing like the real thing.
■ **LP . . . . . . . . . . . . . . . . . . . . . .STML 12163**
■ **MC. . . . . . . . . . . . . . . . . . . . .CSTML 12163**
Motown / Mar '82.
■ **CD . . . . . . . . . . . . . . . . . . . . WD 72041**
Motown / Nov '90.

## DIRTY LOOKS.
**Tracks:** Dirty looks / So close.
■ **12" Remix. . . . . . . . . . . . . . . . 12EMP 2**
■ **12". . . . . . . . . . . . . . . . . . . . 12EM 2**
■ **7". . . . . . . . . . . . . . . . . . . . .EM 2**
EMI / May '87.

## DO YOU KNOW WHERE YOU'RE GOING TO (Theme from 'Mahogany').
**Tracks:** Do you know where you're going to.
■ **7" . . . . . . . . . . . . . . . . . . . .TMG 1010**
Tamla Motown / Apr '76.

## DON'T KNOCK MY LOVE (Ross, Diana & Marvin Gaye).
**Tracks:** Don't knock my love / I'm falling in love with you.
■ **7" . . . . . . . . . . . . . . . . . . TMG 953**
Tamla Motown / Jul '75.

## DOOBEDOOD'NDOOBEDOOBEDOOD'NDOOBE.
**Tracks:** Doobedood'ndoobe, doobedood'ndoobe.
■ **7" . . . . . . . . . . . . . . . . . . TMG 812**
Tamla Motown / May '72.

## DYNAMIC DIANA (Ross, Diana & The Supremes).
**Tracks:** Baby love / Stop, in the name of love / Shake me, wake me / Mother dear / Ask any girl / Hea-twave / I'm so glad / Who could ever doubt my love / Any girl in love (knows what I'm going through) / I'm in love again / Honey boy / Get ready / Always in my heart / Everything is good about you.
■ **LP . . . . . . . . . . . . . . . . . . . . . TMS 3505**
■ **MC. . . . . . . . . . . . . . . . . . . . TMC 3505**
Motown / '82.

## EARLY YEARS 1961-1964 (Ross, Diana & The Supremes).
**Tracks:** Where did our love go / Come see about me / Run, run, run / Long gone lover / Standing at the crossroads of love / Who's loving you / When the lovelight starts shining thru his eyes / Baby love / You've really got a hold on me / Time changes things / You bring back memories / Buttered pop-corn / I want a guy / Do you love me / Let me go the right way / Breathtaking guy.
■ **LP . . . . . . . . . . . . . . . . . . . . STMR 9008**
■ **MC. . . . . . . . . . . . . . . . . . . CSTMR 9008**
Motown / Oct '81.

## EASE ON DOWN THE ROAD (see under Jackson, Michael).

## EATEN ALIVE.
**Tracks:** Eaten alive / Oh teacher / Experience / Chain reaction / More and more / I'm watching you / Love on the line / I love being in love with you / Crime of passion / Don't give up on each other / Eaten alive (extended remix).
■ **LP . . . . . . . . . . . . . . . . . . . . . . ROSS 2**
■ **MC. . . . . . . . . . . . . . . . . . . . . TCROSS 2**
Capitol / Sep '85.
■ **CD . . . . . . . . . . . . . . . . . . CDP 746 184 2**
Capitol / Jan '86.
**CD . . . . . . . . . . . . . . . . . . . . CDEMD 1051**
EMI / Nov '93 / EMI.

## EATEN ALIVE.
**Tracks:** Eaten alive / I'm watching you.
■ **12" . . . . . . . . . . . . . . . . . . 12CL 372**
■ **7" . . . . . . . . . . . . . . . . . . . .CL 372**
Capitol / Sep '85.

## ENDLESS LOVE (Ross, Diana & Lionel Richie).
**Tracks:** Endless love.
■ **7" . . . . . . . . . . . . . . . . . . TMG 1240**
Motown / Oct '81.

## EVENING WITH DIANA ROSS.
**Tracks:** Overture / Here I am / I wouldn't change a thing / Lady is a tramp / Touch me in the morning / Smile / Send in the clowns / Love hangover / I want you back / Motown story: Motown overture / Money (that's what I want) / Please Mr. Postman / Fingertips / Reach out and touch / You keep me hangin' on / Baby love / Someday we'll be together / Stop in the name of love / You can't hurry love / Reflections / My world is empty without you / I hear a symphony / Girls / Point (everything's got 'em) / Me and my arrow / Lifeline / Everything's got 'em (reprise) /

Working girls / Lady sings the blues / T'aint nobody's business if I do / I cried for you / Aux lies Hawaii / Stormy weather / Jump in the pot (and let's get hot) / I need a little sugar in my bowl / My man (mon homme) / One giant step / Chorus line / Music in the mirror / What I did for love / Improvisations / Dance / Ten looks three / Do you know where you're going to / Ain't no mountain high enough.
■ **Double LP. . . . . . . . . . . . . . TMSP 6005**
■ **MC Set . . . . . . . . . . . . . . CTMSP 6005**
Motown / Oct '81.
■ **Double LP. . . . . . . . . . . . . . . WL 72268**
■ **MC. . . . . . . . . . . . . . . . . . WK 72268**
Motown / Aug '85.

## EVERY GREAT NO 1 HIT (Ross, Diana & The Supremes).
**Tracks:** Where did our love go / Baby love / Come see about me / Stop, in the name of love / Back in my arms again / I hear a symphony / You can't hurry love / You keep me hangin' on / Love is here and now you're gone / Happening / Love child / Someday we'll be together.
■ **CD . . . . . . . . . . . . . . . . . . WD 72597**
Motown / Feb '88.

## EVERYTHING IS EVERYTHING.
**Tracks:** My place / Ain't no sad song / Everything is everything / Baby it's love / I'm still waiting / Doobe-dood'ndoobe, doobedood'ndoobe / Come together / Long and winding road / I love you (call me) / How about you / Close to you.
■ **LP . . . . . . . . . . . . . . . . . . . . . .STML 11178**
Tamla Motown / Jun '71.
■ **LP . . . . . . . . . . . . . . . . . . . . . STMS 5047**
■ **MC. . . . . . . . . . . . . . . . . . . . CSTMS 5047**
Motown / '82.

## EXPERIENCE.
**Tracks:** Experience / Oh teacher.
■ **12" . . . . . . . . . . . . . . . . . . 12CL 400**
■ **7" . . . . . . . . . . . . . . . . . . . .CL 400**
Capitol / Apr '86.

## FAREWELL (Ross, Diana & The Supremes).
**Tracks:** T.C.B. / Stop in the name of love / Come-see about me / My world is empty without you / Baby love / Lady is a tramp / Let's get away from it all / Love is here and now you're gone / I'm gonna make you love me / Can't take my eyes off you / Reflec-tions / My man / Didn't we / It's alright with me / Big spender / Falling in love with love / Love child / Aquarius/Let the sunshine in / Impossible dream / Someday we'll be together.
■ **LP Set . . . . . . . . . . . . . . . STML 11154/5**
Tamla Motown / Aug '70.

## FLIP HITS EP.
**Tracks:** Do you know where you're going to / I thought it took a little time / One love in my lifetime / Love hangover.
■ **MC Single. . . . . . . . . . . . . . CTME 2021**
Motown / May '83.

## FORCE BEHIND THE POWER.
**Tracks:** Change of heart / When you tell me that you love me / Battlefield / Blame it on the sun / You're gonna love it / Heavy weather / Force behind the power / Heart (don't change my mind) / Waiting in the wings / You and I (Not on LP) / One shining moment / If we hold on together (Not on LP) / No matter what you do (On CD only).
**CD . . . . . . . . . . . . . . . . . . CDEMD 1023**
**MC. . . . . . . . . . . . . . . . . . TCEMD 1023**
EMI / Aug '91 / EMI.
■ **LP . . . . . . . . . . . . . . . . . . . . .EMD 1023**
EMI / Nov '91.
**MiniDisc. . . . . . . . . . . . . . . . . .797154-3**
EMI / Feb '93 / EMI.
**DCC . . . . . . . . . . . . . . . . . DCCEMD 1023**
EMI / Jan '93 / EMI.

## FORCE BEHIND THE POWER.
**Tracks:** Force behind the power / If we hold on together.
■ **12". . . . . . . . . . . . . . . . . . .12EM 200**
■ **7". . . . . . . . . . . . . . . . . . . EM 200**
■ **CD Single . . . . . . . . . . . . . .CDEM 200**
■ **MC Single. . . . . . . . . . . . . .TCEM 200**
EMI / Aug '91.

## FORCE BEHIND THE POWER (SINGLE) (REMIX).
**Tracks:** Force behind the power / You're gonna love it / Your gonna love it (inst) / Supremes medley.
■ **12". . . . . . . . . . . . . . . . . . .12EM 221**
■ **7". . . . . . . . . . . . . . . . . . . EM 221**
■ **CD Single . . . . . . . . . . . . . .CDEM 221**
■ **MC Single. . . . . . . . . . . . . .TCEM 221**
EMI / Jan '92.

■ **DELETED**

355

## FOREVER CAME TODAY (Ross, Diana & The Supremes).
**Tracks:** Forever came today.
■ 7" . . . . . . . . . . . . . . . . . . . **TMG 650**
Tamla Motown / Apr '68.

## FOREVER DIANA.
**Tracks:** When the lovelight starts shining through his eyes / Breathtaking guy / Where did our love go / Baby love / Come see about me / Stop in the name of love / Back in my arms again / You send me / Nothing but heartaches / Put on a happy face / I hear a symphony / My world is empty without you / Love is like an itching in my heart / I hear a happy symphony / You can't hurry love / You keep me hangin' on / Love is here and now you're gone / Happening / Reflections / In and out of love / Forever came today / Love child / I'm gonna make you love me / Try it baby / I'm livin' in shame / Someday we'll be together / Reach out and touch (somebody's hand) / Ain't no mountain high enough / Remember me / Reach out I'll be there / Surrender / I'm still waiting / Lady sings the blues / Good morning heartache / God bless the child / Touch me in the morning / Brown baby/Save the children (medley) / Last time I saw him / You are everything / My mistake (was to love you) / Theme from Mahogany (do you know where you're going to) / Love hangover / Confide in me / Come in from the rain / Gettin' ready for love / Home / Boss / It's my house / I ain't been licked / Upside down / I'm coming out / It's my turn / Endless love / My old piano / Why do fools fall in love / Mirror mirror / Work that body / Muscles / Missing you / Swept away / Eaten alive / Chain reaction / Family / Ninety nine & a half / What a wonderful world / Amazing Grace / If we hold on together / Workin' overtime / This house / Force behind the power / When you tell me that you love me / One shining moment / Waiting in the wings / Where did we go wrong / Back to the future / Let's make every moment count / Your love / It's a wonderful life / Best years of my life.
CD Set . . . . . . . . . . . . . . . . **DRBOX 1**
EMI / Oct '93 / EMI.

## FUNNY GIRL (Ross, Diana & The Supremes).
**Tracks:** If a girl isn't pretty / I am woman / I'm the greatest star / Funny girl / Music that makes me dance / Don't rain on my parade / People / Cornet man / His love makes me beautiful / Sadie Sadie.
■ LP . . . . . . . . . . . . . . . . .**STML 11088**
Tamla Motown / Feb '69.

## GETTIN' READY FOR LOVE.
**Tracks:** Gettin' ready for love.
■ 7" . . . . . . . . . . . . . . . . . . **TMG 1090**
Motown / Oct '81.

## GREATEST HITS (Ross, Diana & The Supremes).
**Tracks:** Whisper you love me boy / When the lovelight starts shining / Where did our love go / Baby love / Come see about me / Stop in the name of love / Back in my lonely arms again / Nothing but heartaches / Happening / Reflections / I hear a symphony / My world is empty without you / Love is like an itching in my heart / You can't hurry love / You keep me hanging on / Love is here and now you're gone.
■ LP . . . . . . . . . . . . . . . . .**STML 11063**
Tamla Motown / Jan '68.

## GREATEST HITS LIVE, THE.
**Tracks:** Intro - Dirty Diana / I'm coming out / Upside down / What can one person do / Missing you / Mirror, mirror / Chain reaction / Muscles / Dirty looks / Love hangover / Man I love / Do you know where you're going to / Ain't no mountain high enough / Paradise / This house / Workin' overtime / Stop in the name of love / You keep me hangin' on / You can't hurry love / Where did our love go / Baby love / Why do fools fall in love / Endless love / Reach out and touch somebody's hand.
CD . . . . . . . . . . . . . . . . . . **CDEMDC 1001**
■ Double LP . . . . . . . . . . . . . . . **EMDC 1001**
■ MC . . . . . . . . . . . . . . . . **TCEMDC 1001**
EMI / Oct '89 / EMI.

## GREATEST HITS VOL.2 (Ross, Diana & The Supremes).
**Tracks:** Someday we'll be together / I'm gonna make you love me / Love child / I second that emotion / Some things you never get used to / I'll try something new / Honey bee / Forever came today / Weight / In and out of love / No matter what sign you are / Why / Composer / I'm livin' in shame.
■ LP . . . . . . . . . . . . . . . . .**STML 11146**
Tamla Motown / May '70.

## GREATEST HITS: DIANA & MARVIN (Ross, Diana & Marvin Gaye).
**Tracks:** Your precious love / Ain't no mountain high enough / You're all I need to get by / Ain't nothing

like the real thing / Good lovin ain't easy to come by / If this world were mine / Onion song / If I could build my whole world around you / You are everything / Love twins / Don't knock my love / You're a special part of me / Pledging my love / Just say, just say / Stop, look, listen( to your heart) / I'm fallin in love with you / My mistake ( was to love you) / Include me in your life.
■ CD . . . . . . . . . . . . . . . . . **ZD 72454**
Motown / Oct '86.

## GREATEST HITS: DIANA ROSS.
**Tracks:** Remember me / Didn't you know (you'd have to cry sometime) / Doobedood'ndoobe, doobedood'ndoobe / And if you see him / Ain't no mountain high enough / How about you / Reach out and touch / These things will keep me loving you / Reach out I'll be there / Close to you / I'm still waiting.
■ LP . . . . . . . . . . . . . . . . . **STMA 8006**
Tamla Motown / Nov '72.
■ CD . . . . . . . . . . . . . . . . . **WD 72478**
■ LP . . . . . . . . . . . . . . . . . **WL 72478**
■ MC . . . . . . . . . . . . . . . . . **WK 72478**
Motown / Oct '86.

## GREATEST HITS: DIANA ROSS VOL.1 & 2 (2 Classic albums) (Ross, Diana & The Supremes).
**Tracks:** When the lovelight starts shining through his eyes / Where did our love go / Ask any girl / Baby love / Run, run, run / Stop in the name of love / Back in my arms again / Come see about me / Nothing but heartaches / Everything is good about you / I hear a symphony / Love is here and now you're gone / Whisper you love me boy / Happening / You keep me hangin' on / You can't hurry love / Standing at the crossroads of love / Love is like an itching in my heart / There's no stopping us now.
■ CD . . . . . . . . . . . . . . . . . **ZD 72493**
Motown / Nov '86.

## GREATEST HITS: DIANA ROSS VOL.2.
**Tracks:** Touch me in the morning / Love hangover / Sorry doesn't always make it right / Imagine / Last time I saw him / All of my life / Do you know where you're going to / I won't last a day without you / Behind closed doors / Love me / Good morning heartache / I thought it took a little time (but today I fell in love).
■ LP . . . . . . . . . . . . . . . . .**STML 12036**
MC . . . . . . . . . . . . . . . . .**CSTML 12036**
Motown / Oct '81 / PolyGram.
■ LP . . . . . . . . . . . . . . . . . **ZL 72028**
Motown / '86.

## HEART (DON'T CHANGE MY MIND).
**Tracks:** Heart (Don't change my mind) / Endless love / Experience / Ain't no mountain high enough (Live) / Upside down (Live).
■ 7" . . . . . . . . . . . . . . . . . . **EM 261**
■ CD Single . . . . . . . . . . . . . **CDEM 261**
■ MC Single . . . . . . . . . . . . . **TCEM 261**
EMI / Mar '93.

## I SECOND THAT EMOTION (Ross, Diana & The Supremes).
**Tracks:** I second that emotion.
■ 7" . . . . . . . . . . . . . . . . . . **TMG 709**
Tamla Motown / Sep '69.

## I THOUGHT IT TOOK A LITTLE TIME.
**Tracks:** I thought it took a little time.
■ 7" . . . . . . . . . . . . . . . . . .**TMG 1032**
Tamla Motown / Jul '76.

## I'M COMING OUT.
**Tracks:** I'm coming out / Give up.
■ 12" . . . . . . . . . . . . . . . . . **TMGT 1210**
■ 7" . . . . . . . . . . . . . . . . . . **TMG 1210**
Motown / Oct '81.

## I'M GONNA MAKE YOU LOVE ME (Ross, Diana, The Supremes & The Temptations).
**Tracks:** I'm gonna make you love me / I second that emotion.
■ 7" . . . . . . . . . . . . . . . . . . **TMG 685**
Tamla Motown / Jan '69.
■ 7" . . . . . . . . . . . . . . . . . . **TMG 991**
Tamla Motown / Oct '75.
■ 7" . . . . . . . . . . . . . . . . . .**TMG 1045**
Tamla Motown / Sep '76.

## I'M LIVING IN SHAME (Ross, Diana & The Supremes).
**Tracks:** I'm living in shame.
■ 7" . . . . . . . . . . . . . . . . . . **TMG 695**
Tamla Motown / Apr '69.

## I'M STILL WAITING.
**Tracks:** I'm still waiting / Surrender / I can't give back the love I feel for you / Remember me / And if you see him / Reach out I'll be there / Didn't you know (you'd have to cry sometime) / Simple thing like cry / Did you read the morning paper / I'll settle for you / I'm a winner / All the befores.
■ LP . . . . . . . . . . . . . . . . .**STML 11193**
Tamla Motown / Oct '71.
■ LP . . . . . . . . . . . . . . . . . **STMS 5031**
Motown / Jun '82.
■ MC . . . . . . . . . . . . . . . . . **WK 72082**
■ LP . . . . . . . . . . . . . . . . . **WL 72082**
Motown / Apr '84.

## I'M STILL WAITING.
**Tracks:** I'm still waiting / Touch me in the morning.
■ 7" . . . . . . . . . . . . . . . . . .**TMG 1041**
Tamla Motown / Sep '76.

## I'M STILL WAITING.
**Tracks:** I'm still waiting / Touch me in the morning.
■ 7" . . . . . . . . . . . . . . . . . . **TMG 781**
Tamla Motown / Jul '71.

## I'M STILL WAITING & ALL THE GREAT HITS.
**Tracks:** I'm still waiting (1990 remix) / Upside down / My old piano / Tenderness / Boss / It's my turn / Touch me in the morning / Endless love / Love hangover (PWL remix) / Do you know where you're going to / Remember me / Reach out and touch / I'm coming out / It's my house / All of my life / Surrender / Ain't no mountain high enough.
■ CD . . . . . . . . . . . . . . . . . **ZD 72716**
■ LP . . . . . . . . . . . . . . . . . **ZL 72716**
■ MC . . . . . . . . . . . . . . . . . **ZK 72716**
Motown / Aug '90.

## I'M STILL WAITING (1990 REMIX).
**Tracks:** I'm still waiting (1990 remix).
■ 12" . . . . . . . . . . . . . . . . . **ZT 43782**
■ 7" . . . . . . . . . . . . . . . . . . **ZB 43781**
■ CD Single . . . . . . . . . . . . . **ZD 43782**
■ MC Single . . . . . . . . . . . . . **ZK 43781**
Motown / Jun '90.

## I'M STILL WAITING/SURRENDER.
**Tracks:** Not Advised.
■ CD . . . . . . . . . . . . . . . . . .**530251-2**
Motown / Jan '93.

## IF WE HOLD ON TOGETHER.
**Tracks:** Work that body (On Cdems 257 only) / Missing you (On Cdems 257 only) / Chain reaction (Live) (Not on Cdem 257) / Why do fools fall in love (Live) (On Cdem 257 only) / Do you know where you're going to (On Cdem 257 only) / One shining moment (On Cdem 257 only) / If we hold on together.
■ 7" . . . . . . . . . . . . . . . . . . **EM 257**
■ CD Single . . . . . . . . . . . . .**CDEMS 257**
■ CD Single . . . . . . . . . . . . . **CDEM 257**
■ MC Single . . . . . . . . . . . . . **TCEM 257**
EMI / Nov '92.

## IN AND OUT OF LOVE (Ross, Diana & The Supremes).
**Tracks:** In and out of love.
■ 7" . . . . . . . . . . . . . . . . . . **TMG 632**
Tamla Motown / Nov '67.

## IT'S MY HOUSE.
**Tracks:** It's my house / No one gets the prize / Boss.
■ 12" . . . . . . . . . . . . . . . . . **TMGT 1169**
■ 7" . . . . . . . . . . . . . . . . . . **TMG 1169**
Motown / Oct '81.

## IT'S MY TURN.
**Tracks:** It's my turn / Sleepin'.
■ 7" . . . . . . . . . . . . . . . . . . **TMG 1217**
Motown / Oct '81.

## IT'S NEVER TOO LATE.
**Tracks:** It's never too late / Endless love / Sweet surrender.
■ 12" . . . . . . . . . . . . . . . . . **12CL 256**
■ 7" . . . . . . . . . . . . . . . . . . **CL 256**
Capitol / Jul '82.

## LAST TIME I SAW HIM.
**Tracks:** Last time I saw him / No one's gonna be a fool for ever / Love me / Sleepin' / You / Turn around / When will I come home to you / I heard a song / Stone liberty / Behind closed doors.
■ LP . . . . . . . . . . . . . . . . .**STML 11255**
Tamla Motown / Jun '74.
■ LP . . . . . . . . . . . . . . . . . **STMS 5071**
■ MC . . . . . . . . . . . . . . . . .**CSTMS 5071**
Motown / Aug '82.

### LAST TIME I SAW HIM.
**Tracks:** Last time I saw him.
■ 7" . . . . . . . . . . . . . . . . . TMG 893
Tamla Motown / May '74.

### LEGEND (Ross, Diana, The Supremes & The Temptations).
**Tracks:** Not Advised.
CD . . . . . . . . . . . . . . . . . 295 709
EMS / Jul '90.

### LET THE SUN SHINE IN/CREAM OF THE CROP (Ross, Diana & The Supremes).
**Tracks:** Composer / Everyday people / No matter what sign you are / Hey Western Union man / What becomes of the broken hearted / I'm livin' in shame / Aquarius (Medley) / Let the sun shine in (the flesh failures) (medley) / Let the music play / With a child's heart / Discover me (and you'll discover love) / Will this be the day / I'm so glad I got somebody (like you around) / Someday we'll be together / Can't you see it's me / You gave me love / Hey Jude / Young folks / Shadows of society / Loving you is better than ever / When it's to the top (still I won't stop giving you love) / Till Johnny comes / Blowin' in the wind / Beginning of the end.
■ CD . . . . . . . . . . . . . . . . . ZD 72496
Motown / Dec '86.

### LET THE SUNSHINE IN (Ross, Diana & The Supremes).
**Tracks:** Composer / Everyday people / No matter what sign you are / Send a telegram / What becomes of the broken-hearted / I'm livin' in shame / Aquarius/Let the sunshine in / Let the music play / With a child's heart / Discover me / Will this be the day / I'm so glad I got somebody.
■ LP . . . . . . . . . . . . . . . STML 11114
Tamla Motown / Oct '69.
LP . . . . . . . . . . . . . . . . . ML 5305
Milestone / '90 / Jazz Music / Pinnacle / Cadillac.

### LIVE AT CAESAR'S PALACE.
**Tracks:** Overture / Don't rain on my parade / Big Mabel Murphy / Reach out and touch / Stop, in the name of love / My world is empty without you / Baby love / I hear a symphony / Ain't no mountain high enough / Corner of the sky / Being green / I loves you Porgy / Lady sings the blues / God bless the child / Good morning heartache / T'aint nobody's business if I do / Lady is a tramp / My man (mon homme).
■ LP . . . . . . . . . . . . . . . STMS 5019
MC . . . . . . . . . . . . . . . . . CSTMS 5019
Motown / Oct '81 / PolyGram.

### LIVE AT LONDON'S TALK OF THE TOWN (Ross, Diana & The Supremes).
**Tracks:** Michelle / Yesterday / Baby love / More / Happening / Mame / Reflections / Lady is a tramp / Without a song / Stop in the name of love / Second hand Rose / In and out of love.
■ LP . . . . . . . . . . . . . . . MFP 50447
MFP / Jan '80.

### LIVE AT THE TALK OF THE TOWN (Ross, Diana & The Supremes).
**Tracks:** With a song in my heart / Stop in the name of love / Baby love / More / Michelle / Yesterday / In and out of love / Lady is a tramp / Mame / Happening / Secondhand rose / Reflections / and 12 others.
■ LP . . . . . . . . . . . . . . . STML 11070
Tamla Motown / Mar '68.

### LIVE: DIANA ROSS.
**Tracks:** Not Advised.
■ LP . . . . . . . . . . . . . . . .STML 11248
Tamla Motown / Jun '74.
■ LP . . . . . . . . . . . . . . . . WL 72075
■ MC . . . . . . . . . . . . . . . . WK 72075
Motown / '86.

### LOVE CHILD (Ross, Diana & The Supremes).
**Tracks:** Love child / Keep an eye / How long has that evening train been gone / Does your mama know about me / Honey bee (keep on stinging me) / Some things you never get used to / He's my sunny boy / You've been so wonderful to me / Don't break these chains of love / You ain't livin' till you're lovin' / I'll set you free / Can't shake it loose.
■ LP . . . . . . . . . . . . . . . .STML 11095
Tamla Motown / Feb '69.
■ LP . . . . . . . . . . . . . . . STMS 5070
■ MC . . . . . . . . . . . . . . . . CSTMS 5070
Motown / Aug '82.

### LOVE CHILD (Ross, Diana & The Supremes).
**Tracks:** Love child.
■ 7" . . . . . . . . . . . . . . . . . TMG 677
Tamla Motown / Nov '68.

### LOVE HANGOVER.
**Tracks:** Love hangover.
■ 7" . . . . . . . . . . . . . . . . .TMG 1024
Tamla Motown / Apr '76.
■ 12" . . . . . . . . . . . . . . . TMGT 1380
■ 7" . . . . . . . . . . . . . . . . .TMG 1380
Motown / Apr '85.

### LOVE HANGOVER (RE-RELEASE).
**Tracks:** Love hangover / Love hangover (instrumental) / Love hangover (urban remix) (Only on 12" version ZT 42348.) / Love hangover (urban dub) (Only on 12" version ZT 42348.).
■ 12" . . . . . . . . . . . . . . . . ZT 42348
■ 12" . . . . . . . . . . . . . . . . ZT 42308
■ 7" . . . . . . . . . . . . . . . . . ZB 42307
■ CD Single . . . . . . . . . . . . ZD 42308
Motown / Nov '88.

### LOVE ME.
**Tracks:** Love me.
■ 7" . . . . . . . . . . . . . . . . . TMG 917
Tamla Motown / Sep '74.

### LOVE SONGS: DIANA ROSS.
**Tracks:** Do you know where you're going to / Endless love / Love me / Sorry doesn't always make it right / Crying my heart out for you / I thought it took a little time (but today I fell in love) / These things will keep me loving you / It's my turn / Sparkle / Touch me in the morning / I'm still waiting / All night lover / You're all I need to get by / All of my life.
■ LP . . . . . . . . . . . . . . . . . NE 1200
■ MC . . . . . . . . . . . . . . . . CE 2200
K-Tel / Nov '82.

### LOVE SONGS: DIANA ROSS & MICHAEL JACKSON (Ross, Diana & Michael Jackson).
**Tracks:** I'm still waiting / Touch me in the morning / All of my life / Love hangover / Ain't no mountain high enough / Endless love / Reach out and touch / Do you know where you're going / Got to be there / Ain't no sunshine / Farewell my Summer love / Ben / One day in your life / I'll be there / Girl you're so fine / Never can say goodbye.
■ LP . . . . . . . . . . . . . . . STAR 2298
■ MC . . . . . . . . . . . . . . . STAC 2298
Telstar/Ronco / Sep '87.
■ CD . . . . . . . . . . . . . . . . TCD 2298
Telstar/Ronco / Nov '88.

### LOVE SONGS: MICHAEL JACKSON & DIANA ROSS (see under Jackson, Michael).

### LOVE SUPREME (Ross, Diana & The Supremes).
**Tracks:** You can't hurry love / Baby love / Happening / Automatically sunshine / Up the ladder to roof / Stoned love / Where did our love go / Love is here and now you're gone / Reflections / In and out of love / Stop in the name of love / Come see about me / I'm gonna make you love me / Love child / I'm living in shame / Floy joy / You keep me hangin' on / I second that emotion / Nathan Jones / Someday we'll be together.
■ CD . . . . . . . . . . . . . . . . ZD 72701
■ LP . . . . . . . . . . . . . . . . ZL 72701
■ MC . . . . . . . . . . . . . . . . ZK 72701
Motown / Dec '88.

### LOVIN' LIVIN' AND GIVIN'.
**Tracks:** Lovin', livin' and givin'.
■ 7" . . . . . . . . . . . . . . . . .TMG 1112
Tamla Motown / Jul '78.

### MERRY CHRISTMAS.
**Tracks:** Not Advised.
CD . . . . . . . . . . . . . . . . .550 4032
MC . . . . . . . . . . . . . . . . .550 4034
Spectrum (1) / Nov '94 / PolyGram.

### MIRROR MIRROR.
**Tracks:** Mirror mirror.
■ 12" . . . . . . . . . . . . . . . 12CL 234
■ 7" . . . . . . . . . . . . . . . . .CL 234
Capitol / Jan '82.

### MISSING YOU.
**Tracks:** Missing you / Work that body / We are the children of the world.
■ 7" . . . . . . . . . . . . . . . . .CL 348
Capitol / Dec '84.
■ 12" . . . . . . . . . . . . . . . 12CL 348
Capitol / Mar '85.

### MOTOWN SPECIAL (Ross, Diana & The Supremes & The Temptations).
**Tracks:** I'm gonna make you love me / My guy, my girl / Uptight / Sweet inspiration / I'll try something new / Ain't no mountain high enough / I second that

emotion / Why / For better for worse / Weight / I'll be doggone / Stubborn kind of fellow.
■ LP . . . . . . . . . . . . . . . STMX 6003
Motown / Mar '77.

### MOTOWN'S GREATEST HITS: DIANA ROSS.
**Tracks:** Ain't no mountain high enough / Touch me in the morning / I'm still waiting / I'm gonna make you love me / Upside down / My old piano / You keep me hangin' on / Happening / Reflections / Baby love / You can't hurry love / Where did our love go / Stop in the name of love / All of my life.
CD . . . . . . . . . . . . . . . . 5300132
MC . . . . . . . . . . . . . . . . 5300134
■ LP . . . . . . . . . . . . . . . . 5300131
Motown / Feb '92 / PolyGram.
DCC . . . . . . . . . . . . . . . 530 013-5
Motown / Jan '93 / PolyGram.

### MR. LEE.
**Tracks:** Mr. Lee / Mr. Lee (mix).
■ 12" . . . . . . . . . . . . . . . .12EM 73
■ 12" Remix . . . . . . . . . . . . .12EMX 73
■ 7" . . . . . . . . . . . . . . . . . EM 73
■ CD Single . . . . . . . . . . . . CDEM 73
EMI / Sep '88.

### MUSCLES.
**Tracks:** Muscles / I am me.
■ 12" . . . . . . . . . . . . . . . 12CL 268
■ 7" . . . . . . . . . . . . . . . . .CL 268
Capitol / Oct '82.

### MY OLD PIANO.
**Tracks:** My old piano / Where did we go wrong.
■ 7" . . . . . . . . . . . . . . . . .TMG 1202
Motown / Oct '81.
■ 12" . . . . . . . . . . . . . . . TMGT 1387
■ 7" . . . . . . . . . . . . . . . . .TMG 1387
Motown / Apr '85.

### NEVER-BEFORE-RELEASED MASTERS (see under Supremes).

### NO MATTER WHAT SIGN YOU ARE (Ross, Diana & The Supremes).
**Tracks:** No matter what sign you are.
■ 7" . . . . . . . . . . . . . . . . . TMG 704
Tamla Motown / Jul '69.

### NO ONE GETS THE PRIZE.
**Tracks:** No one gets the prize.
■ 7" . . . . . . . . . . . . . . . . .TMG 1160
Motown / Oct '81.

### OLD FUNKY ROLLS.
**Tracks:** Old funky rolls / Boss.
■ 12" . . . . . . . . . . . . . . . TMGT 1273
■ 7" . . . . . . . . . . . . . . . . .TMG 1273
Motown / Aug '82.

### ONE MORE CHANCE.
**Tracks:** One more chance / Confide in me.
■ 7" . . . . . . . . . . . . . . . . .TMG 1227
Motown / Oct '81.

### ONE SHINING MOMENT.
**Tracks:** One shining moment / Waiting in the wings (CD singles only.) / Endless love (CD single (1) only) / When you tell me that you love me (Not on CD single (2).) / Why do fools fall in love (CD single (2) only.) / Muscles (CD single (2) only.).
■ 7" . . . . . . . . . . . . . . . . . EM 239
■ CD Single . . . . . . . . . . . .CDEM 239
■ CD Single . . . . . . . . . . . .CDEMS 239
■ MC Single . . . . . . . . . . . .TCEM 239
EMI / Jun '92.

### ONE WOMAN - THE ULTIMATE COLLECTION.
**Tracks:** Where did our love go / Baby love / You can't hurry love / Reflections / Reach out and touch / Ain't no mountain high enough / Touch me in the morning / Love hangover / I'm still waiting / Upside down / Theme from Mahogany (do you know where you're going to) / Endless love / Why do fools fall in love / Chain reaction / When will you tell me that you love me / One shining moment / If we hold on together / Best years of my life / Your love / Let's make every moment count.
CD . . . . . . . . . . . . . . . . CDONE 1
DCC . . . . . . . . . . . . . . . DCCONE 1
LP . . . . . . . . . . . . . . . . .ONE 1
MC . . . . . . . . . . . . . . . . TCONE 1
MiniDisc . . . . . . . . . . . . .MDONE 1
EMI / Oct '93 / EMI.

### ONE WOMAN - THE VIDEO COLLECTION.
**Tracks:** Theme from Mahogany (do you know where you're going to) / Upside down / My old piano / Why do fools fall in love / Mirror mirror / Work that body /

Muscles / Pieces of ice / Swept away / Eaten alive / Missing you / Chain reaction / Experience / Dirty looks / Mr. Lee / Workin' overtime / Paradise / I'm still waiting / When you tell me that you love me / Force behind the power / One shining moment / Heart don't change my mind.

■ VHS . . . . . . . . . . . . . . . . . MVN 4911553
PMI / Oct '93 / EMI / Gold & Sons / THE.

### PARADISE.
**Tracks:** Paradise (LP version) (7" & Cassingle only.) / We stand together (7" & Cassingle only.) / Paradise (exotic mix) (12" & CD single only.) / Paradise (desert island dub) (12" & CD single only.) / We stand together (edit) (12" & CD single only.) / Paradise (12" remix) (12EMX 94 only.).

■ 12" . . . . . . . . . . . . . . . . . . .12EM 94
■ 12" . . . . . . . . . . . . . . . . . .12EMX 94
■ 12" P.Disc. . . . . . . . . . . . . .12EMP 94
■ 7" . . . . . . . . . . . . . . . . . . . . EM 94
■ CD Single . . . . . . . . . . . . . . . CDEM 94
■ MC Single . . . . . . . . . . . . . . . TCEM 94
EMI / Jul '89.

### PIECES OF ICE.
**Tracks:** Pieces of ice / Still in love.

■ 12" . . . . . . . . . . . . . . . . . . . 12CL 298
■ 7" . . . . . . . . . . . . . . . . . . . .CL 298
Capitol / Jun '83.

### POPS, WE LOVE YOU (Ross, Diana/Stevie Wonder/Marvin Gaye/Smokey Robinson).
**Tracks:** Pops, we love you / Pops, we love you (version).

■ 7" . . . . . . . . . . . . . . . . . . .TMG 1136
Motown / Feb '79.

### PORTRAIT VOL 2.
**Tracks:** Not Advised.
CD . . . . . . . . . . . . . . . . . . . . TCD 2238B
Telstar/Ronco / Jul '86 / BMG.

### PORTRAIT VOLS. 1 & 2.
**Tracks:** Where did our love go / Baby love / Stop in the name of love / You can't hurry love / You keep me hangin on / Happening / Reflections / Love child / I'm gonna make you love me / I second that emotion / Someday we'll be together / Doobedood'ndoobe, doobedood'ndoobe / Ain't no mountain high enough / Remember me / Surrender / Love hangover / I'm still waiting / Reach out and touch / All of my life / Sorry doesn't always make it right / Do you know where your going to / Touch me in the morning / Upside down / It's my house / Boss / My old piano / I'm coming out / It's my turn / Endless love.

CD . . . . . . . . . . . . . . . . . .TCD 2238AR3
■ LP . . . . . . . . . . . . . . . . . . . STAR 2238
■ MC Set . . . . . . . . . . . . . . . STAC 2238
Telstar/Ronco / Apr '86 / BMG.

### REACH OUT AND TOUCH.
**Tracks:** Reach out and touch.

■ 7" . . . . . . . . . . . . . . . . . . . TMG 743
Tamla Motown / Jul '70.

### REACH OUT AND TOUCH.
**Tracks:** Reach out and touch / Surrender.

■ 7" . . . . . . . . . . . . . . . . . . . TMG 988
Tamla Motown / Sep '75.
■ 7" . . . . . . . . . . . . . . . . . . . ZB 41923
Motown / Apr '88.

### RED HOT RHYTHM 'N' BLUES.
**Tracks:** Dirty looks / Stranger in paradise / Shine / Shockwaves / Selfish one / Mr. Lee / Tell mama / There goes my baby / Summertime / Cross my heart / It's hard for me to say (Produced by Luther Vandross) / Tell me again.

■ LP . . . . . . . . . . . . . . . . . . . EMC 3532
■ MC . . . . . . . . . . . . . . . . . . TCEMC 3532
■ CD . . . . . . . . . . . . . . . . . CDEMC 3532
EMI / May '87.

### REFLECTIONS (Ross, Diana & The Supremes).
**Tracks:** Reflections / I'm gonna make it / Forever came today / I can't make it alone / In and out of love / Bah-bah-bah / What the world needs now is love / Up, up and away / Love makes me do foolish things / Then / Misery makes its home in my heart / Ode to Billy Joe.

■ LP . . . . . . . . . . . . . . . . . .STML 11073
Tamla Motown / Jul '68.
■ LP . . . . . . . . . . . . . . . . . . . WL 72368
■ MC . . . . . . . . . . . . . . . . . . WK 72368
Motown / Mar '85.

### REFLECTIONS (Ross, Diana & The Supremes).
**Tracks:** Reflections / Love child.

■ 7" . . . . . . . . . . . . . . . . . . . TMG 960
Tamla Motown / Mar '75.

### REMEMBER ME.
**Tracks:** Remember me / Surrender.

■ 7" . . . . . . . . . . . . . . . . . . . TMG 768
Tamla Motown / Apr '71.
■ 7" . . . . . . . . . . . . . . . . . . . TMG 970
Tamla Motown / May '75.

### RODGERS & HART COLLECTION (Ross, Diana & The Supremes).
**Tracks:** With a song in my heart / My funny valentine / Spring is here / Little Girl Blue / It never entered my mind / Where or when / There's a small hotel / Blue room / You took advantage of me / Manhattan / Bewitched / Blue moon / Wait till you see her / Dancing on the ceiling / Thou swell / I didn't know what time it was / Falling in love with love / Lover / My romance / Mountain greenery / Lady is a tramp / My heart stood still / This can't be love / Johnny One Note.

■ CD . . . . . . . . . . . . . . . . . . . WD 72594
Motown / Nov '87.

### ROSS.
**Tracks:** Not Advised.
■ LP . . . . . . . . . . . . . . . . . . EST 1867051
Capitol / Jul '83.

### SECRETS OF A SPARROW.
**Tracks:** Not Advised.
MC Set . . . . . . . . . . . . . . . . . . RC 163
Random House / Jan '94 / Conifer Records / THE.

### SHOCK WAVE.
**Tracks:** Shockwaves (12" remix) (on 12" only) / Shockwaves (7" remix) / Shockwaves (instrumental) / I am one.

■ 12" . . . . . . . . . . . . . . . . . . .12EM 22
■ 7" . . . . . . . . . . . . . . . . . . . EM 22
EMI / Sep '87.

### SILK ELECTRIC.
**Tracks:** Muscles / So close / Still in love / Fool for your love / Turn me over / Who / Love's lies / In your arms / Anywhere you run to / I am me.

■ LP . . . . . . . . . . . . . . . . . . .EST 27313
■ MC . . . . . . . . . . . . . . . . . TC EST 27313
Capitol / Oct '82.
■ LP . . . . . . . . . . . . . . . . . . . FA 3184
■ MC . . . . . . . . . . . . . . . . . . TCFA 3184
Fame / Jun '87.
■ CD . . . . . . . . . . . . . . . . . . CDEMD 1050
EMI / Nov '93 / EMI.

### SO CLOSE.
**Tracks:** So close / Fool for your love.

■ 12" . . . . . . . . . . . . . . . . . . . 12CL 277
■ 7" . . . . . . . . . . . . . . . . . . . .CL 277
Capitol / Jan '83.

### SOMEDAY WE'LL BE TOGETHER (Ross, Diana & The Supremes).
**Tracks:** Someday we'll be together.

■ 7" . . . . . . . . . . . . . . . . . . . TMG 721
Tamla Motown / Dec '69.
■ 7" . . . . . . . . . . . . . . . . . . . ZB 41925
Motown / Apr '88.

### SORRY DOESN'T ALWAYS MAKE IT RIGHT.
**Tracks:** Sorry doesn't always make it right.

■ 7" . . . . . . . . . . . . . . . . . . . TMG 941
Tamla Motown / Mar '75.

### STOLEN MOMENTS (The Lady Sings Jazz & Blues).
**Tracks:** Fine and mellow / Them there eyes / Don't explain / What a little moonlight can do / Mean to me / Lover man (Oh where can you be) / Gimme a pigfoot and a bottle of beer / Little girl blue / There's a small hotel / I cried for you / Man I love / God bless the child / You've changed / Strange fruit / All of me / Good morning heartache / Ain't nobody's bixness if I do / My man (mon homme) / Wonderful world / Fine and mellow (Reprise).

■ VHS . . . . . . . . . . . . . . . . MVN 4911913
PMI / Apr '93 / EMI / Gold & Sons / THE.

### STOLEN MOMENTS - THE LADY SINGS JAZZ & BLUES LIVE.
**Tracks:** Fine and mellow / Them there eyes / Don't explain / What a little moonlight can do / Mean to me / Lover man (Oh where can you be) / Gimme a pigfoot and a bottle of beer / Little girl blue / There's a small hotel / I cried for you / God bless the child / Love is here to stay / You've changed / Strange fruit / Good morning heartache / Ain't nobody's bizness if I do / My man (mon homme) / Fine and mellow (Reprise) / Where did we go wrong.

CD . . . . . . . . . . . . . . . . . . CDEMD 1044
MC . . . . . . . . . . . . . . . . . . TCEMD 1044
EMI / Apr '93 / EMI.

### STOP IN THE NAME OF LOVE (Ross, Diana & The Supremes).
**Tracks:** Stop in the name of love / Automatically sunshine / Automatically sunshine (medley) (12" only).

■ 12" . . . . . . . . . . . . . . . . . . ZT 41964
■ 7" . . . . . . . . . . . . . . . . . . . ZB 41963
Motown / Feb '89.

### STOP IN THE NAME OF LOVE.
**Tracks:** Baby love / Heat wave / (I'm so glad) heartaches don't last always / Mother dear / (You're gone but) Always in my heart / Get ready / Everything is good about you / Shake me, wake me (when it's over) / Who could ever doubt my love / Honey boy / Ask any girl / I'm in love again / Any girl in love (knows what I'm going through) / Stop in the name of love.

CD . . . . . . . . . . . . . . . . . . . .550 0712
MC. . . . . . . . . . . . . . . . . . . .550 0714
Spectrum (1) / May '93 / PolyGram.

### STOP LOOK LISTEN TO YOUR HEART (Ross, Diana & Marvin Gaye).
**Tracks:** Stop look listen to your heart / Love twins.

■ 7" . . . . . . . . . . . . . . . . . . . TMG 906
Tamla Motown / Jun '74.

### SUPREMES MEDLEY (Ross, Diana & The Supremes).
**Tracks:** Supremes medley.

■ 12" . . . . . . . . . . . . . . . . . . TMGT 1180
■ 7" . . . . . . . . . . . . . . . . . . .TMG 1180
Motown / Oct '81.

### SURRENDER.
**Tracks:** Surrender.

■ 7" . . . . . . . . . . . . . . . . . . . TMG 792
Tamla Motown / Oct '71.

### SWEPT AWAY.
**Tracks:** Missing you / Touch by touch / Rescue me / It's your move / Swept away (Spoken introduction written by Diana Ross.) / Telephone / Nobody makes me crazy like you do / All of you / We are the children of the world / Forever young.

■ CD . . . . . . . . . . . . . . . . . CDP 746 053 2
■ LP . . . . . . . . . . . . . . . . . . . ROSS 1
■ MC . . . . . . . . . . . . . . . . . . TCROSS 1
Capitol / Oct '86.
■ LP . . . . . . . . . . . . . . . . . . . FA 3200
■ MC . . . . . . . . . . . . . . . . . . TCFA 3200
Fame / Jun '88.

### TENDERNESS.
**Tracks:** Tenderness.

■ 12" . . . . . . . . . . . . . . . . . . TMGT 1248
■ 7" . . . . . . . . . . . . . . . . . . .TMG 1248
Motown / Dec '81.

### THEIR VERY BEST - BACK TO BACK (Ross, Diana/Michael Jackson/Gladys Knight/Stevie Wonder).
**Tracks:** Not Advised.

■ CD . . . . . . . . . . . . . . . . . . . PTVCD 2
■ LP . . . . . . . . . . . . . . . . . . . PTVR 2
■ MC . . . . . . . . . . . . . . . . . . PTVT 2
Priority / Nov '86.

### THIS HOUSE.
**Tracks:** This house / Chain reaction (live).

■ 12" . . . . . . . . . . . . . . . . . . .12EM 118
■ 7" . . . . . . . . . . . . . . . . . . . EM 118
■ CD Single . . . . . . . . . . . . . .CDEM 118
■ MC Single. . . . . . . . . . . . . .TCEM 118
EMI / Nov '89.

### TO LOVE AGAIN.
**Tracks:** It's my turn / Stay with me / One more chance / Crying my heart out for you / Do you know where you're going to / I thought it took a little time (but today I fell in love) / To love again / No one's gonna be a fool for ever / Touch me in the morning.

■ LP . . . . . . . . . . . . . . . . . . .STML 12152
■ MC . . . . . . . . . . . . . . . . . .CSTML 12152
Motown / Oct '81.

### TOGETHER (Ross, Diana & The Supremes With The Temptations).
**Tracks:** Stubborn kind of fellow / I'll be doggone / Weight / Ain't nothing like the real thing / Uptight / Sing a simple song / My guy, my girl / For better or worse / Can't take my eyes off you / Why.

■ LP . . . . . . . . . . . . . . . . . . .STML 11122
Tamla Motown / Feb '70.

## TOUCH BY TOUCH.
Tracks: Touch by touch / Fight for it.
■ 7"......................CL 337
Capitol / Sep '84.

## TOUCH ME IN THE MORNING.
Tracks: Touch me in the morning / All of my life / We need you / Leave a little room / I won't last a day without you / Little girl blue / My baby / Imagine / Brown baby / Save the children.
■ LP....................STML 11239
Motown / Oct '81.
■ LP.......................WL 72074
■ MC.......................WK 72074
Motown / May '84.
■ CD.......................WD 72074
Motown / Aug '88.
CD.......................530165-2
Motown / Jan '93 / PolyGram.

## TOUCH ME IN THE MORNING.
Tracks: Touch me in the morning.
■ 7".......................TMG 861
Tamla Motown / Jul '73.

## TOUCH ME IN THE MORNING/BABY IT'S ME.
Tracks: Touch me in the morning / All of my life / We need you / Leave a little room / Little girl blue / My baby (my baby my own) / Imagine / Brown baby (medley) / Save the children (medley) / Gettin' ready for love / You got it / Baby it's me / Too shy to say / Your love is so good for me / Top of the world / All night lover / Confide in me / Same love that made me laugh / Come in from the rain.
■ CD.......................ZD 72490
Motown / Dec '86.

## UP FRONT.
Tracks: Up front / Love or lonliness.
■ 12".......................12CL 306
■ 7".......................CL 306
Capitol / Oct '83.

## UPSIDE DOWN.
Tracks: Upside down.
■ 7".......................TMG 1195
Motown / Jul '80.

## VERY BEST OF DIANA ROSS.
Tracks: Reach out and touch / Ain't no mountain high enough / Now that there's you / Remember me / My place / I'm still waiting / Reach out I'll be there / And if you see him / Touch me in the morning / Good morning heartache / Love is here to stay / Lover man / Baby, I love your way / Young mothers / Imagine / Too shy to say / Do you know where you're going to / Love hangover / Don't knock my love / Last time I saw him / Sleepin' / Same love that made me laugh / Smile / Together / My mistake (was to love you) / Gettin' ready for love / Lovin', livin' and givin' / No one gets the prize / Boss / Now that you're gone / Upside down / Crying my heart out for you / It's my turn / Endless love.
■ Double LP...............TMSP 6017
■ MC Set.................CTMSP 6017
Motown / Dec '83.
■ Double LP...............WL 72135
■ MC Set.................WK 72135
Motown / '86.

## VERY SPECIAL SEASON, A.
Tracks: Winter wonderland / White Christmas / Wonderful Christmastime / What the world needs now / Happy Christmas (war is over) / Let it snow let it snow let it snow / Amazing grace / His eye is on the sparrow / Silent night / Overjoyed / O holy night / Someday at Christmas / Ave Maria / Christmas song.
CD.......................CDEMD 1075
MC.......................TCEMD 1075
EMI / Nov '94 / EMI.

## VISIONS OF DIANA ROSS, THE.
Tracks: Why do fools fall in love / Chain reaction / Swept away / Muscles / Mirror mirror / Eaten alive.
■ VHS....................MVR 99 0049 2
PMI / Mar '86.
VHS.......................MC 2058
Music Club Video / Mar '91 / Video Collection / Gold & Sons / THE.

## WE REMEMBER SAM COOKE (Ross, Diana & The Supremes).
Tracks: Not Advised.
■ LP.......................WL 72445
■ MC.......................WK 72445
Motown / May '86.

## WHAT YOU GAVE ME.
Tracks: What you gave me / Ain't no mountain high enough.

■ 12".......................12TMG 1135
■ 7".......................TMG 1135
Motown / Oct '81.

## WHEN YOU TELL ME THAT YOU LOVE ME.
Tracks: When you tell me that you love me / Chain reaction / You and I (Only on 12" and CD Single.).
■ 12".......................12EM 217
■ 7".......................EM 217
■ CD Single...............CDEM 217
■ MC Single...............TCEM 217
EMI / Nov '91.

## WHY (MUST WE FALL IN LOVE) (Ross, Diana & The Supremes).
Tracks: Why (must we fall in love).
■ 7".......................TMG 730
Tamla Motown / Mar '70.

## WHY DO FOOLS FALL IN LOVE.
Tracks: Why do fools fall in love.
■ 7".......................CL 226
Capitol / Nov '81.

## WHY DO FOOLS FALL IN LOVE.
Tracks: Why do fools fall in love / Sweet surrender / Mirror mirror / Endless love / It's never too late / Think I'm in love / Sweet nothin's / Two can make it / Work that body.
■ LP.......................EST 26733
Capitol / Nov '81.
MC.......................TCFA 3186
■ LP.......................FA 3186
Fame / Sep '87 / EMI.
CD.......................CDFA 3186
Fame / Feb '89 / EMI.
CD.......................CDEMD 1049
EMI / Nov '93 / EMI.

## WHY DO FOOLS FALL IN LOVE.
Tracks: Why do fools fall in love / I'm coming out / Boss (Features on CDS & 12" only.) / Love hangover (Features on CDS only.).
12".......................12 EM 332
7".......................EM 332
CD Single...............CDEM 332
MC Single...............TCEM 332
EMI / Jun '94 / EMI.

## WORK THAT BODY.
Tracks: Work that body / Two can make it.
■ 12".......................12CL 241
■ 7".......................CL 241
Capitol / May '82.

## WORKIN' OVERTIME.
Tracks: Workin' overtime / Say we can / Take the bitter with the sweet / Bottom line / This house / Paradise / Keep on dancing / What can one person do / Going through the motions / We stand together.
■ CD.......................CDEMD 1009
■ LP.......................EMD 1009
■ MC.......................TCEMD 1009
EMI / May '89.

## WORKIN' OVERTIME.
Tracks: Workin' overtime / Workin' overtime (ext. version) (Not on 7".) / Workin' overtime (house mix) (12" only.) / Workin' overtime (Instrumental version) (7" only.) / Workin' overtime (club mix) (CD single only.)
■ 12".......................12EM 91
■ 7".......................EM 91
■ CD Single...............CDEM 91
■ 12" Remix...............12EMX 91
EMI / May '89.

## YOU ARE EVERYTHING (Ross, Diana & Marvin Gaye).
Tracks: You are everything / Stop, look, listen, to your heart.
■ 7".......................TMG 890
Tamla Motown / Nov '75.

## YOU'RE GONNA LOVE IT.
Tracks: You're gonna love it.
■ 12".......................12EM 2211
EMI / Feb '92.

## YOUR LOVE.
Tracks: Your love / Missing you / Love hangover (CDS only) / When you tell me that you love me (CDS only).
■ 7".......................EM 299
■ CD Single...............CDEM 299
■ CD Single...............CDEMS 299
■ MC Single...............TCEM 299
EMI / Nov '93.

## YOUR LOVE IS SO GOOD FOR ME.
Tracks: Your love is so good for me / Baby it's me.
■ 7".......................TMG 1104
Motown / Apr '78.

## Ross, Jackie

### FULL BLOOM.
Tracks: Selfish one / Everything but love / Wasting time / I had to walk with my man / Be sure you know / Summertime / I've got the skill / Change your ways / Don't take my love / Haste makes waste / From you (I wanna hear it) / Misty.
■ LP.......................GCH 8095
MC.......................GCHK 78095
Chess (Charly) / Aug '88 / Charly.

## Ross, James

### FRONT PAGE LOVER.
Tracks: Front page lover / Keep on keepin' on.
■ 7".......................AM 146
A&M / Sep '83.

### SLOW DOWN.
Tracks: Slow down.
■ 12".......................AMX 125
■ 7".......................AM 125
A&M / Jul '83.

## Rotary Connection

### PEACE.
Tracks: Opening round / Silent night / Christmas love / Last call for peace / Shopping bag menagerie / Christmas child / Peace at last / Santa's little helpers / Sidewalk Santa / If peace was all we had / Silent chant.
■ LP.......................GCH 8102
Chess (Charly) / '89.

### ROTARY CONNECTION, THE.
Tracks: Amen / Rapid transit / Turn me on / Pink noise / Lady Jane / Like a rolling stone / Soul man / Sursum mentes / Didn't want to have to do it / Black noise / Memory band / Ruby Tuesday / Rotary connection.
■ LP.......................CRL 4538
Chess / May '68.

## Roundtree, Richard

### MAN FROM SHAFT.
Tracks: Gets hard sometimes / Peace in the morning / I'm here / Street brother / Man from Shaft / Tree of life / Lovin' / Sagittarian lady / Letter.
■ LP.......................2315121
MGM (EMI) / Feb '73.

## Roy, Barbara

### GONNA PUT UP A FIGHT.
Tracks: Gonna put up a fight / Gotta see you tonight.
■ 12".......................PT 49734
■ 7".......................PB 49733
RCA / Mar '87.

### GOT TO SEE YOU TONIGHT.
Tracks: Got to see you tonight.
■ 12".......................PT 49804
■ 7".......................PB 49803
RCA / Aug '86.

### IF YOU WANT ME (Roy, Barbara & Ecstacy, Passion & Pain).
Tracks: If you want me / I've got you.
■ 12".......................EXCL 512
■ 7".......................EXC 512
Excaliber / Jul '81.

### WALKING TALKING DOLLY.
Tracks: Wild mountain / Walking talking dolly.
■ 7".......................GBH 7S 407
August (USA) / Dec '86.

### WITH ALL MY LOVE.
Tracks: With all my love.
■ 12".......................ARIST 12578
■ 7".......................ARIST 578
Arista / Sep '84.

## Roy C

### SHOTGUN WEDDING.
Tracks: Monster mash / Shotgun wedding.
■ 7".......................WI 273
Island / Apr '66.
■ 7".......................UK 19
UK / Nov '72.

**SHOTGUN WEDDING (OLD GOLD).**
Tracks: Shotgun wedding.
■ 7″ . . . . . . . . . . . . . . . . . . . . . . . . .OG 9345
Old Gold / Jul '88.

## Royal Jokers

**DON'T IT MAKE YOU FEEL FUNKY.**
Tracks: Don't it make you feel funky.
■ 7″ . . . . . . . . . . . . . . . . . . . . . . . . SUE 6
Suemi / '81.

## Royalle Delite

**(I'LL BE A) FREAK FOR YOU.**
Tracks: I'll be a freak for you.
■ 7″ . . . . . . . . . . . . . . . . . . . . . . . KHAN 51
Streetwave / Sep '85.

**I'LL COME WHEN YOU CALL.**
Tracks: I'll come when you call / Radio cut.
■ 12″ . . . . . . . . . . . . . . . . . . . . . MKHAN 71
Streetwave / Aug '86.

**SPEND A LITTLE TIME WITH ME.**
Tracks: Send a little time with me.
■ 12″ . . . . . . . . . . . . . . . . . . . . . MKHAN 60
■ 7″ . . . . . . . . . . . . . . . . . . . . . . KHAN 60
■ 7″ P.Disc . . . . . . . . . . . . . . . MKHPX 60
MC. . . . . . . . . . . . . . . . . . . . . . . ZCMK 60
Streetwave / Dec '85.

## Roye, Lee

**TEARS (NOTHING BUT TEARS).**
Tracks: Tears (nothing but tears) / Who am I.
■ 7″ . . . . . . . . . . . . . . . . . . . . . MCA 378
MCA / Jul '79.

## Ruby & The Romantics

**OUR DAY WILL COME.**
Tracks: Our day will come / When you're young and
in love / Nobody but my baby / How deep is the
ocean / Does he really care for me / I'm sorry / By
the way / End of the world / Moonlight and music /
Baby come home / I cry alone / Your baby doesn't
love you anymore / Hey there, lonely boy / What a
difference a day made / I'm much better off than I've
ever been / Young wings can fly.
■ LP . . . . . . . . . . . . . . . . . . . . . .CRM 2030
Charly / Sep '84.

**OUR DAY WILL COME.**
Tracks: Our day will come.
■ 7″ . . . . . . . . . . . . . . . . . . . . . HLR 9679
London-American / Mar '63.

## Rucker, Vernis

**STRANGER IN THE SHEETS.**
Tracks: Fishin' for a man / You've been good for me /
He's cheating on you / There must be someone for
me / Fever / There's a hurt where my heart used to
be / Put love first / Then came you / Stormy Monday /
Dead to right / Strangers in the sheets.
CD. . . . . . . . . . . . . . . . . . . . . .CDCH 508
Ace / Jan '94 / Pinnacle / Complete Record Co. Ltd.

## Ruffin, David

Born in Meridian, Mississippi, in 1941, Ruffin first joined the Temptations as their
drummer in the early '60s; later replacing
Elbridge Bryant as lead tenor. After a series
of hits starring Eddie Kendricks' lighter stylings, Ruffin made a dramatic entrance as
frontman on *My Girl* - the Temps' first
number one and a masterful example of the
broken-hearted soul singer's art. However,
he never settled as merely a group
member, demanding more status and special treatment until, in '68, he was voted out
of the group. A subsequent solo career at
Motown began well and peaked in '76 with
the Van McCoy-produced international hit
*Walk Away From Love.* Thereafter he cut a
couple of very good but overlooked albums
on Warners (*So Soon We Change* and
*Gentleman Ruffin*) and, in '87, enjoyed a
brief revival with his old friend Kendricks;
when, under the auspices of Hall & Oates,
the pair recorded an album for RCA. In '91
he was found dead in a Detroit crack-house,
the second Temptation (after Paul Williams)
to die by his own hand.

**AT HIS BEST.**
Tracks: Walk away from love / I can't stop the rain /
My whole world ended / Heavy love / Ain't too proud

to beg / Everything's coming up love / I wish it would
rain / Got to find myself a brand new baby / You're
my peace of mind / Me and rock 'n' roll / I'm losing
you / I miss you / My girl / World of darkness / Blood
donors needed.
■ LP . . . . . . . . . . . . . . . . . . .STML 12079
Motown / May '78.

**DISCOVER ME.**
Tracks: Discover me / Smiling faces sometimes.
■ 7″ . . . . . . . . . . . . . . . . . . . .TMG 1036
Tamla Motown / Aug '76.

**FEELIN' GOOD.**
Tracks: Loving you / Put a little love in your heart /
I'm so glad I fell for you / Feelin' alright / I could
never be President / I pray everyday you won't
regret loving me / What you gave me / One more
hurt / I let love slip away / I don't know why I love
you / Forgotten man / Letter.
■ LP . . . . . . . . . . . . . . . . . . .STML 11139
Tamla Motown / Apr '70.

**I CAN'T STOP THE RAIN.**
Tracks: I can't stop the rain / My whole world ended.
■ 7″ . . . . . . . . . . . . . . . . . . . .TMG 1078
Motown / Jul '77.

**MY WHOLE WORLD ENDED.**
Tracks: My whole world ended / Pieces of a man /
Somebody stole my dream / I've lost everything I've
ever loved / Everlasting love / I've got to find myself
a brand new baby / Double cross / Message from
Maria / World of darkness / We'll have a good thing
going on / My love is growing stronger / Flower
child.
■ LP . . . . . . . . . . . . . . . . . . .STML 11118
Tamla Motown / Sep '69.

**TAKE ME CLEAR FROM HERE.**
Tracks: Take me clear from here / Blood donors
needed.
■ 7″ . . . . . . . . . . . . . . . . . . . . TMG 936
Tamla Motown / Jan '75.

**WALK AWAY FROM LOVE.**
Tracks: Walk away from love / I'll say forever my
love.
■ 7″ . . . . . . . . . . . . . . . . . . . .TMG 1017
Tamla Motown / Nov '75.
■ 7″ . . . . . . . . . . . . . . . . . . . ZB 41927
Motown / Apr '88.

## Ruffin, Jimmy

**20 GOLDEN CLASSICS: JIMMY RUFFIN.**
Tracks: What becomes of the broken hearted / Don't
you miss me a little bit baby / As long as there is
love love / I'll stay forever my love / Baby I've got it /
I've passed this way before / Sad and lonesome
feeling / Don't let him take your love from me / World
so wild / Nowhere to hide (from your heart) / This
guy's in love with you / Gonna give her all the love
I've got / Let's say goodbye tomorrow / Farewell
is a lonely sound / Living in a world I created for
myself / On the way out (on the way in) / Maria (you
were the only one) / Stand by me / Halfway to
paradise.
■ LP . . . . . . . . . . . . . . . . . . . STMR 9012
■ MC . . . . . . . . . . . . . . . . . . .CSTMR 9012
Motown / Oct '81.

**DON'T YOU MISS ME A LITTLE BIT
BABY.**
Tracks: Don't you miss me a little bit baby / I want
her love.
7″ . . . . . . . . . . . . . . . . . . . . . TMG 617
Tamla Motown / Aug '67 / PolyGram.

**EASY JUST TO SAY (I LOVE YOU).**
Tracks: Easy to say I love you / You never have time
(for me) / Easy just to say (I love you) / Easy just to
say (I love you) (Ext. club mix) / Easy just to say (I
love you) (Eeesay mix).
■ 7″ . . . . . . . . . . . . . . . . . . . . POSP 869
■ 12″ . . . . . . . . . . . . . . . . . . . POSPX 869
Polydor / Jun '87.

**FAREWELL IS A LONELY SOUND.**
Tracks: Farewell is a lonely sound.
■ 7″ . . . . . . . . . . . . . . . . . . . . TMG 726
Tamla Motown / Feb '70.
■ 7″ . . . . . . . . . . . . . . . . . . . . TMG 922
Tamla Motown / Oct '74.

**FOREVER.**
Tracks: Farewell is a lonely sound / Raindrops keep
falling on my head / Our favourite melody / Maria
you were the only one / Living in a world I created
for myself / Let's say goodbye tomorrow / This guy's
in love with you / I'll stay forever my love / Take a
letter Maria / Honey come back / That's me loving

you / You gave me love / If you will let me I know I
can / Don't take away my rose-coloured glasses.
■ LP . . . . . . . . . . . . . . . . . . .STML 11161
Tamla Motown / Oct '70.

**GONNA GIVE HER ALL THE LOVE I'VE
GOT.**
Tracks: Gonna give her all the love I've got / I've
passed this way before.
■ 7″ . . . . . . . . . . . . . . . . . . . . TMG 996
Tamla Motown / Nov '75.

**GONNA GIVE HER ALL THE LOVE I'VE
GOT.**
Tracks: Gonna give her all the love I've got / World
so wide.
■ 7″ . . . . . . . . . . . . . . . . . . . . TMG 603
Tamla Motown / Apr '67.

**GREATEST HITS: JIMMY RUFFIN.**
Tracks: Not Advised.
■ LP . . . . . . . . . . . . . . . . . . .STML 11259
Tamla Motown / Jun '74.

**GREATEST MOTOWN HITS.**
Tracks: What becomes of the broken hearted / Baby
I've got it / I've passed this way before / Gonna give
her all the love I've got / World so wide, nowhere to
hide / Don't you miss me a little bit baby / Everybody
needs love / It's wonderful (to be loved by you) /
Gonna keep on tryin' till I win your love / This guy's
in love with you / Farewell is a lonely sound / Stand
by me / As long as there is l-o-v-e love / Sad and
lonesome feeling / I'll say forever my love / Don't let
him take your love from me / Maria (you were the
only one) / Living in a world I created for myself /
Let's say goodbye tomorrow / He ain't heavy, he's
my brother.
■ CD . . . . . . . . . . . . . . . . . . . WD 72654
■ LP . . . . . . . . . . . . . . . . . . . WL 72654
■ MC . . . . . . . . . . . . . . . . . . . WK 72654
Motown / Aug '89.
CD. . . . . . . . . . . . . . . . . . . . .530057-2
MC. . . . . . . . . . . . . . . . . . . . .530057-4
Motown / Jan '93 / PolyGram.

**HOLD ON TO MY LOVE.**
Tracks: Hold on to my love / Hold on to my love (part
2).
■ 7″ . . . . . . . . . . . . . . . . . . . . . RSO 57
RSO / May '80.

**I'LL SAY FOREVER MY LOVE.**
Tracks: I'll say forever my love / It's wonderful.
■ 7″ . . . . . . . . . . . . . . . . . . . . TMG 740
Tamla Motown / Jul '70.
■ 7″ . . . . . . . . . . . . . . . . . . . . TMG 961
Tamla Motown / Mar '75.

**I'M GONNA LIVE FOREVER.**
Tracks: I'm gonna live forever / I'm gonna live forever (version).
■ 12″ . . . . . . . . . . . . . . . . . . . ERCL 109
■ 7″ . . . . . . . . . . . . . . . . . . . . .ERC 109
ERC / Feb '84.

**I'M GONNA LOVE YOU FOREVER (Ruf-
fin, Jimmy & Jackson Moore).**
Tracks: I'm gonna love you forever.
■ 12″ . . . . . . . . . . . . . . . . . . . ERCRL 109
■ 7″ . . . . . . . . . . . . . . . . . . . . ERCR 109
ERC / Jun '84.

**I'VE PASSED THIS WAY BEFORE.**
Tracks: I've passed this way before / Tomorrow's
tears.
■ 7″ . . . . . . . . . . . . . . . . . . . . TMG 593
Tamla Motown / Feb '67.
■ 7″ . . . . . . . . . . . . . . . . . . . . TMG 703
Tamla Motown / Aug '69.
■ 7″ . . . . . . . . . . . . . . . . . . . . TMG 934
Tamla Motown / Jan '75.

**IT'S WONDERFUL.**
Tracks: It's wonderful.
■ 7″ . . . . . . . . . . . . . . . . . . . . TMG 753
Tamla Motown / Oct '70.

**JIMMY RUFFIN.**
Tracks: What becomes of the broken hearted / It's
wonderful to be loved by you / Farewell is a lonely
sound / I'll say forever my love.
■ MC Single. . . . . . . . . . . . . . CTME 2025
Motown / May '83.

**JIMMY RUFFIN WAY.**
Tracks: Not Advised.
■ LP . . . . . . . . . . . . . . . . . . .STML 11048
Tamla Motown / May '67.

**NIGHT OF LOVE.**
Tracks: Night of love / Songbird.
■ 7″ . . . . . . . . . . . . . . . . . . . .2090 459
RSO / Jun '80.

## RUFF 'N' READY.
Tracks: Don't let him take your love from me / Don't you miss me a little bit baby / Gonna keep on tryin' till I win your love / Farewell is a lonely sound / Everybody needs love / 96 tears / It's wonderful / Sad and lonesome feeling / Love gives, love takes away / I'll say forever my love / You got what it takes / Lonely lonely man am I.
■ LP . . . . . . . . . . . . . . . . . .STML 11106
Tamla Motown / May '69.

## RUFFIN & KENDRICKS (Ruffin & Kendricks).
Tracks: I couldn't believe it / Ordinary girl / One more for the lonely hearts club / Whatever you got / Don't know why you're dreaming / Family affair / One last kiss / You only get what you put out / Goodnight pillow.
■ CD . . . . . . . . . . . . . . . . . PD 86765
■ MC . . . . . . . . . . . . . . . . . PK 86765
■ LP . . . . . . . . . . . . . . . . . PL 86765
RCA / Feb '88.

## SON OF A PREACHER MAN.
Tracks: Not Advised.
CD. . . . . . . . . . . . . . . . . . .550 4092
MC. . . . . . . . . . . . . . . . . . .550 4094
Spectrum (1) / Aug '94 / PolyGram.

## SUNRISE.
Tracks: Hold on / Forever / Night of love / Searchin' / Changin' me / Where do I go / Two people / Jealousy / Songbird.
■ LP . . . . . . . . . . . . . . . . . .2394 258
RSO / Aug '80.

## TELL ME WHAT YOU WANT.
Tracks: Tell me what you want.
■ 7" . . . . . . . . . . . . . . . . . .2058 433
Polydor / Nov '74.

## THAT'S WHEN MY LOVING BEGINS.
Tracks: That's when my loving begins / Don't stop.
■ 12" . . . . . . . . . . . . . . . .12EMI 4424
■ 7" . . . . . . . . . . . . . . . . . EMI 4424
EMI / Jul '85.

## THERE WILL NEVER BE ANOTHER YOU.
Tracks: There will never be another you / Backstabbers.
■ 12" . . . . . . . . . . . . . . . .12EMI 5514
■ 7" . . . . . . . . . . . . . . . . . EMI 5541
EMI / Jan '85.

## WHAT BECOMES OF THE BROKENHEARTED.
Tracks: What becomes of the broken hearted.
■ 7" . . . . . . . . . . . . . . . . . TMG 577
Tamla Motown / Oct '66.
■ 7" . . . . . . . . . . . . . . . . . TMG 911
Tamla Motown / Jul '74.
■ 7" . . . . . . . . . . . . . . . . .TMG 1052
Tamla Motown / Sep '76.

## YOUNG HEART.
Tracks: Young heart / Hold on to my love.
■ 12" . . . . . . . . . . . . . . . . .ERCL 117
■ 7" . . . . . . . . . . . . . . . . . .ERC 117
ERC / Mar '85.

# Rufus

Having evolved from Paulette Williams-fronted American Breed into Rufus, featuring Chaka Khan, this Chicago-based octet struggled as an under-achieving funk-rock act. Then a specially-written Stevie Wonder song, Tell Me Something Good, established them on the R&B and pop charts and their album Rags To Rufus went gold. Later the same year ('74), three hits - Once You Get Started, Please Pardon Me and a cover of Bobby Womack's Stop On By - transformed Rufusized into a number one album and made Al Ciner, Andre Fisher, Kevin Murphy, Bobby Watson, Hawk Wolinski and David Williams, plus later members Tony Maiden and John Robinson, into sought-after session players. Impressed by Khan's extraordinary voice, many saw the band merely as her back-up, and albums the group made after she went solo were underwhelming. But the live double Stompin' At The Savoy proved their compositional and instrumental credentials; Wolinski wrote the hit Ain't Nobody before embarking on a successful production career. Robinson and Watson, meanwhile, played on Michael Jackson's Off The Wall as part of a fruitful relationship with Quincy Jones.

## AIN'T NOBODY LIKE YOU.
Tracks: Ain't nobody like you.
■ 12" . . . . . . . . . . . . . . . . . ABCT 4250
ABC Records / Mar '79.

## ANY LOVE (Rufus & Chaka Khan).
Tracks: Any love / What am I missing.
■ 12" . . . . . . . . . . . . . . . . .MCAT 575
■ 7" . . . . . . . . . . . . . . . . . MCA 575
MCA / Mar '80.

## ASK RUFUS.
Tracks: At midnight (my love will lift you up) / Close the door / Slow screw against the wall / A-flat fry / Earth song / Everlasting love / Hollywood / Magic in your eyes / Better days / Eygptian song.
■ LP . . . . . . . . . . . . . . . . . ABCL 5203
ABC Records / Mar '77.
CD . . . . . . . . . . . . . . . . MCAD 10449
MCA / '88 / BMG.

## AT MIDNIGHT.
Tracks: At midnight / Better days.
■ 7" . . . . . . . . . . . . . . . . . ABC 4165
ABC Records / Feb '77.

## BLUE LOVE.
Tracks: Blue love / Take time.
■ 7" . . . . . . . . . . . . . . . . . ABC 4209
ABC Records / Apr '78.

## DO YOU LOVE WHAT YOU FEEL (Rufus & Chaka Khan).
Tracks: Do you love what you feel / Dancin' mood.
■ 12" . . . . . . . . . . . . . . . . .MCAT 892
■ 7" . . . . . . . . . . . . . . . . . MCA 892
MCA / Jun '84.

## MASTERJAM (Rufus & Chaka Khan).
Tracks: Do you love what you feel.
■ LP . . . . . . . . . . . . . . . . . .MCG 4007
MCA / Jan '80.

## NUMBERS.
Tracks: Not Advised.
■ LP . . . . . . . . . . . . . . . . . ABCL 5263
ABC Records / Apr '79.

## ONE MILLION KISSES (Rufus & Chaka Khan).
Tracks: One million kisses / Any old Sunday / Do you love what you feel.
■ 12" . . . . . . . . . . . . . . . . . W 9244 T
■ 7" . . . . . . . . . . . . . . . . . W 9244
WEA / Jun '84.

## PARTY TIL YOU'RE BROKE.
Tracks: Not Advised.
■ LP . . . . . . . . . . . . . . . . . MCF 3108
MCA / May '81.

## RAGS TO RUFUS.
Tracks: Not Advised.
■ CD . . . . . . . . . . . . . . . DMCL 1909
MCA / Aug '90.
■ CD . . . . . . . . . . . . . . . MCLD 19135
■ MC . . . . . . . . . . . . . . . MCLC 19135
MCA / Dec '92.

## RUFUSIZED.
Tracks: Not Advised.
■ LP . . . . . . . . . . . . . . . . . ABCL 5063
ABC Records / Apr '75.

## STOMPIN' AT THE SAVOY (Rufus & Chaka Khan).
Tracks: Not Advised.
■ Double LP . . . . . . . . . . . . . .923679 1
■ MC . . . . . . . . . . . . . . . . .923679 4
WEA / Sep '83.

## STOP ON BY.
Tracks: Stop on by / Rufusized.
■ 7" . . . . . . . . . . . . . . . . . ABC 4038
Anchor (1) / Feb '75.

## STREET PLAYER.
Tracks: Destiny / Stranger to love / Stay / Bets of your heart / Finale / Take time / Blue love / Turn / Change your ways.
■ LP . . . . . . . . . . . . . . . . . ABCL 5239
ABC Records / Apr '78.

## TAKE IT TO THE TOP.
Tracks: Take it to the top / Distant lover.
■ 12" . . . . . . . . . . . . . . . . . W 9790 T
■ 7" . . . . . . . . . . . . . . . . . W 9790
WEA / Mar '83.

## TONIGHT WE LOVE.
Tracks: Tonight we love / Party til' you're broke.
■ 12" . . . . . . . . . . . . . . . . .MCAT 690

■ 7" . . . . . . . . . . . . . . . . . MCA 690
MCA / Mar '81.

# Rumblers

## SOULFUL JERK.
Tracks: Soulful jerk.
■ 7" . . . . . . . . . . . . . . . . . .KG 1021
King (2) / '65.

# Rush Hour

## CUSTOM MADE LOVE.
Tracks: Custom made love.
■ 12" . . . . . . . . . . . . . . . . . RH 1010
Star Gaze (USA) / Nov '87.

## DEDICATION.
Tracks: Dedication / Stay a while.
■ 7" . . . . . . . . . . . . . . . . . ANC 1056
Anchor (1) / '78.

# Rushen, Patrice

L.A. born child prodigy, Rushen swapped classical for jazz on entering teenage in late '60s. She recorded three albums for Prestige label, last of which - Shout It Out - took first steps into dance. Mid-'70s found her on albums by likes of Lee Ritenour, Blackbyrds and Minnie Riperton, before she re-established solo career in 1978. Chart hits commenced with second album for Elektra, Pizzazz, and peaked with Straight From The Heart in '82; from which Forget Me Nots made U.K. Top 10. Much of her subsequent work was in jazz field, although she toured with Soul II Soul and her Haven't You Heard provided hook for Zhane's '94 hit Groove Thang.

## DON'T BLAME ME.
Tracks: Don't blame me / Time will tell.
■ 12" . . . . . . . . . . . . . . . . . K 12542T
■ 7" . . . . . . . . . . . . . . . . . K 12542
Elektra / Jun '81.

## FEELS SO REAL (WON'T LET GO).
Tracks: Feel so real (won't let go) / Feel so real (won't let go) (version).
■ 12" . . . . . . . . . . . . . . . . .E 9742 T
■ 7" . . . . . . . . . . . . . . . . . E 9742
Elektra / Jun '84.

## FORGET ME NOT.
Tracks: Forget me not / Havent you heard.
■ 12" . . . . . . . . . . . . . . . . . K 13173T
■ 7" . . . . . . . . . . . . . . . . . K 13173
Elektra / Apr '82.

## FORGET ME NOT'S (OLD GOLD).
Tracks: Forget me not's / Haven't you heard.
12" . . . . . . . . . . . . . . . . .OG 4216
Old Gold / '92 / Pickwick.

## GET OFF.
Tracks: Get off / Remind me.
■ 12" . . . . . . . . . . . . . . . . . E 970 T
■ 7" . . . . . . . . . . . . . . . . . E 9702
Elektra / Sep '84.

## HANG IT UP.
Tracks: Hang it up / Just a natural thing.
■ 7" . . . . . . . . . . . . . . . . . K 12336
Elektra / Feb '79.

## HAVEN'T YOU HEARD.
Tracks: Haven't you heard / Keepin' faith in love.
■ 7" . . . . . . . . . . . . . . . . . K 12414
Elektra / Mar '80.

## I WAS TIRED OF BEING ALONE.
Tracks: I was tired of being alone / Number one.
■ 12" . . . . . . . . . . . . . . . . . K 13184T
■ 7" . . . . . . . . . . . . . . . . . K 13184
Elektra / Jun '82.

## LET THERE BE FUNK.
Tracks: Let your heart be free / Let there be funk / What's the story / Shout it out / Yolon / Traverse / Hump / Roll with the punches / Steppin' stones / Sojourn.
■ LP . . . . . . . . . . . . . . . . PR 10110
Prestige / Oct '80.

## LOOK UP.
Tracks: Look up / Dream.
■ 12" . . . . . . . . . . . . . . . . . K 12506T
■ 7" . . . . . . . . . . . . . . . . . K 12506
Elektra / Apr '81.

## MUSIC OF THE EARTH.
**Tracks:** Music of the earth / When I found you / Changes / Wishful thinking / Let's sing a song of love / Hang it up / Cha cha / It's just a natural thing / Didn't you know / Play.
■ **LP** . . . . . . . . . . . . . . . . . **K 52104**
Elektra / Mar '79.

## NEVER GONNA GIVE YOU UP.
**Tracks:** Never gonna give you up / Don't blame me.
■ **12″** . . . . . . . . . . . . . . . . **K 12494T**
■ **7″** . . . . . . . . . . . . . . . . . **K 12494**
Elektra / Nov '80.

## NOW.
**Tracks:** Not Advised.
**MC.** . . . . . . . . . . . . . . . . . **9603604**
■ **LP** . . . . . . . . . . . . . . . . . **9603601**
Elektra / Jul '84 / WEA.

## POSH.
**Tracks:** Never gonna give you up / Don't blame me / Look up / I need your love / Time will tell / Dream / Funk won't let you know / This is all I really know.
■ **LP** . . . . . . . . . . . . . . . . . **6E 302**
Elektra / Jan '81.

## SHOUT IT OUT.
**Tracks:** Hump / Shout it out / Stepping stones / Let your heart be free / Roll with the punches / Let there be funk / Yolon / Sojourn.
■ **LP** . . . . . . . . . . . . . . . . **PR 10101**
Prestige / '79.

## STRAIGHT FROM THE HEART.
**Tracks:** Forget me nots / I was tired of being alone / All we need / Number one / Where there is love / Breakout / If only / Remind me / She will take you down to love.
■ **LP** . . . . . . . . . . . . . . . . . **K 52532**
Elektra / May '82.

## WATCH OUT (OBSERVATION MIX).
**Tracks:** Watch out (observation mix) / Watch out (ext mix) / Over the phone.
■ **12″** . . . . . . . . . . . . . . . . **RIST 12R**
Arista / Apr '87.

## WATCH OUT!.
**Tracks:** Watch out / Breakin' all the rules / Long time coming / All my love / Somewhere / Anything can happen / Burnin' / Till she's out of your mind / Come back to me / Tender lovin'.
■ **CD** . . . . . . . . . . . . . . . . . **257831**
■ **LP** . . . . . . . . . . . . . . . . . **207831**
■ **MC.** . . . . . . . . . . . . . . . . **407831**
Arista / Jan '87.

## Russ, Eddie

### FRESH OUT.
**Tracks:** Lope song / All but blind / Shamanding / Hill where the lord lies / You are the sunshine of my life / Watergate blues.
■ **LP** . . . . . . . . . . . . . . . . **SJC 0004**
Soul Jazz / Nov '92.

## LOPE SONG, THE.
**Tracks:** Lope song.
■ **12″** . . . . . . . . . . . . . . . . **SJC 0002**
Soul Jazz / Feb '92.

## Russell, Brenda

### BRENDA RUSSELL.
**Tracks:** So good so right / In the thick of it / If only for one night / Way back when / Little bit of love / You're free / Think it over / God bless you.
■ **LP** . . . . . . . . . . . . . . . . **AMLJ 739**
A&M / Nov '79.
■ **LP** . . . . . . . . . . . . . . . . **AMA 3174**
■ **CD** . . . . . . . . . . . . . . . . **CDA 3174**
■ **MC.** . . . . . . . . . . . . . . . . **AMC 3174**
A&M / Mar '88.

### GET HERE.
**Tracks:** Gravity / Just a believer / Piano in the dark / This time I need you / Make my day / Le restaurant / Midnight eyes / Get here.
**MC.** . . . . . . . . . . . . . . . . **AMC 5178**
■ **LP** . . . . . . . . . . . . . . . . **AMA 5178**
■ **CD** . . . . . . . . . . . . . . . . **CDA 5178**
Breakout / Feb '88.

### GET HERE.
**Tracks:** Get here / Le restaurant / Little bit of love (Only on 12″) / So good, so right (Only on 12″).
■ **12″** . . . . . . . . . . . . . . . . **USAT 647**
■ **7″** . . . . . . . . . . . . . . . . . **USA 647**
Breakout / Sep '88.

### GRAVITY.
**Tracks:** Gravity / If only for one night.
■ **12″** . . . . . . . . . . . . . . . . **USAT 630**
■ **7″** . . . . . . . . . . . . . . . . . **USA 630**
■ **CD Single** . . . . . . . . . . . . **USACD 630**
Breakout / Jun '88.

### GREATEST HITS.
**Tracks:** Piano in the dark / So good so right / Gravity / Kiss me with the wind / Get here / Dinner with Gershwin / Stop running away / In the thick of it / If only for one night / Way back when / Justice in truth / Le restaurant.
**CD** . . . . . . . . . . . . . . . . **CDMID 171**
**MC.** . . . . . . . . . . . . . . . . **CMID 171**
A&M / Oct '92 / PolyGram.

### KISS ME WITH THE WIND.
**Tracks:** Kiss me with the wind / All American / Waiting for you / Dinner with Gershwin / Night train to Leningrad / On your side / Stupid love / Stop running away / Justice in truth / Good for love / Drive my car ('til sunset).
**CD** . . . . . . . . . . . . . . . . **3952712**
■ **LP** . . . . . . . . . . . . . . . . **3952711**
■ **MC.** . . . . . . . . . . . . . . . . **3952714**
A&M / Jul '90 / PolyGram.

### KISS ME WITH THE WIND.
**Tracks:** Kiss me with the wind.
■ **12″** . . . . . . . . . . . . . . . . **AMY 578**
■ **7″** . . . . . . . . . . . . . . . . . **AM 578**
■ **CD Single** . . . . . . . . . . . . **AMCD 578**

■ **MC Single** . . . . . . . . . . . . **AMMC 578**
A&M / Aug '90.

## PIANO IN THE DARK.
**Tracks:** Piano in the dark / In the thick of it.
■ **12″** . . . . . . . . . . . . . . . . **USAT 623**
■ **7″** . . . . . . . . . . . . . . . . . **USA 623**
Breakout / Feb '88.
■ **CD Single** . . . . . . . . . . . . **USACD 623**
Breakout / Feb '88.

## SO GOOD SO RIGHT.
**Tracks:** So good so right / In the thick of it.
■ **7″** . . . . . . . . . . . . . . . . . **AMS 7515**
A&M / Apr '80.

## SOUL TALKIN'.
**Tracks:** Matters of the heart / Soul talkin' / In over my heart / No time for time / You'll fall in love again / 10,000 Words / Life is waiting / Got to love / Universe is calling you / Who are you.
■ **CD** . . . . . . . . . . . . . . **CDMTL 1076**
■ **MC** . . . . . . . . . . . . . . **TCMTL 1076**
EMI-America / Jul '93.

## SUPERSONIC LOVER (Russell, Brenda & Brian).
**Tracks:** Life could be so grand / That's alright too / You show me your love / Don't let love go / Love and loser / Supersonic lover / Beautiful lie / Who loves you / Think about you / Love is better kept.
■ **LP** . . . . . . . . . . . . . . . . **ROLL 13**
Rocket / Dec '77.

## THAT'S ALL RIGHT TOO (Russell, Brenda & Brian).
**Tracks:** That's all right too / Who loves you.
■ **7″** . . . . . . . . . . . . . . . . . **ROKN 535**
Rocket / Jan '78.

## TWO EYES.
**Tracks:** Two eyes / Stay close.
■ **7″** . . . . . . . . . . . . . . . . . **W 9557**
WEA / Jul '83.

## Russell, Leigh

### HEAD FULL OF DREAMS.
**Tracks:** Head full of dreams (Mixes) / Head full of vibes / Bad love (Mixes) / Bad groove.
**12″** . . . . . . . . . . . . . . . . **VIBE 009**
Phat Vibes / Jul '94 / Vital Distribution.

## Ryan, Roz

### BOY WHERE HAVE YOU BEEN?.
**Tracks:** Boy where have you been / Waiting for my lover.
■ **12″** . . . . . . . . . . . . . . . . **MKHAN 8**
Streetwave / Mar '84.

■ **DELETED**

# S

## S.O.S. Band

### 12" TAPE: S.O.S. BAND.
**Tracks:** Just be good to me / Just the way you like it / Weekend girl / Finest / Borrowed Love..
■ MC. . . . . . . . . . . . . . . . . . . . . . . . 4501324
Tabu / Sep '86.

### BORROWED LOVE.
**Tracks:** Borrowed Love / Do you still want to.
■ 12" . . . . . . . . . . . . . . . . . . . . . . TA 7241
■ 7" . . . . . . . . . . . . . . . . . . . . . . A 7241
Tabu / Jun '86.

### BREAK UP.
**Tracks:** Break up / Body break.
■ 12" . . . . . . . . . . . . . . . . . . . . . . TA 6427
■ 7" . . . . . . . . . . . . . . . . . . . . . . A 6427
Tabu / Jul '85.

### DIAMOND IN THE RAW.
**Tracks:** Not Advised.
CD. . . . . . . . . . . . . . . . . . . . . . . . 4607352
■ LP . . . . . . . . . . . . . . . . . . . . . . 4607351
■ MC. . . . . . . . . . . . . . . . . . . . . . 4607354
Epic / Nov '89 / Sony.

### EVEN WHEN YOU SLEEP.
**Tracks:** Even when you sleep.
■ 12" . . . . . . . . . . . . . . . . . . . . . 650128 6
Tabu / Nov '86.

### FINEST, THE.
**Tracks:** Finest / I don't want nobody else.
■ 12" . . . . . . . . . . . . . . . . . . . . . TA 6997
■ 7" . . . . . . . . . . . . . . . . . . . . . . A 6997
Tabu / Mar '86.

### FINEST, THE (OLD GOLD).
**Tracks:** Finest / Just the way you like it.
12" . . . . . . . . . . . . . . . . . . . . . . . OG 4148
Old Gold / Jan '90 / Pickwick.

### GROOVIN'.
**Tracks:** Groovin' / Take your time.
■ 12" . . . . . . . . . . . . . . . . . . . TBUA 133120
■ 7" . . . . . . . . . . . . . . . . . . . . TBUA 3120
Tabu / Feb '83.

### HIGH HOPES.
**Tracks:** High hopes / Good and plenty.
■ 12" . . . . . . . . . . . . . . . . . . TBU A132936
■ 7" . . . . . . . . . . . . . . . . . . . TBU A2936
Tabu / Nov '82.

### HIT MIXES, THE.
**Tracks:** Just be good to me (vocal remix) / Borrowed love (extended version) / Just the way you like it (long version) / Finest, The (extended version) / No lies (special version) / No lies (dub mix) / Take your time (do it right).
CD. . . . . . . . . . . . . . . . . . . . . . .460189 2
■ LP . . . . . . . . . . . . . . . . . . . . . 460597 1
MC. . . . . . . . . . . . . . . . . . . . . . 460597 4
Tabu / Nov '87 / Sony.

### JUST BE GOOD TO ME.
**Tracks:** Just be good to me.
■ 12" . . . . . . . . . . . . . . . . . . . . . TA 3626
■ 7" . . . . . . . . . . . . . . . . . . . . . . A 3626
Tabu / Apr '84.

### JUST THE WAY YOU LIKE IT.
**Tracks:** No one's gonna love you / Weekend girl / Just the way you like it / Breakup / Feeling / I don't want nobody else / Body break.
■ LP . . . . . . . . . . . . . . . . . . . . TBU 26058
■ MC. . . . . . . . . . . . . . . . . . . . .40 26058
Tabu / Aug '84.
■ CD . . . . . . . . . . . . . . . . . . . . . 467 016 2
■ LP . . . . . . . . . . . . . . . . . . . . . 467 016 1
■ MC. . . . . . . . . . . . . . . . . . . . . 467 016 4
Tabu / Aug '90.

### JUST THE WAY YOU LIKE IT.
**Tracks:** Just the way you like it.
■ 12" . . . . . . . . . . . . . . . . . . . . . TA 4621
■ 7" . . . . . . . . . . . . . . . . . . . . . . A 4621
Tabu / Aug '84.
■ 7" Set . . . . . . . . . . . . . . . . . . . . DA 4621
Tabu / Sep '84.

### NO LIES.
**Tracks:** No lies / Even when you sleep.
■ 7" . . . . . . . . . . . . . . . . . . . . .650444 7
Tabu / Mar '87.

### ON THE RISE.
**Tracks:** Tell me if you still care / Just be good to me / For your love / I'm not runnin' / If you want my love / On the rise / Who's making love / Steppin' the stones.
■ LP . . . . . . . . . . . . . . . . . . . . TBU 25476
Tabu / Oct '83.
■ CD . . . . . . . . . . . . . . . . . . . . . 4501652
■ LP . . . . . . . . . . . . . . . . . . . . . 4501651
■ MC. . . . . . . . . . . . . . . . . . . . . 4501654
Tabu / May '90.

### ONE OF MANY NIGHTS.
**Tracks:** I wanna be the one / Sometimes I wonder / Broken promises / How can we ever get back together / Are you ready / Can't explain / Someone I can love / Get hyped on this / I only want you / One of many nights.
CD. . . . . . . . . . . . . . . . . . . . . .364003 2
■ LP . . . . . . . . . . . . . . . . . . . . .364003 1
MC. . . . . . . . . . . . . . . . . . . . . .364003 4
A&M / Oct '91 / PolyGram.

### S.O.S.
**Tracks:** S.O.S. (Dit, dit, dit, dash, dash, dash, dit, dit, dit) / What's wrong with our love affair / Open letter / Love won't wait for love / Take your time (do it right) / I'm in love / Take love where you find it / S.O.S. (reprise).
■ LP . . . . . . . . . . . . . . . . . . . . TBU 84445
Tabu / Sep '80.
■ MC. . . . . . . . . . . . . . . . . . . . .40 32541
■ LP . . . . . . . . . . . . . . . . . . . . TBU 32541
Tabu / Nov '84.

### SANDS OF TIME.
**Tracks:** Even when you sleep / Sands of time / Borrowed love / Nothing but the best / Finest / No lies / Two time lover / Do you still want to / Sands of time (reprise).
■ LP . . . . . . . . . . . . . . . . . . . . TBU 26863
MC. . . . . . . . . . . . . . . . . . . . . .40 26863
Tabu / Apr '86 / Sony.
CD . . . . . . . . . . . . . . . . . . . . . CD 26863
CBS / Aug '86 / Sony.
■ CD . . . . . . . . . . . . . . . . . . . . .460946 2
■ LP . . . . . . . . . . . . . . . . . . . . .460946 1
■ MC. . . . . . . . . . . . . . . . . . . . .460946 4
Tabu / Nov '88.

### SOS BAND, THE.
**Tracks:** Can't get enough / High hopes / Have it your way / Your love / Good and plenty / Looking for you / These are the things / You shake me up / Groovin'.
■ LP . . . . . . . . . . . . . . . . . . . TBU 25078
Tabu / '83.

### TAKE YOUR TIME (DO IT RIGHT).
**Tracks:** Take your time (do it right) / Take your time (do it right) (part 2).
■ 7" . . . . . . . . . . . . . . . . . . . . . TBU 8564
Tabu / Jul '80.

### TELL ME YOU STILL CARE.
**Tracks:** Tell me you still care / If you want my love.
■ 12" . . . . . . . . . . . . . . . . . . . . . TA 3927
■ 7" . . . . . . . . . . . . . . . . . . . . . . A 3927
Tabu / Jun '84.

### WEEKEND GIRL.
**Tracks:** Weekend girl / For your love.
■ 12" . . . . . . . . . . . . . . . . . . . . . TA 4785
■ 7" . . . . . . . . . . . . . . . . . . . . . . A 4785
Tabu / Oct '84.

## S.O.U.L.

### CAN YOU FEEL IT.
**Tracks:** Tell it like it is / No what's never you want to do / Peace of mind / My cherie amour / Love, peace and power / To mend a broken heart / Sleeping beauty.
■ LP . . . . . . . . . . . . . . . . . . . . NSPL 28162
Pye / Jun '72.

### S.O.U.L. WHAT IS IT.
**Tracks:** Down in the ghetto / Get ready / Burning spear / Express yourself / Soul / Message from a black man / Memphis underground.
CD. . . . . . . . . . . . . . . . . . . . BGPCD 1087
BGP / May '94 / Pinnacle.

## S.W.V.

Teenage trio Cheryl 'Coko' Gamble, Leanne 'Lelee' Lyons and Tamara 'Taj' Johnson took baton from En Vogue to become leading New Jill Swingers. Brooklyn/Bronx-born, gospel-trained Sisters With Voices blew up storm with debut *I'm So Into You*: single sold half-a-million in U.S. and, re-mixed by Teddy Riley with added Wreckx-N-Effect, crashed U.K. Top 20. Group made U.S. chart history by placing this song and follow-up *Weak* in Top 10 simultaneously. Mid-'93 debut album *It's About Time* was further boosted by Riley remix of *Right Here*, which weaved in Michael Jackson's *Human Nature*. Yet another remix, *Anything*, kicked off 1994 *Above The Rim* soundtrack; single version boasted implausible but successful cameo by rap warriors Wu Tang Clan.

### ANYTHING.
**Tracks:** Anything (Mixes).
■ 12" . . . . . . . . . . . . . . . . . 7432121221-1
■ CD Single. . . . . . . . . . . . . . 7432121222-2
■ CD Single. . . . . . . . . . . . . . 7432121221-2
■ MC Single. . . . . . . . . . . . . . 7432121221-4
Arista / May '94.

### DOWNTOWN.
**Tracks:** Downtown (Mixes).
■ 12" . . . . . . . . . . . . . . . . . 7432118901-1
■ CD Single. . . . . . . . . . . . . . 7432118901-2
■ MC Single. . . . . . . . . . . . . . 7432118901-4
Arista / Feb '94.

### I'M SO INTO YOU.
**Tracks:** Not Advised.
■ 7" . . . . . . . . . . . . . . . . . . 7432114497-7
■ CD Single. . . . . . . . . . . . . . 7432114497-2
■ MC Single. . . . . . . . . . . . . . 7432114497-4
Arista / Dec '92.

### IT'S ABOUT TIME.
**Tracks:** Anything / I'm so into you / Right here / Weak / You're always on my mind / Downtown / Coming home / Give it to me / Black pudd'n / It's about time / Think you're gonna like it / That's what I need / SWV (in the house) / Weak (A cappella) (Not available on LP) / Right here (Vibe mix).
LP . . . . . . . . . . . . . . . . . . .7863 660741
■ CD . . . . . . . . . . . . . . . . . .7863 660742
■ MC. . . . . . . . . . . . . . . . . .7863 660744
RCA / Jul '93 / BMG.

### REMIXES, THE.
**Tracks:** Not Advised.
CD. . . . . . . . . . . . . . . . . . . 7863 66401-2
LP . . . . . . . . . . . . . . . . . . . 7863 66401-1
MC. . . . . . . . . . . . . . . . . . . 7863 66401-4
Arista / Jun '94 / BMG.

### RIGHT HERE.
**Tracks:** Right here.
■ 12" . . . . . . . . . . . . . . . . . .74321 16048-1
■ 7" . . . . . . . . . . . . . . . . . . .74321 16048-7
■ CD Single . . . . . . . . . . . . . .74321 16048-2
■ MC Single. . . . . . . . . . . . . . 74321 16048-4
RCA / Aug '93.

### WEAK.
**Tracks:** Weak / SWV (in the house) / I'm so into you / Weak (mixes).
■ 12" . . . . . . . . . . . . . . . . . .74321 153351
■ 7" . . . . . . . . . . . . . . . . . . 74321 153357
■ CD Single . . . . . . . . . . . . . .74321 153352
■ MC Single. . . . . . . . . . . . . . 74321 153354
Arista / Jun '93.

## Saatchi, Phil

### LITTLE IN LOVE.
**Tracks:** Little in love / When we dream.
■ 12" . . . . . . . . . . . . . . . . . . . . . AMY 389
■ 7" . . . . . . . . . . . . . . . . . . . . . . AM 389
A&M / Apr '87.

■ DELETED

## POOR MAN'S PARADISE.
**Tracks:** Poor man's paradise / You should be mine / Cancel my subscriptions (Track on 12" only).
■ 7" . . . . . . . . . . . . . . . . . . . . . . . . . **AM 303**
A&M / Mar '86.

## STRIPPED.
**Tracks:** Little in love / When we dream / King of another country / Build a bridge / Love is a mission / No one gonna love you (like I do) / Wheel of fortune / Poor man's paradise / White flag / People of the New World.
■ CD . . . . . . . . . . . . . . . . . . . . . **CDA 5152**
■ LP . . . . . . . . . . . . . . . . . . . . . **AMA 5152**
■ MC. . . . . . . . . . . . . . . . . . . . . **AMC 5152**
A&M / Apr '87.

## THREE MIRACLES.
**Tracks:** Three miracles / Push a little harder.
■ 12" . . . . . . . . . . . . . . . . . . . . . **AMY 498**
■ 7" . . . . . . . . . . . . . . . . . . . . . . **AM 498**
A&M / Mar '89.

## TRAPPED.
**Tracks:** Not Advised.
■ CD . . . . . . . . . . . . . . . . . . . . . **2410892**
WEA / '88.

## WHEEL OF FORTUNE.
**Tracks:** Wheel of fortune / You should have warned me / White (This track is on the 12" version only).
■ 12" . . . . . . . . . . . . . . . . . . . . . **AMY 327**
■ 7" . . . . . . . . . . . . . . . . . . . . . . **AM 327**
A&M / Jan '87.

## Sabina

## USE WHAT YOU GOT.
**Tracks:** Use what you got.
■ 12" . . . . . . . . . . . . . . . . . . . . . **RBBT 002**
■ 7" . . . . . . . . . . . . . . . . . . . . . . **RBBS 002**
Punch Bag / Oct '89.

## Sadane, Mark

## EXCITING.
**Tracks:** Not Advised.
■ LP . . . . . . . . . . . . . . . . . . . . . **BSK 3675**
WEA / Nov '82.

## ONE MINUTE FROM LOVE.
**Tracks:** One minute from love.
■ 12" . . . . . . . . . . . . . . . . . . . . . **K 17961 T**
■ 7" . . . . . . . . . . . . . . . . . . . . . . **K 17961**
WEA / Oct '82.

## ONE WAY LOVE AFFAIR.
**Tracks:** One way love affair.
■ 12" . . . . . . . . . . . . . . . . . . . . . **K 17816 T**
■ 7" . . . . . . . . . . . . . . . . . . . . . . **K 17816**
WEA / Jun '81.

## ONE WAY LOVE AFFAIR.
**Tracks:** One way love affair / You're the one for me / Fool in me / Never gonna stop this heart of mine / Standing in the shadows of love / Sit up / Girl come on / Love can't wait / Midnight love dance / Make up your mind.
■ LP . . . . . . . . . . . . . . . . . . . . . **K 56895**
Warner Bros. / May '81.

## Sade

Born of a Nigerian father and British mother, Sade studied fashion and designed her own range of clothes before an opening as a background singer with local outfit, Pride offered a first step into music. Her unusually beautiful physical appearance and growing confidence as a songwriter soon led to her fronting her own band, comprising Stuart Matthewman, Andrew Hale and Paul Denman and tagged simply "Sade". Debuting on Epic in '84 with *Diamond Life*, Sade soon developed a reputation as Thatcher-era coffee-table fodder, an unfair accusation that pays little heed to the strength and subtlety of the band's music. In 10 years Sade have released only four albums, each better than its predecessor, culminating in the excellent *Love Deluxe* in '92. And while the press have chased Ms. Adu all over Europe in search of that elusive intro to her private life, the group's record sales - especially in America - have soared. With a greatest hits album released in October, don't expect a new record for at least 18 months.

## BEST OF SADE, THE.
**Tracks:** Your love is king / Hang on to your love / Smooth operator / Jezebel / Sweetest taboo / Is it a crime / Never as good as the first time / Love is stronger than pride / Paradise / Nothing can come between us / No ordinary love / Like a taboo / Kiss of life / Please send someone to love / Cherish the day / Pearls.
CD. . . . . . . . . . . . . . . . . . . . .477793-2
LP. . . . . . . . . . . . . . . . . . . . .477793-1
MC. . . . . . . . . . . . . . . . . . . . .477793-4
MiniDisc. . . . . . . . . . . . . . . . .477793-8
Epic / Oct '94 / Sony.

## CHERISH THE DAY.
**Tracks:** Cherish the day / Cherish the day (mix).
■ 12" P.Disc. . . . . . . . . . . . . . . .659481 6
■ CD Single . . . . . . . . . . . . . . . .659481 2
■ MC Single . . . . . . . . . . . . . . . .659481 4
Epic / Jul '93.

## DIAMOND LIFE.
**Tracks:** Smooth operator / Your love is king / Hang on to your love / When am I gonna make a living / Frankie's first affair / Cherry pie / Sally / I will be your friend / Why can't we live together.
CD. . . . . . . . . . . . . . . . . . . . . CD 26044
MC. . . . . . . . . . . . . . . . . . . . . .40 26044
■ LP . . . . . . . . . . . . . . . . . . . . EPC 26044
Epic / Jul '84 / Sony.
MiniDisc. . . . . . . . . . . . . . . . . .26044-3
Epic / Feb '93 / Sony.

## DIAMOND LIFE/PROMISE.
**Tracks:** Not Advised.
■ CD Set. . . . . . . . . . . . . . . . . .CDSD 241
CBS / '88.

## FEEL NO PAIN.
**Tracks:** Feel no pain / Love is stronger than pride (Mad Professor remix) / Feel no pain (mixes) (On CDs Cat No: 658829-5).
■ 7" . . . . . . . . . . . . . . . . . . . .658829-7
■ CD Single . . . . . . . . . . . . . . .658829-5
■ CD Single . . . . . . . . . . . . . . .658829-2
■ MC Single. . . . . . . . . . . . . . .658829-4
Epic / Nov '92.

## IS IT A CRIME.
**Tracks:** Is it a crime / Punch drunk.
■ 12" . . . . . . . . . . . . . . . . . . . . . TA 6742
■ 7" . . . . . . . . . . . . . . . . . . . . . . A 6742
Epic / Dec '85.

## KISS OF LIFE.
**Tracks:** Kiss of life / Room 55 / Kiss of life (Album version) (Available on CDS & 12" only).
■ 12" . . . . . . . . . . . . . . . . . . . .659254 6
■ 7" . . . . . . . . . . . . . . . . . . . . .659254 7
■ CD Single . . . . . . . . . . . . . . . .659254 2
Epic / Apr '93.

## LOVE DELUXE.
**Tracks:** No ordinary love / Feel no pain / I couldn't love you more / Like a tattoo / Kiss of life / Cherish the day / Pearls / Bulletproof soul / Mermaid.
CD. . . . . . . . . . . . . . . . . . . . . 4726262
■ LP . . . . . . . . . . . . . . . . . . . . 4726261
MC. . . . . . . . . . . . . . . . . . . . . 4726264
Epic / Oct '92 / Sony.
MiniDisc. . . . . . . . . . . . . . . . .472626-3
Epic / Feb '93 / Sony.

## LOVE IS STRONGER THAN PRIDE.
**Tracks:** Love is stronger than pride / Super bien total / Super bien total (extended mix).
■ 12" . . . . . . . . . . . . . . . . . . . . . SADE T1
■ 7" . . . . . . . . . . . . . . . . . . . . . SADE P1
■ 7" . . . . . . . . . . . . . . . . . . . . . . SADE 1
■ 7" . . . . . . . . . . . . . . . . . . . . SADE QT1
■ CD Single . . . . . . . . . . . . . . . CD SADE 1
Epic / Mar '88.

## NEVER AS GOOD AS THE FIRST TIME.
**Tracks:** Never as good as the first time.
■ 12" . . . . . . . . . . . . . . . . . . . . . TA 7061
■ 7" . . . . . . . . . . . . . . . . . . . . . . A 7061
Epic / Mar '86.

## NO ORDINARY LOVE.
**Tracks:** No ordinary love / Paradise / No ordinary love (album version) (On CD Single only).
■ 7" . . . . . . . . . . . . . . . . . . . .658356-7
■ CD Single . . . . . . . . . . . . . . .658356-2
■ MC Single. . . . . . . . . . . . . . .658356-4
Epic / Jun '93.

## NOTHING CAN COME BETWEEN US.
**Tracks:** Nothing can come between us / Make some room / You're not the man (CD only).
■ 12" . . . . . . . . . . . . . . . . . . . . . SADE T3
■ 7" . . . . . . . . . . . . . . . . . . . . . . SADE 3
■ CD Single . . . . . . . . . . . . . . . CDSADE 3
Epic / Aug '88.
■ 12" . . . . . . . . . . . . . . . . . . . . SADE QT3
Epic / Aug '88.

## PARADISE.
**Tracks:** Paradise (remix) (7") / Paradise (inst) (7" & CD single.) / Paradise (ext. remix) (12" & CD single. / Paradise (ext. inst.) (12".) / Paradise (extra beats (12".) / Hang on to your love (U.S. remix) (CD single. / Keep hanging on (live) (CD single.).
■ 12" . . . . . . . . . . . . . . . . . . . . . SADE QT2
■ 12" . . . . . . . . . . . . . . . . . . . . . SADE T2
■ 7" . . . . . . . . . . . . . . . . . . . . . . SADE 2
■ CD Single . . . . . . . . . . . . . . . . .6516172
Epic / May '88.

## PROMISE.
**Tracks:** Is it a crime / Sweetest taboo / War of the hearts / Jezebel / Mr. Wrong / Never as good as the first time / Fear / Tar baby / Maureen / You're not the man (Track on cassette only) / Punch drunk (Or cassette only).
■ LP . . . . . . . . . . . . . . . . . . . . EPC 86318
MC. . . . . . . . . . . . . . . . . . . . . .40 86318
Epic / Nov '85 / Sony.
CD. . . . . . . . . . . . . . . . . . . . . CD 86318
Epic / Jan '86 / Sony.
CD. . . . . . . . . . . . . . . . . . . . . 4655752
MC. . . . . . . . . . . . . . . . . . . . . 4655754
■ LP . . . . . . . . . . . . . . . . . . . . 4655751
Epic / Mar '90 / Sony.
MiniDisc. . . . . . . . . . . . . . . . . MD 86318
Epic / Apr '93 / Sony.

## SADE - LIVE.
**Tracks:** Not Advised.
VHS . . . . . . . . . . . . . . . . . . . . . 2005762
Sony Music Video / Oct '94 / Sony.

## SMOOTH OPERATOR.
**Tracks:** Smooth operator / Spirit / Red eyes (on 12" only).
■ 12" . . . . . . . . . . . . . . . . . . . . . TA 4655
■ 7" . . . . . . . . . . . . . . . . . . . . . . A 4655
Epic / Sep '84.

## STRONGER THAN PRIDE.
**Tracks:** Love is stronger than pride / Paradise / Nothing can come between us / Haunt me / Turn my back on you / Keep looking / Clean heart / Give it up / I never thought I'd see the day / Siempre hay esperanza.
CD. . . . . . . . . . . . . . . . . . . . . 4604972
MC. . . . . . . . . . . . . . . . . . . . . 4604974
■ LP . . . . . . . . . . . . . . . . . . . . 4604971
Epic / May '88 / Sony.
MiniDisc. . . . . . . . . . . . . . . . .460497-3
Epic / Feb '93 / Sony.

## SWEETEST TABOO.
**Tracks:** Sweetest taboo / You're not the man.
■ 12" . . . . . . . . . . . . . . . . . . . . . TA 6609
■ 7" . . . . . . . . . . . . . . . . . . . . . . A 6609
Epic / Oct '85.

## TURN MY BACK ON YOU.
**Tracks:** Turn my back on you (remix) / Turn my back on you (extended remix) (Not on 7".) / Turn my back on you (Heff's mix) (Not on 7".) / Keep looking.
■ 12" . . . . . . . . . . . . . . . . . . . . . SADE T4
■ 7" . . . . . . . . . . . . . . . . . . . . . . SADE 4
■ CD Single . . . . . . . . . . . . . . . CD SADE 4
Epic / Nov '88.

## WHEN AM I GOING TO MAKE A LIVING.
**Tracks:** When am I going to make a living / Should I love you / Why can't we live together (on 12" only).
■ 12" . . . . . . . . . . . . . . . . . . . . . TA 4437
■ 7" . . . . . . . . . . . . . . . . . . . . . . A 4437
Epic / May '84.

## YOUR LOVE IS KING.
**Tracks:** Your love is king / Love affair with life (live) / Smooth operator (Only on 12" single.) / Snake bite (Only on 12" single.).
■ 12" . . . . . . . . . . . . . . . . . . . . . TA 4137
■ 7" . . . . . . . . . . . . . . . . . . . . . . A 4137
Epic / Feb '84.

## YOUR LOVE IS KING (OLD GOLD).
**Tracks:** Your love is king / Smooth operator.
7" . . . . . . . . . . . . . . . . . . . . . .OG 9967
Old Gold / '92 / Pickwick.

## Sae, Kelli

## IT'S TOO LATE.
**Tracks:** It's too late.
■ 12" . . . . . . . . . . . . . . . . . . . .12EASY 100
Easy Street / Nov '89.

■ DELETED

## Sain, Oliver

### BLUE MAX.
Tracks: Party hearty (get up and hustle) / She's a disco queen / London express / Apricot splash (the prayer) / Have you ever been mellow (you are beautiful) / Just a lonely man / Hey butterfly.
- **LP** . . . . . . . . . . . . . . . . . . . . . .CLP 532
Contempo (1).

### BUS STOP.
Tracks: Bus stop / Goin' back to Memphis / Laid back / Sporty Mae / Nightime / Double bump / California sunset / Libra's dream / Blowing for love / Soul serenade.
- **LP** . . . . . . . . . . . . . . . . . . . . . .CLP 518
Contempo (1).

### CONDITION YOUR HEARTS (see under Turner, Ike).

### SHE'S A DISCO QUEEN.
Tracks: She's a disco queen / Get up and hustle.
- **7"** . . . . . . . . . . . . . . . . . . . . . .CS 2077
Contempo (1) / Jan '77.

## Saint & Stephanie

### GOTTA KEEP DANCIN'.
Tracks: Gotta keep dancin' / Standing on the edge of a love affair.
- **7"** . . . . . . . . . . . . . . . . . . . . . .ARIST 283
Arista / Jul '79.

## Salsoul Explosion

### I FEEL HAPPY (Sabor De Salsa).
Tracks: I feel happy (sabor de salsa) / Soul machine.
- **7"** . . . . . . . . . . . . . . . . . . . . . .DAY 109
Calendar / '77.

### SALSOUL INVENTION.
Tracks: Nice 'n' nasty / Be my soul / Fifth of Beethoven / Double action / Soul machine / Nice and slow / Salsoul hustle / Soul for Elisa / Get happy / I feel happy / Follow me into the car.
- **LP** . . . . . . . . . . . . . . . . . . . . . .DAYL 002
Calendar / Sep '77.

## Salsoul Orchestra

### CHRISTMAS TIME.
Tracks: Christmas time / New York medley.
- **12"** . . . . . . . . . . . . . . . . . . . .EPCA 131883
- **7"** . . . . . . . . . . . . . . . . . . . . .EPCA 1883
Epic / Nov '81.

### HOW HIGH.
Tracks: I'll keep you warm / Resorts international / Stop and think / Have a good time / My number's up / How high.
- **LP** . . . . . . . . . . . . . . . . . . . . .SSLP 1518
Salsoul / Dec '79.

### LITTLE DRUMMER BOY.
Tracks: Little drummer boy / Merry Christmas all.
- **7"** . . . . . . . . . . . . . . . . . . . . .SSOL 113
Salsoul / Nov '78.

### OOH I LOVE IT.
Tracks: Ooh I love it.
- **12"** . . . . . . . . . . . . . . . . . . . . .SALT 102
Salsoul / Mar '83.

### SALSOUL ORCHESTRA, THE.
Tracks: Not Advised.
- **CD** . . . . . . . . . . . . . . . . . . . . .CPCD 8059
- **LP** . . . . . . . . . . . . . . . . . . . . .CPLP 8059
Charly / Nov '94 / Charly.

### SHORT SHORTS.
Tracks: Short shorts / It's a new day.
- **7"** . . . . . . . . . . . . . . . . . . . . . .SZ 2037
Salsoul / Jul '77.

### TANGERINE.
Tracks: Tangerine / Get happy.
- **7"** . . . . . . . . . . . . . . . . . . . . .EPC 4003
Epic / Feb '76.

### YOU'RE JUST THE RIGHT SIZE.
Tracks: You're just the right size / Speedy Gonzalez (Not on reissue.) / Runaway (On Reissue only.).
- **7"** . . . . . . . . . . . . . . . . . . . . .SSOL 110
Salsoul / Jun '78.
- **12"** . . . . . . . . . . . . . . . . . . .12 SALSA 9
Salsoul / May '93.

## Sam & Dave

Ex-gospel singers who swapped praise-the-lord for *Hold On! I'm Coming* on signing to Stax. Songwriters Isaac Hayes and David Porter also supplied them with best-remembered hit *Soul Man;* which, like majority of duo's classics, boasted superlative backing from Booker T, Steve Cropper and Memphis Horns. Sworn enemies by 1969, Sam Moore and David Prater split and reformed during '70s; finally calling it a day when even Blues Brothers' revival of *Soul Man* failed to smooth path of reconciliation. Prater died in April 1988; legacy is some of the grittiest soul to bear Stax label (or, indeed, any other).

### 18 GREATEST HITS: SAM & DAVE.
Tracks: Not Advised.
- **LP** . . . . . . . . . . . . . . . . . . . . . . MA 26287
- **MC** . . . . . . . . . . . . . . . . . . . MAMC 926287
Masters (Holland) / Aug '87.

### 20 GREATEST HITS: SAM & DAVE.
Tracks: Not Advised.
- **CD** . . . . . . . . . . . . . . . . . . . .SPEC 85033
Spectrum (CD) / Dec '88 / M.S.D.

### 20 GREATEST HITS: SAM & DAVE (2).
Tracks: Soul man / Hold on I'm coming / Can't you find another way of doing it / Bring it on home to me / Summertime / Wonderful world / Another Saturday night / You got me / Can't find another way / You got me hummin' / I thank you / Soul sister, brown sugar / Sittin' on the dock of the bay / You send me / Don't pull your love / Cupid / Gimme some lovin' / Said I wasn't gonna tell nobody / Soothe me.
- **CD** . . . . . . . . . . . . . . . . . . 266 224 2
- **LP** . . . . . . . . . . . . . . . . . . 226 224 5
- **MC** . . . . . . . . . . . . . . . . . . 216 224 5
Mainline (2) / Jan '90.

### BEST OF SAM & DAVE.
Tracks: Hold on, I'm comin' / When something is wrong with my baby / You don't know like I know / May I baby / Soul man / Soothe me / I thank you / I take what I want / Wrap it up / You don't know what you mean to me / Small portion of your love / You got me hummin' / Can't you find another way / Said I wasn't gonna tell nobody.
- **LP** . . . . . . . . . . . . . . . . . . . . .588 155
Atlantic / Nov '69.

### BEST OF SAM AND DAVE.
Tracks: Soul man / You don't know what you mean to me / Soul sister brown sugar / Hold on I'm coming / Can't you find another way of doing it / Everybody's got to believe in somebody / May I baby / I take what I want / You don't know like I know / When something's wrong with my baby / Soothe me.
- **LP** . . . . . . . . . . . . . . . . . . . .881202 1
Atlantic / Aug '84.
- **MC** . . . . . . . . . . . . . . . . . . . .781202 4
Atlantic / Nov '84 / WEA.
- **CD** . . . . . . . . . . . . . . . . . . . .781279 2
Atlantic / Oct '87 / WEA.

### CAN'T STAND UP FOR FALLING DOWN.
Tracks: Baby baby don't stop now / I can't stand up for falling down / Born again / My reason for living / This is your world / Holdin' on / Come on in / When you steal from me / I'm not an indian giver / Get it / Ooh ooh ooh / Don't pull your love / Knock it out the park / You easily excite me / One part love, two part pain / Jody Ryder got killed.
- **LP** . . . . . . . . . . . . . . . . . . . . . ED 133
Edsel / May '84.

### DOUBLE DYNAMITE.
Tracks: Not Advised.
- **LP** . . . . . . . . . . . . . . . . . . . . . .589003
Stax / Apr '67.

### DOUBLE TROUBLE.
Tracks: You got me hummin' / Said I wasn't gonna tell nobody / That's the way it's gotta be / When something is wrong with my baby / Just can't get enough / Sweet pains / I'm your puppet / Sleep good tonight / I don't need nobody / Home at last / Use me.
- **LP** . . . . . . . . . . . . . . . . . . . . .587 181
Atlantic / Jun '69.

### GREATEST HITS: SAM AND DAVE.
Tracks: Not Advised.
- **LP** . . . . . . . . . . . . . . . . . . . . . .SHLP 119
- **MC** . . . . . . . . . . . . . . . . . . . . . .SHTC 119
Castle Showcase / Apr '86 / Arabesque Ltd.
- **CD** . . . . . . . . . . . . . . . . . . . . . .SHCD 119
Castle Showcase / Dec '87 / Arabesque Ltd.

### HOLD ON I'M A-COMIN'.
Tracks: Hold on I'm a-comin' / I got everything I need.
- **7"** . . . . . . . . . . . . . . . . . . . . . .584003
Atlantic / May '66.

### HOLD ON I'M COMING.
Tracks: Hold on! I'm coming / If you got the loving / I take what I want / Ease me / I got everything I need / Don't make it so hard on me / It's a wonder / Don't help me out / Just me / You got it made / You don't know like I know / Blame me (don't blame my heart).
- **7"** . . . . . . . . . . . . . . . . . . . . .588 045
Atlantic / Jan '67.
- **CD** . . . . . . . . . . . . . . . . . . . . 7567802552
- **MC** . . . . . . . . . . . . . . . . . . . . 7567802554
Atlantic / Jul '91 / WEA.

### HOLD ON I'M COMING.
Tracks: Not Advised.
- **LP** . . . . . . . . . . . . . . . . . . . . . .PLP 5
- **MC** . . . . . . . . . . . . . . . . . . . . .PMC 5
Platinum (W.Germany) / Nov '85.

### HOLD ON I'M COMING.
Tracks: Not Advised.
- **MC** . . . . . . . . . . . . . . . . . .ENT MC 13061
Entertainers / Mar '92.

### HOLD ON, I'M COMING.
Tracks: Hold on I'm coming / Soothe me soul sister.
- **7"** . . . . . . . . . . . . . . . . . . . . . .K 11616
Atlantic / Jan '81.

### I THANK YOU.
Tracks: I thank you.
- **7"** . . . . . . . . . . . . . . . . . . . . . .601 030
Stax / Mar '68.

### I THANK YOU.
Tracks: I thank you / Everybody got to believe in somebody / These arms of mine / Wrap it up / If I didn't have a girl like you / You don't know what you mean to me / Don't turn your heater on / Talk to the man / Love is after me / Ain't that a lot of love / Don't waste that love / That lucky old sun.
- **LP** . . . . . . . . . . . . . . . . . . . . .588 154
Atlantic / Apr '69.
- **CD** . . . . . . . . . . . . . . . . . . .812271012-2
WEA / Mar '93 / WEA.

### LEGENDS IN MUSIC - SAM & DAVE.
Tracks: Not Advised.
- **CD** . . . . . . . . . . . . . . . . . . . . .LECD 063
Wisepack / Jul '94 / THE / Conifer Records.

### ORIGINAL SOUL MAN, THE.
Tracks: Soul sister brown sugar / Hold on I'm coming / I thank you / Soul man / Funky street / Sweet soul music / Funky Broadway / 634 5789 / Love the one you're with / Mustang Sally / How sweet it is (to be loved by you) / I'll be doggone / Respect / Satisfaction.
- **CD** . . . . . . . . . . . . . . . . . . . . .OR 0010
Music Collection International / Aug '87 / THE / Jazz Music.

### R & B.
Tracks: Not Advised.
- **CD** . . . . . . . . . . . . . . . . . . . .RLBTC 001
- **MC** . . . . . . . . . . . . . . . . . . . .RLBTM 001
Realisation / Oct '93 / Prism Leisure PLC.

### SAM & DAVE.
Tracks: It feels so nice / I got a thing going on / My love belongs to you / Listening for my name / No more pain / I found out / It was so nice while it lasted / You ain't no big thing baby / I need love / She's alright / Keep a-walkin' / If she'll still have me / Garden of Earth (On CD only) / Azethoth (On CD only) / Queen Street gang (On CD only) / Clean innocent fun (On CD only) / Metempsychosis (On CD only).
- **LP** . . . . . . . . . . . . . . . . . . . . .MCP 5000
Major Minor / Jul '68.
- **CD** . . . . . . . . . . . . . . . . . . . . .EDCD 388
Demon / Jun '94 / Pinnacle / A.D.A. Distribution.

### SAM & DAVE MEDLEY-SOUL REVIEW.
Tracks: Sam & Dave medley-soul review / Hold on.
- **12"** . . . . . . . . . . . . . . . . . . .POSPX 775
- **7"** . . . . . . . . . . . . . . . . . . . . .POSP 775
Polydor / Nov '85.

### SOOTHE ME.
Tracks: Soothe me / Sweet pains.
- **7"** . . . . . . . . . . . . . . . . . . . . . .601004
Stax / Mar '67.

■ **DELETED**

## SOUL KINGS VOL.2.
**Tracks:** Don't pull your love / Hold on I'm coming / Said I wasn't gonna tell anybody / I thank you / You don't know like I know / You got me hummin' / When something is wrong / Soul sister/Brown sugar / Can't you find another way / Soul man / Soothe me / You don't know what you mean to me.
CD . . . . . . . . . . . . . . . . . . . . . . **SMS 057**
Pickwick / Oct '92 / Pickwick.

## SOUL MAN.
**Tracks:** Soul man.
■ 7" . . . . . . . . . . . . . . . . . . . . . . 601 023
Stax / Nov '67.
■ 12" . . . . . . . . . . . . . . . . **PER 12 8604**
Perfect / May '87.

## SOUL MAN (OLD GOLD).
**Tracks:** Soul man / Soul sister brown sugar.
■ 7" . . . . . . . . . . . . . . . . . . . . .OG 9911
Old Gold / '89.

## SOUL MEN.
**Tracks:** Soul man / May I baby / Broke down piece of man / Let it be me / Hold it baby / I'm with you / Don't knock it / Just keep holding on / Good runs the bad way / Rich kind of poverty / I've seen what loneliness can do.
■ LP . . . . . . . . . . . . . . . . . . . . 589 015
Stax / Mar '68.
■ LP . . . . . . . . . . . . . . . . . . . . 588 185
Atlantic / Aug '69.
CD . . . . . . . . . . . . . . . . . . 8122702962
Atlantic / Jul '93 / WEA.

## SOUL SISTER.
**Tracks:** Not Advised.
■ LP . . . . . . . . . . . . . . . . . . . . . PLP 16
MC. . . . . . . . . . . . . . . . . . . . . . PMC 16
Platinum (W.Germany) / Oct '85.

## SOUL SISTER BROWN SUGAR.
**Tracks:** Soul sister brown sugar.
■ 7" . . . . . . . . . . . . . . . . . . . . 584 237
Atlantic / Jan '69.

## SWEAT AND SOUL.
**Tracks:** Not Advised.
CD Set . . . . . . . . . . . . . . . .812271253-2
Warner Bros. / Dec '93 / WEA.

## SWEET FUNKY GOLD.
**Tracks:** Not Advised.
CD. . . . . . . . . . . . . . . . . . . . .CD 1018
Gusto (USA) / '88.

## SWEET SOUL MUSIC.
**Tracks:** Hold on I'm coming / 634-5789 / Respect / Funky street / How sweet it is (to be loved by you) / I thank you / Soul sister brown sugar / I'll be doggone / Satisfaction / Land of a thousand dances / Funky broadway / Sweet soul music.
■ LP . . . . . . . . . . . . . . . . . . . .TOP 163
MC. . . . . . . . . . . . . . . . . . . . .KTOP 163
Topline / Feb '87 / Charly.

## SWEET SOUL MUSIC.
**Tracks:** Not Advised.
CD. . . . . . . . . . . . . . . . . . . . . 15 076
MC. . . . . . . . . . . . . . . . . . . . . 79 526
Laserlight / Aug '91 / THE / BMG / Target.

## WE CAN WORK IT OUT.
**Tracks:** We can work it out / You don't know like I know / Hold on I'm coming.
■ 7" . . . . . . . . . . . . . . . . . . . .CS 2124
Contempo (1) / Mar '78.

## WHEN SOMETHING IS WRONG WITH MY BABY.
**Tracks:** When something is wrong with my baby / Small portion of your love.
■ 7" . . . . . . . . . . . . . . . . . . . . .601006
Stax / Apr '67.

## YOU DON'T KNOW LIKE I KNOW.
**Tracks:** You don't know like I know / Said I wasn't gonna tell nobody.
■ 7" . . . . . . . . . . . . . . . . . . . . K 10594
Atlantic / Aug '75.

## YOU DON'T KNOW LIKE I KNOW.
**Tracks:** You don't know like I know / Blame me don't blame my heart.
■ 7" . . . . . . . . . . . . . . . . . . . . AT 4066
Atlantic / Jan '66.

## YOU GOT ME HUMMIN'.
**Tracks:** You got me hummin' / Sleep good tonight.
■ 7" . . . . . . . . . . . . . . . . . . . .584064
Atlantic / Jan '67.

# Sample, Joe

## ASHES TO ASHES.
**Tracks:** Ashes to ashes / Road less travelled / Mother's eyes / Last child / Born in trouble / Strike two / I'll love you / Born to be bad / Phoenix.
■ LP . . . . . . . . . . . . . . . . . . 7599263181
■ MC . . . . . . . . . . . . . . . . . . 7599263184
WEA / Nov '90.
CD . . . . . . . . . . . . . . . . . . 7599263182
WEA / Mar '94 / WEA.

## BURNIN' UP THE CARNIVAL.
**Tracks:** Burnin' up the carnival / Dream of dreams.
■ 12" . . . . . . . . . . . . . . . . . .MCAT 671
■ 7" . . . . . . . . . . . . . . . . . . MCA 671
MCA / Feb '81.

## CARMEL.
**Tracks:** Not Advised.
■ LP . . . . . . . . . . . . . . . . . . ABCL 5266
ABC Records / Apr '79.
■ LP . . . . . . . . . . . . . . . . . . GRP 16001
MCA / May '82.
■ CD . . . . . . . . . . . . . . . . . . GRP 01192
GRP / Aug '92.

## CARMEL.
**Tracks:** Carmel / Rainy day in Monterey.
■ 7" . . . . . . . . . . . . . . . . . . . MCA 525
MCA / Oct '79.

## CARMEL/RAINBOW SEEKER.
**Tracks:** Carmel / Painting / Cannery row / Rainy day in Monterey / Sunrise / Midnight and mist / More beautiful each day / Rainbow seeker / In all my wildest dreams / There are many stops along the way / Melodies of love / Fly with wings of love / As long as it lasts / Islands in the rain / Together we'll find a way.
■ MC Set . . . . . . . . . . . . . . . . MCA 2 113
MCA (Twinpax Cassettes) / Oct '83.
■ CD . . . . . . . . . . . . . . . . . . MCAD 37210
MCA / Apr '87.

## COLLECTION: JOE SAMPLE.
**Tracks:** Carmel / Woman you're driving me mad / Rainy day in Monterey / Sunrise / There are many stops alone the way / Rainbow seeker / Fly with the wings of love / Burning up the carnival / Night flight / Oasis.
CD . . . . . . . . . . . . . . . . . . GRP 96582
■ MC . . . . . . . . . . . . . . . . . . GRP 96584
GRP / Oct '91 / BMG / New Note.

## DID YOU FEEL THAT.
**Tracks:** Not Advised.
CD . . . . . . . . . . . . . . . . . . .936245729-2
East West / Aug '94 / WEA.

## FANCY DANCE.
**Tracks:** Children's song / Fancy dance / All the lonely years / Another blues / Svenska flicka / Old town.
■ LP . . . . . . . . . . . . . . . . . . SNTF 788
Sonet / Jan '79.
CD . . . . . . . . . . . . . . . . . . SNTCD 788
Sonet / Oct '86 / Swift / C.M. Distribution / Roots Records / Jazz Music / Sonet Records / Cadillac / Projection / Wellard / Hot Shot.

## HUNTER.
**Tracks:** Not Advised.
■ CD . . . . . . . . . . . . . . . . . . GRP 1182
GRP / Mar '93.

## HUNTER, THE.
**Tracks:** Hunter / Blue ballet / Beauty and the beast / Wings of fire / Just a little higher / Night flight.
■ LP . . . . . . . . . . . . . . . . . . MCF 3164
■ MC . . . . . . . . . . . . . . . . . . MCFC 3164
MCA / Mar '83.

## OASIS.
**Tracks:** Oasis / New places / New faces / Teardrops / Asian eyes / Survivor / Love's paradise / Wonderland / Mirage.
■ LP . . . . . . . . . . . . . . . . . . MCF 3289
■ MC . . . . . . . . . . . . . . . . . . MCFC 3289
MCA / Sep '85.
■ CD . . . . . . . . . . . . . . . . . . DMCF 3289
MCA / Mar '86.
■ CD . . . . . . . . . . . . . . . . . . MCAD 5481
MCA / Oct '87.
■ CD . . . . . . . . . . . . . . . . . . GRP 01212
GRP / Feb '93.

## RAINBOW SEEKER.
**Tracks:** Rainbow seeker / In all my wildest dreams / There are many stops along the way / Melodies of love / Fly with wings of love / As long as it lasts / Islands in the rain / Together we'll find a way.
■ LP . . . . . . . . . . . . . . . . . . MCL 1624
■ MC . . . . . . . . . . . . . . . . . . MCLC 1624

MCA / Aug '81.
■ CD . . . . . . . . . . . . . . . . . . CMCAD 31067
MCA / Jul '87.
CD . . . . . . . . . . . . . . . . . . GRP 01202
GRP / Feb '93 / BMG / New Note.

## ROLES.
**Tracks:** Woman you're drivin' me mad / Gifted / Friends and lovers / Ego mania mambo / Fortune hunter / Ship of fools / Passionist.
■ LP . . . . . . . . . . . . . . . . . . MCF 3371
■ CD . . . . . . . . . . . . . . . . . . DMCF 3371
■ MC . . . . . . . . . . . . . . . . . . MCFC 3371
MCA / Jun '87.
■ CD . . . . . . . . . . . . . . . . . . GRP 01232
GRP / Aug '92.

## SPELLBOUND.
**Tracks:** Seven years of good luck / Spellbound / Somehow our love survives / All God's children / Leading me back to you / U turn / Bones jive / Luna en New York / Sermonized / Looking glass.
■ LP . . . . . . . . . . . . . . . . . . .925781 1
■ MC . . . . . . . . . . . . . . . . . . .925781 4
■ CD . . . . . . . . . . . . . . . . . . .925781 2
WEA / Jan '89.

## SURVIVOR.
**Tracks:** Survivor / Wonderland.
■ 12" . . . . . . . . . . . . . . . . . . MCAT 1004
■ 7" . . . . . . . . . . . . . . . . . . .MCA 1004
MCA / Oct '85.

## SWING STREET CAFE (Sample, Joe & David T.Walker).
**Tracks:** Hallelujah, I love her so / Rock house / Honest I do / Next time U see me / Woke up this morning / C.C. rider / Honky tonk / After hours.
■ LP . . . . . . . . . . . . . . . . . . CRP 16004
MCA / May '82.
■ LP . . . . . . . . . . . . . . . . . . .ICRP 5785
■ MC . . . . . . . . . . . . . . . . . . ICRPC 5785
MCA / Aug '86.
■ CD . . . . . . . . . . . . . . . . . . CRPD 5785
MCA / Jul '87.

## VOICES IN THE RAIN.
**Tracks:** Voices in the rain / Burnin' up the carnival / Greener grass / Eye of the hurricane / Dreams of dreams / Shadows / Sonata in solitude.
■ LP . . . . . . . . . . . . . . . . . . MCG 4016
MCA / '81.
■ LP . . . . . . . . . . . . . . . . . . MCL 1765
■ MC . . . . . . . . . . . . . . . . . . MCLC 1765
MCA / '83.

# San Remo Strings

## FESTIVAL TIME.
**Tracks:** Festival time / All turned on.
■ 7" . . . . . . . . . . . . . . . . . . TMG 795
Tamla Motown / Oct '81.

# Sanborn, David

Sanborn's earliest professional experience was with Paul Butterfield's band where he recorded and played until 1972 when he teamed up with Stevie Wonder for a tour with the Rolling Stones. He then became a sought after session man, working with James Taylor, David Bowie, the Brecker Brothers and many others. Around this time he struck up a more permanent relationship with Gil Evans and recorded the classic *Svengali* with him. In 1975 he released his solo album *Takin' Off*; the first of a string of well received and increasingly successful outings, which included the Grammy winning *Voyeur* - probably his best known work. By '92 he had amassed five Grammies, four gold albums and one platinum.

## ANOTHER HAND.
**Tracks:** First song / Monica Jane / Come to me / Nina / Hobbies / Another hand / Jesus / Weird / Cee / Medley / Dukes and Counts.
CD . . . . . . . . . . . . . . . . . . 7559610882
MC. . . . . . . . . . . . . . . . . . 7559610884
Elektra / Sep '91 / WEA.

## AS WE SPEAK.
**Tracks:** Port of call / Better believe it / Rush hour / Over and over / Back again / As we speak / Straight to the heart / Rain on Christmas / Love will come someday.
■ LP . . . . . . . . . . . . . . . . . . BSK 3650
WEA / Jul '82.
CD . . . . . . . . . . . . . . . . . . .923650 2
MC. . . . . . . . . . . . . . . . . . K4 56975
WEA / Oct '87 / WEA.

■ DELETED

## ACKSTREET.

**acks:** I told U so / When you smile at me / Believer / Backstreet / Tear for crystal / Bums cathedral / ue beach / Neither one of us.

| | |
|---|---|
| C. | .923906 4 |
| LP | .923906 1 |
| EA / Sep '83 / WEA. | |
| D. | .923906 2 |
| EA / Oct '87 / WEA. | |

## ANG BANG (MARDI GRAS DANCE IX).

**acks:** Bang bang (mardi gras dance mix) / Bang ang (mardi gras groove mix).

## ANG BANG (MARDI GRAS EDIT).

**acks:** Bang bang.

| | |
|---|---|
| | .EKR 158 |
| CD Single. | EKR 158 CD |
| MC Single. | EKR 158 C |
| EA / Nov '92. | |

## HANGE OF HEART, A.

**acks:** Chicago song / Imogene / High roller / Tin tin / Breaking point / Change of heart / Summer / ream.

| | |
|---|---|
| D. | .925479 2 |
| LP | .925479 1 |
| C. | .925479 4 |
| EA / Jan '87 / WEA. | |

## HICAGO SONG.

**acks:** Chicago song / Imogene.

| | |
|---|---|
| 12". | .W 8392T |
| 7". | W 8392 |
| EA / May '87. | |

## LOSE UP.

**acks:** Slam / J.T. / Leslie Ann / Goodbye / Same rl / Pyramid / Tough / So far away / You are verything.

| | |
|---|---|
| D. | .925715 2 |
| LP | K 925715 1 |
| MC. | K 925715 4 |
| eprise/Slash (USA) / Jun '88 / Pinnacle. | |

## REAM, THE (REMIX).

**racks:** Dream (remix) / Imogene / Change of heart Extra track on 12" only).

| | |
|---|---|
| 12". | .W 8414T |
| 7". | W 8414 |
| VEA / Feb '87. | |

## HEARSAY.

**racks:** Savanna / Long goodbye / Little face / Got to ave it up / Jaws / Mirage / Big foot / Back to Memphis / Ojiji.

| | |
|---|---|
| D. | PKO 61620-2 |
| lektra / Jun '94 / WEA. | |
| D. | .755961620-2 |
| IC. | .755961620-4 |
| VEA / Jun '94 / WEA. | |

## HIDEAWAY.

**racks:** Hideaway / Carly's song / Anything you want / Seduction / Lisa / If you would be mine / Creeper / gain and again.

| | |
|---|---|
| LP | .BSK 3379 |
| VEA / Mar '81. | |

## ET IT SPEAK.

**racks:** Not Advised.

| | |
|---|---|
| LP | K 56975 |
| VEA / Mar '84. | |

## ET'S JUST SAY GOODBYE.

**racks:** Let's just say goodbye / Seduction.

| | |
|---|---|
| 7". | LV 46 |
| VEA / Jul '81. | |

## OVE AND HAPPINESS.

**racks:** Love and happiness / Run for cover / Hideaway (Only on 12" single.).

| | |
|---|---|
| 12". | W 9015 T |
| 7". | W 9015 |
| VEA / Nov '84. | |

## OVE AND HAPPINESS.

**racks:** Not Advised.

| | |
|---|---|
| HS. | .KJ 077 |
| ay Jazz (Video) / '88 / Gold & Sons / Cadillac / Jazz Ausic. | |

## NEITHER ONE OF US.

**racks:** Neither one of us / Let's just say goodbye / ove is not enough.

| | |
|---|---|
| 12". | .W 9430T |
| 7". | W 9430 |
| VEA / Jan '84. | |

## STRAIGHT TO THE HEART.

**Tracks:** Hideaway / Straight to the heart / Run for cover / Smile / Lisa / Love and happiness / Lotus blossom / One hundred ways.

| | |
|---|---|
| ■ LP | .925150 1 |
| WEA / Nov '84. | |
| CD. | .9251 502 |
| WEA / Jan '86 / WEA. | |

## UPFRONT.

**Tracks:** Snakes / Benny / Crossfire / Full house / Soul serenade / Hey / Bang bang / Ramblin'.

| | |
|---|---|
| CD. | .7559612722 |
| ■ LP | .7559612721 |
| MC. | .7559612724 |
| Elektra / May '92 / WEA. | |

## VOYEUR.

**Tracks:** Let's just say goodbye / It's you / Wake me when it's over / One in a million / Run for cover / All I need is you / Just for you.

| | |
|---|---|
| CD. | .256 900 |
| MC. | .D4 56900 |
| ■ LP | .K 56900 |
| WEA / May '81 / WEA. | |

## Sands, Evie

## KEEP MY LOVELIGHT BURNING.

**Tracks:** Keep my lovelight burning / I can't wait for you.

| | |
|---|---|
| ■ 12". | .PC 1541 |
| ■ 7". | .PB 1541 |
| RCA / May '79. | |

## SUSPENDED ANIMATION.

**Tracks:** Lady of the night / Keep my lovelight burning / Take a little love / I can't wait for you / As we fall in love once more / Get up / You sho' look good to me / You can do it / I don't want to let go / Brain damage.

| | |
|---|---|
| ■ LP | PL 12943 |
| RCA / '79. | |

## TAKE ME FOR A LITTLE WHILE.

**Tracks:** Take me for a little while.

| | |
|---|---|
| ■ 7". | RB 10018 |
| Red Bird / '65. | |

## Santos, Larry

## WE CAN'T HIDE IT ANY MORE.

**Tracks:** We can't hide it any more / Can't get you off my mind.

| | |
|---|---|
| ■ 7". | .CBX 515 |
| Casablanca / Apr '76. | |

## YOU DON'T KNOW WHERE YOU ARE.

**Tracks:** You don't know where you are / Prove my love is true.

| | |
|---|---|
| ■ 12". | CAT 4 |
| Pussycat / '83. | |

## Sapphires

## BEST OF THE SAPPHIRES.

**Tracks:** Where is Johnny now / Your true love / Who do you love / Oh so soon / I found out to late / I've got mine you better get yours / Where is your heart (Moulin rouge) / Gotta be more than friends / Wild child / Come on and love me / Baby you've got me / Hearts are made to be broken / Let's break up for a while / Our love is everything / Thank you for loving me / Gotta have your love / Gee I'm sorry baby / Evil one / How could I say goodbye / Gonna be a big thing / You'll never stop me from loving you / Slow fizz.

| | |
|---|---|
| CD. | .NEMCD 676 |
| Sequel / Aug '94 / Total / BMG. | |

## GONNA BE A BIG THING.

**Tracks:** Gonna be a big thing / Playin' hide and seek.

| | |
|---|---|
| ■ 7". | ABC 4221 |
| ABC Records / Jun '78. | |

## MY BABY MUST BE A MAGICIAN.

**Tracks:** My baby must be a magician / Whatever you want my love.

| | |
|---|---|
| ■ 12". | .BUYIT 179 |
| ■ 7". | .BUY 179 |
| Stiff / Apr '83. | |

## ROCK ME SLOWLY.

**Tracks:** Rock me slowly / Make love to the music.

| | |
|---|---|
| ■ 12". | BKSL 9 |
| Beckett / Jan '84. | |

## SAPPHIRES.

**Tracks:** Dead man's grave / Telling lies / Green umbrella / Crystal ball / Temptation / Restless / No way out / World of confusion / No exception / In your mirror / Rockin' chair.

| | |
|---|---|
| ■ LP | SWN 001 |
| Swinging Door / Jan '88. | |

## Sarr Band

## DOUBLE ACTION.

**Tracks:** Double action / Soul tango.

| | |
|---|---|
| ■ 7". | .DAY 115 |
| Calendar / Mar '78. | |

## MAGIC MANDRAKE.

**Tracks:** Magic mandrake.

| | |
|---|---|
| ■ 7". | .DAY 111 |
| Calendar / Sep '78. | |

## STRUT YOUR STUFF.

**Tracks:** Strut your stuff.

| | |
|---|---|
| ■ 12". | DAY 12 127 |
| Calendar / Mar '80. | |

## Sass

## BABY TALK.

**Tracks:** Baby talk.

| | |
|---|---|
| ■ 7". | .TEN 85 |
| ■ 12". | .TEN 85-12 |
| 10 / Nov '85. | |

## I DIDN'T MEAN IT ALL.

**Tracks:** I didn't mean it all / City life.

| | |
|---|---|
| ■ 12". | .TEN 41-12 |
| ■ 7". | TEN 41 |
| 10 / Jan '85. | |

## Saturday Night Band

## COME ON DANCE DANCE.

**Tracks:** Come on dance dance / Touch me on my hot spot.

| | |
|---|---|
| ■ 7". | .CBS 6367 |
| CBS / Jul '78. | |

## SATURDAY NIGHT BAND.

**Tracks:** Don't take my love away / Touch me on my hot spot / Come on dance, dance.

| | |
|---|---|
| ■ LP | CBS 82887 |
| CBS / Aug '78. | |

## Saulsberry, Rodney

## I WONDER.

**Tracks:** I wonder.

| | |
|---|---|
| ■ 12". | ALES 127 |
| ■ 7". | ALES 7 |
| Allegiance / Nov '84. | |

## RODNEY SAULSBERRY.

**Tracks:** Look watcha done now / I wonder / Poor little rich girl / Hey girl / You gotta hold on to your love / Second chance / Her song / Time is on our side.

| | |
|---|---|
| ■ LP | ALE 5605 |
| MC. | ZCALE 5605 |
| Allegiance / Nov '84. | |

## Savage, Chante

## IF YOU BELIEVE ME.

**Tracks:** If you believe (mixes).

| | |
|---|---|
| ■ 12". | .658831 6 |
| ■ CD Single. | .658831 2 |
| Sony Music / Dec '92. | |

## Savanna

## I CAN'T TURN AWAY.

**Tracks:** I can't turn away.

| | |
|---|---|
| ■ 12". | .RBL 203 |
| ■ 7". | .RBS 203 |
| Red Bus / Sep '81. | |

## NEVER LET YOU GO.

**Tracks:** Never let you go / Never let you go (version).

| | |
|---|---|
| ■ 12". | .RBL 209 |
| ■ 7". | .RBS 209 |
| R & B / Mar '82. | |

## Schifrin, Lalo

## APE SHUFFLE.

**Tracks:** Ape shuffle / Escape from tomorrow.

| | |
|---|---|
| ■ 7". | BTC 2150 |
| 20th Century / Apr '75. | |

## MORE JAZZ MEETS THE SYMPHONY.

**Tracks:** Not Advised.

| | |
|---|---|
| CD. | .450995589-2 |
| Warner Bros. / Aug '94 / WEA. | |

## MOST WANTED.
Tracks: Most wanted / Rollercoaster.
■ 7" . . . . . . . . . . . . . . . . . . . . . . . . . CTSP 8
N/A / Oct '78.

## Scott, Freddie

### AM I GROOVING YOU.
Tracks: Am I grooving you / Never you mind.
■ 7" . . . . . . . . . . . . . . . . . . . . . HLZ 10139
London-American / Jun '67.

### ARE YOU LONELY FOR ME.
Tracks: Are you lonely for me / Let it be me / Open up the door to your heart / Where were you / Spanish Harlem / Shake a hand / He will break your heart / Who could ever love you / Cry to me / For your love / Love of my woman / Bring it on home to me.
■ LP . . . . . . . . . . . . . . . . . . . . . . JOYS 215
Joy / Sep '71.

### ARE YOU LONELY FOR ME.
Tracks: Are you lonely for me / Where were you.
■ 7" . . . . . . . . . . . . . . . . . . . . . HLZ 10103
London / Jan '67.

### CRY TO ME.
Tracks: Cry to me / No one could ever love you.
■ 7" . . . . . . . . . . . . . . . . . . . . . HLZ 10123
London / Apr '67.

## Scott, Gloria

### JUST AS LONG AS WERE TOGETHER.
Tracks: Just as long as were together / There will never be another.
■ 7" . . . . . . . . . . . . . . . . . . . . . . . CBX 512
Casablanca / Aug '75.

## Scott, Jimmy

### DREAM.
Tracks: Not Advised.
CD . . . . . . . . . . . . . . . . . . . . . 936245629-2
Warner Bros. / Jul '94 / WEA.

### HUNT, THE.
Tracks: Hunt / Missing link.
■ 12" . . . . . . . . . . . . . . . . . . . . . . . . MSS 9
■ 7" . . . . . . . . . . . . . . . . . . . . . . . . . MS 9
Move / May '86.

### LITTLE JIMMY SCOTT - VERY TRULY YOURS.
Tracks: Not Advised.
CD . . . . . . . . . . . . . . . . . . . . . . . . SVO 239
Savoy / Jan '94 / Jazz Music / Wellard / Savoy Records / Conifer Records.

### VERY TRULY YOURS.
Tracks: Not Advised.
CD . . . . . . . . . . . . . . . . . . . . . . . SV 0239
Savoy / Nov '93 / Jazz Music / Wellard / Savoy Records / Conifer Records.

### WE ALL NEED A HERO.
Tracks: We all need a hero / Madeleine.
■ 7" . . . . . . . . . . . . . . . . . . . . . . . DM 425
Deram / Jun '75.

## Scott, Marilyn

### I GOT WHAT DADDY LIKE (Scott, Marilyn & Mary Deloatch).
Tracks: Not Advised.
■ LP . . . . . . . . . . . . . . . . . . . . . . . KM 710
Whiskey, Women & Song (Sweden) / Oct '88.

## Scott, Millie

### AUTOMATIC.
Tracks: Automatic / Automatic(instrumental).
■ 7" . . . . . . . . . . . . . . . . . . . . . . . BRW 51
■ 12" . . . . . . . . . . . . . . . . . . . . . 12 BRW 51
4th & Broadway / Aug '86.

### EV'RY LITTLE BIT.
Tracks: Ev'ry little bit.
■ 7" . . . . . . . . . . . . . . . . . . . . . . . BRW 58
■ 12" . . . . . . . . . . . . . . . . . . . . . 12 BRW 58
4th & Broadway / Feb '87.

### I CAN MAKE IT GOOD FOR YOU.
Tracks: I can make it good for you / Maybe tonight / It's my life / Keep it to yourself / I wanna be yours / To the letter / Love of your own / Heaven / Key / Falling in love.
■ MC . . . . . . . . . . . . . . . . . . . . . BRCA 522
■ CD . . . . . . . . . . . . . . . . . . . . . BRCD 522

---

■ LP . . . . . . . . . . . . . . . . . . . . . BRLP 522
4th & Broadway / Aug '88.

### LAUGHING UP MY SLEEVE.
Tracks: Laughing up my sleeve / Who cares.
■ 7" . . . . . . . . . . . . . . . . . . . . . . . JH 328
Strike (60's) / Apr '67.

### LET'S TALK IT OVER.
Tracks: Let's talk it over.
■ 12" . . . . . . . . . . . . . . . . . . . . . 12 BRW 68
■ 7" . . . . . . . . . . . . . . . . . . . . . . . BRW 68
4th & Broadway / Jun '87.

### LOVE ME RIGHT.
Tracks: 2 hot 2 handle / Every little bit / One stop lover / Don't take your lover / Love me right / Let's talk it over / Can't stand the heat / Automatic / Prisoner of love.
■ LP . . . . . . . . . . . . . . . . . . . . . BRLP 511
■ MC . . . . . . . . . . . . . . . . . . . . . BRCA 511
■ CD . . . . . . . . . . . . . . . . . . . . . CCD 4004
4th & Broadway / Mar '87.

### PRISONER OF LOVE.
Tracks: Prisoner of love / Prisoner of the groove.
■ 12" . . . . . . . . . . . . . . . . . . . . . 12 BRW 45
■ 7" . . . . . . . . . . . . . . . . . . . . . . . BRW 45
4th & Broadway / Mar '86.

### TO THE LETTER.
Tracks: To the letter / It's my life / Keep it to yourself (Only on 12" single.).
■ 12" . . . . . . . . . . . . . . . . . . . . . 12 BRW 107
■ 7" . . . . . . . . . . . . . . . . . . . . . . BRW 107
4th & Broadway / Aug '88.

## Scott, Peggy

### I THANK YOU (Scott, Peggy & Jo Jo Benson).
Tracks: I thank you / Spreadin' love.
■ 7" . . . . . . . . . . . . . . . . . . . . . . 2091 066
Atlantic / Mar '71.

### LOVERS' HOLIDAY (see under Benson, Jo Jo).

### SOUL SHAKE (Scott, Peggy & Jo Jo Benson).
Tracks: Lover's holiday / Picking wild mountain berries / Love will come breaking up on you / Pure love and pleasure / Magic fingers / I want to love you baby / It's the only way / Big city blues / Soul shake / Doing our thing / Over the hill underground / True soul lovin' / Money don't satisfy / We got our bag / Every little bit hurts / You can never get something for nothing.
■ LP . . . . . . . . . . . . . . . . . . . . . CRB 1122
Charly R&B / Jun '86.

### YOU'VE GOT IT ALL.
Tracks: You've got it all / Let me untie you.
■ 7" . . . . . . . . . . . . . . . . . . . . . . PIN 73
Pinnacle / F .o '79.

## Scott, Rena

### LOVE ZONE.
Tracks: Not Advised.
LP . . . . . . . . . . . . . . . . . . . . . . SDI 7511
Sedona / May '89 / Jetstar.

## Scott, Tom

### BEST OF TOM SCOTT.
Tracks: New York connection / Spindrift / Breezin' easy / Dirty old man / Nite creatures / Shadows / Rock island rocket / Time and love / Tom cat / Gotcha.
■ LP . . . . . . . . . . . . . . . . . . . . . CBS 84347
CBS / Aug '80.

### BORN AGAIN.
Tracks: Children of the night / Back burner / Free hand / Close view / Silhouettes / Way back when / Song no.1 / Born again.
CD . . . . . . . . . . . . . . . . . . . . . GRP 96752
■ MC . . . . . . . . . . . . . . . . . . . . . GRP 96754
GRP / May '92 / BMG / New Note.

### DESIRE.
Tracks: Desire / Sure enough / Only one / Stride / Johnny B. Badd / Meet somebody / Maybe I'm amazed / Chunk of funk.
■ LP . . . . . . . . . . . . . . . . . . . . . K 52411
Elektra / Aug '82.
CD . . . . . . . . . . . . . . . . . . . . . 9601422
Elektra / Jul '88 / WEA.

---

### FLASHPOINT.
Tracks: Not Advised.
CD . . . . . . . . . . . . . . . . . . . . . GRP 957
■ LP . . . . . . . . . . . . . . . . . . . . . GRPA 957
■ MC . . . . . . . . . . . . . . . . . . . . . GRPM 957
GRP / Oct '88 / BMG / New Note.

### INTIMATE STRANGERS.
Tracks: Intimate strangers / Sudden attractions / steppers / Day and nite out together / Getaway / N creatures / Loving and leaving / Lost inside the lo of you / Do you feel me now / Breezin' easy / You' so good to me / Puttin' the bite on you / Beauti music.
■ LP . . . . . . . . . . . . . . . . . . . . . CBS 833
CBS / Mar '79.

### KEEP THIS LOVE ALIVE.
Tracks: If you're not the one for me (Vocals: Bren Russell and Bill Champlin) / Miz thang (instrumente / Keep this love alive (Vocals: David Pack) / Kilima jaro (instrumental) / Reason for the rain (Vocal: E Champlin) / Givin' our best (instrumental) / Only heartbeat away (Vocal: Will Lee) / You mean ever thing to me / Whenever you dream of me (Voca Diane Schuur).
■ LP . . . . . . . . . . . . . . . . . . . . . GRP 964
■ MC . . . . . . . . . . . . . . . . . . . . . GRP 964
■ CD . . . . . . . . . . . . . . . . . . . . . GRP 964
GRP / Jun '91.

### READ MY LIPS.
Tracks: Upbeat 90's / Sarah Sarah / Reed my lips Jungle wave / Hollywood walk / Every day and eve minute / Walk a mile / G.B.U. / Saxappella / Easy lif
■ CD . . . . . . . . . . . . . . . . . . . . . GRP 975
GRP / Jan '94.

### STREAMLINES.
Tracks: Not Advised.
■ LP . . . . . . . . . . . . . . . . . . . . . GRP 9104
■ MC . . . . . . . . . . . . . . . . . . . . . GRPM 9104
■ CD . . . . . . . . . . . . . . . . . . . . . GRPD 955
GRP / '88.
■ CD . . . . . . . . . . . . . . . . . . . . . GRP 9555
GRP / Jan '93.

### TARGET.
Tracks: Target / Come back to me / Aerobia / He too young / Got to get out of New York / Biggest pa of me / Burindi bump.
CD . . . . . . . . . . . . . . . . . . . . . 780 106-
Atlantic / '86 / WEA.
CD . . . . . . . . . . . . . . . . . . . . . 756780106-
Atlantic / Jun '93 / WEA.

### THEM CHANGES.
Tracks: Zoot suit / Pick up the pieces / Chester an Bruce / Desire / Them changes / Too hot / Serpen tine fire / Dahomey dance / We belong togethe (Only on CD.).
■ LP . . . . . . . . . . . . . . . . . . . . . GRP 9613
■ MC . . . . . . . . . . . . . . . . . . . . . GRP 9613
■ CD . . . . . . . . . . . . . . . . . . . . . GRP 9613
GRP / Jun '90.

## Scott-Heron, Gil

Born in Chicago, though raised in Jackson Tennessee by his grandmother, Scott-Heron wrote novels and poetry before a partner ship with keyboard player, Brian Jackson in the early '70s bore first musical fruit with Flying Dutchman Records. In the beginning it was mostly percussion and rhyme, but as the arrangements grew jazzier and more complex, so too did Gil's reputation for pro vocative thought reach an audience beyond the Eastern Seaboard, beyond even Ameri ca. In '74 the album Winter In America which included The Bottle, made its creato a surprise dancefloor star. A year later and Johannesburg performed the same trick for listeners to radio. The '70s and early '80s were his lucid periods, Clive Davis's Arista sticking with their rebel long after the disc boom had reduced his marketplace appeal One mini-revival in the mid-'80s, when an experiment with Bill Laswell led to a disap pointing 45, Re-Ron, petered out quickly but the current "comeback" through TVT Polydor looks like it may stand on sturdier legs. Let's hope Gil's own increasingly dodgy pins are up to the task.

### 1980 (Scott-Heron, Gil & Brian Jackson)
Tracks: Shut 'um down / Alien (hold on to your dream) / Willing / Corners / 1980 / Push comes to shove / Shah Mot / Late last night.
■ LP . . . . . . . . . . . . . . . . . . . . . 201733
Arista / May '85.

■ DELETED

### BEST OF GIL SCOTT-HERON.
Tracks: Revolution will not be televised / Winter in America / Ain't no such thing as Superman / Re-Ron / Shut 'um down / Angel dust / B movie.
```
■ LP . . . . . . . . . . . . . . . . . . . . . . . .206618
■ MC. . . . . . . . . . . . . . . . . . . . . . . .406618
```
Arista / Sep '84.
```
■ CD . . . . . . . . . . . . . . . . . . . . . . . .256618
```
Arista / Apr '88.

### BOTTLE, THE (Scott-Heron, Gil & Brian Jackson).
Tracks: Bottle.
```
■ 12" . . . . . . . . . . . . . . . . . . . . .HEAT 23 12
■ 7" . . . . . . . . . . . . . . . . . . . . . . .HEAT 23
```
Inferno (1) / Jul '80.
```
12" . . . . . . . . . . . . . . . . . . . . . .VATS 302
7" . . . . . . . . . . . . . . . . . . . . . . .VAT 302
```
Champagne / Jan '81.

### BOTTLE, THE (OLD GOLD).
Tracks: Bottle / Johannesburg / Winter in America.
```
■ 12" . . . . . . . . . . . . . . . . . . . . . .OG 4054
```
Old Gold / Mar '88.

### DON'T GIVE UP.
Tracks: Don't give up / Message to the messengers / Bottle (On CD & 12" only).
```
12" . . . . . . . . . . . . . . . . . . . . . 12MUM 58
CD Single . . . . . . . . . . . . . . . . . MUMCD 58
MC Single . . . . . . . . . . . . . . . . . MUMSC 58
```
Mother / Oct '94 / PolyGram.

### GLORY (The Gil Scott Heron Collection).
Tracks: Revolution will not be televised / Blue collar / New York City / Hello Sunday hello road / We almost lost Detroit / Angel dust / Bottle / Winter in America / Delta man / South Carolina (Barnwell) / Inner city blues / Show bizness / B Movie / Lady Day and John Coltrane / I think I'll call it morning / You can depend on (the train from Washington) / Shut 'um down / Ain't no such thing as Superman / Klan / Fast lane / Race track in France / Storm music / Save the children / Song for Bobby Smith / Beginnings / Legend in his own mind.
```
CD . . . . . . . . . . . . . . . . . . . . . . . .353913
■ Double LP. . . . . . . . . . . . . . . . . .303913
■ MC Set . . . . . . . . . . . . . . . . . . . .503913
```
Arista / Nov '90 / BMG.

### HELLO SUNDAY HELLO ROAD.
Tracks: Hello Sunday, hello road / Bottle.
```
■ 12" . . . . . . . . . . . . . . . . . . . .ARIST 12169
```
Arista / Mar '78.

### JOHANNESBURG.
Tracks: Johannesburg / Waiting for the axe to fall.
```
■ 12" . . . . . . . . . . . . . . . . . . . .ARIST 12527
■ 7" . . . . . . . . . . . . . . . . . . . . . .ARIST 527
```
Arista / Apr '83.

### MINISTER OF INFORMATION.
Tracks: Not Advised.
```
CD . . . . . . . . . . . . . . . . . . . . . . CCSCD 403
MC. . . . . . . . . . . . . . . . . . . . . . CCSMC 403
```
Castle / Apr '94 / BMG.

### MOVING TARGET.
Tracks: Fast lane / Washington DC / No exit / Blue collar / Explanations / Ready or not / Black history of the world.
```
■ LP . . . . . . . . . . . . . . . . . . . . . . . .204921
```
Arista / Sep '82.

### RE-RON.
Tracks: Re-ron / B movie.
```
■ 12" . . . . . . . . . . . . . . . . . . . .ARIST 12573
■ 7" . . . . . . . . . . . . . . . . . . . . . .ARIST 573
```
Arista / Aug '84.

### REFLECTIONS.
Tracks: Storm music / Grandma's hands / Is that jazz / Morning thoughts / Inner city blues / Siege of New Orleans / Gun / B movie.
```
■ LP . . . . . . . . . . . . . . . . . . . . . . SPART 1180
```
Arista / Oct '81.

### REVOLUTION WILL NOT BE TELEVISED, THE.
Tracks: Revolution will not be televised / Sex education - ghetto style / Get out of the ghetto blues / No knock / Lady Day and John Coltrane / Pieces of a man / Home is where the hatred is / Brother / Save the children / Whitey on the moon / Did you hear what they said / When you are who you are / I think I'll call it morning / Sign of the ages / Or down you all / Needle's eye / Prisoner.
```
CD . . . . . . . . . . . . . . . . . . . . . . . ND 86994
LP . . . . . . . . . . . . . . . . . . . . . . . NL 86994
MC. . . . . . . . . . . . . . . . . . . . . . . NK 86994
```
Bluebird / Apr '89 / BMG.

### SHOW BIZNESS.
Tracks: Show bizness / Better days ahead.
```
■ 7" . . . . . . . . . . . . . . . . . . . . . . .ARIST 215
```
Arista / Oct '78.

### SPACE SHUTTLE.
Tracks: Space shuttle.
```
■ 12" . . . . . . . . . . . . . . . . . . . . .GILTY 003
■ 12" . . . . . . . . . . . . . . . . . . . . .GILLT 003
■ 12" Remix. . . . . . . . . . . . . . . . .GILTX 003
■ 7" . . . . . . . . . . . . . . . . . . . . . . GILL 003
```
Peaktop / Feb '90.

### SPIRITS.
Tracks: Message to the messengers / Spirits / Give her a call / Lady's song / Spirits past / Other side (parts 1-3) / Work for peace / Don't give up.
```
CD . . . . . . . . . . . . . . . . . . . . . .MUMCD 9415
MC. . . . . . . . . . . . . . . . . . . . . .MUMC 9415
```
Mother / Aug '94 / PolyGram.

### STORM MUSIC.
Tracks: Storm music / B movie.
```
■ 12" . . . . . . . . . . . . . . . . . . . .ARIST 12452
■ 7" . . . . . . . . . . . . . . . . . . . . . .ARIST 452
```
Arista / '82.

### TALES OF GIL.
Tracks: Washington D.C / Save the children / Angel dust / Gun / Blue collar / Alien (hold on to your dream) / Three miles down / Bottle / Winter in America / Is that jazz / 'B' Movie.
```
CD Set . . . . . . . . . . . . . . . . . . . ESDCD 021
■ Double LP. . . . . . . . . . . . . . . . . ESDLP 021
MC Set . . . . . . . . . . . . . . . . . . . ESDMC 021
```
Essential / Feb '90 / Total / BMG.

### TALES OF GIL.
Tracks: Not Advised.
```
■ VHS . . . . . . . . . . . . . . . . . . . . . HEN 2257
```
Hendring Video / Jun '90.

### WHAT'S THE WORD J'BURG.
Tracks: What's the word J'Burg / Fell together.
```
■ 7" . . . . . . . . . . . . . . . . . . . . . . . ARIST 23
```
Arista / Oct '75.

### WINTER IN AMERICA.
Tracks: Winter in America.
```
■ 10" . . . . . . . . . . . . . . . . . . . .ARIST 10643
■ 7" . . . . . . . . . . . . . . . . . . . . . .ARIST 643
```
Arista / Nov '85.

## Sea Level

### BALL ROOM.
Tracks: La di da / Digital daydream blues / What am I gonna do / Keeping it from the troops / I'm in love again / Losin' you / Dreamin' / No favours, no way / Love today.
```
■ LP . . . . . . . . . . . . . . . . . . . . . SPART 1145
```
Arista / Nov '80.

### FIFTY FOUR.
Tracks: Fifty four / Alottacalada.
```
■ 7" . . . . . . . . . . . . . . . . . . . . . . . POSP 28
```
Polydor / Feb '79.

### ON THE EDGE.
Tracks: Fifty four / King grand / Living in a dream / Lotta colada / This could be the worst / Uptown downtown / Electron cold / On the wong.
```
■ LP . . . . . . . . . . . . . . . . . . . . . 242 917 7
```
Capricorn / Apr '79.

### SEA LEVEL.
Tracks: Rain in Spain / Shake a leg / Tidal wave / Country fool / Nothing matters but the fever / Grand larceny / Scarborough Fair / Just a good feeling.
```
■ LP . . . . . . . . . . . . . . . . . . . . . 2429150
```
Capricorn / '77.

## Seal

### BEGINNING, THE.
Tracks: Beginning.
```
■ CD Single . . . . . . . . . . . . . . . . .ZANG 12CD
■ 7" . . . . . . . . . . . . . . . . . . . . . . ZANG 21
■ MC Single . . . . . . . . . . . . . . . . . ZANG 21C
```
ZTT / Jul '91.

### CRAZY.
Tracks: Crazy / Sparkle.
```
■ CD Single . . . . . . . . . . . . . . . . . ZANG 8CD
■ 12" . . . . . . . . . . . . . . . . . . . . . ZANG 8T
■ 7" . . . . . . . . . . . . . . . . . . . . . . ZANG 8
■ MC Single . . . . . . . . . . . . . . . . . ZANG 8C
```
ZTT / Nov '90.

### FUTURE LOVE (EP).
Tracks: Not Advised.
```
■ CD Single . . . . . . . . . . . . . . . . .ZANG 11CD
■ 12" . . . . . . . . . . . . . . . . . . . . .ZANG 11T
```

```
■ 7" . . . . . . . . . . . . . . . . . . . . . . . ZANG 11
■ MC Single . . . . . . . . . . . . . . . . . ZANG 11C
```
ZTT / May '91.

### KILLER .. DANCE.
Tracks: Killer .. dance.
```
■ 12" . . . . . . . . . . . . . . . . . . . . .ZANG 23T
```
ZTT / Nov '91.

### KISS FROM A ROSE.
Tracks: Kiss from a rose.
```
12" . . . . . . . . . . . . . . . . . . . . .ZANG 52T
CD Single . . . . . . . . . . . . . . . . . ZANG 52CD2
CD Single . . . . . . . . . . . . . . . . . ZANG 52CD1
MC Single . . . . . . . . . . . . . . . . . ZANG 52C
```
ZTT / Jul '94 / WEA.

### NEWBORN FRIEND.
Tracks: Newborn friend (Mixes).
```
12" . . . . . . . . . . . . . . . . . . . . .ZANG 58T
CD Single . . . . . . . . . . . . . . . . . ZANG 58CD
MC Single . . . . . . . . . . . . . . . . . ZANG 58C
```
ZTT / Oct '94 / WEA.

### PRAYER FOR THE DYING.
Tracks: Prayer for the dying / Dreaming in metaphors.
```
■ 7" . . . . . . . . . . . . . . . . . . . . . . ZANG 51
■ CD Single . . . . . . . . . . . . . . . . .ZANG 51CD
■ MC Single . . . . . . . . . . . . . . . . . ZANG 51C
```
ZTT / May '94.

### SEAL.
Tracks: Beginning / Deep water / Crazy / Killer / Whirlpool / Future love paradise / Wild / Show me / Violet.
```
CD. . . . . . . . . . . . . . . . . . . . . . . . ZTT 9CD
■ LP . . . . . . . . . . . . . . . . . . . . . . . ZTT 9
MC. . . . . . . . . . . . . . . . . . . . . . . ZTT 9C
```
ZTT / May '91 / WEA.
```
DCC . . . . . . . . . . . . . . . . . . . . .9031 745575
```
WEA / Jan '93 / WEA.

### SEAL.
Tracks: Not Advised.
```
VHS . . . . . . . . . . . . . . . . . . . . . 9031761283
```
Warner Music Video / Dec '91 / WEA.

### SEAL II.
Tracks: Not Advised.
```
CD. . . . . . . . . . . . . . . . . . . . . .450996256-2
LP . . . . . . . . . . . . . . . . . . . . . .450996256-1
MC. . . . . . . . . . . . . . . . . . . . . .450996256-4
```
ZTT / May '94 / WEA.

### VIOLET.
Tracks: Violet.
```
■ 7" . . . . . . . . . . . . . . . . . . . . . . ZANG 27
■ CD Single . . . . . . . . . . . . . . . . .ZANG 27CD
■ MC Single . . . . . . . . . . . . . . . . . ZANG 27C
```
ZTT / Feb '92.

## Sease, Marvin

### BREAKFAST.
Tracks: Love is a game / Same old woman / I belong to you / Lately / I can't forget you girl / Condom on your tongue / I ate you for my breakfast / Tell me.
```
■ CD . . . . . . . . . . . . . . . . . . . . . 834 633 2
■ LP . . . . . . . . . . . . . . . . . . . . .LONLP 65
■ MC. . . . . . . . . . . . . . . . . . . . .LONC 65
```
London / Jul '88.

### MARVIN SEASE.
Tracks: Double crosser / Let's get married today / Love me or leave me / Ghetto man / You're number one / Dreaming / Candy licker.
```
MC. . . . . . . . . . . . . . . . . . . . . .LONC 33
■ LP . . . . . . . . . . . . . . . . . . . . .LONLP 33
```
London / Apr '87 / PolyGram.

## Seawind

### HOLD ON TO LOVE.
Tracks: Hold on to love / Sound rainbow.
```
■ 7" . . . . . . . . . . . . . . . . . . . . . .AMS 7440
```
A&M / '79.

### SEAWIND.
Tracks: What cha doin' / Two of us / Love him, love her / Everything needs love / Shout / Still in love / Pra vose / I need your love / Long, long time.
```
■ LP . . . . . . . . . . . . . . . . . . . . .AMLH 64824
```
A&M / Nov '80.

### WHAT CHA DOIN'.
Tracks: What cha doin' / I need your love.
```
■ 12" . . . . . . . . . . . . . . . . . . . . .AMSX 7575
■ 7" . . . . . . . . . . . . . . . . . . . . . .AMS 7575
```
A&M / Nov '80.

## Second Image

**(GET YOUR FINGER OUT) PINPOINT THE FEELING.**
Tracks: (Get your finger out) pinpoint the feeling / Cool breeze.
■ 12" . . . . . . . . . . . . . . . . . . . POSPX 263
■ 7" . . . . . . . . . . . . . . . . . . . . . POSP 263
Polydor / May '81.

**BETTER TAKE TIME.**
Tracks: Better take time / Special lady / Can't keep holding on / Images.
■ 12" . . . . . . . . . . . . . . . . . . . POSPX 565
■ 7" . . . . . . . . . . . . . . . . . . . . . POSP 565
Polydor / Mar '83.

**CAN'T KEEP HOLDING ON.**
Tracks: Can't keep holding on / Images.
■ 7" . . . . . . . . . . . . . . . . . . . . . POSP 336
Polydor / Oct '81.

**CAN'T KEEP HOLDING ON (OLD GOLD).**
Tracks: Can't keep holding on / Special lady.
■ 12" . . . . . . . . . . . . . . . . . . . . . OG 4126
Old Gold / '89.

**DANCE DANCE DANCE.**
Tracks: Dance, dance, dance / Jazzy dancer.
■ 12" . . . . . . . . . . . . . . . . . . . POSPX 224
Polydor / Feb '81.

**DON'T YOU.**
Tracks: Don't you.
■ 12" . . . . . . . . . . . . . . . . . . . . MCAT 848
■ 7" . . . . . . . . . . . . . . . . . . . . . MCA 848
MCA / Nov '83.

**FALL IN LOVE.**
Tracks: Fall in love / Take a trip.
■ 12" . . . . . . . . . . . . . . . . . . . POSPX 395
■ 7" . . . . . . . . . . . . . . . . . . . . . POSP 395
Polydor / Feb '82.

**SECOND IMAGE.**
Tracks: Can't keep holding on '83 / Special lady / All been said and done / Life is what you make it / Is it me / Better take time / Star / Love turns me upside down / What's happening.
■ LP . . . . . . . . . . . . . . . . . . . . POLS 1081
Polydor / May '83.

**SING AND SHOUT.**
Tracks: Sing and shout.
■ 12" . . . . . . . . . . . . . . . . . . . . MCAT 882
■ 7" . . . . . . . . . . . . . . . . . . . . . MCA 882
MCA / Aug '84.

**SPECIAL LADY.**
Tracks: Special lady / Star.
■ 12" . . . . . . . . . . . . . . . . . . . POSPX 599
■ 7" . . . . . . . . . . . . . . . . . . . . . POSP 599
Polydor / Jun '83.

**STAR.**
Tracks: Star / Sambolic.
■ 12" . . . . . . . . . . . . . . . . . . . POSPX 457
■ 7" . . . . . . . . . . . . . . . . . . . . . POSP 457
Polydor / Jun '82.

**STARTING AGAIN.**
Tracks: Starting again / Ovo Mexico.
■ 12" . . . . . . . . . . . . . . . . . . . . MCAT 936
■ 7" . . . . . . . . . . . . . . . . . . . . . MCA 936
MCA / Jan '85.

**STRANGE REFLECTIONS.**
Tracks: Not Advised.
■ LP . . . . . . . . . . . . . . . . . . . . . MCF 3255
MCA / Mar '85.

**THERE SHE GOES.**
Tracks: There she goes / Searching but not finding.
■ 12" . . . . . . . . . . . . . . . . . . . . MCAT 863
■ 7" . . . . . . . . . . . . . . . . . . . . . MCA 863
MCA / Jan '84.

**WHAT'S HAPPENING.**
Tracks: What's happening.
■ 12" . . . . . . . . . . . . . . . . . . . POSPX 512
■ 7" . . . . . . . . . . . . . . . . . . . . . POSP 512
Polydor / Sep '82.

## Secret Weapon

**DREAM LOVER.**
Tracks: Dream lover.
■ 12" . . . . . . . . . . . . . . . . . . . REMIX 003
Red Records / Jun '93.

## Seka

**LOVES HYMN.**
Tracks: Not Advised.
CD . . . . . . . . . . . . . . . . . . . . . TG 92972
LP . . . . . . . . . . . . . . . . . . . . . TG 92971
Road Runner / Jul '91 / Pinnacle.

## Senate

**I CAN'T STOP.**
Tracks: I can't stop / Ain't as sweet as you.
7" . . . . . . . . . . . . . . . . . . . . . DB 8110
Columbia / Jan '67 / Sony.

**ORIGINAL SIN, THE.**
Tracks: Original sin / Do you believe in the Westworld.
■ 12" . . . . . . . . . . . . . . . . . . . 12 WAR 1
■ 7" . . . . . . . . . . . . . . . . . . . . . WAR 1
W.A.R. / Jul '84.

**SOCK IT TO YOU ONE MORE TIME.**
Tracks: Sock it to 'em JB / Summertime / Girls are out to get you / Love is after me / Sweet thing / Try a little tenderness / What is soul / Knock on wood / Intro 5 bars (who's afraid of Virginia Woolf) / How sweet is it / You don't know like I know / Shake / Please stay / Can't stop / Invitation / Hold on I'm coming.
CD . . . . . . . . . . . . . . . . . . . . RTCD 901146
Line / Apr '92 / C.M. Distribution / Grapevine Distribution / A.D.A. Distribution / Conifer Records.

## Sensations

**I HEAR A MELODY.**
Tracks: I hear a melody / Baby say you love me.
■ 7" . . . . . . . . . . . . . . . . . . . . . MK 5068
MCA / Jun '71.

**LOOK AT MY BABY.**
Tracks: Look at my baby / What a wonderful feeling.
■ 7" . . . . . . . . . . . . . . . . . . . . . F 12392
Decca / May '66.

## Serenade

**FRIEND NOT A LOVER.**
Tracks: Friend not a lover.
■ 12" . . . . . . . . . . . . . . . . . . . . 12 MISH 4
Mission / Jul '93.

**I LIKE.**
Tracks: I like.
■ 12" . . . . . . . . . . . . . . . . . . . . 12 MISH 2
■ CD Single . . . . . . . . . . . . . . . . CDSMISH 2
Passion/Debut/Scratch Music / Jun '93.

## Serious Intention

**SERIOUS.**
Tracks: Serious / Serious (Dub).
■ 12" . . . . . . . . . . . . . . . . . . . . LONX 93
■ 7" . . . . . . . . . . . . . . . . . . . . . LON 93
London / Mar '86.

**YOU DON'T KNOW.**
Tracks: You don't know.
■ 12" . . . . . . . . . . . . . . . . . . . . . TANT 8
■ 7" . . . . . . . . . . . . . . . . . . . . . TAN 8
Important / Oct '85.

## Serious Rope

**HAPPINESS (Serious Rope Presents Sharon D. Clarke).**
Tracks: Happiness.
■ 12" . . . . . . . . . . . . . . . . . . . RUMAT 64
■ 7" . . . . . . . . . . . . . . . . . . . . RUMA 64
■ CD Single . . . . . . . . . . . . . . . . RUMACD 64
■ MC Single . . . . . . . . . . . . . . . . RUMAMC 64
Rumour / Apr '93.

**HAPPINESS.**
Tracks: Happiness (mixes).
12" . . . . . . . . . . . . . . . . . . . 856 237-2
Phonogram / Sep '94 / PolyGram.

**MUSIC MUSIC MUSIC (Serious Rope & Jonathan King).**
Tracks: Music music music (mixes) / Serious Jake (mixes).
■ 12" . . . . . . . . . . . . . . . . . . . 12CHS 5004
■ 7" . . . . . . . . . . . . . . . . . . . . CHS 5004
■ CD Single . . . . . . . . . . . . . . . CDCHS 5004
■ MC Single . . . . . . . . . . . . . . . TCCHS 5004
Chrysalis / Dec '93.

## Sevelle, Taja

**FOUNTAINS FREE.**
Tracks: Trouble having you near / Chase temptatic / I'm givin' in / Even odd you / Fountains free / Powe of your love (you and I) / Perpetual motion / What state of love / Fierce desire / Forever in love / Die alive / Trouble having you near (radio mix).
CD . . . . . . . . . . . . . . . . . . . . 759926724
■ LP . . . . . . . . . . . . . . . . . . . . 759926724
MC. . . . . . . . . . . . . . . . . . . . . 759926724
WEA / Oct '91 / WEA.

**LOVE IS CONTAGIOUS.**
Tracks: Love is contagious / Mama.
■ 12" . . . . . . . . . . . . . . . . . . . . W 8257
■ 7" . . . . . . . . . . . . . . . . . . . . . W 825
WEA / Feb '88.

**TAJA SEVELLE.**
Tracks: Love is contagious / Wouldn't you love love me / Popular / How could you do me so bad Take me for a ride / If I could get your attention Infatuation / Baby's got a lover / Mama 16 / Fly fo your painted rainbow.
■ LP . . . . . . . . . . . . . . . . . . . . .925546
MC. . . . . . . . . . . . . . . . . . . . . .925546
■ CD . . . . . . . . . . . . . . . . . . . .925546
Paisley Park / Sep '87 / WEA.

**WOULDN'T YOU LOVE TO LOVE ME.**
Tracks: Wouldn't you love to love me / Baby's got lover / Love is contagious (Extra track available o CD format only.).
■ 12" . . . . . . . . . . . . . . . . . . . . W 8127
■ 7" . . . . . . . . . . . . . . . . . . . . . W 812
■ CD Single . . . . . . . . . . . . . . . . W 8127C
Paisley Park / Apr '88.

## Seville

**TAKE A WALK.**
Tracks: Take a walk.
■ 12" . . . . . . . . . . . . . . . . . . . . . CR 21
Cutting (USA) / Sep '87.

## Sexton, Ann

**LOVE TRIALS.**
Tracks: I want to be loved / I'm his wife, you're just friend / Who's gonna love you / I had a fight with love (and I lost) / Be serious / Colour my world blue You've been doing me wrong for so long / Have little mercy / Loving you, loving me / Love, love, love / Come back home / Keep on holding on / You're letting me down / You're gonna miss me.
■ LP . . . . . . . . . . . . . . . . . . . CRB 114
Charly R&B / Jan '87.

**YOU'RE GONNA MISS ME.**
Tracks: I had a fight with love (and I lost) / I'm hi wife, you're just a friend / You got to use what yo got / Color my world blue / I want to be loved You've been doing me wrong for so long / Who' gonna love you / You can't win / Love, love, love You're letting me down / You've been gone too long Come back home / Keep on holding on / Loving you loving me / You're gonna miss me / If I work m, thing on you / You're losing me / Sugar Daddy / B serious / Have a little mercy.
CD . . . . . . . . . . . . . . . . . . . . CPCD 801
Charly / Feb '94 / Charly.

**YOU'VE BEEN GONE TOO LONG.**
Tracks: You've been gone too long.
■ 7" . . . . . . . . . . . . . . . . . . . . .HEAT 2
Inferno (1) / Jul '80.

## Sha Sha

**DO RE MI.**
Tracks: Do re mi.
■ 12" . . . . . . . . . . . . . . . . . . . .JIVET 28
Jive / Oct '91.

**LIES.**
Tracks: Lies (remix).
■ 12" Remix . . . . . . . . . . . . . . . .SHASHA 1
■ 7" . . . . . . . . . . . . . . . . . . . SHASHA 1
White / Jul '89.
■ 12" . . . . . . . . . . . . . . . . . . . . . NST 1
White / May '89.

**MADE IT OVER.**
Tracks: Made it over.
■ 12" . . . . . . . . . . . . . . . . . . . . AMA 005
Ama Productions / Jun '93.

■ DELETED

## Shabazz

### LAD YOU'RE IN MY LIFE.
acks: Glad you're in my life.
7" ........................ PB 49291
12" ........................ PT 49292
CA / Mar '90.

### AKES ME HIGHER.
acks: Takes me higher.
12" ........................ CR 10002
oslit (USA) / Sep '87.

## Shai

### I EVER FALL IN LOVE.
acks: If i ever fall in love.
12" ........................ MCST 1727
CD Single. ................. MCSTD 1727
MC Single. ................. MCSC 1727
7" ........................ MCS 1727
CA / Nov '92.

### I EVER FALL IN LOVE.
acks: Sexual interlude / Comforter / If I ever fall in
ve / sexual / Together forever / If I ever fall in love
ccapella) / Flava / Baby I'm yours / Waiting for the
ay / Changes / Don't wanna play / Lord I've come.
D .......................... MCD 10762
C. .......................... MCC 10762
LP .......................... MCA 10762
CA / Jan '93 / BMG.

## Shakatak

### ITTER SWEET.
racks: Don't start giving up / Blue / Bitter sweet /
ool down / Don't look back / They call that cool /
olding on / Fly away / Shake it down / You'll never
now.
MC. ........................ 847 910-4
CD ......................... 847 910-2
LP ......................... 847 910-1
olydor / Apr '91.

### RAZILIAN DAWN.
racks: Brazilian dawn / You'll never know.
12" ........................ POSPX 282
7" ......................... POSP 282
olydor / Jul '81.

### RAZILIAN LOVE AFFAIR.
acks: Brazilian love affair.
2" ......................... 12 INZ 2
D Single ................... CDSINZ 2
cratch (2) / Oct '94 / 3MV / Sony.

### HRISTMAS ALBUM, THE.
racks: Happy Christmas to ya / Winter wonderland /
hite Christmas / O little town of Bethlehem / Silent
ght / Christmas time again / Christmas in Rio /
ood King Wenceslas / Let it snow, let it snow, let it
now / Sing (Little one) / God rest ye merry gentle-
en / Lonely on Christmas day / Jingle bells /
hristmas song / Away in a manger / Auld lang
yne.
D .......................... CDINZ 3
C. .......................... MCINZ 3
assion/Debut/Scratch Music / Dec '93 / Pinnacle /
MV.

### ITY RHYTHM.
racks: Invitations / City rhythm / Climbing high /
hina Bay / Rio nights / Brazilian dawn / Doctor,
octor / Down on the street / Takin' off / Covina /
ight moves / Out of the blue / Fly the wind / Feels
ke the right time / Night bird.
D .......................... PWKS 4103P
C. .......................... PWKMC 4103P
ckwick / Mar '92 / Pickwick.

### ITY RHYTHM.
racks: City rhythm / round and 'round.
12" ........................ POSPX 754
7" ......................... POSP 754
olydor / Aug '85.

### OOLEST CUTS, THE.
racks: Down on the street / Invitations / Living in
e UK / Slip way / Stranger / Steppin' (live) /
razilian dawn / Easier said than done / Night birds /
reetwalkin' / Dark is the night / City rhythm / Walk
e walk / Rio nights / Mr. Manic & Sister Cool.
CD ......................... NCD 2422
LP ......................... NE 1422
MC. ........................ CE 2422
-Tel / Oct '88.

### ARK IS THE NIGHT.
racks: Dark is the night / I lose myself.
12" ........................ POSPX 595
7" ......................... POSP 595
olydor / Jun '83.

---

### DAY BY DAY.
Tracks: Day by day / Once upon a time / Secret /
Physical attraction / City rhythm / I must be dream-
ing / Africa / Goodbye / Mickey Mouse / Vive la
fantasy.
■ LP ....................... POLH 24
■ MC. ...................... POLHC 24
■ CD ....................... 827 485-2
Polydor / Dec '85.

### DAY BY DAY (Shakatak & Al Jarreau).
Tracks: Day by day / Don't push me.
■ 12" ...................... POSPX 770
■ 7" ....................... POSP 770
Polydor / Nov '85.

### DOCTOR DOCTOR.
Tracks: Doctor doctor / Doctor doctor (mix).
■ 12" ...................... DTRX 1
■ 7" ....................... DTR 1
Polydor / Apr '88.

### DOCTOR MANIC, SISTER COOL (CD VIDEO).
Tracks: Dr. Manic, sister cool.
CD Video ................... 080 432 2
Polygram Music Video / Oct '88 / PolyGram.

### DON'T BLAME IT ON LOVE.
Tracks: Don't blame it on love / Nightbirds.
■ 12" ...................... POSPX 699
■ 7" ....................... POSP 699
Polydor / Sep '84.

### DOWN ON THE STREET.
Tracks: Down on the street / Holding on / Summer
sky / Hypnotised / Watching you / Don't blame it on
love / Photograph / Fire dance / Lady (to Billie
Holiday).
■ MC. ...................... POLDC 5148
■ CD ....................... 823 304-2
Polydor / Aug '84.
■ LP ....................... SPELP 109
■ MC. ...................... SPEMC 109
Polydor / Jun '87.

### DOWN ON THE STREET.
Tracks: Down on the street / Holding on.
■ 7" ....................... POSP 688
Polydor / Jul '84.

### DOWN ON THE STREET.
Tracks: Down on the street.
CD Video ................... 080 008 2
Polygram Music Video / Oct '88 / PolyGram.

### DOWN ON THE STREET (OLD GOLD).
Tracks: Down on the street / Dark is the night.
■ 12" ...................... OG 4129
Old Gold / '89.

### DRIVING HARD.
Tracks: Livin' in the UK / Into the night / Toot the
shoot / Lumiere / Late night flight / Waves / Steppin'
/ Covina / You never know / Brazilian dawn.
■ LP ....................... POLS 1030
Polydor / Jan '82.

### DRIVING HARD/NIGHTBIRDS.
Tracks: Into the night / Toot the shoot / Lumiere /
Late night flight / Waves / Covina / You never know /
Brazilian dawn / Living in the UK / Steppin (Live) /
Steppin' / Night birds / Streetwalkin' / Rio nights / Fly
the wind / Easier said than done / Bitch to the boys /
Light of my life / Taking off.
■ MC. ...................... 3574 136
Polydor / Feb '83.
■ LP ....................... SPELP 100
■ MC. ...................... SPEMC 100
■ CD ....................... 823 017-2
Polydor / Jun '86.

### EASIER SAID THAN DONE.
Tracks: Easier said than done / Continental shelf.
■ 12" ...................... POSPX 375
■ 7" ....................... POSP 375
Polydor / Nov '81.

### EASIER SAID THAN DONE (OLD GOLD).
Tracks: Easier said than done / Nightbirds.
■ 12" ...................... OG 4079
Old Gold / Oct '88.

### FEELS LIKE THE RIGHT TIME.
Tracks: Feels like the right time.
■ 7" ....................... POSP 188
Polydor / Nov '80.

### FULL CIRCLE.
Tracks: Brazillian love affair / Catwalk / Out of my
sight / Sweet Sunday / You are / Walk in the night /
Haze / Diamond in the night / Midnight temptation /
Havana express / Tonights the night / Blue azure.
CD ......................... CDINZ 4

---

MC. ........................ MCINZ 4
Passion/Debut/Scratch Music / Oct '94 / Pinnacle /
3MV.

### GREATEST GROOVES.
Tracks: Down on the street / Doctor doctor / Photo-
graph / Invitations / Holding on / Streetwalkin' /
Feels like the right time / Takin' off / Africa / City
rhythm / Watching you / Dark is the night / Physical
attraction / Walk the walk / I must be dreaming / Day
by day / Nightbirds / Covina / Lady / Love of all time
/ Fly like the wind / Easier said than done.
■ CD ....................... VSOPCD 142
■ Double LP. ............... VSOPLP 142
■ MC. ...................... VSOPMC 142
Connoisseur Collection / Mar '90.

### IF YOU COULD SEE ME NOW.
Tracks: If you could see me now / Fly the wind.
■ 12" ...................... POSPX 635
■ 7" ....................... POSP 635
Polydor / Aug '83.

### INTO THE BLUE.
Tracks: Not Advised.
■ CD ....................... 829 923-1
Polydor / Aug '89.

### INVITATIONS.
Tracks: Lose myself / Lonely afternoon / Steppin out
/ Stranger / Invitations / Usual situation / Sol fuego /
In shadows.
■ LP ....................... POLD 5068
Polydor / Nov '82.
■ CD ....................... 810 068-2
Polydor / Jan '83.
■ LP ....................... SPELP 86
■ MC. ...................... SPEMC 86
Polydor / Feb '85.

### INVITATIONS.
Tracks: Invitations / In the shadows.
■ 12" ...................... POSPX 502
■ 7" ....................... POSP 502
Polydor / Sep '82.

### LIVE: SHAKATAK.
Tracks: Dark is the night / Streetwalkin / Watching
you / Invitations / Nightbirds / Don't blame it on love
/ Easier said than done / Down on the street.
■ LP ....................... POLH 21
■ CD ....................... 823 899-2
Polydor / Feb '85.
■ MC. ...................... POLHC 21
Polydor / Feb '85.

### LIVING IN THE UK.
Tracks: Living in the UK / Esperito.
■ 12" ...................... POSPX 230
■ 7" ....................... POSP 230
Polydor / Mar '81.

### MANIC AND COOL.
Tracks: Mr. Manic & Sister Cool / Slow dancing /
Time of my life / M.O.N.E.Y / Nobody holds me (quite
the way you do) / Doctor doctor / Walk the walk /
Releasin' the feeling / Something special / Stop /
Love of all time / Orient express.
■ CD ....................... 835 577-2
■ LP ....................... POLD 5222
■ MC. ...................... POLDC 5222
Polydor / Apr '88.

### MR. MANIC & SISTER COOL.
Tracks: Mr. Manic & Sister Cool / One for Cara / Mr.
Manic & Sister Cool (mix).
■ 12" ...................... MANIX 1
■ 7" ....................... MANIC 1
Polydor / Sep '87.

### NIGHT BIRDS.
Tracks: Night birds / Rio nights.
■ 7" ....................... POSP 407
Polydor / Apr '82.

### NIGHTBIRDS.
Tracks: Taking off / Lisa / Go for it / Rio nights /
Nightbirds / Fly the wing / Easier said than done /
Bitch to the boys / Light of my life.
■ LP ....................... POLS 1059
■ MC. ...................... POLSC 1059
Polydor / May '82.
■ CD ....................... 810 829-2
Polydor / Jan '83.

### ON THE STREET.
Tracks: Down on the street / Easier said than done /
Invitations / Out of this world / Holding on / Lights on
my life / Lady (To Billie Holiday) / Dark is the night /
Dr Dr / Something special / Mr. Manic & Sister cool /
Turn the music up / Bitter sweet / You'll never know.
CD ......................... 550 0082
MC. ........................ 550 0084
Spectrum (1) / May '93 / PolyGram.

## OUT OF THIS WORLD.
**Tracks:** Dark is the night / Don't say that again / Slip away / On nights like tonight / Out of this world / Let's get together / If you can see me now / Sanur.
■ **CD** ............................. 815 304-2
■ **LP** ............................... POLD 5115
Polydor / Jan '83.
CD ........................................ OW 30014
One Way / Sep '94 / Direct Distribution.

## OUT OF THIS WORLD.
**Tracks:** Out of this world / Sanur.
■ **12"** ............................... POSPX 648
■ **7"** ................................. POSP 648
Polydor / Sep '83.

## SOMETHING SPECIAL.
**Tracks:** Something special / Cavalcante.
■ **12"** ............................... POSPX 863
■ **7"** ................................. POSP 863
Polydor / May '87.

## STEPPIN'.
**Tracks:** Steppin' / Killing time.
■ **12"** ............................... POSPX 163
■ **7"** ................................. POSP 163
Polydor / Aug '80.

## STRANGER.
**Tracks:** Stranger / Sol Fuego.
■ **12"** ............................... POSPX 530
■ **7"** ................................. POSP 530
Polydor / Nov '82.

## STREET LEVEL.
**Tracks:** One day at a time / Street level / Sleepin' alone / Siberian breeze / Anyway you want it / Night ain't over yet / Watchin' the rain / Without you / Jump 'n' pump / Empty skies / Calm before the storm / Vibe tribe.
CD ....................................... CDINZ 1
MC ....................................... MCINZ 1
Passion/Debut/Scratch Music / Mar '93 / Pinnacle / 3MV.

## STREETWALKIN'.
**Tracks:** Streetwalkin' / Go for it.
■ **12"** ............................... POSPX 452
■ **7"** ................................. POSP 452
Polydor / Jun '82.

## TURN THE MUSIC UP.
**Tracks:** Turn the music up / Be bop.
■ **12"** .................................. PZ 49
■ **7"** .................................... PO 49
■ **CD Single** ......................... PZCD 49
Polydor / Jul '89.

## TURN THE MUSIC UP.
**Tracks:** Turn the music up / Better believe it.
■ **LP** ................................ 841 077-1
■ **MC** ............................... 841 077-4
■ **CD** ................................ 841 077-2
Polydor / Sep '89.

## UNDER THE SUN.
**Tracks:** Soul destination / Don't walk away / Paradise island / Rest of your life / Crosstown / One for the boyz / Beyond the reach / Can't stop running / Sweat / It's over / Fly by night / Shine your light.
CD ....................................... CDINZ 2
MC ....................................... MCINZ 2
Passion/Debut/Scratch Music / Nov '92 / Pinnacle / 3MV.

## WATCH YOU.
**Tracks:** Watch you / Bitch to the boys.
■ **12"** .............................. SANGRIA 12 1
■ **7"** ............................... SANGRIA 1
Loose / Nov '84.

## Shalamar

Chic wannabes established by *Soul Train* booking agent Dick Griffey, whose best-known line-up featured Howard Hewitt, Jeffrey Daniels and Jody Watley. Biggest act on Griffey's LA-based Solar label, group enjoyed more success in U.K. than U.S.: biggest of four Top 10 hits was 1982's *Night To Remember*. Daniels and Watley quit in '83; latter pursuing intermittently successful solo career. New personnel won Grammy for track from *Beverly Hills Cop*, but were terminally crippled by Hewitt's departure in '86. Later incarnations are best ignored in favour of original line-up's various hits collections.

## AMNESIA.
**Tracks:** Amnesia / You're the one for me.
■ **12"** ................................. SHALT 1

■ **7"** .................................. SHAL 1
MCA / Nov '84.

## BEST OF SHALAMAR.
**Tracks:** Night to remember / Make that move / Take that to the bank / Uptown festival (part 1) / I can make you feel good / Friends / Amnesia / Second time around / I owe you one / Over and over / There it is / Disappearing act / Dead giveaway / My girl loves me.
■ **LP** ................................ MCG 6080
■ **CD** .............................. DMCG 6080
■ **MC** ............................. MCGC 6080
MCA / Mar '90.

## BIG FUN.
**Tracks:** Right time for us / Take me to the river / Right in the socket / Second time around / I owe you one / Let's find the time for love / Girl.
■ **LP** ................................. FL 13479
Grunt / Feb '80.

## CIRCUMSTANTIAL EVIDENCE.
**Tracks:** Circumstantial evidence / Games / Love's grown deep / Plaything / Female / Born to love / Worth waitin' for / Imaginary love.
■ **CD** .............................. DMCF 3387
■ **LP** ................................. MCF 3387
■ **MC** ............................. MCFC 3387
MCA / Jul '87.

## CIRCUMSTANTIAL EVIDENCE.
**Tracks:** Circumstantial evidence.
■ **12"** ................................ SHALT 6
■ **7"** ................................. SHAL 6
MCA / Aug '87.

## COLLECTION.
**Tracks:** Not Advised.
CD ..................................... CCSCD 390
MC. ................................... CCSMC 390
Castle / Apr '94 / BMG.

## DANCING IN THE STREETS.
**Tracks:** Dancing in the street.
■ **12"** ................................. TA 4171
■ **7"** .................................. A 4171
CBS / Jun '84.

## DEAD GIVEAWAY.
**Tracks:** Dead giveaway / I don't wanna be the last to know.
■ **7"** ................................. E 9818
Solar / Jun '83.

## DEADLINE USA.
**Tracks:** Deadline USA / Knock me off my feet.
■ **12"** ............................... MCAT 866
■ **7"** ................................ MCA 866
MCA / Mar '84.

## DISAPPEARING ACT.
**Tracks:** Disappearing act / No limits.
■ **12"** ............................... E 9807T
■ **7"** ................................. E 9807
Solar / Aug '83.

## DISCO GARDENS.
**Tracks:** Tossing, turning and swinging / Disco gardens / Take that to the bank / Stay close to love / Leave it all up to love / Lovely lady / Cindy, Cindy.
■ **LP** ................................. FL 12895
RCA / Nov '78.

## FRIENDS.
**Tracks:** Night to remember / Don't try to change me / Help me / On top of the world / I don't wanna be the last to know / Friends / Playing to win / I just stopped by because I had to / There it is / I can make you feel good.
■ **LP** ................................. K 52345
Solar / Mar '82.
■ **CD** ................................ 252 345
Sire / Jan '83.

## FRIENDS.
**Tracks:** Friends / I just stopped because I had to.
■ **7"** ................................. CHUM 1
Solar / Nov '82.

## GO FOR IT.
**Tracks:** Go for it / Appeal / Final analysis / You've got me running / Sweeter as the days go by / Talk to me / Good feelings / Rocker.
■ **LP** ................................ SOLA 10
MC. ................................... SOLC 10
Solar / Dec '81 / Sony.

## GREATEST HITS: SHALAMAR.
**Tracks:** Over and over / Night to remember / Uptown festival (part 1) / There it is / I can make you feel good / Disappearing act / Dead giveaway / Friends / Amnesia / My girls love me / Make that move /

Second time around / Take that to the bank / I ow you one.
■ **CD** ................................. DSMR 86
MCA / '86.
■ **CD** .............................. DMCG 402
MCA / '88.

## GREATEST HITS: SHALAMAR.
**Tracks:** Attention my baby / Second time around Make that move / This is for the lover in you / Full fire / Take that to the bank / I owe you one / Sweete as the days go by / Somewhere there's a love / Rig in the socket.
■ **LP** ................................. SOLA 30(
MC. ................................... SOLC 30(
Solar / Aug '82 / Sony.

## HEARTBREAK.
**Tracks:** Amnesia / Dancing in the street / Wheneve you need me / Heartbreak / Don't get stopped Beverly Hills / My girl loves me / Melody (an ero affair) / Deceiver.
■ **LP** ................................. MCF 32(
MCA / Jan '85.
CD ..................................... VG 600 0
Vogue / Jan '87 / BMG.
■ **LP** ................................. MCL 18
■ **MC** ............................... MCLC 18
MCA / Jun '87.

## HERE IT IS .. THE BEST OF SHALAMAF
**Tracks:** There it is / Take that to the bank / Friends Second time around / My girl loves me / Dancing the sheets / Disappearing act / Amnesia / Night remember / I owe you one / Full of fire / Sweeter the days go by / Uptown festival (part one) / Going a go go / I can't help myself (sugar pie, honey bunc / Uptight (everything's alright) / Stop, in the name love / It's the same old song / Right in the socke Make that move / Dead giveaway / Over and over can make you feel good.
■ **CD** ................................. 47204(
■ **MC** ............................... 47204(
Solar / Jul '92.

## I CAN MAKE YOU FEEL GOOD.
**Tracks:** I can make you feel good / Help me.
■ **7"** .................................. K 125(
Solar / Mar '82.

## I OWE YOU ONE.
**Tracks:** I owe you one / Right time for us.
■ **12"** ................................ SO 12 (
■ **7"** ................................... SO (
Solar / Aug '80.

## LOOK.
**Tracks:** Closer / Dead giveaway / You can count c me / Right here / No limits / Disappearing act / Ove and over / You're the one for me / You won't mis love / Look.
■ **LP** ............................... K 960239
WEA / Aug '83.

## MAKE THAT MOVE.
**Tracks:** Make that move / Pop along kid.
■ **12"** ................................ SOT (
■ **7"** .................................. SO (
Solar / Mar '81.

## MY GIRL LOVES ME.
**Tracks:** My girl loves me / Mix to remember.
■ **12"** ................................ SHALT (
■ **7"** ................................. SHAL (
MCA / Jan '85.

## NIGHT TO REMEMBER.
**Tracks:** Night to remember / Take that to the bank Uptown festival / I can make you feel good.
■ **7"** ................................. K1316
Solar / '82.
■ **12"** ................................ SHALT (
■ **7"** ................................. SHAL (
I.R.S. (Illegal) / May '87.

## NIGHT TO REMEMBER (OLD GOLD).
**Tracks:** Night to remember / I can make you fee good.
■ **12"** ................................. OG 405
Old Gold / Jul '89.

## NIGHT TO REMEMBER, A (RE-MIX).
**Tracks:** Night to remember (re-mix).
■ **7"** ................................. SHAL (
MCA / Apr '86.

## OVER AND OVER.
**Tracks:** Over and over / You're the one for me.
■ **12"** ................................ E 9792
■ **7"** ................................. E 979
Solar / Oct '83.

## HIS TOP HITS.
Tracks: Not Advised.
MC. . . . . . . . . . . . . . . . . . . . . . . . . .810
Timeless Treasures / Jul '86 / THE.

## IF LOVING YOU IS WRONG.
Tracks: If loving you is wrong I don't want to be right / When a man loves a woman / Take time to know her / Warm and tender love / It tears me up / Behind closed doors / Try a little tenderness / (Sittin' on) the dock of the bay / Tell it like it is / You send me / Bring it on home to me / My special prayer / I've been loving you too long / Cover me.
■ LP . . . . . . . . . . . . . . . . . . . . CRB 1138
Charly R&B / Aug '87.
CD . . . . . . . . . . . . . . . . . . . . . CDCD 1064
Charly / Mar '93 / Charly.

## IT TEARS ME UP (The Best Of Percy Sledge).
Tracks: When a man loves a woman / I'm hanging up my heart for you / Put a little lovin' on me / Love me like you mean it / It tears me up / Warm and tender love / Love me tender / Dark end of the street / Take time to know her / Try a little tenderness / Bless your sweet little soul / True love travels on a gravel road / Sudden stop / Stop the world tonight / It's all wrong but it's alright / Drown in my own tears / Out of left field / Kind woman / Cover me / That's the way I want to live my life / Push Mr.Pride aside / It can't be stopped / Rainbow road.
CD . . . . . . . . . . . . . . . . . . .812270285-2
WEA / Mar '93 / WEA.

## IT TEARS ME UP.
Tracks: It tears me up / Oh how happy.
■ 7" . . . . . . . . . . . . . . . . . . . . .584071
Atlantic / Jan '67.

## JUST CAN'T STOP.
Tracks: Just can't stop.
■ 7" . . . . . . . . . . . . . . . . . . . SON 2335
Sonet / Feb '88.

## LEGENDS IN MUSIC - PERCY SLEDGE.
Tracks: Not Advised.
CD . . . . . . . . . . . . . . . . . . . . . LECD 065
Wiseback / Jul '94 / THE / Conifer Records.

## OUT OF LEFT FIELD.
Tracks: My adorable one / Take time to know her / My special prayer / Thief in the night / Out of left field / It tears me up / When a man loves a woman / Just out of reach (of my two empty arms) / Cover me / Warm and tender love.
■ LP . . . . . . . . . . . . . . . . . . . BDL 3007
President / Oct '90.
CD . . . . . . . . . . . . . . . . . . . . TKOCD 008
MC. . . . . . . . . . . . . . . . . . . . . TKOCS 008
TKO Records / '92 / TKO Records Ltd / President Records.

## OUT OF LEFT FIELD.
Tracks: Out of left field / It can't be stopped.
■ 7" . . . . . . . . . . . . . . . . . . . .584108
Atlantic / Apr '67.

## PERCY.
Tracks: Bring your lovin' to me / You had to be there / All night train / She's too pretty to cry / I still miss someone / Faithful kind / Home type thing / Personality / I'd put angels around you / Hard lovin' woman / When a man loves a woman.
CD . . . . . . . . . . . . . . . . . . . CDCHARLY 95
■ LP . . . . . . . . . . . . . . . . . . . CRB 1152
MC. . . . . . . . . . . . . . . . . . . . TCCRB 1152
Charly R&B / Jul '87 / Charly.

## PERCY SLEDGE - GREATEST HITS.
Tracks: Not Advised.
MC. . . . . . . . . . . . . . . . . . . . . GM 0204
-Tel Goldmasters / Aug '84 / C.M. Distribution / Arabesque Ltd. / Ross Records / PolyGram.

## PERCY SLEDGE WAY, THE.
Tracks: Dark end of the street / You send me / I had a walk / What am I living for / I've been loving you too long / My special prayer / Drown in my own tears / Just out of reach / Pledging my love / You don't miss your water.
■ LP . . . . . . . . . . . . . . . . . . . 587 081
Atlantic / Nov '67.

## PLEDGING MY LOVE.
Tracks: Pledging my love / You don't miss your water.
■ 7" . . . . . . . . . . . . . . . . . . . .584140
Atlantic / Oct '67.

## SOUL SENSATION (see under Franklin, Aretha).

## SPOTLIGHT ON PERCY SLEDGE.
Tracks: Warm and tender love / Cover me / You're pouring water on a drowning man / My special prayer / Take time to know her / My adorable one / Sudden stop / Good love / Walking in the sun / It tears me up / Make it good, make it last / Out of left field / Behind closed doors / Just out of reach / Thief in the night / When a man loves a woman.
CD . . . . . . . . . . . . . . . . . . . HADCD 125
MC. . . . . . . . . . . . . . . . . . . . HADMC 125
Javelin / Feb '94 / THE.

## WANTED AGAIN.
Tracks: Keep the fire burning / Kiss an angel good morning / If you've got the money honey / Today I started loving you again / Wabash cannonball / Wanted again / Hey good lookin' / He'll have to go / She thinks I still care / For the good times.
CD . . . . . . . . . . . . . . . . . . . FIENDCD 140
■ LP . . . . . . . . . . . . . . . . . . . FIEND 140
Demon / Jul '89 / Pinnacle / A.D.A. Distribution.

## WARM AND TENDER LOVE.
Tracks: Make it good and make it last / When a man loves a woman / Walkin' in the sun / Warm and closed doors / Jst out of reach / I believe in you / Take time to know her.
■ LP . . . . . . . . . . . . . . . . . . . BMM 006
Blue Moon (1) / Aug '86.

## WARM AND TENDER LOVE.
Tracks: Warm and tender love.
■ 7" . . . . . . . . . . . . . . . . . . . 584 034
Atlantic / Aug '66.

## WHEN A MAN.
Tracks: When a man loves a woman / Walkin' in the sun / Behind closed doors / Make it good and make it last / Good love / I believe in you / My special prayer / I'll be your everything / If this is the last time / Hard to be friends / Blue water / Love among people.
CD . . . . . . . . . . . . . . . . . . . . OR 0013
Music Collection International / Aug '87 / THE / Jazz Music.

## WHEN A MAN.
Tracks: Not Advised.
CD . . . . . . . . . . . . . . . . . . . .266221 2
Mainline (2) / Feb '89.

## WHEN A MAN LOVES A WOMAN.
Tracks: Warm and tender love.
■ 7" . . . . . . . . . . . . . . . . . . . K 10104
Atlantic / '79.
■ 12" . . . . . . . . . . . . . . . . . . . YZ 96T
■ 7" . . . . . . . . . . . . . . . . . . . TZ 96
Atlantic / Jan '87.
■ CD Single . . . . . . . . . . . . . . . . 500 068
Intertape / Jul '87.

## WHEN A MAN LOVES A WOMAN.
Tracks: When a man loves a woman / Love me like you mean it.
■ 7" . . . . . . . . . . . . . . . . . . . 584 001
Atlantic / May '66.

## WHEN A MAN LOVES A WOMAN.
Tracks: When a man loves a woman / Warm and tender love.
7" . . . . . . . . . . . . . . . . . . . .A 7221
CD Single . . . . . . . . . . . . . . . . A 7221CD
MC Single . . . . . . . . . . . . . . . . A 7221C
Atlantic / Sep '94 / WEA.

## WHEN A MAN LOVES A WOMAN.
Tracks: Come softly to me / You don't miss your water / Heart of a child / Out of left fielf / You send me / Oh, how happy / When a man loves a woman / My special prayer / I love everything about you / High cost of leaving / Love me tender / Warm and tender love.
■ LP . . . . . . . . . . . . . . . . . . . .2464 002
Atlantic / Jun '70.

## WHEN A MAN LOVES A WOMAN (1).
Tracks: I'll be your everything / If this is the last time / Hard to be friends / Blue water / Love away people / Take time to know her / Out of left field / Warm and tender love / It tears me up / When a man loves a woman / Walkin' in the sun / Behind closed doors / Make it good and make it last / Good love / I believe in you / My special prayer.
MC. . . . . . . . . . . . . . . . . . . . KTOP 113
Topline / Jan '85 / Charly.
CD . . . . . . . . . . . . . . . . . . . TOP CD 502
■ LP . . . . . . . . . . . . . . . . . . . .TOP 113
Topline / Apr '87 / Charly.

## WHEN A MAN LOVES A WOMAN (2).
Tracks: When a man loves a woman / Warm and tender love / Just out of reach / Dark end of the street / Cover me / My special prayer / Sudden stop /
You're all around me / It tears me up / Out of left field / Take time to know her / Baby help me.
■ LP . . . . . . . . . . . . . . . . . . . SHM 3064
■ MC. . . . . . . . . . . . . . . . . . . HSC 3064
Hallmark / Jan '81.
■ LP P.Disc . . . . . . . . . . . . . . . AR 30065
Exclusive Picture Discs / Nov '87.
CD . . . . . . . . . . . . . . . . . . . .PWKS 547
MC. . . . . . . . . . . . . . . . . . . . HSC 3287
Pickwick / Oct '89 / Pickwick.

## WHEN A MAN LOVES A WOMAN (3).
Tracks: Not Advised.
MC. . . . . . . . . . . . . . . . . . . . .510439.4
Magnum Music / Dec '88 / Magnum Music Group / THE.

## WHEN A MAN LOVES A WOMAN (EP).
Tracks: When a man loves a woman / Warm and tender love / What is soul / Stand by me.
■ EP . . . . . . . . . . . . . . . . . . . .ATM 3
Atlantic / Apr '80.

## WHEN A MAN LOVES A WOMAN (OLD GOLD).
Tracks: When a man loves a woman / Warm and tender love.
7" . . . . . . . . . . . . . . . . . . . .OG 9496
Old Gold / Mar '90 / Pickwick.

# Sleeque

## ONE FOR THE MONEY.
Tracks: One for the money / One for the (dub).
■ 12" . . . . . . . . . . . . . . . . . MAL 12 033
Malaco / Jun '86.

# Slick

## FORGET YOU (IT'S TOO LATE).
Tracks: Forget you (it's too late) / Betcha bottom dollar.
■ 12" . . . . . . . . . . . . . . . . . . FTCT 193
■ 7" . . . . . . . . . . . . . . . . . . . FTC 193
Fantasy / Nov '80.

## SEXY CREAM.
Tracks: Sexy cream / Put your pants on.
■ 7" . . . . . . . . . . . . . . . . . . . FTC 182
Fantasy / Sep '79.

## SPACE BASS.
Tracks: Space bass / Whole world is dancing.
■ 12" . . . . . . . . . . . . . . . . .12FTC 176
■ 7" . . . . . . . . . . . . . . . . . . . FTC 176
Fantasy / May '79.

## SPACE BASS.
Tracks: Space bass / Feeling good / Sexy cream / Put your pants on / Whole world is dancing.
■ LP . . . . . . . . . . . . . . . . . . . .FT 560
Fantasy / '79.

# Slim

## IT'S IN THE MIX.
Tracks: It's in the mix.
■ 12" . . . . . . . . . . . . . . . . . . GRPT 104
Greyhound / Jul '83.

# Smith & Mighty

## ANYONE.
Tracks: Anyone / Dark.
■ 12" . . . . . . . . . . . . . . . . . . . SAM 111
3 Stripe / Feb '88.
■ 12" . . . . . . . . . . . . . . . . . . BEATM 212
■ 7" . . . . . . . . . . . . . . . . . . . BEATM 2
Beatmaster / Jun '88.

## ANYONE (REISSUES) (Smith & Mighty Featuring Jackie Jackson).
Tracks: Anyone / Anyone (Instrumental) (7" and Cassingle.) / Anyone (Remix) (12" only.) / Anyone (Mellow mix) (12" single only.) / Anyway you want to (12" single only.) / Anyone (Full length mix) / Anyone (Bell mix) (12" remix & CD single only.) / Loving (12" only.)
■ 12" . . . . . . . . . . . . . . . . . . . SNMX 3
■ 12" Remix. . . . . . . . . . . . . . . . SNMXR 3
■ 7" . . . . . . . . . . . . . . . . . . . SNM 3
■ CD Single. . . . . . . . . . . . . . . . SNMCD 3
■ MC Single. . . . . . . . . . . . . . . . SNMCS 3
3 Stripe / Sep '90.

## ANYONE(REMIX).
Tracks: Anyone (remix).
■ 12" . . . . . . . . . . . . . . . . . . SAM 111R
3 Stripe / Feb '89.

## REMEMBER ME.
Tracks: Remember me / Come fly away.
| | |
|---|---|
| 12" | SNMX 6 |
| 7" | SNM 6 |
| CD Single | SNMCD 6 |
| MC Single | SNMC 6 |
3 Stripe / Aug '94 / PolyGram.

## STEPPERS DELIGHT.
Tracks: Steppers delight.
| | |
|---|---|
| ■ 12" | SNMX 5 |
3 Stripe / Apr '92.

## WALK ON BY.
Tracks: Walk on by / Travellin'.
| | |
|---|---|
| ■ 12" | SNM 1114 |
| ■ 12" Remix | SAM 114R |
| ■ 7" | 7 SNM 1114 |
3 Stripe / Nov '88.

## Smith, Charlene

### FEEL THE GOOD TIMES.
Tracks: Feel the good times.
| | |
|---|---|
| 12" | ID 008T |
| CD Single | ID 008CD |
| MC Single | ID 008MC |
Indochina / Jul '94 / Pinnacle.

### I LEARNED MY LESSON.
Tracks: I learned my lesson.
| | |
|---|---|
| CD Single | ID 014CD |
Indochina / Oct '94 / Pinnacle.
| | |
|---|---|
| MC Single | ID 014MC |
China / Oct '94 / Pinnacle.

## Smith, Lonnie Liston

### BEST OF LONNIE LISTON SMITH.
Tracks: Quiet moments / Space princess / In the park / Give peace a chance / Fruit music / Gift of love / Journey into love.
| | |
|---|---|
| ■ LP | CBS 84348 |
| MC | 40 84348 |
CBS / Jan '81 / Sony.

### BEST OF LONNIE LISTON SMITH, THE.
Tracks: Expansions / Love beams / Song of love / Meditations / Voodoo woman / Space lady / Starlight and you starbeams.
| | |
|---|---|
| ■ LP | PL 12897 |
RCA / Apr '80.

### DANCE FLOOR.
Tracks: Dance floor.
| | |
|---|---|
| ■ 12" | 12 PO 50 |
Ichiban / Sep '90.

### DREAMS OF TOMORROW.
Tracks: Lonely way to be / Mystic woman / Love I see in your eyes / Dreams of tomorrow / Never too late / Rainbows of love / Divine light / Garden of peace.
| | |
|---|---|
| ■ LP | ASLP 1000 |
| MC | ZCAS 1000 |
Doctor Jazz (USA) / Jul '83.
| | |
|---|---|
| CD | 26 10 522 |
| MC | 26 10524 |
Dillion / '92 / Sound Solutions.

### DRIVES.
Tracks: Twenty five miles / Psychedelic PI / Spinning wheel / Who's afraid of Virginia Woolf / Seven steps to heaven.
| | |
|---|---|
| CD | CDP 8282662 |
| LP | B1 28266 |
Blue Note / Mar '94 / EMI.

### EXPANSIONS.
Tracks: Expansions / Voodoo woman.
| | |
|---|---|
| ■ 12" | BRT 4 |
Blue Bird (2) / Nov '83.

### EXPANSIONS.
Tracks: Expansions / Dessert nights / Summer days / Voodoo woman / Peace / Shadows / My love.
| | |
|---|---|
| ■ LP | NL 80934 |
| ■ MC | NK 80934 |
RCA / Jun '91.
| | |
|---|---|
| CD | ND 80934 |
RCA / Mar '94 / BMG.

### FUNK REACTION.
Tracks: Funk reaction / When the night is right.
| | |
|---|---|
| ■ 7" | TKR 6021 |
TK / Feb '78.

### GET DOWN EVERYBODY (IT TIME FOR WORLD PEACE).
Tracks: Get down everybody (it time for world peace) / Inner beauty.
| | |
|---|---|
| ■ 7" | RCA 2727 |
RCA / Aug '76.

## GIVE PEACE A CHANCE.
Tracks: Give peace a chance / Sunburst.
| | |
|---|---|
| ■ 12" | 13 8660 |
CBS / Jun '80.

## GOLDEN DREAMS.
Tracks: Get down everybody (it's time for world peace) / Quiet dawn / Sunbeams / Meditations / Peace & love / Goddess of love / Inner beauty / Golden dreams / Journey into space / Astral travelling / Let us go into the house of the Lord / I mani / In search of truth.
| | |
|---|---|
| ■ CD | ND 86886 |
Bluebird / Nov '88.

## GOTCHA.
Tracks: Sweet honey wine / I need your love / What's done is done / Do it / Journey to within / My Latin sky.
| | |
|---|---|
| ■ LP | TKR 83356 |
TK / Apr '79.

## IF YOU TAKE CARE OF ME.
Tracks: If you take care of me / Just us two.
| | |
|---|---|
| ■ 7" | 7AS 3500 |
Doctor Jazz (USA) / Feb '85.

## LOVE GODDESS.
Tracks: Love goddess / Obsession / Heaven / Monk's mood / Star flower / Giving you the best that I've got / Don't write cheques that your body can't cash / Dance floor / I'm your melody / Blue in green / Blue Bossa / Child is born.
| | |
|---|---|
| ■ LP | STA 4021 |
Star Track / Mar '90.
| | |
|---|---|
| CD | STACD 4021 |
| MC | STAMC 4021 |
Star Track / Mar '94 / ACD Trading Ltd.

## LOVE IS THE ANSWER.
Tracks: In the park / Love is the answer / Speak about it / Bridge through time / On the real side / Enchantress / Give peace a chance / Free and easy.
| | |
|---|---|
| ■ LP | CBS 84365 |
CBS / Jul '80.

## LOVELAND.
Tracks: Sunburst / Journey into love / Floating through space / Bright moments / We can dream / Springtime magic / Loveland / Explorations.
| | |
|---|---|
| ■ LP | 82837 |
CBS / '74.

## MAGIC LADY.
Tracks: Not Advised.
| | |
|---|---|
| LP | STA 1000 |
Startrak / Oct '91 / Backs Distribution.

## MOVE YOUR HAND.
Tracks: Charlie Brown / Layin' in the cut / Move your hand / Sunshine superman.
| | |
|---|---|
| LP | B1 84326 |
Blue Note / Aug '94 / EMI.

## NEVER TOO LATE.
Tracks: Never too late / Divine light.
| | |
|---|---|
| ■ 12" | ASL 100 |
| ■ 7" | 7 AS 100 |
Doctor Jazz (USA) / Jul '83.

## OBSESSION (Featuring Phyllis Hyman).
Tracks: Obsession / Obsession (version).
| | |
|---|---|
| ■ 12" | 12 PO 44 |
Ichiban / Apr '90.

## REJUVENATION.
Tracks: Not Advised.
| | |
|---|---|
| ■ LP | ASLP 810 |
| ■ MC | ZCAS 810 |
Doctor Jazz (USA) / Mar '86.

## RENAISSANCE.
Tracks: Space lady / Mardi gras / Starlight and you / Mongotee / Song of love / Between here and there / Renaissance.
| | |
|---|---|
| ■ LP | PL 11822 |
RCA / Jan '77.

## SILHOUETTES.
Tracks: Warm / If you take care of me I'll take care of you / Silhouettes / Summer afternoon / Enlightenment / City of lights / Once again love / Just us two.
| | |
|---|---|
| ■ LP | ASLP 805 |
| MC | ZCAS 805 |
Doctor Jazz (USA) / Nov '84.
| | |
|---|---|
| CD | 26 10 512 |
| MC | 26 10 514 |
Dillion / '92 / Sound Solutions.

## SONG FOR THE CHILDREN.
Tracks: Song for the children / Lover's dream / Aquarian cycle / Street festival / Midsummer magic / Nightlife / Gift of love / Fruit music.
| | |
|---|---|
| ■ LP | 83809 |
CBS / Feb '80.

## STAR FLOWER.
Tracks: Star flower.
| | |
|---|---|
| ■ 12" | 12 PO 56 |
Star Track / Jan '91.

## THINK.
Tracks: Son of Ice Bag / Call of the wild / Think / Three blind mice / Slouchin'.
| | |
|---|---|
| ■ CD | BNZ 136 |
| ■ LP | BST 84290 |
Blue Note / Jul '89.
| | |
|---|---|
| LP | B1 842901 |
Blue Note / Sep '93 / EMI.

## VERY BEST OF LONNIE LISTON SMITH, THE.
Tracks: Space princess / Get down everybody (it's time for world peace) / Desert nights / Voodoo woman / Chance for peace / Visions of a new world / Song for the children / Fruit music / Quiet moments / Quiet dawn / Sunbeams / Expansions / Prelude (live) (Available on CD only) / Expansions (live) (Available on CD only).
| | |
|---|---|
| CD | 74321 13761-2 |
| LP | 74321 13761-1 |
RCA / Jul '93 / BMG.

## WATERCOLORS.
Tracks: Watercolors / Sunset / Starlight and you / My love / Expansions / Song for love / Renaissance / Devika / Summer nights / Aspirations / Colors of the rainbow.
| | |
|---|---|
| CD | ND 83099 |
Novus / Jan '92 / BMG.

## Smith, Marvin

### KEEPER OF THE DRUMS.
Tracks: Just have fun / Miss Ann / Love will find a way / Song of joy / Creeper / Now I know / Thinking of you / Simple samba song.
| | |
|---|---|
| ■ LP | CJ 325 |
| MC | CJC 325 |
Concord Jazz / Sep '87 / New Note.
| | |
|---|---|
| CD | CCD 4325 |
Concord Jazz / Sep '87 / New Note.

### ROAD LESS TRAVELLED, THE (Smith, Marvin 'Smitty').
Tracks: Neighbourhood / Wish you were here with me part 1 / Gothic 17 / Road less travelled / I'll love you always / Salsa blue / Concerto in B.G. / Wish you were here with me part 2.
| | |
|---|---|
| CD | CCD 4379 |
| ■ LP | CJ 379 |
| ■ MC | CJ 379C |
Concord / Jul '89 / New Note.

## Smith, O.C.

### COLLECTION: O.C. SMITH.
Tracks: Honey / That's life / Son of Hickory Holler's tramp / Moody / Me and you / Together / Simple life / Primrose Lane / Pretending / Love song / Empty hearts / Little green apples / You and I / Sweet loveliness.
| | |
|---|---|
| ■ Double LP | PDA 068 |
Pickwick / Sep '80.

### DOWNTOWN U.S.A.
Tracks: Downtown U.S.A. / That's what life is all about.
| | |
|---|---|
| ■ 7" | S 7064 |
CBS / Mar '71.

### DYNAMIC O.C. SMITH.
Tracks: That's life / Seasons / South side of Chicago / My romance / Work song / Fever / Georgia Rose / Here's that rainy day / Quiet nights of quiet stars / What now my love / On a clear day.
| | |
|---|---|
| ■ LP | SBPG 63147 |
CBS / Apr '68.

### HICKORY HOLLER REVISITED.
Tracks: Not Advised.
| | |
|---|---|
| ■ LP | CBS 63362 |
CBS / Aug '68.

### SIMPLE LIFE.
Tracks: Simple life / I found the secret.
| | |
|---|---|
| ■ 7" | CRB 5325 |
Caribou / Jun '77.

### SON OF HICKORY HOLLER'S TRAMP.
Tracks: Son of Hickory Holler's tramp.
| | |
|---|---|
| ■ 7" | CBS 3343 |
CBS / May '68.

■ DELETED

## SON OF HICKORY HOLLER'S TRAMP (OLD GOLD).
**Tracks:** Son of Hickory Holler's tramp / Together.
■ 7" . . . . . . . . . . . . . . . . . . . . **OG 9179**
Old Gold / Jul '82.

## TOGETHER.
**Tracks:** Together / Just couldn't help myself.
■ 7" . . . . . . . . . . . . . . . . . . . . **CRB 4910**
Caribou / Mar '77.

## TOGETHER.
**Tracks:** You and I / Together / Simple life / Sweet lov'liness / Wham bam / Come with me / Pretending / Love song / Empty hearts / I found the secret.
■ LP . . . . . . . . . . . . . . . . . . . . **CRB 81848**
Caribou / Jun '77.

# Smith, Richard Jon

## (MY HOME TOWN) MEADOWLANDS.
**Tracks:** (My home town) Meadowlands / Shout it out.
■ 12" . . . . . . . . . . . . . . . . . . . **CYZ 126**
■ 7" . . . . . . . . . . . . . . . . . . . **CYZ 7 126**
Charly Groove / Jun '88.

## ABC OF KISSING.
**Tracks:** ABC of kissing / Jessica.
■ 12" . . . . . . . . . . . . . . . . . . **JIVET 85**
■ 7" . . . . . . . . . . . . . . . . . . **JIVE 85**
Jive / Mar '85.
■ 7" P.Disc . . . . . . . . . . . . . . . **JIVEP 95**
Jive / May '85.

## BABY'S GOT ANOTHER.
**Tracks:** Baby's got another / This is the moment.
■ 12" . . . . . . . . . . . . . . . . . . **JIVET 29**
■ 7" . . . . . . . . . . . . . . . . . . **JIVE 29**
Jive / Mar '83.

## DANCE WITH ME.
**Tracks:** Dance with me / Jump for you.
■ 12" . . . . . . . . . . . . . . . . . . **JIVET 69**
■ 7" . . . . . . . . . . . . . . . . . . **JIVE 69**
Jive / Jul '84.

## DANCIN' IN AFRICA.
**Tracks:** Dancin' in Africa (African ecstacy mix) / (My home town) Meadowlands (Indian summer mix).
■ 12" . . . . . . . . . . . . . . . . . . **CYZ 129**
■ 7" . . . . . . . . . . . . . . . . . . **CYZ 7 129**
Charly Groove / Sep '88.

## DON'T GO WALKING OUT THAT DOOR.
**Tracks:** Don't go walking out that door / Keep on walking out that door.
■ 12" . . . . . . . . . . . . . . . . . . **JIVET 19**
■ 7" . . . . . . . . . . . . . . . . . . **JIVE 19**
Jive / Aug '82.

## HOLD ON.
**Tracks:** Hold on / Hands off / ABC of kissing (Only on 12" single.) / Baby's got another (Only on 12" single.) / She's the master of the game (Only on 12" single.) / Stay with me tonight (Only on 12" single.)
■ 12" . . . . . . . . . . . . . . . . . **JIVET 104**
■ 7" . . . . . . . . . . . . . . . . . **JIVE 104**
Jive / Sep '85.

## IN THE NIGHT.
**Tracks:** In the night / I need you.
■ 12" . . . . . . . . . . . . . . . . . **JIVET 53**
■ 7" . . . . . . . . . . . . . . . . . **JIVE 53**
Jive / Jan '84.

## RICHARD JON SMITH.
**Tracks:** Stay with me tonight / Don't go walking out that door / Baby's got another.
■ LP . . . . . . . . . . . . . . . . . . **HIP 5**
■ MC. . . . . . . . . . . . . . . . . . **HIPC 5**
Jive / Oct '83.

## SHE'S THE MASTER OF THE GAME.
**Tracks:** She's the master of the game / Love is what I'm after.
■ 12" . . . . . . . . . . . . . . . . . **JIVET 38**
■ 7" . . . . . . . . . . . . . . . . . **JIVE 38**
Jive / Jul '83.

## STAY WITH ME TONIGHT.
**Tracks:** Stay with me tonight.
■ 12" . . . . . . . . . . . . . . . . . **JIVET 10**
■ 7" . . . . . . . . . . . . . . . . . **JIVE 10**
Jive / Feb '82.

# Smith, Toni

## OOH I LIKE THE WAY IT FEELS.
**Tracks:** Ooh, I like the way it feels / Ooh, I like the way it feels (dub).
■ 12" . . . . . . . . . . . . . . . . . **MAL 12 013**
■ 7" . . . . . . . . . . . . . . . . . **MAL 013**
Malaco / Jan '84.

# Smoke

## MY FRIEND JACK.
**Tracks:** Not Advised.
■ LP . . . . . . . . . . . . . . . . . . **MBT 5001**
Morgan Blue Town / May '88.

## MY FRIEND JACK.
**Tracks:** My friend Jack.
■ 7" . . . . . . . . . . . . . . . . . . **DB 8115**
Columbia / Mar '67.

# Snow, Phoebe

## AGAINST THE GRAIN.
**Tracks:** Every night / Do right woman, dor right man / He's not just another man / Random time / In my life / You have not won / Mama don't break down / Oh L.A. / Married men / Keep a watch on the shoreline.
■ LP . . . . . . . . . . . . . . . . . . **CBS 82915**
CBS / Feb '79.

## BEST OF PHOEBE SNOW.
**Tracks:** Two fisted love / All over / Poetry man / Teach me tonight / Don't let me down / Shaky ground / Love makes a woman / Never letting go / Every night / Harpo's blues.
■ LP . . . . . . . . . . . . . . . . . . **CBS 84909**
CBS / Jun '81.
■ LP . . . . . . . . . . . . . . . . . . **CBS 32643**
MC. . . . . . . . . . . . . . . . . . . **40 32643**
CBS / Apr '85 / Sony.

## EVERY NIGHT.
**Tracks:** Every night / Keep a watch on the shoreline.
■ 7" . . . . . . . . . . . . . . . . . . **CBS 6842**
CBS / Jan '79.

## GAMES.
**Tracks:** Games / Down in the basement.
■ 7" . . . . . . . . . . . . . . . . . . **K 11566**
Atlantic / Apr '81.

## GASOLINE ALLEY.
**Tracks:** Gasoline Alley / I believe in you.
■ 7" . . . . . . . . . . . . . . . . . . **K 11663**
Mirage (USA) / Jun '81.

## IF I CAN JUST GET THROUGH THE NIGHT.
**Tracks:** If I can just get through the night / Soothin' / Our love is insane.
■ 12" . . . . . . . . . . . . . . . . . **EKR 91T**
■ 7" . . . . . . . . . . . . . . . . . **EKR 91**
■ CD Single . . . . . . . . . . . . . **EKR 91CD**
Elektra / Apr '89.

## IT LOOKS LIKE SNOW.
**Tracks:** Autobiography / Teach me tonight / Stand up on the rock / In my girlish days / Mercy on those / Don't let me down / Drink up the melody / Fat chance / My faith is blind / Shakey ground.
■ LP . . . . . . . . . . . . . . . . . . **CBS 81714**
CBS / Feb '77.

## NEVER LETTING GO.
**Tracks:** Love makes a woman / Majesty of life / Ride the elevator / Something so right / Never letting go / We're children / Middle of the night / Garden of joy blues.
■ LP . . . . . . . . . . . . . . . . . . **CBS 82224**
CBS / Dec '77.

## PHOEBE SNOW.
**Tracks:** Good times / Harpo's blues / Poetry man / Either or both / San Francisco Bay blues / I don't want the night to end / Take your children home / It must be Sunday / No show tonight.
■ CD . . . . . . . . . . . . . . . . . **NEXCD 143**
Sequel / Oct '90.

## POETRY MAN.
**Tracks:** Poetry man / Neither or both.
■ 7" . . . . . . . . . . . . . . . . . . **AMS 7147**
A&M / Feb '75.

## POETRY MAN.
**Tracks:** Poetry man / San Francisco Bay blues.
■ 7" . . . . . . . . . . . . . . . . . . **WIP 6484**
Island / '79.

## ROCK AWAY.
**Tracks:** Cheap thrills / Baby please / Gasoline Alley / Rock away / Mercy, mercy, mercy / Games / Down in the basement / Shoo-rah-shoo-rah / Something good / I believe in you / Two fisted love / All over / Poetry man / Teach me tonight / Don't let me down / Shakey ground / Love makes a woman / Never letting go / Every night / Harpo's blues.
■ LP . . . . . . . . . . . . . . . . . . **K 50780**
MC. . . . . . . . . . . . . . . . . . . **K4 50780**
Mirage (USA) / Apr '81 / Pinnacle.

## SOMETHING REAL.
**Tracks:** Mr. Wondering / Touch your soul / I'm your girl / Soothin' / Cardiac arrest / Something real / We might never feel this way / If I can just get through the night / Best of my love.
■ CD . . . . . . . . . . . . . . . . . **9608522**
■ LP . . . . . . . . . . . . . . . . . **EKT 56**
■ MC. . . . . . . . . . . . . . . . . **EKT 56 C**
Elektra / Apr '89.

# Soccio, Gino

## CLOSER.
**Tracks:** Try it out / Street talk / It's been too long / Hold tight / Love is / Closer.
■ LP . . . . . . . . . . . . . . . . . **K 50790**
Atlantic / May '81.

## DANCE TO DANCE.
**Tracks:** Dance to dance / Visitors.
■ 7" . . . . . . . . . . . . . . . . . **K 17412**
WEA / '79.

## DANCER.
**Tracks:** Dancer / So lonely.
■ 7" . . . . . . . . . . . . . . . . . **K 17357**
WEA / Apr '79.

## HUMAN NATURE.
**Tracks:** Human nature.
■ 12" . . . . . . . . . . . . . . . . **12 CHALD 101**
Noir / Oct '85.

## OUTLINE.
**Tracks:** Dancer / So lonely / Visitors / Dance to dance / There's a woman.
■ LP . . . . . . . . . . . . . . . . . **K 56620**
WEA / '77.

## SOCIAL HARP.
**Tracks:** Not Advised.
■ LP . . . . . . . . . . . . . . . . . **ROUNDER 0094**
Rounder / May '79.

## TODAY.
**Tracks:** Today / Bully boys / World at ransom.
■ 7" . . . . . . . . . . . . . . . . . **KILL 18**
Karnage / Mar '83.

## TRY IT OUT.
**Tracks:** Try it out / Closer.
■ 12" . . . . . . . . . . . . . . . . **K 11594 T**
■ 7" . . . . . . . . . . . . . . . . **K 11594**
Atlantic / Jun '81.

# Softones

## WHERE DO I BEGIN.
**Tracks:** Where do I begin / Laundromat.
■ 7" . . . . . . . . . . . . . . . . . **6105 078**
H & L (USA) / Jun '77.

# Solid State Sound

## DO YOU WANNA CHILL WITH ME?.
**Tracks:** Do you wanna chill with me.
■ 12" . . . . . . . . . . . . . . . . **12 MISH 3**
Passion/Debut/Scratch Music / Aug '93.

# Sonique

## LET ME HOLD YOU.
**Tracks:** Let me hold you.
■ 12" . . . . . . . . . . . . . . . . **COOLX 114**
■ 7" . . . . . . . . . . . . . . . . **COOL 114**
Cool Tempo / Aug '85.

# Sons Of Champlin

## HERE IS WHERE YOUR LOVE BELONGS.
**Tracks:** Here is where your love belongs / Rainbow's end.
■ 7" . . . . . . . . . . . . . . . . . **AA 112**
Ariola / Feb '77.

## LOVING IS WHY.
**Tracks:** Loving is why / Doin' it for you.
■ 7" . . . . . . . . . . . . . . . . . **AA 115**
Ariola / Sep '77.

## MARIN COUNTY SUNSHINE (1968-1971).
**Tracks:** 1982-A / Black and blue rainbow / Hello sunlight / Everywhere / Don't fight it, do it / Jesus is coming / It's time / Love a woman / Terry's tune / Headway / Follow your heart.
■ LP . . . . . . . . . . . . . . . . . **LIK 21**
Decal / Mar '88.

## Sons Of Moses

**SOUL SYMPHONY.**
Tracks: Soul symphony / Fatback.
■ 7" .............................. MCA 169
MCA / Jan '75.

## Sorokus

**SOROKUS.**
Tracks: It's going on / Think about it / Cruizin' / Brown eyes / Where would I be / One more lady / Take me to your place / Gentle touch.
■ LP ............................ TRLP 122
Timeless (Soul) / Apr '88.
■ CD ............................ TLCD 516
■ LP ............................ TRPL 122
Timeless (Soul) / Jan '90.

## Soskin, Mark

**CALYPSO & JAZZ.**
Tracks: This one is Benjamin's / Beautiful love / Around the corner / Slider / Crazy she calls me / Once was / Never never land / Glance backward / Lament / This one is Benjamin's (Reprise).
CD ............................ KICJ 175
Paddlewheel / Feb '94 / New Note.

**OVERJOYED.**
Tracks: Not Advised.
CD ............................ 66053020
Jazz City / Mar '91 / New Note.

**RHYTHMIC VISION.**
Tracks: Colossus / Mambo mio / Walk tall / Caribbean party / Stomp / That's what friends are for / Opening / Bolinas.
■ LP ............................ PR 10109
Prestige / Oct '80.

**VIEWS FROM HERE.**
Tracks: Not Advised.
■ CD ............................ KICJ 126
Bellaphon / Feb '93.

**WALK TALL.**
Tracks: Walk tall / Colossus.
■ 12" ............................ PRC 105
Prestige / Jun '80.

## Soul

**TRIBES.**
Tracks: Tribes / Love.
■ 7" ............................ CHERRY 27
Cherry Red / Jul '81.

## Soul

**BROKEN.**
Tracks: Broken / So long ago / Through before we started.
■ CD Single ................... CDEM 274
EMI / Aug '93.

## Soul Affair

**ABC.**
Tracks: ABC / Sugar daddy.
■ 12" ......................... 12ROO 106
■ 7" .......................... ROO 106
Rooster (Europe) / Mar '84.

## Soul Brothers Six

**SOME KIND OF WONDERFUL.**
Tracks: Some kind of wonderful / I'll be loving you.
■ 7" .......................... 584118
Atlantic / Jun '67.

## Soul Children

The late '60s creation of David Porter and Isaac Hayes, Soul Children was intended to be the ultimate soul vocal group, starring four potential lead singers, each of heart-stirring quality. Well, two out of four wasn't bad: John Colbert and Shelbra Bennett definitely outshone Norman West and Anita Louis, but nobody felt like quibbling once they heard the records. The group released two moderately successful albums, *Soul Children* and *Best Of Two Worlds*, but it was 1972's *Genesis*, featuring the hit *Hearsay*, that confirmed their potential. The Soul Children's speciality was the eternal triangle, and in the early '70s the "slippin' around" lyric was right in vogue. Their best

work is all in the superb album *Friction*, from which *I'll Be The Other Woman* was their biggest hit (US R&B Top 3). They had one album on Epic in the late '70s before splitting. Colbert enjoyed further success as J. Blackfoot (as he had previously), with *Taxi* in '83.

**CAN'T GIVE UP A GOOD THING.**
Tracks: Can't give up a good thing / Signed, sealed, delivered, I'm yours.
■ 7" .......................... STAX 503
Stax / Jun '78.

**FRICTION.**
Tracks: I'll be the other woman / What's happening baby / Can't let you go / It's out of my hands / Just one moment / We're gettin' too close / Love makes it right.
■ LP .......................... STS 5507
Stax / '74.

**FRICTION/ BEST OF TWO WORLDS.**
Tracks: I'll be the other woman / What's happening baby / Can't let you go / It's out of my hands / Just one moment / We're gettin' too close / Love makes it right / Bring it here / Thanks for a precious nothing / Put your world in my world / Give me one good reason / Got to get away from it all / Hang ups of holding on / Wrap it up tonight / Let's make a sweet thing sweeter / Finish me off / Don't break away.
CD ......................... CDSXD 056
Ace / Jun '93 / Pinnacle / Complete Record Co. Ltd.

**GENESIS.**
Tracks: I want to be loved / Don't take my sunshine / Hearsay / All that shines ain't gold / It hurts me to my heart / I'm loving you more everyday / Just the one / Never get enough of your love / All day preachin' / Get up about yourself.
■ LP .......................... 2325076
Stax / Sep '72.

**GIVE ME ONE GOOD REASON.**
Tracks: Give me one good reason / Bring it here.
■ 7" .......................... 2025 050
Stax / Aug '71.

**SINGLES, THE/OPEN DOOR POLICY.**
Tracks: Don't take my kindness for weakness / It ain't always what you do (It's who you let see you do it) / Hold on I'm coming / Make it good / Ridin' on love's merry go-round / Love is a hurtin' thing / Poem on the school house door / Come back kind of love / Signed, sealed and delivered / I don't know what this world is coming to / Hearsay / Stir up the boogie, Part II / Who you used to be / Strangers / Summer in the shade / Can't give up a good thing / Butt la rose / Hard living with a man / Beleiving.
CD ......................... CDSXD 101
Stax / Jan '94 / Pinnacle.

**SOUL CHILDREN/GENESIS.**
Tracks: I'll understand / Move over / When tomorrow comes / Sweeter he is (part 1) / Sweeter he is (part 2) / Tighten up my thang / Give 'em love / Doing our thang / Take up the slack / Super soul / My baby specializes / I want to be loved / Don't take my sunshine / Hearsay / All that shines ain't gold / It hurts me to my heart / I'm loving you more every day / Just the one (I've been looking for) / Never get enough of your love / All day preaching / Get up about yourself.
CD ......................... CDSXD 944
Stax / Aug '90 / Pinnacle.

## Soul City

**EVERYBODY DANCE NOW.**
Tracks: Everybody dance now / Who knows.
■ 7" .......................... C 103
Cameo Parkway / Feb '67.

## Soul Club

**I WANT YOUR GUY.**
Tracks: I want your guy / I want your guy (dub).
■ 7" .......................... COOL 135
■ 12" ......................... COOLX 135
Cool Tempo / Feb '87.

## Soul Expression

**FEELINGS.**
Tracks: Feelings.
12" .......................... DJR 1001
Dessy Jay / Jun '94 / Jetstar.

## Soul Family Sensation

**BEAUTIFUL MORNING.**
Tracks: Beautiful morning.
■ 12" ......................... 87TP 12
■ CD Single ................... 87TP7 CD
One Little Indian / Jun '93.

**BURGER HABIT.**
Tracks: Not Advised.
CD ........................... TPLP 45CD
LP ........................... TPLP 45
MC ........................... TPLP 45C
One Little Indian / Sep '93 / Pinnacle.

**DON'T EVEN KNOW IF I CALL YOU BABY.**
Tracks: Don't even know if I call you baby.
■ 12" ......................... 47TP 12
■ 12" Remix .................. 47TP 12 L
■ 7" .......................... 47TP 7
■ CD Single ................... 47TP 12 CD
■ MC Single .................. 47TP 12 C
One Little Indian / Apr '91.

**HIGH ON THE GRASS.**
Tracks: High on the grass.
■ 12" ......................... .97 TP 12
■ CD Single ................... 97 TP 7CD
■ MC Single .................. 97 TP 7C
One Little Indian / Jul '93.

**I DON'T EVEN KNOW IF I SHOULD CALL YOU BABY.**
Tracks: I don't even know if I should call you baby.
■ 12" ......................... 12TP 42
■ 7" .......................... 7TP 42
One Little Indian / Oct '90.
■ 12" Remix .................. 12TP 42 R
One Little Indian / Apr '91.

**NEW WAVE.**
Tracks: Not Advised.
CD ........................... TPLP 35CD
LP ........................... TPLP 35
MC ........................... TPLP 35C
One Little Indian / Sep '91 / Pinnacle.

**PERFECT LIFE.**
Tracks: Perfect life.
■ 12" ......................... 67 TP 712
■ 7" .......................... 67 TP 7
■ CD Single ................... 67 TP 7 CD
■ MC Single .................. 67 TP 7 C
One Little Indian / Sep '91.

## Soul Generation

**BABY BE GOOD TO ME (Soul Generation featuring Latice & Seven T).**
Tracks: Baby be good to me.
■ 12" ......................... STD 20
■ 7" .......................... STS 20
Soul Train / Dec '90.

**HOLD ON.**
Tracks: Hold on / Lonely sea.
■ 7" .......................... GRP 131
Grapevine (Northern Soul) / Dec '79.

## Soul Iberica Band

**BABY SITTER.**
Tracks: Baby sitter / I'm looking for Jeremy.
■ 7" .......................... EMI 2762
EMI / Mar '78.

## Soul II Soul

Once the biggest and best on the block, Soul II Soul were largely the creation of London DJ and entrepreneur Jazzie B. Group evolved from sound system into group, whose 1989 debut *Club Classics Vol. 1* provided formula for dance music at turn of decade. Sung by Caron Wheeler, *Back To Life* and *Keep On Movin'* were major Tansatlantic hits. Success continued with *Get A Life* and *Dream's A Dream* in 1990, despite departure of Wheeler for ill-fated solo career. Third album, *Just Right*, was comparatively minor success and seemed to mark end of Soul II Soul empire (which expanded into shops and community projects). However, successful hits collection in '93 and mooted return of Wheeler bode well for the future. Former Soul II Soul/Wild Bunch honcho Nellee Hooper ranks among top producers of '90s.

■ DELETED

**BACK TO LIFE.**
**Tracks:** Back to life / Back to the beats / Back to life (mixes) (Only on 12" version.).
■ **MC Single** . . . . . . . . . . . . . . . . . TENW 265
■ **12"** . . . . . . . . . . . . . . . . . TENX 265
■ **7"** . . . . . . . . . . . . . . . . . TEN 265
■ **MC Single** . . . . . . . . . . . . . . . . . TENC 265
■ **CD Single** . . . . . . . . . . . . . . . . . TENCD 265
10 / May '89.

**CLUB CLASSICS VOL.1.**
**Tracks:** Keep on movin' / Back to life / Feel free / Live rap / Dance / Jazzie's groove / Fairplay / Happiness / Holdin' on Bambelea / African dance / Acapella.
**CD** . . . . . . . . . . . . . . . . . DIXCD 82
**MC** . . . . . . . . . . . . . . . . . CDIX 82
■ **LP** . . . . . . . . . . . . . . . . . DIX 82
10 / Mar '89 / EMI.

**DREAMS A DREAM, A.**
**Tracks:** Dreams a dream (Not on 12" single) / Dreams a dream, A (instrumental) (Only on MC and 7" singles.) / Dreams a dream, A (night at the opera mix) (Only on 12" and CD single) / Courtney blows (Only on 12" and CD single) / Dreams a dream, A (club dub) (Only on CD single).
■ **12"** . . . . . . . . . . . . . . . . . TENX 300
10 / Jun '90.
■ **7"** . . . . . . . . . . . . . . . . . TEN 300
■ **7" Set** . . . . . . . . . . . . . . . . . TENB 300
■ **MC Single** . . . . . . . . . . . . . . . . . TENC 300
■ **CD Single** . . . . . . . . . . . . . . . . . TENCD 300
10 / Jun '90.

**FAIRPLAY.**
**Tracks:** Fairplay (On TENX 228) / Fairplay (radio mix) (On all versions) / Fairplay (bonus beats) (NOT on TENR 228) / Fairplay (freestyle horns) (On TENR 228 only) / Ambition (rap) (On TENR 228).
■ **7"** . . . . . . . . . . . . . . . . . TEN 228
■ **12"** . . . . . . . . . . . . . . . . . TENX 228
■ **12" Remix** . . . . . . . . . . . . . . . . . TENR 228
10 / May '88.

**FEEL FREE (Featuring Do'reen).**
**Tracks:** Feel free (7" version also on CD) / Fairplay (On all versions) / Feel free (extended version) (On CD & 12" only) / Feel free (instrumental) (On CD & 12" only).
■ **7"** . . . . . . . . . . . . . . . . . TEN 239
■ **CD Single** . . . . . . . . . . . . . . . . . TENCD 239
■ **12"** . . . . . . . . . . . . . . . . . TENX 239
■ **12" Remix** . . . . . . . . . . . . . . . . . TENR 239
10 / Sep '88.

**FUNKY DREDS' VIDEO (Live from Brixton Academy).**
**Tracks:** Not Advised.
**VHS** . . . . . . . . . . . . . . . . . VVD 787
Virgin Vision / Nov '90 / Gold & Sons / THE.

**GET A LIFE.**
**Tracks:** Get a life (Only on 7", MC and 3" CD single) / Jazzie's groove (Only on 12" single (TENX 284)) / Back to life (Only on 12" singles (TENR 284 & TENP 284)) / Keep on movin' (Only on CD single).
■ **12"** . . . . . . . . . . . . . . . . . TENR 284
10 / Dec '89.
■ **7"** . . . . . . . . . . . . . . . . . TEN 284
■ **7" P.Disc** . . . . . . . . . . . . . . . . . TENP 284
■ **MC Single** . . . . . . . . . . . . . . . . . TENC 284
■ **12"** . . . . . . . . . . . . . . . . . TENX 284
■ **CD Single** . . . . . . . . . . . . . . . . . TENCD 284
10 / Nov '89.

**JOY.**
**Tracks:** Joy.
■ **12"** . . . . . . . . . . . . . . . . . TENX 350
■ **7"** . . . . . . . . . . . . . . . . . TEN 350
■ **CD Single** . . . . . . . . . . . . . . . . . TENDG 350
■ **MC Single** . . . . . . . . . . . . . . . . . TENC 350
10 / Mar '92.

**JUST RIGHT (Volume III).**
**Tracks:** Joy / Take me higher / Storm / Direction / Just right / Move me no mountain / Intelligence / Future / Mood / Everywhere.
**CD** . . . . . . . . . . . . . . . . . DIXCD 100
**MC** . . . . . . . . . . . . . . . . . CDIX 100
■ **LP** . . . . . . . . . . . . . . . . . DIX 100
10 / Apr '92 / EMI.
**MiniDisc** . . . . . . . . . . . . . . . . . DIXMD 100
10 / Feb '93 / EMI.

**JUST RIGHT.**
**Tracks:** Just Right / Just Right (mix) / Intelligence.
■ **MC Single** . . . . . . . . . . . . . . . . . MCS 410
■ **12"** . . . . . . . . . . . . . . . . . TENX 410
■ **7"** . . . . . . . . . . . . . . . . . TEN 410
■ **CD Single** . . . . . . . . . . . . . . . . . TENDG 410
10 / Sep '92.

**KEEP ON MOVIN' (Soul II Soul & Caron Wheeler).**
**Tracks:** Keep on movin' (Only on 7" and CD single (TENCD 263)) / Keep on movin' (instrumental) (Only on 7" and 12" single) / Keep on movin' (club mix) (Only on 12" and CD single (TENCD 263)) / Feel free (Only on CD single (TENCD 263)) / Keep on movin' (New York mix) (Only on CD single (TENRD 263)) / Keep on movin' (the 1st movement) (Only on CD single (TENRD 263)) / Keep on movin' (a dub in the sun) (Only on CD single (TENRD 263)) / Keep on movin' (big beat accapella) (Only on 12" single) / Keep on movin' (pianopella) (Only on 12" single).
■ **7"** . . . . . . . . . . . . . . . . . TEN 263
■ **CD Single** . . . . . . . . . . . . . . . . . TENRD 263
■ **12"** . . . . . . . . . . . . . . . . . TENX 263
■ **12" Remix** . . . . . . . . . . . . . . . . . TENR 263
■ **CD Single** . . . . . . . . . . . . . . . . . TENCD 263
10 / May '89.

**MISSING YOU (Soul II Soul & Kym Mazelle).**
**Tracks:** Missing you.
■ **12"** . . . . . . . . . . . . . . . . . TENX 345
■ **12" Remix** . . . . . . . . . . . . . . . . . TENR 345
■ **7"** . . . . . . . . . . . . . . . . . TEN 345
■ **MC Single** . . . . . . . . . . . . . . . . . TENC 345
■ **CD Single** . . . . . . . . . . . . . . . . . TENCD 345
10 / Nov '90.

**MOVE ME NO MOUNTAIN.**
**Tracks:** Move me no mountain.
■ **12"** . . . . . . . . . . . . . . . . . TENX 400
■ **7"** . . . . . . . . . . . . . . . . . TEN 400
■ **CD Single** . . . . . . . . . . . . . . . . . TENDG 400
■ **MC Single** . . . . . . . . . . . . . . . . . TENC 400
10 / Jun '92.

**VOLUME II - 1990 A NEW DECADE.**
**Tracks:** Get a life / Jazzie B / Daddae Harvey / Love comes through / People / Missing you / Courtney blows / 1990 a new decade / Dreams a dream / Time (untitled) / In the heat of the night / Our time has now come / Nomsa caluza / Sonti mndebele.
■ **LP** . . . . . . . . . . . . . . . . . DIX 90
■ **MC** . . . . . . . . . . . . . . . . . CDIX 90
10 / May '90.
**CD** . . . . . . . . . . . . . . . . . DIXCD 90
**MC** . . . . . . . . . . . . . . . . . OVEDC 395
10 / Apr '92 / EMI.

**VOLUME IV - THE CLASSIC SINGLES 1988-93.**
**Tracks:** Back to life / Keep on movin' / Get a life / Dreams a dream / Missing you / Just right / Move me no mountain / People / Fairplay / Jazzie's groove / Wish / Joy / Keep on movin' (mixes) / Fairplay (mixes) / Back to life (mixes).
**CD** . . . . . . . . . . . . . . . . . CDV 2724
**LP** . . . . . . . . . . . . . . . . . V 2724
**MC** . . . . . . . . . . . . . . . . . TCV 2724
Virgin / Oct '93 / EMI.

**WISH.**
**Tracks:** Wish.
■ **12"** . . . . . . . . . . . . . . . . . VST 1480
■ **7"** . . . . . . . . . . . . . . . . . VS 1480
■ **CD Single** . . . . . . . . . . . . . . . . . VSCDG 1480
■ **MC Single** . . . . . . . . . . . . . . . . . VSC 1480
Virgin / Oct '93.

## Soul Inspirations

**TRY MY LUV.**
**Tracks:** Try my love.
■ **12"** . . . . . . . . . . . . . . . . . SR 001
Solution Records / Oct '92.

## Soul Stirrers

**GOD SAID IT.**
**Tracks:** Not Advised.
**LP** . . . . . . . . . . . . . . . . . SL 14569
Savoy / Apr '90 / Jazz Music / Wellard / Savoy Records / Conifer Records.

**HEAVEN IS MY HOME.**
**Tracks:** Christ is all / He's my rock (wait on Jesus) (Take 2) / He's my rock (wait on Jesus) (Take 3) / In a few more days / Golden bells (Take 1) / Golden bells (Take 2) / Sinner run to Jesus / Heaven is my home (Take 1) / Heaven is my home (Take 2) / Until then / Out on a hill (Take 1-alternate) / Swing low, sweet chariot (Take 1) / Swing low, sweet chariot (Take 2) / Loved ones are waiting / Love of God (Take 2 - alternate) / Love of God (Take 3 - alternate) / Love of God (Take 4 - alternate) / When the gates swing open / Lord laid his hands on me / That's all I need to know / My life belongs to him / There's not a friend like Jesus / Heaven is my home.
**CD** . . . . . . . . . . . . . . . . . CDCHD 478
Ace / Jul '93 / Pinnacle / Complete Record Co. Ltd.

**I CAN SEE THE LIGHT SHINING.**
**Tracks:** Not Advised.
**LP** . . . . . . . . . . . . . . . . . SL 14635
Savoy / Apr '90 / Jazz Music / Wellard / Savoy Records / Conifer Records.

**I'VE GOT SO MUCH TO BE THANKFUL FOR.**
**Tracks:** Not Advised.
**LP** . . . . . . . . . . . . . . . . . SL 14611
Savoy / Apr '90 / Jazz Music / Wellard / Savoy Records / Conifer Records.

**JESUS GAVE ME WATER.**
**Tracks:** Jesus gave me water / Christ is all / Come, lets us go back to god / I'm on the firing line / How far am I from canaan / Jesus done just what he said / He's my rock (wait on jesus) / Joy, joy to my soul / I'm gonna build (right) on that shore / Until Jesus calls me home / Jesus will lead me to the promise land / It wont' be long / Let me go home / Someday somewhere / Jesus paid the debt / End of my journey / He's my friend until the end / I have a friend above all others / I gave up everything to follow him / Come & go to that land / I'm so happy in the sevice of the lord / Any day now / Jesus I'll never forget / All right now / Pray / Come to go to that land / I'm so happy in the service of the lord.
**CD** . . . . . . . . . . . . . . . . . CDCHD 464
Ace / Mar '93 / Pinnacle / Complete Record Co. Ltd.

**LAST MILE OF THE WAY, THE.**
**Tracks:** Last mile of the way / Mean old way / That's heaven to me / Were you there (false starts) / Were you there / Lord remember me / Pilgrim of sorrow / He's my guide / He's my guide (incomplete) / Last mile of the way (incomplete) / All right now / He'll make a way / Jesus, I'll never forget / Come and go to that land / Just as I am (incomplete) / He'll welcome me / He's my friend until the end / Jesus paid the debt / Jesus will lead me to that promised land (incomplete) / Jesus will lead me to that promised land / It won't be very long / How far am I from Canaan (incomplete) / How far am I from Canaan / Let me go home.
**CD** . . . . . . . . . . . . . . . . . CDCHD 563
Ace / Mar '94 / Pinnacle / Complete Record Co. Ltd.

**LIVE IN CONCERT.**
**Tracks:** Introduction / He's my friend / Be with me, Jesus / I'm travelling on / Wade in the water / God is able / Lord, remember me / When the gates swing open / Touch the hem of his garment / If you love Jesus / Raise your hand / Amazing grace / I will trust in the Lord.
**CD** . . . . . . . . . . . . . . . . . MIR 5025CD
**LP** . . . . . . . . . . . . . . . . . MIR 5025
**MC** . . . . . . . . . . . . . . . . . MIR 5025MC
Miracle / Nov '90 / Backs Distribution.

**SHE'S GONE ON HOME.**
**Tracks:** Not Advised.
**LP** . . . . . . . . . . . . . . . . . SL 14530
Savoy / Apr '90 / Jazz Music / Wellard / Savoy Records / Conifer Records.

**STAND BY ME FATHER.**
**Tracks:** Put a little love in your heart / Stand by me Father / He's my guide / Without God in my life / Set me free / In Heaven with him / Glory bound train / Amazing grace.
■ **LP** . . . . . . . . . . . . . . . . . MIR 5013
**MC** . . . . . . . . . . . . . . . . . ZCMIR 5013
Miracle / Jul '89 / Backs Distribution.

**WILL THE REAL SOUL STIRRERS PLEASE STAND UP.**
**Tracks:** If you love Jesus raise your hand / Nobody's child / Hey brother / Are you holding on / Until then / Touch the hem of His garment / He'll welcome us / They crucified Him / Walk along with me / Stop on board and follow me.
**MC** . . . . . . . . . . . . . . . . . ZCMIR 5006
Miracle / Aug '88 / Backs Distribution.
■ **LP** . . . . . . . . . . . . . . . . . MIR 5006
Miracle / Aug '88.

## Soul Survivors

**EXPRESSWAY TO YOUR HEART.**
**Tracks:** Expressway to your heart / Hey gyp.
■ **7"** . . . . . . . . . . . . . . . . . SS 2057
Stateside / Oct '67.

**SOUL SOUNDS.**
**Tracks:** Jump back / See saw / You can't sit down / How sweet it is / Soul soup / Sunshine superman /

Last night / When something is wrong with my baby / I feel good / Philly dog / Soul survival / Night train.
- **LP** . . . . . . . . . . . . . . . . . . . . . . SCX 6158
Columbia / Dec '67.
- **CD**. . . . . . . . . . . . . . . . . . . RTCD 901145
Line / Sep '94 / C.M. Distribution / Grapevine Distribution / A.D.A. Distribution / Conifer Records.

## Soul Train

### JAZZ IN SWEDEN 1986.
Tracks: Not Advised.
- **CD**. . . . . . . . . . . . . . . . . . . . . . . . 1335
- **LP** . . . . . . . . . . . . . . . . . . . . . . . 1335-1
Caprice Records / Feb '90 / C.M. Distribution / Complete Record Co. Ltd / Cadillac.

## Soul Train Gang

### SOUL TRAIN GANG.
Tracks: That certain way / Ooh cha / How much longer / All my life / Soul train theme / If it takes all night / Country girl.
- **LP** . . . . . . . . . . . . . . . . . . . . . FL 11844
RCA / Jul '77.

## Soul Twins

### QUICK CHANGE ARTIST.
Tracks: Quick change artist / Give the man a chance.
- **7"** . . . . . . . . . . . . . . . . . . . . .GRP 101
Grapevine (Northern Soul) / Oct '77.

## Sounds Of Blackness

### AFRICA TO AMERICA: THE JOURNEY OF THE DRUM.
Tracks: Hold on (Part 1) / I'm going all the way / Ah been 'buked (Part 1) / Hold on (Part 2) / Everything is gonna be alright / Sun up to sundown / Lord will make a way / He took away all my pain / Place in my heart / Harder they are, the bigger they fall / Drum (Africa to America) / African medley (Royal Kingdoms/Rise/My Native Land) / Very special love / Strange fruit / Black butterfly / You've taken by blues and gone / Livin' the blues / Ah been 'buked (Part 2) / I'm going all the way (Brixton flavour).
- **CD**. . . . . . . . . . . . . . . . . . . . .549009-2
- **LP Set**. . . . . . . . . . . . . . . . . .549009-1
- **MC**. . . . . . . . . . . . . . . . . . . . . .549009-4
Perspective / Apr '94 / PolyGram.

### EVERYTHING'S GONNA BE ALRIGHT.
Tracks: Everything's gonna be alright (Mixes).
- 12". . . . . . . . . . . . . . . . . . . . . . .587467-1
- CD Single. . . . . . . . . . . . . . . . . .587467-2
- MC Single . . . . . . . . . . . . . . . . .587467-4
Perspective / Aug '94 / PolyGram.

### EVOLUTION OF GOSPEL.
Tracks: Chains / Optimistic / Ah been workin' / Pressure, The (pt.1) / Testify / Gonna be free one day / Stand / Pressure, The (pt.2) / Your wish is my command / Hallelujah Lord / We give you thanks / He holds the future / What shall I call him / Better watch your behaviour / Please take my hand / I'll fly away / Harambee.
- **CD**. . . . . . . . . . . . . . . . . . . . . .3953612
- **LP** . . . . . . . . . . . . . . . . . . . . . .3953611
- **MC**. . . . . . . . . . . . . . . . . . . . . .3953614
A&M / Oct '91 / PolyGram.

### I BELIEVE.
Tracks: I believe (Mixes).
- **12"**. . . . . . . . . . . . . . . . . . . . .587451-1
- **CD Single** . . . . . . . . . . . . . . . .587451-2
A&M / Mar '94.

### I'M GOING ALL THE WAY.
Tracks: I'm going all the way / I'm going all the way mixes.
- **12"**. . . . . . . . . . . . . . . . . . . . .587424-1
- **7"** . . . . . . . . . . . . . . . . . . . . .587424-7
- **CD Single** . . . . . . . . . . . . . . . .587424-2
- **MC Single** . . . . . . . . . . . . . . . .587424-4
A&M / Apr '93.

### NIGHT BEFORE CHRISTMAS, THE.
Tracks: Born in a manger / Soul holidays / It's Christmas time / Away in a manger / O come all ye faithful / O', Holy night / Peace on earth for everyone / Children go / Santa's comin' to town / Dance, chitlins, dance / Holiday love / Santa won't you come by / Jolly one's here / Dash away all / Reindeer revolt / Give us a chance / Santa watch yo' step / Why don't you believe me / Merry Christmas to the world.
- **CD**. . . . . . . . . . . . . . . . . . . . 549 000-2
A&M / Oct '92 / PolyGram.

---

### OPTIMISTIC.
Tracks: Optimistic.
- **12"** . . . . . . . . . . . . . . . . . . . AMY 786
- **7"** . . . . . . . . . . . . . . . . . . . . AM 786
- **CD Single** . . . . . . . . . . . . . . . AMCD 786
- **MC Single** . . . . . . . . . . . . . . AMMC 786
Perspective / Oct '91.

### OPTIMISTIC.
Tracks: Optimistic / Testify.
- **12"** . . . . . . . . . . . . . . . . . . . PERT 849
- **12" Remix**. . . . . . . . . . . . . . . PERX 849
- **7"** . . . . . . . . . . . . . . . . . . . . . PER 849
- **MC Single** . . . . . . . . . . . . . . PERCS 849
Perspective / Feb '92.

### PRESSURE (PART 1).
Tracks: Pressure (part 1).
- **12"** . . . . . . . . . . . . . . . . . . . PERT 816
- **7"** . . . . . . . . . . . . . . . . . . . PERSS 816
- **CD Single** . . . . . . . . . . . . . . . PERD 816
- **MC Single** . . . . . . . . . . . . . . PERCS 816
A&M / Oct '91.

### PRESSURE PART 1.
Tracks: Pressure.
- **12"** . . . . . . . . . . . . . . . . . . . PERT 867
- **7"** . . . . . . . . . . . . . . . . . . . PERSS 867
Perspective / Apr '92.

### SOUL HOLIDAYS/JOY.
Tracks: Soul holidays / Joy.
- **12"** . . . . . . . . . . . . . . . . . . . PERT 7414
- **7"** . . . . . . . . . . . . . . . . . . . PERS 7414
- **CD Single** . . . . . . . . . . . . . . . PERD 7414
- **MC Single** . . . . . . . . . . . . . . PERC 7414
Perspective / Nov '92.

## South, Joe

### GAMES PEOPLE PLAY.
Tracks: Games people play.
- **7"** . . . . . . . . . . . . . . . . . . . CL 15579
Capitol / Mar '69.

### INTROSPECT.
Tracks: All my hard times / Rose garden / Mirror of your mind / Redneck / Don't throw your love to the wind / Greatest love / Games people play / These are not my people / Don't you be ashamed / Birds of a feather / Gabriel.
- **LP** . . . . . . . . . . . . . . . . . . . . . SEE 69
See For Miles / Jun '86.

### JOE SOUTH STORY.
Tracks: So fine / Silly little girl / Will the real you please stand up / Masquerade / Deep inside me / I've got to be somebody / You're the reason / I'm sorry for you / Hiding place / Let the party roll on.
- **LP** . . . . . . . . . . . . . . . . . . . JSX 2006
Jay Boy / Apr '71.

### WALK A MILE IN MY SHOES.
Tracks: Walk a mile in my shoes / Clock up on the wall / What makes lovers hurt one another / Children / Shelter / Be a believer / Don't it make you want to go home / Hush / Party people / Hole in your soul / Untie me / Hearts desire / Million miles away / Leaning on you.
- **LP** . . . . . . . . . . . . . . . . . . . ST 21548
Capitol / May '70.

## Sovereign

### I LUV U.
Tracks: I Luv U.
- **12"** . . . . . . . . . . . . . . . . . . . EZY 1206
Passion/Debut/Scratch Music / Oct '93.

## Spank

### OH BABY.
Tracks: Oh baby.
- **12"** . . . . . . . . . . . . . . . . . . .CHAMP 121
- **7"** . . . . . . . . . . . . . . . . . . . . CHAMP 1
Champion / Apr '85.

### SPANK YOU.
Tracks: Spank you.
- **7"** . . . . . . . . . . . . . . . . . . .CHAMP 101
Champion / Mar '85.

## Special Delivery

### ANGEL SMILE.
Tracks: Angel smile / Let's turn the smile.
- **7"** . . . . . . . . . . . . . . . . . . .1992 001
1992 / Apr '90.

---

## Spellbinders

### CHAIN REACTION.
Tracks: Chain reaction / For you.
- **■** . . . . . . . . . . . . . . . . . . . . .202622
CBS / Mar '67.

### HELP ME (GET MYSELF BACK TO-GETHER ON).
Tracks: Help me (get myself back together) / Danny boy.
- **7"** . . . . . . . . . . . . . . . . . .CBS 202453
CBS / '66.

### SINCE I DON'T HAVE YOU.
Tracks: Since I don't have you / I believe.
- **7"** . . . . . . . . . . . . . . . . . . . . 2776
CBS / May '67.

## Spellman, Benny

### CALLING ALL CARS.
Tracks: Not Advised.
- **LP** . . . . . . . . . . . . . . . . . . .BANDY 70018
Bandy (USA) / Jul '84.

### FORTUNE TELLER.
Tracks: Fortune teller / Lipstick traces.
- **7"** . . . . . . . . . . . . . . . . . . . HLP 9570
London-American / '62.
- **7"** . . . . . . . . . . . . . . . . . . BANDY 1492
Bandy (USA) / Mar '83.

### FORTUNE TELLER.
Tracks: Fortune teller / Stickin' wit cha baby / In the night / Every now and then / T'aint it the truth / Life is too short / You don't love me no more / Talk about love / I feel good / Liptsick traces (on a cigarette) / I'll never leave you / It's for you / Word game / You got to get it / Anywhere you go / 10-4 (calling all cars).
- **LP** . . . . . . . . . . . . . . . . . . . CRB 1168
- **MC**. . . . . . . . . . . . . . . . . . . TCCRB 1168
Charly R&B / Jan '88 / Charly.

## Spiral Starecase

### MORE TODAY THAN YESTERDAY.
Tracks: More today than yesterday.
- **7"** . . . . . . . . . . . . . . . . . . . CBS 4187
CBS / May '69.

## Spirit Traveller

### PLAYING HITS FROM MOTOR CITY.
Tracks: Signed, sealed, delivered I'm yours / Since I lost my baby / Ain't that peculiar / Ain't nothing like the real thing / You keep me hangin' on / OOO baby baby / Tracks of my tears / Ain't no mountain high enough / I love you / It's growing / You've really got a hold on me.
- **CD**. . . . . . . . . . . . . . . . . . . .JVC 20292
JVC / Feb '94 / New Note.

## Springer, Marvin

### MERRY CHRISTMAS.. (Springer, Marvin & The Children of the World Choir).
Tracks: Merry Christmas..
- **7"** . . . . . . . . . . . . . . . . . . . S 110
Sold / Dec '86.

### WHERE'S MY LOVE GONE.
Tracks: Where's my love gone.
- **12"** . . . . . . . . . . . . . . . . . . . CCYT 2
- **7"** . . . . . . . . . . . . . . . . . . . CCY 2
Circle City / Nov '87.
- **12"** . . . . . . . . . . . . . . . . . . . CLEF 7
Treble Clef / May '93.

## Spyder D

### HOW YA LIKE ME NOW.
Tracks: How ya like me now.
- **12"** . . . . . . . . . . . . . . . . . . .PRO 7158
Profile (USA) / Sep '87.

### I CAN'T WAIT (To rock the mike).
Tracks: I can't wait.
- **7"** . . . . . . . . . . . . . . . . . . . CHAMP 14
- **12"** . . . . . . . . . . . . . . . . . . . CHAMP 1214
Champion / Jun '86.

## Spyro Gyra

### ACCESS ALL AREAS.
Tracks: Shaker song / Serpent in Paradise. / Heliopolis / Harbour nights / Conversations / Schu's blues / Morning dance / Island in the sky / Sea biscuit / Latin streets.

**■ DELETED**

■ **Double LP** . . . . . . . . . . . . . . . . .MCSP 310
MCA / Aug '84.
■ **CD** . . . . . . . . . . . . . . . . . . . . . GRP 01322
GRP / Feb '93.

## ALTERNATING CURRENTS.
**Tracks:** Not Advised.
■ **CD** . . . . . . . . . . . . . . . . . . . GRP 01102
GRP / Oct '92.

## BREAKOUT.
**Tracks:** Bob goes to the store / Freefall / Doubletake / Breakout / Body wave / Whirlwind / Swept away / Guiltless.
■ **LP** . . . . . . . . . . . . . . . . . . . . MCF 3334
■ **MC** . . . . . . . . . . . . . . . . . . . MCFC 3334
MCA / Aug '86.
■ **CD** . . . . . . . . . . . . . . . . . . . MCAD 5753
MCA / '87.
■ **CD** . . . . . . . . . . . . . . . . . . . GRP 01092
GRP / Oct '92.

## CARNAVAL.
**Tracks:** Cafe amore / Dizzy / Awakening / Cashaca / Foxtrot / Sweet 'n' savvy / Bittersweet / Carnaval.
■ **LP** . . . . . . . . . . . . . . . . . . . . MCF 3087
MCA / Dec '80.
■ **LP** . . . . . . . . . . . . . . . . . . . . MCL 1711
■ **MC** . . . . . . . . . . . . . . . . . . . MCLC 1711
MCA / Sep '82.
■ **CD** . . . . . . . . . . . . . . . . . . . MCAD 1663
MCA / '87.
■ **CD** . . . . . . . . . . . . . . . . . . . GRP 01302
GRP / Aug '92.

## CATCHING THE SUN.
**Tracks:** Catching the sun / Cockatoo / Autumn of our love / Laser material / Percolator / Philly / Lovin' you (interlude) lovin' you / Here again / Safari.
■ **LP** . . . . . . . . . . . . . . . . . . . .MCG 4009
MCA / Feb '80.
■ **LP** . . . . . . . . . . . . . . . . . . . . MCL 1763
■ **MC** . . . . . . . . . . . . . . . . . . . MCLC 1763
MCA / '83.
■ **CD** . . . . . . . . . . . . . . . . . . . MCAD 1487
MCA / Apr '87.
■ **CD** . . . . . . . . . . . . . . . . . . . GRP 01282
GRP / Aug '92.

## CATCHING THE SUN.
**Tracks:** Catching the sun / Percoloator / Cockatoo.
■ **7"** . . . . . . . . . . . . . . . . . . . . MCA 568
MCA / Feb '80.

## CITY KIDS.
**Tracks:** City kids / Serpent in Paradise / Ballad / Nightlife / Islands in the sky / Conversations / Silver lining / Haverstraw road.
■ **LP** . . . . . . . . . . . . . . . . . . . . MCF 3178
■ **MC** . . . . . . . . . . . . . . . . . . . MCFC 3178
MCA / Aug '83.

## COLLECTION.
**Tracks:** You can count on me / What exit / Nu sungo / Unknown soldier / Morning dance / Old San Juan / Shakedown / Mallet ballet / Catching the sun / Para ti latino / Incognito / Harbour nights / Limelight / Breakout.
■ **LP** . . . . . . . . . . . . . . . . . . . . GR 9642
■ **MC** . . . . . . . . . . . . . . . . . . . GRC 9642
■ **CD** . . . . . . . . . . . . . . . . . . . GRD 9642
GRP / May '91.
■ **DCC** . . . . . . . . . . . . . . . . . . GRX 9642 5
GRP / Jan '93.

## DREAMS BEYOND CONTROL.
**Tracks:** Walk the walk / Patterns in the rain / Breakfast at Igor's / Waltz for Isabel / South beach / Send me one line / Bahia / Kindred spirit / Birks law / Same difference / Delicate prey / Friendly fire.
**CD** . . . . . . . . . . . . . . . . . . . GRP 97432
GRP / Sep '93 / BMG / New Note.

## FAST FORWARD.
**Tracks:** Bright lights / Para ti latino / Alexandra / Ocean parkway / Speak easy / Futurephobia / 4MD / Shadow play / Escape hatch / Tower of Babel.
■ **CD** . . . . . . . . . . . . . . . . . . . GRD 96082
■ **LP** . . . . . . . . . . . . . . . . . . . . GR 9608
■ **MC** . . . . . . . . . . . . . . . . . . . GRC 9608
GRP / Aug '90.

## FREETIME.
**Tracks:** Freetime / Telluride / Summer strut / Elegy for 'Trane / Pacific sunrise / Amber dream / String soup.
■ **LP** . . . . . . . . . . . . . . . . . . . . MCF 3119
MCA / Oct '81.
■ **CD** . . . . . . . . . . . . . . . . . . . MCAD 1468
MCA / '87.

## FREETIME.
**Tracks:** Freetime / String soup.
■ **12"** . . . . . . . . . . . . . . . . . . .MCAT 746

■ **7"** . . . . . . . . . . . . . . . . . . . MCA 746
MCA / Nov '81.

## GRAFFITI.
**Tracks:** Shake down / Bob goes to the store / Nu sungo / Yosemite.
■ **VHS** . . . . . . . . . . . . . . . . . . . GRV 9513
GRP Video / Feb '92.

## INCOGNITO.
**Tracks:** Not Advised.
■ **LP** . . . . . . . . . . . . . . . . . . . . MCF 3151
MCA / Dec '82.
■ **CD** . . . . . . . . . . . . . . . . . . . MCAD 5368
MCA / Feb '87.
■ **CD** . . . . . . . . . . . . . . . . . . . GRP 01312
GRP / Oct '92.

## MORNING DANCE.
**Tracks:** Morning dance / Jubilee / Rasul / Song for Lorraine / Starburst / It does'nt matter / Little Linda / End of Romanticism / Heliopolis.
■ **LP** . . . . . . . . . . . . . . . . . . . . INS 2003
Infinity / Jul '79.
■ **CD** . . . . . . . . . . . . . . . . . . . DIDX 201
■ **LP** . . . . . . . . . . . . . . . . . . . . MCL 1788
■ **MC** . . . . . . . . . . . . . . . . . . . MCLC 1788
MCA / Feb '84.
■ **CD** . . . . . . . . . . . . . . . . . . . DMCL 1788
MCA / Apr '89.
**CD** . . . . . . . . . . . . . . . . . . . 7432120261-2
MCA / May '94 / BMG.

## MORNING DANCE.
**Tracks:** Morning dance.
■ **7"** . . . . . . . . . . . . . . . . . . . . INF 111
Infinity / Jul '79.

## MORNING DANCE/CATCHING THE SUN.
**Tracks:** Catching the sun / Cockatoo / Autumn of our love / Laser material / Percolator / Philly / Loving you / Here again / Safari / Morning dance / Jubilee / Rasul / Song for Lorraine / Starburst / Heliopolis / It doesn't matter / Little Linda / End of romanticism.
■ **MC Set** . . . . . . . . . . . . . . . . MCA 2 100
MCA (Twinpax Cassettes) / Apr '82.

## POINT OF VIEW.
**Tracks:** Slow burn / Swing street / Fairweather / Unknown soldier / Hannibal's boogie / No limits / Carolina / Riverwalk / Swamp thing / Counterpoint / Gotcha.
**CD** . . . . . . . . . . . . . . . . . . . MCAD 6309
■ **LP** . . . . . . . . . . . . . . . . . . . . MCA 6309
**MC** . . . . . . . . . . . . . . . . . . . MCAC 6309
MCA (Jazz Today) / Jun '89 / Pinnacle.
**CD** . . . . . . . . . . . . . . . . . . . GRP 01072
BMG / Oct '92 / BMG.

## RITES OF SUMMER.
**Tracks:** Not Advised.
**CD** . . . . . . . . . . . . . . . . . . . GRP 01082
GRP / Oct '92 / BMG / New Note.

## SPYRO GYRA.
**Tracks:** Shaker song / Opus O'opus / Mallet ballet / Pygmy funk / Cascade / Leticia / Mead / Paula / Paw prints / Galadriel / Cafe Amore / Dizzy / Awakening / Cashaca / Foxtrot / Sweet and savvy / Bittersweet / Carnival.
■ **LP** . . . . . . . . . . . . . . . . . . . . INS 2008
Infinity / Nov '79.
■ **LP** . . . . . . . . . . . . . . . . . . . . MCL 1626
■ **MC** . . . . . . . . . . . . . . . . . . . MCLC 1626
MCA / Aug '81.
■ **CD** . . . . . . . . . . . . . . . . . . . GRP 01292
GRP / Aug '92.

## SPYRO GYRA/ CARNAVAL.
**Tracks:** Shaker song / Opus d'opus / Mallet ballet / Pygmy funk / Cascade / Leticia / Mead / Paula/paw prints / Galadriel / Cafe amore / Dizzy / Awakening / Cashaca / Foxtrot / Sweet and savvy / Bittersweet / Carnival.
■ **MC Set** . . . . . . . . . . . . . . . . MCA 2110
MCA (Twinpax Cassettes) / Oct '83.

## STORIES WITHOUT WORDS.
**Tracks:** Cayo Hueso / Serpentine shelly / Del corazon / Early light / Nu sungo / Chrysalis / Joy ride / Pyramid.
■ **LP** . . . . . . . . . . . . . . . . . . . . MCF 3390
■ **MC** . . . . . . . . . . . . . . . . . . . MCFC 3390
■ **CD** . . . . . . . . . . . . . . . . . . . DMCF 3390
MCA / Jul '87.
■ **CD** . . . . . . . . . . . . . . . . . . . GRP 01112
GRP / Oct '92.

## THREE WISHES.
**Tracks:** Pipo's song / Introduction to breathless / Breathless / Real time / Jennifer's lullaby / Whitewater / Inside your love / Nothing to lose / Three wishes / Gliding / Yemanja / Rollercoaster / Three wishes (reprise).

**CD** . . . . . . . . . . . . . . . . . . . GRP 96742
■ **MC** . . . . . . . . . . . . . . . . . . . GRP 96744
GRP / May '92 / BMG / New Note.

# St. James, Phyllis

## AIN'T NO TURNING BACK.
**Tracks:** Candlelight afternoon / Ain't no turnin' back / Ruler of the hunt / Phonemate / This time / If you believe / Livin' on the border / Sweet rhythm / Back in the race.
■ **LP** . . . . . . . . . . . . . . . . . . . . ZL 72298
Motown / Nov '84.

## CANDLELIGHT AFTERNOON.
**Tracks:** Candlelight afternoon / Back in the race.
■ **7"** . . . . . . . . . . . . . . . . . . . .TMG 1358
■ **12"** . . . . . . . . . . . . . . . . . . .TMGT 1358
Motown / Sep '84.

# St. John, Barry

## COME AWAY MELINDA.
**Tracks:** Come away Melinda.
■ **7"** . . . . . . . . . . . . . . . . . . . .DB 7783
Columbia / Dec '65.

## EVERYTHING I TOUCH TURNS TO TEARS.
**Tracks:** Everything I touch turns to tears / Sounds like my baby.
■ **7"** . . . . . . . . . . . . . . . . . . . .DB 7688
Columbia / '66.

## MY MAN.
**Tracks:** My man (mon homme) / Bright shines the light.
■ **7"** . . . . . . . . . . . . . . . . . . . . F 13529
Decca / Jun '74.

# St. Paul

## INTIMACY.
**Tracks:** Intimacy.
■ **12"** . . . . . . . . . . . . . . . . . . .MCAT 1245
■ **7"** . . . . . . . . . . . . . . . . . . . .MCA 1245
MCA / Apr '88.

# Stairsteps

## STAIRSTEPS.
**Tracks:** My sweet Lord / Hush child / Everybody is a star / Peace is gonna come / I love you.. stop / Snow / Didn't it look so easy / Easy way / Look out / I feel a song.
■ **LP** . . . . . . . . . . . . . . . . . . . . 2365016
Buddah / Jun '72.

## STEP BY STEP BY STEP.
**Tracks:** We must be in love / Baby you make me feel so good / Stay close to me / Ooh baby baby / Because I love you / Behind curtains / Ooh child / World of fantasy / Come back to me / Don't waste your time / Playgirl's love / You waited too long / Touch of you / Danger - She's a stranger.
■ **LP** . . . . . . . . . . . . . . . . . . . .2359 021
Buddah / Aug '71.

# Stanley, Chuck

## DAY BY DAY.
**Tracks:** Day by day / Finer things in life.
■ **12"** . . . . . . . . . . . . . . . . . . .6504996
■ **7"** . . . . . . . . . . . . . . . . . . . .6504997
Def Jam / Apr '87.

## FINER THINGS IN LIFE,THE.
**Tracks:** Day by day / Love toy / Never gonna let you go / Burning up / Make you mine tonight / Jammin' to the bells / All and all / Real soon / When it all falls down.
■ **LP** . . . . . . . . . . . . . . . . . . . . 4504831
Def Jam / Mar '87.
**MC.** . . . . . . . . . . . . . . . . . . . 4504834
■ **CD** . . . . . . . . . . . . . . . . . . . 4504832
Def Jam / May '87 / PolyGram.

# Stansfield, Lisa

## AFFECTION.
**Tracks:** This is the right time / Mighty love / Sincerity / Love in me / All around the world / What did I do to you / Live together / You can't deny it / Poison / When are you coming back / Affection / Wake up baby (Only on cassette and CD.) / Way you want it.
**CD** . . . . . . . . . . . . . . . . . . . .260379
■ **LP** . . . . . . . . . . . . . . . . . . . . .210379
**MC.** . . . . . . . . . . . . . . . . . . . .410379
Arista / Nov '89 / BMG.

DCC . . . . . . . . . . . . . . . . . . . . . . 07822185545
Arista / Jan '93 / BMG.

## ALL AROUND THE WORLD.
Tracks: All around the world / Wake up baby / All around the world (around the house mix) (12" remix only.) / This is the right time (accapella) (12" remix only.) / All around the world (runaway love mix) (12" remix only.) / Way you want it (Not on 7".).
■ 7" . . . . . . . . . . . . . . . . . . . . . . .112757
■ 7" . . . . . . . . . . . . . . . . . . . . . . .112693
■ 12" . . . . . . . . . . . . . . . . . . . . . .612857
■ MC Single. . . . . . . . . . . . . . . . . .410308
Arista / Oct '89.

## ALL AROUND THE WORLD.
Tracks: This is the right time / Mighty love / You can't deny it / Love in me / Sincerity / Poison / Live together / Good morning heartache / What did I do to you / All around the world / People hold on / Affection / Way you want it.
VHS . . . . . . . . . . . . . . . . . . . . . 790 443
BMG Video / Apr '94 / BMG.

## ALL WOMAN.
Tracks: All woman / Everything will get better.
■ 12" . . . . . . . . . . . . . . . . . . . . . .615000
■ 7" . . . . . . . . . . . . . . . . . . . . . . .115000
■ CD Single. . . . . . . . . . . . . . . . . .665000
■ MC Single. . . . . . . . . . . . . . . . . .412475
Arista / Dec '91.

## CHANGE.
Tracks: Change / Little more love.
■ 12" . . . . . . . . . . . . . . . . . . . . . 614 820
■ 7" . . . . . . . . . . . . . . . . . . . . . . 114 820
■ CD Single. . . . . . . . . . . . . . . . . 664 820
■ MC Single. . . . . . . . . . . . . . . . . 412 206
Arista / Oct '91.

## I GOT A FEELING.
Tracks: I got a feeling / Red lights.
■ 7" . . . . . . . . . . . . . . . . . . . . . POSP 651
Polydor / Oct '83.

## IN ALL THE RIGHT PLACES.
Tracks: In all the right places.
■ 12" . . . . . . . . . . . . . . . . . . . . MCST 1780
■ 7" . . . . . . . . . . . . . . . . . . . . . MCS 1780
■ MC Single . . . . . . . . . . . . . . . . MCSC 1780
MCA / May '93.

## LISTEN TO YOUR HEART.
Tracks: Listen to your heart / Thought police.
■ 7" . . . . . . . . . . . . . . . . . . . . . POSP 566
Polydor / Feb '83.

## LITTLE BIT OF HEAVEN, A.
Tracks: Little bit of heaven.
■ 12" . . . . . . . . . . . . . . . . . . . . 7432117820-1
■ 7" . . . . . . . . . . . . . . . . . . . . . 7432117820-7
Arista / Nov '93.
MC Single . . . . . . . . . . . . . . . . . 7432117820-4
■ CD Single . . . . . . . . . . . . . . . . . 7432117820-2
Arista / Aug '94 / BMG.

## LIVE AT WEMBLEY.
Tracks: Set your loving free / I will be waiting / Symptoms of loneliness and heartache / Little more love / Love in me / What did I do to you / All woman / Soul deep / Time to make you mine / Tenderly / All around the world / Change / This is the right time / People hold on / Live together/Young hearts run free / It's got to be real.
■ VHS . . . . . . . . . . . . . . . . . MVN 4910403
PMI / Oct '92.

## LIVE TOGETHER.
Tracks: Live together / Sing it / Live together (ext. version) / Live together (big beat mix).
■ 12" . . . . . . . . . . . . . . . . . . . . .612914
■ 12" Remix . . . . . . . . . . . . . . . . .612943
■ 7" . . . . . . . . . . . . . . . . . . . . . .112914
■ CD Single . . . . . . . . . . . . . . . . .662914
■ MC Single . . . . . . . . . . . . . . . . .410459
Arista / Feb '90.

## ONLY WAY.
Tracks: Only way / Only love.
■ 7" . . . . . . . . . . . . . . . . . . . . . POSP 521
Polydor / Oct '82.

## REAL LIFE.
Tracks: Change / Real love / Set your loving free / I will be waiting / All woman / Soul deep / Make love to ya / Time to make you mine / Symptoms of loneliness and heartache / It's got to be real / First joy (Only on cassette and CD.) / Tenderly (Only on cassette and CD.) / Little more love.
CD . . . . . . . . . . . . . . . . . . . . . . .262300
MC . . . . . . . . . . . . . . . . . . . . . . .412300
■ LP . . . . . . . . . . . . . . . . . . . . . .212300
Arista / Nov '91 / BMG.

---

DCC . . . . . . . . . . . . . . . . . . . . . . 07822186795
Arista / Jan '93 / BMG.

## REAL LIFE.
Tracks: Change / This is the right time / All around the world / Live together / Down in the depths (Red, Hot and Blue) / All woman / Time to make you mine / What did I do to you (Live).
Laser Disc . . . . . . . . . . . . . . . . . 781.236
■ VHS . . . . . . . . . . . . . . . . . . . 791.236
BMG Video / Mar '92 / BMG.

## SET YOUR LOVING FREE.
Tracks: Set your loving free / Whenever you're gone / Make love to ya (12" only).
■ 12" . . . . . . . . . . . . . . . . . 74321100581
■ 7" . . . . . . . . . . . . . . . . . . 74321100587
■ CD Single . . . . . . . . . . . . . . 74321100582
■ MC Single. . . . . . . . . . . . . . 74321100584
Arista / May '92.

## SO NATURAL.
Tracks: So natural / So natural (mixes).
■ 7" . . . . . . . . . . . . . . . . . .74321 16913-7
■ 12" . . . . . . . . . . . . . . . . . .74321 16913-1
■ CD Single . . . . . . . . . . . . . .74321 16913-2
■ MC Single. . . . . . . . . . . . . .74321 16913-4
Arista / Oct '93.

## SO NATURAL.
Tracks: So natural / I give you everything / Marvellous & mine / Little bit of heaven / Goodbye / Sweet memories / She's always there / Turn me on / Never set me free / Wish I could always be this way / In all the right places.
CD . . . . . . . . . . . . . . . . . . . .74321 17231-2
DCC . . . . . . . . . . . . . . . . . . .74321 17231-5
LP . . . . . . . . . . . . . . . . . . . .74321 17231-1
MC. . . . . . . . . . . . . . . . . . . .74321 17231-4
Arista / Nov '93 / BMG.

## SOME DAY.
Tracks: Not Advised.
■ 7" . . . . . . . . . . . . . . . . . 74321 1123561
■ CD Single . . . . . . . . . . . . . 74321 1123562
■ MC Single . . . . . . . . . . . . . 74321 1123564
Arista / Dec '92.

## SOMEDAY (I'M COMING BACK).
Tracks: Someday (I'm coming back) / Tenderly / Someday (I'm coming back) (absolute remix) (On 12" only) / Live Together/Young hearts run free (On 12"/ CDs only).
■ 12" . . . . . . . . . . . . . . . . . 74321 123561
■ 7" . . . . . . . . . . . . . . . . . . 74321 123567
■ CD Single . . . . . . . . . . . . . 74321 123562
■ MC Single . . . . . . . . . . . . . 74321 123564
Arista / Dec '92.

## THIS IS THE RIGHT TIME.
Tracks: This is the right time / Affection.
■ 12" . . . . . . . . . . . . . . . . . . . . .612517
■ CD Single . . . . . . . . . . . . . . . . .662512
■ 12" Remix . . . . . . . . . . . . . . . . .612512
■ 7" . . . . . . . . . . . . . . . . . . . . . .112512
■ MC Single . . . . . . . . . . . . . . . . .409517
Arista / Aug '89.

## TIME TO MAKE YOU MINE.
Tracks: Time to make you mine / All around the world.
■ 12" . . . . . . . . . . . . . . . . . . . . 6115113
■ MC Single. . . . . . . . . . . . . . . . .412637
■ CD Single . . . . . . . . . . . . . . . . .665113
Arista / Mar '92.
■ 7" . . . . . . . . . . . . . . . . . . . . . .115113
Arista / Mar '92.

## WHAT DID I DO TO YOU.
Tracks: What did I do to you? (remix) / My apple heart / Lay me down / Something's happenin'.
■ 12" . . . . . . . . . . . . . . . . . . . . .613168
■ 7" . . . . . . . . . . . . . . . . . . . . . .113168
■ CD Single . . . . . . . . . . . . . . . . .663168
■ MC Single. . . . . . . . . . . . . . . . .410865
Arista / Apr '90.

## YOUR ALIBIS.
Tracks: Your alibis / Thought police.
■ 7" . . . . . . . . . . . . . . . . . . . . . DEV 2
Devil / Mar '82.

## Staple Singers

Roebuck "Pops" Staples may be 79 years old, but he shows few signs yet of turning in his guitar for a bus-pass, having recently embarked on a solo career to fill in gaps between family gigs. With daughters Cleotha, Yvonne and Mavis he's been performing both gospel and soul material since the early '50s, heading up from Winona, Mississippi to Memphis, where they recorded for Stax in '68. Heavy Makes You

---

Happy ('71) marked their switch to mainstream soul, but the big attractions arrived the following year in the shape of Respect Yourself and I'll Take You There, both million sellers Stateside. Reaching their artistic peak on 74's Be What You Are LP (which included Come Go With Me), the group then suffered from the break-up of the Stax label, resurfacing briefly on the Curtis Mayfield written soundtrack to the Let's Do It Again movie. Eighties success was limited to one single for Private I/CBS, Slippery People ('84), but their status as America's senior family gospel-soul group has been maintained. Mavis has most recently been recording for Prince and another family album is imminent.

## ARE YOU READY.
Tracks: Are you ready / Love works in strange ways.
■ 12" . . . . . . . . . . . . . . . . . . . . TA 6580
■ 7" . . . . . . . . . . . . . . . . . . . . . .A 6580
Epic / Oct '85.

## AT THEIR BEST.
Tracks: Not Advised.
MC. . . . . . . . . . . . . . . . . . . . . . . 2651214
Supreme / May '88 / Pinnacle.

## BE WHAT YOU ARE.
Tracks: Be what you are / If you're ready (Come go with me) / Love comes in all colors / Tellin' lies / Touch a hand, make a friend / Drown yourself / I ain't raisin' no sand / Grandma's hands / Bridges instead of walls / I'm on your side / That's what friends are for / Heaven.
■ LP . . . . . . . . . . . . . . . . . . . . . STS 3015
Stax / '73.

## BEALTITUDE: RESPECT YOURSELF.
Tracks: This world / Respect yourself / Name the missing word / I'll take you there / This old town / We the people / Are you sure / Who do you think you are / I'm just another soldier / Who.
■ LP . . . . . . . . . . . . . . . . . . . . . 2325069
Stax / Jun '72.
■ LP . . . . . . . . . . . . . . . . . . . . . SXE 001
Stax / Aug '87.
CD. . . . . . . . . . . . . . . . . . . . . CDSXE 001
Stax / May '91 / Pinnacle.

## BRAND NEW DAY.
Tracks: Brand new day / Child's life / Come out of your shell / If it wasn't for a woman / He / Garden party / I believe in music / Which way did it go / This time around / You've got to make an effort / Unity.
■ LP . . . . . . . . . . . . . . . . . . . . . STM 7009
Stax / Apr '80.

## GREAT DAY.
Tracks: Gloryland / Everybody will be happy / Here me call, here / Nobody knows the trouble I've seen / I'm willin' (Part 1) / I'm willin' (Part 2) / Great day / Do you know him / New-born soul / Dying man's plea / New home / Wish I had answered / Better home / Old time religion / Swing down, chariot / Motherless children / Gamblin' man / I know I've been changed / Jesus is all / You got shoes / What are they doing (in heaven today) / Will the Lord rememeber me / My dying bed / Let Jesus lead you / Praying time / I can't help from cryin' sometime / Masters of war.
CD. . . . . . . . . . . . . . . . . . . . . .CDCH 391
Ace / May '92 / Pinnacle / Complete Record Co. Ltd.

## HEAVY MAKES YOU HAPPY.
Tracks: Heavy makes you happy / Love is plentiful.
■ 7" . . . . . . . . . . . . . . . . . . . . . 2025019
Stax / Apr '71.

## HOLD ON TO YOUR DREAM.
Tracks: Ride it on out / There's got to be rain in your life / Message in our music / Cold and windy nights / Stupid Louie / Hold on to your dream / Show off the real you / Old flames / Love came knocking.
■ LP . . . . . . . . . . . . . . . . . . . . . T 636
MC. . . . . . . . . . . . . . . . . . . . . . C 636
20th Century / Oct '81.

## I'LL TAKE YOU THERE.
Tracks: I'll take you there / I'm just another soldier.
■ 7" . . . . . . . . . . . . . . . . . . . . .2025 110
Stax / Jun '72.
■ 7" . . . . . . . . . . . . . . . . . . . . . STAX 1002
Stax / Mar '82.
■ 7" . . . . . . . . . . . . . . . . . . . . . STAX 815
Stax / Sep '87.

## IF YOU'RE READY (COME GO WITH ME).
Tracks: If you're ready (come go with me).
■ 7" . . . . . . . . . . . . . . . . . . . . .2025 224
Stax / Jun '74.

## LONG WALK TO DC.
Tracks: Long walk to D.C.
■ 7" . . . . . . . . . . . . . . . . . . . STAX 817
Stax / Oct '87.

## PRAY ON.
Tracks: Pray on / Don't drive me away / Downward road / Will the circle be unbroken / Stand by me / Ain't that good news / If I could hear my mother / Going away / Don't knock / Uncloudy day / I know I got religion / Somebody save me / Let's go home / This may be the last time / I had a dream / Calling me.
■ LP . . . . . . . . . . . . . . . . . . . GNC 1002
New Cross / Apr '86.
■ CD . . . . . . . . . . . . . . . . . CDCHARLY 220
Charly / Jun '90.

## RESPECT YOURSELF.
Tracks: Respect yourself / This world / Heavy makes you happy / Long walk to DC.
■ 7" . . . . . . . . . . . . . . . . . . . STAX 805
■ 12" . . . . . . . . . . . . . . . . . . . STAT 805
Stax / Jun '87.

## RESPECT YOURSELF - THE BEST OF THE STAPLE SINGERS.
Tracks: Heavy makes you happy / Long walk to DC / This world / Respect yourself / I see it / We'll get over / Take you there / Oh la de da / Are you sure / If you're ready (come go with me) / Touch a hand, make a friend / City in the sky / People come out of your shell / You've got to earn it (Available on CD only) / Love is plentiful (Available on CD only) / Got to be some changes (Available on CD only) / Be what you are (Available on CD only) / This old town (Available on CD only) / Slow train (Available on CD only) / My main man (Available on CD only).
CD . . . . . . . . . . . . . . . . . . . CDSX 006
Stax / Oct '87 / Pinnacle.
■ LP . . . . . . . . . . . . . . . . . . . SX 006
■MC . . . . . . . . . . . . . . . . . . . SXC 006
Stax / Mar '88 / Pinnacle.

## SLIPPERY PEOPLE.
Tracks: Slippery people.
■ 12" . . . . . . . . . . . . . . . . . . . TA 4784
■ 7" . . . . . . . . . . . . . . . . . . . A 4784
Epic / Sep '84.

## SOUL FOLK IN ACTION.
Tracks: We've got to get ourselves together / Dock of the bay / Top of the mountain / Slow train / Weight / Long walk to D.C. / Got to be some changes made / Ghetto / People, my people / I see it / This year.
■ LP . . . . . . . . . . . . . . . . . . . SXATS 1004
Stax / May '69.
■ LP . . . . . . . . . . . . . . . . . . . 2363011
Stax / Aug '71.

## SOUL FOLK IN ACTION/WE'LL GET OVER.
Tracks: We've got to get ourselves together / (Sittin' on the) Dock of the bay / Top of the mountain / Slow train / Weight / Long walk to D.C. / Got to be some changes made / Ghetto / People, my people / I see it / This year / We'll get over / Give a damn / Everyday people / End of our road / Tend to your own business / Solon bushi / Challenge / God bless the children / Games people play / Wednesday in your garden / Gardener / When will be paid (For the work we did).
CD Set . . . . . . . . . . . . . . . . CDSXD 109
Stax / Jul '94 / Pinnacle.

## STAND BY ME.
Tracks: Stand by me / If I could hear my mother pray / God's wonderful love / Calling me / Uncloudy day / I know I've got religion / Swing low, sweet chariot / On my way to heaven / I'm coming home / I had a dream / Help me Jesus / Love is the way / Let's go home / This may be the last time / I'm leaning / Going away / Downward road / Pray on / Good news / Day is passed and gone / Don't knock / Will the circle be unbroken / Born in Bethlehem / I've been scorned / Sit down servant / Two wings.
■ Double LP . . . . . . . . . . . . . . . DJD 28028
JM / Jan '77.

## STAPLE SINGERS.
Tracks: Are you ready / Life during wartime / Nobody can make it on there own / Back to the war / Reason to love / We stand (together, forever) / Start walking / Love works in strange ways.
■ LP . . . . . . . . . . . . . . . . . . . EPC 26537
MC . . . . . . . . . . . . . . . . . . . 40 26537
Epic / Nov '85 / Sony.

## STAPLE SINGERS.
Tracks: This is a perfect world / What's your thing / You've got to earn it / You're gonna make me cry / Little boy / How do you move a mountain / Almost / I'm a lover / Love is plentiful / Heavy makes you

happy / I like the things about you / Give a hand, take a hand.
■ LP . . . . . . . . . . . . . . . . . . . 2362005
Stax / May '71.

## STAPLE SINGERS AT THEIR BEST.
Tracks: If you're ready (come go with me) / Respect yourself / This world / You're gonna make me cry / Touch a hand, make a friend / City in the sky / I'll take you there / You've got to earn it / Oh la de da / Heavy makes you happy / Be what you are / My main man / Long walk to DC.
■ LP . . . . . . . . . . . . . . . . . . . STAXL 5004
MC . . . . . . . . . . . . . . . . . . . STAXK 5004
Stax / Mar '82 / Pinnacle.

## STAPLE SINGERS, THE.
Tracks: Not Advised.
MC . . . . . . . . . . . . . . . . . . . ZCGAS 745
Audio Fidelity / Oct '84 / Telstar/Ronco.

## STAPLE SWINGERS.
Tracks: This is a perfect world / What's your thing / You've got to earn it / You're gonna make me cry / Little boy / How do you move a mountain / Almost / I'm a lover / Love is plentiful / Heavy makes you happy / I like the things about you / Give a hand take a hand.
CD . . . . . . . . . . . . . . . . . . . CDSXE 035
Stax / Feb '91 / Pinnacle.

## SWING LOW.
Tracks: Born in Bethlehem / Stand by me / I've been scorned / Two things / Calling me / Swing low, sweet chariot / Sit down servant / Day is passed and gone / Good news / Let's go home / This may be the last time.
■ LP . . . . . . . . . . . . . . . . . . . JS 5014
Joy / Jan '72.

## THIS IS OUR NIGHT.
Tracks: This is our night / Turning point.
■ 12" . . . . . . . . . . . . . . . . . . . TA 5008
■ 7" . . . . . . . . . . . . . . . . . . . A 5008
Epic / Jan '85.

## TURNING POINT.
Tracks: This is our night / Slippery people / Bridges instead of walls / Turning point / Right decision / H-a-t-e / On my own again / That's what friends are for.
■ LP . . . . . . . . . . . . . . . . . . . EPC 26212
Epic / Dec '84.

## UNCLOUDY DAY.
Tracks: Uncloudy day / Let me ride / God's wonderful love / Help me Jesus / I'm coming home / If I could hear Jesus / Low is the way / I had a dream / On my way to heaven / Going away / I'm leaning / I know I got religion.
■ LP . . . . . . . . . . . . . . . . . . . JS 5019
Joy / Jun '72.

## WE'LL GET OVER.
Tracks: Give a damn / Everyday people / End of the road / Tend to your own business / Solon Bushi (Japanese folk song) / Challenge / God bless the children / Games people play / Wednesday in your garden / Gardener / When will we be paid / We'll get over.
■ LP . . . . . . . . . . . . . . . . . . . SXATS 1018
Stax / Nov '69.
■ LP . . . . . . . . . . . . . . . . . . . MPS 8532
MC . . . . . . . . . . . . . . . . . . . MPS 585532
Stax / Jan '87 / Pinnacle.

# Staples, Mavis

## DON'T CHANGE ME NOW.
Tracks: Ready for the heartbreak / Sweet things you do / Chokin' kind / House is not a home / Security / Good to me / You send me / I'm tired / Why can't it be like it used to be (Available on CD only) / You're the fool (Available on CD only) / You're all I need / I have learned to do without you / How many times / Endlessly / Since I fell for you / Since you became a part of my life / Don't change me now / You're driving me (to the arms of a stranger) (Available on CD only) / Pick up the pieces (Available on CD only) / Chains of love (Available on CD only) / What happened to the real me (Available on CD only) / It makes me wanna cry.
CD . . . . . . . . . . . . . . . . . . . CDSX 014
■ MC . . . . . . . . . . . . . . . . . . . SXC 014
■ LP . . . . . . . . . . . . . . . . . . . SX 014
Stax / Aug '88 / Pinnacle.

## MAVIS STAPLES.
Tracks: Until I met you / Sweet things you do / Chokin' kind / You're driving me / House is not a home / Security / Son of a preacher man / Pick up the pieces / Chained / Good to me / You send me.

## MELODY COOL.
■ LP . . . . . . . . . . . . . . . . . . . SXATS 1026
Stax / Feb '70.

## MELODY COOL.
Tracks: Melody cool.
■ 12" . . . . . . . . . . . . . . . . . . . W 9728 T
■ 7" . . . . . . . . . . . . . . . . . . . W 9728
■ CD Single . . . . . . . . . . . . . . . . W 9728 CD
■ MC Single. . . . . . . . . . . . . . . . W 9728 C
WEA / Aug '90.

## ONLY FOR THE LONELY.
Tracks: I have learned to do without you / How many times / Endlessly / You're the fool / Since I fell for you / What happened to the real me / Since you became a part of my life / It makes me wanna cry / Don't change me now.
■ LP . . . . . . . . . . . . . . . . . . . 2362007
Stax / Mar '71.

## TIME WAITS FOR NO-ONE.
Tracks: Not Advised.
■ CD . . . . . . . . . . . . . . . . . . . K 925798-2
■ LP . . . . . . . . . . . . . . . . . . . K 925798-1
■ MC . . . . . . . . . . . . . . . . . . . K 925798-4
WEA / May '89.

## TONIGHT I FEEL LIKE DANCING.
Tracks: Tonight I feel like dancing / If I can't have you.
■ 7" . . . . . . . . . . . . . . . . . . . K 17410
WEA / '79.

# Staples, Pops

## FATHER FATHER.
Tracks: Father Father / Why am I treated so bad / Too big for your britches / Jesus is going to make up (My dying bed) / Downward road / People get ready / Hope in a hopeless world / You got to serve somebody / Waiting for my child / Simple man / Glory glory.
CD. . . . . . . . . . . . . . . . . . . VPBCD 19
MC . . . . . . . . . . . . . . . . . . . VPBTC 19
Virgin / May '94 / EMI.

## JAMMED TOGETHER (see under Cropper, Steve).

## PEACE IN THE NEIGHBORHOOD.
Tracks: Not Advised.
CD . . . . . . . . . . . . . . . . . . . VPBCD 8
MC. . . . . . . . . . . . . . . . . . . VPBTC 8
■ LP . . . . . . . . . . . . . . . . . . . VPBLP 8
Point Blank / Mar '92 / EMI.

# Starguard

## BACK 2 BACK.
Tracks: You're the one / Here comes love / Just one love / Back to the funk / High on the boogie / Cat and me / It's your love that I'm missing / Diary.
■ LP . . . . . . . . . . . . . . . . . . . K 56854
WEA / Jul '81.

## LOVE IS SO EASY.
Tracks: Love is so easy / Three girls.
■ 7" . . . . . . . . . . . . . . . . . . . MCA 354
MCA / Apr '78.

## SENSUOUS WOMAN.
Tracks: Sensuous woman / How come I can't see you.
■ 7" . . . . . . . . . . . . . . . . . . . MCA 404
MCA / Jan '79.

## WEAR IT OUT.
Tracks: Wear it out / Wear it out (instrumental).
■ 7" . . . . . . . . . . . . . . . . . . . K 17475
WEA / Jan '80.

## WHAT YOU WAITING FOR.
Tracks: What you waiting for / Smile.
■ 7" . . . . . . . . . . . . . . . . . . . MCA 382
MCA / Sep '78.

# Starpoint

## BRING YOUR SWEET LOVIN' BACK.
Tracks: Bring your sweet lovin' back / I want you closer.
■ 12" . . . . . . . . . . . . . . . . . . . CANX 1013
■ 7" . . . . . . . . . . . . . . . . . . . CAN 1013
Casablanca / Jan '82.

## EMOTIONS.
Tracks: Emotions / Send me a letter / Breakout (Only on 12" single.).
■ 12" . . . . . . . . . . . . . . . . . . . EKR 22 T
■ 7" . . . . . . . . . . . . . . . . . . . EKR 22
Elektra / Sep '85.

## HAVE YOU GOT WHAT IT TAKES.
**Tracks:** Not Advised.
CD . . . . . . . . . . . . . . . . . . . . 7559609232
■ LP . . . . . . . . . . . . . . . . . . . . EKT 71
MC. . . . . . . . . . . . . . . . . . . . EKT 71 C
Elektra / Apr '90 / WEA.

## HE WANTS MY BODY.
**Tracks:** He wants my boys / Satisfy me love.
■ 12" . . . . . . . . . . . . . . . . . . . . EKR 55 T
■ 7" . . . . . . . . . . . . . . . . . . . . EKR 55
Elektra / Apr '87.

## HOT TO TOUCH.
**Tracks:** Fresh start / Tough act to follow / Hot to the touch / After all is said and done / Park it / One step closer to your love / Say you will / Swept away / Heart attack.
CD . . . . . . . . . . . . . . . . . . . . K 960810 2
■ LP . . . . . . . . . . . . . . . . . . . . K 960810 1
■ MC. . . . . . . . . . . . . . . . . . . . K 960810 4
Elektra / Oct '88 / WEA.

## I JUST WANNA DANCE WITH YOU.
**Tracks:** I just wanna dance with you / Get ready get down / Gonna lift you up.
■ 12" . . . . . . . . . . . . . . . . . . . . CANL 205
■ 7" . . . . . . . . . . . . . . . . . . . . CAN 205
Casablanca / Aug '80.

## I JUST WANT TO BE YOUR LOVER.
**Tracks:** I just want to be your lover / Keep it on.
■ 12" . . . . . . . . . . . . . . . . . . . . CANX 1001
■ 7" . . . . . . . . . . . . . . . . . . . . CAN 1001
Casablanca / May '81.

## IT'S ALL YOURS.
**Tracks:** It's all yours / Something in your eyes.
■ 7" . . . . . . . . . . . . . . . . . . . . E 6964
■ 12" . . . . . . . . . . . . . . . . . . . . E 6964 T
Elektra / May '84.

## OBJECT OF MY DESIRE.
**Tracks:** Object of my desire / Am I still the one.
■ 12" . . . . . . . . . . . . . . . . . . . . EKR 26 T
■ 7" . . . . . . . . . . . . . . . . . . . . EKR 26
Elektra / Jan '86.

## RESTLESS.
**Tracks:** What you been missing / One more night / Restless / See the light / Til the end of time / Don't take your love away / Emotions / Objects of my desire.
■ LP . . . . . . . . . . . . . . . . . . . . EKT 11
Elektra / Aug '85.

## SENSATIONAL.
**Tracks:** He wants my body / D.Y.B.O. / Prove it tonight / Sensational / Another night / More we love / Touch of your love / Second chance.
■ LP . . . . . . . . . . . . . . . . . . . . K 960722 1
MC. . . . . . . . . . . . . . . . . . . . K 960722 4
Elektra / Feb '87 / WEA.

## Starr, Edwin

### 20 GREATEST MOTOWN HITS.
**Tracks:** Stop her on sight (S.O.S.) / 25 miles / Headline news / Agent double o soul / Backstreet / I want my baby back / Funky music sho nuff turns me on / Soul master / You've got my soul on fire / Who's right or wrong / War / Stop the war now / Way over there / Take me clear from here / Cloud 9 / There you go / Gonna keep on tryin' till I win your love / Time / My weakness is you / Harlem.
■ LP . . . . . . . . . . . . . . . . . . . . WL 72429
■ MC . . . . . . . . . . . . . . . . . . . . WK 72429
Motown / '86.
■ CD . . . . . . . . . . . . . . . . . . . . WD 72429
Motown / Mar '89.
CD. . . . . . . . . . . . . . . . . . . . .530064-2
MC. . . . . . . . . . . . . . . . . . . . .530064-4
Motown / Jan '93 / PolyGram.

### 25 MILES.
**Tracks:** 25 miles / I'm still a struggling man / Backyard lovin' man / He who picks up a rose / Soul City / You beat me to the punch / Gonna keep on tryin' till I win your love / Pretty little angel / If my heart could tell the story / Who cares if you're happy or not / 24 hours / Mighty good lovin'.
■ LP . . . . . . . . . . . . . . . . . . . .STML 11115
Tamla Motown / Sep '69.

### 25 MILES/WAR AND PEACE (2 Classic Albums).
**Tracks:** Twenty five miles / I'm still a struggling man / Backyard lovin' man / He who picks a rose / Soul city (open your arms to me) / You beat me to the punch / Gonna keep on tryin' till I win your love / Pretty little angel / If my heart could tell the story / Who cares if you're happy or not (I do) / 24 hours to find my baby / Mighty good lovin' / War / Running

back and forth / Adios senorita / All around the world / I can't escape your memory / At last / I just wanted to cry / Raindrops keep falling on my head / Time / California soul / I can't replace my old love / She should have been home.
■ CD . . . . . . . . . . . . . . . . . . . . ZD 72484
Motown / '86.

### AFTERNOON SUNSHINE.
**Tracks:** Overture to afternoon sunshine / Pretty girl / Ruby Begonia / Eavesdropper / I just wanna do my thing / Mr. Davenport and Mr. James / Not having you / Accident / Everybody needs love / Edge of insanity.
■ LP . . . . . . . . . . . . . . . . . . . .GTLP 19
GTO / Feb '77.

### AGENT DOUBLE O SOUL.
**Tracks:** Agent double o soul.
■ 7" . . . . . . . . . . . . . . . . . . . . TMG 790
Tamla Motown / Oct '71.

### AIN'T NO STOPPIN' US NOW (Starr, Edwin & David Saylor).
**Tracks:** Ain't no stoppin' us now.
■ 12" . . . . . . . . . . . . . . . . . . . .SOVT 102
■ 7" . . . . . . . . . . . . . . . . . . . .SOV 102
Sovereign / Jul '90.

### CLEAN.
**Tracks:** I'm so into you / Jealous / Contact / Storm clouds on the way / Don't waste your time / Music brings out the beast in me / Working song.
■ LP . . . . . . . . . . . . . . . . . . . .BT 559
20th Century / Jan '79.

### CONTACT.
**Tracks:** Contact.
■ 7" . . . . . . . . . . . . . . . . . . . .GOLD 508
RCA Golden Grooves / Jul '81.

### CONTACT (OLD GOLD).
**Tracks:** Contact / Get down.
■ 7" . . . . . . . . . . . . . . . . . . . .OG 9487
Old Gold / Jun '88.

### CONTACT (OLD GOLD) (2).
**Tracks:** Contact / H.A.P.P.Y. radio.
12" . . . . . . . . . . . . . . . . . . . .OG 4161
Old Gold / Mar '90 / Pickwick.

### CONTACT (RE-RELEASE).
**Tracks:** Contact / Don't waste your time.
■ 7" . . . . . . . . . . . . . . . . . . . . BTC 2396
20th Century / Jan '79.

### GET UP WHIRLPOOL.
**Tracks:** Get up whirlpool / Stronger than you think I am.
■ 7" . . . . . . . . . . . . . . . . . . . . STARR 1
20th Century / Jan '80.

### GRAPEVINE.
**Tracks:** Grapevine / I need your love / Grapevine (parts 1 and 2) ('Grapevine (parts 1 & 2)' on 12" only.).
■ 12" . . . . . . . . . . . . . . . . . . . .12 HIPPO 107
■ 7" . . . . . . . . . . . . . . . . . . . . HIPPO 107
Hippodrome / Mar '86.

### H.A.P.P.Y. RADIO.
**Tracks:** H.A.P.P.Y. radio.
■ 7" . . . . . . . . . . . . . . . . . . . . TC 2408
RCA / May '79.

### HEADLINE NEWS.
**Tracks:** Headline news.
■ 7" . . . . . . . . . . . . . . . . . . . . 56 717
Polydor / Aug '66.

### HITS OF EDWIN STARR.
**Tracks:** Headline news / My weakness is you / Stop her on sight / I want my baby back / Time / I'm still a struggling man / Agent Double O Soul / 25 miles / Soul master / Way over there / War / Stop the war now / Funky music sho nuff turns me on / Take me clear from here.
■ LP . . . . . . . . . . . . . . . . . . . .STML 11209
Tamla Motown / Sep '72.

### I WANNA TAKE YOU HOME.
**Tracks:** I wanna take you home / Hit the nail on your head.
■ 12" . . . . . . . . . . . . . . . . . . . . AVATX 2
■ 7" . . . . . . . . . . . . . . . . . . . . AVAT 2
Avatar / Jan '83.

### I'M SO INTO YOU.
**Tracks:** I'm so into you / Don't waste your time.
■ 7" . . . . . . . . . . . . . . . . . . . . BTC 2389
20th Century / Nov '78.

### INVOLVED.
**Tracks:** War / Ball of confusion / Funky music sho nuff turns me on / Stop the war now / Cloud nine / Stand / Way over there / My sweet Lord.
■ LP . . . . . . . . . . . . . . . . . . . .STML 11199
Tamla Motown / Feb '72.

### IT AIN'T FAIR.
**Tracks:** It ain't fair.
■ 12" . . . . . . . . . . . . . . . . . . . . 12 HIP 101
■ 7" . . . . . . . . . . . . . . . . . . . . HIP 101
Hippodrome / May '85.

### JUST ANOTHER FOOL IN LOVE.
**Tracks:** Just another fool in love.
■ 12" . . . . . . . . . . . . . . . . . . . .12MOTC 82
Motor City / Nov '91.

### MARVIN.
**Tracks:** Marvin / Happy song.
■ 12" . . . . . . . . . . . . . . . . . . . . MKHAN 12
■ 7" . . . . . . . . . . . . . . . . . . . . KHAN 12
Streetwave / May '84.

### MISSILES(WE DONT WANT TO DIE).
**Tracks:** Missiles (we don't want to die).
■ 12" . . . . . . . . . . . . . . . . . . . .12 HIPPO 105
■ 7" . . . . . . . . . . . . . . . . . . . . HIPPO 105
Hippodrome / Oct '85.

### SMOOTH.
**Tracks:** Smooth.
■ 12" . . . . . . . . . . . . . . . . . . . . CABL 114
■ 7" . . . . . . . . . . . . . . . . . . . .CAB 114
Calibre / Aug '83.

### SOUL MASTER.
**Tracks:** Agent double o soul / I am the man for you baby / S.O.S. / Oh how happy / Way over there / My weakness is you / Headline news / Soul master / I want my baby back / Love is my destination / I am your man / Time is passin' by.
■ LP . . . . . . . . . . . . . . . . . . . .STML 11093
Tamla Motown / Sep '69.

### SOUL SINGER.
**Tracks:** Soul singer / Eye to eye contact (remake).
■ 12" . . . . . . . . . . . . . . . . . . . .12 HIPPO 108
■ 7" . . . . . . . . . . . . . . . . . . . . HIPPO 108
Hippodrome / Jul '86.

### STONGER THAN YOU THINK I AM.
**Tracks:** Never turn my back on you / Tell a star Sweet / Upside down / Bigger and better / Stronger than you think I am / Get up whirlpool / Bop bop song.
■ LP . . . . . . . . . . . . . . . . . . . . T 615
20th Century / Jul '80.

### STOP HER ON SIGHT (SOS).
**Tracks:** Stop her on sight (SOS) / Headline news.
■ 7" . . . . . . . . . . . . . . . . . . . .56 153
Polydor / Dec '68.

### STOP HER ON SIGHT (SOS)(REISSUES)
**Tracks:** Stop her on sight (SOS) / Headline news.
■ 7" . . . . . . . . . . . . . . . . . . . . 56183
Polydor / Dec '68.
■ 7" . . . . . . . . . . . . . . . . . . . . TMG 905
Tamla Motown / Jun '74.

### STOP HER ON SIGHT (SOS).
**Tracks:** S.O.S. (stop her on sight) / I have faith in you.
■ 7" . . . . . . . . . . . . . . . . . . . . BM 56702
Polydor / '66.

### STOP THE WAR NOW.
**Tracks:** Stop the war now.
■ 7" . . . . . . . . . . . . . . . . . . . . TMG 764
Tamla Motown / Feb '71.

### STORM CLOUDS ON THE WAY.
**Tracks:** Storm clouds on the way / Music brings out the beast in me.
■ 7" . . . . . . . . . . . . . . . . . . . . BTC 1044
20th Century / May '79.

### TELESTAR.
**Tracks:** Telestar / Bop bop song.
■ 7" . . . . . . . . . . . . . . . . . . . . TC 2450
20th Century / May '80.

### TIME.
**Tracks:** Time.
■ 7" . . . . . . . . . . . . . . . . . . . .TMG 1028
Tamla Motown / May '76.

### TWENTY FIVE MILES.
**Tracks:** Twenty five miles / Never turn my back on you.
■ 12" . . . . . . . . . . . . . . . . . . . . TCD 247
20th Century / Jan '81.
■ 7" . . . . . . . . . . . . . . . . . . . . TMG 673
Tamla Motown / Oct '81.

## TWENTY FIVE MILES ('89 REMIX).
Tracks: Twenty five miles ('89 remix) / Twenty five miles (original instrumental) / Twenty five miles (12" dub) (Only on 12" single.).
■ 12". . . . . . . . . . . . . . . . . . . . . ZT 41966
■ 7". . . . . . . . . . . . . . . . . . . . . ZB 41965
Motown / Jul '89.

## WAR.
Tracks: War.
■ 7". . . . . . . . . . . . . . . . . . . . . TMG 754
Tamla Motown / Oct '70.
■ 7". . . . . . . . . . . . . . . . . . . . . TMG 984
Tamla Motown / Aug '75.

## WAR.
Tracks: War / Indiana wants me.
■ 7". . . . . . . . . . . . . . . . . . . . . TMG 968
Tamla Motown / Apr '75.

## WAR AND PEACE.
Tracks: War / Running back and forth / Adios Senorita / All around the world / I can't escape your memory / At last I found a love / I just wanted to cry / Raindrops keep fallin' on my head / Time / California soul / I can't replace my old love / She should have been home.
■ LP. . . . . . . . . . . . . . . . . . STML 11171
Tamla Motown / Jan '71.

## WHATEVER MAKES OUR LOVE GROW.
Tracks: Whatever makes our love grow / Whatever makes our love grow (instrumental).
■ 7". . . . . . . . . . . . . . . . . . . . . TEN 199
■ 12". . . . . . . . . . . . . . . . . . . . TENT 199
0 / Sep '87.

## WHERE IS THE SOUND.
Tracks: Not Advised.
■ CD. . . . . . . . . . . . . . . . . . . MOTCCD 73
Motor City / Oct '92.

# Starr, Stella

## BRING HIM BACK.
Tracks: Bring him back / Say it.
■ 7". . . . . . . . . . . . . . . . . . . . . 7N 35366
Piccadilly / Feb '67.

## STELLA'S STARR HITS.
Tracks: Not Advised.
■ LP. . . . . . . . . . . . . . . . . . . PELICAN 21
Pelican / Sep '81.

# Starship Orchestra

## CELESTIAL SKY.
Tracks: You're a star / New York, New York / Waiting Game / Aquelas coisas todas / Genie / Celestial sky / Yesterday / Serious business / Give me some skin.
■ LP. . . . . . . . . . . . . . . . . . . CBS 84558
BS / Sep '80.

## YOU'RE A STAR.
Tracks: You're a star / Celestial sky.
■ 12". . . . . . . . . . . . . . . . . . CBS 138898
■ 7". . . . . . . . . . . . . . . . . . . . CBS 8898
BS / Aug '80.

# Staton, Candi

Deep soul singer discovered and promptly married by Clarence Carter in late '60s. After U.S. hits including million-selling In The Ghetto, she divorced Carter, who no doubt left with Staton's successful version of Stand By Your Man ringing in his ears. Switching from Muscle Shoals-based Fame label to Warner Brothers, she made huge international splash with Young Hearts Run Free in 1976. Other U.K. hits included Nights On Broadway in 1977 and Suspicious Minds in '82. She subsequently returned to first love gospel, although 1986 recording with the Source, haunting You Got The Love, resurfaced as club classic and chart smash in '91.

## CANDI STATON.
Tracks: Looking for love / Halfway to heaven / One more try / If you feel the need / Hunter gets captured by the game / It's real / Betcha I'm gonna get ya.
■ LP. . . . . . . . . . . . . . . . . . . K 56803
WEA / Aug '80.

## CHANCE.
Tracks: I ain't got nowhere to go / When you wake up / Rock / Chance / I live / Me and my music.
■ LP. . . . . . . . . . . . . . . . . . . K 56641
WEA / '77.

## COUNT ON ME.
Tracks: Count on me / Hurry sundown.
■ 12". . . . . . . . . . . . . . . . . . . SHL 115
■ 7". . . . . . . . . . . . . . . . . . . . . SH 115
Sugarhill / Jul '82.

## DESTINY.
Tracks: Destiny.
■ 7". . . . . . . . . . . . . . . . . . . . . K 16806
WEA / Sep '76.

## GLORIFY.
Tracks: Sing a song / He is Lord / To glorify your name / It's not easy / Have you tried God / First face / I want to see / God's got it / He's coming back.
CD. . . . . . . . . . . . . . . . . . . CDBM 075
LP. . . . . . . . . . . . . . . . . . . BMLP 075
Blue Moon (1) / '91 / Roots Records / Jazz Music / Swift / Projection / THE / Hot Shot.

## HONEST I DO LOVE YOU.
Tracks: Honest I do love you / So blue.
■ 7". . . . . . . . . . . . . . . . . . . . . K 17164
WEA / Jun '78.

## HOUSE OF LOVE.
Tracks: Victim / Honest I do love you / Yesterday evening / I wonder will I ever get over it / I'm gonna make you love me / So blue / Take my hand.
■ LP. . . . . . . . . . . . . . . . . . . K 56510
WEA / Aug '78.

## I'M JUST A PRISONER.
Tracks: Someone you use / I'd rather be an old man's sweetheart / Heart on a string / You don't love me no more / Evidence / For you / Sweet feeling do your duty / That's how strong my love is / I'm just a prisoner / Another man's woman, another woman's man / Never in public / Get it when I.
■ LP. . . . . . . . . . . . . . . . . . . ST 21631
Capitol / Oct '70.

## LISTEN TO THE MUSIC.
Tracks: Listen to the music / Music speaks louder than words.
■ 7". . . . . . . . . . . . . . . . . . . . . K 17080
WEA / Jan '78.

## LOOKING FOR LOVE.
Tracks: Looking for love / It's real.
■ 7". . . . . . . . . . . . . . . . . . . . . K 17656
WEA / Aug '80.

## MAKE ME AN INSTRUMENT.
Tracks: Sin doesn't live here anymore / God can make something out of nothing / Let go and tell God / Make me an instrument / He is no farther than a thought away / Oh how He must love me / God specialises / Nothing can separate me (from your love).
■ LP. . . . . . . . . . . . . . . . . . . MYR 1180
MC. . . . . . . . . . . . . . . . . . . MC 1180
Myrrh / May '85 / Word Records (UK) / Sony.

## MUSIC SPEAKS LOUDER THAN WORDS.
Tracks: Nights on Broadway / You are / Dreamer of a dream / Music speaks louder than words / Cotton Candi / Listen to the music / When you want love / One more chance / On love / Main thing / Before the next teardrop falls / Music speaks louder than words (reprise).
■ LP. . . . . . . . . . . . . . . . . . . K 56360
WEA / Jul '77.

## MUSIC SPEAKS LOUDER THAN WORDS.
Tracks: Music speaks louder than words / Dreamer of dreams.
■ 7". . . . . . . . . . . . . . . . . . . . . K 17029
WEA / Nov '77.

## NIGHTLITES.
Tracks: Love and be free / Suspicious minds / In the still of the night / Sunshine of our love / Hurry sundown / Tender hooks / Count on me.
CD. . . . . . . . . . . . . . . . . . . NEMCD 624
Sequel / Jun '92 / Total / BMG.

## NIGHTS ON BROADWAY.
Tracks: Nights on Broadway / You are.
■ 7". . . . . . . . . . . . . . . . . . . . . K 16972
WEA / Jul '77.

## STAND BY YOUR MAN.
Tracks: Stand by your man / How can I put out the flame.
■ 7". . . . . . . . . . . . . . . . . . . . . CL 15658
Capitol / Jul '71.

## STAND UP AND BE A WITNESS.
Tracks: Stand up / I'm depending on you / You don't know / He's always there / Advance / God's got an answer / Until you make it through / Glory of Jesus / Hallel.
CD. . . . . . . . . . . . . . . . . . . CDBM 077

## STANDING ON THE PROMISES.
Tracks: Not Advised.
CD. . . . . . . . . . . . . . . . . . . CDBM 096
Blue Moon (1) / Oct '93 / Roots Records / Jazz Music / Swift / Projection / THE / Hot Shot.

LP. . . . . . . . . . . . . . . . . . . BMLP 077
Blue Moon (1) / Apr '90 / Roots Records / Jazz Music / Swift / Projection / THE / Hot Shot.

## SUSPICIOUS MINDS.
Tracks: Love and be free / Suspicious minds / In the still of the night / Sunshine of our love / Hurry sundown / Tender hooks / Count on me.
■ LP. . . . . . . . . . . . . . . . . . . SHLP 1005
MC. . . . . . . . . . . . . . . . . . . ZCSH 1005
Sugarhill / Jul '82 / Roots Records / C.M. Distribution / A.D.A. Distribution / Direct Distribution.

## SUSPICIOUS MINDS.
Tracks: Suspicious minds / Nights on Broadway.
■ 12". . . . . . . . . . . . . . . . . . . SHL 112
■ 7". . . . . . . . . . . . . . . . . . . . . SH 112
Sugarhill / Mar '82.

## TELL IT LIKE IT IS (Staton, Candi & Bettye Swann).
Tracks: Someone you use / I'd rather be an old man's sweetheart (Full title: I'd rather be an old man's sweetheart (than a young man's) / Evidence / Sweet feeling / I'm just a prisoner (of your good lovin') / Do your duty / Get it when I want it / Tell it like it is / These arms of mine / No faith, no love / Cover me / Don't you ever get tired (of hurtin' me) / You're up to your same old tricks again / Today I started loving you again / Willie and Laura Mae Jones.
■ MC. . . . . . . . . . . . . . . . . . . TCSSL 6003
■ LP. . . . . . . . . . . . . . . . . . . SSL 6003
Stateside / Apr '86.

## VICTIM.
Tracks: Victim / Yesterday evening.
■ 7". . . . . . . . . . . . . . . . . . . . . K 17221
WEA / Aug '78.

## WHEN YOU WAKE UP TOMORROW.
Tracks: When you wake up tomorrow / Rough times.
■ 7". . . . . . . . . . . . . . . . . . . . . K 17370
WEA / '79.

## YOU'VE GOT THE LOVE (Staton, Candi Featuring The Source).
Tracks: You've got the love (mix).
■ 12". . . . . . . . . . . . . . . . . . . MKHAN 78
■ 7". . . . . . . . . . . . . . . . . . . . . KHAN 78
Streetwave / Nov '86.

## YOUNG HEARTS RUN FREE.
Tracks: Run to me / Destiny / What a feeling / You bet your sweet / Sweet love / Young hearts run free / Living for you / Summer time with you / I know.
■ LP. . . . . . . . . . . . . . . . . . . K 56259
WEA / Jul '76.

## YOUNG HEARTS RUN FREE.
Tracks: Young hearts run free / I know.
■ 7". . . . . . . . . . . . . . . . . . . . . K 16730
WEA / May '76.

## YOUNG HEARTS RUN FREE (OLD GOLD).
Tracks: Young hearts run free / Nights on Broadway.
■ 7". . . . . . . . . . . . . . . . . . . . . OG 9518
Old Gold / Sep '85.

## YOUNG HEARTS RUN FREE (REMIX).
Tracks: Young hearts run free / Young hearts run free (M & M '86 remix).
■ 12". . . . . . . . . . . . . . . . . . . W 8680T
■ 7". . . . . . . . . . . . . . . . . . . . . W 8680
WEA / May '86.

# Status IV

## LOVIN' YOU.
Tracks: Loving you.
■ 12". . . . . . . . . . . . . . . . . . . DEST 8
■ 7". . . . . . . . . . . . . . . . . . . . . DES 8
Design Communications / Mar '84.

## YOU AIN'T REALLY DOWN.
Tracks: You ain't really down.
■ 12". . . . . . . . . . . . . . . . . . . TMTT 4
■ 7". . . . . . . . . . . . . . . . . . . . . TMT 4
T.M.T. / Jul '83.
■ 12". . . . . . . . . . . . . . . . . . . DOM T1
Domino (1) / May '85.

■ DELETED

395

## Steele, Jevetta

### CALLING YOU (Steele, Jevetta & Deinnger Blasmusik).
Tracks: Calling you / Calling you (inst) / Zweisach.
■ CD Single . . . . . . . . . . . . . . . . CID 385
Island / Apr '89.
■ 7" . . . . . . . . . . . . . . . . . . . IS 385
Island / Mar '89.

### HERE IT IS.
Tracks: Say a little prayer for you / Baby are you / And how / You're gonna love me / Here it is / Calling you / In this man's world / Good foot / Skip 2 my u my darling / Where do we go from here / Love will follow.
CD . . . . . . . . . . . . . . . . . . . .108772
Musidisc / Mar '92 / Vital Distribution / Discovery / A.D.A. Distribution / Harmonia Mundi (UK).

## Stephenson, Van

### MODERN DAY DELILAH.
Tracks: Modern day Delilah / Don't do that.
■ 7" . . . . . . . . . . . . . . . . . . MCA 891
MCA / Jun '84.

### RIGHTEOUS ANGER.
Tracks: Modern day Delilah / I know who you are (and I saw what you did) / What the big girls do / Don't do that / Others only dream / Righteous anger / Cure will kill you / You've been lied to before / Heart over mind / All american boy.
■ LP . . . . . . . . . . . . . . . . . . MCF 3229
MCA / Sep '84.
■ LP . . . . . . . . . . . . . . . . . . MCL 1854
■ MC . . . . . . . . . . . . . . . . . . MCLC 1854
MCA / Jun '87.

### SUSPICIOUS HEART.
Tracks: Not Advised.
■ LP . . . . . . . . . . . . . . . . . . MCF 3336
■ MC . . . . . . . . . . . . . . . . . . MCFC 3336
MCA / Aug '86.

### WE'RE DOIN' ALRIGHT.
Tracks: We're doin' alright / Suspicious heart / What the big girls do (Extra track on 12" version only) / Modern day Delilah (Extra track on 12" version only).
■ 12" . . . . . . . . . . . . . . . . . MCAT 1082
■ 7" . . . . . . . . . . . . . . . . . . MCA 1082
MCA / Sep '86.

## Stereotype

### FREESTYLE.
Tracks: Freestyle.
■ 12" . . . . . . . . . . . . . . . . . . STING 1
Big Buzz / Mar '89.

## Stevens, April

### ALONE.
Tracks: Not Advised.
■ LP . . . . . . . . . . . . . . . . . . . SAM 1
MC . . . . . . . . . . . . . . . . . . . SAMC 1
Mr.Sam / Jul '85 / M.I.S.Records.

### ONCE UPON A VERY SPECIAL TIME.
Tracks: Once upon a very special time.
■ 7" . . . . . . . . . . . . . . . . . . SAS 101
Mr.Sam / May '85.

### WANTING YOU.
Tracks: Falling in love / Wanting you.
■ 7" . . . . . . . . . . . . . . . . . .2006 603
MGM (EMI) / Jul '77.

## Stevens, Kenni

### 24-7-365.
Tracks: 24-7-365 / 24-7-365 (remix) (Only on 12" single.) / Who's been loving you.
■ 12" . . . . . . . . . . . . . . . . . DEBTX 3051
■ 7" . . . . . . . . . . . . . . . . . . DEBT 3051
Debut (1) / Jun '88.

### ALL DAY ALL NIGHT.
Tracks: All day, all night / All day all night (keep on loving mix) / All day all night (jazz mix) / All day all night (funk mix).
■ 12" . . . . . . . . . . . . . . . . . . DAZZ 50
Elite Records / Feb '86.

### BLUE MOODS.
Tracks: Not Advised.
CD . . . . . . . . . . . . . . . . . . CDKEN 1
■ LP . . . . . . . . . . . . . . . . . KENILLP 1
MC . . . . . . . . . . . . . . . . . . . ZKEN 1
Jam Today / Apr '87 / Jetstar.

### CANNOT LIVE WITHOUT YOUR LOVE (AT LAST THE DANCE MIX).
Tracks: Cannot live without your love (dance mix) / Passionate (jam today remix).
■ 12" . . . . . . . . . . . . . . . . . 12 KST 1
■ 7" . . . . . . . . . . . . . . . . . . KST 1
Elite Records / Jul '87.

### LIVING ON THE EDGE.
Tracks: Living on the edge / Love takes over the dance / Gonna take time / Sailing / Living on the edge (reprise) / I know how / You're a sin / Someone / After all.
LP . . . . . . . . . . . . . . . . . . DBLP 505
MC. . . . . . . . . . . . . . . . . . ZCDB 505
Debut (1) / Feb '90 / Pinnacle.

### NIGHT MOVIES.
Tracks: Night movies.
■ 12" . . . . . . . . . . . . . . . . . . DAZZ 41
■ 7" . . . . . . . . . . . . . . . . . . DAZZ 417
Elite Records / Jul '85.

### SAILING.
Tracks: Sailing.
■ 12" . . . . . . . . . . . . . . . . . DEBTX 3066
■ 7" . . . . . . . . . . . . . . . . . . DEBT 3066
Debut (1) / Mar '89.

### TOO MUCH TOO SOON.
Tracks: Too much too soon / Night moves (ultra-sensual remix) / Too much too soon (Inst).
■ 12" . . . . . . . . . . . . . . . . . . DAZZ 59
Elite Records / Oct '86.

### YOU.
Tracks: Who's been loving you / Hurt this way / Never gonna give you up / 24-7-365 / You don't know / I bleed for you / You / Didn't mean to hurt you / Work me up (Extra track on cassette & CD.) / Anne (Extra track on cassette & CD.).
CD. . . . . . . . . . . . . . . . . . .CDDB 502
■ LP . . . . . . . . . . . . . . . . . DBLP 502
MC. . . . . . . . . . . . . . . . . . ZCDB 502
Debut (1) / May '88 / Pinnacle.

## Stevens, Mike

### C'EST L'AFFAIRE.
Tracks: C'est l'affaire / C'est l'affair (pure sax mix) / C'est l'affaire (sax maniax mix) (extra track on 12") / C'est l'affaire (no sax please..) (extra track on 12").
■ 12" . . . . . . . . . . . . . . . . . . PT 41752
■ 7" . . . . . . . . . . . . . . . . . . PB 41751
RCA / Feb '88.

### CATHY'S CLOWN.
Tracks: Cathy's clown / Go-go train.
■ 7" . . . . . . . . . . . . . . . . . . 7N 17243
Pye / Jan '67.

### LIGHT UP THE NIGHT.
Tracks: Time with you / C'est l'affaire / Looks like rain / Sao Paulo / Tapestry / Joy and pain / Light up the night / My funny valentine / Into the heat / Easy way out.
■ LP . . . . . . . . . . . . . . . . . CGILLP 3
MC. . . . . . . . . . . . . . . . . . ZCCHIL 3
Jam Today / Nov '87 / Jetstar.
■ CD . . . . . . . . . . . . . . . . . . PD 71641
■ LP . . . . . . . . . . . . . . . . . PL 71641
■ MC . . . . . . . . . . . . . . . . . PK 71641
RCA / Mar '88.

### SET THE SPIRIT FREE.
Tracks: Cool with your love / Set the spirit free / Sunset trip / Love TKO / Tell her / I'm a romantic / Ride the bullet train / Precious / Latinesque / Finest one / Roxanne (Only on CD.) / Living groove (Only on CD.) / Sparkle (in your eyes).
CD. . . . . . . . . . . . . . . . . . CDCHIL 9
LP . . . . . . . . . . . . . . . . . . CHILLP 9
MC. . . . . . . . . . . . . . . . . . ZCCHIL 9
Jam Today / May '90 / Jetstar.

## Stevie B

### BECAUSE I LOVE YOU (THE POSTMAN SONG).
Tracks: Because I love you (The postman song) / We're jammin' now.
■ 12" . . . . . . . . . . . . . . . . . . PZ 126
■ 7" . . . . . . . . . . . . . . . . . . PO 126
■ CD Single. . . . . . . . . . . . . . PZCD 126
■ MC Single. . . . . . . . . . . . . . POCS 126
Polydor / Feb '91.

### I'LL BE BY YOUR SIDE.
Tracks: I'll be by your side.
■ CD Single . . . . . . . . . . . . . . PO 145
■ CD Single . . . . . . . . . . . . . PZCD 145
■ MC Single. . . . . . . . . . . . . . POCS 145

### ■ 12" . . . . . . . . . . . . . . . . . .PZ 145
Polydor / Mar '91.

### LOVE AND EMOTION.
Tracks: Love and emotion / Because I love you (The postman song) / Forever more / Broken hearted / Facts of love / Who's loving you tonight / We re jammin now / Memories of loving you / I'll be by your side.
■ LP . . . . . . . . . . . . . . . . . 849 012-1
■ CD . . . . . . . . . . . . . . . . . 849 012-2
■ MC . . . . . . . . . . . . . . . . . 849 012-4
Polydor / Apr '91.

### SPRING LOVE COME BACK TO ME.
Tracks: Spring love come back to me.
■ 12" . . . . . . . . . . . . . . . . . LMR 4002
LMR / Jul '88.

## Stewart, Amii

### AMII.
Tracks: Time is tight / Power play / Easy on your love / Love's in disguise / Lover to lover / Break these chains / Love ain't no toy / Mystery of love / Conspiracy / This generation.
■ LP . . . . . . . . . . . . . . . . . . PL 70112
■ MC . . . . . . . . . . . . . . . . . . PK 70112
RCA / Jan '87.

### AMII STEWART.
Tracks: Knock on wood / You really touched my heart / Light my fire / 137 disco heaven / Bring it or back to me / Closest thing to heaven / Am I losing you / Get your love back / Only a child in your eyes.
■ LP . . . . . . . . . . . . . . . . . . K 50593
■ MC . . . . . . . . . . . . . . . . . . K4 50593
Atlantic / May '79.

### BEST OF AND THE REST OF, THE.
Tracks: Knock on wood / You really touch my heart / 137 disco heaven / Paradise bird / My guy, my girl / Light my fire / Only a child in your eyes / Step into the love line / Ash 48 / Jealousy.
■ CD . . . . . . . . . . . . . . . . . . CDAR 1023
■ MC . . . . . . . . . . . . . . . . . . ARLC 1023
Action Replay / Mar '91.

### FRIENDS.
Tracks: Friends / Picture.
■ 7" . . . . . . . . . . . . . . . . . . .RCA 471
■ 12" . . . . . . . . . . . . . . . . . RCAT 471
RCA / Jan '85.

### FRIENDS '91.
Tracks: Friends.
■ 12" . . . . . . . . . . . . . . . . . FLYUK 41
Flying UK / Sep '91.

### HITS, THE.
Tracks: Knock on wood / Ash 48 / Light my fire / 137 disco heaven / You really touch my heart.
■ LP . . . . . . . . . . . . . . . . . . SED 9000
MC. . . . . . . . . . . . . . . . . . ZCSED 9000
Sedition / Nov '85.

### JEALOUSY.
Tracks: Jealousy.
■ 7" . . . . . . . . . . . . . . . . . . K 11386
Atlantic / Nov '79.

### KNOCK ON WOOD.
Tracks: Knock on wood / When you are beautiful.
■ 7" . . . . . . . . . . . . . . . . . . K 11214
Atlantic / '79.
■ 12" . . . . . . . . . . . . . . . . . EDITL 3303
■ 7" . . . . . . . . . . . . . . . . . . EDIT 3303
Sedition / Jul '85.

### KNOCK ON WOOD (1985 REMIX).
Tracks: Knock on wood (1985 remix) / Light my fire (1985 remix).
■ 12" . . . . . . . . . . . . . . . . . . OG 4120
Old Gold / May '89.

### KNOCK ON WOOD (OLD GOLD).
Tracks: Knock on wood / Light my fire.
7" . . . . . . . . . . . . . . . . . . .OG 6512
Old Gold / '92 / Pickwick.

### LIGHT MY FIRE.
Tracks: Light my fire / Knock on wood.
■ 12" . . . . . . . . . . . . . . . . . EDITX 3303
Sedition / Aug '85.

### LIGHT MY FIRE (ORIGINAL).
Tracks: Light my fire / Bring it on home to me.
■ 7" . . . . . . . . . . . . . . . . . . K 11276
WEA / '79.

### LOVE AIN'T NO TOY.
Tracks: Lover to lover / Friends (Available on 12" version).
■ 12" . . . . . . . . . . . . . . . . . PT 41106

■ DELETED

7" . . . . . . . . . . . . . . . . . . . . PB 41105
CA / Feb '87.

## MY GUY, MY GIRL (Stewart, Amii & Leon Estus).
**Tracks:** My guy, my girl / Bring it on back to me / Knock on wood (Track included in double pack) / Light my fire (Track included in double pack).
■ 12" . . . . . . . . . . . . . . . EDITL 3310
■ 12" Remix. . . . . . . . . . . . EDITX 3310
■ 7" . . . . . . . . . . . . . . . . EDIT 3310
edition / Nov '85.

## MY GUY, MY GIRL (Stewart, Amii & Johnny Bristol).
**Tracks:** My guy, my girl.
■ 7" . . . . . . . . . . . . . . . . . K 11550
tlantic / Jul '80.

## PARADISE BIRD.
Tracks: Letter / Paradise bird / He's a burglar / Jealousy / Right place, wrong time / Step into the Love line / Paradise found.
■ LP . . . . . . . . . . . . . . . . K 50673
■ MC. . . . . . . . . . . . . . . . K4 50673
tlantic / Oct '79.

## PARADISE BIRD.
Tracks: Paradise bird / Letter.
■ 7" . . . . . . . . . . . . . . . . K 11424
tlantic / Jan '80.

## HAT LOVING FEELING.
Tracks: That loving feeling / Fever line.
■ 12" . . . . . . . . . . . . . . . PT 40018
■ 7" . . . . . . . . . . . . . . . PB 40017
CA / Mar '85.

## WHERE DID OUR LOVE GO.
Tracks: Where did our love go / Premiere.
■ 12" . . . . . . . . . . . . . . K 11580 T
■ 7" . . . . . . . . . . . . . . . K 11580
tlantic / Apr '81.

## YOU REALLY TOUCH MY HEART.
Tracks: You really touch my heart / Closest to Heaven.
■ 7" . . . . . . . . . . . . . . . . K 11178
tlantic / Aug '78.
■ 12" . . . . . . . . . . . . . . EDITL 3307
■ 7" . . . . . . . . . . . . . . . EDIT 3307
edition / Oct '85.
■ 7" Set . . . . . . . . . . . . . EDITP 3307
edition / Oct '85.

# Stewart, Billy

## BECAUSE I LOVE YOU.
Tracks: Because I love you / Mountain of love.
■ 7" . . . . . . . . . . . . . . . CRS 8028
hess / Jan '66.

## BILLY STEWART TEACHES OLD STAN-DARDS NEW TRICKS.
Tracks: Temptation / Exodus / Fly me to the moon / Let's fall in love / Somewhere / Ol' man river / Every Day I Have the blues / Who can I turn to / Moonlight In Vermont / Secret love / When I fall in love / It's Alright with me.
■ LP . . . . . . . . . . . . . . . .GCH 8089
■ MC. . . . . . . . . . . . . . GCHK 78089
hess (Charly) / Jul '88 / Charly.

## EVERY DAY I HAVE THE BLUES.
Tracks: Not Advised.
CD. . . . . . . . . . . . . . . . RTS 33206
Roots / Nov '90 / Pinnacle / Target.

## GOLDEN DECADE.
Tracks: Summertime / I do love you / Temptation's About to get me / Fat boy / Scramble / Cross my heart I'm no Romeo / Sitting in the park / Secret love / Because I love you / Reap what you sow / Strange Feeling / Why do I love you so / Keep lovin' / Once Again / Billy's blues.
■ LP . . . . . . . . . . . . . . . 6310125
hess / Nov '72.

## LOVE ME.
Tracks: Love me / Why am I lonely.
■ 7" . . . . . . . . . . . . . . . CRS 8038
hess / Jun '66.

## OL' MAN RIVER.
Tracks: Ol' man river / Every day I have the blues.
■ 7" . . . . . . . . . . . . . . . CRS 8050
hess / Jan '67.

## ONE MORE TIME.
Tracks: Billy's blues part 2 / Fat boy / Reap what you Sow / Sugar and spice / Strange Feeling / Count me Out / Keep lovin' / I do love you / Sitting in the park / Love me / Summertime / How nice it is / Because I

---

love you / Over the rainbow / Everyday I have the blues / Secret love / Temptaion 'bout to get me / Why do I love you so / Cross my heart / Golly golly gee / One more time / Tell me the truth / I'm in love (oh yes I am) / We'll always be together.
■ LP . . . . . . . . . . . . . . . LPM 7004
Chess (Charly) / '89.

## SECRET LOVE.
Tracks: Secret love / Look back and smile.
■ 7" . . . . . . . . . . . . . . . CRS 8045
Chess / Oct '66.

## SUMMERTIME.
Tracks: Summertime / Secret love / Sitting in the park / I do love you.
■ 7" . . . . . . . . . . . . . . . CRS 8040
Chess / Sep '66.
■ 7" . . . . . . . . . . . . . . . CHES 4007
Chess (PRT) / Jul '85.

## THINK BEFORE YOU THINK.
Tracks: Think before you think / Faces / Dewey said / When you're smiling / Goodbye / Processional / I'm gettin' sentimental over you / Rain / Deed-Lee-Yah / Little Niles.
CD. . . . . . . . . . . . . . . . 66053024
Jazz City / Jun '91 / New Note.

# Stewart, Denise

## TAKE ME IN YOUR ARMS.
Tracks: Take me in your arms / Take me in your arms (version).
■ 12" . . . . . . . . . . . . . . . ELLT 3
■ 7" . . . . . . . . . . . . . . . ELL 3
Ellorac / Nov '89.

# Stewart, Jermaine

## DON'T EVER LEAVE ME.
Tracks: Give your love to me / Don't ever leave me.
■ 12" . . . . . . . . . . . . . . TENT 157
■ 7" . . . . . . . . . . . . . . . TEN 157
10 / Jan '87.

## DON'T TALK DIRTY TO ME.
Tracks: Don't talk dirty to me (7" only) / Places / Don't talk dirty to me (radio edit) (On CD only) / Don't talk dirty to me (edited remix) (On CD only) / Get lucky (New York mix) (On CD only).
■ 12" . . . . . . . . . . . . . . .SRNT 86
■ 7" . . . . . . . . . . . . . . . SRNP 86
■ 7" . . . . . . . . . . . . . . . SRN 86
■ CD Single. . . . . . . . . . . .SRNCD 86
Siren / Sep '88.
■ 7" P.Disc . . . . . . . . . . . . SRNY 86
Siren / Sep '88.

## EVERY WOMAN WANTS TO.
Tracks: Every woman wants to / Holes in my jeans / Every woman wants to (new mix) (Only on 12" and CD single.) / Every woman wants to (album version) (Only on 12" and CD single.).
■ 12" . . . . . . . . . . . . . . TENX 296
■ 7" . . . . . . . . . . . . . . . TEN 296
■ CD Single. . . . . . . . . . . TENCD 296
10 / Feb '90.

## FRANTIC ROMANTIC.
Tracks: We don't have to take our clothes off / Versatile / Moonlight carnival / Don't ever leave me / Dance floor / Jody / Give your love to me / Out to punish / Frantic romantic / Word is out / Word is out, The (West mix-ext. version) (CD & Cassette only) / We don't have to take our clothes off (spec (CD & Cassette only).
■ CD . . . . . . . . . . . . . . DIXCD 26
■ LP . . . . . . . . . . . . . . . DIX 26
■ MC. . . . . . . . . . . . . . . CDIX 26
10 / Jul '87.

## GET LUCKY.
Tracks: Get lucky (Not on 12") / Get lucky (extended remix) (Not on 7") / Imagine (On all versions) / Say it again (remix) (CD & Cassette only) / Get lucky (dub) (12" only).
■ 12" . . . . . . . . . . . . . . .SRNT 82
■ 12" P.Disc. . . . . . . . . . . SRNTP 82
■ 7" . . . . . . . . . . . . . . . SRN 82
■ CD Single. . . . . . . . . . . .SRNCD 82
Siren / Mar '88.
■ MC Single. . . . . . . . . . . SRNC 82
Siren / Mar '88.

## GET OVER IT.
Tracks: Get over it.
■ 12" . . . . . . . . . . . . . . TEN 23-12
■ 7" . . . . . . . . . . . . . . . TEN 23
10 / Jun '84.

---

## I LIKE IT.
Tracks: I like it / Month of Mondays.
■ 12" . . . . . . . . . . . . . . TEN 50-12
■ 7" . . . . . . . . . . . . . . . TEN 50
10 / May '85.

## JODY.
Tracks: Jody / Dance floor.
■ 12" . . . . . . . . . . . . . . TENT 143
■ 7" . . . . . . . . . . . . . . . TEN 143
10 / Oct '86.

## SAY IT AGAIN.
Tracks: Don't talk dirty to me / Say it again / Get lucky / Got to be love / Dress it up / Don't have sex with your ex / Is it really love / Call it a miracle / Eyes / My house / She's a teaser / My body.
■ CD . . . . . . . . . . . . . . .CDSRN 14
■ LP . . . . . . . . . . . . . . . SRNLP 14
■ MC . . . . . . . . . . . . . . SRNMC 14
Siren / Feb '88.

## SAY IT AGAIN.
Tracks: Say it again (On all versions) / You promise (On all versions) / Say it again (extended remix) (On 12" only) / We don't have to take our clothes off (On CD only) / Dress it up (On CD only).
■ 12" . . . . . . . . . . . . . . TENT 188
■ 7" . . . . . . . . . . . . . . . TENM 188
■ CD Single . . . . . . . . . . . SAYCD 188
■ 7" . . . . . . . . . . . . . . . TEN 188
■ MC Single. . . . . . . . . . . TENC 188
10 / Oct '87.

## TREN DE AMOR.
Tracks: Tren de amor / When sex becomes a religion / Tren di amour (express mix) (Only on 12" and CD single.) / Tren di amour (acappella mix) (Only on 12" single.) / Tren di amour (cymone mix) (Only on CD" single.).
■ 12" . . . . . . . . . . . . . . TENX 292
■ MC Single . . . . . . . . . . . TENC 292
■ 7" . . . . . . . . . . . . . . . TEN 292
■ 7" P.Disc . . . . . . . . . . . TENP 292
■ CD Single . . . . . . . . . . . TENCD 292
10 / Nov '89.

## WE DON'T HAVE TO TAKE OUR CLOTHES OFF.
Tracks: We don't have to take our clothes off / Brilliance / We don't have to take our clothes off (extended0 (12" only).
■ 12" . . . . . . . . . . . . . . TEN 96-12
■ 7" . . . . . . . . . . . . . . . TEN 96
10 / Feb '86.

## WHAT BECOMES A LEGEND MOST.
Tracks: Tren de amor / Set me free / State of my heart / I'd rather be with you / Every woman wants to / Lies / One lover / Call me before you come / Gourmet love / Please say you will / Betty Blue / Holes in my jeans.
■ CD . . . . . . . . . . . . . . DIXCD 88
■ LP . . . . . . . . . . . . . . . DIX 88
■ MC. . . . . . . . . . . . . . . CDIX 88
10 / Mar '90.

## WORD IS OUT.
Tracks: Word is out / I like it / In love again / Debbie / Reasons why / Get over it / Month of Mondays / You / Spies / Brilliance.
CD P.Disc. . . . . . . . . . . . CDPSRN 14
Siren / Dec '88 / EMI.
■ LP . . . . . . . . . . . . . . . XID 4
■ MC. . . . . . . . . . . . . . . CXID 4
Siren / Jun '88.

## WORD IS OUT.
Tracks: Word is out / Word is out, The (instrumental).
■ 12" . . . . . . . . . . . . . . TEN 10-12
■ 7" . . . . . . . . . . . . . . . TEN 10
10 / Mar '84.

# Stikki Stuff

## SCHOOL.
Tracks: School / Wiggle.
■ 7" . . . . . . . . . . . . . . . .CAR 206
Carrere / Aug '81.

## YO YO.
Tracks: Yo yo / For all those who sail with us.
■ 7" . . . . . . . . . . . . . . . TECLR 1
Total Eclipse / Oct '86.

# Stirling McLean

## COMING OR GOING.
Tracks: Coming or going / Hey boy.
12" . . . . . . . . . . . . . . . CALL 100T
Callisto / Sep '94 / Timewarp.

## Stone

### CRAZY.
**Tracks:** Crazy / That girl is hot.
- **7"** . . . . . . . . . . . . . . . . . . . . SYN 4
Sound Of New York (USA) / Jul '83.
- **12"** . . . . . . . . . . . . . . . . . . . SNYL 4
Sound Of New York (USA) / Jul '85.

### GIRL I LIKE THE WAY YOU MOVE.
**Tracks:** Girl I like the way you move.
- **12"** . . . . . . . . . . . . . . . . . . CART 261
- **7"** . . . . . . . . . . . . . . . . . . . CAR 261
Carrere / Jan '83.

### TIME.
**Tracks:** Time.
- **12"** . . . . . . . . . . . . . . . . . . CART 236
- **7"** . . . . . . . . . . . . . . . . . . . CAR 236
Carrere / Apr '82.
- **12"** . . . . . . . . . . . . . . . . BC 12205640
BCM / Nov '87.

## Stone City Band

### ALL DAY AND ALL OF THE NIGHT.
**Tracks:** All day and all of the night.
- **12"** . . . . . . . . . . . . . . . . . TMGT 1221
- **7"** . . . . . . . . . . . . . . . . . . TMG 1221
Motown / Oct '81.

### BOYS ARE BACK.
**Tracks:** All day and all of the night / Feel good 'bout yourself / Keep love happy / Ganja / Freaky / Funky reggae / Lovin' you is easy / Tin soldier.
- **LP** . . . . . . . . . . . . . . . . . STML 12150
Motown / Oct '81.

### FUNKY REGGAE.
**Tracks:** Funky reggae / Ganja.
- **7"** . . . . . . . . . . . . . . . . . . TMG 1239
Motown / Jul '81.

### LADIES CHOICE.
**Tracks:** Ladies choice.
- **12"** . . . . . . . . . . . . . . . . . TMGT 1316
- **7"** . . . . . . . . . . . . . . . . . . TMG 1316
Motown / Sep '83.

### OUT FROM THE SHADOW.
**Tracks:** Not Advised.
- **LP** . . . . . . . . . . . . . . . . . STML 12190
- **MC** . . . . . . . . . . . . . . . . CSTML 12190
Motown / Nov '83.

### STRUT YOUR STUFF.
**Tracks:** Strut your stuff / F.I.M.A.
- **7"** . . . . . . . . . . . . . . . . . . TMG 1181
Motown / Oct '81.

## Stone, Sly

Exasperated by attempts to produce Jefferson Airplane, Sylvester Stewart turned back on acid rock and formed Sly & the Family Stone in 1967. Result was sequence of funkiest singles ever recorded by anyone whose name wasn't James Brown; including *Dance To The Music*, *Everyday People* and *Thank You (Falettinme Be Mice Elf Agin)*. '70s saw darkening of Sly's vision; *There's A Riot Goin' On* was bitter contrast to optimism of earlier work, while drugs and egos took their toll on group. 1973's *Fresh* was effectively epitaph for career, although Sly would periodically attempt comebacks (meeting his match in George Clinton). A hugely-influential and much-sampled performer, Sly's keenest disciple is Prince, whose multi-racial, mixed-gender bands are obvious derivations of Family Stone template.

### ANTHOLOGY - SLY & THE FAMILY STONE (Sly & The Family Stone).
**Tracks:** Dance to the music / M'lady / Life / Fun / Sing a simple song / Everyday people / Stand / I want to take you higher / Don't call me nigger, whitey / You can make it if you try / Hot fun in the summertime / Thank you (falletinme be mice elf agin) / Everybody is a star / Family affair / Runnin' away / You caught me smilin' / Thank you for talking to me Africa / Babies makin' babies / If you want me to stay / Que sera sera.
- **Double LP** . . . . . . . . . . . EPC 22119
Epic / Jun '82.
- **LP** . . . . . . . . . . . . . . . . . . 4601751
- **MC** . . . . . . . . . . . . . . . . . . 4601754
Epic / Sep '87.

### BACK ON THE RIGHT TRACK (Sly & The Family Stone).
**Tracks:** Remember who you are / Back on the right track / If it's not addin' up / Same thing / It takes all kinds / Who's to say / Sheer energy.
- **LP** . . . . . . . . . . . . . . . . . . K 56640
WEA / Jan '80.

### BEST OF SLY AND THE FAMILY STONE (Sly & The Family Stone).
**Tracks:** Dance to the music / I want to take you higher / Family affair / Thank you / I get high on you / Stand / M'lady / Skin I'm in / Everyday people / Sing a simple song / Hot fun in the summertime / Don't call me nigger, whitey / Brave and strong / Life / Everybody is a star / If you want me to stay / (You caught me) smilin' / Que sera sera / Runnin' away / Family affair (remix).
- **CD** . . . . . . . . . . . . . . . . . . 4717582
- **MC** . . . . . . . . . . . . . . . . . . 4717584
Epic / Jul '92 / Sony.
- **CD** . . . . . . . . . . . . . . . . . . 477506 2
Epic / Oct '94 / Sony.

### COLLECTION: SLY & THE FAMILY STONE (Sly & The Family Stone).
**Tracks:** Not Advised.
- **CD** . . . . . . . . . . . . . . . . . CCSCD 307
- **MC** . . . . . . . . . . . . . . . . CCSMC 307
Castle Collector Series / Sep '91 / BMG / Pinnacle / Castle Communications.

### DANCE TO THE MUSIC (Sly & The Family Stone).
**Tracks:** You're my only love / Heavenly angel / Oh what a night / You've forgotten me / Yellow moon / Honest / Nerves / Help me with my broken heart / Long time alone / Uncle Sam needs you my friend.
- **CD** . . . . . . . . . . . . . . . . . CDTB 1.029
Thunderbolt / Nov '87 / THE / Jazz Music.
- **LP** . . . . . . . . . . . . . . . . . THBL 1.029
Thunderbolt / Nov '87.

### DANCE TO THE MUSIC (Sly & The Family Stone).
**Tracks:** Dance to the music.
- **7"** . . . . . . . . . . . . . . . . . . EPC 8017
Epic / Dec '79.
- **12"** . . . . . . . . . . . . . . . . . . . SLY T1
- **7"** . . . . . . . . . . . . . . . . . . . SLY 1
Portrait / Sep '87.

### DANCE TO THE MUSIC (Sly & The Family Stone).
**Tracks:** Dance to the music.
- **7"** . . . . . . . . . . . . . . . . . . . 583568
Direction / Mar '69.

### DANCE TO THE MUSIC (Sly & The Family Stone).
**Tracks:** Dance to the music / Higher / I ain't got nobody / Dance to the medley / Music is alive / Dance in music lover / Ride the rhythm / Color me true / Are you ready / I'll never fall in love again / Don't burn baby.
- **LP** . . . . . . . . . . . . . . . . . . 8 63412
Direction / Oct '68.

### DANCE TO THE MUSIC (OLD GOLD) (Sly & The Family Stone).
**Tracks:** Dance to the music / Everyday people.
- **7"** . . . . . . . . . . . . . . . . . . OG 9188
Old Gold / Aug '82.

### EVERYDAY PEOPLE (Sly & The Family Stone).
**Tracks:** Everyday people.
- **7"** . . . . . . . . . . . . . . . . . . . 583938
Direction (CBS) / Mar '69.

### FAMILY AFFAIR (Sly & The Family Stone).
**Tracks:** Family affair.
- **7"** . . . . . . . . . . . . . . . . . . EPC 7632
Epic / Jan '72.

### FAMILY AFFAIR (Sly & The Family Stone).
**Tracks:** My woman's head / New breed / As I get older / Somethin' bad / Fire in my heart / She's my baby / Free as a bird / Girl won't you go / Everything I need / Why can't you stay / Off the hook / Dance your pants off / Under the influence of love / Crazy love song / Seventh son.
- **CD** . . . . . . . . . . . . . . . . . CDTB 119
- **MC** . . . . . . . . . . . . . . . . . THBC 119
Thunderbolt / Apr '91 / THE / Jazz Music.

### FRESH (Sly & The Family Stone).
**Tracks:** In time / If you want me to stay / Let me have it all / Frisky / Thankful 'n' thoughtful / Skin I'm in / I

don't know / Keep on dancing / Que sera sera / If were left up to me / Babies makin' blues.
- **CD** . . . . . . . . . . . . . . . . . . EDCD 23
Edsel / Aug '87.
- **LP** . . . . . . . . . . . . . . . . . . XED 23
**MC** . . . . . . . . . . . . . . . . . . CED 23
Edsel / Jun '87 / Pinnacle.

### GREATEST HITS: SLY & THE FAMILY STONE (Sly & The Family Stone).
**Tracks:** I want to take you higher / Everybody is star / Stand / Life / Fun / You can make it if you try Dance to the music / Everyday people / Hot fun in the summertime / M'lady / Sing a simple song / Than you.
- **LP** . . . . . . . . . . . . . . . . . . 6900
Epic / Feb '71.
- **LP** . . . . . . . . . . . . . . . . . CBS 3202
**MC** . . . . . . . . . . . . . . . . . .40 3202
CBS / Mar '81 / Sony.
- **CD** . . . . . . . . . . . . . . . . . 462524
- **LP** . . . . . . . . . . . . . . . . . 462524
- **MC** . . . . . . . . . . . . . . . . . 462524
Epic / Sep '90 / Sony.

### I GET HIGH ON YOU.
**Tracks:** I get high on you / That's lovin' you.
- **7"** . . . . . . . . . . . . . . . . . . EPC 359
Epic / Oct '75.

### IN THE STILL OF THE NIGHT (Sly & The Family Stone).
**Tracks:** In the still of the night / Searchin' / Don't say didn't warn you / Ain't that lovin' you babe / Swim Every dog has his day / Suki suki pt. 1 / Suki suki p 2 / Seventh son / I can't turn you loose / Take m advice / Watermelon man / I ain't got nobody / I yo were blue / Rock dirge / High love / Life of fortune and fame.
- **CD** . . . . . . . . . . . . . . . . . CDTB 12
Thunderbolt / Sep '91 / THE / Jazz Music.

### LOOSE BOOTY (Sly & The Family Stone).
**Tracks:** Loose booty / Can't strain my brain.
- **7"** . . . . . . . . . . . . . . . . . . EPC 288
Epic / Jan '75.

### M'LADY (Sly & The Family Stone).
**Tracks:** M'lady.
- **7"** . . . . . . . . . . . . . . . . . . . .58370
Direction (CBS) / Oct '68.

### M'LADY (Sly & The Family Stone).
**Tracks:** Dynamite / Chicken / Plastic Jim / Fun / Int my own thing / Harmony / Life / Love city / I'm a animal / M'lady / Jane is a groupee.
- **LP** . . . . . . . . . . . . . . . . . . 8 6346
Direction / Feb '69.

### PEARLS FROM THE PAST - SLY STONE
**Tracks:** Not Advised.
- **CD** . . . . . . . . . . . . . . . . . KLMCD 00
Scratch / Nov '93 / Scratch Records / BMG / Grape vine Distribution.

### REMEMBER WHO YOU ARE.
**Tracks:** Remember who you are / Sheer energy.
- **7"** . . . . . . . . . . . . . . . . . . K 1747
WEA / '79.

### RUNNIN' AWAY (Sly & The Famil Stone).
**Tracks:** Runnin' away.
- **7"** . . . . . . . . . . . . . . . . . . EPC 781
Epic / Apr '72.

### SHINE IT ON (Sly & The Family Stone).
**Tracks:** Shine it on / Back on the right track / It take all kinds / Do the rattleshake / Seventh son / Sear chin' / Swim / Google eyes / Somebody to you Things that'll make you laugh / If it's not adding up Buttermilk (part 1) / Remember who you are / In the still of the night / Ain't that lovin' you baby.
- **CD** . . . . . . . . . . . . . . . . . .16222CI
Success (3) / Sep '94 / Pickwick.

### SPOTLIGHT ON SLY & FAMILY STONE (Sly & The Family Stone).
**Tracks:** Honest / Ain't that lovin' you babe / Water melon man / Hi love / Life of fortune and fame / Don say I didn't warn you / Take my advice / In the still o the night / If you were blue / Searchin' / Every do has his day / I ain't got nobody (for real) / Seventh son / I can't turn you loose / Swim / Nerves.
- **CD** . . . . . . . . . . . . . . . . . HADCD 11
- **MC** . . . . . . . . . . . . . . . . HADMC 11
Javelin / Feb '94 / THE.

### STAND (Sly & The Family Stone).
**Tracks:** Stand / Don't call me nigger, Whitey / I wan to take you higher / Somebody's watching you / Sine a simple song / Everyday people / Sex machine You can make it if you try.

■ DELETE

■ LP . . . . . . . . . . . . . . . . . . . . . . 63655
CBS / Aug '69.

## TEN YEARS TOO SOON (Sly & The Family Stone).
Tracks: Dance to the music / Sing a simple song / I get high on you / Everyday people / You can make it if you try / Stand / This is love.
■ LP . . . . . . . . . . . . . . . . . . . EPC 83640
Epic / Feb '80.

## THERE'S A RIOT GOING ON (Sly & The Family Stone).
Tracks: Luv'n'Haight / Just like a baby / Poet / Family affair / Africa talks to you - 'The Asphalt Jungle' / There's a riot goin' on / Brave and strong / (You caught me) smilin' / Time / Spaced cowboy / Runnin' away / Thank you for talking to me Africa.
■ LP . . . . . . . . . . . . . . . . . . EPC 64613
Epic / Feb '72.
MC. . . . . . . . . . . . . . . . . . . . . CED 165
■ LP . . . . . . . . . . . . . . . . . . . . XED 165
Edsel / Feb '86 / Pinnacle.
■ CD . . . . . . . . . . . . . . . . . . EDCD 165
Edsel / Dec '90.
LP. . . . . . . . . . . . . . . . . . . . . . ED 165
Edsel / Feb '91 / Pinnacle.
CD. . . . . . . . . . . . . . . . . . . . 467063 2
MC. . . . . . . . . . . . . . . . . . . . 467063 4
Epic / Apr '94 / Sony.

## Stone, Tony

### FOR A LIFETIME.
Tracks: This is serious / Can't say bye / Heartbreak in the making / For a lifetime / Life after romance / Love don't come no stronger / Instant love / Why does living / My good friend James / Something about your..
■ LP. . . . . . . . . . . . . . . . . . . CHR 1614
MC. . . . . . . . . . . . . . . . . . . ZCHR 1614
■ CD . . . . . . . . . . . . . . . . . . CCD 1614
Chrysalis / Oct '88 / EMI.

### INSTANT LOVE.
Tracks: Instant love / I don't want to be lonely.
■ 12". . . . . . . . . . . . . . . . . . ENYX 609
■ 7". . . . . . . . . . . . . . . . . . . ENY 609
Ensign / Nov '87.

### LIVING ON SUNSHINE.
Tracks: Living on sunshine.
CD Single. . . . . . . . . . . . . . . PELCD 103
Equity / Aug '94 / Intoto Records / BMG.

### LOVE DON'T COME NO STRONGER.
Tracks: Love don't come no stronger / No more those lies.
■ 7". . . . . . . . . . . . . . . . . . . ENY 617
Ensign / Oct '88.

### THIS IS SERIOUS.
Tracks: This is serious / Fooling around and having fun / Leaving on a night train (Only on CD.) / Can't say bye (Only on CD.).
■ 7". . . . . . . . . . . . . . . . . . . ENY 615
Ensign / Jun '88.
CD. . . . . . . . . . . . . . . . . . . NYCD 615
Chrysalis / Jun '88 / EMI.
■ 12". . . . . . . . . . . . . . . . . . ENYX 615
Ensign / Jun '88.

## Street, Judy

### WHAT.
Tracks: What / You turn me on.
■ 7" . . . . . . . . . . . . . . . . . . . GRP 106
Grapevine (Northern Soul) / '78.
■ 7" . . . . . . . . . . . . . . . . . . . SS 3003
Soul Stop / Aug '82.

## Strikers

### BODY MUSIC.
Tracks: Body music.
■ 12". . . . . . . . . . . . . . . . EPCA 131290
■ 7" . . . . . . . . . . . . . . . . . EPC A 1290
Epic / Jun '81.

### CONTAGIOUS.
Tracks: Contagious.
■ 12". . . . . . . . . . . . . . . . PRLA 122970
■ 7" . . . . . . . . . . . . . . . . . PRLA 2970
Prelude / Nov '82.

### INCH BY INCH.
Tracks: Inch by inch.
■ 12". . . . . . . . . . . . . . . . . EPCA 131628
■ 7" . . . . . . . . . . . . . . . . . EPCA 1628
Epic / Oct '81.

## Striplin, Sylvia

### GIVE ME YOUR LOVE.
Tracks: Give me your love / Give me your love (alternative mix) / You can't turn me away.
■ 12". . . . . . . . . . . . . . . . . FIZY 504
■ 7". . . . . . . . . . . . . . . . . . FIZZ 504
Champagne / Feb '81.
■ 12". . . . . . . . . . . . . . . . . . MOLS 8
Music Of Love / Oct '86.

### GOING HOME.
Track: Going home.
■ 12 . . . . . . . . . . . . . . . . . . DFT 1211
Dancefloor / May '89.

### YOU CAN'T TURN ME AWAY.
Tracks: You can't turn me away.
■ 12". . . . . . . . . . . . . . . . . UMD 7001
UMD (USA) / Nov '87.
■ 12". . . . . . . . . . . . . . . . . EXPAND 47
Expansion / May '94.

## Strong, Barrett

### LOVE IS YOU.
Tracks: You are my one and only love / All I wanna do is be with you / I'm so in love with you / You're a mighty good love / You turn me on / You make me feel the way I do / Love is you / When you're truly in love.
■ LP . . . . . . . . . . . . . . . . . . TRLP 101
Timeless (Soul) / Dec '87.
■ CD . . . . . . . . . . . . . . . . . TLCD 369
■ LP . . . . . . . . . . . . . . . . . . TRPL 101
Timeless (Soul) / Jan '90.

## Stubbs, Joe

### PRESSURE POINT.
Tracks: Not Advised.
■ CD . . . . . . . . . . . . . . . MOTCCD 80
Motor City / Oct '92.

## Stuff

### STUFF.
Tracks: Foots / My sweetness / Do you want some of this / Looking for the juice / Reflections on divine love / How long will it last / Sun song / Happy farms / Dixie up on the roof.
■ LP . . . . . . . . . . . . . . . . . . K 56305
WEA / Jan '77.

## Stylistics

Philadelphia band who, like Delfonics, specialised in soulful smooch. Unlike Delfonics, Stylistics lasted beyond early '70s, although their domestic success faded after fourth Top Ten hit *You Make Me Feel Brand New* in '74. By this time, however, they were chart regulars in U.K.: peaking in '75/'76 with two No. 1 hits albums and chart-topping single *Can't Give You Anything (But My Love)*. Subsequent decade saw band moving from Avco label to Philadelphia International, then on to Arthur Baker's Streetwise label and Virgin; all with non-charting results.

### 16 BARS.
Tracks: 16 bars.
■ 7" . . . . . . . . . . . . . . . . . . . 6105059
H & L (USA) / Aug '76.

### 1982.
Tracks: We should be lovers / United / Call on you / My heart / Always something there to remind me / You're leaving / Don't come telling me lies / Lighten up.
■ LP . . . . . . . . . . . . . . . . . PIR 85791
Philadelphia Int. / Sep '82.

### 7000 DOLLARS AND YOU.
Tracks: 7000 dollars and you / That don't shake me.
■ 7" . . . . . . . . . . . . . . . . . . . 6105073
H & L (USA) / Mar '77.

### ALL ABOUT LOVE.
Tracks: Can't give you anything but my love / Na na is the saddest word / Jenny / Honky tonk cafe / I will love you always / I plead guilty / Can't help falling in love / Let's put it all together / You are beautiful / Funky weekend.
■ LP . . . . . . . . . . . . . . . . . . CN 2044
■ MC. . . . . . . . . . . . . . . . . . CN4 2044
Contour / Sep '81.

### BEST OF THE STYLISTICS.
Tracks: Not Advised.
■ LP . . . . . . . . . . . . . . . . . .9109 003
Avco-Embassy / Apr '75.

### BEST OF THE STYLISTICS (1990).
Tracks: Not Advised.
CD. . . . . . . . . . . . . . . . . . . 842 936 2
■ LP . . . . . . . . . . . . . . . . . PRICE 23
MC. . . . . . . . . . . . . . . . . . PRIMC 23
Mercury / May '90 / PolyGram.

### BEST OF THE STYLISTICS VOL.2.
Tracks: Not Advised.
■ LP . . . . . . . . . . . . . . . . . .9109 010
Avco-Embassy / Sep '76.

### BETCHA BY GOLLY WOW.
Tracks: Betcha by golly wow.
■ 7" . . . . . . . . . . . . . . . . . .6105 011
Avco-Embassy / Jun '72.

### BLACK SATIN.
Tracks: Could this be the end / Country living / Doin' the streets / I won't give up / It's too late / Keeping my fingers crossed / Let them work it out / Love comes easy / Make it last / Only for the children / Pay back is a dog / Point of no return / Satin doll / There's no reason / You'll never get to heaven / You're as right as rain.
■ LP . . . . . . . . . . . . . . . . . . 9198230
H & L (USA) / '79.

### BREAK UP TO MAKE UP.
Tracks: Break up to make up.
■ 7" . . . . . . . . . . . . . . . . . .6105 020
Avco-Embassy / Mar '73.

### CAN'T GIVE YOU ANYTHING (BUT MY LOVE).
Tracks: Can't give you anything (but my love).
■ 7" . . . . . . . . . . . . . . . . . .6105 039
Avco-Embassy / Jul '75.

### CAN'T HELP FALLING IN LOVE.
Tracks: Can't help falling in love.
■ 7" . . . . . . . . . . . . . . . . . .6105 050
Avco-Embassy / Apr '76.

### CLOSER THAN CLOSE.
Tracks: What's your name / I've got this feeling / Mine all mine / Habit / Searchin' / It's only love / Closer than close / Almost there.
■ LP . . . . . . . . . . . . . . . . . PIR 85159
Philadelphia Int. / Nov '81.

### FABULOUS.
Tracks: Not Advised.
■ LP . . . . . . . . . . . . . . . . . .9109 008
Avco-Embassy / Jun '76.

### FROM THE MOUNTAIN.
Tracks: Not Advised.
■ LP . . . . . . . . . . . . . . . . . .9109 002
Avco-Embassy / Mar '75.

### FUNKY WEEKEND.
Tracks: Funky weekend / If you are there.
■ 7" . . . . . . . . . . . . . . . . . .6105 044
Avco-Embassy / Feb '76.

### GIVE A LITTLE LOVE FOR LOVE.
Tracks: Give a little love for love.
■ 12". . . . . . . . . . . . . . . . . VS 769-12
■ 7". . . . . . . . . . . . . . . . . . . VS 769
Virgin / May '85.

### GREAT LOVE HITS, THE.
Tracks: Rock 'n' roll baby / You make me feel brand new / I'm stone in love with you / Hey girl, come and get it / We can make it happen again / Peek-a-boo / You are everything / You'll never get to heaven / I will love you always / Love comes easy / Betcha by golly wow / If you are there / Break up to make up / People make the world go round.
■ LP . . . . . . . . . . . . . . . . . . CN 2063
MC. . . . . . . . . . . . . . . . . . . CN4 2063
Contour / Apr '83 / Pickwick.
CD. . . . . . . . . . . . . . . . . . . PWK 139
Pickwick / Jul '90 / Pickwick.

### GREATEST HITS: STYLISTICS.
Tracks: Not Advised.
CD. . . . . . . . . . . . . . . . . . . BRCD 43
■ LP . . . . . . . . . . . . . . . . . .BRLP 43
MC. . . . . . . . . . . . . . . . . . BRMC 43
BR Music/BR Music (Holland) / Oct '88 / BMG.

### HITS, THE.
Tracks: Betcha by golly wow / Break up to make up / I can't give you anything but love / Can't help falling in love / Funky weekend / I'm stone in love with you / Let's put it all together / Na na is the saddest word / Peek a boo / Rockin' roll baby / 7000 dollars and you

/ Sing baby sing / Sixteen bars / Star on a TV show /
You make me feel brand new / You'll never get to
heaven.
■ **LP** . . . . . . . . . . . . . . . . . . . . . . . . . . . 6467650
H & L (USA) / Dec '79.

## HURRY UP THIS WAY AGAIN.
**Tracks:** Driving me wild / It started out / And I'll see
you no more / Found a love you couldn't handle /
Maybe it's love this time / Hurry up this way again / I
have you, you have me / Is there something on your
mind.
■ **LP** . . . . . . . . . . . . . . . . . . . . . . . . . PIR 84323
■ **MC** . . . . . . . . . . . . . . . . . . . . . . . .40 84323
Philadelphia Int. / Oct '80.

## HURRY UP THIS WAY AGAIN.
**Tracks:** Hurry up this way again / It started out.
■ **7"** . . . . . . . . . . . . . . . . . . . . . . . . . PIR 8907
Philadelphia Int. / Sep '80.

## I PLEAD GUILTY.
**Tracks:** I plead guilty / So what.
■ **7"** . . . . . . . . . . . . . . . . . . . . . . . . . 6105085
H & L (USA) / Aug '77.

## I'M STONE IN LOVE WITH YOU.
**Tracks:** I'm stone in love with you.
■ **7"** . . . . . . . . . . . . . . . . . . . . . . . . . 6105 015
Avco-Embassy / Nov '72.

## I'M STONE IN LOVE WITH YOU (OLD GOLD).
**Tracks:** I'm still in love with you / Betcha by golly
wow.
■ **7"** . . . . . . . . . . . . . . . . . . . . . . . . . OG 9568
Old Gold / Sep '85.

## LET'S PUT IT ALL TOGETHER.
**Tracks:** Not Advised.
■ **LP** . . . . . . . . . . . . . . . . . . . . . . . . . 6466 013
Avco-Embassy / Mar '75.

## LET'S PUT IT ALL TOGETHER.
**Tracks:** Let's put it all together.
■ **7"** . . . . . . . . . . . . . . . . . . . . . . . . . 6105 032
Avco-Embassy / Oct '74.

## LOVE IS NOT THE ANSWER.
**Tracks:** Love is not the answer / Just the two of us.
■ **12"** . . . . . . . . . . . . . . . . . . . . . . . VS 793-12
■ **7"** . . . . . . . . . . . . . . . . . . . . . . . . . VS 793
Virgin / Jul '85.

## LOVE TALK.
**Tracks:** Not Advised.
**CD** . . . . . . . . . . . . . . . . . . . . . . . .MYCD 301
**MC** . . . . . . . . . . . . . . . . . . . . . . . .MYMC 301
Mythical Records / Feb '93 / Pinnacle.

## NA NA IS THE SADDEST WORD.
**Tracks:** Na na is the saddest word.
■ **7"** . . . . . . . . . . . . . . . . . . . . . . . . . 6105 041
Avco-Embassy / Nov '75.

## PEEK A BOO.
**Tracks:** Peek-a-boo.
■ **7"** . . . . . . . . . . . . . . . . . . . . . . . . . 6105 023
Avco-Embassy / Jun '73.

## ROCKIN' ROLL BABY.
**Tracks:** Not Advised.
■ **LP** . . . . . . . . . . . . . . . . . . . . . . . . . 6466 012
Avco-Embassy / Aug '74.

## ROCKIN' ROLL BABY.
**Tracks:** Rockin' roll baby.
■ **7"** . . . . . . . . . . . . . . . . . . . . . . . . . 6105 026
Avco-Embassy / Jan '74.

## SETTING THE SCENE.
**Tracks:** You make me feel brand new / Sing baby
sing / You'll never get to heaven (if you break my
heart) / You are everything / I plead guilty / You make
go round / I plead guilty / You are beautiful / Break
up to make up / Only for the children / Jenny / Love
at first sight / You're a big girl now / Stop, look, listen
(to your heart) / Peek a boo.
**CD** . . . . . . . . . . . . . . . . . . . . . . . .550 0312
**MC** . . . . . . . . . . . . . . . . . . . . . . . .550 0314
Spectrum (1) / May '93 / PolyGram.

## SING BABY SING.
**Tracks:** Sing baby sing.
■ **7"** . . . . . . . . . . . . . . . . . . . . . . . . . 6105 036
Avco-Embassy / May '75.

## SOME THINGS NEVER CHANGE.
**Tracks:** Some things never change / Give a little love
for love / Don't change / Girl in yellow / Row your
love / Love is not the answer / Hooked on your lovin'
/ When will I learn / Just the two of us.
■ **LP** . . . . . . . . . . . . . . . . . . . . . . . . . OVED 186
■ **MC** . . . . . . . . . . . . . . . . . . . . . . . OVEDC 186

Virgin / May '85.
**CD** . . . . . . . . . . . . . . . . . . . . . . 290 10 001
Bellaphon / '86 / New Note.

## SPOTLIGHT ON THE STYLISTICS.
**Tracks:** Not Advised.
■ **LP** . . . . . . . . . . . . . . . . . . . . . . . . . 6641622
H & L (USA) / Jul '77.

## STAR ON A TV SHOW.
**Tracks:** Star on a TV show.
■ **7"** . . . . . . . . . . . . . . . . . . . . . . . .6105 035
Avco-Embassy / Jan '75.

## STOP, LOOK, LISTEN (TO YOUR HEART).
**Tracks:** Stop, look, listen (To your heart) / If I love
you.
■ **7"** . . . . . . . . . . . . . . . . . . . . . . . 61005004
Avco-Embassy / Jul '71.

## STYLISTICS.
**Tracks:** Stop, look, listen / Point of no return / Betcha
by golly, wow / Country living / You're a big girl now
/ You are everything / People make the world round /
Ebony eyes / If I love you.
■ **LP** . . . . . . . . . . . . . . . . . . . . . . . . . 6466008
Avco-Embassy / Aug '72.

## SUN & SOUL.
**Tracks:** I plead guilty / I run to you / I'm coming home
/ I'm sorry / My love, come live with me / Our love
will never die / Put a little love away / 7,000 dollars
and you / Shame and scandal in the family / So what.
■ **LP** . . . . . . . . . . . . . . . . . . . . . . . . . 9109014
H & L (USA) / May '77.

## THANK YOU BABY.
**Tracks:** Not Advised.
■ **LP** . . . . . . . . . . . . . . . . . . . . . . . . . 9109 005
Avco-Embassy / Jul '75.

## TWO.
**Tracks:** I'm stone in love with you / If you don't watch
out / You & me / It's too late / Children of the night /
You'll never got to heaven / Break up to make up /
Peek-a-boo / You're as right as rain / Pieces.
■ **LP** . . . . . . . . . . . . . . . . . . . . . . . . . 6466010
Avco-Embassy / Feb '73.

## VERY BEST OF THE STYLISTICS.
**Tracks:** Can't give you anything but my love / Let's
put it all together / I'm stone in love with you / You
make me feel brand new / Sing baby sing / Na na is
the saddest word / Sixteen bars / Betcha by golly
wow / Rock 'n' roll baby / Star on a TV show / Funky
weekend / Break up to make up / Can't help falling in
love / Peek-a-boo / 7000 dollars and you / You'll
never get to heaven.
■ **LP** . . . . . . . . . . . . . . . . . . . . . . . . . PRICE 23
**MC** . . . . . . . . . . . . . . . . . . . . . . . PRIMC 23
H & L (USA) / Jun '83.

## WONDER WOMAN.
**Tracks:** Wonder woman / Lucky me.
■ **7"** . . . . . . . . . . . . . . . . . . . . . . . 6105086
H & L (USA) / Aug '78.

## WONDER WOMAN.
**Tracks:** Fool of the year / Give a little love / Good
thing goin' on / Green grass, shade trees / I think
about you / Lucky me / One way trip to paradise /
Rock & a hard place / Same old feeling / Wonder
woman.
■ **LP** . . . . . . . . . . . . . . . . . . . . . . . . . 9109016
H & L (USA) / Mar '78.

## YOU ARE BEAUTIFUL.
**Tracks:** Not Advised.
■ **LP** . . . . . . . . . . . . . . . . . . . . . . . . . 9109 006
Avco-Embassy / Dec '75.

## YOU MAKE ME FEEL BRAND NEW.
**Tracks:** You make me feel brand new / Only for the
children.
■ **7"** . . . . . . . . . . . . . . . . . . . . . . . .6105 028
Avco-Embassy / Jul '74.

## YOU MAKE ME FEEL BRAND NEW (OLD GOLD).
**Tracks:** You make me feel brand new / I can't give
you anything (but my love).
■ **7"** . . . . . . . . . . . . . . . . . . . . . . . . . OG 9248
Old Gold / Jul '82.

## YOU'LL NEVER GET TO HEAVEN.
**Tracks:** You'll never get to heaven / Country living /
You are beautiful / Miracle.
■ **EP** . . . . . . . . . . . . . . . . . . . . . . . STYL 001
H & L (USA) / Nov '76.

# Sudden Impact

## CLEAR SPACE (Sudden Impact & Jessica Lauren).
**Tracks:** Clear space / Freestyle / Baby Batu.
**12"** . . . . . . . . . . . . . . . . . . . . . . . SJR 016
Soul Jazz / Jun '94 / New Note.

# Sue & Sunny

## YOU CAN'T BYPASS LOVE.
**Tracks:** You can't bypass love / I like your style.
■ **7"** . . . . . . . . . . . . . . . . . . . . . . . .DB 8099
Columbia / Jan '67.

# Sugar Loaf

## SOUL STRUTTING.
**Tracks:** Time is tight / Papa's got a brand new bag /
Baby you turn me on / Soulful strut / Black / Soul
walk / Pearl time / Hard down / Cleo's mood / Soul
clap '69 / If I had a hammer / You can't sit down.
■ **LP** . . . . . . . . . . . . . . . . . . . . . . . INTS 1113
RCA Victor / Aug '70.

# Summer, Donna

## ALL SYSTEMS GO.
**Tracks:** All systems go / Bad reputation / Love shock
/ Jeremy / Only the fool survives / Dinner with
Gershwin / Fascination / Voices cryin' out / Thinkin'
bout my baby.
**CD** . . . . . . . . . . . . . . . . . . . . . . .252953 2
**MC** . . . . . . . . . . . . . . . . . . . . . . . WX 130C
■ **LP** . . . . . . . . . . . . . . . . . . . . . . . WX 130
WEA / Oct '87 / WEA.

## ALL SYSTEMS GO.
**Tracks:** All systems go / Bad reputation.
■ **12"** . . . . . . . . . . . . . . . . . . . . . . . U 8122 T
■ **7"** . . . . . . . . . . . . . . . . . . . . . . . .U 8122
WEA / Jan '88.

## ANOTHER PLACE AND TIME.
**Tracks:** This time I know it's for real / I don't wanna
get hurt / In another place and time / Whatever your
heart desires / If it makes you feel good / When love
takes over you / Only one / Sentimental / Breakaway
/ Love's about to change my heart.
**CD** . . . . . . . . . . . . . . . . . . . . . . .255976 2
■ **LP** . . . . . . . . . . . . . . . . . . . . . . . WX 219
**MC** . . . . . . . . . . . . . . . . . . . . . . . WX 219C
WEA / Jan '89 / WEA.

## ANTHOLOGY.
**Tracks:** Love to love you baby / Could it be magic /
Try me I know we can make it / Spring affair / Love's
unkind / I feel love / Once upon a time / Rumour has
it / I love you / Last dance / Macarthur Park / Heaven
knows / Hot stuff / Bad girls / Dim all the lights /
Sunset people.
**CD Set** . . . . . . . . . . . . . . . . . . . . . 518 144-2
Phonogram / Oct '93 / PolyGram.

## BACK IN LOVE AGAIN.
**Tracks:** Back in love again / Try me / I know we can
make it / Wasted.
■ **7"** . . . . . . . . . . . . . . . . . . . . . . . . . GT 117
GTO / Apr '78.

## BAD GIRLS.
**Tracks:** Hot stuff / Bad girls / Love will always find
you / Walk away / Dim all the lights / Journey to the
centre of your heart / One night in a lifetime / Can't
get to sleep at night / On my honour / There will
always be you / All through the night / My baby
understands / One love / Lucky / Sunset people.
■ **LP** . . . . . . . . . . . . . . . . . . . . . . . CALD 5007
Casablanca / Jun '79.
■ **Double LP**. . . . . . . . . . . . . . . . . . . 6685031
Casablanca / Nov '81.
**MC Set** . . . . . . . . . . . . . . . . . . . .7599 493
**CD** . . . . . . . . . . . . . . . . . . . . . . . 822 557-2
Casablanca / Feb '87.

## BAD GIRLS.
**Tracks:** Bad girls / On my honour.
■ **12"** . . . . . . . . . . . . . . . . . . . . . . . CANL 155
■ **7"** . . . . . . . . . . . . . . . . . . . . . . . .CAN 155
Casablanca / Jul '79.

## BEST OF DONNA SUMMER, THE.
**Tracks:** I feel love / Macarthur park / Hot stuff /
Wanderer / Love's unkind / On the radio / State of
independence / Breakaway / Love is in control
(finger on the trigger) / Dinner with Gershwin / I
don't wanna get hurt / This time I know it's for real /
Love's about to change my heart (Not available on
LP).
**CD**. . . . . . . . . . . . . . . . . . . . . . . . 9031729092
■ **LP** . . . . . . . . . . . . . . . . . . . . . . . . . WX 397

MC. . . . . . . . . . . . . . . . . . . . . . . . **WX 397C**
East West / Nov '90 / WEA.

## BREAKAWAY.
**Tracks:** Breakaway.
■ CD Single. . . . . . . . . . . . . . . . **U 3308 CD**
■ 12". . . . . . . . . . . . . . . . . . . . . . **U 3308 T**
■ 7". . . . . . . . . . . . . . . . . . . . . . . .**U 3308**
WEA / Dec '90.

## CATS WITHOUT CLAWS.
**Tracks:** Supernatural love / It's not the way / There goes my baby / Suzanna / Cats without claws / Oh Billy please / Eyes / Maybe it's over / I'm free / Forgive me.
CD. . . . . . . . . . . . . . . . . . . . . . . . **2508062**
■ LP. . . . . . . . . . . . . . . . . . . . . . . **2508061**
■ MC. . . . . . . . . . . . . . . . . . . . . . . **2508064**
WEA / Sep '84 / WEA.

## COLD LOVE.
**Tracks:** Cold love / Grand illusion.
■ 7". . . . . . . . . . . . . . . . . . . . . . . **K 79193**
WEA / Dec '80.

## COULD IT BE MAGIC.
**Tracks:** Could it be magic.
■ 7". . . . . . . . . . . . . . . . . . . . . . . . **GT 60**
GTO / May '76.

## DANCE COLLECTION.
**Tracks:** I feel love / With your love / Last dance / Macarthur Park / One of a kind / Heaven knows / Hot stuff / Walk away / Dim all the lights / No more tears (enough is enough).
CD. . . . . . . . . . . . . . . . . . . . . **830 534-2**
Phonogram / Nov '90 / PolyGram.

## DIM ALL THE LIGHTS.
**Tracks:** Dim all the lights.
■ 7". . . . . . . . . . . . . . . . . . . . . . .**CAN 162**
Casablanca / Sep '79.

## DINNER WITH GERSHWIN.
**Tracks:** Dinner with Gershwin / Tearing down the walls (Available on 12" only).
■ 12". . . . . . . . . . . . . . . . . . . . . **U 8237T**
■ 7". . . . . . . . . . . . . . . . . . . . . . .**U 8237**
WEA / Sep '87.

## DONNA SUMMER.
**Tracks:** Love is in control / Mystery of love / Woman in me / State of independence / Live in America / Protection / (If it) hurts just a little / Love is just a breath away / Lush life.
CD. . . . . . . . . . . . . . . . . . . . . **K2 99163**
■ LP. . . . . . . . . . . . . . . . . . . . . **K 99163**
■ MC. . . . . . . . . . . . . . . . . . . . **K4 99163**
WEA / Jul '82 / WEA.

## DONNA SUMMER.
**Tracks:** Not Advised.
CD. . . . . . . . . . . . . . . . . . .**KLMCD 026**
Scratch / May '94 / Scratch Records / BMG / Grapevine Distribution.

## DONNA SUMMER.
**Tracks:** Not Advised.
CD. . . . . . . . . . . . . . . . . . . . . . . . . **12397**
MC. . . . . . . . . . . . . . . . . . . . . . . . . **72397**
Laserlight / Sep '94 / THE / BMG / Target.

## DONNA SUMMER GREATEST HITS.
**Tracks:** Not Advised.
VHS . . . . . . . . . . . . . . . . . . . . . **6323523**
Polygram Music Video / Oct '94 / PolyGram.

## DOWN DEEP INSIDE.
**Tracks:** Down deep inside.
■ 7". . . . . . . . . . . . . . . . . . . . . . .**CAN 111**
Casablanca / Aug '77.

## ENDLESS SUMMER - THE BEST OF DONNA SUMMER.
**Tracks:** Melody of love (Wanna be loved) / Love to love you baby / Could it be magic / I feel love / Love's unkind / I love you / Last dance / MacArthur park / Hot stuff / Bad girls / No more tears (Enough is enough) / On the radio / Love is in control (Finger on the trigger) / State of independence / She works hard for the money / Unconditional love / This time I know it's for real / I don't wanna get hurt / Any way at all.
CD. . . . . . . . . . . . . . . . . . . . .**526217-2**
MC. . . . . . . . . . . . . . . . . . . . .**526217-4**
Polygram / Nov '94 / PolyGram.

## EYES.
**Tracks:** Eyes / It's not the way.
■ 12". . . . . . . . . . . . . . . . . . . . . **U 9103T**
■ 7". . . . . . . . . . . . . . . . . . . . . . .**U 9103**
WEA / Apr '85.

## FOUR SEASONS OF LOVE.
**Tracks:** Spring affair / Summer fever / Autumn changes / Winter melody / Spring reprise.
■ LP. . . . . . . . . . . . . . . . . . . . . **GTLP 018**
GTO / Nov '76.
CD. . . . . . . . . . . . . . . . . . . . . **826 236-2**
Phonogram / Aug '91 / PolyGram.

## GREATEST HITS: DONNA SUMMER VOL.1.
**Tracks:** Love to love you baby / I feel love / I remember yesterday / I love you / Heaven knows / Last dance.
■ LP. . . . . . . . . . . . . . . . . . . . . **GTLP 028**
GTO / Jan '78.
■ LP. . . . . . . . . . . . . . . . . . . . . **9128 032**
MC. . . . . . . . . . . . . . . . . . . . . . **7268 023**
Casablanca / Apr '82.

## GREATEST HITS: DONNA SUMMER VOL.2.
**Tracks:** MacArthur Park / Hot stuff / Bad girls / Dim all the lights / Sunset people / No more tears / On the radio.
■ LP. . . . . . . . . . . . . . . . . . . . . **9128 033**
MC. . . . . . . . . . . . . . . . . . . . . . **7268 024**
Casablanca / Apr '82.

## HEAVEN KNOWS.
**Tracks:** Heaven knows / Only one man.
■ 7". . . . . . . . . . . . . . . . . . . . . .**CAN 141**
Casablanca / Feb '79.

## HOT STUFF.
**Tracks:** Hot stuff.
■ 7". . . . . . . . . . . . . . . . . . . . . .**CAN 151**
Casablanca / May '79.

## HOT SUMMER NIGHT, A.
**Tracks:** Not Advised.
VHS . . . . . . . . . . . . . . . . . . . **CFV 00242**
Channel 5 / '88 / Channel 5 Video / P.R.O. Video / Gold & Sons.

## I DON'T WANNA GET HURT.
**Tracks:** I don't wanna get hurt / Dinner with Gershwin.
■ 12". . . . . . . . . . . . . . . . . . . . . **U 7567T**
■ 7". . . . . . . . . . . . . . . . . . . . . . .**U 7567**
■ CD Single. . . . . . . . . . . . . . . . **U 7567CD**
■ MC Single. . . . . . . . . . . . . . . . **U 7567C**
WEA / May '89.

## I FEEL LOVE.
**Tracks:** I feel love / Can't we just sit down.
■ 7". . . . . . . . . . . . . . . . . . . . . . .**GT 100**
GTO / Jul '77.

## I FEEL LOVE (OLD GOLD).
**Tracks:** Love to love you baby / I feel love.
■ 7". . . . . . . . . . . . . . . . . . . . . . .**OG 9771**
Old Gold / Feb '88.

## I FEEL LOVE (RE-RELEASE).
**Tracks:** I feel love.
■ 12". . . . . . . . . . . . . . . . . . . . . **FEEL 12**
■ 7". . . . . . . . . . . . . . . . . . . . . . .**FEEL 7**
Casablanca / Oct '84.

## I LOVE TO DANCE.
**Tracks:** Not Advised.
■ LP. . . . . . . . . . . . . . . . . . . **PER 33 8601**
MC. . . . . . . . . . . . . . . . . . .**PER 733 8601**
Perfect / Aug '87 / Pinnacle.

## I LOVE YOU.
**Tracks:** I love you.
■ 7". . . . . . . . . . . . . . . . . . . . . .**CAN 114**
Casablanca / Dec '77.

## I REMEMBER YESTERDAY.
**Tracks:** I remember yesterday / Love's unkind / Back in love again / Black lady / Take me / Can't we just sit down and talk it over / I feel love.
■ LP. . . . . . . . . . . . . . . . . . . . . **GTLP 025**
GTO / Jun '77.
■ LP. . . . . . . . . . . . . . . . . . . . . **CBS 31718**
CBS / '79.
CD. . . . . . . . . . . . . . . . . . . . . **826 237-2**
Phonogram / '83 / PolyGram.
■ LP. . . . . . . . . . . . . . . . . . . . . **PRICE 3**
■ MC. . . . . . . . . . . . . . . . . . . . . **PRIMC 3**
Casablanca / May '83.

## I REMEMBER YESTERDAY.
**Tracks:** I remember yesterday.
■ 7". . . . . . . . . . . . . . . . . . . . . . .**GT 107**
GTO / Sep '77.

## LAST DANCE.
**Tracks:** Last dance / With your love.
■ 7". . . . . . . . . . . . . . . . . . . . . . .**TGIF 2**
Casablanca / Jun '78.

## LIVE AND MORE.
**Tracks:** Once upon a time / Fairytale high / Faster and faster to nowhere / Spring affair / Rumour has it / I love you / Only one man / I remember yesterday / Love's unkind / Man I love / I got it bad (and that ain't good) / Some of these days / Way we were / Mimi's song / Try me, I know we can make it / Love to love you, baby / I feel love / Last dance / MacArthur Park / One of a kind / Heaven knows.
■ Double LP. . . . . . . . . . . . . . . **CALD 5006**
Casablanca / Nov '78.
■ Double LP. . . . . . . . . . . . . . . .**6685 030**
MC Set . . . . . . . . . . . . . . . . . . . .**7599 492**
Casablanca / Nov '81.

## LOVE HAS A MIND OF IT'S OWN.
**Tracks:** Love has a mind of it's own / People people / She works hard for the money (Available on 12" only).
■ 12". . . . . . . . . . . . . . . . . . . **DONNA 4 12**
■ 7". . . . . . . . . . . . . . . . . . . . . **DONNA 4**
Mercury / Apr '84.

## LOVE IS IN CONTROL.
**Tracks:** Love is in control / Sometimes.
■ 12". . . . . . . . . . . . . . . . . . . . **K 79302 T**
■ 7". . . . . . . . . . . . . . . . . . . . . **K 79302**
WEA / Jun '82.

## LOVE TO LOVE YOU BABY.
**Tracks:** Love to love you baby / Full of emptiness / Need-a-man blues / Whispering waves / Pandora's box / Full of emptiness (reprise).
■ LP. . . . . . . . . . . . . . . . . . . . . **GTLP 008**
GTO / Jan '76.
■ LP. . . . . . . . . . . . . . . . . . . . . **PRICE 21**
Casablanca / Jul '83.
CD. . . . . . . . . . . . . . . . . . . . . **822 792-2**
Phonogram / '93 / PolyGram.

## LOVE TO LOVE YOU BABY.
**Tracks:** Love to love you baby.
■ 7". . . . . . . . . . . . . . . . . . . . . . .**GT 17**
GTO / Jan '76.
■ 12". . . . . . . . . . . . . . . . . . . . **CANX 1014**
■ 7". . . . . . . . . . . . . . . . . . . **CAN 1014**
Casablanca / Apr '83.

## LOVE TRILOGY.
**Tracks:** Try me I know we can make it better / Could it be magic / Wasted / Prelude to love / Come with me.
■ LP. . . . . . . . . . . . . . . . . . . . . **PRICE 22**
Phonogram / Jul '83.

## LOVE TRILOGY, A.
**Tracks:** Not Advised.
■ LP. . . . . . . . . . . . . . . . . . . . . **GTLP 010**
GTO / May '76.

## LOVE'S ABOUT TO CHANGE MY HEART.
**Tracks:** Love's about to change my heart / Love's about to change my heart (Inst.).
■ 12". . . . . . . . . . . . . . . . . . . . . **U 7494 T**
■ 7". . . . . . . . . . . . . . . . . . . . . . .**U 7494**
WEA / Aug '89.

## LOVE'S UNKIND.
**Tracks:** Love's unkind.
■ 7". . . . . . . . . . . . . . . . . . . . . . .**GT 113**
GTO / Dec '77.

## LOVE'S UNKIND (OLD GOLD).
**Tracks:** Love's unkind / Winter melody.
■ 7". . . . . . . . . . . . . . . . . . . . . . .**OG 9565**
Old Gold.

## MACARTHUR PARK.
**Tracks:** Macarthur Park / Once upon a time.
■ 7". . . . . . . . . . . . . . . . . . . . . .**CAN 131**
Casablanca / Oct '78.

## MELODY OF LOVE.
**Tracks:** Melody of love (Mixes).
12". . . . . . . . . . . . . . . . . . . . . .**MERX 418**
CD Single. . . . . . . . . . . . . . . . **MERCD 418**
CD Single. . . . . . . . . . . . . . . . **MERDD 418**
MC Single . . . . . . . . . . . . . . . **MERMC 418**
Mercury / Oct '94 / PolyGram.

## MISTAKEN IDENTITY.
**Tracks:** Get ethnic / Body talk / Work that magic / When love cries / Heaven's just a whisper away / Cry of a waking heart / Friends unknown / Fred Astaire / Say a little prayer / Mistaken identity / What is it you want / Let there be peace.
CD. . . . . . . . . . . . . . . . . . . . **9031751592**
■ LP. . . . . . . . . . . . . . . . . . . **9031751591**
MC. . . . . . . . . . . . . . . . . . . . **9031751594**
WEA / Sep '91 / WEA.

■ DELETED

## NEVER LOSE YOUR SENSE OF HUMOUR (Summer, Donna & Paul Jabara).
Tracks: Never lose your sense of humour / Just you and me.
■ 12" . . . . . . . . . . . . . . . . . . . . . NBL 1002
■ 7" . . . . . . . . . . . . . . . . . . . . . . NB 1002
Casablanca / Mar '80.

## NO MORE TEARS (Summer, Donna & Barbara Streisand).
Tracks: No more tears.
■ 12" . . . . . . . . . . . . . . . . . . . . CBS 8000
■ 7" . . . . . . . . . . . . . . . . . . . . .CAN 174
Casablanca / Nov '79.

## ON THE RADIO.
Tracks: On the radio / Love to love you baby / Try me, I know we can make it / I feel love / Our love / I remember yesterday / I love you / Heaven knows / Last dance / MacArthur Park / Hot stuff / Bad girls / Dim all the lights / Sunset people / No more tears / Niagra / I ain't gonna cry tonight / Kiss me in the rain.
■ LP . . . . . . . . . . . . . . . . . . . . CALD 5008
Casablanca / Nov '79.
■ CD . . . . . . . . . . . . . . . . . . . . 822 558-2
Casablanca / Feb '87.

## ON THE RADIO.
Tracks: On the radio / There will always be a you.
■ 7" . . . . . . . . . . . . . . . . . . . . . NB 2236
Casablanca / Feb '80.

## ONCE UPON A TIME.
Tracks: Once upon a time / Faster and faster to nowhere / Fairy tale high / Say something nice / Now I need you / Working the midnight shift / Queen for a day / If you got it flaunt it / Man like you / Sweet romance / Dance into my life / Rumour has it / I love you / Happily ever after.
■ LP . . . . . . . . . . . . . CALD 5003
Casablanca / Nov '77.
■ CD . . . . . . . . . . . . . . . . . . . . 826 238-2
Casablanca / Feb '87.

## RUMOUR HAS IT.
Tracks: Rumour has it.
■ 7" . . . . . . . . . . . . . . . . . . . . .CAN 122
Casablanca / Feb '78.

## SHE WORKS HARD FOR THE MONEY.
Tracks: She works hard for the money / Stop, look and listen / He's a rebel / Woman / Unconditional love / Love has a mind of its own / Tokyo / People people / I do believe (I fell in love).
■ LP . . . . . . . . . . . . . . . . . . . . MERL 21
Mercury / Jul '83.
■ CD . . . . . . . . . . . . . . . . . . . . 812 265-2
Mercury / Jul '84.

## SHE WORKS HARD FOR THE MONEY.
Tracks: She works hard for the money / I do believe (I fell in love).
■ 7" . . . . . . . . . . . . . . . . . . . . DONNA 1
Mercury / Jun '83.

## SHOUT IT OUT.
Tracks: Fun Street / Little Marie / Shout it out / They can't take away our music / Back off boogaloo / Jeannie / Nice to see you / Na na hey hey / Do what mothers do.
CD . . . . . . . . . . . . . . . . . . . . CDBM 078
■ LP . . . . . . . . . . . . . . . . . . . . BMLP 078
Blue Moon (1) / Oct '89 / Roots Records / Jazz Music / Swift / Projection / THE / Hot Shot.

## STATE OF INDEPENDENCE.
Tracks: State of independence / Love is just a breath away.
■ 7" . . . . . . . . . . . . . . . . . . . . K 79344
■ 12" . . . . . . . . . . . . . . . . . . . K 79344T
WEA / Nov '82.
■ 12" . . . . . . . . . . . . . . . . . . . U 2857T
■ 7" . . . . . . . . . . . . . . . . . . . . .U 2857
■ CD Single . . . . . . . . . . . . . . . . U 2857CD
■ MC Single . . . . . . . . . . . . . . . . U 2857C
East West / Oct '90.

## STOP LOOK AND LISTEN.
Tracks: Stop look and listen / Tokyo.
■ 7" . . . . . . . . . . . . . . . . . . . . DONNA 3
Mercury / Jan '84.

## SUMMER COLLECTION, THE.
Tracks: She works hard for the money / Bad girls / On the radio / Stop, look and listen / Last dance / MacArthur Park / Heaven knows / Unconditional love / I love you / Enough is enough (no more tears).
■ LP . . . . . . . . . . . . . . . . . . . . MERH 84
■ CD . . . . . . . . . . . . . . . . . . . . 826 144-2
■ MC . . . . . . . . . . . . . . . . . . . . MERHC 84
Mercury / Nov '85.

## SUNSET PEOPLE.
Tracks: Sunset people / Our love.
■ 12" . . . . . . . . . . . . . . . . . . . CANL 198
■ 7" . . . . . . . . . . . . . . . . . . . . .CAN 198
Casablanca / Jun '80.

## SUPERNATURAL LOVE.
Tracks: Supernatural love / Suzanna.
■ 12" . . . . . . . . . . . . . . . . . . . U 9254T
■ 7" . . . . . . . . . . . . . . . . . . . . .U 9254
WEA / Nov '84.

## THERE GOES MY BABY.
Tracks: There goes my baby / Maybe it's over.
■ 12" . . . . . . . . . . . . . . . . . . . U 9438T
■ 7" . . . . . . . . . . . . . . . . . . . . .U 9438
WEA / Aug '84.

## THIS TIME I KNOW IT'S FOR REAL.
Tracks: This time I know it's for real / Whatever your heart desires.
■ 12" . . . . . . . . . . . . . . . . . . . U 7780 T
■ 7" . . . . . . . . . . . . . . . . . . . . .U 7780
■ CD Single . . . . . . . . . . . . . . . . U 7780 CD
Atlantic / Jan '89.

## THIS TIME I KNOW IT'S FOR REAL.
Tracks: Not Advised.
CD . . . . . . . . . . . . . . . . . . . . 9548318232
MC . . . . . . . . . . . . . . . . . . . . 9548318234
Pickwick / Apr '93 / Pickwick.

## UNCONDITIONAL LOVE (Summer, Donna & Musical Youth).
Tracks: Unconditional love / Woman.
■ 12" . . . . . . . . . . . . . . . . . . . DONNA 212
■ 7" . . . . . . . . . . . . . . . . . . . . DONNA 2
Mercury / Sep '83.

## WALK AWAY.
Tracks: Bad girls / Hot stuff / On the radio / I feel love / Walk away / Last dance / Sunset people / MacArthur park.
■ LP . . . . . . . . . . . . . . . . . . . . NBLP 7244
Casablanca / Dec '80.
■ LP . . . . . . . . . . . . . . . . . . .6302 070
MC . . . . . . . . . . . . . . . . . . . .7144 070
Casablanca / Nov '81.
■ CD . . . . . . . . . . . . . . . . . . . . 810 011-2
Casablanca / Jan '83.

## WALK AWAY.
Tracks: Walk away / Could it be magic.
■ 7" . . . . . . . . . . . . . . . . . . . . .CAN 211
Casablanca / Oct '80.

## WANDERER, THE.
Tracks: Cold love / Who do you think you're foolin' / Night life / Stop me / I believe in Jesus / Looking up / Wanderer / Grand illusion / Breakdown / Running for cover.
■ LP . . . . . . . . . . . . . . . . . . . . K 99124
Geffen / Nov '80.

## WANDERER, THE.
Tracks: Wanderer.
■ 7" . . . . . . . . . . . . . . . . . . . . K 79180
WEA / Sep '80.

## WHEN LOVE TAKES OVER YOU.
Tracks: When love takes over you / Whatever your heart desires.
■ 12" . . . . . . . . . . . . . . . . . . . U 7780T
■ 7" . . . . . . . . . . . . . . . . . . . . .U 7780
WEA / Nov '88.
■ 12" . . . . . . . . . . . . . . . . . . . U 7361T
■ 7" . . . . . . . . . . . . . . . . . . . . .U 7361
■ CD Single . . . . . . . . . . . . . . . . U 7361CD
WEA / Nov '89.

## WHO DO YOU THINK YOUR FOOLING.
Tracks: Who do you think you're foolin'.
■ 7" . . . . . . . . . . . . . . . . . . . . K 79201
Geffen / Mar '81.

## WINTER MELODY.
Tracks: Winter melody.
■ 7" . . . . . . . . . . . . . . . . . . . . GT 76
GTO / Dec '76.

## WOMAN IN ME.
Tracks: Woman in me / Livin' in America.
■ 12" . . . . . . . . . . . . . . . . . . . W 69983 T
■ 7" . . . . . . . . . . . . . . . . . . . . W 9983
WEA / Nov '83.

## WORK THAT MAGIC.
Tracks: Work that magic.
■ 12" . . . . . . . . . . . . . . . . . . . U 5937T
■ 7" . . . . . . . . . . . . . . . . . . . . .U 5937
■ CD Single . . . . . . . . . . . . . . . . U 5937CD
■ MC Single . . . . . . . . . . . . . . . . U 5937C
WEA / Nov '91.

# Summers, Bill

## CALL IT WHAT YOU WANT.
Tracks: Call it what you want / Your style ain't that way.
■ 12" . . . . . . . . . . . . . . . . . . . MCAT 689
■ 7" . . . . . . . . . . . . . . . . . . . . MCA 689
MCA / Mar '81.

## ON SUNSHINE.
Tracks: Walking on sunshine / You've got me lovin' again / She's gone / Musicland / Dancin' lady / Love's all we need / Feel the heat / Learn to live as one / Samba de Oakland.
■ LP . . . . . . . . . . . . . . . . . . . . PR 10107
Prestige / Oct '79.

## STRAIGHT TO THE BANK.
Tracks: Straight to the bank / Yours love.
■ 12" . . . . . . . . . . . . . . . . . . .PRC 101
RCA / Feb '79.

# Sun

## DANCE.
Tracks: Dance / Reggae man.
■ 12" . . . . . . . . . . . . . . . . . . . AIR 3701 12
■ 7" . . . . . . . . . . . . . . . . . . . . AIR 3701 7
Air City / Mar '85.

## DESTINATION SUN.
Tracks: Radiation level / Pure fire / I wanna be with you / Disco down / Light of the universe / Deep rooted feeling / Baby I confess / Hallelujah feeling.
■ LP . . . . . . . . . . . . . . . . . . . . .EST 11941
Capitol / '79.

## LEGS.
Tracks: Legs / Heartbreak hideaway.
■ 12" . . . . . . . . . . . . . . . . . . . 12 AIR 3704
■ 7" . . . . . . . . . . . . . . . . . . . . 7 AIR 3704
Air City / Dec '85.

## RADIATION LEVEL.
Tracks: Radiation level.
■ 7" . . . . . . . . . . . . . . . . . . . . CL 16092
Capitol / Nov '79.

## SPACE RANGER.
Tracks: Space ranger / Hot spot / Quest.
■ 12" . . . . . . . . . . . . . . . . . . . 12CL 16157
Capitol / Jul '80.

## START THE COUNTDOWN.
Tracks: Start the countdown / X factor.
■ 7" . . . . . . . . . . . . . . . . . . . . CHEVY 001
Chevy / Sep '83.

## SUN IS HERE.
Tracks: Sun is here / Dance (do what you wanna do).
■ 7" . . . . . . . . . . . . . . . . . . . . CL 15979
Capitol / Apr '78.

# Sunfire

## MA, MA, MA MEXICO.
Tracks: Ma, ma, ma Mexico / Deep song.
■ 7" . . . . . . . . . . . . . . . . . . . .7P 115
Pye / Nov '79.

## STEP IN THE NIGHT.
Tracks: Step in the night / Sexy lady.
■ 12" . . . . . . . . . . . . . . . . . . . W 9642 T
■ 7" . . . . . . . . . . . . . . . . . . . . W 9642
WEA / May '83.

## SUNFIRE.
Tracks: Shake your body / Step in the light / Feet / Givin' away my heart / Keep rockin' my love / Millionaire / Sexy lady / Young, free and single.
■ LP . . . . . . . . . . . . . . . . . . . . W 3730
WEA / Jun '83.

## YOUNG FREE AND SINGLE.
Tracks: Young free and single / Shake your body.
■ 7" . . . . . . . . . . . . . . . . . . . . W 9897
WEA / Mar '83.

# Sunrise

## CALL ON ME.
Tracks: Call on me / Land.
■ 7" . . . . . . . . . . . . . . . . . . . . 2041936
Polydor / Apr '78.

## LET'S PUT OUR HEARTS TOGETHER.
Tracks: Let's put our hearts together / One more chance.
■ 7" . . . . . . . . . . . . . . . . . . . . 7N 46012
Pye / Sep '77.

## Supercharge

**BODY RHYTHMS.**
Tracks: Not Advised.
■ LP . . . . . . . . . . . . . . . . . . . . . . . . . .V 2118
Virgin / '79.

**I CAN SEE RIGHT THRU YOU.**
Tracks: I can see right thru you.
■ 7" . . . . . . . . . . . . . . . . . . . . . . . . . .VS 243
Virgin / Jun '79.

**I THINK I'M GONNA FALL IN LOVE.**
Tracks: I think I'm gonna fall in love / I think I'm gonna fall in love (version).
■ 7" . . . . . . . . . . . . . . . . . . . . . . . . . .VS 202
Virgin / Feb '78.

**LONELY AND IN LOVE.**
Tracks: Lonely and in love / Give it the nasty.
■ 7" . . . . . . . . . . . . . . . . . . . . . . . . . .VS 145
Virgin / Apr '76.

**PEACHES 'N' CREAM.**
Tracks: Peaches 'n' cream.
■ 7" . . . . . . . . . . . . . . . . . . . . . SWAG 20
Criminal (1) / Oct '80.

**TIMES.**
Tracks: Times / I'll give anything / Get down boogie / Celebrate.
■ LP . . . . . . . . . . . . . . . . . . . . . . . .VEP 101
Virgin / Oct '76.

## Supremes

In 1959, Detroit concert-goers could enjoy gigs by the Primes and Primettes, latter featuring one Diane Ross. Primes eventually evolved into Temptations, but not before Primettes signed to Motown as Supremes. Ross, Florence Ballard and Mary Wilson graduated from backing vocals to headline status when Berry Gordy teamed them with Holland-Dozier-Holland. *Where Did Our Love Go* was first of hits - including 12 U.S. chart-toppers - that made Supremes most successful female group ever. From '66, Diane Ross' name was added to group billing and her departure for solo career after '69 hit *Someday We'll Be Together* was no surprise. Less predictable was group's continuing success, notably with *Up The Ladder To The Roof*, *Nathan Jones*, and *Stoned Love*. Hits dried up in '72, although Supremes maintain cult following today and continue to tour, despite featuring no original members.

**AT THE COPA.**
Tracks: Put on a happy face / I am woman / Baby love / Stop in the name of love / Boy from Ipanema / Make someone happy / Come see about me / Rock-a-bye your baby with a Dixie melody / Queen of the house / Group introduction / Somewhere / Back in my arms again / You're nobody loves you.
■ LP . . . . . . . . . . . . . . . . . . . . TML 11026
Tamla Motown / Feb '66.
■ LP . . . . . . . . . . . . . . . . . . . . STMS 5045
■ MC . . . . . . . . . . . . . . . . . . . CSTMS 5045
Motown / Mar '82.

**AT THEIR BEST.**
Tracks: Stoned love / I'm gonna let my heart do the walking / Floy joy / Nathan Jones / Everybody's got the right to love / High inergy / Automatically sunshine / Up the ladder to the roof / You're my driving wheel / Bad weather / Love train / Sha-la bandit / He's my man / You're what's missing in my life.
■ LP . . . . . . . . . . . . . . . . . . . .STML 12091
Motown / Oct '78.

**AUTOMATICALLY SUNSHINE.**
Tracks: Automatically sunshine.
■ 7" . . . . . . . . . . . . . . . . . . . . . TMG 821
Tamla Motown / Jul '72.

**BABY LOVE.**
Tracks: Baby love / Stop in the name of love.
■ 7" . . . . . . . . . . . . . . . . . . . . . TMG 915
Tamla Motown / Aug '74.
■ 7" . . . . . . . . . . . . . . . . . . . . .TMG 1044
Tamla Motown / Sep '76.

**BABY LOVE.**
Tracks: baby love.
■ 7" . . . . . . . . . . . . . . . . . . . . . .SS 350
Stateside / Oct '64.

**BACK IN MY ARMS AGAIN.**
Tracks: Back in my arms again.
■ 7" . . . . . . . . . . . . . . . . . . . . . TMG 516
Tamla Motown / Jun '65.

**BAD WEATHER.**
Tracks: Bad weather.
■ 7" . . . . . . . . . . . . . . . . . . . . . TMG 847
Tamla Motown / Apr '73.

**BEST OF THE SUPREMES & FOUR TOPS (Supremes & Four Tops).**
Tracks: River deep, mountain high / If I could build my whole world around you / You gotta have love in your heart / Hello stranger / Without the one you love / I'll try not to cry / Baby (you've got what it takes) / Call me / Don't let me lose this dream / I can't believe you love me / Good lovin' ain't easy to come by / One more bridge to cross / Melodie / If you could see me now / Do you love me just a little honey / If.
■ CD . . . . . . . . . . . . . . . . . . . . . WD 72776
Motown / Dec '91.

**COME SEE ABOUT ME.**
Tracks: Come see about me.
■ 7" . . . . . . . . . . . . . . . . . . . . . .SS 376
Stateside / Jan '65.

**CREAM OF THE CROP (see under Ross, Diana).**

**DIANA ROSS & THE SUPREMES JOIN THE TEMPTATIONS (see under Ross, Diana).**

**DYNAMITE (Supremes & Four Tops).**
Tracks: It's impossible / Bigger you love / Hello stranger / Love the one you're with / Good lovin' ain't easy to come by / Melodie / If / If I could build my whole world around you / Don't let me lose this dream / Do you love me just a little, honey.
■ LP . . . . . . . . . . . . . . . . . . . .STML 11203
Motown / Apr '72.

**FLOY JOY.**
Tracks: Floy joy / Bad weather.
■ 7" . . . . . . . . . . . . . . . . . . . . . TMG 974
Tamla Motown / May '75.

**FLOY JOY.**
Tracks: You wonderful, sweet sweet love / Floy joy / Heart like mine / Over & over / Precious little things / Now the bitter, now the sweet / Automatically sunshine / Wisdom of time / Oh be my love.
■ LP . . . . . . . . . . . . . . . . . . . .STML 11210
Tamla Motown / Sep '72.

**FUNNY GIRL (see under Ross, Diana).**

**GREATEST HITS (see under Ross, Diana).**

**GREATEST HITS AND RARE CLASSICS.**
Tracks: Up the ladder to the roof / Nathan Jones / I guess I'll miss the man / Stoned love / Everybody's got the right to love / Floy joy / Bad weather / Automatically sunshine / Paradise / Tossin' and turnin' / Il voce de silenzio (Silent voices) / Love train / I had to fall in love / He's my man / Color my world blue / You turn me around / Sha-la bandit / This is why I believe in you / I'm gonna let my heart do the walking / You're my driving wheel / When I looked at your face / Another life from now.
■ CD . . . . . . . . . . . . . . . . . . . . . WD 72773
Motown / Dec '91.
CD . . . . . . . . . . . . . . . . . . . . . .530050-2
MC . . . . . . . . . . . . . . . . . . . . . .530050-4
Motown / Jan '93 / PolyGram.

**GREATEST HITS: SUPREMES.**
Tracks: Up the ladder to the roof / Bad weather / Nathan Jones / Everybody's got the right to love / Automatically sunshine / Touch / I guess I'll miss the man / Stoned love / River deep, mountain high / Floy Joy / Together we can make such sweet music / Your wonderful sweet sweet love / You gotta have love in your heart / Bill, when are you coming back / Reach out and touch.
■ LP . . . . . . . . . . . . . . . . . . . . STMR 9010
Tamla Motown / Apr '80.
■ LP . . . . . . . . . . . . . . . . . . . . STMS 5098
MC . . . . . . . . . . . . . . . . . . . . CSTMS 5098
Motown / Jun '83 / PolyGram.
MC . . . . . . . . . . . . . . . . . . . . . . WK 72124
■ LP . . . . . . . . . . . . . . . . . . . . . WL 72124
Motown / '86 / PolyGram.

**HAPPENING, THE.**
Tracks: Happening / All I know about you.
■ 7" . . . . . . . . . . . . . . . . . . . . . TMG 607
Tamla Motown / May '67.

**HE'S MY MAN.**
Tracks: He's my man / Give out, but don't give up.
■ 7" . . . . . . . . . . . . . . . . . . . . . TMG 950
Tamla Motown / Aug '75.

**HIT AND MISS.**
Tracks: Hit and miss.
■ 12" . . . . . . . . . . . . . . . . . . . .12MOTC 88
Motor City / Nov '91.

**I HEAR A SYMPHONY.**
Tracks: Stranger in Paradise / Yesterday / I hear a symphony / Unchained melody / With a song in my heart / Without a song / My world is empty without you / Lover's concerto / Any girl in love (knows what I'm going through) / Wonderful, wonderful / Everything is good about you / He's all I got.
■ LP . . . . . . . . . . . . . . . . . . . . STMS 5012
■ MC . . . . . . . . . . . . . . . . . . . CSTMS 5012
Motown / Oct '81.

**I HEAR A SYMPHONY.**
Tracks: I hear a symphony.
■ 7" . . . . . . . . . . . . . . . . . . . . . TMG 543
Tamla Motown / Dec '65.

**I'M GONNA MAKE YOU LOVE ME (Supremes and Temptations).**
Tracks: I'm gonna make you love me / My guy, my girl / Uptight (everything's alright) / Sweet inspiration / I'll try something new / Ain't no mountain high enough / I second that emotion / Why (must we fall in love) / For better or worse / Weight / I'll be doggone / Stubborn kind of fellow.
CD . . . . . . . . . . . . . . . . . . . . . .550 0752
MC . . . . . . . . . . . . . . . . . . . . . .550 0754
Spectrum (1) / May '93 / PolyGram.

**LOOKING BACK WITH.. (Supremes & Eddie Floyd).**
Tracks: Tears of sorrow / Pretty baby / Return of Stagger Lee / Searching for my baby / Baby won't you change your mind / I'll get along / All I need is you / Bye bye baby / Never get enough of your love / I am her yo-yo man / Lonely / Please don't leave me dear / I'll never find another girl like you / When you're in love / Whip.
■ LP . . . . . . . . . . . . . . . . . . . .EMB 3398
Ember / Aug '68.

**LOVE CHILD/SUPREMES A GO GO.**
Tracks: Love child / Keep an eye / How long has that evening train been gone / Does your Mama know about me / Honey bee (keep on stinging me) / Some things you never get used to / He's my sunny boy / You've been so wonderful to me / Chains of love (Don't break these) / You ain't livin' till you're lovin' / I'll set you free / Can't shake it loose / Love is like an itching in my heart / This old heart of mine / You can't hurry love / Shake me wake me / Baby I need your loving / These boots are made for walking / I can't help myself / Get ready / Put yourself in my place / Money (that's what I want) / Come and get these memories / Hang on Sloopy.
■ CD . . . . . . . . . . . . . . . . . . . . . ZD 72485
Motown / Nov '86.

**LOVE I NEVER KNEW YOU COULD FEEL SO GOOD.**
Tracks: Love I never knew you could feel so good / This is why I believe in you.
■ 7" . . . . . . . . . . . . . . . . . . . . . TMG 1064
Motown / Mar '77.

**LOVE IS HERE AND NOW YOU'RE GONE.**
Tracks: Love is here and now you're gone / Back in my arms again.
■ 7" . . . . . . . . . . . . . . . . . . . . . TMG 981
Tamla Motown / Jun '75.

**LOVE IS HERE AND NOW YOU'RE GONE.**
Tracks: Love is here and now you're gone / There's no stopping us now.
■ 7" . . . . . . . . . . . . . . . . . . . . . TMG 597
Tamla Motown / Mar '67.

**LOVE IS LIKE AN ITCHING IN MY HEART.**
Tracks: Love is like an itching in my heart / He's all I got.
■ 7" . . . . . . . . . . . . . . . . . . . . . TMG 560
Tamla Motown / May '66.

**MAGNIFICENT 7, THE (Supremes & Four Tops).**
Tracks: Knock on my door / For your love / Without the one you love / Reach out and touch / Stoned soul picnic / Baby (you've got what it takes) / River deep, mountain high / Ain't nothing like the real thing / Everyday people / It's got to be a miracle (this thing called love) / Taste of honey / Together we can make such sweet music.
■ LP . . . . . . . . . . . . . . . . . . . .STML 11179
Tamla Motown / May '71.
■ LP . . . . . . . . . . . . . . . . . . . . STMS 5016

■ MC. . . . . . . . . . . . . . . . . . . CSTMS 5016
Motown / Oct '81.

## MEET THE SUPREMES.
**Tracks:** Not Advised.
■ LP . . . . . . . . . . . . . . . . . . . . SL 10109
Stateside / Dec '64.

## MERRY CHRISTMAS.
**Tracks:** White Christmas / Silver bells / Born of Mary / Children's Christmas song / Little drummer boy / My Christmas tree / Rudolph the red nosed reindeer / Santa Claus is coming to town / My favourite things / Twinkle twinkle little me / Little bright star / Joy to the world.
■ LP . . . . . . . . . . . . . . . . . . . STMS 5084
■ MC. . . . . . . . . . . . . . . . . . CSTMS 5084
Motown / Nov '82.
■ MC. . . . . . . . . . . . . . . . . . . WK 72113
■ LP . . . . . . . . . . . . . . . . . . . . WL 72113
Motown / '86.

## MORE HITS BY THE SUPREMES.
**Tracks:** Ask any girl / Nothing but heartaches / Mother dear / Honey boy / Back in my arms again / Whisper you love me, boy / Only time I'm happy / He holds his own / Who could ever doubt my love / Heartaches don't last always / I'm in love again.
■ LP . . . . . . . . . . . . . . . . . . . STMR 9006
■ MC. . . . . . . . . . . . . . . . . . CSTMR 9006
Motown / Oct '81.
MC. . . . . . . . . . . . . . . . . . . . WK 72117
■ LP . . . . . . . . . . . . . . . . . . . . WL 72117
Motown / '86 / PolyGram.
■ CD . . . . . . . . . . . . . . . . . . . WD 72117
Motown / Feb '91.

## MOTOWN SPECIAL.
**Tracks:** You keep me hangin' on / This old heart of mine / Stop, in the name of love / Mother, you smother me / Put yourself in my place / There's no stopping us now / Baby love / Come and get these memories / Baby, I need your loving / I guess I'll always love you / I can't help myself / Love is in our hearts.
■ LP . . . . . . . . . . . . . . . . . . . STMX 6001
■ MC. . . . . . . . . . . . . . . . . . CSTMX 6001
Motown / Oct '81.

## MOTOWN SPECIAL (see under Ross, Diana).

## MY WORLD IS EMPTY WITHOUT YOU.
**Tracks:** My world is empty without you / Everything is good about you.
■ 7" . . . . . . . . . . . . . . . . . . . TMG 548
Tamla Motown / Feb '66.

## NATHAN JONES.
**Tracks:** Nathan Jones.
■ 7" . . . . . . . . . . . . . . . . . . . TMG 782
Tamla Motown / Aug '71.

## NEVER-BEFORE-RELEASED MASTERS.
**Tracks:** Sweet thing / It's going all the way(to true,-true love) / Little breeze / Am I asking too much / Stormy / Slow down / Don't let true love die / Too much, a little too soon / Too hurt to cry,too in love to say goodbye / Can I get a witness / Come into my palace / I'm the exception to the rule / Our day will come / Save me a star / Mr. Blues / Little Miss Loser / Fancy passes / Ballad of Davy Crockett / Supercalifragilisticexpialidocious / Whistle while you work / I've got no strings / Dream is a wish your heart makes / Land of make believe / Toyland / Won't be long before Christmas / Christmas song / Silent night.
■ CD . . . . . . . . . . . . . . . . . . . WD 72600
Motown / Feb '88.

## NEW WAYS BUT LOVE STAYS.
**Tracks:** Together we can make such sweet music / Stoned love / It's time to break down / Bridge over troubled water / I wish I were your mirror / Come together / Is there a place / Na na hey hey kiss him goodbye / Shine on me / Thank him for today.
■ LP . . . . . . . . . . . . . . . . . . . STML 11175
Tamla Motown / Feb '71.

## NOTHING BUT HEARTACHES.
**Tracks:** Nothing but heartaches.
■ 7" . . . . . . . . . . . . . . . . . . . TMG 527
Tamla Motown / Aug '65.

## REACH OUT AND TOUCH (Supremes & Four Tops).
**Tracks:** Reach out and touch.
■ 7" . . . . . . . . . . . . . . . . . . . TMG 836
Tamla Motown / Nov '72.

## REFLECTIONS.
**Tracks:** Reflections.
■ 7" . . . . . . . . . . . . . . . . . . . TMG 616
Tamla Motown / Aug '67.

## RETURN OF THE MAGNIFICENT 7 (Supremes & Four Tops).
**Tracks:** You gotta have love in your heart / I wonder where we're going / Call me / One more bridge to cross / If you could see me now / I'll try not to cry / I'm glad about it / Let's make love now / I can't believe you love me / Where would I be without you baby / What do you have to do.
■ LP . . . . . . . . . . . . . . . . . . . STML 11192
Tamla Motown / Nov '71.

## RIGHT ON.
**Tracks:** Up the ladder to the roof / Then we can try again / Everybody's got the right to love / Wait a minute before you leave me / You move me / But I love you more / I got hurt / Baby baby / Take a closer look at me / Then I met you / Bill, when are you coming back / Loving country.
■ LP . . . . . . . . . . . . . . . . . . . STML 11157
Tamla Motown / Aug '70.

## RIVER DEEP MOUNTAIN HIGH (Supremes & Four Tops).
**Tracks:** River deep, mountain high / You gotta have more love in your heart.
■ 7" . . . . . . . . . . . . . . . . . . . TMG 777
Tamla Motown / Jun '71.
■ 7" . . . . . . . . . . . . . . . . . . . TMG 971
Tamla Motown / May '75.

## RODGERS & HART COLLECTION (see under Ross, Diana).

## SHAKE.
**Tracks:** Shake / Chain gang / Havin' a party / Good news.
■ EP . . . . . . . . . . . . . . . . . . . TME 2011
Tamla Motown / Feb '66.

## SOME THINGS YOU NEVER GET USED TO.
**Tracks:** Some things you never get used to.
■ 7" . . . . . . . . . . . . . . . . . . . TMG 662
Tamla Motown / Jul '68.

## SOMEDAY WE'LL BE TOGETHER.
**Tracks:** My world is empty without you / Someday we'll be together.
■ 7" . . . . . . . . . . . . . . . . . . . TMG 1080
Motown / '80.

## STONED LOVE.
**Tracks:** Stoned love.
■ 7" . . . . . . . . . . . . . . . . . . . TMG 760
Tamla Motown / Jan '71.

## STONED LOVE.
**Tracks:** Stoned love / Nathan Jones.
■ 7" . . . . . . . . . . . . . . . . . . . TMG 1046
Tamla Motown / Sep '76.

## STONED LOVE.
**Tracks:** Not Advised.
■ LP . . . . . . . . . . . . . . . . . . . MFP 50421
MFP / Feb '79.

## STOP IN THE NAME OF LOVE.
**Tracks:** Stop in the name of love.
■ 7" . . . . . . . . . . . . . . . . . . . TMG 501
Tamla Motown / Mar '65.

## SUPREMES A GO GO.
**Tracks:** Love is like an itching in my heart / This old heart of mine / You can't hurry love / Shake me, wake me / Baby, I need your loving / These boots are made for walking / I can't help myself / Get ready / Put yourself in my place / Money (that's what I want) / Come and get these memories / Hang on, Sloopy.
■ LP . . . . . . . . . . . . . . . . . . . STML 11039
Tamla Motown / Dec '66.
■ LP . . . . . . . . . . . . . . . . . . . STMS 5013
■ MC. . . . . . . . . . . . . . . . . . CSTMS 5013
Motown / Oct '81.
■ LP . . . . . . . . . . . . . . . . . . . WL 72072
Motown / '86.

## SUPREMES SING MOTOWN (Ross, Diana & The Supremes).
**Tracks:** You keep me hangin' on / You're gone, but always in my heart / Love is here and now you're gone / Mother, you smother you / I guess I'll always love you / I'll turn to stone / It's the same old song / Going down for the third time / Love is in our hearts / Remove the doubt / There's no stopping us now / Heatwave.
■ LP . . . . . . . . . . . . . . . . . . . STML 11047
Tamla Motown / May '67.
■ LP . . . . . . . . . . . . . . . . . . . STMS 5014
■ MC. . . . . . . . . . . . . . . . . . CSTMS 5014
Motown / Oct '81.

## SUPREMES SING RODGERS & HART.
**Tracks:** Not Advised.
■ LP . . . . . . . . . . . . . . . . . . . STML 1105
Tamla Motown / Sep '67.

## TOUCH.
**Tracks:** This is the story / Nathan Jones / Here comes the sunrise / Love it came to me this time / Johnny Raven / Have I lost you / Time and love / Touch / Happy (is a bumpy road) / It's so hard for me to say goodbye.
■ LP . . . . . . . . . . . . . . . . . . . STML 11189
Tamla Motown / Sep '71.
■ CD . . . . . . . . . . . . . . . . . . . WD 72742
■ MC. . . . . . . . . . . . . . . . . . WK 72742
Motown / May '91.
CD. . . . . . . . . . . . . . . . . . . . 530211-2
Motown / Jan '93 / PolyGram.

## UP THE LADDER TO THE ROOF.
**Tracks:** Up the ladder to the roof.
■ 7" . . . . . . . . . . . . . . . . . . . TMG 735
Tamla Motown / May '70.

## UP THE LADDER TO THE ROOF.
**Tracks:** Floy joy / Up the ladder to the roof.
■ 7" . . . . . . . . . . . . . . . . . . . TMG 964
Tamla Motown / Mar '75.
■ 7" . . . . . . . . . . . . . . . . . . . ZB 41931
Tamla Motown / Apr '88.

## WHERE DID OUR LOVE GO.
**Tracks:** Where did our love go.
■ 7" . . . . . . . . . . . . . . . . . . . SS 327
Stateside / Sep '64.

## WHERE DID OUR LOVE GO.
**Tracks:** Where did our love go / Run, run, run / Baby love / When the lovelight starts shining through his eyes / Come see about me / Long gone lover / I'm giving you your freedom / Breathtaking guy / He means the world to me / Standing at the crossroads of love / Your kiss of fire / Ask any girl.
■ CD . . . . . . . . . . . . . . . . . . . WD 72735
■ MC. . . . . . . . . . . . . . . . . . WK 72735
Motown / Mar '91.

## WHERE DID OUR LOVE GO.
**Tracks:** Where did our love go.
■ 7" . . . . . . . . . . . . . . . . . . . TMG 925
Tamla Motown / Nov '74.
■ CD Single . . . . . . . . . . . . . . . ZD 41957
Motown / Jun '89.

## WHERE DID OUR LOVE GO/I HEAR A SYMPHONY.
**Tracks:** Where did our love go / Run, run, run / Baby love / When the lovelight starts shining through his eyes / Come see about me / Long gone lover / I'm giving you your freedom / Breathtaking guy / He means the world to me / Standing at the crossroads of love / Your kiss of fire / Ask any girl / Stranger in paradise / Yesterday / I hear a symphony / Unchained melody / With a song in my heart / Without a song / My world is empty without you / Lover's concerto / Any girl in love (knows what I'm going through) / Wonderful, wonderful / Everything is good about you / He's all I got.
■ CD . . . . . . . . . . . . . . . . . . . ZD 72459
Motown / Dec '86.

## YOU CAN'T HURRY LOVE.
**Tracks:** You can't hurry love.
■ 7" . . . . . . . . . . . . . . . . . . . TMG 575
Tamla Motown / Sep '66.
■ 7" . . . . . . . . . . . . . . . . . . . TMG 956
Tamla Motown / Feb '75.

## YOU GOTTA HAVE LOVE IN YOUR HEART (Supremes & Four Tops).
**Tracks:** You gotta have love in your heart.
■ 7" . . . . . . . . . . . . . . . . . . . TMG 793
Tamla Motown / Nov '71.

## YOU KEEP ME HANGIN ON.
**Tracks:** You keep me hangin on / Come see about me / I hear a symphony / Your love is like an itching in my heart.
■ 7" . . . . . . . . . . . . . . . . . . . TMG 992
Tamla Motown / Oct '75.
■ 7" . . . . . . . . . . . . . . . . . . . ZB 40709
■ 12" . . . . . . . . . . . . . . . . . . ZT 40710
Motown / Apr '86.

## YOU KEEP ME HANGIN' ON.
**Tracks:** You keep me hangin' on / Come see about me.
■ 7" . . . . . . . . . . . . . . . . . . . TMG 585
Tamla Motown / Dec '66.

## Sure, Al B.

### F I'M NOT YOUR LOVER.
**Tracks:** If I'm not your lover / Noche y dia.

| | | |
|---|---|---|
| 12" | | W 2908 T |
| 7" | | W 2908 |
| MC Single | | W 2908 C |

WEA / Jun '89.

### N EFFECT MODE.
**Tracks:** Nite and day / Oooh, this love is so / Killing me softly with her song / Naturally mine / If I'm not your lover / Off on your own / Rescue me.

| | | |
|---|---|---|
| D | | .925662 2 |
| LP | | WX 173 |
| MC | | WX 173C |

WEA / Apr '88 / WEA.

### MISUNDERSTANDING.
**Tracks:** Misunderstanding / Misunderstanding (version).

| | | |
|---|---|---|
| 12" | | W 9590 T |
| 7" | | W 9590 |
| CD Single | | W 9590 CD |
| MC Single | | W 9590 C |

WEA / Oct '90.

### NITE AND DAY.
**Tracks:** Nite and day / Nuit et jour.

| | | |
|---|---|---|
| 7" | | W 8192 |
| 12" | | W 8192T |

WEA / Mar '88.

### OFF ON YOUR OWN.
**Tracks:** Off on your own.

| | | |
|---|---|---|
| 7" | | W 7870 |
| 12" | | W 7870 T |

WEA / Jul '88.

### PRIVATE TIMES.AND THE WHOLE 9.
**Tracks:** Hotel California / Touch you / So special / I want to know / No matter what you do / Shades of grey / Private times / Missunderstanding / Channel J / Had enuff / Just for the moment / Sure thang.

| | | |
|---|---|---|
| D | | 7599260052 |
| LP | | WX 395 |
| MC | | WX 395C |

Uptown / Nov '90 / WEA.

### RESCUE ME (I'M NOT MAD).
**Tracks:** Rescue me (I'm not mad).

| | | |
|---|---|---|
| 7" | | 0-21038 |

Uptown / Oct '88.

### SEXY VERSUS.
**Tracks:** Right now / U & I / Playing games / Natalie / Ooh 4 you girl / Kick in the head / Turn you out / See the lady / Thanks 4 a great time last nite / I don't wanna cry / Die for you / I'll never hurt you again / Capes in the end.

| | | |
|---|---|---|
| CD | | 7599269732 |
| MC | | 7599269734 |

Warner Bros. / Nov '92 / WEA.

## Surface

### ND WAVE.
**Tracks:** Shower me with your love / Closer than friends / Can we spend some time / You are my everything / I missed / Black shades / Hold on to love / Where's that girl.

| | | |
|---|---|---|
| LP | | 4629801 |
| MC | | 4629804 |
| CD | | 4629802 |

CBS / Nov '88.

### DEEP.
**Tracks:** First time / Give her love / Rainbow (reprise) / All I want is you / Tomorrow / You're the one / We don't have to say goodbye / Never gonna let you down / "10" / Don't wanna turn you off / Kid stuff (young love) (interlude) / When it comes to love / Echoes / Ain't givin' up / Love x trust / Kid stuff (believe in yourself).

| | | |
|---|---|---|
| LP | | 4673381 |
| CD | | 4673382 |
| MC | | 4673384 |

Columbia / Feb '91.

### BEST OF SURFACE, THE (A Nice Time 4 Lovin').
**Tracks:** Nice time 4 lovin' / Happy / Closer than friends / You are my everything / I missed (title song reprise) / Shower me with your love / First time / Never gonna let you down / World of own / Christmas time is here.

| | | |
|---|---|---|
| CD | | 4690542 |
| LP | | 4690541 |
| MC | | 4690544 |

Columbia / Feb '92.

### FALLING IN LOVE.
**Tracks:** Falling in love.

| | | |
|---|---|---|
| 12" | | SALT 104 |
| 7" | | SAL 104 |

Salsoul / Jun '83.

### FIRST TIME, THE.
**Tracks:** First time / Closer than friends / Happy (12" & CD single only.) / Shower me with your love (12" & CD single only.).

| | | |
|---|---|---|
| 12" | | 6564766 |
| 7" | | 6564767 |
| CD Single | | 6564762 |
| MC Single | | 6564764 |

CBS / Nov '90.

### HAPPY.
**Tracks:** Let's try again / Happy.

| | | |
|---|---|---|
| 12" | | 6503936 |
| 7" | | 6503937 |

CBS / Aug '87.

### I MISSED.
**Tracks:** I missed (7" edit) (Only on 7" version.) / I missed (Only on 7" version.) / I missed (12" version) (Only on 12" version.) / I missed (dub version) (Only on 12" version.) / I missed (acappella) (Only on 12" version.).

| | | |
|---|---|---|
| 12" | | 6530098 |
| 12" | | 6530091 |
| 7" | | 6530097 |

CBS / Nov '88.

### RACE THE NIGHT.
**Tracks:** Intro / Someday / Paris / It's no good / Night creature / Don't try / Hideaway / Bad girls / Story teller.

| | | |
|---|---|---|
| LP | | KILP 4002 |

Killerwatt / May '86.

### SHOWER ME WITH YOUR LOVE.
**Tracks:** Shower me with your love / Shower me with your love (instrumental) / Shower me with your love (remix) (Only on 12" and CD single) / Happy (remix) (Only on 12" and CD single).

| | | |
|---|---|---|
| 12" | | 6552456 |
| 12" | | 6552457 |
| 7" | | 6552450 |
| CD Single | | 6552452 |

CBS / Aug '89.

### SURFACE.
**Tracks:** Let's try again / Happy / We're all searching / Lately / Gotta make love tonight / Who loves you / You're fine / Lady wants a man / Girls were made to love and kiss / Feels so good.

| | | |
|---|---|---|
| MC | | 4500994 |
| LP | | 4500991 |

CBS / Dec '86.

### WHEN YOUR EX WANTS YOU BACK.
**Tracks:** When your ex wants you back.

| | | |
|---|---|---|
| 12" | | SALT 106 |
| 7" | | SAL 106 |

Salsoul / Jun '84.

## Surface Noise

### DANCING ON A WIRE.
**Tracks:** Dancing on a wire / Love groove.

| | | |
|---|---|---|
| 7" | | GP 102 |

Groove Records / Aug '80.

### RIGHT BETWEEN THE EYES.
**Tracks:** Right between the eyes / Zero one.

| | | |
|---|---|---|
| 7" | | K 18396 |

WEA / Jan '81.

### SCRATCH, THE.
**Tracks:** Scratch.

| | | |
|---|---|---|
| 7" | | K 18291 |

WEA / May '80.

## Swann, Bettye

### MAKE ME YOURS.
**Tracks:** Make me yours / Fall in love with me / Don't look back / Don't wait too long / Don't take my mind / I can't stop loving you / I think I'm falling in love / Heartache is gone / I will not cry / What is my life coming to / Change is gonna come.

| | | |
|---|---|---|
| LP | | CLP 541 |

Contempo (1) / Feb '77.

## Sweat, Keith

Former stockbroker and integral member of G.Q. Sweat made sprightly solo debut in 1988 with new jack classic and U.K. hit *I Want Her*, produced by Teddy Riley. By '92, *Keep It Comin'* album - his third - boasted

only one Riley credit, but still topped U.S. R&B chart, going platinum in process. He also enjoyed success as producer of Silk, who scored U.S. hit with *Freak Me* (on Sweat's label Keia). 1994 *How Do You Like It* single, featuring cameo by TLC's Lisa Lopez, previewed album *Get Up On It*, on which Sweat showed few signs of updating tired (albeit massively profitable) style.

### DON'T STOP YOUR LOVE.
**Tracks:** Don't stop your love / Don't stop your love (version).

| | | |
|---|---|---|
| 12" | | EKR 84 T |
| 7" | | EKR 84 |

Elektra / Nov '88.

### GET UP ON IT.
**Tracks:** Interlude (how do you like it) / How do you like it (part 1) / It gets better / Get up on it / Feels so good / How do you like it (part 2) / Intermission break / My whole world / Grind on you / When I give my love / Put your lovin' through the test / Telephone love / Come into my bedroom / For you (you just everything).

| | | |
|---|---|---|
| CD | | 755961550-2 |
| MC | | 755961550-4 |

WEA / May '94 / WEA.

### HOW DO YOU LIKE IT.
**Tracks:** How do you like it (Mixes).

| | | |
|---|---|---|
| 12" | | EKR 185T |
| 7" | | EKR 185 |
| CD Single | | EKR 185CD |
| MC Single | | EKR 185C |

Elektra / May '94.

### I WANT HER.
**Tracks:** I want her.

| | | |
|---|---|---|
| 7" | | EKR 68 |
| 12" | | EKR 68T |

Elektra / Feb '88.

### I'LL GIVE YOU ALL MY LOVE.
**Tracks:** I'll give all my love to you / Make you sweat / Come back / Merry go round / Your love / Your love - part 2 / Just one of them thangs / I knew that you were cheatin / Love to love you.

| | | |
|---|---|---|
| CD | | 7559608612 |
| MC | | EKT 60 C |
| LP | | EKT 60 |

Elektra / Jun '90 / WEA.

### I'LL GIVE YOU ALL MY LOVE.
**Tracks:** I'll give you all my love / I want her.

| | | |
|---|---|---|
| 12" | | EKR 120T |
| 7" | | EKR 120 |
| CD Single | | EKR 120CD |
| MC Single | | EKR 120C |

Elektra / Mar '91.

### KEEP IT COMIN'.
**Tracks:** Keep it comin'.

| | | |
|---|---|---|
| CD | | EKT 103CD |
| LP | | EKT 103 |
| MC | | EKT 103MC |

Elektra / Nov '91 / WEA.

### KEEP IT COMIN'.
**Tracks:** Keep it comin'.

| | | |
|---|---|---|
| 12" | | EKR 140T |
| 7" | | EKR 140 |
| CD Single | | EKR 140CD |
| MC Single | | EKR 140C |

Elektra / Jan '92.

### MAKE IT LAST FOREVER.
**Tracks:** Something just ain't right / Right and a wrong way / Tell me it's me you want / I want her / Make it last forever / In the rain / How deep is your love / Don't stop your love.

| | | |
|---|---|---|
| LP | | 9607611 |
| MC | | 9607634 |

Elektra / Dec '87 / WEA.

| | | |
|---|---|---|
| CD | | 9607632 |

Elektra / Jul '88 / WEA.

### MAKE YOU SWEAT.
**Tracks:** Make you sweat.

| | | |
|---|---|---|
| 7" | | EKR 96 |

Elektra / Oct '89.

### MAKE YOU SWEAT (NORMAN COOK 1990 REMIX).
**Tracks:** Make you sweat (1990 remix).

| | | |
|---|---|---|
| 12" | | EKR 113 T |
| 7" | | EKR 113 |
| CD Single | | EKR 113 CD |
| MC Single | | EKR 113 C |

Elektra / Jul '90.

### SOMETHING JUST AIN'T RIGHT.
**Tracks:** Something just ain't right.

| | | |
|---|---|---|
| 12" | | EKR 72T |

■ 7″ . . . . . . . . . . . . . . . . . . . . . . . EKR 72
■ CD Single . . . . . . . . . . . . . . . . . .EKR 72CD
Elektra / Mar '88.

## Sweet Inspirations

### ESTELLE, MYRNA AND SYLVIA.
Tracks: Wishes and dishes / You roam when you don't get it at home / Slipped and tripped / All it takes is you and me / Pity yourself / Emergency / Call me when all else fails / Whole world is out / Why marry / Sweet inspiration / Why (am I treated so bad).
CD. . . . . . . . . . . . . . . . . . . . . . . CDSXE 062
Stax / Jul '92 / Pinnacle.

### HOT BUTTERFLY.
Tracks: Hot fun / Face to face / That's when you know / Hot butterfly / It's the simple things you do / Do it right.
■ LP . . . . . . . . . . . . . . . . . . . . . . . . RSS 12
RSO / Nov '79.

### LET IT BE ME.
Tracks: Let it be me / When something is wrong with my baby.
■ 7″ . . . . . . . . . . . . . . . . . . . . . . .584132
Atlantic / Sep '67.

### SWEET INSPIRATIONS, THE.
Tracks: Oh what a fool I've been / Blues stay away from me / Don't let me lose this dream / Knock on wood / Do right woman / Don't fight it / Sweet inspiration / Let it be me / I'm blue / Reach out for me / Here I am / Why am I treated so bad.
■ LP . . . . . . . . . . . . . . . . . . . . . . . 587 090
Atlantic / Mar '68.

### SWEET SWEET SOUL.
Tracks: Shut up / Give my love to somebody / Two can play the game / Gotta find a brand new lover / Ain't nothin' in the world / Them boys / Flash in the pan / At last I've found a love / That's the way my baby is.
■ LP . . . . . . . . . . . . . . . . . . . . . . . 2465 003
Atlantic / Jul '70.

### SWEETS FOR MY SWEET.
Tracks: But you know I love you / It's not easy / Get a little order / Don't go / It's worth it all / Sweets for my sweet / Every day will be like a holiday / Let me be lonely / Crying in the rain / Always David.
■ LP . . . . . . . . . . . . . . . . . . . . . . . 588 194
Atlantic / Oct '69.

### WHAT THE WORLD NEEDS NOW IS LOVE.
Tracks: Alfie / What the world needs now is love / To love somebody / Watch the one who brings you the news / Am I ever gonna see my baby again / Unchained melody / You really didn't mean it / Walk in my shoes / Where did it go / I could leave you alone / That's how strong my love is / I don't want to go on without you.
■ LP . . . . . . . . . . . . . . . . . . . . . . . 588 137
Atlantic / Apr '69.

### WHY AM I TREATED SO BAD.
Tracks: Why am I treated so bad / Sweet inspiration / I don't want to go on without you.
■ 7″ . . . . . . . . . . . . . . . . . . . . . . .584117
Atlantic / Jun '67.
■ 7″ . . . . . . . . . . . . . . . . . . . . . . . K 10593
Atlantic / Aug '75.

## Sweet Lamont

### DEFINITION OF A TRACK.
Tracks: Not Advised.
■ 12″ . . . . . . . . . . . . . . . . . . . . .12CTL 002
White / Jul '89.

## Sweet Talks

### HOLLYWOOD HIGHLIFE PARTY.
Tracks: Not Advised.
CD. . . . . . . . . . . . . . . . . . . . . . . .ADC 301
P.A.M. / Feb '94 / Topic Records / Direct Distribution.

## Sweet Thunder

### EVERYBODY'S SINGING LOVE SONGS.
Tracks: Everybody's singing love songs / Space bass.
■ 12″ . . . . . . . . . . . . . . . . . . . . . SWAVE 5
Streetwave / Dec '85.

### EVERYBODY'S SINGING LOVE SONGS.
Tracks: Everybody's singing love songs / Joyful noise.
■ 7″ . . . . . . . . . . . . . . . . . . . . . . . FTC 158
Fantasy / Jun '78.

## Sweethearts

### YOU'RE WEARING ME OUT.
Tracks: You're wearing me out.
■ 12″ . . . . . . . . . . . . . . . . . . . . MKHAN 52
Streetwave / Sep '85.

## Switch

### AM I STILL YOUR BOYFRIEND?.
Tracks: Treason / Am I still your boyfriend / Just can't pull away / I won't give up / Spend my life with you / Forever my love / I'm so satisfied / Switch it baby / It's all up to you / Lovers don't hold back / Keeping secrets.
■ LP . . . . . . . . . . . . . . . . . . . . . . . FL 89407
Total Experience / Jan '85.

### BEST BEAT IN TOWN.
Tracks: Best beat in town / It's so real.
■ 12″ . . . . . . . . . . . . . . . . . . . 12TMG 1148
■ 7″ . . . . . . . . . . . . . . . . . . . . . TMG 1148
Motown / '79.

### DON'T TAKE OUR LOVE AWAY.
Tracks: Don't take our love away.
■ 7″ . . . . . . . . . . . . . . . . . . . . . TMG 1187
Motown / May '80.

### KEEPING SECRETS.
Tracks: Keeping secrets / Switch it baby.
■ 12″ . . . . . . . . . . . . . . . . . . . . . XET 502
■ 7″ . . . . . . . . . . . . . . . . . . . . . . .XE 502
Total Experience / Nov '84.

### REACHING FOR TOMORROW.
Tracks: Power to dance / My friend in the sky / Don't take my love away / Keep movin' on / Brighter tomorrow / Reaching for tomorrow / I finally found someone new / Honey I love you / Get back with you.
■ LP . . . . . . . . . . . . . . . . . . . .STML 12135
Motown / May '80.

### SWITCH II.
Tracks: You're the one for me / Next to you / Best beat in town / Calling on all girls / Go on doin' what you feel / Fallin' / I call your name.
■ LP . . . . . . . . . . . . . . . . . . . .STML 12112
Motown / '79.

### THERE'LL NEVER BE.
Tracks: There'll never be / You pulled a switch.
■ 7″ . . . . . . . . . . . . . . . . . . . . . TMG 1123
Motown / Oct '78.

### WE LIKE TO PARTY.
Tracks: We like to party / Somebody's watchin' you.
■ 7″ . . . . . . . . . . . . . . . . . . . . . TMG 1132
Motown / Jan '79.

## Sybil

### ALL THRU THE NIGHT.
Tracks: All through the night.
■ 12″ . . . . . . . . . . . . . . . . . CHAMP 12225
■ 12″ Remix. . . . . . . . . . . . . CHAMX 12225
■ 7″ . . . . . . . . . . . . . . . . . . .CHAMPX 225
■ CD Single . . . . . . . . . . . . . .CHAMPCD 225
Champion / Dec '89.

### BEYOND YOUR WILDEST DREAMS.
Tracks: Beyond your wildest dreams.
■ 12″ . . . . . . . . . . . . . . . . . . . PWLT 265
■ 7″ . . . . . . . . . . . . . . . . . . . . .PWL 265
■ CD Single . . . . . . . . . . . . . . PWCD 265
■ MC Single. . . . . . . . . . . . . . PWMC 265
PWL / Jun '93.

### CAN'T WAIT ON TOMORROW.
Tracks: Can't wait on tomorrow.
■ 12″ . . . . . . . . . . . . . . . . . . CHAMP 1282
■ 7″ . . . . . . . . . . . . . . . . . . . CHAMP 82
Champion / '88.

### CRAZY FOR YOU.
Tracks: Crazy for you.
■ 12″ . . . . . . . . . . . . . . . . . . . PWLT 53
■ 7″ . . . . . . . . . . . . . . . . . . . . PWL 53
■ CD Single . . . . . . . . . . . . . . PWCD 53
■ MC Single. . . . . . . . . . . . . . PWMC 53
PWL / Apr '90.

### DON'T MAKE ME OVER.
Tracks: Don't make me over / Don't make me over (version).
■ 12″ . . . . . . . . . . . . . . . . CHAMP 12213
■ 12″ Remix . . . . . . . . . . . . CHAMX 12213
■ 7″ . . . . . . . . . . . . . . . . . . .CHAMP 213
■ CD Single . . . . . . . . . . . . .CHAMPCD 213
Champion / Jul '89.

### FALLING IN LOVE.
Tracks: Falling in love / Falling in love (dub mix).
■ 12″ . . . . . . . . . . . . . . . . . . CHAMP 12
■ 7″ . . . . . . . . . . . . . . . . . . . CHAMP
Champion / Oct '86.

### GOOD 'N' READY.
Tracks: Not Advised.
CD. . . . . . . . . . . . . . . . . . . . . . . HFCD
LP. . . . . . . . . . . . . . . . . . . . . . . HF
MC. . . . . . . . . . . . . . . . . . . . . . . HFC
PWL / May '93 / WEA.

### LET YOURSELF GO.
Tracks: Falling in love (remix) / Let yourself go (ins / Let yourself go / Don't make me over / My love guaranteed / U and me 2 nite / Falling in love Walkin' in the moonlight / All through the night / C our way to love.
■ CD . . . . . . . . . . . . . . . . . .CHAMPCD 10
■ LP . . . . . . . . . . . . . . . . . . . CHAMP 10
■ MC . . . . . . . . . . . . . . . . . CHAMPK 10
Champion / Aug '87.
■ LP . . . . . . . . . . . . . . . . . . . CHAMPX 10
MC. . . . . . . . . . . . . . . . . . CHAMXK 10
Champion / Jan '90 / BMG.

### LET YOURSELF GO.
Tracks: Let yourself go.
■ 12″ . . . . . . . . . . . . . . . . . . CHAMP 12
■ 7″ . . . . . . . . . . . . . . . . . . . CHAMP
Champion / Apr '87.

### LOVE I LOST, THE (see under Westend

### LOVE SO SPECIAL.
Tracks: Love so special.
■ 7″ . . . . . . . . . . . . . . . . . . . . .A 77
■ 12″ . . . . . . . . . . . . . . . . . . . A 7779
East West / Nov '90.

### MAKE IT EASY ON ME.
Tracks: Make it easy on me.
■ 12″ . . . . . . . . . . . . . . . . . . . PWLT
■ 7″ . . . . . . . . . . . . . . . . . . . . PWL
■ CD Single . . . . . . . . . . . . . . PWLCD
■ MC Single. . . . . . . . . . . . . . PWLMC
PWL / Sep '90.

### MY LOVE IS GUARANTEED.
Tracks: My love is guaranteed / Red ink mix part (on 12″ special edition only) / Red ink mix part 2 (c 12″ special edition only).
■ 12″ . . . . . . . . . . . . . . . . . . CHAMP 125
■ 12″ Remix . . . . . . . . . . . . CHAMP 1255
■ 7″ . . . . . . . . . . . . . . . . . . . CHAMP 5
Champion / Aug '87.

### MY LOVE IS GUARANTEED.
Tracks: My love is guaranteed / My love is guara teed (remix).
■ 12″ . . . . . . . . . . . . . . . . . . . PWLT 27
■ 7″ . . . . . . . . . . . . . . . . . . . . PWL 27
■ CD Single . . . . . . . . . . . . . . PWCD 27
■ MC Single. . . . . . . . . . . . . . PWMC 27
PWL / Dec '93.

### STRONGER TOGETHER.
Tracks: Stronger together.
■ 12″ . . . . . . . . . . . . . . . . . . . PWLT 26
■ 7″ . . . . . . . . . . . . . . . . . . . . PWL 26
■ CD Single . . . . . . . . . . . . . . PWCD 26
■ MC Single. . . . . . . . . . . . . . PWMC 26
PWL / Aug '93.

### SYBILIZATION.
Tracks: Not Advised.
CD. . . . . . . . . . . . . . . . . . . . . . . HFCD
■ LP . . . . . . . . . . . . . . . . . . . . . . HF 1
MC. . . . . . . . . . . . . . . . . . . . . . . HFC 1
PWL / Nov '90 / WEA.

### WALK ON BY.
Tracks: Not Advised.
CD. . . . . . . . . . . . . . . . . . . . . . . HFCD 1
■ LP . . . . . . . . . . . . . . . . . . . . . . HF 1
MC. . . . . . . . . . . . . . . . . . . HFMC 1
PWL / Feb '90 / WEA.

### WALK ON BY.
Tracks: Walk on by / Here comes my love.
■ 12″ . . . . . . . . . . . . . . . . . . . PWLT
■ 7″ . . . . . . . . . . . . . . . . . . . . PWL
PWL / Jan '90.

### WHEN I'M GOOD AND READY.
Tracks: When I'm good and ready / When I'm goo and ready (mixes).
■ 12″ . . . . . . . . . . . . . . . . . . . PWLT 26
■ 7″ . . . . . . . . . . . . . . . . . . . . PWL 26
■ CD Single . . . . . . . . . . . . . . PWCD 26
■ MC Single. . . . . . . . . . . . . . PWMC 26
PWL / Mar '93.

■ DELETE

# Sylvers

## BIZARRE.
**Tracks:** Tension / Bottom line / Falling for your love / Boomerang / Bizzare / In one love and out the other / Got to be crazy / You turn me on / Let my love shine in / Something's gotta give.
- ■ LP . . . . . . . . . . . . . . . . . . . . . GEF 26019
Geffen / Jan '85.

## BOOGIE FEVER.
**Tracks:** Boogie fever / Free style.
- ■ 7" . . . . . . . . . . . . . . . . . . . . . . CL 15850
Capitol / Feb '76.

## CONCEPT.
**Tracks:** Heart repair man / Come back lover, come back / P.S. / Just when I thought it was over / I'm gettin' over / Take it to the top / Reach out / There's a place / Taking over.
- ■ LP . . . . . . . . . . . . . . . . . . . . . K 52307
Solar / Nov '81.

## DISCO FEVER.
**Tracks:** Mahogany / Is everybody happy / Come and stay all night / Dancing right now / Gimme gimme your lovin' / I feel so good tonight / Hoochie coochie dancin' / Forever.
- ■ LP . . . . . . . . . . . . . . . . . . . . . CAL 2050
Casablanca / '79.

## FOREVER YOURS.
**Tracks:** Don't stop, get off / Love changes / Forever yours / Swept for you baby / Play this one last record / Come dance with me / Come on down to my house / Diamonds are rare / Love won't let me go / Just a little bit longer.
- ■ LP . . . . . . . . . . . . . . . . . . . . . CAL 2045
Casablanca / Apr '79.

## HIGH SCHOOL DANCE.
**Tracks:** High school dance / Lovin' you is like lovin' the wind / Boogie fever / Hot line.
- ■ 7" . . . . . . . . . . . . . . . . . . . . . CLX 102
Capitol / Jul '77.

## HOOCHIE COOCHIE DANCIN'.
**Tracks:** Hoochie coochie dancin' / I feel so good tonight.
- ■ 7" . . . . . . . . . . . . . . . . . . . . . CAN 153
Casablanca / Nov '79.

## IN ONE LOVE AND OUT THE OTHER.
**Tracks:** In one love and out the other / Falling for your love.
- ■ 12" . . . . . . . . . . . . . . . . . . . . . TA 4852
- ■ 7" . . . . . . . . . . . . . . . . . . . . . A 4852
Geffen / Nov '84.

## MAHOGANY.
**Tracks:** Mahogany / I feel so good tonight.
- ■ 7" . . . . . . . . . . . . . . . . . . . . . CAN 167
Casablanca / Oct '79.

# Sylvers, Leon III

## LEON SYLVERS III.
**Tracks:** Make it count / Gotta find a way / Time machine / Help me find love / So hung up on you / Safe and sound / Living life at the maximum / All or nothing / Let's go thru it / When love moves in / Make it count (12" version) (Only on CD.)
- ■ CD . . . . . . . . . . . . . . . . . . . . . ZD 72681
- ■ LP . . . . . . . . . . . . . . . . . . . . . ZL 72681
- ■ MC . . . . . . . . . . . . . . . . . . . . . ZK 72681
Motown / Nov '89.

## LET'S GO THROUGH IT.
**Tracks:** Let's go thru it / Make it count.
- ■ 12" . . . . . . . . . . . . . . . . . . . . . ZT 43554
- ■ 7" . . . . . . . . . . . . . . . . . . . . . ZB 43553
Motown / Feb '90.

# Sylvester

## BAND OF GOLD.
**Tracks:** Band of gold.
- ■ 12" . . . . . . . . . . . . . . . . . . . . . LONX 33
- ■ 7" . . . . . . . . . . . . . . . . . . . . . LON 33
London / Aug '83.

## CALL ME.
**Tracks:** Trouble in paradise / Call me / Good feeling / He'll understand / One night only / Too late / Power of love / Band of gold.
- ■ LP . . . . . . . . . . . . . . . . . . . . . XTLP 3
- ■ MC . . . . . . . . . . . . . . . . . . . . . XTCC 3
Ecstasy / Apr '84.

## COLLECTION.
**Tracks:** Not Advised.
- ■ CD . . . . . . . . . . . . . . . . . . . . . CCSCD 393
- ■ MC . . . . . . . . . . . . . . . . . . . . . CCSMC 393

Castle Collector Series / May '94 / BMG / Pinnacle / Castle Communications.

## DANCE (DISCO HEAT).
**Tracks:** Dance (disco heat) / Grateful.
- ■ 7" . . . . . . . . . . . . . . . . . . . . . FTC 163
- ■ 12" . . . . . . . . . . . . . . . . . . . . 12FTC 163
Fantasy / Nov '78.

## DO YA WANNA FUNK (Sylvester & Patrick Cowley).
**Tracks:** Do ya wanna funk (Housey, housey mix) / Menergy / Do ya wanna funk (original mix) / Do ya wanna funk.
- ■ 12" . . . . . . . . . . . . . . . . . . . . . DOM T4
Domino (1) / Aug '86.

## DO YA WANNA FUNK (Sylvester & Patrick Cowley).
**Tracks:** Do ya wanna funk.
- ■ 12" . . . . . . . . . . . . . . . . . . . . . LONX 13
- ■ 7" . . . . . . . . . . . . . . . . . . . . . LON 13
- ■ MC Single. . . . . . . . . . . . . . . . . LONCS 13
London / Sep '82.

## DON'T STOP.
**Tracks:** Don't stop.
- ■ 12" . . . . . . . . . . . . . . . . . . . . . LONX 23
- ■ 7" . . . . . . . . . . . . . . . . . . . . . LON 23
London / May '83.

## DOWN DOWN DOWN.
**Tracks:** Down down down / Changes.
- ■ 7" . . . . . . . . . . . . . . . . . . . . . FTC 152
Fantasy / Mar '78.

## GREATEST HITS: SYLVESTER.
**Tracks:** Not Advised.
- ■ LP . . . . . . . . . . . . . . . . . . . . . XL 89106
- MC. . . . . . . . . . . . . . . . . . . . . . XK 89106
Fantasy / Nov '83 / Pinnacle / Jazz Music.

## HEAVEN.
**Tracks:** Heaven / Sex.
- ■ 12" . . . . . . . . . . . . . . . . . . . . . COOLX 106
- ■ 7" . . . . . . . . . . . . . . . . . . . . . COOL 106
Cool Tempo / Jan '85.

## HERE IS MY LOVE.
**Tracks:** Here is my love / Give it up.
- ■ 12" . . . . . . . . . . . . . . . . . . . . . FTCT 197
Fantasy / Aug '81.

## I (WHO HAVE NOTHING).
**Tracks:** I (who have nothing) / You make me feel mighty real.
- ■ 12" . . . . . . . . . . . . . . . . . . . . 12FTC 171
- ■ 7" . . . . . . . . . . . . . . . . . . . . . FTC 171
Fantasy / Mar '79.

## LIVING FOR THE CITY.
**Tracks:** Living for the city / Living for the city (dub mix).
- ■ 12" . . . . . . . . . . . . . . . . . . . . . CRT 90
- ■ 7" . . . . . . . . . . . . . . . . . . . . . CR 90
Creole / Mar '86.

## LIVING PROOF.
**Tracks:** Overture / Blackbird / This could be magic / Song for you / Happiness / Loverman / You are my friend / Can't stop dancing / In my fantasy.
- ■ LP . . . . . . . . . . . . . . . . . . . . . FT 573
Fantasy / Jan '80.

## M1015.
**Tracks:** Rock the box / Sex / I don't wanna think about it / Taking love into my own hands / Take me to heaven / How do you like your love / Lovin' is really my game / Shadow of a heart.
- ■ LP . . . . . . . . . . . . . . . . . . . . . CHR 1492
Chrysalis / Dec '84.

## MENERGY.
**Tracks:** Menergy / Won't you let me love you.
- ■ 12" . . . . . . . . . . . . . . . . . . . . . ERCL 200
- ■ 7" . . . . . . . . . . . . . . . . . . . . . ERC 200
ERC / Aug '84.

## MIGHTY REAL.
**Tracks:** Stars / Body strong / Down down down / You make me feel mighty real / I / I need somebody to love tonight / Over and over / Dance.
- ■ LP . . . . . . . . . . . . . . . . . . . . . FTA 3009
Fantasy / Jun '79.

## MUTUAL ATTRACTION.
**Tracks:** Someone like you / Living for the city / Summertime / Mutual attraction / Talk to me / Cool of the evening / Sooner or later / Anything can happen.
- ■ LP . . . . . . . . . . . . . . . . . . . . . 925527 1
- ■ MC . . . . . . . . . . . . . . . . . . . . . 925527 4
WEA / Jan '87.

## MUTUAL ATTRACTION.
**Tracks:** Mutual attraction.
- ■ 12" . . . . . . . . . . . . . . . . . . . . . W 8382T
- ■ 7" . . . . . . . . . . . . . . . . . . . . . W 8382
WEA.

## ROCK THE BOX.
**Tracks:** Rock the box / Rock the box (dub).
- ■ 12" . . . . . . . . . . . . . . . . . . . . . COOLX 104
- ■ 7" . . . . . . . . . . . . . . . . . . . . . COOL 104
Cool Tempo / Oct '84.

## SELL MY SOUL.
**Tracks:** I need you / I'll dance to that / Change up / Sell my soul / Doin' it for the real thing / Cry me a river / My life is loving you / Fever.
- ■ LP . . . . . . . . . . . . . . . . . . . . . F 9601
Fantasy / Nov '80.

## SELL MY SOUL.
**Tracks:** Sell my soul / Sell my soul (pt 2).
- ■ 12" . . . . . . . . . . . . . . . . . . . . . FTCT 192
- ■ 7" . . . . . . . . . . . . . . . . . . . . . FTC 192
Fantasy / Oct '80.

## STAR - BEST OF SYLVESTER.
**Tracks:** Stars (everybody is one) / Dance (disco heat) / Down, down, down / I need somebody to love tonight / I (who have nothing) / You make me feel (mighty real) / My life is loving you / Can't stop dancing / Body strong (On CD/MC only) / Over and over (On CD/MC only) / Disco international (ON CD/MC only).
- CD . . . . . . . . . . . . . . . . . . . . . CDSEW 007
- ■ LP . . . . . . . . . . . . . . . . . . . . . SEW 007
- ■ MC . . . . . . . . . . . . . . . . . . . . . SEWC 007
South Bound / Jun '89 / Pinnacle.

## STARS.
**Tracks:** Stars / Never too late.
- ■ 7" . . . . . . . . . . . . . . . . . . . . . FTC 177
Fantasy / Aug '79.

## STARS.
**Tracks:** Stars / Body strong / I / I need somebody to love tonight.
- ■ LP . . . . . . . . . . . . . . . . . . . . . FT 556
Fantasy / '79.

## STEP II.
**Tracks:** You make me feel mighty real / Dance / Grateful / I took my strength from you / Was it something I said / Just you & I forever.
- ■ LP . . . . . . . . . . . . . . . . . . . . . FT 549
Fantasy / Oct '78.

## SYLVESTER.
**Tracks:** Over and over / I tried to forget you / Changes / Tipsong / Down down down / Loving grows up slow / I been down / Never too late.
- ■ LP . . . . . . . . . . . . . . . . . . . . . FT 538
Fantasy / Apr '78.

## SYLVESTER & GRIFFIN (Sylvester & Griffin).
**Tracks:** Please come into my life / Till midnight / Rozanne / Never alone / Wolf river / Light that shone / You go your way / Girl be here tonight / If you give your love to me / Did you hear the news today.
- ■ LP . . . . . . . . . . . . . . . . . . . . . POLD 5063
Polydor / Aug '82.

## SYLVESTER: GREATEST HITS.
**Tracks:** Do you wanna funk / Dance (disco heat) / You make me feel (mighty real) / I need somebody to love / 'Stars' intro / Can't stop dancing / Stars.
- ■ LP . . . . . . . . . . . . . . . . . . . . . 8170441
Fantasy / Jun '86.

## TOO HOT TO SLEEP.
**Tracks:** New beginnings / Thinking right / Can't forget the love / Too hot to sleep / Give it up / Here is my love / Can't you see / Oooh baby baby / I can't believe I'm in love.
- ■ LP . . . . . . . . . . . . . . . . . . . . . F 9607
Fantasy / Aug '81.

## YOU MAKE ME FEEL (MIGHTY REAL).
**Tracks:** You make me feel (mighty real) / Was it something I said.
- ■ 7" . . . . . . . . . . . . . . . . . . . . . FTC 160
Fantasy / Jul '78.

## YOU MAKE ME FEEL (MIGHTY REAL).
**Tracks:** You make me feel (mighty real) / Stars (everybody is one) (Only on 12" and CD single.) / Over and over (Available on CD single only).
- ■ 12" . . . . . . . . . . . . . . . . . . . . . SEWT 700
- ■ 12" Remix . . . . . . . . . . . . . . . . . SEWT 703
- ■ 7" . . . . . . . . . . . . . . . . . . . . . SEWS 700
- ■ CD Single . . . . . . . . . . . . . . . . . CDSEWT 700
South Bound / May '89.
- 12" . . . . . . . . . . . . . . . . . . . . . BSTNT 110
- 12" Remix . . . . . . . . . . . . . . . . . BSTNTR 110

CD Single. . . . . . . . . . . . . . . . BSTNCD 110
MC Single . . . . . . . . . . . . . . BSTNMC 110
Bosting Records / Oct '94 / Pinnacle.

## Sylvia

**PILLOW TALK.**
Tracks: Pillow talk.
■ 7" . . . . . . . . . . . . . . . . . . . . . HL 10415
London-American / Jun '73.

## Synethia

**I'VE GOT THE LOVE YOU'VE BEEN MISSING.**
Tracks: I've got the love you've been missing.
■ 12". . . . . . . . . . . . . . . . . . . . 12 PO 47
Ichiban / Jun '90.

**SYNETHIA.**
Tracks: Really good lovin' / I've got the love you've been missing / It be's that way sometimes / Come back into my life / Ladies, men get lonely too / Whatever, whenever, whomever / In my arms / You were doing bad when I met cha / What a feeling.
CD. . . . . . . . . . . . . . . . . . . . . JSX 4025 CD
LP . . . . . . . . . . . . . . . . . . . . . . JSX 4025
MC. . . . . . . . . . . . . . . . . . . . JSX 4025 MC
JS / Apr '90 / Backs Distribution / Ichiban Records (UK).

## Syreeta

**BEST OF SYREETA.**
Tracks: With you I'm born again / He's gone / To know you is to love you / Go for it / Just a little piece of you / I can't give you back the love I feel for you / One more time for love / Something on my mind / Harm our love / Spinnin' and spinnin' / Your kiss is sweet / Let's make a deal / Love fire / She's leaving home / Keep him like he is / I like every little thing about you / I'm going left / It will come.
■ LP . . . . . . . . . . . . . . . . . . . STMR 9014
■ MC. . . . . . . . . . . . . . . . CSTMR 9014
Motown / Oct '81.

**CAN'T SHAKE YOUR LOVE.**
Tracks: Can't shake your love / Wish upon a star.
■ 12". . . . . . . . . . . . . . . . . . . TMGT 1275
■ 7" . . . . . . . . . . . . . . . . . . . .TMG 1275
Motown / Aug '82.

**FOREVER IS NOT ENOUGH.**
Tracks: Forever is not enough / She's leaving home.
■ 12". . . . . . . . . . . . . . . . . . . TMGT 1306
■ 7" . . . . . . . . . . . . . . . . . . . .TMG 1306
Motown / May '83.

**GO FOR IT (see under Preston, Billy).**

**HARMOUR LOVE.**
Tracks: Harmour love.
■ 7" . . . . . . . . . . . . . . . . . . . TMG 954
Tamla Motown / Aug '75.

**HE'S GONE.**
Tracks: He's gone / Here's my love.
■ 7" . . . . . . . . . . . . . . . . . . . .TMG 1200
Motown / Oct '81.

**I MUST BE IN LOVE.**
Tracks: I must be in love / Out of the box.
■ 12". . . . . . . . . . . . . . . . . . . TMGT 1258
■ 7" . . . . . . . . . . . . . . . . . . . .TMG 1258
Motown / Apr '82.

**IT WILL COME IN TIME (see under Preston, Billy).**

**ONE TO ONE.**
Tracks: One to one / I don't know / Rest yourself / I too am wanting / Tika tiki danga / Don't cry / Harmour love.
■ LP . . . . . . . . . . . . . . . . . . SYML 12053
Motown / Mar '77.

**PLEASE STAY (see under Preston, Billy).**

**QUICK SLICK.**
Tracks: Quick slick / I don't know.
■ 12". . . . . . . . . . . . . . . . . . . TMGT 1247
Motown / Dec '81.
■ 7" . . . . . . . . . . . . . . . . . . . .TMG 1247
Motown / Dec '81.

**RICH LOVE, POOR LOVE (Syreeta & G.C. Cameron).**
Tracks: Rich love, poor love / I'll try love again / Let's make a deal / Station break for love / Made from love / Love to the rescue / All things happen for a reason.
■ LP . . . . . . . . . . . . . . . . . . .STML 12073
Motown / Dec '77.

**SET MY LOVE IN MOTION.**
Tracks: Quick slick / Move it do it / You set my love in motion / There's nothing like a woman in love / Can't shake your love / I must be in love / Wish upon a star / Out the box / I know the way to your heart / I love you.
■ LP . . . . . . . . . . . . . . . . . . .STML 12162
■ MC. . . . . . . . . . . . . . . . .CSTML 12162
Motown / Dec '81.

**SPINNIN' AND SPINNIN'.**
Tracks: Spinnin' and spinnin'.
■ 7" . . . . . . . . . . . . . . . . . . . TMG 912
Tamla Motown / Sep '74.

**STEVIE WONDER PRESENTS SYREETS.**
Tracks: I'm going left / Spinnin' and spinnin' / Your kiss is sweet / Come and get this stuff / Heavy day / Cause we've ended as lovers / Just a little piece of you / Waiting for the postman / When your daddy's not around / I wanna be by your side / Universal sound of the world.
■ LP . . . . . . . . . . . . . . . . . . STMS 5079
■ MC. . . . . . . . . . . . . . . . CSTMS 5079
Motown / Oct '82.

**SYREETA.**
Tracks: Blame it on the sun / Let me be the one you need / You bring out the love in me / Please stay / He's gone / Love fire / Here's my love / Signed, sealed, delivered, I'm yours / Dance for me children / One more time for love.
■ LP . . . . . . . . . . . . . . . . . . .STML 12137
■ MC. . . . . . . . . . . . . . . . .CSTML 12137
Motown / Oct '81.

**WITH YOU I'M BORN AGAIN (see under Preston, Billy).**

**YOUR KISS IS SWEET.**
Tracks: Your kiss is sweet.
■ 7" . . . . . . . . . . . . . . . . . . . TMG 933
Tamla Motown / Jan '75.

## System

**60 WATT PEARL.**
Tracks: 60 watt pearl / Fergie.
■ 7" . . . . . . . . . . . . . . . . . . . . MCA 731
MCA / Jul '81.

**COME AS YOU ARE (SUPERSTAR).**
Tracks: Modern girl / Come as you are (superstar).
■ 12". . . . . . . . . . . . . . . . . . . A 9297 T
■ 7" . . . . . . . . . . . . . . . . . . . .A 9297
Atlantic / Feb '87.

**COMING TO AMERICA.**
Tracks: Coming to America (part one) / Coming to America (part two).
■ 12". . . . . . . . . . . . . . . . . . . A 9320 T
■ 7" . . . . . . . . . . . . . . . . . . . .A 9320
Atlantic / Aug '88.

**DON'T DISTURB THIS GROOVE.**
Tracks: Don't disturb this groove / Come as you are (Superstar) / Save me / Heart beat of the city / Groove / Nightmare lover / House of rhythm / Didn't I (blow your mind this time) / Soul boy / Modern girl.
■ LP . . . . . . . . . . . . . . . . . . K 781 691-1
MC. . . . . . . . . . . . . . . . . . . . K 781 691-4
Atlantic / Mar '87 / WEA.

**I WANNA MAKE YOU FEEL GOOD.**
Tracks: I wanna make you feel good / Promises can break.
■ 12". . . . . . . . . . . . . . . . . . . POSPX 685
■ 7" . . . . . . . . . . . . . . . . . . . .POSP 685
Polydor / Jun '84.

**NIGHT TIME LOVER.**
Tracks: Night time lover / Save me.
■ 12". . . . . . . . . . . . . . . . . . . A 922 T
■ 7" . . . . . . . . . . . . . . . . . . . .A 9222
Atlantic / Nov '87.

**PLEASURE SEEKERS.**
Tracks: Pleasure seekers.
■ 12". . . . . . . . . . . . . . . . . . . POSPX 753
■ 7" . . . . . . . . . . . . . . . . . . . .POSP 753
Polydor / Aug '85.

**PLEASURE SEEKERS, THE.**
Tracks: Pleasure seekers / It takes two / Big city beat / Love won't wait for lovin' / This is for you / My radio rocks / Did in by a friend / I don't run from danger.
■ LP . . . . . . . . . . . . . . . . . . POLD 5182
MC. . . . . . . . . . . . . . . . . . . POLDC 5182
Polydor / Aug '85 / PolyGram.

**RHYTHM AND ROMANCE.**
Tracks: Not Advised.
■ CD . . . . . . . . . . . . . . . . . . K 781896-2
■ LP . . . . . . . . . . . . . . . . . . K 781896-1
■ MC. . . . . . . . . . . . . . . . . . K 781896-4
WEA / May '89.

**THIS FOR YOU.**
Tracks: This is for you / Love won't wait for lovin' / You are in my system.
■ 12". . . . . . . . . . . . . . . . . . . POSPX 76
■ 7" . . . . . . . . . . . . . . . . . . . .POSP 76
■ 7" Set . . . . . . . . . . . . . . . . POSPXX 76
Polydor / Oct '85.

**WARFARE (EP).**
Tracks: Warfare.
■ 7" . . . . . . . . . . . . . . . . . . . . SDL
Spiderleg / Jun '82.

**YOU ARE MY SYSTEM.**
Tracks: You are my system / Now I am electric.
■ 12". . . . . . . . . . . . . . . . . . . POSPX 58
■ 7" . . . . . . . . . . . . . . . . . . . .POSP 58
Polydor / Apr '83.

## Szabo, Gabor

**BELSTA RIVER.**
Tracks: Not Advised.
■ LP . . . . . . . . . . . . . . . . . . . FLC 503
Four Leaf Clover / '88.

**HIGH CONTRAST (Szabo, Gabor & Bobby Womack).**
Tracks: Breezin' / Amazon / Fingers / Azure blue / Just a little communication / If you don't want my love, give it back / I remember when.
■ LP . . . . . . . . . . . . . . . . . . . AFF 19
MC. . . . . . . . . . . . . . . . . . . . TCAFF 19
Affinity / Sep '88 / Charly / Cadillac / Swift / Jazz Music.

**SMALL WORLD.**
Tracks: Not Advised.
■ LP . . . . . . . . . . . . . . . . . . . FLC 600
Four Leaf Clover / '88.

**SORCERER, THE.**
Tracks: Not Advised.
CD . . . . . . . . . . . . . . . . . . . MCAD 3311
Impulse Jazz / Apr '90 / New Note.

# T

## T-Connection

**AT MIDNIGHT.**
**Tracks:** At midnight (mixes) / Playin' games (7" only).
■ 7" . . . . . . . . . . . . . . . . . . . . . . TKR 7517
TK / Feb '79.
12" . . . . . . . . . . . . . . . . . . . . . . WIZZ 016
Wizz / Nov '94 / Vital Distribution.

**DO WHAT YOU WANNA DO.**
**Tracks:** Do what you wanna do / Got to see my baby.
■ 7" . . . . . . . . . . . . . . . . . . . . . . XC 9109
TK / Jun '77.

**DO WHAT YOU WANNA DO (OLD GOLD).**
**Tracks:** Do what you wanna do / Haven't you stopped dancing yet (Only on 12" single) / At midnight (Only on CD single).
■ CD Single . . . . . . . . . . . . . . . . . OG 6522
Old Gold / Jul '90.
12" . . . . . . . . . . . . . . . . . . . . . . OG 4221
Old Gold / '92 / Pickwick.

**ECSTACY.**
**Tracks:** Ecstacy / Danger zone.
■ 7" . . . . . . . . . . . . . . . . . . . . . TKR 771
TK / Jan '80.

**EVERYTHING IS COOL.**
**Tracks:** Everything is cool / Paradise / We've got a good thing.
■ 12" . . . . . . . . . . . . . . . . . . . 12CL 16187
■ 7" . . . . . . . . . . . . . . . . . . . . CL 16187
Capitol / Mar '81.

**FUNKANNECTION.**
**Tracks:** Funkannection / Coming back for more / Funky lady / Don't stop the music / Saturday night / At midnight / Midnight train / Love supreme.
■ LP . . . . . . . . . . . . . . . . . . . TKR 82546
TK / Mar '79.

**LET YOURSELF GO.**
**Tracks:** Let yourself go / Groove to get down.
■ 7" . . . . . . . . . . . . . . . . . . . . TKR 6024
TK / Jun '78.

**LOVE ODYSSEY.**
**Tracks:** Love odyssey / Might as well dance.
■ 12" . . . . . . . . . . . . . . . . . . . 12CL 287
■ 7" . . . . . . . . . . . . . . . . . . . . CL 287
Capitol / Mar '83.

**MAGIC.**
**Tracks:** Do what you wanna do / Disco magic / Go back home / Got to see my lady / Crazy mixed up world / Mother's love / Monday morning / Peace one.
■ LP . . . . . . . . . . . . . . . . . . . . XL 14054
TK / Jul '77.
■ LP . . . . . . . . . . . . . . . . . . . TKR 82508
TK / Apr '78.

**ON FIRE.**
**Tracks:** On fire / Cush.
■ 7" . . . . . . . . . . . . . . . . . . . . TKR 6006
TK / Jan '78.

**ON FIRE.**
**Tracks:** Your love is rated X / Stormy / Here I go / Did we make love to you / I panicked / Love is better in the a.m. / It ain't what you do / Not just another booty song / I'm just a shoulder to cry on / Stop giving people hard luck stories.
■ LP . . . . . . . . . . . . . . . . . . . TKR 82502
TK / Feb '78.

**PURE AND NATURAL.**
**Tracks:** Girl watching / Party night / Little more love / Slippin' away / Might as well dance / Rushing through the crowd / Best of my love / Groombay line.
■ LP . . . . . . . . . . . . . . . . . . . EST 12191
Capitol / May '82.

**SATURDAY NIGHT.**
**Tracks:** Saturday night.
■ 7" . . . . . . . . . . . . . . . . . . . . TKR 7536
TK / May '79.

## T-Life

**SOMETHING THAT YOU DO TO ME.**
**Tracks:** Something that you do to me / Lonely.
■ 12" . . . . . . . . . . . . . . . . . . ARIST 12431
Arista / Sep '81.
■ 7" . . . . . . . . . . . . . . . . . . . . ARIST 431
Arista / Sep '81.

## T.F.O.

**MY SUMMER LOVE.**
**Tracks:** My summer love / My summer love (version).
■ 12" . . . . . . . . . . . . . . . . . . . 12PO 37
Gemc / Dec '89.

## Ta Mara & The Seen

**AFFECTION.**
**Tracks:** Affection / Everybody dance / Summertime love (Track on 12" version only).
■ 12" . . . . . . . . . . . . . . . . . . . AMY 301
■ 7" . . . . . . . . . . . . . . . . . . . . AM 301
A&M / Feb '86.

## Tafuri

**WHAT AM I GONNA DO ABOUT YOUR LOVE.**
**Tracks:** What am I gonna do about your love.
■ 12" . . . . . . . . . . . . . . . . . . . SBUK R20T
■ 7" . . . . . . . . . . . . . . . . . . . . SBUK R20
■ CD Single . . . . . . . . . . . . . . SBUKSCD 020
Sleeping Bag / Apr '90.

**YOU KNOW HOW TO LOVE ME.**
**Tracks:** You know how to love me.
■ 12" . . . . . . . . . . . . . . . . . . . . FX 172
■ 7" . . . . . . . . . . . . . . . . . . . . F 172
■ CD Single . . . . . . . . . . . . . . . . FCD 172
■ MC Single . . . . . . . . . . . . . . . . FCS 172
FFRR / Oct '91.

## Take 6

Christian jazz acapella? It just can't work. Nobody will buy it. In fact, nobody's likely to get the chance, 'cause no self-respecting A&R will sign it. How Take 6 must have chortled as they stepped forward to collect their Grammies. All five of them. Nobody expected that an unheard of gospel sextet from a small Huntsville, Alabama college might put the American R&B charts in its pocket, but from the release of the group's debut album in '88, so it has proved. Boasting influences as widely spaced as Miles Davis, Stevie Wonder and The Persuasions, Take 6 have in three albums taken the art of acapella singing to new heights. Some of the effects on their second album, *So Much To Say*, have to be heard to be believed. Their latest album, however, *Join The Band*, for the first time incorporates instruments and has had the effect of swapping their uniqueness for perceived commercial possibilities. A bad move?

**HE IS CHRISTMAS.**
**Tracks:** Silent night / Oh! He is Christmas / Hark! the herald angels sing / Away in a manger / Amen / Little drummer boy / 'Twas da nite / Sweet little Jesus boy / God rest ye merry gentlemen / O come all ye faithful.
■ CD . . . . . . . . . . . . . . . . . . 7599266652
■ MC . . . . . . . . . . . . . . . . . . 7599266654
WEA / Nov '91.

**JOIN THE BAND.**
**Tracks:** Not Advised.
CD . . . . . . . . . . . . . . . . . . 936245497-2
MC . . . . . . . . . . . . . . . . . . 936245497-4
Warner Bros. / Jun '94 / WEA.

**SO MUCH 2 SAY.**
**Tracks:** So much 2 say / I L-O-V-E U / Something within me / Time after time (the savior is waiting) / Come unto me / I'm on my way / I believe / Sunday's on the way / Where do the children play.
CD . . . . . . . . . . . . . . . . . . 7599258922

■ LP . . . . . . . . . . . . . . . . . . 7599258921
MC . . . . . . . . . . . . . . . . . . 7599258924
Reprise / Nov '90 / WEA.

**TAKE 6.**
**Tracks:** Gold mine / If we ever / Mary / Get away Jordan / Milky-white way / Spread love / Quiet place / David and Goliath / He never sleeps / Let the words.
CD . . . . . . . . . . . . . . . . . . . 925670 2
■ LP . . . . . . . . . . . . . . . . . . K 925670 1
■ MC . . . . . . . . . . . . . . . . . . K 925670 4
WEA / Feb '88 / WEA.

## Tamangoes

**I REALLY LOVE YOU.**
**Tracks:** I really love you.
■ 7" . . . . . . . . . . . . . . . . . . . . GRP 122
Grapevine (Northern Soul) / Jun '79.

## Tams

**18 GREATEST HITS.**
**Tracks:** Not Advised.
CD . . . . . . . . . . . . . . . . . . . . 2636052
MC . . . . . . . . . . . . . . . . . . . . 2636054
Black Tulip / Oct '89.

**ATLANTA SOUL CONNECTION.**
**Tracks:** Hey girl don't bother me / It's alright / You lied to your daddy / What kind of fool / Untie me / What do you do / LAugh it off / Don't you just know it / Concrete jungle / Letter / Shelter / There's a great big change in me / Trouble maker / Standing in / Anna / It's better to have loved a little / Be young, be foolish, be happy.
■ LP . . . . . . . . . . . . . . . . . . . CRB 1064
Charly R&B / Nov '83.

**BE YOUNG, BE FOOLISH, BE HAPPY.**
**Tracks:** Be young, be foolish, be happy.
■ 7" . . . . . . . . . . . . . . . . . . . . SS 2123
Stateside / Feb '70.

**BE YOUNG, BE FOOLISH, BE HAPPY.**
**Tracks:** Be young, be foolish, be happy / Greatest love / That same old song / Sunshine, rainbow, blue sky, brown-eyed girl / Thank you for my baby / Whose little girl are you / All my hard times / Concrete jungle / Letter / Shelter / There's a great big change in me / Trouble maker / Makin' music / Down in the Boondocks.
■ LP . . . . . . . . . . . . . . . . . . SSL 10304
Stateside / Jun '70.

**BEACH MUSIC FROM..THE TAMS.**
**Tracks:** There ain't nothin' like shaggin' / Thank you John / Making true love / Showtime / Get a job / My baby sure can shag.
■ LP . . . . . . . . . . . . . . . . . . CLTLB 6500
Compleat (USA) / Jul '84.

**BEST OF THE TAMS.**
**Tracks:** I've been hurt / Go away little girl / Take away / Be young, be foolish, be happy / It's all right / Letter / Hey girl don't bother me / Laugh it off / Greatest love / You lied to your Daddy / Shelter / All my hard times / Weep little girl / What kind of fool.
■ LP . . . . . . . . . . . . . . . . . . SPB 1044
Probe / Dec '71.

**BEST OF THE TAMS, THE.**
**Tracks:** Not Advised.
CD . . . . . . . . . . . . . . . . . . CDSGP 0110
Prestige / Sep '94 / Total / BMG.

**HEY GIRL DON'T BOTHER ME.**
**Tracks:** Hey girl don't bother me / Our love is getting stronger.
■ 7" . . . . . . . . . . . . . . . . . . . . PRO 532
Probe / Jun '71.
■ 7" . . . . . . . . . . . . . . . . . . . . CC 17
Casino Classics / Apr '86.

**HEY GIRL DON'T BOTHER ME (OLD GOLD).**
**Tracks:** Hey girl don't bother me.
■ 7" . . . . . . . . . . . . . . . . . . . . OG 9219
Old Gold / Jul '82.

## LITTLE MORE SOUL.
**Tracks:** Laugh it off / Untie me / Holding on / Get away / Mary Mary / Unlove you / What do you do / I've been hurt (and 8 others).
■ **LP** . . . . . . . . . . . . . . . . . . . .SSL 10258
Stateside / Nov '68.

## MY BABY SURE CAN SHAG.
**Tracks:** My baby sure can shag / Thank you John.
■ **12"** . . . . . . . . . . . . . . . . . . . . VST 1037
■ **7"** . . . . . . . . . . . . . . . . . . . . . VS 1037
Virgin / Dec '87.

## THERE AIN'T NOTHING LIKE SHAGGIN'.
**Tracks:** There ain't nothing like shaggin' / Hey girl, don't bother me / Making true love / Thank you John / Get a job / Be young, be foolish, be happy / Showtime / Weep little girl / What kind of fool (do you think I am) / My baby sure can shag.
■ **LP** . . . . . . . . . . . . . . . . . . . . .V 2499
■ **MC** . . . . . . . . . . . . . . . . . . . TCV 2499
Virgin / Dec '87.
■ **CD** . . . . . . . . . . . . . . . . . . CDV 2499
■ **LP** . . . . . . . . . . . . . . . . . . .OVED 303
■ **MC** . . . . . . . . . . . . . . . . OVEDC 303
Virgin / Apr '90.

## THERE AIN'T NOTHING LIKE SHAGGIN'.
**Tracks:** There ain't nothing like shaggin' / Get a job.
■ **12"** . . . . . . . . . . . . . . . . . . . VST 1029
■ **7"** . . . . . . . . . . . . . . . . . . . . VS 1029
Virgin / Nov '87.

## Tapestry

## CARNABY STREET.
**Tracks:** Carnaby Street / Taming of the shrew.
■ **7"** . . . . . . . . . . . . . . . . . . . HLZ 10138
London-American / Jun '67.

## Tashan

Tashan Rashad grew up in the hip hop era but loved '60s/'70s soul, concisely explaining why his solo albums have largely been an intriguing blend of the two genres. New Yorker Tashan made his first professional appearance as a songwriter for rap group Whodini in '83, aged 20, when his tune *Yours For A Night* made their Jive album. Two years later he was signed by Russell Simmons to Def Jam, along with Chuck Stanley, Juice Jones and Alyson Williams, providing the soul alternative to the company's very successful hip hop stars. Two albums, *Chasin' A Dream* and *On The Horizon* were released, neither selling well, though they did have the effect of making him something of a cult hero in Britain. A third album, *For The Sake Of Love* was recorded for Columbia Records, mostly in London under the guidance of Martyn Ware, but again, achieved only further underground notoriety and the withdrawl of his contract. Let's hope there's a fourth.

## BLACK MAN.
**Tracks:** Black man (radio version) / On the horizon (Not on cassingle.) / Black man (club mix) / Black man (alternative club mix) / Chasing a dream (long version) (Not on cassingle.) / Black man (full mix) / Black man (dub mix).
■ **12"** . . . . . . . . . . . . . 655 640 6
■ **7"** . . . . . . . . . . . . . . 655 640 7
■ **CD Single** . . . . . . . . . . . . . . . 655 640 2
■ **MC Single.** . . . . . . . . . . . . . . 655 640 4
O.B.R. / Feb '90.
■ **12"** . . . . . . . . . . . . . 655 640 8
O.B.R. / Mar '90.

## CHASIN' A DREAM.
**Tracks:** Chasin' a dream.
■ **12"** . . . . . . . . . . . . . . . . 6503590
■ **7"** . . . . . . . . . . . . . . . . . 6503597
■ **12"** . . . . . . . . . . . . . . . . 6503596
Def Jam / Jul '87.

## CHASING A DREAM.
**Tracks:** Read the dream / Strung out on you / If words can express / Thank you father / Love is / I don't ever / So much in love / Read my mind / Ooh wee baby / Chasing a dream / Got the right attitude.
■ **LP** . . . . . . . . . . . . . . . . . 4501581
■ **MC** . . . . . . . . . . . . . . . . 4501584
Def Jam / Dec '86.
■ **CD** . . . . . . . . . . . . . . . . 4501582
Def Jam / Oct '87.

## FOR THE SAKE OF LOVE.
**Tracks:** Tempted / Been a long time / Ecstatic / For the sake of love / Single and lonely / Still in love / Love is forever / Romantically inspired / Control of me / Insane / All I ever do / Love of my life.

---

## CD
**CD** . . . . . . . . . . . . . . . .472411-2
**LP** . . . . . . . . . . . . . . . . .472411-1
**MC.** . . . . . . . . . . . . . . . .472411-4
Columbia / Mar '94 / Sony.

## LOVE IS FOREVER.
**Tracks:** Love is forever (mixes).
■ **12"** . . . . . . . . . . . . . . . . .660045 6
Columbia / Feb '94.

## ON THE HORIZON.
**Tracks:** Black man / Howya livin' / Keep movin' on / Save the family / Heaven / Tears of joy / Think about you all the time / Do you wanna know / Lovin' great feelin' / Changes / On the horizon / This one's for James.
**MC.** . . . . . . . . . . . . . . . . 465 521 4
■ **CD** . . . . . . . . . . . . . . . . 465 521 2
■ **LP** . . . . . . . . . . . . . . . . 465 521 1
ORB / Nov '89 / Sony.

## READ MY MIND.
**Tracks:** Read my mind / Got the right attitude.
■ **12"** . . . . . . . . . . . . . . . . TASH T1
■ **7"** . . . . . . . . . . . . . . . TASH 1
Def Jam / Oct '87.

## SAVE THE FAMILY.
**Tracks:** Save the family.
■ **12"** . . . . . . . . . . . . . . . . 4473386
ORB / Jun '90.

## THANK YOU FATHER.
**Tracks:** Thank you father / Got the right attitude / Love is".
■ **12"** . . . . . . . . . . . . . . . . 6507796
■ **7"** . . . . . . . . . . . . . . . . 6507797
Def Jam / Apr '87.

## Taste Of Honey

## BOOGIE OOGIE OOGIE.
**Tracks:** Boogie oogie oogie / We've got the groove.
■ **7"** . . . . . . . . . . . . . . . CL 15988
Capitol / Jul '78.
■ **7"** . . . . . . . . . . . . . . . . .CL 357
Capitol / Apr '85.
■ **12"** . . . . . . . . . . . . . . 12CL 357
Capitol / May '85.

## BOOGIE OOGIE OOGIE (OLD GOLD).
**Tracks:** Boogie oogie oogie / Heaven must be missing an angel.
■ **7"** . . . . . . . . . . . . . . . .OG 9713
Old Gold / Apr '87.

## DO IT GOOD.
**Tracks:** Do it good / I love you.
■ **7"** . . . . . . . . . . . . . . . CL 16085
Capitol / '79.

## GOLDEN SHOWER.
**Tracks:** Golden shower.
■ **12"** . . . . . . . . . . . . . . . SUB 45
■ **7"** . . . . . . . . . . . . .SUB 045-7
Subway / Dec '88.

## I'LL TRY SOMETHING NEW.
**Tracks:** I'll try something new / Goodbye baby.
■ **7"** . . . . . . . . . . . . . . . .CL 249
Capitol / Jun '82.

## LADIES OF THE EIGHTIES.
**Tracks:** Sayonara / We've got the groove / I'll try something new / Lies / Diamond real / Never go wrong / Midnight snack / Leavin' tomorrow.
■ **LP** . . . . . . . . . . . . . . . .EST 12173
Capitol / Jul '82.

## RESCUE ME.
**Tracks:** Rescue me / Say that you'll stay / Boogie oogie oogie.
■ **12"** . . . . . . . . . . . . . . 12CL 16156
■ **7"** . . . . . . . . . . . . . . . CL 16156
Capitol / Aug '80.

## SUKIYAKI.
**Tracks:** Sukiyaki / Don't you lead on me.
■ **7"** . . . . . . . . . . . . . . . CL 16194
Capitol / Apr '81.

## TWICE AS SWEET.
**Tracks:** Ain't nothin' but a party / Rescue me / Goodbye baby / I'm talkin' 'bout you / Superstar superman / She's a dancer / Sukiyaki / Don't you lead me on / Say that you'll stay.
■ **LP** . . . . . . . . . . . . . . . .EST 12089
Capitol / Sep '80.

---

## Tate, Howard

## BABY I LOVE YOU.
**Tracks:** Baby I love you / How blue can you get.
■ **7"** . . . . . . . . . . . . . . . .VS 555
Verve / Jun '67.

## GET IT WHILE YOU CAN.
**Tracks:** Ain't nobody home / Part time love / Glad I knew better / How blue can you get / Get it while you can / baby I love you / I learnd it all the hard way / Everyday I have the blues / How come my bull dog don't bark / Look at granny run run.
■ **LP** . . . . . . . . . . . . . . . POLD 5096
Verve / Mar '83.

## GET IT WHILE YOU CAN.
**Tracks:** Get it while you can / Glad I knew better.
■ **7"** . . . . . . . . . . . . . . . .VS 552
Verve / May '67.

## LOOK AT GRANNY RUN RUN.
**Tracks:** Look at granny run run / I learned it all the hard way.
■ **7"** . . . . . . . . . . . . . . . POSP 584
Verve / Apr '83.

## Tate, Tommy

## BIG BLUE DIAMONDS.
**Tracks:** Big blue diamonds / Lover's reward.
■ **7"** . . . . . . . . . . . . . . . .DB 8047
Columbia / Oct '66.

## LOVE ME NOW.
**Tracks:** Good medicine / Slow rain (fast train) / forget to be your lover / Midnight holiday / Tear this house down / Love me now / When a fool takes his turn / Never let you see me cry / Big blue sky.
■ **CD** . . . . . . . . . . . . . . CDCHARLY 255
Charly / Dec '90.

## TOMMY TATE.
**Tracks:** For the dollar bill / On the real side / Listen to the children / Castles in the sky / This train / I just don't know / Let me entertain you / We don't.
■ **LP** . . . . . . . . . . . . . . . .MS 3
Move / Nov '85.
■ **LP** . . . . . . . . . . . . . . . TRLP 107
Timeless (Soul) / Jul '86.
■ **CD** . . . . . . . . . . . . . . TLCD 363
■ **LP** . . . . . . . . . . . . . . TRPL 107
Timeless (Soul) / Jan '90.

## Tavares

## BAD TIMES.
**Tracks:** Bad times / Got to have your love.
■ **7"** . . . . . . . . . . . . . . . CL 1611?
Capitol / Jan '80.

## BEST OF TAVARES.
**Tracks:** Heaven must be missing an angel / She's gone / Mighty power of love / Check it out / One step with you / It only takes a minute / Love I never had My ship / Don't take away the music.
■ **LP** . . . . . . . . . . . . . . . .EST 1170
Capitol / Apr '78.
■ **LP** . . . . . . . . . . . . . . . FA 302
Fame / May '82.
■ **MC** . . . . . . . . . . . . . . TCFA 302
Capitol (Specials) / Dec '88.
**MC.** . . . . . . . . . . . . . . . 4XL 940
Capitol (Specials) / Dec '88.

## CAPITOL GOLD: THE BEST OF TAVARES.
**Tracks:** What can I do / Check it out / That's the sound that lonely makes / Remember what I told you to forget / Too late / She's gone / It only takes minute / Love I never had / Heaven must be missing an angel / Don't take away the music / Whodunit (Goodbye my love) Pleasant dreams / More than woman / Never had love like this before / Bad times Loveline.
**CD** . . . . . . . . . . . . . . . C2 8938
Capitol / Aug '93 / EMI.

## CHECK IT OUT.
**Tracks:** If that's the way you want it / Strangers dark corners / That's the sound that lonely makes Check it out / Wish you were with me Mary / I never say never again / Little girl / Let's make the best of what we've got / I'm in love / Mama's little girl.
■ **LP** . . . . . . . . . . . . . . . .EST 1125
Capitol / Jan '77.

## DEEPER IN LOVE.
**Tracks:** Deeper in love / I really miss you baby.
■ **12"** . . . . . . . . . . . . . . . . RCAT 353
■ **7"** . . . . . . . . . . . . . . . .RCA 353
RCA / Sep '83.

## ON'T TAKE AWAY THE MUSIC.
acks: Don't take away the music.
7" . . . . . . . . . . . . . . . . . . . . . . . CL 15876
pitol / Oct '76.

## HOST OF LOVE, THE.
acks: Ghost of love / Bein' with you.
7" . . . . . . . . . . . . . . . . . . . . . . . CL 15968
pitol / Mar '78.

## EART AND SOUL OF TAVARES.
acks: Heaven must be missing an angel / Bein'
th you / Love uprising / She's gone / Never had
ve like this before / That's the sound that lonely
akes.
CD . . . . . . . . . . . . . . . . . . . . . KNCD 12054
MC . . . . . . . . . . . . . . . . . . . . . KNMC 12054
ight / May '90.

## EAVEN MUST BE MISSING AN ANGEL.
acks: Heaven must be missing an angel / Don't
ke away the music / Whodunnit (12" only).
7" . . . . . . . . . . . . . . . . . . . . . . . CL 15876
pitol / Jun '76.
7" . . . . . . . . . . . . . . . . . . . . . . . TAV 1
12" . . . . . . . . . . . . . . . . . . . . . . . 12TAV 1
pitol / Feb '86.

## TS OF TAVARES.
acks: Not Advised.
) . . . . . . . . . . . . . . . . . . . . . KLMCD 024
ratch / Apr '94 / Scratch Records / BMG / Grape-
he Distribution.

## OON'T WANT YOU ANY MORE.
acks: I don't want you any more / Never had a love
e this before.
7" . . . . . . . . . . . . . . . . . . . . . . . CL 16146
pitol / May '80.

## WANNA SEE YOU SOON.
acks: I wanna see you soon / Keep in touch.
7" . . . . . . . . . . . . . . . . . . . . . . . CL 15945
pitol / Oct '77.

## ONLY TAKES A MINUTE.
acks: It only takes a minute / I hope she chooses
e.
7" . . . . . . . . . . . . . . . . . . . . . . . CL 15893
pitol / Aug '75.

## ONLY TAKES A MINUTE.
acks: It only takes a minute / More than a woman /
he minute (instrumental) (Available on 12 Version
ily).
7" . . . . . . . . . . . . . . . . . . . . . . . TAV 2
12" . . . . . . . . . . . . . . . . . . . . . . . 12TAV 2
pitol / Apr '86.

## VE HITS.
acks: Not Advised.
a . . . . . . . . . . . . . . . . . . . . . . CDCD 1149
arly / Feb '94 / Charly.

## OVE UPRISING.
acks: Only one I need to love / Break down for love
Love uprising / Loneliness / Knock the wall down /
et love / Don't wanna say goodnight / Do you
lieve in love / She can wait forever / In this lovely
orld / Lifetime of love.
LP . . . . . . . . . . . . . . . . . . . . . EST 12117
pitol / Mar '81.

## ADAME BUTTERFLY.
acks: Straight from your heart / Games, games /
adame Butterfly / Let me heal the bruises / Never
ad a love like this before / One telephone call away
My love calls / Positive forces / I'm back for more.
LP . . . . . . . . . . . . . . . . . . . . EA ST 11874
pitol / Mar '79.

## IGHTY POWER OF LOVE.
acks: Mighty power of love / I hope she chooses
e / My ship / Strangers in dark corners.
7" . . . . . . . . . . . . . . . . . . . . . . . CL 15905
pitol / Jan '77.

## ORE THAN A WOMAN.
acks: More than a woman / We're both ready for
ve.
7" . . . . . . . . . . . . . . . . . . . . . . . CL 15977
pitol / May '78.

## EVER HAD A LOVE LIKE THIS
EFORE.
acks: Never had a love like this before / Turn out
e nightlight.
7" . . . . . . . . . . . . . . . . . . . . . . . CL 218
pitol / Mar '79.
12" . . . . . . . . . . . . . . . . . . . . . . . 12CL 16032
pitol / Mar '79.

## NEW DIRECTIONS.
Tracks: Penny for your thoughts / I hope you'll be
very unhappy without me / Got to find my way back
to you / Mystery lady / Maybe we'll fall in love again
/ Abracadabra love you too / Skin you're in / Wanna
be close to you.
LP . . . . . . . . . . . . . . . . . . . . RCALP 3103
MC . . . . . . . . . . . . . . . . . . . . RCAK 3103
RCA / Nov '82 / BMG.

## ONE STEP AWAY.
Tracks: One step away / Out of the picture.
■ 7" . . . . . . . . . . . . . . . . . . . . . . . CL 15930
Capitol / Jul '77.

## REMEMBER WHAT I TOLD YOU TO FORGET.
Tracks: Remember what I told you to forget / My
ship.
■ 7" . . . . . . . . . . . . . . . . . . . . . . . CL 15809
Capitol / Feb '75.

## SKY HIGH.
Tracks: Not Advised.
■ LP . . . . . . . . . . . . . . . . . . . . . EST 11533
Capitol / Aug '76.

## SLOW TRAIN TO PARADISE.
Tracks: Slow train to paradise / Timber.
■ 7" . . . . . . . . . . . . . . . . . . . . . . . CL 15996
Capitol / Aug '78.

## STRAIGHT FROM YOUR HEART.
Tracks: Straight from your heart / Let me heal the
bruises.
■ 7" . . . . . . . . . . . . . . . . . . . . . . . CL 16081
Capitol / May '79.

## TAVARES LIVE IN CONCERT.
Tracks: Not Advised.
CD . . . . . . . . . . . . . . . . . . . . . JHD 104
MC . . . . . . . . . . . . . . . . . . . . MCJHD 104
Tring / Aug '93 / Prism Leisure PLC / Midland
Records.

## VERY BEST OF TAVARES, THE.
Tracks: Heaven must be missing an angel,(remixed
12" v angel mix) / She's gone / Mighty power of love
/ Check it out / One step away / I wanna see you
soon / More than a woman (remixed version) /
Whodunnit (remixed 12" version) / Bein' with you / It
only takes a minute / Love I never had / My ship /
Don't take away the music (remixed 12" version.
■ LP . . . . . . . . . . . . . . . . . . . . . EMS 1165
■ MC . . . . . . . . . . . . . . . . . . . . TCEMS 1165
Capitol / Mar '86.

## WHODUNNIT.
Tracks: Whodunnit / Fool of the year.
■ 7" . . . . . . . . . . . . . . . . . . . . . . . CL 15914
Capitol / Apr '77.

## WORDS & MUSIC.
Tracks: Ten to one / Deeper in love / Caught short /
My all in all / Words and music / Baby I want you
back / I really miss you baby / Don't play so hard to
get / Us and love.
■ LP . . . . . . . . . . . . . . . . . . . . . PL 84700
RCA / Jan '84.

## Taylor, Bobby

## BOBBY TAYLOR & THE VANCOUVERS (Taylor, Bobby & The Vancouvers).
Tracks: Does your man know about me / I am your
man / So this is love / I heard it through the grapevine / Malinda / Fading away / You gave me something / It's growing / If you love her / One girl / Try a
little tenderness / Day by day or never.
■ LP . . . . . . . . . . . . . . . . . . . . . STML 11093
Tamla Motown / Mar '69.

## DOES YOUR MAMA KNOW ABOUT ME (Taylor, Bobby & The Vancouvers).
Tracks: Does your mama know about me.
■ 7" . . . . . . . . . . . . . . . . . . . . . . . TMG 654
Tamla Motown / Mar '68.

## FIND MY WAY BACK (Taylor, Bobby & The Vancouvers).
Tracks: Not Advised.
■ LP . . . . . . . . . . . . . . . . . . . . MOTCLP 46
■ CD . . . . . . . . . . . . . . . . . . CDMOTCLP 46
Motor City / Dec '90.

## TAYLOR MADE SOUL.
Tracks: Out in the country / Oh, I've been bless'd /
How long has that evening train been gone / My girl
has gone / Eleanor Rigby / I just can't carry on / I
need to belong / Don't be afraid / One too many
heartaches / It should have been me loving you /
Little Miss Sweetness.

## LP . . . . . . . . . . . . . . . . . . . . . STML 11125
Tamla Motown / Apr '70.

## Taylor, Brenda

## YOU CAN'T HAVE YOUR CAKE AND EAT IT TOO.
Tracks: You can't have your cake and eat it too.
■ 12" . . . . . . . . . . . . . . . . . . . . . EXCL 526
■ 7" . . . . . . . . . . . . . . . . . . . . . . . EXC 526
Excaliber / Nov '82.

## Taylor, Debbie

## JUST DON'T PAY (OLD GOLD) (Taylor, Debbie & Jeff Perry).
Tracks: Just don't pay / Love don't come no stranger.
■ 12" . . . . . . . . . . . . . . . . . . . . . OG 4509
Old Gold / Apr '89.

## Taylor, Felice

## I FEEL LOVE COMIN' ON.
Tracks: I feel love comin' on.
■ 7" . . . . . . . . . . . . . . . . . . . . . . . PT 155
President / May '80.

## I'M UNDER THE INFLUENCE OF LOVE.
Tracks: I'm under the influence of love / Love theme.
■ 7" . . . . . . . . . . . . . . . . . . . . . . . PT 133
President / Apr '67.

## IT MAY BE WINTER OUTSIDE.
Tracks: It may be winter outside / Winter again.
■ 7" . . . . . . . . . . . . . . . . . . . . . . . PT 120
President / Jan '67.

## Taylor, Gary

## A.P.B.
Tracks: A.P.B.
■ 12" . . . . . . . . . . . . . . . . . . . . EXPAND 38
■ CD Single . . . . . . . . . . . . . . . . CDSEXP 38
Passion/Debut/Scratch Music / Jun '93.

## COMPASSION.
Tracks: Compassion / Tease me / Lonely heart /
Easier said than done / Love you to the limit / Don't
ask my neighbour / I won't stop / I'll always be /
Follow (CD & Cassette only).
■ LP . . . . . . . . . . . . . . . . . . . . . DIX 77
■ MC . . . . . . . . . . . . . . . . . . . . CDIX 77
■ CD . . . . . . . . . . . . . . . . . . . . DIXCD 77
10 / May '88.

## COMPASSION.
Tracks: Compassion (7" only) / Compassion (club
remix) (12" only) / Follow / Compassion (acapella
mix) (12" only) / Compassion (dub instrumental) (12"
only).
■ 12" . . . . . . . . . . . . . . . . . . . . . TENX 232
■ 7" . . . . . . . . . . . . . . . . . . . . . . . TEN 232
10 / May '88.

## RESTLESS.
Tracks: Restless.
12" . . . . . . . . . . . . . . . . . . . . . EXPAND 52
Expansion / Nov '94 / Pinnacle / Sony / 3MV.

## SQUARE ONE.
Tracks: Hold me accountable / Irresistible love /
A.P.B. / Pieces / Square one / Read between the
lines / Never too blue / I need you now / Eye to eye /
One and only.
CD . . . . . . . . . . . . . . . . . . . . . EXCD 6
LP . . . . . . . . . . . . . . . . . . . . . EXLP 6
MC . . . . . . . . . . . . . . . . . . . . . EXMC 6
Expansion / Mar '93 / Pinnacle / Sony / 3MV.

## TAKE CONTROL.
Tracks: Take control / Whatever / I need / In and out
of love / Wishful thinking / Don't be so distant / I live
4 U / Sign my life away / Time after time.
CD . . . . . . . . . . . . . . . . . . . . EXCDP 5
Expansion / Jun '90 / Pinnacle / Sony / 3MV.
LP . . . . . . . . . . . . . . . . . . . . . EXLP 05
Expansion / Nov '90.

## Taylor, J.T.

## ALL I WANT IS FOREVER (Taylor, JT & Regina Belle).
Tracks: All I want is forever / Innocent / Lovers
intuition.
■ 12" . . . . . . . . . . . . . . . . . . . . . 6558726
■ 7" . . . . . . . . . . . . . . . . . . . . . . . 6558727
■ CD Single . . . . . . . . . . . . . . . . . 6558722
■ MC Single. . . . . . . . . . . . . . . . . 6558724
Epic / Apr '90.

## FEEL THE NEED.
Tracks: Not Advised.
CD . . . . . . . . . . . . . . . . . . . . . MCAD 10306
■ LP . . . . . . . . . . . . . . . . . . . . MCA 10306
MC. . . . . . . . . . . . . . . . . . . . . MCAC 10306
MCA / Aug '91 / BMG.

## FEEL THE NEED.
Tracks: Feel the need.
■ 12" . . . . . . . . . . . . . . . . . . . . MCST 1592
■ 7" . . . . . . . . . . . . . . . . . . . . . MCS 1592
■ CD Single . . . . . . . . . . . . . . . MCSTD 1592
MCA / Nov '91.

## FOLLOW ME.
Tracks: Follow me.
■ 12" . . . . . . . . . . . . . . . . . . . . MCST 1617
■ 7" . . . . . . . . . . . . . . . . . . . . . MCS 1617
■ CD Single . . . . . . . . . . . . . . . MCSTD 1617
■ MC Single . . . . . . . . . . . . . . . MCSC 1617
MCA / Apr '92.

## LONG HOT SUMMER NIGHT.
Tracks: Long hot summer night.
■ 12" . . . . . . . . . . . . . . . . . . . . MCST 1567
■ 7" . . . . . . . . . . . . . . . . . . . . . MCS 1567
■ CD Single . . . . . . . . . . . . . . . MCSTD 1567
■ MC Single . . . . . . . . . . . . . . . MCSC 1567
MCA / Aug '91.

## Taylor, Johnnie

One might say that 56 year old coronary survivors ought to be thinking about putting their feet up, but Arkansas-born Johnnie Taylor, now resident in Dallas, just rolls on as ever, recording a new (and inevitably very good) album for Malaco Records each year and undertaking as much live work as he can fit in. He's not as bluesy as he once was, but then Taylor's real successes came as a soulman with Stax and later CBS. At Stax, Taylor scored hits with *Jody Got Your Girl And Gone, I Believe In You* and *Cheaper To Keep Her*. At CBS, he provided the label with their biggest selling single ever - *Disco Lady* in '76, which sold 2 million copies in the US alone. Most of the real good stuff is on Stax though, his *Taylored In Silk* and *Super Taylor* albums in the early '70s cruising into the "essential" category, while a double CD, *Chronicle*, gathers together most of his best sixties work. If you can find it, the very rare *A New Day*, from '80, should not be overlooked.

## 20 GREATEST HITS: JOHNNIE TAYLOR.
Tracks: Not Advised.
CD . . . . . . . . . . . . . . . . . . . . . FCD 60006
London / Apr '87 / PolyGram.

## AIN'T THAT LOVIN' YOU.
Tracks: Ain't that lovin' you / Outside love.
■ 7" . . . . . . . . . . . . . . . . . . . . . .601003
Stax / Mar '67.

## BEST OF JOHNNIE TAYLOR ON MALA-CO VOL.1.
Tracks: Not Advised.
CD . . . . . . . . . . . . . . . . . . . . . MALCD 7463
Malaco / Mar '93 / C.M. Distribution / Charly / Pinnacle.

## CHRONICLE.
Tracks: Who's making love / Take care of your homework / Testify / I could never be president / Love bones / Steal away / I am somebody / Jody's got your girl and gone / I don't wanna lose you / Hijackin' love / Standin' in for Jody / Doin' my own thing / Doing my own thing, part 1 / Stop doggin' me / I believe in you (You believe in me) / Cheaper to keep her / We're getting careless with our love / I've been born again / It's September / Try me tonight / Just keep on lovin' me.
■ LP . . . . . . . . . . . . . . . . . . . . STM 7001
Stax / Mar '78.
CD. . . . . . . . . . . . . . . . . . . . . CDSXE 084
Stax / Jul '93 / Pinnacle.

## CHRONICLE VOL. 2.
Tracks: Shackin' up / Stop doggin' me / Stop teasin' me / Don't you fool with your soul / I believe in you / Cheaper to keep her / We're getting careless with our love / I've been born again / It's September / Try me tonight / Just keep on lovin' me / Steal it.
■ LP . . . . . . . . . . . . . . . . . . . . STM 7002
Stax / May '78.

## CRAZY 'BOUT YOU.
Tracks: Not Advised.
■ LP . . . . . . . . . . . . . . . . . . . . MALP 7452
MC. . . . . . . . . . . . . . . . . . . . . MALC 7452
Malaco / '89 / C.M. Distribution / Charly / Pinnacle.

CD . . . . . . . . . . . . . . . . . . . . . MALCD 7452
Malaco / Apr '93 / C.M. Distribution / Charly / Pinnacle.

## DISCO LADY.
Tracks: Disco lady.
■ 7" . . . . . . . . . . . . . . . . . . . . . CBS 4044
CBS / Apr '76.

## EVER READY.
Tracks: Hey Mr. Melody / Ever ready / Keep on dancing / I gotta keep groovin' / You / Soul fillet / Bittersweet love / I love to make love / When it's raining / Give me my baby.
■ LP . . . . . . . . . . . . . . . . . . . . CBS 82776
CBS / Jun '78.

## GREATEST HITS.
Tracks: Steal away / Who can I turn to / I ain't particular / Mr Nobody is somebody now / I could never be President / Testify / Who's making love / Love bones / Hold on this time / I'm not the same person / Take care of your homework / Somebody's sleeping in my bed.
■ LP . . . . . . . . . . . . . . . . . . . . 2362015
Stax / Jul '71.

## HEY MISTER MELODY MAKER.
Tracks: Hey Mister Melody Maker / Give me my baby.
■ 7" . . . . . . . . . . . . . . . . . . . . . CBS 6516
CBS / Sep '78.

## IN CONTROL.
Tracks: Not Advised.
■ LP . . . . . . . . . . . . . . . . . . . . MAL 7446
MC. . . . . . . . . . . . . . . . . . . . . MALC 7446
Malaco / Mar '89 / C.M. Distribution / Charly / Pinnacle.
CD. . . . . . . . . . . . . . . . . . . . . MALCD 7446
Malaco / Mar '93 / C.M. Distribution / Charly / Pinnacle.

## IT'S SEPTEMBER.
Tracks: It's September.
■ 7" . . . . . . . . . . . . . . . . . . . . . STAX 2021
Stax / Jan '85.

## JODY GOT YOUR GIRL AND GONE.
Tracks: Jody got your girl and gone / Fool like me.
■ 7" . . . . . . . . . . . . . . . . . . . . . .2025 021
Stax / Apr '71.

## JOHNNIE TAYLOR PHILOSOPHY CONTI-NUES/ONE STEP BEYOND.
Tracks: (I wanna) Testify / Separation line / Love bones / Love is a hurtin' thing / I had a fight with love / I could never be president / It's amazing / Who can I turn to / Games people play / It's your thing / Time after time / Party life / Will you love me forever / I am somebody (Parts 1 & 2) / I don't wanna lose you (Parts 1 & 2) / Don't take my sunshine / Jody's got your girl and gone / Fool like me.
CD Set . . . . . . . . . . . . . . . . . . CDSXD 108
Stax / Jul '94 / Pinnacle.

## JUST AIN'T GOOD ENOUGH.
Tracks: Not Advised.
CD . . . . . . . . . . . . . . . . . . . . . BGCD 10001
LP . . . . . . . . . . . . . . . . . . . . . BG 10001
MC. . . . . . . . . . . . . . . . . . . . . BGCX 10001
Beverly Glen (USA) / Sep '90 / Jetstar / RTM / Pinnacle.

## KEEP ON DANCING.
Tracks: Keep on dancing / I love to make love when it's raining.
■ 7" . . . . . . . . . . . . . . . . . . . . . CBS 6304
CBS / May '78.

## LOOKING FOR..
Tracks: I got to love somebody's baby / Just the one I've been lookin' for / Watermelon man / Where can a man go from here / Toe hold / Outside love / Ain't that loving you / Blues in the night / I had a dream / Sixteen tons / Little bluebird.
■ LP . . . . . . . . . . . . . . . . . . . . 228 008
Atco / Jul '69.

## LOVE IS BETTER IN THE A.M.
Tracks: Love is better in the A.M. / Love is better in the A.M. (version).
■ 7" . . . . . . . . . . . . . . . . . . . . . CBS 5041
CBS / Mar '77.

## LOVERBOY.
Tracks: Don't make me late / Loverboy / Lately / You can't win / Something is going wrong / If I lose your love / Girl of my dreams / Nothing like a lady / Happy times / Universal lady.
■ LP . . . . . . . . . . . . . . . . . . . . MALP 012
Malaco / Feb '87.
MC. . . . . . . . . . . . . . . . . . . . . MALC 7440

Malaco / Mar '89 / C.M. Distribution / Charly / Pinnacle.

## PHILOSOPHY CONTINUES.
Tracks: Not Advised.
■ LP . . . . . . . . . . . . . . . . . . . . .SXATS 1024
Stax / Nov '69.

## RAW BLUES/LITTLE BLUEBIRD.
Tracks: Not Advised.
CD. . . . . . . . . . . . . . . . . . . . . CDSXD 051
Stax / Jun '92 / Pinnacle.

## ROOTS OF JOHNNIE TAYLOR.
Tracks: In love with you / Rome wasn't built in a day / Never, never / Getting married soon / Run but you can't hide / Whole lotta woman / Dance what you wanna / Oh how I love you / Baby we've got love / I need lots of love / Shine, shine, shine / Why, why, why.
■ LP . . . . . . . . . . . . . . . . . . . . SCB 2
Soul City / May '70.

## SOMEBODY'S GETTIN' IT.
Tracks: Disco lady / Somebody's gettin' it / Pick up the pieces / Running out of lines / Did he make love to you / Your love is rated X / I'm just a shoulder to cry on / Love is better in the a.m. / Just a happy song / Right now.
CD. . . . . . . . . . . . . . . . . . . . . CDCHARLY 160
Charly / Mar '89 / Charly.
■ LP . . . . . . . . . . . . . . . . . . . . CRB 1216
MC. . . . . . . . . . . . . . . . . . . . . TCCRB 1216
Charly R&B / Mar '89 / Charly.

## TESTIFY (I WANNA).
Tracks: Testify.
■ 7" . . . . . . . . . . . . . . . . . . . . . STAX 820
Stax / Oct '87.

## THIS IS YOUR NIGHT.
Tracks: Not Advised.
■ LP . . . . . . . . . . . . . . . . . . . . MAL 7421
Malaco / Dec '84.
MC. . . . . . . . . . . . . . . . . . . . . MALC 7421
Malaco / Mar '89 / C.M. Distribution / Charly / Pinnacle.

## WALL TO WALL.
Tracks: Not Advised.
■ LP . . . . . . . . . . . . . . . . . . . . MAL 7431
Malaco / Feb '86.
MC. . . . . . . . . . . . . . . . . . . . . MALC 7431
Malaco / Feb '86 / C.M. Distribution / Charly / Pinnacle.
■ LP . . . . . . . . . . . . . . . . . . . . MALP 003
Malaco / '88.

## WHO'S MAKING LOVE?.
Tracks: Who's making love / I'm not the same person / Hold on this time / Woman across the river / Can't trust your neighbour / Take care of your homework / I'm trying / Poor make believer / Payback hurts / Mr Nobody is somebody now / I'd rather drink muddy water.
■ LP . . . . . . . . . . . . . . . . . . . . .SXATS 1006
Stax / May '69.
■ LP . . . . . . . . . . . . . . . . . . . . 2363009
Stax / Aug '71.
■ LP . . . . . . . . . . . . . . . . . . . . SXE 004
Stax / Sep '87.

## WHO'S MAKING LOVE?.
Tracks: Who's making love / I'm trying.
■ 7" . . . . . . . . . . . . . . . . . . . . . STAX 1006
Stax / Mar '82.
■ 7" . . . . . . . . . . . . . . . . . . . . . STAX 80
Stax / Jun '87.

## WHO'S MAKING LOVE? (OLD GOLD).
Tracks: Who's making love / Private number.
■ 7" . . . . . . . . . . . . . . . . . . . . . OG 953
Old Gold / Sep '85.

## Taylor, Linda

## EVERY WAKING HOUR.
Tracks: Every waking hour (inst).
■ 12" . . . . . . . . . . . . . . . . . . . . MARE
■ 7" . . . . . . . . . . . . . . . . . . . . . MARES
Nightmare / Jan '87.

## LOVE IN THE SHADOWS.
Tracks: Love in the shadows / Move over.
12". . . . . . . . . . . . . . . . . . . . .ALMY 02
CD Single . . . . . . . . . . . . . . . . CDALMY 02
Almighty / Jan '93 / Total / BMG.

## MOVE OVER DARLING.
Tracks: Move over darling.
12". . . . . . . . . . . . . . . . . . . . .ALMY 01
Almighty / Jan '93 / Total / BMG.

**AYLOR MADE.**
racks: Not Advised.
■ LP . . . . . . . . . . . . . . . . . . . . . . .GPLP 31
roove PR / May '82.

**OU AND ME JUST STARTED.**
racks: You and me just started.
■ 12" . . . . . . . . . . . . . . . . . . . . . . . GP 3112
■ 7" . . . . . . . . . . . . . . . . . . . . . . . . GP 317
roove PR / Apr '82.

**OU'RE IN THE POCKET.**
racks: You're in the pocket / Steal your love.
■ 12" . . . . . . . . . . . . . . . . . . . . . . .GP 109T
■ 7" . . . . . . . . . . . . . . . . . . . . . . . GP 109
roove PR / Sep '81.

## Taylor, Little Johnny

**S LONG AS I DON'T SEE YOU.**
racks: As long as I don't see you.
■ 7" . . . . . . . . . . . . . . . . . . . . . . . .CTD 118
harly / Jul '80.

**VERYBODY KNOWS ABOUT MY GOOD HING.**
racks: Baby get hip to yourself / How are you fixed
r love / How can a broke man survive / Keep on
eeping on / Everybody knows about my good thing /
ere's something on your mind / You've got the
ve I need / It's my fault darling / Make love to me
aby / Sweet soul woman.
■ LP . . . . . . . . . . . . . . . . . . . . . 2916015
ojo / Aug '72.

**ALAXY YEARS, THE.**
racks: You'll need another favor / What you need is
ball / Part time love / Somewhere down the line /
nce I found a new love / My heart is filled with pain
First class love / If you love me (like you say) / You
n, I lose / Nightingale melody / I smell trouble /
rue love / For your precious love / I've never had a
oman like you before / Somebody's got to pay /
elp yourself / One more chance / Please come
ome for Christmas / All I want is you / Zig zag
ghtning / Things that I used to do / Big blue dia-
onds / I know you hear me calling / Driving wheel /
ometimey woman / Double or nothing.
■ O . . . . . . . . . . . . . . . . . . . .CDCHD 967
ce / Apr '91 / Pinnacle / Complete Record Co. Ltd.

**SHOULDA BEEN A PREACHER.**
racks: Somebody's got to pay / Help yourself /
hings I used to do / Driving wheel / True love / I
mell trouble / Double or nothing / Sometimey wo-
an / All I want is you / You'll need another favour /
rst class love / If you love me / My heart is filled
ith pain / Since I found a new love / Please come
ome for Christmas.
■ LP . . . . . . . . . . . . . . . . . . . . . .RL 030
ed Lightnin' / Sep '82.

**NE MORE CHANCE.**
racks: One more chance / Looking at the future.
■ 7" . . . . . . . . . . . . . . . . . . . . . . . VP 9264
ocalion / Feb '66.

**ART-TIME LOVE.**
acks: You're the one / As quick as I can / What you
eed is a ball / You gotta go on / She tried to
aderstand / Since I found a new love / Darling,
elieve me / She's yours, she's mine / Stay sweet /
omewhere down the line / Part time love.
■ LP . . . . . . . . . . . . . . . . . . . . . CRB 1012
harly R&B / Mar '81.
■ O . . . . . . . . . . . . . . . . . . . . . . . CD 229
hris Wellard / Dec '87 / Wellard.
■ LP . . . . . . . . . . . . . . . . . . . . . CH 229
ce / Nov '87.

**TUCK IN THE MUD.**
acks: Stuck in the mud / Full Time Love / I will give
all / Back To You / First Class Love / There Is
omething On Your Mind / Everybody Knows About
y Good Thing / You can help yourself / Your fade is
rther on down the road.
■ LP . . . . . . . . . . . . . . . . . . . . ICH 1022
■ C. . . . . . . . . . . . . . . . . . . . . .ZCICH 1022
hiban / Apr '88 / A.D.A. Distribution / Pinnacle /
CD Trading Ltd. / Koch International / Direct
stribution.

**GLY MAN.**
acks: Have you ever been to Kansas City / Never
e lonely and blue / LJT / Ugly man / It's my fault,
arlin' / I enjoy you / How can a broke man survive /
ng-size souvenir / Have you ever been to Kansas
ty (Reprise).
■ C. . . . . . . . . . . . . . . . . . . . . ICH 1042
■ C. . . . . . . . . . . . . . . . . . .ZCICH 1042
hiban / Sep '89 / A.D.A. Distribution / Pinnacle /
CD Trading Ltd. / Koch International / Direct
stribution.

---

■ CD . . . . . . . . . . . . . . . . . . . . .CDICH 1042
Ichiban / Oct '93 / A.D.A. Distribution / Pinnacle /
ACD Trading Ltd. / Koch International / Direct
Distribution.

## Taylor, R. Dean

**GOTTA SEE JANE.**
Tracks: Gotta see Jane.
■ 7" . . . . . . . . . . . . . . . . . . . TMG 656
Tamla Motown / Jun '68.

**GOTTA SEE JANE.**
Tracks: Gotta see Jane.
■ 7" . . . . . . . . . . . . . . . . . . . TMG 918
Tamla Motown / Sep '74.

**INDIANA WANTS ME.**
Tracks: Indiana wants me.
■ 7" . . . . . . . . . . . . . . . . . . . TMG 763
Tamla Motown / Apr '71.

**INDIANA WANTS ME.**
Tracks: Gotta see Jane / Fire and rain / Woman alive
/ Ain't a sad thing / Indiana wants me / Back street
/ Two of us / Sunday morning coming down / Gonna
give her all the love I've got / Love's your name.
■ LP . . . . . . . . . . . . . . . . . .STML 11185
Tamla Motown / Aug '71.

**THERE'S A GHOST IN MY HOUSE.**
Tracks: There's a ghost in my house / Let's go
somewhere.
■ 7" . . . . . . . . . . . . . . . . . . . TMG 896
Tamla Motown / May '74.

**WINDOW SHOPPING.**
Tracks: Window shopping.
■ 7" . . . . . . . . . . . . . . . . . . .2058 502
Polydor / Aug '74.

## Taylor, Ted

**IT'S TOO LATE.**
Tracks: It's too late.
■ 7" . . . . . . . . . . . . . . . . . . . .CTD 111
Charly / Jul '80.

**KEEP WALKING ON.**
Tracks: Not Advised.
■ LP . . . . . . . . . . . . . . . . . . . CRB 1011
Charly R&B / Mar '81.

**SOMEBODY'S ALWAYS TRYING (1958-66).**
Tracks: Not Advised.
■ LP . . . . . . . . . . . . . . . . . . . RB 1005
Mr.R&B (Sweden) / '88.

**TED TAYLOR 1976.**
Tracks: Somebody's getting it / Steal away / Stick by
me / Standing in the wings of a heartache / Caught
up in a good woman's love / I'm gonna hate myself
in the morning / It takes a fool to be a fool again /
You make loving easy / High heel sneakers.
■ LP . . . . . . . . . . . . . . . . . . . CLP 538
Contempo (1) / Feb '77.

## Team

**WE ARE THE TEAM (Team, Featuring Gee Bello).**
Tracks: We are the Team / Rock creek park.
■ 12" . . . . . . . . . . . . . . . . . .12EMI 5533
■ 7" . . . . . . . . . . . . . . . . . . . EMI 5533
EMI / Oct '85.

**WICKI WACKY HOUSE PARTY.**
Tracks: Wicki wacky house party.
■ 12" . . . . . . . . . . . . . . . . . .12EMI 5519
■ 12" Remix . . . . . . . . . . . . . . .12EMIX 5519
■ 7" . . . . . . . . . . . . . . . . . . . EMI 5519
EMI / Jun '85.

## Tease

**FIRESTARTER.**
Tracks: Firestarter / Baby, be mine.
■ 12" . . . . . . . . . . . . . . . . . . . TA 7084
■ 7" . . . . . . . . . . . . . . . . . . . .A 7084
Epic / Apr '86.

**TEASE.**
Tracks: Note / Better wild (than mild) / Firestarter /
Body heat / Total control / Soft music / Baby be mine
/ I wish you were here.
■ LP . . . . . . . . . . . . . . . . . . . EPC 26963
■ MC. . . . . . . . . . . . . . . . . . . .40 26963
Epic / Jun '86.

---

## Tee Cee's

**DISCO LOVE BITE.**
Tracks: Disco love bite / Disco love bite (version).
■ 7" . . . . . . . . . . . . . . . . . . .DJS 10842
DJM / Feb '78.

**ECSTASY.**
Tracks: Ecstasy (pt 1) / Ecstasy (pt 2).
■ 7" . . . . . . . . . . . . . . . . . . .DJS 10898
DJM / '79.

## Tee, Richard

**BOTTOM LINE.**
Tracks: If you want it / What can I say / Bottom line /
Nippon lights / Rhapsody in blue / Miss-Understand-
ing / Spring is you / No real way / Moving on.
■ LP . . . . . . . . . . . . . . . . . K 28P 6364
King (Japan) / Jul '86.

**NATURAL INGREDIENTS.**
Tracks: What a woman really means / Now / Nut's off
the screw / Tell it like it is / Us / Back door man /
Spinning song.
■ LP . . . . . . . . . . . . . . . . . . CBS 84194
CBS / Aug '80.

**STROKIN'.**
Tracks: First love / Everyday / Strokin' / I wanted it
too / Virginia Sunday / Jesus children of America /
Take the 'A' train.
■ LP . . . . . . . . . . . . . . . . . . CBS 83339
CBS / '79.

## Tee, Willie

**KEYS TO THE CRESCENT (see under Neville, Art).**

**THANK YOU JOHN.**
Tracks: Thank you John / Walking up a one way
street.
■ 7" . . . . . . . . . . . . . . . . . . . .584116
Atlantic / Jun '67.

**WALKING UP A ONE WAY STREET.**
Tracks: Walking up a one way street / Thank you
John.
■ 7" . . . . . . . . . . . . . . . . . . . CS 8002
Contempo (1) / Mar '78.

## Teen Queens

**GOOD ROCKIN' DADDY.**
Tracks: Good rockin' daddy / Eddie my love.
■ 7" . . . . . . . . . . . . . . . . . . . NS 66
Ace / Mar '81.

**ROCK EVERYBODY.**
Tracks: Rock everybody / Red top / Eddie my love /
Zig zag / All my love / Baby mine / Riding the boogie
/ Just goofed / Love sweet love / So all alone / My
heart's desire / Teenage gold / Let's make up / Billy
Boy.
■ LP . . . . . . . . . . . . . . . . . . . CH 186
Ace / Oct '86.

## Television

**BEVERLY HILLS 90210 (Various Artists).**
Tracks: Bend time back around / Got 2 have U / Right
kind of love / Love is / Just wanna be your friend /
Let me be your baby / Saving forever for you / All the
way to heaven / Why / Time to be lovers / Action
speaks louder than words / Theme from Beverly
Hills 90210.
■ CD . . . . . . . . . . . . . . . . . 7599244652
■ MC . . . . . . . . . . . . . . . . . 7599244654
WEA / Nov '92.
CD. . . . . . . . . . . . . . . . . 74321 14798 20
MC. . . . . . . . . . . . . . . . . 74321 14798 44
Giant / Nov '94 / BMG.

**BEVERLY HILLS 90210 - THE COLLEGE YEARS (Various Artists).**
Tracks: Make it right / Not one more time / Every day
of the week / Not enough hours in the.. / S.O.S. / No
intermission / Cantaloop (Flip fantasia) / Moving on
up / Saturday / Touch my light / I'll love you anyway /
What your love means to me / Forever yours.
CD . . . . . . . . . . . . . . . . 74321 20303 27
MC. . . . . . . . . . . . . . . . 74321 20303 41
Giant / Nov '94 / BMG.

**DIANA (TV Soundtrack) (Ross, Diana).**
Tracks: Don't rain on my parade / Close to you /
Remember me / Ain't no mountain high enough / I
love you / Love story / Mama's Pearl / Walk on by /
Love you save / I'll be there / Feelin' alright.

■ LP . . . . . . . . . . . . . . . . . STMA 8001
Tamla Motown / Oct '71.

### DIANA (TV SPECIAL) (Ross, Diana).
Tracks: Don't rain on my parade / Long to be (close to you) / Remember me / Ain't no mountain high enough / I love you (call me) / Love story / Bill Cosby entertains / Danny Thomas entertains.
■ LP . . . . . . . . . . . . . . . . . STMS 5048
■ MC . . . . . . . . . . . . . . . . . CSTMS 5048
Motown / Mar '82.

### DIANA (TV SPECIAL) (Ross, Diana).
Tracks: Not Advised.
■ LP . . . . . . . . . . . . . . . . . SHM 3203
MC . . . . . . . . . . . . . . . . . HSC 3203
Pickwick / '88 / Pickwick.

### MOONLIGHTING (Television Soundtrack) (Various Artists).
Tracks: Moonlighting / Limbo rock / This old heart of mine / I told ya I love ya, now get out / Good lovin' / Since I fell for you / When a man loves a woman / Someone to watch over me / Stormy weather.
■ CD . . . . . . . . . . . . . . . . . DMCF 3386
■ LP . . . . . . . . . . . . . . . . . MCF 3386
■ MC . . . . . . . . . . . . . . . . . MCFC 3386
MCA / Jul '87.
■ CD . . . . . . . . . . . . . . . . . DMCL 1873
MCA / Jul '88.
CD . . . . . . . . . . . . . . . . . 2414382
WEA / Nov '88 / WEA.
MC . . . . . . . . . . . . . . . . . MCLD 10991
MCA / Oct '92 / BMG.
■ MC . . . . . . . . . . . . . . . . . MCLC 10991
MCA / Jan '93.

### STAY OUT OF MY LIFE (Theme From TV's 'How Dare You') (Five Star).
Tracks: Stay out of my life / How dare you stay out of my life / If I say yes (Lew Hahn US dub mix') (* Available on 12" version only).
■ 12" . . . . . . . . . . . . . . . . . PT 41132
Tent / Jan '87.
■ 7" . . . . . . . . . . . . . . . . . PB 41131
RCA / Jan '87.

### TALES OF THE CITY (Various Artists).
Tracks: Love to love you baby / Never can say goodbye / Jive talkin' / Philadelphia freedom / That's the way I like it / Lady marmalade / You sexy thing / H.A.P.P.Y. radio / You're the first, the last, my everything / It's a man's man's world / Cry me a river / I'm not in love / Cocaine / Hang on in there / Don't take away the music / Disco inferno.
CD . . . . . . . . . . . . . . . . . 5165152
MC . . . . . . . . . . . . . . . . . 5165154
Polygram T.V. / Oct '93 / PolyGram.

## Tella, Sylvia

### HE'S MY BABY.
Tracks: He's my baby.
■ 12" . . . . . . . . . . . . . . . . . BS 002
Boss / Oct '85.

### I STILL FEEL.
Tracks: I still feel / I still feel (version).
■ 12" . . . . . . . . . . . . . . . . . BS 001
Boss / Nov '84.

### PEACE AND LOVE.
Tracks: Peace & love / Peace and love (version).
■ 12" . . . . . . . . . . . . . . . . . BZT 06
Body Music / Nov '87.

### PEOPLE OF THE WORLD.
Tracks: People of the world.
12" . . . . . . . . . . . . . . . . . STR 016
Sting Ray / Aug '94 / Jetstar.

### SPELL.
Tracks: Not Advised.
■ LP . . . . . . . . . . . . . . . . . SRL 1005
Sarge / Apr '86.

### SWEETER HE IS.
Tracks: Sweeter he is.
■ 12" . . . . . . . . . . . . . . . . . SRLDD 1
SRL / Apr '82.

### WILL YOU STILL WANT ME.
Tracks: Not Advised.
■ LP . . . . . . . . . . . . . . . . . SYLVIA 01
Body Music / Nov '87.

## Temple, Richard

### THAT BEATIN' RHYTHM.
Tracks: That beatin' rhythm / Could it be.
■ 7" . . . . . . . . . . . . . . . . . CS 9040
Contempo (1) / Feb '76.

## Temprees

### LOVEMEN.
Tracks: Explain it to her mama / If I could say what's on my mind / I love you, you love me / We've only just begun / Dedicated to the one I love / My baby love / I'm for you, you for me / Love can be so wonderful.
■ LP . . . . . . . . . . . . . . . . . 2325083
Stax / Nov '72.

## Temptations

Temptations are yardstick against which all male vocal groups must be measured. Motown's finest debuted in early '60s, using producers Smokey Robinson and Norman Whitfield for classics like My Girl, Ain't Too Proud To Beg and I Wish It Would Rain. However, greatest period came when Whitfield sought to out-do young pretenders like Hendrix and Sly. Results were extraordinary eleven hits between '68 and '72, cream of which included I Can't Get Next To You, Ball of Confusion, Just My Imagination and Papa Was A Rollin' Stone. Now minus David Ruffin (whose arrival in '63 coincided with their breakthrough), group also enjoyed hit collaborations with Diana Ross & the Supremes, I'm Gonna Make You Love Me and I Second That Emotion. Group lost Whitfield, several key members (including Eddie Kendricks) and much of its momentum in mid-'70s. Later efforts, including reunions involving Kendricks and Ruffin in '80s, were generally less successful, but first decade's recordings alone earn them 'Emperors of Soul' title.

### (I KNOW) I'M LOSING YOU.
Tracks: (I know) I'm losing you.
■ 7" . . . . . . . . . . . . . . . . . TMG 587
Tamla Motown / Dec '66.

### 17 GREATEST HITS.
Tracks: Girl (why you wanna make me blue) / My girl / Since I lost my baby / Ain't too proud to beg / (I know) I'm losing you / You're my everything / I wish it would rain / I can never love another (after loving you) / Cloud 9 / Runaway child running wild / I can't get next to you / Psychedelic shack / Ball of confusion / Just my imagination (running away with me) / Superstar (remember how you do you are) / Papa was a rollin' stone / Hey girl (I like your style).
■ CD . . . . . . . . . . . . . . . . . ZD 72365
Motown / Jul '85.

### 20 GOLDEN GREATS: TEMPTATIONS.
Tracks: Just my imagination (running away with me) / I wish it would rain / I second that emotion / Beauty is only skin deep / I'm losing you / Cloud 9 / Take a look around / Superstar / Papa was a rollin' stone / Power / I'm gonna make you love me / My girl / You're my everything / I can't get next to you / Get ready / Ain't too proud to beg / I could never love another (after loving you) / Ball of confusion / Psychedelic shack / Law of the land.
■ LP . . . . . . . . . . . . . . . . . STML 12140
■ MC . . . . . . . . . . . . . . . . . CSTML 12140
Motown / Oct '81.
■ LP . . . . . . . . . . . . . . . . . ZL 72160
Motown / '86.

### 25TH ANNIVERSARY: TEMPTATIONS.
Tracks: I want a love I can see / So much joy / It don't have to be this way / Further you look the less you see / My girl / Since I lost my baby / I can't get next to you / Cloud 9 / Just my imagination (running away with me) / Come to me / Soulmate / Tear from a woman's eyes / Wherever I lay my hat / Don't look back / Get ready / Ain't too proud to beg / Truly yours / Papa was a rollin' stone / Thanks to you / Glasshouse / Power / Treat her like a lady.
■ MC . . . . . . . . . . . . . . . . . WK 72435
■ LP . . . . . . . . . . . . . . . . . WL 72435
Tamla Motown / Jun '86.

### AIMING AT YOUR HEART.
Tracks: Aiming at your heart / Life of a cowboy.
■ 12" . . . . . . . . . . . . . . . . . TMGT 1243
■ 7" . . . . . . . . . . . . . . . . . TMG 1243
Motown / Oct '81.

### AIN'T TOO PROUD TO BEG.
Tracks: Ain't too proud to beg / You'll lose a precious love.

■ 7" . . . . . . . . . . . . . . . . . TMG 565
Tamla Motown / Jul '66.

### ALL DIRECTIONS.
Tracks: Funky music sho nuff turns me on / Run Charlie run / Papa was a rollin' stone / Love woke me up this morning / I ain't got nothin' / First time ever I saw your face / Mother nature / Do your thing.
■ LP . . . . . . . . . . . . . . . . . STML 11218
Tamla Motown / Jan '73.
■ LP . . . . . . . . . . . . . . . . . STMS 5052
■ MC . . . . . . . . . . . . . . . . . CSTMS 5052
Motown / Mar '82.
■ LP . . . . . . . . . . . . . . . . . WL 72321
Motown / '86.
■ CD . . . . . . . . . . . . . . . . . WD 72321
Motown / Jun '89.
CD . . . . . . . . . . . . . . . . . 530 155-2
Motown / Sep '93 / PolyGram.

### ALL I NEED.
Tracks: All I need / Sorry is a sorry word.
■ 7" . . . . . . . . . . . . . . . . . TMG 610
Tamla Motown / '67.

### ALL I WANT FROM YOU.
Tracks: All I want from you / All I want from you (instrumental) / Treat her like a lady (Available on 12" format only.) / Papa was a rolling stone (Available on 12" only).
■ 12" . . . . . . . . . . . . . . . . . ZT 43234
■ 7" . . . . . . . . . . . . . . . . . ZB 43233
■ CD Single . . . . . . . . . . . . . . ZD 43234
Motown / Sep '89.

### ALL THE MILLION SELLERS.
Tracks: My girl / Ain't too proud to beg / I wish it would rain / Cloud 9 / Runaway child, running wild / I can't get next to you / Psychedelic shack / Ball of confusion (that's what the world is today) / Just my imagination (running away with me) / Papa was a rollin' stone.
■ CD . . . . . . . . . . . . . . . . . WD 72096
■ LP . . . . . . . . . . . . . . . . . WL 72096
■ MC . . . . . . . . . . . . . . . . . WK 72096
Motown / '91.

### ANTHOLOGY - TEMPTATIONS (Volumes 1 & 2).
Tracks: Way you do the things you do / I'll be in trouble / Girl's alright with me / Girl (why you wanna make me blue) / My girl / It's growing / Since I lost my baby / My baby / Don't look back / Get ready / Ain't too proud to beg / Beauty is only skin deep / I'm losing you / All I need / You're my everything / It's you that I need (loneliness made me realise) / I wish it would rain / I truly, truly believe / I could never love another (after loving you) / Runaway child running wild / Ol' man river / Try to remember / Impossible dream / I'm gonna make you love me (with Diana Ross & The Supremes.) / Please return your love to me / Cloud 9 / Don't let the Joneses get you down / I can't get next to you / Psychedelic shack / Ball of confusion / Funky music sho nuff turns me on / I ain't got nothin' / Just my imagination (running away with me) / Superstar (remember how you got where you are) / Mother nature / Love woke me up this morning / Papa was a rollin' stone / Masterpiece / Shakey ground / Power / Sail away / Treat her like a lady.
■ Double LP . . . . . . . . . . . . . . TMSP 6003
■ MC Set . . . . . . . . . . . . . . . CTMSP 6003
Motown / Oct '81.
■ Double LP . . . . . . . . . . . . . . ZL 72178
Motown / '86.
■ CD Set . . . . . . . . . . . . . . . ZD 72528
Motown / Jan '87.
■ CD Set . . . . . . . . . . . . . . . WD 72528
Motown / Apr '89.

### BACK TO BASICS.
Tracks: Miss busy body (get your body busy) / Sail away / Outlaw / Stop the world right here (I wanna get off) / Battle song, The (I'm the one) / Hollywood / Isn't the night fantastic / Make me believe in love again.
■ LP . . . . . . . . . . . . . . . . . STML 12190
■ MC . . . . . . . . . . . . . . . . . CSTML 12190
Motown / Dec '83.

### BALL OF CONFUSION.
Tracks: Ball of confusion / Take a look around.
■ 7" . . . . . . . . . . . . . . . . . TMG 749
Tamla Motown / Sep '70.

### BALL OF CONFUSION.
Tracks: Ball of confusion.
■ 7" . . . . . . . . . . . . . . . . . TMG 961
Tamla Motown / Apr '75.

### BARE BACK.
Tracks: Bare back / Ever ready love.
■ 7" . . . . . . . . . . . . . . . . . K 11183
Atlantic / Sep '78.

414

■ DELETE

**BARE BACK.**
**Tracks:** Mystic woman / I just don't know how to let you go / That's when you need love / Bare back / Ever ready love / Wake up to me / You're so easy to love / I see my child / Touch me again.
■ **LP** . . . . . . . . . . . . . . . . . . . . **K 50504**
Warner Bros. / Sep '78.

**BEAUTY IS ONLY SKIN DEEP.**
**Tracks:** Beauty is only skin deep.
■ **7"** . . . . . . . . . . . . . . . . . . . **TMG 578**
Tamla Motown / Oct '66.

**BEST OF THE TEMPTATIONS.**
**Tracks:** Not Advised.
■ **LP** . . . . . . . . . . . . . . . . . . . . **STAR 2281**
■ **MC** . . . . . . . . . . . . . . . . . . . . **STAC 2281**
Telstar/Ronco / Nov '86.

**BEST OF THE TEMPTATIONS, THE.**
**Tracks:** Not Advised.
**MC** . . . . . . . . . . . . . . . . . . . . . **3127-4**
Scratch / Oct '94 / Scratch Records / BMG / Grapevine Distribution.
**CD** . . . . . . . . . . . . . . . . . . . . . **3127-2**
Scratch / Oct '94 / Scratch Records / BMG / Grapevine Distribution.

**CLOUD NINE.**
**Tracks:** Cloud 9 / I heard it through the grapevine / Runaway child running wild / Love is a hurtin' thing / Hey girl (I like your style) / Why did she have to leave me (why did she have to go?) / I need your lovin' / Don't let him take your love from me / I gotta find a way (to get you back) / Gonna keep on tryin' till I win your love.
■ **LP** . . . . . . . . . . . . . . . . . . . . **STML 11109**
Motown / Sep '69.
■ **LP** . . . . . . . . . . . . . . . . . . . . **STMS 5020**
■ **MC** . . . . . . . . . . . . . . . . . . . . **CSTMS 5020**
Motown / Oct '81.
**CD** . . . . . . . . . . . . . . . . . . . . . **5301532**
Motown / Aug '93 / PolyGram.

**CLOUD NINE.**
**Tracks:** Cloud 9 / Psychedelic shacks.
■ **7"** . . . . . . . . . . . . . . . . . . . **TMG 982**
Tamla Motown / Aug '75.

**CLOUD NINE.**
**Tracks:** Cloud 9.
■ **7"** . . . . . . . . . . . . . . . . . . . **TMG 707**
Tamla Motown / Aug '69.

**CLOUD NINE/PUZZLE PEOPLE.**
**Tracks:** Cloud 9 / I heard it through the grapevine / Runaway child, running wild / Love is a hurtin' thing / Hey girl(I like your style) / Why did she have to leave me (why did she have to go) / I need your lovin' / Don't let him take your love from me / I gotta find a way ( to get you back) / Gonna keep on tryin' till I win your love / I can't get next to you / Hey Jude / Don't let the Joneses get you down / Message from a black man / It's your thing / Little green apples / You don't love me no more / Since I've lost you / Running away (ain't gonna help you) / That's the way love is / Slave.
■ **CD** . . . . . . . . . . . . . . . . . . . . **ZD 72460**
Motown / Jan '87.

**COMPACT COMMAND PERFORMANCES.**
**Tracks:** My girl / Since I lost my baby / Just my imagination (running away with me) / Ain't too proud to beg / Psychedelic shack / Cloud 9 / (I know) I'm losing you / I wish it would rain / You're my everything / I could never love another (after loving you) / Runaway child, running wild / I can't get next to you / Ball of confusion / Superstar (remember how you got where you are) / Hey girl (I like your style) / Papa was a rollin' stone.
■ **CD** . . . . . . . . . . . . . . . . . . . . **WD 72365**
Motown / Apr '89.

**DIANA ROSS JOINS THE TEMPTATIONS/TOGETHER (see under Ross, Diana).**

**DO YOU REALLY LOVE YOUR BABY.**
**Tracks:** Do you really love your baby.
■ **12"** . . . . . . . . . . . . . . . . . . . **ZT 40454**
■ **7"** . . . . . . . . . . . . . . . . . . . **ZB 40453**
Motown / Nov '85.

**EMPERORS OF SOUL.**
**Tracks:** Come on / Oh mother of mine / Romance without finance / Check yourself / Dream come true / Mind over matter (I'm gonna make you mine) / I'll love you 'til I die / Paradise / Slow down heart / I couldn't cry if I wanted to / Witchcraft (for your love) / I want a love I can see / Further you look the less you see / Farewell my love / Tear from a woman's eyes / Way you do the things you do / I'll be in trouble / Girl's alright with me / Girl (Why you wanna make me blue) / Baby, baby I need you / My girl / (Talking 'bout) Nobody but my baby / It's growing / You'll lose a precious love / Since I lost my baby / You've got to earn it / My baby / Don't look back / Get ready / Fading away / Ain't too proud to beg / Too busy thinking about my baby / Who you gonna run to / Beauty is only skin deep / I got heaven right here on earth / (I know) I'm losing you / All I need / Sorry is a sorry word / I'm doing it all / No more water in the well / You're my everything / Just one last look / Angel doll / (Loneliness made me realize) It's you that I need / Don't send me away / Hello young lovers / Ol' man river / I wish it would rain / I truly, truly believe / I could never love another (after loving you) / Please return your love to me / How can I forget / For once in my life (live) / Cloud nine / Why did she have to leave me (Why did she have to go) / I'm goona make you love me / I'll try something new / Runaway child, running wild / Don't let the Joneses get you down / I can't get next to you / Message from a black man / War / Psychedelic shack / Hum along and dance / Ball of confusion (That's what the world is today) / Ungena za ulimwengu (Unite the world) / Just my imagination (Running away with me) / Take a look around / It's summer / Superstar (Remember how you got where you are) / I ain't got nothin' / Mother nature / Papa was a rolling stone / Masterpiece / Plastic man / Hey girl (I like your style) / Law of the land / Let your hair down / Heavenly / You've got my soul on fire / Happy people / Shakey ground / Glasshouse / Song for you / Memories / Keep holdin' on / Darling, stand by me (Song for my woman) / Who are you / In a lifetime / Power / Isn't the night fantastic / Aiming at your heart / Standing on the top, part 1 / Sail away / Treat her like a lady / My love is true (Truly for you) / Do you really love your baby / Magic / Lady soul / I wonder who she's seeing now / Look what you started / Soul to soul / Special / My kind of woman / Hoops of fire / Error of our ways / Givin' u the best / Elevator eyes / Blueprint for love.
**CD Set** . . . . . . . . . . . . . . . . . . . **530338-2**
Polygram / Sep '94 / PolyGram.

**GET READY.**
**Tracks:** You're the one I need / Too busy thinking about my baby / I gotta know now / Just another lonely night / Say you / Fading away / It's a lonely world without your love / Get ready / Everybody needs love / Born to love you / You'll lose a precious love / You've got to earn it.
■ **LP** . . . . . . . . . . . . . . . . . . . . **TMS 3507**
■ **MC** . . . . . . . . . . . . . . . . . . . . **TMC 3507**
Motown / '82.

**GET READY.**
**Tracks:** Get ready.
■ **7"** . . . . . . . . . . . . . . . . . . . **TMG 688**
Tamla Motown / Mar '69.

**GET READY.**
**Tracks:** Get ready.
■ **7"** . . . . . . . . . . . . . . . . . . . **TMG 557**
Tamla Motown / '66.

**GET READY.**
**Tracks:** Papa was a rollin' stone / Psychedelic shack / Ball of confusion / Just my imagination (running away with me) / Way you do the things you do / Since I lost my baby / You're my everything / All I need / Get ready / Heavenly / Beauty is only skin deep / Ol' man river / Cloud 9 / Ain't too proud to beg / My girl / I can't get next to you / Thank you / I wonder.
■ **VHS** . . . . . . . . . . . . . . . . . . . **MVPTEM3 1**
■ **VHS** . . . . . . . . . . . . . . . . . . . **MVP 99 1165 3**
PMI / Sep '88.
**VHS** . . . . . . . . . . . . . . . . . . . . **MC 2097**
Music Club / Oct '92 / Gold & Sons / THE / Video Collection / C.M. Distribution.

**GETTING READY.**
**Tracks:** Not Advised.
■ **LP** . . . . . . . . . . . . . . . . . . . . **STML 11035**
Tamla Motown / Dec '66.

**GIVE LOVE AT CHRISTMAS.**
**Tracks:** Give love on Christmas day / Christmas song / Love comes with Christmas / Everything for Christmas / Christmas everyday / Silent night.
■ **LP** . . . . . . . . . . . . . . . . . . . . **STMS 5085**
■ **MC** . . . . . . . . . . . . . . . . . . . . **CSTMS 5085**
Motown / Nov '85.
■ **MC** . . . . . . . . . . . . . . . . . . . . **WK 72356**
Motown / '86.
■ **LP** . . . . . . . . . . . . . . . . . . . . **WL 72356**
Motown / '88.

**GREATEST HITS, VOL 2: TEMPTATIONS.**
**Tracks:** Cloud 9 / I wish it would rain / Ball of confusion (that's what the world is today) / (I know) I'm losing you / I can't get next to you / You're my everything / Psychedelic shack / Please return your love to me / Runaway child, running wild / I could never love another (after loving you) / Don't let the Joneses get you down / (Loneliness made me realize) It's you that I need.
■ **LP** . . . . . . . . . . . . . . . . . . . . **STML 11170**
Tamla Motown / Dec '70.
■ **MC** . . . . . . . . . . . . . . . . . . . . **WK 72647**
■ **CD** . . . . . . . . . . . . . . . . . . . . **WD 72647**
■ **LP** . . . . . . . . . . . . . . . . . . . . **WL 72647**
Motown / Sep '88.

**GREATEST HITS: TEMPTATIONS.**
**Tracks:** Way you do the things you do / My girl / Ain't too proud to beg / Don't look back / Get ready / Beauty is only skin deep / Since I lost my baby / Girls alright with me / My baby / It's growing / I'll be in trouble / Girl (why you wanna make me blue).
■ **CD** . . . . . . . . . . . . . . . . . . . . **WD 72646**
■ **LP** . . . . . . . . . . . . . . . . . . . . **WL 72646**
■ **MC** . . . . . . . . . . . . . . . . . . . . **WK 72646**
Motown / Sep '88.

**GREATEST HITS: TEMPTATIONS.**
**Tracks:** Not Advised.
**CD** . . . . . . . . . . . . . . . . . . . . . **PA 714-2**
Paradiso / Mar '94 / BMG.

**HEAR TO TEMPT YOU.**
**Tracks:** Think for yourself / In a lifetime / Can we come and share in love / She's all I've got / Snake in the grass / It's time for life / Let's live in peace / Read between the lines / I could never stop loving you.
■ **LP** . . . . . . . . . . . . . . . . . . . . **K 50413**
Atlantic / Mar '78.

**HUM ALONG AND DANCE - MORE BEST OF THE TEMPTATIONS (1963-74).**
**Tracks:** I want a love i can see / What love has joined together / You've got to earn it / No more water in the well / Ain't no sun since you've been gone / Gonna give her all the love I've got / He who picks a rose / Fan the flame / Don't let him take your love from me / Gonna keep on tryin' 'til I win your love / Hum along and dance / Ungena za ulimwengu / It's summer / Stop the war now / Take a look around / Plastic man / Heavenly / You've got my soul on fire.
**CD** . . . . . . . . . . . . . . . . . . . . . **812271180-2**
**MC** . . . . . . . . . . . . . . . . . . . . . **812271180-4**
WEA / Jun '93 / WEA.

**I CAN'T GET NEXT TO YOU.**
**Tracks:** I can't get next to you / I know I'm losing you.
■ **7"** . . . . . . . . . . . . . . . . . . . **TMG 722**
Tamla Motown / Jan '70.
■ **7"** . . . . . . . . . . . . . . . . . . . **ZB 41933**
Motown / Apr '88.

**I COULD NEVER LOVE ANOTHER.**
**Tracks:** I could never love another (after loving you).
■ **7"** . . . . . . . . . . . . . . . . . . . **TMG 658**
Tamla Motown / Jun '68.

**I WISH IT WOULD RAIN.**
**Tracks:** I wish it would rain.
■ **7"** . . . . . . . . . . . . . . . . . . . **TMG 641**
Tamla Motown / Mar '68.

**I WISH IT WOULD RAIN.**
**Tracks:** I could never love another / Cindy / Please return your love to me / Fan the flame / I wish it would rain / He who picks a rose / Why did you leave me darling / This is my beloved / I truly believe / Gonna give her all the love I've got / I've passed this way before / No man can love her like I do.
■ **LP** . . . . . . . . . . . . . . . . . . . . **STML 11079**
Tamla Motown / Aug '68.

**I WONDER WHO SHE'S SEEING NOW?.**
**Tracks:** I wonder who she's seeing now / Girls (they like it) / I wonder who she's seeing now (extended) / I wonder who she's seeing now (7") (On 12" version only.).
■ **12"** . . . . . . . . . . . . . . . . . . . **ZT 41548**
■ **7"** . . . . . . . . . . . . . . . . . . . **ZB 41547**
Motown / Oct '87.

**I'M GONNA MAKE YOU LOVE ME (see under Ross, Diana).**

**I'M SO FASCINATED.**
**Tracks:** I'm fascinated / How can you say that it's over / Treat her like a lady (On 12" version only) / M and M (remix) (On 12" version only).
■ **12"** . . . . . . . . . . . . . . . . . . . **ZT 40622**
■ **7"** . . . . . . . . . . . . . . . . . . . **ZB 40621**
Motown / Mar '86.

**IN A MELLOW MOOD.**
**Tracks:** Hello young lovers / Taste of honey / For once in my life / Somewhere / Old man river / I'm ready for love / Try to remember / Who can I turn to / What now my love / That's life / With these hands / Impossible dream.

■ **LP** . . . . . . . . . . . . . . . . . . . . . .STML 11068
Tamla Motown / Mar '68.

### IT'S GROWING.
**Tracks:** It's growing.
■ **7"** . . . . . . . . . . . . . . . . . . . . . . . . TMG 504
Tamla Motown / Apr '65.

### IT'S THE TEMPTATIONS.
**Tracks:** My baby / Sice I lost my baby / It's growing / Way you do the things you do.
■ **EP** . . . . . . . . . . . . . . . . . . . . . . . TME 2010
Tamla Motown / Feb '66.

### JONES', THE.
**Tracks:** Jones'.
■ **7"** . . . . . . . . . . . . . . . . . . . . . . .TMG 1403
■ **CD Single** . . . . . . . . . . . . . . . TMGCD 1403
■ **MC Single** . . . . . . . . . . . . . . . TMGCS 1403
Motown / Feb '92.

### JUST MY IMAGINATION.
**Tracks:** Just my imagination (running away with me) / Get ready.
■ **7"** . . . . . . . . . . . . . . . . . . . . . . . TMG 773
Tamla Motown / Apr '71.
■ **7"** . . . . . . . . . . . . . . . . . . . . . . .TMG 1043
Tamla Motown / Sep '76.

### LADY SOUL.
**Tracks:** Lady soul / Fine mess (A) / Papa was a rollin' stone (On 12" version only).
■ **12"** . . . . . . . . . . . . . . . . . . . . . . ZT 40850
■ **7"** . . . . . . . . . . . . . . . . . . . . . . ZB 40850
Motown / Aug '86.

### LAW OF THE LAND.
**Tracks:** Law of the land / Beauty is only skin deep.
■ **7"** . . . . . . . . . . . . . . . . . . . . . . . TMG 866
Tamla Motown / Sep '73.
■ **7"** . . . . . . . . . . . . . . . . . . . . . . . TMG 990
Tamla Motown / Sep '75.

### LEGEND (see under Ross, Diana).

### LIVE AT THE COPA.
**Tracks:** Introduction / Get ready / You're my every-thing / I truly, truly believe / I wish it would rain / For once in my life / I could never love another / Intro-duction of band and group / Hello young lovers / With these hands / Swanee / Impossible dream / Please return your love to me / I'm losing you.
■ **LP** . . . . . . . . . . . . . . . . . . . . . .STML 11104
Tamla Motown / May '69.

### LIVE AT THE COPA/WITH A LOT O' SOUL.
**Tracks:** Introduction / Get ready / You're my every-thing / I truly, truly believe / I wish it would rain / For once in my life / I could never love another (after loving you) / Introduction to Band and Group / Hello young lovers / With these hands / Swanee / Imposs-ible dream / Please return your love to me / I'm losing you / Ain't no sun since you've been gone / All I need / It's you that I need (loneliness made me realise) / No more water in the well / Save my love for a rainy day / Just one last look / Sorry is a sorry word / Now that you've won me / Two sides to love / Don't send me away.
■ **CD** . . . . . . . . . . . . . . . . . . . . . . ZD 72501
Motown / Feb '87.

### LIVE AT THE TALK OF THE TOWN.
**Tracks:** Get ready / Girl / Beauty is only skin deep / You're my everything / My girl / Ain't too proud to beg / I'm gonna make you love me / Impossible dream / Run away child, running wild / Don't let the Joneses get you down / Time for us / I can't get next to you / This guy's in love with you / I've gotta be me / I'm losing you / Cloud nine / Everything is going to be alright.
■ **LP** . . . . . . . . . . . . . . . . . . . . . .STML 11141
Tamla Motown / Apr '70.

### LOOK WHAT YOU STARTED.
**Tracks:** Look what you started.
■ **MC Single** . . . . . . . . . . . . . . . . ZV 41733
Motown / Feb '88.
■ **12"** . . . . . . . . . . . . . . . . . . . . . . ZT 41734
■ **7"** . . . . . . . . . . . . . . . . . . . . . . ZB 41733
Motown / Jan '88.

### LOVE ON MY MIND.
**Tracks:** Love on my mind / Bring your body here.
■ **12"** . . . . . . . . . . . . . . . . . . . . . TMGT 1297
■ **7"** . . . . . . . . . . . . . . . . . . . . . . TMG 1297
Motown / Mar '83.

### MASTERPIECE.
**Tracks:** Hey girl (I like your style) / Masterpiece / Ma / Law of the land / Plastic man / Hurry tomorrow.
■ **LP** . . . . . . . . . . . . . . . . . . . . . .STML 11229
Tamla Motown / Jul '73.
■ **LP** . . . . . . . . . . . . . . . . . . . . . . STMS 5021

■ **MC** . . . . . . . . . . . . . . . . . . . . CSTMS 5021
Motown / Oct '81.
■ **MC** . . . . . . . . . . . . . . . . . . . . . WK 72076
■ **LP** . . . . . . . . . . . . . . . . . . . . . WL 72076
Motown / '86.
■ **CD** . . . . . . . . . . . . . . . . . . . . . WD 72076
Motown / Oct '89.
CD . . . . . . . . . . . . . . . . . . . . . . .530100-2
■ **MC** . . . . . . . . . . . . . . . . . . . . .530100-4
Motown / Jan '93 / PolyGram.

### MEDLEY OF HITS (Temptations & Four Tops).
**Tracks:** Medley of hits.
■ **12"** . . . . . . . . . . . . . . . . . . . . TMGT 1320
■ **7"** . . . . . . . . . . . . . . . . . . . . . TMG 1320
Motown / Oct '83.

### MILESTONE.
**Tracks:** Eenie, meenie, minie, moe / Any old lovin' (just won't do) / Hoops of fire / We should be makin' love / Jones / Get ready / Corner of my heart / Whenever you're ready / Do it easy / Wait a minute / Celebrate (Cassette & CD only).
■ **CD** . . . . . . . . . . . . . . . . . . . . ZD 72768
■ **LP** . . . . . . . . . . . . . . . . . . . . . ZL 72768
■ **MC** . . . . . . . . . . . . . . . . . . . . ZK 72768
Motown / Dec '91.
CD . . . . . . . . . . . . . . . . . . . . . .530005-2
■ **MC** . . . . . . . . . . . . . . . . . . . . .530005-4
Motown / Jan '93 / PolyGram.

### MOTOWN SPECIAL (see under Ross, Diana).

### MOTOWN SPECIAL.
**Tracks:** Ball of confusion / Cloud nine / Since I lost you / You need love like I do / Runaway child, running wild / I can't get next to you / I gotta find my way / Message from a black man / Running way / War / You don't love me no more.
■ **LP** . . . . . . . . . . . . . . . . . . . . . STMX 6002
Motown / Mar '77.

### MOTOWNS GREATEST HITS: TEMPTATIONS.
**Tracks:** Not Advised.
CD . . . . . . . . . . . . . . . . . . . . . . .530015-2
DCC . . . . . . . . . . . . . . . . . . . . . 530 015-5
MC . . . . . . . . . . . . . . . . . . . . . .530154-4
Motown / Jan '93 / PolyGram.

### MY BABY.
**Tracks:** My baby.
■ **7"** . . . . . . . . . . . . . . . . . . . . . . TMG 541
Tamla Motown / Nov '65.

### MY GIRL.
**Tracks:** My girl.
■ **7"** . . . . . . . . . . . . . . . . . . . . . . . SS 395
Stateside / Mar '65.
■ **7"** . . . . . . . . . . . . . . . . . . . . . . 6576767
■ **CD Single** . . . . . . . . . . . . . . . . 6576762
■ **MC Single** . . . . . . . . . . . . . . . 6576764
Epic / Feb '92.

### MY GIRL.
**Tracks:** My girl / Wherever I lay my hat / Way you do the things you do (on 12" version only) / My baby (On 12" version only).
■ **7"** . . . . . . . . . . . . . . . . . . . . . ZB 40743
■ **12"** . . . . . . . . . . . . . . . . . . . . . ZT 40744
Motown / Jun '86.

### MY LOVE IS TRUE (TRULY FOR YOU).
**Tracks:** My love is true / I'll keep my light in my window / Treat her like a lady (on 12" only).
■ **12"** . . . . . . . . . . . . . . . . . . . . TMGT 1373
■ **7"** . . . . . . . . . . . . . . . . . . . . . TMG 1373
Motown / Mar '85.

### ORIGINAL LEAD SINGERS.
**Tracks:** Not Advised.
CD . . . . . . . . . . . . . . . . . . . . KWEST 5409
MC . . . . . . . . . . . . . . . . . . . . KWEST 4409
Kwest / Dec '92 / THE.

### PAPA WAS A ROLLIN' STONE.
**Tracks:** Papa was a rollin' stone.
■ **7"** . . . . . . . . . . . . . . . . . . . . . . TMG 839
Tamla Motown / Jan '73.

### PAPA WAS A ROLLIN' STONE.
**Tracks:** Ain't too proud to beg / Papa was a rollin' stone.
■ **12"** . . . . . . . . . . . . . . . . . . . . . ZT 41432
■ **7"** . . . . . . . . . . . . . . . . . . . . . ZB 41431
Motown / Aug '87.

### POWER.
**Tracks:** Power / Struck by lightning twice / Isn't the night fantastic / How can I resist your love / Can't you see sweet thing / Go for it / I'm coming home.

■ **LP** . . . . . . . . . . . . . . . . . . . . . .STML 12136
Motown / Oct '81.

### POWER.
**Tracks:** Power (part 1) / Power (part 2).
■ **7"** . . . . . . . . . . . . . . . . . . . . . TMG 1186
Motown / May '80.

### PSYCHEDELIC SHACK.
**Tracks:** Psychedelic shack / You make your own heaven and hell right here on earth / Hum along and dance / Take a stroll thru your mind / It's summer / War / You need love like I do / Friendship train.
■ **LP** . . . . . . . . . . . . . . . . . . . . . .STML 11147
Tamla Motown / Jul '70.
■ **LP** . . . . . . . . . . . . . . . . . . . . . STMS 5051
■ **MC** . . . . . . . . . . . . . . . . . . . . CSTMS 5051
Motown / Mar '82.

### PSYCHEDELIC SHACK.
**Tracks:** Psychedelic shack.
■ **7"** . . . . . . . . . . . . . . . . . . . . . . TMG 741
Tamla Motown / Jun '70.

### PSYCHEDELIC          SHACK/ALL DIRECTIONS.
**Tracks:** Psychedelic shack / You make your own heaven and hell right here on Earth / Hum along and dance / Take a stroll thru your mind / It's Summer / War / You need love like I do / Friendship train / Funky music sho nuff turns me on / Run Charlie run / Papa was a rollin' stone / Love woke me up this morning / I ain't got nothin' / First time ever I saw your face / Mother nature / Do your thing.
■ **CD** . . . . . . . . . . . . . . . . . . . . ZD 72486
Motown / Nov '86.

### PUZZLE PEOPLE.
**Tracks:** I can't get next to you / Hey Jude / Don't let the Joneses get you down / Message from a black man / It's your thing / Little green apples / Don't you love me no more / Since I've lost you / Running away (ain't gonna help you) / That's the way love is / Slave.
■ **LP** . . . . . . . . . . . . . . . . . . . . . .STML 11133
Tamla Motown / Feb '70.
■ **LP** . . . . . . . . . . . . . . . . . . . . . STMS 5050
■ **MC** . . . . . . . . . . . . . . . . . . . . CSTMS 5050
Motown / Mar '82.

### SHAKY GROUND.
**Tracks:** Shaky ground / I'm a bachelor.
■ **7"** . . . . . . . . . . . . . . . . . . . . . TMG 1063
Motown / Feb '77.

### SINCE I LOST MY BABY.
**Tracks:** Since I lost my baby / You've got to earn it.
■ **7"** . . . . . . . . . . . . . . . . . . . . . . TMG 526
Tamla Motown / '65.

### SKY'S THE LIMIT.
**Tracks:** Gonna keep on tryin' till I win your love / Just my imagination (running away with me) / I'm the exception to the rule / Smiling faces sometimes / Man / Throw a farewell kiss / Ungena za ulimwengu (unite the world) / Love can be anything (can't no-thing be love but love).
■ **LP** . . . . . . . . . . . . . . . . . . . . . .STML 11184
Tamla Motown / Aug '71.
■ **CD** . . . . . . . . . . . . . . . . . . . . . WD 72743
■ **MC** . . . . . . . . . . . . . . . . . . . . . WK 72743
Motown / May '91.

### SOLID ROCK.
**Tracks:** Take a look around / Ain't no sunshine / Stop the war now / What is is / Smooth sailing / Superstar / It's summer / End of our road.
■ **LP** . . . . . . . . . . . . . . . . . . . . . .STML 11202
Tamla Motown / Apr '72.

### SONG FOR YOU/MASTERPIECE.
**Tracks:** Happy people (2) / Glasshouse / Shakey ground / Prophet / Happy people (1) / Song for you / Memories / I'm a bachelor / Firefly / Hey girl (I like your style) / Masterpiece / Ma / Law of the land / Plastic man / Hurry tomorrow.
■ **CD** . . . . . . . . . . . . . . . . . . . . ZD 72499
Motown / Dec '86.

### SPECIAL.
**Tracks:** Friends / Special / All I want from you / She's better than money / One step at a time / Fill me up / Go ahead / Loveline / Soul to soul / O.A.O. lover (CD only.)
■ **CD** . . . . . . . . . . . . . . . . . . . . ZD 72667
■ **LP** . . . . . . . . . . . . . . . . . . . . . ZL 72667
■ **MC** . . . . . . . . . . . . . . . . . . . . ZK 72667
Motown / Oct '89.

### STANDING ON THE TOP (Temptations Featuring Rick James).
**Tracks:** Standing on the top / Standing on the top (part 2).
■ **12"** . . . . . . . . . . . . . . . . . . . . TMGT 1263

■ 7" . . . . . . . . . . . . . . . . . . . TMG 1263
Motown / May '82.

## STRUCK BY LIGHTNING TWICE.
Tracks: Struck by lightning twice / I'm coming home.
■ 7" . . . . . . . . . . . . . . . . . . . TMG 1197
Motown / Oct '81.

## SUPERSTAR.
Tracks: Superstar (remember how you got where you are).
■ 7" . . . . . . . . . . . . . . . . . . . TMG 800
Tamla Motown / Feb '72.

## SURFACE THRILLS.
Tracks: Surface thrills / Love on my mind / Tonight / One man woman / Show me your love / Seeker, (The) / What a way to put it / Bring your body here (exercise chant) / Made in America.
■ LP . . . . . . . . . . . . . . . . . . .STML 12182
■ MC . . . . . . . . . . . . . . . . . .CSTML 12182
Motown / Mar '83.

## TAKE A LOOK AROUND.
Tracks: Take a look around.
■ 7" . . . . . . . . . . . . . . . . . . . TMG 808
Tamla Motown / Apr '72.

## TAKE ME AWAY.
Tracks: Take me away / There's more where that came from.
■ 7" . . . . . . . . . . . . . . . . . . . TMG 1216
Motown / Oct '81.

## TEMPTATION'S GREATEST HITS.
Tracks: Not Advised.
■ LP . . . . . . . . . . . . . . . . . .STML 11042
Tamla Motown / Feb '67.

## TEMPTATIONS.
Tracks: Take a look around / Ball of confusion / Get ready / Beauty is only skin deep.
■ MC Single . . . . . . . . . . . . . . CTME 2024
Motown / May '83.

## TEMPTATIONS AND THE FOUR TOPS (Temptations & Four Tops).
Tracks: Standing in the shadows of love / Stop in the name of love / Reach out I'll be there / Papa was a rollin' stone.
VHS . . . . . . . . . . . . . . . . . . VC 4047
Video Collection / Aug '88 / Gold & Sons / Video Collection / THE.

## TEMPTATIONS LIVE.
Tracks: Not Advised.
■ LP . . . . . . . . . . . . . . . . . .STML 11053
Tamla Motown / Jul '67.

## TEMPTATIONS SING SMOKEY.
Tracks: Way you do the things you do / Baby baby I need you / My girl / What love has joined together / You'll lose a precious love / Who's lovin' you / It's growing / What's so good about goodbye.
■ LP . . . . . . . . . . . . . . . . . STMR 9005
■ MC . . . . . . . . . . . . . . . . . CSTMR 9005
Motown / Oct '81.

## TEMPTATIONS WITH A LOT OF SOUL.
Tracks: Not Advised.
■ LP . . . . . . . . . . . . . . . . . .STML 11057
Tamla Motown / Nov '67.

## TEMPTATIONS XMAS CARD.
Tracks: Not Advised.
■ LP . . . . . . . . . . . . . . . . . .SHM 3202
MC. . . . . . . . . . . . . . . . . . .HSC 3202
Pickwick / '88 / Pickwick.

## TEMPTATIONS, THE.
Tracks: Aiming at your heart / Evil woman (gonna take your love) / Best of both worlds / Ready willing and able / Open their eyes / Oh what a night / Life of a cowboy / Just ain't havin' fun / What else / Your lovin' is magic.
■ LP . . . . . . . . . . . . . . . . . .STML 12159
■ MC . . . . . . . . . . . . . . . . . .CSTML 12159
Motown / Jun '82.

## TEMPTATIONS: LIVE IN CONCERT.
Tracks: Not Advised.
VHS . . . . . . . . . . . . . . . . . . SVM 802
Start (Video) / Nov '92 / Sony Video Software.

## TO BE CONTINUED..
Tracks: Lady soul / Message to the world / To be continued / Put us together again / Someone / Girls (they like it) / More love, your love / Fine mess (from 'A Fine Mess'.) / You're the one / Love me right.
■ LP . . . . . . . . . . . . . . . . . . ZL 72515
■ MC . . . . . . . . . . . . . . . . . . ZK 72515
Motown / Sep '86.

## TOGETHER AGAIN.
Tracks: I got your number / Look what you started / I wonder who she's seeing now / 10 x 10 / Do you wanna go with me / Little things / Every time I close my eyes / Lucky / Put your foot down.
■ LP . . . . . . . . . . . . . . . . . . ZL 72616
■ MC . . . . . . . . . . . . . . . . . . ZK 72616
■ CD . . . . . . . . . . . . . . . . . . ZD 72616
Motown / Nov '87.

## TOUCH ME.
Tracks: Magic / Give her some attention / Deeper than love / I'm fascinated / Touch me / Don't break your promise to me / She got tired of loving me / Do you really love your baby / Oh lover.
■ LP . . . . . . . . . . . . . . . . . . ZL 72413
■ MC . . . . . . . . . . . . . . . . . . ZK 72413
Motown / Nov '85.

## TREAT HER LIKE A LADY.
Tracks: Treat her like a lady / Isn't the night fantastic.
■ 12" . . . . . . . . . . . . . . . . . TMGT 1365
■ 7" . . . . . . . . . . . . . . . . . . TMG 1365
Tamla Motown / Nov '84.

## TRULY FOR YOU.
Tracks: Running / Treat her like a lady / How can you say that it's over / My love is true / Memories / Just to keep you in my life / Set your love right / I'll keep my light in my window.
■ LP . . . . . . . . . . . . . . . . . . ZL 72342
MC. . . . . . . . . . . . . . . . . . . ZK 72342
Motown / Dec '84 / PolyGram.
■ LP . . . . . . . . . . . . . . . . . . WL 76244
■ MC . . . . . . . . . . . . . . . . . . WK 76244
■ CD . . . . . . . . . . . . . . . . . . WD 76244
Motown / Oct '88.

## WHO ARE YOU.
Tracks: Who are you / Let me count the ways.
■ 7" . . . . . . . . . . . . . . . . . . TMG 1057
Motown / Oct '76.

## YOU'RE MY EVERYTHING.
Tracks: You're my everything.
■ 7" . . . . . . . . . . . . . . . . . . TMG 620
Tamla Motown / Sep '67.

# Ten City

Formerly Ragtyme, Ten City hooked up with fellow Chicago resident and top house producer Marshall Jefferson for 1989 Foundation debut. Atlantic release spawned first and last Top 10 hit, That's The Way Love Is. Band persevered into '90s; ending up on Columbia after minor stint with East West. Latest album ranges from swing to more traditional dance sound, topped by vocals of spendidly-monickered leader Byron Stingily.

## (IS IT LOVE) ONLY TIME WILL TELL.
Tracks: (Is it love) Only time will tell / (Is it love) only time will tell (mix) / My piece of heaven / My piece of heaven (mix).
■ 12" . . . . . . . . . . . . . . . . . A 8516T
■ 7" . . . . . . . . . . . . . . . . . .A 8516
■ CD Single . . . . . . . . . . . . . . A 8516CD
■ MC Single . . . . . . . . . . . . . . A 8516C
Atlantic / Aug '92.

## DEVOTION.
Tracks: Devotion (halla-pela).
■ 7" . . . . . . . . . . . . . . . . . .A 9153
Atlantic / Nov '87.

## DEVOTION.
Tracks: Devotion.
■ 12" . . . . . . . . . . . . . . . . . A 8916 T
■ 7" . . . . . . . . . . . . . . . . . .A 8916
■ CD Single . . . . . . . . . . . . . . A 8916 CD
Atlantic / Mar '89.
■ 12" . . . . . . . . . . . . . . . . . A 8916 TX
Atlantic / May '89.

## FANTASY.
Tracks: Fantasy / Joy and pain / Fantasy (mixes) (On CD single only).
■ 12" . . . . . . . . . . . . . . . . . .659504 6
■ CD Single . . . . . . . . . . . . . . .659504 2
■ MC Single . . . . . . . . . . . . . . .659504 4
Columbia / Sep '93.

## FOUNDATION.
Tracks: That's the way love is / Where do we go / Suspicious / Close and slow / One kiss will make it better / Devotion / Satisfaction / You must be the one / For you / Foundation.
■ CD . . . . . . . . . . . . . . . . . . 781 939-2
■ CD . . . . . . . . . . . . . . . . . . WX 249CD
■ LP . . . . . . . . . . . . . . . . . . WX 249

## MC. . . . . . . . . . . . . . . . . . . WX 249C
Atlantic / Feb '89 / WEA.

## NO HOUSE BIG ENOUGH.
Tracks: My peace of heaven / Only time will tell / She all that and more / Come this way again / School me / Keep kiss / All loved out / You'll never know lonely / You need a love of your own / Midnight / Thick & thin.
CD. . . . . . . . . . . . . . . . . . . 7567921702
■ LP . . . . . . . . . . . . . . . . . . 7567921701
MC. . . . . . . . . . . . . . . . . . . 7567921704
East West / Aug '92 / WEA.

## RIGHT BACK TO YOU.
Tracks: Right back to you / One kiss will make it better.
■ 12" . . . . . . . . . . . . . . . . . A 9088 T
■ 7" . . . . . . . . . . . . . . . . . .A 9088
Atlantic / May '88.

## STATE OF MIND.
Tracks: State of mind / Livin' easy / Whatever makes you happy / I should learn to love you / Superficial people / Put love where you want it / Destiny / Nothing's changed / It ain't no big thing / Heartache (Not available on LP).
CD. . . . . . . . . . . . . . . . . . . 7567921462
■ LP . . . . . . . . . . . . . . . . . . WX 393
■ MC . . . . . . . . . . . . . . . . . . WX 393C
Atlantic / Oct '90 / WEA.

## SUPERFICIAL PEOPLE.
Tracks: Superficial people / Nothing's changed / Superficial people (version) (Only on 12" and CD single) / Where do we go (Only on 12" and CD single).
■ 12" . . . . . . . . . . . . . . . . . A 7780TC
■ 7" . . . . . . . . . . . . . . . . . .A 7780
■ CD Single . . . . . . . . . . . . . . A 7780CD
Atlantic / Dec '90.

## THAT WAS THEN, THIS IS NOW.
Tracks: Fantasy (Demo version) / Way you make me feel / Goin' up in smoke / When I'm gone, I'm gone / Love in a day / Whay my love can do / Interlude / Then / Under you / All this love / Joy and pain / All I want / Say something / Fantasy (Funky ginger mix) / Now.
CD. . . . . . . . . . . . . . . . . . . .474594 2
LP . . . . . . . . . . . . . . . . . . .474594 1
MC. . . . . . . . . . . . . . . . . . . .474594 4
Columbia / May '94 / Sony.

## THAT'S THE WAY LOVE IS.
Tracks: That's the way love is / That's the way love is (version) / Devotion (Only on 12" version).
■ 12" . . . . . . . . . . . . . . . . . A 8963 T
■ 7" . . . . . . . . . . . . . . . . . .A 8963
Atlantic / Jan '89.

## WHATEVER MAKES YOU HAPPY.
Tracks: Whatever makes you happy / Whatever makes you happy (version).
■ 12" . . . . . . . . . . . . . . . . . A 7819T
■ 7" . . . . . . . . . . . . . . . . . .A 7819
■ CD Single . . . . . . . . . . . . . . A 7819CD
■ MC Single . . . . . . . . . . . . . . A 7819C
Atlantic / Oct '90.

## WHERE DO WE GO.
Tracks: Where do we go / Where do we go (version).
■ 12" . . . . . . . . . . . . . . . . . A 8864 T
■ 7" . . . . . . . . . . . . . . . . . .A 8864
■ CD Single . . . . . . . . . . . . . . A 8864 CD
■ MC Single . . . . . . . . . . . . . . A 8864 C
Atlantic / Jul '89.

# Terrell, Dino

## YOU CAN DO IT.
Tracks: You can do it / You can do it (instrumental) / Acal-poco (On 12" track only) / You can do it (dub) (On 12" version only).
■ 12" . . . . . . . . . . . . . . . . . LOVT 3
■ 7" . . . . . . . . . . . . . . . . . . LOV 3
Lovebeat Int. / Mar '86.

# Terrell, Tammi

## 2 CLASSIC ALBUMS : GREATEST HITS
(see under Gaye, Marvin).

## COME ON AND SEE ME.
Tracks: Come on and see me / Baby don'tcha worry.
■ 7" . . . . . . . . . . . . . . . . . . TMG 561
Tamla Motown / May '66.

## EASY (see under Gaye, Marvin).

## GREATEST HITS: TAMMI TERRELL (see under Gaye, Marvin).

## IRRESISTIBLE.

Tracks: I can't believe you love me / That's what boys are made for / Come on and see me / What a good man he is / Tears at the end of a love affair / This old heart of mine / He's the one I love / Can't stop now / Just too much to hope for / Hold me oh my darling / I can't go on without you.
■ **LP** . . . . . . . . . . . . . . . . . . . . . . . **STML 11103**
Tamla Motown / May '69.

## IRRESISTIBLE TAMMI TERRELL.

Tracks: Not Advised.
■ **LP** . . . . . . . . . . . . . . . . . . . . . . . . **M 652**
Tamla Motown / Jan '68.

## ONION SONG (see under Gaye, Marvin).

## TWO CAN HAVE A PARTY (see under Gaye, Marvin).

## UNITED (see under Gaye, Marvin).

## YOU'RE ALL I NEED (see under Gaye, Marvin).

# Terri & Monica

## SYSTA.

Tracks: Uh huh / Lisa listen to me / Over it / Intentions / Super-natural thing / Next time / I've been waiting / I need your love / Way you make me feel / Temptation / Where are you now / When the tables turn.
LP . . . . . . . . . . . . . . . . . . . . . . . .474741 1
Epic / Dec '93 / Sony.
CD . . . . . . . . . . . . . . . . . . . . . . . .477108 2
LP . . . . . . . . . . . . . . . . . . . . . . . .477108 1
MC . . . . . . . . . . . . . . . . . . . . . . . .477108 4
Epic / Jun '94 / Sony.

## UH-HUH.

Tracks: Uh-huh (Mixes).
■ 12" . . . . . . . . . . . . . . . . . . . . . .660418 6
■ CD Single . . . . . . . . . . . . . . . . . .660418 2
■ MC Single . . . . . . . . . . . . . . . . . .660418 4
Epic / May '94.

# Terry, Ruby

## CHAPTER ONE.

Tracks: Not Advised.
■ **LP** . . . . . . . . . . . . . . . . . . . . **MALP 4433**
MC . . . . . . . . . . . . . . . . . . . . . **MALC 4433**
Malaco / '89 / C.M. Distribution / Charly / Pinnacle.

# Terry, Tony

## FOREVER YOURS.

Tracks: Forever yours / Lovey dovey / Fulltime girl / Daydreaming / Here with me / She's fly / Wassup wit u / Up and down love / Young love / What would it take / Forever yours (late night version) / Lovey dovey (remix).
■ **MC** . . . . . . . . . . . . . . . . . . . . . . **4605044**
■ **LP** . . . . . . . . . . . . . . . . . . . . . . **4605041**
Epic / Dec '87.
CD . . . . . . . . . . . . . . . . . . . . . . . **4605042**
Epic / Dec '87 / Sony.

## FOREVER YOURS.

Tracks: Forever yours / Here with me / Forever yours (LP version) (Only on 12".) / Forever yours (Late night version) (Only on 12".) / Forever yours (inst) (Only on 12".).
■ 12" . . . . . . . . . . . . . . . . . . . . . . **TONY T3**
■ 12" Remix . . . . . . . . . . . . . . . . . **TON QT3**
■ 7" . . . . . . . . . . . . . . . . . . . . . . . **TONY 3**
■ CD Single . . . . . . . . . . . . . . . . **CD TONY 3**
Epic / May '88.

## FORGET THE GIRL.

Tracks: Forget the girl (extended remix) / Forget the girl (Midtown mix) / Forget the girl (accapella).
■ 12" . . . . . . . . . . . . . . . . . . . . . . **6550216**
Epic / Jun '89.

## HEAD OVER HEELS.

Tracks: Head over heels (LP edit) (Available on 7" and CD single formats only.) / Head over heels (easy listening version) (Available on 7" and CD single formats only.) / Forget the girl (extended remix) (Available on 12" and CD single formats only.) / Lovey dovey (long version) (Available on 12" single format only.) / Head over heels (LP version) / Lovey dovey (remix) (Available on CD single format only.) / Head over heels (heads up mix) (Second 12" only.) / She's fly (long version) (Second 12" only.).
■ 7" . . . . . . . . . . . . . . . . . . . . . . . **6565517**
Epic / Dec '90.
■ 12" . . . . . . . . . . . . . . . . . . . . . . **6565516**
■ 12" . . . . . . . . . . . . . . . . . . . . . . **6565518**

■ CD Single . . . . . . . . . . . . . . . . . . **6565512**
■ MC Single . . . . . . . . . . . . . . . . . . **6565514**
Epic / Dec '90.

## LOVEY DOVEY.

Tracks: Lovey dovey (long version) / Lovey dovey (dub) / Lovey dovey (Charlie Dee dub) / Lovey dovey (dove-tale mix) (Track on special remix.) / Lovey dovey (Charlie Dee dub - new speed) (Track on special remix.).
■ 12" . . . . . . . . . . . . . . . . . . . . . . **TONY QT2**
■ 12" . . . . . . . . . . . . . . . . . . . . . . **TONY T2**
■ 12" Remix . . . . . . . . . . . . . . . . . **TONY QR 2**
■ 7" . . . . . . . . . . . . . . . . . . . . . . . **TONY 2**
Epic / Feb '88.

## SHE'S FLY.

Tracks: She's fly.
■ 12" . . . . . . . . . . . . . . . . . . . . . . **TONY T1**
■ 7" . . . . . . . . . . . . . . . . . . . . . . . **TONY 1**
Epic / Oct '87.

## TONY TERRY.

Tracks: Head over heels / Bad girl / Baby love / Friends and lovers / With you / Come home with me / That kind of guy / Tongue tied / Let me love you / Read my mind / Everlasting love.
CD . . . . . . . . . . . . . . . . . . . . . . . .4658282
MC . . . . . . . . . . . . . . . . . . . . . . . .4658284
■ **LP** . . . . . . . . . . . . . . . . . . . . . . .4658281
Epic / Dec '90 / Sony.

## WITH YOU.

Tracks: With you / Head over heels / Young love (Only on 12" Single.) / Forget the girl (Only on 12" Single.) / Lovey dovey.
■ 12" . . . . . . . . . . . . . . . . . . . . . . **6576456**
■ 7" . . . . . . . . . . . . . . . . . . . . . . . **6576457**
■ CD Single . . . . . . . . . . . . . . . . . . **6576452**
■ MC Single . . . . . . . . . . . . . . . . . . **6576454**
Epic / Nov '91.

## YOUNG LOVE.

Tracks: Young love / Young love (acid mix) (TONY QT4 only.) / Young love (age of consent mix) (TONY QT4 only.) / Young love (oh oh Omar dubb mix) (TONY QT4 only.).
■ 12" . . . . . . . . . . . . . . . . . . . . . . **TONY QT4**
■ 12" . . . . . . . . . . . . . . . . . . . . . . **TONY T4**
■ 7" . . . . . . . . . . . . . . . . . . . . . . . **TONY 4**
Epic / Sep '88.

# Tex, Joe

*Hold What You've Got* was not only Joe Tex's first hit but also southern soul's first crossover success. The former Joseph Arrington Jr, whose home state was Texas, had spent nearly a decade in the wilderness, despite having his songs recorded by likes of James Brown. After '64, however, he regularly hit R&B and pop charts, declining only at the end of the decade. Success returned in '72 with his biggest domestic hit, *I Gotcha*, and peaked again in '77 with international smash *Ain't Gonna Bump No More (With No Big Fat Woman)*. He withdrew from public eye in subsequent years and died in 1982.

## AIN'T GONNA BUMP NO MORE.

Tracks: Ain't gonna bump no more / I mess up everything I get my hands on.
■ 7" . . . . . . . . . . . . . . . . . . . . . . **EPC 5035**
Epic / Apr '77.

## AIN'T GONNA BUMP NO MORE.

Tracks: Ain't gonna bump no more / Be cool / Leaving you dinner / I mess eveything up / We held on / Music ain't got no colour / Loose caboose / Rub down / Congratulations / You can be my star / You might be diggin' the garden (but somebody's picking your / Give the baby anything the baby wants / Takin' a chance / You're in too deep / God of love / Baby let me steal you / Woman cares / Love me right girl / I gotcha.
CD . . . . . . . . . . . . . . . . . . . . **CDSEWD 043**
Ace / Jun '93 / Pinnacle / Complete Record Co. Ltd.

## AIN'T GONNA BUMP NO MORE (OLD GOLD).

Tracks: Ain't gonna bump no more / Play that funky music.
■ 7" . . . . . . . . . . . . . . . . . . . . . . .OG 9192
Old Gold / Jul '82.

## AIN'T I A MESS.

Tracks: All I could do was cry (parts 1 and 2) / You keep her / Ain't I a mess / Baby you're right / Sit yourself down / Don't play / Get closer together / I'll never break your heart pts 1 + 2.
■ **LP** . . . . . . . . . . . . . . . . . . . . . **GCH 8120**
Chess (Charly) / '89.

## BEST OF JOE TEX.

Tracks: Sysljfm (the letter song) / Hold what you've got / One monkey don't stop no show / You better get it / You got what it takes / I believe I'm gonna make it / Show me / Papa was too / Woman can change a man / Love you save / Build your love / I've got to do a little bit better.
■ **LP** . . . . . . . . . . . . . . . . . . . . . **780 173-1**
■ **MC** . . . . . . . . . . . . . . . . . . . . . **780 173-4**
Atlantic / Jul '84.

## BUMPS & BRUISES.

Tracks: Ain't gonna bump no more / Leaving you dinner / Be cool / I mess up everything I get my hands on / We held on / I almost got to heaven once / Hungry for love / Jump bad / There's something wrong.
■ **LP** . . . . . . . . . . . . . . . . . . . . . **EPC 81931**
Epic / Jun '77.

## BUYING A BOOK.

Tracks: We can't sit down now / Sure is good / That's the way / Anything you wanna know / It ain't sanitary / Only way / Grandma Mary / Get your lies together / Same things you did to get me / Buying a book.
■ **LP** . . . . . . . . . . . . . . . . . . . . . **588 193**
Atlantic / Oct '69.

## DIFFERENT STROKES.

Tracks: Have you ever / My neighbours got the gimmes / Mrs. Wiggles / Baby it's rainin' / Under your powerful love / Don't play with me / Same things it took to get me / All a man needs is his woman's love / When a woman stops loving a man / I can see everybody's baby / She said yeah / Time brings about a change / I don't want you to love me / I'm gonna try love again / This time we'll make it all the way / It's ridiculous / We're killing ourselves / Back off / Does it run in your family / Living in the last days / I've seen enough.
CD . . . . . . . . . . . . . . . . . . **CDCHARLY 161**
■ Double LP . . . . . . . . . . . . . . . . . . **CDX 41**
MC . . . . . . . . . . . . . . . . . . . . . **TCCDX 41**
Charly / Jan '89 / Charly.

## GET BACK LEROY.

Tracks: Get back Leroy / You can be my star.
■ 7" . . . . . . . . . . . . . . . . . . . . . . **EPC 6303**
Epic / May '78.

## GREATEST HITS.

Tracks: Hold what you got / You got what it takes / Woman / I want to / I believe I'm gonna make it / I've got to do a little bit better / Letter song / Papa was too / Show me / Sweet woman like you / Love you save / You better get it.
■ **LP** . . . . . . . . . . . . . . . . . . . . . **588 079**
Atlantic / Nov '67.

## GREATEST HITS: JOE TEX.

Tracks: Not Advised.
CD . . . . . . . . . . . . . . . . . . . . **KWEST 5259**
MC . . . . . . . . . . . . . . . . . . . . **KWEST 4259**
Kwest / Jul '92 / THE.

## HOLD WHAT YOU'VE GOT.

Tracks: Hold what you've got / Sweet woman like you.
■ 7" . . . . . . . . . . . . . . . . . . . . . . .584096
Atlantic / Mar '67.

## I GOT 'CHA.

Tracks: I got 'cha / You said a bad word.
■ 7" . . . . . . . . . . . . . . . . . . . . . . .6167 548
Mercury / Jun '77.

## I GOTCHA.

Tracks: I gotcha / Give the baby anything the baby wants / Takin' a chance / Baby let me steal you / It ain't gonna work baby / God of love / You said a bad word / Bad feet / Woman cares / Love me right girl / For my woman / You're in too deep.
■ **LP** . . . . . . . . . . . . . . . . . . . . . . **6338093**
Mercury / Jul '72.

## I GOTCHA (His Greatest Hits).

Tracks: Hold what you've got / You got what it takes / Woman can change a man / One monkey don't stop no show / I want (to do everything for you) / Sweet woman like you / Love you save (may be your own) / S.Y.S.L.J.F.M. (The letter song) / I believe I'm gonna make it / I've got to do a little bit better / Papa was. too (Tramp) / Show me / Woman like that, yeah / Woman's hands / Skinny legs and all / Men are gettin' scarce / I'll never do you wrong / Keep the one you got / Buying a book / I gotcha.
CD . . . . . . . . . . . . . . . . . . . . **CPCD 8015**
Charly / Feb '94 / Charly.

## I KNEW HIM.

Tracks: I knew him / Bad feet.
■ 7" . . . . . . . . . . . . . . . . . . . . . . **6052067**
Mercury / Apr '71.

## I WANT TO.
**Tracks:** I want to / Funny bone.
■ 7" . . . . . . . . . . . . . . . . . . . . . AT 4045
Atlantic / Sep '65.

## LIVE AND LIVELY.
**Tracks:** Show me / Do right woman / Get out of my life woman / Wooden spoon / That's life / Love is a hurtin' thing / Don't give up / Woman's hands / You're gonna thank me / Papa was too / Skinny legs and all.
■ LP . . . . . . . . . . . . . . . . . . . . 588 104
Atlantic / Apr '68.

## LOVE YOU SAVE, THE.
**Tracks:** Love you save / If sugar was as sweet as you.
■ 7" . . . . . . . . . . . . . . . . . . . . . AT 4081
Atlantic / Mar '66.

## PAPA WAS TOO.
**Tracks:** Papa was too / Truest woman in the world.
■ 7" . . . . . . . . . . . . . . . . . . . . .584068
Atlantic / Jan '67.

## RUB DOWN.
**Tracks:** Rub down / Be kind to old people.
■ 7" . . . . . . . . . . . . . . . . . . . . EPC 6068
Epic / Feb '78.

## RUB DOWN.
**Tracks:** Rub down / You can be my star / Get it / Get back / Leroy / Be kind to old people / You might be digging the garden / Don't cry over spilled milk / I gotcha / I know how you like your loving / Congratulations.
■ LP . . . . . . . . . . . . . . . . . . . EPC 82481
Epic / Apr '78.

## S.Y.S.L.J.F.M. (LETTER SONG).
**Tracks:** S.Y.S.L.J.F.M. (Letter song) / I'm a man.
■ 7" . . . . . . . . . . . . . . . . . . . . .584016
Atlantic / Jun '66.

## SHOW ME.
**Tracks:** Show me / Hold what you've got.
■ 7" . . . . . . . . . . . . . . . . . . . . CS 8001
Cool Tempo / Mar '78.

## SHOW ME.
**Tracks:** Show me / I want to / Papa was too / You better believe it, baby / I'm a man / Hold what you've got / Skinny legs and all / If sugar was as sweet as you / I'll never do you wrong / What in the world / Woman sees a hard time / S.Y.S.L.J.F.M.
■ LP . . . . . . . . . . . . . . . . . . . .2464 004
Atlantic / Jun '70.
CD . . . . . . . . . . . . . . . . . . . .FCD 104
Fan Club / Mar '92 / Pinnacle.

## SHOW ME.
**Tracks:** Show me / Woman sees a hard time.
■ 7" . . . . . . . . . . . . . . . . . . . . .584102
Atlantic / Apr '67.

## SHOW ME EP.
**Tracks:** Show me / Hold what you've got / Ooh Otis, ooh Carla / Tramp.
■ EP . . . . . . . . . . . . . . . . . . . . ATM 5
Atlantic / Apr '80.

## SHOW ME THE HITS AND MORE.
**Tracks:** Not Advised.
CD . . . . . . . . . . . . . . . . . . .ICH 1149CD
Ichiban / Jan '94 / A.D.A. Distribution / Pinnacle / ACD Trading Ltd. / Koch International / Direct Distribution.

## SINGS WITH STRINGS AND THINGS.
**Tracks:** Everything happens on time / Same old soup / I love you and I thank you / Little friendly advice / Take my baby a little love / You're right, Ray Charles / She might need me / Daddy's got a bad back / My wife my woman / When Johnny comes marching home again / I can't see you no more.
■ LP . . . . . . . . . . . . . . . . . . . .2465 001
Atlantic / Aug '70.

## SKINNY LEGS AND ALL.
**Tracks:** S.Y.S.L.J.F.M. (The letter song) / Love you save (may be your own) / Show me / Hold what you've got / Heep see few know / Someone to take your place / One monkey don't show no show / If sugar was as sweet as you / Meet me in church / You got what it takes / I had a good home but I left (part 1) / Don't let your left hand know / Woman can change a man / Skinny legs and all / I want to (do everything for you) / Sweet woman like you / I believe I'm gonna make it / Men are getting scarce / I'm a man / I've got to do a little bit better / Papa was too / Watch the one (that brings the bad news) / Truest woman in the world / Chicken crazy.
CD . . . . . . . . . . . . . . . . . . .CDKEND 114
Kent / Mar '94 / Pinnacle.

## SOUL COUNTRY.
**Tracks:** I'll never do you wrong / Ode to Billie Joe / Dark end of the street / Funny how time slips away / Enging engine no. 9 / Skip a rope / Green green grass of home / Set me free / By the time I get to Phoenix.
■ LP . . . . . . . . . . . . . . . . . . . . 588 118
Atlantic / Oct '68.

## STONE SOUL COUNTRY.
**Tracks:** Just out of reach / Detroit city / Set me free / Heartbreak Hotel / Together again / King of the road / At the dark end of the street / I'll never do you wrong / Make the world go away / Funny how time slips away / Ode to Billy Joe / Release me / Skip a rope / Engine engine / Honey / By the time I get to Phoenix / Green green grass of home / Papa's dreams.
CD . . . . . . . . . . . . . . . . CDCHARLY 184
■ LP . . . . . . . . . . . . . . . . . . . CRB 1215
MC . . . . . . . . . . . . . . . . . . . TCCRB 1215
Charly R&B / Jun '89 / Charly.

## SWEET WOMAN LIKE YOU, A.
**Tracks:** Sweet woman like you / Close the door.
■ 7" . . . . . . . . . . . . . . . . . . . . AT 4058
Atlantic / Dec '65.

## VERY BEST OF JOE TEX, THE.
**Tracks:** Hold what you've got / One monkey don't stop no show / Woman (can change a man) / I want (do everything for you) / Don't make your children pay (for your mistakes) / Sweet woman like you / Love you save / You better believe it baby / I've got to do a little bit better / S.Y.S.L.J.F.M. (The letter song) / I believe I'm gonna make it / Woman sees a hard time (when her man is gone) / Watch the one (that brings the bad news) / Papa was too / Truest woman in the world / Show me / Woman like that, yeah / Woman's hands / Skinny legs and all / Men are getting scarce / I'll never do you wrong / Keep the one you've got / You need me, baby / Buying a book / It ain't sanitary / You're right, Ray Charles / I gotcha.
CD . . . . . . . . . . . . . . . . CDCHARLY 133
■ Double LP . . . . . . . . . . . . . . . . CDX 29
MC . . . . . . . . . . . . . . . . . . .TCCDX 29
Charly / Jul '88 / Charly.

## YOU BETTER GET IT.
**Tracks:** You got what it takes / Tell me right now / One monkey don't stop no show / Are we ready / Hold what you've got / I'm not going to work today / You better get it / Heep see few know / You can stay / Fresh out of tears / There is a girl / Together we stand.
■ LP . . . . . . . . . . . . . . . . . . . . 588 130
Atlantic / Dec '68.

## Think 2wice

### ALCOHOLIC BLUES.
**Tracks:** Alcoholic blues.
■ 12" . . . . . . . . . . . . . . . . . . . . CFT 1
■ 7" . . . . . . . . . . . . . . . . . . . . CSE 1
Conscience / Jul '88.

### HEAVEN IN YOUR EYES.
**Tracks:** Heaven in your eyes / Ease the pressure.
■ 12" . . . . . . . . . . . . . . . . . . . . IB-1
Internal Bass / Feb '92.

### WAITING 4 YOU.
**Tracks:** Waiting 4 you.
■ 12" . . . . . . . . . . . . . . . . . . . 12IB 5
■ CD Single . . . . . . . . . . . . . . . . CDIB 5
■ MC Single . . . . . . . . . . . . . . . . CAIB 5
Internal Bass / Sep '93.

## Third Party

### BORDERLINE E.P.
**Tracks:** Not Advised.
12" . . . . . . . . . . . . . . . . . . . KM 3RD1
Kemet / Jun '94 / Jetstar.

## Thomas & Taylor

### I GIVE YOU ME.
**Tracks:** I give you me / You can't blame love (1990 extended mix).
■ 12" . . . . . . . . . . . . . . . . . . ICHT 710
Ichiban / Nov '90.

### I LOVE YOU.
**Tracks:** Love and affection.
■ 12" . . . . . . . . . . . . . . . . . . . .INRT 3
■ 7" . . . . . . . . . . . . . . . . . . . . INT 3
In Recordings / Feb '87.

## TRUE LOVE (BOOK 1).
**Tracks:** Lonely too long / True love / You can't blame love (remix) / You can't blame love / Freedom / My room / Love and affection (remix) / Call me / I love you.
■ LP . . . . . . . . . . . . . . . . . . . .INRLP 1
MC . . . . . . . . . . . . . . . . . . . . INRC 1
In Recordings / Jan '87.

## YOU CAN'T BLAME LOVE.
**Tracks:** You can't blame love / We need company.
■ 12" . . . . . . . . . . . . . . . . . . COOLX 123
■ 7" . . . . . . . . . . . . . . . . . . .COOL 123
Cool Tempo / May '86.

## YOU CAN'T BLAME LOVE - AN ANTHOLOGY.
**Tracks:** City lights / Who can the winner be / I'll be waiting (radio) / You can't blame love (original radio mix) / Why don't you try me / Don't let it be (all in my mind) / I don't want to go through love again / Try me / Freedom / My room / Love and affection / My life / Give it up / Snake in the grass (radio) / Freedom (extended mix) / Snake in the grass (extended) / I'll be waiting (extended mix) / I love you / Lonely (too long) / True love / Call me / Hey brother / Don't forget (who you are) / You can't blame love (original extended mix).
CD Set . . . . . . . . . . . . . . NED CD 227
Sequel / Oct '92 / Total / BMG.

# Thomas, B.J.

## 16 GREATEST HITS.
**Tracks:** Not Advised.
■ CD . . . . . . . . . . . . . . . . . .CD 1014
Gusto (USA) / '88.

## AMAZING GRACE.
**Tracks:** Amazing grace / His eye is on the sparrow / Unclouded day / In the garden / You'll never walk alone / Old rugged cross / Just a closer walk with thee / I believe / Just as I am / Beyond the sunset.
■ LP . . . . . . . . . . . . . . . . . . .WST 9611
MC . . . . . . . . . . . . . . . . . . . .WC 9611
Word (UK) / May '82 / Word Records (UK) / Sony.

## ANOTHER SOMEBODY DONE SOMEBODY WRONG SONG.
**Tracks:** Another somebody done somebody wrong song / City boys.
■ 7" . . . . . . . . . . . . . . . . . . .ABC 4043
ABC Records / '75.

## B.J.THOMAS.
**Tracks:** Not Advised.
MC . . . . . . . . . . . . . . . . . . ZCGAS 723
Audio Fidelity / Oct '84 / Telstar/Ronco.

## BEST OF B.J. THOMAS.
**Tracks:** Not Advised.
MC . . . . . . . . . . . . . . . . . . . . . 16-14
Creole (Everest-Europa) / Jul '84.

## BILLY JOE THOMAS.
**Tracks:** That's what friends are for / Rock'n'roll lullaby / Happier than the morning sun / Roads / Sweet cherry wine / Song for my brother / Fine way to go / Just as gone / I get enthused / Are we losing touch / We have to get our ship together / Stories we can tell.
■ LP . . . . . . . . . . . . . . . . . . . WNS 17
Wand / Aug '72.

## CLOSE TO YOU.
**Tracks:** Not Advised.
MC . . . . . . . . . . . . . . . . . . . ORC 008
Orchid Music / Feb '82 / Pinnacle.

## DON'T WORRY BABY.
**Tracks:** Don't worry baby / My love.
■ 7" . . . . . . . . . . . . . . . . . . . MCA 313
MCA / Aug '77.

## EVERYBODY LOVES A RAIN SONG.
**Tracks:** Everybody loves a rain song / Dusty roads.
■ 7" . . . . . . . . . . . . . . . . . . . MCA 351
MCA / Feb '78.

## I CAN'T HELP IT.
**Tracks:** I can't help it / Baby cried.
■ 7" . . . . . . . . . . . . . . . . . . 7N 25426
Pye / Jul '67.

## MIGHTY CLOUDS OF JOY.
**Tracks:** Mighty clouds of joy / Life.
■ 7" . . . . . . . . . . . . . . . . . . . . WN 19
Wand / Jul '71.

## MIRACLE.
**Tracks:** Not Advised.
■ LP . . . . . . . . . . . . . . . . . . .MYR 1128

**THOMAS, B.J.**

MC. . . . . . . . . . . . . . . . .MC 1128
Myrrh / May '82 / Word Records (UK) / Sony.

**NEW LOOKS.**
Tracks: New looks from an old lover / Wind beneath my wings / I'm saving all the good times for you / You keep the man in me happy (and the child in me alive) / Whatever happened to old-fashioned love / Rock and roll you're beautiful / Memory machine / I love us / I just sing.
■ LP . . . . . . . . . . . . . . . . . EPC 25378
MC. . . . . . . . . . . . . . . . . .40 25378
Epic / Aug '83 / Sony.

**NO LOVE AT ALL.**
Tracks: No love at all / Have a heart.
■ 7". . . . . . . . . . . . . . . . . . WN 16
Wand / May '71.

**RAINDROPS KEEP FALLING ON MY HEAD.**
Tracks: Raindrops keep falling on my head.
■ 7". . . . . . . . . . . . . . . . . . WN 1
Wand / Feb '70.

**WHATEVER HAPPENED TO OLD FAS-HIONED LOVE.**
Tracks: Whatever happened to old fashioned love / I just sing.
■ 7". . . . . . . . . . . . . . . . . EPCA 3244
Epic / Jul '83.

**YOU GAVE ME LOVE.**
Tracks: Not Advised.
■ LP . . . . . . . . . . . . . . . . .WRD 3006
MC. . . . . . . . . . . . . . . . .TC WRD 3006
Word (UK) / Jun '84 / Word Records (UK) / Sony.

## Thomas, Carla

**B-A-B-Y.**
Tracks: B-A-B-Y / Let me be good to you.
■ 7". . . . . . . . . . . . . . . . . K 10597
Atlantic / Aug '75.

**B-A-B-Y.**
Tracks: B-A-B-Y / What have you got to offer me.
■ 7". . . . . . . . . . . . . . . . . .584042
Atlantic / Oct '66.

**BEST OF CARLA THOMAS, THE.**
Tracks: Where do I go / I've fallen in love / I like what you're doing (to me) / Strung out over you / Just keep on loving me / My life / I need you woman / I can't stop / Some other man (is beating your time) / Guide me well / Time for love / (I'm going back to) living in the City / All I have to do is dream / I loved you like I love my very life / Hi de ho (that old sweet roll) / You've got a cushion to fall on / Love means you never have to say you're sorry / Sugar / I may not be all you want (but I'm all you got) / Love among people / I have a God who loves / Gee whiz / I'll never stop loving you.
CD. . . . . . . . . . . . . . . . . CDSXD 093
Stax / Aug '93 / Pinnacle.

**CARLA.**
Tracks: Not Advised.
CD. . . . . . . . . . . . . . . . . 7567823402
Atlantic / Jul '93 / WEA.

**COMFORT ME.**
Tracks: Comfort me / I'm for you.
■ 7". . . . . . . . . . . . . . . . . AT 4074
Atlantic / Feb '66.

**COMFORT ME.**
Tracks: Not Advised.
CD. . . . . . . . . . . . . . . . .756780329-2
Atlantic / Jun '93 / WEA.

**HIDDEN GEMS.**
Tracks: I'll never stop loving you / I wonder about love / Little boy / Loneliness / (Your love is a) lifesaver / Sweet sensation / You'll lose a good thing / I've made up my mind / My man believes in me / I like it / Run around / Good good lovin' / That beat keeps disturbing my sleep / If it's not asking too much / It ain't no easy thing / Toe hold / Good man / I can't hide it / Thump in my heart / Goodbye my love.
CD. . . . . . . . . . . . . . . . . CDSXD 039
Stax / Oct '91 / Pinnacle.

**I LIKE WHAT YOU'RE DOING TO ME.**
Tracks: I like what you're doing (to me).
■ 7". . . . . . . . . . . . . . . . . STAX 819
Stax / Oct '87.

**LOVE MEANS.**
Tracks: Didn't we / Are you sure / What is love / Daughter, you're still your daddy's child / Love means you never have to say you're sorry / You've got a cushion to fall on / Il est plus doux que / Cherish / I wake up wanting you.

■ LP . . . . . . . . . . . . . . . . . 2362023
Stax / May '72.
CD. . . . . . . . . . . . . . . . . CDSXE 060
Stax / Jul '92 / Pinnacle.

**MEMPHIS QUEEN.**
Tracks: I like what you're doing (to me) / Don't say no more / Strung out over you / Guide me well / Where do I go / I play for keeps / I've fallen in love / How can you throw my love away / Precious memor-ies / Unyielding / More man than I ever had / He's beating your time.
■ LP . . . . . . . . . . . . . . . .SXATS 1019
Stax / Nov '69.
■ LP . . . . . . . . . . . . . . . . . 2363004
Stax / Jul '71.
CD. . . . . . . . . . . . . . . . . CDSXE 027
Stax / Mar '90 / Pinnacle.

**QUEEN ALONE, THE.**
Tracks: Not Advised.
CD. . . . . . . . . . . . . . . . . 8122710152
WEA / Jul '93 / WEA.

**SOMETHING GOOD.**
Tracks: Something good / It's starting to grow.
7". . . . . . . . . . . . . . . . . .601002
Stax / Mar '67 / Pinnacle.

**WHEN TOMMOROW COMES.**
Tracks: When tommorow comes / Unchanging love.
■ 7". . . . . . . . . . . . . . . . . .601008
Stax / Apr '67.

## Thomas, Chris

**BEGINNING, THE.**
Tracks: Not Advised.
■ LP . . . . . . . . . . . . . . . ARHOOLIE 1096
MC. . . . . . . . . . . . . . . . . ARHC 1096
Arhoolie (USA) / '88 / Pinnacle / Cadillac / Swift / Projection / Hot Shot / A.D.A. Distribution / Jazz Music.

**CRY OF THE PROPHETS.**
Tracks: Angel lady / Wanna die with a smile on my face / Dance to the music till my savior comes / Alpha omega / Last real man / Cry of the prophets / Heart and soul / Help us, somebody / I'm gonna make it / All nite long / I need you.
CD. . . . . . . . . . . . . . . . . 7599261862
■ LP . . . . . . . . . . . . . . . . 7599261861
MC. . . . . . . . . . . . . . . . . 7599261864
Sire / Jul '90 / WEA.

**SIMPLE.**
Tracks: Not Advised.
CD. . . . . . . . . . . . . . . . . HCD 8043
Hightone / Jun '94 / A.D.A. Distribution / Koch International.

## Thomas, Don

**COME ON TRAIN.**
Tracks: Come on train / Come on train (version).
■ 7". . . . . . . . . . . . . . . . . DJS 670
DJM / May '76.

## Thomas, Evelyn

**COLD SHOULDER.**
Tracks: Cold shoulder / Hot mix (Track on 12" remix version only.).
■ 12". . . . . . . . . . . . . . . . .SOHOT 60
■ 7". . . . . . . . . . . . . . . . . SOHO 60
Record Shack / Mar '86.

**DOOMSDAY.**
Tracks: Doomsday / Day after doomsday.
■ 7". . . . . . . . . . . . . . . . . BTC 1017
20th Century / Apr '76.

**HEARTLESS.**
Tracks: Heartless / Heartless (part 2).
■ 12". . . . . . . . . . . . . . . . .SOHOT 30
■ 7". . . . . . . . . . . . . . . . . SOHO 30
Record Shack / Nov '84.

**HIGH ENERGY.**
Tracks: Not Advised.
■ LP . . . . . . . . . . . . . . . . SOHOLP 4
Record Shack / Oct '86.

**HIGH ENERGY.**
Tracks: High energy.
■ 12". . . . . . . . . . . . . . . . .SOHOT 18
■ 7". . . . . . . . . . . . . . . . . SOHO 18
■ 7" P.Disc . . . . . . . . . . . . . SOHOP 18
Record Shack / May '84.

**HIGH ENERGY (90 REMIX).**
Tracks: High energy (90 remix) / Only once in a lifetime.

■ 12". . . . . . . . . . . . . . . . PASH 96(12)
Passion (1) / Nov '89.

**HIGH ENERGY (OLD GOLD).**
Tracks: High energy / Masquerade.
■ 12". . . . . . . . . . . . . . . . .OG 4137
Old Gold / '89.

**HIGH ENERGY (SINGLE) (RE-RELEASE).**
Tracks: Hi energy / Primitive desire.
■ 12". . . . . . . . . . . . . . . . .SOHOB 2
Record Shack / Feb '88.

**I WANNA MAKE IT ON MY OWN.**
Tracks: I wanna make it on my own / It's the magic of your touch / Look no further / Thanks for being there / Back to reality.
■ LP . . . . . . . . . . . . . . . . CAL 2041
Casablanca / Dec '78.

**MASQUERADE.**
Tracks: Masquerade.
■ 12". . . . . . . . . . . . . . . . .SOHOT 25
■ 7". . . . . . . . . . . . . . . . . SOHO 25
Record Shack / Aug '84.

**MASQUERADE (RE-RELEASE).**
Tracks: Masquerade / Reflections / Vanity.
■ 12". . . . . . . . . . . . . . . . .SOHOB 4
Record Shack / Feb '88.

**MY HEAD IN THE STARS.**
Tracks: My head in the stars / Stargazin'.
■ 7". . . . . . . . . . . . . . . . . BTC 1029
20th Century / Mar '77.

**ONE WORLD.**
Tracks: One world.
12". . . . . . . . . . . . . . . . XCLV 009CA
CD Single . . . . . . . . . . . . . XCLV 009CD
■ 12". . . . . . . . . . . . . . . . XCLV 009TB
■ 12". . . . . . . . . . . . . . . . XCLV 009TA
Exclusive (2) / Jul '94 / Pinnacle.

**REFLECTIONS.**
Tracks: Reflections / Running wild in the night.
■ 7". . . . . . . . . . . . . . . . . SOHO 53
Record Shack / Sep '83.
■ 12". . . . . . . . . . . . . . . . .SOHOT 53
Record Shack / Nov '85.
12". . . . . . . . . . . . . . . . .ALMY 017
Almighty / Jan '93 / Total / BMG.

**SORRY WRONG NUMBER.**
Tracks: Sorry wrong number.
■ 12". . . . . . . . . . . . . . . . .SOHOT 41
■ 7". . . . . . . . . . . . . . . . . SOHO 41
Record Shack / Apr '85.

**STANDING AT THE CROSS ROADS.**
Tracks: Standing at the crossroads / Standing at the crossroads (inst).
■ 12". . . . . . . . . . . . . . . . . MARE 31
■ 7". . . . . . . . . . . . . . . . . MARES 31
Nightmare / Apr '87.

**STANDING AT THE CROSSROADS.**
Tracks: Standing at the crossroads / How many hearts / Cold shoulder / Sorry wrong number / Reflections suite / Reflections (love tempo) / Number one lover / Reflections / Tightrope.
■ LP . . . . . . . . . . . . . . . .SOHOLP 10
MC. . . . . . . . . . . . . . . . .SOHOTC 10
Record Shack / Sep '86.

**THANKS FOR BEING THERE.**
Tracks: Thanks for being there / Back to reality.
■ 7". . . . . . . . . . . . . . . . .CAN 192
Casablanca / Apr '80.

**TIGHTROPE.**
Tracks: Tightrope / Tightrope (inst).
■ 12". . . . . . . . . . . . . . . . . MARE 1
■ 7". . . . . . . . . . . . . . . . . MARES 1
Nightmare / Oct '86.

**WEAK SPOT.**
Tracks: Weak spot / Dancin' is my weak spot.
■ 7". . . . . . . . . . . . . . . . . BTC 1014
20th Century / Jan '76.

## Thomas, Irma

**BREAKAWAY.**
Tracks: Without love / Take a look / Time is on my side / Wish someone would care / It's starting to get to me now / He's my guy / What are you trying to do / I'm gonna cry till my tears run dry / You don't miss a good thing (until it's gone) / Anyone who knows what love is (will understand) / It's raining / Please send me someone to love / Another woman's man / While the city sleeps / Straight from the heart / It's a man's woman's world / I've been there before / I need you so / Breakaway.

■ DELETED

■ MC. . . . . . . . . . . . . . . . . . . . . . TC-SSL 6032
■ LP . . . . . . . . . . . . . . . . . . . . . . . SSL 6032
Stateside / Sep '87.

## DOWN AT MUSCLE SHOALS.
Tracks: We got something good / Good to me / Here I am, take me / Security / Let's do it over / Somewhere crying / Woman will do wrong / Yours until tomorrow / I gave you everything / I've been loving you too long / Don't make me stop now / Cheater man / Good things don't come easy (CD only).
■ LP . . . . . . . . . . . . . . . . . . . . . GCH 8104
Chess (Charly) / '89.
CD . . . . . . . . . . . . . . . . . . . . . .CDRED 28
Charly / Sep '91 / Charly.

## HIP SHAKING MAMA.
Tracks: Not Advised.
■ LP . . . . . . . . . . . . . . . . . . . . . .CRM 2019
Charly / Dec '81.

## IN BETWEEN TEARS.
Tracks: Not Advised.
■ LP . . . . . . . . . . . . . . . . . . . . . . CRB 1020
Charly R&B / Mar '81.

## IRMA THOMAS SINGS (Minit And Bandy Originals).
Tracks: Not Advised.
■ LP . . . . . . . . . . . . . . . . . . . . BANDY LP 101
Bandy (USA) / Apr '79.

## LIVE - SIMPLY THE BEST.
Tracks: Breakaway / Time is on my side / Hip shakin' mama / That's what love is all about / Thinking of you / I need somebody / I've been loving you too long / Please please please / It's raining / I done got over/Iko iko/Hey pocky way / Wish someone would care / You can have my husband / Oh me oh my (I'm a fool for you) / Simply the best.
■ CD . . . . . . . . . . . . . . . . . . . . .NETCD 25
Nettwerk / May '91.

## LIVE: IRMA THOMAS.
Tracks: Not Advised.
■ LP . . . . . . . . . . . . . . . . . . . . . . . .HELP 29
Island / Feb '77.

## NEW RULES, THE.
Tracks: New rules / Gonna cry til my tears run dry / I needed somebody / Good things don't come easy / Love of my man / One more time / Thinking of you / Wind beneath my wings / I gave you everything / Yours until tomorrow.
CD . . . . . . . . . . . . . . . . . . . . . . . .CD 2046
Rounder / '86 / Roots Records / C.M. Distribution / Topic Records / A.D.A. Distribution / Direct Distribution.
■ LP . . . . . . . . . . . . . . . . . . . . . REU 1001
Rounder Europa (USA) / Feb '87.
■ LP . . . . . . . . . . . . . . . . . . . . ROUNDER 2046
MC. . . . . . . . . . . . . . . . . . . . .ROUNDER 2046C
Rounder / '88 / Roots Records / C.M. Distribution / Topic Records / A.D.A. Distribution / Direct Distribution.

## RULER OF HEARTS.
Tracks: I did my part / Cry on / For goodness sake / It's raining / Look up / It's too soon to know / Somebody told you / Your love is true / (You ain't) hittin' on nothing / Gone / Two winters long / I done got over it / That's all I ask / Ruler of my heart / Girl needs boy.
CD . . . . . . . . . . . . . . . . . . . . . CDCHARLY 195
Charly / Aug '89 / Charly.
■ LP . . . . . . . . . . . . . . . . . . . . . . CRB 1226
MC. . . . . . . . . . . . . . . . . . . . . . TCCRB 1226
Charly R&B / Aug '89 / Charly.

## RULER OF HEARTS/SHOW ME THE WAY (Thomas, Irma & Aaron Neville).
Tracks: Not Advised.
MC. . . . . . . . . . . . . . . . . . . . . . . . TCAD 24
Charly / Dec '90 / Charly.

## SAFE WITH ME.
Tracks: Safe with me / Don't stop.
■ 12". . . . . . . . . . . . . . . . . . . . . .POLO 12-10
■ 7" . . . . . . . . . . . . . . . . . . . . . . . POLO 10
Polo / Apr '81.

## SOMETHING GOOD.
Tracks: Not Advised.
■ CD . . . . . . . . . . . . . . . . . . . . . CHD 93004
Chess (MCA) / Sep '90.
■ CD . . . . . . . . . . . . . . . . . . . . .CHLD 19103
Chess (MCA) / Mar '93.

## SOUL QUEEN OF NEW ORLEANS.
Tracks: It's raining / Ruler of my heart / I did my part / Cry on / Look up / It's too soon to know / I done got over / That's all I ask / For goodness sake / Gone / Somebody told you / Two winters long / (You ain't) hittin' on nothing / Girl needs boy / In between tears

---

(On CD only) / She'll never be your wife (On CD only) / These four walls (On CD only) / What's so wrong with you loving me (On CD only) / You're the dog (I do the barking myself) (On CD only) / Coming from behind (On CD only) / Wish someone would care (On CD only) / Turn my world around (On CD only).
■ LP . . . . . . . . . . . . . . . . . . . . . . . . .1005
■ MC. . . . . . . . . . . . . . . . . . . . . . . .1005 TC
Maison De Soul / Mar '79.
CD . . . . . . . . . . . . . . . . . . . . . . CPCD 8010
Charly / Feb '94 / Charly.

## TAKE A LOOK.
Tracks: Teasing but you're pleasing / I haven't got time to cry / You don't miss a good thing / Some things you never get used to / It's starting to get me now / Times have changed / He's my guy / Don't look down / What are you trying to do / Wait wait wait.
■ LP . . . . . . . . . . . . . . . . . . . . . MLS 40004
Minit / Aug '68.

## TIME IS ON MY SIDE.
Tracks: Take a look / Time is on my side / Baby don't look down / Times have changed / I done got over it / It's raining / Somebody told you / Wait, wait, wait / Breakaway / I haven't got time to cry / Some things you never get used to / Ruler of my heart / I need your love so bad / Wish someone would care / I want a true true love.
MC. . . . . . . . . . . . . . . . . . . . . . .KENC 010
Kent / Jan '85 / Pinnacle.
■ LP . . . . . . . . . . . . . . . . . . . . . . KENT 010
Kent / Dec '88.

## TIME IS ON MY SIDE - THE BEST OF IRMA THOMAS.
Tracks: Girl needs boy / It's too soon to know / Gone / It's raining / Two winters long / Ruler of my heart / While the city sleeps / Wish someone would care / Breakaway / Time is on my side / Anyone who knows what love is (will understand / (I want a) true, true love / Think again / Long after tonight / Times have changed / He's my guy / Maybe / I'm gonna cry till my tears run dry / Hurt's all gone / Live again / Some things you never get used to / It's starting to get to me now / Take a look.
■ CD . . . . . . . . . . . . . . . . . . . . . . CZ 502
Capitol / Jun '92.

## WALK AROUND HEAVEN.
Tracks: Not Advised.
CD . . . . . . . . . . . . . . . . . . . . ROU 2128CD
Rounder / Apr '94 / Roots Records / C.M. Distribution / Topic Records / A.D.A. Distribution / Direct Distribution.

## WAY I FEEL, THE.
Tracks: Old records / Baby I love you / Sorry wrong number / You can think twice / Sit down and cry / All I know is the way I feel / I'm gonna hold you to your promise / I'll take care of you / Dancing in the street / You don't know nothing about love.
CD . . . . . . . . . . . . . . . . . . . . . . .CD 2058
■ LP . . . . . . . . . . . . . . . . . . . . . ROUNDER 2058
MC. . . . . . . . . . . . . . . . . . . . . ROUNDER 2058 C
Rounder / '88 / Roots Records / C.M. Distribution / Topic Records / A.D.A. Distribution / Direct Distribution.
■ LP . . . . . . . . . . . . . . . . . . . . . .FIEND 112
Demon / Feb '88.
■ CD . . . . . . . . . . . . . . . . . . . . .FIENDCD 112
Demon / Sep '91 / Pinnacle / A.D.A. Distribution.

## WISH SOMEONE WOULD CARE.
Tracks: Not Advised.
■ LP . . . . . . . . . . . . . . . . . . . . . . .LAX 313
Flyover / Apr '79.

## Thomas, Jano

## I SPY FOR THE FBI.
Tracks: I spy for the FBI.
■ 7" . . . . . . . . . . . . . . . . . . . . . . . . 56755
Polydor / Feb '69.

## Thomas, Jimmy

## ALL GOD'S CHILDREN.
Tracks: All God's children.
■ 7" . . . . . . . . . . . . . . . . . . . . . . . . .C 8
Contempo (1) / Apr '73.

## HANG RIGHT ON IN THERE (2 Parts).
Tracks: Hang right on in there / Hang right on in there (part 2).
■ 7" . . . . . . . . . . . . . . . . . . . . . . . .OSC 2
Osceola / Feb '82.

## STANDING ALONE IN A CROWD.
Tracks: Standing alone in a crowd.
■ 7" . . . . . . . . . . . . . . . . . . . . . . . LBW 002
Cricket International / Oct '82.

---

## Thomas, Joe

## BLOWNIN' IN FROM K.C.
Tracks: Not Advised.
■ LP . . . . . . . . . . . . . . . . . . . . . . UP 27 12
Uptown (USA) / Jul '83.

## JUMPING WITH JOE.
Tracks: Not Advised.
■ LP . . . . . . . . . . . . . . . . . . . . . . . ST 1017
Swingtime / Sep '87.

## MAKE YOUR MOVE.
Tracks: Make your move / Your love is so good to me / Caught you lying again / Plato's retreat / Let me be the one / Get on back / Sugar shack.
■ LP . . . . . . . . . . . . . . . . . . . . . TKR 83374
TK / '79.

## MAKE YOUR MOVE.
Tracks: Make your move / Get on back.
■ 7" . . . . . . . . . . . . . . . . . . . . . . TKR 7544
TK / Jun '79.

## PLATO'S RETREAT.
Tracks: Plato's retreat / Place in space.
■ 7" . . . . . . . . . . . . . . . . . . . . . . TKR 6049
TK / Sep '78.

## RAW MEAT.
Tracks: Not Advised.
■ LP . . . . . . . . . . . . . . . . . . . . . . UP 27 01
Uptown (USA) / Feb '83.

## Thomas, Kenny

## BEST OF YOU, THE.
Tracks: Best of you.
■ 12". . . . . . . . . . . . . . . . . . . COOXS 243
■ 7" . . . . . . . . . . . . . . . . . . . . . COOL 243
■ CD Single. . . . . . . . . . . . . . . . COOLCD 243
■ MC Single. . . . . . . . . . . . . . . COOLXMC 243
Chrysalis / Oct '91.

## DESTINY.
Tracks: Destiny / Destiny (mixes).
■ 12". . . . . . . . . . . . . . . . . . 12COOL 289
■ 7" . . . . . . . . . . . . . . . . . . . .COOL 289
■ CD Single. . . . . . . . . . . . . . . . CDCOOL 289
■ MC Single. . . . . . . . . . . . . . . . TCCOOL 289
Chrysalis / May '94.

## I WANNA MAKE LOVE TO YOU, BABY.
Tracks: I wanna make love to you, baby / In my arms.
■ 12". . . . . . . . . . . . . . . . . . . . . PT 12-575
■ 7" . . . . . . . . . . . . . . . . . . . . . .PT 575
President / Aug '88.

## OUTSTANDING.
Tracks: Outstanding / Outstanding (Touchdown mix) (12" & CD single only.) / Outstanding (Bust A Cone mix) (12" & CD single only.) / W.L.N. (7" & cassingle only.)
■ 12". . . . . . . . . . . . . . . . . . . . . COOLX 215
■ 7" . . . . . . . . . . . . . . . . . . . . . COOL 215
■ CD Single. . . . . . . . . . . . . . . . COOLCD 215
■ MC Single. . . . . . . . . . . . . . . . COOLC 215
Cool Tempo / Jul '90.
■ 12". . . . . . . . . . . . . . . . . . . . . COOLX 227
■ 7" . . . . . . . . . . . . . . . . . . . . . COOL 227
■ CD Single. . . . . . . . . . . . . . . . COOLCD 227
■ MC Single. . . . . . . . . . . . . . . . COOLMC 227
Cool Tempo / Jan '91.

## PIECE BY PIECE.
Tracks: Piece by piece.
■ 7" . . . . . . . . . . . . . . . . . . . CDCOOLS 283
■ CD Single. . . . . . . . . . . . . . . . CDCOOL 283
■ CD Single. . . . . . . . . . . . . . . . TCCOOL 283
■ MC Single. . . . . . . . . . . . . . . . TCCOOL 283
Cool Tempo / Nov '93.

## STAY.
Tracks: Stay / Womans world (On 7", CD & cassette only) / Stay (mixes).
■ 12". . . . . . . . . . . . . . . . . . . R2COOL 271
■ 7" . . . . . . . . . . . . . . . . . . . .COOL 271
■ CD Single. . . . . . . . . . . . . . . . CDCOOL 271
■ MC Single. . . . . . . . . . . . . . . . TCCOOL 271
Chrysalis / Jun '93.

## TENDER LOVE.
Tracks: Tender love / Will I ever see your face.
■ 12". . . . . . . . . . . . . . . . . . . . COOLX 247
■ 7" . . . . . . . . . . . . . . . . . . . . . COOL 247
■ MC Single. . . . . . . . . . . . . . . . COOLMC 247
■ CD Single. . . . . . . . . . . . . . . . COOLCD 247
Cool Tempo / Nov '91.

## THINKING ABOUT YOUR LOVE.
Tracks: Thinking about your love (One world mix) (Only on 7" and CD Single) / Thinking about your

421

■ DELETED

love (Lonsdale) / Thinking about your love (7" edit)
(Only on 12" Single).

| | |
|---|---|
| ■ 12".................... | COOLX 235 |
| ■ MC Single. | COOLMC 235 |
| ■ 12" Remix. | COOLXR 235 |
| ■ 7". | COOL 235 |
| ■ CD Single. | COOLCD 235 |

Cool Tempo / May '91.

## TRIPPIN' ON YOUR LOVE.
**Tracks:** Trippin' on your love (Mixes) / Outstanding.

| | |
|---|---|
| ■ 12". | 12COOL 277 |
| ■ 7". | COOL 277 |
| ■ CD Single. | CDCOOL 277 |
| ■ MC Single. | TCCOOL 277 |

Chrysalis / Aug '93.

## VOICES.
**Tracks:** Outstanding / Best of you / Tender love / Will
I ever see your face / Something special / If you
believe / Thinking about your love / Voices / Girlfriend / Were we ever in love.

| | |
|---|---|
| CD. | CCD 1890 |
| MC. | ZCTLP 24 |
| ■ LP. | CTLP 24 |

Cool Tempo / Oct '91 / EMI.

| | |
|---|---|
| CD. | CD25CR 16 |

Chrysalis / Mar '94 / EMI.

## WAIT FOR ME.
**Tracks:** Stay / Destiny / Piece by piece / Can't hide
love / Wait for me / Keep forgettin' / Trippin' on your
love / Hold you close / Separate lives / Same old
story / Garden of pain / Reprise (wait for me).

| | |
|---|---|
| CD. | CTCD 36 |
| LP. | CTLP 36 |
| MC. | CTTC 36 |

Cool Tempo / Sep '93 / EMI.

# Thomas, Lillo

## ALL OF YOU.
**Tracks:** Your love's got a hold on me / Holding on /
Show me / Settle down / All of you / My girl / Never
give you up / I like your style.

| | |
|---|---|
| ■ LP. | EJ 2402171 |

EMI / May '85.

## DOWNTOWN.
**Tracks:** Downtown / I'm in love.

| | |
|---|---|
| ■ 12". | 12CL 453 |
| ■ 7". | CL 453 |

Capitol / Jul '87.

## I LOVE IT.
**Tracks:** I love it / Trust me.

| | |
|---|---|
| ■ 12". | 12CL 313 |
| ■ 7". | CL 313 |

Capitol / Oct '83.

## I'M IN LOVE (RADIO MIX).
**Tracks:** I'm in love / I'm in love (short love dub) / I've
been loving you too long to stop now (Extra track on
12" only).

| | |
|---|---|
| ■ 12". | 12CL 450 |
| ■ 12" Remix. | 12CLD 450 |
| ■ 7". | CL 450 |

Capitol / May '87.

## LET ME BE YOURS.
**Tracks:** I love it / Trust me / Who do you think you
are / Just my imagination / Hot love / Good girl / Joy
of your love / Let me be yours.

| | |
|---|---|
| MC. | TC-EST 7122904 |
| ■ LP. | EST 7122901 |

Capitol / Sep '83 / EMI.

## LILLO.
**Tracks:** I'm in love / Her love / Sweet surrender /
That guy (could have been me) / Sexy girl / Wanna
make love (all night long) / I've been loving you too
long (to stop now) / Downtown / Put your foot down.

| | |
|---|---|
| ■ CD. | CDP 746 811 2 |
| ■ LP. | EST 2031 |
| ■ MC. | TCEST 2031 |

Capitol / Apr '87.

## SETTLE DOWN.
**Tracks:** Settle down / I like your style.

| | |
|---|---|
| ■ 12". | 12CL 356 |
| ■ 7". | CL 356 |

Capitol / Apr '85.

## SEXY GIRL.
**Tracks:** Sexy girl.

| | |
|---|---|
| ■ 12". | 12CL 445 |
| ■ 7". | CL 445 |

Capitol / Mar '87.

# Thomas, Philip Michael

## JUST THE WAY I PLANNED IT.
**Tracks:** Just the way I planned it / All my love.

| | |
|---|---|
| ■ 12". | B 9581 T |
| ■ 7". | B 9581 |

WEA / Jan '86.

## LIVIN' THE BOOK OF LIFE.
**Tracks:** Livin' the book of life / Just the way I planned
it / You might be the lucky one / Fish and chips /
Everything happens in it's own time / She's a liar /
I'm in love with the love that you give me / Stay (in
my loving arms tonight) / All my love / La Mirada.

| | |
|---|---|
| ■ LP. | WX 34 |
| ■ MC. | WX 34 C |

Atlantic / Mar '86.

## SOMEBODY.
**Tracks:** Not Advised.

| | |
|---|---|
| CD. | 790 960-2 |
| MC. | 790 960-4 |
| ■ LP. | 790 960-1 |

Atlantic / Sep '88 / WEA.

# Thomas, Rufus

Self-proclaimed "world's oldest teenager"
was born in 1917 and scored first hit with
*Bear Cat* in 1959 (song also marked Sun
label's R&B chart debut). After successful
spell as disc jockey, Thomas joined fledgling Stax; duet with daughter Carla, *Cause
I Love You* was label's first hit. Drawing on
early career as comic with Rabbit Foot Min-
strels, he became known for irresistably
nonsensical songs like *Walking the Dog*
(1963) and *Do The Funky Chicken* (1970).
These 'novelty' (albeit classic) hits belied
Thomas' flair for R&B; talent which kept him
going into '90s.

## BEST OF - THE SINGLES, THE.
**Tracks:** Funky Mississippi / So hard to get along with
/ Funky way / I want to hold you / Do the funky
chicken / Preacher and the bear / Sixty minute man,
Part II / Do the push and pull (part 2) / World is round
1) / Breakdown (part 2) / Do the funky penguin (part
1) / Do the funky penguin (part 2) / 6-3-8 (that's the
number to play) / Itch and scratch (part 1) / Funky
robot (part 1) / I know (I love you so) / I'll be your
santa baby / Funky bird / Boogie ain't nuttin' (but
gettin' down) / Do the double bump (part 1) / Jump
back '75 (part 1) / Lookin' for a love (part 1).

| | |
|---|---|
| CD. | CDSXD 094 |

Stax / Oct '93 / Pinnacle.

## CAN'T GET AWAY FROM THIS DOG.
**Tracks:** Walking the dog / Can't get away from this
dog / Forty four long / Strolling Beale no.1 / Cherry
red blues / Carry me back to old Virginny / Barefoo-
tin' / Story that's never been told / Last clean shirt /
Show me the way to go home / Jump back / My girl /
We're gonna make it / Don't mess up a good thing / I
want to hold you / Can your monkey do the dog /
Stop kicking my dog around / Wang dang doodle /
Reconsider baby.

| | |
|---|---|
| CD. | CDSXD 038 |

Stax / Oct '91 / Pinnacle.

## CROWN PRINCE OF DANCE.
**Tracks:** Git on up and do it / I know you don't want
me no more / Funkiest man alive / Tutti Frutti / Funky
robot / I wanna sang / Baby it's real / Steal a little /
I'm still in love with you / Funky bird.

| | |
|---|---|
| CD. | CDSXE 054 |

Stax / Nov '92 / Pinnacle.

## DID YOU HEARD ME.
**Tracks:** (Do the) Push & pull parts 1 & 2 / World is
round / (I love you) for sentimental reasons / Breakdown Part 1 / Breakdown Part 2 / Love trap / Do the
funky penguin Part 1 / Do the Funky Penguin Part 2 /
Ditch digging / 6-3-8 (That's the number to play).

| | |
|---|---|
| ■ LP. | 2362028 |

Stax / '72.

| | |
|---|---|
| CD. | CDSXE 050 |

Stax / Nov '92 / Pinnacle.

## DO THE DOUBLE BUMP.
**Tracks:** Do the double bump.

| | |
|---|---|
| ■ 7". | STXS 2029 |

Stax / Jun '75.

## DO THE FUNKY CHICKEN.
**Tracks:** Do the funky chicken.

| | |
|---|---|
| ■ 7". | STAX 144 |

Stax / Apr '70.

## DO THE FUNKY CHICKEN.
**Tracks:** Do the funky chicken.

| | |
|---|---|
| ■ 7". | STAX 814 |

Stax / Sep '87.

## DO THE FUNKY CHICKEN.
**Tracks:** Do the funky chicken / Let the good times roll
/ Sixty minute man / Lookin' for a love / Bearcat / Old
McDonald had a farm (parts 1 and 2) / Rufus Rastus
Johnson Brown / Soul food / Turn your damper down
/ Preacher and the bear.

| | |
|---|---|
| ■ LP. | SXATS 1033 |

Stax / Jul '70.

| | |
|---|---|
| ■ LP. | 2363 001 |

Polydor / Mar '71.

| | |
|---|---|
| CD. | CDSXE 036 |

Stax / Mar '91 / Pinnacle.

## DO THE PUSH AND PULL.
**Tracks:** Do the push and pull.

| | |
|---|---|
| ■ 7". | 2025 016 |

Stax / Jan '71.

## GREASY SPOON.
**Tracks:** Greasy spoon / Sophisticated sissy.

| | |
|---|---|
| ■ 7". | 601013 |

Stax / Jul '67.

## IF THERE WERE NO MUSIC.
**Tracks:** Who's makin' love to your old lady / If there
was no music / Don't let hate taer the whole world
down / Hot grits / I got to be myself / Today I started
loving you again / Blues in the basement / You send
me / Little joint around the corner.

| | |
|---|---|
| ■ LP. | NSPL 28241 |

Pye / Mar '78.

## JUMP BACK.
**Tracks:** Jump back / All night worker / Little Sally
Water / Chicken scratch / World is round / Sister's
got a boyfriend / Talkin' about true love / Sophisticated cissy / Memphis train / Greasy spoon / Dog /
Walking the dog / Can your monkey do the dog / I
want to be loved / I want to get married / Fine and
mellow.

| | |
|---|---|
| ■ LP. | ED 134 |

Edsel / May '84.

## JUMP BACK.
**Tracks:** Jump back / All night worker.

| | |
|---|---|
| ■ 7". | AT 4009 |

Atlantic / '65.

## JUMP BACK 75.
**Tracks:** Jump back 75.

| | |
|---|---|
| ■ 7". | STXS 2037 |

Stax / Jan '76.

## LIVE DOING THE PUSH AND PULL AT PJ'S.
**Tracks:** Monologue / Ooh poo pah do / Old McDonald
had a farm / Walking the dog / Preacher and the bear
/ Night time is the right time / Push and pull / Do the
funky chicken.

| | |
|---|---|
| ■ LP. | 2362010 |

Stax / Jun '71.

## RUFUS THOMAS.
**Tracks:** Not Advised.

| | |
|---|---|
| CD. | CD 1016 |

Gusto (USA) / '88.

## RUFUS THOMAS EP.
**Tracks:** Bear cat / Walkin' in the rain / Tiger man /
Save that money.

| | |
|---|---|
| ■ EP. | CEP 101 |

Charly / Feb '77.

## THAT WOMAN IS POISON.
**Tracks:** That woman is poison / Big fine hunk of
woman / Somebody's got to go / Walk / I just got to
know / Blues in the basement / Breaking my back /
All night worker.

| | |
|---|---|
| ■ LP. | AL 4769 |

Alligator / Jan '89.

| | |
|---|---|
| MC. | ALCS 4769 |

Alligator / Aug '92 / Topic Records / Direct Distribution / C.M. Distribution / A.D.A. Distribution / Jazz
Music.

| | |
|---|---|
| CD. | ALCD 4769 |

Alligator / May '93 / Topic Records / Direct Distribution / C.M. Distribution / A.D.A. Distribution / Jazz
Music.

## TIMELESS FUNK.
**Tracks:** Not Advised.

| | |
|---|---|
| CD. | CDSGP 036 |
| ■ MC. | CASSGP 036 |

Prestige (Total) / Nov '92 / BMG.

## TIMELESS FUNK.
**Tracks:** Timeless funk.

| | |
|---|---|
| ■ 12". | VSSGP 1002 |

Prestige (Total) / Jan '93.

■ DELETED

## WALKING THE DOG.
**Tracks:** Dog / Mashed potatoes / Ooh-poo-pah-doo / You said / Boom boom / It's aw'rite / Walking the dog / Ya, ya / Land of 1,000 dances / Can your monkey do the dog / 'Cause I love you / I want to be loved.
CD . . . . . . . . . . . . . . . . . . . . . . 7567822542
MC . . . . . . . . . . . . . . . . . . . . . . 7567822544
East West / Jul '91 / WEA.

## WILLY NILLY.
**Tracks:** Willy nilly / Sister's got a boyfriend.
■ 7" . . . . . . . . . . . . . . . . . . . . . . K 10596
Atlantic / Aug '75.

# Thomas, Sybil

## RESCUE ME.
**Tracks:** Rescue me.
. . . . . . . . . . . . . . . . . . . . . .WEND 124
Arista / '83.

## RESCUE ME.
**Tracks:** Rescue me.
■ 12" . . . . . . . . . . . . . . . . . . . .WEND 124
■ 7" . . . . . . . . . . . . . . . . . . . . . WEND 4
West End / Nov '84.

# Thomas, Tasha

## MIDNIGHT RENDEZVOUS.
**Tracks:** Midnight rendezvous / Street fever / Shoot me / Hot buttered boogie / You put the music in me / Wake up morning glory / You're the one I love / Drinking again.
■ LP . . . . . . . . . . . . . . . . . . . . . K 50572
Atlantic / '77.

## SHOOT ME.
**Tracks:** Shoot me (with your love).
■ 7" . . . . . . . . . . . . . . . . . . . . . . LV 4
Atlantic / Jan '79.

## STREET FEVER.
**Tracks:** Street fever / Drinking again.
■ 7" . . . . . . . . . . . . . . . . . . . . . K 11346
WEA / '79.

# Thomas, Timmy

## MAGICIAN.
**Tracks:** Magician / Don't put it down.
■ 7" . . . . . . . . . . . . . . . . . . . . . XB 9052
TK / Mar '77.

## MAGICIAN.
**Tracks:** Magician / Say love, can you chase away my blues / Stone to the bone / Show me tenderness / Watch it, Watch it, watch it for Dudley Dudley Dorite / Make peace with yourself / Let my people go / Don't put it down / Running out of time.
■ LP . . . . . . . . . . . . . . . . . . . . . XL 14044
TK / May '77.

## NEW YORK EYES (see under Nicole (1)).

## TOUCH TO TOUCH.
**Tracks:** Touch to touch / When a house got music.
■ 7" . . . . . . . . . . . . . . . . . . . . TKR 6017
TK / Jul '78.

## TOUCH TO TOUCH.
**Tracks:** Touch to touch / Africano / When a house got music / Game of life / Love for the people / Torrid zone / Diane / Sweet music.
■ LP . . . . . . . . . . . . . . . . . . . . TKR 82510
TK / Mar '78.

## WHY CAN'T WE LIVE TOGETHER.
**Tracks:** Why can't we live together.
■ 7" . . . . . . . . . . . . . . . . . . . . .2027 012
Mojo / Feb '73.

## WHY CAN'T WE LIVE TOGETHER.
**Tracks:** Why can't we live together / Rainbow people / Take care of home / First time ever I saw your face / Coldest day of my life / In the beginning / Cold cold people / Opportunity / Dizzy dizzy world / Funky me.
■ LP . . . . . . . . . . . . . . . . . . . 33 6501
Glades / Jan '72.

## WHY CAN'T WE LIVE TOGETHER.
**Tracks:** Why can't we live together (war & peace edit) (7" & cassingle only.) / Why can't we live together (original version) / Why can't we live together (war & peace mix) (12" & CD single only.) / Why can't we live together (lasting peace mix) (12" & CD single only.)
■ MC Single . . . . . . . . . . . . . . . . TCTKR 1
■ 12" . . . . . . . . . . . . . . . . . . . .12TKR 1
■ 7" . . . . . . . . . . . . . . . . . . . . . TKR 1
■ CD Single . . . . . . . . . . . . . . . CDTKR 1
TK / Jul '90.

## YOU'RE THE SONG I'VE ALWAYS WANTED TO SING.
**Tracks:** You're the song I've always wanted to sing / I've got to see you tonight.
■ 7" . . . . . . . . . . . . . . . . . . . . 2001545
Polydor / Jan '75.

# Thomas, Vaneese

## LET'S TALK IT OVER.
**Tracks:** Let's talk it over / Love in your eyes.
■ 12" . . . . . . . . . . . . . . . . . . . .GEFT 26
■ 7" . . . . . . . . . . . . . . . . . . . . . GEF 26
Geffen / Aug '87.

## VANEESE THOMAS.
**Tracks:** (I wanna get) close to you / Let's talk it over / Keep it up / Heading in the right direction / Rockin' and lovin' / Ultimate love / I'm gonna love you.
■ LP . . . . . . . . . . . . . . . . . . . . . 9241411
MC . . . . . . . . . . . . . . . . . . . . . . 9241414
Geffen / Jul '87 / BMG.

# Thornton, Fonzi

## BEVERLEY.
**Tracks:** Beverley / Looking up to you.
■ 12" . . . . . . . . . . . . . . . . . . . .OG 4512
Old Gold / Apr '89.

# Three Caps

## COOL JERK.
**Tracks:** Cool jerk / Hello stranger.
■ 7" . . . . . . . . . . . . . . . . . . . . .2091 105
Atlantic / Jul '71.

# Three Degrees

## 20 GOLDEN GREATS: THREE DEGREES.
**Tracks:** Not Advised.
■ LP . . . . . . . . . . . . . . . . . . . . . SHM 3155
■ MC . . . . . . . . . . . . . . . . . . . . . HSC 3155
Hallmark / Sep '84.

## 20 GREATEST HITS: THREE DEGREES.
**Tracks:** When will I see you again / Can't you see what you're doing to me / Toast of love / We're all alone / Long lost lover / Get your love back / I like being a woman / What I did for love / Standing up for love / Take good care of yourself / Dirty ol' man / Loving cup / Woman needs a good man / T.S.O.P. (The sound of Philadelphia) / Another heartache / Distant lover / Together / Here I am / Year of decision / Love train (live version).
■ LP . . . . . . . . . . . . . . . . . . EPC 32478
■ MC . . . . . . . . . . . . . . . . . .40 32478
Epic / Jun '84.
CD . . . . . . . . . . . . . . . . . . .982585-2
Pickwick/Sony Collector's Choice / Mar '94 / Pickwick / Pinnacle.

## 3D.
**Tracks:** Jump the gun / Red light / Set me free / Starlight / My simple heart / Without you / Bodycheck.
■ LP . . . . . . . . . . . . . . . . . . . . . 3DLP 1
Ariola / Dec '79.

## 6 TRACK HITS.
**Tracks:** Woman in love / Magic in the air / My simple heart / Jump the gun / Without you / Runner.
■ EP . . . . . . . . . . . . . . . . . . . . . 7SR 5005
■ MC Single. . . . . . . . . . . . . . . . . 7SC 5005
Scoop 33 / Sep '83.

## BEST OF THE THREE DEGREES, THE.
**Tracks:** When will I see you again / Year of decision / Toast of love / This is the house / Starlight / Love Train / Woman in love / Get your love back / Dirty ol' man / Without you / TSOP(the sound of Philadelphia) / My simple heart / Long lost lover / Heaven I need / I didn't know / Givin' up givin' in / Take good care of yourself / Golden lady / Love is the message / Distant lover / Jump the gun / Runner.
LP . . . . . . . . . . . . . . . . . . . VSOPLP 149
■ CD . . . . . . . . . . . . . . . . . . VSOPCD 149
■ MC . . . . . . . . . . . . . . . . . . VSOPMC 149
Connoisseur Collection / Apr '90 / Pinnacle.

## COLLECTION OF THEIR 20 GREATEST HITS, A.
**Tracks:** Not Advised.
■ LP . . . . . . . . . . . . . . . . . . . . EPC 10013
Epic / Mar '79.

## COMPLETE SWAN RECORDINGS.
**Tracks:** Gee baby (I'm sorry) / Do what you're supposed to do / Let's shindig / You're gonna miss me / How did that happen / Little red riding hood (that's what they call me) / I'm gonna need you / Just right

for love / I'll weep for you / Don't (leave me lover) / Someone (who will be true) / Bongo's on the beach / Close your eyes / Gotta draw the line / Mine all mine / Are you satisfied / And in return / Heartbroken memories / Signs of love / Look in my eyes / Drivin' me mad / Maybe / Yours / Tales are true / I wanna be your baby / Love of my life.
CD . . . . . . . . . . . . . . . . . .NEMCD 631
Sequel / Nov '92 / Total / BMG.

## DIRTY OLD MAN.
**Tracks:** Dirty old man / Can't you see what you're doing to me.
■ 7" . . . . . . . . . . . . . . . . . . . . PIR 5944
Philadelphia Int. / Jan '78.

## GET YOUR LOVE BACK.
**Tracks:** Get your love back.
■ 7" . . . . . . . . . . . . . . . . . . . . PIR 2737
Philadelphia Int. / Nov '74.

## GIVIN' UP GIVIN' IN.
**Tracks:** Givin' up givin' in.
■ 7" . . . . . . . . . . . . . . . . . . . . ARO 130
Ariola / Oct '78.

## GOLD.
**Tracks:** Not Advised.
■ LP . . . . . . . . . . . . . . . . . . . . NE 1089
■ MC . . . . . . . . . . . . . . . . . . . . CE 2089
K-Tel / Aug '80.

## GOLD (2).
**Tracks:** Not Advised.
■ LP . . . . . . . . . . . . . . . . . . . . 3DLP 2
Ariola / Sep '80.

## GOLD (EPIC).
**Tracks:** Dirty ol' man / We're all alone / I didn't know / I like being a woman / What I did for love / Take good care of yourself / Year of decision / Another heartache / Can't you see what you're doing to me / Distant lover / Toast of love / Get your love back / When will I see you again / Long lost lover / Macaroni man / In love we grow / Gee baby / Standing up for love / T.S.O.P. / Free ride / Love train / Don't let the sun go down on me / Living for the city / For the love of money.
■ Double LP . . . . . . . . . . . . . . . EPC 22110
Epic / Nov '80.

## GOLDEN HOUR OF THE THREE DEGREES.
**Tracks:** You're the one / Love the one you're with / Who is she and what is she to you / Magic mirror / There's so much love all around me / Rose garden / Caught between two fires / Collage / Lonely man / Maybe / Ebb tide / Tradewinds / I do take you / If you must leave my life / Magic door / Stardust / You're the fool / Sugar on Sunday / MacArthur Park.
■ LP . . . . . . . . . . . . . . . . . . . . GH 881
Golden Hour / Mar '79.

## GOLDEN LADY, THE.
**Tracks:** Golden lady / Sophisticated like you.
■ 7" . . . . . . . . . . . . . . . . . . . . ARO 170
Ariola / Jun '79.

## HEAVEN I NEED, THE.
**Tracks:** Heaven I need.
■ 12" . . . . . . . . . . . . . . . . . . . . SUPET 102
■ 7" . . . . . . . . . . . . . . . . . . . . SUPE 102
Supreme / Sep '85.

## HITS HITS HITS.
**Tracks:** Woman in love / My simple heart / We are family / Falling in love again / Givin' up, givin' in / Without you / Magic in the air / I'll never love this way again / Starlight / Jump the gun / You light up my life / Red light / Bodycheck.
■ LP . . . . . . . . . . . . . . . . . . . . SHM 3086
■ MC . . . . . . . . . . . . . . . . . . . . HSC 3086
Hallmark / Sep '81.

## JUMP THE GUN.
**Tracks:** Jump the gun.
■ 7" . . . . . . . . . . . . . . . . . . . . ARO 183
Ariola / Sep '79.

## LET'S GET IT ON.
**Tracks:** Not Advised.
CD . . . . . . . . . . . . . . . . . . . . . RLBTC 004
MC . . . . . . . . . . . . . . . . . . . . . RLBTM 004
Realisation / Oct '93 / Prism Leisure PLC.

## LIAR (YOU'VE BEEN CHEATING ON ME).
**Tracks:** Liar (you've been cheating on me).
■ 7" . . . . . . . . . . . . . . . . . . . . 3D 1
3D / Nov '83.

## LOCK IT UP.
**Tracks:** Lock it up.
■ 12" . . . . . . . . . . . . . . . . . . . . ICHT 707

■ 7″ . . . . . . . . . . . . . . . . . . . . . . ICHS 707
Ichiban / Sep '89.

**LONG LOST LOVER.**
Tracks: Long lost lover / Lonelier are fools.
■ 7″ . . . . . . . . . . . . . . . . . . . . . . PIR 3352
Philadelphia Int. / Jul '75.

**MAKE IT EASY ON YOURSELF.**
Tracks: Make it easy on yourself / Play me / Alone
again / Where is the love / Goodbye to love / Too
young / Lean on me / How can I be sure / Run to me /
Sung sung blue / He ain't heavy he's my brother.
■ 12″ . . . . . . . . . . . . . . . . . . . . 12 PO 36
Ichiban / '88.

**MY SIMPLE HEART.**
Tracks: My simple heart / Hot summer night.
■ 7″ . . . . . . . . . . . . . . . . . . . . . . ARO 202
Ariola / Nov '79.

**NEW DIMENSIONS.**
Tracks: Givin' up, givin' in / Falling in love again /
Looking for love / Runner / Woman in love / Magic in
the air.
■ LP . . . . . . . . . . . . . . . . . . . . . ARL 5012
■ MC . . . . . . . . . . . . . . . . . . . ZCARL 5012
Ariola / Feb '79.

**RUNNER, THE.**
Tracks: Runner.
■ 12″ . . . . . . . . . . . . . . . . . . . .AROD 154
■ 7″ . . . . . . . . . . . . . . . . . . . . . ARO 154
Ariola / Mar '79.

**SATIN AND SOUL.**
Tracks: Woman in love / My simple heart / Golden
lady / Without you / Set me free / Starlight / Runner /
Givin' up, givin' in / Falling in love again / Body-
check / Red light / Out of love again / Magic in the air
/ Jump the gun.
■ CD . . . . . . . . . . . . . . . . . . . 260.362
■ MC . . . . . . . . . . . . . . . . . . . 410.362
RCA / Dec '89.

**STANDING UP FOR LOVE.**
Tracks: Standing up for love / In love we grow.
■ 7″ . . . . . . . . . . . . . . . . . . . . . EPC 4992
Epic / Feb '77.

**STANDING UP FOR LOVE.**
Tracks: Stand up for love / What I did for love / Just
leave me alone / Macaroni man / Gee baby / People
with feeling / In love we grow / We're all alone.
■ LP . . . . . . . . . . . . . . . . . . . EPC 81694
Epic / Mar '77.

**STARLIGHT.**
Tracks: Starlight / Set me free.
■ 7″ . . . . . . . . . . . . . . . . . . . . . ARO 228
Ariola / May '80.

**SUGAR ON SUNDAY.**
Tracks: Sugar on Sunday / Maybe.
■ 7″ . . . . . . . . . . . . . . . . . . . . 7N 25671
Pye International / Feb '75.

**TAKE GOOD CARE OF YOURSELF.**
Tracks: Not Advised.
■ LP . . . . . . . . . . . . . . . . . . . PIR 69137
Philadelphia Int. / May '75.

**TAKE GOOD CARE OF YOURSELF.**
Tracks: Take good care of yourself.
■ 7″ . . . . . . . . . . . . . . . . . . . . PIR 3177
Philadelphia Int. / Apr '75.

**TENDER LIE.**
Tracks: Tender lie / Vital signs.
■ 12″ . . . . . . . . . . . . . . . . . . . ICHT 706
■ 7″ . . . . . . . . . . . . . . . . . . . ICHS 706
Ichiban / May '89.

**THIS IS THE HOUSE.**
Tracks: This is the house / This is the house (mega
dance version) / Senza voce / Heaven I need /
Gimme gimme gimme.
■ 12″ . . . . . . . . . . . . . . . . . . SUPET 104
■ 12″ P.Disc. . . . . . . . . . . . . . . SUPETP 104
Supreme / Mar '86.

**THREE DEGREES.**
Tracks: Collage / You're the one / Sugar on Sunday /
Maybe / MacArthur Park / Rose garden / Stardust /
Lonely town / Magic door.
■ LP . . . . . . . . . . . . . . . . . . . 2916 002
Mojo / Aug '71.

**THREE DEGREES.**
Tracks: When will I see you again / I didn't know /
Dirty ol' man / Loving cup / Lonelier are fools / TSOP
/ Long lost lover / Can't you see what you're doing to
me / Together / If and when / Get your love back.

■ LP . . . . . . . . . . . . . . . . . . . CBS 31644
Embassy (1) / May '78.

**THREE DEGREES, THE.**
Tracks: Jump the gun / Red light / Set me free /
Bodycheck / Givin' up, givin' in / Starlight / My
simple heart / Without you / Stardust / We are family.
■ LP . . . . . . . . . . . . . . . . . . . 65858
Philadelphia Int. / Aug '74.
■ LP . . . . . . . . . . . . . . . . . . . PIR 32044
■ MC . . . . . . . . . . . . . . . . . . . .40 32044
Philadelphia Int. / Jun '81.

**THREE DEGREES, THE.**
Tracks: Not Advised.
■ LP . . . . . . . . . . . . . . . . . . MFP 50543
■ MC . . . . . . . . . . . . . . . . .TCMFP 50543
MFP / Oct '81.

**THREE DEGREES, THE.**
Tracks: Giving up, giving in / Falling in love again /
Looking for love / Runner / Woman in love / Magic in
the air.
■ LP . . . . . . . . . . . . . . . . . . . ARLH 5012
Ariola / Oct '78.

**THREE DEGREES.. AND HOLDING, THE.**
Tracks: Tie u up / Win, place or show / Make it easy
on yourself / Lock it up / Vital signs / Tender lie /
After the night is over / Are you that kind of guy.
■ LP . . . . . . . . . . . . . . . . . . . ICH 1041
MC. . . . . . . . . . . . . . . . . . . ZCICH 1041
Ichiban / May '89 / A.D.A. Distribution / Pinnacle /
ACD Trading Ltd. / Koch International / Direct
Distribution.
CD. . . . . . . . . . . . . . . . . . . .CDICH 1041
Ichiban / Oct '93 / A.D.A. Distribution / Pinnacle /
ACD Trading Ltd. / Koch International / Direct
Distribution.

**TIE U UP.**
Tracks: Tie u up.
■ 12″ . . . . . . . . . . . . . . . . . . . 12 PO 27
Ichiban / '88.

**TOAST OF LOVE.**
Tracks: Toast of love.
■ 7″ . . . . . . . . . . . . . . . . . . . . . EPC 4215
Epic / May '76.

**WE'RE ALL ALONE.**
Tracks: We're all alone / We grow in love.
■ 7″ . . . . . . . . . . . . . . . . . . . . . EPC 5112
Epic / Mar '77.

**WHEN WILL I SEE YOU AGAIN.**
Tracks: When will I see you again / I didn't know.
■ 7″ . . . . . . . . . . . . . . . . . . . . . PIR 2155
Philadelphia Int. / Jul '74.

**WHEN WILL I SEE YOU AGAIN (OLD
GOLD).**
Tracks: When will I see you again / Take good care
of yourself.
7″ . . . . . . . . . . . . . . . . . . . . . OG 9307
Old Gold / Mar '90 / Pickwick.

**WITHOUT YOU.**
Tracks: Without you / Magic in the air.
■ 7″ . . . . . . . . . . . . . . . . . . . . . ARO 308
Ariola / Feb '80.
■ 7″ . . . . . . . . . . . . . . . . . . . . . ARO 208
Ariola / May '82.

**WOMAN IN LOVE.**
Tracks: Woman in love / Out of love again.
■ 7″ . . . . . . . . . . . . . . . . . . . . . ARO 141
Ariola / Dec '78.

**WOMAN IN LOVE.**
Tracks: Not Advised.
CD. . . . . . . . . . . . . . . . . . . . .290403
■ MC . . . . . . . . . . . . . . . . . . . .490403
Ariola / Dec '92 / BMG.

**WOMAN IN LOVE.**
Tracks: Not Advised.
■ CD Single . . . . . . . . . . . . . . . PWKS 4118
■ MC Single. . . . . . . . . . . . . . PWKMC 4118
Pickwick / Oct '92.

**WOMAN IN LOVE (OLD GOLD).**
Tracks: Woman in love / Runner.
■ 7″ . . . . . . . . . . . . . . . . . . . .OG 9703
Old Gold / Apr '87.

**YEAR OF DECISION.**
Tracks: Year of decision.
■ 7″ . . . . . . . . . . . . . . . . . . . . . PIR 2073
Philadelphia Int. / Apr '74.

**YOU'RE THE ONE.**
Tracks: You're the one / Rose garden.
■ 7″ . . . . . . . . . . . . . . . . . . . . . 2092002
Mojo / Jun '71.

## Three Ounces Of Love

**GIVE ME SOME FEELING.**
Tracks: Give me some feeling / Don't worry 'bout my
love.
■ 7″ . . . . . . . . . . . . . . . . . . . . .TMG 1119
Motown / Sep '78.

**STAR LOVE.**
Tracks: Star love / I found the feeling.
■ 7″ . . . . . . . . . . . . . . . . . . . . .TMG 1105
Motown / Mar '78.

## Three Sounds

**BABE'S BLUES.**
Tracks: Babe's blues / Wait a minute / Work song /
Blue Daniel / Sweet and lovely / Shiny stockings /
Walking the floor over you / Between the Devil and
the deep blue sea / Stairway to the stars / Lazy cat
■ LP . . . . . . . . . . . . . . . . . . . BST 84434
Blue Note / Dec '86.
■ CD. . . . . . . . . . . . . . . . . . . .BNZ 137
Blue Note / Mar '89.

**INTRODUCING THE THREE SOUNDS.**
Tracks: Tenderly / Willow weep for me / Both sides
Blue bells / It's nice / Going home / Would'n you / O
sole mio / Bobby / Mo-ge / It might as well be Spring
/ Soft touch / Don't get around much anymore /
Going home (alternative take).
■ CD. . . . . . . . . . . . . . . . . . . . BNZ 95
Blue Note / May '87.

## Thrills

**SHOW THE WORLD WHERE IT'S AT.**
Tracks: Show the world where it's at / What can go
wrong.
■ 7″ . . . . . . . . . . . . . . . . . . . . .GRP 126
Grapevine (Northern Soul) / Aug '79.

## Thurston, Bobby

**CHECK OUT THE GROOVE.**
Tracks: Check out the groove / Sitting in the park.
■ 7″ . . . . . . . . . . . . . . . . . . . . . EPC 8348
Epic / Mar '80.

**MAIN ATTRACTION.**
Tracks: Is something wrong with you / Main attrac
tion / Love makes it complete / Keep it going / I know
you feel like I feel / Very last drop / I really don'
mean it / Life is what you make it.
■ LP . . . . . . . . . . . . . . . . . . . EPC 8507
Epic / Jul '81.

**SWEETEST PIECE OF THE PIE.**
Tracks: Not Advised.
■ LP . . . . . . . . . . . . . . . . . . . .HH 113
Hi-Hut / Nov '88.

**VERY LAST DROP.**
Tracks: Very last drop / Life is what you make it.
■ 12″ . . . . . . . . . . . . . . . . . . .EPCA 13130
■ 7″ . . . . . . . . . . . . . . . . . . . . EPCA 130
Epic / Jun '81.

**YOU GOT WHAT IT TAKES.**
Tracks: You got what it takes / I wanna do it with you
/ Check out the groove / I want your body / Sittin' i
the park.
■ LP . . . . . . . . . . . . . . . . . . . EPC 8425
Epic / May '80.

**YOU GOT WHAT IT TAKES.**
Tracks: You got what it takes / I wanna do it with you
■ 7″ . . . . . . . . . . . . . . . . . . . . . EPC 859
Epic / Jun '80.

## Time

**COOL.**
Tracks: Cool 1 / Cool 2.
■ 12″ . . . . . . . . . . . . . . . . . . . .K 17920
■ 7″ . . . . . . . . . . . . . . . . . . . . . K 1792
WEA / Feb '82.

**GOT YOUR NUMBER.**
Tracks: Got your number / Grace.
■ 12″ . . . . . . . . . . . . . . . . . . . . W 9982
■ 7″ . . . . . . . . . . . . . . . . . . . . . W 99
WEA / Jan '83.

■ DELETE

## ICE CREAM CASTLE.
Tracks: Ice cream castles / My drawers / Chilli sauce / Jungle love / If the kid can't make you come / Bird.
- **LP** . . . . . . . . . . . . . . . . . . .925109 1
WEA / Aug '84.
- **CD** . . . . . . . . . . . . . . . . . . .925109 2
WEA / Jul '86.

## ICE CREAM CASTLES.
Tracks: Ice cream castles / Tricky.
- **12"** . . . . . . . . . . . . . . . . . . W 9247T
- **7"** . . . . . . . . . . . . . . . . . . . W 9247
WEA / Sep '84.

## JERK OUT.
Tracks: Jerk out.
- **12"** . . . . . . . . . . . . . . . . W 9750 T
- **7"** . . . . . . . . . . . . . . . . . W 9750
- **CD Single** . . . . . . . . . . . W 9750 CD
- **MC Single** . . . . . . . . . . . W 9750 C
WEA / Aug '90.

## PANDEMONIUM.
Tracks: Dreamland / Pandemonium / Sexy socialites / Ycount / Donald Trump (black version) / Cooking class / It's your world / Data bank / Pretty little women / Jerk out / Blondie / Chocolate / Skillet / Sometimes I get lonely / My summertime thang.
- **CD** . . . . . . . . . . . . . . . . . . WX 336CD
- **LP** . . . . . . . . . . . . . . . . . . WX 336
- **MC** . . . . . . . . . . . . . . . . . . WX 336C
WEA / Jul '90 / WEA.

## TIME.
Tracks: Not Advised.
- **LP** . . . . . . . . . . . . . . . . . . . K 56947
- **MC** . . . . . . . . . . . . . . . . . . K4 56947
WEA / Mar '82.

## WHAT TIME IS IT?.
Tracks: Wild and loose / 777-9311 / Onedayi'mgonna-besomebody / Walk / Gigolos get lonely too / I don't wanna leave you.
- **LP** . . . . . . . . . . . . . . . . . . . K 57017
WEA / Jan '83.

# Timex Social Club

## MIXED UP WORLD.
Tracks: Mixed up world.
- **7"** . . . . . . . . . . . . . . . . . .COOL 138
- **12"** . . . . . . . . . . . . . . . . .COOLX 138
Cool Tempo / Nov '86.

## RUMOURS.
Tracks: Rumours / Rumours (Shep's version).
- **12"** . . . . . . . . . . . . . . . . .COOLX 13
- **7"** . . . . . . . . . . . . . . . . . .COOL 133
Cool Tempo / '86.

## VICIOUS RUMORS.
Tracks: Rumours / Thinkin' about ya / Just kickin' it / Only you / mixed up world / Cokelife / Go away little girl / 363 (Natty Prep) / Vicious rumors.
- **LP** . . . . . . . . . . . . . . . . . . . CTLP 2
- **MC** . . . . . . . . . . . . . . . . . . .ZCTLP 2
Cool Tempo / Jan '87 / EMI.

# Titiyo

## AFTER THE RAIN (Titiyo & Papa Dee).
Tracks: After the rain / After the rain (raga rap) / After the rain (new life mix) (12" and CD only) / After the rain (Raga muffin style) (12" only).
- **12"** . . . . . . . . . . . . . . . . . .612735
- **12"** . . . . . . . . . . . . . . . . . .612722
- **7"** . . . . . . . . . . . . . . . . . .112722
- **CD Single** . . . . . . . . . . . . .662722
- **MC Single** . . . . . . . . . . . . .410516
Arista / Feb '90.

## BACK AND FORTH.
Tracks: Back and forth.
- **12"** . . . . . . . . . . . . . . 7432118185-1
- **CD Single** . . . . . . . . . 7432118224-2
RCA / Nov '93.

## FLOWERS.
Tracks: Flowers / Doin' his thing.
- **12"** . . . . . . . . . . . . . . . . . .613212
- **7"** . . . . . . . . . . . . . . . . . .113212
- **CD Single** . . . . . . . . . . . . .663212
- **MC Single** . . . . . . . . . . . . .411213
Arista / Sep '90.
- **12" Remix** . . . . . . . . . . . .613213
Arista / Sep '90.

## MY BODY SAYS YES.
Tracks: My body says yes / My body says yes (instrumental) (On 12" and CD single only).
- **CD Single** . . . . . . . . . . . . .662733
- **12"** . . . . . . . . . . . . . . . . . .612733
- **12" Remix** . . . . . . . . . . . .614 278

---

- **7"** . . . . . . . . . . . . . . . . . .112733
Arista / Apr '91.

## TELL ME (I'M NOT DREAMING).
Tracks: Tell me (I'm not dreaming) / Human climate / Tell me (I'm not dreaming) (mixes).
- **12"** . . . . . . . . . . . . . .74321 18562-1
- **7"** . . . . . . . . . . . . . . .74321 18562-7
- **CD Single** . . . . . . . . . .74321 18562-2
- **MC Single** . . . . . . . . . .74321 18562-4
Arista / Jan '94.

## THIS IS.
Tracks: This is / Back and forth / Hot gold / Deep down underground / Make my day / Way you make me feel / Spinnin' / Human climate / Defended / Never let me go / Man in the moon.
- **CD** . . . . . . . . . . . . . . .74321 18882-2
- **LP** . . . . . . . . . . . . . . .74321 18882-1
- **MC** . . . . . . . . . . . . . . .74321 18882-4
Arista / Jan '94 / BMG.

## TITIYO.
Tracks: Flowers / Do my thing / Peace and quiet / I know you better / Waiting for you / After the rain / Body and mind / Break my heart / L.O.V.E. / Man in the moon / Doin' his thing.
- **MC** . . . . . . . . . . . . . . . . . . .410977
- **CD** . . . . . . . . . . . . . . . . . . .260977
- **LP** . . . . . . . . . . . . . . . . . . .210977
RCA / Aug '90 / BMG.

# TLC

## AIN'T 2 PROUD 2 BEG.
Tracks: Ain't 2 proud 2 beg.
- **12"** . . . . . . . . . . . . . . . . . 615 265
- **7"** . . . . . . . . . . . . . . . . . 115 265
- **CD Single** . . . . . . . . . . . 665 265
Arista / May '92.

## BABY BABY BABY.
Tracks: Baby baby baby.
- **12"** . . . . . . . . . . . . . . 74321111291
- **CD Single** . . . . . . . . . 74321111292
- **MC Single** . . . . . . . . . 74321111294
- **7"** . . . . . . . . . . . . . . 74321111297
Arista / Aug '92.

## OOOOOOOH.. ON THE TLC TIP.
Tracks: Ain't 2 proud 2 beg / Shock dat monkey / Intermission I / Hat 2 da bak / Das da way we like 'em / What about your friends / His story / Intermission II / Bad my myself / Somethin' you wanna know / Baby-baby-baby / This is how it should be done / Depend on myself / Conclusion.
- **CD** . . . . . . . . . . . . . . . . . 262 878
- **MC** . . . . . . . . . . . . . . . . . 412 878
Arista / Aug '92 / BMG.

## WHAT ABOUT YOUR FRIENDS.
Tracks: What about your friends.
- **7"** . . . . . . . . . . . . . . 74321118177
- **12"** . . . . . . . . . . . . . . 74321118171
- **CD Single** . . . . . . . . . 74321118172
- **MC Single** . . . . . . . . . 74321118174
RCA / Oct '92.

# Today

## GIRL I GOT MY EYES ON YOU.
Tracks: Girl I got my eyes on you.
- **12"** . . . . . . . . . . . . . . . . ZT 42684
- **7"** . . . . . . . . . . . . . . . . ZB 42683
Motown / Mar '89.

## HIM OR ME.
Tracks: Him or me / Him or me (inst) (7" only) / Him or me (dub mix) (12" only) / Bonus beats (12" only).
- **12"** . . . . . . . . . . . . . . . . ZT 42262
- **7"** . . . . . . . . . . . . . . . . ZB 42261
Motown / Oct '88.

## NEW FORMULA, THE.
Tracks: I got the feelin' / Every little thing about you / Self centred / Let me know / Why you get funky on me / Trying to get over you / I wanna come back home / Home is where you belong / Tennis anyone / Gonna make you mine / No need to worry (On CD only.) / My happiness (On CD only.).
- **LP** . . . . . . . . . . . . . . . . ZL 72727
- **CD** . . . . . . . . . . . . . . . . ZD 72727
- **MC** . . . . . . . . . . . . . . . . ZK 72727
Motown / Nov '90.

## TODAY.
Tracks: Him or me / Girl I got my eyes on you / Take it off / Take your time / Style / You stood me up / Your love is not true / Lady sexy lady.
- **CD** . . . . . . . . . . . . . . . . ZD 72650
- **LP** . . . . . . . . . . . . . . . . ZL 72650
- **MC** . . . . . . . . . . . . . . . . ZK 72650
Motown / Apr '89.

---

## WHY YOU GET FUNKY ON.
Tracks: Why you get funky on.
- **12"** . . . . . . . . . . . . . . . . ZT 43618
- **7"** . . . . . . . . . . . . . . . . ZB 43617
Motown / May '90.

# Todd, Pam

## BAISEZ MOI (Todd, Pam & Golden Bullion Band).
Tracks: Baisez moi / Baisez moi (version).
- **7"** . . . . . . . . . . . . . . . . EPC 6939
Epic / Feb '79.

# Tolbert, Israel

## POPPER STOPPER.
Tracks: Big leg woman / Lost love / You'll lose a good thing / Kentucky waltz / Happy birthday misses / Saving my love for you / Shake your big hips / Darling, I love you / Driving wheel / Bitter tears / I'm in love.
- **LP** . . . . . . . . . . . . . . . . . 2362020
Stax / Aug '71.

# Tom & Jerrio

## BOO-GA-LOO.
Tracks: Boo-ga-loo / Boomerang.
- **7"** . . . . . . . . . . . . . . . POP 1435
H.M.V. / '65.

# Tomlin, Lee

## SWEET SWEET LOVIN'.
Tracks: Sweet sweet lovin'.
- **7"** . . . . . . . . . . . . . .CBS 202455
CBS / '66.

# Tomorrow's Edition

## YOU TURN ME ON.
Tracks: You turn me on.
- **12"** . . . . . . . . . . . . . . . . A 13 2099
- **7"** . . . . . . . . . . . . . . . .A 2099
CBS / Feb '82.

# Toney, Kevin

## LOVESCAPE.
Tracks: Not Advised.
- **CD** . . . . . . . . . . . . . . . .ICH 1167CD
Ichiban / Jan '94 / A.D.A. Distribution / Pinnacle / ACD Trading Ltd. / Koch International / Direct Distribution.

# Toney, Oscar Jr.

## FOR YOUR PRECIOUS LOVE.
Tracks: For your precious love / Ain't that true love.
- **7"** . . . . . . . . . . . . . . . SS 2033
Stateside / Jun '67.

## PAPA DON'S PREACHER.
Tracks: For your precious love / Dark end of the street / Turn on your lovelight / Mon river / Any day now / You can lead your woman to the altar / Unlucky guy / He will break your heart / Without love / Down in Texas / Love that never grows old / Ain't that true love / Do right woman, do right man / That's all I want from you / Never get enough of your love / No sad songs.
- **LP** . . . . . . . . . . . . . . . . CRB 1183
- **MC** . . . . . . . . . . . . . . . TCCRB 1183
Charly R&B / Jun '88 / Charly.

## TURN ON YOUR LOVE LIGHT.
Tracks: Turn on your love light / Any day now.
- **7"** . . . . . . . . . . . . . . . . SS 2046
Stateside / Sep '67 / EMI.

# Tongue 'N' Cheek

## DON'T STOP THE LOVE.
Tracks: Don't stop the love / Don't stop the love (version).
- **12"** . . . . . . . . . . . . . . . . BUST 4
Criminal (1) / Jul '87.

## ENCORE.
Tracks: Encore / Freestyle / Encore (slammin' mix) (Special product only.) / Encore (slammin' dub 1) (Special product only.) / Encore (slammin' dub 2) (Special product only.)
- **12"** . . . . . . . . . . . . . . . .12SY 33
- **12" Remix** . . . . . . . . . . 12SYX 33
- **7"** . . . . . . . . . . . . . . . . . SY 33
- **MC Single** . . . . . . . . . . .TCSY 33

■ CD Single . . . . . . . . . . . . . . . . . CDSY 33
Syncopate / Nov '89.

### FORGET ME NOTS.
Tracks: Forget me nots - The DNA mix / Forget me nots - The slammer mix / Forget me nots - The slammer mix (ext.) (12SYX 39 only.) / Forget me nots - The slam jam mix (12" only.) / Cushion of love (12" only.).
■ 12" . . . . . . . . . . . . . . . . . . . 12SY 39
■ 12" Remix. . . . . . . . . . . . . . . 12SYX 39
■ 7" . . . . . . . . . . . . . . . . . . . . SY 39
■ CD Single . . . . . . . . . . . . . . . . CDSY 39
■ MC Single. . . . . . . . . . . . . . . .TCSY 39
Syncopate / Nov '90.

### NOBODY.
Tracks: Nobody - blue edit (Not on 12".) / Nobody - original version / Nobody - street mix (12" & CD single only.) / Nobody - blue mix (12" & CD single only.) / Tommorrow - The manana mix (12" only.).
■ 12" . . . . . . . . . . . . . . . . . . . 12SY 37
■ 7" . . . . . . . . . . . . . . . . . . . . SY 37
■ CD Single . . . . . . . . . . . . . . . . CDSY 37
■ MC Single. . . . . . . . . . . . . . . .TCSY 37
Syncopate / Jul '90.
■ 12" Remix. . . . . . . . . . . . . . 12SYX 37
Syncopate / Jul '90.

### NOBODY CAN LOVE ME.
Tracks: Nobody can love me.
■ 12" . . . . . . . . . . . . . . . . . . . BUSTR 6
Criminal (1) / Jan '88.

### THIS IS TONGUE 'N' CHEEK.
Tracks: This is Tongue 'N' Cheek / Forget me nots / Nobody / So fine / Street thang / Tomorrow / Cushion of love / It's a crime / Don't stop the love / Why / Encore / Nobody - blue mix (CD only.) / Tomorrow - warehouse mix (CD only.) / Encore - 12" version (CD only.).
■ CD . . . . . . . . . . . . . . . . .CDSYLP 6006
■ LP . . . . . . . . . . . . . . . . . . SYLP 6006
■ MC. . . . . . . . . . . . . . . . . TCSYLP 6006
Syncopate / Aug '90.

### TOMORROW.
Tracks: Tomorrow (warehouse edit) (Not on 12") / Encore (Recall rap mix) (Not on 12SYX 34.) / Tomorrow (Def piano dub) (12SY 34 only.) / Tomorrow (Accapella version) (CD single only.) / Tomorrow (original version) (CD single only.) / Encore (Frankies favourite garage mix) (12SYX 34 only.) / Encore (Slammin mix) (12SYX 34 only.) / Tomorrow (Frankie's def dub) (12SYX 34 only.).
■ MC Single. . . . . . . . . . . . . . . .TCSY 34
■ 12" . . . . . . . . . . . . . . . . . . . 12SY 34
■ 7" . . . . . . . . . . . . . . . . . . . . SY 34
■ CD Single . . . . . . . . . . . . . . . . CDSY 34
■ 12" Remix. . . . . . . . . . . . . . 12SYX 34
Syncopate / Mar '90.

### WHY.
Tracks: Why (you could have had it all) / Nobody (remix).
■ 12" . . . . . . . . . . . . . . . . . . .BUSTR 11
Criminal (1) / Nov '88.

### WHY (YOU COULD HAVE HAD IT ALL).
Tracks: Why (you could have had it all) / Throw down.
■ 12" . . . . . . . . . . . . . . . . . . .BUST 11
■ 7" . . . . . . . . . . . . . . . . . . . . BUS 11
Criminal (1) / Sep '88.

## Tony B

### SO NATURAL.
Tracks: So natural.
■ 12" . . . . . . . . . . . . . . . . . . . VIC 38
■ CD Single . . . . . . . . . . . . . . . . VIC 38CD
■ MC Single. . . . . . . . . . . . . . . VIC 38MC
Victim / Dec '93.

## Tony Toni Tone

Oakland swing trio who scored instant success with 1988 Who? debut, largely produced by En Vogue masterminds Foster & McElroy. Band included ex-Lionel Richie/Sheila E backing musicians, for whom 'Tony' equalled 'looking sharp'. They maintained momentum with cut on Boyz 'N The Hood soundtrack and platinum Revival album. Self-composed and produced 1993 album Sons of Soul was TTT's first to chart in U.K., though they previously hit with brilliant Oakland Stroke single.

### BLUES, THE.
Tracks: Blues.
■ 12". . . . . . . . . . . . . . . . . . WING 8 T
■ 7" . . . . . . . . . . . . . . . . . . . WING 8

---

■ MC Single. . . . . . . . . . . . . . . WING 8 C
■ CD Single . . . . . . . . . . . . . . WING 8 CD
Wing (USA) / Aug '90.

### FEELS GOOD.
Tracks: Feels good / Little Walter.
■ 12" . . . . . . . . . . . . . . . . . . . WINGX 9
■ 7" . . . . . . . . . . . . . . . . . . . . WING 9
■ CD Single . . . . . . . . . . . . . . .WINGCD 9
■ MC Single. . . . . . . . . . . . . . .WINGCS 9
Polydor / Sep '90.

### IF I HAVE NO LOOT.
Tracks: If I have no loot.
■ 12" . . . . . . . . . . . . . . . . . . . .PZ 292
■ 7" . . . . . . . . . . . . . . . . . . . . PO 292
■ CD Single . . . . . . . . . . . . . . . .PZCD 292
■ MC Single. . . . . . . . . . . . . . . .POCS 292
Polydor / Aug '93.

### IT NEVER RAINS (IN SOUTHERN CALIFORNIA).
Tracks: It never rains (in Southern California).
■ 12" . . . . . . . . . . . . . . . . . . .WINGX 10
■ 7" . . . . . . . . . . . . . . . . . . . .WING 10
■ CD Single . . . . . . . . . . . . . . .WINCD 10
■ MC Single. . . . . . . . . . . . . . . WINCS 10
Polydor / Feb '91.

### LITTLE WALTER.
Tracks: Little Walter / Little Walter (instrumental).
■ 12" . . . . . . . . . . . . . . . . . . . WINGX 2
■ 7" . . . . . . . . . . . . . . . . . . . . WING 2
Polydor / Jun '88.

### MY EX-GIRLFRIEND.
Tracks: My ex-girlfriend (Mixes).
■ 12" . . . . . . . . . . . . . . . . . . . .PZ 313
■ 7" . . . . . . . . . . . . . . . . . . . . PO 313
■ CD Single . . . . . . . . . . . . . . . .PZCD 313
■ MC Single. . . . . . . . . . . . . . . .POCS 313
Polydor / May '94.

### OAKLAND STROKE.
Tracks: Oakland stroke.
■ 12" . . . . . . . . . . . . . . . . . . . WINGX 7
■ 12" Remix. . . . . . . . . . . . . . .WINXR 7
■ 7" . . . . . . . . . . . . . . . . . . . . WING 7
■ CD Single . . . . . . . . . . . . . . .WINCD 7
■ MC Single. . . . . . . . . . . . . . . WINCS 7
Wing (USA) / Jun '90.

### REVIVAL, THE.
Tracks: Feels good / Oakland stroke / Let's have a good time / Whatever you want / Sky's the limit / Don't talk about me / Jo-Jo / All the way / Blues / It never rains / I care / All my love / Skin tight / Those were the days.
■ CD . . . . . . . . . . . . . . . . . . 841 902-2
■ LP . . . . . . . . . . . . . . . . . . 841 902-1
■ MC. . . . . . . . . . . . . . . . . . 841 902-4
Polydor / May '90 / PolyGram.

### SONS OF SOUL.
Tracks: If I had no loot / What goes around comes around / My ex-girlfriend / Tell me mama / Leavin' / Slow wine (slow grind) / Lay your head on my pillow / I couldn't keep it to myself / Gangsta groove / Tonyies! In the wrong key / Dance hall / Time Square 2:30 AM (Segue) / Fun / Anniversary / Castleers.
■ CD . . . . . . . . . . . . . . . . . . .514933-2
■ LP . . . . . . . . . . . . . . . . . . .514933-1
■ MC. . . . . . . . . . . . . . . . . . .514933-4
Polydor / Jul '93 / PolyGram.

## Total Contrast

### BE WITH YOU TONIGHT.
Tracks: Be with you tonight / Ourselves.
■ 12" . . . . . . . . . . . . . . . . . . . TCRS 1
■ 7" . . . . . . . . . . . . . . . . . . . . TCR 1
Total Contrast / Jan '84.
■ 12" . . . . . . . . . . . . . . . . . . . LONX 76
■ 7" . . . . . . . . . . . . . . . . . . . . LON 76
London / Oct '85.

### BEAT TO BEAT.
Tracks: Jody / Painting by numbers / Found somebody / Help me / Just a little bit / Kiss / Hidden in a heartbeat / Same old story / Teach me to forget / Jody - the dance hall version (On CD only).
■ CD . . . . . . . . . . . . . . . . . . 828 068 2
■ LP . . . . . . . . . . . . . . . . . . .LONLP 45
■ MC. . . . . . . . . . . . . . . . . . . LONC 45
London / Nov '87.

### JODY.
Tracks: Jody / Jody (inst).
■ 12" . . . . . . . . . . . . . . . . . . . LONX 142
■ 7" . . . . . . . . . . . . . . . . . . . .LON 142
London / Aug '87.

---

### KISS.
Tracks: Kiss / Dance.
■ 12" . . . . . . . . . . . . . . . . . . . LONX 155
■ 7" . . . . . . . . . . . . . . . . . . . .LON 155
London / Oct '87.

### LOVE FEVER.
Tracks: Love fever.
■ 12" . . . . . . . . . . . . . . . . . . . BUST 018
Criminal (1) / May '89.

### NEXT TIME I'LL KNOW BETTER.
Tracks: Next time I'll know better / Sunshine.
■ 12" . . . . . . . . . . . . . . . . . . . TCR 2
Total Contrast / Nov '84.

### RIVER, THE.
Tracks: River / River, the(Instrumental) / Takes a Little time (US Remix) (12"recording only).
■ 12" . . . . . . . . . . . . . . . . . . . LONX 83
■ 7" . . . . . . . . . . . . . . . . . . . . LON 83
London / Feb '86.

### TAKES A LITTLE TIME.
Tracks: Takes a little time / Takes a little mirage style.
■ 12" . . . . . . . . . . . . . . . . . . . LONX 71
■ 7" . . . . . . . . . . . . . . . . . . . . LON 71
London / Jul '85.

### TAKES A LITTLE TIME (OLD GOLD).
Tracks: Takes a little time / Hit and run.
■ 12" . . . . . . . . . . . . . . . . . . .OG 4080
Old Gold / Oct '88.

### TOTAL CONTRAST.
Tracks: Hit and Run / River / Where is love / How many reasons / Takes a Little time / What you gonna do about it / Sunshine / Entangled.
MC . . . . . . . . . . . . . . . . . . . LONC 15
■ LP . . . . . . . . . . . . . . . . . . .LONLP 15
London / Nov '85 / PolyGram.
■ CD . . . . . . . . . . . . . . . . . . 828 002 2
London / Mar '86.

### WAITING IN VAIN.
Tracks: Waiting in vain.
■ 12" . . . . . . . . . . . . . . . . . . . BARB T1
■ 7" . . . . . . . . . . . . . . . . . . . . BUS 14
■ 7" . . . . . . . . . . . . . . . . . . . . BARB 2
Criminal (1) / Dec '88.
■ 12" . . . . . . . . . . . . . . . . . . .BUST 14
Criminal (1) / Dec '88.

### WHAT YOU GONNA DO ABOUT IT.
Tracks: What you gonna do about it / I'm still waiting.
■ 12" . . . . . . . . . . . . . . . . . . . LONX 9
■ 7" . . . . . . . . . . . . . . . . . . . . LON 9
London / Apr '86.

## Touch Of Class

### I'M IN HEAVEN.
Tracks: I'm in heaven.
■ 7" . . . . . . . . . . . . . . . . . . . . GT 9
GTO / May '77.

### KEEP DANCING.
Tracks: Keep dancing.
■ 12" . . . . . . . . . . . . . . . . . . . A 9643
■ 7" . . . . . . . . . . . . . . . . . . . .A 964
Atlantic / Nov '84.

### LET ME BE YOUR EVERYTHING.
Tracks: Let me be your everything / Keep dancing
■ 12" . . . . . . . . . . . . . . . . . . . A 9550
■ 7" . . . . . . . . . . . . . . . . . . . .A 955
Atlantic / Jun '85.

## Touchdown

### BREAKOUT.
Tracks: Breakout.
■ 12" . . . . . . . . . . . . . . . . . . . EXCL 52
■ 7" . . . . . . . . . . . . . . . . . . . .EXC 52
Excalibur / Oct '82.

### DO YOU NEED?.
Tracks: Do you need.
■ 12" . . . . . . . . . . . . . . . . . . . SUE 100
Krack / Dec '84.

### EASE YOUR MIND.
Tracks: Ease your mind / Aquadance.
■ 12" . . . . . . . . . . . . . . . . . . . SHACK 12
■ 7" . . . . . . . . . . . . . . . . . . . .SHACK
Arista / Jun '81.

### EASE YOUR MIND.
Tracks: Ease your mind / Ritmo suave.
■ 12" . . . . . . . . . . . . . . . . . . . EXCL 57
■ 7" . . . . . . . . . . . . . . . . . . . .EXC 57
Excaliber / May '82.

■ DELETE

**EASE YOUR MIND '89.**
Tracks: Ease your mind '89.
■ 12" . . . . . . . . . . . . . . . . . . . . . BBOXT 5
■ 7" . . . . . . . . . . . . . . . . . . . . . . BBOX 5
Beat Box / May '89.

**ENDZONE, THE.**
Tracks: Endzone.
■ 12" . . . . . . . . . . . . . . . . . . . DEBTX 3004
Debut (1) / Apr '86.

## Toussaint, Allen

A handful of solo releases do not do justice to this legendary New Orleans pianist and producer, who is better known as a song-writer for acts including Dixie Cups, Irma Thomas and Aaron Neville, and collabora-tor with acts ranging from Dr John to Paul Simon. Among his more enduring relation-ships were those with Lee Dorsey (associa-tion which stretched from *Ya Ya* in '61 to later, pre-funk classics like *Get Out Of My Life Woman*) and the Neville clan (including the Meters) acclaimed '70s work). Tous-saint's name appeared with less frequency in the '80s, although he resurfaced in 1987 Broadway musical *Staggerlee* and has tragically recently recorded an album of Andrew Lloyd Webber material.

**20 FAMOUS THEMES OF ANDREW LLOYD WEBBER (Toussaint, Allen Orchestra).**
Tracks: Phantom of the opera / Wishing you were somehow here again / All I ask of you / Music of the night / Jesus Christ superstar / I don't know how to love him.
CD . . . . . . . . . . . . . . . . . . . . . 26 68 282
MC . . . . . . . . . . . . . . . . . . . . . 26 68 284
Point (2) / '92 / Sound Solutions.

**20 GREAT GERSHWIN GREATS (Tous-saint, Allen Orchestra).**
Tracks: Rahpsody in blue / I got rhythm / Swanee / Our love is here to stay / Summertime / Let's call the whole thing off / Embraceable you / But not for me / I got plenty of nothing.
CD . . . . . . . . . . . . . . . . . . . . . 26 68 272
MC . . . . . . . . . . . . . . . . . . . . . 26 68 274
Point (2) / '92 / Sound Solutions.

**20 SUPERHERO THEMES (Toussaint, Al-len Orchestra).**
Tracks: Batdance / Licence to kill / Raider's march / On our own / Roadhouse blues / Wonder woman / Batman theme / Star wars suite / Superman theme.
CD . . . . . . . . . . . . . . . . . . . . . 26 38 382
MC . . . . . . . . . . . . . . . . . . . . . 26 38 384
Point (2) / '92 / Sound Solutions.

**24 CHRISTMAS SONGS (Toussaint, Al-len Orchestra).**
Tracks: Wonderful christmas time / Have yourself a merry little christmas / Little drummer boy / Mary's little boy child / Rudolph, the red nosed reindeer / Good King Wenceslas / First Noel.
CD . . . . . . . . . . . . . . . . . . . . . 26 60 042
MC . . . . . . . . . . . . . . . . . . . . . 26 60 044
Point (2) / '92 / Sound Solutions.

**40 ALL TIME FILM AND TV GREATEST (Toussaint, Allen Orchestra).**
Tracks: Not Advised.
CD . . . . . . . . . . . . . . . . . . . . . 26 68 362
MC . . . . . . . . . . . . . . . . . . . . . 26 68 364
Point (2) / '92 / Sound Solutions.

**O'S MASTERS, THE.**
Tracks: Whirlaway / Happy times / Up the crek / Tim jam / Me and you / Bono / Java / Wham tousan / Nowhere to go / Nashua / Po boy walk / Pelican parade / Chico / Back home again in Indiana / Second liner / Cow cow blues / Moo moo / Sweetie pie (twenty years later) / You didn't know, did you / Up right / Blue mood / Lazy day / Naomi / Real hurchy / Real church (2).
CD . . . . . . . . . . . . . . . . . . . . . BCD 15641
Bear Family / Mar '92 / Rollercoaster Records / Swift Direct Distribution / Topic Records.

**BEATLES SONGBOOK (24 Memorable Themes) (Toussaint, Allen Orchestra).**
Tracks: Hard day's night / Can't buy me love / I feel fine / She loves you / I want to hold your hand / Help / Ticket to ride / Yesterday / We can work it out / Paperback writer.
CD . . . . . . . . . . . . . . . . . . . . . 26 68 312
MC . . . . . . . . . . . . . . . . . . . . . 26 68 314
Point (2) / '92 / Sound Solutions.

**CLASSIC ROCK SYMPHONIES (Tous-saint, Allen Orchestra).**
Tracks: Layla / Bohemian rhapsody / Another brick in the wall / MacArthur park / Nights in white satin / Whiter shade of pale / In love / Question / Stairway to heaven / Day in the life.
CD . . . . . . . . . . . . . . . . . . . . . 26 68 252
MC . . . . . . . . . . . . . . . . . . . . . 26 68 254
Point (2) / '92 / Sound Solutions.

**FROM A WHISPER TO A SCREAM (Retro 87-88).**
Tracks: From a whisper to a scream / Chokin' kind / Sweet touch of love / What is success / Working in a coalmine / Everything I do gonna be funky / Either / Louie / Cast your fate to the wind / Number nine / Pickles.
■ LP . . . . . . . . . . . . . . . . . . . KENT 036
Kent / Mar '85.
CD . . . . . . . . . . . . . . . . . . . CDKENM 036
Kent / Mar '91 / Pinnacle.

**I GET A KICK OUT OF .. COLE POTER (Toussaint, Allen Orchestra).**
Tracks: Begine the beguine / I get a kick out of you / Let's do it / Just one of those things / Anything goes / Night and day / What is this thing called love / Don't fence me in.
CD . . . . . . . . . . . . . . . . . . . . . 26 68 302
MC . . . . . . . . . . . . . . . . . . . . . 26 68 304
Point (2) / '92 / Sound Solutions.

**IRVING BERLIN'S 20 GRESTEST THEMES (Toussaint, Allen Orchestra).**
Tracks: Alexander's ragtime band / Blue skies / Cheek to cheek / There's no business like show business / Top hat, white tie & tails / God bless America / Let's face the music and dance.
CD . . . . . . . . . . . . . . . . . . . . . 26 68 322
MC . . . . . . . . . . . . . . . . . . . . . 26 68 324
Point (2) / '92 / Sound Solutions.

**LIFE, LOVE AND FAITH.**
Tracks: Victims of the darkness / Am I expecting too much / My baby is the real thing / Goin' down / She once belonged to me / Out of the city / Soul sister / Fingers & toes / I've got to convince myself / On your way down / Gone too far / Electricity.
■ LP . . . . . . . . . . . . . . . . . . . K 44202
Reprise / Nov '72.
CD . . . . . . . . . . . . . . . . . . . CPCD 8032
Charly / Feb '94 / Charly.

**MOTION.**
Tracks: Night people / Just a kiss away / With you in mind / Lover of love / To be with you / Motion / Viva la money / Declaration of love / Happiness / Op-timism blues.
■ LP . . . . . . . . . . . . . . . . . . . K 56473
Warner Bros. / Jul '78.

**SOUTHERN NIGHTS.**
Tracks: Last train / Worldwide / Back in baby's arms / Country John / Basic lady / Southern nights / You will not lose / What do you want the girl to do / When the party's over / Cruel way to go down.
■ LP . . . . . . . . . . . . . . . . . . . ED 155
Edsel / Mar '85.

**TOUSSAINT.**
Tracks: From a whisper to a scream / Chokin' kind / Sweet touch of love / What is success / Working in the coalmine / Everything I do gonna be funky / Pickles / Louie / Either / Cast your fate to the wind.
■ LP . . . . . . . . . . . . . . . . . . . WNS 14
Wand / Feb '72.
■ LP . . . . . . . . . . . . . . . . . . . DJM 22070
DJM / Sep '77.

**WILD SOUNDS OF NEW ORLEANS.**
Tracks: Up the creek / Tim Tam / Me And You / Bono / Java / Happy Times / Nowhere to go / Nashua / Po' Boy Walk / Pelican parade.
■ LP . . . . . . . . . . . . . . . . . . . ED 275
Edsel / Apr '88.
CD . . . . . . . . . . . . . . . . . . . EDCD 275
Edsel / Apr '91 / Pinnacle.

**WITH THE STOKES.**
Tracks: Not Advised.
■ LP . . . . . . . . . . . . . . . . . . . BANDY 70014
Bandy (USA) / Jul '84.

**WORKING IN THE COALMINE.**
Tracks: Working down the coal mine / Down in the sewer.
■ 7" . . . . . . . . . . . . . . . . . . . MAG 170
Magnet / Apr '80.

## Tower Of Power

Brass-heavy R&B act from San Francisco, Tower of Power acquired formidable repu-tation in early '70s: memorable evening at Fillmore West found them supporting Ar-etha Franklin and King Curtis. Rockier side found audience on 1975 Warner Brothers package tour of Europe, also boasting Doo-bie Brothers and Graham Central Station. By this time they had several million-sellers under their belts, including Steve Cropper-produced *Bump City* album. Second lead singer Lenny Williams (their first, Rich Ste-vens, having left and been convicted of murder) launched successful solo career in late '70s, by which time TOP's star was beginning to fade. However, they continued to record and were still active in late '80s; 10-piece line-up included new vocalist Tom Bowes. TOP are among acts who made strong impression on youthful Prince Roger Nelson.

**BUMP CITY.**
Tracks: Not Advised.
CD . . . . . . . . . . . . . . . . . . . . . 7599263482
Warner Bros. / Sep '93 / WEA.

**DIRECT.**
Tracks: Not Advised.
CD . . . . . . . . . . . . . . . . . . . . . CD 17
Sheffield Treasury / '88.

**IN THE SLOT.**
Tracks: Not Advised.
CD . . . . . . . . . . . . . . . . . . . . . 7599263502
Warner Bros. / Sep '93 / WEA.

**LOVIN' YOU IS GONNA SEE ME THRU.**
Tracks: Lovin' you is gonna see me thru / Am I a fool.
■ 7" . . . . . . . . . . . . . . . . . . . CBS 6318
CBS / May '78.

**POWER.**
Tracks: Baby's got the power / Some days were meant for rain / Ball and chain / Count on me / Up against yourself / Credit / Boys night out / Through lovers eyes / On the one.
CD . . . . . . . . . . . . . . . . . . . . . YD 0106
■ LP . . . . . . . . . . . . . . . . . . . YL 0106
Cypress / Nov '88 / Sonet Records / Jazz Music / Wellard / C.M. Distribution.

**TOWER OF POWER.**
Tracks: Not Advised.
■ LP . . . . . . . . . . . . . . . . . . . LAB 17
Sheffield Treasury / Oct '82.

**URBAN RENEWAL.**
Tracks: Not Advised.
CD . . . . . . . . . . . . . . . . . . . . . 7599263492
Warner Bros. / Sep '93 / WEA.

**WE CAME TO PLAY.**
Tracks: We came to play / Lovin' you is gonna see me thru / Let me touch you / Yin-yang thang / Share my life / Bittersweet soul music / Am I a fool / Love bug / Somewhere down the road.
■ LP . . . . . . . . . . . . . . . . . . . CBS 82239
CBS / Jul '78.

**WHAT IS HIP.**
Tracks: Maybe it'll rub off / On the serious side / Just enough and too much / So very hard to go / Soul vaccination / Don't change horses in the middle of a stream / What is hip / Get yo' feet back on the ground / Both sorry over nothing / Clean slate / Treat me like your man / Give me the proof / (To say the least) you're the most.
■ LP . . . . . . . . . . . . . . . . . . . ED 206
Edsel / Nov '86.

**YOU OUGHT TO BE HAVIN' FUN.**
Tracks: You ought to be havin' on / While we went to the moon.
■ 7" . . . . . . . . . . . . . . . . . . . CBS 4675
CBS / Oct '76.

## Toys

**ATTACK.**
Tracks: Attack.
■ 7" . . . . . . . . . . . . . . . . . . . SS 483
Stateside / Jan '66.

**CIAO BABY.**
Tracks: Ciao baby / I got carried away.
■ 7" . . . . . . . . . . . . . . . . . . . BF 1563
Philips / Mar '67.

**LOVER'S CONCERTO (OLD GOLD).**
Tracks: Lover's concerto / Walking my cat named dog.

■ 7″ . . . . . . . . . . . . . . . . . . . . . . . .OG 9416
Old Gold / Jul '84.

## LOVER'S CONCERTO, A.
**Tracks:** Lovers concerto.
■ 7″ . . . . . . . . . . . . . . . . . . . . . . . .SS 460
Stateside / '65.

## MY LOVE SONATA.
**Tracks:** My love sonata / I close my eyes.
■ 7″ . . . . . . . . . . . . . . . . . . . . . . .BF 1581
Philips / Jun '67.

## Tracy, Jeanie

### DO YOU BELIEVE IN THE WONDER.
**Tracks:** Do you believe in the wonder.
12″ . . . . . . . . . . . . . . . . . . . . .12 LOSE 74
7″ . . . . . . . . . . . . . . . . . . . . . . .LOSE 74
CD Single . . . . . . . . . . . . . . . . .CDLOSE 74
MC Single . . . . . . . . . . . . . . . .CALOSE 74
Pulse 8 / Oct '94 / Sony / 3MV.

### DON'T LEAVE ME THIS WAY.
**Tracks:** Don't leave me this way (Sylvester mix).
■ 12″ . . . . . . . . . . . . . . . . . . . . .DOM T2
■ 7″ . . . . . . . . . . . . . . . . . . . . . . .DOM 2
Domino (1) / Aug '86.

### IT'S MY TIME.
**Tracks:** It's my time.
■ 7″ . . . . . . . . . . . . . . . . . . . . . . .3 BT29
■ MC Single . . . . . . . . . . . . . . . .3 BTCA 29
■ 12″ . . . . . . . . . . . . . . . . . . . . .3 BTT 29
■ CD Single . . . . . . . . . . . . . . . .3 BTCD 29
3 Beat / Nov '93.

### ME AND YOU.
**Tracks:** Sing your own song / Your old stand by / I
feel like dancing / Me and you / I'm your jeanie /
Come make love to me / I want you / Tears on my
pillow.
■ LP . . . . . . . . . . . . . . . . . . . .FASLP 3001
Fantasy / Mar '82.

## Tramaine

### FALL DOWN (SPIRIT OF LOVE).
**Tracks:** Fall down (spirit of love).
■ 12″ . . . . . . . . . . . . . . . . . . . . .AMY 281
■ 7″ . . . . . . . . . . . . . . . . . . . . . . .AM 281
A&M / Oct '85.

## Trammps

Early Philadelphia disco favourites founded
by drummer Earl Young. 1972 update of
Zing Went the Strings of My Heart began
series of hits that climaxed with Disco Inferno, from Saturday Night Fever. Thereafter,
group disappeared from charts, but periodically recorded in 1980s, and sang on KWS's
1992 remake of their '75 smash Hold Back
the Night. Tina Turner successfully covered
Disco Inferno in 1993.

### BEST OF THE TRAMMPS.
**Tracks:** Disco inferno / Night the lights went out /
That's where the happy people go / Hooked for life /
Disco party / Soul searchin' time / Body contact
contract / I feel like I been livin' / Seasons for girls.
■ LP . . . . . . . . . . . . . . . . . . . . . .K 50511
Atlantic / Feb '79.

### DISCO INFERNO.
**Tracks:** Disco inferno / You touch my hot line.
■ 7″ . . . . . . . . . . . . . . . . . . . . .K 10914
Atlantic / Apr '77.

### DISCO INFERNO.
**Tracks:** Disco inferno / Where the happy people go.
■ 7″ . . . . . . . . . . . . . . . . . . . . .K 11135
Atlantic / Jun '78.

### DISCO INFERNO.
**Tracks:** Bocy contact contract / Starvin' / I feel like
I've been livin' (on the dark side of the moon) / Disco
inferno / Don't burn no bridges / You touch my hot
line.
■ LP . . . . . . . . . . . . . . . . . . . . . .K 50339
Atlantic / '77.

### DISCO INFERNO (OLD GOLD).
**Tracks:** Disco inferno / That's where the happy people go.
12″ . . . . . . . . . . . . . . . . . . . . . .OG 4186
Old Gold / Jul '90 / Pickwick.

### HARD ROCK & DISCO.
**Tracks:** Hard rock and disco (part 1) / Hard rock and
disco (part 2).
■ 7″ . . . . . . . . . . . . . . . . . . . . .K11438
Atlantic / Apr '80.

---

## HOLD BACK THE NIGHT.
**Tracks:** Hold back the night / Tom's song.
■ 7″ . . . . . . . . . . . . . . . . . . . . .BDS 437
Buddah / Oct '75.

## HOLD BACK THE NIGHT (OLD GOLD).
**Tracks:** Hold back the night / Zing went the strings of
my heart.
■ 7″ . . . . . . . . . . . . . . . . . . . . .OG 9297
Old Gold / Apr '83.
7″ . . . . . . . . . . . . . . . . . . . . . . .OG 9921
Old Gold / Jan '90 / Pickwick.

## I FEEL LIKE I'VE BEEN LIVIN'.
**Tracks:** I feel like I've been livin' / Don't burn no
bridges.
■ 7″ . . . . . . . . . . . . . . . . . . . . .K 10982
Atlantic / Jul '77.

## LEGENDARY ZING ALBUM, THE.
**Tracks:** Penguin at the big apple/Zing went the
strings of my heart / Pray all you sinners / Sixty
minute man / Scruboard / Tom's song / Rubber band
/ Hold back the night / Penguin at the big apple.
CD . . . . . . . . . . . . . . . . . . .CDKENM 088
■ LP . . . . . . . . . . . . . . . . . . .KENT 088
Kent / Oct '88 / Pinnacle.

## LOOKING FOR YOU.
**Tracks:** Looking for you / Love land.
■ 7″ . . . . . . . . . . . . . . . . . . . . .K 11654
Atlantic / Feb '81.

## LOVE EPIDEMIC.
**Tracks:** Love epidemic / I know that feeling.
■ 7″ . . . . . . . . . . . . . . . . . . .PIR 1989
Philadelphia Int. / Feb '76.

## MIXIN' IT UP.
**Tracks:** Hard rock and disco / You can make it /
Music freek / Let me dance real close / Dance
contest / Everybody boogie / V.I.P. / Wake up from
yesterday.
■ LP . . . . . . . . . . . . . . . . . . . . .K 50704
Atlantic / Jun '80.

## SIXTY MINUTE MAN.
**Tracks:** Sixty minute man.
■ 7″ . . . . . . . . . . . . . . . . . . . . .BDS 415
Buddah / Feb '75.

## SLIPPING OUT.
**Tracks:** Loveland / Trained - eye / Mellow out /
Groove all mighty / Looking for you / Our thought
(slipping away) / I don't want to ever lose your love /
Is there any room for me / Breathtaking view.
■ LP . . . . . . . . . . . . . . . . . . . . .K 50769
Atlantic / Jan '81.

## SOUL SEARCHIN' TIME.
**Tracks:** Soul searchin' time.
■ 7″ . . . . . . . . . . . . . . . . . . . . .K 10797
Atlantic / Jul '76.

## THAT'S WHERE THE HAPPY PEOPLE
GO.
**Tracks:** That's where the happy people go.
■ 7″ . . . . . . . . . . . . . . . . . . . . .K 10703
Atlantic / Mar '76.

## TRAMMPS (CD EP).
**Tracks:** Hold back the night / Sixty minute man / Zing
went the strings of my heart / Penguin at the big
apple.
■ CD Single . . . . . . . . . . . . . . . . .CD3-18
Special Edition / '88.

## TRAMMPS DISCO THEME.
**Tracks:** Trammps disco theme / Love epidemic.
■ 7″ . . . . . . . . . . . . . . . . . . . . .PIR 5452
Philadelphia Int. / Jul '77.

## TRAMMPS III.
**Tracks:** Night the lights went out / Love per hour /
People of the world rise / Living the life / Seasons for
girls / Life ain't been easy / I'm so glad you came
along / It don't take too much.
■ LP . . . . . . . . . . . . . . . . . . . . .K 50425
Atlantic / Feb '78.

## WHOLE WORLD'S DANCING, THE.
**Tracks:** Love insurance policy / Teaser / Whole
world's dancing / My love, it's never been better /
Soul bones / Love magnet / More good times to
remember.
■ LP . . . . . . . . . . . . . . . . . . . . .K 50599
Atlantic / '78.

## ZING WENT THE STRINGS OF MY
HEART.
**Tracks:** Zing went the strings of my heart.
■ 7″ . . . . . . . . . . . . . . . . . . . . .BDS 405
Buddah / Nov '74.

---

## TRELLINI.
**Tracks:** Tell me baby / Stay with me / Spastic ass
Don't call me baby / U said U loved me / Eddie Mille
/ Crazy bout you / Come inside / Intermission /
wanna be yours / Follow my heart / Together foreve
/ Dinner date / True 2 me / Take it slow / What's up
CD . . . . . . . . . . . . . . . . . . . . . .11393
LP . . . . . . . . . . . . . . . . . . . . . .11393
MC . . . . . . . . . . . . . . . . . . . . . .11393
Musidisc / Sep '94 / Vital Distribution / Discovery
A.D.A. Distribution / Harmonia Mundi (UK).

## Tresvant, Ralph

### RALPH TRESVANT.
**Tracks:** Not Advised.
■ CD . . . . . . . . . . . . . . . . . . .DMCG 612
■ LP . . . . . . . . . . . . . . . . . . . .MCG 612
■ MC . . . . . . . . . . . . . . . . . . .MCGC 612
MCA / Dec '90.

### SENSITIVITY.
**Tracks:** Sensitivity.
■ 12″ . . . . . . . . . . . . . . . . . . .MCAT 146
■ 12″ Remix . . . . . . . . . . . . . . .MCAX 146
■ 7″ . . . . . . . . . . . . . . . . . . . . .MCA 146
■ CD Single . . . . . . . . . . . . . .DMCAT 146
■ MC Single . . . . . . . . . . . . . . .MCAC 146
MCA / Nov '90.

### STONE COLD GENTLEMAN.
**Tracks:** Stone cold gentleman.
■ 12″ . . . . . . . . . . . . . . . . . . .MCST 152
■ 12″ Remix . . . . . . . . . . . . . .MCSTR 152
■ 7″ . . . . . . . . . . . . . . . . . . . . .MCS 152
■ CD Single . . . . . . . . . . . . . .MCSTD 152
■ MC Single . . . . . . . . . . . . . . .MCSC 152
MCA / Mar '91.

## Triple S Connection

### MY CHERIE AMOUR.
**Tracks:** My cherie amour / Back in your arms agair
■ 7″ . . . . . . . . . . . . . . . . . . . . .TC 241
20th Century / Nov '79.

## Troop

### MAMACITA.
**Tracks:** Mamacita.
■ 12″ . . . . . . . . . . . . . . . . . . . . .A 8979
■ 7″ . . . . . . . . . . . . . . . . . . . . . .A 897
WEA / Nov '88.

### THAT'S MY ATTITUDE.
**Tracks:** That's my attitude / That's my attitud
(remix).
■ 12″ . . . . . . . . . . . . . . . . . . .A 7810
■ 7″ . . . . . . . . . . . . . . . . . . . . .A 781
East West / Oct '90.

### TROOP.
**Tracks:** Not Advised.
■ LP . . . . . . . . . . . . . . . . . . . . .81851
Atlantic / Aug '88.

## Trouble Funk

Trouble Funk were leading lights of massi
vely-hyped and microscopically-purchased
Go-Go genre. Formed in Washington ir
1978, quintet recorded for Sugarhill; rein
forcing their hip-hop connections in '8
when Trouble Over Here, Trouble Ove
There album boasted Bootsy Collins and
Kurtis Blow. By this time, group were or
Island, with whom they managed a couple
of minor U.K. chart successes. Failure to
cross over can largely be attributed to es
sentially live nature of band's pounding
sound.

### BOMB HAS DROPPED, THE.
**Tracks:** Pump me up / Hey fellas / Let's get hot
Drop the bomb / Get on up / Don't try to use me.
■ LP . . . . . . . . . . . . . . . . . . . .BLAT 5
MC . . . . . . . . . . . . . . . . . . . .BLATMC 5
■ CD . . . . . . . . . . . . . . . . . . .BLATCD 5
Blatant / Apr '88 / Roots Records.

### DROP THE BOMB.
**Tracks:** Hey fellas / Get on up / Let's get hot / Dro
the bomb / Pump me up / Don't try to use me / My
love (burning love) / Caravan to midnight / I'm out to
get you / Lost in love / Fool / It's for you / Birthda
boy / King of the dances / Sail on / Supergrit (On CI
only) / Hey Fellas (2) (On CD only).
■ LP . . . . . . . . . . . . . . . . . . . .SHLP 1000
Sugarhill / Sep '82.

■ DELETE

■ LP . . . . . . . . . . . . . . . . . SHLP 5554
Sugarhill / Feb '85.
CD . . . . . . . . . . . . . . . . . NEBCD 663
Sequel / Oct '93 / Total / BMG.

**DROP THE BOMB.**
Tracks: Drop the bomb.
■ 12″ . . . . . . . . . . . . . . . . . SHL 140
Sugarhill / Feb '85.

**GOOD TO GO.**
Tracks: Good to go / Say what / Good to go (instrumental).
■ 7″ . . . . . . . . . . . . . . . . . . . GO 6
■ 12″ . . . . . . . . . . . . . . . . . 12GO 6
Island / Jul '86.

**LIVE IN JAPAN.**
Tracks: Fusion / U should be dancing / Hey T bone / Say what / Mr. Magic / Trouble / Good to go / Trouble in the pocket / Drop the bomb / Don't touch that stereo.
VHS . . . . . . . . . . . . . . . . . IVA 009
Island Visual Arts / Nov '88 / PolyGram / THE.

**SAY WHAT.**
Tracks: Not Advised.
■ LP . . . . . . . . . . . . . . . . . DCLP 101
■ MC . . . . . . . . . . . . . . . . . DCCA 101
4th & Broadway / Oct '86.

**STILL SMOKIN'.**
Tracks: Still smokin' / Beat is bad / Don't touch that stereo / It's all in the mix (don't touch that stereo) (MC single only).
■ 12″ . . . . . . . . . . . . . . . 12 GOGO 5
4th & Broadway / Oct '85.
■ 7″ . . . . . . . . . . . . . . . . . GOGO 5
■ MC Single. . . . . . . . . . . . . GOGOC 5
4th & Broadway / Oct '86.

**TROUBLE FUNK EXPRESS.**
Tracks: Trouble Funk express.
■ 12″ . . . . . . . . . . . . . . . . . GRPT 105
Greyhound / Jun '83.

**TROUBLE OVER HERE TROUBLE OVER THERE.**
Tracks: Break it up / Sexy / New money / Stroke / All over the world / Hey tee bone / Woman of principle / Trouble.
■ CD . . . . . . . . . . . . . . . . . BRCD 513
■ LP . . . . . . . . . . . . . . . . . BRLP 513
■ MC . . . . . . . . . . . . . . . . . BRCA 513
4th & Broadway / Jul '87.
■ CD . . . . . . . . . . . . . . . . . IMCD 47
4th & Broadway / '89.
MC . . . . . . . . . . . . . . . . . ICM 2052
MC . . . . . . . . . . . . . . . . . 842 711 4
4th & Broadway / '90 / PolyGram.

**TROUBLE, STILL SMOKIN'.**
Tracks: Trouble, still smokin' / Drop the bomb.
■ 12″ . . . . . . . . . . . . . . . . 12 BRW 80
4th & Broadway / Oct '87.

**WOMAN OF PRINCIPLE.**
Tracks: Woman of principle / Don't touch that stereo (live in Montreux.) / Woman of principle (special remix) (Special remix Bootsy Collins. Track on 12″ version only.).
■ 12″ . . . . . . . . . . . . . . . . 12 BRW 70
■ 7″ . . . . . . . . . . . . . . . . . BRW 70
■ MC Single . . . . . . . . . . . . . BRWC 70
4th & Broadway / Jun '87.

## Troy, Doris

**ANYTHING HE WANTS ME TO DO.**
Tracks: Anything he wants me to do / Just like that.
■ 7″ . . . . . . . . . . . . . . . . . C 101
Cameo / Feb '66.

**DORIS TROY.**
Tracks: Ain't that cute / Special care / Give me back my dynamite / You tore me up inside / Games people play / Gonna get my baby back / I've got to be strong / Hurry / So far / Exactly like you / You give me joy / Don't call me no more / Jacob's ladder / All that I got (Not on LP) / Get back (Not on LP) / Dearest darling (Not on LP) / What you will blues (Not on LP) / Vaya con dios (Not on LP).
LP . . . . . . . . . . . . . . . . . SAPCOR 13
Apple / Oct '70.
CD . . . . . . . . . . . . . . . CDP 7987012
MC . . . . . . . . . . . . . . . TCSAPCOR 13
Apple / Jun '92 / EMI.

**JUST ONE LOOK.**
Tracks: What'cha gonna do about it / Bossa nova blues / Just one look / Trust in me / Lazy days / Are you coming home / Somewhere along the way / Draw me closer / School for fools / Be sure / Someone ain't right / Stormy weather / Time.

---

■ LP . . . . . . . . . . . . . . . . . 2464 001
Atlantic / Jun '70.

**LYIN' EYES.**
Tracks: Lyin' eyes / Give God glory.
■ 7″ . . . . . . . . . . . . . . . . . MID 5
Not Advised / Dec '76.

**RAINBOW TESTAMENT (Troy, Doris & The Gospel Truth).**
Tracks: Testify / Games people play / Everything's alright / Steal away / Nitty gritty / Put your hand on the hand / My father's house / Morning train.
■ LP . . . . . . . . . . . . . . . . . 2956001
Mojo / Jan '73.

**WHAT'CHA GONNA DO ABOUT IT.**
Tracks: What'cha gonna do about it.
■ 7″ . . . . . . . . . . . . . . . . . AT 4011
Atlantic / '64.

## True, Andrea

**MORE MORE MORE.**
Tracks: More, more, more.
■ 7″ . . . . . . . . . . . . . . . . . BDS 442
Buddah / Apr '76.

**MORE MORE MORE (OLD GOLD) (True, Andrea Connection).**
Tracks: More, more, more / This is it.
7″ . . . . . . . . . . . . . . . . . OG 9922
Old Gold / Jan '90 / Pickwick.

**WHAT'S YOUR NAME WHAT'S YOUR NUMBER.**
Tracks: What's your name what's your number / Fill me up.
■ 7″ . . . . . . . . . . . . . . . . . BDS 467
Buddah / Mar '78.

## Trusay

**THAT'S THE WAY.**
Tracks: That's the way (Mixes).
12″ . . . . . . . . . . . . . . . . . SIP 001
SP / Sep '94 / Jetstar.

## Trussel

**LOVE INJECTION.**
Tracks: Love injection / Gone for the weekend.
■ 7″ . . . . . . . . . . . . . . . . . K 12412
Elektra / Mar '80.

## Tuff Crew

**DANGER ZONE.**
Tracks: Not Advised.
LP . . . . . . . . . . . . . . . . . WAR 2705
Warlock / Jul '88 / Jetstar.

**MY PART OF TOWN.**
Tracks: My part of town.
■ 12″ . . . . . . . . . . . . . . . . WAR 020
Soo Def / Feb '89.

## Turner, Ike

**1958-59 TITLES FOR COBRA AND ARTISTIC.**
Tracks: Matchbox / I know you don't love me / You keep on worrying me / Box top / I'm gonna / Forget about you / Down and out / You've got to lose / Walking down the aisle.
CD . . . . . . . . . . . . . . . . . FLYCD 39
Flyright / Oct '91 / Hot Shot / Roots Records / Wellard / Charly / Swift / Projection / Jazz Music.

**BLUES ROOTS.**
Tracks: You're still my baby / Tacks in my shoes / Things I used to do / Goin' home / Lawdy Miss Clawdy / Right on / Think / Rockin' blues / That's alright / My babe / Broken hearted / If you love me like you say.
■ LP . . . . . . . . . . . . . . . . . UAG 29362
United Artists / Aug '72.

**IKE TURNER AND HIS KINGS OF RHYTHM.**
Tracks: Not Advised.
■ LP . . . . . . . . . . . . . . . . . CH 22
Ace / Dec '88.

**IKE TURNER AND HIS KINGS OF RHYTHM VOL.2.**
Tracks: Not Advised.
■ LP . . . . . . . . . . . . . . . . . CHD 146
Ace / '88.

---

**IKE TURNER AND THE KINGS OF RHYTHM.**
Tracks: Not Advised.
■ LP . . . . . . . . . . . . . . . . . FLY 578
Flyright / Jun '88.

**ROCKS THE BLUES.**
Tracks: Hey Miss Tina / Stringin' along / I miss you so / Nobody wants me / Way you treat me / Bayou rock / Wild one / All the blues all the time.
■ LP . . . . . . . . . . . . . . . . . EMB 3395
Ember / Sep '68.

**TRAILBLAZER (Turner, Ike & The Kings of Rhythm).**
Tracks: Big question / Just one more time / Mistreater / No coming back / You found the time / She made my blood run cold / I'm tore up / Trail blazer / You've changed my love / Let's call it a day / Much later / Miserable / Do you mean it / Gonna wait for my chance / If I never had known you / Rock-a-bucket / Sad as a man can be / What can it be / Do right baby / My baby's tops / Take your fine frame home.
CD . . . . . . . . . . . . . . . . CDCHARLY 263
Charly / Feb '91 / Charly.

## Turner, Ike & Tina

**40 RARE RECORDINGS.**
Tracks: Not Advised.
CD . . . . . . . . . . . . . . . . . 26 20 212
Point (2) / '92 / Sound Solutions.

**BABY GET IT ON.**
Tracks: Baby get it on (2 pts).
■ 7″ . . . . . . . . . . . . . . . . . UP 35766
United Artists / Jul '75.

**BEST OF IKE AND TINA TURNER.**
Tracks: I idolize you / Fool in love / Sexy Ida (part 2) / It's gonna work out fine / Stagger Lee and Billy / Man's crazy / Letter from Tina / River deep, mountain high / Working together / Nutbush City Limits / Proud Mary / Acid Queen / Baby get it on / Honky tonk women / Funky Street (live).
■ CD . . . . . . . . . . . . . . CDP 746 599 2
United Artists / Jun '87.

**BLACK ANGEL.**
Tracks: Not Advised.
■ LP . . . . . . . . . . . . . . . . . CV 1342
Musidisc / Oct '76.

**BLACK BEAUTY.**
Tracks: Not Advised.
■ LP . . . . . . . . . . . . . . . . . CV 1323
■ MC . . . . . . . . . . . . . . . . . C 20195
Musidisc / Jan '77.

**COLLECTION: IKE AND TINA TURNER.**
Tracks: Mississippi rolling stone / Living for the city / Golden empire / I'm looking for my mind / Shake a hand / Bootsie Whitelaw / Too much man for one woman / I know (you don't want me no more) / Rockin' and rollin' / Never been to spain / Sugar sugar / Push / Raise your hand / Tinas prayer / Chicken / If you want it / Let's get it on / You're up to something / You're still my baby / Jesus.
CD . . . . . . . . . . . . . . . . . CCSCD 170
■ Double LP . . . . . . . . . . . . . CCSLP 170
■ MC . . . . . . . . . . . . . . . . . CCSMC 170
Castle Collector Series / '88 / BMG / Pinnacle / Castle Communications.

**CRAZY 'BOUT YOU.**
Tracks: Not Advised.
■ LP . . . . . . . . . . . . . . . . . PLP 30
MC . . . . . . . . . . . . . . . . . PMC 30
Platinum (W.Germany) / Oct '85.

**CUSSIN', CRYIN' AND CARRYIN' ON.**
Tracks: Black angel / Getting nasty / It sho' ain't me / Fool in love / Nothing you can do boy / I better get ta steppin' / Shake a tailfeather / We need an understanding / You're so fine / Too hot to hold / I'm fed up / You got what you wanted / Betcha can't kiss me (just one time) / Cussin, cryin, and carryin, on / Ain't nobody's business / Funky mule / Thinking black / Black beauty / Ghetto funk / Black's alley.
CD . . . . . . . . . . . . . . . . . CDSM 014

**IKE & TINA TURNER SHOW, THE (Turner, Ike & Tina).**
Tracks: Finger poppin' / Tell her I'm not home / Good times / You are my sunshine / Good time tonight / Twist and shout / Something's got a hold on me / I know you don't want me no more / Hi-heel sneakers / My man he's a loving man / I can't stop loving you / Tell the truth.
■ LP . . . . . . . . . . . . . . . . . W 1579
Warner / Aug '66.

■ LP . . . . . . . . . . . . . . . . . . .SMT 014
Starburst / Aug '88 / THE / Jazz Music.

## DELILA'S POWER.
**Tracks:** Delila's power / That's my purpose.
■ 7" . . . . . . . . . . . . . . . . . . . . . UP 26028
United Artists / Nov '75.

## DYNAMIC DUO, THE.
**Tracks:** If I can't be first / Goodbye so long / I don't need / Flee flee flee / It's crazy baby / Hard times / Don't you blame it on me / Gonna have fun / I wish my dream would come true / Am I a fool in love / Something came over me / Hurt is all you gave me.
■ LP . . . . . . . . . . . . . . . . . . . GEM 004
■ MC. . . . . . . . . . . . . . . . . . . GEMC 004
Crown / Feb '86.

## FANTASTIC IKE & TINA.
**Tracks:** Not Advised.
■ LP . . . . . . . . . . . . . . . . . . SLS 50205
■ MC . . . . . . . . . . . . . . . . . . TCS 50205
Sunset (Liberty) / '74.

## FEEL GOOD.
**Tracks:** Chopper / Kay got laid / Feel good / I like it / If you can hully gull / Black coffee / She came in through the bathroom window / If I knew then / You better think of something / Bolic.
■ LP . . . . . . . . . . . . . . . . . UAS 29377
United Artists / '72.

## FINGERPOPPIN' - THE WARNER BROS YEARS.
**Tracks:** Finger poppin' / Tell her I'm not home / (Please) leave me alone / Just so I can be with you / Too many tears / No tears to cry / Merry Christmas baby / Somebody (somewhere) needs you / All I could do was cry / You must believe (in) me / It's all over / Fool for you.
■ LP . . . . . . . . . . . . . . . . . . ED 243
Edsel / Feb '88.

## FOOL IN LOVE, A.
**Tracks:** Not Advised.
CD . . . . . . . . . . . . . . . . . . 120 101
MCS Look Back / Jul '87.

## GOLDEN EMPIRE.
**Tracks:** Mississippi rolling stone / Living for the city / Golden empire / I'm looking for my mind / Shake a hand / Bootsie Whitelaw / Too much man for one woman / I know (you don't want me no more) / Rockin' and rollin' / Never been to Spain.
■ LP . . . . . . . . . . . . . . . . . 6 26297
MC. . . . . . . . . . . . . . . . . . 4 26297
Teldec (1) / Apr '86 / Pinnacle / C.M. Distribution / Swift.

## GOLDEN EMPIRE.
**Tracks:** Not Advised.
CD Set . . . . . . . . . . . . . . . . 24052
Laserlight / Sep '92 / THE / BMG / Target.

## GOLDEN EMPIRE 1 & 2.
**Tracks:** Mississippi rolling stone / Living in the city / Golden empire / I'm looking for my mind / Shake a hand / Bootsie Whitelaw / Too much man for one woman / I know (you don't want me no more) / Rockin' and rollin' / Never been to Spain.
■ LP . . . . . . . . . . . . . . . . . . . . SPDP 2
Spartan / Aug '86.

## GOOD OLD TIMES.
**Tracks:** Let's get it on / Mr. Right / Bootsie Whitelaw / Oh my my / Games people play / So fine / Something / Soul deep / You got to work it / I can't believe what you say / Stormy weather / Night time is the right time / It's gonna work out fine / Proud Mary / Endlessly.
CD. . . . . . . . . . . . . . . . . . . .662171
FNAC Music / Dec '92 / New Note.

## GREAT ALBUM, THE.
**Tracks:** Not Advised.
■ Double LP . . . . . . . . . . . . . . .ALB 148
Musidisc / Jun '84.

## GREATEST HITS.
**Tracks:** Tell the truth / Good times / You are my sunshine / It's all over / All I can do is cry / Something's got a hold on me / Early in the mornin' / I can't stop loving you / Somebody needs you / Fool for you.
■ LP . . . . . . . . . . . . . . . . . . .WS 1810
Warner Bros. / Dec '69.

## GREATEST HITS.
**Tracks:** Fool in love / Poor fool / Tra la la / Mojo queen / Good lovin' / It's gonna work out fine / You should have treated me right / Mind in a whirl / I idolise you / Letter from Tina.
■ LP . . . . . . . . . . . . . . . . . . HM 563
Hallmark / Jul '68.

## HER MAN..HIS WOMAN.
**Tracks:** Get it - get it / I believe / I can't believe (what you say) / My babe / Strange / You weren't ready / That's alright / Rooster / Five long years / Things I used to do.
■ LP . . . . . . . . . . . . . . . . . . E-ST 571
Capitol / Jun '71.
MC. . . . . . . . . . . . . . . . . . ZCGAS 716
Audio Fidelity / Oct '84 / Telstar/Ronco.
■ MC. . . . . . . . . . . . . . . . . EG 2607334
■ LP . . . . . . . . . . . . . . . . . EG 2607331
Stateside / Oct '85.

## HEY HEY.
**Tracks:** Hey hey / Why should I / Jack Rabbit / Ho ho / In your eyes baby / Star above / Prancing / Angel of love / I do love you / You're the only one / Look at that chick / Gotta have you for myself / Shirley can't you see / I don't want to lose your love / Bag pipe special / Moving slow / Evening train / East St. Louis rock / Dear lovin' man / Leaving Kansas city.
■ LP . . . . . . . . . . . . . . . . . . RL 0047
Red Lightnin' / Apr '84.

## HUNTER.
**Tracks:** Hunter / You don't love me / You got me running / Bold soul sister / I smell trouble / Things I used to do / Early in the morning / You're still my baby / I know.
■ LP . . . . . . . . . . . . . . . . SHSP 4001
Harvest / Sep '70.

## I'M TORE UP.
**Tracks:** Sad as a man can be / If I never had known you / I'm tore up / Let's call it a day / Take your fine frame home / Do right, baby / No coming back / Just one more time / Gonna wait for my chance / What can it be / Big question, (The) / She made my blood run cold / Do you mean it / Hoo doo say / I'm tired of beggin' / You don't love me (I know) / Rock a bucket.
■ LP . . . . . . . . . . . . . . . . . .RL 016
Red Lightnin' / Sep '82.

## IKE & TINA TURNER SHOW LIVE, THE.
**Tracks:** Finger poppin' / Down in the valley / Good times / You are my sunshine / Havin' a good time / Twist and shout / I know (you don't want me no more) / Tight pants / My man, he's a lovin' man / I can't stop loving you / To tell the truth.
■ LP . . . . . . . . . . . . . . . . . . ED 152
Edsel / Apr '85.

## IKE AND TINA SESSIONS.
**Tracks:** Lose my cool / Goodbye, so long / You can't miss nothing / My baby now / Flee flee flee / Makin' plans together / It's crazy baby / I wish my dreams would come true / Something came over me / If I can't be first / Hurt is all you gave me / Gonna have fun / I don't need / Give me your love / I can't believe what you say / I need a man / Baby don't do it / Over you / He's the one / Don't you blame it on me.
■ LP . . . . . . . . . . . . . . . . . KENT 065
■ CD . . . . . . . . . . . . . . . . CDKEN 065
■ MC . . . . . . . . . . . . . . . . KENC 065
Kent / Feb '87.

## IKE AND TINA TURNER (1).
**Tracks:** Not Advised.
■ LP . . . . . . . . . . . . . . . . . .SM 3913
Joker (USA) / '88.

## IKE AND TINA TURNER (2).
**Tracks:** Not Advised.
■ CD . . . . . . . . . . . . . . . . . 500 055
Intertape / Jul '87.

## IKE AND TINA TURNER REVUE LIVE, THE.
**Tracks:** Please, please, please / If I can't be the first / Feelin' good / Love of my man / Think / Drown in my own tears / I love the way you love / For your precious love / All in my mind / Am I fool in love / All I could do was cry / My man he's a loving man / I know you don't love me no more / It's gonna work out fine / Way you love me / I can't stop lovin' you / You should have treated me right / He's mine.
■ CD . . . . . . . . . . . . . . . CDKEND 102
Kent / Jun '93.

## IN PERSON VOL. 1 (Turner, Ike & Tina & The Ikettes).
**Tracks:** Everyday people / Gimme some loving / Sweet soul music / Son of a preacher man / I saw through the grapevine / Respect / There was a time / African boo's / Funky Street / Fool in love / Sumit / All I could do was cry / Please please please / Baby I love you / Goodbye, so long.
■ LP . . . . . . . . . . . . . . . . MLS 40014
Minit / Nov '69.

## IT'S ALL OVER.
**Tracks:** Not Advised.
CD . . . . . . . . . . . . . . . . . CDSGP 058

MC. . . . . . . . . . . . . . . . . . CASSGP 058
Prestige / Oct '93 / Total / BMG.

## IT'S GONNA WORK OUT FINE.
**Tracks:** It's gonna work out fine / I idolize you / Fool in love / This man's crazy.
■ EP . . . . . . . . . . . . . . . . . . . ENS 1
Ensign / Oct '83.

## JUKE BOX GIANTS.
**Tracks:** Betcha can't kiss me (just one time) / Ghetto funk / Black angel / Poor fool (fool to long) / It sho ain't me / We need an understanding / Blacks alley / Too hot to hold / I'm fed up / Make 'em wait / Black beauty / Poor little fool / Nothing you can do boy / Nuttin up / Scotty souling / So blue over you / Sad Sam / Thinking black / I better get ta steppin' / Getting nasty.
■ LP . . . . . . . . . . . . . . . . . AFEMP 1021
Audio Fidelity / May '82.

## LEGENDS IN MUSIC - IKE & TINA TURNER.
**Tracks:** Not Advised.
CD. . . . . . . . . . . . . . . . . . LECD 102
Wisepack / Sep '94 / THE / Conifer Records.

## LET ME TOUCH YOUR MIND.
**Tracks:** Let me touch your mind / Annie had a baby / Don't believe her / I had a notion / Popcorn / Early one morning / Help him / Up on the roof / Born free / Heaven help us all.
■ LP . . . . . . . . . . . . . . . . . UAS 29423
United Artists / Feb '73.

## LIVE AT CIRCUS KRONE 1973.
**Tracks:** Not Advised.
CD . . . . . . . . . . . . . . . . . . ZYX 36082
ZYX / Oct '93 / Arabesque Ltd. / BMG.

## LIVE IN PARIS.
**Tracks:** Grumbling / You got me hummin' / Everyday people / Shake a tailfeather / Gimme some loving:Sweet soul music / Son of a preacher man / Come together / Proud Mary / Love like yours don't come knocking everyday / I smell trouble / Respect / Honky tonk woman / I've been loving you too long / I want to take you higher / Land of 1000 dances.
CD . . . . . . . . . . . . . . . . . . .662173
FNAC Music / Dec '92 / New Note.

## LIVING FOR THE CITY.
**Tracks:** Living for the city / Push.
■ 12" . . . . . . . . . . . . . . . . . 12SP 136
■ 7" . . . . . . . . . . . . . . . . . .SP 136
Spartan / Apr '86.

## LOVE LIKE YOURS, A.
**Tracks:** Love like yours.
■ 7" . . . . . . . . . . . . . . . . . HL 10083
London-American / Oct '66.

## M.R.S.
**Tracks:** Not Advised.
CD. . . . . . . . . . . . . . . . . .GRF 218
MC. . . . . . . . . . . . . . . . . MCGRF 218
Tring / Mar '93 / Prism Leisure PLC / Midland Records.

## MOVIN' ON.
**Tracks:** Not Advised.
CD . . . . . . . . . . . . . . . . . CDCD 1134
Charly / Mar '93 / Charly.

## NEW BREED.
**Tracks:** New breed.
■ 7" . . . . . . . . . . . . . . . . . 45FV 303
Fleetville / '85.

## NICE 'N' ROUGH.
**Tracks:** Funky street / I heard it through the grapevine / Honky tonk women / Baby get it on / Working together / I've been loving you too long / Proud Mary / Nutbush City Limits / Acid Queen / Come together / Get back / Sweet Rhode Island red / I want to take you higher / River deep, mountain high (Live.) / Goodbye, so long.
■ LP . . . . . . . . . . . . . . . . LBR 2600211
■ MC . . . . . . . . . . . . . . . TCLBR 2600214
Liberty / Feb '84.

## NUFF SAID.
**Tracks:** I love what you do to me / Baby / Sweet frustrations / What you don't see / Nuff said / Tell the truth / Pick me up / Moving into hip style / I love baby / Can't you hear me callin'.
■ LP . . . . . . . . . . . . . . . . . UAG 2925
United Artists / Mar '72.

## NUTBUSH CITY LIMITS.
**Tracks:** Nutbush City Limits.
■ 7" . . . . . . . . . . . . . . . . . UP 3558
United Artists / Sep '73.

## NUTBUSH CITY LIMITS.
Tracks: Nutbush City Limits / Loco-motion / It's gonna work out fine / I'm blue / River deep, mountain high / I'm falling in love / Fool in love / I idolize you / Come together / Shake, rattle and roll / If you can hully gully (I can hully gully too) / Fool for you / You can't blame me / This man's crazy / Good good lovin' / Stagger Lee.
■ CD .................................16217CD
Success (3) / Oct '94 / Pickwick.

## OOH POO PAH DOO.
Tracks: Ooh poo pah doo / I wanna jump.
■ 7" ...................................UP 35245
United Artists / Jun '71.

## OUTTA SEASON.
Tracks: I've been loving you too long / Mean old world / 3 o'clock in the morning blues / Five long years / Dust my broom / Grumbling / I am a motherless child / Crazy 'bout you baby / Reconsider baby / Honest I do / Please love me / My babe / Rock me baby.
■ LP ................................. LBS 83241
Liberty / Jun '69.
■ LP .................................SLS 50314
Sunset (France) / Jul '72.

## PEARLS FROM THE PAST.
Tracks: Not Advised.
■ CD ...............................KLMCD 019
Scratch / Apr '94 / Scratch Records / BMG / Grapevine Distribution.

## PROUD MARY (And Other Hits).
Tracks: Not Advised.
■ CD ....................................15 090
■ MC ....................................79 539
Laserlight / Aug '91 / THE / BMG / Target.

## PROUD MARY.
Tracks: Proud Mary / Funkier than a mosquito's tweeter.
■ 7" .................................LBF 15432
Liberty / Jan '71.

## PROUD MARY - THE BEST OF IKE & TINA TURNER (Legendary Masters Series).
Tracks: Fool in love / I idolize you / I'm jealous / It's gonna work out fine / Poor fool / Tra la la la la / You should'a treated me right / Come together / Honky tonk women / I want to take you higher / Workin' together / Proud Mary / Funkier than a mosquita's tweeter / Ooh poo pah doo / I'm yours (use me anyway you wanna) / Up in heah / River deep, mountain high / Nutbush City Limits / Sweet Rhode Island Red / Sexy Ida (part 1) / Sexy Ida (part 2) / Baby - get it on / Acid Queen.
■ CD ....................................CZ 422
■ MC ................................. TCEMS 1431
EMI / Apr '91 / EMI.

## RIVER DEEP, MOUNTAIN HIGH.
Tracks: River deep, mountain high / I idolize you / Love like yours / Fool in love / Make 'em wait / Hold on baby / Save the last dance for me / Oh baby / Everyday I have to cry / Such a fool for you / It's gonna work out fine / I'll never need you more than this.
■ LP ................................. HAU 8396
London-American / Oct '66.
■ LP ................................. AMLS 971
A&M / Apr '70.
■ LP ................................. AMLB 1021
Mayfair / Apr '71.
■ LP ................................. MFP 50443
MFP / Dec '79.
■ LP ....................................SPR 8548
■ MC ....................................SPC 8548
Spot / May '84.
■ CD ................................. 393 179-2
■ LP ................................. AMA 3179
■ MC ................................. AMC 3179
A&M / '88 / PolyGram.
■ CD ................................. CDMID 134
■ MC ................................. CMID 134
A&M / Oct '92 / PolyGram.

## RIVER DEEP, MOUNTAIN HIGH.
Tracks: River deep, mountain high.
■ LP ................................. HLU 10242
London-American / Feb '69.

## RIVER DEEP, MOUNTAIN HIGH.
Tracks: River deep, mountain high / I'll keep you happy.
■ 7" ................................. HL 10046
London-American / Jun '66.

## RIVER DEEP, MOUNTAIN HIGH.
Tracks: River deep, mountain high / Oh baby.
■ 7" ....................................AMS 829
A&M / Feb '71.

## RIVER DEEP, MOUNTAIN HIGH (OLD GOLD).
Tracks: River deep, mountain high / Love like yours.
■ 7" ....................................OG 9147
Old Gold / Jul '82.

## ROCK ME BABY.
Tracks: Crazy 'bout you baby / Too hot to hold / Please love me / I smell trouble / It sho' ain't me / We need an understanding / Beauty is just skin deep / Shake a tailfeather / Rock me baby / So fine / My babe / Ain't nobody's business / I better get ta steppin' / Betcha can't kiss me (just one time) / Fool in love / You're so fine.
■ LP ....................................TOP 111
■ MC ...................................KTOP 111
Topline / Nov '84 / Charly.
■ CD ................................. TOP CD 511
Topline / Apr '87 / Charly.

## ROCK ME BABY.
Tracks: Not Advised.
■ LP ................................. BDL 1045
■ MC ................................. BDC 1045
Bulldog Records / Sep '82 / President Records / Jazz Music / Wellard / TKO Records Ltd.

## ROCK ME BABY.
Tracks: Not Advised.
■ LP ....................................20015
■ MC ....................................40015
Astan / Nov '84.

## ROCKIN' BLUES.
Tracks: Prancing / Things I used to do / Gully / Think / You're still my baby / Katanga / Tacks in my shoes / Right on / Rockin' blues / That's alright / Broken hearted / If you love me like you say / Bootie lip / City / Neckin' / These dreams / Soppin' molasses.
■ LP ....................................SSL 6008
■ MC ................................. TC-SSL 6008
Stateside / Oct '86.

## SO FINE.
Tracks: My babe / I better get ta steppin' / Shake a tailfeather / We need an understanding / You're so fine / Here's your heart / Please love me / Freedom sound / Crazy 'bout you baby.
■ LP ....................................B 80054
■ MC ................................. MB 980054
Happy Bird (Germany) / Jun '83.
■ LP ................................. LILP 400158
Line / Mar '88.

## SO FINE.
Tracks: Betcha can't kiss me / Ain't nobody's business / It sho' ain't me / Too hot to hold / Fool in love / So fine / Poor little fool / I better get to steppin' / Shake a tail feather / We need an understanding / You're so fine / Poor Sam.
■ LP ....................................SHU 8370
London / Jan '69.

## SOUL OF IKE & TINA, THE.
Tracks: Goodbye, so long / It can't be first / Chicken shack / I don't ne d / I wish my dreams would come true / Hard times / It's crazy, baby / Gonna have fun / Am I a fool in love / Something came over me / Hurt is all you gave me / Don't blame it on me / I can't believe what you say.
■ LP ....................................KENT 014
Kent / Apr '84.

## SOUL SELLERS.
Tracks: Not Advised.
■ MC ................................. TCR 1002
■ LP ................................. LBR 1002
Liberty / Nov '79.

## SPOTLIGHT ON IKE & TINA TURNER.
Tracks: It's gonna work out fine / Fool for you / Crazy 'bout you baby / I can't stop loving you / Somebody somewhere needs you / Too hot to hold / Cussin', cryin' and carryin' on / I know / It sho' ain't me / You got what you wanted / Ain't nobody's business / Betcha can't kiss me / I smell trouble / It's all over / Nothing you can do baby / All I do is cry.
■ CD ................................. HADCD 127
■ MC ................................. HADMC 127
Javelin / Feb '94 / THE.

## SUPERGOLD.
Tracks: Nutbush City Limits / River deep, mountain high / Living for the city / Proud Mary / Honky tonk women / Baby get it on.
■ Double LP ................... 1C 13482758/9
EMI (Import) / Jul '82.

## TALENT SCOUT BLUES.
Tracks: Take the world by storm / Back stabbing / Make some noise / Woman just won't do / I'm tired of being / Nobody seems to want me / I miss you / Nobody wants me / Why did you leave me / Everybody's talkin' / Love is a gamble / Feeling good / I smell trouble / Five long years / Mother in law blues / Dust my blues / That's alright / Twistin' the night away.
■ LP ....................................CHD 244
Ace / Apr '88.

## TELL HER I'M NOT HOME.
Tracks: Tell her I'm not home.
■ 7" ....................................WB 5753
WEA / Jun '66.

## THOSE WERE THE DAYS.
Tracks: Sugar sugar / Never been to Spain / Too much for one woman / Stormy weather / Into to it / Trying to find my mind / I want to take you higher / Fool in love / I idolize you / Poor fool / Lay it down / Freedom to stay / Loving him was easier / Rescue me / Father alone / What a friend / When the saints / Near the corss / Nutbush City Limits.
■ CD ....................................662172
FNAC Music / Dec '92 / New Note.

## TINA'S PRAYER.
Tracks: Not Advised.
■ MC ................................. ENT MC 13054
Entertainers / May '92 / BMG.

## TOO HOT TO HANDLE.
Tracks: Not Advised.
■ MC ....................................ORC 001
Orchid Music / Feb '82 / Pinnacle.

## TOO HOT TO HOLD.
Tracks: Not Advised.
■ CD ................................. CDCD 1042
Charly / Mar '93 / Charly.

## TOUGH ENOUGH.
Tracks: Stagger Lee and Billy / This man's crazy / Foolish / Two is a couple / Prancing (instrumental) / Worried and hurtin' inside / Dear John / You should've treated me right / Too many ties (you've got) / Gonna find me a substitute / Sleepless / Groove (instrumental) / Fool in love / It's gonna work out fine / I'm gonna do all I can to do right by my man / Can't chance a break up.
■ MC ................................. EG 2602514
■ LP ................................. EG 2602511
Liberty / Sep '84.

## WHAT YOU HEAR IS WHAT YOU GET.
Tracks: Piece of my heart / Everyday people / Doin' the Tina Turner / Sweet soul music / Ooh poo pah doo / Honky tonk women / Love like yours / Proud Mary / I smell trouble / Ike's tune / I want to take you higher / I've been loving you too long.
■ LP Set ............................. UAD 60005/6
United Artists / Oct '71.

## WHAT YOU SEE (IS WHAT YOU GET).
Tracks: What you see / Down in the valley / Proud Mary / Shake / Locomotion / I know.
■ CD ................................. SMCD 18
■ LP ................................. STMDL 18
■ MC ................................. STMDC 18
Start / Oct '88 / THE / Koch International.

# Turner, Ruby

## BABY I NEED YOUR LOVING.
Tracks: Baby I need your loving / If you're ready, come go with me / Hurting inside.
■ 12" ....................................RTST 6
■ 7" ....................................RTS 6
■ CD Single ............................ RTSCD 6
Jive / Feb '89.

## BYE BABY.
Tracks: Bye Baby / Story of a man and a woman / If you're ready come go with me (Track in Double pack only.) / Still on my mind (Track in Double pack only.) / Won't cry no more.
■ 12" ................................. JIVET 126
■ 7" ................................. JIVE 126
■ 7" Set ................................. JIVED 126
Jive / Aug '86.

## CHECKING IT OUT (EP).
Tracks: Checking it out.
■ 12" ....................................SF 2
Sunflower / Apr '82.

## EVERY SOUL.
Tracks: Every soul / First step.
■ 12" ....................................12SF 3
■ 7" ....................................SF 3
Sunflower / Mar '83.

## I'D RATHER GO BLIND.
Tracks: I'd rather go blind / I'm livin' a life of love / Ooo baby baby (12" only) / If you're ready (come go with me) (CD only (Extended version)) / Bye baby (CD only).
- 12" . . . . . . . . . . . . . . . . . . . . . . RTST 1
- 7" . . . . . . . . . . . . . . . . . . . . . . . RTS 1
- 7" Set . . . . . . . . . . . . . . . . . . . . . RTSD 1
- CD Single . . . . . . . . . . . . . . . . . . . RTCD 1
Jive / Feb '87.

## I'M IN LOVE.
Tracks: I'm in love / Story of a man and a woman / Living the life of love / Feel my love / Someday soon / Still on my mind.
- 12" . . . . . . . . . . . . . . . . . . . . . . JIVET 118
- 12" Remix . . . . . . . . . . . . . . . . . . JIVER 5
- 7" . . . . . . . . . . . . . . . . . . . . . . . JIVE 118
Jive / Mar '86.
- 12" . . . . . . . . . . . . . . . . . . . . . . RSTS 2
- 7" . . . . . . . . . . . . . . . . . . . . . . . RTS 2
- CD Single . . . . . . . . . . . . . . . . . . . RTCD 2
Jive / May '87.

## IF YOU'RE READY (COME GO WITH ME).
Tracks: If you're ready (come go with me) / Still on my mind / I won't cry no more.
- 12" . . . . . . . . . . . . . . . . . . . . . . JIVET 109
- 7" . . . . . . . . . . . . . . . . . . . . . . . JIVE 109
- CD Single . . . . . . . . . . . . . . . . . . . JIVEX 109
Jive / Jan '86.

## IF YOU'RE READY COME GO WITH ME (OLD GOLD).
Tracks: If you're ready come go with me / Lies.
- 12" . . . . . . . . . . . . . . . . . . . . . . OG 4123
Old Gold / '89.

## IN MY LIFE.
Tracks: In my life / He's mine.
- 12" . . . . . . . . . . . . . . . . . . . . . . RTST 3
- 7" . . . . . . . . . . . . . . . . . . . . . . . RTS 3
Jive / Jun '87.

## IT'S A CRYIN' SHAME.
Tracks: It's a crying shame.
- 12" . . . . . . . . . . . . . . . . . . . . . . JIVET 260
- 7" . . . . . . . . . . . . . . . . . . . . . . . JIVE 260
- CD Single . . . . . . . . . . . . . . . . . . . JIVECD 260
Jive / Oct '90.

## IT'S GONNA BE ALRIGHT.
Tracks: It's gonna be alright / Sexy.
- 12" . . . . . . . . . . . . . . . . . . . . . . RTS T7
- 12" . . . . . . . . . . . . . . . . . . . . . . RTSR 7
- 7" . . . . . . . . . . . . . . . . . . . . . . . RTS 7
- CD Single . . . . . . . . . . . . . . . . . . . RTCD 7
Jive / Oct '89.

## LYSANDER'S THEME (Turner, Ruby & Junior).
Tracks: Lysander's Theme.
- CD Single . . . . . . . . . . . . . . . . . . . JILLYCD 1
- MC Single . . . . . . . . . . . . . . . . . . . JILLYMC 1
Intoto / May '93.

## MOTOWN SONGBOOK, THE.
Tracks: Not Advised.
- LP . . . . . . . . . . . . . . . . . . . . . . . HIP 58
- CD . . . . . . . . . . . . . . . . . . . . . . . CHIP 58
- MC . . . . . . . . . . . . . . . . . . . . . . . HIPC 58
Jive / Sep '88.

## OTHER SIDE, THE.
Tracks: Not Advised.
- CD . . . . . . . . . . . . . . . . . . . . . . . CHIP 111
- LP . . . . . . . . . . . . . . . . . . . . . . . HIP 111
- MC . . . . . . . . . . . . . . . . . . . . . . . HIPC 111
Jive / May '91.

## PARADISE.
Tracks: Paradise / It's gonna be alright / It's a crying shame / Leaves in the wind / There's no better love / Everytime I breathe / Sexy / See me / Surrender / It's you my heart beats for.
- CD . . . . . . . . . . . . . . . . . . . . . . . CHIP 89
- LP . . . . . . . . . . . . . . . . . . . . . . . HIP 89
- MC . . . . . . . . . . . . . . . . . . . . . . . HIPC 89
Jive / Feb '90.

## PARADISE.
Tracks: Paradise / I'm livin' a life of love.
- 12" . . . . . . . . . . . . . . . . . . . . . . RTST 8
- 7" . . . . . . . . . . . . . . . . . . . . . . . RTS 8
- CD Single . . . . . . . . . . . . . . . . . . . RTSCD 8
Jive / Feb '90.

## RESTLESS MOODS.
Tracks: Not Advised.
CD . . . . . . . . . . . . . . . . . . . . . . . MAGCD 1058
MC . . . . . . . . . . . . . . . . . . . . . . . MAGCS 1058
Polygram / Oct '94 / PolyGram.

## RUMOURS.
Tracks: Rumours.
- 12" . . . . . . . . . . . . . . . . . . . . . . JIVET 285
- CD Single . . . . . . . . . . . . . . . . . . . JIVECD 285
Jive / Sep '91.

## SEPARATE WAYS.
Tracks: Separate ways / I shall be released.
- 7" . . . . . . . . . . . . . . . . . . . . . . . SF 1
Sunflower / Sep '80.

## SIGNED SEALED DELIVERED.
Tracks: Signed sealed delivered.
- 12" . . . . . . . . . . . . . . . . . . . . . . RTST 4
- 7" . . . . . . . . . . . . . . . . . . . . . . . RTS 4
Jive / Aug '88.
- 12" Remix . . . . . . . . . . . . . . . . . . RTSR 4
- CD Single . . . . . . . . . . . . . . . . . . . RTS CD 4
Jive / Aug '88.

## STAY WITH ME BABY.
Tracks: Stay with me baby.
- 7" . . . . . . . . . . . . . . . . . . . . . . . MAGS 53
- CD Single . . . . . . . . . . . . . . . . . . . MAGCD 53
- MC Single . . . . . . . . . . . . . . . . . . . MAGCS 53
M & G / Jan '94.

## VIBE IS RIGHT, THE.
Tracks: Vibe is right.
- 12" . . . . . . . . . . . . . . . . . . . . . . JIVET 278
- 7" . . . . . . . . . . . . . . . . . . . . . . . JIVE 278
- CD Single . . . . . . . . . . . . . . . . . . . JIVECD 278
Jive / Jun '91.

## WHAT BECOMES OF THE BROKEN HEARTED.
Tracks: What becomes of the broken hearted / Still waters run deep / Signed, sealed, delivered, I'm yours / (If you're ready) come go with me.
- 12" . . . . . . . . . . . . . . . . . . . . . . RTST 5
- 7" . . . . . . . . . . . . . . . . . . . . . . . RTS 5
- CD Single . . . . . . . . . . . . . . . . . . . RTSCD 5
Jive / Nov '88.

## WITH LOVE.
Tracks: What becomes of the brokenhearted / I'd rather go blind / Tracks of my tears / Just my imagination (Running away with me) / Ooh baby baby / Bye baby / Still waters run deep / Signed sealed delivered I'm yours / Baby I need your lovin' / How sweet it to be loved by you / It's a crying shame / Surrender / Someday soon / Still on my mind.
CD . . . . . . . . . . . . . . . . . . . . . . . 5501152
MC . . . . . . . . . . . . . . . . . . . . . . . 5501154
Spectrum (1) / Oct '93 / PolyGram.

## WOMEN HOLD UP HALF THE SKY.
Tracks: Not Advised.
MC . . . . . . . . . . . . . . . . . . . . . . . HIPC 36
- CD . . . . . . . . . . . . . . . . . . . . . . . CHIP 36
- LP . . . . . . . . . . . . . . . . . . . . . . . HIP 36
Jive / Apr '87 / BMG.

# Turner, Sammy

## ALWAYS.
Tracks: Always.
- 7" . . . . . . . . . . . . . . . . . . . . . . . HLX 8963
London-American / Nov '59.

# Turner, Spyder

## SPYDERMAN.
Tracks: Spyderman / Spyderman (version).
- 12" . . . . . . . . . . . . . . . . . . . . . . SH 1964 12
- 7" . . . . . . . . . . . . . . . . . . . . . . . SH 1964
Shatter / Nov '83.

## STAND BY ME.
Tracks: Stand by me / You're good enough for me.
- 7" . . . . . . . . . . . . . . . . . . . . . . . MGM 1332
MGM (EMI) / Feb '67.

# Turner, Tina

Tina Turner's return to limelight in 1984 was probably nearest rock/pop/soul will ever get to Second Coming. Having established name as half of Ike & Tina Turner, she spent decade in chart wilderness after duo's 1973 hit Nutbush City Limits. However, enduring live reputation won large audiences and place on 1983 album by UK synth duo Martyn Ware and Ian Marsh. Pair were instrumental in creation of her 1984 album Private Dancer, which - together with hit cover of Al Green's Let's Stay Together - initiated spectacular career rejuvenation. Of 25+ ensuing hits, most inclined towards Turner's first love, rock, rather than soul; tendency indicated by collaborators David Bowie,

Eric Clapton, Rod Stewart and Brya Adams. However, songs like What's Lov Got To Do With It and cover of Ann Peeble I Can't Stand the Rain were powerful re minders of Turner's more passionate side

## ACID QUEEN.
Tracks: Under my thumb / Let's spend the nig together / Acid queen / I can see for miles / Who lotta love / Baby git it on / Bootsie Whitelaw / Pi me tonight / Rockin' and rollin'.
MC . . . . . . . . . . . . . . . . . . . . . . . TCFA 314
- LP . . . . . . . . . . . . . . . . . . . . . . . FA 314
Fame / Nov '85 / EMI.
- CD . . . . . . . . . . . . . . . . . . . . . . . CDFA 314
Fame / Oct '91.
CD . . . . . . . . . . . . . . . . . . . . . . . CDEST 223
MC . . . . . . . . . . . . . . . . . . . . . . . TCEST 223
Capitol / Aug '94 / EMI.

## ACID QUEEN.
Tracks: Acid queen / Rockin' and rollin'.
- 7" . . . . . . . . . . . . . . . . . . . . . . . UP 3604
United Artists / Jan '76.

## ADDICTED TO LOVE.
Tracks: Addicted to love / Overnight sensation / Leg (12" and CD versions only.).
- 12" . . . . . . . . . . . . . . . . . . . . . . 12CL 48
- 7" . . . . . . . . . . . . . . . . . . . . . . . CL 48
- CD Single . . . . . . . . . . . . . . . . . . . CDCL 48
Capitol / Mar '88.

## BACKSTABBERS.
Tracks: Backstabbers / Sunset on sunset.
- 7" . . . . . . . . . . . . . . . . . . . . . . . BP 320
Liberty / Jan '80.

## BALL OF CONFUSION.
Tracks: Ball of confusion / Ball of confusion (part 2
- 7" . . . . . . . . . . . . . . . . . . . . . . . VS 50
Virgin / May '82.

## BE TENDER WITH ME BABY.
Tracks: Be tender with me baby (LP version) / B tender with me baby (live - edit) (Not on 12" or Cl single.) / Be tender with me baby (live) (12" & Cl single.) / You know who (is doing you know what) (L version) (12" & CD single.)
- 12" . . . . . . . . . . . . . . . . . . . . . . 12CL 59
- 7" . . . . . . . . . . . . . . . . . . . . . . . CL 59
- 7" P.Disc . . . . . . . . . . . . . . . . . . . CLPD 59
- CD Single . . . . . . . . . . . . . . . . . . . CDCL 59
- MC Single . . . . . . . . . . . . . . . . . . . TCCL 59
Capitol / Oct '90.

## BEST, THE.
Tracks: Best / Undercover agent for the blues / Bol and reckless (12" & CD single only.).
- 12" . . . . . . . . . . . . . . . . . . . . . . 12CL 54
- 7" . . . . . . . . . . . . . . . . . . . . . . . CLS 543
- 7" . . . . . . . . . . . . . . . . . . . . . . . CL 54
- CD Single . . . . . . . . . . . . . . . . . . . CDCL 54
- MC Single . . . . . . . . . . . . . . . . . . . TCCL 54
Capitol / Aug '89.

## BETTER BE GOOD TO ME.
Tracks: Better be good to me / When I was young.
- 12" . . . . . . . . . . . . . . . . . . . . . . 12CL 33
- 7" P.Disc . . . . . . . . . . . . . . . . . . . CLP 33
- 7" . . . . . . . . . . . . . . . . . . . . . . . CL 33
Capitol / Jan '86.

## BREAK EVERY RULE.
Tracks: What you get is what you see / Change i gonna come / Addicted to love / In the midnight hou / 634-5789 / Land of a thousand dances / Typica male / Two people / Till the right man comes along Afterglow / Girls / Back where you started / Brea every rule / Overnight sensation / Paradise is here I'll be thunder.
CD . . . . . . . . . . . . . . . . . . . . . . . CDP 746 323 2
MC . . . . . . . . . . . . . . . . . . . . . . . TCEST 2018
- LP . . . . . . . . . . . . . . . . . . . . . . . EST 2018
Capitol / Sep '86 / EMI.

## BREAK EVERY RULE.
Tracks: Break every rule.
- 12" . . . . . . . . . . . . . . . . . . . . . . 12CL 452
- 7" . . . . . . . . . . . . . . . . . . . . . . . CL 452
- 7" P.Disc . . . . . . . . . . . . . . . . . . . CLP 452
Capitol / May '87.

## BREAK EVERY RULE.
Tracks: Not Advised.
- VHS . . . . . . . . . . . . . . . . . . . . . . MVP 99 1148 2
PMI / Feb '87.
- VHS . . . . . . . . . . . . . . . . . . . . . . MVA 003
PMI / Mar '90.
VHS . . . . . . . . . . . . . . . . . . . . . . MC 2053

■ DELETED

usic Club Video / Mar '91 / Video Collection / Gold
Sons / THE.

## HANGE IS GONNA COME, A.
acks: Change is gonna come, A (LP version)'
rack on 12" version only) / Change is gonna come
utbush City Limits.
```
12" .................................. 12CL 495
7" ................................... .CL 495
```
apitol / May '88.

## OLLECTED RECORDINGS: SIXTIES TO
NINETIES, THE.
acks: Fool in love / It's gonna work out fine / I
olize you / Poor fool / Letter from Tina / Finger
oppin' / River deep mountain high / Crazy 'bout you
old soul sister / I want to take you higher / Come
gether / Honky tonk women / Proud Mary / Nutbush
ty limits / Sexy Ida (part 1) / Sexy Ida (part 2) / It
n't right (lovin) to be lovin' / Acid Queen / Whole
tta love / Ball of confusion / Change is gonna come
Johnny & Mary / Games (unreleased demos) /
hen I was young / Total control (unreleased mas-
er) / Let's pretend we're married / It's only love /
on't turn around / Legs (live at the Blockbuster
avillion) / Addicted to love (live) / Tearing us apart /
takes two / Let's stay together (LP edit) / What's
ve got to do with it (LP edit) / I can't stand the
P edit) / Private dancer (LP edit) / I can't stand the
ain / Help (LP studio version) / We don't need
nother hero (thunderdome LP edit) / Typical male
P edit) / What you get is what you see (LP Edit) /
aradise is here / Back where you started / Best (LP
dit) / Steamy windows (LP edit) / Foreign affair (LP
dit) / I don't wanna fight.
```
D Set ............................. CDESTX 2240
D Set .............................. CDEST 2240
```
apitol / Nov '94 / EMI.

## OUNTRY CLASSICS.
acks: Lay it down / Lovin' him was easier / Good
earted woman / If this was our last time / Stand by
our man / Freedom to stay / We had it all / Soul
eep / If it's alright with you / You ain't woman
ough to take my man.
```
D ................................. HADCD 166
C ................................. HADMC 166
```
velin / May '94 / THE.

## OUNTRY IN MY SOUL.
acks: Not Advised.
```
D ................................. DFG 8416
```
xie Frog / Sep '90 / New Note / MMG Distribution.

## SCO INFERNO.
acks: Disco inferno / Disco inferno (mixes) (Avail-
le on 12 and CDS only) / I don't wanna fight (Not
ailable on 12).
```
CD Single ......................... CDR 6357
MC Single ......................... TCR 6357
12" ............................... 12R 6357
7" ................................. .R 6357
```
MI / Aug '93.

## O YOU WANT SOME ACTION (Live
rom Barcelona 1990).
acks: Steamy windows / Typical male / Foreign
fair / Undercover agent / Ask me how I feel / We
n't need another hero / Private dancer / Nutbush
ty Limits / Addicted to love / Best / I don't wanna
se you / What's love got to do with it / Let's stay
gether / Proud Mary / Better be good to me / Be
nder with me baby.
```
............................. CFM 2842
```
hannel 5 / Nov '90 / Channel 5 Video / P.R.O. Video
Gold & Sons.

## OREIGN AFFAIR.
acks: Steamy windows / Best / You know who (is
oing you know what) / Undercover agent for the
ues / Look me in the heart / Be tender with me
aby / You can't stop me loving you / Ask me how i
el / Falling like rain / I don't wanna lose you / Not
ough romance / Foreign affair.
```
D ................................. CDESTU 2103
C ................................. TCESTU 2103
LP ................................ ESTU 2103
```
apitol / Sep '89 / EMI.

## OREIGN AFFAIR.
acks: Steamy windows / Best / I don't wanna lose
ou / Look me in the heart / Foreign affair.
```
VHS ............................... MVL 990 087 3
```
MI / Jul '90.

## IRL FROM NUTBUSH, THE.
acks: Not Advised.
```
VHS ............................... MVN 4910253
```
MI / Oct '92.

## ELP.
acks: Help / Rock 'n' roll widow.
```
7" ................................. .CL 325
```

DELETED

---

```
7" P.Disc ......................... CLP 325
```
Capitol / Feb '84.

## I CAN'T STAND THE RAIN.
Tracks: I can't stand the rain / Let's pretend we're
married.
```
12" ............................... 12CL 352
7" ................................. .CL 352
```
Capitol / Feb '85.

## I DON'T WANNA FIGHT.
Tracks: I don't wanna fight (Single edit) / Best (Single
edit) (Features on ⅋ MCS only.) / Tina's wish
(Features on CDS only.) / I don't wanna fight (Urban
mix) (Features on CDS only.)
```
7" ................................. .R 6346
CD Single ......................... CDRS 6346
MC Single ......................... TCR 6346
```
EMI / May '93.

## I DON'T WANNA FIGHT.
Tracks: Best, The (single eca.t) / I don't wanna lose
you / What's love got to do with it.
```
CD Single ......................... CDR 6346
```
EMI / May '93.

## I DON'T WANNA LOSE YOU.
Tracks: I don't wanna lose you / Not enough romance / Stronger than the wind (12" only.) / We don't
need another hero (Thunderdome) (CD single only.).
```
12" ............................... 12CL 553
12" P.Disc ........................ 12CLP 553
7" ................................. .CL 553
CD Single ......................... CDCL 553
MC Single ......................... TCCL 553
```
Capitol / Oct '89.

## I WANT YOU NEAR ME.
Tracks: I want you near me / Let's stay togther /
Land of the 1,000 dances (live) (Only available on CD
Single.) / In the midnight hour (live) (Only available
on CD Single.) / 634-5789 (live) (Only available on CD
Single.).
```
7" ................................. .CL 659
MC Single ......................... TCCL 659
CD Single ......................... CDCLS 659
```
Capitol / Jun '92.

## LET'S STAY TOGETHER.
Tracks: Let's stay together / I wrote a letter.
```
12" ............................... 12CL 316
12" P.Disc ........................ 12CLP 316
7" ................................. .CL 316
```
Capitol / Nov '83.

## LIVE IN EUROPE: TINA TURNER.
Tracks: What you get is what you see / Break every
rule / I can't stand the rain / Two people / Typical
male / Better be good to me / Addicted to love /
Private dancer / We don't need another hero /
What's love got to do with it / Let's stay together /
Show some respect / Land of a thousand dances / In
the midnight hour / 634-5789 / Change is gonna
come / Tearing us apart / Proud Mary / Help /
Tonight / It's only love / Nutbush City Limits / Paradise is here / Let's dance / Girls (Extra track on
cassette & CD only) / Back where you started (Extra
track on cassette & CD only) / River deep, mountain
high (Extra track on cassette & CD only) / Overnight
sensation (Extra track on cassette & CD only.).
```
CD Set ............................ .CDESTD 1
MC Set ............................ TCESTD 1
Double LP ......................... ESTD 1
```
Capitol / Mar '88 / EMI.

## LOOK ME IN THE HEART.
Tracks: Look me in the heart (LP version) (Not on
12".) / Steel claw (live) / Look me in the heart (12"
remix) (12" & CD single only.) / Look me in the heart
(inst.) (12" & CD single only.).
```
CD ................................ CDCLX 584
```
EMI / Jul '90.
```
12" ............................... 12CL 584
7" ................................. .CL 584
CD Single ......................... CDCL 584
MC Single ......................... TCCL 584
```
Capitol / Jul '90.

## LOVE EXPLOSION.
Tracks: Love explosion / Fool for your love / Sunset
on sunset / Music keeps me dancin' / I see home /
Backstabbers / Just a little lovin' (early in the morning) / You got what I'm gonna get / On the radio.
```
LP ................................ UAG 30267
```

---

United Artists / Nov '79.
```
CD ................................ CZ 358
LP ................................ ATAK 155
MC. ............................... TCATAK 155
```
Parlophone / Oct '90 / EMI.

## LOVE THING.
Tracks: Love thing / Way of the world / I'm a lady
(Only on CD Single.).
```
7" ................................. .CL 644
CD Single ......................... CDCL 644
MC Single. ........................ TCCL 644
```
Capitol / Jan '92.

## NICE 'N' ROUGH.
Tracks: River deep, mountain high / Nutbush City
Limits / Proud Mary / Honky tonk women / Jumpin'
Jack Flash / Hollywood nights / Crazy in the night /
Giving it up for your love / Acid queen / Tonight's the
night / It's only rock 'n' roll / Kill his wife (foolish
behaviour).
```
VHS ............................... TVE 90 0986 2
```
EMI / Nov '82 / EMI.
```
VHS ............................... .PM 0004
```
Video Collection / '88 / Gold & Sons / Video Collec-
tion / THE.
```
VHS ............................... .MC 2014
```
Music Club Video / Jun '89 / Video Collection / Gold
& Sons / THE.

## NUTBUSH CITY LIMITS (90'S VERSION).
Tracks: Nutbush city limits (90's version) / Best /
Addicted to love (Only on CD Single.).
```
12" ............................... 12CL 630
7" ................................. .CL 630
CD Single ......................... CDCL 630
MC Single. ........................ TCCL 630
```
Capitol / Oct '91.

## ONE OF THE LIVING.
Tracks: One of the living / One of the living (version).
```
12" ............................... 12CL 376
7" ................................. .CL 376
```
Capitol / Sep '85.

## PARADISE IS HERE.
Tracks: In the midnight hour / Paradise is here.
```
12" ............................... 12CL 459
7" ................................. .CL 459
7" P.Disc ......................... CLP 459
```
Capitol / Aug '87.

## PRIVATE DANCER.
Tracks: I might have been queen / Whats love got to
do with it / Show some respect / I can't stand the rain
/ Private dancer / Lets stay together / Better be good
to me / Steel claw / Help.
```
LP ................................ .TINA 1
MC. ............................... TCTINA 1
CD ................................ CDP 746 041 2
```
Capitol / Jun '84 / EMI.
```
LP P.Disc ......................... TINAP 1
```
Capitol / Apr '85.

## PRIVATE DANCER.
Tracks: Private dancer / Nutbush City Limits.
```
12" ............................... 12CL 343
7" ................................. .CL 343
```
Capitol / Nov '84.

## PRIVATE DANCER LIVE (CD & Video
Double Pack).
Tracks: Show some respect / I might have been
Queen (Soul survivor) / What's love got to do with it /
I can't stand the rain / Better be good to me / Private
dancer / Let's stay together / Help / It's only love /
Tonight / Let's dance (Version 1) / Let's dance (Ver-
sion 2).
```
VHS ............................... SAV 4913083
```
PMI / Jul '94 / EMI / Gold & Sons / THE.

## PRIVATE DANCER TOUR.
Tracks: Show some respect / I might have been
queen (soul survivor) / What's love got to do with it /
I can't stand the rain / Better be good to me / Private
dancer / Let's stay together / Help / It's only love /
Tonight / Let's dance.
```
VHS ............................... MVP 99 1085 2
```
PMI / Jul '85.

## PRIVATE DANCER VIDEO EP.
Tracks: What's love got to do with it / Let's stay
together / Private dancer.
```
VHS ............................... MVS 99 0035 2
```
PMI / Feb '85.
```
VHS ............................... .MC 2025
```
Music Club Video / Jun '89 / Video Collection / Gold
& Sons / THE.

## RIO '88.
Tracks: Not Advised.
```
VHS ............................... 041 661 2
```
Polygram Music Video / Apr '88 / PolyGram.
```
CD Video .......................... 080 348 1
```

433

Polygram Music Video / Oct '88 / PolyGram.
**VHS** . . . . . . . . . . . . . . . . . . . . . . . . **CFV 08102**
Channel 5 / Sep '89 / Channel 5 Video / P.R.O. Video
/ Gold & Sons.
**VHS** . . . . . . . . . . . . . . . . . . . . . . . . **LED 80172**
4 Front / May '91 / PolyGram Video.

## RIVER DEEP, MOUNTAIN HIGH.
**Tracks:** Not Advised.
**CD** . . . . . . . . . . . . . . . . . . . . . . . . **YDG 74615**
**MC** . . . . . . . . . . . . . . . . . . . . . . . . **YDG 45715**
Yesterday's Gold / Aug '93 / Target / Midland Records / Target Sales & Marketing.

## ROOT TOOT UNDISPUTABLE ROCK 'N' ROLLER.
**Tracks:** Root toot undisputable rock 'n' roller / Fire down below.
■ **7"** . . . . . . . . . . . . . . . . . . . . . . . . **UP 36485**
United Artists / '79.

## ROUGH.
**Tracks:** Fruits of the night / Bitch is back / Woman I'm supposed to be / Viva la money / Funny how time slips away / Earthquake hurricane / Root toot undisputable rock 'n' roller / Fire down below / Sometimes when we touch / Woman in a man's world / Night time is the right time.
■ **LP** . . . . . . . . . . . . . . . . . . . . . . . . **UAG 30211**
United Artists / Apr '79.
■ **LP** . . . . . . . . . . . . . . . . . . . . . . . . **ATAK 154**
**MC** . . . . . . . . . . . . . . . . . . . . . . . . **TCATAK 154**
■ **CD** . . . . . . . . . . . . . . . . . . . . . . . . **CZ 357**
Parlophone / Oct '90 / EMI.

## SIMPLY THE BEST.
**Tracks:** Best / What's love got to do with it / I don't wanna lose you / Nutbush City limits / Let's stay together / Private dancer / We don't need another hero / Better be good to me / River deep, mountain high / Steamy windows / Typical male / It takes two / Addicted to love / Be tender with me baby / I want you near me / Love thing.
**CD** . . . . . . . . . . . . . . . . . . . . . . . . **CDESTV 1**
■ **Double LP** . . . . . . . . . . . . . . . . . . . . **ESTV 1**
**MC** . . . . . . . . . . . . . . . . . . . . . . . . **TCESTV 1**
Capitol / Oct '91 / EMI.
**MiniDisc** . . . . . . . . . . . . . . . . . . . . . **796630-3**
Capitol / Feb '93 / EMI.

## SIMPLY THE BEST.
**Tracks:** Best / Better be good to me / I can't stand the rain / What's love got to do with it / Typical male / Private dancer / We don't need another hero / What you get is what you see / I don't wanna lose you / Look me in the heart / Addicted to love / Steamy windows / Break every rule / Foreign affair / Tonight / Let's stay together / Be tender with me baby / It takes two / Nutbush City Limits / Love thing / What's love got to do with it (secret version).
**VHS** . . . . . . . . . . . . . . . . . . . . . . . . **MVD 9913083**
PMI / Oct '91 / EMI / Gold & Sons / THE.

## SIMPLY THE BEST '94.
**Tracks:** Simply the best / Better be good to me / I can't stand the rain / What's love got to do with it / Typical male / Private dancer / We don't need another hero / What you get is what you see / I don't wanna lose you / Look me in the heart / Addicted to love / Steamy windows / Break every rule / Foreign affair / Tonight / Let's stay together / Be tender with me baby / It takes two / Nutbush City limits / Love thing / I don't wanna fight / Disco inferno / Why must we wait until tonight.
**Video CD** . . . . . . . . . . . . . . . . . . . . . **PMCD 4913032**
PMI / Jul '94 / EMI / Gold & Sons / THE.

## SO FINE.
**Tracks:** Not Advised.
**CD** . . . . . . . . . . . . . . . . . . . . . . . . **ENT CD 202**
Entertainers / Sep '87 / BMG.

## SOMETIMES WHEN WE TOUCH.
**Tracks:** Sometimes / Earthquake & hurricane.
■ **7"** . . . . . . . . . . . . . . . . . . . . . . . . **UP 36513**
United Artists / Apr '79.

## STEAMY WINDOWS.
**Tracks:** Steamy windows (Not on 12".) / Best, The (Single muscle mix) (7" & Cassingle only.) / Steamy windows (vocal mix) (12" & CD single only.) / Best, The (muscle mix) (12" only.) / Steamy windows (musle mix) (12" only.) / Steamy windows (house mix) (12" only.) / Best, The (ext. muscle mix) (CD single only.)
■ **CD Single** . . . . . . . . . . . . . . . . . . . . **CDCL 560**
■ **12"** . . . . . . . . . . . . . . . . . . . . . . . . **12CL 560**
■ **7"** . . . . . . . . . . . . . . . . . . . . . . . . **CL 560**
■ **MC Single** . . . . . . . . . . . . . . . . . . . . **TCCL 560**
Capitol / Jan '90.

## TINA TURNER.
**Tracks:** Not Advised.
■ **LP** . . . . . . . . . . . . . . . . . . . . . . . . **ENT LP 13004**

**MC.** . . . . . . . . . . . . . . . . . . . . . . . . **ENT MC 13004**
Entertainers / '88 / BMG.

## TINA TURNER BOX SET.
**Tracks:** Not Advised.
■ **LP Set.** . . . . . . . . . . . . . . . . . . . . . . **TTGIFT 1**
■ **CD Set.** . . . . . . . . . . . . . . . . . . . . . . **CDP 795 246 2**
■ **MC Set** . . . . . . . . . . . . . . . . . . . . . . **TCTTGIFT 1**
Capitol / Oct '90.

## TINA TURNER GOES COUNTRY.
**Tracks:** Lay it down / Lovin' him was easier / Good hearted woman / If this is our last time / Stand by your man / Freedom to stay / We had it all / Soul deep / If it's alright with you / You ain't woman enough to take my man.
**CD** . . . . . . . . . . . . . . . . . . . . . . . . **NSPCD 501**
**LP** . . . . . . . . . . . . . . . . . . . . . . . . **NSPLP 501**
**MC.** . . . . . . . . . . . . . . . . . . . . . . . . **NSPMC 501**
Connoisseur Collection / Feb '91 / Pinnacle.

## TINA TURNER: INTERVIEW PICTURE DISC.
**Tracks:** Not Advised.
■ **LP P.Disc.** . . . . . . . . . . . . . . . . . . . . **BAK 2076**
Baktabak / Nov '87.

## TWO PEOPLE.
**Tracks:** Two people / Havin' a party.
■ **12"** . . . . . . . . . . . . . . . . . . . . . . . . **12CL 430**
■ **12"** . . . . . . . . . . . . . . . . . . . . . . . . **12CLD 430**
■ **7"** . . . . . . . . . . . . . . . . . . . . . . . . **CL 430**
Capitol / Oct '86.

## TYPICAL MALE.
**Tracks:** Typical male / Don't turn around / Typical male (version) (Available on 12" only.)
■ **12" P.Disc.** . . . . . . . . . . . . . . . . . . . . **12CLP 419**
■ **12"** . . . . . . . . . . . . . . . . . . . . . . . . **12CL 419**
■ **7"** . . . . . . . . . . . . . . . . . . . . . . . . **CL 419**
Capitol / Aug '86.

## WAY OF THE WORLD.
**Tracks:** Way of the world / I don't wanna lose you / Foreign affair (Only on 12" and CD single).
■ **12"** . . . . . . . . . . . . . . . . . . . . . . . . **12CL 637**
■ **7"** . . . . . . . . . . . . . . . . . . . . . . . . **CL 637**
■ **CD Single** . . . . . . . . . . . . . . . . . . . . **CDCL 637**
■ **MC Single.** . . . . . . . . . . . . . . . . . . . . **TCCL 637**
Capitol / Oct '91.

## WHAT YOU GET IS WHAT YOU SEE.
**Tracks:** What you get is what you see (dance mix) / Tina Turner montage mix.
■ **7" Set** . . . . . . . . . . . . . . . . . . . . . . **7CLD 439**
■ **12"** . . . . . . . . . . . . . . . . . . . . . . . . **12CL 439**
■ **12" Remix.** . . . . . . . . . . . . . . . . . . . . **12 CLX 439**
■ **7"** . . . . . . . . . . . . . . . . . . . . . . . . **CL 439**
Capitol / Feb '87.

## WHAT YOU GET IS WHAT YOU SEE.
**Tracks:** Typical male / Two people / What you get is what you see / Break every rule / Two people (Tina's Hollywood version).
■ **VHS** . . . . . . . . . . . . . . . . . . . . . . . . **MVR 99 0069 2**
PMI / Jul '87.

## WHAT'S LOVE GOT TO DO WITH IT.
**Tracks:** What's love got to do with it / Don't rush the good things.
■ **12"** . . . . . . . . . . . . . . . . . . . . . . . . **12CL 334**
■ **7"** . . . . . . . . . . . . . . . . . . . . . . . . **CL 334**
Capitol / Jun '84.

## WHAT'S LOVE LIVE.
**Tracks:** Steamy windows / Typical male / Foreign affair / Undercover agent for the blues / Private dancer / We don't need another hero / I can't stand the rain / I don't wanna fight no more / Let's stay together / What's love got to do with it / Proud Mary / Legs / Better be good to me / Why must we wait until tonight.
**Laser Disc** . . . . . . . . . . . . . . . . . . . . **PLMPB 00121**
Pioneer LDCE / Sep '94 / Video Collection / THE.
**VHS** . . . . . . . . . . . . . . . . . . . . . . . . **MVN 4912803**
PMI / Sep '94 / EMI / Gold & Sons / THE.

## WHY MUST WE WAIT UNTIL TONIGHT.
**Tracks:** Why must we wait until tonight / Shake a tailfeather / Best.
■ **7"** . . . . . . . . . . . . . . . . . . . . . . . . **R 6366**
■ **CD Single** . . . . . . . . . . . . . . . . . . . . **CDRS 6366**
■ **CD Single** . . . . . . . . . . . . . . . . . . . . **CDR 6366**
■ **MC Single.** . . . . . . . . . . . . . . . . . . . . **TCR 6366**
Parlophone / Oct '93.

## WILD LADY OF ROCK.
**Tracks:** Not Advised.
■ **VHS** . . . . . . . . . . . . . . . . . . . . . . . . **HEN 2089**
Hendring Video / Apr '92.

# Turner, Titus

## JAMIE RECORDINGS, THE.
**Tracks:** Not Advised.
**CD** . . . . . . . . . . . . . . . . . . . . . . . . **BCD 155**
Bear Family / Feb '92 / Rollercoaster Records / Sw
/ Direct Distribution / Topic Records.

## TITANS OF R&B (Turner, Titus & Tomm Tucker).
**Tracks:** Leave my kitten alone / Gavadonius love
Keep on loving me baby / Help the blind / I am
member of the club / Sportin' Tom / I need your lo
to carry on / Silly dilly / Slow drag one more time
Roll on / You're the top crust / That's al right / She
the one I love / Come on in / High heel sneakers
Tell me who's wrong / Lean greens / Satifyin' feeli
/ Is that the way God planned it / Ooh baby / Si
little Cynthia / Never let me go / Your loves a hal
with me / Drunk.
**CD** . . . . . . . . . . . . . . . . . . . . . . . . **RLCD 00**
Red Lightnin' / Nov '90 / A.D.A. Distribution / Swi
C.M. Distribution / Jazz Music / Cadillac / Arabesqu
Ltd. / Topic Records / Direct Distribution.

# Twilight 22

## MYSTERIOUS.
**Tracks:** Mysterious.
■ **12"** . . . . . . . . . . . . . . . . . . . . . . . . **YZ 3**
WEA / Mar '85.

# Two Tons

## TWO TONS O'FUN/BACKATCHA.
**Tracks:** Do you wanna boogie, hunh / Just us / I g
the feeling / Gone away / Earth can be just lil
heaven / Make someone feel happy today / Takin
away your space / One-sided love affair / Never lil
this / I depend on you / Your love is gonna see n
through / It's true I do / Can't do it by myself / Clou
with a chance of rain / I've got to make it on my own
I been down.
**CD** . . . . . . . . . . . . . . . . . . . . . . . . **CDSEWD 0**
South Bound / Jul '93 / Pinnacle.

# Tymes

## DIGGIN' THEIR ROOTS.
**Tracks:** I can't explain / Who, what, when, wher
why / It wasn't the right time / As time goes by / Ho
am I to know / Girl, you blew it / I'll take you there
Kunte Kinte.
■ **LP** . . . . . . . . . . . . . . . . . . . . . . . . **PL 124**
RCA / Oct '77.

## GOD'S GONNA PUNISH YOU.
**Tracks:** God's gonna punish you.
■ **7"** . . . . . . . . . . . . . . . . . . . . . . . . **RCA 262**
RCA / Jan '76.

## MS. GRACE.
**Tracks:** Ms. Grace / You little trust maker.
■ **7"** . . . . . . . . . . . . . . . . . . . . . . . . **RCA 249**
RCA / Dec '74.

## MS. GRACE.
**Tracks:** Ms. Grace.
■ **7"** . . . . . . . . . . . . . . . . . . . . . . . . **GOLD 50**
RCA Golden Grooves / Jul '78.

## MS. GRACE (OLD GOLD).
**Tracks:** Ms. Grace.
■ **7"** . . . . . . . . . . . . . . . . . . . . . . . . **OG 970**
Old Gold / Apr '87.

## PEOPLE.
**Tracks:** People.
■ **7"** . . . . . . . . . . . . . . . . . . . . . . . . **5839C**
Direction (CBS) / Jan '69.

## PEOPLE.
**Tracks:** Look of love / Alfie/For once in my life / Lov
that you're looking for / For love of Ivy / City / Wichit
lineman / People / Way of the crowd / Those wer
the days / God bless the child / Make someon
happy.
■ **LP** . . . . . . . . . . . . . . . . . . . . . . . . **8 6355**
Direction / May '69.

## SO MUCH IN LOVE.
**Tracks:** So much in love.
■ **7"** . . . . . . . . . . . . . . . . . . . . . . . . **P 87**
Cameo Parkway / Jul '63.

## SOUL GEMS.
**Tracks:** Not Advised.
■ **LP** . . . . . . . . . . . . . . . . . . . . . . . . **PRST 50**
■ **CD** . . . . . . . . . . . . . . . . . . . . . . . . **CDPT 50**
■ **MC.** . . . . . . . . . . . . . . . . . . . . . . . . **ZPRST 50**
Prestige (Total) / Jul '90.

■ **DELETE**

**YOU LITTLE TRUST MAKER.**
Tracks: You little trust maker.
■ 7″ . . . . . . . . . . . . . . . . . . . . . . RCA 2456
RCA / Sep '74.

## Tyrone, Michael

**ALWAYS.**
Tracks: Always.
■ 12″ . . . . . . . . . . . . . . . . . . . . SDT 62 R
■ 12″ . . . . . . . . . . . . . . . . . . . . . SDT 62
Sure Delight / Jan '93.

## Tyrrel Corporation

**BOTTLE, THE.**
Tracks: Bottle.
■ 12″ . . . . . . . . . . . . . . . . . . . . . TYRX 1
■ 7″ . . . . . . . . . . . . . . . . . . . . . . TYR 1
■ CD Single . . . . . . . . . . . . . . . . . TYRCD 1
■ MC Single . . . . . . . . . . . . . . . . . TYRMC 1
Cool Tempo / Mar '92.

**GOING HOME.**
Tracks: Going home.
■ 12″ . . . . . . . . . . . . . . . . . . . . . TYRX 2

■ 12″ Remix. . . . . . . . . . . . . . . . TYRXR 2
■ 7″ . . . . . . . . . . . . . . . . . . . . . . TYR 2
■ CD Single. . . . . . . . . . . . . . . . . TYRCD 2
Cool Tempo / Sep '92.

**NORTH EAST OF EDEN.**
Tracks: Bottle / 6 O'Clock / Ballad of British justice / Freedom / Going home / One day / Waking with a stranger / Lies before breakfast / Grapes of wrath / Cheated.
CD . . . . . . . . . . . . . . . . . . . . . . CTCD 29
■ LP . . . . . . . . . . . . . . . . . . . . . . CTLP 29
MC. . . . . . . . . . . . . . . . . . . . . . . CTTC 29
Cool Tempo / Oct '92 / EMI.
MiniDisc. . . . . . . . . . . . . . . . . . . CTMD 29
Cool Tempo / Jan '93 / EMI.

**SIX O'CLOCK.**
Tracks: Six o'Clock.
■ 12″ . . . . . . . . . . . . . . . . . . . . . .FLYRX 3
■ 7″ . . . . . . . . . . . . . . . . . . . . . . FLYR 3
■ CD Single. . . . . . . . . . . . . . . . . .FLYRCD 3
■ MC Single. . . . . . . . . . . . . . . . . FLYRMC 3
Cool Tempo / Oct '91.

**WAKING WITH A STRANGER/ONE DAY.**
Tracks: One day / One day (mixes) / Waking with a stranger.

■ 12″ . . . . . . . . . . . . . . . . . . . . 12 TYRS 3
■ 7″ . . . . . . . . . . . . . . . . . . . . . TYRS 3
■ CD Single. . . . . . . . . . . . . . . . . .CDTYRS 3
■ MC Single. . . . . . . . . . . . . . . . . TCTYR 3
Cool Tempo / Sep '92.

**YOU'RE NOT HERE.**
Tracks: You're not here (mixes).
12″ . . . . . . . . . . . . . . . . . . . . 12COOL 292
12″ Remix. . . . . . . . . . . . . . . . .12COOLX 292
CD Single . . . . . . . . . . . . . . . . . CDCOOL 292
MC Single . . . . . . . . . . . . . . . . TCCOOL 292
Cool Tempo / Sep '94 / EMI.

## Tyson

**GROOVIN.**
Tracks: Groovin.
12″ . . . . . . . . . . . . . . . . . . . . 12LOSE 65
7″ . . . . . . . . . . . . . . . . . . . . . .LOSE 65
CD Single. . . . . . . . . . . . . . . . . CDLOSE 65
MC Single . . . . . . . . . . . . . . . . . CALOSE 65
Pulse 8 / Aug '94 / Sony / 3MV.

# U

## U.N.V.

### 2 B OR NOT 2 B.
Tracks: 2 B or not 2 B (Mixes).
- 12"............................W 0233T
- 7"..............................W 0233
- CD Single.....................W 0233CD
- MC Single.....................W 0233C
Warner Bros. / Feb '94.

### SOMETHING'S GOIN ON.
Tracks: UNV thang / When will I know / Who will it be / Close tonight / Gonna give U what U want / Something's goin' on / 2 B or not 2 B / Straight from my heart / Hold on / No one compares to you.
CD..........................9362452874-2
East West / Nov '93 / WEA.

### SOMETHING'S GOIN' ON.
Tracks: Something's goin' on / Flipside / Something's goin' on (Mixes) / Tempted.
- 12"............................W 0201T
- 7"..............................W 0201
- CD Single.....................W 0201CD
- MC Single.....................W 0201C
WEA / Sep '93.

## UK Players

### EVERYBODY GETS UP.
Tracks: Everybody gets up / Rivers.
- 12"..........................AMSX 7580
- 7"...........................AMS 7580
A&M / Nov '80.

### GIRL.
Tracks: Girl / Jim's jam.
- 12"..........................AMSP 8169
- 7"...........................AMS 8169
A&M / Sep '81.

### LOVE'S GONNA GET YOU.
Tracks: Love's gonna get you.
- 12"..........................RCAT 326
- 7"...........................RCA 326
RCA / Apr '83.

### MIDNIGHT.
Tracks: Midnight / Exist.
- 12"..........................AMSP 8137
- 7"...........................AMS 8137
A&M / May '81.

### MISSBEHAVIN.
Tracks: Missbehavin / Can't shake your love.
- 12"..........................AMSX 8238
- 7"...........................AMS 8238
A&M / Jul '82.

### NO WAY OUT.
Tracks: Dancing in the street / So good to be alive / No way out / Missbehavin' / Saving up your love / Can't shake your love / First time out / Star of my show / Killing time.
- LP............................AMLH 68544
A&M / Aug '82.

### NO WAY OUT.
Tracks: No way out / So good to be alive.
- 12"..........................AMSX 8220
- 7"...........................AMS 8220
A&M / May '82.

### YOU MAKE ME FEEL.
Tracks: You make me feel / Landslide.
- 12"..........................RCAT 347
- 7"...........................RCA 347
RCA / Aug '83.

## Ultimate Kaos

### SOME GIRLS.
Tracks: Some girls (mixes) / Love you like this.
- 12"..........................CARDX 12
- 7"...........................CARD 12
- CD Single....................CARDD 12
- MC Single....................CARDC 12
Wild Card / Oct '94 / PolyGram.

## Ultrafunk

### GOTHAM CITY BOOGIE.
Tracks: Gotham City boogie / Indigo country.
- 7"............................CS 2100
Contempo (1) / Jan '77.

### MEAT HEAT.
Tracks: Gotham City boogie / Sunrise / I wish / Temptation / Meat heat.
- LP............................CLP 601
Contempo (1) / Dec '77.

### SWEET F.A. (FUNKY AL).
Tracks: Sweet F.A. (Funky Al) / Use me.
- 7"............................CS 2020
Contempo (1) / May '75.

## Undisputed Truth

Undisputed Truth were second outlet for innovative Motown producer Norman Whitfield. Latter's main charges were Temptations, whose *Smiling Faces Sometimes* was U.S. No. 3 for Truth; Temptations regained advantage when their version of *Papa Was A Rolling Stone* rose 62 places higher than rivals', topping U.S. chart. Ensuing turbulence prompted departure of original singers; among them Billie Calvin, whose song *Wishing On A Star* became hit for another Whitfield discovery, Rose Royce. Renewed and funkier line-up scored hit with *You + Me = Love* (among first commercially-released 12" singles in U.K.). However, although they were now signed to Whitfield's self-named label, producer's attention shifted to Rose Royce and Truth were virtually forgotten.

### BEST OF THE UNDISPUTED TRUTH.
Tracks: Smiling faces sometimes / Save my love for a rainy day / You make your own heaven and hell right here on earth / What it is / Papa was a rollin' stone / Girl you're alright / Mama I got a brand new thing (don't say no) / Law of the land / Help yourself / I'm a fool for you / UFO's / Higher than high.
- LP............................STMA 8029
Motown / Sep '77.
- CD............................WD 72778
Motown / Dec '91.

### FACE TO FACE WITH THE TRUTH.
Tracks: You make your own heaven & hell right here on earth / What is it / Ungena za ulimwengu / Friendship train / Superstar / Take me in your arms and love me / Don't let him take your love from me / What's going on.
- LP............................STMA 8004
Tamla Motown / Jul '72.

### HIGHER THAN HIGH.
Tracks: Higher than high / Spaced out.
- 7"............................TMG 1014
Tamla Motown / Nov '75.

### METHOD TO THE MADNESS.
Tracks: Cosmic contact / Method to the madness / Sunshine / You + me = love / Hole in the wall / Loose life ain't so easy / Take a vacation / From life (and visit your dreams) / Let's go down to the disco.
- LP............................K 56289
Whitfield (USA) / '77.

### SAVE MY LOVE FOR A RAINY DAY.
Tracks: Save my love for a rainy day.
- 7"............................TMG 776
Tamla Motown / Jun '71.

### SMOKIN'.
Tracks: Show time / Talkin' to the wind / Atomic funk / I can't get enough of your love / Misunderstood / Sandman / Tazmanian monster / Space machine.
- LP............................K 56497
Whitfield (USA) / '77.

### UNDISPUTED TRUTH.
Tracks: You got the love I need / Save my love for a rainy day / California soul / Aquarius / Ball of confusion / Smiling faces sometimes / We've got a way out love / Since I've lost you / Ain't no sun since you've been gone / I heard it through the grapevine / Like a rolling stone.

- LP............................STML 11197
Tamla Motown / Feb '72.

### YOU + ME = LOVE.
Tracks: You + me = love / You + me = love (version).
- 7"............................K 16804
WEA / Jan '77.

## Unique

### WHAT I GOT IS WHAT YOU NEED.
Tracks: What I got is what you need.
- 12"..........................TA 3707
- 7"...........................A 3707
Prelude / Sep '83.

## Uniques

### BEST OF THE UNIQUES (1967-1969).
Tracks: Not Advised.
- CD............................CDTRL 340
Trojan / Jun '94 / Jetstar / Total / BMG.

### SHOWCASE VOLUME 1.
Tracks: Not Advised.
- LP............................TWS 935
Third World / Jun '78.

### YOU DON'T MISS YOUR WATER.
Tracks: You don't miss your water.
- 7"............................CTD 121
Charly / Jul '80.

## Universal Robot Band

### BARELY BREAKING EVEN.
Tracks: Barely breaking even.
- 12"..........................MKHAN 48
Streetwave / Aug '85.

## Unlimited Touch

### I HEAR DANCING IN THE STREETS.
Tracks: I hear dancing in the streets / In the middle.
- 12"..........................13-9477
- 7"...........................EPC 9477
Epic / Feb '81.

### SEARCHING TO FIND THE ONE.
Tracks: Searching to find the one / Carry one.
- 7"............................EPCA 145
Epic / Jul '81.

### YES WE'RE READY.
Tracks: Yes i'm ready / Your love is serious / Love explosion / No one can love me / Good living.
- LP............................PRL 2529
Prelude / May '83.

## Upchurch, Phil

### ALL I WANT.
Tracks: Poison / When we need it bad / 12/25 / 516 Grace / What will I do / All I want from you / U god gowin on.
- LP............................ICH 112
- MC...........................MCICH 112
Ichiban / Feb '92 / A.D.A. Distribution / Pinnacle ACD Trading Ltd. / Koch International / Direct Distribution.
- CD............................ICH 1127CD
Ichiban / Jan '94 / A.D.A. Distribution / Pinnacle ACD Trading Ltd. / Koch International / Direct Distribution.

### COMPANIONS.
Tracks: Companions / Song for Lenny / Mr. T.B.A. song / Show your love / Tell me I'm not dreaming / Blues in the middle / Rosanna / c.c. rider.
- LP............................PAL
- MC...........................PADC
Paladin / Apr '85 / EMI / Pinnacle / Cadillac.

### MIDNIGHT BLUE.
Tracks: Name of the game / round and 'round / People get ready / Chicago stomp / Need to belong / Midnite blue / Bluz / Welcome.
- CD............................KICJ 5
King/Electric Bird / Aug '91.

436

■ DELETE

**WHATEVER HAPPENED TO THE BLUES.**
Tracks: Not Advised.
CD. . . . . . . . . . . . . . . . . . . . . VBR 20662
Go Jazz / Jul '92 / New Note.

**WHEN AND IF I FALL IN LOVE.**
Tracks: When and if I fall in love.
■ 12". . . . . . . . . . . . . . . . . . . . FIZ 1T
■ 7". . . . . . . . . . . . . . . . . . . . . FIZ 1
Physical / Jul '83.

**YOU CAN'T SIT DOWN.**
Tracks: You can't sit down.
■ 7". . . . . . . . . . . . . . . . . . . WI 4005
Sue / May '66.

## Urban Species

**BROTHER.**
Tracks: Brother (Mixes) / Consequence (On CDs only).
■ 7". . . . . . . . . . . . . . . . . . . TLK 47
■ CD Single. . . . . . . . . . . . . . . .TLKX 47
■ CD Single. . . . . . . . . . . . . . . TLKDD 47
■ MC Single. . . . . . . . . . . . . . . TLKMC 47
Talkin' Loud / Apr '94.

**EXPERIENCE, THE.**
Tracks: Experience / Experience (mixes).
■ 12". . . . . . . . . . . . . . . . . . .TLKX 40
■ CD Single. . . . . . . . . . . . . . .TLKCD 40
Talkin' Loud / Sep '93.

**LISTEN.**
Tracks: Hide & seek / Gotta have it / No particular title / Ropes / Spiritual love / Just a matter of time / Listen / Consequence / Experience / Musikism / Brother / Light at the end of the tunnel.
■ CD. . . . . . . . . . . . . . . . . . . . . 518 648-2
■ LP. . . . . . . . . . . . . . . . . . . . . 518 648-1
■ MC. . . . . . . . . . . . . . . . . . . . . 518 648-4
Talkin' Loud / Feb '94.

**LISTEN.**
Tracks: Listen (mixes).
12". . . . . . . . . . . . . . . . . . . . .TLKXX 50
CD Single. . . . . . . . . . . . . . . . .TLKCD 50
Talkin' Loud / Aug '94 / PolyGram.

**SPIRITUAL LOVE.**
Tracks: Spiritual love / Spiritual love (mixes).
■ 12". . . . . . . . . . . . . . . . . . . .TLKX 45
■ CD Single. . . . . . . . . . . . . . . .TLKCD 45
■ MC Single. . . . . . . . . . . . . . .TLKMC 45
Talkin' Loud / Jan '94.

## Urbanator

**URBANATOR.**
Tracks: Not Advised.
CD. . . . . . . . . . . . . . . . . . . . . .HIBD 8001
LP. . . . . . . . . . . . . . . . . . . . . . HIB 8001
MC. . . . . . . . . . . . . . . . . . . . . .HIBC 8001
Hib Bop / Jun '94 / Conifer Records.

## Usher, Raymond

**CAN U GET WIT IT.**
Tracks: Can U get wit it (Mixes).
12". . . . . . . . . . . . . . . . . . . . . 7432124009-1
CD Single. . . . . . . . . . . . . . . . . 7432124009-2
MC Single . . . . . . . . . . . . . . . . 7432124009-4
LaFace/Arista / Oct '94 / BMG.

**USHER.**
Tracks: Not Advised.
CD. . . . . . . . . . . . . . . . . . . . . 7300826008-2
MC. . . . . . . . . . . . . . . . . . . . . 7300826008-4
Arista / Oct '94 / BMG.

## Usry, Johnny

**HEALING.**
Tracks: Healing / Forgotten heroes / Johnny's rap (give peace a chance) / Chu-lai Charlie / Healing (reprise) / Girl of the night / When love is gone / Mom / Homeless / Girl of the night (instrumental).
CD. . . . . . . . . . . . . . . . . . . . . CDUSC 4006
■ LP. . . . . . . . . . . . . . . . . . . . . USC 4006
MC. . . . . . . . . . . . . . . . . . . . . ZCUSC 4006
Ichiban / Jul '89 / A.D.A. Distribution / Pinnacle / ACD Trading Ltd. / Koch International / Direct Distribution.

# V

## Valadiers

### I FOUND A GIRL.
**Tracks:** I found myself a brand new baby.
- ■ 7" . . . . . . . . . . . . . . . . . . . . . . CBA 1775
Oriole / '62.

## Valentin, Dave

### FLUTE JUICE.
**Tracks:** Crotona Park / Loquita (crazy lady) / Flute juice / Latin jazz dance / Foot-prints / Merle the pearl / Crotona Park (reprise).
- ■ LP . . . . . . . . . . . . . . . . . . . . GRPA 1004
- ■ MC . . . . . . . . . . . . . . . . . . . . GRPC 1004
GRP / Jun '84.

### HAWK.
**Tracks:** Not Advised.
- ■ CD . . . . . . . . . . . . . . . . . . . . GRP 95152
GRP / Jul '92.

### JUNGLE GARDEN.
**Tracks:** Awakening / Oasis / Bones / Love light in flight / Jungle garden / Very nice indeed / I loves you Porgy / Eighty-one / Tabasco.
- ■ LP . . . . . . . . . . . . . . . . . . . . GRP 91016
- ■ MC . . . . . . . . . . . . . . . . . . . GRPC 1016
- ■ CD . . . . . . . . . . . . . . . . . . . . GRPD 9523
GRP / Jul '85.
- ■ CD . . . . . . . . . . . . . . . . . . . . GRP 95232
GRP / Jan '93.

### KALAHARI.
**Tracks:** Not Advised.
- ■ MC . . . . . . . . . . . . . . . . . . . . . C 1009
GRP / Sep '84.
- ■ LP . . . . . . . . . . . . . . . . . . . . GRP 91009
- ■ CD . . . . . . . . . . . . . . . . . . . . GRP 95082
GRP / Sep '88.

### LEGENDS.
**Tracks:** Not Advised.
- ■ CD . . . . . . . . . . . . . . . . . . . . GRP 95192
GRP / Sep '88.

### LIGHT STRUCK.
**Tracks:** Miss V. / One thing I can't change is my heart / Grand slam / Village / AM-FM / Chris-cross / Prince of wands / Prelude to a kiss.
- ■ LP . . . . . . . . . . . . . . . . . . . . GRP 91028
- ■ MC . . . . . . . . . . . . . . . . . . . GRPM 91028
GRP / Jul '86.
- ■ CD . . . . . . . . . . . . . . . . . . . . GRP 95372
GRP / Jan '93.

### LIVE AT THE BLUE NOTE.
**Tracks:** Not Advised.
- ■ LP . . . . . . . . . . . . . . . . . . . . . GR 9568
- ■ MC . . . . . . . . . . . . . . . . . . . . GRC 9568
- ■ CD . . . . . . . . . . . . . . . . . . . . GRPD 9568
GRP / Sep '88.
- ■ CD . . . . . . . . . . . . . . . . . . . . GRP 95682
GRP / Jan '93.

### MIND TIME.
**Tracks:** Not Advised.
- ■ LP . . . . . . . . . . . . . . . . . . . . GRP 91043
- MC . . . . . . . . . . . . . . . . . . . . GRPM 91043
- ■ CD . . . . . . . . . . . . . . . . . . . . GRPD 9554
GRP / Sep '88 / BMG / New Note.
- ■ CD . . . . . . . . . . . . . . . . . . . . GRP 95542
GRP / Jan '93.

### MUSICAL PORTRAITS.
**Tracks:** Musical portraits / Lady Laurie / Cat tail / Winter sunset / Firecracker / Day that you love me / Venus. Brazil / King of the white cloth / Little Puerto Rico / Prelude to a kiss.
- ■ CD . . . . . . . . . . . . . . . . . . . . GRP 96642
GRP / Jun '92.

### RED SUN.
**Tracks:** With a little help from my friends / Red sun / Two steps ahead / We'll be together again / Beyond the ridge / Lia's song / Loco motion / Little sunflower / Pensativa.

- CD . . . . . . . . . . . . . . . . . . . . GRP 96992
GRP / Apr '93 / BMG / New Note.

### TWO AMIGOS (Valentin, Dave & Herbie Mann).
**Tracks:** Bronx bad boys / Moonlight walk / Jesse's samba / First date / Rambo the cat / Two amigos / Old hill (morro velho) / Savana / Obsession.
- ■ LP . . . . . . . . . . . . . . . . . . . . GRP 96061
- ■ MC . . . . . . . . . . . . . . . . . . . . GRP 96064
- ■ CD . . . . . . . . . . . . . . . . . . . . GRP 96062
GRP / Jun '90.

### WE CAN ONLY DREAM.
**Tracks:** We can only dream.
- ■ 7" . . . . . . . . . . . . . . . . . . . . . AUS 150
Aura / Jul '86.

## Valentine Brothers

Natives of Columbus, Ohio, John and Billy Valentine exchanged their middle-class business backgrounds for the less reliable environs of the record industry in the late '70s, recording their debut set for Source in '79. But it was their second album that caused all the fuss: *First Take*, cut in '82 with pianist/producer Bobby Lyle, spawned the massive hit *Money's Too Tight To Mention* (later covered to successful effect by Simply Red) as well as its excellent follow-up *Just Let Me Be Close To You*. Since then their undoubted talent has suffered at the hands of record company recklessness: an album for A&M in '84 suffering from an A&R decision to change direction in mid-project, while an excellent set for EMI, *Picture This*, wasn't even released in America. More recently Billy Valentine has been the most visible of the brothers, working as a writer/producer in Los Angeles in the early '90s and contributing vocals to the soundtrack of the movie *The Five Heartbeats*. A recent reformation of the Valentine Brothers as a duo has produced little beyond a single for the UK indie Expansion Records.

### MONEY'S TOO TIGHT.
**Tracks:** Money's too tight.
- ■ 12" . . . . . . . . . . . . . . . . . . . . 12 NGY 1
- ■ 7" . . . . . . . . . . . . . . . . . . . . . NGY 1
Energy Acid / Mar '83.

### MONEY'S TOO TIGHT TO MENTION.
**Tracks:** Not Advised.
- CD . . . . . . . . . . . . . . . . . . . . TKOCD 016
- MC . . . . . . . . . . . . . . . . . . . . TKOCS 016
TKO Records / '92 / TKO Records Ltd / President Records.

### PICTURE THIS.
**Tracks:** Somebody took my love / No better love / She loves me / In my time / Cut backs / Used to be lovers / What you gonna do with love / Ladies' delight / Funk attack / Starship.
- ■ CD . . . . . . . . . . . . . . . . . . . . CDP 7469552
- ■ LP . . . . . . . . . . . . . . . . . . . . AML 3123
- ■ MC . . . . . . . . . . . . . . . . . . . . TCAML 3123
EMI-America / Aug '87.

### THIS KIND OF LOVE (IS SO SPECIAL).
**Tracks:** This kind of love (is so special).
- ■ 7" . . . . . . . . . . . . . . . . . . . . EXPAND 43
Expansion / Mar '94.

## Valentine, Billy

### MISS ME.
**Tracks:** Miss me.
- ■ 12" . . . . . . . . . . . . . . . . . . . . EXPAND 44
Expansion / Feb '94.

## Valentinos

### DON'T RAISE YOUR HANDS IN ANGER.
**Tracks:** Don't raise your hands in anger / Stand up and be counted.
- ■ 7" . . . . . . . . . . . . . . . . . . . . 2058 090
Polydor / Mar '71.

## Van Dyke, Earl

### 6 X 6.
**Tracks:** 6 x 6 / All for you.
- ■ 7" . . . . . . . . . . . . . . . . . . . . TMG 7?
Tamla Motown / Nov '70.

### ALL FOR YOU (Van Dyke, Earl & Th Soul Brothers).
**Tracks:** All for you.
- ■ 7" . . . . . . . . . . . . . . . . . . . . TMG 5?
Tamla Motown / '65.

## Vandross, Luther

Born in The Bronx in '51, Luther's adhe ence to the female vocalists of the sixtie drew him to the Apollo Theatre at ever opportunity, sometimes to watch those c stage, but mostly to indulge in his favouri hobby of diva spotting in the guest boxe Since he loved Aretha, Dionne and Dian the most, the fact that he subsequent oversaw albums by each of his heroines undoubtedly a source of enormous pride. I the mid-70's Vandross worked as an a jingle singer, but by '76 he'd formed his ow group, Luther, and released two albums fe Cotillion. *Luther* and *This Close To You* a now extremely rare for the reason that Va dross himself owns the rights to the recor ings and refuses to re-issue them. Betwee the trio's demise and his first solo album I '81, Vandross returned to the session ci cuit, singing backgrounds for, among others, Quincy Jones, Peabo Bryson, R berta Flack (he previously made a cele brated contribution to David Bowie's *Your Americans*). In the 13 years and 10 album since, Luther has traversed the board fro fashionable, cult-ish soulman to twinkl jacketed megastar, in all but a few case justifying his status as the leading mai stream black male vocalist. Best albums Try *Forever, For Always, For Love* ('82) ar *Any Love* ('88).

### ANY LOVE.
**Tracks:** Any love / Any love (album version) (C single) / Any love (inst.) (CD single) / Superstar (C single) / Until you come back to me (CD single) Better love (1989 12" & CD only) / You stopped lovi me / How many times can we say goodbye.
- ■ 12" . . . . . . . . . . . . . . . . . . . . LUTH ?
- ■ 7" . . . . . . . . . . . . . . . . . . . . LUTH
- ■ CD Single . . . . . . . . . . . . . . . . LUTH C
Epic / Sep '88.
- ■ 12" . . . . . . . . . . . . . . . . . . . . LUTH T
- ■ 7" . . . . . . . . . . . . . . . . . . . . LUTH
- ■ CD Single . . . . . . . . . . . . . . . CD LUTH
Epic / Jun '89.

### ANY LOVE.
**Tracks:** I wonder / She won't talk to me / I know ye want to / Come back / Any love / Love won't let m wait / Are you gonna love me / For you to love Second time around.
- ■ LP . . . . . . . . . . . . . . . . . . . . 46290#
- ■ CD . . . . . . . . . . . . . . . . . . . . 46290#
- ■ MC . . . . . . . . . . . . . . . . . . . . 46290#
Epic / Oct '88.

### BAD BOY HAVIN' A PARTY.
**Tracks:** Bad boy havin' a party / Once you know.
- ■ 12" . . . . . . . . . . . . . . . . . . . . EPCA 1327
- ■ 7" . . . . . . . . . . . . . . . . . . . . EPCA 27?
Epic / Nov '82.

### BEST OF LUTHER VANDROSS, THE (TH best of love).
**Tracks:** Searching / Glow of love / Never too much If this world were mine / Bad boy / Having a party Since I lost my baby / Promise me / Til my ba comes home / In only for one night / Creepin' supe star / Until you come back to me / Stop to love / ? amazing / There's nothing better than love / Give n the reason / Any love / I really didn't mean it / Lc won't let me wait / Treat you right / Here and nov
- CD . . . . . . . . . . . . . . . . . . . . 46580#
- MC . . . . . . . . . . . . . . . . . . . . 46580#
- ■ LP . . . . . . . . . . . . . . . . . . . . 46580#
Epic / Oct '89 / Sony.

438

■ DELET?

## BEST OF LUTHER VANDROSS, THE.
Tracks: Power of love/Love power / Don't want to be a fool / Rush / Here and now / She won't talk to me / Any love / Stop to love / There's nothing better than love / Give me the reason / Anyone who had a heart / It's over now / Superstar / Never too much / House is not a home.
VHS . . . . . . . . . . . . . . . . . . . .490952
Sony Music Video / Mar '94 / Sony.

## BEST THINGS IN LIFE ARE FREE, THE (Vandross, Luther & Janet Jackson).
Tracks: Best things in life are free.
■ CD Single . . . . . . . . . . . . . . . . PERD 7400
■ 12" . . . . . . . . . . . . . . . . . . . PERT 7400
■ 7" . . . . . . . . . . . . . . . . . . . PERSS 7400
■ MC Single . . . . . . . . . . . . . . PERCS 7400
Perspective / Jul '92.

## BUSY BODY.
Tracks: I wanted your love / Busy body / I'll let you slide / Make me a believer / For the sweetness of your love / How many times can we say goodbye / Superstar / Until you come back to me.
■ LP . . . . . . . . . . . . . . . . . . . EPC 25608
MC . . . . . . . . . . . . . . . . . . . .40 25608
Epic / Jan '84 / Sony.
■ LP . . . . . . . . . . . . . . . . . . . 460183 1
■ MC . . . . . . . . . . . . . . . . . . . 460183 4
Epic / Mar '88.

## BUSY BODY/THE NIGHT I FELL IN LOVE.
Tracks: Not Advised.
■ CD Set . . . . . . . . . . . . . . . . CDLV 241
CBS / '88.

## COME BACK.
Tracks: Come back / Second time around / She loves me back / Come back (Keith Cohen extended remix).
■ 12" . . . . . . . . . . . . . . . . . LUTHQT 10
■ 12" . . . . . . . . . . . . . . . . . LUTHGT 10
■ 7" . . . . . . . . . . . . . . . . . . . LUTH 10
■ CD Single . . . . . . . . . . . . . . CDLUTH 10
Epic / Apr '89.

## DON'T WANT TO BE A FOOL.
Tracks: Don't want to be a fool / Bad boy / Having a party / Busy body.
■ 12" . . . . . . . . . . . . . . . . . . . 6573996
■ 7" . . . . . . . . . . . . . . . . . . . 6573997
■ CD Single . . . . . . . . . . . . . . . 6573995
■ MC Single . . . . . . . . . . . . . . . 6573998
Epic / Aug '91.

## FOREVER, FOR ALWAYS, FOR LOVE.
Tracks: Bad boy/Having a party / You're the sweetest one / Since I lost my baby / Forever, for always, for love / Better love / Promise me / She loves me back / Once you know how.
■ LP . . . . . . . . . . . . . . . . . . . EPC 25013
Epic / Jul '87.
CD . . . . . . . . . . . . . . . . . . . CD 25013
Epic / Mar '88 / Sony.
CD . . . . . . . . . . . . . . . . . . . 4630012
MC . . . . . . . . . . . . . . . . . . . 4630014
■ LP . . . . . . . . . . . . . . . . . . . 4630011
Epic / Nov '88 / Sony.

## GIVE ME THE REASON.
Tracks: Stop to love / See me / I gave it up (when I fell in love) / So amazing / Give me the reason / There's nothing better than love / I really didn't mean it / Because it's really love / Anyone who had a heart.
■ LP . . . . . . . . . . . . . . . . . . . 4501341
■ CD . . . . . . . . . . . . . . . . . . . 4501342
■ MC . . . . . . . . . . . . . . . . . . . 4501344
Epic / Jan '87.

## GIVE ME THE REASON.
Tracks: Give me the reason.
■ 7" . . . . . . . . . . . . . . . . . . . .A 7288
Epic / Jul '86.
■ 12" . . . . . . . . . . . . . . . . . . . LUTH T5
■ 12" P.Disc. . . . . . . . . . . . . . . LUTH P5
■ 7" . . . . . . . . . . . . . . . . . . . LUTH 5
■ CD Single . . . . . . . . . . . . . . CD LUTH 5
Epic / Jan '88.

## GIVE ME THE REASON (OLD GOLD).
Tracks: Give me the reason / I really didn't mean it.
■ 7" . . . . . . . . . . . . . . . . . . . .OG 9961
Old Gold / '92 / Pickwick.

## GIVE ME THE REASON/NEVER TOO MUCH.
Tracks: Not Advised.
CD Set . . . . . . . . . . . . . . . . .4501342 0
Epic / Feb '93 / Sony.

## HEAVEN KNOWS.
Tracks: Heaven knows / I want the night to stay / Heaven knows (mixes) (On CD single & 12" only).
■ 12" . . . . . . . . . . . . . . . . . .659652 6
■ CD Single . . . . . . . . . . . . . . .659652 2
■ MC Single . . . . . . . . . . . . . . .659652 4
Epic / Sep '93.

## HERE AND NOW.
Tracks: Here and now / For you to love / Mix by Ben Liebrand (Only on 12" and CD single) / Never too much (Ben Liebrand mix) (Only on 12" (LUTHQT 13)).
■ 12" . . . . . . . . . . . . . . . . . LUTHQT 13
■ 12" . . . . . . . . . . . . . . . . . . LUTH 13T
■ 7" . . . . . . . . . . . . . . . . . . . LUTH 13
■ CD Single . . . . . . . . . . . . . . CDLUTH 13
■ MC Single . . . . . . . . . . . . . . LUTHMT 13
Epic / Dec '89.

## I DIDN'T REALLY MEAN IT.
Tracks: I didn't really mean it.
■ 12" . . . . . . . . . . . . . . . . . . . LUTH T3
■ 12" . . . . . . . . . . . . . . . . . LUTH QT3
Epic / Jun '87.

## I GAVE IT UP (WHEN I FELL IN LOVE).
Tracks: I gave it up (when I fell in love) / She's a super lady / Luther in love (mega mix) (Extra track on 12").
■ 12" . . . . . . . . . . . . . . . . . LUTH QT6
■ 12" . . . . . . . . . . . . . . . . . . LUTH T6
■ 7" . . . . . . . . . . . . . . . . . . . LUTH 6
■ CD Single . . . . . . . . . . . . . . CD LUTH 6
Epic / Apr '88.

## I WANTED YOUR LOVE.
Tracks: I wanted your love / Superstar / Until you come back to me.
■ 12" . . . . . . . . . . . . . . . . . . . TA 4279
■ 7" . . . . . . . . . . . . . . . . . . . .A 4279
Epic / Aug '87.

## I'LL LET YOU SLIDE.
Tracks: I'll let you slide.
■ 12" . . . . . . . . . . . . . . . . . . . TA 3978
■ 7" . . . . . . . . . . . . . . . . . . . .A 3978
Epic / Dec '83.

## IT'S OVER NOW.
Tracks: It's over now.
■ 12" . . . . . . . . . . . . . . . . . . . TA 6414
■ 7" . . . . . . . . . . . . . . . . . . . .A 6414
Epic / Jun '85.

## LITTLE MIRACLES (HAPPEN EVERY DAY).
Tracks: Little miracles (Happen every day) / I'm gonna start today / Heart of a hero (Avaialble on CDS only).
■ 7" . . . . . . . . . . . . . . . . . . . .659044 7
■ CD Single . . . . . . . . . . . . . . .659044 2
■ MC Single . . . . . . . . . . . . . . .659044 4
Epic / May '93.

## LIVE AT WEMBLEY.
Tracks: Never too much / Any love / Come back / Love won't let me wait / Give me the reason / Searching / For you to love / Superstar / House is not a home / She won't talk to me / Stop to love.
VHS . . . . . . . . . . . . . . . . . . . .490232
CMV Enterprises (Video) / Dec '89 / Sony.

## LOVE IS ON THE WAY (REAL LOVE).
Tracks: Love is on the way (Real love) / Never let me go.
■ 12" . . . . . . . . . . . . . . . . . .659959 6
■ CD Single . . . . . . . . . . . . . . .659959 2
■ MC Single . . . . . . . . . . . . . . .659959 4
Epic / Nov '93.

## LUTHER VANDROSS.
Tracks: Bad boy / Having a party / Since I lost my baby / She loves me back / House is not a home / Never too much / She's a super lady / Sugar and spice (I found me a girl) / Better love / You're the sweetest one.
■ LP . . . . . . . . . . . . . . . . . . . EPC 25220
MC . . . . . . . . . . . . . . . . . . . .40 25520
Epic / Dec '82 / Sony.
■ LP . . . . . . . . . . . . . . . . . . . 4606971
Epic / Oct '90.
CD . . . . . . . . . . . . . . . . . . . 4606972
MC . . . . . . . . . . . . . . . . . . . 4606974
Epic / Feb '94 / Sony.

## LUTHER VANDROSS - THE 12" TAPE.
Tracks: Never too much / I gave it up (when I fell in love) / Stop to love / It's over now.
MC . . . . . . . . . . . . . . . . . . . 4689864
Epic / Sep '91 / Sony.

## NEVER LET ME GO.
Tracks: Little miracles (happen every day) / Heaven knows / Love me again / Can't be doin' that now / Too far down / Love is on the way / Hustle / Emotion eyes / Lady, lady / Medley: How deep is your love/ Love don't love nobody.

CD . . . . . . . . . . . . . . . . . . . 473598 2
LP . . . . . . . . . . . . . . . . . . . 473598 1
MC . . . . . . . . . . . . . . . . . . . 473598 4
MiniDisc. . . . . . . . . . . . . . . . 473598 8
Epic / Jun '93 / Sony.

## NEVER TOO MUCH.
Tracks: Never too much / Sugar and spice (I found me a girl) / Don't you know that / I've been working / She's a super lady / You stopped loving me / House is not a home.
■ LP . . . . . . . . . . . . . . . . . . . EPC 85275
Epic / Dec '81.
■ LP . . . . . . . . . . . . . . . . . . . EPC 32807
■ MC . . . . . . . . . . . . . . . . . . . .40 32807
Epic / Aug '86.
CD . . . . . . . . . . . . . . . . . . . 32807 2
Epic / May '90 / Sony.

## NEVER TOO MUCH.
Tracks: Never too much / Superstar (don't you remember) / See me (Old Gold release only).
■ 12" . . . . . . . . . . . . . . . . . . . A 133101
■ 7" . . . . . . . . . . . . . . . . . . . .A 3101
Epic / Feb '83.
12" . . . . . . . . . . . . . . . . . . . .OG 4225
Old Gold / Apr '92 / Pickwick.

## NEVER TOO MUCH (OLD GOLD).
Tracks: Never too much / Your the sweetest one.
7" . . . . . . . . . . . . . . . . . . . .OG 9948
Old Gold / Sep '90 / Pickwick.

## NEVER TOO MUCH (REMIX).
Tracks: Never too much (remix) / Glow of love.
■ 12" . . . . . . . . . . . . . . . . . . . LUTH T12
■ 7" . . . . . . . . . . . . . . . . . . . .LUTH 12
■ CD Single . . . . . . . . . . . . . . CDLUTH 12
■ MC Single . . . . . . . . . . . . . . .LUTH M12
■ Special . . . . . . . . . . . . . . . . LUTH QT12
Epic / Oct '89.

## NIGHT I FELL IN LOVE, THE.
Tracks: Till my baby comes home / Night I fell in love / If only for one night / Creepin' / It's over now / Wait for love / My sensitivity (Gets in the way) / Other side of the world.
CD . . . . . . . . . . . . . . . . . . . CD 26387
■ LP . . . . . . . . . . . . . . . . . . . EPC 26387
MC . . . . . . . . . . . . . . . . . . . .40 26387
Epic / Mar '85 / Sony.
CD . . . . . . . . . . . . . . . . . . . 4624892
MC . . . . . . . . . . . . . . . . . . . 4624894
■ LP . . . . . . . . . . . . . . . . . . . 4624891
Epic / Mar '90 / Sony.

## POWER OF LOVE.
Tracks: She doesn't mind / Power of love/ Love power / I'm gonna start today / Rush / I want the night to stay / Don't want to be a fool / I can tell you that / Sometimes it's only love / Emotional love / I who have nothing.
CD . . . . . . . . . . . . . . . . . . . 4680122
■ LP . . . . . . . . . . . . . . . . . . . 4680121
■ MC . . . . . . . . . . . . . . . . . . . 4680124
Epic / May '91 / Sony.
MiniDisc. . . . . . . . . . . . . . . . 4680123
Epic / Feb '93 / Sony.

## POWER OF LOVE.
Tracks: Power of love / Love power (Not on MC single) / Love power (instrumental) (Only on MC & CD single) / I wanted your love (Only on 12" single. Original release only) / Any love (Only on CD single and original 12").
■ 12" . . . . . . . . . . . . . . . . . . . 6568226
■ 7" . . . . . . . . . . . . . . . . . . . 6568227
■ CD Single . . . . . . . . . . . . . . . 6568222
■ MC Single . . . . . . . . . . . . . . . 6568224
■ MC Single . . . . . . . . . . . . . . . 6568228
Epic / Feb '92.

## RUSH, THE.
Tracks: Rush.
■ 12" . . . . . . . . . . . . . . . . . . . 6577236
■ 7" . . . . . . . . . . . . . . . . . . . 6577237
■ CD Single . . . . . . . . . . . . . . . 6577232
■ MC Single . . . . . . . . . . . . . . . 6577234
Epic / Jan '92.

## SEE ME.
Tracks: See me / House is not a home.
■ 12" . . . . . . . . . . . . . . . . . . . LUTH T1
■ 7" . . . . . . . . . . . . . . . . . . . LUTH 1
Epic / Mar '87.
■ 12" . . . . . . . . . . . . . . . . . . . LUTH QT1
Epic / May '87.

## SHE WON'T TALK TO ME.
Tracks: She wont talk to me / Creepin'.
■ 12" . . . . . . . . . . . . . . . . . . .LUTH QT9
■ 12" . . . . . . . . . . . . . . . . . . .LUTH T9
■ 7" . . . . . . . . . . . . . . . . . . . LUTH 9
■ CD Single . . . . . . . . . . . . . . .CDLUTH 9

■ EP . . . . . . . . . . . . . . . . . . . . . . .LUTHEP 9
Epic / Dec '88.

**SO AMAZING.**
Tracks: So amazing / If only for one night / So amazing (instrumental) (On 12" version.) / If only for one night (version) (On LUTH P4 only) / House is not a home (On 12" version.).
■ 12" . . . . . . . . . . . . . . . . . . . . . . LUTH P4
■ 12" . . . . . . . . . . . . . . . . . . . . . . .LUTH T4
■ 7" . . . . . . . . . . . . . . . . . . . . . . . LUTH 4
■ CD Single . . . . . . . . . . . . . . . . . CD LUTH 4
Epic / Oct '87.

**SONGS.**
Tracks: Love the one you're with / Killing me softly / Endless love / Evergreen / Reflections / Hello / Ain't no stoppin' us now / Always and forever / Going in circles / Since you've been gone / All the woman I need / What the world needs now / Impossible.
MiniDisc. . . . . . . . . . . . . . . . . . . . . .476656 6
Epic / Oct '94 / Sony.
CD. . . . . . . . . . . . . . . . . . . . . . . . 4766562
LP . . . . . . . . . . . . . . . . . . . . . . . .476656 1
MC. . . . . . . . . . . . . . . . . . . . . . . . 4766564
Epic / Sep '94 / Sony.

**STOP TO LOVE.**
Tracks: Stop to love / Stop to love (instrumental).
■ 12" . . . . . . . . . . . . . . . . . . . . . . .LUTH T2
■ 7" . . . . . . . . . . . . . . . . . . . . . . . LUTH 2
■ EP . . . . . . . . . . . . . . . . . . . . . . .LUTH QT2
Epic / Sep '87.

**SUGAR AND SPICE (I FOUND ME A GIRL).**
Tracks: Sugar and spice (I found me a girl).
■ 7" . . . . . . . . . . . . . . . . . . . . . . . EPCA 1662
Epic / Oct '81.

**THERE'S NOTHING BETTER THAN LOVE.**
Tracks: There's nothing better than love (with Gregory Hines) / Anyone who had a heart / There's nothing better than love (instrumental) / My sensitivity (gets in the way).
■ 12". . . . . . . . . . . . . . . . . . . . . . .LUTH T7
■ 7" . . . . . . . . . . . . . . . . . . . . . . . LUTH 7
■ CD Single . . . . . . . . . . . . . . . . . CD LUTH 7
Epic / Jun '88.

**TILL MY BABY COMES HOME.**
Tracks: Till my baby comes home.
■ 12" . . . . . . . . . . . . . . . . . . . . . . TA 6074
■ 7" . . . . . . . . . . . . . . . . . . . . . . . A 6074
Epic / Mar '85.

**TREAT YOU RIGHT.**
Tracks: Treat you right / I know you want to.
■ 12" . . . . . . . . . . . . . . . . . . . . . . LUTH T14
■ 7" . . . . . . . . . . . . . . . . . . . . . . .LUTH 14
■ CD Single . . . . . . . . . . . . . . . CDLUTH 14
Epic / Jun '90.

**TWELVE INCH MIXES.**
Tracks: Never too much / I gave it up (when I fell in Love) / It's over now (special version) / Never too much (mix).
CD. . . . . . . . . . . . . . . . . . . . . . . . .468986-2
Epic / Nov '92 / Sony.

**YOU'RE THE SWEETEST ONE.**
Tracks: You're the sweetest one / She's a super lady.
■ 12" . . . . . . . . . . . . . . . . . . . . . . TA 3313
■ 7" . . . . . . . . . . . . . . . . . . . . . . . A 3313
Epic / Apr '83.

## Vanity

**MECHANICAL EMOTION.**
Tracks: Mechanical emotion / Crazy maybe.
■ 12" . . . . . . . . . . . . . . . . . . . . . . TMGT 1369
■ 7" . . . . . . . . . . . . . . . . . . . . . . . TMG 1369
Motown / Jan '85.

**PRETTY MESS.**
Tracks: Pretty mess / Pretty mess (instr.).
■ 12" . . . . . . . . . . . . . . . . . . . . . . TMGT 1360
■ 7" . . . . . . . . . . . . . . . . . . . . . . . TMG 1360
Motown / Sep '84.

**SKIN ON SKIN.**
Tracks: Under the influence / Manhunt / Romantic voyage / Confidential / Animals / Skin on skin / Gun shy / Ouch / In the jungle.
■ LP . . . . . . . . . . . . . . . . . . . . . . . ZL 72399
■ MC. . . . . . . . . . . . . . . . . . . . . . . ZK 72399
Motown / Jun '86.

**UNDER THE INFLUENCE.**
Tracks: Under the influence / Wild animal.
■ 12". . . . . . . . . . . . . . . . . . . . . . ZT 40610

■ 7" . . . . . . . . . . . . . . . . . . . . . . . ZB 40609
Motown / Apr '86.

**WILD ANIMAL.**
Tracks: Flippin' out / Pretty mess / Samuelle / Strap on Robbie baby / Wild animal / Crazy maybe / Mechanical emotion.
■ LP . . . . . . . . . . . . . . . . . . . . . . . ZL 72283
■ MC. . . . . . . . . . . . . . . . . . . . . . . ZK 72283
Motown / Oct '84.

## Vannelli, Gino

**BIG DREAMERS NEVER SLEEP.**
Tracks: Not Advised.
CD. . . . . . . . . . . . . . . . . . . . . .FDM 362112
Dreyfus / Oct '93 / Topic Records / A.D.A. Distribution / Direct Distribution / New Note.

**BLACK CARS.**
Tracks: Black cars / Other man / It's over / Here she comes / Hurts to be in love / Total stranger / Just a motion away / Imagination / How much.
CD. . . . . . . . . . . . . . . . . . . . . . 825 108-2
■ LP . . . . . . . . . . . . . . . . . . . . . . . 825 108-1
MC. . . . . . . . . . . . . . . . . . . . . . 825 108-4
Polydor/Dreyfus (USA) / Apr '85.
CD. . . . . . . . . . . . . . . . . . . . . .FDM 362102
Dreyfus / Oct '93 / Topic Records / A.D.A. Distribution / Direct Distribution / New Note.

**BROTHER TO BROTHER.**
Tracks: Appaloosa / River must flow / I just wanna stop / Love and emotion / Feel like flying / Brother to brother / Wheels of fire / Evil eye / People I belong to.
■ LP . . . . . . . . . . . . . . . . . . . . . . . AMLH 64722
A&M / '78.

**I JUST WANNA STOP.**
Tracks: I just wanna stop / Surest things never change.
■ 7" . . . . . . . . . . . . . . . . . . . . . . .AMS 7397
A&M / Nov '78.

**INCONSOLABLE MAN.**
Tracks: Rhythm of romance / If I should lose this love / Shame / Sunset on L.A. / Moment to moment / Cry of love / Time of day / Bound to cry / Joker's wild / Inconsolable man.
■ CD. . . . . . . . . . . . . . . . . . . . . . 843 639-2
■ MC. . . . . . . . . . . . . . . . . . . . . . 843 639-4
Polydor / Aug '91.

**LIVING INSIDE MYSELF.**
Tracks: Living inside myself / Stay with me.
■ 7" . . . . . . . . . . . . . . . . . . . . . . .ARIST 390
Arista / Apr '81.

**NIGHTWALKER.**
Tracks: Nightwalker / Seek and you shall find / Put the weight on my shoulders / I believe / Santa Rosa / Living inside myself / Stay with me / Sally, she says the sweetest things.
■ LP . . . . . . . . . . . . . . . . . . . . . . . SPART 1148
Arista / Apr '81.
■ CD . . . . . . . . . . . . . . . . . . . . . . 253 178
RCA / Oct '87.

**PAUPER IN PARADISE.**
Tracks: Mardi gras / Valleys of Valhalla / Surest things can change / One night with you / Song and dance / Black and blue / Pauper in paradise.
■ LP . . . . . . . . . . . . . . . . . . . . . . . AMLH 68443
A&M / Jan '78.

**POWERFUL PEOPLE.**
Tracks: People gotta move / Lady / Son of a New York gun / Jack miraculous / Jo Jo / Powerful people / Felicia / Work verse / Poor happy Jimmy.
■ LP . . . . . . . . . . . . . . . . . . . . . . . AMLS 63630
A&M / '79.

**WHEELS OF LIFE.**
Tracks: Wheels of life / Powerful people.
■ 7" . . . . . . . . . . . . . . . . . . . . . . .AMS 7420
A&M / Mar '79.

## Veal, Charles

**ONLY THE BEST.**
Tracks: Happy is the man / We can / It's alright / Prelude / What good is a song / How does it feel / Live your life and let live / If you ever need somebody / I believe in you / This must be magic / Someday we'll all be free / Thankful.
■ LP . . . . . . . . . . . . . . . . . . . . . . .EST 12095
Capitol / Nov '80.

## Vega, Tata

**GET IT UP FOR LOVE.**
Tracks: Get it up for love.
■ 12" . . . . . . . . . . . . . . . . . . . . . . TMGT 1140
■ 7" . . . . . . . . . . . . . . . . . . . . . . . TMG 1140
Motown / Oct '81.

**GIVING ALL MY LOVE.**
Tracks: Giving all my love / You keep me hangin' on / Abandoned / Reachin' all around my love / There's love in the world / You better watch out / Love your neighbour / Second wind / I get so used to you being around.
■ LP . . . . . . . . . . . . . . . . . . . . . . .STML 12138
Motown / '81.

**IF LOVE MUST GO.**
Tracks: If love must go / Come in heaven.
■ 7" . . . . . . . . . . . . . . . . . . . . . . .TMG 1157
Motown / Aug '79.

**LOVE YOUR NEIGHBOUR.**
Tracks: Love your neighbour / There's love in the world.
■ 12" . . . . . . . . . . . . . . . . . . . . . . TMGT 1236
■ 7" . . . . . . . . . . . . . . . . . . . . . . . TMG 1236
Motown / Oct '81.

**MISS CELIE'S BLUES (SISTER).**
Tracks: Celie shaves Mr. / Sarification ceremony.
■ 7" . . . . . . . . . . . . . . . . . . . . . . . W 875
Qwest / Jul '86.

**TIME'S SO RIGHT.**
Tracks: Not Advised.
CD. . . . . . . . . . . . . . . . . . . . . . RMCD 03
■ LP . . . . . . . . . . . . . . . . . . . . . . .RMLP 03
MC. . . . . . . . . . . . . . . . . . . . . . . RMC 03
Word (UK) / Jan '89 / Word Records (UK) / Sony.

**TOTALLY TATA.**
Tracks: Mr. Troublemaker / Blame it on the sun / Come in heaven / Deep inside / Jesus take me higher / Love comes from unexpected places / It' too late / You'll never rock alone / Ever so lovingly.
■ LP . . . . . . . . . . . . . . . . . . . . . . .STML 12051
Tamla Motown / May '88.

**TRY LOVE FROM THE INSIDE.**
Tracks: Try love from the inside / Just as long as there is you.
■ 7" . . . . . . . . . . . . . . . . . . . . . . .TMG 1051
Tamla Motown / Oct '76.

**TRY MY LOVE.**
Tracks: Come on and try my love / I need you now / Get it up, for love / If love must go / Magic feeling / Gonna do my best to love you / I just keep thinking about you baby / Whoppre bopper show stopper / In the morning.
■ LP . . . . . . . . . . . . . . . . . . . . . . .STML 12100
Motown / '79.

**YOU KEEP ME HANGIN' ON.**
Tracks: You keep me hangin' on / You better watc out.
■ 12" . . . . . . . . . . . . . . . . . . . . . . TMGT 12
■ 7" . . . . . . . . . . . . . . . . . . . . . . . TMG 12
Motown / Oct '81.

## Velvelettes

**HE WAS REALLY SAYIN' SOMETHIN'.**
Tracks: He was really saying something.
■ 7" . . . . . . . . . . . . . . . . . . . . . . . SS 3
Stateside / Feb '65.

**IT KEEPS REMINDING ME.**
Tracks: It keeps reminding me.
■ 12" . . . . . . . . . . . . . . . . . . . . . . 12 MOTC
Motor City / Jun '92.

**LONELY LONELY GIRL AM I.**
Tracks: Lonely lonely girl am I.
■ 7" . . . . . . . . . . . . . . . . . . . . . . . TMG 5
Tamla Motown / '65.

**NEEDLE IN A HAYSTACK.**
Tracks: Needle in a haystack / He was really sayi something.
■ 7" . . . . . . . . . . . . . . . . . . . . . . . SS 3
Stateside / Jun '64.
■ 7" . . . . . . . . . . . . . . . . . . . . . . . TMG 5
Tamla Motown / '66.
■ 7" . . . . . . . . . . . . . . . . . . . . . . . TMG 8
Tamla Motown / Mar '72.
■ 7" . . . . . . . . . . . . . . . . . . . . . . . TMG 1
Motown / Mar '83.

## THESE THINGS WILL KEEP ME LOVING YOU.
Tracks: These things will keep me loving you / Since you've been loving me.
■ 7" . . . . . . . . . . . . . . . . . . . . . **TMG 580**
Tamla Motown / Oct '66.
■ 7" . . . . . . . . . . . . . . . . . . . . . **TMG 780**
Tamla Motown / Jul '71.

# Verdell, Jackie

## LAY MY BURDEN DOWN.
Tracks: Lay my burden down / Praise him / Can I get a witness / Storm is passing over / Walk all over God's heaven / When the saints go marching in / Let me be / I want Jesus to walk with me.
■ CD . . . . . . . . . . . . . . . . . . **CDCH 375**
Ace / Jun '93 / Pinnacle / Complete Record Co. Ltd.

## WHEN THE SAINTS GO MARCHING IN.
Tracks: When the saints go marching in / Can I get a witness.
■ 7" . . . . . . . . . . . . . . . . . . . . . **YZ 27**
WEA / Nov '84.

# Vertical Hold

## SUMMERTIME.
Tracks: Summertime / Summertime (jazzy dub) / Summertime (percapella) (Available on 12" single only.).
■ 12" . . . . . . . . . . . . . . . . **12 BRW 109**
■ 7" . . . . . . . . . . . . . . . . . **BRW 109**
4th & Broadway / Jul '88.

# Vibe

## MORE I KEEP WISHING, THE (Vibe & Elroy Pinnock).
Tracks: More I keep wishing (Mixes).
■ 12" . . . . . . . . . . . . . . . . . .**TCUE 16**
Cue / May '94.

# Vibrations

## CANADIAN SUNSET.
Tracks: Canadian sunset / Story of a starry night.
■ 7" . . . . . . . . . . . . . . . . . . . . . **DB 7895**
Columbia / Mar '66.

## PICK ME.
Tracks: Pick me / You better beware.
■ 7" . . . . . . . . . . . . . . . . . . . . . **DB 8175**
Columbia / Apr '67.

## SOMBRAS.
Tracks: Not Advised.
■ CD . . . . . . . . . . . . . . . . . . **CDART 101**
Arc / Oct '94 / ARC Music Distribution Ltd / Koch International / BMG / Total.

# Village People

## BEST OF VILLAGE PEOPLE, THE.
Tracks: Not Advised.
■ VHS . . . . . . . . . . . . . . . . . **WNR 2038**
Warnervision Video / Jan '94 / VCI Distribution / THE.

## CAN'T STOP THE MUSIC.
Tracks: Can't stop the music / I love you to death.
■ 7" . . . . . . . . . . . . . . . . . . . . . **MER 16**
Mercury / Aug '80.

## CRUISIN'.
Tracks: Y.M.C.A. / Women / I'm a cruiser / Hot cop / My room mate / Ups and downs.
■ LP . . . . . . . . . . . . . . . . . . . **9109 614**
Mercury / Jan '79.

## DO YOU WANNA SPEND THE NIGHT.
Tracks: Do you wanna spend the night / Food fight.
■ 12" . . . . . . . . . . . . . . . . . . **MERX 75**
■ 7" . . . . . . . . . . . . . . . . . . . **MER 75**
Mercury / Jul '81.

## GO WEST.
Tracks: Go West / Citizens of the world.
■ 12" . . . . . . . . . . . . . . . . . .**9198 274**
■ 7" . . . . . . . . . . . . . . . . . . **6007 221**
Mercury / Jun '79.

## GO WEST.
Tracks: In the navy / Go West / Citizens of the world / I wanna shake your hand / Get away holiday / Manhattan woman / Y.M.C.A.
■ LP . . . . . . . . . . . . . . . . . . **9109 621**
Mercury / May '79.

## GREATEST HITS.
Tracks: YMCA (93 remix) / In the navy (93 remix) / Can't stop the music (93 remix) / San Francisco (93

remix) / Macho man (92 remix) / Go west / Fire island / Ready for the 80's / Sex over the phone / New York City / Just a gigolo/I ain't go nobody / 5 o'clock in the morning / In Hollywood / YMCA (93 12" remix).
■ CD . . . . . . . . . . . . . . . . **7432117831-2**
■ MC . . . . . . . . . . . . . . . **7432117831-4**
Arista / Nov '93 / BMG.

## GREATEST HITS: VILLAGE PEOPLE (REMIX).
Tracks: Y.M.C.A. / Macho man / San Francisco / Can't stop the music / In the navy / In Hollywood / Fire island.
■ CD . . . . . . . . . . . . . . . . . **GMCD 1003**
■ LP . . . . . . . . . . . . . . . . . **GMLP 1003**
■ MC . . . . . . . . . . . . . . . . **GMMC 1003**
Groove & Move (G&M) / Dec '89 / Groove & Move Records.

## HITS, THE.
Tracks: Not Advised.
■ LP . . . . . . . . . . . . . . . . . . . **QUALP 1**
Quazar / Nov '87.

## I AM WHAT I AM.
Tracks: I am what I am / Key West.
■ 7" . . . . . . . . . . . . . . . . . . **DJS 10892**
DJM / Feb '79.

## IN THE NAVY.
Tracks: In the Navy.
■ 12" . . . . . . . . . . . . . . . . . . **9198144**
■ 7" . . . . . . . . . . . . . . . . . . **6007 209**
Mercury / Mar '79.

## IN THE NAVY.
Tracks: In the navy (Mixes).
■ 12" . . . . . . . . . . . . . . **7432119819-1**
■ 7" . . . . . . . . . . . . . . **7432119819-7**
■ CD Single . . . . . . . . . . . . **7432119819-2**
■ MC Single . . . . . . . . . . . **7432119819-4**
Arista / May '94.

## JUST A GIGOLO.
Tracks: Just a gigolo / I ain't got nobody / In Hollywood.
■ 7" . . . . . . . . . . . . . . . . . . **DJS 10899**
DJM / Feb '79.

## LIVE AND SLEAZY.
Tracks: Fire island / Hot cop / San Francisco / In Hollywood / Macho man / In the navy / Y.M.C.A. / Sleazy / Rock and roll is back again / Ready for the 80's / Save me.
■ Double LP . . . . . . . . . . . . . . . **6641980**
Mercury / Nov '79.

## MACHO MAN.
Tracks: Macho man / In Hollywood.
■ 7" . . . . . . . . . . . . . . . . . . **DJS 10856**
DJM / Apr '78.

## MACHO MAN.
Tracks: Mach man / I am what I am / Key west / Just a gigolo / I ain't got nobody / Snoop & Gommorrah.
■ LP . . . . . . . . . . . . . . . . . **DJF 20538**
DJM / Apr '78.

## MAGIC NIGHT.
Tracks: Magic night / Can't stop the music.
■ 12" . . . . . . . . . . . . . . . . . . **MERX 39**
■ 7" . . . . . . . . . . . . . . . . . . . **MER 39**
Mercury / Oct '80.

## MEDLEY - IN THE NAVY.
Tracks: In the navy.
■ 12" . . . . . . . . . . . . . . . . . **SOHOT 51**
■ 7" . . . . . . . . . . . . . . . . . . **SOHO 51**
Record Shack / Nov '85.

## NEW YORK CITY.
Tracks: New York City (vocal) / New York City (Instrumental).
■ 12" . . . . . . . . . . . . . . . . . **SOHOT 39**
■ 7" . . . . . . . . . . . . . . . . . . **SOHO 39**
Record Shack / Mar '85.

## NEW YORK CITY.
Tracks: Not Advised.
■ LP . . . . . . . . . . . . . . . . . **SOHOLP 5**
■ MC. . . . . . . . . . . . . . . . . **SOHOTC 5**
Record Shack / Mar '85.

## READY FOR THE 80'S.
Tracks: Ready for the 80's / Save me.
■ 7" . . . . . . . . . . . . . . . . . . **6007 244**
Mercury / Nov '79.

## RENAISSANCE.
Tracks: Do you wanna spend the night / 5 o'clock in the morning / Fireman / Jungle city / Action man / Diet / Food fight.
■ LP . . . . . . . . . . . . . . . . . . **6399 204**

## MC. . . . . . . . . . . . . . . . . . . . **7199 204**
Mercury / Jul '81 / PolyGram.

## SAN FRANCISCO.
Tracks: San Francisco / Fire Island.
■ 7" . . . . . . . . . . . . . . . . . . **DJS 10817**
DJM / Nov '77.

## SAN FRANCISCO (REISSUES).
Tracks: San Francisco / Macho man.
■ 7" . . . . . . . . . . . . . . . . . . **DJS 15001**
DJM / Nov '78.
■ 7" . . . . . . . . . . . . . . . . . . **DJS 18003**
DJM / Feb '79.

## SEX OVER THE PHONE.
Tracks: Sex over the phone.
■ 12" . . . . . . . . . . . . . . . . . . **SOHOT 34**
■ 7" . . . . . . . . . . . . . . . . . . . **SOHO 34**
Record Shack / Jan '85.

## VILLAGE PEOPLE MEGAMIX.
Tracks: Village People megamix / YMCA ('89').
■ 12" . . . . . . . . . . . . . . . . . . **GMT 129**
■ 7" . . . . . . . . . . . . . . . . . . . **GMT 9**
■ CD Single . . . . . . . . . . . . . . **GMCS 9**
Groove & Move (G&M) / Nov '89.

## VILLAGE PEOPLE: THE HITS.
Tracks: YMCA / Macho man / San Francisco (you've got me) / Can't stop the music / Megamix / In the navy / In Hollywood / Fire island / Go West / Village people / Ready for the 80's / Do you wanna spend the night.
■ CD . . . . . . . . . . . . . . . . . **MCCD 004**
■ MC. . . . . . . . . . . . . . . . . **MCTC 004**
Music Club / Feb '91 / Gold & Sons / THE / Video Collection / C.M. Distribution.

## Y.M.C.A.
Tracks: Y.M.C.A.
■ 7" . . . . . . . . . . . . . . . . . . **6007 192**
Mercury / Nov '78.

## Y.M.C.A. (OLD GOLD).
Tracks: Y.M.C.A. / In the navy / Can't stop the music (Only on CD single.).
■ 12" . . . . . . . . . . . . . . . . . . **OG 4091**
Old Gold / Jan '89.
CD Single . . . . . . . . . . . . . . . **OG 6510**
Old Gold / Jul '90 / Pickwick.
7" . . . . . . . . . . . . . . . . . . . **OG 9836**
Old Gold / '92 / Pickwick.

## Y.M.C.A. 93.
Tracks: Y.M.C.A. 93 (mixes) / Go west.
■ 7" . . . . . . . . . . . . . . . . **7432117718 7**
■ CD Single . . . . . . . . . . . . **7432117718 2**
■ MC Single . . . . . . . . . . . . **7432117718 4**
■ 12" . . . . . . . . . . . . . . . **7432117718 1**
Arista / Nov '93.

# Virginia Wolves

## STAY.
Tracks: Stay.
■ 7" . . . . . . . . . . . . . . . . . . . **SS 563**
Stateside / '66.

# Viscount Oliver

## JUST ONE MOMENT.
Tracks: Not Advised.
■ CD . . . . . . . . . . . . . . . . . . **FECD 13**
First Edition / Apr '93 / Jetstar.

# Vision

## DO IT TONIGHT.
Tracks: Do it tonight / Seduction.
■ 12" . . . . . . . . . . . . . . . . . . **DOM T8**
Domino (1) / Sep '87.

## EXPOSED.
Tracks: Exposed / Victim / Can't let her go / Do it tonight / Kisses don't lie / Seduction / Private passion / Where did our love go / Lust 4 U.
■ LP . . . . . . . . . . . . . . . . . **DOM LP 1**
Domino (1) / May '87.
■ LP . . . . . . . . . . . . . . . . . **WIL 3002**
WRC / '88.

# Visual

## MUSIC GOT ME (2 PARTS).
Tracks: Music got me.
■ 12" . . . . . . . . . . . . . . . **PRLA 13 3237**
■ 7" . . . . . . . . . . . . . . . . **PRLA 13 3237**
Prelude / Apr '83.

## Voices Of East Harlem

### RIGHT ON BE FREE.
**Tracks:** Right on be free / Simple song of freedom / Proud Mary / Music in the air / Oh yeah / For what it's worth / Let it be me / No no no / Gotta be a change / Run shaker Kife.
■ **LP** . . . . . . . . . . . . . . . . . . . . . . .2469 007
Elektra / Nov '70.

## Vontastics

### LADY LOVE.
**Tracks:** Lady love.
■ **7"** . . . . . . . . . . . . . . . . . . . . . . . . **SS 2002**
Stateside / Mar '67.

## Voyage

### FROM EAST TO WEST.
**Tracks:** From east to west / Scots machine.
■ **7"** . . . . . . . . . . . . . . . . . . . . . **GT 224**
GTO / Jun '78.

### LET'S FLY AWAY.
**Tracks:** Let's fly away / Ketchak fantasy.
■ **7"** . . . . . . . . . . . . . . . . . . . . . **GT 245**
GTO / Mar '79.

### POINT ZERO.
**Tracks:** Point zero / Latin odyssey.
■ **7"** . . . . . . . . . . . . . . . . . . . . . **GT 235**
GTO / Sep '78.

### SOUVENIRS.
**Tracks:** Souvenirs.
■ **7"** . . . . . . . . . . . . . . . . . . . . . **GT 241**
GTO / Nov '78.

### VOYAGE.
**Tracks:** Not Advised.
■ **LP** . . . . . . . . . . . . . . . . . . . . . **GTLP 030**
GTO / Sep '78.

## Wade, Adam

**AKE GOOD CARE OF HER.**
acks: Take good care of her.
7"..................................POP 843
M.V. / Jun '61.

## Walden, Narada Michael

**WAKENING.**
acks: Love me only / I don't want nobody else /
ive your love a chance / They want the feeling /
wakening suite (part 1) / Awakening / Listen to me /
oll and satisfied / Will you ever know.
LP.................................K 50570
ntlantic / Apr '79.

**ONFIDENCE.**
acks: You're my number 1 / Summer lady / I'm
ady / Safe in my arms / Confidence / Holiday / You
ught to love me / Blue side of midnight.
LP.................................K 50883
lantic / Jun '82.

**ARDEN OF LOVE LIGHT.**
acks: White night / Garden of love light / Delightful
First love / Meditation / Sun is dancing / You got the
oul / Saint and the rascal / You are love.
LP.................................K 50329
tlantic / '79.

**IMME,GIMME,GIMME.**
acks: Gimme gimme gimme / Wear your love.
12"...............................W 9077T
7".................................W 9077
EA / Mar '85.

**CRY, I SMILE.**
acks: I need your love / Better man / Soul bird / I
member / Oneness-cry / Mango bop / Rainbow sky
cry, I smile / Heaven's just a step ahead / So long.
LP.................................K 50417
lantic / Jun '78.

**DON'T WANT NOBODY ELSE (TO
ANCE WITH YOU).**
acks: I don't want nobody else (to dance with you)
You're so good.
7".................................K 11549
lantic / Jul '80.

**DON'T WANT NOBODY ELSE (TO
ANCE WITH YOU).**
acks: I don't want nobody else (to dance with you)
Will you ever know.
.................................K 11269
EA / '79.

**SHOULDA LOVED YA.**
acks: I shoulda loved ya / Carry on.
7".................................K 11413
lantic / Apr '80.

**SHOULDA LOVED YA (OLD GOLD).**
acks: I shoulda loved ya / Tonight i'm alright.
.................................OG 4206
d Gold / Jun '91 / Pickwick.

**WANT YOU.**
acks: I want you / Get up.
12"...............................K 11634 T
7".................................K 11634
lantic / Nov '80.

**M READY.**
acks: I'm ready / Holiday.
12"...............................A 9949 T
7".................................A 9949
lantic / Jan '83.

**ATURE OF THINGS.**
acks: That's the way it is / High above the clouds /
mme gimme gimme / Live it up / Nature of things /
uspicion / Dancin' on main street / Wear your love.
LP...............................925176 1
C.................................925176 4
EA / Feb '85 / WEA.

**ATURE OF THINGS.**
acks: Nature of things / Dancin' on Main Street.
12"...............................W 9017T
7".................................W 9017
EA / Jun '85.

---

**REACH OUT.**
Tracks: Reach out / Shake it off.
12"................................A 9858T
7".................................A 9858
Atlantic / Mar '83.

**REAL THANG.**
Tracks: Real thang / Take it to the bassman.
12"...............................K 11659 T
7".................................K 11659
Atlantic / Mar '81.

**SUMMER LADY.**
Tracks: Summer lady / Confidence.
12"...............................K 11752 T
7".................................K 11752
Atlantic / Aug '82.

**TONIGHT I'M ALL RIGHT.**
Tracks: Tonight I'm all right / Dance of life.
7".................................K 11437
Atlantic / Feb '80.

**VICTORY.**
Tracks: Real thing / Take it to the bossman / Alone
without you / Get up / Lucky fella / You will find your
way / Victory suite / Theme / Battle (hero soldiers
battle the hostile forces) / Victory for the hero
soldiers.
LP.................................K 50743
MC.................................K4 50743
Atlantic / Oct '80 / WEA.

**YOU OUGHTA LOVE ME.**
Tracks: You oughta love me / I shoulda loved ya.
12"...............................K 11739 T
7".................................K 11739
Atlantic / Jun '82.

## Walker, Chris

**FIRST TIME.**
Tracks: Little more amore / Make me feel / Someday
/ I just can't stop / Giving you all my love / Take time
/ I need you / Missing you / No place like love / First
time ever (I saw your face) / You've been gone
(Available on CD only).
CD.................................7559611362
LP.................................7559611361
MC.................................7559611364
WEA / Nov '91 / WEA.

## Walker, David

**RING THE CHANGES.**
Tracks: Ring the changes.
7".................................RCA 1664
RCA / Feb '68.

## Walker, David T.

**SWING STREET CAFE (see under Sam-
ple, Joe).**

## Walker, Junior

Scorching saxophonist Walker added grit to
Motown's mid-'60s output: *Shotgun* and
*Roadrunner* are among most exciting records of era. Biggest international success,
however, rewarded smoothing of sound for
1969's *What Does It Take (To Win Your
Love)*. Declining fortunes in subsequent
years were briefly turned around by cameo
on Foreigner's 1981 hit *Urgent*, after which
Walker returned to club circuit.

**19 GREATEST HITS: JUNIOR WALKER.**
Tracks: Not Advised.
CD.................................530033-2
MC.................................533033-4
Motown / Jan '93 / PolyGram.

**ANTHOLOGY - JUNIOR WALKER
(Walker, Junior & The All Stars).**
Tracks: Shotgun / Do the boomerang / Shake and
fingerpop / Cleo's back / Cleo's mood / I'm a roadrunner / How sweet it is (to be loved by you) / Money
(that's what I want) / Pucker up buttercup / Shoot
your shot / Come see about me / Hip city (part 1) /

---

Home cooking / What does it take (to win your love) /
These eyes / I've got to find a way to win Maria back
/ Gotta hold on to this feeling / Do you see my love
(for you growing) / Holy holy / Take me girl I'm ready
/ Right on brothers and sisters / Don't blame the
children / Moody junior / Way back home / Walk in
the night.
Double LP..........................TMSP 1129
Motown / Oct '81.

**BACK STREET BOOGIE.**
Tracks: Backstreet boogie / Girl I wanna marry you /
Wishing on a star / Hole in the wall / Don't let me go
astray / Tiger in my tank / Sax attack.
LP.................................K 56668
WEA / Feb '80.

**BEST OF JUNIOR WALKER & THE ALL
STARS, THE (Walker, Junior & The All
Stars).**
Tracks: Not Advised.
CD Set..............................530293-2
Motown / Apr '94 / PolyGram.

**BLOW THE HOUSE DOWN.**
Tracks: Sex pot / Rise and shine / Closer than close /
Ball baby / T-oo (t double oo) / Urgent / In and out /
Blow the house down.
LP.................................STML 12194
MC.................................CSTML 12194
Motown / Oct '83.

**BLOW THE HOUSE DOWN.**
Tracks: Blow the house down / Ball baby.
12"...............................TMGT 1318
7".................................TMG 1318
Motown / Oct '83.

**CLEO'S MOOD.**
Tracks: Cleo's mood.
7".................................TMG 550
Tamla Motown / '66.

**COMPACT COMMAND PERFORM-
ANCES (Walker, Junior & The All Stars).**
Tracks: Shotgun / Do the boomerang / Shake and
fingerpop / Cleo's back / Road runner / How sweet
it is (to be loved by you) / Money (that's what I want)
/ Pucker up buttercup / Shoot your shot / Come see
about me / Hip city, part 2 / Home cooking / What
does it take (to win your love) / These eyes / Gotta
hold on to this feeling / Do you see love (for you
growing) / Take me girl, I'm ready / Way back home /
Walk in the night.
CD.................................WD 72511
Motown / Mar '87.

**DO THE BOOMERANG (Walker, Junior &
The All Stars).**
Tracks: Do the boomerang / Tune up.
7".................................TMG 520
Tamla Motown / '65.

**GAS, A (Walker, Junior & The All Stars).**
Tracks: Do you see my love / And when I die / I was
made to love her / Carry your own load / Shut up,
don't interrupt me / Groove and move / Holly holy /
Honey come back / Riding high on love / Hey Jude /
At a Saturday matinee.
LP.................................STML 11167
Tamla Motown / Nov '70.

**HOME COOKIN' (Walker, Junior & The
All Stars).**
Tracks: Come see about me / What does it take to
win your love / Home cookin' / Sweet soul / Sweet
Daddy Deacon / Hip city / Fannie Mae / Things I do
for you / Baby ain't you shame.
LP.................................STML 11097
Tamla Motown / Feb '69.

**HOW SWEET IT IS (Walker, Junior & The
All Stars).**
Tracks: How sweet it is (to be loved by you) / Nothing
but soul.
7".................................TMG 571
Tamla Motown / Aug '66.
7".................................ZB 41935
Motown / Apr '88.

## I AIN'T GOING NOWHERE (Walker, Junior & The All Stars).
Tracks: I ain't going nowhere / What does it take / Take me girl, I'm ready.
■ 7"..............................TMG 1070
Motown / May '77.

## JUNIOR WALKER & THE ALL STARS (EP) (Walker, Junior & The All Stars).
Tracks: Road runner / Take me girl I'm ready / Walk in the night / What does it take (to win your love).
■ MC Single...............CTME 2026
Motown / Jun '83.

## JUNIOR WALKER'S GREATEST HITS.
Tracks: Shotgun / How sweet it is (to be loved by you) / Road runner / Hip city part 1 / Cleo's mood / Money (that's what I want) / Shoot your shot / Pucker up buttercup / Come see about me / What does it take (to win your love) / Shake and fingerpop / Home cooking / Baby you know it ain't right / Anyway you wanna.
■ LP...............................STML 11120
Tamla Motown / Nov '69.
■ LP...............................STMS 5054
■ MC...............................CSTMS 5054
Motown / Mar '82.
■ LP...............................WL 72097
■ MC...............................WK 72097
Motown / '86.
■ CD...............................WD 72097
Motown / Aug '88.

## LIVE (Walker, Junior & The All Stars).
Tracks: Hip city parts 1 and 2 / Sweet soul / Home cookin' / Something you got / I'm losing you / Come see about me / What does it take / Shotgun.
■ LP...............................STML 11152
Tamla Motown / Jul '70.

## MONEY.
Tracks: Money.
■ 7"................................TMG 586
Tamla Motown / '66.

## MOODY JUNIOR.
Tracks: Way back home / I don't want to do wrong / Bristol's way / Don't blame the children / Me and my family / Groove thang / Still water medley / Never can say goodbye / Moody Junior.
■ LP...............................STML 11211
Tamla Motown / Aug '72.

## MOTOWN SPECIAL (Walker, Junior & The All Stars).
Tracks: What does it take / Take me girl I'm ready / Shotgun / I was made to love her / Carry your own load / Pychedelic shack / Road runner / Ame cherie / Honey come back / Riding high on love / Shut up, don't interrupt me / San-ho-zay.
■ LP...............................STMX 6005
Motown / Mar '77.

## PUCKER UP BUTTERCUP.
Tracks: Pucker up buttercup / Anyway you wanta.
■ 7"................................TMG 596
Tamla Motown / Feb '67.

## RAINBOW FUNK (Walker, Junior & The All Stars).
Tracks: Way back home / Take me girl, I'm ready / Feelin' alright / Right on brothers and sisters / Teach them to pray / Something / Psychedelic shack / Pieces of a man / These things will keep me loving you.
■ LP...............................STML 11198
Tamla Motown / Feb '72.

## ROAD RUNNER.
Tracks: Road runner / Shoot your shot.
■ 7"................................TMG 559
Tamla Motown / '66.

## ROAD RUNNER (Walker, Junior & The All Stars).
Tracks: Road runner / Shotgun.
■ 7"................................TMG 691
Tamla Motown / Feb '69.

## ROAD RUNNER (Walker, Junior & The All Stars).
Tracks: How sweet it is / Last call / Anyway you wanta / Money / Mutiny / Baby you know you ain't right / Pucker up buttercup / Ame' che'rie / Twist Lackawana / Road runner / San Ho-zay.
■ LP...............................STML 11038
Tamla Motown / Jun '69.

## SHAKE AND FINGERPOP.
Tracks: Shake and fingerpop / Cleo's back.
■ 7"................................TMG 529
Tamla Motown / '65.

## SHAKE AND FINGERPOP.
Tracks: Shotgun / How sweet it is (to be loved by you) / Home cooking / Money / Pucker up buttercup / What does it take (to win your love) / Come see about me / Hip city / Cleo's mood / Shake and fingerpop / Shoot your shot.
CD...............................CDBM 072
■ LP...............................BMLP 072
Blue Moon (1) / Apr '89 / Roots Records / Jazz Music / Swift / Projection / THE / Hot Shot.

## SHAKE AND FINGERPOP (Walker, Junior & The All Stars).
Tracks: Shake and fingerpop / Do the boomerang / Cleo's back / Shotgun.
■ EP...............................TME 2013
Tamla Motown / Feb '66.

## SHOTGUN.
Tracks: Shotgun.
■ 7"................................TMG 509
Tamla Motown / '65.

## SHOTGUN/ ROADRUNNER (Walker, Junior & The All Stars).
Tracks: Cleo's mood / Do the boomerang / Shake and fingerpop / Shoot your shot / Tune up / Hot cha / Tally ho / Monkey jump / Cleo's back / Ain't that the truth / Road runner / How sweet it is (to be loved by you) / Pucker up Buttercup / Money (that's what I want) / Last call / Anyway you wanna / Baby, you know you ain't right / Ame' cherie (soul darling) / Twist lackawanna / San-ho-zay / Mutiny.
■ CD...............................ZD 72487
Motown / Dec '86.

## SMOOTH SOUL.
Tracks: I need you right now / I can see clearly now / Waht becomes of the brokenhearted / These things will keep me loving you / It's too late / I want you / It takes two to make love / Walk in the night / Climb on up / Never say goodbye / I don't want to do wrong / All the way.
■ LP...............................STML 12089
Motown / Sep '78.

## TAKE ME GIRL I'M READY (Walker, Junior & The All Stars).
Tracks: Take me girl I'm ready.
■ 7"................................TMG 840
Tamla Motown / Jan '73.

## THESE EYES (Walker, Junior & The All Stars).
Tracks: What does it take / These eyes / Proud Mary / Ame Cherie / Clinging to the thought that she's coming back / Cleo's mood / Hot cha / I've got to find a way to win Maria back / Sweet soul / Gotta hold on to this feeling / How sweet it is / San Ho Zay.
■ LP...............................STML 11140
Tamla Motown / Apr '70.

## WALK IN THE NIGHT (Walker, Junior & The All Stars).
Tracks: Walk in the night.
■ 7"................................TMG 824
Tamla Motown / Aug '72.
■ 7"................................TMG 1118
Motown / Sep '78.

## WAY BACK HOME (Walker, Junior & The All Stars).
Tracks: Way back home.
■ 7"................................TMG 857
Tamla Motown / Jun '73.

## WHAT DOES IT TAKE (Walker, Junior & The All Stars).
Tracks: What does it take / Take me girl, I'm ready.
■ 7"................................TMG 712
Tamla Motown / Oct '69.
■ 7"................................TMG 962
Tamla Motown / Mar '75.

## WHOPPER BOPPER SHOW STOPPER.
Tracks: Whopper bopper show stopper / You are the sunshine of my life / You're on fire / Leap and peep / Don't make no plans / I could never love another (after loving you) / I want you / Love ain't enough / My love.
■ LP...............................STML 12048
Motown / Jan '77.

## Wansel, Dexter

## ALL NIGHT LONG.
Tracks: All night long / What the world is coming to.
■ 12"...............................12PIR 6255
■ 7"................................PIR 6255
Philadelphia Int. / May '78.

## CAPTURED.
Tracks: Captured / Do what you wanna do / Year living dangerously / Heart on the line / Each mome / Conversations / Turn me on / Nam (I can't sleep night) / in the wind / East meets west.
■ LP...............................DIX 3
■ MC...............................CDIX 3
10 / Jul '86.

## CAPTURED (Wansel, Dexter Featurin The Jones Girls).
Tracks: Captured / Conversations.
■ 12"...............................TEN 80-1
■ 7"................................TEN 8
10 / May '86.

## I'M IN LOVE.
Tracks: I'm in love / Solutions.
■ 7"................................PIR 649
Philadelphia Int. / Jul '78.

## LIFE ON MARS.
Tracks: Life on mars / Always there.
■ 12"...............................SWAVE
Streetwave / Apr '86.

## VOYAGER.
Tracks: All night long / Solutions / Voyager / I ju want to love you / Time is the teacher / Latin love I'm in love.
■ LP...............................PIR 8271
■ MC...............................40 8271
Philadelphia Int. / Jun '78.

## War

Playing as an instrumental group in Califo nia in 1969, they were spotted by produce Jerry Goldstein and ex-Animal Eric Burdor who immediately adopted them as his bac king band. Their first album *Eric Burdor Declares War* was highly acclaimed an contained the U.S. No. 3 hit *Spill The Win* They split with Burdon in 1971 but continue to develop their unique style with Goldstein incorporating soul, rock, latin and jazz in fluences. Signed to United Artists they ha various hits thoughout the early seventie including *The World Is A Ghetto* in 1972 an *Cisco Kid* the following year. Disputes wit management prevented success in 1974 be once resolved they returned to the top the charts with the aptly titled *Why Can't W Be Friends* and followed this with 1976 *Summer*. Up to this point they had not pene trated the U.K. charts but in 1976 *Low Ride* reached No. 12. Their second U.K. chart hi *Galaxy* in 1978 was also ironically one their last U.S. hits as sales declined. Wa are still recording sporadically with littl commercial success, but their sell-ou shows at London's Jazz Cafe in 1993 ar evidence of their enduring popularity.

## ALL DAY MUSIC.
Tracks: All day music / Get down / That's what you will do / There must be a reason / Nappy head Slippin' into darkness / Baby brother.
■ LP...............................UAS 2926
United Artists / Feb '72.

## BABY FACE (SHE SAID 'DO DO DO DO").
Tracks: Baby face (she said 'do do do do').
■ 7"................................MCA 38
MCA / Aug '78.

## BEST OF WAR AND MORE.
Tracks: Not Advised.
CD...............................CDLAX 10
Chord / '88 / EMI.

## BEST OF WAR..AND MORE.
Tracks: Livin' on the red / Low rider / Cisco kid Slippin' into darkness / Me and baby brother / Ga laxy / Spill the wine / All day music / Why can't w be friends / Summer / City country city / Whos Cadillac is that / Low rider (remix).
CD...............................R2 7002
Rhino (USA) / '87 / WEA.

## BLACK CAUCUS CONCERT (War/Curti Mayfield/Kool & The Gang).
Tracks: Wild and peaceful / Give me your love / C and on / Gypsy man / Going down slow.
■ LP...............................GCH 803
MC...............................GCHK 7803
Chess (Charly) / '87 / Charly.

## GALAXY.
Tracks: Galaxy.
■ 7"................................MCA 33
MCA / Dec '77.

■ DELETE

## GALAXY.
Tracks: Galaxy / Baby face / Sweet fighting lady / Hey senorita / Seven tin soldiers.
■ LP . . . . . . . . . . . . . . . . . . MCF 2822
MCA / Mar '78.

## GOOD GOOD FEELIN'.
Tracks: Good good feelin' / Music band.
■ 12" . . . . . . . . . . . . . . . . . . . MCAT 418
■ 7" . . . . . . . . . . . . . . . . . . . MCA 418
MCA / Apr '79.

## GROOVIN'.
Tracks: Groovin' (vocal) / Groovin' (instrumental).
■ 12" . . . . . . . . . . . . . . . . . . . BRT 16
■ 7" . . . . . . . . . . . . . . . . . . . BR 16
Blue Bird (2) / Aug '86.

## HEY SENORITA.
Tracks: Hey senorita / Sweet fighting lady.
■ 7" . . . . . . . . . . . . . . . . . . . MCA 359
MCA / Apr '78.

## I'LL BE AROUND.
Tracks: I'll be around / Music band 2.
■ 7" . . . . . . . . . . . . . . . . . . . MCA 593
MCA / Jun '80.

## I'M THE ONE WHO UNDERSTANDS.
Tracks: I'm the one who understands / Corns and callouses.
■ 7" . . . . . . . . . . . . . . . . . . . MCA 514
MCA / Aug '79.

## JUST BECAUSE.
Tracks: Just because / I'm about somebody.
■ 7" . . . . . . . . . . . . . . . . . . .RCA 240
RCA / Jul '82.

## LIFE.
Tracks: Happiness / W.W.III / Dawning of night / Waiting at the church / When the nightmare comes / Shaking it down / Summerdreams / U-2 medley.
■ LP . . . . . . . . . . . . . . . . . . . RCALP 3113
RCA / Sep '83.

## LOVE IS ALL AROUND (War Featuring Eric Burdon).
Tracks: Love is all around / Tobacco Road / Day in the life / Magic mountain / Home dream / Paint it black.
■ LP . . . . . . . . . . . . . . . . . . . ABCL 5207
ABC Records / Jan '77.

## LOW RIDER.
Tracks: Low rider (remix) / Low rider (orig) / Flippin' to darkness (Extra track on 12" only).
■ 7" . . . . . . . . . . . . . . . . . . . WIP 6267
Island / Jan '76.
■ 12" . . . . . . . . . . . . . . . . . . . XLAX 100
■ 7" . . . . . . . . . . . . . . . . . . . XLAX 1
Fax / May '87.

## ME AND BABY BROTHER.
Tracks: Me and baby brother.
■ 7" . . . . . . . . . . . . . . . . . . . WIP 6303
Island / Jun '76.

## ON FIRE.
Tracks: On fire / Roses are blue / Ripe bananas / Exodus / Churchin' / Nothing you can do / Cup of soul / Afro cuban opus No. 1 / God is love / Glorissa superba.
■ LP . . . . . . . . . . . . . . . . . . . THBL 1.041
Thunderbolt / Jun '87.

## OUTLAW.
Tracks: You got the power / Outlaw / Jungle (medley) / Beware it's a jungle out there / Street of walls / Street of lights / Street of now / Just because / Baby it's cold outside / I'm about somebody / Cinco de Mayo.
■ LP . . . . . . . . . . . . . . . . . . . RCALP 3069
RCA / Mar '82.

## REMIXES, THE.
Tracks: Not Advised.
■ . . . . . . . . . . . . . . . . . . . CDLAX 001
Record / '88 / EMI.

## SLIPPIN' INTO DARKNESS.
Tracks: Slippin' into darkness / Nappy head.
■ 7" . . . . . . . . . . . . . . . . . . . WIP 6359
Island / Dec '76.

## SUN OH SON.
Tracks: Sun oh son / Lonely feelin'.
■ 7" . . . . . . . . . . . . . . . . . . .LBF 15443
Liberty / Mar '71.

## WAR - GREATEST HITS.
Tracks: Not Advised.
■ LP . . . . . . . . . . . . . . . . . . . ILPS 9413
Island / Nov '76.

## WAR GIVE YOU..THE FREEDOM TO ROCK.
Tracks: Not Advised.
■ LP . . . . . . . . . . . . . . . . . . . WARLP 8621
MC . . . . . . . . . . . . . . . . . . . ZCWARLP 8621
W.A.R. / Nov '85 / W.A.R. Records.

## WHY CAN'T WE BE FRIENDS.
Tracks: Why can't we be friends / In mazatlan.
■ 7" . . . . . . . . . . . . . . . . . . . UP 35836
United Artists / May '75.

## WORLD IS A GHETTO.
Tracks: World is a ghetto / I'll take care of you.
■ 12" . . . . . . . . . . . . . . . . . . .MCAT 557
■ 7" . . . . . . . . . . . . . . . . . . . MCA 557
MCA / Jan '80.

## WORLD IS A GHETTO.
Tracks: Cisco kid / City, country, city / Beetles in a bog / Four cornered room / Where was you at / World is a ghetto.
■ LP . . . . . . . . . . . . . . . . . . . UAS 29400
United Artists / Feb '73.

## YOU GOT THE POWER.
Tracks: You got the power.
■ 12" . . . . . . . . . . . . . . . . . . . RCAT 201
■ 7" . . . . . . . . . . . . . . . . . . .RCA 201
RCA / Mar '82.

## YOUNGBLOOD.
Tracks: Youngblood / Youngblood (version).
■ 7" . . . . . . . . . . . . . . . . . . . MCA 399
MCA / Dec '78.

# Ward, Anita

## ANITA WARD.
Tracks: I'm ready for your love / Curtains up / This must be love / Ring my bell / Sweet splendour / There's no doubt about it / You lied / Make believe lovers / If I could feel that old feeling again / Spoiled by your love / I won't stop loving you.
CD . . . . . . . . . . . . . . . . . . . TLCD 900404
Line / '89 / C.M. Distribution / Grapevine Distribution / A.D.A. Distribution / Conifer Records.
■ CD . . . . . . . . . . . . . . . . . . . CDTR 4
■ LP . . . . . . . . . . . . . . . . . . . TRPL 115
Timeless (Soul) / Jan '90.

## RING MY BELL.
Tracks: Ring my bell / If I could feel that old feeling again.
■ 7" . . . . . . . . . . . . . . . . . . . TKR 7543
TK / Jun '79.

## RING MY BELL (1990 RE-ISSUE).
Tracks: Ring my bell.
■ 12" . . . . . . . . . . . . . . . . . . .12FRS 3
■ 7" . . . . . . . . . . . . . . . . . . . FRS 3
■ CD Single . . . . . . . . . . . . . . . CDFRS 3
Freestyle (1) / Sep '90.

## RING MY BELL (OLD GOLD).
Tracks: Ring my bell / If I could feel that old feeling again.
■ 12" . . . . . . . . . . . . . . . . . . .OG 4154
Old Gold / '88.

## SONGS OF LOVE.
Tracks: Make believe lovers / If I could feel that old feeling again / Spoiled by your love / I won't stop loving you / Ring my bell / Sweet splendor / There's no doubt about it / You lied.
■ LP . . . . . . . . . . . . . . . . . . . TKR 83371
TK / '79.

# Ward, Billy

## 14 ORIGINAL GREATEST HITS : BILLY WARD (Ward, Billy & His Dominoes).
Tracks: Not Advised.
■ LP . . . . . . . . . . . . . . . . . . .K 5005
King (USA) / Mar '88.

## 21 ORIGINAL GREATEST HITS (Ward, Billy & His Dominoes).
Tracks: Not Advised.
■ LP . . . . . . . . . . . . . . . . . . .K 5008
King (USA) / Mar '88.

## BILLY WARD & HIS DOMINOES (Ward, Billy & His Dominoes).
Tracks: Sixty minute man / Do something for me / That's what you're doing to me / Deep sea blues / Pedal pushin' papa / Don't leave me this way / Have mercy hurry I am with you / Chicken blues / Weeping willow blues / Love, love, love / Bells.
■ LP . . . . . . . . . . . . . . . . . . . SING 559
Sing / '88.

## CD.
CD . . . . . . . . . . . . . . . . . . . .KCD 559
King / Mar '90 / New Note / Koch International.

## BILLY WARD AND HIS DOMINOES (Ward, Billy & The Dominoes).
Tracks: Not Advised.
■ LP . . . . . . . . . . . . . . . . . . . BID 8005
Bellaphon / Jul '88.

## BILLY WARD AND HIS DOMINOES VOL.2.
Tracks: Not Advised.
■ LP . . . . . . . . . . . . . . . . . . . BID 8008
Bellaphon / Jul '88.

## DEEP PURPLE.
Tracks: Deep purple.
■ 7" . . . . . . . . . . . . . . . . . . . HLU 8502
London-American / Nov '57.

## FEAT (Ward, Billy & His Dominoes).
Tracks: Tenderly / Over the rainbow / Learnin' the blues / When the swallows come back to Capistano / Harbour lights / These foolish things / Three coins in the fountain / Little things mean a lot / Rags to riches / May I never love again / Lonesome road / Until the real thing comes along.
■ LP . . . . . . . . . . . . . . . . . . . SING 733
Sing / '88.
CD . . . . . . . . . . . . . . . . . . . .KCD 733
King / Mar '90 / New Note / Koch International.

## SIXTY MINUTE MAN (Ward, Billy & The Dominoes).
Tracks: Sixty minute man / Chicken blues / Don't leave me this way / Do something for me / That's what you're doing to me / Weeping willow blues / How long blues / I am with you / Have mercy baby / If I ever get to heaven / Pedal pushin' papa / I'd be satisfied / 'Deed I do / Bells / My baby's 3-D / Tenderly / I ain't gonna cry for you / You can't keep a good man down / I really don't want to know / I'm gonna move to the outskirts of town.
CD . . . . . . . . . . . . . . . . . . . CDCHARLY 242
Charly / Oct '90 / Charly.

## STARDUST.
Tracks: Stardust.
■ 7" . . . . . . . . . . . . . . . . . . . HLU 8465
London-American / Sep '57.

# Ware, Leon

## LEON WARE.
Tracks: Not Advised.
■ LP . . . . . . . . . . . . . . . . . . . E 160050
Elektra / Jul '82.

## MUSICAL MESSAGE.
Tracks: Learning to love you / Instant love / Body heat / Share your love / Holiday / Phantom lover / Journey into you / Musical message / French waltz / Turn out the light.
■ LP . . . . . . . . . . . . . . . . . . .STML 12050
Motown / Feb '77.

## ROCKING YOU ETERNALLY.
Tracks: Little boogie / Baby don't stop me / Sure do want you now / Our time / Rocking you eternally / Got to be loved / Don't stay away / In our garden.
■ LP . . . . . . . . . . . . . . . . . . . K 52282
Asylum / Apr '81.

## SHOULDA BEEN YOU.
Tracks: Shoulda been you / Heartbeat.
■ 12" . . . . . . . . . . . . . . . . . . . EXPAND 21
Expansion / Nov '90.

## UNDERCOVER LOVER.
Tracks: Not Advised.
LP . . . . . . . . . . . . . . . . . . . LP 80017
Slingshot / May '89 / Jetstar.

# Warp 9

## FADE IN FADE OUT.
Tracks: Skips a beat / Dirty looks / Big fun / Reach for your star / Cutting edge / You'll get over it / To the last drop.
■ LP . . . . . . . . . . . . . . . . . . . ZL 72414
■ MC . . . . . . . . . . . . . . . . . . . ZK 72414
Motown / Mar '86.

## LIGHT YEARS AWAY.
Tracks: Light years away.
■ 12" . . . . . . . . . . . . . . . . . . . ARIST 12531
Arista / May '83.

## MASTER OF THE MIX.
Tracks: Master of the mix.
■ 7" . . . . . . . . . . . . . . . . . . . BRW 11
4th & Broadway / Aug '84.

## NO MAN IS AN ISLAND.
**Tracks:** No man is an island / Island jam.
- ■ 7" . . . . . . . . . . . . . . . . . . . . . . . . . . . . .BRW 6
- ■ 12" . . . . . . . . . . . . . . . . . . . . . . 12 BRW 6
4th & Broadway / Jun '84.

## NUNK.
**Tracks:** Nunk.
- ■ 12" . . . . . . . . . . . . . . . . . . ARIST 12509
- ■ 7" . . . . . . . . . . . . . . . . . . . . .ARIST 509
Arista / Nov '82.

## SKIPS A BEAT.
**Tracks:** Skips a beat / Skips a beat (dub).
- ■ 12" . . . . . . . . . . . . . . . . . . . . ZT 40504
- ■ 7" . . . . . . . . . . . . . . . . . . . . ZB 40503
Motown / Feb '86.

## WHAMMER SLAMMER.
**Tracks:** Whammer slammer (Mixes).
- 12" . . . . . . . . . . . . . . . . . . . . .KGBT 014
- CD Single . . . . . . . . . . . . . . . . . .KGBD 014
- MC Single . . . . . . . . . . . . . . . . . KGBM 014
Internal Affairs / Aug '94 / BMG.

## Warren, Aleysha

### DISCOVER ME.
**Tracks:** Discover me / Touch me (the amore mix) (Available on 12" and CD single only) / Touch me / Discover me (a cappella) (Available on 12" and CD single only).
- ■ 12" . . . . . . . . . . . . . . . . . . . . PT 43493
- ■ MC Single . . . . . . . . . . . . . . . . PK 43491
- ■ 7" . . . . . . . . . . . . . . . . . . . . PB 43491
- ■ CD Single . . . . . . . . . . . . . . . . PD 43492
RCA / Apr '90.

### TOUCH ME.
**Tracks:** Touch me / Touch me (version).
- ■ 12" . . . . . . . . . . . . . . . . . . . . PT 42824
- ■ 7" . . . . . . . . . . . . . . . . . . . . PB 42823
- ■ CD Single . . . . . . . . . . . . . . . . PD 42824
RCA / Jul '89.
- ■ 12" . . . . . . . . . . . . . . . . . . . . PT 43222
RCA / Sep '89.

## Warrèn, Alysha

### I'M SO IN LOVE.
**Tracks:** I'm so in love (Mixes) / All the man i need.
- 12" . . . . . . . . . . . . . . . . . . . . .CARDX 10
- 7" . . . . . . . . . . . . . . . . . . . . . CARD 10
- MC Single . . . . . . . . . . . . . . . . CARDC 10
Wild Card / Sep '94 / PolyGram.
- CD Single . . . . . . . . . . . . . . . . CARDD 10
Wild Card / Sep '94 / PolyGram.

## Warren, Nikita

### I NEED YOU.
**Tracks:** I need you.
- ■ 12" . . . . . . . . . . . . . . . . . . . . RADZR 5
Raiders/Polydor / Jan '92.

## Warwick, Dee Dee

### COLD NIGHT IN GEORGIA.
**Tracks:** Cold night in Georgia / Searching.
- ■ 7" . . . . . . . . . . . . . . . . . . . .2091 057
Atlantic / Mar '71.

### LOVER'S CHANT.
**Tracks:** Lover's chant / Worth every tear I cry.
- ■ 7" . . . . . . . . . . . . . . . . . . . . MF 909
Mercury / Mar '66.

### SUSPICIOUS MIND.
**Tracks:** Suspicious mind / I'm glad I'm a woman.
- ■ 7" . . . . . . . . . . . . . . . . . . . . 2091092
Atlantic / May '71.

### TURNING AROUND.
**Tracks:** If this was the last song / More today than yesterday / Who will the next fool be / I'm glad I'm a woman / She didn't know / Girl who'll satisfy her man / I ain't got to love nobody else / I'm only human / Make love to me / Down so low.
- ■ LP . . . . . . . . . . . . . . . . . . . . .2465 018
Atco / Dec '70.

### WE'RE DOING FINE.
**Tracks:** We're doing fine / Goptta get a hold of myself / Alfie / Another lonely Saturday.
- ■ LP . . . . . . . . . . . . . . . . . . 10036 MCE
Mercury / Aug '66.

### WHEN LOVE SLIPS AWAY.
**Tracks:** When love slips away / House of gold.
- ■ 7" . . . . . . . . . . . . . . . . . . . . MF 974
Mercury / Mar '67.

## Warwick, Dionne

### 20 GOLDEN PIECES: DIONNE WARWICK.
**Tracks:** I'll never fall in love again / Anyone who had a heart / I say a little prayer / Do you know the way to San Jose / Raindrops keep falling on my head / Don't make me over / Alfie / I just don't know what to do with myself / Make it easy on yourself / This girl's in love with you / Walk on by / Trains and boats and planes / You'll never get to Heaven / Wives and lovers / As long as he needs me / Message to Michael / Didn't we / Games people play / My way / Promises, promises.
- ■ LP . . . . . . . . . . . . . . . . . . . . BDL 2029
- MC . . . . . . . . . . . . . . . . . . . . . BDC 2029
Bulldog Records / Oct '82 / President Records / Jazz Music / Wellard / TKO Records Ltd.

### 20 GREATEST HITS: DIONNE WARWICK.
**Tracks:** Walk on by / I say a little prayer / Valley of the dolls, Theme from / I'll never fall in love again / Anyone who had a heart / Message to Michael / Do you know the way to San Jose / Are you there (with another girl) / Who can I turn to / House is not a home / Don't make me over / You'll never get to heaven / Make it easy on yourself / Reach out for me / Alfie / You've lost that lovin' feelin' / Trains and boats and planes / I just don't know what to do with myself / Window of the world / Promises, promises.
- CD . . . . . . . . . . . . . . . . . . . . . CD 36
Bescol / May '87 / C.M. Distribution.

### 25TH ANNIVERSARY COLLECTION.
**Tracks:** Walk On By / Close To You / There's always something there to remind me / Wishin' and hopin' / Look of love / Message To Michael / I Just Don't Know What To Do With Myself / Wives and lovers / Reach Out For Me / Are you there (with another girl) / Do you know the way to San Jose / I say a little prayer.
- CD . . . . . . . . . . . . . . . . . . .PWKS 512
- ■ LP . . . . . . . . . . . . . . . . . . .SHM 3243
- MC . . . . . . . . . . . . . . . . . . . . HSC 3243
Pickwick / Sep '88 / Pickwick.

### 6 TRACK HITS: DIONNE WARWICK.
**Tracks:** Walk on by / Reach out for me / Do you know the way to San Jose / You'll never get to Heaven / Valley of the dolls / Anyone who had a heart.
- ■ EP . . . . . . . . . . . . . . . . . . . . 7SR 5001
- MC . . . . . . . . . . . . . . . . . . . . . 7SC 5001
Scoop 33 / Sep '83.

### ALFIE.
**Tracks:** Alfie / Beginning of lonliness.
- ■ 7" . . . . . . . . . . . . . . . . . . . . 7N 25424
Pye International / Jun '67.

### ALL THE LOVE IN THE WORLD.
**Tracks:** All the love in the world / It makes no difference.
- ■ 12" . . . . . . . . . . . . . . . . . . ARIST 12507
- ■ 7" . . . . . . . . . . . . . . . . . . . .ARIST 507
Arista / Dec '82.

### ANTHOLOGY - DIONNE WARWICK (1962-1971).
**Tracks:** Not Advised.
- ■ Double LP . . . . . . . . . . . . . . . RNDA 1100
Rhino (USA) / Feb '85.

### ANYONE WHO HAD A HEART.
**Tracks:** Not Advised.
- CD . . . . . . . . . . . . . . . . . . . . . 2636232
- MC . . . . . . . . . . . . . . . . . . . . . 2636234
Black Tulip / Nov '89.

### ANYONE WHO HAD A HEART.
**Tracks:** Anyone who had a heart / Walk on by / Do you know the way to San Jose.
- ■ 7" . . . . . . . . . . . . . . . . . . . . 7N 25234
Pye International / Feb '64.

### ANYONE WHO HAD A HEART (OLD GOLD).
**Tracks:** Anyone who had a heart / Walk on by / Do you know the way to San Jose.
- ■ CD Single . . . . . . . . . . . . . . . .OG 6140
Old Gold / Apr '89.

### BEST OF DIONNE WARWICK.
**Tracks:** Then came you / One less bell to answer / Love in the afternoon / Ronnie Lee / Close to you / I think you need love / If we only have to love / You're gonna need me / Do you believe in love at first sight / Track of the cat / We'll burn our bridges behind us / Just being myself.
- ■ LP . . . . . . . . . . . . . . . . . . . . W 3814
- MC . . . . . . . . . . . . . . . . . . . . .W 38144
WEA / Jun '83 / WEA.

### BEST OF DIONNE WARWICK.
**Tracks:** Not Advised.
- MC . . . . . . . . . . . . . . . . . . . . . 16-10
Creole (Everest-Europa) / Jul '84.

### BEST OF DIONNE WARWICK.
**Tracks:** Anyone who had a heart / Don't make me over / House is not a home / Wishin' and hopin' / Unchained melody / What'd I say / Make it easy on yourself / Zip-a-dee-doo-dah / You'll never get to heaven / Wives and lovers / Walk on by / You can have him.
- ■ LP . . . . . . . . . . . . . . . . . . NPL 28079
Pye / Feb '66.

### COMPACT MOMENTS (Warwick, Dionne/Roger Whittaker/Gilbert O'Sullivan/Cleo Lain).
**Tracks:** Not Advised.
- CD Set . . . . . . . . . . . . . . . . . CD BOX 11
IMS / Jul '87 / PolyGram.

### DEJA VU.
**Tracks:** Deja vu / My everlasting love.
- ■ 7" . . . . . . . . . . . . . . . . . . . .ARIST 310
Arista / Oct '79.

### DIONNE.
**Tracks:** Who, what, when, where and why / After you / Letter / I'll never love this way again / Deja vu / Feeling old feelings / In your eyes / My everlasting love / Out of my hands / All the time.
- ■ LP . . . . . . . . . . . . . . . . . SPART 1096
- ■ MC . . . . . . . . . . . . . . . . . TCART 1096
Arista / Jun '79.
- CD . . . . . . . . . . . . . . . . . . . MCCD 169
- MC . . . . . . . . . . . . . . . . . . .MCTC 169
Music Collection International / Sep '94 / THE / Jazz Music.

### DIONNE WARWICK.
**Tracks:** Walk on by / Anyone who had a heart / Reach out for me / I just don't know what to do with myself / Don't make me over / Always something there to remind me / Do you know the way to San Jose / Trains and boats and planes / Wishin' and hopin' / Valley of the dolls / House is not a home / I'll never fall in love again.
- ■ LP . . . . . . . . . . . . . . . . . . COUNT 6
- ■ MC . . . . . . . . . . . . . . . . . . ZC CNT 6
Dakota / Oct '82.

### DIONNE WARWICK.
**Tracks:** Not Advised.
- ■ CD . . . . . . . . . . . . . . . . . . RC 83109
- ■ MC . . . . . . . . . . . . . . . . . . RC 82109
Royal Collection / Mar '93.

### DIONNE WARWICK CLASSICS.
**Tracks:** Not Advised.
- ■ CD . . . . . . . . . . . . . . . . . . ONCD 511
K-Tel / '86.

### DIONNE WARWICK COLLECTION.
**Tracks:** Not Advised.
- ■ Double LP . . . . . . . . . . . . . . . .PDA 00
Pickwick / Mar '76.
- ■ MC Set . . . . . . . . . . . . . . . . .PDC 00
Pickwick / Dec '79.

### DIONNE WARWICK COLLECTION, THE.
**Tracks:** Heartbreaker / I'll never love this way again / Friends in love / Deja vu / No night so long / Take the short way home / All the love in the world / Love so right / Letter / Betcha by golly wow / Easy love / Our day will come / Yours / Who, what, when, where and why / It's the falling in love / With a touch / All the time / What is this / Walk on by / Anyone who had a heart / You'll never get to heaven / House is not home / Message to Michael / Trains and boats and planes / Look of love / Close to you / Do you know the way to San Jose / Valley of the dolls / There's always something there to remind me / Make it easy on yourself / Promises, promises / What the world needs now is love.
- ■ Double LP . . . . . . . . . . . . . . .DIONE
- MC Set . . . . . . . . . . . . . . . . .ZCDIO
Starblend / May '83.
- CD . . . . . . . . . . . . . . . . . CDTRACK 4
Starblend / '86.

### DIONNE WARWICK GOLDEN C COLLECTION.
**Tracks:** Not Advised.
- CD . . . . . . . . . . . . . . . . . . . BDCD 202
Bulldog Records / May '89 / President Records / Jazz Music / Wellard / TKO Records Ltd.

### DIONNE WARWICK IN CONCERT.
**Tracks:** Not Advised.
- VHS . . . . . . . . . . . . . . . . . . . VC 400
Video Collection / May '87 / Gold & Sons / Video Collection / THE.

VHS . . . . . . . . . . . . . . . . . . . . . . MC 2009
Music Club Video / Jun '89 / Video Collection / Gold & Sons / THE.

## DIONNE WARWICK IN CONCERT.
Tracks: Not Advised.
VHS . . . . . . . . . . . . . . . . . . . . SVM808
Start (Video) / Nov '92 / Sony Video Software.

## DIONNE WARWICK SINGS BACHARACH.
Tracks: Not Advised.
■ LP . . . . . . . . . . . . . . . . . . ENT LP 13050
MC. . . . . . . . . . . . . . . . . . ENT MC 13050
Entertainers / Jul '88 / BMG.

## DIONNE WARWICK SINGS COLE PORTER.
Tracks: Night and day / I love Paris / I get a kick out of you / What is thing called love / So in love (medley) / You're the top / I've got you under my skin / Begin the beguine / It's alright with me / Anything goes / You'd be so nice to come home to / All of you / I concentrate on you / Night and day (jazz version) Only on CD and Cassette.) / Just one of those things.
CD. . . . . . . . . . . . . . . . . . . . . . . . 260918
■ LP . . . . . . . . . . . . . . . . . . . . . . 210918
■ MC. . . . . . . . . . . . . . . . . . . . . . 410918
Arista / Oct '90 / BMG.

## DIONNE WARWICK VOL 1.
Tracks: Not Advised.
MC. . . . . . . . . . . . . . . . . . . . . ZCGAS 715
Audio Fidelity / Oct '84 / Telstar/Ronco.

## DIONNE WARWICK VOL 3.
Tracks: Not Advised.
MC. . . . . . . . . . . . . . . . . . . . . ZCGAS 735
Audio Fidelity / Oct '84 / Telstar/Ronco.

## DIONNE WARWICK VOL 4.
Tracks: Not Advised.
MC. . . . . . . . . . . . . . . . . . . . . ZCGAS 744
Audio Fidelity / Oct '84 / Telstar/Ronco.

## DIONNE WARWICK VOL.1.
Tracks: Not Advised.
VHS . . . . . . . . . . . . . . . . . . . . NBD 2139
Pickwick Video / '92 / THE / Gold & Sons.

## DIONNE WARWICK VOL.2.
Tracks: Not Advised.
VHS . . . . . . . . . . . . . . . . . . . . NBD 3073
Pickwick Video / '92 / THE / Gold & Sons.

## DO YOU BELIEVE IN LOVE AT FIRST SIGHT.
Tracks: Do you believe in love at first sight / Do I have to cry.
■ 7" . . . . . . . . . . . . . . . . . . . . K 17104
WEA / Mar '78.

## DO YOU KNOW THE WAY TO SAN JOSE.
Tracks: Do you know the way to san jose.
■ 7" . . . . . . . . . . . . . . . . . . . . 7N 25457
Pye International / May '68.

## DO YOU KNOW THE WAY TO SAN JOSE (OLD GOLD).
Tracks: Do you know the way to san jose / You'll never get to heaven.
■ 7" . . . . . . . . . . . . . . . . . . . . OG 9285
Old Gold / Apr '83.

## EVENING WITH DIONNE WARWICK, AN.
Tracks: Not Advised.
VHS . . . . . . . . . . . . . . . . . . . . V 9051
MSD / Sep '87 / Multiple Sound Distributors / Gold & Sons.

## FREEWHEELIN'.
Tracks: I say a little prayer / This girl's in love with you / Little green apples / Where is love / Who is gonna love me / Windows of the world / Where am I going / Silent voices / Lonely in my heart / Yesterday I heard the rain.
■ LP . . . . . . . . . . . . . . . . . . . . NSPL 28120
Pye / Apr '69.

## FRIENDS.
Tracks: That's what friends are for / Whisper in the dark / Remember your heart / Love at second sight / Moments are moments / Stronger than before / Stay devoted / No one there to sing me a love song / How long / Extravagant gestures.
■ CD. . . . . . . . . . . . . . . . . . . . . 610556
■ LP . . . . . . . . . . . . . . . . . . . . . 207438
■ MC. . . . . . . . . . . . . . . . . . . . . 407438
Arista / Dec '85.
■ LP . . . . . . . . . . . . . . . . . . . . . 209652
■ MC. . . . . . . . . . . . . . . . . . . . . 409652
■ CD. . . . . . . . . . . . . . . . . . . . . 259652
Arista / Mar '89.

## FRIENDS CAN BE LOVERS.
Tracks: Where my lips have been / Sunny weather lover / Age of miracles / Love will find a way / Much to much / Til the end of time / Woman that I am / Fragile / Can't break this heart / Superwoman.
CD . . . . . . . . . . . . . . . . . . . 7822 18682-2
MC. . . . . . . . . . . . . . . . . . 7822 18682-4
Arista / Mar '93 / BMG.

## FRIENDS IN LOVE.
Tracks: For you / Friends in love / Never gonna let you go / Can't hide love / Betcha by golly wow / More than fascination / Got you where I want you / With a touch / What is this / Love so right.
■ LP . . . . . . . . . . . . . . . . . . . . SPART 1192
■ MC. . . . . . . . . . . . . . . . . . . . . TCART 1192
Arista / May '82.

## FRIENDS IN LOVE.
Tracks: Friends in love.
■ 7" . . . . . . . . . . . . . . . . . . . . . A 2371
CBS / May '82.

## FROM WITHIN VOL. 1.
Tracks: Battle hymn of the Republic / Somebody bigger than you & I / Grace / Steal away / Much to much / You'll never walk alone / If you want me to make love to you then why can't I touch you / Stand / Games people play / Loving you is sweeter than ever / You're all I need to get by / Everyday people.
■ LP . . . . . . . . . . . . . . . . . . . . WCS 1007
Wand / Aug '72.

## FROM WITHIN VOL. 2.
Tracks: People got to be free / Reach out & touch / All kinds of people / MacArthur Park / Young, gifted & black / Give a damn / This little light / Love of my man / Do right woman - do right man / Hurts so bad / Weight / Our ages of our hearts / Someday we'll be together.
■ LP . . . . . . . . . . . . . . . . . . . . WCS 1008
Wand / Aug '72.

## GOLDEN HITS: DIONNE WARWICK, VOL 1.
Tracks: Don't make me over / Wishin' and hopin' / You'll never get to Heaven / Say on yourself / Any old time of day / Walk on by / Reach out for me / Anyone who had a heart / Always something there to remind me.
■ LP . . . . . . . . . . . . . . . . . . . . PHX 1015
Phoenix (2) / Oct '82.

## GOLDEN HITS: DIONNE WARWICK, VOL 2.
Tracks: Do you know the way to San Jose / I just don't know what to do with myself / Message to Michael / Trains and boats and planes / Are you there (with another girl) / I say a little prayer / What the world needs now is love / Windows of the world / Who can I turn to.
■ LP . . . . . . . . . . . . . . . . . . . . PHX 1023
Phoenix (2) / Oct '82.

## GOT A DATE.
Tracks: Got a date / Two ships passing in the night.
■ 12" . . . . . . . . . . . . . . . . . . ARIST 12552
■ 7" . . . . . . . . . . . . . . . . . . . ARIST 552
Arista / Jan '84.

## GOT YOU WHERE I WANT YOU (Warwick, Dionne & Johnny Mathis).
Tracks: Got you where I want you / Lately.
■ 7" . . . . . . . . . . . . . . . . . . . . . A 3005
CBS / Jan '83.

## GREAT SONGS OF THE SIXTIES.
Tracks: Not Advised.
CD . . . . . . . . . . . . . . . . . . . PWKS 4191
MC. . . . . . . . . . . . . . . . . . PWKMC 4191
Pickwick / Mar '94 / Pickwick.

## GREATEST HITS VOL 2: DIONNE WARWICK.
Tracks: What the world needs now / Message to Michael / Are you there with another girl / I just don't know what to do with myself / Do you know the way to San Jose / I say a little prayer for you / Who can I turn to / Unchained melody / Forever my love / Trains, boat and planes / In between heartaches / Windows of the world.
■ LP . . . . . . . . . . . . . . . . . . . . WNS 2
Wand / Jun '70.

## GREATEST HITS: DIONNE WARWICK.
Tracks: I say a little prayer / Do you know the way to San Jose / You'll never get to Heaven / Alfie / Hurt so bad / Somewhere / Who can I turn to / In between the heartaches / Anyone who had a heart / I just don't know what to do with myself.
MC Set . . . . . . . . . . . . . . . . DTO 10002
Ditto / Jul '82 / Pickwick.

## GREATEST HITS: DIONNE WARWICK.
Tracks: Don't make me over / Anyone who had a heart / Make it easy on yourself / I smiled sweetly / Wishin' and hopin' / Walk on by / Reach out for me / You'll never get to heaven / This empty place / It's love that really counts / Always something there to remind me / Any old time of the day.
■ LP . . . . . . . . . . . . . . . . . . . . WNS 1
Wand / May '70.

## GREATEST HITS: DIONNE WARWICK.
Tracks: Not Advised.
■ LP . . . . . . . . . . . . . . . . . . . . 2236235
MC. . . . . . . . . . . . . . . . . . . . . 2136235
Black Tulip / May '88.

## GREATEST HITS: DIONNE WARWICK.
Tracks: Not Advised.
LP . . . . . . . . . . . . . . . . . . . . FUN 9037
MC. . . . . . . . . . . . . . . . . . . . . FUNC 9037
Fun (Holland) / Oct '88 / Pinnacle.

## GREATEST MOTION PICTURE HITS.
Tracks: Look of love / Alfie / Valley of the Dolls, Theme from / People / House is not a home / Wives and lovers / April fools / Slaves / One hand, one heart / With these hands / Here I am / As long as he needs me / Somewhere.
■ LP . . . . . . . . . . . . . . . . . . . . NSPL 28126
Pye / Nov '69.
■ LP . . . . . . . . . . . . . . . . . . . . WNS 9
Wand / Aug '71.

## GREEN GRASS STARTS TO GROW.
Tracks: Green grass starts to grow / They don't give medals to yesterday's heroes.
■ 7" . . . . . . . . . . . . . . . . . . . . WN 12
Wand / Jan '71.

## HEARTBREAKER.
Tracks: All the love in the world / I can't see anything but you / You are my love / Just one more night / Our day will come / Heartbreaker / Yours / Take the short way home / It makes no difference / Misunderstood.
■ LP . . . . . . . . . . . . . . . . . . . . 204974
Arista / Oct '82.
CD. . . . . . . . . . . . . . . . . . . . . 258719
■ LP . . . . . . . . . . . . . . . . . . . . 208719
MC. . . . . . . . . . . . . . . . . . . . . 408719
Arista / Oct '87 / BMG.
■ CD. . . . . . . . . . . . . . . . . . . . . 610002
Arista / '88.

## HEARTBREAKER.
Tracks: Heartbreaker.
■ 7" . . . . . . . . . . . . . . . . . . . . ARIST 496
Arista / Oct '82.
■ CD Single . . . . . . . . . . . . . . . . . 162055
Arista / Jun '89.

## HERE I AM.
Tracks: Here I am / If you see Bill / How many days of sadness / Looking with my eyes.
■ EP . . . . . . . . . . . . . . . . . . . . NEP 44061
Pye / Feb '66.

## HERE WHERE THERE IS LOVE.
Tracks: Not Advised.
■ LP . . . . . . . . . . . . . . . . . . . . NPL 28096
Pye / Feb '67.

## HOT, LIVE AND OTHERWISE.
Tracks: What you won't do for love / Don't make me over / Alfie / One-in-a-million you / Walk on by / Anyone who had a heart / You'll never get to Heaven / House is not a home / Message to Michael / Trains and boats and planes / Look of love / Close to you / Do you know the way to San Jose / Valley of the dolls / There's always something there to remind me / Make it easy on yourself / Promises, promises / What the world needs now is love / Then came you / Deja vu / Easy love / No night so long / We never said goodbye / I'll never lose this way again / There's a long road ahead of us / Dedicate this heart / Some changes are for good / Even a fool would let go / Now we're starting over again.
■ Double LP. . . . . . . . . . . . . . . . DARTY 10
■ MC Set . . . . . . . . . . . . . . . . TCDAR 10
Arista / Jun '81.

## HOW MANY TIMES CAN WE SAY GOODBYE.
Tracks: How many times can we say goodbye / What can a miracle do.
■ 7" . . . . . . . . . . . . . . . . . . . . ARIST 544
Arista / Oct '83.

## HOW MANY TIMES CAN WE SAY GOODBYE.
Tracks: Got a date / So amazing / I do it 'cause I like it / How many times can we say goodbye (Duet with Luther Vandross) / What can a miracle do / Two

ships passing in the night / I can let you go / Will you love me tomorrow.
■ CD.....................259051
Arista / Jun '88.

## I DON'T CARE WHAT PEOPLE SAY.
Tracks: I don't care what people say / More than fascination.
■ 7".....................ARIST 475
Arista / Jul '82.

## I'LL NEVER LOVE THIS WAY AGAIN.
Tracks: I'll never love this way again / In your eyes.
■ 7".....................ARIST 276
Arista / '79.

## I'LL NEVER LOVE THIS WAY AGAIN.
Tracks: I'll never love this way again / Hit medley.
■ 12"....................ARIST 12530
■ 7".....................ARIST 530
Arista / May '83.

## IN BETWEEN THE HEARTACHES.
Tracks: In between the heartaches / Long day, short night.
■ 7"...................7N 25357
Pye / Mar '66.

## JUST BEING MYSELF.
Tracks: Not Advised.
CD.....................JHD 002
MC.....................MCJHD 002
IMD / Jun '92 / BMG.

## JUST DIONNE WARWICK.
Tracks: Not Advised.
■ LP.....................SM 4046
Joker (USA) / '88.

## LOVE AT FIRST SIGHT.
Tracks: Keepin' my head above water / Love in the afternoon / Long way to go / Do I have to cry / Don't ever take your love away / One thing on my mind / Early morning strangers / Livin' it up is starting to get me down / Since you stayed here / Do you believe in love at first sight.
■ LP.....................K 56429
Warner Bros. / Dec '77.

## LOVE POWER (Warwick, Dionne & Jeffrey Osbourne).
Tracks: Love power / In a world such as this / No one in the world* (*Extra track on 12").
■ 12"....................RIST 27
■ 7".....................RIS 27
Arista / Jul '87.

## LOVE SONGS COLLECTION.
Tracks: I'll never fall in love again / Let it be me / Here where there is love / I love Paris / Hurt so bad / As long as he needs me / Blowin' in the wind / One hand, one heart / You can have him / People / This girl's in love with you / You're all I need to get by / Baubles, bangles & beads / Getting ready for the heartbreak / Who can I turn to / People got to be free / It's the good life / Somewhere / Unchained melody / Valley of the dolls.
CD.....................PWKS 525
■ LP.....................SHM 3258
MC.....................HSC 3258
Pickwick / Feb '89 / Pickwick.

## LOVE SONGS, THE.
Tracks: Heartbreaker / I'll never love this way again / Walk on by / Deja vu / No one in this world / Run to me / How many times can we say goodbye / Take good care of me and you / All the love in the world / Love power / Do you know the way to San Jose / Reservations for two / Yours / You'll never get to heaven / So amazing / That's what friends are for.
CD.....................260441
MC.....................410441
■ LP.....................210441
Arista / Dec '89 / BMG.

## MESSAGE TO MICHAEL.
Tracks: Message to Michael / Here where there is love.
■ 7"...................7N 25368
Pye / Mar '66.

## MESSAGE TO MICHAEL.
Tracks: Message to Michael / I cry alone / Here where there is love / Put yourself in my place.
■ LP.....................NEP 44067
Pye / Aug '66.

## MOVE ME NO MOUNTAIN.
Tracks: Move me no mountain / We'll burn our bridges behind us.
■ 7"...................K 16595
WEA / Aug '75.

## NO NIGHT SO LONG.
Tracks: Easy love / No night so long / It's the falling in love / When the world runs out of love / We never said goodbye / How you once loved me / Reaching for the sky / Sweetie pie / Somebody's angel / We had this time.
■ LP.................SPART 1132
■ MC.................TCART 1132
Arista / Aug '80.

## NO NIGHT SO LONG.
Tracks: No night so long / Reaching for the sky.
■ 7".....................ARIST 256
Arista / Sep '80.

## NOW WE'RE STARTING OVER AGAIN.
Tracks: Now we're starting over again / Hits medley.
■ 7".....................ARIST 419
Arista / Jul '81.

## ORIGINAL HITS 1962-1972, THE.
Tracks: Not Advised.
CD.....................DCD 5366
Disky / Apr '94 / THE.

## ORIGINAL SOUL OF DIONNE WARWICK, THE.
Tracks: Don't make me over / I smiled yesterday / This empty place / Wishin' and hopin' / Make the music play / Please make him love me / Love of a boy / It's love that really counts / Make it easy on yourself / Anyone who had a heart / Walk on by / Any old time of day / Getting ready for the heartbreak / Oh Lord what are you doing to me / You'll never get to Heaven / Reach out for me / You can have her / Looking with my eyes / Are you there (with another girl) / Message to Michael / I just don't know what to do with myself / Windows of the world / I say a little prayer / Do you know the way to San Jose / Who is gonna love me / Lonely in my heart / Yesterday I heard the rain / Do right woman, do right man / I've been loving you too long / I'm your puppet / Walk the way you talk / Love of my man.
■ Double LP..............CDX 18
MC....................TCCDX 18
Charly / Sep '87 / Charly.

## PRESENTING DIONNE WARWICK.
Tracks: Not Advised.
■ LP.................NPL 28037
Pye / May '64.

## PROMISES, PROMISES.
Tracks: Promises, promises / This girl's in love with you / Little green apples / Where love is / Who is gonna love me / Walk little Dolly / Whoever you are, I love you / Where am I going / Wanting things / Lonely in my heart / Yesterday I heard the rain / Love.
■ LP.....................WNS 11
Wand / Aug '71.

## REACH OUT FOR ME.
Tracks: Reach out for me.
■ 7"...................7N 25265
Pye International / Oct '64.

## RESERVATIONS.
Tracks: Reservations for two / For everything you are / Love power / You're my hero / Close enough / In a world such as this / Another chance to love / Cry on me / Heartbreak of love / No one in the world.
■ LP.....................208213
■ CD.....................258213
■ MC.....................408213
Arista / Aug '87.

## RESERVATIONS FOR TWO (Warwick, Dionne & Kashif).
Tracks: Reservations for two (single).
■ 7".....................RIS 44
Arista / Oct '87.

## RUN TO ME (Warwick, Dionne & Barry Manilow).
Tracks: Run to me / Heartbreaker / Paradise Cafe.
■ 12"....................ARIST 12610
■ 7".....................ARIST 610
Arista / Mar '85.

## SAY A LITTLE PRAYER.
Tracks: Not Advised.
CD.....................DZS 008
Dunhill (USA) / '86 / Silver Sounds (CD).

## SINGS BURT BACHARACH.
Tracks: Not Advised.
CD.................ENT CD 268
Entertainers / Mar '92 / BMG.

## SO AMAZING.
Tracks: How many times can we say goodbye / I do it 'cause I like it / Will you love me tomorrow / Got a

date / I can let go now / So amazing / What can a miracle do / Two ships passing in the night.
■ LP.....................205755
■ MC.....................405755
Arista / Oct '83.
■ CD....................1610099
Arista / Apr '84.

## SOULFUL.
Tracks: You've lost that lovin' feelin' / I'm your puppet / People got to be free / You're all I need to get by / We can work it out / Silent voices (Not on Pye LP) / Hard day's night / Do right woman - do right man / I've been loving you too long / People get ready / Hey Jude / What's good about goodbye (Not on Pye LP).
■ LP.................NSPL 28122
Pye / Aug '69.
■ LP.....................WNS 12
Wand / Aug '71.
CD.....................DCD 5401
Disky / Oct '94 / THE.

## TAKE GOOD CARE OF YOU AND ME (Warwick, Dionne & Jeffrey Osbourne).
Tracks: Take good care of you and me / Heartbreaker / Love power (Available on 12" format).
■ 12"....................612894
■ 7".....................112894
■ CD Single..............662894
Arista / Dec '89.

## THAT'S WHAT FRIENDS ARE FOR (Warwick & Friends).
Tracks: That's what friends are for / Two ships passing in the night.
■ 12"..................ARIST 12638
■ 7".....................ARIST 638
Arista / Oct '85.

## THEN CAME YOU (Warwick, Dionne & The Detroit Spinners).
Tracks: Then came you.
■ 7".....................K 10495
Atlantic / Oct '74.

## THIS GIRL'S IN LOVE.
Tracks: Do you know the way to San Jose / Who can I turn to / Reach out for me / Loneliness remembers / Make it easy on yourself / Wives and lovers / Goin' out of my head / Trains and boats and planes / I say a little prayer / This girl's in love with you / Look of love / Valley of the dolls, Theme from / House is not a home / What the world needs now is love / You'll never get to heaven / I'll never fall in love again / Message to Michael / Let me be lonely / Windows of the world / Promises, promises / There's always something there to remind me / Raindrops keep falling on my head / Walk on by / Alfie / Don't make me over / I just don't know what to do with myself.
■ Double LP................CR 031
■ MC Set..................CRT 031
Cambra / Feb '85.

## TRACK OF THE CAT.
Tracks: Track of the cat / Ronnie Lee.
■ 7".....................K 16698
WEA / Apr '76.

## UNFORGETTABLE: DIONNE WARWICK (16 Golden Classics).
Tracks: Games people play / Hey Jude / Look of love / If I ruled the world / Goin' out of my head / Unchained melody / Yesterday / You'll never walk alone / Alfie / Trains and boats and planes / You've lost that lovin' feelin' / Anyone who had a heart / Walk on by / Always something there to remind me.
CD...................UNCD 005
■ LP...................UNLP 005
MC...................UNMC 005
Unforgettable / Dec '86 / BMG.

## VALLEY OF THE DOLLS.
Tracks: As long as there's an apple tree / Up up and away / You're my world / Do you know the way to San Jose / Valley of the dolls / Silent voices / For the rest of my life / Let me be lonely / Where would I go / Walking backwards down the road.
■ LP.................NSPL 28114
Pye / May '68.

## VALLEY OF THE DOLLS.
Tracks: Valley of the dolls.
■ 7"...................7N 25445
Pye International / Mar '68.

## VERY BEST OF DIONNE WARWICK THE.
Tracks: Walk on by / Don't make me over / One hand one heart / With these hands / Baubles, bangles & beads / Trains and boats and planes / Getting ready

■ DELETED

for the heartbreak / Make the music play / Un-chained melody / Here where there is love / You can have him / House is not a home / Close to you / What'd I say / Make it easy on yourself / Always something there to remind me / Wishin' and hopin' / Another night / If I ever make you cry / Blowin' in the wind / Look of love / People / Wives and lovers / Message to Michael / Are you there (with another girl).
■ **MC Set** . . . . . . . . . . . . . . . . . DTO 10059
Ditto / Aug '83.

## VERY DIONNE.
**Tracks:** Check out time / Yesterday / We've only just begun / Here's that rainy day / Green grass starts to grow / Where would I go / They don't give medals / Walk the way you talk / Make it easy on yourself / Goin' out of my head / I got love / Let me be lonely.
■ **LP** . . . . . . . . . . . . . . . . . . . . . . . WNS 10
Wand / Aug '71.

## WALK AWAY.
**Tracks:** Walk away.
■ **7"** . . . . . . . . . . . . . . . . . . . . . . .113101
■ **CD Single** . . . . . . . . . . . . . . . . .663101
Arista / Mar '90.

## WALK ON BY.
**Tracks:** Walk on by.
■ **7"** . . . . . . . . . . . . . . . . . . . 7N 25241
Pye International / Apr '64.
■ **7"** . . . . . . . . . . . . . . . . . . . . BAK 13
Dakota / Aug '82.

## WALK ON BY (OLD GOLD).
**Tracks:** Walk on by / Anyone who had a heart.
■ **7"** . . . . . . . . . . . . . . . . . . . . .OG 9284
Old Gold / Mar '83.
**12"** . . . . . . . . . . . . . . . . . . . . . .OG 9966
Old Gold / '92 / Pickwick.

## WALK ON BY AND OTHER FAVOURITES.
**Tracks:** Don't make me over / This empty place / Wishin' and hopin' / Anyone who had a heart / Make it easy on yourself / It's love that really counts / Walk on by / You'll never get to Heaven / Reach out for me / I just don't know what to do with myself / I say a little prayer / Do you know the way to San Jose / I'm your puppet / Trains and boats and planes / Here where there is love / Are you there (with another girl) / Wives and lovers / Valley of the Dolls, Theme from / I'll never fall in love again / Make the music play.
**CD** . . . . . . . . . . . . . . . . . . . CDCHARLY 101
Charly / Oct '87 / Charly.

## WE'LL BURN OUR BRIDGES BEHIND US.
**Tracks:** We'll burn our bridges behind us / Track of the cat.
■ **7"** . . . . . . . . . . . . . . . . . . . . . . W 9762
WEA / Mar '83.

## WHISPER IN THE DARK.
**Tracks:** Whisper in the dark / Extravagent gestures / No one there (to sing me a love song)* (* = Track available on 12" version only).
■ **12"** . . . . . . . . . . . . . . . . . . . ARIST 12652
■ **7"** . . . . . . . . . . . . . . . . . . . . .ARIST 652
Arista / Apr '86.

## WHO GETS THE GUY.
**Tracks:** Who gets the guy / Walk the way you talk.
■ **7"** . . . . . . . . . . . . . . . . . . . . . . WN 15
Wand / Apr '71.

## WINDOWS OF THE WORLD.
**Tracks:** Windows of the world / Walk little dolly.
■ **7"** . . . . . . . . . . . . . . . . . . . 7N 25428
Pye / Aug '67.

## WINDOWS OF THE WORLD.
**Tracks:** Walk little Dolly / Another night / Windows of the world / Somewhere / You're gonna hear from me / Love / etc.
■ **LP** . . . . . . . . . . . . . . . . . . . .NSPL 28105
Pye / Dec '67.

## WITHOUT YOUR LOVE.
**Tracks:** No one in the world / Without your love / Run to me / Finder of lost loves / Love don't live here anymore / It's you / It's love / Bedroom eyes / Weakness / You made me want to love again.
■ **CD** . . . . . . . . . . . . . . . . . . . .610316
■ **LP** . . . . . . . . . . . . . . . . . . . .206571
■ **MC** . . . . . . . . . . . . . . . . . . . .406571
Arista / Feb '85.
■ **CD** . . . . . . . . . . . . . . . . . . . .258553
■ **LP** . . . . . . . . . . . . . . . . . . . .208553
■ **MC** . . . . . . . . . . . . . . . . . . . .408553
Arista / May '88.

## WITHOUT YOUR LOVE.
**Tracks:** Without your love / It's love / Got a date.
■ **12"** . . . . . . . . . . . . . . . . . . . ARIST 12605
■ **7"** . . . . . . . . . . . . . . . . . . . . .ARIST 605
Arista / Dec '84.

## YOU CAN HAVE HIM.
**Tracks:** You can have him.
■ **7"** . . . . . . . . . . . . . . . . . . . 7N 25290
Pye International / Apr '65.

## YOU'LL NEVER GET TO HEAVEN.
**Tracks:** You'll never get to heaven.
■ **7"** . . . . . . . . . . . . . . . . . . . 7N 25256
Pye International / Jul '64.

## YOU'LL NEVER GET TO HEAVEN (OLD GOLD).
**Tracks:** You'll never get to heaven.
■ **7"** . . . . . . . . . . . . . . . . . . . . .OG 9968
Old Gold / Feb '92.

## YOURS.
**Tracks:** Yours / Take the short way home.
■ **12"** . . . . . . . . . . . . . . . . . . . ARIST 12518
■ **7"** . . . . . . . . . . . . . . . . . . . . .ARIST 518
Arista / Feb '83.

# Was Not Was

## ANYTHING CAN HAPPEN.
**Tracks:** Anything can happen (R&B mix) / Anything can happen / Anything can happen (acid condomi-nium mix) (Only on 12" single.).
■ **12"** . . . . . . . . . . . . . . . . . . . WAS 612
■ **7"** . . . . . . . . . . . . . . . . . . . . .WAS 6
■ **CD Single** . . . . . . . . . . . . . . . . .WASCD 6
■ **MC Single** . . . . . . . . . . . . . . . . WASMC 6
Fontana / Aug '89.

## ANYTHING CAN HAPPEN (CD VIDEO).
**Tracks:** Anything can happen.
**CD Video** . . . . . . . . . . . . . . . . . . 080 454 2
Polygram Music Video / Oct '88 / PolyGram.

## ARE YOU OKAY?.
**Tracks:** Are you okay / I feel better than James Brown / Papa was a rollin' stone / How the heart behaves / Maria Novarro / In K Mart wardrobe / Dressed to be killed / You, you, you / I blew up the United States / Elvis' Rolls Royce / Just another couple broken hearts / Look what's back.
■ **CD** . . . . . . . . . . . . . . . . . . . 8463512
■ **LP** . . . . . . . . . . . . . . . . . . . 8463511
■ **MC** . . . . . . . . . . . . . . . . . . . 8463514
Fontana / Jul '90.

## BORN TO LAUGH AT TORNADOS.
**Tracks:** Out come the freaks / Professor night / Party broke up / Smile / Zaz turned blue / Knocked down / Made small / Bow wow wow wow / Betrayal / Shake your head / Man vs the empire brain building.
■ **LP** . . . . . . . . . . . . . . . . . . . GEF 25922
Geffen / Dec '83.

## BOY'S GONE CRAZY, THE.
**Tracks:** Boy's gone crazy.
■ **12"** . . . . . . . . . . . . . . . . . . . SFSP 912
■ **7"** . . . . . . . . . . . . . . . . . . . . .SFSP 9
Fontana / Nov '87.

## HELLO DAD.. I'M IN JAIL.
**Tracks:** Listen like thieves / Shake your head / Tell me that I'm dreaming / Papa was a rolling stone / Are you okay / Spy in the house of love / I feel better than James Brown / Somewhere in America / There's a street named after my dad / Out come the freaks / How the heart behaves / Walk the dinosaur / Hello dad.. I'm in jail.
**CD** . . . . . . . . . . . . . . . . . . . 512 464-2
■ **LP** . . . . . . . . . . . . . . . . . . . 512 464-1
■ **MC** . . . . . . . . . . . . . . . . . . . 512 464-4
Fontana / Jun '92 / PolyGram.

## HOW THE HEART BEHAVES.
**Tracks:** How the heart behaves / Wierd and wonder-ful world / Anything can happen (Not on 7" single.).
■ **12"** . . . . . . . . . . . . . . . . . . . WAS 812
■ **7"** . . . . . . . . . . . . . . . . . . . . .WAS 8
■ **CD Single** . . . . . . . . . . . . . . . . .WASCD 8
■ **MC Single** . . . . . . . . . . . . . . . . WASMC 8
Fontana / Jul '90.

## I FEEL BETTER THAN JAMES BROWN.
**Tracks:** I feel better than James Brown.
■ **12"** . . . . . . . . . . . . . . . . . . . WASXR 9
■ **12"** . . . . . . . . . . . . . . . . . . . WAS 912
■ **12" Remix** . . . . . . . . . . . . . . . . WASR 912
■ **7"** . . . . . . . . . . . . . . . . . . . . .WAS 9
■ **CD Single** . . . . . . . . . . . . . . . . .WASCD 9
Fontana / Nov '90.

## LISTEN LIKE THIEVES.
**Tracks:** Listen like thieves / Hello operator / Go..now (Available on 12" and CD single format only.) / Wedding vows in Vegas.
■ **12"** . . . . . . . . . . . . . . . . . . . WASX 10
■ **7"** . . . . . . . . . . . . . . . . . . . . .WAS 10
■ **CD Single** . . . . . . . . . . . . . . . . .WASCD 10
■ **MC Single** . . . . . . . . . . . . . . . . WASMC 10
Fontana / May '92.

## OUT COME THE FREAKS.
**Tracks:** Not Advised.
■ **LP** . . . . . . . . . . . . . . . . . . . . . IMA 10
■ **MC** . . . . . . . . . . . . . . . . . . . . . IMC 10
Island / Apr '84.

## OUT COME THE FREAKS.
**Tracks:** Out come the freaks / Earth to Doris / Return to the valley of out come the freaks (Track on 12" and CD versions only.) / Stuck inside of Detroit with the out come the freaks (Track on CD version only.) / Out come the freaks (again) (Track on CD version only.).
■ **12"** . . . . . . . . . . . . . . . . . . . .12WIP 6709
■ **7"** . . . . . . . . . . . . . . . . . . . . .WIP 6709
Island / Jul '81.
■ **12"** . . . . . . . . . . . . . . . . . . . . TA 4178
■ **7"** . . . . . . . . . . . . . . . . . . . . .A 4178
Geffen / Mar '84.
■ **12"** . . . . . . . . . . . . . . . . . . . . WAS 412
■ **7"** . . . . . . . . . . . . . . . . . . . . .WAS 4
■ **CD Single** . . . . . . . . . . . . . . . . .WASCD 4
Fontana / Apr '88.

## PAPA WAS A ROLLING STONE.
**Tracks:** Papa was a rolling stone / Ballad of you / Papa was a rolling stone (instrumental) (Only on 12" and CD single.).
■ **MC Single** . . . . . . . . . . . . . . . . WASMC 7
■ **12"** . . . . . . . . . . . . . . . . . . . WAS 712
■ **12" Remix** . . . . . . . . . . . . . . . . WASR 712
■ **7"** . . . . . . . . . . . . . . . . . . . . .WAS 7
■ **CD Single** . . . . . . . . . . . . . . . . .WASCD 7
Fontana / May '90.

## PROFESSOR NIGHT.
**Tracks:** Professor Night / Bow wow wow wow.
■ **12"** . . . . . . . . . . . . . . . . . . . . TA 4412
■ **7"** . . . . . . . . . . . . . . . . . . . . .A 4412
Geffen / Apr '84.

## ROBOT GIRL.
**Tracks:** Robot girl / Earth to doris.
■ **12"** . . . . . . . . . . . . . . . . . . . .WASR 112
■ **7"** . . . . . . . . . . . . . . . . . . . . .WAS 1
Fontana / Dec '86.

## SHAKE YOUR HEAD.
**Tracks:** Shake your head / I blew up the United States.
■ **12"** . . . . . . . . . . . . . . . . . . . WASX 11
■ **7"** . . . . . . . . . . . . . . . . . . . . .WAS 11
■ **CD Single** . . . . . . . . . . . . . . . . .WASCD 11
■ **MC Single** . . . . . . . . . . . . . . . . WASMC 11
Fontana / Jun '92.

## SMILE.
**Tracks:** Smile / Jason blew in from Peoria.
■ **7"** . . . . . . . . . . . . . . . . . . . . .A 3835
Geffen / Oct '83.

## SPY IN THE HOUSE OF LOVE.
**Tracks:** Spy in the house of love / Dad I'm in jail.
■ **12"** . . . . . . . . . . . . . . . . . . . WAS 212
■ **12" Remix** . . . . . . . . . . . . . . . . WASX 2
■ **7"** . . . . . . . . . . . . . . . . . . . . .WAS 2
■ **CD Single** . . . . . . . . . . . . . . . . .WASCD 2
Fontana / Jun '87.

## TELL ME THAT I'M DANCING.
**Tracks:** Tell me that I'm dancing.
■ **12"** . . . . . . . . . . . . . . . . . . . .12WIP 6776
■ **7"** . . . . . . . . . . . . . . . . . . . . .WIP 6776
Island / Mar '82.

## WALK THE DINOSAUR.
**Tracks:** Walk the dinosaur / 11 miles an hour.
■ **12"** . . . . . . . . . . . . . . . . . . . WAS 312
■ **7"** . . . . . . . . . . . . . . . . . . . . .WAS 3
Fontana / Sep '87.

## WALK THE DINOSAUR (CD VIDEO).
**Tracks:** Walk the dinosaur.
**CD Video** . . . . . . . . . . . . . . . . . . 080 452 2
Polygram Music Video / Oct '88 / PolyGram.

## WAS (NOT WAS).
**Tracks:** Not Advised.
**MC.** . . . . . . . . . . . . . . . . . . . .ICT 7015
■ **LP** . . . . . . . . . . . . . . . . . . . .ILPS 7015
Island / Jul '81 / PolyGram.
■ **LP** . . . . . . . . . . . . . . . . . . . 842 683 1
■ **MC** . . . . . . . . . . . . . . . . . . . 842 683 4
■ **CD** . . . . . . . . . . . . . . . . . . . 842 683 2
Island / May '90.

■ **DELETED**

449

## WHAT UP, DOG.
**Tracks:** Spy In The House of Love / Boy's gone crazy / Anything Can Happen / Somewhere in America / Out Come The Freaks / What up dog / Love can be bad luck / 11 Miles An Hour.
■ CD . . . . . . . . . . . . . . . . . . . 8342912
■ LP . . . . . . . . . . . . . . . . . . . SFLP 4
■ MC . . . . . . . . . . . . . . . . . . . SFMC 4
Fontana / Mar '88.

## WHERE DID YOUR HEART GO.
**Tracks:** Where did your heart go / Wheel me out.
■ 12" . . . . . . . . . . . . . . . . . 12WIP 6716
■ 7" . . . . . . . . . . . . . . . . . . WIP 6716
Island / Sep '81.

## Wash. Martha

### CARRY ON.
**Tracks:** Carry on.
■ 12" . . . . . . . . . . . . . . . . 74321 125451
■ 7" . . . . . . . . . . . . . . . . . 74321 125457
■ CD Single . . . . . . . . . . . . 74321 125452
■ MC Single . . . . . . . . . . . . 74321 125454
RCA / Nov '92.

### GIVE IT TO YOU.
**Tracks:** Give it to you / Give it to you (mixes).
■ 7" . . . . . . . . . . . . . . . . . 74321 136567
■ CD Single . . . . . . . . . . . . 74321 136582
■ MC Single . . . . . . . . . . . . 74321 136564
■ 12" . . . . . . . . . . . . . . . . 74321 136561
RCA / Feb '93.

### MARTHA WASH.
**Tracks:** Someone who believes in you (prelude) / So whatcha gonna do / Give it to you / Runaround / Now that you're gone / Things we do for love / Just us (dancin') / Leave a light on / Carry on / Someone who believes in you / Hold on (part 1) / Hold on (part 2) / When it's in my heart / Just us (singin').
CD . . . . . . . . . . . . . . . . . . 07863 66052-27
LP . . . . . . . . . . . . . . . . . . 07863 66052-10
MC. . . . . . . . . . . . . . . . . . 07863 66052-41
RCA / Aug '93 / BMG.

### RUNAROUND.
**Tracks:** Runaround / Carry on / Runaround (remix) (On CD single & 12" only) / Carry on (remix) (On CD single & 12" only) / Runaround (mixes) / Carry on (mixes).
■ 12" Remix . . . . . . . . . . . . 74321 156161
■ 12" . . . . . . . . . . . . . . . . 74321 153701
■ CD Single . . . . . . . . . . . . 74321 153702
■ MC Single . . . . . . . . . . . . 74321 153704
RCA / Jun '93.

## Washburn, Lalomie

### MY MUSIC IS HOT.
**Tracks:** Give me love with the music / Double funkin' / My love is hot / Man power / Shade of blue / Freaky strangeness / What's love.
■ LP . . . . . . . . . . . . . . . . . . . RRL 2002
Parachute (USA) / Feb '78.

### NOW OR NEVER.
**Tracks:** Not Advised.
■ 12" . . . . . . . . . . . . . . . . . . . BBR 006
Boogie Back Records / Nov '92.

### TRY MY LOVE.
**Tracks:** Try my love / Mother may I.
■ 12" . . . . . . . . . . . . . . . . . . . CON 5 0
Conscious / Nov '91.
■ 12" . . . . . . . . . . . . . . . . . 12BRW 249
■ 7" . . . . . . . . . . . . . . . . . . BRW 249
■ CD Single . . . . . . . . . . . . . . BRCD 249
4th & Broadway / Apr '92.

## Washington, Baby

### I CAN'T WAIT UNTIL I SEE MY BABY'S FACE.
**Tracks:** I can't wait until I see my baby's face / Who's gonna take care of me.
■ 7" . . . . . . . . . . . . . . . . . . . WI 321
Sue / Aug '64.

### ONLY THOSE IN LOVE.
**Tracks:** Only those in love / Ballad of Bobby Dawn.
■ 7" . . . . . . . . . . . . . . . . . . HLC 9987
London-American / Aug '65.

### THAT'S HOW HEARTACHES ARE MADE.
**Tracks:** That's how heartaches are made / Real thing / I can't stand it / I know.
■ 7" . . . . . . . . . . . . . . . . . . . ENS 3
Ensign / Nov '83.

## THAT'S HOW HEARTACHES ARE MADE.
**Tracks:** Ballad of Bobby Dawn / Leave me alone / There he is / Doodlin' / You and the night and the music / That's how heartaches are made / Standing on the pier / I've got a feeling / Careless hands / Hush heart / Go on / Handful of memories.
■ LP . . . . . . . . . . . . . . . . . . HAC 8260
London-American / '65.

## Washington, Bernadette

### CROSSING THE BEAT.
**Tracks:** Crossing the beat / Second time around / Crossing the beat (inst.).
■ 12" . . . . . . . . . . . . . . . . . 12 IS 451
■ 7" . . . . . . . . . . . . . . . . . . IS 451
■ CD Single . . . . . . . . . . . . . . CID 451
■ MC Single . . . . . . . . . . . . . . CIS 451
Island / Jan '90.

### STRAIGHT TO MY HEART.
**Tracks:** Straight to my heart (On 7", MC and CD only) / Second time around / Straight to my heart (Instrumental) (On 12" only).
■ MC Single . . . . . . . . . . . . . . CIS 465
■ 12" . . . . . . . . . . . . . . . . . 12 IS 465
■ 7" . . . . . . . . . . . . . . . . . . IS 465
■ CD Single . . . . . . . . . . . . . . CID 465
Island / May '90.

## Washington, Cecil

### I DON'T LIKE TO LOSE.
**Tracks:** I don't like to lose / Something's bad.
■ 7" . . . . . . . . . . . . . . . . . . 7SS 105
Soul Supply / Dec '84.

## Washington, Ella

### NOBODY BUT ME.
**Tracks:** All the time / Stop giving your man away / I'm losing the feeling / Doin' the best I can / Starving for love / He'll be back / Too weak to fight / Nobody but me / Sweet talking candy man / Cry cry cry (You're gonna) / Sit down and cry / He called me baby / Grass is always greener / I want to walk through this life with you.
■ LP . . . . . . . . . . . . . . . . . . CRB 1144
Charly R&B / Feb '87.

## Washington, Geno

### ALLISON PLEASE.
**Tracks:** Allison please / Each and every part of me.
■ 7" . . . . . . . . . . . . . . . . . 7N 45019
Pye / Jan '71.

### BABY COME BACK.
**Tracks:** Baby come back / Caught in the middle.
■ 12" . . . . . . . . . . . . . . . . . DJR 18008
■ 7" . . . . . . . . . . . . . . . . . .DJS 10926
DJM / Oct '79.

### CATCH ME.
**Tracks:** Rock the car / Catch me.
■ 12" . . . . . . . . . . . . . . . . . MILT 001
■ 7" . . . . . . . . . . . . . . . . . MILS 001
MIL / Jun '88.

### FEELING SO GOOD.
**Tracks:** Feeling so good / Would you believe my little chick-a-dee.
■ 7" . . . . . . . . . . . . . . . . . 7N 45085
Pye / Jul '71.

### HAND CLAPPIN'-FOOT STOMPIN'-FUNKY BUTT-LIVE (Washington, Geno & The Ram Jam Band).
**Tracks:** Philly dog / Ride your pony / Up tight / Road runner / Hold on / Don't fight it / Land of a thousand dances / Respect / Willy nilly / Get down with it / Michael / Que sera sera / You don't know.
■ LP . . . . . . . . . . . . . . . . . . NPL 38026
Piccadilly / Dec '66.
■ LP . . . . . . . . . . . . . . . . . .NSPL 18618
Pye / Aug '80.
CD. . . . . . . . . . . . . . . . . . .REP 4189-WZ
Repertoire (Germany) / Aug '91 / Pinnacle.

### HAND CLAPPIN'-FOOT STOMPIN'-FUNKY BUTT-LIVE & (HIPSTERS, FLIPSTERS, FINGER POPPIN' DADDIES) (Washington, Geno & The Ram Jam Band).
**Tracks:** Philly dog / Up tight (everything's alright) / Hold on I'm coming / Land of a thousand dances / Willy nilly / Michael / You don't know (like I know) / Day tripper / You left the water running / High heel sneakers / Raise your hand / Things get better / She shot a hole in my soul / Ride your pony / (I'm a)

roadrunner / Don't fight it / Respect / Get down with it / Que sera sera / Herk's works / I can't turn you loose / In the midnight hour / Shotgun / Who's foolin who / It's a wonder / Wild thing.
CD. . . . . . . . . . . . . . . . . . . . C5CD 581
C5 / Mar '92 / Pinnacle.

### HI HI HAZEL (Washington, Geno & The Ram Jam Band).
**Tracks:** Hi hi hazel.
■ 7" . . . . . . . . . . . . . . . . . 7N 35329
Piccadilly / Jul '66.

### HIP-SHAKIN' SOUL-BREAKIN' EARTH-QUAKIN' LIVE! (Washington, Geno & The Ram Jam Band).
**Tracks:** Not Advised.
■ CD. . . . . . . . . . . . . . . . . . PYC 4018
■ LP . . . . . . . . . . . . . . . . . . PYL 4018
■ MC . . . . . . . . . . . . . . . . . PYM 4018
PRT / Oct '88.

### HIPSTERS, FLIPSTERS AND FINGER POPPIN' DADDIES.
**Tracks:** Not Advised.
■ LP . . . . . . . . . . . . . . . . . .NSPL 38032
Piccadilly / Sep '67.
CD . . . . . . . . . . . . . . . . . . .REP 4190-W2
Repertoire (Germany) / Aug '91 / Pinnacle.

### HOLD ON MOMMA (Washington, Geno & The Ram Jam Band).
**Tracks:** Hold on Momma / Help I'm in love again.
■ 7" . . . . . . . . . . . . . . . . . DJS 392
DJM / Jul '75.

### JINGLE BELLS.
**Tracks:** Jingle bells / Rock the car.
■ 7" . . . . . . . . . . . . . . . . . GKA 001
G Kap / Dec '88.

### LIVE SIDEWAYS (Washington, Geno & The Ram Jam Stars).
**Tracks:** Not Advised.
■ LP . . . . . . . . . . . . . . . . . GENOLP 1
Ammunition / Dec '86.

### MICHAEL (Washington, Geno & The Ram Jam Band).
**Tracks:** Michael / Hold on to my love.
■ 7" . . . . . . . . . . . . . . . . . 7N 35359
Piccadilly / Feb '67.

### MY MONEY, YOUR MONEY.
**Tracks:** My money, your money / Get some bad tonight.
■ 12" . . . . . . . . . . . . . . . . . DJR 10919
■ 7" . . . . . . . . . . . . . . . . . .DJS 10919
DJM / Jul '79.

### NO HOLDS BARRED (Washington, Geno & Jimmy James).
**Tracks:** Not Advised.
CD. . . . . . . . . . . . . . . . . . .NEXCD 169
Sequel / Jul '91 / Total / BMG.

### PROUD MARY.
**Tracks:** Proud Mary / Stir it up.
■ 7" . . . . . . . . . . . . . . . . . .DJS 10825
DJM / Dec '77.

### PUT OUT THE CAT.
**Tracks:** Not Advised.
■ LP . . . . . . . . . . . . . . . . . . 6.24665
Teldec (1) / Sep '81.

### QUE SERA SERA (Washington, Geno & The Ram Jam Band).
**Tracks:** Que sera sera.
■ 7" . . . . . . . . . . . . . . . . . 7N 35346
Piccadilly / Oct '66.

### QUE SERA SERA (EP) (Washington, Geno & The Ram Jam Band).
**Tracks:** Que sera sera / Hi hi Hazel / You got me hummin' / Different strokes.
■ EP . . . . . . . . . . . . . . . . . FBEP 103
Flashback / Jul '80.

### RUNNING WILD.
**Tracks:** Knock on wood / Gimme little sign / Raise your hand / Michael / Que sera sera / Rock me baby / Hi heel sneakers / Mary Ann / Day tripper / Baby come back.
■ LP . . . . . . . . . . . . . . . . . . NPL 18219
Pye / Oct '68.

### SHAKE A TAIL FEATHER.
**Tracks:** Raise your hand / You got me hummin' / Three time loser / Tell it like it is / Use me / Understanding / Knock on wood / Bonie Moronie / Never like this before / I'm your puppet / Who's foolin' who / Hold on to my love.

■ **LP** . . . . . . . . . . . . . . . . . . .NSPL 38029
Piccadilly / Feb '68.

## SHE SHOT A HOLE IN MY SOUL.
**Tracks:** She shot a hole in my soul / I've been hurt by love.
■ **7"** . . . . . . . . . . . . . . . . . . . . 7N 35392
Piccadilly / Jun '67.

## SMALL PACKAGE OF HIPSTERS (Washington, Geno & The Ram Jam Band).
**Tracks:** Philly dog / Ride your pony / Uptight / Respect.
■ **7"** . . . . . . . . . . . . . . . . . . NEP 24302
Pye / Dec '68.

## SOOTHE ME.
**Tracks:** Soothe me / My kind of love.
■ **7"** . . . . . . . . . . . . . . . . . . .DJS 10761
DJM / Mar '77.

## TAKE THAT JOB AND STUFF IT.
**Tracks:** Not Advised.
■ **LP** . . . . . . . . . . . . . . . . KOMO 788027
Konnexion / Aug '87.

## TELL IT LIKE IT IS.
**Tracks:** Tell it like it is / Girl I want to marry you.
■ **7"** . . . . . . . . . . . . . . . . . . 7N 35403
Piccadilly / Sep '67.

## THAT'S WHY HOLLYWOOD LOVES ME.
**Tracks:** That's why Hollywood loves me / Get some bad tonight / Thanks for loving me / Baby come back / Caught in the middle / My money, your money.
■ **LP** . . . . . . . . . . . . . . . . . . .DJF 20561
DJM / Oct '79.

## UPTIGHT (Washington, Geno & The Ram Jam Band).
**Tracks:** Herks works / Day tripper / You left the water running / In the midnight hour / High heel sneakers / Shotgun / Philly dog / Ride your pony / Uptight / Road runner / Hold on / Don't fight it.
■ **LP** . . . . . . . . . . . . . . . . . MALS 1162
Marble Arch / Oct '69.

## WATER (Washington, Geno & The Ram Jam Band).
**Tracks:** Water / Understanding.
■ **7"** . . . . . . . . . . . . . . . . . . 7N 35312
Piccadilly / May '66.

---

## Washington, Grover Jr.

Having built a reputation as an accomplished jazz-fusion sax player in the early 70's, Washington moved further towards pop with the 1975 Top 10 album *Feels So Good*. Signed to Motown, he released the self-produced *Reed Seed* in 1978 but despite the relative success of this record found he was unhappy at the label. Although still contractually obliged to issue alternate releases through Motown he was signed to Elektra and here had his greatest commercial success. 1981's *Winelight* mixed soul, jazz and pop and was hugely popular, selling over two million copies and being awarded two Grammy's. It included the single *Just The Two Of Us*, featuring Bill Withers on vocals, which shot to No. 2 on the U.S. chart. Subsequent releases have achieved more limited success while Washington's style has become less jazz-influenced.

## ALL THE KING'S HORSES.
**Tracks:** No tears / In the end / All the king's horses / Where is the love / Body & soul / Lean on me / Lover man / Interlude No. 2 / Love song 1700.
■ **LP** . . . . . . . . . . . . . . . . . STMS 5056
■ **MC** . . . . . . . . . . . . . . . . . CSTMS 5056
Motown / Mar '82.

## ANTHOLOGY (ELEKTRA): GROVER WASHINGTON JR.
**Tracks:** Best is yet to come / East River drive / Be mine tonight / Can you dig it / In the name of love / Just the two of us / Jamming / Little black samba / Jet stream / Let it flow.
■ **LP** . . . . . . . . . . . . . . . . . . . EKT 17
MC. . . . . . . . . . . . . . . . . . . .EKT 17C
Elektra / Nov '85 / WEA.
CD. . . . . . . . . . . . . . . . . . . 9604152
Elektra / '89 / WEA.

## ANTHOLOGY (MOTOWN): GROVER WASHINGTON JR.
**Tracks:** Inner city blues / Mercy mercy me / Where is the love / Mr. Magic / It feels so good / Secret place / Masterpiece / Trouble man / Summer song / Santa Cruzin' / Snake eyes.

---

■ **Double LP**. . . . . . . . . . . . . . . TMSP 6015
■ **MC Set** . . . . . . . . . . . . . . CTMSP 6015
Motown / Sep '82.
■ **Double LP**. . . . . . . . . . . . . . . ZL 72168
Motown / '86.

## AT HIS BEST.
**Tracks:** It feels so good / Mr. Magic / Do dat / Summer song / Secret place / Ain't no sunshine / Masterpiece.
■ **CD**. . . . . . . . . . . . . . . . . WD 72366
Motown / Apr '85.

## BADDEST.
**Tracks:** Black frost / Do dat / Summer song / Secret place / Ain't no sunshine / Mercy mercy me / It feels so good / Mr. Magic / No tears in the end / Inner city blues / Lean on me / Masterpiece.
■ **Double LP**. . . . . . . . . . . . . . . TMSP 6011
■ **MC**. . . . . . . . . . . . . . . . . CTSMP 6011
Motown / Oct '81.

## BE MINE.
**Tracks:** Be mine / Little black samba.
■ **7"** . . . . . . . . . . . . . . . . . . K 12600
Elektra / Feb '82.

## BEST IS YET TO COME.
**Tracks:** Can you dig it / Best is yet to come / More than meets the eye / Things are getting better / Mixed emotions / Brazilian memories / I'll be with you / Cassie's theme.
■ **LP** . . . . . . . . . . . . . . . . . . .E 0215
MC. . . . . . . . . . . . . . . . . . . . E 02154
Elektra / Jan '83 / WEA.
CD. . . . . . . . . . . . . . . . . . . 9602152
Elektra / Feb '87 / WEA.

## COME MORNING.
**Tracks:** East River drive / Come morning / Be mine (tonight) / Reaching out / Jamming / Little black samba / Making love to you / I'm all yours.
■ **LP** . . . . . . . . . . . . . . . . . . . K 52337
MC. . . . . . . . . . . . . . . . . . . K 452337
Elektra / Nov '81 / WEA.
CD. . . . . . . . . . . . . . . . . . . .252337
Elektra / Apr '84 / WEA.

## DO DAT.
**Tracks:** Do dat / Reed seed.
■ **7"** . . . . . . . . . . . . . . . . . .TMG 1131
Motown / Jan '79.

## FEELS SO GOOD.
**Tracks:** Sea lion / Knucklehead / Moonstreams / Feels so good / Hydra.
■ **LP** . . . . . . . . . . . . . . . . . STMS 5028
■ **MC** . . . . . . . . . . . . . . . . CSTMS 5028
Motown / Oct '81.
■ **LP** . . . . . . . . . . . . . . . . . WL 72080
■ **CD** . . . . . . . . . . . . . . . . . WD 72080
Motown / Aug '88.

## GREATEST PERFORMANCES.
**Tracks:** Mr. Magic / It feels so good / Secret place / Do dat / Lean on me.
■ **LP** . . . . . . . . . . . . . . . . . STMS 5099
■ **MC** . . . . . . . . . . . . . . . . CSTMS 5099
Motown / Jun '83.
■ **LP** . . . . . . . . . . . . . . . . . WL 72125
■ **MC** . . . . . . . . . . . . . . . . WK 72125
Motown / '86.

## INNER CITY BLUES.
**Tracks:** Inner city blues / Georgia on my mind / Mercy mercy me / Ain't no sunshine / Better days / Until it's time for you to go / I loves you Porgy.
■ **LP** . . . . . . . . . . . . . . . . . . KUL 1
Creed Taylor / Jul '72.
■ **LP** . . . . . . . . . . . . . . . . . STMS 5055
MC. . . . . . . . . . . . . . . . . . CSTMS 5055
Motown / Mar '82 / PolyGram.
■ **MC** . . . . . . . . . . . . . . . . . WK 72098
■ **CD** . . . . . . . . . . . . . . . . . WD 72098
■ **LP** . . . . . . . . . . . . . . . . . WL 72098
Motown / Feb '88.

## INSIDE MOVES.
**Tracks:** Inside moves / Dawn song / Watching you watching me / Secret sounds / Jet stream / When I look at you / Sassy stew.
■ **MC** . . . . . . . . . . . . . . . . . 9603184
■ **LP** . . . . . . . . . . . . . . . . . 9603181
Elektra / Oct '84.
**CD**. . . . . . . . . . . . . . . . . . 9603182
Elektra / Feb '87 / WEA.
**CD**. . . . . . . . . . . . . . . . . 7559603182
Pickwick/Warner / Oct '94 / Pinnacle.

## JAMMING.
**Tracks:** Jamming / East River drive.
■ **7"** . . . . . . . . . . . . . . . . . . K 13161
Elektra / Apr '82.

---

## JUST THE TWO OF US.
**Tracks:** Just the two of us / Make me a memory.
■ **7"** . . . . . . . . . . . . . . . . . . K 12514
Elektra / May '81.

## JUST THE WAY YOU ARE.
**Tracks:** Just the way you are / Lorans dance.
■ **7"** . . . . . . . . . . . . . . . . . .TMG 1153
Motown / Oct '81.

## LET IT FLOW (FOR DR J).
**Tracks:** Let it flow / Winelight.
■ **12"**. . . . . . . . . . . . . . . . . K 12495T
■ **7"** . . . . . . . . . . . . . . . . . K 12495
Asylum / Dec '80.

## LIVE AT THE BIJOU.
**Tracks:** On the cusp / You make me dance / Lock it in the pocket / Sausalito / Funkfoot / Summer song / Juffure / Days in our lives / Mr. Magic.
■ **Double LP** . . . . . . . . . . . . . . . WL 72267
■ **MC Set** . . . . . . . . . . . . . . . WK 72267
Motown / Jun '86.

## LOVE AT THE BIJOU.
**Tracks:** On the cusp / You make me dance / Lock it in the pocket / Summer song / Juffure / Sausalito / Funkfoot.
■ **LP Set**. . . . . . . . . . . . . . . SOULD 002
Polydor / Feb '78.

## MISTER MAGIC.
**Tracks:** Earth tones / Passion flower / Mr. Magic / Black frost.
■ **LP** . . . . . . . . . . . . . . . . . STMS 5027
■ **MC** . . . . . . . . . . . . . . . . CSTMS 5027
Motown / Oct '81.
**CD**. . . . . . . . . . . . . . . . . . .530103-2
■ **MC**. . . . . . . . . . . . . . . . .530103-4
Motown / Jan '93 / PolyGram.

## MISTER MAGIC/FEELS SO GOOD.
**Tracks:** Earth tones / Passion flower / Mr. Magic / Black frost / Sea lion / Moonstreams / Knucklehead / It feels so good / Hydra.
■ **CD** . . . . . . . . . . . . . . . . . ZD 72452
Motown / Nov '86.

## MR. MAGIC.
**Tracks:** Mr. Magic / Sausalito.
■ **7"** . . . . . . . . . . . . . . . . .KUDUX 100
Kudu / Oct '80.

## NEXT EXIT.
**Tracks:** Take five / Your love / Only for you (siempre para d'sers) / Greene street / Next exit / I miss home / Love like this / Summer chill / Till you return to me / Get on up / Check out Grover.
CD. . . . . . . . . . . . . . . . . . . 4690882
■ **LP** . . . . . . . . . . . . . . . . . 4690881
■ **MC** . . . . . . . . . . . . . . . . . 4690884
Columbia / Jul '92 / Sony.

## PARADISE.
**Tracks:** Paradise / Icey / Answer in your eyes / Asia's theme / Shana / Tell me about it / Feel it comin'.
■ **LP** . . . . . . . . . . . . . . . . . . K 52130
Elektra / Jun '79.
■ **CD** . . . . . . . . . . . . . . . . . K 252130
Elektra / Jul '87.

## PLAYBOY JAZZ FESTIVAL (Washington Grover, Jr & Weather Report).
**Tracks:** Not Advised.
■ **LP** . . . . . . . . . . . . . . . . . . 9602981
Elektra / May '84.

## REED SEED.
**Tracks:** Do dat / Step 'n' thru / Reed seed / Maracas beach / Santa Cruzin' / Just the way you are / Loran's dance.
■ **LP** . . . . . . . . . . . . . . . . . STMS 5072
■ **MC** . . . . . . . . . . . . . . . . CSTMS 5072
Motown / Jun '82.
■ **LP** . . . . . . . . . . . . . . . . . WL 72106
■ **MC** . . . . . . . . . . . . . . . . WK 72106
Motown / '86.

## SECRET PLACE, A.
**Tracks:** Secret place / Dolphine dance / Not yet / Love makes it better.
■ **LP** . . . . . . . . . . . . . . . . . STMS 5029
■ **MC** . . . . . . . . . . . . . . . . CSTMS 5029
Motown / Oct '81.
■ **LP** . . . . . . . . . . . . . . . . . WL 70281
Motown / '86.

## SECRET PLACE, A/ALL THE KING'S HORSES.
**Tracks:** Secret place / Dolphin dance / Not yet / Love makes it better / No tears, in the end / All the king's

horses / Where is the love / Body & soul / Lean on me / Lover man / Love song 1700.
■ CD. . . . . . . . . . . . . . . . . . . . . . ZD 72494
Motown / Jan '87.

## SKYLARKIN'.
Tracks: Easy loving you / Bright moments / Snake eyes / I can't help it / Love / Open up your mind.
■ LP. . . . . . . . . . . . . . . . . . . . .STML 12131
Motown / Apr '80.
■ LP. . . . . . . . . . . . . . . . . . . . . . WL 72107
■ MC. . . . . . . . . . . . . . . . . . . . . WK 72107
Motown / Apr '84.

## STRAWBERRY MOON.
Tracks: Strawberry moon / Look of love / Shivaree Ride / Caught a touch of your love / Maddie's Blues / I will be here for you / Keep in touch / Summer nights.
■ MC. . . . . . . . . . . . . . . . . . . . . 4504644
■ LP. . . . . . . . . . . . . . . . . . . . . 4504641
CBS / Aug '87 / Sony.
■ CD. . . . . . . . . . . . . . . . . . . . . 4504642
CBS / Sep '87.

## THEN AND NOW.
Tracks: Blues for D.P. / Just enough / French connections / Something borrowed, something blue / Lullaby for Shana Bly / In a sentimental mood / Stella by starlight.
■ LP. . . . . . . . . . . . . . . . . . . . . 4625161
■ MC. . . . . . . . . . . . . . . . . . . . . 4625164
■ CD. . . . . . . . . . . . . . . . . . . . . 4625162
CBS / Oct '88.

## TIME OUT OF MIND.
Tracks: Jamaica / Gramercy Park / Sacred kind of love / Brand new age / Fly away / Don't take your love from me / Time out of mind / Spilt second (Act II, The Bar Scene) / Nice-n-easy / Unspoken love / Protect the dream.
■ LP. . . . . . . . . . . . . . . . . . . . . 4655261
MC. . . . . . . . . . . . . . . . . . . . . . 4655264
■ CD. . . . . . . . . . . . . . . . . . . . . 4655262
CBS / Oct '89 / Sony.

## WINELIGHT.
Tracks: Winelight / Let it flow / In the name of love / Take me there / Just the two of us / Make me a memory.
CD. . . . . . . . . . . . . . . . . . . . . . 252 262
■ LP. . . . . . . . . . . . . . . . . . . . . K 52262
Asylum / Nov '80 / WEA.

## WINELIGHT/PARADISE.
Tracks: Not Advised.
■ MC. . . . . . . . . . . . . . . . . . . . . K 462039
Elektra / Oct '82.

## Washington, Joey

### KEEP IT DANCE.
Tracks: Keep it dance (mixes).
12". . . . . . . . . . . . . . . . . . . . . LIBT 12008
4 Liberty / Oct '94 / SRD.

## Washington, Keith

### KISSING YOU.
Tracks: Kissing you.
■ 12". . . . . . . . . . . . . . . . . . . . .W 0041T
■ 7". . . . . . . . . . . . . . . . . . . . . W 0041
■ CD Single. . . . . . . . . . . . . . . . . W 0041CD
■ MC Single. . . . . . . . . . . . . . . . . W 0041C
WEA / Nov '91.

### MAKE TIME FOR LOVE.
Tracks: Make time for love.
■ 12". . . . . . . . . . . . . . . . . . . . .7599265281
Qwest / May '91.

### MAKE TIME FOR LOVE.
Tracks: All night / Make time for love / Kissing you / Are you still in love with me / When you love somebody / Ready, willing and able / I'll be there / When it comes to you / Lovers after all / Closer.
CD. . . . . . . . . . . . . . . . . . . . . .759926528-2
■ LP. . . . . . . . . . . . . . . . . . . . .759926528-1
MC. . . . . . . . . . . . . . . . . . . . . .759926528-4
Warner Bros. / Mar '91 / WEA.

### YOU MAKE IT EASY.
Tracks: Let me make love to you / Stay in my corner / Don't leave me in the dark / You always gotta go / What it takes / We need to talk/Before I let go / trippin' / Do what you like / Believe that / No one / You make it easy.
CD. . . . . . . . . . . . . . . . . . . . . . 9362453362
MC. . . . . . . . . . . . . . . . . . . . . . 9362453364
Warner Bros. / Sep '93 / WEA.

## Washington, Steve

### PLEASE DON'T GO.
Tracks: Please don't go / Like a shot.
■ 12". . . . . . . . . . . . . . . . . . MKHAN 27
■ 7". . . . . . . . . . . . . . . . . . . KHAN 27
Streetwave / Sep '84.

## Watford, Michael

Watford first came to prominence with club hit *Holdin' On*, from *Underground Dance Vol. 1* compilation. Further singles paved way for eponymous debut on Atlantic. Released in early '94, album elicited comparisons with Marvin Gaye.

### HOLDIN' ON.
Tracks: Holdin' on.
■ 12". . . . . . . . . . . . . . . . . . A 7512T
■ 7". . . . . . . . . . . . . . . . . . .A 7512
■ CD Single. . . . . . . . . . . . . . A 7512CD
■ MC Single. . . . . . . . . . . . . . A 7512C
Atlantic / Feb '92.

### LOVE TO THE WORLD.
Tracks: Love to the world (Mixes).
12". . . . . . . . . . . . . . . . . . .A 8252T
CD Single. . . . . . . . . . . . . . . A 8252CD
MC Single. . . . . . . . . . . . . . . A 8252C
Atlantic / Oct '94 / WEA.

### MICHAEL WATFORD.
Tracks: Luv 4-2 / Love me tonight / First mistake / Holdin' on / Happy man / Interlude / So into you / Love to the world / Yesterday love / Michael's prayer.
CD. . . . . . . . . . . . . . . . . . .756792323-2
LP. . . . . . . . . . . . . . . . . . .756792323-1
MC. . . . . . . . . . . . . . . . . . .756792323-4
East West / Jan '94 / WEA.

### SO INTO YOU.
Tracks: So into you (Mixes).
■ 12". . . . . . . . . . . . . . . . . . A 8309T
■ 12" Remix. . . . . . . . . . . . . . A 8309TX
■ CD Single. . . . . . . . . . . . . . A 8309CD
■ MC Single. . . . . . . . . . . . . . A 8309C
Atlantic / Feb '94.

## Watley, Jody

### AFFAIRS OF THE HEART.
Tracks: I want you / Call on me / I'm the one you need / Affairs of the heart / Commitment to love / It all begins with you / Dance to the music / Strange way / Always and forever / Until the last goodbye / Stolen moments.
■ CD. . . . . . . . . . . . . . . . . . MCAD 10355
■ LP. . . . . . . . . . . . . . . . . . MCA 10355
■ MC. . . . . . . . . . . . . . . . . . MCAC 10355
MCA / Apr '92.
■ DCC. . . . . . . . . . . . . . . . . MCX 10355
MCA / Jan '93.

### DON'T YOU WANT ME.
Tracks: Don't you want me / Don't you want me (dub) / Don't you want me (acappella) (Available on 12" only.).
■ 12". . . . . . . . . . . . . . . . . . MCAT 1198
■ 7". . . . . . . . . . . . . . . . . . .MCA 1198
MCA / Sep '87.

### ECSTACY.
Tracks: Not Advised.
■ 12". . . . . . . . . . . . . . . . . . MCSX 1964
MCA / May '94.

### ECSTASY.
Tracks: Ecstasy.
■ 12". . . . . . . . . . . . . . . . . . MCST 1964
■ CD Single. . . . . . . . . . . . . . MCSTD 1964
■ MC Single. . . . . . . . . . . . . . MCSC 1964
MCA / May '94.

### EVERYTHING.
Tracks: Everything / Everything (instrumental).
■ 12". . . . . . . . . . . . . . . . . . MCAT 1395
■ 7". . . . . . . . . . . . . . . . . . .MCA 1395
■ CD Single. . . . . . . . . . . . . . DMCAT 1395
MCA / Jan '90.

### FRIENDS.
Tracks: Friends / Private life.
■ 12". . . . . . . . . . . . . . . . . . MCAT 1352
■ 12" Remix. . . . . . . . . . . . . . MCAX 1352
■ 7". . . . . . . . . . . . . . . . . . .MCA 1352
■ CD Single. . . . . . . . . . . . . . MCAD 1352
■ MC Single. . . . . . . . . . . . . . MCAC 1352
MCA / Jul '89.

## I'M THE ONE YOU NEED.
Tracks: I'm the one you need.
■ 12". . . . . . . . . . . . . . . . . . MCST 1608
■ 7". . . . . . . . . . . . . . . . . . .MCS 1608
■ CD Single. . . . . . . . . . . . . . MCSTD 1608
■ MC Single. . . . . . . . . . . . . . MCSC 1608
MCA / Mar '92.

### INTIMACY.
Tracks: Workin' on a groove / When a man loves awoman / Are you the one / Too shy to say / Your love keeps working on me / Ecstacy / To be with you / Together / Take me in your arms / Best of me.
CD. . . . . . . . . . . . . . . . . . . MCD 10947
■ LP. . . . . . . . . . . . . . . . . . MCA 10947
■ MC. . . . . . . . . . . . . . . . . . MCC 10947
MCA / Nov '93 / BMG.

### JODY WATLEY.
Tracks: Looking for a new love / Still a thrill / Some kind of lover / For the girls / Love injection / Don't you want me / Do it to the beat / Most of all / Learn to say no / Looking for a new love (extended club version) (Extra track available on cassette and compact disc only.)
■ CD. . . . . . . . . . . . . . . . . . .DMCG 6024
■ LP. . . . . . . . . . . . . . . . . . .MCG 6024
■ MC. . . . . . . . . . . . . . . . . . MCGC 6024
MCA / Feb '87.
■ CD. . . . . . . . . . . . . . . . . . .DMCL 1889
MCA / Jan '90.
■ CD. . . . . . . . . . . . . . . . . . MCLD 19064
■ MC. . . . . . . . . . . . . . . . . . MCLC 19064
MCA / Oct '92.

### LARGER THAN LIFE.
Tracks: Real love / Everything / L.O.V.E.R. / Lifestyle / Something new / Come into my life / Friends / What'cha gonna do for me / For love's sake / Precious love / Once you leave / Only you.
■ LP. . . . . . . . . . . . . . . . . . .MCG 6044
■ CD. . . . . . . . . . . . . . . . . . .DMCG 6044
■ MC. . . . . . . . . . . . . . . . . . MCGC 6044
MCA / Apr '89.

### LOOKING FOR A NEW LOVE.
Tracks: Looking for a new love / Looking for a new love (acappella).
■ 12". . . . . . . . . . . . . . . . . . MCAT 1107
■ 7". . . . . . . . . . . . . . . . . . .MCA 1107
MCA / Apr '87.

### PRECIOUS LOVE.
Tracks: Precious love.
■ 12". . . . . . . . . . . . . . . . . . MCAT 1410
■ 7". . . . . . . . . . . . . . . . . . .MCA 1410
■ CD Single. . . . . . . . . . . . . . DMCAT 1410
MCA / Jun '90.

### REAL LOVE.
Tracks: Real love.
■ 12". . . . . . . . . . . . . . . . . . MCAT 1324
■ 12" Remix. . . . . . . . . . . . . . MCAX 1324
■ 7". . . . . . . . . . . . . . . . . . .MCA 1324
■ CD Single. . . . . . . . . . . . . . DMCAT 1324
MCA / Mar '89.

### SOME KIND OF LOVER.
Tracks: Some kind of lover / Some kind of lover (dub version) / Some kind of lover (ext. version) / Some kind of lover (bonus beats) / Looking for a new love / Some kind of lover (10" extended mix).
■ 12". . . . . . . . . . . . . . . . . . MCAT 1236
■ 7". . . . . . . . . . . . . . . . . . .MCA 1236
MCA / Feb '88.

### STILL A THRILL.
Tracks: Still a thrill / Looking for a new love (acappella).
■ 12". . . . . . . . . . . . . . . . . . MCAT 1168
■ 7". . . . . . . . . . . . . . . . . . .MCA 1168
MCA / Jul '87.

### WHATCHA GONNA DO FOR ME.
Tracks: Whatcha gonna do for me.
■ 12". . . . . . . . . . . . . . . . . . MCAT 1382
■ 7". . . . . . . . . . . . . . . . . . .MCA 1382
■ CD Single. . . . . . . . . . . . . . DMCAT 1382
MCA / Nov '89.

## Watts 103rd Street..

### 'TIL YOU GET ENOUGH (Watts 103rd Street Rhythm Band).
Tracks: 'Til you get enough / Light my fire.
■ 7". . . . . . . . . . . . . . . . . . .WB 7298
Warner Bros. / Aug '69.

### DO YOUR OWN THING (Watts 103rd Street Rhythm Band).
Tracks: Do your own thing / Dance, a kiss, a song.
■ 7". . . . . . . . . . . . . . . . . . .WB 7250
Warner Bros. / May '69.

### EXPRESS YOURSELF (Watts 103rd Street Rhythm Band).
**Tracks:** Express yourself / Living on borrowed time.
■ 7" .................................WB 7417
Warner Bros. / Nov '70.

### LOVE LAND (Watts 103rd Street Rhythm Band).
**Tracks:** Love land.
■ 7" .................................WB 7365
Warner Bros. / Mar '70.

## Watts, Ernie

### AFOXE (Watts, Ernie & Gilberto Gil).
**Tracks:** Green giant, The (part 1) / Show me / You're my thrill / From Japan / Meditation / Rituals of spring / A raca humana / Afoxe / Gondwana / Oriente / Green giant, The (part 3).
CD ................................ R2 79479
CTI (1) / May '92 / New Note.

### CHARIOTS OF FIRE.
**Tracks:** Chariots of fire / Hold on / Lady / Gigolo / Valdez in the country / Abraham's theme / Five circles.
■ LP .............................. K 56982
Qwest / Feb '82.

### CHARIOTS OF FIRE.
**Tracks:** Chariots of fire.
■ 7" .............................. K 17958
WEA / Jun '82.

### ERNIE WATTS QUARTET (Watts, Ernie Quartet).
**Tracks:** Not Advised.
CD ................................ JD 3309
■ LP .............................. JLP 3309
MC. ............................... JC 3309
JVC / Sep '88 / New Note.

### JUST HOLDIN' ON.
**Tracks:** Just holdin' on / Look in your heart.
■ 7" .............................. K 12489
Elektra / Dec '80.

### LOOK IN YOUR HEART.
**Tracks:** Look in your heart / Just holdin' on / Dance music, makin' music / Let's sail away / Beyond the cosmic void suite (starship outness) / Love in transit / Marching to Cretonia.
■ LP .............................. E 6285
Elektra / Oct '80.

### MUSICIAN.
**Tracks:** Music prayer for peace / Where the spirit lives / Rock camping / One love / Red dress / Looking glass / Don't you know / Urban renewal / Keepin' on.
■ LP .............................. 925283 1
Qwest / Aug '85.

### REACHING UP.
**Tracks:** Reaching up / Mr. Sums / I hear a rhapsody / Transparent sea / High road / Inward glance / You leave me breathless / Juice Lucy / Angels flight / Sweet solitude.
CD ................................ JVC 20312
JVC / Feb '94 / New Note.

## Wavelinx

### SECOND HAND WORDS.
**Tracks:** Second hand words / Oracabesa / Believe it's real.
■ 12" ............................. MBX 004
Southside / Sep '90.

### WE FOUND LOVE.
**Tracks:** We found love / Happiness.
■ 12" ............................. MBMPX 001
MGX / Jun '87.

## Weather Girls

### BIG GIRLS DON'T CRY.
**Tracks:** Lock me up / Big girls don't cry / Well-a-wiggy / No-one can love you more than me / Down on the corner / March / Laughter in the rain / You can do it.
■ LP .............................. CBS 26474
MC. ............................... .40 26474
CBS / Sep '85 / Sony.

### DEAR SANTA, BRING ME A MAN FOR CHRISTMAS.
**Tracks:** Dear Santa, bring me a man for Christmas.
■ 7" .............................. A 4072
CBS / Dec '83.

### DOUBLE TONS OF FUN.
**Tracks:** Not Advised.
CD ................................ 450994018-2
MC. ............................... 450994018-4
WEA / Mar '94 / WEA.

### I'M GONNA WASH THAT MAN RIGHT OUTA MY HAIR.
**Tracks:** I'm gonna wash that man right outa my hair / Ladies' hotline.
■ 12" ............................. TA 3716
■ 7" .............................. A 3716
CBS / Jul '84.

### IT'S RAINING MEN (OLD GOLD).
**Tracks:** It's raining men / I'm gonna wash that man right outa my hair / Success.
■ 12" ............................. OG 4022
Old Gold / Sep '87.
CD Single ......................... OG 6513
Old Gold / '92 / Pickwick.

### LAND OF THE BELIEVER.
**Tracks:** Land of the believer / It's raining men / I'm gonna wash that man right outa my hair.
■ 12" ............................. 6513729
■ 7" .............................. 6513727
CBS / May '88.

### NO ONE CAN LOVE YOU MORE.
**Tracks:** No one can love you more / You can do it.
■ 12" ............................. QTA 6488
■ 7" .............................. A 6488
CBS / Aug '85.

### SUCCESS.
**Tracks:** Not Advised.
■ LP .............................. CBS 25719
CBS / Nov '83.

### SUCCESS.
**Tracks:** Success / Hungry for love / Dear santa / Hope / Its raining men / I'm gonna wash that man right outa my hait.
■ 12" ............................. TA 4401
■ 7" .............................. A 4401
CBS / May '84.

### WEATHER GIRLS.
**Tracks:** Land of the believer / Love's on the way / Why can't we show our love / Opposite directions / Love you like a train / Worth my weight in love / Burn me / Something for nothing.
■ CD .............................. 4604702
■ LP .............................. 4604701
■ MC. ............................. 4604704
CBS / May '88.
CD ................................ 983315-2
Pickwick/Sony Collector's Choice / Apr '94 / Pickwick / Pinnacle.

## Weather Report

### 8.30.
**Tracks:** Black market / Scarlet woman / Teen town / Remark you made / Slang / In a silent way / Birdland / Thanks for the memory / Badia / Boogie woogie waltz medley / 8.30 / Brown Street / Orphan / Sightseeing.
■ Double LP ....................... CBS 88455
CBS / Nov '79.
■ Double LP ....................... 22134
CBS / '88.

### BIRDLAND.
**Tracks:** Birdland / Juggler.
■ 7" .............................. CBS 5205
CBS / May '77.

### BIRDLAND (RE-ISSUES).
**Tracks:** Birdland / Remark you made / River people (Only on 12" single).
■ 12" ............................. CBS 137701
■ 7" .............................. CBS 7701
CBS / Jul '79.

### BLACK MARKET.
**Tracks:** Not Advised.
■ CD .............................. CD 81325
■ LP .............................. CBS 32226
CBS / May '87.

### COLLECTION: WEATHER REPORT.
**Tracks:** Birdland / Teen town / Juggler / Pursuit of the woman with the feathered hat / Elders / Punk jazz / And then / Black market (live) / Night passage / Rockin' in rhythm / Fast city / Madagascar / Remark you made (live).
CD ................................ CCSCD 244
MC. ............................... CCSMC 244
■ Double LP ....................... CCSLP 244
Castle Collector Series / Aug '90 / BMG / Pinnacle / Castle Communications.

### DOMINO THEORY.
**Tracks:** Can it be done / D flat waltz / Peasant / Predator / Blue sound-note / Swamp cabbage / Domino theory.
■ LP .............................. CBS 25839
■ MC. ............................. .40 25839
■ CD .............................. CD 25839
CBS / Feb '84.

### GREATEST HITS: WEATHER REPORT.
**Tracks:** Not Advised.
■ LP .............................. 4669961
MC. ............................... 4669964
CBS / Apr '91 / Sony.

### HEAVY WEATHER.
**Tracks:** Birdland / Remark you made / Teen town / Harlequin / Rumba mama / Palladium / Juggler / Havona.
■ LP .............................. CBS 81775
CBS / Apr '77.
MC. ............................... .40 32358
■ LP .............................. CBS 32358
CBS / Sep '83 / Sony.
■ CD .............................. CD 81775
CBS / Nov '87.
CD ................................ CD 32358
CBS / Mar '91 / Sony.
CD ................................ 4682092
Columbia / Jan '92 / Sony.

### I SING THE BODY ELECTRIC.
**Tracks:** Not Advised.
■ LP .............................. CBS 32062
CBS / Oct '82.

### JAPAN DOMINO THEORY.
**Tracks:** Not Advised.
■ VHS ............................. HEN 2030
Hendring Video / '88.

### MR GONE.
**Tracks:** Pursuit of the woman in the feathered hat / River people / Young and fine / Elders / Mr. Gone / Punk jazz / Pinocchio / And then.
■ LP .............................. CBS 82775
CBS / Nov '78.
■ LP .............................. 32790
MC. ............................... .40 32790
Prix D'Ami (France) / Sep '86.

### MYSTERIOUS TRAVELLER.
**Tracks:** Not Advised.
■ CD .............................. CD 80027
CBS / '84.

### NEW ALBUM.
**Tracks:** Not Advised.
■ CD .............................. CD 26367
CBS / '88.

### NIGHT PASSAGE.
**Tracks:** Dream clock / Port of entry / Forlorn / Rockin' in rhythm / Fast city / Night passage / Three views of a secret / Madagascar.
■ LP .............................. CBS 84597
■ CD .............................. CD 84597
CBS / '83.

### PROCESSION.
**Tracks:** Procession / Plaza real / Two lines / Where the moon goes / Well / Molasses run.
CD ................................ CD 25241
■ LP .............................. CBS 25241
MC. ............................... .40 25241
CBS / Feb '83 / Sony.

### RIVER PEOPLE.
**Tracks:** River people / Birdland.
■ 7" .............................. CBS 6743
CBS / Oct '78.

### SPORTIN' LIFE.
**Tracks:** Corner pocket / Indiscretions / Hot cargo / Confians / Pearl on the half-shell / What's going on / Face on the bar room floor / Icepick Willy.
■ LP .............................. CBS 26367
■ MC. ............................. .40 26367
CBS / Jun '85.

### THIS IS THIS.
**Tracks:** This is this / Face the fire / I'll never forget you / Jungle stuff (part 1) / Man with the copper fingers / Consequently / Update / China blues.
■ LP .............................. CBS 57052
■ MC. ............................. .40 57052
CBS / Jul '86.

### WEATHER REPORT.
**Tracks:** Volcano for hire / Current affairs / N.Y.C. / Dara factor one / When it was now / Speechless.
■ LP .............................. CBS 85326
CBS / Feb '82.
CD ................................ 983339 2

Pickwick/Sony Collector's Choice / Mar '94 / Pickwick / Pinnacle.

## WEATHER REPORT (2).
**Tracks:** Milky way / Umbrellas / Seventh arrow / Orange lady / Morning lake / Waterfall / Tears / Eurydice.
■ CD.................... 4682122
Columbia / Jan '92.

## Weathers, Barbara

### BARBARA WEATHERS.
**Tracks:** Barbi doll / My only love / Master key / All I know / Our love runs deep / Our love will last forever / Where can you run / Where did our love go / Anywhere.
■ CD.................... 7599261662
■ LP.................... 7599261661
MC.................... 7599261664
WEA / Jun '90 / WEA.

## Webb, Rick

### THINK ABOUT IT.
**Tracks:** Think about it / You are my one and only love.
■ 12".................... EXPAND 42
Expansion / Jul '93.

## Weeks & Co

### ROCK CANDY.
**Tracks:** Rock candy / Knock knock.
■ 12".................... SALT 103
■ 7".................... SAL 103
Salsoul / Jun '83.

## Weeks, Richie

### FORBIDDEN FRUIT.
**Tracks:** Forbidden fruit / Centrefold / Sugar daddy.
■ 12".................... MKHAN 42
■ 7".................... KHAN 42
Streetwave / May '85.

## Well Red

### GET LUCKY.
**Tracks:** Get lucky / Get lucky (master mix) / Get lucky (dub).
■ 12".................... VS 977-12
■ 7".................... VS 977
Virgin / Jul '87.

### HARD.
**Tracks:** Hard (Extended version on 12") / Mixed up (Glutus maximus alignment).
■ 12".................... VST 1112
■ 7".................... VS 1112
Virgin / Aug '88.

### HONEY.
**Tracks:** Honey (2 skin mix) / Saturday (garage mix).
■ 12".................... VS 943-12
Virgin / '87.

### LIMIT OF YOUR LOVING.
**Tracks:** Limit of your loving.
■ 12".................... PALS 101 12
■ 7".................... PALS 101
Paladin / May '85.

### LOVE GONE CRAZY.
**Tracks:** Love gone crazy.
■ 12".................... VS 826-12
■ 7".................... VS 826
Virgin / Nov '85.

### M.F.S.B.
**Tracks:** M.F.S.B. (7" only) / System (first cut) (NOT on VSR 1079).
■ 12" Remix.................... VSR 1079
■ 7".................... VS 1079
■ 12".................... VST 1079
Virgin / Apr '88.

### MOTION.
**Tracks:** Yes we can / Love gone crazy (LP only) / Come back / System / Get lucky / Mixed up / Turn me on / Honey (12" version) / Saturday (garage mix) (CD only) / Limit of your loving (12" version) (CD only) / Let me out (CD only) / Love gone crazy (12" version) (CD & MC only) / Saturday (MC only).
■ CD.................... CDV 2418
■ LP.................... V 2418
■ MC.................... TCV 2418
Virgin / Jun '87.
■ LP.................... OVED 264
■ MC.................... OVEDC 264
Virgin / '90.

## RESPECT DUE.
**Tracks:** Rocketship of love / Baby / Use me / Keep those wheels turning / Jungle life / More (CD & MC only) / Minute of your time / Hard / Sugar Kane / M.F.S.B. / Love gone crazy (CD & MC only).
■ LP.................... V 2548
■ MC.................... TCV 2548
■ CD.................... CDV 2548
Virgin / Sep '88.

## ROCKETSHIP OF LOVE.
**Tracks:** Rocketship of love / My way.
■ 7".................... VS 1137
■ 12".................... VST 1137
Virgin / Nov '88.

## YES WE CAN.
**Tracks:** Don't rush me.
■ 12".................... VS 925-12
■ 7".................... VS 925
Virgin / Jan '87.

## Wells, Bobby

### BE'S THAT WAY SOMETIMES.
**Tracks:** Be's that way sometimes / Recipe for love.
■ 7".................... GRP 124
Grapevine (Northern Soul) / Aug '79.

## Wells, Brandi

### FANTASY.
**Tracks:** Fantasy / Golden moment / I love you.
■ 12".................... VS 515-12
■ 7".................... VS 515
W.M.O.T.(USA) / Jul '82.

### WATCH OUT.
**Tracks:** Watch out.
■ 12".................... VS 479-12
■ 7".................... VS 479
Virgin / Jan '82.

### WATCH OUT.
**Tracks:** Not Advised.
■ LP.................... V 2224
■ MC.................... TCV 2224
Virgin / Jan '82.

### WHITE BOY DANCE.
**Tracks:** White boy dance.
■ 12".................... VS 492-12
■ 7".................... VS 492
Virgin / Apr '82.

## Wells, James

### ALL I EVER NEED IS MUSIC.
**Tracks:** All I ever need is music / If you lead me into temptation.
■ 7".................... 2058 824
Polydor / Jan '77.

### LOVE THE CURE FOR ME (Wells, James & Susan).
**Tracks:** Love the cure for me.
■ 12".................... MARE 6
■ 7".................... MARES 6
Nightmare / Dec '86.

### MIRROR IMAGE (Wells, James & Susan).
**Tracks:** Mirror image.
■ 12".................... FAN 122901
■ 7".................... FAN 2901
Fanfare / Jun '85.

### RSVP (Wells, James & Susan).
**Tracks:** RSVP.
■ 12".................... 12 FAN 2900
■ 7".................... FAN 2900
Fanfare / Feb '85.

## Wells, Jean

### SOUL ON SOUL.
**Tracks:** Have a little mercy / I'll drown in my own tears / After loving you / Sit down and cry / Ease away a little bit at a time / Our sweet love turned bitter / Somebody's been loving you (but it ain't been me) / Keep your mouth shut and your eyes open / If you've ever loved someone / Broomstick horse cowboy / I couldn't love you (more than I do now) / I feel good / With my love and what you've got (we could turn this love a / Keep on doin' it / Take time to make time for me / Try me and see / Roll up your sleeves, come on lovin' (winner takes all) / What have I got to lose / Puttin' the best on the outside / He ain't doin' bad / Hello baby, goodbye too.
CD.................... CDKEND 113
Ace / Jun '94 / Pinnacle / Complete Record Co. Ltd.

## Wells, Mary

Among the first and best-loved Motown stars, Mary Wells scored eleven Smokey Robinson-penned U.S. hits between 1961 and '64, culminating with classic no. 1 *My Guy*. Lured from Motown by 20th Century Fox, Wells' stock plummeted: final 'good year' was 1966, when she married Cecil Womack and scored hit with *Dear Lover* on Atco. Persistent attempts at comeback were halted by contraction of throat cancer, from which she died in July 1992.

### AIN'T IT THE TRUTH.
**Tracks:** Ain't it the truth.
■ 7".................... SS 372
Stateside / '64.

### COMPACT COMMAND PERFORMANCES (22 Greatest Hits).
**Tracks:** Bye bye baby / I don't want to take a chance / One who really loves you / You beat me to the punch / Two lovers / Laughing boy / Your old standby / Old love (let's try it again) / Oh little boy / What love has joined together / You lost the sweetest boy / What's easy for two is so hard for one / My guy / Two wrongs don't make a right / Everybody needs love / I'll be available / One block from Heaven / When I'm gone / He's the one I love / Whisper you love me boy / Does he love me / Was it worth it.
■ CD.................... WD 72448
Motown / Nov '87.
CD.................... 530104-2
MC.................... 530104-4
Motown / Jan '93 / PolyGram.

### COMPLETE JUBILEE SESSIONS, THE.
**Tracks:** Soul train / Apples, peaches, pumpkin pie / Stag-o-lee / Make me yours / Two lovers history / Can't get away from your love / Doctor / Don't look back / Sunny / Woman in love / 5000 Miles / Bye bye baby / Love shooting bandit / Mind reader / Sometimes I wonder / Dig the way I feel / Brand new me / Hold on / Leaving on a jet plane / Come together / Sweet love / Mister touch / Never give a man the world / Raindrops keep falling on my head / It must be me / Love and tranquility.
CD.................... NEXCD 257
Sequel / Nov '93 / Total / BMG.

### DEAR LOVER.
**Tracks:** Dear lover / Can't you see you're losing me.
■ 7".................... AT 4067
Atlantic / Feb '66.

### DOCTOR, THE.
**Tracks:** Doctor.
■ 7".................... SS 2111
Stateside / May '68.

### DON'T BURN YOUR BRIDGES.
**Tracks:** Don't burn your bridges / Don't burn your bridges (inst).
■ 12".................... MARE 33
■ 7".................... MARES 33
Nightmare / May '87.

### GREATEST HITS: MARY WELLS.
**Tracks:** My guy / What's easy for two is so hard for one / One who really loves you / You lost the sweetest boy / You beat me to the punch / Operator / Two lovers / Laughing boy / I don't want to take a chance / My baby just cares for me / Your old stand by / Strabge love / What love has joined us together / Oh little boy / Old love / Bye bye baby.
■ LP.................... STMS 5093
■ MC.................... CSTMS 5093
Motown / Feb '83.
■ LP.................... SPR 90008
Sounds Superb / Aug '87.

### HE'S A LOVER.
**Tracks:** He's a lover / I'm learnin'.
■ 7".................... SS 439
Stateside / '65.

### KEEPING MY MIND ON LOVE.
**Tracks:** Not Advised.
■ LP.................... MOTCLP 40
■ CD.................... CDMOTCLP 40
Motor City / Dec '90.

### MARY WELLS SINGS MY GUY.
**Tracks:** He's the one I love / Whisper you love me boy / My guy / Does he love me / How / When my heart belongs to you / He holds his own / My baby just cares for me / I only have eyes for you / You do something to me / It had to be you / If you love me / At last.
■ LP.................... STMS 5057
■ MC.................... CSTMS 5057
Motown / Mar '82.

■ DELETED

## MY GUY.
**Tracks:** My guy.
■ 7″ . . . . . . . . . . . . . . . . . . . . . . . . . SS 288
Stateside / May '64.
■ 7″ . . . . . . . . . . . . . . . . . . . . . . . TMG 820
Tamla Motown / Jul '72.
■ . . . . . . . . . . . . . . . . . . . . . . . . . TMG 1100
Motown / Feb '78.
■ 12″ . . . . . . . . . . . . . . . . . . . . . . . ALES 121
■ 7″ . . . . . . . . . . . . . . . . . . . . . . . . ALES 1
Allegiance / Feb '84.

## MY GUY.
**Tracks:** He's the one I love / Whisper you love me
boy / My guy / Does he love me / How / When my
heart belongs to you / He holds his own / My baby
just cares for me / I only have eyes for you / You do
something to me / It had to be you / If you love me,
really love me / At last.
■ CD . . . . . . . . . . . . . . . . . . . . . . . WD 72730
■ MC . . . . . . . . . . . . . . . . . . . . . . WK 72730
Motown / Feb '91.
CD . . . . . . . . . . . . . . . . . . . . . . . CDCD 1146
Charly / Feb '94 / Charly.

## MY GUY.
**Tracks:** One who really loves you / You beat me to
the punch / Two lovers / Your old stand-by / What's
easy for two is so hard for one / My guy / Laughing
boy / What love has joined together / Oh little boy /
Old love / You lost the sweetest boy / Bye bye baby.
■ LP . . . . . . . . . . . . . . . . . . . . . . SRS 5040
Starline / Oct '70.

## MY GUY - THE BEST OF MARY WELLS.
**Tracks:** Not Advised.
CD . . . . . . . . . . . . . . . . . . . . . . . CDSGP 057
MC . . . . . . . . . . . . . . . . . . . . . . CASSGP 057
Prestige / May '93 / Total / BMG.

## MY HANDS ARE TIED.
**Tracks:** My hands are tied / My hands are tied (dub
mix).
■ 12″ . . . . . . . . . . . . . . . . . . . . . . . MARE 18
■ 7″ . . . . . . . . . . . . . . . . . . . . . . . MARES 18
Nightmare / May '87.

## OLD, NEW AND BEST OF MARY WELLS.
**Tracks:** My guy / One who really loves you / Two
lovers / You beat me to the punch / Oh little boy what
did you do to me / Bye bye baby / Whats easy for two
is hard for one / What love has joined together / You
lost the sweetest boy / Old love, let's try again.
■ LP . . . . . . . . . . . . . . . . . . . . . . ALE 5601
MC . . . . . . . . . . . . . . . . . . . . . . ZCALE 5601
Allegiance / Apr '84.

## SERVIN' UP SOME SOUL.
**Tracks:** Soul train / Apples, peaches, pumpkin pie /
Stagger Lee / Make me yours / Doctor / Two lovers'
history / Can't get away from your love / Don't look
back / Sunny / Woman in love / 500 miles / Bye bye
baby.
■ LP . . . . . . . . . . . . . . . . . . . . . . SSL 10266
Stateside / Jan '69.

## SET MY SOUL ON FIRE.
**Tracks:** Set my soul on fire / Coming home.
■ 7″ . . . . . . . . . . . . . . . . . . . . . . . . 584104
Atlantic / Apr '67.

## SISTERS OF SOUL.
**Tracks:** Not Advised.
CD . . . . . . . . . . . . . . . . . . . . . . . RSACD 806
Sequel / Oct '94 / Total / BMG.

## USE YOUR HEAD.
**Tracks:** Use your head / Everlovin' boy.
■ 7″ . . . . . . . . . . . . . . . . . . . . . . . . SS 396
Stateside / '65.

## YOU BEAT ME TO THE PUNCH.
**Tracks:** You beat me to the punch / Oh little boy,
what did you do to me.
■ 7″ . . . . . . . . . . . . . . . . . . . . . . . . ALES 5
Allegiance / Jun '84.

## YOU LOST THE SWEETEST BOY.
**Tracks:** You lost the sweetest boy / What's easy for
two (is so hard for one).
■ 7″ . . . . . . . . . . . . . . . . . . . . . . . . SS 242
Stateside / '63.

# Wells, Terri

## I'LL BE AROUND.
**Tracks:** I'll be around / You make it heaven.
■ 7″ . . . . . . . . . . . . . . . . . . . . . . . LON 48
London / May '84.

## I'LL BE AROUND (OLD GOLD).
**Tracks:** I'll be around / You make it heaven.
■ 12″ . . . . . . . . . . . . . . . . . . . . . . . OG 4056
Old Gold / Apr '88.

## JUST LIKE DREAMIN'.
**Tracks:** I'm givin' all my love / Just like dreamin'
Falling leaves / Can't stop / I already know / I'll be
around / Who's that stranger / Don't make me wait in
line.
■ LP . . . . . . . . . . . . . . . . . . . . . . LONLP 4
■ MC . . . . . . . . . . . . . . . . . . . . . . LONC 4
London / Sep '84 / PolyGram.

## YOU MAKE IT HEAVEN.
**Tracks:** You make it heaven.
■ 12″ . . . . . . . . . . . . . . . . . . . . . . . PWSL 111
■ 7″ . . . . . . . . . . . . . . . . . . . . . . . PWS 111
Philly World (USA) / Jun '83.

# Wendy & Lisa

## ARE YOU MY BABY.
**Tracks:** Are you my baby / Happy birthday / Honeymoon express (Available on 12″ format only.) / Are
you my baby (12″ mix) (Only on 12″ and CD single).
■ CD Single . . . . . . . . . . . . . . . . . . VSCD 1156
■ 12″ . . . . . . . . . . . . . . . . . . . . . . . VST 1156
■ 7″ . . . . . . . . . . . . . . . . . . . . . . . VS 1156
Virgin / Dec '88.

## CLOSING OF THE YEAR.
**Tracks:** Closing of the year / Closing of the year
(instrumental).
■ 7″ . . . . . . . . . . . . . . . . . . . . . . . ZANG 36
■ CD Single . . . . . . . . . . . . . . . . . . ZANG 36 CD
■ MC Single . . . . . . . . . . . . . . . . . . ZANG 36 C
WEA / Nov '92.

## DON'T TRY TO TELL ME.
**Tracks:** Don't try to tell me / Balance.
■ CD Single . . . . . . . . . . . . . . . . . . VSCDX 1337
■ 12″ . . . . . . . . . . . . . . . . . . . . . . . VST 1337
■ 7″ . . . . . . . . . . . . . . . . . . . . . . . VS 1337
■ CD Single . . . . . . . . . . . . . . . . . . VSCDT 1337
■ MC Single . . . . . . . . . . . . . . . . . . VSC 1337
Virgin / Jan '91.

## EROICA.
**Tracks:** Rainbow lake / Strung out / Mother of pearl /
Don't try to tell me / Crack in the pavement / Porch
swing / Why wait for heaven / Turn me inside out /
Skeleton key / Valley vista / Staring at the sun.
■ LP . . . . . . . . . . . . . . . . . . . . . . V 2633
■ MC . . . . . . . . . . . . . . . . . . . . . . TCV 2633
Virgin / Jul '90.
■ MC . . . . . . . . . . . . . . . . . . . . . . OVEDC 412
■ CD . . . . . . . . . . . . . . . . . . . . . . CDV 2633
Virgin / Apr '92.

## FRUIT AT THE BOTTOM.
**Tracks:** Lolly lolly / Satisfaction / Everyday / Tears of
joy / Fruit at the bottom / Are you my baby / Always
in my dreams / From now on / I think it was De-
cember / Someday.
■ LP . . . . . . . . . . . . . . . . . . . . . . V 2580
■ MC . . . . . . . . . . . . . . . . . . . . . . TCV 2580
Virgin / Feb '89.
■ CD . . . . . . . . . . . . . . . . . . . . . . CDVWL 2580
■ LP . . . . . . . . . . . . . . . . . . . . . . VWL 2580
■ MC . . . . . . . . . . . . . . . . . . . . . . TCVWL 2580
Virgin / Nov '89.
CD . . . . . . . . . . . . . . . . . . . . . . . CDV 2580
■ MC . . . . . . . . . . . . . . . . . . . . . . OVEDC 411
Virgin / Apr '92 / EMI.

## HONEYMOON EXPRESS.
**Tracks:** Honeymoon express (7″ only) / Chance to
grow / Honeymoon express (12″ version).
■ 12″ . . . . . . . . . . . . . . . . . . . . . . . VST 1052
■ 7″ . . . . . . . . . . . . . . . . . . . . . . . VS 1052
Virgin.

## LOLLY LOLLY.
**Tracks:** Lolly lolly / Hip hop love / Lolly lolly (version)
(12″ only).
■ CD Single . . . . . . . . . . . . . . . . . . VSCD 1175
■ 12″ . . . . . . . . . . . . . . . . . . . . . . . VSTP 1175
■ 12″ . . . . . . . . . . . . . . . . . . . . . . . VST 1175
■ 7″ . . . . . . . . . . . . . . . . . . . . . . . VS 1175
Virgin / Feb '89.

## RAINBOW LAKE.
**Tracks:** Rainbow lake.
■ MC Single . . . . . . . . . . . . . . . . . . VSC 1280
■ 12″ . . . . . . . . . . . . . . . . . . . . . . . VST 1280
■ 7″ . . . . . . . . . . . . . . . . . . . . . . . VS 1280
■ CD Single . . . . . . . . . . . . . . . . . . VSCDT 1280
Virgin / Oct '90.

## SATISFACTION.
**Tracks:** Satisfaction / Stay / Satisfaction (12″ dance
mix) (Only on 12″ and CD single) / Satisfaction (12″
dance dub) (Only on 12″ and CD single).
■ CD Single . . . . . . . . . . . . . . . . . . VSCD 1194
■ 12″ . . . . . . . . . . . . . . . . . . . . . . . VST 1194
■ 12″ Remix . . . . . . . . . . . . . . . . . . VSTX 1194

■ 7″ . . . . . . . . . . . . . . . . . . . . . . . VS 1194
Virgin / Jun '89.

## SIDESHOW.
**Tracks:** Sideshow (Extended version on CD & 12″) /
Chance to grow / Waterfall (CD only) / Sideshow
(extended version) (Only on 12″ and CD single).
■ 12″ . . . . . . . . . . . . . . . . . . . . . . . VST 1012
■ 7″ . . . . . . . . . . . . . . . . . . . . . . . VS 1012
Virgin / Jan '88.

## STRUNG OUT.
**Tracks:** Strung out / Stones and birth / Strung out (g
strung mix) (Only on 12″ and CD single).
■ 12″ . . . . . . . . . . . . . . . . . . . . . . . VST 1272
■ 7″ . . . . . . . . . . . . . . . . . . . . . . . VS 1272
■ CD Single . . . . . . . . . . . . . . . . . . VSCDT 1272
■ MC Single . . . . . . . . . . . . . . . . . . VSC 1272
Virgin / Jun '90.

## WATERFALL.
**Tracks:** Waterfall / Life / To trip is to fall (Not on 7″).
■ 12″ . . . . . . . . . . . . . . . . . . . . . . . VS 999-12
■ 7″ . . . . . . . . . . . . . . . . . . . . . . . VS 999
■ MC Single . . . . . . . . . . . . . . . . . . VSC 999-12
Virgin / Aug '87.

## WATERFALL 89.
**Tracks:** Always in my dreams / Waterfall 89 (Alice
and sundial seven) / Waterfall (psychedelic teepee
twelve) (Only on 12″ and CD single) / Waterfall
(original version) (Only on CD single).
■ 12″ . . . . . . . . . . . . . . . . . . . . . . . VST 1223
■ 7″ . . . . . . . . . . . . . . . . . . . . . . . VS 1223
■ CD Single . . . . . . . . . . . . . . . . . . VSCD 1223
Virgin / Nov '89.

## WENDY AND LISA.
**Tracks:** Honeymoon express / Sideshow / Waterfall /
Stay / White / Blues away / Song about / Chance to
grow / Life / Everything but you / Light.
CD . . . . . . . . . . . . . . . . . . . . . . . CDV 2444
■ LP . . . . . . . . . . . . . . . . . . . . . . V 2444
■ MC . . . . . . . . . . . . . . . . . . . . . . TCV 2444
Virgin / Sep '87 / EMI.
■ LP . . . . . . . . . . . . . . . . . . . . . . OVED 343
■ MC . . . . . . . . . . . . . . . . . . . . . . OVEDC 343
Virgin / Sep '90.

## WENDY AND LISA: INTERVIEW PIC DISC.
**Tracks:** Not Advised.
■ LP P.Disc . . . . . . . . . . . . . . . . . . BAK 2136
Baktabak / Jun '89.

# Wesley, Fred

## BLOW FOR ME AND A TOOT TO YOU, A (Wesley, Fred & The Horny Horns).
**Tracks:** Not Advised.
CD . . . . . . . . . . . . . . . . . . . . . . . NEDCD 268
■ LP . . . . . . . . . . . . . . . . . . . . . . NEXLP 268
Sequel / May '94 / Total / BMG.

## FINAL BLOW, THE (Wesley, Fred & The Horny Horns).
**Tracks:** Not Advised.
CD . . . . . . . . . . . . . . . . . . . . . . . NEDCD 270
LP . . . . . . . . . . . . . . . . . . . . . . . NEXLP 270
Sequel / May '94 / Total / BMG.

## HOUSE PARTY.
**Tracks:** House party / I make music.
■ 12″ . . . . . . . . . . . . . . . . . . . . . . . RSOX 67
■ 7″ . . . . . . . . . . . . . . . . . . . . . . . RSO 67
RSO / Oct '80.

## HOUSE PARTY.
**Tracks:** Not Advised.
■ CD . . . . . . . . . . . . . . . . . . . . . . BB 0001
■ LP . . . . . . . . . . . . . . . . . . . . . . BB 001
Back Black / Jun '93.

## NEW FRIENDS.
**Tracks:** Rockin' in rhythm / Blue monk / Plenty plenty
soul / Birks works / Peace fugue / Eyes to beautiful /
Bright Mississippi.
CD . . . . . . . . . . . . . . . . . . . . . . . ANCD 8758
LP . . . . . . . . . . . . . . . . . . . . . . . AN 8758
MC . . . . . . . . . . . . . . . . . . . . . . . ANC 8758
Antilles/New Directions / Jun '91 / Grapevine
Distribution.

## SAY BLOW BY BLOW BACKWARDS (Wesley, Fred & The Horny Horns).
**Tracks:** Not Advised.
CD . . . . . . . . . . . . . . . . . . . . . . . NEXCD 269
■ LP . . . . . . . . . . . . . . . . . . . . . . NEXLP 269
Sequel / May '94 / Total / BMG.

## TO SOMEONE.
**Tracks:** Not Advised.
CD . . . . . . . . . . . . . . . . . . . . . . . HNCD 2002

■ DELETED

LP . . . . . . . . . . . . . . . . . . . . . HNL 2002
Hi-Note / May '90 / De-Mix.

**WHAT GOES AROUND COMES AROUND**
(see under Byrd, Bobby).

## Wesley Ryles, John

**WHEN A MAN LOVES A WOMAN.**
Tracks: When a man loves a woman / I'm gonna make it without you.
■ 7" . . . . . . . . . . . . . . . . . . . . . . BD 9
Bulldog Records / Mar '77.

## Westend

**LOVE I LOST, THE (Westend Featuring Sybil).**
Tracks: Love I lost.
■ 12" . . . . . . . . . . . . . . . . . . . PWLT 253
■ 7" . . . . . . . . . . . . . . . . . . . . .PWL 253
■ CD Single . . . . . . . . . . . . . . . . PWCD 253
■ MC Single. . . . . . . . . . . . . . . . PWMC 253
PWL / Oct '92.

## Weston, Kim

**FOR THE FIRST TIME.**
Tracks: Where am I going / Free again / Everything in the world / When the sun comes out / I got what you need / etc.
■ LP . . . . . . . . . . . . . . . . . . . . . CS 8055
MGM (EMI) / Dec '67.

**HELPLESS.**
Tracks: Helpless / Love like yours.
■ 7" . . . . . . . . . . . . . . . . . . . . . TMG 554
Tamla Motown / Mar '66.

**I GOT WHAT YOU NEED.**
Tracks: I got what you need / Someone like you.
■ 7" . . . . . . . . . . . . . . . . . . . . . . 1338
MGM (EMI) / Apr '67.

**I'M STILL LOVING YOU.**
Tracks: I'm still loving you.
■ 7" . . . . . . . . . . . . . . . . . . . . . TMG 511
Tamla Motown / '65.

**IT TAKES TWO (see under Gaye, Frankie).**

**IT TAKES TWO (see under Gaye, Marvin).**

**KIM WESTON & JOHNNY NASH (Weston, Kim & Johnny Nash).**
Tracks: It's gonna be better / Just losing you / Baby don't leave me / Without you / They're just gonna have to try / We try harder / But you know I love you / Stranded in the middle / Letter / My time / What could be better.
■ LP . . . . . . . . . . . . . . . . . . . . . SMLP 54
Major Minor / Jun '69.

**KIM, KIM, KIM.**
Tracks: You just don't know / Love I've been looking for / What could be better / When something is wrong with my baby / Love vibrations / Buy myself a man / Got to get you off my mind / Soul on fire / Brothers and sisters (get together) / Penny blues / Choice is up to you (Walk with me Jesus).
■ LP . . . . . . . . . . . . . . . . . . . . . 2362021
Stax / Oct '71.
CD . . . . . . . . . . . . . . . . . . . . CDSXE 063
Stax / Jul '92 / Pinnacle.

**LITTLE MORE LOVE, A.**
Tracks: Little more love.
■ 7" . . . . . . . . . . . . . . . . . . . . .SS 359
Stateside / '64.

**TAKE ME IN YOUR ARMS (ROCK ME A LITTLE WHILE).**
Tracks: Take me in your arms (rock me a little while) / Don't compare me with her.
■ 7" . . . . . . . . . . . . . . . . . . . TMG 538
Tamla Motown / Oct '65.

**THAT'S GROOVY.**
Tracks: That's groovy / Land of tomorrow.
7" . . . . . . . . . . . . . . . . . . . . MGM 1357
MGM (EMI) / Oct '67 / EMI.

## Wheeler, Audrey

**IRRESISTIBLE.**
Tracks: Irresistible.
■ 12" . . . . . . . . . . . . . . . . . . . 12CL 471
■ 12" Remix. . . . . . . . . . . . . . . . 12CLX 471
■ 7" . . . . . . . . . . . . . . . . . . . . .CL 471
Capitol / Oct '87.

**LET IT BE ME.**
Tracks: Irresistible / Love on the inside / Forget about her / Somewhere in your life / Time for passion / I miss you, love / Don't lose your touch / Let it be me.
■ LP . . . . . . . . . . . . . . . . . . . . EST 2050
■ MC. . . . . . . . . . . . . . . . . . . TC EST 2050
Capitol / Dec '87.

## Wheeler, Caron

Caron Wheeler sang with pop-reggae bands Brown Sugar and Afrodiziak and earned name as a session vocalist (Elvis Costello, Erasure, Phil Collins) before joining Soul II Soul. Her most notable lead performances for Jazzie B's group are the hits *Keep On Movin'* and *Back To Life*, whereafter she signed a deal as a solo artist with RCA. The *UK Blak* album followed in '90, garnering ecstatic reviews but disappointing sales, leading to her being dropped from the label. Immediately signed to US Capitol Records, an equally superb second album - *Beach Of The War Goddess* - met a similar fate and wasn't even released in the UK. In '94 she rejoined Soul II Soul to work on an album due in spring '95.

**BEACH OF THE WAR GODDESS.**
Tracks: Respect to the Mother / In our love / I adore you / Wonder / Gotta give it up / Beach of the War Goddess / Soul Street / Lite as a feather / Need a man / Father / Naughty eyes / Wind cries Mary / Do you care / Land of life.
■ CD . . . . . . . . . . . . . . . . . . . CDMTL 1075
■ MC. . . . . . . . . . . . . . . . . . . TCMTL 1075
EMI-America / Jul '93.

**BEACH OF THE WAR GODDESS.**
Tracks: Beach of the war goddess / Beach of the war goddess (mixes) (Available on 12 and CDS only) / I adore you.
■ MC Single. . . . . . . . . . . . . . . . TCEM 282
■ 12" . . . . . . . . . . . . . . . . . . . 12EM 282
■ 7" . . . . . . . . . . . . . . . . . . . . EM 282
■ CD Single . . . . . . . . . . . . . . . .CDEM 282
EMI / Aug '93.

**BLUE (IS THE COLOUR OF PAIN).**
Tracks: Blue (is the colour of pain) / Blue (is the colour of pain) (Blak + Blue mix) / This is mine (remix) / Blue (is the colour of pain) (Perfect shade of aqua mix) / Jamaica.
■ 12" . . . . . . . . . . . . . . . . . . . PT 44535
■ 12" Remix. . . . . . . . . . . . . . . . PT 44538
■ 7" . . . . . . . . . . . . . . . . . . . PB 44535
■ CD Single . . . . . . . . . . . . . . . PD 44536
■ MC Single. . . . . . . . . . . . . . . . PK 44535
RCA / Jun '91.

**DON'T QUIT.**
Tracks: Don't quit / My time / Livin' in the light (remix) (Only on CD and MC single).
■ 7" . . . . . . . . . . . . . . . . . . . PB 44259
■ CD Single . . . . . . . . . . . . . . . PD 44260
■ MC Single. . . . . . . . . . . . . . . . PK 44259
■ 12" . . . . . . . . . . . . . . . . . . . PT 44260
RCA / Feb '91.

**I ADORE YOU.**
Tracks: I adore you (LP radio mix) / I adore you (Club house edit) / I adore you (I adore dubb) / I adore you (Catch the groove mix) / I adore you (Club house mix) / I adore you (LP version) / I adore you (Dance hall version).
■ CD Single . . . . . . . . . . . . . . . PERD 7407
■ 12" . . . . . . . . . . . . . . . . . . . PERT 7407
■ 7" . . . . . . . . . . . . . . . . . . . PERSS 7407
■ MC Single. . . . . . . . . . . . . . . . PERCS 7407
A&M / Oct '92.

**LIVIN' IN THE LIGHT.**
Tracks: Livin' in the light.
■ 12" Remix. . . . . . . . . . . . . . . . PT 43942
■ 7" . . . . . . . . . . . . . . . . . . . PB 43939
■ MC Single. . . . . . . . . . . . . . . . PK 43939
■ CD Single . . . . . . . . . . . . . . . PD 43940
■ 12" . . . . . . . . . . . . . . . . . . . PT 43940
RCA / Aug '90.

**UK BLAK.**
Tracks: UK blak / Livin' in the light (remix) / Blue (is the colour of pain) / No regrets / This is mine / Don't

quit (Only on CD) / Jamaica / Never lonely / Song for you / Somewhere / Enchanted / Proud / Kama ye (Only on CD) / Livin' in the light (original story).
■ CD. . . . . . . . . . . . . . . . . . . . PD 7475
■ LP. . . . . . . . . . . . . . . . . . . . PL 7475
■ MC. . . . . . . . . . . . . . . . . . . . PK 7475
RCA / Sep '90.
CD . . . . . . . . . . . . . . . . . 74321 14774:
RCA / Jun '93 / BMG.

**UK BLAK.**
Tracks: UK Blak / Burn inside / UK blak (dub) (12 only.).
■ 7" . . . . . . . . . . . . . . . . . . . PB 43711
■ MC Single. . . . . . . . . . . . . . . . PK 43711
■ 12" . . . . . . . . . . . . . . . . . . . PT 43721
■ 12" Remix. . . . . . . . . . . . . . . . PT 43722
■ CD Single . . . . . . . . . . . . . . . PD 4372
RCA / Oct '90.

## Which Is Which

**I CAN'T GET ENOUGH.**
Tracks: I can't get enough.
■ 12" . . . . . . . . . . . . . . . . . . . . .HA 106
Pulse / Jul '89.

## Whispers

Led by brothers Wallace and Walter Scott Whispers were already veterans when their career received well-earned boost in mid 70's. Having scored minor soul hits for various small labels, quintet signed with Soul Train Records, offshoot of TV's most important black music show. With new backing, group made R&B Top Ten twice, with *One For The Money* and unlikely remake of Bread's *Make It With You*. In '78, Soul Train evolved into SOLAR (Sound Of Los Angeles Records). Solar production supremo Leon Sylvers gave Whispers their first and biggest international smash with 1980's *And The Beat Goes On*. However, after second transatlantic hit with *It's A Love Thing* group's success began to slide; although unlike most disco stars, they were still charting in late '80s, in U.K. pop and U.S. soul listings. Among these later successes was *LA & Babyface-produced '87 single *Rock Steady*.

**30TH ANNIVERSARY ANTHOLOGY.**
Tracks: Seems like I gotta do wrong / There's a love for everyone / Can't help but love you / I only mean to wet my feet / Somebody loves you / Mother for my children / Bingo / One for the money / Living together (In sin) / Make it with you / (Let's go) All the way / (Olivia) Lost and turned out / Can't do without love / Song for Donny / Beat goes on / Lady my girl It's a love thing / I'm the one for you / I can make it better / This kind of lovin' / In the raw / Emergency Tonight / Keep on loving me / Contagious / Some kinda lover / Rock steady / Just gets better with time / In the mood / No pain no gain / Say yes / Special F/X.
CD Set . . . . . . . . . . . . . . . . NEDCD 26
Sequel / Aug '94 / Total / BMG.

**AND THE BEAT GOES ON.**
Tracks: Some kinda lover / It's a love thing (Extra track on 12" only) / Contagious (Extra track on 12" only) / And the beat goes on.
■ 7" . . . . . . . . . . . . . . . . . . . . .SO
Solar / Feb '80.
■ 12" . . . . . . . . . . . . . . . . . . . SO 121 8
Soul Train / Jul '81.
■ 12" . . . . . . . . . . . . . . . . . . . MCAT 1126
■ 7" . . . . . . . . . . . . . . . . . . . .MCA 1126
MCA / Mar '87.

**AND THE BEAT GOES ON (OLD GOLD).**
Tracks: And the beat goes on / It's a love thing / Rock steady.
■ 12" . . . . . . . . . . . . . . . . . . . .OG 406
Old Gold / Jul '89.
CD Single . . . . . . . . . . . . . . . . .OG 6514
Old Gold / '92 / Pickwick.

**BEST OF THE WHISPERS.**
Tracks: Beat goes on / Make it with you / Lost & turned out / Loving together / One for the money / I can make it better / It's a love thing.
■ LP . . . . . . . . . . . . . . . . . . . . SOLA 12
MC. . . . . . . . . . . . . . . . . . . . SOLC 12
Solar / '82 / Sony.

**BINGO.**
Tracks: Bingo / Someone's waiting.
■ 7" . . . . . . . . . . . . . . . . . . . . 6146026
Janus / Jun '74.

456

■ DELETED

## CONTAGIOUS.
Tracks: Contagious / Keep your love around.
■ 12" . . . . . . . . . . . . . . . . . . . MCAT 937
■ 7" . . . . . . . . . . . . . . . . . . . MCA 937
MCA / Jan '85.

## EMERGENCY.
Tracks: Emergency / Only you.
■ 12" . . . . . . . . . . . . . . . . . . K 13171 T
■ 7" . . . . . . . . . . . . . . . . . . . K 13171
Solar / Apr '82.

## HEADLIGHTS.
Tracks: Headlights / (Olivia) Lost and turned out / Let's go) All the way / (You're a) Special part of my life / Planets of life / Try and make it better / Disco melody / Children of tomorrow.
■ LP . . . . . . . . . . . . . . . . . . . FL 12774
■ MC . . . . . . . . . . . . . . . . . . . FK 12774
RCA / Jul '78.

## HEADLIGHTS.
Tracks: Headlights / (Let's go) All the way.
■ 12" . . . . . . . . . . . . . . . . . . . FC 9287
Grunt / '79.

## I CAN MAKE IT BETTER.
Tracks: I can make it better / Say you.
■ 12" . . . . . . . . . . . . . . . . . . . SOT 19
■ 7" . . . . . . . . . . . . . . . . . . . SO 19
Solar / May '81.

## IMAGINATION.
Tracks: It's a love thing / Say you would love for me too / Continental shuffle / I can make it better / Imagination / Girl I need you / Up on soul train / Fantasy.
■ LP . . . . . . . . . . . . . . . . . . . SOLA 7
Solar / Mar '81.

## IN THE RAW.
Tracks: In the raw / Small talkin'.
■ 12" . . . . . . . . . . . . . . . . . . K 12597 T
■ 7" . . . . . . . . . . . . . . . . . . . K 12597
Solar / Jan '82.

## IT'S A LOVE THING.
Tracks: It's a love thing / Girl I need you.
■ 12" . . . . . . . . . . . . . . . . . . . SOT 16
■ 7" . . . . . . . . . . . . . . . . . . . SO 16
Solar / Feb '81.

## JUST GETS BETTER WITH TIME.
Tracks: I want you / Special FX / Rock steady / No pain, no gain / In the mood / Just gets better with time / Love's calling / Give it to me.
■ LP . . . . . . . . . . . . . . . . . . . MCF 3381
■ CD . . . . . . . . . . . . . . . . . . . DMCF 3381
■ MC . . . . . . . . . . . . . . . . . . . MCFC 3381
MCA / May '87.

## LADY.
Tracks: Lady / I love you.
■ 12" . . . . . . . . . . . . . . . . . . . SO 12 4
■ 7" . . . . . . . . . . . . . . . . . . . SO 4
Solar / May '80.

## LIVING TOGETHER IN SIN.
Tracks: Living together in sin / I've got a feeling.
■ 7" . . . . . . . . . . . . . . . . . . . FB 0773
Soul Train / Jan '77.

## LOVE FOR LOVE.
Tracks: Tonight / Keep on lovin' me / Love for love / This time / Had it not been for you / Try it again / Do they turn you on / Keep your love around / Lay it on me.
■ LP . . . . . . . . . . . . . . . . . . . E0216
Solar / May '83.

## LOVE IS WHERE YOU FIND IT.
Tracks: In the raw / Turn me out / Cruisin' in / Emergency / Say yes / Love is where you find it / Only you / Small talkin'.
■ LP . . . . . . . . . . . . . . . . . . . K 52344
Solar / Apr '82.

## MAKE IT WITH YOU.
Tracks: Make it with you / You are Number One.
■ 12" . . . . . . . . . . . . . . . . . . . FC 0996
■ 7" . . . . . . . . . . . . . . . . . . . FB 0996
Grunt / '79.

## MORE OF THE NIGHT.
Tracks: Innocent / Girl don't make me wait / Misunderstanding / Forever lover / Babes / More of the night / My heart your heart / Mind blowing / Is it good for you / Don't be late for love (Cassette & CD only.) / You are the one (Cassette & CD only.) / I want 2B the U (Cassette & CD only.) / Help them see the light (Cassette & CD only.).
CD . . . . . . . . . . . . . . . . . . . CDEST 2130
■ LP . . . . . . . . . . . . . . . . . . . EST 2130

■ MC . . . . . . . . . . . . . . . . . . . TCEST 2130
Capitol / Aug '90 / EMI.

## MY GIRL.
Tracks: My girl / Olivia lost and turned out.
■ 12" . . . . . . . . . . . . . . . . . . . SO 12 8
■ 7" . . . . . . . . . . . . . . . . . . . SO 8
Solar / Jul '80.

## NO PAIN, NO GAIN.
Tracks: No pain, no gain / Uptown mix / No pain, no gain (extended) (On 12" version only.).
■ 12" . . . . . . . . . . . . . . . . . . . MCAT 1212
■ 7" . . . . . . . . . . . . . . . . . . . MCA 1212
MCA / Oct '87.

## OPEN UP YOUR LOVE.
Tracks: Make it with you / Chocolate girl / Love is a dream / Open up your love / I fell in love last night (at the disco) / You are Number One / You never miss your water / I'm gonna make you my wife.
■ LP . . . . . . . . . . . . . . . . . . . FL 12270
Grunt / '79.

## OUT OF THE BOX.
Tracks: Out of the box / Welcome into my dream.
■ 12" . . . . . . . . . . . . . . . . . . . SOT 12
■ 7" . . . . . . . . . . . . . . . . . . . SO 12
Solar / Sep '80.

## ROCK STEADY.
Tracks: Rock steady / Are you going my way.
■ 12" . . . . . . . . . . . . . . . . . . . MCAT 1152
■ 7" . . . . . . . . . . . . . . . . . . . MCA 1152
MCA / May '87.

## SO GOOD.
Tracks: Some kinda lover / Contagious / Sweet sensation / Impact / Romancin'III / Suddenly / Don't keep me waiting / Are you going my way / Never too late / So good.
■ LP . . . . . . . . . . . . . . . . . . . MCF 3252
■ MC . . . . . . . . . . . . . . . . . . . MCFC 3252
MCA / Jan '85.
■ MC . . . . . . . . . . . . . . . . . . . MCLC 1845
■ LP . . . . . . . . . . . . . . . . . . . MCL 1845
MCA / Mar '87.
■ LP . . . . . . . . . . . . . . . . . . . 603 561
Solar / Dec '88.

## SOME KINDA LOVER.
Tracks: Some kinda lover.
■ 12" . . . . . . . . . . . . . . . . . . . MCAT 951
■ 7" . . . . . . . . . . . . . . . . . . . MCA 951
MCA / Apr '85.

## SPECIAL FX.
Tracks: Special FX.
■ 12" . . . . . . . . . . . . . . . . . . . MCAT 1178
■ 7" . . . . . . . . . . . . . . . . . . . MCA 1178
MCA / Aug '87.

## THIS KIND OF LOVIN.
Tracks: This kind of lovin' / World of a thousand dreams / I'm the one for you / Got to get away / I'm gonna love you more / Can't stop loving you baby / What will I do / Bright lights and you girl.
■ LP . . . . . . . . . . . . . . . . . . . SOLA 9
■ MC . . . . . . . . . . . . . . . . . . . SOLC 9
Solar / Oct '81 / Sony.

## THIS KIND OF LOVIN.
Tracks: This kind of lovin.
■ 12" . . . . . . . . . . . . . . . . . . . SOT 22
■ 7" . . . . . . . . . . . . . . . . . . . SO 22
Solar / Sep '81.

## THIS TIME.
Tracks: This time / Tonight.
■ 12" . . . . . . . . . . . . . . . . . . . E 9878 T
■ 7" . . . . . . . . . . . . . . . . . . . E 9878
Solar / Mar '83.

## WHISPER IN YOUR EAR.
Tracks: Homemade livin' / If I don't get your love / Whisper in your ear / Love at its best / Can't do without love / Pretty lady / You'll never get away.
■ LP . . . . . . . . . . . . . . . . . . . FL 13105
Solar / '79.

## WHISPERS.
Tracks: Song for Donny / My girl / Lady can you do the boogie / Beat goes on / I love you / Out the box / Welcome into my dream.
■ LP . . . . . . . . . . . . . . . . . . . SOLA 1
Solar / Apr '80.

## WHISPERS.
Tracks: You must be doing all right / Seems like I gotta do wrong / Planets of life / They're going to hear from me / Sing of songs / I can remember / Needle in a haystack / Creation of love / I'm the one / You've made me so very happy.

■ LP . . . . . . . . . . . . . . . . . . . .2916 003
Mojo / Aug '71.

## White, Anthony

### I CAN'T TURN YOU LOOSE.
Tracks: I can't turn you loose / Block party.
■ 7" . . . . . . . . . . . . . . . . . . . SSOL 103
Salsoul / Mar '78.

## White, Artie

### BEST OF ARTIE WHITE, THE.
Tracks: Today I started loving you again / Nothing takes the place of you / Tore up / Tired of sneaking around / Jodie / Dark end of the street / That's where it's at / Nobody wants you when you're old and grey / Funny how time slips away / Hattie MAe / Thangs got to change / I need someone.
LP . . . . . . . . . . . . . . . . . . . ICH 1131
MC . . . . . . . . . . . . . . . . . . . MCICH 1131
Ichiban / Feb '92 / A.D.A. Distribution / Pinnacle / ACD Trading Ltd. / Koch International / Direct Distribution.
CD . . . . . . . . . . . . . . . . . . . CDICH 1131
Ichiban / Oct '93 / A.D.A. Distribution / Pinnacle / ACD Trading Ltd. / Koch International / Direct Distribution.

### DARK END OF THE STREET.
Tracks: Tore up / Clock don't tick / Nite before pay day / Not in the begging business / Somebody changed my sweet baby's mind / Dark end of the street / Hit the nail on the head / I intend to take your place / Darlin' you know I love you / I'm mean.
■ LP . . . . . . . . . . . . . . . . . . . ICH 1117
■ MC . . . . . . . . . . . . . . . . . . . ICH 1117MC
Ichiban / Sep '91.
■ CD . . . . . . . . . . . . . . . . . . . CDICH 1117
Ichiban / Oct '93.

### HIT AND RUN.
Tracks: Not Advised.
■ CD . . . . . . . . . . . . . . . . . . . ICH 1136CD
■ MC . . . . . . . . . . . . . . . . . . . ICH 1136MC
Ichiban / Jun '92.

### NOTHING TAKES THE PLACE OF YOU.
Tracks: Wondering how you keep your man / How could you do it to me / Lies I want to hear / All you got / Funny how time slips away / Nothing takes the place of you / Ever loving man / I found a woman / I need someone.
LP . . . . . . . . . . . . . . . . . . . ICH 1008
MC . . . . . . . . . . . . . . . . . . . ZCICH 1008
Ichiban / Aug '87 / A.D.A. Distribution / Pinnacle / ACD Trading Ltd. / Koch International / Direct Distribution.

### THINGS GOT TO CHANGE.
Tracks: Things got to change / Rainy day / I ain't taking no prisoners / You upset me baby / Thank you pretty baby / Hattie Mae / I wonder why / Reconsider baby / Somebody's on my case.
LP . . . . . . . . . . . . . . . . . . . ICH 1044
MC . . . . . . . . . . . . . . . . . . . ZCICH 1044
Ichiban / Sep '89 / A.D.A. Distribution / Pinnacle / ACD Trading Ltd. / Koch International / Direct Distribution.
CD . . . . . . . . . . . . . . . . . . . CDICH 1044
Ichiban / Oct '93 / A.D.A. Distribution / Pinnacle / ACD Trading Ltd. / Koch International / Direct Distribution.

### TIRED OF SNEAKIN' AROUND.
Tracks: Today I started loving you / Thinking about making a change / Jodie / Peeping Tom / Tired of sneaking around / Don't pet my dog / Can't get you off my mind / I can't seem to please you / Turn about is fair play / Nose to the grindstone.
LP . . . . . . . . . . . . . . . . . . . ICH 1061
MC . . . . . . . . . . . . . . . . . . . ICH 1061MC
Ichiban / Jul '90 / A.D.A. Distribution / Pinnacle / ACD Trading Ltd. / Koch International / Direct Distribution.
CD . . . . . . . . . . . . . . . . . . . CDICH 1061
Ichiban / Oct '93 / A.D.A. Distribution / Pinnacle / ACD Trading Ltd. / Koch International / Direct Distribution.

### WHERE IT'S AT.
Tracks: Not Advised.
LP . . . . . . . . . . . . . . . . . . . ICH 1026
MC . . . . . . . . . . . . . . . . . . . ZCICH 1026
Ichiban / Nov '88 / A.D.A. Distribution / Pinnacle / ACD Trading Ltd. / Koch International / Direct Distribution.
CD . . . . . . . . . . . . . . . . . . . CDICH 1026
Ichiban / Oct '93 / A.D.A. Distribution / Pinnacle / ACD Trading Ltd. / Koch International / Direct Distribution.

## White, Barry

Having produced several minor '60s acts, White formed Love Unlimited in early '70s, scoring international hit with *Walking In The Rain (With The One I Love)*. Single featured White's wife Glodean James and cameo from man himself, thus forming prelude to latter's solo career. Bridging gap between Isaac Hayes and disco, White gained massive sales for his extravagant 'lurve' anthems, biggest of which was '74's *You're The First, The Last, My Everything*. Last major hit was cover of Billy Joel's *Just The Way You Are*. Despite brief renaissance with *Sho' You Right* in '88, White has yet to recapture limelight; instead guesting on records by Big Daddy Kane, Lisa Stansfield and Quincy Jones (other collaborators included Ray Parker Jr, Lee Ritenour, Nathan East and Jermaine Jackson). White compilations are guaranteed money-spinners, and '93 box-set *Just For You* is appropriately bulging tribute.

### ALL IN THE RUN OF A DAY.
**Tracks:** All in the run of a day / Don't take your love from me.
■ 7" . . . . . . . . . . . . . . . . . . . . . . . . . . .PT 139
President / Jun '67.

### BABY WE BETTER TRY AND GET IT TOGETHER.
**Tracks:** Baby we better try and get it together.
■ 7" . . . . . . . . . . . . . . . . . . . . . . . . . BTC 2298
20th Century / Aug '76.

### BARRY AND GLODEAN (White, Barry & Glodean).
**Tracks:** Our theme / I want you / You're the only one for me / This love / Better love is / You / We can't let go of love / You make my life easy livin' / Didn't we make it happen baby.
■ LP . . . . . . . . . . . . . . . . . . . ULG 84870
MC. . . . . . . . . . . . . . . . . . . . .40 84870
Unlimited Gold(USA) / May '81 / Sony.
CD. . . . . . . . . . . . . . . . . . . .CDSEWM 073
South Bound / Mar '93 / Pinnacle.

### BARRY WHITE-HEART AND SOUL.
**Tracks:** You're the first, the last, my everything / I'm gonna love you just a little bit more baby / Standing in the shadows of love / What am I gonna do about you / Never never gonna give you up / I love to sing the songs I sing / Don't make me wait too long / You see the trouble with me / Love serenade / It's ecstasy when you lay down next to me / I can't get enough of your love / I'm qualified to satisfy you / Sha la la means I love you / Honey please can't you see / I've found someone / Let me live my life loving you babe / Let the music play / Baby we better try and get it together / Playing your game baby / I've got so much to give / September when I first met you / Love's theme.
■ LP . . . . . . . . . . . . . . . . . . . . . NE 1314
■ MC. . . . . . . . . . . . . . . . . . . . . CE 2314
K-Tel / Nov '85.

### BARRY WHITE: COLLECTION.
**Tracks:** Out of the shadows / I've got the world to hold me up / Under the influence of love / Where can I turn to / Long black veil / All in the run of a day / Come on in love / Fragile - handle with care / Your heart and soul / Big man / My buddy / I owe it all to you / Lady sweet lady / I like you to like me / Change / I found love.
CD. . . . . . . . . . . . . . . . . . . . . . RC 81115
MC. . . . . . . . . . . . . . . . . . . . . . RC 82115
Royal Collection / Sep '93 / BMG.

### BEST OF BARRY WHITE.
**Tracks:** I've got so much to give / Midnight and you / Bring back my yesterdays / Love's theme / I've found someone / Under the influence of love / You're the first, the last, my everything / Together brothers (From the film.) / I'll do for you anything you want me to / I belong to you.

### BEST OF BARRY WHITE AND LOVE UNLIMITED ORCHESTRA.
**Tracks:** Let the music play / Midnight and you / Don't make me wait too long / I'm qualified to satisfy you / Under the influence of love / Love's theme / Your sweetness is my weakness / I'll do for you anything you want me / I belong to you.
■ LP . . . . . . . . . . . . . . . . . . . . . 8129431
MC. . . . . . . . . . . . . . . . . . . . . . 8129434
Casablanca / Jun '88.

### BEST OF OUR LOVE.
**Tracks:** I love to sing the songs I sing / Let me live my life loving you babe / It's ecstasy when you lay down next to me / I'm gonna love you just a little bit more / Can't get enough of your love babe / You're

the first the last my everything / You see the trouble with me / Playing your game baby / September when I first met you / Just the way you are / Oh love well we finally made it / I'm under the influence of love / I belong to you / Walking in the rain with the one I love / I guess I'm just (another girl in love) / My sweet summer suite / Midnight and you / Satin soul / Baby blues / Love's theme.
■ LP . . . . . . . . . . . . . . . . . . . ULG 88520
Unlimited Gold(USA) / Mar '81.

### BEWARE.
**Tracks:** Beware / Relax to the max / Let me in and let's begin with love / Your love, your love / Rio de janeiro / You're my high / Ooooo..ahhh / I won't settle for less than the best (you baby) / Louie Louie.
CD. . . . . . . . . . . . . . . . . . . . .CDSEWM 074
South Bound / Mar '93 / Pinnacle.

### CAN'T GET ENOUGH.
**Tracks:** Not Advised.
■ LP . . . . . . . . . . . . . . . . . . . . . .BT 444
20th Century / Nov '74.

### CAN'T GET ENOUGH OF YOUR LOVE BABE.
**Tracks:** Can't get enough of your love babe.
■ 7" . . . . . . . . . . . . . . . . . . . . . 7N 25661
Pye International / Aug '74.

### CHANGE.
**Tracks:** Change / Turnin' on, tunin' in / Don't tell me about heartaches / Passion / I've got that love fever / I like you, you like me / It's all about love / Let's make tonight (An evening to remember) / I've got that lover fever.
■ LP . . . . . . . . . . . . . . . . . . . ULG 85788
Unlimited Gold(USA) / Dec '82.
CD. . . . . . . . . . . . . . . . . . . .CDSEWM 075
South Bound / Apr '93 / Pinnacle.

### COLLECTION: BARRY WHITE.
**Tracks:** You're the first, the last, my everything / You see the trouble with me / Can't get enough of your love babe / I'll do for you anything you want me to / Just the way you are / Walking in the rain (with the one I love) / It may be Winter outside / Love's theme / Sho' you right / What am I gonna do with you / Never never gonna give you up / Baby we better try and get it together / Let the music play / Don't make me wait too long / I'm gonna love you just a little more baby / Right night.
■ CD . . . . . . . . . . . . . . . . . BWTVCD 1
■ LP . . . . . . . . . . . . . . . . . . BWTV 1
■ MC . . . . . . . . . . . . . . . . . . BWTVC 1
Polydor / Jun '88.
CD. . . . . . . . . . . . . . . . . . . . . 8347902
MC. . . . . . . . . . . . . . . . . . . . . 8347904
Polygram T.V. / Feb '94 / PolyGram.

### COLLECTION: BARRY WHITE.
**Tracks:** Never never gonna give you up / What am I gonna do with you / Playing your games / You see the trouble with me / You're the first, the last, my everything / I wanna do it good to ya / Just the way you are / Can't get enough of your love babe / Let the music play / Follow that and see (where it leads y'all) / Sho' you right.
■ VHS . . . . . . . . . . . . . . . . . . 792.103
BMG Video / '91.
VHS . . . . . . . . . . . . . . . . . .WNR 2019
Wienerworld Video / Feb '91 / VCI Distribution / THE.

### COME IN LOVE.
**Tracks:** Not Advised.
CD . . . . . . . . . . . . . . . . . . . CDCD 1188
Charly / Sep '94 / Charly.

### DEDICATED.
**Tracks:** America / Free / Don't forget.. remember / Life / Love song / All in the run of a day / Don't let 'em blow your mind / Dreams.
■ LP . . . . . . . . . . . . . . . . . . . ULG 25474
MC. . . . . . . . . . . . . . . . . . . . .40 25474
Unlimited Gold(USA) / Sep '83 / Sony.
CD. . . . . . . . . . . . . . . . . . . .CDSEWM 076
South Bound / Apr '93 / Pinnacle.

### DIDN'T WE MAKE IT HAPPY BABY.
**Tracks:** Didn't we make it happy baby / I'll sing.
■ 7" . . . . . . . . . . . . . . . . . . . . . .A 1125
Unlimited Gold(USA) / Apr '81.

### DON'T MAKE ME WAIT TOO LONG.
**Tracks:** Don't make me wait too long.
■ 7" . . . . . . . . . . . . . . . . . . . . BTC 2309
20th Century / Nov '76.

### FOLLOW THAT AND SEE (WHERE IT LEADS Y'ALL).
**Tracks:** Follow that and see (where it leads y'all) / Follow that and see (instrumental).
■ 7" . . . . . . . . . . . . . . . . . . . . .USA 670
Breakout / Oct '89.

### FOR YOUR LOVE.
**Tracks:** For your love / Love is in your eyes / As time goes by.
■ 12" . . . . . . . . . . . . . . . . . . . . USAT 61
■ 7" . . . . . . . . . . . . . . . . . . . . .USA 61
Breakout / Jan '88.

### GREATEST HITS: BARRY WHITE, VOL 2.
**Tracks:** Not Advised.
■ LP . . . . . . . . . . . . . . . . . . . BTH 800
20th Century / Apr '77.

### GREATEST HITS: BARRY WHITE, VOL.1
**Tracks:** What am I gonna do with you / You're the first, the last, my everything / Can't get enough of your love, babe / Honey please can't you see / Love serenade / Never never gonna give ya up / I'm gonna love you just a little more baby / I've found someone / I've too much to give / Standing in the shadows of love.
■ LP . . . . . . . . . . . . . . . . . . . BTH 800
20th Century / Nov '75.
■ LP . . . . . . . . . . . . . . . . . . . . T 49
20th Century / Feb '80.
■ LP . . . . . . . . . . . . . . . . . . PRICE 1
20th Century / Feb '80.
MC. . . . . . . . . . . . . . . . . . . .PRIMC 1
20th Century / May '83.

### HEART AND SOUL.
**Tracks:** Not Advised.
■ LP . . . . . . . . . . . . . . . . . . . . NE 131
K-Tel / Dec '85.

### I LOVE TO SING THE SONGS I SING.
**Tracks:** I love to sing the songs I sing / Girl, what's your name / Once upon a time / Oh me oh my / I can't leave you alone / Call me baby / How did you know it was me.
■ LP . . . . . . . . . . . . . . . . . . . . T 59
20th Century / Feb '80.

### I WANNA DO IT TO YA.
**Tracks:** I wanna do it to ya.
■ CD Single . . . . . . . . . . . . . USACD 68
■ 12" . . . . . . . . . . . . . . . . . . USAT 68
■ 7" . . . . . . . . . . . . . . . . . . . .USA 68
A&M / May '90.

### I'LL DO FOR YOU ANYTHING YOU WANT ME TO.
**Tracks:** I'll do for you anything you want me to.
■ 7" . . . . . . . . . . . . . . . . . . . BTC 220
20th Century / May '75.

### I'M GONNA LOVE YOU JUST A LITTLE BIT MORE BABY.
**Tracks:** I'm gonna love you just a little bit more baby
■ 7" . . . . . . . . . . . . . . . . . . . 7N 2561
Pye International / Jun '73.

### I'M QUALIFIED TO SATISFY.
**Tracks:** I'm qualified to satisfy you.
■ 7" . . . . . . . . . . . . . . . . . . . BTC 232
20th Century / Mar '77.

### ICON IS LOVE, THE.
**Tracks:** Practice what you preach / There it is / I only want to be with you / Time is right / Baby's home / Come on / Love is the icon / Sexy undercover / Don' you want to know / Whatever we had, we had.
CD. . . . . . . . . . . . . . . . . . .540280-2
MC. . . . . . . . . . . . . . . . . . .540280-4
A&M / Oct '94 / PolyGram.

### IT'S ECSTASY WHEN YOU LAY DOWN NEXT TO ME.
**Tracks:** It's ecstasy when you lay down next to me / never thought I'd fall in love with you.
■ 7" . . . . . . . . . . . . . . . . . . . BTC 235
20th Century / Oct '77.

### JUST ANOTHER WAY TO SAY I LOVE YOU.
**Tracks:** Not Advised.
■ LP . . . . . . . . . . . . . . . . . . . .BT 46
20th Century / Apr '75.

### JUST FOR YOU.
**Tracks:** Not Advised.
CD. . . . . . . . . . . . . . . . . . . .514143
Phonogram / Jan '93 / PolyGram.

### JUST THE WAY YOU ARE.
**Tracks:** Just the way you are / Your sweetness is my weakness.
■ 7" . . . . . . . . . . . . . . . . . . . BTC 238
20th Century / Dec '78.

### LET THE MUSIC PLAY.
**Tracks:** You're the first, the last, my everything / Your sweetness is my weakness / I feel love coming on / Midnight and you / Barry's theme / Oh love, we

■ DELETE

we finally made it / I'm qualified to satisfy / Oh what a night for dancing / You see the trouble with me / Sha la la means I love you / It's ecstasy when you lay next to me / Standing in the shadows of love / What a groove / Honey, please can't you see / Rhapsody in white / Let the music play on.

■ LP . . . . . . . . . . . . . . . . . . . . . . . . . . . . . BT 502
20th Century / Feb '76.
CD . . . . . . . . . . . . . . . . . . . . . . . . . PWKS 4128P
MC . . . . . . . . . . . . . . . . . . . . . . . PWKMC 4128P
Pickwick / Oct '92 / Pickwick.

### LET THE MUSIC PLAY.
Tracks: Let the music play.
■ 7" . . . . . . . . . . . . . . . . . . . . . . . . . . BTC 2265
20th Century / Dec '75.
■ 7" . . . . . . . . . . . . . . . . . . . . . . . . . GOLD 533
RCA Golden Grooves / Oct '81.

### LOVE AIN'T EASY.
Tracks: Love ain't easy / I'm on fire.
■ 7" . . . . . . . . . . . . . . . . . . . . . . . . . ULG 7778
Unlimited Gold(USA) / Aug '79.

### MAN IS BACK, THE.
Tracks: Responsible / Super lover / L.A. my kinda place / Follow that and see (where it leads y'all) / When will I see you again / I wanna do it good to ya / It's getting harder all the time / Don't let go / Loves interlude / Goodnight my love.
CD . . . . . . . . . . . . . . . . . . . . . . . . . CDA 5256
MC . . . . . . . . . . . . . . . . . . . . . . . . . AMC 5256
■ LP . . . . . . . . . . . . . . . . . . . . . . . . . AMA 5256
A&M / Aug '89 / PolyGram.

### MAN, THE.
Tracks: Look at her / Your sweetness is my weakness / Sha la la means I love you / September when I first met you / It's only love doing it's thing / Just the way you are / Early years.
■ LP . . . . . . . . . . . . . . . . . . . . . . . . . . BT 571
20th Century / Dec '78.

### MESSAGE IS LOVE, THE.
Tracks: It ain't love baby / Hung up in your love / You're the one I need / Any fool could see / Love ain't easy / I'm on fire / I found love.
■ LP . . . . . . . . . . . . . . . . . . . . . . . . ULG 83475
MC . . . . . . . . . . . . . . . . . . . . . . . . .40 83475
Unlimited Gold(USA) / Apr '79.
CD . . . . . . . . . . . . . . . . . . . . . . . CDSEWM 071
South Bound / Feb '93 / Pinnacle.

### NEVER NEVER GONNA GIVE YOU UP.
Tracks: Never never gonna give you up (Paul Hardcastle remix) / September when I first met you / Never never gonna give you up (mammoth mix) Extra track, available on 12" only.) / Never never gonna give you up (ext. mix) (Extra track, available on 12" only.).
■ 7" . . . . . . . . . . . . . . . . . . . . . . . . 7N 25633
Pye International / Jan '74.
■ 12" . . . . . . . . . . . . . . . . . . . . . . . . JABX 59
■ 7" . . . . . . . . . . . . . . . . . . . . . . . . . JAB 59
Club / Sep '87.

### NEVER NEVER GONNA GIVE YOU UP (OLD GOLD).
Tracks: Never never gonna give you up / I'm gonna love you just a little bit more.
■ 7" . . . . . . . . . . . . . . . . . . . . . . . . OG 9768
Old Gold / Oct '88.

### OH WHAT A NIGHT FOR DANCING.
Tracks: Oh what a night for dancing / You're so good, you're so bad.
■ 7" . . . . . . . . . . . . . . . . . . . . . . . . BTC 2365
20th Century / Aug '78.

### PUT ME IN YOUR MIX.
Tracks: Put me in your mix / I wanna do it good to ya.
■ 12" . . . . . . . . . . . . . . . . . . . . . . . . AMY 833
■ CD Single . . . . . . . . . . . . . . . . . . . AMCD 833
■ MC Single . . . . . . . . . . . . . . . . . . . AMMC 833
■ 7" . . . . . . . . . . . . . . . . . . . . . . . . . AM 833
A&M / Oct '91.

### PUT ME IN YOUR MIX.
Tracks: Let's get busy / Love is good for you / For real chill / Break it down with you / Volare / Put me in your mix / Who you giving your love to / Love will find us / We're gonna have it all / Dark and lovely (you over there) / Sho' you right (remix).
CD . . . . . . . . . . . . . . . . . . . . . . . . .394377 2
■ LP . . . . . . . . . . . . . . . . . . . . . . . .395377 1
MC . . . . . . . . . . . . . . . . . . . . . . . . .395377 4
A&M / Oct '91 / PolyGram.

### RHAPSODY IN WHITE.
Tracks: Not Advised.
■ LP . . . . . . . . . . . . . . . . . . . . . . . NSPL 28191
Pye / Apr '74.

### RIGHT NIGHT AND BARRY WHITE, THE.
Tracks: Sho' you right / For your love / There is a place / Love is in your eyes / Right night / I'm ready for love / Share / Who's the fool.
■ CD . . . . . . . . . . . . . . . . . . . . . . . . CDA 5154
■ LP . . . . . . . . . . . . . . . . . . . . . . . . AMA 5154
■ MC . . . . . . . . . . . . . . . . . . . . . . . . AMC 5154
A&M / Oct '87.
CD . . . . . . . . . . . . . . . . . . . . . . . . CDMID 155
MC . . . . . . . . . . . . . . . . . . . . . . . . CMID 155
A&M / Oct '92 / PolyGram.

### RIGHT NIGHT, THE.
Tracks: Right night / Right night, The (baad remix) (Extra track on 12".) / Right night, The (baad dub) (Extra track on 12".) / There's a place.
■ 12" . . . . . . . . . . . . . . . . . . . . . . . . USAT 626
■ 7" . . . . . . . . . . . . . . . . . . . . . . . . . USA 626
Breakout / Mar '88.

### RUM AND COCA COLA.
Tracks: Rum and coca cola / Everything to me.
■ 7" . . . . . . . . . . . . . . . . . . . . . . . . ULG 8901
Unlimited Gold(USA) / Aug '80.

### SATIN AND SOUL.
Tracks: You're the first, the last, my everything / Can't get enough of your love babe / It may be Winter outside / I'll do for you anything you want me to / Honey please can't you see / Satin soul / Never gonna give ya up / I love to sing the songs I sing / You see the trouble with me / Playing your game / I needed your love, you were there / Hard to believe that I found you / Standing in the shadows of love / I can't let him down / Only you can make me blue / Heavenly that's what you are to me / Oh love we finally made it / Love serenade / Just the way you are / Bring back my yesterdays / Baby blues / Midnight and you / September when I first met you / Love's theme.
■ LP . . . . . . . . . . . . . . . . . . . . . . . VSOPLP 101
■ MC . . . . . . . . . . . . . . . . . . . . . . VSOPMC 101
Connoisseur Collection / Nov '87.
■ CD . . . . . . . . . . . . . . . . . . . . . . VSOPCD 101
Connoisseur Collection / Jan '90.

### SEPTEMBER WHEN I FIRST MET YOU.
Tracks: September when I first met you / Early years.
■ 12" . . . . . . . . . . . . . . . . . . . . . . . BTCL 1045
■ 7" . . . . . . . . . . . . . . . . . . . . . . . . BTC 1045
20th Century / Jul '79.

### SHA LA LA MEANS I LOVE YOU.
Tracks: Sha la la means I love you / It's only love doing its thing.
■ 12" . . . . . . . . . . . . . . . . . . . . . . . BTCL 1041
■ 7" . . . . . . . . . . . . . . . . . . . . . . . . BTC 1041
20th Century / Mar '79.

### SHEET MUSIC.
Tracks: Sheet music / Sheet music (part 2) / Lady, sweet lady / Ghetto letto / Rum and coca cola / She's everything to me / Love makin' music / I believe in love.
■ LP . . . . . . . . . . . . . . . . . . . . . . . ULG 83927
MC . . . . . . . . . . . . . . . . . . . . . . . . .40 83927
Unlimited Gold(USA) / Jul '80 / Sony.
CD . . . . . . . . . . . . . . . . . . . . . . . CDSEWM 072
South Bound / Feb '93 / Pinnacle.

### SHEET MUSIC.
Tracks: Sheet Music.
■ 7" . . . . . . . . . . . . . . . . . . . . . . . . ULG 8563
Unlimited Gold(USA) / May '80.

### SHO' YOU RIGHT.
Tracks: Sho' you right / You're what's on my mind.
■ 12" . . . . . . . . . . . . . . . . . . . . . . . . USAT 614
■ 7" . . . . . . . . . . . . . . . . . . . . . . . . . USA 614
Breakout / Oct '87.

### SINGS FOR SOMEONE YOU LOVE.
Tracks: Playing your game babe / It's ecstacy when you lay down next to me / You're so good you're bad / I never thought I'd fall in love with you / You turned my world around / Oh what a night for dancing / Of all the guys in the world.
■ LP . . . . . . . . . . . . . . . . . . . . . . . . BTH 8004
20th Century / Nov '77.

### SOUL SEDUCTION.
Tracks: Never never gonna give you up / Standing in the shadows of love / What am I gonna do with you / Honey please cant' you see / Your sweetness is my weakness / I love to sing the songs I sing / It's only love doing it's thing / Bring back my yesterday / I've got so much to give / You see the trouble with me / Playing your game baby / You're so good, you're so bad / Oh me oh my (I'm such a lucky guy).
CD . . . . . . . . . . . . . . . . . . . . . . . . 5500902
MC . . . . . . . . . . . . . . . . . . . . . . . . 5500904
Spectrum (1) / Oct '93 / PolyGram.

### SPOTLIGHT ON BARRY WHITE.
Tracks: My buddy / Long black veil / Where can I turn to / I've got the world to hold me up / Your heart and soul / Out of the shadows of love / Under the influence of love / Fragile - handle with care / All in the run of love / Come on in love / I owe it all to you.
CD . . . . . . . . . . . . . . . . . . . . . . . HADCD 142
MC . . . . . . . . . . . . . . . . . . . . . . . HADMC 142
Javelin / Feb '94 / THE.

### WHAT AM I GONNA DO WITH YOU.
Tracks: What am I gonna do with you.
■ 7" . . . . . . . . . . . . . . . . . . . . . . . . BTC 2177
20th Century / Mar '75.

### WHEN WILL I SEE YOU AGAIN.
Tracks: When will I see you again.
■ 12" . . . . . . . . . . . . . . . . . . . . . . . . AMY 593
■ 7" . . . . . . . . . . . . . . . . . . . . . . . . . AM 593
A&M / Sep '90.

### WITH LOVE UNLIMITED.
Tracks: Walking in the rain with the one I love / Don't make me wait too long / Don't tell me about heartaches / I won't settle for less than the best / Didn't we make it happen baby / Let me in, let's begin with love / Let the music play / Lady sweet lady / I like you, you like me / Change / Gotta be where you are / What am I gonna do with you / You're the one I need / Life / Any fool could see / I found love / Our theme (part 2) / Baby we better try and get it together / She's everything to me / Let's make tonight an evening to remember / I can't let him down / You're the only one for me.
CD Set . . . . . . . . . . . . . . . . . . . . DVSOPCD 154
■ Double LP . . . . . . . . . . . . . . . . . . VSOPLP 154
MC Set . . . . . . . . . . . . . . . . . . . . VSOPMC 154
Connoisseur Collection / Dec '90 / Pinnacle.

### YOU SEE THE TROUBLE WITH ME.
Tracks: You see the trouble with me.
■ 7" . . . . . . . . . . . . . . . . . . . . . . . . BTC 2277
20th Century / Mar '76.

### YOU'RE THE FIRST, THE LAST MY EVERYTHING (OLD GOLD).
Tracks: You're the first, the last, my everything / Just the way you are.
■ 7" . . . . . . . . . . . . . . . . . . . . . . . . OG 9770
Old Gold / Oct '88.

### YOU'RE THE FIRST, THE LAST, MY EVERYTHING.
Tracks: You're the first, the last, my everything.
■ 7" . . . . . . . . . . . . . . . . . . . . . . . . BTC 2133
20th Century / Nov '74.
■ 7" . . . . . . . . . . . . . . . . . . . . . . . . GOLD 516
RCA Golden Grooves / Jul '81.

### YOUR HEART & SOUL.
Tracks: Not Advised.
CD . . . . . . . . . . . . . . . . . . . . . . . . JHD 001
MC . . . . . . . . . . . . . . . . . . . . . . . MCHJD 001
IMD / Jun '92 / BMG.

# White, Karyn

### HUNGAH.
Tracks: Hungah (Mixes).
12" . . . . . . . . . . . . . . . . . . . . . . . . W 0264T
CD Single . . . . . . . . . . . . . . . . . . . W 0264CD
MC Single . . . . . . . . . . . . . . . . . . . W 0264C
Warner Bros. / Sep '94 / WEA.

### KARYN WHITE.
Tracks: Way you love me / Secret rendezvous / Slow down / Super woman / Family man / Love saw it / Don't mess with me / Tell me tomorrow / One wish.
■ LP . . . . . . . . . . . . . . . . . . . . . . . . WX 235
WEA / Oct '88.
CD . . . . . . . . . . . . . . . . . . . . . . . K 9256372
MC . . . . . . . . . . . . . . . . . . . . . . . WX 235C
WEA / Mar '94 / WEA.

### MAKE HIM DO RIGHT.
Tracks: Not Advised.
CD . . . . . . . . . . . . . . . . . . . . . . 936245400-2
MC . . . . . . . . . . . . . . . . . . . . . . 936245400-4
Warner Bros. / Sep '94 / WEA.

### RITUAL OF LOVE.
Tracks: Romantic / Ritual of love / Way I feel about you / Hooked on you / Walking the dog / Love that's mine / How I want you / One heart / Tears of joy / Beside you / Do unto me / Hard to say goodbye.
CD . . . . . . . . . . . . . . . . . . . . . . 7599263202
MC . . . . . . . . . . . . . . . . . . . . . . . WX 411C
■ LP . . . . . . . . . . . . . . . . . . . . . . . WX 411
WEA / Sep '91 / WEA.

■ DELETED

459

## SECRET RENDEZVOUS.
**Tracks:** Secret rendezvous / Language of love.
- 12"...................................W 2855T
- 7".....................................W 2855
- CD Single..........................W 2855CD
- MC Single.......................W 2855MC
WEA / Aug '89.
- 12"...................................W 7562T
- 7".....................................W 7562
- CD Single..........................W 7562CD
WEA / Jan '89.

## SUPERWOMAN.
**Tracks:** Superwoman / Way you love me.
- 12"..................................W 2920 T
- 12" Remix......................W 2920 TW
- 7"..................................W 2920
- CD Single.......................W 2920 CD
WEA / Jun '89.

## WAY I FEEL ABOUT YOU, THE.
**Tracks:** Way I feel about you.
- 12"..................................W 0073T
- 7"..................................W 0073
- MC Single......................W 0073C
WEA / Jan '92.

## WAY YOU LOVE ME, THE.
**Tracks:** Way you love me / Tell me tomorrow.
- 12"..................................W 2681 T
- 7"..................................W 2681
WEA / Nov '89.

## WAY YOU LOVE ME, THE.
**Tracks:** Way you love me.
- 12"..................................W 7773 T
- 7"..................................W 7773
WEA / Oct '88.

# White, Lenny

## KIDS STUFF.
**Tracks:** Kids stuff / Slip away / Fancy dancer.
- 12".....................................LV 43
- 7"....................................K 12500
Asylum / Feb '81.

## LADY MADONNA.
**Tracks:** Lady Madonna / 12 bars from Mars.
- 7"....................................K 12328
Elektra / Jan '79.

## PEANUT BUTTER.
**Tracks:** Peanut butter / Citi dancing / Oh Sylvie.
- EP......................................LV 37
Asylum / Jun '80.

## STREAMLINE.
**Tracks:** Struttin' / Lady Madonna / 12 bars from Mars / Earthlings / Spazmo strikes again / Time / Pooh bear / Lockie's inspiration / I'll see you soon / Night games / Cosmic indigo.
- LP....................................K 52108
Elektra / '78.

## TWENNYNINE WITH LENNY WHITE.
**Tracks:** Just right for me / It's music, it's magic / My melody / Kid stuff / Fancy dancer / Love & be loved / Back to you / Slip away / We had to break away / 11th fanfare.
- LP....................................K 52257
Asylum / Oct '80.

# White, Lynn

## I DON'T KNOW WHY.
**Tracks:** I don't know why (Mixes).
- 12"..............................EXPAND 45
Expansion / Mar '94.

## LOVE AND HAPPINESS.
**Tracks:** See you later bye / Eight men, four women / Your woman is home tonight / If you think you're lonely now / Steal away / Love me like you do / I'm gonna find me a lover tonight / Love and happiness / Fool don't live here anymore / Don't quit.
- CD...................................TLCD 123
- LP...................................TRPL 123
Total / Nov '89 / Total / BMG.

## SUCCESS.
**Tracks:** Don't let success / I made a mistake / Anyway the wind blows / Baby for you / Giving it all I got / I can't give you what you want / Sorry / Gonna be some changes made / Caught you with your love down / All because of your love.
- LP....................................TRLP 105
Timeless (Soul) / Jun '87.
- CD...................................TLCD 361
Timeless (Soul) / Jan '90.

---

**YES I'M READY.**
**Tracks:** Not Advised.
- CD................................WAY 2695052
- LP................................WAY 2695051
- MC...............................WAY 2695054
Waylo / Apr '90 / Charly.

# White, Maurice

While history elects not to remember Salty Peppers, Maurice White's next endeavour are more celebrated. Before Earth Wind & Fire, however, White was bandmate of Booker T. Jones and house drummer for Chess label in '60s (he can be heard on classics like Fontella Bass' *Rescue Me* and Billy Stewart's *Summertime*). He capped this with four years in Ramsey Lewis' band around turn of decade. Such experience made White better equipped to tailor EWF's output to singles chart, while exploring grander vision with own production company and record label. Among many artists with whom he has been associated are Deniece Williams, Emotions and Atlantic Starr. His solo album came out in 1985.

## MAURICE WHITE.
**Tracks:** Switch on your radio / Jamboree / Stand by me / Sea of glass / I need you / Believe in magic / Lady is love / Invitation / Sleeping flame / Alpha dance / Children of Africa.
- LP...............................CBS 26637
- MC.................................40 26637
- CD................................CD 26637
CBS / Oct '85 / Sony.

## STAND BY ME.
**Tracks:** Stand by me.
- 12".................................TA 6512
- 7"..................................A 6512
CBS / Aug '85.

# White, Michael

## HOW STRONG WE BELIEVE.
**Tracks:** You are the one / One more time / So far away / Fe-fe / How strong we believe / Song for Rachel / I want you.
CD...................................K32Y 6279
King/Electric Bird / Aug '91 / Pinnacle.

## MICHAEL WHITE.
**Tracks:** Fantasy / I know you need someone / Bring on the night / Matriach / One good turn / Psychometry / Deja vu / Jumpin' the fence / Radio.
- LP................................781 753-1
- MC...............................781 753-4
Atlantic / Aug '87 / WEA.

## MICHAEL WHITE'S NEW ORLEANS MUSIC.
**Tracks:** Shake it and break it / Am I blue / Please don't talk about me when I'm gone / In the upper garden / Mama Inez / It's a sin to tell a lie / Apex blues / Girl of my dreams / Baby won't you please come home / Exactly like you.
- LP..............................NOLALP 022
Nola / Jul '82.

## NO RULES.
**Tracks:** Don't stop the music / Late night / Rock witcha / Round midnight / Let's stay together / Any love / No rules.
- CD..................................KICJ 82
King / Jun '92.

## SHAKE IT BREAK IT.
**Tracks:** Not Advised.
- LP....................................LPS 6
504 / Aug '81.

## X FACTOR, THE.
**Tracks:** Not Advised.
- LP...................................K 52095
Elektra / Aug '78.

# White, Scott

## I DON'T UNDERSTAND IT.
**Tracks:** I don't understand it.
- 12"...................................8792 RD
RCA / Nov '88.

## SUCCESS NEVER ENDS.
**Tracks:** Hypnotised / Never ends / Love emergency / Success / I don't understand it / Friends / Time has hold on love / Let me be.
- MC..................................PK 90246
- LP..................................PL 90246
RCA / Sep '88.

---

# Whithead, John

## I NEED MONEY BAD.
**Tracks:** Not Advised.
- LP.................................834 310-1
Mercury / Jul '88.

# Whitley, Ray

## I'VE BEEN HURT.
**Tracks:** I've been hurt.
- 7"....................................POP 1473
H.M.V. / '65.

# Whitney, Marva

## IT'S MY THING.
**Tracks:** It's my thing - parts 1 & 2 / Things got to get better / What kind of man / If you love me / In the middle / Unwind yourself / You got to have a job / I'I work it out / Get out of my life / I'm tired, I'm tired I'm tired / Shades of brown.
- LP.................................583 762
Polydor / Nov '69.

# Whycliffe

## HEAVEN.
**Tracks:** Heaven (mixes).
- 12"...............................MCST 1944
- 7"................................MCS 1944
- CD Single......................MCSTD 1944
- MC Single......................MCSC 1944
MCA / Nov '93.

## I TRIED.
**Tracks:** I tried.
- 12"...............................MCST 1549
- 7"................................MCS 1549
- CD Single......................MCSTD 1549
MCA / Jul '91.

## LOVESPEAKUP.
**Tracks:** Lovespeakup / Roughside.
- 12"...............................MCAT 1451
- 12" Remix.....................MCAX 1451
- 7"................................MCA 1451
- CD Single......................DMCAT 1451
- MC Single......................MCAC 1451
MCA / Oct '90.

## MAGIC GARDEN.
**Tracks:** Magic garden.
- 12"...............................MCST 1508
- 12" Remix.....................MCSX 1508
- 7"................................MCS 1508
MCA / Feb '91.

## ONE MORE TIME.
**Tracks:** One more time.
- 12"...............................MCST 1955
- CD Single......................MCSTD 1955
- MC Single......................MCSC 1955
MCA / Mar '94.

## ROUGHSIDE.
**Tracks:** Not Advised.
- LP................................MCA 10282
- MC..............................MCAC 10282
- CD..............................MCAD 10282
MCA / May '91.

## WHATEVER IT IS.
**Tracks:** Whatever it is.
- 12"...............................MCST 1518
- 7"................................MCS 1518
MCA / Apr '91.

# Wigan's Ovation

## AFTER LOVING YOU.
**Tracks:** After loving you (part 1) / After loving you (part 2).
- 7"....................................RK 1008
RK / Apr '78.

## NORTHERN SOUL DANCER.
**Tracks:** Northern soul dancer / Upon my soul / Let's get together / Be with me tonight / Stand in line / Skiing in the snow / Superlove / Sign on the dotted line / Personally / What's wrong with me baby / Ten miles high / My girl.
- CD.................................C5CD 592
See For Miles / Oct '92.

## PER-SO-NAL-LY.
**Tracks:** Per-so-nal-ly.
- 7"...................................SRL 1129
Spark (3) / Jun '75.

■ DELETED

## SKIING IN THE SNOW.
Tracks: Skiing in the snow.
■ 7" . . . . . . . . . . . . . . . . . . . . . SRL 1122
Spark (3) / Mar '75.

## SUPER LOVE.
Tracks: Super love.
■ 7" . . . . . . . . . . . . . . . . . . . . . SRL 1133
Spark (3) / Nov '75.

# Wiggins, Percy

## BOOK OF MEMORIES.
Tracks: Book of memories / Can't find nobody.
■ 7" . . . . . . . . . . . . . . . . . . . .584113
Atlantic / Jun '67.

# Wild Cherry

## 1-2-3 KIND OF LOVE.
Tracks: 1-2-3 kind of love / Fools fall in love.
■ 7" . . . . . . . . . . . . . . . . . . . . EPC 6497
Epic / Jul '78.

## BABY, DON'T YOU KNOW?.
Tracks: Baby, don't you know / Get it up.
■ 7" . . . . . . . . . . . . . . . . . . . . EPC 4919
Epic / Jan '77.

## ELECTRIFIED FUNK.
Tracks: Baby don't you know / Are you boogieing around your Daddy / Dancin' music band / Put yourself in my shoes / Closest to my mind / Electrified funk / Hole in the wall / Hot to trot / Hold on / It's all up to you.
■ LP . . . . . . . . . . . . . . . . . . . . EPC 81846
Epic / Jun '77.

## LOVE MY MUSIC.
Tracks: I love my music / Don't stop, get off.
■ 7" . . . . . . . . . . . . . . . . . . . . EPC 6173
Epic / Mar '78.

## LOVE MY MUSIC.
Tracks: I love my music / Lana / It's the same old song / Try one more time / Don't stop get off / 1-2-3 kind of love / No way out love affair / If you want my love / Fools fall in love / This old heart of mine.
■ LP . . . . . . . . . . . . . . . . . . . . EPC 82326
Epic / Jun '78.

## PLAY THAT FUNKY MUSIC.
Tracks: Play that funky music.
■ 7" . . . . . . . . . . . . . . . . . . . . EPC 4593
Epic / Oct '76.

# Wild Magnolias

## SMOKE MY PEACE PIPE.
Tracks: Smoke my peace pipe / Handa wanda.
■ 7" . . . . . . . . . . . . . . . . . . . . BAR 30
Barclay (France) / Jan '75.

# Wild Tchoupitoulas

## WILD TCHOUPITOULAS, THE.
Tracks: Brother John / Meet de boys on de battle-front / Here dey come / Hey pocky a-way / Indian red / Big chief got a golden crown / Hey mama / Hey hey.
■ CD . . . . . . . . . . . . . . . . . . . . CID 9360
■ LP . . . . . . . . . . . . . . . . . . . . ILPS 9360
■ MC . . . . . . . . . . . . . . . . . . . . ICT 9360
Mango / Apr '88.
CD . . . . . . . . . . . . . . . . . . . . IMCD 89
MC . . . . . . . . . . . . . . . . . . . . ICM 89
Island / Feb '90 / PolyGram.

# Wild-Life

## ZOO.
Tracks: Zoo (mixes) / Cats dance / Walking in the park (mixes) / Theme track.
LP Set . . . . . . . . . . . . . . . . . . . . KG 002-3
Cooky Grooves / Sep '94 / SRD.

# Wilde, Dee Dee

## FOUND YOU.
Tracks: I found you / I found you (instrumental) / I found you (extended) (on 12" only).
■ 12" . . . . . . . . . . . . . . . . . . . . 12 BRW 87
■ 7" . . . . . . . . . . . . . . . . . . . . BRW 87
4th & Broadway / Mar '88.

## LAP OF LUXURY.
Tracks: Lap of luxury / I found you.
■ 12" . . . . . . . . . . . . . . . . . . . .12 BRW 117
■ 7" . . . . . . . . . . . . . . . . . . . . BRW 117

■ CD Single . . . . . . . . . . . . . . . .BRCD 117
4th & Broadway / Oct '88.

## NO WAY OUT.
Tracks: Not Advised.
CD . . . . . . . . . . . . . . . . . . . . .BRCD 527
■ LP . . . . . . . . . . . . . . . . . . . . BRLP 527
■ MC . . . . . . . . . . . . . . . . . . . . BRCA 527
4th & Broadway / May '89 / PolyGram.
MC . . . . . . . . . . . . . . . . . . . . ICM 2066
MC . . . . . . . . . . . . . . . . . . . . 846 605 4
Island / '90 / PolyGram.

## NO WAY OUT.
Tracks: No way out / No way out (Instrumental).
■ CD Single . . . . . . . . . . . . . . . .BRCD 127
■ 12" . . . . . . . . . . . . . . . . . . . .12 BRW 127
■ 7" . . . . . . . . . . . . . . . . . . . . BRW 127
4th & Broadway / Apr '89.

# Wilde, Eugene

## CHEY CHEY KULE.
Tracks: Chey chey kule / Rainbow.
■ 7" . . . . . . . . . . . . . . . . . . . . BRW 30
■ 12" . . . . . . . . . . . . . . . . . . . . 12 BRW 30
4th & Broadway / Jul '85.

## DIANA.
Tracks: Diana / I want you / Diana (instrumental) (on 12" only).
■ 12" . . . . . . . . . . . . . . . . . . . . MCAT 1046
■ 7" . . . . . . . . . . . . . . . . . . . . MCA 1046
MCA / Jun '86.

## DON'T SAY NO TONIGHT.
Tracks: Don't say no tonigt / Let her feel it.
■ 12" . . . . . . . . . . . . . . . . . . . . 12 BRW 35
■ 7" . . . . . . . . . . . . . . . . . . . . BRW 35
4th & Broadway / Nov '85.

## EUGENE WILDE.
Tracks: Not Advised.
■ MC . . . . . . . . . . . . . . . . . . . .BRCA 502
■ LP . . . . . . . . . . . . . . . . . . . . BRLP 502
4th & Broadway / Nov '84.

## GOTTA GET YOU HOME TONIGHT.
Tracks: Gotta get you home tonight / Gotta get you home tonight (version).
■ 12" P.Disc. . . . . . . . . . . . . . . 12 PBRW 15
■ 12" . . . . . . . . . . . . . . . . . . . . 12 BRW 15
■ 7" . . . . . . . . . . . . . . . . . . . . BRW 15
4th & Broadway / Sep '84.

## I CHOOSE YOU TONIGHT.
Tracks: Not Advised.
CD . . . . . . . . . . . . . . . . . . . . MCAD 42282
MC . . . . . . . . . . . . . . . . . . . . MCAC 42282
MCA / Jul '89 / BMG.

## PERSONALITY.
Tracks: Personality / Let her feel it.
■ 7" . . . . . . . . . . . . . . . . . . . . BRW 18
■ 12" . . . . . . . . . . . . . . . . . . . . 12 BRW 18
4th & Broadway / Jan '85.

## SERENADE.
Tracks: Not Advised.
■ LP . . . . . . . . . . . . . . . . . . . . MCF 3321
■ MC . . . . . . . . . . . . . . . . . . . . MCFC 3321
MCA / May '86.

# Williams, Al

## I AM NOTHING.
Tracks: I am nothing / Brand new love.
■ 7" . . . . . . . . . . . . . . . . . . . .GRP 136
Grapevine (Northern Soul) / Apr '80.

# Williams, Alyson

## ALYSON WILLIAMS.
Tracks: Can't have my man / Just my luck / Here comes the rain / So special / Just the way I like it / Heaven / Everybody knew but me / Your love is all I need / She's not your fool / Second X around.
■ LP . . . . . . . . . . . . . . . . . . . . 4681621
■ CD . . . . . . . . . . . . . . . . . . . . 4681622
■ MC . . . . . . . . . . . . . . . . . . . . 4681624
O.B.R. / May '92.

## COOKED - THE REMIX ALBUM (Re-mixed Tracks From The 'Raw' Album).
Tracks: Not Advised.
CD . . . . . . . . . . . . . . . . . . . . 4667992
■ LP . . . . . . . . . . . . . . . . . . . . 4667991
MC . . . . . . . . . . . . . . . . . . . . 4667994
Def Jam / May '90 / PolyGram.

## I NEED YOUR LOVIN'.
Tracks: I need your lovin' (7" remix) (Only on 7" single.) / Make you mine tonight (Not on CD single.) /

My love is so raw (baby love mix) (Only on 12" single.) / I need your lovin' (extended remix) (Only on CD single.) / My love is so raw (album raw mix) (Only on CD single.).
■ 12" . . . . . . . . . . . . . . . . . . . . 6551438
■ 12" . . . . . . . . . . . . . . . . . . . . 6551436
■ 7" . . . . . . . . . . . . . . . . . . . . 6551437
■ CD Single . . . . . . . . . . . . . . . . 6551432
■ MC Single . . . . . . . . . . . . . . . . 6551434
Def Jam / Jul '89.

## I SECOND THAT EMOTION.
Tracks: I second that emotion / Still my no.1.
■ 12" . . . . . . . . . . . . . . . . . . . . 655 456 6
■ 12" . . . . . . . . . . . . . . . . . . . . 655 456 8
■ 7" . . . . . . . . . . . . . . . . . . . . 655 456 7
■ CD Single . . . . . . . . . . . . . . . . 655 456 2
■ MC Single . . . . . . . . . . . . . . . . 655 456 4
Def Jam / Nov '89.

## MY LOVE IS SO RAW.
Tracks: My love is so raw / We're gonna make it / My love is so raw (extended club mix) / I second that emotion.
■ 12" . . . . . . . . . . . . . . . . . . . . 6548988
■ 12" . . . . . . . . . . . . . . . . . . . . 6548986
■ 7" . . . . . . . . . . . . . . . . . . . . 6548987
■ CD Single . . . . . . . . . . . . . . . . 6548982
■ MC Single . . . . . . . . . . . . . . . . 6548984
Def Jam / Apr '89.

## RAW.
Tracks: Just call my name / We're gonna make it / I looked into your eyes / Not on the outside / Masquerade / I'm so glad / My love is so raw / On the rocks / Still my No.1 / I need your lovin' / Sleep talk.
■ LP . . . . . . . . . . . . . . . . . . . . 4632931
■ CD . . . . . . . . . . . . . . . . . . . . 4632932
■ MC . . . . . . . . . . . . . . . . . . . . 4632934
Def Jam / Mar '89.
CD . . . . . . . . . . . . . . . . . . . . .983314 2
MC . . . . . . . . . . . . . . . . . . . . .983314 4
Pickwick/Sony Collector's Choice / Oct '93 / Pickwick / Pinnacle.

## SLEEP TALK.
Tracks: Sleep talk / I'm so glad (with Chuck Stanley) / How to love again (With Oran 'Juice' Jones) / Make you mine tonight / Still my No.1 (Only on 12" version.) / Sleep talk (extended version) (Only on 12" version.).
■ 12" . . . . . . . . . . . . . . . . . . . . 6546568
■ 12" . . . . . . . . . . . . . . . . . . . . 6546566
■ 7" . . . . . . . . . . . . . . . . . . . . 6546567
■ CD Single . . . . . . . . . . . . . . . . 6546562
Def Jam / Feb '89.

## SLEEP TALK (OLD GOLD).
Tracks: Sleep talk / I need your lovin'.
12" . . . . . . . . . . . . . . . . . . . .OG 4230
Old Gold / Jun '92 / Pickwick.

# Williams, Beau

## STAY WITH ME.
Tracks: Not Advised.
CD . . . . . . . . . . . . . . . . . . . .MAUCD 636
Mau Mau / Apr '93 / Pinnacle.

# Williams, Bobby

## LET'S JAM.
Tracks: Let's jam / You're my baby.
■ 7" . . . . . . . . . . . . . . . . . . . . CS 9028
Contempo (1) / May '75.

# Williams, Christopher

## ADVENTURES IN PARADISE.
Tracks: Not Advised.
CD . . . . . . . . . . . . . . . . . . . .K 9242202
■ LP . . . . . . . . . . . . . . . . . . . . K 9242201
■ MC . . . . . . . . . . . . . . . . . . . . K 9242204
Elektra / May '89 / WEA.

## CHANGES.
Tracks: All I see / Don't u wanna make love / Good Luvin' / Come on and go with me / When a fool becomes a man / Changes / Where is the love / Let's get right / Where are u now / Every little thing u do / Please, please, please.
CD . . . . . . . . . . . . . . . . . . . . MCD 10751
■ LP . . . . . . . . . . . . . . . . . . . . MCA 10751
■ MC . . . . . . . . . . . . . . . . . . . . MCC 10751
MCA / Jan '93 / BMG.

## TALK TO MYSELF.
Tracks: Talk to myself.
■ 7" . . . . . . . . . . . . . . . . . . . . GEF 62
Geffen / Sep '89.

■ DELETED

## Williams, Deniece

Williams first attracted attention as one of Stevie Wonder's backing group Wonderlove. She sang with Stevie between 1971 and '76, before Earth Wind & Fire's Maurice White helped launch her solo career. 1977 single *Free* became U.S. smash and cruised to top of U.K. chart. In 1978 she teamed with Johnny Mathis for *Too Much, Too Little, Too Late*, which reached No. 1 in U.S. and No. 3 in Britain. Six years later, Williams enjoyed her first solo U.S. chart-topper: *Let's Hear It For The Boy* - also first U.S. No. 1 for producer, George Duke. Recent recordings have seen Williams turn to gospel.

### AS GOOD AS IT GETS.
**Tracks:** I can't wait / This is as good as it gets / We are here to change the world / All I need / Memories / There's no other / I am sure / It's you I'm after / Don't stop the love / Hold me tight.
| | |
|---|---|
| ■ CD | 4629202 |
| ■ LP | 4629201 |
| ■ MC | 4629204 |
CBS / Nov '88 / Sony.

### BABY BABY MY LOVE'S ALL FOR YOU.
**Tracks:** Baby baby my love's all for you.
| | |
|---|---|
| ■ 7" | CBS 5779 |
CBS / Nov '77.

### BLACK BUTTERFLY.
**Tracks:** Black butterfly / I want you / It's gonna take a miracle (on 12" only) / I've got the next dance (on 12" only).
| | |
|---|---|
| ■ 12" | TA 4564 |
| ■ 7" | A 4564 |
CBS / Sep '84.

### DO WHAT YOU FEEL.
**Tracks:** Do what you feel / Love peace and unity.
| | |
|---|---|
| ■ 7" | A 3409 |
CBS / May '83.

### EVERY MOMENT.
**Tracks:** Every moment.
| | |
|---|---|
| ■ 12" | PX 27 |
| ■ 7" | P 27 |
Power / Nov '89.

### FREE.
**Tracks:** Free / Could you love me baby.
| | |
|---|---|
| ■ 7" | CBS 4978 |
CBS / Feb '77.

### FREE (OLD GOLD).
**Tracks:** Free / That's what friends are for.
| | |
|---|---|
| ■ 7" | OG 9318 |
Old Gold / Apr '83.

### FREE (RE-RELEASE).
**Tracks:** Free / That's what friends are for.
| | |
|---|---|
| ■ 7" | A 4586 |
CBS / Jul '84.

### FROM THE BEGINNING.
**Tracks:** Not Advised.
| | |
|---|---|
| ■ CD | SPCD 1256 |
| ■ LP | SPR 1256 |
| MC. | SPC 1256 |
Sparrow / Jan '91 / Word Records (UK) / Sony.

### HOT ON THE TRAIL.
**Tracks:** Wiser and weaker / Hot on the trail / He loves me, he loves me not / Video / I feel the night / We're together / Straight from the heart / Healing.
| | |
|---|---|
| ■ LP | CBS 26690 |
| ■ MC. | 40 26690 |
CBS / Sep '86.

### I CAN'T WAIT.
**Tracks:** I can't wait / Free (12" & CD single only.) / I've got the next dance (CD single only.) / Cause you love me baby (Only on (6530618) 12".).
| | |
|---|---|
| ■ 12" | 6530616 |
| ■ 12" | 6530618 |
| ■ 7" | 6530617 |
| ■ CD Single | 6530612 |
CBS / Oct '88.

### I'M SO PROUD.
**Tracks:** Do what you feel / I'm so proud / So deep in love / I'm glad it's you / Heaven in your eyes / They say / Love / Peace and unity / It's OK.
| | |
|---|---|
| ■ LP | CBS 25352 |
| MC. | 40 25352 |
CBS / Jul '83 / Sony.

### I'VE GOT THE NEXT DANCE.
**Tracks:** I've got the next dance / When love comes calling.
| | |
|---|---|
| ■ 12" | CBS 137399 |

| | |
|---|---|
| ■ 7" | CBS 7399 |
CBS / Jun '79.

### IT'S GONNA TAKE A MIRACLE.
**Tracks:** It's gonna take a miracle / Part of love.
| | |
|---|---|
| ■ 7" | A 2336 |
CBS / Feb '83.

### IT'S YOUR CONSCIENCE.
**Tracks:** It's your conscience / Sweet surrender.
| | |
|---|---|
| ■ 7" | A 1341 |
CBS / Jun '81.

### LET'S HEAR IT FOR THE BOY.
**Tracks:** Let's hear it for the boy / I want you / Picking up the pieces / Black butterfly / Next love / Haunting me / Don't tell me we have nothing / Blind dating / Wrapped up / Whiter than snow.
| | |
|---|---|
| ■ LP | CBS 26010 |
CBS / Aug '84.
| | |
|---|---|
| CD. | 982981 2 |
Pickwick/Sony Collector's Choice / Sep '93 / Pickwick / Pinnacle.

### LET'S HEAR IT FOR THE BOY.
**Tracks:** Let's hear it for the boy.
| | |
|---|---|
| ■ 12" | TA 3419 |
| ■ 7" | A 3419 |
CBS / May '84.

### LET'S HEAR IT FOR THE BOY (OLD GOLD).
**Tracks:** Let's hear it for the boy / Holding out for a hero.
| | |
|---|---|
| 7" | OG 9947 |
Old Gold / Sep '90 / Pickwick.

### MY MELODY.
**Tracks:** My melody / It's your conscience / Silly / Strangers / What two can do / You're all that matters / Suspicious / Sweet surrender.
| | |
|---|---|
| ■ LP | CBS 84874 |
CBS / Jun '81.

### NEVER SAY NEVER.
**Tracks:** Never say never / Love finds you.
| | |
|---|---|
| ■ 12" | 6507366 |
| ■ 7" | 6507367 |
CBS / Apr '87.

### NEXT LOVE.
**Tracks:** Next love / Picking up the pieces.
| | |
|---|---|
| ■ 12" | TA 4618 |
| ■ 7" | A 4618 |
CBS / Jul '84.

### NIECY.
**Tracks:** Waiting by the hot line / It's gonna take a miracle / Love notes / I believe in miracles / How does it feel / Waiting / Now it's time for love / Part of love.
| | |
|---|---|
| ■ LP | CBS 85602 |
CBS / Jun '82.

### SEASON.
**Tracks:** Season / God is amazing.
| | |
|---|---|
| ■ 7" | CBS 6324 |
CBS / May '78.

### SILLY.
**Tracks:** Silly / My melody.
| | |
|---|---|
| ■ 7" | A 1535 |
CBS / Nov '81.

### SO GLAD I KNOW.
**Tracks:** Just in time / Wings of an eagle / My soul desire / They say / Straight ahead / So glad I know / I surrender all / If we are the light / What you do for me.
| | |
|---|---|
| ■ LP | BIRD R 177 |
| ■ MC. | BIRD C 177 |
Birdwing / Jul '86.
| | |
|---|---|
| ■ CD | BIRDCD 177 |
Birdwing / Jul '88.

### SONGBIRD.
**Tracks:** After you / We have love for you / Baby, baby, my love's all for you / Paper / Be good to me / Season / Time / God is amazing / Boy I left behind.
| | |
|---|---|
| ■ LP | CBS 86046 |
CBS / Dec '77.

### SPECIAL LOVE.
**Tracks:** Not Advised.
| | |
|---|---|
| ■ CD | SP D 1174 |
| ■ LP | SP R 1174 |
| ■ MC. | SP C 1174 |
Sparrow / Nov '89.

### THAT'S WHAT FRIENDS ARE FOR.
**Tracks:** That's what friends are for.
| | |
|---|---|
| ■ 7" | CBS 5432 |
CBS / Jul '77.

### THIS IS NIECY.
**Tracks:** It's important to me / That's what friends are for / How'd I know that love would slip away / 'Cause you love me, baby / Free / Watching over / If you don't believe.
| | |
|---|---|
| ■ LP | CBS 8186 |
CBS / May '77.
| | |
|---|---|
| ■ MC. | 40 3253 |
| ■ LP | CBS 3253 |
CBS / Nov '84.
| | |
|---|---|
| CD. | 983396-2 |
Pickwick/Sony Collector's Choice / Mar '94 / Pickwick / Pinnacle.

### TOO MUCH, TOO LITTLE, TOO LATE
**(Williams, Deniece & Johnny Mathis).**
**Tracks:** Too much, too little too late / Emotions.
| | |
|---|---|
| ■ 7" | CBS 6161 |
CBS / Mar '78.

### WAITING BY THE HOTLINE.
**Tracks:** Waiting by the hotline / Love notes.
| | |
|---|---|
| ■ 7" | A 2651 |
CBS / Sep '82.

### WATER UNDER THE BRIDGE.
**Tracks:** I confess / Never say never / Water under the bridge / Love finds you / Not by chance / One less lonely heart / I believe in you / Someone for someone / Baby this is love / Don't blame it on my heart.
| | |
|---|---|
| CD. | 4505982 |
| ■ LP | 4505981 |
| MC. | 4505984 |
CBS / May '87 / Sony.

### WE HAVE LOVE FOR YOU.
**Tracks:** We have love for you / Boy I left behind.
| | |
|---|---|
| ■ 7" | CBS 5931 |
CBS / Jan '78.

### WHAT TWO CAN DO.
**Tracks:** What two can do / Sweet surrender.
| | |
|---|---|
| ■ 7" | A 1137 |
CBS / Apr '81.

### WHEN LOVE COMES CALLING.
**Tracks:** When love comes calling / Why can't we fall in love / God knows / Like magic / I found love / Turn around / I've got the next dance / Are you thinking / Touch me again / My prayer.
| | |
|---|---|
| ■ LP | CBS 83202 |
CBS / '79.

## Williams, Geoffrey

### BARE.
**Tracks:** Deliver me up / Let's go it on / I'll get over you / Moonchild / Don't make me love you / Let me be your baby / It's not a love thing / This is not a love song / Deeper within / Save another prayer / Bare.
| | |
|---|---|
| ■ CD | CDEMC 3618 |
| ■ LP | EMC 3618 |
| ■ MC. | TCEMC 3618 |
EMI / Feb '92.

### BLUE.
**Tracks:** Blue / The world is full of other people.
| | |
|---|---|
| ■ 12" | A 7962 |
| ■ 7" | A 7962 |
| ■ CD Single | A 7962CD |
| ■ MC Single | A 7962C |
Atlantic / Feb '90.

### CINDERELLA.
**Tracks:** Cinderella / She used to be / Cinderella (12" mix).
| | |
|---|---|
| ■ 12" | PZ 3 |
| ■ 7" | PO 3 |
Polydor / Jun '88.

### DELIVER ME UP.
**Tracks:** Deliver me up / It's not a love thing (live (Not on 12") / Summer breeze (CD single only).
| | |
|---|---|
| ■ 12" | 12EM 237 |
| ■ 7" | EM 237 |
| ■ CD Single | CDEM 237 |
| ■ MC Single | TCEM 237 |
EMI / Jun '92.

### IT'S NOT A LOVE THING.
**Tracks:** It's not a love thing / This is not a love song.
| | |
|---|---|
| ■ 12" | 12EM 228 |
| ■ 7" | EM 228 |
| ■ CD Single | CDEM 228 |
| ■ MC Single | TCEM 228 |
EMI / Mar '92.

### LIPSTICK.
**Tracks:** Lipstick / Walk like a man.
| | |
|---|---|
| ■ 12" | A 8863 |
| ■ 7" | A 8863 |

■ DELETED

■ CD Single . . . . . . . . . . . . . . . A 8863CD
Atlantic / Aug '89.

## PRISONER OF LOVE.
Tracks: Not Advised.
CD . . . . . . . . . . . . . . . . . . . . . . K 781 998 2
■ LP . . . . . . . . . . . . . . . . . . . . . . WX 298
MC . . . . . . . . . . . . . . . . . . . . . WX 298C
Atlantic / Aug '89 / WEA.

## SUMMER BREEZE.
Tracks: Summer breeze / Would I die for you (Not on 12") / Deliver me up (12" only).
■ 12" . . . . . . . . . . . . . . . . . . . 12EM 245
■ 7" . . . . . . . . . . . . . . . . . . . . . . EM 245
■ CD Single . . . . . . . . . . . . . . . . . CDEM 245
■ MC Single . . . . . . . . . . . . . . . . . TCEM 245
EMI / Sep '92.

## THERE'S A NEED IN ME.
Tracks: There's a need in me / There's a need in me (New York '88 mix) (Track on 12" and CD.) / There's a need in me (the other mix) (Track on 12".) / Shadows / Gypsy (Track on CD.).
■ 12" . . . . . . . . . . . . . . . . . . . POSPX 906
■ 7" . . . . . . . . . . . . . . . . . . . . POSP 906
■ CD Single . . . . . . . . . . . . . . . . . POCD 906
Polydor / Mar '88.

# Williams, James

## IN YOUR EYES (Williams, James 'D-Train').
Tracks: In your eyes / Order in the house / With all my heart / If you knew what I know / Shadow of another love / Runner / Curious / Child of love / Diamond in the night / My friend / Smile.
CD . . . . . . . . . . . . . . . . . . . . . . 4610462
■ LP . . . . . . . . . . . . . . . . . . . . . . 4610461
■ MC . . . . . . . . . . . . . . . . . . . . . 4610464
CBS / Oct '88 / Sony.

## MIRACLES OF THE HEART (Williams, James 'D-Train').
Tracks: You are everything / Oh how I love you (girl) / Miracle of the heart / Misunderstandings / Let me love you / Ice melts into rain / I got your number / Stand up and fight.
■ LP . . . . . . . . . . . . . . . . . . . . . . 4500661
■ MC . . . . . . . . . . . . . . . . . . . . . 4500664
CBS / Sep '86.

## MISUNDERSTANDING (Williams, James 'D-Train').
Tracks: Misunderstanding.
■ 7" . . . . . . . . . . . . . . . . . . . . . 6504317
CBS / Feb '87.

## RUNNER (Williams, James 'D-Train').
Tracks: Runner / Runner (accapella) / Runner (12" version) (Only on 12", 12" picture bag & CD single.) / Runner (dub mix) (Only on 12" & CD single.) / In your eyes (Only on 12" picture bag version.) / Misunderstanding (Only on 12" picture bag version.) / You are everything (Only on 12" picture bag version.).
■ 12" . . . . . . . . . . . . . . . . . . . . 6531166
■ 12" . . . . . . . . . . . . . . . . . . . . 6531168
■ 7" . . . . . . . . . . . . . . . . . . . . . 6531167
■ CD Single . . . . . . . . . . . . . . . . . 6531162
CBS / Oct '88.

# Williams, Jerry

## CRUISIN' ON A SATURDAY NIGHT (Williams, Jerry 'Swamp Dogg').
Tracks: Cruisin' on a Saturday night / Big black Chevrolet.
■ 7" . . . . . . . . . . . . . . . . . . . . SON 2249
Sonet / Sep '82.

## DANCIN' WITH SOUL (Williams, Jerry 'Swamp Dogg' & Michelle Williams).
Tracks: Some kind of wonderful / Hold on I'm coming Funktastic / Galacticlerock / This is it / All she wants is reggae music / Foxy foxy rapp / Loverise / Don't stop the boogie / Mad love / Make me yours.
■ LP . . . . . . . . . . . . . . . . . . . . . RARE LP 1
Neon / Jan '84.

## GOD BLESS ROCK'N'ROLL (Williams, Jerry 'Swamp Dogg').
Tracks: God bless rock 'n' roll / Big black Chevrolet.
■ 7" . . . . . . . . . . . . . . . . . . . . SON 2251
Sonet / Oct '82.

## TOO FAST TO LIVE, TOO FAST TO DIE (Williams, Jerry 'Swamp Dogg').
Tracks: No money down / Git it / Guitar Nelly / Serving time / Rock on / Look out heart / Slow down / That'll be the day / Willie and the hand jive / Burn out / Little honda.

---

■ LP . . . . . . . . . . . . . . . . . . . . . SNTF 791
Sonet / Feb '79.

# Williams, Jessica

## AND THEN, THERE'S THIS.
Tracks: Bemsha swing / And then, there's this / All alone / Nichol's bag / Child within / Elaine / House that Rouse, built / Newk's fluke / Swanee / I mean you.
CD . . . . . . . . . . . . . . . . . . . . . CDSJP 345
Timeless (Jazz) / Feb '91 / New Note / Jazz Music.

## CASANOVA.
Tracks: Casanova / Casanova (inst).
■ 12" . . . . . . . . . . . . . . . . . PASH 73(12)
Passion (1) / '88.

## IN THE POCKET.
Tracks: Weirdo / Gal in calico / I really love you / Driftin' / For you again / Cheek to cheek / I remember Bill / Ghost of a chance / Pfrancing.
CD . . . . . . . . . . . . . . . . . . . HEPCD 2055
Hep / Jun '94 / Cadillac / Pinnacle / Jazz Music.

## NEXT STEP, THE.
Tracks: Taking a chance on love / Stonewall blues / Easter parade / Bongo's waltz / I didn't know until you told me / Quilt / Clear blue Lou / I should care / Theme for Lester Young / Like someone in love / I'll always be in love with you / I got it bad / Little waltz.
CD . . . . . . . . . . . . . . . . . . . HEPCD 2054
Hep Jazz / Sep '93 / C.M. Distribution / Cadillac / Jazz Music / New Note / Wellard / Zodiac Records.

## NOTHIN' BUT THE BLUES.
Tracks: Not Advised.
■ LP . . . . . . . . . . . . . . . . . . BKH 51301
Blackhawk / Aug '86.

## QUEEN OF FOOLS.
Tracks: Queens of fools / I close my eyes and count to ten.
■ 12" . . . . . . . . . . . . . . . . . PASH 06(12)
Passion (1) / Sep '83.

## QUEEN OF FOOLS (REISSUES).
Tracks: Queen of fools.
■ 12" . . . . . . . . . . . . . . . . . PASH 25(12)
Passion (1) / '87.
■ 12" . . . . . . . . . . . . . . . . . PASH 05(12)
Passion (1) / '88.

# Williams, Lenny

## CHOOSING YOU.
Tracks: Choosing you / Trust in me.
■ 7" . . . . . . . . . . . . . . . . . . . . ABC 4198
ABC Records / Feb '78.

## GIVIN' UP ON LOVE.
Tracks: Givin' up on love.
■ 12" . . . . . . . . . . . . . . . . . . . ONE 6603
■ 7" . . . . . . . . . . . . . . . . . . . . ONE 6103
■ CD Single . . . . . . . . . . . . . . . . . ONE 6903
K-Tel / Jan '89.

## LOOK UP WITH YOUR MIND.
Tracks: Look up with your mind / Riding the high wire.
■ 7" . . . . . . . . . . . . . . . . . . . . ABC 4214
ABC Records / Apr '78.

## LOVE CURRENT.
Tracks: Not Advised.
■ LP . . . . . . . . . . . . . . . . . . . MCF 3014
MCA / '79.

## OOH CHILD.
Tracks: Ooh child / Let's do it today.
■ 7" . . . . . . . . . . . . . . . . . . . . MCA 660
MCA / Jan '81.

## SHOO DOO FU FU OOH.
Tracks: Shoo doo fu fu ooh.
■ 7" . . . . . . . . . . . . . . . . . . . . ABC 4194
ABC Records / Nov '77.

## SPARK OF LOVE.
Tracks: I still reach out / You got me running / Midnight girl / Think what we have / 'Cause I love you / Changes / Half past love / Love came and rescued me.
■ LP . . . . . . . . . . . . . . . . . . . ABCL 5251
ABC Records / Aug '78.

## TEN WAYS OF LOVING YOU.
Tracks: Ten ways of loving you / Waiting for your love.
■ 7" . . . . . . . . . . . . . . . . . . . . MALD 2
Malaco Dance / Sep '86.

---

## YOU GOT ME RUNNING.
Tracks: You got me running / Come reap my love.
■ 7" . . . . . . . . . . . . . . . . . . . . ABC 4228
ABC Records / Sep '78.

# Williams, Maurice

## MAURICE WILLIAMS & THE ZODIACS (Williams, Maurice & The Zodiacs).
Tracks: Not Advised.
■ LP . . . . . . . . . . . . . . . . . . . HERALD 5017
Herald / Aug '87.

## SPOTLIGHT ON MAURICE WILLIAMS.
Tracks: High heeled sneakers / Bare footin' / Spanish harlem / Up on the roof / On broadway / Corrina, Corrina / Driftaway / Save the last dance for me / Raindrops keep falling on my head / Mustang Sally / Running around / Little darling / This feeling / Stay.
CD . . . . . . . . . . . . . . . . . . . . HADCD 120
MC . . . . . . . . . . . . . . . . . . . HADMC 120
Javelin / Feb '94 / THE.

## STAY (JUST A LITTLE BIT LONGER).
Tracks: Stay (just a little bit longer).
■ 7" . . . . . . . . . . . . . . . . . . . . JAR 526
Top Rank (1) / Jan '61.

## STAY (JUST A LITTLE BIT LONGER) (OLD GOLD) (Williams, Maurice & The Zodiacs).
Tracks: Stay (just a little bit longer) / Get a job.
■ 7" . . . . . . . . . . . . . . . . . . . . OG 9093
Old Gold / Jul '82.

# Williams, Michelle

## DANCIN' WITH SOUL (see under Williams, Jerry 'Swamp Dogg').

## I FEEL MUCH BETTER NOW.
Tracks: I feel much better now.
■ 7" . . . . . . . . . . . . . . . . . . . DJS 10921
DJM / Aug '79.

# Williams, Sam

## LOVE SLIPPED THROUGH MY FINGERS.
Tracks: Love slipped through my fingers / You don't mean it.
■ 7" . . . . . . . . . . . . . . . . . . . GRP 116
Grapevine (Northern Soul) / Apr '79.

# Williams, Vanessa

## DREAMIN'.
Tracks: Dreamin'.
■ 12" . . . . . . . . . . . . . . . . . . . WINGX 4
■ 7" . . . . . . . . . . . . . . . . . . . . WING 4
■ 7" . . . . . . . . . . . . . . . . . . . WINGG 4
■ CD Single . . . . . . . . . . . . . . . 871 749-2
Polydor / Mar '89.

## IN THE COMFORT ZONE.
Tracks: Not Advised.
CD . . . . . . . . . . . . . . . . . . . . . 5112672
■ LP . . . . . . . . . . . . . . . . . . . . . 5112671
MC . . . . . . . . . . . . . . . . . . . . . 5112674
Wing / Oct '91 / PolyGram.

## JUST FOR TONIGHT.
Tracks: Just For Tonight.
■ 12" . . . . . . . . . . . . . . . . . . . PZ 213
■ 7" . . . . . . . . . . . . . . . . . . . . PO 213
■ CD Single . . . . . . . . . . . . . . . PZCD 213
■ MC Single . . . . . . . . . . . . . . . POCS 213
Polydor / May '92.

## RIGHT STUFF, THE.
Tracks: Not Advised.
CD . . . . . . . . . . . . . . . . . . . 835 694-2
■ LP . . . . . . . . . . . . . . . . . . . WNGLP 1
■ MC . . . . . . . . . . . . . . . . . . WNGMC 1
Wing / Sep '88 / PolyGram.

## RIGHT STUFF, THE.
Tracks: Right stuff (mixes) / Darlin I (Only on WINR 3 & WINGR 3).
12" . . . . . . . . . . . . . . . . . . . WINGX 3
12" . . . . . . . . . . . . . . . . . . . 8873861
7" . . . . . . . . . . . . . . . . . . . . WING 3
Polydor / Jul '88 / PolyGram.
12" . . . . . . . . . . . . . . . . . . . WINGR 3
7" . . . . . . . . . . . . . . . . . . . . WINR 3
Polydor / Aug '89 / PolyGram.

## RUNNING BACK TO YOU.
Tracks: Running back to you.
■ 12" . . . . . . . . . . . . . . . . . . . PZ 172

■ 7″ . . . . . . . . . . . . . . . . . . . . . . . . PO 172
■ CD Single . . . . . . . . . . . . . . . PZCD 172
■ MC Single . . . . . . . . . . . . . . . POCS 172
Polydor / Sep '91.

## SAVE THE BEST FOR LAST.
**Tracks:** Save the best for last.
■ 12″ . . . . . . . . . . . . . . . . . . . . . . .PZ 192
■ 7″ . . . . . . . . . . . . . . . . . . . . . . . . PO 192
■ CD Single . . . . . . . . . . . . . . . PZCD 192
■ MC Single . . . . . . . . . . . . . . . POCS 192
Polydor / Mar '92.

## Williams, Vesta

### CONGRATULATIONS.
**Tracks:** Congratulations / Once bitten twice shy.
■ CD Single . . . . . . . . . . . . . . USACD 680
■ 12″ . . . . . . . . . . . . . . . . . . . . USAT 680
■ 7″ . . . . . . . . . . . . . . . . . . . . . USA 680
Breakout / Oct '89.

### DON'T BLOW A GOOD THING.
**Tracks:** Don't blow a good thing / You make me want
to (love again).
■ 12″ . . . . . . . . . . . . . . . . . . . . USAT 600
■ 7″ . . . . . . . . . . . . . . . . . . . . . USA 600
Breakout / Mar '87.

### ONCE BITTEN, TWICE SHY.
**Tracks:** Once bitten twice shy / My heart is yours.
■ 12″ . . . . . . . . . . . . . . . . . . . . AMY 362
■ 7″ . . . . . . . . . . . . . . . . . . . . . . AM 362
A&M / Nov '86.

### SUDDENLY IT'S MAGIC.
**Tracks:** Suddenly it's magic / Don't let me down.
■ 7″ . . . . . . . . . . . . . . . . . . . . . USA 603
Breakout / May '87.

### VESTA.
**Tracks:** Something about you / Sweet thang / Don't
blow a good thing / Get out of my life / I can make
your dreams come true / My heart is yours / You
make me want to (love again) / It's you / Don't let me
down / Once bitten twice shy.
■ CD . . . . . . . . . . . . . . . . . . . . CDA 5118
■ LP . . . . . . . . . . . . . . . . . . . . AMA 5118
■ MC . . . . . . . . . . . . . . . . . . . AMC 5118
A&M / Nov '86.

### VESTA 4 U.
**Tracks:** Hearsay / Sweet sweet love / How u feel /
Hunger / All on u / 4 U / Best I ever had /
Congratulations.
CD . . . . . . . . . . . . . . . . . . . . CDA 5223
■ LP . . . . . . . . . . . . . . . . . . . . AMA 5223
■ MC . . . . . . . . . . . . . . . . . . . AMC 5223
A&M / Oct '88 / PolyGram.

## Wills, Viola

### BOTH SIDES NOW.
**Tracks:** Both sides now.
■ 7″ . . . . . . . . . . . . . . . . . . . . KHAN 66
Streetwave / Mar '86.

### DARE TO DREAM.
**Tracks:** Dare to dream.
■ 12″ . . . . . . . . . . . . . . . . . . MKHAN 66
Streetwave / Feb '86.

### GONNA GET ALONG WITHOUT YOU NOW.
**Tracks:** Gonna get along without you now.
■ 7″ . . . . . . . . . . . . . . . . . . . . AHA 546
Ariola Hansa / Sep '82.
■ 12″ . . . . . . . . . . . . . . . . . . 12TOU 05
Touch / Jul '84.
■ 12″ . . . . . . . . . . . . . . . . . MMPT 12006
■ 7″ . . . . . . . . . . . . . . . . . . MMPS 7006
Music Man / Jul '89.

### I'VE GOT TO HAVE ALL OF YOU.
**Tracks:** I've got to have all of you / Night scene.
■ 7″ . . . . . . . . . . . . . . . . . . . . PT 152
President / Oct '67.

### IF YOU COULD READ MY MIND.
**Tracks:** If you could read my mind / Somebody's
eyes.
■ 7″ . . . . . . . . . . . . . . . . . . . . AHA 577
Ariola Hansa / Mar '80.

### LET'S LOVE NOW.
**Tracks:** Let's love now part 1 / Let's love now part 2.
■ 7″ . . . . . . . . . . . . . . . . . . . . ARIST 151
Arista / Jan '78.

### LOVE LETTERS.
**Tracks:** Love letters.
■ 7″ . . . . . . . . . . . . . . . . . . . . CYS 1062
Charly / Mar '80.

## REGGAE HIGH.
**Tracks:** Reggae high.
■ 12″ . . . . . . . . . . . . . . . . . . . 12IS 329
■ 7″ . . . . . . . . . . . . . . . . . . . . . IS 329
Island / Aug '87.

### SECRET LOVE.
**Tracks:** Secret love.
■ 12″ . . . . . . . . . . . . . . . . . . . . SH 29T
■ 7″ . . . . . . . . . . . . . . . . . . . . . SH 29
Light House / Jan '89.

### SOMEBODY'S EYES.
**Tracks:** Somebody's eyes / You love.
■ 12″ . . . . . . . . . . . . . . . . . . EDITL 3313
■ 7″ . . . . . . . . . . . . . . . . . . . EDIT 3313
Sedition / Sep '86.

### TAKE ONE STEP FORWARD (Wills, Viola & Noel McCalla).
**Tracks:** Take one step forward (Inst).
■ 12″ . . . . . . . . . . . . . . . . . . . MARE 7
■ 7″ . . . . . . . . . . . . . . . . . . . MARES 7
Nightmare / Dec '86.

### THESE THINGS HAPPEN.
**Tracks:** These things happen.
■ 12″ . . . . . . . . . . . . . . . . . . .LEFT 23 T
■ 7″ . . . . . . . . . . . . . . . . . . . .LEFT 23
Rhythm King / Sep '88.

### TOGETHER FOREVER.
**Tracks:** Together forever / Don't kiss me hello and
mean goodbye.
■ 7″ . . . . . . . . . . . . . . . . . . . . PT 150
President / Aug '67.

### UP ON THE ROOF.
**Tracks:** Up on the roof / Let me be your rock.
■ 12″ . . . . . . . . . . . . . . . . . . AHAD 564
■ 7″ . . . . . . . . . . . . . . . . . . . AHA 564
Ariola Hansa / Jul '80.

### YOU ARE THE REASON WHY.
**Tracks:** You are the reason why / You are the reason
why (alternative version).
■ 12″ . . . . . . . . . . . . . . . . . . MKHAN 70
■ 7″ . . . . . . . . . . . . . . . . . . . KHAN 70
Streetwave / May '86.

## Wilson, Al

### COUNT THE BOYS.
**Tracks:** Earthquake / You got it / Count the boys /
Save a dance / Is this the end / Since I'm without you
/ You really turn me on / Tomorrow's sun.
■ LP . . . . . . . . . . . . . . . . . . . FL 13215
RCA / '79.

### DANCING HAMMOND.
**Tracks:** Mr. Sandman / Mack the knife / Un-senti-
mental / I'll be seeing you / Come fly with me / Yeh,
yeh / When the red, red robin comes bob, bob,
bobbin' along / Bye bye blackbird / Nikita / This is all
I ask / Once in a while / If love is good to me / You
always hurt the one you love / I know I'll never love
this way again / I'll get a kick out of you.
■ LP . . . . . . . . . . . . . . . . . . . SUS 513
MC . . . . . . . . . . . . . . . . . . . . CSUS 513
Sounds Ultimate / Dec '85 / Savoy Records / Sounds
Ultimate Records.

### EARTHQUAKE.
**Tracks:** Earthquake / Is this the end.
■ 12″ . . . . . . . . . . . . . . . . . . FC 9399
■ 7″ . . . . . . . . . . . . . . . . . . . PB 9399
RCA / Jul '79.

### SEARCHING FOR THE DOLPHINS.
**Tracks:** Dolphins / By the time I get to Phoenix / I
stand accused / Summer rain / Do what you gotta do
/ Snake / Who could be lovin' you / Poor side of town
/ Shake me, wake me / This guy's in love with you /
Brother, where are you.
■ LP . . . . . . . . . . . . . . . . . . . LBS 83173
Liberty / Jul '69.

### SNAKE, THE.
**Tracks:** Snake / Lovers concerto.
■ 7″ . . . . . . . . . . . . . . . . . . . BELL 1436
Bell / Aug '75.
■ 7″ . . . . . . . . . . . . . . . . . . . CC 16
Casino Classics / Aug '84.

## Wilson, Bobby

### I'LL BE YOUR RAINBOW.
**Tracks:** Deeper and deeper / Hey girl (Tell me) / Let
me (Put love back in your life) / I'll be your rainbow /
Here is where the love is / Don't shut me out / You
make me feel good all over / I'll take good care of
you / All I need (I've got) / When I don't see a smile
on your face.

CD . . . . . . . . . . . . . . . . . . . . NEMCD 635
Sequel / Mar '93 / Total / BMG.

## Wilson, Frank

### DO I LOVE YOU (INDEED I DO).
**Tracks:** Do I love you (indeed I do).
■ 7″ . . . . . . . . . . . . . . . . . . . TMG 1170
Motown / Oct '81.

## Wilson, Jackie

Born in Detroit in 1934, the indefatigable
Wilson sampled life both as a boxer and on
the assembly line before taking over Clyde
McPhatter's lead role in The Dominoes in
'53. Three years later he met Berry Gordy,
went solo and saw their first tune together,
*Reet Petite*, reach the UK Top 10. A series
of hits over the next few years, including
*Lonely Teardrops* and *Talk That Talk*, plus
an unbelievably energetic live show, installed him as one of the first great soul
stars. A bullet from a female fan in '61
stopped him for a couple of years, and sales
dwindled as Wilson dabbled in melodrama-
tic orchestral and big band arrangements.
Hugley successful return to form came in
the form of hits *Whispers* and *Higher And
Higher* in 1966 and 1967 respectively. Hits
continued, most notably for Brunswick Records until '75 when he suffered a severe
stroke on stage and lay in a coma until '84,
when he died. These posthumous hits followed *Reet Petite* became Christmas No. 1
in '86, followed up the charts by *I Get The
Sweetest Feeling* and *Higher And Higher* in
'87.

### 14 ORIGINAL GREATEST HITS:JACKIE WILSON/BILLY WARD (Wilson, Jackie & Billy Ward).
**Tracks:** Not Advised.
■ LP . . . . . . . . . . . . . . . . . . . . K 5007
King (USA) / Mar '88.

### 20 GREATEST HITS - JACKIE WILSON.
**Tracks:** Not Advised.
CD . . . . . . . . . . . . . . . . . . . . BRCD 48
■ LP . . . . . . . . . . . . . . . . . . . BRLP 48
MC . . . . . . . . . . . . . . . . . . . . BRMC 48
BR Music/BR Music (Holland) / Oct '88 / BMG.

### 20 GREATEST HITS: JACKIE WILSON.
**Tracks:** Your love keeps lifting me / Lonely teardrops
/ Reet petite / That's why I love you so / To be loved /
Tear of the year / No pity (in the naked city) / Am I
the man / I'm comin' on back to me / Whispers /
Night / Baby workout / You were made for all /
Please tell me why / You better know it / I just can't
help it / I get the sweetest feeling / Doggin' around /
Woman, a lover, a friend.
CD . . . . . . . . . . . . . . . . . . . . 2662542
LP . . . . . . . . . . . . . . . . . . . . 2662541
MC . . . . . . . . . . . . . . . . . . . . 2662544
Mainline (2) / Apr '90.

### ALL MY LOVE.
**Tracks:** All my love.
■ 7″ . . . . . . . . . . . . . . . . . . . Q 72407
Coral / Sep '60.

### ALONE AT LAST.
**Tracks:** Alone at last.
■ 7″ . . . . . . . . . . . . . . . . . . . Q 72412
Coral / Dec '60.

### BABY WORKOUT.
**Tracks:** Baby workout / Lonely teardrops.
■ 12″ . . . . . . . . . . . . . . . . . . SKM 11(12)
■ 7″ . . . . . . . . . . . . . . . . . . . SKM 11
■ CD Single . . . . . . . . . . . . . . SKMCD 11
SMP (2) / Nov '87.

### CLASSIC JACKIE WILSON.
**Tracks:** Reet petite / To be loved / Lonely teardrops /
That's why (I love you so) / I'll be satisfied / You
better know it / Talk that talk / Night / Doggin' around
/ Passing through / Woman, a lover, a friend / Am I
the man / Please tell me why / I'm coming on back to
you / You don't know what it means / I just can't help
it / Baby workout / Danny boy / I get the sweetest
feeling / No pity (in the naked city) / She's alright /
Whispers / Your love keeps lifting me higher and
higher / You got me walking.
■ LP . . . . . . . . . . . . . . . . . . . JAK 101
MC . . . . . . . . . . . . . . . . . . . . ZCJAK 101
SMP (2) / Jun '84 / PRT Distribution.

### DO YOUR THING.
**Tracks:** To change my love / This guy's in love with
you / Why don't you do your thing / This bitter earth ▲

                                              ■ DELETED

Helpless / Light my fire / That lucky old sun / With these hands / Hold on, I'm coming / Eleanor Rigby.
■ LP . . . . . . . . . . . . . . . . . . . . . . . . . . MUPS 405
MCA / Jun '70.

### DYNAMIC JACKIE WILSON.
Tracks: (Your love keeps lifting me) Higher and higher / I get the sweetest feeling / Squeeze her (ease her (but love her) / She's all right / Think twice Duet with LaVern Baker) / I've got to get back Country boy) / Whispers (gettin' louder) / Just be sincere / Since you showed me how to be happy / I won't want to lose you / I've lost you / Stop lying / Who am I / I believe / Even when you cry (With Count asie) / (I can feel those vibrations) This love is real You got me walking / No more goodbyes / Don't urn no bridges (With the Chi-Lites) / Open the door your heart.
D . . . . . . . . . . . . . . . . . . . . . . . . . CPCD 8018
harly / Feb '94 / Charly.

### FIFTEEN CLASSIC TRACKS.
Tracks: Reet petite / Tear of the year / Your one and only love / Alone at last / Greatest hurt / Years from now / Baby work out / Shake, shake, shake / Higher and higher / For your precious love / Think twice / chain gang / To change my love / Uptight / Doggin' round.
■ LP . . . . . . . . . . . . . . . . . . . . . . . . . 4504551
■ MC . . . . . . . . . . . . . . . . . . . . . . . . . 4504554
BS / '87.

### GREATEST HITS: JACKIE WILSON.
Tracks: Reet petite / Baby workout / To be loved / oggin' around / All my love / Whispers (gettin' ouder) / Woman a lover a friend / I get the sweetest eeling / (Your love keeps lifting me) higher and igher / I'll be satisfied / You better know it / I'm oming on back to you / Am I the man / Chain gang / lone at last / Lonely teardrops.
■ CD . . . . . . . . . . . . . . . . . . . . . . . . .261854
■ LP . . . . . . . . . . . . . . . . . . . . . . . . .211854
■ MC . . . . . . . . . . . . . . . . . . . . . . . . .411854
rista / Aug '91.

### HIGHER AND HIGHER.
Tracks: Soul galore / I've lost you / I don't want to ose you / Who who song / Nothing but blue skies / I et the sweetest feeling / You brought about a hange in me / I'm the one to do it / Nobody but you / igher and higher / Uptight / Whispers (gettin' ouder) / You got me walking / Because of you / Wat'cha gonna do about ove / This love is real / Since you showed me how to e happy.
D . . . . . . . . . . . . . . . . . . . . . . . . . CDKEN 901
ent / May '86 / Pinnacle.

### HIGHER AND HIGHER.
Tracks: Higher and higher / Who who song.
■ 7" . . . . . . . . . . . . . . . . . . . . . . . . . BAG 2
CA / May '69.
I 12" . . . . . . . . . . . . . . . . . . . . . . SKM 10(12)
■ 7" . . . . . . . . . . . . . . . . . . . . . . . . SKM 10
MP (2) / Jun '87.

### HIGHER AND HIGHER.
Tracks: Reet petite / Lonely teardrops / Come back me / Danny boy / Why can't you be mine / If I can't ave you / That's why (I love you so) / I'll be satisfied You better know it / Talk that talk / I know I'll always in love with you / Doggin' around / Woman a over, a friend / Am I the man / Tear of the year / ease tell me why / I'm coming back to you / You on't know what it means / I just can't help it / Baby workout / Shake, shake, shake / No pity (in the naked ity) / Whispers (Gettin' louder) / (Your love keeps ting me) Higher and higher / I get the sweetest eeling.
D . . . . . . . . . . . . . . . . . . . . . . . . . CPCD 8005
harly / Oct '93 / Charly.

### HIGHER AND HIGHER.
Tracks: Higher and higher / I'm the one to do it.
■ 7" . . . . . . . . . . . . . . . . . . . . . . . . Q 72493
oral / Sep '67.

### HIGHER AND HIGHER.
Tracks: I don't need you around / I've lost you / nose heartaches / Soulville / Open the door to your eart / I'm the one to do it / You can count on me / gher and higher / I need your loving / Somebody o there likes you / When will our day come.
LP . . . . . . . . . . . . . . . . . . . . . . . MUPS 304
CA / May '68.

### IS STORY VOL. 1.
acks: Not Advised.
D . . . . . . . . . . . . . . . . . . . . . . . . . RTS 33050
ovogue / Apr '93 / Pinnacle.

### HIS STORY VOL. 2.
Tracks: Not Advised.
CD . . . . . . . . . . . . . . . . . . . . . . . RTS 33051
Provogue / Apr '93 / Pinnacle.

### I BELIEVE I'LL LOVE ON.
Tracks: I believe I'll love on / Lonely teardrops.
■ 7" . . . . . . . . . . . . . . . . . . . . . . . . Q 72482
Coral / Dec '65.

### I GET THE SWEETEST FEELIN'.
Tracks: You keep me hangin' on / For once in my life / Who can I turn to / People / Don't go to strangers / I get the sweetest feeling / You brought about a change in me / Nothing but blue skies / Woman needs to be loved / Growin' tall / Since you showed me how to be happy.
■ LP . . . . . . . . . . . . . . . . . . . . . . . MUPS 361
MCA / Apr '69.

### I GET THE SWEETEST FEELING.
Tracks: I get the sweetest feeling / Whisper / Higher and higher / Who who song / Nothing but blue skies.
■ 7" . . . . . . . . . . . . . . . . . . . . . . . . MU 1160
MCA / Jul '72.
■ 7" . . . . . . . . . . . . . . . . . . . . . . . . BR 18
Brunswick / Mar '75.
■ 12" . . . . . . . . . . . . . . . . . . . . . . SKM 0121
SMP (2) / Feb '87.

### I GET THE SWEETEST FEELING (OLD GOLD).
Tracks: I get the sweetest feeling / Higher and higher / Whispers (getting louder).
■ CD Single . . . . . . . . . . . . . . . . . . . OG 6109
Old Gold / Nov '88.
■ 12" . . . . . . . . . . . . . . . . . . . . . . OG 4118
Old Gold / May '89.

### I'M GONNA GET YOU (see under Baker, LaVern).

### IT ONLY HAPPENS WHEN I LOOK AT YOU.
Tracks: It only happens when I look at you / Just as soon as the feelings over.
■ 7" . . . . . . . . . . . . . . . . . . . . . . . . BR 43
Brunswick / Jul '77.

### JACKIE WILSON.
Tracks: Not Advised.
■ LP . . . . . . . . . . . . . . . . . . . . . . . BID 8007
Bellaphon / Jul '88.

### JACKIE WILSON.
Tracks: Not Advised.
DCC . . . . . . . . . . . . . . . . . . . . . DCC 8105
MiniDisc . . . . . . . . . . . . . . . . . . MDISC 810
Disky / Apr '93 / THE.

### JACKIE WILSON - GREATEST HITS.
Tracks: Not Advised.
■ LP . . . . . . . . . . . . . . . . . . . . . . . MA 18287
MC . . . . . . . . . . . . . . . . . . . . MAMC 918287
Masters (Holland) / '88.

### NO PITY (IN THE NAKED CITY).
Tracks: No pity (in the naked city) / I'm so lonely.
■ 7" . . . . . . . . . . . . . . . . . . . . . . . . Q 72481
Coral / Aug '65.

### REET PETITE.
Tracks: Shake, shake, shake / Why can't you be mine / I'm wanderin' / Lonely teardrops / Yeah yeah / It's so fine / Come back to me / Shake a hand / Reet petite / If I can't have you / All my love / So much / I know I'll always be in love with you / Danny boy / Doggin' around / Do Lord.
■ LP . . . . . . . . . . . . . . . . . . . . . . . CH 125
MC . . . . . . . . . . . . . . . . . . . . . . .CHC 125
Ace / Mar '85 / Pinnacle / Complete Record Co. Ltd.
CD . . . . . . . . . . . . . . . . . . . . . . . CDCH 902
Ace / May '86 / Pinnacle / Complete Record Co. Ltd.

### REET PETITE.
Tracks: Reet petite / You brought about a change in me / I'm the one to do it.
■ 7" . . . . . . . . . . . . . . . . . . . . . . . . SKM 03
SMP (2) / Mar '85.
■ 12" . . . . . . . . . . . . . . . . . . . . . . SKM 0123
SMP (2) / Nov '86.

### REET PETITE.
Tracks: Reet petite / I get the sweetest feeling.
VHS . . . . . . . . . . . . . . . . . . . . . . . VC 4014
Gold Rushes / Mar '87 / Gold & Sons.

### REET PETITE (ORIGINAL).
Tracks: Reet petite.
■ 7" . . . . . . . . . . . . . . . . . . . . . . . . Q 72290
Coral / Nov '57.

### REET PETITE AND OTHER CLASSICS.
Tracks: Reet petite / That's why I love you so / Lonely teardrops / Night / I'm wandering / Singing a song / We have love / It's so fine / By the light of the silvery moon / Come back to me / To be loved / Only you, only me / Stormy weather / Lonely life / Ask / Magic of love / Happiness / Never go away / Thrill of love / Danny boy.
CD . . . . . . . . . . . . . . . . . . . . . . . CDCD 1142
Charly / Nov '93 / Charly.

### SOUL YEARS VOL.2, THE.
Tracks: Whispers / Since you showed me how to be happy / Uptight / You can count on me / Somebody up there likes you / My heart is calling / Hard to get a thing called love / Those heartaches / Don't you know I love you / I've learned about life / It's all over / Do it the right way / You keep me hangin' on / To change my love / Love is funny that way / Nobody but you.
■ LP . . . . . . . . . . . . . . . . . . . . . . . KENT 054
Kent / May '86.

### SOUL YEARS, THE.
Tracks: Soul galore / I've lost you / Who who song / I don't want to lose you / Just be sincere / I'm the one to do it / I get the sweetest feeling / Nothing but blue skies / I can feel those vibrations (this love is real) / Because of you / Try it again / What 'cha gonna do about love / You left the fire burning / You got me walking / You brought about a change in me / Open the door to your heart.
■ LP . . . . . . . . . . . . . . . . . . . . . . . KENT 027
■ MC . . . . . . . . . . . . . . . . . . . . . . KENC 027
Kent / Jan '85.

### SPOTLIGHT ON JACKIE WILSON.
Tracks: Over the rainbow / Pledging my love / Georgia on my mind / You'll never walk alone / Rags to riches / You don't know / What kind of fool am I / I wanna be around / Until the real thing coms along / I apologise / Lonely teardrops / We have love.
■ LP . . . . . . . . . . . . . . . . . . . . . . . LVA 9231
Coral / Jan '66.

### THRU THE YEARS.
Tracks: Right now / I'm wanderin' / We have love / So much / Way I am / You only live twice / Do lord / Silent one / Think twice / Since you showed me how to be happy / I still love you / Didn't I / Love is funny that way / You left the fire burning.
■ LP . . . . . . . . . . . . . . . . . . . . . RNLP 70230
MC . . . . . . . . . . . . . . . . . . . . . RNC 70230
Rhino (USA) / Oct '87 / WEA.

### TO BE LOVED.
Tracks: To be loved.
■ 7" . . . . . . . . . . . . . . . . . . . . . . . . Q 72306
Coral / Mar '58.

### TO MAKE A BIG MAN CRY.
Tracks: To make a big man cry / Be my love.
■ 7" . . . . . . . . . . . . . . . . . . . . . . . . Q 72484
Coral / May '66.

### TWO MUCH (Wilson, Jackie & Count Basie).
Tracks: Funky Broadway / For your precious love / In the midnight hour / Ode to Billy Joe / Chain gang / I was made to love her / Uptight / I never loved a woman / Respect / Even when you cry / My girl.
■ LP . . . . . . . . . . . . . . . . . . . . . . . MUPS 333
MCA / Sep '68.

### TWO ON ONE: SAM COOKE & JACKIE WILSON (see under Cooke, Sam).

### VERY BEST OF JACKIE WILSON, THE.
Tracks: Reet petite / Lonely teardrops / To be loved / That's why / I'll be satisfied / Doggin' around / Lonely life / Night / You better know it / Talk talk talk / Am I the man / I'm comin' on back to you / Woman, a lover, a friend / Baby workout / Squeeze her, tease her (but love her) / No pity (in the naked city) / Whispers (gettin' louder) / I get the sweetest feeling / Since you showed me how to be happy / Love is funny that way / Just be sincere / Your love keeps lifting me higher and higher / You got me walking / This love is real (I can feel those...
CD . . . . . . . . . . . . . . . . . . . . . . . CDCH 913
Ace / Jun '87 / Pinnacle / Complete Record Co. Ltd.

### VERY BEST OF JACKIE WILSON, THE (2).
Tracks: Reet petite / Lonely teardrops / That's why I love you so / Night / You better know it / Talk that talk / to be loved / I'll be satisfied / Whispers (gettin' louder) / Your love keeps lifting me higher and

DELETED

higher / I get the sweetest feeling / Doggin' around /
Am I the man / I'm comin' on back to you / Woman, a
lover, a friend / No pity (in the naked city).
**CD** .................................... **MCCD 017**
■ **MC** .................................... **.MCTC 017**
Music Club / Feb '91 / Gold & Sons / THE / Video
Collection / C.M. Distribution.

### WHISPERS.
**Tracks:** Whispers / Fairest of them all.
■ **7"** .................................... **Q 72487**
Coral / Nov '66.

## Wilson, Nancy

### BEST OF CAPITOL YEARS.
**Tracks:** Hello young lovers / You leave me breathless / Teach me tonight / Lot of living to do /
Sophisticated lady / Tonight / Midnight sun / There
will never be another you / What a little moonlight
can do / Very thought of you / Satin doll / Make
someone happy / Like someone in love / Try a little
tenderness / Quiet nights of quiet stars / Your name
is love / This dream / Days of wine and roses / Boy
from Ipanema / As you desire me / I'm all smiles /
Close your eyes / Back in your own backyard.
**CD** .................................... **CDEMS 1462**
■ **MC** .................................... **TCEMS 1462**
Capitol / Oct '92 / EMI.

### BUT BEAUTIFUL.
**Tracks:** Prelude to a kiss / For heaven's sake /
Happiness is a thing called Joe / I'll walk alone /
Supper time / Oh look at me now / Glad to be
unhappy / In a sentimental mood / I thought about
you / Easy living / Do it again / Darn that dream.
■ **CD** .................................... **CDP 792 868 2**
Pacific Jazz / Apr '90.

### END OF OUR LOVE, THE.
**Tracks:** End of our love / Face it, girl, it's over.
■ **7"** .................................... **CL 15547**
Capitol / Feb '77.

### FORBIDDEN LOVER.
**Tracks:** Forbidden lover / I was telling him about you
/ If you only knew / Deeper / Puttin' my trust / You
know / Too good to be true / I never held your heart /
What will it take this time / Song for you.
**CD** .................................... **.983326 2**
Pickwick/Sony Collector's Choice / Oct '93 / Pickwick
/ Pinnacle.

### GODSEND.
**Tracks:** Feel like makin' love / Dindi / It's all been
said / Loneliness / Godsend / Ribbon in the sky /
Heart to heart / How could I have know / I believe in
you / Another place in time.
■ **CD** .................................... **C38 7188**
Denon / Dec '84.

### LADY WITH A SONG, A.
**Tracks:** Do you still dream about me / Now I know /
Time out for love / Don't ask my neighbours / Lady
with a song / That's what I remember / This love is
what I need / Other side of the storm / Melody is you
/ Heavens hands.
■ **CD** .................................... **4664325**
■ **LP** .................................... **4664331**
■ **MC** .................................... **4664334**
CBS / Sep '90.

### LIFE, LOVE AND HARMONY.
**Tracks:** Life, love and harmony / Here's to us / This
is our song / Sunshine / You're the one / Open up
your heart / Wrapped up in the comfort of your love /
Best of the woman in me / Heaven.
■ **LP** .................................... **.EST 11943**
Capitol / '79.

### LIVE AT CARNEGIE HALL.
**Tracks:** Not Advised.
**VHS** .................................... **IGU 0002**
Iguana Video / '92 / Video Collection.

### LIVE IN EUROPE.
**Tracks:** Not Advised.
**CD** .................................... **JD 1264**
Jazz Door / Aug '94 / Charly / Koch International /
A.D.A. Distribution.

### LUSH LIFE.
**Tracks:** Free again / Midnight sun / Only the young /
When the world was young / Right to love / Lush life /
Over the weekend / You've changed / River shallow
/ Sunny / I stayed too long at the fair.
■ **MC** .................................... **TCCAPS 2600064**
■ **LP** .................................... **CAPS 2600061**
Capitol / Apr '84.

### MERCY, MERCY, MERCY.
**Tracks:** Mercy, mercy, mercy / Don't look over your
shoulder.

■ **7"** .................................... **CL 15508**
Capitol / Jul '67.

### MUSIC ON MY MIND.
**Tracks:** I'm gonna let ya / Music on my mind / I'm a
balloon / Let it flow / Easy / he makes me feel good
'bout myself / I'm in love / I really need him / Light.
■ **LP** .................................... **.EST 11786**
Capitol / Aug '78.

### NANCY WILSON & CANNONBALL AD-
### DERLEY (Wilson, Nancy & Cannonball
### Adderley).
**Tracks:** Save your love for me / Never will I marry /
Old country / Happy talk / Masquerade is over /
Sleepin' bee / Little unhappy boy / Teaneck / I can't
get started / One man's dream / Never say yes / Unit
7.
■ **CD** .................................... **CDP 7812042**
Capitol Jazz / Mar '93.

### NANCY WILSON'S GREATEST HITS.
**Tracks:** How glad I am / Face it girl it's over / Can't
take my eyes off you / Uptight / Peace of mind / Now
I'm a woman / Tell me the truth / I want to be with
you / Don't come running back to me.
**MC** .................................... **4XL 9449**
Capitol (Specials) / Dec '88.

### NOW I'M A WOMAN.
**Tracks:** Now I'm a woman / Close to you / Long and
winding road / Bridge over troubled water / Let's fall
in love all over / Lonely, lonely / How many broken
wings / Real me / Make it with you.
■ **LP** .................................... **E-ST 541**
Capitol / Oct '71.

### POWER OF LOVE.
**Tracks:** Power of love / Rain sometimes.
■ **7"** .................................... **CL 15443**
Capitol / Mar '66.

### TEN YEARS OF TEARS.
**Tracks:** Ten years of tears / Willow weep for me.
■ **7"** .................................... **CL 15503**
Capitol / May '67.

### TOUCH OF TODAY, A.
**Tracks:** You've got your troubles / I love him /
Uptight / Have a heart / Before the rain / Shadow of
your smile / Call me / Yesterday / Wasn't it wonder-
ful / Your gonna hear from me / No one else but you
/ Goin' out of my head.
■ **LP** .................................... **.T 2495**
Capitol / Sep '66.

### TWO OF US, THE.
**Tracks:** Ram / Midnight rendezvous / Breaker beat /
Slippin' away / Two of us / Quiet storm / Never
wanna say goodnight / Closer than close / Song
without words.
■ **LP** .................................... **CBS 25976**
■ **MC** .................................... **.40 25976**
CBS / Sep '84.

### UPTIGHT (EVERYTHING'S ALRIGHT).
**Tracks:** Uptight (everything's alright).
■ **7"** .................................... **CL 15466**
Capitol / '66.

### WELCOME TO MY LOVE.
**Tracks:** In the heat of the night / May I come in /
Angel eyes / It never entered my mind / I'm always
drunk in San Francisco (and I don't drink at all) /
Theme from Hotel / For once in my life / You don't
know me / Why try to change me now / Welcome to
my love / Ode to Billy Joe / Let's make the most of a
beautiful thing.
**CD** .................................... **CDP 8289802**
Capitol Jazz / Jul '94 / EMI.

### WHERE DOES THAT LEAVE ME.
**Tracks:** Where does that leave me.
■ **7"** .................................... **CL 15412**
Capitol / '66.

### WITH MY LOVER BESIDE ME.
**Tracks:** With my lover beside me / Look at you/
Something tells me I'm falling in love / When Oc-
tober goes / Love is where you find it / At last / I
can't teach my old heart new tricks / When the
meadow was bloomin' / Heart of mine, cry on / Just
remember / Last dream home / Epilogue.
■ **CD** .................................... **4690032**
■ **MC** .................................... **4690034**
Columbia / Nov '91.

### YESTERDAY'S LOVE SONGS..TODAY'S
### BLUES.
**Tracks:** Song is you / Very thought of you / Satin doll
/ Bewitched / Sufferin' with the blues / Someone to
watch over me / Best is yet to come / Never let me
go / Send me yesterday / All my tomorrows / Please
send me someone to love / Blue prelude / What are

you doing New Year's Eve / Show goes on / Wes[t]
Coast blues / Tell me the truth / My sweet thing.
■ **CD** .................................... **CZ 44[?]**
■ **MC** .................................... **B4 9626[?]**
Capitol Jazz / Jun '91.

### YOU'RE AS RIGHT AS RAIN.
**Tracks:** You're as right as rain / There'll always b[e]
forever.
■ **7"** .................................... **CL 1581[?]**
Capitol / Feb '75.

## Wilson, Nicky

### STONE SOUL LOVING.
**Tracks:** Stone soul loving / Cry like a child.
■ **7"** .................................... **.CC[?]**
Casino Classics / '79.

## Wilson, Precious

### CRY TO ME.
**Tracks:** Cry to me / Stop running.
■ **7"** .................................... **EPCA 133[?]**
Epic / Jun '81.

### I MAY BE RIGHT 4 U.
**Tracks:** I may be right 4 u / I may be right 4 [u]
(instrumental).
■ **12"** .................................... **12SAV 10[?]**
■ **7"** .................................... **.SAV 10[?]**
S & M / Feb '90.

### I NEED YOU.
**Tracks:** I need you / Valley of the dolls.
■ **7"** .................................... **EPCA 185[?]**
Epic / Jan '82.

### I'LL BE YOUR FRIEND.
**Tracks:** I'll be your friend.
■ **12"** .................................... **JIVET 1[?]**
■ **7"** .................................... **.JIVE 1[?]**
Jive / Sep '85.

### IF I LOVE YOU LESS.
**Tracks:** If I love you less / Stop runnin'.
■ **7"** .................................... **EPC 955[?]**
Epic / Feb '81.

### JEWEL OF THE NILE.
**Tracks:** Jewel of the nile / Didn't take it away.
■ **12"** .................................... **JIVET 11[?]**
■ **7"** .................................... **.JIVE 11[?]**
Jive / Apr '86.

### NICE GIRLS DON'T LAST.
**Tracks:** Nice girls don't last / Nice girls don't last (L[?]
mix).
■ **12"** .................................... **JIVET 12[?]**
■ **7"** .................................... **.JIVE 12[?]**
Jive / Jul '86.

### ON THE RACE TRACK (Wilson, Preciou[s]
### & Sky Train).
**Tracks:** We are on the race track / Cry to me / Sto[p]
running / Stay by my side / You ain't got love [/]
Together forever / Mr. Pilot man / Funky dancer [/]
Killing me softly.
■ **LP** .................................... **EPC 8489[?]**
Country Roads Records / Sep '81.

### ONLY THE STRONG SURVIVE.
**Tracks:** Only the strong survive.
■ **12"** .................................... **JIVET 14[?]**
■ **7"** .................................... **.JIVE 14[?]**
Jive / Jul '87.

### PRECIOUS WILSON.
**Tracks:** I'll be your friend / Love can't wait / Sh[?]
don't really wanna know / Letter / Nice girls don['t]
last / State of relations / Jewel of the nile / Ne[w]
moon in the summer / Don't take it away.
■ **LP** .................................... **HIP 3[?]**
■ **MC** .................................... **HIPC 3[?]**
Jive / Sep '86.

### RED LIGHT.
**Tracks:** Red light / I don't know why / Why don't I r[un]
away from you / Kisuraheli / You haven't heard th[e]
last of me / Raising my family / Night the music die[d]
/ All coloured in love / Every day will be like
holiday / Your face stays on my mind / I need you[r]
■ **LP** .................................... **EPC 2505[?]**
Epic / Dec '82.

### RED LIGHT.
**Tracks:** Red light / Night the music died.
■ **7"** .................................... **EPCA 273[?]**
Epic / Oct '82.

■ **DELETE[D]**

## OU HAVEN'T HEARD THE LAST OF
E.
racks: You haven't heard the last of me / isuraheli.
■ 7" . . . . . . . . . . . . . . . . . . . . EPCA 3095
pic / Feb '83.

## Wilson, Reuben

### LUE MODE.
racks: Bambu / Knock on wood / Bus ride / Orange eel / Twenty-five miles / Blue mode.
P . . . . . . . . . . . . . . . . . . . . . B1 84343
lue Note / Aug '94 / EMI.

### ISCO KID, THE.
racks: Not Advised.
■ LP . . . . . . . . . . . . . . . . . . . . PLEO 1
ot Advised / '87.

### OVE BUG.
racks: Hot rod / I'm gonna make you love me / I say little prayer / Love bug / Stormy / Back out.
P . . . . . . . . . . . . . . . . . . . . . B1 84317
lue Note / Aug '94 / EMI.

## Wilson, Tony

### EST OF TONY WILSON, THE.
racks: Give your lady what she wants / Lay nest to ou / Africa / New Orleans music / Love, I thought I ould never find love / I like your style / New York ity life / Politician (A man of many words) / What oes it take / Gotta make love to you / Loving you sn't the same / Better of just loving you / Legal aper / Just when I need you most / Try love / orever young / Anything that keeps you satisfied / I an't leave it alone.
. . . . . . . . . . . . . . . . . . . . . SEECD 323
ee For Miles / May '93 / Pinnacle.

### ATCH ONE.
racks: Give your lady what she wants / Lay next to ou / Fool around / Just when I needed you most / frica / Try love / New Orleans music / Love, I ought I would never find love / I really love you / orever young.
■ LP . . . . . . . . . . . . . . . . . . . . K 55526
earsville (USA) / Apr '79.

### LIKE YOUR STYLE.
racks: Not Advised.
D . . . . . . . . . . . . . . . . . . REP 4076-WZ
P . . . . . . . . . . . . . . . . . . . . REP 2076
C . . . . . . . . . . . . . . . . . . REP 2076-TS
epertoire (Germany) / Aug '91 / Pinnacle.

### UST PART OF WHAT YOU'LL GET.
racks: Not Advised.
CD . . . . . . . . . . . . . . . . . . CDSGP 028
MC . . . . . . . . . . . . . . . . . . CASSGP 028
restige (Total) / Nov '92.

### EW YORK CITY LIFE.
racks: New York City life / Politician.
■ 7" . . . . . . . . . . . . . . . . . . . . K 15533
earsville (USA) / May '77.

### ART OF WHAT YOU GET.
racks: Part of what you get / Walk on the beach.
■ 7" . . . . . . . . . . . . . . . . . . . SDZ 001
and Dollar (USA) / Jan '89.

### ALKING THE HIGHWIRE.
racks: Not Advised.
D . . . . . . . . . . . . . . . . . . LICD 901222
ne / Nov '92 / C.M. Distribution / Grapevine Distri- ution / A.D.A. Distribution / Conifer Records.

### HAT DID I DO.
racks: What did I do / Can't waste a good thing.
■ 7" . . . . . . . . . . . . . . . . . . . DB 8153
olumbia / Mar '67.

## Wilson-James, Victoria

### WANT YOU IN MY MOVIE.
acks: I want you in my movie.
12" . . . . . . . . . . . . . . . . . . RAHT 101
7" . . . . . . . . . . . . . . . . . . . RAH 101
sing / Jun '88.

### ERSEVERANCE.
racks: Through / Bright lights / One world / 2nd ature / Angel calling / Through (classic club mix) / omen of colours / Perseverance works / Rest of ur life / Future world / Works (instrumental).
D . . . . . . . . . . . . . . . . . . . . 4674732
LP . . . . . . . . . . . . . . . . . . . . 4674731
C . . . . . . . . . . . . . . . . . . . . 4674734
ic / Apr '91 / Sony.

### THROUGH.
Tracks: Through.
■ 12" . . . . . . . . . . . . . . . . . . 6566556
■ 7" . . . . . . . . . . . . . . . . . . . 6566557
■ 7" . . . . . . . . . . . . . . . . . . . 6566550
■ CD Single . . . . . . . . . . . . . . 6566552
■ MC Single . . . . . . . . . . . . . . 6566558
Epic / Mar '91.

## Winans

Four brothers from Detroit who made their debut as the Testimonial Singers before turning professional in 1981 as the Winans. Thier first three albums were released through Light Records between 1981 and 1985. Having seen them in concert in Los Angeles, Quincy Jones signed them to his Qwest label and they released their most commercially successful single *Let My People Go* in 1985. Subsequent albums featured renowned soul artists such as Anita Baker and Stevie Wonder and production credits included Teddy Riley and Michael Powell. In return they provided backing vocals for Michael Jackson's *Man In The Mirror* and featured on the film soundtrack *Lean On Me*.

### AIN'T NO NEED TO WORRY (Winans with Anita Baker).
Tracks: Ain't no need to worry.
■ 12" . . . . . . . . . . . . . . . . . . W 8274T
■ 7" . . . . . . . . . . . . . . . . . . W 8274
Qwest / Aug '87.

### ALL OUT.
Tracks: Payday / It's not heaven if you're not there / If he doesn't come tonight / That extra mile / Tradewinds / All you ever been was good / Money motive / Love will never die / Heaven belongs to you / He said go.
CD . . . . . . . . . . . . . . . . . . 9362452132
MC . . . . . . . . . . . . . . . . . . 9362452134
Qwest / Aug '93 / WEA.

### LET MY PEOPLE GO.
Tracks: Choose ye / Redeemed / Perfect love / Straighten my life out / Let my people go / I'll follow where you lead / Special lady / Very real way.
■ LP . . . . . . . . . . . . . . . . . . .925344 1
Qwest / Dec '85.

### LET MY PEOPLE GO.
Tracks: Let my people go.
■ 12" . . . . . . . . . . . . . . . . . . W 8874 T
■ 7" . . . . . . . . . . . . . . . . . . W 8874
WEA / Jan '86.

### LOVE HAS NO COLOUR (Winans featuring Michael McDonald).
Tracks: Love has no colour / What can I say.
■ 12" . . . . . . . . . . . . . . . . . . W 8147T
■ 7" . . . . . . . . . . . . . . . . . . W 8147
Qwest / Nov '87.

### RETURN.
Tracks: It's time / Everyday the same / Don't leave me / Friend / Gonna be alright / When you cry / Together we stand / This time it's personal / Free / Wherever I go.
CD . . . . . . . . . . . . . . . . . . 7599261612
■ LP . . . . . . . . . . . . . . . . . . 7599261611
MC . . . . . . . . . . . . . . . . . . 7599261614
WEA / Apr '90 / WEA.

### TOMORROW.
Tracks: Not Advised.
■ LP . . . . . . . . . . . . . . . . . . LS 7073
MC . . . . . . . . . . . . . . . . . . LC 7073
Light / Mar '84 / Word Records (UK) / Sony.

### VERY REAL WAY.
Tracks: Very real way / Let my people go.
■ 12" . . . . . . . . . . . . . . . . . . W 8744 T
■ 7" . . . . . . . . . . . . . . . . . . W 8744
Qwest / Mar '86.

### WINANS.
Tracks: Not Advised.
■ LP . . . . . . . . . . . . . . . . . . LS 7063
MC . . . . . . . . . . . . . . . . . . LC 7063
Light / May '82 / Word Records (UK) / Sony.

### WINANS - LIVE AT CARNEGIE HALL.
Tracks: Ain't no need to worry / Tomorrow / What a friend we have in Jesus.
■ Double LP . . . . . . . . . . . . . . SL R 7501
MC Set . . . . . . . . . . . . . . . . SL C 7501
Word (UK) / '88 / Word Records (UK) / Sony.

## Winans, Bebe & Cece

### BEBE & CECE WINANS.
Tracks: I O U Me / No hiding place / Call me / In return / I don't know why / For always / Change your nature / He's coming soon.
■ CD . . . . . . . . . . . . . . . . . BIRDCD 193
■ LP . . . . . . . . . . . . . . . . . . BIRD R 193
■ MC . . . . . . . . . . . . . . . . . . BIRD C 193
Sparrow / Oct '88.

### CELEBRATE NEW LIFE.
Tracks: Celebrate new life (Celebration edit) (Not on 12".) / Bridge over troubled water (Not on 12".) / Celebrate new life (Celebration mix) (12" only.) / Celebrate new life (Milkyway beats) (12" only.) / Heaven (mix) / Heaven (LP version) (CD single only.) / Celebrate new life (dub life mix) (CD single only.)
■ 12" . . . . . . . . . . . . . . . . . . 12CL 551
■ 7" . . . . . . . . . . . . . . . . . . .CL 551
■ CD Single . . . . . . . . . . . . . . CDCL 551
Capitol / Oct '89.

### DECISIONS.
Tracks: Ain't no need to worry / Millions / Breaking of day / What can I say / Right, left in a wrong world / Don't let the sun go down on me / Love has no colour / Give me you / How can you live without Christ.
CD . . . . . . . . . . . . . . . . . . .925510 2
■ LP . . . . . . . . . . . . . . . . . . K 925510 1
MC. . . . . . . . . . . . . . . . . . K 925510 4
Qwest / Oct '87 / WEA.

### DIFFERENT LIFESTYLES.
Tracks: Not Advised.
CD . . . . . . . . . . . . . . . . . . CDEST 2146
MC . . . . . . . . . . . . . . . . . .TCEST 2146
Capitol / Jun '91 / EMI.

### HEAVEN.
Tracks: Heaven / Celebrate new life / Lost without you / You / Wanna be more / Hold up the light (With Whitney Houston.) / Meantime / Don't cry / Trust him / Bridge over troubled water.
■ CD . . . . . . . . . . . . . . . . . . CDEST 2081
■ LP . . . . . . . . . . . . . . . . . . EST 2081
■ MC . . . . . . . . . . . . . . . . . .TCEST 2081
Capitol / Dec '88.

### I.O.U. ME.
Tracks: I.O.U. me / No hiding place / Love said not so (Track on 12" only.).
■ 12" . . . . . . . . . . . . . . . . . . 12CL 472
■ 7" . . . . . . . . . . . . . . . . . . .CL 472
Capitol / Jan '88.

### RELATIONSHIPS.
Tracks: Count it all joy / Love of my life / Don't let me walk down this road alone / Both day and night / Stay with me / He's always there / Right away / If anything ever happened to you / These what about's / (If I was only) Welcomed in / We can make a difference.
CD . . . . . . . . . . . . . . . . . . CDEST 2237
Capitol / Sep '94 / EMI.

## Winbush, Angela

A native of St Louis, Missouri, Winbush relocated to LA during the seventies and cut first musical teeth as a member of Stevie Wonder's band, Wonderlove. In 1977 she met Rene Moore and formed the writing/ performance duo Rene & Angela, recording several albums for Capitol records, the most successful of which was *Street Named Desire*. The biggest hit on that LP was *Your Smile*, led by a solo lead vocal from Winbush and, after a public and bitter professional divorce from Moore in '86, Angela decided to seek a solo career. The following year her solo debut *Sharp* was released. At the same time she formed a private and professional relationship with Ronald Isley, whom she later married. As a writer she has provided hits for Stephanie Mills (*I Have Learned To Respect The Power Of Love*) and Lalah Hathaway (*Baby Don't Cry*) and she recently produced a reformed Isley Brothers. Her most recent album, *Angela Winbush*, included a killer cover of Marvin Gaye's *Inner City Blues* and generally confirmed her reputation as one of America's leading female singer/songwriter/ producers.

### ANGEL.
Tracks: Angel / Angel (insrumental) / Angel (extended) (On 12" only).
■ 12" . . . . . . . . . . . . . . . . . . JABX 60
■ 7" . . . . . . . . . . . . . . . . . . JAB 60
Club / Oct '87.

## ANGELA WINBUSH.
Tracks: Not Advised.
| | |
|---|---|
| CD | .755961591-2 |
| LP | .755961685-1 |
Elektra / Apr '94 / WEA.

### C'EST TOI.
Tracks: C'est toi / Hello beloved.
| | |
|---|---|
| ■ 12″ | .JABX 67 |
| ■ 7″ | .JAB 67 |
Club / Jul '88.

### INNER CITY BLUES.
Tracks: Inner city blues (mixes).
| | |
|---|---|
| 12″ | .EKR 187T |
| CD Single | .EKR 187CD |
| MC Single | .EKR 187C |
Elektra / Jul '94 / WEA.

### REAL THING, THE.
Tracks: Not Advised.
| | |
|---|---|
| ■ CD | .838 866 2 |
| ■ LP | .838 866 1 |
| ■ MC | .838 866 4 |
Mercury / Nov '89.

---

## Windjammer

### LIVE WITHOUT YOUR LOVE.
Tracks: Live without your love.
| | |
|---|---|
| ■ 12″ | .MCAT 921 |
| ■ 7″ | .MCA 921 |
MCA / Sep '84.

### TOSSING AND TURNING.
Tracks: Tossing and turning / Live without your love.
| | |
|---|---|
| ■ 7″ | .MCA 897 |
| ■ 12″ | .MCAT 897 |
MCA / Jun '84.

### TOSSING AND TURNING (89 REMIX).
Tracks: Tossing and turning (89 remix).
| | |
|---|---|
| ■ 12″ | .DEBTX 3077 |
Debut (1) / Sep '89.

### TOSSING AND TURNING (OLD GOLD).
Tracks: Tossing and turning / Live without your love.
| | |
|---|---|
| ■ 12″ | .OG 4062 |
Old Gold / May '88.

### UNDER YOUR SPELL.
Tracks: Under your spell / Winter love.
| | |
|---|---|
| ■ 12″ | .DYAAT 101 |
| ■ 7″ | .DYNS 101 |
Dynatrack / Jan '88.

### WINDJAMMER II.
Tracks: Live without your love / Tossing and turning / Anxiously waiting / Am I right / Call me up / You're out the box / Sneak attack / Stay, part II / I'll always love you / Dive inside my love.
| | |
|---|---|
| ■ LP | .MCF 3231 |
| ■ MC | .MCFC 3231 |
MCA / Jul '84.

### WINDJAMMER III.
Tracks: Not Advised.
| | |
|---|---|
| ■ LP | .MCF 3290 |
| ■ MC | .MCFC 3290 |
MCA / Oct '85.

---

## Wingfield, Pete

### EIGHTEEN WITH A BULLET.
Tracks: Eighteen with a bullet / Shadow of a doubt.
| | |
|---|---|
| ■ 7″ | .WIP 6231 |
Island / Jun '75.

### THEY ALL CAME BACK.
Tracks: They all came back / Too much of a good thing.
| | |
|---|---|
| ■ 7″ | .CHIP 5 |
Chipping Norton / Jun '81.

---

## Winters, Robert

### MAGIC MAN.
Tracks: Magic man.
| | |
|---|---|
| ■ 12″ | .BDSL 496 |
| ■ 7″ | .BDS 496 |
Buddah / Aug '81.

### MAGIC MAN (Winters, Robert & Fall).
Tracks: Face the music / Into my world / Touched by you / She beieves in me / Magic man / When will my love be right / Watchin' you / How can love be wrong / Happiness.
| | |
|---|---|
| ■ LP | .BDLP 4068 |
Buddah / Jul '81.

---

## Winters, Shelley

### NINE TIMES OUT OF TEN.
Tracks: Nine times out of ten.
| | |
|---|---|
| ■ 7″ | .HEAT 24 |
Inferno (1) / Oct '79.

---

## Wish

### MR. D.J.
Tracks: Mr. D.J.
| | |
|---|---|
| ■ 7″ | .WAVE 1 |
Streetwave / Apr '83.

### NICE AND SOFT.
Tracks: Nice and soft / Nice and soft (part 2).
| | |
|---|---|
| ■ 12″ | .EXCL 511 |
| ■ 7″ | .EXC 511 |
Excaliber / Jul '81.

### TOUCH ME (ALL NIGHT LONG).
Tracks: Touch me (all night long).
| | |
|---|---|
| ■ 12″ | .KN 1001 |
KN (USA) / Sep '87.

---

## Withers, Bill

Made famous by 1971 hit Ain't No Sunshine, Withers was 33 when he became successful (previous careers included bricklaying, nine years in U.S. Navy and aircraft manufacturing). Debut LP Just As I Am was produced by Booker T. Jones (of the MGs). 1972 maintained momentum with U.S. No. 1 Lean On Me and No. 2 Use Me; former shared U.K. Top 20 with Michael Jackson's version of Ain't No Sunshine (first of several Witherspenned hit covers). After mid-'70s slump, he returned to charts in '78 with Lovely Day. In 1981 he made acclaimed cameo on Just The Two Of Us, a U.S. hit for Grover Washington Jr. His first solo album in seven years, 1985's Watching You Watching Me, yielded modestly successful Oh Yeah, and he returned to U.K. Top Five in '88 with remixed Lovely Day.

### 'BOUT LOVE.
Tracks: All because of you / Dedicated to you my love / Don't it make it better / You got the stuff / Look to each other for love / Love / Love is / Memories are the way.
| | |
|---|---|
| ■ LP | .CBS 83176 |
CBS / Apr '79.

### AIN'T NO SUNSHINE.
Tracks: Ain't no sunshine (eclipse mix) / Ain't no sunshine (original version) / Ain't no sunshine (total eclipse mix) (Only on 12″) / Oh yeah (Only on 12″) / I want to spend the night (Only on 12″).
| | |
|---|---|
| ■ 12″ | .6531986 |
| ■ 7″ | .6531987 |
| ■ CD Single | .6531982 |
CBS / Nov '88.

### DON'T IT MAKE BETTER.
Tracks: Don't it make it better / Love is.
| | |
|---|---|
| ■ 7″ | .CBS 7052 |
CBS / '79.

### EVERYBODY'S TALKIN'.
Tracks: Everybody's talkin' / Harlem.
| | |
|---|---|
| ■ 7″ | .AMS 845 |
A&M / May '71.

### GREATEST HITS: BILL WITHERS.
Tracks: Just the two of us / Use me / Ain't no sunshine / Lovely day / I want to spend the night / Soul shadows / Lean on me / Grandma's hands / Hello like before / Who is he, what is he to you.
| | |
|---|---|
| ■ LP | .CBS 84710 |
CBS / Feb '81. | |
| ■ LP | .CBS 85049 |
CBS / Jun '81. | |
| MC | .40 32343 |
| | .32343 |
CBS / '87 / Sony. | |
| CD | .CD 32343 |
CBS / Sep '88 / Sony. | |
| CD | .477503-2 |
Columbia / Oct '94 / Sony.

### HARLEM (BEN LIEBRAND REMIX).
Tracks: Haarlem (Ben Liebrand remix) / Haarlem (original version) / Ain't no sunshine / I don't know.
| | |
|---|---|
| ■ 12″ | .6548315 |
| ■ 12″ | .6548318 |
| ■ 7″ | .6548310 |
| ■ CD Single | .6548312 |
| ■ MC Single | .6548314 |
CBS / Apr '90.

---

### I WANT TO SPEND THE NIGHT.
Tracks: I want to spend the night.
| | |
|---|---|
| ■ 7″ | .A 1403 |
CBS / Jul '81.

### JUST AS I AM.
Tracks: Harlem / Ain't no sunshine / Grandma's hands / Sweet Wanomi / Everybody's talkin' / Do it good / Hope she'll be happier / Let it be / I'm her Daddy / In my heart / Moanin' and groanin' / Better off dead.
| | |
|---|---|
| ■ LP | .AMLS 65002 |
A&M / Aug '71.

### LEAN ON ME.
Tracks: Lean on me / Use me.
| | |
|---|---|
| ■ 7″ | .AMS 7004 |
A&M / Aug '72. | |
| ■ 7″ | .SXX 9 |
Sussex / Apr '75.

### LEAN ON ME (OLD GOLD).
Tracks: Lean on me.
| | |
|---|---|
| ■ 7″ | .OG 9186 |
Old Gold / Jul '82.

### LOVELY DAY.
Tracks: Lovely day / Lovely night for dancing / Oh yeah.
| | |
|---|---|
| ■ 7″ | .CBS 5773 |
CBS / Jan '78.

### LOVELY DAY.
Tracks: Lovely day (Sunshine mix) / Lovely day (Original version) / Lean on me / Ain't no sunshine.
| | |
|---|---|
| ■ 12″ | .6509926 |
| ■ 7″ | .6509927 |
CBS / Jul '87. | |
| ■ 12″ | .6530016 |
| ■ 7″ | .6530017 |
| ■ CD Single | .6530012 |
CBS / Sep '88.

### LOVELY DAY (OLD GOLD).
Tracks: Lovely day / Oh yeah.
| | |
|---|---|
| ■ 7″ | .OG 9729 |
Old Gold / Nov '87.

### LOVELY DAYS.
Tracks: Lovely day / Use me / Ain't no sunshine / Harlem / Kissing my love / Lean on me / Steppin' right along / Grandma's hands / Lonely town, lonely street / Who is he what is he to you.
| | |
|---|---|
| ■ LP | .4668241 |
| ■ LP | .4668240 |
| ■ CD | .4668243 |
| ■ MC | .4668244 |
CBS / Apr '90.

### LOVELY NIGHT FOR DANCING.
Tracks: Lovely night for dancing / Let me be the one you need.
| | |
|---|---|
| ■ 7″ | .CBS 6193 |
CBS / Mar '78.

### MENAGERIE.
Tracks: Lovely day / I want to spend the night / Lovely night for dancing / Then you smile at me / She wants to (get on down) / It ain't because of me baby / Tender things / Winter time / Let me be the one you need.
| | |
|---|---|
| ■ LP | .CBS 82265 |
CBS / Feb '78. | |
| ■ LP | .CBS 32694 |
| ■ MC | .40 32694 |
CBS / Nov '85.

### OH YEAH.
Tracks: Oh yeah / Just like the first time.
| | |
|---|---|
| ■ 12″ | .TA 6154 |
| ■ 7″ | .A 6154 |
CBS / May '85.

### SOUND OF SOUL, THE.
Tracks: Not Advised.
| | |
|---|---|
| CD | .BLATCD 13 |
| MC | .BLATMC 13 |
| ■ LP | .BLATLP 13 |
Blatant / Apr '89 / Roots Records.

### USA.
Tracks: U.S.A. / Paint your pretty picture.
| | |
|---|---|
| ■ 7″ | .A 2006 |
CBS / Jan '82.

### WATCHING YOU, WATCHING ME.
Tracks: Oh yeah / Something that turns you on / Don't make me wait / Heart in your life / Watchin you watching me / We could be sweet lovers / You just can't smile it away / Steppin' right along / Whatever happens / You try to find a place.
| | |
|---|---|
| ■ LP | .CBS 2620 |
| ■ MC | .40 2620 |
CBS / Jun '85.

■ DELETE

# COMPILATIONS

## NUMERICAL

### 1-800 NEW FUNK.
Tracks: Minneapolis: *MPLS* / Hollywood: *Clinton, George* / Love sign: *Gaye, Nona & Prince* / If I love U 2nite: *Mayte* / Colour: *Steeles* / 2gether: *N.P.G.* / Standing at the altar: *Cox, Margie* / You will be moved: *Staples, Mavis* / 17: *Madhouse* / Woman's gotta have it: *Gaye, Nona* / Minneapolis reprise: *MPLS*.
CD . . . . . . . . . . . . . . . . . . . . NPG 60512
LP . . . . . . . . . . . . . . . . . . . . NPG 60511
MC. . . . . . . . . . . . . . . . . . . . NPG 60514
New Power Generation / Aug '94 / Grapevine Distribution / THE.

### 10 BY 12.
Tracks: Livin' in America: *Brown, James* / Alice, I want you just for me: *Full Force* / I wonder if I take you home: *Lisa Lisa & Cult Jam with Full Force* / House rocker: *Lovebug Starski* / Hot: *Ayers, Roy* / Saturday love: *Cherrelle & Alexander O'Neal* / Sugar free: *Juicy* / New York eyes: *Nicole & Timmy Thomas* / If I were here tonight: *O'Neal, Alexander* / Finest: *S.O.S. Band*.
MC. . . . . . . . . . . . . . . . . . . . . .40 26920
■ LP . . . . . . . . . . . . . . . . . . PRT 26920
Portrait / Apr '86.

### 10 DANCE RECORD, A.
Tracks: Tell me (how it feels) (M+M stylee): *52nd Street* / We don't have to take our clothes off: *Stewart, Jermaine* / This house is haunted: *Arnold, P.P.* / Ain't that the truth: *Kelly, Frankie* / Keep on: *Mardis, Bobby* / Warrior groove: *D.S.M.* / More than one night: *Roberts, Julie* / Galveston bay: *Hill, Lonnie* / Raise the roof: *Conway Brothers* / Good to the last drop (Featuring Eleanor Mills): *C-Bank*.
MC. . . . . . . . . . . . . . . . . . . . . TDRC 1
10 / Jan '88 / EMI.

### 10 SOUL STARS VOL.1.
Tracks: Not Advised.
CD . . . . . . . . . . . . . . . . . . . . STACD 063
Wisepack / Nov '93 / THE / Conifer Records.

### 10 SOUL STARS VOL.2.
Tracks: Not Advised.
CD . . . . . . . . . . . . . . . . . . . . STACD 064
Wisepack / Nov '93 / THE / Conifer Records.

### 10 SOUL STARS VOL.3.
Tracks: Not Advised.
CD . . . . . . . . . . . . . . . . . . . . STACD 065
Wisepack / Nov '93 / THE / Conifer Records.

### 10 SOUL STARS VOL.4.
Tracks: Sanctified lady: *Gaye, Marvin* / My love is waiting: *Gaye, Marvin* / Always and forever: *Heatwave* / Jitterbugging: *Heatwave* / That lady: *Isley Brothers* / Harvest for the world: *Isley Brothers* / Cuba: *Gibson Brothers* / Ooh what a life: *Gibson Brothers* / I'm in a philly mood: *La Belle, Patti* / people: *La Belle, Patti* / Please don't go: *K.C. & The Sunshine Band* / That's the way I like it: *K.C. & The Sunshine Band* / Dominoes: *Nevil, Robbie* / C'est la vie: *Nevil, Robbie* / Slowhand: *Pointer Sisters* / Jump (for my love): *Pointer Sisters* / Heaven must be missing an angel: *Tavares* / Don't take away the music: *Tavares* / Ain't no sunshine: *Withers, Bill* / Lean on me: *Withers, Bill*.
CD . . . . . . . . . . . . . . . . . . . . STACD 066
Wisepack / Nov '93 / THE / Conifer Records.

### 16 BIG HITS FROM THE EARLY 60'S.
Tracks: Shop around / Please Mr. Postman: *Marvelettes* / Do you love me: *Contours* / You've really got a hold on me / Fingertips (part 2): *Wonder, Stevie* / Heatwave: *Reeves, Martha* / My guy: *Wells, Mary* / Where did our love go: *Supremes* / Baby love: *Supremes* / Come see about me: *Supremes* / My girl: *Temptations* / Shotgun: *Walker, Junior & The All Stars* / Stop in the name of love: *Supremes* / I can't help myself: *Four Tops* / Back in my arms again: *Supremes* / I hear a symphony: *Supremes*.
■ CD . . . . . . . . . . . . . . . . . . WD 72386
Motown / Feb '88.
■ LP . . . . . . . . . . . . . . . . . . WL 72386
■ MC . . . . . . . . . . . . . . . . . WK 72386
Motown / '91.

### 16 BIG HITS FROM THE LATE 60'S.
Tracks: You can't hurry love: *Supremes* / Uptight: *Wonder, Stevie* / Get ready: *Temptations* / Ain't too proud to beg: *Temptations* / Reach out I'll be there: *Four Tops* / You keep me hangin' on: *Supremes* / (I know) I'm losing you: *Temptations* / Love is here & now you're gone: *Supremes* / Happening: *Supremes* / I was made to love her: *Wonder, Stevie* / I second that emotion: *Robinson, Smokey & The Miracles* / I wish it would rain: *Temptations* / Love child: *Supremes* / I heard it through the grapevine: *Knight, Gladys & The Pips* / I can't get next to you: *Temptations* / Someday we'll be together: *Ross, Diana & The Supremes*.
■ CD . . . . . . . . . . . . . . . . . . WD 72385
Motown / Feb '88.
■ LP . . . . . . . . . . . . . . . . . . WL 72385
■ MC . . . . . . . . . . . . . . . . . WK 72385
Motown / '91.

### 18 SOUL CLASSICS FROM 60'S & 70'S (Volume 3).
Tracks: Letter: *Box Tops* / Kissing in the back row: *Drifters* / Hang on in there baby: *Bristol, Johnny* / Reunited: *Peaches & Herb* / Best thing that ever happened to me: *Knight, Gladys & The Pips* / Didn't I (blow your mind this time): *Delfonics* / Me and Mrs. Jones: *Paul, Billy* / Running away: *Sly & The Family Stone* / Love Train: *O'Jays* / What a diff'rence a day makes: *Phillips, Esther* / Betcha by golly wow: *Stylistics* / I'm your puppet: *Purify, James & Bobby* / That lady: *Isley Brothers* / I can see clearly now: *Nash, Johnny* / L.O.D. (love on delivery): *Ocean, Billy* / Can't get enough of your love babe: *White, Barry* / Where did our love go: *Elbert, Donnie* / Get up offa that thing: *Brown, James*.
CD . . . . . . . . . . . . . . . . . . . . PMP 106
Pickwick / May '93 / Pickwick.

### 18 SOUL CLASSICS FROM THE 70'S & 80'S (Volume 2).
Tracks: Do what you do: *Jackson, Jermaine* / All the love in the world: *Warwick, Dionne* / Joanna: *Kool & The Gang* / Night to remember: *Shalamar* / Your love is king: *Sade* / Never knew love like this before: *Mills, Stephanie* / Secret lovers: *Atlantic Starr* / Stay with me tonight: *Osbourne, Jeffrey* / There goes my first love: *Drifters* / Reach out I'll be there: *Gaynor, Gloria* / One hundred ways: *Jones, Quincy & James Ingram* / You make me feel brand new: *Stylistics* / Never, never gonna give you up: *White, Barry* / Woman in love: *Three Degrees* / Summer breeze: *Isley Brothers* / My love is waiting: *Gaye, Marvin* / Lovely day(remix): *Withers, Bill* / What a fool believes: *Franklin, Aretha*.
CD . . . . . . . . . . . . . . . . . . . . PMP 105
Pickwick / May '93 / Pickwick.

### 18 SOUL CLASSICS FROM THE 70'S & 80'S (Volume 1).
Tracks: Just an illusion: *Imagination* / I'm so excited: *Pointer Sisters* / System addict: *Five Star* / Going back to my roots: *Odyssey* / (You said) You'd gimme more time: *K.C. & The Sunshine Band* / She's strange: *Cameo* (1) / Rock the boat: *Hues Corporation* / Jumpin' Jack flash: *Franklin, Aretha* / Let the music play: *White, Barry* / Fantasy: *Earth, Wind & Fire* / Can you feel it: *Jacksons* / Burn rubber on me: *Gap Band* / Love come down: *King, Evelyn 'Champagne'* / Mama used to say: *Giscombe, Junior* / Rockit: *Hancock, Herbie* / Fight the power: *Isley Brothers* / Livin' in America: *Brown, James*.
CD . . . . . . . . . . . . . . . . . . . . PMP 104
Pickwick / May '93 / Pickwick.

### 18 SOUL CLASSICS FROM THE 70'S & 80'S (Volume 4).
Tracks: Loco in acapulco: *Four Tops* / Wishing well: *D'Arby, Terence Trent* / Jump (for my love): *Pointer Sisters* / Who's zoomin' who: *Franklin, Aretha* / Get outta my dreams, get into my car: *Ocean, Billy* / Star: *Earth, Wind & Fire* / Can't wait another minute: *Five Star* / Best of my love: *Emotions* (2) / Always and forever: *Heatwave* / Lies: *Butler, Jonathan* / Caravan of love: *Isley-Jasper-Isley* / Why (Can't we live together): *Sade* / I won't cry: *Goldsmith, Glen* / I'd rather go blind: *Turner, Ruby* / On the wings of love: *Osbourne, Jeffrey* / Sweetest sweetest: *Jackson, Jermaine* / Hurt: *Manhattans* / Never too much: *Vandross, Luther*.
CD . . . . . . . . . . . . . . . . . . . . PMP 107
Pickwick / May '93 / Pickwick.

### 20 DETROIT CHARTBUSTERS VOL.1.
Tracks: Not Advised.
■ LP . . . . . . . . . . . . . . . . . MOTCLP 21
Motor City / Mar '90.

### 20 GOSPEL GREATS.
Tracks: Love of God: *Taylor, Johnnie* / Trouble in my way: *Swan Silvertones* / My rock: *Swan Silvertones* / Get away Jordan (I want to cross over): *Love Coates, Dorothy* / You better run: *Love Coates, Dorothy* / Ninety nine and a half (won't do): *Love Coates, Dorothy* / Straight Street: *Pilgrim Travelers* / Jesus hits like the atom bomb: *Cleveland, James* / Living for my Jesus: *Five Blind Boys Of Alabama* / Alone and motherless: *Five Blind Boys Of Alabama* / This may be the last time: *Five Blind Boys Of Alabama* / Ball game: *Carr, Sister Wynona* / Touch the hem of his garment: *Cooke, Sam & The Soul Stirrers* / Prayer for the doomed: *Chosen Gospel Singers* / Holy ghost: *Bradford, Alex* / Lifeboat: *Bradford, Alex* / Whosoever will: *Griffin, Bessie* / Wade in the water: *Original Gospel Harmonettes*.
CD . . . . . . . . . . . . . . . . . . . . CDROP 1017
LP . . . . . . . . . . . . . . . . . . . . DROP 1017
■ MC . . . . . . . . . . . . . . . . . CROP 1017
Cascade / May '90.

### 20 GREAT UNKNOWN SOUL CLASSICS OF THE 60'S AND 70'S.
Tracks: And the rains came: *Millionaires* / Ain't that soul: *Millionaires* / Hey stoney face: *Love, Mary* / Dance, children, dance / Think it over baby: *Love, Mary* / Slow and easy / If I could turn back the hands of time: *Garett, Vernon* / Get lost: *King, Al* / Sweet temptation: *Watson, Cressa* / You just cheat and lie: *Hill, Z.Z.* / If I could do it all over again: *Hill, Z.Z.* / You are my sunshine: *Shane, Jackie* / Let freedom ring: *Turner, Frank* / I've got a right to lose my mind / I'm not ashamed / With all my heart: *White, Margo* / You know it ain't right: *Lil' Bob & The Lollipops* / Blue on blue: *Ikettes* / Woman needs a man: *Baker, Yvonne* / It's raining: *Thomas, Irma*.
MC. . . . . . . . . . . . . . . . . . . . . CROP 1013
■ LP . . . . . . . . . . . . . . . . . . DROP 1013
Cascade / Aug '86.

### 20 GREATEST SONGS IN MOTOWN HISTORY.
Tracks: Three times a lady: *Commodores* / Touch me in the morning: *Ross, Diana* / I heard it through the grapevine: *Gaye, Marvin* / For once in my life: *Wonder, Stevie* / Never can say goodbye: *Jackson Five* / My girl: *Temptations* / Love hangover: *Ross, Diana* / Where did our love go: *Ross, Diana & The Supremes* / Dancing in the street: *Reeves, Martha* / Still: *Commodores* / Stop, In the name of love: *Ross, Diana & The Supremes* / Tracks of my tears: *Robinson, Smokey & The Temptations* / You keep me hangin' on: *Ross, Diana & The Supremes* / Easy: *Commodores* / Reach out I'll be there: *Four Tops* / Ain't no mountain high enough: *Gaye, Marvin & Tammi Terrell* / You can't hurry love: *Ross, Diana & The Supremes* / Standing in the shadows of love: *Four Tops* / Just my imagination (running away with me): *Temptations* / How sweet it is (to be loved by you): *Gaye, Marvin*.
■ CD . . . . . . . . . . . . . . . . . . ZD 72400
Motown / Mar '86.

### 20 MOD CLASSICS.
Tracks: Can I get a witness: *Gaye, Marvin* / You're a wonderful one: *Gaye, Marvin* / How sweet it is (to be loved by you): *Gaye, Marvin* / Heatwave: *Reeves, Martha & The Vandellas* / Quicksand: *Reeves, Martha & The Vandellas* / Dancing in the street: *Reeves, Martha & The Vandellas* / I gotta dance to keep from crying: *Robinson, Smokey & The Miracles* / That's what love is made of: *Robinson, Smokey & The Miracles* / When the lovelight starts shining thru' his eyes: *Ross, Diana & The Supremes* / Come see about me: *Ross, Diana & The Supremes* / As long as I know he's mine: *Marvelettes* / You're my remerdy: *Marvelettes* / Too many fish in the sea: *Marvelettes* / My guy: *Wells, Mary* / Girl's alright with me: *Temptations* / Girl (why you wanna make me blue): *Temptations* / My girl: *Temptations* / Hey harmonica man: *Wonder, Stevie* / Needle in a haystack: *Velvelettes* / He was really saying somethin': *Velvelettes*.
■ LP . . . . . . . . . . . . . . . . . STML 12125
■ MC . . . . . . . . . . . . . . . . CSTML 12125
Tamla Motown / Oct '81.

■ LP . . . . . . . . . . . . . . . . . . . . . ZL 72032
Motown / '86.

## 20 MOD CLASSICS - VOL.2.

**Tracks:** Fingertips (part 2): *Marvelettes* / Baby love: *Ross, Diana & The Supremes* / Uptight (everything's alright): *Wonder, Stevie* / Come and get these memories: *Reeves, Martha & The Vandellas* / In my lonely room: *Reeves, Martha & The Vandellas* / Nowhere to run: *Reeves, Martha & The Vandellas* / Mickey's monkey: *Robinson, Smokey & The Miracles* / I like it like that: *Robinson, Smokey & The Miracles* / Way you do the things you do: *Temptations* / Shotgun: *Walker, Junior & The All Stars* / (I'm a) road runner: *Walker, Junior & The All Stars* / When I'm gone: *Holloway, Brenda* / I'll be doggone: *Gaye, Marvin* / Ain't that perculiar: *Gaye, Marvin* / Back in my arms again: *Ross, Diana & The Supremes* / I can't help myself: *Four Tops* / Lonely lonely girl am I: *Velvelettes* / I'll always love you: *Detroit Spinners* / First I look at the purse: *Contours* / Take me in your arms (rock me a little while): *Weston, Kim* / Helpless: *Weston, Kim*.
■ LP . . . . . . . . . . . . . . . . . . . .STML 12133
■ MC. . . . . . . . . . . . . . . . . . . .CSTML 12133
Tamla Motown / Oct '81.
■ LP . . . . . . . . . . . . . . . . . . . . . ZL 72033
Motown / '86.

## 20TH ANNIVERSARY ALBUM.

**Tracks:** Money (that's what I want): *Strong, Barrett* / Shop around: *Robinson, Smokey & The Miracles* / You've really got a hold on me: *Robinson, Smokey & The Miracles* / Tears of clown: *Robinson, Smokey & The Miracles* / Fingertips (part 2): *Wonder, Stevie* / You are the sunshine of my life: *Wonder, Stevie* / Living for the city: *Wonder, Stevie* / Uptight (everything's alright): *Wonder, Stevie* / For once in my life: *Wonder, Stevie* / Superstition: *Wonder, Stevie* / Heatwave: *Reeves, Martha & The Vandellas* / Dancing in the street: *Reeves, Martha & The Vandellas* / My guy: *Wells, Mary* / Baby love: *Ross, Diana & The Supremes* / You keep me hangin' on: *Ross, Diana & The Supremes* / Shotgun: *Walker, Junior & The All Stars* / Ben: *Jackson, Michael* / Touch me in the morning: *Ross, Diana* / Do you know where you're going to: *Ross, Diana* / Love hangover: *Ross, Diana* / I'm still waiting: *Ross, Diana* / Don't leave me this way: *Houston, Thelma* / Three times a lady: *Commodores* / Machine gun: *Commodores* / With you I'm born again: *Preston, Billy & Syreeta* / This old heart of mine (is weak for you): *Isley Brothers* / What becomes of a brokenhearted: *Ruffin, Jimmy* / Reach out I'll be there: *Four Tops* / Bernadette: *Four Tops* / You're all I need to get by: *Gaye, Marvin & Tammi Terrell* / I heard it through the grapevine: *Gaye, Marvin* / What's going on: *Gaye, Marvin* / Cloud 9: *Temptations* / Papa was a rollin' stone: *Temptations* / I want you back: *Jackson Five* / I'll be there: *Jackson Five* / War: *Starfighters* / Indiana wants me: *Taylor, R. Dean* / Help me make it through the night: *Knight, Gladys & The Pips*.
■ LP . . . . . . . . . . . . . . . . . . . . . ZL 72132
■ MC. . . . . . . . . . . . . . . . . . . . . ZK 72132
Motown / '86.

## 25 USA NO.1 HITS FROM 25 YEARS.

**Tracks:** Please Mr. Postman: *Marvelettes* / My girl: *Temptations* / You can't hurry love: *Ross, Diana & The Supremes* / I heard it through the grapevine: *Gaye, Marvin* / ABC: *Jackson Five* / Just my imagination (running away with me): *Temptations* / Papa was a rollin' stone: *Temptations* / Let's get it on: *Gaye, Marvin* / Baby love: *Ross, Diana & The Supremes* / I can't help myself: *Four Tops* / Reach out I'll be there: *Four Tops* / I want you back: *Jackson Five* / Ain't no mountain high enough: *Ross, Diana* / Tears of a clown: *Robinson, Smokey* / What's going on: *Gaye, Marvin* / You are the sunshine of my life: *Wonder, Stevie* / Keep on truckin': *Kendricks, Eddie* / Don't leave me this way: *Houston, Thelma* / Three times a lady: *Commodores* / Give it to me baby: *James, Rick* / Superstition: *Wonder, Stevie* / Got to give it up: *Gaye, Marvin* / Still: *Commodores* / Endless love: *Ross, Diana & Lionel Richie*.
■ Double LP. . . . . . . . . . . . . . . . . TMSP 6018
■ MC Set . . . . . . . . . . . . . . . . . CTMSP 6018
Motown / Oct '83.
■ CD Set. . . . . . . . . . . . . . . . . . . ZD 72136
■ Double LP. . . . . . . . . . . . . . . . . WL 72136
■ MC Set . . . . . . . . . . . . . . . . . . WK 72136
Motown / '86.
■ CD Set. . . . . . . . . . . . . . . . . . WD 72136
Motown / Apr '89.
CD. . . . . . . . . . . . . . . . . . . . . .530032-2
■ MC. . . . . . . . . . . . . . . . . . . . .530032-4
Motown / Jan '93.

## 32 BIG HITS (Early & Late 1960's).

**Tracks:** Not Advised.
■ Double LP. . . . . . . . . . . . . . . . . STMF 7001
■ MC Set . . . . . . . . . . . . . . . . . CSTMF 7001
Motown / Oct '82.

## 33 MINITS OF BLUES AND SOUL.

**Tracks:** We got a good thing goin': *Holiday, Jimmy* / Beauty of a girl in love: *Holiday, Jimmy* / Give me your love: *Holiday, Jimmy* / Let the door hit you: *McCracklin, Jimmy* / Dog: *McCracklin, Jimmy* / I wanna testify: *Dozier, Gene* / Hunk o' funk: *Dozier, Gene* / Get right: *Players* / Look at me: *Greene, Vernon* / I'll never stop loving you: *King, Clydie* / Trust me: *Womack, Bobby* / Soulin' and rollin': *Trensations* / Hooked by love: *Banks, Homer* / Working on your case: *O'Jays*.
■ LP . . . . . . . . . . . . . . . . . . . . MLS 40002
Minit / Apr '68.

## 60'S SOUL.

**Tracks:** Not Advised.
CD. . . . . . . . . . . . . . . . . . . . . .WPCD 009
Stardust / Oct '90 / Pickwick / Conifer Records.

## 60'S SOUL.

**Tracks:** Not Advised.
■ LP . . . . . . . . . . . . . . . . . . . . .KNLP 15006
■ CD . . . . . . . . . . . . . . . . . . . . KNCD 15006
■ MC. . . . . . . . . . . . . . . . . . . . KNMC 15006
Replay / May '89.

## 60'S SOUL CLASSICS.

**Tracks:** Rescue me: *Fontella Bass* / Hi-heel sneakers: *Tucker, Tommy* / Clapping song: *Ellis, Shirley* / Holy cow: *Dorsey, Lee* / In crowd: *Gray, Dobie* / Private number: *Clay, Judy & William Bell* / Twist and shout: *Isley Brothers* / Wade in the water: *Lewis, Ramsey* / I can't believe what you say: *Turner, Ike & Tina* / Hey girl don't bother me: *Tams* / It's allright: *Impressions* / Knock on wood: *Floyd, Eddie* / Working in a coalmine: *Dorsey, Lee* / Peaches n cream: *Ikettes* / (I don't know why) But I do: *Henry, Clarence 'Frogman'* / Barefootin: *Parker, Robert* / Tell it like it is: *Neville, Aaron* / Shoop shoop (It's in his kiss): *Everett, Betty* / Time is tight: *Booker T & The MG's* / Keep on pushing: *Impressions*.
CD. . . . . . . . . . . . . . . . . . . . . . PWKS 4196
MC. . . . . . . . . . . . . . . . . . . . . PWKMC 4196
Pickwick / Oct '94 / Pickwick.

## 60'S SOUL CLUB.

**Tracks:** Summertime: *Stewart, Billy* / Farther on up the road: *Simon, Joe* / Show me: *Tex, Joe* / How I miss you baby: *Womack, Bobby* / Barefootin': *Parker, Robert* / Getting mighty crowded: *Everett, Betty* / Get on up: *Esquires* / Rescue me: *Bass, Fontella* / Come on sock it to me: *Johnson, Syl* / Land of a thousand dances: *Kenner, Chris* / Ride your pony: *Dorsey, Lee* / Selfish one: *Ross, Jackie* / Lover's holiday: *Scott, Peggy & Jo Jo Benson* / Nothing can stop me: *Chandler, Gene*.
CD. . . . . . . . . . . . . . . . . . . . . .CDINS 5005
■ LP . . . . . . . . . . . . . . . . . . . . . INS 5005
MC. . . . . . . . . . . . . . . . . . . . . .TCINS 5005
Instant (2) / Jul '89 / Charly.

## 60'S SOUL/90'S SOUL.

**Tracks:** Sittin' on the dock of the bay: *Redding, Otis* / Now I know what made Otis blue: *Young, Paul* / I say a little prayer: *Franklin, Aretha* / You're all that matters to me: *Stigers, Curtis* / When a man loves a woman: *Sledge, Percy* / When you tell me that you love me: *Ross, Diana* / What becomes of the broken hearted: *Ruffin, Jimmy* / Move closer: *Nelson, Phyllis* / Stand by me: *King, Ben E.* / All woman: *Stansfield, Lisa* / Piece of my heart: *Franklin, Erma* / Dreams: *Gabrielle* / In the midnight hour: *Pickett, Wilson* / I don't wanna fight: *Turner, Tina* / I heard it through the grapevine: *Gaye, Marvin* / Would I lie to you: *Charles & Eddie* / Tracks of my tears: *Robinson, Smokey* / So close: *Carroll, Dina* / Rescue me: *Bass, Fontella* / Come in out of the rain: *Moten, Wendy*.
CD. . . . . . . . . . . . . . . . . . . . . .CDPCSTV 4
MC. . . . . . . . . . . . . . . . . . . . . .TCPCSTV 4
EMI / Aug '94 / EMI.

## 70'S SOUL HOT WAX 3.

**Tracks:** I've got to have your love: *Hunt, Pierre* / I'm your pimp: *Skull Snaps* / Man of money: *Barkley, Tyrone* / I can see him loving you: *Anderson Brothers* / Your smallest wish: *21st Century Ltd* / Dancing on a daydream: *Soulvation Army* / Time passed by: *Bynum, James* / You only live once: *Imperial Wonders* / Happy: *Velvet Hammer* / It's not where you start: *Davis, Luckey* / Sweet love: *Cody, Black* / Like taking candy from a baby: *Brown, J.T.* / Mama, I wish I stayed at home: *Chandler, Denice* / Take me as I am: *Hughes, Freddie* / When you see what you want: *Weathers, Oscar* / Operataor operator: *Baker, Johnny* / I'm gonna get you: *Floyd, Frankie* / World world: *Drinkyard, Kevin* / Paradise: *Neo Experience* / Love will turn around: *Entertains* / My baby's gone: *Blade Family* / I'm a winner: *Just Bobby* / I won't be completely happy: *Carlena* / Don't waste your time girl: *Miller, Catherine*.
CD. . . . . . . . . . . . . . . . . . . . . . .GSCD 037
Goldmine / Aug '94 / Vital Distribution.

## 70'S SOUL HOTWAX VOL.2.

**Tracks:** Don't hurt me no more: *Woods, Wendy* / All want from you is your love: *Neal, C.C.* / Come & ask me: *5 Wagers* / Something fishy going on: *Universal Mind* / What's bothering me: *Thomas, Timmy* / You can win: *Bileo* / Heartaches & pain: *Pages* / Some kind of man: *Pride, Passion & Pain* / From the top of my heart: *Wells, Wes & the Steelers* / Wrong crowd: *Prince George* / You're mine: *Veroneeca* / Lord what's happening to your people: *Smith, Kenny* / Come back: *Fantastic Puzzles* / He's always somewhere around: *Gerrard, Donny* / I can make it on my own: *Simmons, Vessie* / Bet you if you ask around: *Velvet* / Strange: *Tradewinds* / I want to be loved: *Stevens & Foster* / Let's spend some time together: *Houston, Larry* / Love built on a strong foundation: *Big Jim's Border Crossing* / Oh happy day: *Flame'n'King* / Turning point: *Simmons, Mack* / Have love, will travel: *Jones, Rosey* / Let's get nasty: *Stephens, Chuck* / Honey vision: *Innervision* / Alone with no love: *Rock Candy*.
CD. . . . . . . . . . . . . . . . . . . . . . .GSCD 035
Goldmine / Apr '94 / Vital Distribution.

## 70'S SOUL SEARCHERS.

**Tracks:** It really hurts me girl: *Carstairs* / Ain't nothin' wrong makin' love: *Jones, Jimmy (2)* / Economy: *Mitchell, Lee* / Shady lady: *Newton, Bobby* / Spellbound: *Everett, Frank* / You better keep her: *Holmes, Marvin & Justice* / When the fuel runs out: *Ambitions* / I can't let you walk away: *Caress* / I've got to start my life over: *Houston, Larry* / You're my main squeeze: *Crystal Motion* / Loneliness: *Will, David* / Shy guy: *Baker, Johnny* / Baby hard times: *Love, Dave* / Dance all nite: *Master Plan* / If it wasn't for my baby: *Four Sonics* / Secret place: *Brothers* / In a world so cold: *St. Germain, Tyrone* / I hope you really love me: *Family Circle* / Give in to the power: *Committee* / Over the top: *Dawson, Roy*.
CD. . . . . . . . . . . . . . . . . . . . . . .GSCD 024
Goldmine / Nov '93 / Vital Distribution.

## 94 & 10TH - A DECADE OF 4TH & BROADWAY.

**Tracks:** Somebody else's guy: *Brown, Jocelyn* / Thinking about your love: *Skipworth & Turner* / Seventh heaven: *Guthrie, Gwen* / Gotta get you home tonight: *Wilde, Eugene* / I surrender to your love: *By All Means* / Let's start over: *Jaye, Miles* / My one temptation: *Paris, Mica* / Love supreme: *Downing, Will* / Teardrops: *Womack & Womack* / Love makes the world go round: *Don-E* / Where is the love: *Paris, Mica & Will Downing* / Real love: *Driza Bone* / Try my love: *Washburn, Lalomie* / Way we are: *Affair (1)* / Lite up your life: *Act Of Faith* / King of rock: *Run D.M.C.* / Drop the bomb: *Trouble Funk* / Boops (here to go): *Sly & Robbie* / Chief Inspector: *Badarou, Wally* / Paid in full: *Eric B & Rakim* / Friends & countrymen: *Wild Bunch (2)* / Straight outta Compton: *N.W.A.* / Television, the drug of the nation: *Disposable Heroes Of Hiphoprisy* / Wash your face in my sink: *Dream Warriors* / Turn on, tune in, cop out: *Freakpower* / Connected: *Stereo MC's* / It was a good day: *Ice Cube* / Aftermath: *Tricky* / Braindead: *Bomb The Bass* / Best at slavery: *Silent Eclipse*.
CD Set . . . . . . . . . . . . . . . . . . BRCDD 614
LP Set. . . . . . . . . . . . . . . . . . . BRLPD 614
MC Set . . . . . . . . . . . . . . . . . . .BRCAD 614
4th & Broadway / Aug '94 / PolyGram.

## 94 & 10TH E.P.

**Tracks:** Teardrops: *Womack & Womack* / Funky cold medina: *Tone Loc* / Paid in full: *Eric B & Rakim* / Love supreme: *Downing, Will*.
■ 12". . . . . . . . . . . . . . . . . . . . .12BRW 307
■ CD. . . . . . . . . . . . . . . . . . . . . .BRCD 307
4th & Broadway / Aug '94.

## 100 ALL TIME CLASSIC DANCE HITS OF THE 1970'S.

**Tracks:** Shaft, Theme from: *Hayes, Isaac* / That lady: *Isley Brothers* / Move on up: *Mayfield, Curtis* / I'm doing fine now: *New York City* / Mrs. Grace: *Tymes* / Family affair: *Sly & The Family Stone* / Groovin' with Mr Bloe: *Mr. Bloe* / Get up I feel like a sex machine: *Brown, James* / I'll take you there: *Staple Singers* / Summer breeze: *Isley Brothers* / Higher and higher: *Wilson, Jackie* / Pick up the pieces: *Average White Band* / Only the strong survive: *Paul, Billy* / Hang on in there baby: *Bristol, Johnny* / I get the sweetest feeling: *Wilson, Jackie* / You can do magic: *Limmie & Family Cooking* / On the pony express: *Johnson, Johnny & Bandwagon* / Backstabbers: *O'Jays* / Walking in rhythm: *Blackbyrds* / Sunshine day: *Osibisa* / Satisfaction guaranteed: *Melvin, Harold & The Bluenotes* / Love train: *O'Jays* / When will I see you again: *Three Degrees* / Rock the boat: *Hues Corporation* / Shame, shame, shame: *Shirly & Company* / Get dancing: *Disco Tex & The Sexolettes* / Ain't gonna bump no more: *Tex, Joe* / Swing your daddy: *Gilstrap, Jim* / Come back and finish what you started: *Knight, Gladys & The Pips* / You'll never find

482

■ DELETED

another love like mine: *Rawls, Lou* / Sweet inspiration: *Johnson, Johnny & Bandwagon* / Take good care of yourself: *Three Degrees* / Soul city walk: *Bell, Archie & The Drells* / Be thankful for what you've got: *DeVaughan, William* / Lady Marmalade: *Labelle* / Native New Yorker: *Odyssey* / Nice and slow: *Green, Jesse* / I wanna dance wit choo: *Disco Tex & The Sexolettes* / Dr. Kiss Kiss: *5000 Volts* / More, more, more: *Andrea True Connection* / You to me are everything: *Real Thing* / You don't have to go: *Chi-Lites* / Sixty minute man: *Trammps* / First impression: *Impressions* / You little trust maker: *Tymes* / Ride a wild horse: *Clark, Dee* / Gonna get along without you now: *White, Barry* / What it is: *Mimms, Garnet* / This is it: *Moore, Melba* / You're the first, the last, my everything: *White, Barry* / Do the bus stop: *Fatback Band* / Never can say goodbye: *Gaynor, Gloria* / Now is the time: *James, Jimmy & The Vagabonds* / Too good to be forgotten: *Chi-Lites* / Dolly my love: *Moments* / If I can't have you: *Elliman, Yvonne* / Don't leave me this way: *Melvin, Harold & The Bluenotes* / Let the music play: *White, Barry* / Isn't she lovely: *Parton, David* / Hold back the night: *Trammps* / Shuffle: *McCoy, Van* / Walkin' miracle: *Limmie & Family Cooking* / There goes my first love: *Drifters* / Sixteen bars: *Stylistics* / I'll go where the music takes me: *James, Jimmy & The Vagabonds* / Sing baby sing: *Stylistics* / You're more than a number in my little red book: *Drifters* / Can't get by without you: *Real Thing* / I'm on fire: *5000 Volts* / Spanish hustle: *Fatback Band* / Sad sweet dreamer: *Sweet Sensation* / Hustle: *McCoy, Van & Soul City Symphony* / Jack in the box: *Moments* / Ain't no stoppin' us now: *McFadden & Whitehead* / Let's do the latin hustle: *M & O Band* / Get down: *Chandler, Gene* / Shame: *King, Evelyn 'Champagne'* / I thought it was you: *Hancock, Herbie* / Strawberry letter 23: *Brothers Johnson* / September: *Earth, Wind & Fire* / Highwire: *Carr, Linda* / Ladies night: *Kool & The Gang* / Stuff like that: *Jones, Quincy* / H.A.P.P.Y. radio: *Starr, Edwin* / Ain't we funkin' now: *Brothers Johnson* / Ring my bell: *Ward, Anita* / I will survive: *Gaynor, Gloria* / Got to get you into my life: *Earth, Wind & Fire* / Strut your funky stuff: *Frantique* / Jack & Jill: *Raydio* / You bet your love: *Hancock, Herbie* / Light my fire: *Stewart, Amii* / Rappers delight: *Sugarhill Gang* / You make me feel: *Sylvester* / Knock on wood: *Stewart, Amii* / I lost my heart to a starship trooper: *Brightman, Sarah* / Contact: *Starr, Edwin* / I love America: *Juvet, Patrick* / Yes sir I can boogie: *Baccara* / In the bush: *Musique*.

**CD Set** . . . . . . . . . . . . . . . . . . . **DHOSCD 100**
**■ LP Set** . . . . . . . . . . . . . . . . . . **DHOSLP 100**
**■ MC Set** . . . . . . . . . . . . . . . . . **DHOSMC 100**
Connoisseur Collection / Oct '88.

## 100 DANCE HITS OF THE 80'S.

**Tracks:** Ride on time: *Black Box* / Pump up the jam: *Technotronic featuring Felly* / Only way is up: *Yazz & The Plastic Population* / Doctorin' the house: *Coldcut Featuring Yazz & The Plastic Population* / People hold on: *Coldcut & Lisa Stansfield* / Numero uno (radio edit): *Starlight* / Lambada: *Kaoma* / Don't make me over: *Sybil* / Fake '88: *O'Neal, Alexander* / Who found who: *Jellybean & Elisa Fiorillo* / Lovely day (sunshine mix): *Withers, Bill* / I really didn't mean it: *Vandross, Luther* / Tribute (right on): *Pasadenas* / Hustle (to the music) (radio 1): *Funky Worm* / Roadblock: *Stock/Aitken/Waterman* / Respectable: *Mel & Kim (1)* / Loco in Acapulco: *Four Tops* / Shake you down: *Abbott, Gregory* / Real thing: *Jellybean featuring Steven Dante* / Automatic: *Pointer Sisters* / Midas touch: *Midnight Star* / In the name of love '88: *Thompson Twins* / Let's hear it for the boy: *Williams, Deniece* / Now that we've found love: *Third World* / Lost in music: *Sister Sledge* / Ghostbusters: *Parker, Ray Jnr.* / System addict: *Five Star* / Wap bam boogie: *Matt Bianco* / Dance sucker: *Set The Tone* / Dr. Beat: *Estefan, Gloria & Miami Sound Machine* / Takes a little time: *Total Contrast* / Let the music play: *Shannon* / Gotta get you home tonight: *Wilde, Eugene* / I wonder if I take you home: *Lisa Lisa & Cult Jam* / She's strange: *Cameo (1)* / Money's too tight to mention: *Simply Red* / I found lovin': *Fatback Band* / Finest: *S.O.S. Band* / I can't wait: *Nu Shooz* / Going to the bank: *Commodores* / Jump (for my love): *Pointer Sisters* / Dancin' in the key of life (remix): *Arrington, Steve* / Showing out (get fresh at the weekend): *Mel & Kim (1)* / Rappers delight: *Sugarhill Gang* / Breaks: *Blow, Kurtis* / Message: *Grandmaster Flash* / Get on the dancefloor: *Base, Rob & D.J. E-Z Rock* / I know you got soul: *Eric B & Rakim* / White lines (don't do it): *Grandmaster Flash & Melle Mel* / (Nothin' serious) just buggin': *Whistle* / Break 4 love: *Raze* / Alice I want you just for me: *Full Force* / (Bang Zoom) let's go go: *Real Roxanne* / Let's get brutal: *Nitro Deluxe* / Jack the groove: *Raze* / Jack le freak: *Chic* / Jack to the sound of the underground: *Hithouse* / Don't stop the music: *Yarbrough & Peoples* / Jump to the beat: *Lattisaw, Stacy* / Get down on it: *Kool & The Gang* / Jump to it: *Franklin, Aretha* / Stomp: *Brothers Johnson* / Love come down: *King, Evelyn 'Champagne'* / Funkin' for Jamaica: *Browne, Tom* / Searching: *Change* / I'll be good: *Rene & Angela* / Razzamatazz: *Jones, Quincy* / She's a bad mama jama: *Carlton, Carl* / Once bitten twice shy: *Williams, Vesta* / Back and forth: *Cameo (1)* / Groove: *Franklin, Rodney* / Who's zoomin' who: *Franklin, Aretha* / I'm in love: *King, Evelyn 'Champagne'* / Walking on sunshine: *Rockers Revenge* / Juicy fruit: *Mtume* / Silver shadow: *Atlantic Starr* / Keepin' love new: *Johnson, Howard* / Save your love (for number one): *Rene & Angela* / Night to remember: *Shalamar* / Love town: *Newberry, Booker III* / We got the funk: *Positive Force* / Let's groove: *Earth, Wind & Fire* / Inside out: *Odyssey* / Going back to my roots: *Odyssey* / Rockit: *Hancock, Herbie* / Celebration: *Kool & The Gang* / Mama used to say: *Giscombe, Junior* / (Sexual) healing: *Gaye, Marvin* / Make that move: *Shalamar* / There it is: *Shalamar* / Candy girl: *New Edition (1)* / I.O.U.: *Freeez* / 19: *Hardcastle, Paul* / Funky town: *Lipps Inc.* / Walking into sunshine: *Central Line* / Southern Freeez: *Freeez* / Ai no corrida: *Jones, Quincy* / Everybody salsa: *Modern Romance* / Flashback: *Imagination* / And the beat goes on: *Whispers*.

**CD Set** . . . . . . . . . . . . . . . . . . **DBOXCD 101**
**LP Set** . . . . . . . . . . . . . . . . . . **DBOXLP 101**
**■ MC Set** . . . . . . . . . . . . . . . . **DBOXMC 101**
Connoisseur Collection / Sep '90.

## 100 SOUL HITS.

**Tracks:** Soul man: *Sam & Dave* / Papa's got a brand new bag: *Brown, James* / Knock on wood: *Floyd, Eddie* / Under the boardwalk: *Drifters* / Rescue me: *Bass, Fontella* / It's just a matter of time: *Benton, Brook* / In crowd: *Grey, Dobie* / Oh no not my baby: *Brown, Maxine* / Every beat of my heart: *Knight, Gladys* / Rock your baby: *McCrae, George* / Barefootin': *Parker, Robert* / When a man loves a woman: *Sledge, Percy* / Backfield in motion: *Mel & Tim* / You don't know what you mean to me: *Sam & Dave* / Expressway to my heart: *Soul Survivors* / Save the last dance for me: *Drifters* / When something is wrong with my baby: *Sam & Dave* / If you need me: *Pickett, Wilson* / Do the funky chicken: *Thomas, Rufus* / Please, please, please: *Brown, James* / Rainy night in Georgia: *Benton, Brook* / Hold on I'm coming: *Burke, Solomon* / Bring it on home to me: *Floyd, Eddie* / Stand by me: *King, Ben E.* / I got the feeling: *Brown, James* / On broadway: *Drifters* / Hold on I'm coming (2): *Sam & Dave* / It's a man's man's world: *Brown, James* / Oh what a night: *Drells* / California girl: *Floyd, Eddie* / Spanish Harlem: *King, Ben E.* / True love: *Drifters* / Soul man (2): *Lewis, Ramsey* / So many ways: *Benton, Brook* / Letter full of tears: *Knight, Gladys* / Walking the dog: *Thomas, Rufus* / Hi heel sneakers: *Lewis, Ramsey* / All in my mind: *Brown, Maxine* / Best thing that ever happened to me: *Knight, Gladys* / Turn it loose: *Brown, James* / Said I wasn't gonna tell nobody: *Sam & Dave* / I who have nothing: *King, Ben E.* / My guy: *Wells, Mary* / Sweets for my sweet: *Drifters* / Georgia on my mind: *Knight, Gladys* / Boll weevil song: *Benton, Brook* / You don't know like I know: *Sam & Dave* / Get up off that thang: *Brown, James* / Warm & tender love: *Sledge, Percy* / Challenge: *Butler, Jerry* / It's too funky here: *Brown, James* / Kiddio: *Benton, Brook* / Tighten up: *Bell, Archie & The Drells* / I thank you: *Sam & Dave* / Lovin' arms: *Grey, Dobie* / Supernatural thing: *King, Ben E.* / Dancing in the street: *Lewis, Ramsey* / There goes my baby: *Drifters* / Operator: *Knight, Gladys & The Pips* / I wanna go home: *Drells* / Try me: *Brown, James* / Uptight: *Lewis, Ramsey* / So sad the song: *Knight, Gladys & The Pips* / Fools rush in: *Benton, Brook* / Girls: *Moments* / This magic moment: *Drifters* / Behind closed doors: *Sledge, Percy* / Listen: *Impressions* / Hard day's night: *Lewis, Ramsey* / Duke of Earl: *Chandler, Gene* / You got me hummin': *Sam & Dave* / Think twice: *Benton, Brook* / Since you've been gone: *Lewis, Ramsey* / Cold sweat/I can't stand myself (medley): *Brown, James* / I who have nothing (2): *King, Ben E.* / Soul sister brown sugar: *Sam & Dave* / Sex machine: *Brown, James* / Love me again: *Knight, Gladys & The Pips* / Up on the roof: *Drifters* / Look at me I'm in love: *Moments* / Drift away: *Grey, Dobie* / It's too late: *Pickett, Wilson* / She does it right: *King, Ben E.* / Hotel happiness: *Benton, Brook* / Louie, louie: *Kingsmen* / Get on the good foot: *Brown, James* / Soul twist: *Curtis, King* / Never found a girl: *Floyd, Eddie* / Don't pull your love out on me baby: *Sam & Dave* / Dance with me: *Drifters* / If ever I should fall in love: *Knight, Gladys & The Pips* / In crowd (2): *Lewis, Ramsey* / Love on a two way street: *Moments* / Take time to know her: *Sledge, Percy* / I need your love: *Impressions* / Can't you find another way: *Sam & Dave* / Some kind of wonderful: *Drifters* / Thank you pretty baby: *Benton, Brook* / What shall I do: *Knight, Gladys & The Pips* / I feel good: *Brown, James*.

**CD Set** . . . . . . . . . . . . . . . . . . . . **TFP 001**
**MC Set** . . . . . . . . . . . . . . . . . . . **MCTFP 001**
Tring / Nov '92 / Prism Leisure PLC / Midland Records.

## 150 MOTOWN HITS OF GOLD.

**Tracks:** Not Advised.

**■ LP Set** . . . . . . . . . . . . . . . . . . **WL 72410**
**■ MC Set** . . . . . . . . . . . . . . . . . . **WK 72410**
Motown / Oct '85.

## 1000 VOLTS OF STAX.

**Tracks:** Hide away: *Booker T & The MG's* / Sittin' on the dock of the bay: *Booker T & The MG's* / Don't you lie to me: *King, Albert* / Cupid: *Redding, Otis* / I've got dreams to remember: *Redding, Otis* / Don't worry about tomorrow: *Marchan, Bobby* / Walking the dog: *Thomas, Rufus* / Run around: *Thomas, Carla* / Floyd's beat: *Newman, Floyd* / When my love comes down: *Johnson, Ruby* / She won't be like you: *Bell, William* / Never let me go: *Bell, William* / Sweet devil: *John, Mable* / Cloudburst: *Mad Lads (1)* / Hippy dippy: *Mar-Keys* / Don't mess up a good thing: *Thomas, Rufus & Carla* / Just enough to hurt me: *Astors* / Knock on wood: *Floyd, Eddie*.

**CD** . . . . . . . . . . . . . . . . . . . . . . **CDSXD 042**
Stax / Sep '91 / Pinnacle.

## 1320 SOUTH LAUDARDALE AVENUE.

**Tracks:** Listen (take 1): *Green, Al* / Get back baby: *Green, Al* / Starting over again: *Green, Al* / Everything to me: *Green, Al* / Sweet song: *Green, Al* / Listen (take 2): *Green, Al* / Nothing impossible with love: *Green, Al* / Fool can't see the light: *Wright, O.V.* / I'm gonna be a big man some day: *Wright, O.V.* / Did you ever have the blues: *Bryant, Don* / With your hand: *Bryant, Don* / Run to me: *Bryant, Don* / It ain't easy: *Bryant, Don* / Coming on strong: *Bryant, Don*.

**■ LP** . . . . . . . . . . . . . . . . . . . . **HIUKLP 430**
Hi / Apr '89.

## 2000 VOLTS OF STAX.

**Tracks:** Kinda easy like: *Booker T & The MG's* / Ride your pony: *Thomas, Rufus* / You don't know like I know: *Taylor, Johnnie* / Pain in my heart: *Redding, Otis* / It's not that easy: *Johnson, Ruby* / How about you: *Parker, Deanie* / Hotshot: *Bar-Kays* / Come out tonight: *Astors* / Bark at the moon: *Floyd, Eddie* / I found a brand new love: *Kirk, Eddie* / Please don't go: *Tonettes* / Try me: *Thomas, Carla* / Slinky: *Mar-Keys* / Crosscut saw: *King, Albert* / She's the one: *Mad Lads (1)* / You don't miss your water: *Bell, William* / I say a little prayer: *Booker T & The MG's* / Try a little tenderness: *Redding, Otis*.

**CD** . . . . . . . . . . . . . . . . . . . . . . **CDSXD 074**
Stax / Oct '92 / Pinnacle.

# A

## ACID JAZZ AND OTHER ILLICIT GROOVES.

**Tracks:** Introduction: *Ace Of Clubs* / Ace of clubs: *Ace Of Clubs* / Jalal: *Jalal* / Push: *Traffic* / Shaft in action: *Acid Jazz* / Galliano: *Six Sharp Fists* / And now we have rhythm: *Night Trains* / Doin' it naturally: *Rhythm Blades* / Jazz renegades.

**CD** . . . . . . . . . . . . . . . . . . . . . . . **837 347-2**
**■ LP** . . . . . . . . . . . . . . . . . . . . . **URBLP 16**
**MC** . . . . . . . . . . . . . . . . . . . . . . **URBMC 16**
Urban / Sep '88 / PolyGram.

## ACID JAZZ AND OTHER ILLICIT GROOVES VOL.2.

**Tracks:** Not Advised.

**■ MC** . . . . . . . . . . . . . . . . . . . . . **837 925-4**
**■ CD** . . . . . . . . . . . . . . . . . . . . . **837 925-2**
**■ LP** . . . . . . . . . . . . . . . . . . . . . **837 925-1**
Urban / Feb '89.

## ACID JAZZ VOL.1.

**Tracks:** Better half: *Funk Inc.* / Got myself a good man: *Pucho* / Houston Express: *Houston Person* / Grits and gravy: *Kloss, Eric* / Hoochie coo chickie: *Jones, Ivan "Boogaloo Joe"* / Lady Mama: *Ammons, Gene* / Hip shaker: *Spencer, Leon* / Psychedelic Sally.

**■ LP** . . . . . . . . . . . . . . . . . . . . . **BGP 1015**
BGP / Sep '88.
**CD** . . . . . . . . . . . . . . . . . . . . . . **CDBGP 1015**
BGP / Oct '91 / Pinnacle.

**ACID JAZZ VOL.2.**
**Tracks:** Super bad: *Muhammad, Idris* / Cold sweat: *Purdie, Bernard* / Wildfire: *Bryant, Rusty* / Hot barbecue: *McDuff, Jack* / Reelin' with the feelin': *Kynard, Charles* / Spinky: *Earland, Charles* / Who's gonna take the weight: *Sparks, Melvin*.
■ LP . . . . . . . . . . . . . . . . . . . . BGP 1017
BGP / Oct '88.
CD. . . . . . . . . . . . . . . . . . . . CDBGP 1017
BGP / Oct '91 / Pinnacle.

**ACID JAZZ VOL.3.**
**Tracks:** I want you back: *Mabern, Harold* / Psychedelic Pucho: *Pucho* / Zebra walk: *Kynard, Charles* / Akilah: *Sparks, Melvin* / What it is: *Jones, Ivan "Boogaloo Joe"* / Bad Montana: *Parker, Maynard* / Dig on it: *Smith, Johnny "Hammond"* / Bowlegs: *Funk Inc.*.
■ LP . . . . . . . . . . . . . . . . . . . . BGP 1025
BGP / Mar '89.
CD. . . . . . . . . . . . . . . . . . . . CDBGP 1025
BGP / Oct '91 / Pinnacle.

**ACID JAZZ VOL.4.**
**Tracks:** Soul dance: *Person, Houston* / Sing a simple song: *Earland, Charles* / Twang thang: *Butler, Billy* / Shaft, Theme from: *Purdie, Bernard* / Sure 'nuff, sure 'nuff: *Phillips, Sonny* / Mamblues: *Tjader, Cal & Bernard Purdie* / Haw right now: *Rushen, Patrice* / Life is funky: *Round Robin Monopoly*.
■ LP . . . . . . . . . . . . . . . . . . . . BGP 1029
BGP / Jul '89.
CD. . . . . . . . . . . . . . . . . . . . CDBGP 1029
BGP / Oct '91 / Pinnacle.

**AFTER DARK.**
**Tracks:** Where do broken hearts go: *Houston, Whitney* / Just another day: *Secada, Jon* / She's gone: *Hall & Oates* / House is not a home: *Vandross, Luther* / Tired of being alone: *Green, Al* / If you're looking for a way out: *Odyssey* / I keep forgettin': *McDonald, Michael* / Wishing on a star: *Rose Royce* / Different corner: *Michael, George* / Why: *Lennox, Annie* / Just my imagination (running away with me): *Temptations* / Let the music play: *White, Barry* / Oh girl: *Young, Paul* / Don't leave me this way: *Melvin, Harold & The Bluenotes* / Teardrops: *Womack & Womack* / Heartbreaker: *Warwick, Dionne* / What's love got to do with it: *Turner, Tina* / I wonder why: *Stigers, Curtis*.
CD. . . . . . . . . . . . . . . . . . . . SETVCD 5
MC. . . . . . . . . . . . . . . . . . . . SETVC 5
Epic / Aug '93 / Sony.

**AFTER MIDNIGHT.**
**Tracks:** What a difference a day made: *Washington, Dinah* / Unforgettable: *Washington, Dinah* / Just a matter of time: *Benton, Brook* / Endlessly: *Benton, Brook* / Broken hearted melody: *Vaughan, Sarah* / Misty: *Vaughan, Sarah* / Twilight time: *Platters* / Smoke gets in your eyes: *Platters* / In the dark: *Jo, Damita* / You won't let me go: *Jo, Damita* / I apologise: *Eckstine, Billy* / Guilty: *Eckstine, Billy*.
■ LP . . . . . . . . . . . . . . . . . . . . SMWL 21018
Mercury / Feb '69.

**AFTER THE SESSION.**
**Tracks:** Not Advised.
■ LP . . . . . . . . . . . . . . . . . . . . LPSS 108
Soul Supply / May '86.

**AIN'T NOTHIN' BUT A HOUSE PARTY.**
**Tracks:** Bless your soul: *Dreamlovers* / You gave me somebody to love: *Dreamlovers* / You ain't sayin' nothin' new: *Virgil, Henry* / You fooled me: *Virgil, Henry* / Ain't nothin' but a houseparty: *Showstoppers* / What a man can do: *Showstoppers* / Eeeny meeny: *Showstoppers* / How easy your heart forgets me: *Showstoppers* / Suddenly: *Cherry People* / Father's angels: *Cherry People* / Bok to bak: *Cherry People* / I've been hurt: *Deal, Bill & The Rhondells* / Baby show it: *Festival* / Green grow the lilacs: *Festival* / You're gonna make it: *Devonnes* / Mob: *Devonnes* / I dig everything about you: *Devonnes* / Loan shark: *Chapter One* / Money won't do it, love will: *Chapter One* / I'll get by without you: *Gamble, Kenny & Tommy Bell* / Someday you'll be my love: *Gamble, Kenny & Tommy Bell*.
CD. . . . . . . . . . . . . . . . . . . . NEMCD 678
Sequel / Apr '94 / Total / BMG.

**ALABAMA SOUL.**
**Tracks:** Not Advised.
■ LP . . . . . . . . . . . . . . . . . . . . RPL 113
Timeless (Jazz) / Aug '87.

**ALBUM FULL OF SOUL.**
**Tracks:** Everybody's somebody's fool: *McPhatter, Clyde* / I belong to you: *McPhatter, Clyde* / Stand by me: *Little Eva* / You better make up your mind: *O'Dell, Brooks* / Work, work, work: *Dorsey, Lee* / Lovers always forgive: *Knight, Gladys* / Stop and get a hold of myself: *Knight, Gladys* / I'm counting on you: *Freeman Brothers* / My faith in you: *Billups, Eddie* / Something touched me: *Woods, Pearl* / I'm a member of your club: *Turner, Titus* / You satisfy my needs: *Irwin, Big Dee* / What a sad feeling: *Harris, Betty* / I love you: *Townsend, Ed* / You'll remind me: *King, Earl* / Wait: *Smith, Bobby*.
■ LP . . . . . . . . . . . . . . . . . . . . SL 10172
Stateside / Feb '66.

**ALL PLATINUM.**
**Tracks:** Not Advised.
■ LP . . . . . . . . . . . . . . . . . . . . CXMP 2001
Chess (PRT) / Apr '81.

**ALL SPICE.**
**Tracks:** Never like this: *Two Tons Of Fun* / I think I love you: *Shock* / Slipped away: *Allspice* / Give it up (don't make me wait): *Sylvester* / Rainy day stormy nights: *Impact* / Hungry for your love: *Allspice* / Keep it up: *Everett, Betty* / Lovin': *Hurtt, Phil* / Just us: *Two Tons Of Fun* / I ain't into that: *Rappin' Reverend* / S.O.S.: *Side Effect* / Feel good all over: *McWilliams, Paulette* / For you: *Reason, Johnny* / I believe in you: *Muhammad, Idris* / Love's such a wonderful sound: *Reason, Johnny* / Finally found someone: *Side Effect* / Never been here before: *McWilliams, Paulette*.
CD. . . . . . . . . . . . . . . . . . . . CDBGPD 074
BGP / Oct '93 / Pinnacle.
LP . . . . . . . . . . . . . . . . . . . . BPGD 1074
BGP / Oct '93 / Pinnacle.

**ALL THE GREAT MOTOWN LOVE DUETS.**
**Tracks:** It takes two: *Gaye, Marvin & Kim Weston* / I'm gonna make you love me: *Ross, Diana & The Supremes* / Ain't nothing like the real thing: *Gaye, Marvin & Tammi Terrell* / Blame it on love: *Robinson, Smokey & Barbara Mitchell* / You're a special part of me: *Gaye, Marvin & Diana Ross* / With you I'm born again: *Preston, Billy & Syreeta* / You're all I need to get by: *Gaye, Marvin & Tammi Terrell* / Fire and desire: *James, Rick & Teena Marie* / My mistake (was to love you): *Gaye, Marvin & Diana Ross* / If this world were mine: *Gaye, Marvin & Tammi Terrell* / Endless love: *Ross, Diana & Lionel Richie*.
■ LP . . . . . . . . . . . . . . . . . . . . WL 72367
■ MC. . . . . . . . . . . . . . . . . . . . WK 72367
Motown / Mar '85.
■ CD. . . . . . . . . . . . . . . . . . . . WD 72367
Motown / Oct '89.

**ALL THESE THINGS (The Sound Of New Orleans).**
**Tracks:** Barefootin': *Parker, Robert* / Tell it like it is: *Neville, Aaron* / Mother in law: *Doe, Ernie K.* / Working in a coalmine: *Dorsey, Lee* / I like it like that: *Kenner, Chris* / Ooh poo pah doo: *Hill, Jessie* / It will stand: *Showman* / You always hurt the one you love: *Henry, Clarence 'Frogman'* / Fortune teller: *Spellman, Benny* / All these things: *Neville, Art* / Iko iko: *Dixie Cups* / Ruler of my heart: *Thomas, Irma* / Rockin' pneumonia and the boogie woogie flu: *Smith, Huey "Piano"* / Chicken strut: *Meters* / Release me: *Adams, Johnny* / Something you got: *George, Barbara*.
CD. . . . . . . . . . . . . . . . . . . . CDINS 5024
LP . . . . . . . . . . . . . . . . . . . . INS 5024
MC. . . . . . . . . . . . . . . . . . . . TCINS 5024
Instant (2) / Feb '90 / Charly.

**ALWAYS AND FOREVER (20 Soulful Hits).**
**Tracks:** That lady: *Isley Brothers* / You're love is king: *Sade* / I don't love you anymore: *Pendergrass, Teddy* / Rain or shine: *Five Star* / Best of my love: *Emotions (2)* / I will survive: *Gaynor, Gloria* / Jack & Jill: *Raydio* / It's a man's man's man's world: *Brown, James* / Inside out: *Odyssey* / If you were here tonight: *O'Neal, Alexander* / September: *Earth, Wind & Fire* / Used ta be my girl: *O'Jays* / Hold on to my love: *Ruffin, Jimmy* / Like sister and brother: *Drifters* / Friends: *Stewart, Amii* / Always and forever: *Heatwave* / Heartbreaker: *King, Evelyn 'Champagne'* / I'm your puppet: *Purify, James & Bobby* / Night I fell in love: *Vandross, Luther* / Greatest love of all: *Benson, George*.
CD. . . . . . . . . . . . . . . . . . . . STDCD 31
MC. . . . . . . . . . . . . . . . . . . . STDMC 31
Solitaire / Mar '90 / BMG.

**ALWAYS AND FOREVER.**
**Tracks:** Still / Lovely day / Heartbreaker / If you don't know me by now / You make me feel brand new / You'll never find another love like mine / Touch me in the morning / Three times a lady / Jack & Jill / Me and Mrs. Jones / Tears on my pillow / How 'bout us / Always and forever / Do you know where you're going to.
■ LP . . . . . . . . . . . . . . . . . . . . LPIMP 4
MC. . . . . . . . . . . . . . . . . . . . TCIMP 4
Impression / Aug '84 / Pinnacle.

**ALWAYS AND FOREVER.**
**Tracks:** Not Advised.
■ LP . . . . . . . . . . . . . . . . . . . . STAR 2301
■ CD. . . . . . . . . . . . . . . . . . . . TCD 2301
■ MC. . . . . . . . . . . . . . . . . . . . STAC 2301
Telstar/Ronco / '87.

**AMERICAN SOUL 1966-72.**
**Tracks:** Not Advised.
■ LP . . . . . . . . . . . . . . . . . . . . CGB 1003
Capitol / Dec '81.

**AMERICA'S MUSIC - R & B VOL. 1.**
**Tracks:** Not Advised.
VHS . . . . . . . . . . . . . . . . . . . . MMGV 043
MMG Video / Jul '92 / THE.

**AMERICA'S MUSIC - SOUL VOL. 1.**
**Tracks:** Rap payback / Jam / Spanish Harlem / I who have nothing / This is it / Turn back the hands of time / Turning point / Lead me on / I don't miss you at all / Right back where we started from / In the mood / Man understand.
VHS . . . . . . . . . . . . . . . . . . . . MMGV 036
MMG Video / Feb '92 / THE.

**AND THE BEAT GOES ON (34 Dance Hits Of The 70's).**
**Tracks:** Boogie wonderland: *Earth, Wind & Fire* / I will survive: *Gaynor, Gloria* / Young hearts run free: *Staton, Candi* / Lady marmalade: *Labelle* / Nutbush City Limits: *Turner, Ike & Tina* / Car wash: *Rose Royce* / Love train: *O'Jays* / You're the first, the last, my everything: *White, Barry* / Ain't no stoppin' us now: *McFadden & Whitehead* / Show you the way to go: *Jacksons* / Don't take away the music: *Tavares* / Get down: *Chandler, Gene* / Baby don't change your mind: *Knight, Gladys & The Pips* / If I can't have you: *Elliman, Yvonne* / Streetlife: *Crusaders* / Ring my bell: *Ward, Anita* / Play that funky music: *Wild Cherry* / Best of my love: *Emotions (1)* / Dance, dance, dance: *Chic* / He's the greatest dancer: *Sister Sledge* / Contact: *Starr, Edwin* / I'm on fire: *5000 Volts* / Y.M.C.A.: *Village People* / Rock your baby: *McCrae, George* / Le freak: *Chic* / Disco stomp: *Bohannon, Hamilton* / Hold back the night: *Trammps* / Everyone's a winner: *Hot Chocolate* / You bet your love: *Hancock, Herbie* / And the beat goes on: *Whispers*.
■ Double LP. . . . . . . . . . . . . . . . . STAR 2338
■ CD. . . . . . . . . . . . . . . . . . . . TCD 2338
■ MC. . . . . . . . . . . . . . . . . . . . STAC 2338
Telstar/Ronco / Sep '88.

**ANTHOLOGY OF HOT R&B FROM BATON ROUGE.**
**Tracks:** Not Advised.
CD. . . . . . . . . . . . . . . . . . . . FLYCD 41
Flyright / Oct '91 / Hot Shot / Roots Records / Wellard / Charly / Swift / Projection / Jazz Music.

**APOLLO SATURDAY NIGHT.**
**Tracks:** Not Advised.
■ LP . . . . . . . . . . . . . . . . . . . . SD 33159
Atco / Jun '88.

**ARISTA FUNKSTERS.**
**Tracks:** Baby not tonight / Song for Jeremy / Red piper / Saturday night.
■ 12". . . . . . . . . . . . . . . . . . . . ARIST 12430
Arista / Sep '81.

**ART OF THE SOUL BALLAD, THE.**
**Tracks:** Not Advised.
CD. . . . . . . . . . . . . . . . . . . . CDCD 1096
MC. . . . . . . . . . . . . . . . . . . . CDMC 1096
Charly / Jun '93 / Charly.

**ATLANTA GOSPEL.**
**Tracks:** I don't..: *Peach, Georgia & Reliables* / Open up: *Reliable Jubiliee Singers* / God shall wipe all tears away: *Reliable Jubiliee Singers* / On Mount Olive: *National Independent Gospel Singers* / I got it right: *National Independent Gospel Singers* / Evening sun: *Echoes Of Zion* / Keep still: *Echoes Of Zion* / Awful day will..: *Starlight Spiritual Singers* / Tone the bell easy: *Five Trumpets* / I can see: *Five Trumpets* / Ten commandments: *Five Trumpets* / Bread of heaven: *Five Trumpets* / My chains fell off: *Five Trumpets* / Servant's prayer: *Five Trumpets* / Stand by me: *Five Trumpets* / How I got over: *Five Trumpets*.
■ LP . . . . . . . . . . . . . . . . . . . . HT 312
Heritage / Jan '87.

**ATLANTIC DISCO YEARS 1974-79.**
**Tracks:** Not Advised.
CD. . . . . . . . . . . . . . . . . . . . 241 678-2
Atlantic / '87 / WEA.

**ATLANTIC GROOVES - THE FUNK & JAZZ EXPERIENCE VOL. 1.**
**Tracks:** Not Advised.
CD. . . . . . . . . . . . . . . . . . . . 954832771-2

**MC.** . . . . . . . . . . . . . . . . . . . . . . **954832771-4**
Atlantic / Aug '94 / WEA.

### ATLANTIC MASTERS STARTRACKS, PART 1.
**Tracks:** Not Advised.
■ **LP** . . . . . . . . . . . . . . . . . . . . . . **K 50732**
Atlantic / Jun '80.

### ATLANTIC R & B (1947-1974).
**Tracks:** Not Advised.
**CD Set** . . . . . . . . . . . . . . . . . . . . **781 292-2**
**MC Set** . . . . . . . . . . . . . . . . . . . . **781 620-4**
■ **LP Set** . . . . . . . . . . . . . . . . . . . **781 620-1**
Atlantic / Apr '87.

### ATLANTIC R & B VOL 1 (1947-1952).
**Tracks:** Lowe groovin': *Morris, Joe* / That old black magic: *Grimes, Tiny* / Annie Laurie: *Grimes, Tiny* / Midnight special: *Grimes, Tiny* / Applejack: *Morris, Joe* / Drinkin' wine spo-dee-o-dee: *McGhee, Sticks* / Coleslaw: *Culley, Frank* / So long: *Brown, Ruth* / I'll get along somehow (parts 1&2): *Brown, Ruth* / Hey little girl: *Professor Longhair* / Mardi Gras in New Orleans: *Professor Longhair* / Tee nah nah: *Van Walls, Harry* / Anytime, anyplace, anywhere: *Morris, Joe* / Teardrops from my eyes: *Brown, Ruth* / One monkey don't stop no show: *McGhee, Sticks* / Don't you know I love you: *Clovers* / Shouldn't I know: *Cardinals* / Chill is on: *Turner, Big Joe* / Chains of love: *Turner, Big Joe* / Fool, fool, fool: *Clovers* / One mint julep: *Clovers* / Wheel of fortune: *Cardinals* / Sweet sixteen: *Turner, Big Joe* / 5-10-15 hours: *Brown, Ruth* / Ting a ling: *Clovers* / Gator's groove: *Jackson, Willis* / Daddy, daddy: *Brown, Ruth* / Midnight hour: *Charles, Ray.*
**CD** . . . . . . . . . . . . . . . . . . . . . . **781 293-2**
Atlantic / Apr '87 / WEA.

### ATLANTIC R & B VOL 2 (1952-1955).
**Tracks:** Beggar for your kisses: *Diamonds* / Mama, he treats your daughter mean: *Brown, Ruth* / Good lovin: *Clovers* / Wild wild young men: *Brown, Ruth* / Mess around: *Charles, Ray* / Hush hush: *Turner, Big Joe* / Soul on fire / Money honey: *McPhatter, Clyde & Drifters* / Such a night: *McPhatter, Clyde & Drifters* / Tipitina: *Professor Longhair* / White Christmas: *McPhatter, Clyde & Drifters* / Honey love: *McPhatter, Clyde* / Watcha gonna do: *McPhatter, Clyde* / Shake, rattle & roll: *Turner, Big Joe* / Sh'boom: *Chords* / Jam up: *Ridgley, Tommy* / Tomorrow night / Tweedlee dee / I got a woman: *Charles, Ray* / Door is still open: *Cardinals* / Flip flop and fly: *Turner, Big Joe* / Fool for you: *Charles, Ray* / This little girl of mine: *Charles, Ray* / Play it fair / Adorable: *Drifters* / Smokey Joe's cafe: *Robins.*
**CD** . . . . . . . . . . . . . . . . . . . . . . **781 294-2**
Atlantic / Apr '87 / WEA.

### ATLANTIC R & B VOL 3 (1955-1958).
**Tracks:** Ruby baby: *Drifters* / In paradise: *Cookies* / Chicken and the hawk: *Turner, Big Joe* / Devil or angel: *Clovers* / Drown in my own tears: *Charles, Ray* / Hallelujah, I love her so: *Charles, Ray* / Jim Dandy: *Baker, LaVern* / Down in Mexico: *Coasters* / Corina Corina: *Turner, Big Joe* / Treasure of love: *McPhatter, Clyde* / Love, love, love: *Clovers* / It's too late: *Willis, Chuck* / Lonely avenue: *Charles, Ray* / Since I met you baby: *Hunter, Lloyd Serenaders* / Lucky lips: *Brown, Ruth* / Without love: *McPhatter, Clyde* / Fools fall in love: *Drifters* / Midnight special train: *Turner, Big Joe* / Empty arms: *Hunter, Ivory Joe* / C.C. rider: *Willis, Chuck* / Betty and Dupree: *Bobbettes* / What am I living for: *Willis, Chuck* / Hang up my rock 'n' roll shoes: *Willis, Chuck* / Yakety yak: *Coasters* / Lover's question: *McPhatter, Clyde* / I cried a tear: *Charles, Ray* / Right time: *Charles, Ray* / What'd I say (parts 1&2): *Charles, Ray* / There goes my baby: *Drifters.*
**CD** . . . . . . . . . . . . . . . . . . . . . . **781 295-2**
Atlantic / Apr '87 / WEA.

### ATLANTIC R & B VOL 4 (1958-1962).
**Tracks:** Along came Jones: *Coasters* / Let the good times roll: *Charles, Ray* / Poison ivy: *Coasters* / Dance with me: *Drifters* / Just for a thrill: *Charles, Ray* / This magic moment: *Charles, Ray* / Save the last dance for me: *Charles, Ray* / Shopping for clothes: *Coasters* / Spanish Harlem: *King, Ben E.* / Young boy blues: *King, Ben E.* / Stand by me: *King, Ben E.* / Gee whiz: *Thomas, Carla* / Saved / Just out of reach: *Burke, Solomon* / Little Egypt: *Coasters* / Amor: *King, Ben E.* / Last night: *Mar-Keys* / I'm blue (the gong-gong song): *Ikettes* / You don't miss your water: *Bell, William* / I found a love: *Falcons (1)* / Cry to me: *Burke, Solomon* / Don't play that song: *King, Ben E.* / Green onions: *Booker T & The MG's.*
**CD** . . . . . . . . . . . . . . . . . . . . . . **781 296-2**
Atlantic / Apr '87 / WEA.

### ATLANTIC R & B VOL 5 (1962-1966).
**Tracks:** Up on the roof: *Drifters* / c.c. rider / I (who have nothing): *King, Ben E.* / If you need me: *Burke, Solomon* / These arms of mine: *Redding, Otis* / Hello stranger: *Lewis, Barbara* / On Broadway: *Drifters* / Just one look: *Troy, Doris* / Do the mashed potatoes (parts 1&2): *Kindricks, Nat & The Swans* / Land of a thousand dances: *Kenner, Chris* / Walking the dog: *Kenner, Chris* / Release me: *Phillips, Esther* / Mercy, mercy: *Covay, Don* / Under the boardwalk: *Drifters* / And I love him: *Phillips, Esther* / Hold what you've got: *Tex, Joe* / Mr. Pitiful: *Redding, Otis* / Baby I'm yours: *Lewis, Barbara* / Teasin' you: *Tee, Willie* / I've been loving you too long: *Redding, Otis* / In the midnight hour: *Pickett, Wilson* / See-saw: *Covay, Don* / Respect: *Redding, Otis* / You don't know like I know: *Sam & Dave* / When a man loves a woman: *Sledge, Percy* / Hold on I'm coming: *Sam & Dave* / Cool jerk: *Capitols (1)* / Neighbour, neighbour: *Hughes, Jimmy.*
**CD** . . . . . . . . . . . . . . . . . . . . . . **781 297-2**
Atlantic / Apr '87 / WEA.

### ATLANTIC R & B VOL 6 (1966-1969).
**Tracks:** Land of a thousand dances: *Pickett, Wilson* / Knock on wood: *Floyd, Eddie* / Try a little tenderness: *Redding, Otis* / Mustang Sally: *Pickett, Wilson* / When something is wrong with my baby: *Sam & Dave* / Sweet soul music: *Conley, Arthur* / Soul man: *Sam & Dave* / I never loved a man (the way I love you): *Franklin, Aretha* / Do right woman, do right man: *Franklin, Aretha* / Show me: *Tex, Joe* / Tramp: *Redding, Otis & Carla Thomas* / Funky Broadway: *Pickett, Wilson* / Hip hug her: *Booker T & The MG's* / Respect: *Franklin, Aretha* / You make me feel like a natural woman: *Franklin, Aretha* / Soul finger: *Bar-Kays* / Baby I love you: *Franklin, Aretha* / Skinny legs and all: *Tex, Joe* / Chain of fools: *Franklin, Aretha* / I'm in love: *Pickett, Wilson* / Memphis soul stew: *King Diamond* / (Sittin' on) the dock of the bay: *Redding, Otis* / Tighten up: *Redding, Otis* / Slip away: *Carter, Clarence* / Think: *Franklin, Aretha* / First time ever I saw your face: *Flack, Roberta* / Take a letter, Maria: *Greaves, R.B.* / Rainy night in Georgia: *Charles, Ray* / Ghetto: *Hathaway, Donny.*
**CD** . . . . . . . . . . . . . . . . . . . . . . **781 298-2**
Atlantic / Apr '87 / WEA.

### ATLANTIC R & B VOL 7 (1969-1974).
**Tracks:** Turn back the hands of time: *Davis, Walter* / Compared to what: *McCann, Les* / Don't play that song: *Franklin, Aretha* / Groove me: *Floyd, King* / Patches: *Carter, Clarence* / Funky Nassau (parts 1&2): *Beginning Of The End* / Thin line between love and hate: *Persuaders* / Rock steady: *Franklin, Aretha* / You've got a friend: *Flack, Roberta & Donny Hathaway* / Clean up woman: *Wright, Betty* / Could it be I'm falling in love: *Spinners* / Killing me softly with his song: *Flack, Roberta* / Where is the love: *Flack, Roberta & Donny Hathaway* / I'll be around: *Spinners* / Feel like makin' love: *Flack, Roberta* / Mighty love: *Spinners* / Love won't let me wait: *Major Harris.*
**CD** . . . . . . . . . . . . . . . . . . . . . . **781 299-2**
Atlantic / Apr '87 / WEA.

### ATLANTIC RECORDS HISTORY OF R&B VOCAL GROUPS.
**Tracks:** Sh'boom: *Chords* / Come back my love: *Cardinals* / Devil or angel: *Clovers* / She's mine all mine: *Royal Jokers* / Adorable: *Drifters* / Smokey Joe's cafe: *Robins* / Ruby baby: *Drifters* / Fools fall in love: *Drifters* / Yes sir that's my baby: *Sensations featuring Yvonne Mills* / Please me disc jockey: *Sensations featuring Yvonne Mills* / Mr. Lee: *Bobbettes* / Down in Mexico: *Coasters.*
■ **LP** . . . . . . . . . . . . . . . . . . . . . . **790 132-1**
Atlantic / Mar '84.

### ATLANTIC SOUL BALLADS.
**Tracks:** Try a little tenderness: *Redding, Otis* / I say a little prayer: *Franklin, Aretha* / Save the last dance for me: *Drifters* / I'm in love: *Pickett, Wilson* / Warm and tender love: *Sledge, Percy* / Patches: *Carter, Clarence* / Thin line between love and hate: *Persuaders* / Spanish Harlem: *King, Ben E.* / When something is wrong with my baby: *Sam & Dave* / My girl: *Redding, Otis* / Love won't let me wait: *Harris, Major* / On Broadway: *Drifters* / Baby I'm yours: *Lewis, Barbara* / Rainy night In Georgia: *Benton, Brook* / Hey Jude: *Pickett, Wilson.*
**CD** . . . . . . . . . . . . . . . . . . . . . . **241 136-2**
■ **LP** . . . . . . . . . . . . . . . . . . . . . . **WX 98**
■ **MC** . . . . . . . . . . . . . . . . . . . . . . **WX 98 C**
Atlantic / Jun '88.

### ATLANTIC SOUL CLASSICS.
**Tracks:** Sweet soul music: *Conley, Arthur* / In the midnight hour: *Pickett, Wilson* / Knock on wood: *Floyd, Eddie* / Soul man: *Sam & Dave* / Respect: *Franklin, Aretha* / See-saw: *Convoy, Don* / Everybody needs somebody to love: *Burke, Solomon* / Soul finger: *Bar-Kays* / Stand by me: *King, Ben E.* / B-A-B-Y: *Thomas, Carla* / Under the boardwalk: *Drifters* / Tramp: *Redding, Otis & Carla Thomas* / Green onions: *Booker T & The MG's* / When a man loves a woman: *Sledge, Percy* / Tribute to a king: *Bell, William* / (Sittin' on) the dock of the bay: *Redding, Otis.*
**CD** . . . . . . . . . . . . . . . . . . . . . . **241 138-2**
■ **LP** . . . . . . . . . . . . . . . . . . . . . . **WX 105**
**MC** . . . . . . . . . . . . . . . . . . . . . . **WX 105C**
Atlantic / May '87 / WEA.

### ATLANTIC STORY, THE.
**Tracks:** Drinkin' wine spo-dee-o-dee: *McGhee, Sticks* / 5-10-15 hours: *Brown, Ruth* / One mint julep: *Clovers* / Shake, rattle and roll: *Turner, Joe* / Jim Dandy: *Baker, LaVern* / Lover's question: *McPhatter, Clyde* / What'd I say: *Charles, Ray* / Mack the knife: *Darin, Bobby* / Giant steps: *Coltrane, John* / Poison ivy: *Coasters* / Save the last dance for me: *Drifters* / Stand by me: *King, Ben E.* / Deep purple: *Tempo, Nino & April Stevens* / I got U babe: *Sonny & Cher* / Green onions: *Booker T & The MG's* / Hold on, I'm comin': *Sam & Dave* / Knock on wood: *Floyd, Eddie* / When a man loves a woman: *Sledge, Percy* / Got to get you off my mind: *Burke, Solomon* / In the midnight hour: *Pickett, Wilson* / I say a little prayer: *Franklin, Aretha* / Sweet soul music: *Conley, Arthur* / (Sittin' on) the dock of the bay: *Redding, Otis* / Groovin': *Young Rascals* / You keep me hangin' on: *Vanilla Fudge* / In-A-Gadda-Da-Vida: *Iron Butterfly* / For what it's worth: *Buffalo Springfield* / Sweet Jane: *Velvet Underground* / Rock and roll: *Led Zeppelin* / Can't get enough: *Bad Company* / Could it be I'm falling in love: *Detroit Spinners* / Such a night: *Dr. John* / Chanson d'amour: *Manhattan Transfer* / Soul man: *Blues Brothers* / Good times: *Chic* / We are family: *Sister Sledge* / Gloria: *Branigan, Laura* / I want to know what love is: *Foreigner* / Casanova: *Levert* / From a distance: *Levert* / Black velvet: *Myles, Alannah* / Walking in Memphis: *Cohn, Marc* / It's a shame about Ray: *Lemonheads* / Silent all these years: *Amos, Tori* / Hold on: *En Vogue.*
**CD Set** . . . . . . . . . . . . . . . . . . . . **954832424-2**
Atlantic / Dec '92 / WEA.

## B

### B & G PARTY.
**Tracks:** Rock Creek Park: *Blackbyrds* / Glide: *Pleasure (2)* / Straight to the bank: *Summers, Bill* / I've learned from my burns: *Spyders Webb* / Keep that same old feeling: *Side Effect* / Ghettos of the mind: *Pleasure (2)* / Sister Jane: *Funk Inc..*
■ **LP** . . . . . . . . . . . . . . . . . . . . . . **BGP 1006**
BGP / Feb '88.

### BABY LOVE.
**Tracks:** Not Advised.
**CD** . . . . . . . . . . . . . . . . . . . . . . **01373062**
Compact Leisure / Jun '89.

### BACK ON THE RIGHT TRACK BABY.
**Tracks:** Walking up a one way street: *Tee, Willie* / See-saw: *Covay, Don* / Candy: *Astors* / Someday we're gonna love again: *Lewis, Barbara* / Get on the right track baby: *Charles, Ray* / Soul man: *Sam & Dave* / (Ain't that) just like me: *Coasters* / It's in his kiss: *King, Ramona* / Comin' home baby: *Torme, Mel* / Here I go again: *Bell, Archie & The Drells* / Respect: *Redding, Otis* / Last night: *Mar-Keys* / Stupidity: *Burke, Solomon* / Tramp: *Redding, Otis & Carla Thomas* / Beat goes on: *Sonny & Cher* / Stay with me (baby): *Ellison, Lorraine.*
■ **LP** . . . . . . . . . . . . . . . . . . . . . . **KENT 091**
■ **MC** . . . . . . . . . . . . . . . . . . . . . . **KENC 091**
Kent / May '89.

### BACK TO STAX, VOL. 1.
**Tracks:** Not Advised.
**VHS** . . . . . . . . . . . . . . . . . . . . . . **CFV 10652**
Channel 5 / May '90 / Channel 5 Video / P.R.O. Video / Gold & Sons.

### BACK TO STAX, VOL. 2.
**Tracks:** Not Advised.
**VHS** . . . . . . . . . . . . . . . . . . . . . . **CFV 10662**
Channel 5 / May '90 / Channel 5 Video / P.R.O. Video / Gold & Sons.

### BAD, BAD WHISKEY (The Galaxy Masters).
**Tracks:** She's looking good: *Collins, Rodger* / Rufus Jr: *Merced Blue Notes* / I got to tell somebody: *Everett, Betty* / Chicken heads: *Rush, Bobby* / Get

your lie straight: *Coday, Bill* / (Tell me) Why do you have to lie: *Right Kind* / You better stop: *Rhodes, Sonny* / Nightingale melody: *Taylor, Little Johnny* / I pity the fool: *Saunders, Merl* / It's a shame: *Malone, J.J.* / Rainbow 71: *Holloway, Loleatta* / Foxy girls in Oakland: *Collins, Rodger* / When you find a fool bump his head: *Coday, Bill* / Mama Rufus: *Merced Blue Notes* / For your precious love: *Taylor, Little Johnny* / Abraham Martin and John: *Brown, Charles* / Bad bad whiskey: *Merced Blue Notes* / How can I forget you: *Williams, Lenny* / Ain't nothing gonna change me: *Everett, Betty* / Woman rules the world: *Coday, Bill* / Why did our love go: *Huey, Claude 'Baby'* / Let me be your handy man: *Coday, Bill* / Fever fever fever: *Eaton, Bobby* / Lisa'a gone: *Williams, Lenny* / Don't want to be a lone ranger: *Watson, Johnny 'Guitar'*.
**CD** . . . . . . . . . . . . . . . . . . . . . . **CDCHD 516**
Ace / Jan '94 / Pinnacle / Complete Record Co. Ltd.

**BATTIN' THE BOOGIE.**
**Tracks:** One note boogie: *Restum, Willie* / Good morning Mary: *Restum, Willie* / What'd he say: *Restum, Willie* / Rock-a-beatin' boogie: *Restum, Willie* / Kiss me: *Restum, Willie* / Off and on: *Restum, Willie* / Do it easy: *Restum, Willie* / Restum in peace blues: *Restum, Willie* / Save me a boogie: *Johnson, Marvin* / Hello: *Williams, Paul (1)* / You're breaking my heart no more: *Williams, Paul (1)* / It's over: *Williams, Paul (1)* / Rock it Davy Crockett: *Williams, Paul (1)* / Battin' the boogie: *Johnson, Joshua* / Ramblin' woman: *Johnson, Joshua* / Your love has me rockin' and reelin': *Valentine, Billy*.
■ **LP** . . . . . . . . . . . . . . . . . . . . . **CRB 1127**
Charly R&B / Aug '86.

**BEAT IS ON (Sue instrumentals 1959-67).**
**Tracks:** I got a woman: *McGriff, Jimmy* / Going home: *Turner, Ike* / Fat back: *Doggett, Bill* / June's blues: *Commandos* / So far away: *Jacobs, Hank* / Stick shift: *Duals* / Good time tonight: *Doggett, Bill* / New breed, The (pt.1): *Turner, Ike & The Kings of Rhythm* / Chicken scratch: *Commandos* / Monkey hips and rice: *Jacobs, Hank* / Soul at sunrise: *Juggy* / All about my girl: *McGriff, Jimmy* / New breed, The (pt.2): *Turner, Ike & The Kings of Rhythm* / M.G. blues: *McGriff, Jimmy*.
■ **MC** . . . . . . . . . . . . . . . . . . . . **TCSSL 6029**
■ **LP** . . . . . . . . . . . . . . . . . . . . . **SSL 6029**
Stateside / Jul '87.

**BELL'S CELLAR OF SOUL - VOL. 1.**
**Tracks:** I need a lot of lovin': *Mighty Sam* / In the same old way: *Mighty Sam* / Can't last much longer: *Harris, Betty* / I'm gonna git ya: *Harris, Betty* / What'd I do wrong: *Harris, Betty* / I believe I'll go back home: *Ovations* / Woman is a man's best friend: *Carr, James* / You hurt me so good: *Carr, James* / How to pick a winner: *Diamond Joe* / Either way I lose: *Knight, Gladys* / Giving up: *Knight, Gladys* / Sinner girl: *Spellman, Benny* / My ship is comin' in: *Radcliffe, Jimmy* / Don't pity me: *Moore, Curley* / She shot a hole in my soul: *Curry, Clifford* / Say you need it: *Perry, Barbara*.
■ **LP** . . . . . . . . . . . . . . . . . . . . . **MBLL 102**
Bell / Mar '68.

**BELL'S CELLAR OF SOUL - VOL. 2.**
**Tracks:** Not Advised.
■ **LP** . . . . . . . . . . . . . . . . . . . . . **MBLL 107**
Bell / Nov '68.

**BELL'S CELLAR OF SOUL 89.**
**Tracks:** She shot a hole in my soul: *Curry, Clifford* / Don't you know a true love: *O'Jays* / Sock it to em soul brother: *Moss, Bill* / I'm just an average guy: *Masqueraders* / Believe in me: *Henley, Floyd* / Love bug: *Davis, Melvin* / On the other side: *Jones, Lee* / Choice: *O'Jays* / I miss you: *O'Jays* / Love that never ..: *Tig & Co* / I ain't got love: *Williams/Weston* / Don't be afraid: *Henley, Floyd* / Love bug got a bear hug: *Davis, Melvin*.
■ **LP** . . . . . . . . . . . . . . . . . . . . . **CRB 1221**
Charly R&B / Feb '89.

**BEST FROM BELL - VOL.2.**
**Tracks:** Not Advised.
■ **LP** . . . . . . . . . . . . . . . . . . . . . **SBLL 124**
Bell / Nov '69.

**BEST OF 12" GOLD VOL.1.**
**Tracks:** Boogie wonderland: *Earth, Wind & Fire* / Disco nights (rock freak): *G.Q.* / You can do it: *Hudson, Al & The Partners* / I thought it was you: *Hancock, Herbie* / Street life: *Crusaders* / You know how to love me: *Hyman, Phyllis* / It's a disco night (rock don't stop): *Isley Brothers* / Stuff like that: *Jones, Quincy*.
**CD** . . . . . . . . . . . . . . . . . . . . . . **OG 3401**
■ **LP** . . . . . . . . . . . . . . . . . . . . . **OG 1401**
**MC** . . . . . . . . . . . . . . . . . . . . . . **OG 2401**
Old Gold / Oct '88 / Pickwick.

**BEST OF 12" GOLD VOL.10.**
**Tracks:** Let the music play: *Shannon* / Hip hop, be bop: *Man Parrish* / Alice, I want you just for me: *Full Force* / Haunted house of rock: *Whodini* / Body work: *Hot Streak* / Street dance: *Break Machine* / Sexomatic: *Bar-Kays* / Rock it: *Hancock, Herbie*.
**CD** . . . . . . . . . . . . . . . . . . . . . . **OG 3410**
■ **LP** . . . . . . . . . . . . . . . . . . . . . **OG 1410**
**MC** . . . . . . . . . . . . . . . . . . . . . . **OG 2410**
Old Gold / Nov '89 / Pickwick.

**BEST OF 12" GOLD VOL.14.**
**Tracks:** Love me like this: *Real To Reel* / My love is waiting: *Gaye, Marvin* / Risin' to the top: *Burke, Keni* / Girl from Ipanema: *Gilberto, Astrud* / Does she have a friend: *Chandler, Gene* / Mind blowin' decisions: *Heatwave* / Mellow mellow right on: *Lowrell* / Pillow talk: *Sylvia (1)*.
**CD** . . . . . . . . . . . . . . . . . . . . . . **OG 3414**
**LP** . . . . . . . . . . . . . . . . . . . . . . **OG 1414**
**MC** . . . . . . . . . . . . . . . . . . . . . . **OG 2414**
Old Gold / Jul '90 / Pickwick.

**BEST OF 12" GOLD VOL.16.**
**Tracks:** Somebody's else's guy: *Brown, Jocelyn* / Thinking of you: *Sister Sledge* / Change of heart: *Change* / Tuch me: *Rae, Fonda* / Who do you love: *Intruders* / You're the one for me (medley): *Hardcastle, Paul* / Feel so real: *Arrington, Steve* / Say I'm your number one: *Princess*.
**CD** . . . . . . . . . . . . . . . . . . . . . . **OG 3416**
**MC** . . . . . . . . . . . . . . . . . . . . . . **OG 2416**
Old Gold / Jun '91 / Pickwick.

**BEST OF 12" GOLD VOL.17.**
**Tracks:** He's the greatest dancer: *Sister Sledge* / Contact: *Starr, Edwin* / I will survive: *Gaynor, Gloria* / Ladies night: *Kool & The Gang* / Get down: *Chandler, Gene* / Good times: *Chic* / Shoulda loved ya, I: *Walden, Narada Michael* / Searching: *Change*.
**LP** . . . . . . . . . . . . . . . . . . . . . . **OG 3417**
**MC** . . . . . . . . . . . . . . . . . . . . . . **OG 2417**
Old Gold / Jun '91 / Pickwick.

**BEST OF 12" GOLD VOL.18.**
**Tracks:** Forget me nots: *Rushen, Patrice* / I wish you would: *Brown, Jocelyn* / Love wars: *Womack & Womack* / Dancing in the key of life: *Arrington, Steve* / You are my melody: *Change* / In your car: *Cool Notes* / After the love has gone: *Princess* / Rain forest: *Hardcastle, Paul*.
**CD** . . . . . . . . . . . . . . . . . . . . . . **OG 3418**
**MC** . . . . . . . . . . . . . . . . . . . . . . **OG 2418**
Old Gold / '92 / Pickwick.

**BEST OF 12" GOLD VOL.19.**
**Tracks:** Best disco in town: *Ritchie Family* / Shame: *King, Evelyn 'Champagne'* / Don't leave me this way: *Melvin, Harold & The Bluenotes* / You to me are everything: *Real Thing* / Native New Yorker: *Odyssey* / Take that to the bank: *Shalamar* / Groove line: *Heatwave* / Galaxy of love: *Crown Heights Affair*.
**CD** . . . . . . . . . . . . . . . . . . . . . . **OG 3419**
Old Gold / Apr '92 / Pickwick.

**BEST OF 12" GOLD VOL.2.**
**Tracks:** And the beat goes on: *Whispers* / Check out the groove: *Thurston, Bobby* / Music: *Miles, John* / You're lying: *Linx* / Stomp: *Brothers Johnson* / Star: *Earth, Wind & Fire* / You bet you're love: *Hancock, Herbie* / I don't wanna be a freak: *Dynasty*.
**CD** . . . . . . . . . . . . . . . . . . . . . . **OG 3402**
■ **LP** . . . . . . . . . . . . . . . . . . . . . **OG 1402**
**MC** . . . . . . . . . . . . . . . . . . . . . . **OG 2402**
Old Gold / Oct '88 / Pickwick.

**BEST OF 12" GOLD VOL.20.**
**Tracks:** Get down on it: *Kool & The Gang* / Just an illusion: *Imagination* / Inside out: *Odyssey* / Walking on sunshine: *Rockers Revenge* / Message: *Grandmaster Flash & The Furious Five* / Automatic: *Pointer Sisters* / Try jah love: *Third World* / Night to remember: *Shalamar*.
**CD** . . . . . . . . . . . . . . . . . . . . . . **OG 3420**
**MC** . . . . . . . . . . . . . . . . . . . . . . **OG 2420**
Old Gold / Apr '92 / Pickwick.

**BEST OF 12" GOLD VOL.21.**
**Tracks:** Word up: *Cameo (1)* / Spend the night: *Cool Notes* / Fresh: *Kool & The Gang* / Sleeptalk: *Williams, Alyson* / All and all: *Sims, Joyce* / Never too much: *Vandross, Luther* / Tribute: *Pasadenas* / Midas touch: *Midnight Star*.
**CD** . . . . . . . . . . . . . . . . . . . . . . **CD 3421**
**MC** . . . . . . . . . . . . . . . . . . . . . . **MC 2421**
Pickwick / Sep '92 / Pickwick.

**BEST OF 12" GOLD VOL.3.**
**Tracks:** Let's groove: *Earth, Wind & Fire* / I'm in love: *King, Evelyn 'Champagne'* / Ai no corrida: *Jones, Quincy* / Groove: *Franklin, Rodney* / Funkin' for Jamaica: *Browne, Tom* / Don't stop the music: *Yarbrough & Peoples* / Strut your funky stuff: *Frantique* / Don't push it don't force it: *Haywood, Leon*.
**CD** . . . . . . . . . . . . . . . . . . . . . . **OG 3403**
■ **LP** . . . . . . . . . . . . . . . . . . . . . **OG 1403**
**MC** . . . . . . . . . . . . . . . . . . . . . . **OG 2403**
Old Gold / Oct '88 / Pickwick.

**BEST OF 12" GOLD VOL.4.**
**Tracks:** Jump to it: *Franklin, Aretha* / I can make you feel good: *Shalamar* / Put our heads together: *O'Jays* / I've had enough: *Earth, Wind & Fire* / Love come down: *King, Evelyn 'Champagne'* / Get down Saturday night: *Cheatham, Oliver* / Crazy: *Manhattans* / It's a love thing: *Whispers*.
**CD** . . . . . . . . . . . . . . . . . . . . . . **OG 3404**
■ **LP** . . . . . . . . . . . . . . . . . . . . . **OG 1404**
**MC** . . . . . . . . . . . . . . . . . . . . . . **OG 2404**
Old Gold / Oct '88 / Pickwick.

**BEST OF ACID JAZZ.**
**Tracks:** Chicken lickin': *Funk Inc.* / Zebra walk: *Kynard, Charles* / Reelin' with the feelin': *Kynard, Charles* / Dig on it: *Smith, Johnny "Hammond"* / Got myself a good man: *Pucho* / Super bad: *Muhammad, Idris* / Who's gonna take the weight: *Sparks, Melvin* / Sure 'nuff, sure 'nuff: *Phillips, Sonny* / Cold sweat: *Purdie, Bernard* / Psychadelic Sally: *Jefferson, Eddie* / Soul dance: *Houston Person* / Houston Express: *Houston Person* / Smokin' at Tiffany's: *Funk Inc.*.
**CD** . . . . . . . . . . . . . . . . . . . . . **CDBGP 921**
**MC** . . . . . . . . . . . . . . . . . . . . . **BGPC 921**
BGP / Jun '89 / Pinnacle.

**BEST OF ACID JAZZ VOL.2.**
**Tracks:** Don't let it go to your head: *Brand New Heavies* / Masterplan: *Brown, Diana & Barrie K Sharpe* / Peace & love: *Sewell, Janette* / Watch my garden grow: *Humble Souls* / Jazz Jupiter: *A-Zel* / Hope you're feeling better: *Mother Earth (2)* / E-type: *Corduroy* / Lucky fellow: *Snowboy* / Ain't no use: *Pure Wildness* / Girl overboard: *Snowboy* / Living life your own way (CD only): *Windross, Rose*.
**CD** . . . . . . . . . . . . . . . . . . . . **JAZIDCD 066**
**LP** . . . . . . . . . . . . . . . . . . . . **JAZIDLP 066**
**MC** . . . . . . . . . . . . . . . . . . . . **JAZIDMC 066**
Acid Jazz / May '93 / Vital Distribution.

**BEST OF ACID JAZZ, THE.**
**Tracks:** Not Advised.
**CD** . . . . . . . . . . . . . . . . . . . . . **JAZIDCD 29**
**LP** . . . . . . . . . . . . . . . . . . . . . **JAZIDLP 29**
**MC** . . . . . . . . . . . . . . . . . . . . . **JAZIDMC 29**
Acid Jazz / Jan '91 / Vital Distribution.

**BEST OF ALL PLATINUM.**
**Tracks:** Shame, shame, shame: *Shirley & Company* / Suspicious minds: *Staton, Candi* / Where did our love go: *Elbert, Donnie* / Love on a two way street: *Moments* / It won't rain in my backyard: *Moments* / Girls: *Moments & Whatnauts* / Dolly my love: *Moments* / Jack in the box: *Moments* / Pillow talk: *Sylvia (1)* / 7654321 (blow your whistle): *Rimshots* / Sending out an S.O.S.: *Young, Retta* / We got the funk: *Positive Force*.
■ **CD** . . . . . . . . . . . . . . . . . . . . **BLATCD 3**
■ **LP** . . . . . . . . . . . . . . . . . . . . **BLATLP 3**
■ **MC** . . . . . . . . . . . . . . . . . . . . **BLATMC 3**
Blatant / May '88.

**BEST OF BELL RECORDS.**
**Tracks:** Working in a coalmine: *Dorsey, Lee* / Letter: *Box Tops* / Didn't I (blow your mind this time): *Delfonics* / Captain of your ship: *Reparata & The Delrons* / Angel of the morning: *Rush, Merrilee* / Ride your pony: *Dorsey, Lee* / I'm your puppet: *Purify, James & Bobby* / Shake a tailfeather: *Purify, James & Bobby* / La la la means I love you: *Delfonics* / Ready or not here I come: *Delfonics* / Get out of my life woman: *Dorsey, Lee* / Proud Mary: *Burke, Solomon* / Cry like a baby: *Box Tops* / Keep on: *Channel, Bruce* / Little girl: *Syndicate Of Sound* / I can remember (not so long ago): *Purify, James & Bobby* / Sea of love/Dock of the bay: *Tempo, Nino & April Stevens* / Aquarius/Let the sun shine in: *5th Dimension*.
**CD** . . . . . . . . . . . . . . . . . . . . . **KAZCD 25**
**MC** . . . . . . . . . . . . . . . . . . . . . **KAZMC 25**
Kaz / Jul '92 / BMG.

**BEST OF BLUES AND SOUL.**
**Tracks:** Not Advised.
**CD** . . . . . . . . . . . . . . . . . . . . . **MALCD 341**
Malaco / Apr '87 / C.M. Distribution / Charly / Pinnacle.

**BEST OF BRITISH FUNK.**
**Tracks:** Love games / Starchild / Feels like the right time / Easier said than done / Can't keep holding on / Fall in love / Walking into sunshine / Mama used to say.
■ **LP** . . . . . . . . . . . . . . . . . . . . . **2480 659**

486

■ DELETED

**MC.** . . . . . . . . . . . . . . . . . . . . . . . . . .3194 659
Polydor / May '82 / PolyGram.

## BEST OF BRITISH JAZZ FUNK VOL.2.
**Tracks:** I'm for real: *Gee, Roy & Energee* / Body shake: *Curtis, T.C.* / One to one / You and me just started: *Taylor, Linda* / Magic: *Side On* / Somebody help me out: *Beggar & Co* / Play the game: *Cool Runners* / Love train: *Light Of The World* / Come and get me: *Morrissey-Mullen* / Don't be mistaken: *First Light* / You're lying: *Linx* / North London boy / Tarantula walk: *Carless, Ray* / Time's running out: *Direct Drive.*
■ **LP** . . . . . . . . . . . . . . . . . . . . . BEGA 41
Beggars Banquet / Oct '82.

## BEST OF CAPITOL CLASSICS VOL.1 & 2.
**Tracks:** Key to the world: *Reynolds, L.J.* / On the beat: *B B & Q Band* / Prance on: *Henderson, Eddie* / Love on a summer night: *McCrarys* / It's a pleasure: *Brown, Sheree* / Sound of music: *Dayton* / Doin' alright: *O'Bryan* / Music is my sanctuary: *Bartz, Gary* / Be thankful for what you've got / Hard to get around: *B B & Q Band* / Before you break my heart: *Dunlap, Gene* / Really, really love you: *Parker, Cecil* / There ain't nothin' (like your lovin'): *Laurence, Paul* / It's just the way I feel: *Dunlap, Gene & The Ridgeways.*
**CD** . . . . . . . . . . . . . . . . . . . . . . . CZ 208
Capitol / Jun '89 / EMI.

## BEST OF CHESS R & B VOL.1.
**Tracks:** Not Advised.
■ **CD** . . . . . . . . . . . . . . . . . . . CHD 31317
Chess (MCA) / Sep '90.
**CD** . . . . . . . . . . . . . . . . . . . . . .CHLD 19160
Chess / Nov '91 / BMG.

## BEST OF CHESS R & B VOL.2.
**Tracks:** Not Advised.
■ **CD** . . . . . . . . . . . . . . . . . . . CHD 31318
Chess (MCA) / Sep '90.
**CD** . . . . . . . . . . . . . . . . . . . . . .CHLD 19161
Chess / Nov '91 / BMG.

## BEST OF CHESS RHYTHM & BLUES, THE.
**Tracks:** Please send me someone to love: *Moonglows* / Bad girl: *Miracles* / Walk: *McCracklin, Jimmy* / Smokey places: *Corsairs* / Watusi: *Vibrations* / But I do: *Henry, Clarence 'Frogman'* / Searching for my love: *Moore, Bobby & The Rhythm Aces* / Mama didn't lie: *Bradley, Jan* / I do love you: *Stewart, Billy* / We're gonna make it: *Little Milton* / Summertime: *Stewart, Billy* / Entertainer: *Clarke, Tony* / I had a talk with my man: *Collier, Mitty* / Voice your choice: *Radiants* / Stay in my corner: *Dells* / Rescue me: *Bass, Fontella* / In crowd: *Lewis, Ramsey Trio* / Soulful dress: *Desanto, Sugar Pie* / Selfish one: *Ross, Jackie* / Tell mama: *James, Etta.*
■ **Double LP** . . . . . . . . . . . . . . . .GCH 2-6022
**MC Set** . . . . . . . . . . . . . . . . . . . .GCHK 2-6022
Chess (Charly) / Dec '87 / Charly.
**CD** . . . . . . . . . . . . . . . . . . . . .CDCHESS 1006
Chess (Charly) / '89 / Charly.

## BEST OF CHESS, CHECKER, CADET SOUL.
**Tracks:** Not Advised.
■ **LP** . . . . . . . . . . . . . . . . . . . . CXMP 2003
Checker (USA) / Apr '81.

## BEST OF HIGH ENERGY.
**Tracks:** Not Advised.
■ **LP** . . . . . . . . . . . . . . . . . . . .LELEP 1001
■ **MC** . . . . . . . . . . . . . . . . . . . .CELEP 1001
Electricity / Dec '84.

## BEST OF NEWPORT IN NEW YORK '72 - THE SOUL SESSIONS.
**Tracks:** Medley: Ode to Billy Joe/Please send me someone to love / I apologise / Jelly jelly / Stone junkie / Pusherman / I need you baby / Hold on I'm coming / Price you got to pay to be free / Ain't no mountain high enough / Somewhere.
**CD** . . . . . . . . . . . . . . . . . . . . . .NEMCD 634
Sequel / Feb '93 / Total / BMG.

## BEST OF NORTHERN TRACKS.
**Tracks:** Superlove: *Wigan's Ovation* / Get out: *Hunt, Tommy* / Love feeling: *McKenna, Val* / Sign on the dotted line: *Latter, Gene* / We ain't here looking for trouble: *Thomas, Jimmy* / Heartbreaker: *Honeyend* / Northern soul dancer: *Wigan's Ovation* / Skiing in the snow: *Wigan's Ovation* / Tainted love: *Swann, Ruth* / Honey (I need your love) / Boy, you'd better move on / I love you / Stand in line / Crackin' up.
■ **LP** . . . . . . . . . . . . . . . . . . . . . .SRLM 502
Spark (3) / May '74.

## BEST OF OKEH VOL.1.
**Tracks:** Not Advised.
■ **LP** . . . . . . . . . . . . . . . . . . . . . . . 81224
Epic / '76.

## BEST OF OKEH VOL.2.
**Tracks:** Not Advised.
■ **LP** . . . . . . . . . . . . . . . . . . . . . . . 81532
Epic / '76.

## BEST OF RARE, THE.
**Tracks:** Expansions: *Smith, Lonnie Liston* / Oops here I go again: *Wright, Edna* / Till you take me love: *Mason, Harvey* / Never (gonna let you go): *Charme* / Miss Cheryl: *Banda Black Rio* / Delerium: *McGhee, Fancine* / Stick by me: *Serenade* / Haboglabotribin: *Wright, Bernard* / Holding you loving you: *Blackman, Donald* / Work to do: *Main Ingredient* / Action speaks louder than words: *Chocolate Milk* / Love me like this: *Real To Reel* / Close Encounters of the Third Kind: *Page, Gene* / Mr. Business: *Browne, Tom.*
■ **CD** . . . . . . . . . . . . . . . . . . . . . . . .261083
**MC** . . . . . . . . . . . . . . . . . . . . . . . . . .411083
■ **LP** . . . . . . . . . . . . . . . . . . . . . . . .211083
RCA / Apr '91.

## BEST OF RIC RECORDS VOL. 1.
**Tracks:** Carnival Time: *Johnson, Al* / Cotton candy: *Capello, Lenny* / Check Mr. Popeye: *Bo, Eddie* / I don't talk too much: *Nelson, Martha* / Let's stop and talk it over: *Ridgley, Tommy* / Lena: *Johnson, Al* / 90 pound weakling: *Capello, Lenny* / Losing battle: *Adams, Johnny* / Let's Get It: *Blanchard, Edgar* / She's got what it takes: *Ridley, Tommy* / Feeling right Sat: *Velvetiers.*
■ **LP** . . . . . . . . . . . . . . . . . . . . . . ED 257
Edsel / Feb '88.

## BEST OF TK VOL. 1.
**Tracks:** Do what you wanna do: *T-Connection* / One love: *Celi Bee & The Buzzy Bunch* / That's the way I like it: *K.C. & The Sunshine Band* / Dance across the floor: *Horne, Jimmy 'Bo'* / Get off: *Foxy* / Do ya wanna get funky with me: *Brown, Peter* / Jazz freak: *Reeves, Paulette* / What you won't do for love: *Caldwell, Bobby* / Groove on: *Hale, Willie 'Little Beaver'* / Rock your baby: *McCrae, George.*
■ **Double LP** . . . . . . . . . . . . . . . . ROUS 1041
■ **CD** . . . . . . . . . . . . . . . . . . CDP 797 773 2
■ **MC Set** . . . . . . . . . . . . . . . . TCROUS 1041
Roulette (EMI) / Aug '91.

## BEST SOUL, THE.
**Tracks:** Not Advised.
**CD** . . . . . . . . . . . . . . . . . . . . . . . . CD 905
Sound / Jun '89 / Direct Distribution.

## BETTER DANCE 2.
**Tracks:** Humpin' around: *Brown, Bobby (1)* / Everything's gonna be alright: *Father* / Let's get to it: *Pagano, John* / Rump shaker: *Wreckx N Effect* / Big idea: *Brecker Brothers* / Real love: *Blige, Mary J.* / Relax with pep: *Eric B & Rakim* / Sprung on me: *Wilson, Charlie* / You can't see what I can see: *Heavy D & The Boyz* / It's alright: *Jodeci* / On a corner called jazz: *Mr. Fingers.*
**LP** . . . . . . . . . . . . . . . . . . . . . . . MCA 30175
■ **CD** . . . . . . . . . . . . . . . . . . . . . MCD 30175
■ **MC** . . . . . . . . . . . . . . . . . . . . . MCC 30175
MCA / Jan '93.

## BIG CITY SOUL SOUND.
**Tracks:** Not Advised.
■ **LP** . . . . . . . . . . . . . . . . . . . . . . KENT 061
Kent / Dec '86.

## BIG CITY SOUL VOL.1.
**Tracks:** Looking for you: *Mimms, Garnet* / Love is not a game: *Soul, Sam E* / My Dear heart: *Robinson, Shawn* / Mend my broken heart: *St. John, Rose & The Wonderettes* / Hold on: *O'Jays* / Ready willing and able: *Holiday, Jimmy & Clydie King* / Lot of love: *Banks, Homer* / Hooked by love: *Banks, Homer* / I lost a true love: *Wagner, Danny & The Kindred Soul* / Then came heart break: *Jive Five* / Strange neighbourhood: *McDaniels, Gene* / Stick close: *Brown, Estelle* / Be careful girl: *Turner, Betty* / I'll never forget you: *O'Jays* / It's what's underneath that counts: *Jackson, June* / Working on your case: *O'Jays* / My heart is in danger: *Ray, Alder* / Honest to goodness: *Diplomats (1)* / Are you trying to get rid of me baby: *Crystals (1)* / Breakaway part 1: *Karman, Steve* / I only get this feeling: *Irwin, Dee* / Living above your head: *Jay & The Americans* / Don't: *Josie, Marva* / It's a sad thing: *Pollard, Ray* / Walk with a winner: *McDaniels, Gene* / Drifter: *Pollard, Ray* / It'll never be over for me: *Yuro, Timi.*
**CD** . . . . . . . . . . . . . . . . . . . . . . .GSCD 042
Goldmine / Jul '94 / Vital Distribution.

## BIG CITY SOUL VOL.2.
**Tracks:** I'm stepping out of the picture: *Maestro, Johnny & The Crests* / (There goes) the forgotten man: *Radcliffe, Jimmy* / Givin' up: *Lewis, Junior Trio* / Who's gonna mention my name: *Sattin, Lonnie* / Is he all right: *St. Clair, Syliva* / Love of my man: *Kilgore, Theola* / Losing my touch: *Brown, Maxine* / What'cha gonna say tomorrow: *Jackson, Chuck* / I just don't know what to do with myself: *Hunt, Tommy* / Haunted house: *Wilson, Jackie* / Lonely people do foolish things: *Clay, James* / Try to get you out of my heart: *Toys (1)* / Come the night: *Knight, Marie* / Nobody cares (about me): *Washington, Jeanette* / Remember me: *Shirelles* / How do you feel now: *Big Maybelle.*
■ **LP** . . . . . . . . . . . . . . . . . . . . . . KENT 087
Kent / Nov '88.

## BIG CITY SOUL VOLUME 2.
**Tracks:** Stop and think it over: *Mimms, Garnet* / I love you baby: *Ambers* / Pretty little face: *Four Hi's* / You can split: *Youngblood Smith* / What would I do: *Superiors* / Living a lie: *High Keys* / Stop and take a look at yourself: *Shalimars* / Take a step in my direction: *Little Eva* / Real jive guy: *Ahres, Dajh* / Walkin' the duck: *Triumphs* / I can't make it without you baby: *Banks, Bessie* / Just a fool: *Gainey, Jerry* / I watched you slowly slip away: *Guyton, Howard* / Mighty good way: *Banks, Robert* / Right direction: *Ward, Clara* / My heart belongs to you: *Pickett, Wilson* / I don't want to lose your love: *Woods, Billy* / Love I give: *Murray, Louise* / (You'd better) Straighten up and fly right: *Bryant, Terry* / Born to please: *Prince Harold* / Baby I love you: *Tate, Howard* / I'm a practical guy: *Gardner, Don* / (Git your) Backfield in motion: *Poindexter Brothers* / I don't need no doctor: *Ashford, Nick* / Can't deny the hurt: *Rakes, Pal & The Prophets* / Picture me gone: *Brooks, Diane* / Let's take a chance: *High Keys* / Let me be your boy: *Pickett, Wilson.*
**CD** . . . . . . . . . . . . . . . . . . . . . . .GSCD 044
Goldmine / Sep '94 / Vital Distribution.

## BIG MOTOWN HITS AND HARD-TO-FIND CLASSICS VOL 1.
**Tracks:** Helpless: *Weston, Kim* / You've made me so very happy: *Holloway, Brenda* / Love's gone bad: *Clark, Chris* / I got a feeling: *Randolph, Barbara* / Baby I'm for real: *Originals* / Does your mama know about me: *Taylor, Bobby & The Vancouvers* / Bells: *Originals* / What becomes of the broken hearted: *Ruffin, Jimmy* / I've passed this way before: *Ruffin, Jimmy* / Walk away from love: *Ruffin, David* / My world ended (the moment you left me): *Ruffin, David* / Get ready: *Rare Earth* / I'm losing you: *Rare Earth* / War: *Starr, Edwin* / Twenty five miles: *Starr, Edwin* / It's a shame: *Detroit Spinners* / I'll always love you: *Detroit Spinners* / Darling baby: *Elgins* / Heaven must have sent you: *Elgins* / Just look what you've done: *Holloway, Brenda.*
■ **MC** . . . . . . . . . . . . . . . . . . . . . WK 72431
■ **CD** . . . . . . . . . . . . . . . . . . . . . WD 72513
■ **LP** . . . . . . . . . . . . . . . . . . . . . WL 72431
Motown / '87.

## BIG MOTOWN HITS AND HARD-TO-FIND CLASSICS VOL 2.
**Tracks:** When I'm gone: *Holloway, Brenda* / Jamie: *Holland, Eddie* / Indiana wants me: *Taylor, R. Dean* / He was really saying something: *Velvelettes* / Born to wander: *Rare Earth* / With you I'm born again: *Preston, Billy & Syreeta* / Every little bit hurts: *Holloway, Brenda* / Needle in a haystack: *Velvelettes* / Lonely, lonely girl am I: *Velvelettes* / I can't believe you love me: *Terrell, Tammi* / Money (that's what I want): *Strong, Barrett* / Take me in your arms: *Isley Brothers* / I guess I'll always love you: *Isley Brothers* / Here comes the judge: *Long, Shorty* / Function at the junction: *Long, Shorty* / Smiling faces sometimes: *Undisputed Truth* / I just want to celebrate: *Rare Earth* / River deep, mountain high: *Supremes & Four Tops* / I've never been to me: *Charlene* / What the world needs now is love: *Clay, Tom.*
■ **LP** . . . . . . . . . . . . . . . . . . . . . WL 72432
■ **MC** . . . . . . . . . . . . . . . . . . . . . WK 72432
Motown / Jun '86.
■ **CD** . . . . . . . . . . . . . . . . . . . . . WD 72514
Motown / Oct '87.

## BIG MOTOWN HITS AND HARD-TO-FIND CLASSICS VOL 3.
**Tracks:** Take me in your arms (rock me a little while) / Looking for the right guy: *Weston, Kim* / Love me all the way: *Weston, Kim* / Bird in the hand (is worth two in the bush): *Velvelettes* / Come and see me: *Terrell, Tammi* / Operator: *Holloway, Brenda* / I'll be available: *Holloway, Brenda* / I'll always love you: *Holloway, Brenda* / Devil with the blue dress: *Long, Shorty* / He's my man: *Supremes* / Agent double o soul: *Starr, Edwin* / Stop her on sight (S.O.S.) / Leaving here: *Holland, Eddie* / Just ain't enough love: *Holland, Eddie* / Candy to me: *Holland, Eddie* /

■ DELETED

This old heart of mine: *Isley Brothers* / Behind a painted smile: *Isley Brothers* / Truly yours: *Detroit Spinners* / Just a little misunderstanding: *Contours* / Do you love me: *Contours* / First I look at the purse: *Contours* / Why do you want to let me go: *Johnson, Marv* / Stay in my lonely arms: *Elgins* / Put yourself in my place: *Elgins* / I wouldn't change the man he is: *Blinky*.
■ **CD** . . . . . . . . . . **WD 72548**
Motown / Feb '88.

## BIG SOUL SOUND.
**Tracks:** Not Advised.
■ **LP** . . . . . . . . . . **NE 1216**
■ **MC** . . . . . . . . . . **CE 2216**
K-Tel / Jun '83.

## BIG WHEELS OF MOTOWN.
**Tracks:** I heard it through the grapevine: *Gaye, Marvin* / Too busy thinking about my baby: *Gaye, Marvin* / Tears of a clown: *Robinson, Smokey & The Miracles* / Tracks of my tears: *Robinson, Smokey & The Miracles* / My guy: *Wells, Mary* / I can't help myself: *Four Tops* / Reach out I'll be there: *Four Tops* / Get ready: *Temptations* / I'm still waiting: *Ross, Diana* / I want you back: *Jackson Five* / Jimmy Mack: *Reeves, Martha* / Dancing in the street: *Reeves, Martha* / Yester-me, yester-you, yesterday: *Wonder, Stevie* / I'm gonna make you love me: *Ross, Diana & The Supremes & The Temptations* / Stoned love: *Supremes* / For once in my life: *Wonder, Stevie* / Help me make it through the night: *Knight, Gladys* / What becomes of the broken hearted: *Ruffin, Jimmy* / This old heart of mine: *Isley Brothers* / Where did our love go: *Ross, Diana & The Supremes*.
■ **LP** . . . . . . . . . . **MTV 12**
■ **MC** . . . . . . . . . . **CMTV 12**
Motown / Oct '81.
■ **LP** . . . . . . . . . . **ZL 72006**
■ **MC** . . . . . . . . . . **ZK 72006**
Motown / '86.

## BLACK ATLANTIC 45'S 1965-67.
**Tracks:** Record: *King, Ben E.* / I'm gonna run away from you: *Lynn, Tammi* / Outside world: *Drifters* / Just say goodbye: *Phillips, Esther* / Scratchy: *Wammack, Travis* / Philly dog: *Mar-Keys* / Smokey Joe's la-la: *Rene, Googie* / Love makes the world go round: *Jackson, Deon* / Can't you see you're losing me: *Wells, Mary* / There's no place to hide: *King, Ben E.* / Candy: *Astors* / Dear lover: *Wells, Mary*.
■ **LP** . . . . . . . . . . **ATLM 123**
Atlantic / '79.

## BLACK MAGIC.
**Tracks:** Maybellene: *Berry, Chuck* / Keep on knockin': *Little Richard* / Rockin' Robin: *Day, Bobby* / Lover's question: *McPhatter, Clyde* / Dedicated to the one I love: *Shirelles* / Girl I love: *Benton, Brook* / Tears on my pillow: *Imperials* / You're just too marvellous: *Holiday, Billie* / Please love me forever: *Edwards, Tommy* / All in my mind: *Brown, Maxine* / 16 candles: *Crests* / Unforgettable: *Washington, Dinah* / Let the good times roll: *Shirley & Lee* / Misty: *Vaughan, Sarah* / C.C. rider: *Charles, Ray* / Dance with me, Henry: *James, Etta* / Chains of love: *Phillips, Esther* / My way: *Simone, Nina* / Alley oop: *Hollywood Argyles* / Earth angel: *Penguins* / Baby it's you: *La Belle, Patti* / Duke of Earl: *Chandler, Gene*.
**CD** . . . . . . . . . . **C5LCD 586**
**MC** . . . . . . . . . . **C5LK 586**
See For Miles / Apr '92 / Pinnacle.

## BLACK MAGIC.
**Tracks:** Not Advised.
■ **Double LP** . . . . . . . . . . **SMR 619**
■ **MC Set** . . . . . . . . . . **SMC 619**
Stylus / Sep '86.

## BLACK MAGIC.
**Tracks:** Not Advised.
■ **LP** . . . . . . . . . . **PLD 8000**
Pickwick / Oct '79.

## BLACK MUSIC IS OUR BUSINESS (A Galaxy Of Soul).
**Tracks:** Drifting: *Huey, Claude 'Baby'* / Why would you blow it: *Huey, Claude 'Baby'* / Zig zag lightning: *Taylor, Little Johnny* / Big blue diamonds: *Taylor, Little Johnny* / I finally got wise: *Keen, Billy* / I got to tell somebody: *Everett, Betty* / Man don't cry: *Witherspoon, Jimmy* / Love me right: *Witherspoon, Jimmy* / Why do you have to lie: *Right Kind* / She's looking good: *Collins, Rodger* / Lover set me free: *Grier, Roosevelt* / Thompin': *Merced Blue Notes* / When you find a fool bump his head: *Coday, Bill* / How can I forget you: *Williams, Lenny* / My babe: *McCoy, Freddie* / Doing the best I can (with what I got): *Williams, Larry & The ATS Express*.
■ **LP** . . . . . . . . . . **KENT 085**
Kent / Oct '88.

## BLACK SATIN.
**Tracks:** When a man loves a woman: *Sledge, Percy* / Hold on I'm coming: *Sam & Dave* / Heatwave: *Reeves, Martha* / Knock on wood: *Floyd, Eddie* / Up on the roof: *Drifters* / Rescue me: *Bass, Fontella* / Do the funky chicken: *Thomas, Rufus* / Hey there lonely girl: *Holman, Eddie* / Everlasting love: *Knight, Robert* / Jimmy Mack: *Reeves, Martha* / If loving you is wrong I don't want to be right: *Sledge, Percy* / Hey girl don't bother me: *Tams* / B.A.B.Y.: *Thomas, Carla* / Patches: *Carter, Clarence* / I heard it through the grapevine: *Reeves, Martha* / (Sittin' on) the dock of the bay: *Sledge, Percy* / Harlem shuffle: *Bob & Earl* / Lover's concerto: *Toys (1)* / Best thing that ever happened to me: *Knight, Gladys & The Pips* / Under the boardwalk: *Drifters* / Softly whispering I love you: *New Congregation* / Da doo ron ron: *Crystals (1)* / Midnight train to Georgia: *Knight, Gladys & The Pips* / Try a little tenderness: *Sledge, Percy* / My guy: *Wells, Mary* / You little trust maker: *Tymes* / Soul man: *Sam & Dave* / Quicksand: *Reeves, Martha* / Then he kissed me: *Crystals (1)* / Tighten up: *Bell, Archie & The Drells*.
■ **MC Set** . . . . . . . . . . **CRT 022**
Cambra / '83.

## BLACK SOUL.
**Tracks:** Dancing in the street: *Reeves, Martha* / Hold on: *Sam & Dave* / Harlem shuffle: *Bob & Earl* / Every beat of my heart: *Knight, Gladys* / He's so fine: *Chiffons* / Walking the dog: *Thomas, Rufus* / My guy: *Wells, Mary* / Save the last dance for me: *Drifters* / Love on a mountain top: *Knight, Robert* / Da doo ron ron: *Crystals (1)* / Something old, something new: *Fantastics* / Knock on wood: *Floyd, Eddie* / Do the funky chicken: *Thomas, Rufus* / B.A.B.Y.: *Thomas, Carla* / Heatwave: *Reeves, Martha* / Will you love me tomorrow: *Shirelles* / Rescue me: *Bass, Fontella* / Soul man: *Sam & Dave* / Sweet talking guy: *Chiffons* / Saturday night at the movies: *Drifters*.
■ **LP** . . . . . . . . . . **PAST 2**
Creole / Nov '83.

## BLACK SOUL EXPLOSION.
**Tracks:** Everyday fun / Compared to what / Learn how to love / Skeletons in my closet / Why can't there be love / Hey Blackman / There's gotta be a way / Oh Lord, oh I feel good / Whip your lovin' on me / Hurt a little everyday.
■ **LP** . . . . . . . . . . **SE 8009**
Ember / Jan '72.

## BLAME IT ON THE BOOGIE.
**Tracks:** Blame it on the boogie: *Jacksons* / Boogie nights: *Heatwave* / Dance, dance, dance (yowsah, yowsah, yowsah): *Chic* / He's the greatest dancer: *Sister Sledge* / Get down on it: *Kool & The Gang* / Oops up side your head: *Gap Band* / Play that funky music (white boy): *Wild Cherry* / Let's groove: *Earth, Wind & Fire* / Use it up and wear it out: *Odyssey* / Never can say goodbye: *Gaynor, Gloria* / That's the way (I like it): *K.C. & The Sunshine Band* / Lady Marmalade: *Labelle* / Night to remember: *Shalamar* / Hot stuff: *Summer, Donna* / Rock the boat: *Hues Corporation* / Funky town: *Lipps Inc.* / Boogie oogie oogie: *Taste Of Honey* / More, more, more: *Andrea True Connection* / Disco inferno: *Trammps* / I haven't stopped dancing yet: *Gonzales*.
**CD** . . . . . . . . . . **5155172**
■ **LP** . . . . . . . . . . **5155171**
**MC** . . . . . . . . . . **5155174**
Polygram T.V. / Jul '92 / PolyGram.

## BLUES & SOUL ESSENTIALS.
**Tracks:** Not Advised.
**CD** . . . . . . . . . . **STYLECD 1**
**LP** . . . . . . . . . . **STYLELP 1**
**MC** . . . . . . . . . . **STYLEMC 1**
Blues & Soul / Nov '94 / Total / BMG.

## BLUES AND SOUL.
**Tracks:** Not Advised.
■ **LP** . . . . . . . . . . **MLS 40007**
Minit / Oct '68.

## BLUES AND SOUL POWER.
**Tracks:** Not Advised.
■ **LP** . . . . . . . . . . **KENT 068**
Kent / Jun '87.

## BLUES BROTHER, SOUL SISTER.
**Tracks:** Not Advised.
**CD** . . . . . . . . . . **DINCD 56**
**MC** . . . . . . . . . . **DINMC 56**
■ **LP** . . . . . . . . . . **DINTV 56**
Dino / Jan '93.

## BLUES BROTHER, SOUL SISTER VOL.3.
**Tracks:** Not Advised.
**CD** . . . . . . . . . . **DINCD 85**
**LP** . . . . . . . . . . **DINTV 85**
**MC** . . . . . . . . . . **DINMC 85**
Dino / Apr '94 / Pinnacle.

## BOOGIE NIGHTS 1973 - 1980.
**Tracks:** Best of my love: *Emotions (2)* / More, more, more: *True, Andrea Connection* / You can do magic: *Limmie & Family Cooking* / I love the nightlife: *Bridges, Alicia* / Gonna get along without you now: *Wills, Viola* / I will survive: *Gaynor, Gloria* / Love train: *O'Jays* / Don't leave me this way: *Melvin Harold* / Contact: *Starr, Edwin* / Shame: *King, Evelyn 'Champagne'* / Boogie nights: *Heatwave* / Blame it on the boogie: *Jacksons* / Celebration: *Kool & The Gang* / It's a disco night (rock don't stop): *Isley Brothers* / Best disco in town: *Ritchie Family* / Ain't gonna bump no more: *Tex, Joe* / Disco lady: *Taylor, Johnny* / Fantasy: *Earth, Wind & Fire* / YMCA: *Village People* / This is it: *Moore, Melba* / What it is: *Mimms Garnet* / You can do it: *Hudson, Al & The Partners* / Turn the music up: *Players Association* / Use it up and wear it out: *Odyssey*.
**CD Set** . . . . . . . . . . **OG 3210**
**MC Set** . . . . . . . . . . **OG 2210**
Old Gold / Oct '90 / Pickwick.

## BOY MEETS GIRL.
**Tracks:** I'm trying / Never, never let you go / My life, thank you / Don't make me a storyteller / Leave the girl alone / Just keep on loving me / Soul-a-lujah / It's our time / That's the way love is / All I have to do is dream / It's too late / It's unbelievable / Ain't that good / I need you woman.
■ **LP** . . . . . . . . . . **SXATS 1027**
Stax / Feb '70.

## BRAINSTORMERS.
**Tracks:** Just one more chance: *Bradley, Patrick* / Gee baby I love you: *Malibus* / Stop, leave my heart alone: *2 People* / Getting used to the blues: *Bland, Bobby* / I had a good time: *Taylor, Little Eddie* / Bye bye baby: *Everett, Betty* / Lend a hand: *Hutton, Bobby* / Love runs out: *Hutch, Willie* / Wherever you were: *Harper, Bud* / That's when I need you: *Butler, Freddie* / It's a heartache: *Little Charles & The Sidewinders* / Ain't that good enough: *Green, Garland* / You're too much a part of me: *Austin, Patti* / My heart's not in it anymore: *Steinways* / Kid: *Brasseur, Andre*.
■ **LP** . . . . . . . . . . **KENT 042**
Kent / Aug '85.

## BRIT FUNK 1.
**Tracks:** (Somebody) Help me out: *Beggar & Co* / Feel the real (again): *Beggar & Co* / Parisienne Girl: *Incognito* / Time: *Light Of The World* / I hate hate: *Williams, Danny* / Amigo: *Black Slate* / London Town '85: *Light Of The World* / Destination: *Warriors* / Head over heels: *Galaxy (1)* / Tarantula walk: *Careless, Ray*.
**CD** . . . . . . . . . . **CDCHEN 32**
■ **LP** . . . . . . . . . . **CHEN 32**
■ **MC** . . . . . . . . . . **TCCHEN 32**
Ensign / Oct '92.

## BRITISH MOTOWN CHARTBUSTERS VOL.1.
**Tracks:** Blowin' in the wind: *Wonder, Stevie* / You keep me hangin' on: *Ross, Diana & The Supremes* / Standing in the shadows of love: *Four Tops* / It takes two: *Gaye, Marvin & Kim Weston* / When you're young and in love: *Marvelettes* / (I know) I'm losing you: *Temptations* / What becomes of the broken hearted: *Ruffin, Jimmy* / Happening: *Ross, Diana & The Supremes* / 7 rooms of gloom: *Four Tops* / How sweet it is (to be loved by you): *Walker, Junior & The All Stars* / I'm ready for love: *Reeves, Martha* / Love is here and now you're gone: *Ross, Diana & The Supremes* / Gonna give her all the love I've got: *Ruffin, Jimmy* / I was made to love her: *Wonder, Stevie* / Take me in your arms and love me: *Knight, Gladys & The Pips* / Jimmy Mack: *Reeves, Martha*.
■ **LP** . . . . . . . . . . **WL 72671**
■ **CD** . . . . . . . . . . **WD 72671**
■ **MC** . . . . . . . . . . **WK 72671**
Motown / Nov '89.
**CD** . . . . . . . . . . **530066-2**
**MC** . . . . . . . . . . **530066-4**
Motown / Jan '93 / PolyGram.

## BRITISH MOTOWN CHARTBUSTERS VOL.2.
**Tracks:** Ain't nothing like the real thing: *Gaye, Marvin & Tammi Terrell* / Reflections: *Ross, Diana & The Supremes* / If you can want: *Robinson, Smokey & The Miracles* / You keep running away: *Four Tops* / I could never love another (after loving you): *Temptations* / I heard it through the grapevine: *Knight, Gladys & The Pips* / I'm wondering: *Wonder, Stevie* / I've passed this way before: *Ruffin, Jimmy* / Some things you never get used to: *Ross, Diana & The Supremes* / Gotta see Jane: *Taylor, R. Dean* / Shoo-be-doo-be-doo-da-day: *Wonder, Stevie* / You're my everything: *Temptations* / Honey chile: *Reeves,*

488 ■ DELETED

lartha & The Vandellas / If I were a carpenter: *Four ops* / I second that emotion: *Robinson, Smokey & he Miracles* / If I could build my whole world around ou: *Gaye, Marvin & Tammi Terrell*.
■ CD. . . . . . . . . . WD 72672
■ LP . . . . . . . . . . WL 72672
■ MC. . . . . . . . . . WK 72672
lotown / Nov '89.
D. . . . . . . . . . .530067-2
IC. . . . . . . . . . .530067-4
lotown / Jan '93 / PolyGram.

## ROWNSWOOD WORKSHOP.
racks: Not Advised.
D. . . . . . . . . . .518960-2
P . . . . . . . . . . .518960-1
IC. . . . . . . . . . .518960-4
alkin' Loud / Mar '94 / PolyGram.

# C

## CAPITOL CLASSICS VOL. 1.
**racks:** Key to the world: *Reynolds, L.J.* / Boogie ogie oogie: *Taste Of Honey* / On the beat: *B B & Q and* / Prance on: *Henderson, Eddie* / Love on a ımmer night: *McCrarys* / It's a pleasure: *Brown, heree* / Sound of music: *Dayton* / Doin' alright: *'Bryan* / Just can't give you up: *Mystic Merlin* / lusic is my sanctuary: *Bartz, Gary*.
■ LP . . . . . . . . . . EMS 1316
■ MC. . . . . . . . . . TCEMS 1316
MI / Feb '89.

## CAPITOL CLASSICS VOL. 2.
**racks:** Be thankful for what you've got: *DeVaughan, Villiam* / Hard to get around: *B B & Q Band* / Before ou break my heart: *Dunlap, Gene* / Call on me: *laze* / Work that sucker to death: *Xavier* / Really, eally love you: *Parker, Cecil* / There ain't nothin' ike your lovin'): *Laurence, Paul* / Promise me: *ayton* / It's just the way I feel: *Dunlap, Gene & The idgeways* / Annie Mae: *Cole, Natalie*.
LP . . . . . . . . . . EMS 1338
MC. . . . . . . . . . TCEMS 1338
apitol / Jun '89.

## CAPITOL CLASSICS VOL. 3.
**racks:** I ain't with it (heart to heart mix): *Laurence, aul* / Magic spell (hocus pocus mix): *Lynch* / I romise: *Bleu, Mikki* / Gitchi U (ext. dance mix): *'Looke* / Have you had your love today: *O'Jays* / ising to the top: *Pieces Of A Dream* / Wanna make ve: *Sun* / Tender moments: *Blu, Peggi* / Feeling ıcky lately: *High Fashion* / I am down: *Bryson, eabo* / Call on me (CD only.): *Maze* / Annie Mae CD only.): *Cole, Natalie* / Just can't give you up (CD nly.): *Mystic Merlin* / Boogie oogie oogie (CD only.): *aste Of Honey*.
■ LP . . . . . . . . . . EMS 1344
■ MC. . . . . . . . . . TCEMS 1344
■ CD. . . . . . . . . . CZ 227
apitol / Feb '90.

## CAPITOL COLLECTABLES.
**racks:** I'm in love: *Thomas, Lillo* / Why should I cry: *endryx, Nona* / All because of you: *Williams, Beau* / you want me: *Hyman, Phyllis* / Take it to the limit: *ay,Goodman & Brown* / Betcha don't know: *Najee* / you were mine: *Lynn, Cheryl* / Working up a sweat: *ull Circle* / Tender moments: *Blu, Peggi* / Little bit ore: *Jackson, Freddie & Melba Moore* / Don't take iy love away: *O'Jays*.
■ CD. . . . . . . . . . CDEST 2038
apitol / Aug '87.
LP . . . . . . . . . . EST 2038
MC. . . . . . . . . .TCEST 2038
apitol / Jul '87.

## CAPITOL COLLECTABLES II.
**racks:** Hold on to what you've got: *King, Evelyn Champagne'* / Da'butt: *E.U.* / Wishing you were ere: *Gyrlz* / You're my one and only love: *Connors, orman* / Personality: *Najee* / Irresistible: *Wheeler, udrey* / Rising to the top: *Pieces Of A Dream* / Off e hook: *RJ's Latest Arrival* / Wasn't I good to ya: *akrash* / Keeps me runnin' back: *Moore, Melba* / irt: *King, Evelyn 'Champagne'*.
LP . . . . . . . . . . CMP 1001
MC. . . . . . . . . . TCCMP 1001

■ CD. . . . . . . . . . CDCMP 1001
Capitol / Aug '88.

## CAPITOL RARE (Funky Notes From The West Coast).
**Tracks:** Music is my sanctuary: *Bartz, Gary* / Sky islands: *Caldera* / Annie Mae: *Cole, Natalie* / Sunshine: *Wilson, Nancy* / As: *Harris, Gene* / Genie: *Lyle, Bobby* / I love you: *Taste Of Honey* / While I'm alone: *Maze* / Peace of mind: *Allen, Rance Group* / Inside you: *Henderson, Eddie* / Every generation: *Laws, Ronnie* / She's my summer breeze: *Reflections (1)* / Losalamitos (Latinfunklovesong): *Harris, Gene* / About love: *Sidran, Ben* / Dindi: *Lawson, Janet* / Woman of the ghetto: *Shaw, Marlena* / Cheshire cat: *Foster, Ronnie*.
CD. . . . . . . . . . CDP 8298652
LP Set. . . . . . . . . . B1 29865
Blue Note / Jun '94 / EMI.

## CAPITOL SOUL CASINO.
**Tracks:** Heartbeat: *Jones, Gloria* / I walked away: *Paris, Bobby* / They'll be coming: *Ambrose, Sammy* / Ten miles high: *David & The Giants* / Lonely man: *Outsiders (1)* / By yourself: *Martin, Jay D* / Love slipped through my fingers: *Williams, Sam* / End of our love: *Wilson, Nancy* / Nobody but me: *Human Beinz* / Right on: *Delory, Al* / So is the sun: *World Column* / Police Story: *Williams, Pat Orchestra* / Baby mine: *Houston, Thelma* / Coloured Man, Theme from: *Vann, Teddy*.
■ LP . . . . . . . . . . CAPS 1025
Capitol / Dec '78.

## CARNIVAL OF SOUL VOLUME 1: WISHES.
**Tracks:** Wishes: *Metrics* / She's so fine: *Topics* / All I need is your love: *Manhattans* / Me myself and I: *Jenkins, Norma* / I need a guy: *Lovettes* / Forget him: *Brown, Barbara* / Nobody loves me (like my baby): *Caldwell, Harry* / I love you more: *Williams, Lee & The Cymbals* / I'll keep holding on: *Ruffin, Kenneth* / Nothing will ever change (this love of mine): *Jules, Jimmy* / My love is yours tonight: *Turner Brothers* / It's everything about you (that I love): *Williams, Lee & The Cymbals* / I wanna be (your everything): *Pretenders (2)* / Love has passed me by: *Terrell, Phil* / I say yeah: *Pets* / I'll catch you on the rebound: *Leon & The Metronomes* / Can I come in: *Terrell, Phil* / Come home to Daddy: *Goggins, Curby* / I can tell: *Little Royal* / I'm gonna be missing you: *Bailey, Rene* / My baby's gone: *Tren-Teens* / I call it love: *Pretenders (2)* / Til you come back to me: *Manhattans* / Go right on: *Three Reasons*.
CD. . . . . . . . . . CDKEND 108
Kent / Oct '94 / Pinnacle.

## CARNIVAL TIME: THE BEST OF RIC RECORDS (Vol. 1).
**Tracks:** Not Advised.
CD. . . . . . . . . . CD 2075
■ LP . . . . . . . . . . ROUNDER 2075
MC. . . . . . . . . .ROUNDER 2075C
Rounder / '88 / Roots Records / C.M. Distribution / Topic Records / A.D.A. Distribution / Direct Distribution.

## CASEY KASEM'S ROCK 'N' ROLL GOLDMINE (Soul Years).
**Tracks:** I feel good: *Brown, James* / Try a little tenderness: *Redding, Otis* / Respect: *Franklin, Aretha* / Stand by me: *King, Ben E.* / Hold on I'm coming: *Sam & Dave* / My girl: *Temptations* / Fingertips: *Wonder, Stevie* / River deep, mountain high: *Turner, Ike & Tina* / When a man loves a woman: *Sledge, Percy*.
VHS . . . . . . . . . . VIDJAM 22
Charly Video / Mar '90 / Charly / THE.

## CASINO CLASSICS CHAPTER 1.
**Tracks:** Touch of velvet, a sting of brass: *Grainer, Ron Orchestra* / Lost summer love: *Silver, Lorraine* / Joe 90: *Grainer, Ron Orchestra* / Panic: *Reparata & The Delrons* / Shake a tailfeather: *Purify, James* / I'll do anything: *Gamble, Lenny* / Six by six: *All Night Band* / Joker: *All Night Band* / Little darlin': *Flirtations* / I'm gonna share it with you: *Foster, Diana* / I go to pieces: *Granger, Gerri* / Long after tonight is all over: *Radcliffe, Jimmy* / Time will pass you by: *Tobi Legend* / I'm on my way: *Parrish, Dean*.
■ LP . . . . . . . . . . CCLP 1001
Casino Classics / Feb '83.

## CASINO CLASSICS CHAPTER 2.
**Tracks:** Tainted love: *Jones, Gloria* / Ain't nothing but a house party: *Show Stoppers* / Sliced tomatoes: *Just Brothers* / You got me where you want me: *Hunt, Tommy* / I can't seem to hold you: *Foster, Diana* / I've got a feeling: *Foster, Diana* / Sign on the dotted line: *Latter, Gene* / Better late than never: *Ducane, Diane* / It really hurts me girl: *Carstairs* / Love factory: *Laws, Eloise* / When loves grows cold: *Grainer, Ron Orchestra* / Gonna love you longer stronger baby / Loving on the losing side: *Hunt, Tommy* / Why'd you put it to me baby: *Short People*.
■ LP . . . . . . . . . . CCLP 1002
Casino Classics / Dec '79.

## CELEBRATION OF SOUL.
**Tracks:** Not Advised.
CD. . . . . . . . . . VSD 5486
Colosseum / Oct '94 / Pinnacle.

## CELEBRATION OF SOUL VOL. 1, A.
**Tracks:** Not Advised.
CD. . . . . . . . . . VSD 5488
Varese Sarabande Records / Oct '94 / Silva Screen / Pinnacle.

## CHAMPAIGN 4.
**Tracks:** Not Advised.
CD. . . . . . . . . . MALCD 7461
Malaco / Mar '93 / C.M. Distribution / Charly / Pinnacle.

## CHARLY BLACK MUSIC SAMPLER.
**Tracks:** Not Advised.
■ LP . . . . . . . . . . CRM 2018
Charly / Jul '81.

## CHARLY DANCE PARTY.
**Tracks:** Let's go, let's go, let's go / Shake your moneymaker / I'm gonna love you / Stormy weather / Rebound / Surely I love you / Feeling good / Look out Mabel / Convention / She's the most / Sapphire / I wanna know / Wildcat tamer / Black diamond / Breaking up the house.
■ LP . . . . . . . . . . CR 30261
Charly / Oct '86.

## CHARLY R & B PARTY.
**Tracks:** Barefootin': *Parker, Robert* / Ride your pony: *Harris, Betty* / Picking wild mountain berries: *Scott, Peggy & Jo Jo Benson* / Neighbour neighbour: *Hughes, Jimmy* / I stand accused: *Butler, Jerry* / Shame, shame, shame: *Reed, Jimmy* / If you gotta make a fool of somebody: *Ray, James (2)* / Let's stick together: *Harrison, Wilbert* / It's alright: *Impressions* / Hey girl don't bother me: *Tams* / Tell it like it is: *Neville, Aaron* / Get out of my life woman: *Dorsey, Lee* / Boom boom: *Hooker, John Lee* / Dust my broom: *James, Elmore* / Nothing can stop me: *Chandler, Gene* / It's in his kiss: *Everett, Betty*.
■ LP . . . . . . . . . . CRB 1088
MC. . . . . . . . . . TCCRB 1088
Charly R&B / Jun '85 / Charly.

## CHESS EP COLLECTION, THE.
**Tracks:** Long tall shorty: *Tucker, Tommy* / Susie Q: *Hawkins, Dale* / Ain't got no home: *Henry, Clarence 'Frogman'* / Rescue: *Fontella Bass* / You all green: *Diddley, Bo* / I got to find my baby: *Little Walter* / Good morning little school girl: *Don & Bob* / Oh baby: *Williams, Larry* / Walk: *McCracklin, Jimmy* / I don't want 'cha: *Tucker, Tommy* / When the lights go out: *Witherspoon, Jimmy* / Entertainer: *Clarke, Tony* / Summertime: *Stewart, Billy* / I had a talk with my man: *Collier, Mitty* / Sitting in the park: *Stewart, Billy* / Who's cheating who: *Little Milton* / In crowd: *Lewis, Ramsey Trio* / Leave my baby alone: *Guy, Buddy* / High heel sneakers: *Tucker, Tommy* / Soulful dress: *Desanto, Sugar Pie* / Crazy for my baby: *Dixon, Willie* / I can tell: *Diddley, Bo* / You gonna wreck my life: *Howlin' Wolf* / Messin' with the man: *Waters, Muddy* / Promised land: *Berry, Chuck*.
CD. . . . . . . . . . SEECD 380
See For Miles / Oct '93 / Pinnacle.

## CHESS MASTERS.
**Tracks:** Not Advised.
■ Double LP. . . . . . . . . . CXMD 4010
Chess (PRT) / Apr '82.

## CHESS NEW ORLEANS R&B.
**Tracks:** Not Advised.
■ LP . . . . . . . . . . DET 205
Chess (Charly) / Nov '87.

## CHESS SISTERS OF SOUL.
**Tracks:** Wang dang doodle: *Taylor, Koko* / Selfish one: *Ross, Jackie* / Mama didn't lie: *Bradley, Jan* / Two sides (to every story): *James, Etta* / Take me for a little while: *Ross, Jackie* / Rescue me: *Bass, Fontella* / Only time will tell: *James, Etta* / I had a talk with my man: *Collier, Mitty* / Lovin' you more every day: *James, Etta*.
■ LP . . . . . . . . . . CXMP 2052
■ MC. . . . . . . . . . ZCCXMP 2052
Chess (PRT) / Jun '84.

## CHESS SOUL CLASSICS.
**Tracks:** Not Advised.
CD. . . . . . . . . . CD CHESS 100
Greenline / '88 / Charly.

**CHESS STORY - VOL. 1, THE (From Blues To Doo Wop).**
**Tracks:** Gypsy woman: *Waters, Muddy* / Anna Lee: *Nighthawk, Robert* / That's all right: *Rogers, Jimmy* / Rocket 88: *Brenston, Jackie* / Walkin the boogie: *Hooker, John Lee* / I don't know: *Mabon, Willie* / White cliffs of Dover: *Blue Jays* / Third degree: *Boyd, Eddie* / I'm your hoochie coochie man: *Waters, Muddy* / Reconsider baby: *Fulson, Lowell* / Sincerely: *Moonglows* / My babe: *Little Walter* / Bo Diddley: *Diddley, Bo* / Maybellene: *Berry, Chuck* / Later alligator: *Charles, Bobby* / I'll be home: *Flamingos (1)* / Smokestack lightning: *Howlin' Wolf* / Ain't got no home: *Henry, Clarence* / Susie Q: *Hawkins, Dale* / Long lonely nights: *Andrew, Lee And The Hearts* / Happy happy birthday baby: *Tune Weavers* / Walk: *McCracklin, Jimmy* / Johnny B. Goode: *Berry, Chuck* / Book of love: *Monotones* / First time I met the blues: *Guy, Buddy.*
**CD** . . . . . . . . . . . . . . . . . . . . . **CDINS 5033**
Instant (2) / Sep '90 / Charly.
**CD** . . . . . . . . . . . . . . . . . . . . . **CDCD 1123**
Charly / Oct '93 / Charly.

**CHESS STORY - VOL. 2, THE (From R'N'B To Soul).**
**Tracks:** Sun is shining: *James, Elmore* / Wang dang doodle: *Howlin' Wolf* / But I do: *Henry, Clarence 'Frogman'* / Watusi: *Vibrations* / I'm a little mixed up: *James, Betty* / Let me in: *Sensations (1)* / Smokey places: *Corsairs* / You can't judge a book by the cover: *Diddley, Bo* / Mama didn't lie: *Bradley, Jan* / Help me: *Williamson, Sonny Boy (1)* / Hi heal sneaker: *Tucker, Tommy* / Soulful dress: *Sugar Pie Desanto* / Selfish one: *Ross, Jackie* / I had a talk with my man last night: *Collier, Mitty* / Voice your choice: *Radiants* / Entertainer: *Clarke, Tony* / We're gonna make it: *Little Milton* / In crowd: *Lewis, Ramsey* / Rescue me: *Bass, Fontella* / Summertime: *Stewart, Billy* / Searching for my love: *Moore, Bobby & The Rhythm Aces* / Dirty man: *Lee, Laura* / I'd rather go blind: *James, Etta* / Stay in the corner: *Dells* / Here come the judge: *Markham, Pigmeat.*
**CD** . . . . . . . . . . . . . . . . . . . . . **CDINS 5034**
Instant (2) / Sep '90 / Charly.
**CD** . . . . . . . . . . . . . . . . . . . . . **CDCD 1124**
Charly / Oct '93 / Charly.

**CHESS STORY 1954-1969.**
**Tracks:** Bye bye Johnny: *Berry, Chuck* / Suzie Q: *Hawkins, Dale* / Rinky dink: *Cortez, Dave 'Baby'* / In the mood: *Hooker, John Lee* / Madison blues: *James, Elmore* / Ain't got no home: *Henry, Clarence 'Frogman'* / Sincerely: *Moonglows* / Sneakin' around: *Little Milton* / Rescue me: *Bass, Fontella* / Stop around: *Guy, Buddy* / Bring it to Jerome: *Diddley, Bo* / High heel sneakers: *Tucker, Tommy* / Mannish boy: *Waters, Muddy* / Smokestack lightnin': *Howlin' Wolf* / In crowd: *Lewis, Ramsey Trio* / Peanut butter: *Marathons* / Only time will tell: *James, Etta* / Get closer together: *Tex, Joe* / Selfish one: *Ross, Jackie.*
**CD** . . . . . . . . . . . . . . . . . . . **VSOPCD 130**
**■ Double LP** . . . . . . . . . . . . . . **VSOPLP 130**
**MC** . . . . . . . . . . . . . . . . . . . **VSOPMC 130**
Connoisseur Collection / Apr '89 / Pinnacle.

**CHESS:THE RHYTHM AND THE BLUES.**
**Tracks:** Not Advised.
**CD** . . . . . . . . . . . . . . . . . . . . . **CDSAM 500**
**■ LP** . . . . . . . . . . . . . . . . . . . . . **SAM 500**
**MC** . . . . . . . . . . . . . . . . . . . . . **TCSAM 500**
Chess (Charly) / Jul '88 / Charly.

**CHICAGO GOSPEL.**
**Tracks:** Not Advised.
**CD** . . . . . . . . . . . . . . . . . . . . . . . **HTCD 08**
Heritage / '92 / Swift / Roots Records / Wellard / Topic Records / Hot Shot / Jazz Music / Direct Distribution.

**CHICAGO SOUL UPRISING (The Real Sound of Chicago 1967-1975).**
**Tracks:** Since you showed me how to be happy: *Wilson, Jackie* / I love you: *Leavill, Otis* / Give it away: *Chi-Lites* / Girl don't care: *Chandler, Gene* / Am I the same girl: *Acklin, Barbara* / Sly slick and wicked: *Lost Generation* / I'll be right there: *Davis, Tyrone* / Funky chicken: *Henderson, Willie* / Follow the leader: *Lance, Major* / Love uprising: *Leavill, Otis* / Let me be the man my daddy was: *Chi-Lites* / Could I forget you: *Davis, Tyrone* / Got to find me a lover: *Franklin, Erma* / Girl I need you: *Artistics* / Wait a minute: *Lost Generation* / Don't burn no bridges: *Wilson, Jackie & The Chi-Lites.*
**■ LP** . . . . . . . . . . . . . . . . . . . . . **CRB 1160**
**MC** . . . . . . . . . . . . . . . . . . . . **TCCRB 1160**
Charly R&B / Jul '87 / Charly.

**CHRISTMAS CLASSICS VOL. 1.**
**Tracks:** White Christmas: *Ross, Diana & The Supremes* / Rudolph the red nosed reindeer: *Temptations* / Frosty the snowman: *Jackson Five* / What Christmas means to me: *Wonder, Stevie* / Twinkle twinkle little me: *Ross, Diana & The Supremes* / Santa Claus is coming to town: *Jackson Five* / Jingle bells: *Robinson, Smokey & The Miracles* / Little Christmas tree: *Jackson, Michael* / Someday at Christmas: *Wonder, Stevie* / Let it snow, let it snow, let it snow: *Temptations* / I saw Mommy kissing Santa Claus: *Jackson Five* / Christmas lullaby: *Robinson, Smokey & The Miracles* / My Christmas tree: *Ross, Diana & The Supremes* / Up on the house top: *Jackson Five* / Christmas song: *Wonder, Stevie* / Little bright star: *Ross, Diana & The Supremes* / Silent night: *Temptations* / God rest ye merry gentlemen: *Robinson, Smokey & The Miracles* / Christmas won't be the same this year: *Jackson Five* / Silver bells: *Ross, Diana & The Supremes.*
**CD** . . . . . . . . . . . . . . . . . . . . . **530 109-2**
**MC** . . . . . . . . . . . . . . . . . . . . . **530 109-4**
Polydor / Nov '93 / PolyGram.

**CHRISTMAS SOUL SPECIAL.**
**Tracks:** Jingle bells / Silent night / Drummer boy / Oh holy night / Jingle bell rock / Christmas song / Santa Claus is coming to town / Noel / Winter wonderland / Oh come all ye faithful / Frosty the snowman / Silver bells.
**■ LP** . . . . . . . . . . . . . . . . . . . . . **BMLP 056**
Blue Moon (1) / Nov '87.
**CD** . . . . . . . . . . . . . . . . . . . . . **CDVR 015**
**■ LP** . . . . . . . . . . . . . . . . . . . . . . . **V 015**
**MC** . . . . . . . . . . . . . . . . . . . . . . **V 015 C**
Varrick (USA) / '88 / Roots Records / Topic Records / Duncans / C.M. Distribution / Jazz Music / Ross Records / Projection / Hot Shot / Direct Distribution / A.D.A. Distribution.

**CHUNKS OF FUNK.**
**Tracks:** Not Advised.
**■ LP** . . . . . . . . . . . . . . . . . . . . . . **CHUNK 1**
MCA / Oct '84.

**CLASSIC 80'S GROOVE MASTERCUTS VOLUME 1.**
**Tracks:** Do it to the music: *Raw Silk* / So fine: *Johnson, Howard* / After the dance is through: *Krystol* / (I'll be a) freak for you: *Royalle Delite* / Main thing: *Shot* / You used to hold me so tight: *Houston, Thelma* / Fool's paradise: *Morgan, Meli'sa* / Who do you love: *Wright, Bernard* / Hangin' on a string: *Loose Ends* / Change of heart: *Change* / Settle down: *Thomas, Lillo* / Encore: *Lynn, Cheryl.*
**CD** . . . . . . . . . . . . . . . . . . . . . **CUTSCD 15**
**LP** . . . . . . . . . . . . . . . . . . . . . . **CUTSLP 15**
**MC** . . . . . . . . . . . . . . . . . . . . **CUTSMC 15**
Beechwood / Nov '93 / Pinnacle.

**CLASSIC CLUB COLLECTIVE (A Classic Collection Of Club Anthems).**
**Tracks:** Got to have your love: *Mantronix* / Let the beat hit 'em: *Lisa Lisa & Cult Jam* / Optimistic: *Sounds Of Blackness* / Love under moonlight: *Graham, Jaki* / Twilight: *Maze Featuring Frankie Beverly* / Secret rendezvous: *Rene & Angela* / Laughin' at you: *Dazz Band* / Come into my life: *Sims, Joyce* / Got to be real: *Lynn, Cheryl* / Sleep talk: *Williams, Alyson* / You and me tonight: *Aurra* / Good lovin': *Belle, Regina* / Heaven: *Chimes (1)* / Can't stop: *After 7.*
**CD** . . . . . . . . . . . . . . . . . . . . . **CDUBC 01**
**LP** . . . . . . . . . . . . . . . . . . . . . . **LPUBC 01**
**MC** . . . . . . . . . . . . . . . . . . . . . **MCUBC 01**
Passion/Debut/Scratch Music / Jan '94 / Pinnacle / 3MV.

**CLASSIC FUNK MASTERCUTS VOL. 1.**
**Tracks:** Who is he and what is he to you: *Creative Source* / Wicki-wacky: *Fatback Band* / Gimme some more: *J.B.'s* / For the love of money: *O'Jays* / Fire: *Ohio Players* / Pusherman: *Mayfield, Curtis* / Blow your head: *Wesley, Fred & The J.B.'s* / Fencewalk: *Mandrill* / Pick up the pieces: *Average White Band* / Rock creek park: *Blackbyrds* / N.T. Pts 1 & 2: *Kool & The Gang* / Stone to the bone: *Brown, James.*
**CD** . . . . . . . . . . . . . . . . . . . . . . **CUTSCD 6**
**■ LP** . . . . . . . . . . . . . . . . . . . . . **CUTSLP 6**
**MC** . . . . . . . . . . . . . . . . . . . . . **CUTSMC 6**
Beechwood / May '92 / Pinnacle.

**CLASSIC FUNK MASTERCUTS VOL. 2.**
**Tracks:** Movin': *Brass Construction* / Express yourself Pt.1: *Wright, Charles & The Watts 103rd St.Rhythm Band* / You can have your watergate: *J.B.'s* / It's alright now: *Harris, Eddie* / Funky stuff/ More funky stuff: *Kool & The Gang* / Keep on steppin': *Fatback Band* / Jive turkey: *Ohio Express* / Ghetto: *Hathaway, Donny* / Baby let me take you (in my arms): *Detroit Emeralds* / Boss: *Brown, James* / Do it fluid: *Blackbyrds* / Stomp & buck dance: *Crusaders.*
**CD** . . . . . . . . . . . . . . . . . . . . . **CUTSCD 14**
**LP Set** . . . . . . . . . . . . . . . . . . . . **CUTSLP 14**
**MC** . . . . . . . . . . . . . . . . . . . . **CUTSMC 14**
Beechwood / Sep '93 / Pinnacle.

**CLASSIC JAZZ-FUNK MASTERCUTS.**
**Tracks:** Expansions: *Smith, Lonnie Liston* / Always there: *Laws, Ronnie* / Bottle: *Scott-Heron, Gil* / Change (makes you want to hustle): *Byrd, Donald* / Inherit the wind: *Felder, Wilton* / Shaker song: *Spyro Gyra* / Jazz carnival: *Azymuth* / Los conquistadores chocolates: *Hammond, Johnny* / Say you will: *Henderson, Eddie* / Brasilia: *Klemmer, John* / Till you take my love: *Mason, Harvey* / Unicorn: *Gillespie, Dizzy.*
**CD** . . . . . . . . . . . . . . . . . . . . . . **CUTSCD 2**
**■ Double LP** . . . . . . . . . . . . . . . . **CUTSLP 2**
**MC** . . . . . . . . . . . . . . . . . . . . . **CUTSMC 2**
Beechwood / Sep '91 / Pinnacle.

**CLASSIC JAZZ-FUNK MASTERCUTS 2.**
**Tracks:** Could heaven ever be like this: *Muhammad, Idris* / Brazilian love affair: *Duke, George* / Easy: *Jarreau, Al* / Dominoes: *Byrd, Donald* / To prove my love: *Doheny, Ned* / Snowblower: *Baker, B* / Poo poo la la: *Ayers, Roy* / Come with me: *Maria, Tania* / Rotation: *Alpert, Herb* / Chicago song: *Sanborn, David* / New killer Joe: *Golson, Benny* / Keep that same old feeling: *Crusaders.*
**CD** . . . . . . . . . . . . . . . . . . . . . . **CUTSCD 4**
**■ LP** . . . . . . . . . . . . . . . . . . . . . **CUTSLP 4**
**MC** . . . . . . . . . . . . . . . . . . . . . **CUTSMC 4**
Beechwood / Nov '91 / Pinnacle.

**CLASSIC JAZZ-FUNK MASTERCUTS 3.**
**Tracks:** Feel the real: *Bendeth, David* / Roller jubilee: *Di Meola, Al* / Saturday night: *Hancock, Herbie* / Love has come around: *Byrd, Donald* / Spring high: *Lewis, Ramsey* / Love will bring us back together: *Ayers, Roy* / Westchester lady: *James, Bob* / Summer madness: *Kool & The Gang* / Sun goddess: *Lewis, Ramsey with Earth, Wind & Fire* / Darlin' darlin' baby: *Khan, Steve* / You're a star: *Aquarian Dream* / Best of friends: *White, Lenny.*
**CD** . . . . . . . . . . . . . . . . . . . . . . **CUTSCD 7**
**■ LP** . . . . . . . . . . . . . . . . . . . . . **CUTSLP 7**
**MC** . . . . . . . . . . . . . . . . . . . . . **CUTSMC 7**
Beechwood / Jun '92 / Pinnacle.

**CLASSIC JAZZ-FUNK MASTERCUTS 4.**
**Tracks:** Birdland: *Weather Report* / I thought it was you: *Hancock, Herbie* / Can't you see me: *Ayers, Roy* / Dancing in outer space: *Atmosfear* / You got the floor: *Adams, Arthur* / Whistle bump: *Deodato, Eumir* / Real thing: *Mendes, Sergio* / Magic fingers: *Hamilton, Chico* / Strawberry letter: *Brothers Johnson* / Chief inspector: *Badarou, Wally* / Funkin' for Jamaica: *Browne, Tom* / Street life: *Crusaders.*
**CD** . . . . . . . . . . . . . . . . . . . . . **CUTSCD 16**
**LP** . . . . . . . . . . . . . . . . . . . . . . **CUTSLP 16**
**MC** . . . . . . . . . . . . . . . . . . . . . **CUTSMC 16**
Beechwood / Jan '94 / Pinnacle.

**CLASSIC JAZZ-FUNK MASTERCUTS 5.**
**Tracks:** Not Advised.
**CD** . . . . . . . . . . . . . . . . . . . . . **CUTSCD 23**
**LP Set** . . . . . . . . . . . . . . . . . . . . **CUTSLP 23**
**MC** . . . . . . . . . . . . . . . . . . . . . **CUTSMC 23**
Beechwood / Nov '94 / Pinnacle.

**CLASSIC MELLOW MASTERCUTS VOL 1.**
**Tracks:** She's so good to me: *Vandross, Luther* / Risin' to the top: *Burke, Keni* / Outstanding: *Gap Band* / Joy and pain: *Maze* / Give me the sunshine: *Leo's Sunshipp* / Hold me tighter in the rain: *Griffin, Billy* / I'm out of your life: *Arnie's Love* / You'll never know: *Hi-Gloss* / What you won't do for love: *Caldwell, Bobby* / I'm back for more: *Johnson, Al & Jean Carn* / Fruit song: *Reynolds, Jeannie* / Mellow mellow right on: *Lowrell.*
**CD** . . . . . . . . . . . . . . . . . . . . . . **CUTSCD**
**■ LP** . . . . . . . . . . . . . . . . . . . . . **CUTSLP**
**MC** . . . . . . . . . . . . . . . . . . . . . **CUTSMC**
Beechwood / Sep '91 / Pinnacle.

**CLASSIC MELLOW MASTERCUTS VOL 2.**
**Tracks:** Don't look any further: *Edwards, Dennis* / Baby I'm scared of you: *Womack & Womack* / Mind blowing decisions: *Heatwave* / I don't think that man should sleep alone: *Parker, Ray Jnr.* / All night long: *Mary Jane Girls* / Sweet sticky thing: *Ohio Players* / It's ecstasy when you lay down next to me: *White, Barry* / Juicy fruit: *Mtume* / Whatcha see is whatcha get: *Dramatics* / Yu-ma/Go away little boy: *Shaw, Marlena* / I choose you: *Paris (1)* / So delicious: *Fatback Band.*
**CD** . . . . . . . . . . . . . . . . . . . . . . **CUTSCD**
**■ LP** . . . . . . . . . . . . . . . . . . . . . **CUTSLP**
**MC** . . . . . . . . . . . . . . . . . . . . . **CUTSMC**
Beechwood / Jul '92 / Pinnacle.

**CLASSIC MELLOW MASTERCUTS VOL 3.**
**Tracks:** Never too much: *Vandross, Luther* / You're gonna get next to me: *Kirkland, Bo & Ruth Davis*

490

■ DELETED

lights over Egypt: *Jones Girls* / Now that we've found love: *O'Jays* / Don't let it go to your head: *Carne, Jean* / Do you get enough love: *Jones, Shirley* / You are my starship: *Connors, Norman* / Reasons (Live): *Earth, Wind & Fire* / Rock me tonight For old time's sake): *Jackson, Freddie* / Gotta get you home tonight: *Jackson, Freddie* / Wilde, Eugene: *Jackson, Freddie* / Sweet love: *Baker, Anita* / We're n this love together: *Jarreau, Al.*

| CD | CUTSCD 17 |
| P Set | CUTSLP 17 |
| MC | CUTSMC 17 |

Beechwood / Feb '94 / Pinnacle.

## CLASSIC MIX MASTERCUTS VOL.1.

**Tracks:** Yah mo be there: *Ingram, James* / Medicine song: *Mills, Stephanie* / You're the one for me: *D-Train* / Seventh heaven: *Guthrie, Gwen* / You don't now: *Serious Intention* / Searchin' to find the one: *Unlimited Touch* / Beat the street: *Redd, Sharon* / You can't hide your love: *Joseph, David* / Ain't nothn' goin' on but the rent: *Guthrie, Gwen* / Thinking of you: *Sister Sledge* / Searching: *Change* / Running away: *Ayers, Roy.*

| CD | CUTSCD 1 |
| Double LP | CUTSLP 1 |
| MC | CUTSMC 1 |

Beechwood / Sep '91 / Pinnacle.

## CLASSIC NEW JACK SWING MASTERCUTS VOL.1.

**Tracks:** Rub you the right way: *Gill, Johnny* / Her: *Guy* / I got the feeling: *Today* / New Jack swing: *Wreckx N Effect* / She's got that vibe: *R. Kelly* / Do me right: *Guy* / Sensitivity: *Tresvant, Ralph* / So you ike what you see: *Samuelle* / Poison: *Bell Biv Devoe* Treat them like they want to be treated: *Father* / Another like my lover: *Guy, Jasmine* / Mama told ne: *Jackson, Keisha.*

| CD | CUTSCD 5 |
| LP | CUTSLP 5 |
| MC | CUTSMC 5 |

Beechwood / Mar '92 / Pinnacle.

## CLASSIC NEW JACK SWING MASTERCUTS VOL.2.

**Tracks:** Is it good to you: *Lucas, Tammy & Teddy Riley* / Don't be afraid: *Hall, Aaron* / Yo that's a lot of body: *Ready For The World* / I like your style: *Bubba* Whatever it takes: *Basic Black* / Swinging single: *Groove B Chill* / Just got paid: *Kemp, Johnny* / My antasy: *Guy* / Why you get funky on me: *Today* / *Coool aid express card: *Nation Funktasia* / Serious: *La Rue* / My prerogative: *Brown, Bobby* (1).

| CD | CUTSCD 9 |
| LP | CUTSLP 9 |
| MC | CUTSMC 9 |

Beechwood / Oct '92 / Pinnacle.

## CLASSIC NEW JACK SWING MASTERCUTS VOL.3.

**Tracks:** Ain't too proud to beg: *TLC* / I want her: *Sweat, Keith* / I just can't handle it: *Hi-Five* / Judy had a boyfriend: *Riff* (2) / Somebody for me: *Heavy D & The Boyz* / I'm dreaming: *Williams, Christopher* / O.G. me out: *Guy* / Rump shaker: *Wreckx N Effect* / 9: *Father* / I'm so into you: *S.W.V.* / Real love: *Blige, Mary J.* / Love thang: *Intro.*

| CD | CUTSCD 18 |
| P | CUTSLP 18 |
| MC | CUTSMC 18 |

Beechwood / Mar '94 / Pinnacle.

## CLASSIC P-FUNK MASTERCUTS VOL.1.

**Tracks:** Not Advised.

| CD | CUTSCD 12 |
| P | CUTSLP 12 |
| MC | CUTSMC 12 |

Beechwood / Jan '93 / Pinnacle.

## CLASSIC PRELUDES.

**Tracks:** Check out the groove: *Thurston, Bobby* / In the bush (remix): *Musique* / Body music: *Strikers* / tretchin' out (remix): *Adams, Gayle* / Never give ou up: *Redd, Sharon* / You're the one for me: *D-Train* / You'll never know: *Hi-Gloss* / Come on dance dance: *Saturday Night Band* / What I got is what you eed: *Unique* / Can U handle it (remix): *Redd, haron.*

| CD | 260.376 |
| LP | 210.376 |
| MC | 410.376 |

Ariola / Dec '89.

## CLASSIC RARE GROOVE MASTERCUTS VOL.1.

**Tracks:** Turned on to you: *80's Ladies* / Riding high: *aze-O* / Why I came to California: *Ware, Leon* / Say ou love me girl: *Break Water* / Movin' in the right rection: *Parks, Steve* / Number one: *Rushen, Patrice* / Good love: *Jeffries, Rome* / So different: *Kinky xxx* / Much too much: *Sass* / All I want is my baby:

Gilliam, Roberta / Moonshadow: *Labelle* / It's your love: *Beatty, Ethel.*

| CD | CUTSCD 11 |
| LP Set | CUTSLP 11 |
| MC | CUTSMC 11 |

Beechwood / Apr '93 / Pinnacle.

## CLASSIC RARE GROOVE MASTERCUTS VOL.2.

**Tracks:** Caveman boogie: *Wilson, Lesette* / LA nights: *Agawu, Yasuko* / No.1 girl: *Light Of The World* / You need a change of mind: *Brooklyn Express* / There's a reason: *Hi-Tension* / Work it out: *Break Water* / Barely breaking even: *Universal Robot Band* / I'd like to get into you: *Kelly, Denise & Fame* / Windy city theme: *Davis, Carl* / Bump & hustle music: *Stewart, Tommy* / God made me funky: *Head Hunters* / Give me some: *L.A. Boppers.*

| CD | CUTSCD 21 |
| CD | CUTSMC 21 |
| LP Set | CUTSLP 21 |

Beechwood / Sep '94 / Pinnacle.

## CLASSIC SOUL.

**Tracks:** Not Advised.

| CD | STACD 057 |

Stardust / Aug '93 / Pickwick / Conifer Records.

## CLASSIC SOUL MIX.

**Tracks:** Not Advised.

| CD | NCD 5161 |

K-Tel / Feb '88.

## CLASSIC SOUL YEARS SERIES 1964.

**Tracks:** Hey girl don't bother me: *Tams* / Lovers always forgive: *Knight, Gladys & The Pips* / It's in his kiss: *Everett, Betty* / Chapel of love: *Dixie Cups* / Gonna send you back to Georgia: *Shaw, Timmy* / I just don't know what to do with myself: *Hunt, Tommy* / Do wah diddy: *Exciters* / Loving you more everyday: *James, Etta* / I had a talk with my man: *Collier, Mitty* / Sha-la-la: *Shirelles* / Let it be me: *Everett, Betty & Jerry Butler* / Soulville: *Franklin, Aretha* / Um, um, um, um, um, um: *Lance, Major* / Soul serenade: *Curtis, King* / Selfish one: *Ross, Jackie* / Hurt by love: *Foxx, Inez & Charlie* / Quiet place: *Mimms, Garnet* / Beg me: *Jackson, Chuck* / So far away: *Jacobs, Hank* / Keep on pushing: *Impressions* / I can't stand it: *Soul Sisters* / Time is on my side: *Thomas, Irma.*

| Double LP | CSYR LP 64 |
| CD | CSYR CD 64 |
| MC | CSYR MC 64 |

Connoisseur Collection / May '89.

## CLASSIC SOUL YEARS SERIES 1965.

**Tracks:** Rescue me: *Bass, Fontella* / Duck: *Lee, Jackie* / Sitting in the park: *Stewart, Billy* / Who's that lady: *Isley Brothers* / Lipstick traces: *O'Jays* / Getting mighty crowded: *Everett, Betty* / Come tomorrow: *Knight, Marie* / Goin' out of my head: *Imperials* / Birds and the bees: *Akens, Jewel* / Baby I'm yours: *Lewis, Barbara* / If you gotta make a fool: *Brown, Maxine* / Boy from New York City: *Ad Libs* / Gee baby: *Three Degrees* / We're gonna make it: *Little Milton* / In crowd: *Ramsey, Lewis Trio* / Misty: *Vibrations* / Jerk: *Larks* (2) / Iko iko: *Dixie Cups* / It was easier to hurt her: *Mimms, Garnet* / Hold what you've got: *Tex, Joe* / I can't work no longer: *Butler, Billy* / I don't know what ..: *Little Richard* / You're gonna make me cry: *Wright, O.V.* / Stay in my corner: *Dells.*

| CD | CSYRCD 65 |
| LP | CSYRLP 65 |
| MC | CSYRMC 65 |

Connoisseur Collection / Jul '89 / Pinnacle.

## CLASSIC SOUL YEARS SERIES 1966.

**Tracks:** Barefootin': *Parker, Robert* / I spy for the F.B.I.: *Thomas, Jano* / Lot of love: *Banks, Homer* / Holy cow: *Dorsey, Lee* / Karate: *Emperors* / I'm gonna make you love me: *Warwick, Dee Dee* / I'm your puppet: *Purify, James & Bobby* / Love is a hurting thing: *Rawls, Lou* / When a woman loves a man: *Lester, Ketty* / Sweet talking guy: *Chiffons* / Searching for my love: *Moore, Bob* / Summertime: *Stewart, Billy* / Sunny: *Herb, Bobby* / Maybe: *Three Degrees* / Tell it like it is: *Neville, Aaron* / I fooled you this time: *Chandler, Gene* / No man is an island: *Van Dykes* / Soul at sunrise: *Juggy* / What did I do wrong: *Harris, Betty* / Bad mouthin': *Brown, James* / It's a man's man's man's world: *Brown, James* / There's something on my mind: *Baby Ray* / Hurt: *Imperials* / For you precious love: *Butler, Jerry.*

| CD | CSYR CD 66 |
| LP | CSYR LP 66 |
| MC | CSYR MC 66 |

Connoisseur Collection / Jul '89.

## CLASSIC SOUL YEARS SERIES 1967.

**Tracks:** Dance to the music: *Sly & The Family Stone* / O - O - I love you: *Dells* / Dirty man: *Lee, Laura* / Gimme little sign: *Wood, Brenton* / River of soul:

Capel, Larry / For your precious love: *Toney, Oscar Jr.* / Show me: *Tex, Joe* / Never let me go: *Dykes, Van* / No more tears: *Jive Five* / Everlasting love: *Knight, Robert* / Do what you gotta do: *Wilson, Al* / I believe in you: *Baker, Sam* / My ship is coming in: *Jackson, Walter* / Girl from Texas: *Lewis, Jimmy* / When she touches me: *Mighty Sam* / Can't last much longer: *Harris, Betty* / Working on your case: *O'Jays* / Hunk of funk: *Dozier, Gene* / Nothing takes the place of ..: *McCall, Toussaint* / Money: *Little Richard* / Rough dried woman: *Big Mac* / Everybody needs help: *Holiday, Jimmy* / 60 minutes of your love: *Banks, Homer* / Get on up: *Esquires.*

| CD | CSYR CD67 |
| LP | CSYR LP67 |
| MC | CSYR MC67 |

Connoisseur Collection / Aug '89.

## CLASSIC SOUL YEARS SERIES 1968.

**Tracks:** Nothing can stop me: *Chandler, Gene* / Without love: *Toney, Oscar Jr.* / Cry baby cry: *Van & Titus* / Cowboys to girls: *Intruders* / Uptight good man: *Lee, Laura* / Please don't change me now: *Dells* / Yesterday has gone: *Imperials* / Good to me: *Thomas, Irma* / Snake: *Wilson, Al* / At the dark end of the tunnel: *Little Milton* / Baby you got it: *Wood, Brenton* / Look over your shoulder: *O'Jays* / I'd rather go blind: *James, Etta* / We got a good thing going: *King, Clydie* / I've got love for my baby: *Young Hearts* / Where is my baby: *Neville, Aaron* / Baby make your own sweet music: *Johnson, Johnny* / And black is beautiful: *Lee, Nickie* / When a man cries: *Robinson, Johnny* / Gonna get that boat (part 1): *Lytle, Johnny* / Lover's holiday: *Scott, Peggy* / I'm glad it's over: *Mack, Oscar* / Love that never grows: *Tig, J & L.*

| CD | CSYR CD68 |
| LP | CSYR LP68 |
| MC | CSYR MC68 |

Connoisseur Collection / Aug '89.

## CLASSICS AND RARITIES.

**Tracks:** Not Advised.

| LP | 2429193 |

Capricorn / Nov '79.

## CLUB CLASSICS.

**Tracks:** Soul city walk: *Bell, Archie & The Drells* / Love is lost: *Melvin, Harold & The Bluenotes* / I don't love you anymore: *Pendergrass, Teddy* / It ain't reggae (but its funky): *Instant Funk* / Life on Mars: *Wansel, Dexter* / I'll always love my mama: *Intruders* / Do it anyway you wanna: *People's Choice* / You'll never find another love like mine: *Rawls, Lou* / If you wanna go back: *Carne, Jean* / Come go with me: *Pockets.*

| LP | VAULT 1 |
| MC | VAULT 401 |

CBS / Nov '84.

## CLUB SOUL.

**Tracks:** Dearly beloved: *Montgomery, Jack* / Let's get back together: *Honey Bees* / Honey boy: *Dodds, Nella* / Rainmaker: *Moods* / Since I found you: *Brown, Maxine* / It's me: *Copeland, Johnny* / Two stupid feet: *Jackson, Chuck* / Oh Lord what are you doing to me: *Big Maybelle* / Hand it over: *Jackson, Chuck* / I never want to lose my sweet thing: *Charles, Lee* / Let love win: *Candy & The Kisses* / Too much of a good thing: *Shirelles* / You've got the power: *Esquires* / Mr. Schemer: *Wood, Brenton* / I thank you kindly: *Lewis, Diane* / So help me woman: *Tindley, George.*

| LP | KENT 022 |

Kent / Aug '84.

## CLUB UK (Ten Extended UK Club Hits).

**Tracks:** Down on the street: *Shakatak* / Magic touch: *Loose Ends* / Minefield: *Level* / Hi-Tension: *Hi-Tension* / Southern freeez: *Freeez* / You're lying: *Linx* / Spend the night: *Cool Notes* / London town: *Light Of The World* / Love games: *Level 42* / You can't hide your face: *Joseph, David.*

| CD | OG 3801 |
| LP | OG 1801 |
| MC | OG 2801 |

Old Gold / Jul '90 / Pickwick.

## CLUB UK VOL.2.

**Tracks:** Somebody help me out: *Beggar & Co* / As time goes by: *Funkapolitan* / Tears not enough: *ABC* / Flashback: *Imagination* / Time like this: *Haywoode* / All fall down: *Five Star* / Riding on a train: *Pasadenas* / Chant no.1 (I don't need this pressure): *Spandau Ballet* / Half the day's gone and we haven't earned a penny: *Lynch, Kenny* / Guilty: *Hardcastle, Paul.*

| CD | OG 3804 |
| LP | OG 1804 |
| MC | OG 2804 |

Old Gold / Oct '90 / Pickwick.

## C'MON & DANCE TOO.

**Tracks:** I'm comin' home in the mornin': *Pride, Lou* / R & B time (part 1): *Jones, E.Rodney* / Airplane song: *Jenkins, Norma & The Dolls* / Fine, fine, fine: *Hughes, Judy* / Wee oo, I'll let it be your babe: *Hughes, Judy* / Stronger than love: *Flirtations* / Love you baby: *Parker, Eddie* / My terms: *Ferguson, Helena* / I gotta know: *Tonnettes* / You'll never make the grade: *Sunlovers* / Where can my baby be: *Martells* / We must be doing something right: *Moody, Joan* / Goose pimples: *Scott, Shirley J.* / You've got to love your baby: *Millionaires* / Walkin' by: *Boss Four* / You gotta do what you gotta do: *Contenders* / Can't get over these memories: *John & The Weirdest* / Baby I dig you: *Anderson, Gene* / Ever again: *Woodberry, Gene* / It's all gone: *Magicians* / You won't say nothing: *Lewis, Tamala* / We've got a love that's out of sight: *Spencer* / I can't change: *Baker, Yvonne* / Poor unfortunate me: *Taylor, Gloria*.
**CD** . . . . . . . . . . . . . . . . . . . . . . **GSCD 017**
Goldmine / Jul '93 / Vital Distribution.

## C'MON & DANCE VOL 3.

**Tracks:** Black power: *Coit, James* / Cool aid: *Humphrey, Paul & his Cool Aid Chemists* / Dancin' a hole in the world: *Esquires* / Come go with me: *Paramounts* / Easy baby: *Adventures* / Just as much: *Peterson, Kris* / Prepared to love you: *Lindsay, Thelma* / How good can it get: *Lyle, Jay* / Babysitter: *Turner, Duke & Chitowns* / Running wild: *Ex Saveyons* / What have I got now: *Fletcher, Darrow* / I can't give up on losing you: *Remarkables* / Feel good all over: *Huey, Claude 'Baby'* / Dancin' everywhere: *Bob & Earl* / I wouldn't come: *Mask Man & the Agents* / My heart is calling: *Magnificents* / Mine exclusively: *Olympics* / Ain't nobody's business: *Marbray, Ernie* / Just a little while: *Jackson, Ollie* / Love bandit: *Chi-Lites* / I'm looking for my baby: *Sull, Eddie* / I'm gonna love you: *Hamilton, Edward & Arabians* / You got me where you want me: *Santos, Larry* / Personally: *Paris, Bobby* / Hold on: *Generation* / Build your house on a strong foundation: *Given & Rae* / Job opening (Part 1): *Del-Larks* / What good am I: *Champion, Mickey* / Don't it make you feel funky: *Hicks, Joe* / I've got something good: *Sam & Kitty*.
**CD** . . . . . . . . . . . . . . . . . . . . . . **GSCD 033**
Goldmine / Apr '94 / Vital Distribution.

## C'MON & DANCE VOL1.

**Tracks:** Not Advised.
**CD** . . . . . . . . . . . . . . . . . . . . . . **GSCD 008**
Goldmine / Nov '92 / Vital Distribution.

## COLLECTION OF BIG HITS - VOL.8.

**Tracks:** Not Advised.
■ **LP** . . . . . . . . . . . . . . . . . . . . . . **STML 11130**
Tamla Motown / Feb '70.

## COLLECTION OF MODERN SOUL CLASSICS, A.

**Tracks:** Just loving you: *Andrews, Ruby* / Come back baby: *Justice Department* / I'm so glad you're mine: *Perkins, George* / Lonely girl: *Side Show* / Talkin': *Vee Gees* / Making new friends: *Tracy, Jeanie* / Girl, you're my kind of wonderful: *Relf, Bob* / Girl I've been trying to tell you: *Ultimates* / Lightin' up: *Karim, Ty* / Teasin you again: *Tee, Willie* / Let's go fishing: *Turner Bros* / Dream: *Creations* / I need your love: *Woods, Ella* / Here stands a man who needs you: *Wilson, George* / Given up on love: *Thompson, Johnny* / If it's not love don't waste my time: *Johnson, Dorothy* / Have I relly loved you: *Smoke* / Footsteps across your mind: *Shock* / Girl I love you: *Fisher, Shelley* / You're gone: *Hardin, Celest* / Better to bend than break: *Simmons, Cissie* / Colour him father: *Winstons* / Wash & wear love: *Vernado, Lynne*.
**CD** . . . . . . . . . . . . . . . . . . . . . . **GSCD 009**
**LP** . . . . . . . . . . . . . . . . . . . . . . **GSLP 009**
Goldmine / Jan '93 / Vital Distribution.

## COLLECTION OF SOUL SMASHES.

**Tracks:** Soul man: *Sam & Dave* / Knock on wood: *Floyd, Eddie* / That's the way I feel about cha: *Floyd, Eddie* / Ruler of my heart: *Womack, Bobby* / Rainy night in Georgia: *Benton, Brook* / Hold what you've got: *Tex, Joe* / Hello stranger: *Lewis, Barbara* / If you need me: *Burke, Solomon* / Patches: *Carter, Clarence* / Rescue me: *Fontella Bass* / Gimme little sign: *Wood, Brenton* / Walking the dog: *Thomas, Rufus* / Turn back the hand of time: *Davis, Tyrone* / B.A.B.Y.: *Thomas, Carla* / Troilodyte: *Castor, Jimmy Bunch* / Snake: *Wilson, Al*.
**CD** . . . . . . . . . . . . . . . . . . . . . . **CDCD 1026**
Charly / Mar '93 / Charly.

## COLUMBIA 60'S SOUL.

**Tracks:** Brand new man: *Wylie, Richard 'Popcorn'* / Little bit of something: *Little Richard* / I don't want to discuss it: *Little Richard* / Poor dog: *Little Richard* / Quitter never wins: *Williams, Larry & Johnny Watson* / It's an uphill climb to the bottom: *Jackson, Walter* / Everything I touch turns to tears: *St. John, Barry* / Monkey time: *Lance, Major* / Matador: *Lance, Major* / Investigate: *Lance, Major* / Ain't no soul: *Lance, Major* / Dance to the music: *Sly & The Family Stone* / You're ready now: *Bennett, Bobby* / Just come closer to me: *Korda, Paul* / One in a million: *Keyes, Karol* / Candy to me: *Raynor, Martin* / These things will keep me loving you: *Carr, Romey* / On the brink: *Vickers, Mike* / Stop and you will become aware: *Shapiro, Helen* / Foxy: *Guest, Earl* / This beautiful day: *Jackson, Levy* / You can't bypass love: *Sue & Sunny*.
■ **Double LP** . . . . . . . . . . . . . . . . . . **SX 4231**
Columbia / '79.

## COME WITH CLUB - 2.

**Tracks:** Ladies night: *Kool & The Gang* / I'm out to catch: *Haywood, Leon* / Something special: *Harvey, Steve* / Surprise surprise: *Central Line* / Love town: *Newbury, Booker* / Come with me: *Maria, Tania* / You're a winner: *Cameo (1)* / Mi sabrina tequana: *Ingram*.
■ **LP** . . . . . . . . . . . . . . . . . . . . . . **CLUBL 002**
**MC** . . . . . . . . . . . . . . . . . . . . . . **CLUBC 002**
Club / Aug '83 / PolyGram.

## COMMITTED TO SOUL.

**Tracks:** Not Advised.
**CD** . . . . . . . . . . . . . . . . . . . . . . **ARC 3100142**
**MC** . . . . . . . . . . . . . . . . . . . . . . **ARC 3100154**
Arcade / Jul '94 / Sony / Grapevine Distribution.

## COMPACT DISCO.

**Tracks:** Funky town: *Lipps Inc.* / Love party: *Taka Boom* / Break it out: *Lisa* / Medicine song: *Mills, Stephanie* / Shaft, Theme from: *Eddie & The Soulband* / She's strange: *Cameo (1)* / Sexomatic: *Bar-Kays* / Too tight: *Con Funk Shun* / Breaks: *Blow, Kurtis*.
**CD** . . . . . . . . . . . . . . . . . . . . . . **824642 2**
Mercury / '86 / PolyGram.

## COMPACT DISCO VOLUME 2.

**Tracks:** Not Advised.
■ **CD** . . . . . . . . . . . . . . . . . . . . . . **830976-2**
Mercury / Jul '87.

## COMPACT DISCO VOLUME 3.

**Tracks:** Not Advised.
■ **CD** . . . . . . . . . . . . . . . . . . . . . . **816417-2**
Mercury.

## COMPACT DISCO VOLUME 4.

**Tracks:** Not Advised.
■ **CD** . . . . . . . . . . . . . . . . . . . . . . **836644-2**
Mercury / May '89.

## COMPACT SOUL.

**Tracks:** It's alright: *Mayfield, Curtis & The Impressions* / Hey girl don't bother me: *Tams* / Picking wild mountain berries: *Scott, Peggy & Jo Jo Benson* / He made a woman out of me: *Lavette, Betty* / He will break your heart: *Butler, Jerry with Curtis Mayfield* / Neighbour, neighbour: *Hughes, Jimmy* / You're gonna make me cry: *Wright, O.V.* / Giving up: *Knight, Gladys & The Pips* / Pity the fool: *Bland, Bobby* / You threw a lucky punch: *Chandler, Gene* / Cry, cry, cry: *Bland, Bobby* / Shell of a woman: *Allen, Doril* / Either way I lose: *Knight, Gladys & The Pips* / Eight men, four women: *Wright, O.V.* / I stand accused: *Butler, Jerry* / Reconsider me: *Adams, Johnny* / Just be true: *Chandler, Gene* / Stay in my corner: *Dells* / You can make it if you try: *Allison, Gene* / People get ready: *Mayfield, Curtis & The Impressions* / Steal away: *Hughes, Jimmy* / Lover's holiday: *Scott, Peggy & Jo Jo Benson*.
■ **CD** . . . . . . . . . . . . . . . . . . . . . . **CDCHARLY 10**
Charly / Apr '86.

## COMPLETE STAX/VOLT SOUL SINGERS, VOL.2.

**Tracks:** I was born to love you: *Walton, Shirley* / Precious, precious: *Hayes, Isaac* / Send peace and harmony home: *Walton, Shirley* / Soul limbo: *Booker T & The MG's* / I've never found a girl: *Floyd, Eddie* / It's been a long time coming: *Delaney & Bonnie* / What a man: *Lyndell, Linda* / I like everything about you: *Hughes, Jimmy* / Stay baby stay: *Daye, Johnny* / Private number: *Clay, Judy & William Bell* / So nice: *Mad Lads (1)* / Long walk to D.C.: *Staple Singers* / Give 'em love: *Soul Children* / Funky Mississippi: *Thomas, Rufus* / Lovin' feeling: *Charmels* / Where do I go: *Thomas, Carla* / Bed of roses: *Clay, Judy* / Bring it on home to me: *Floyd, Eddie* / It's unbelievable (how you control my soul): *Jeanne & The Darlings* / Who's making love: *Taylor, Johnnie* / Mighty cold Winter: *Dino & Doc* / Hang 'em high: *Booker T & The MG's* / You're leaving me: *Ollie & The Nightingales* / Copy kat: *Bar-Kays* / I forgot to be your lover: *Bell, William* / Running out: *John, Mable* / My baby specializes: *Bell, William & Judy Clay* / I'll understand: *Soul Children* / Ghetto: *Staple Singers* / Blues power: *King, Albert* / Echo: *Epsilons* / Funky way: *Thomas, Rufus* / Take care of your homework *Taylor, Johnnie* / I like what you're doing (to me) *Thomas, Carla* / I've got to have your love: *Floyd Eddie* / Let 'em down baby: *Hughes, Jimmy* / Love i here today and gone tomorrow: *Mad Lads (1)* / I ain't long enough: *Clay, Judy* / Mellow way you trea your man: *Ollie & The Nightingales* / Private numbe (2): *Stitt, Sonny* / Time is tight: *Booker T & The MG'* / Double or nothing: *Mar-Keys* / (Sittin' on) The doc of the bay: *Staple Singers* / So I can love you *Emotions (1)* / Don't stop dancing (to the music) par 1: *Bar-Kays* / One more chance: *Joseph, Margie* / wanna be good (to you): *Dotson, Jimmy* / Finge lickin' good: *Miller, Art Jerry* / Tighten up my thang *Soul Children* / Whole world is falling down: *Bel William* / Testify (I wonna): *Taylor, Johnnie* / Drown ing on dry land: *King, Albert* / Do the cissy: *Stingers* Don't tell your mama (where you've been): *Floyd Eddie* / Mrs. Robinson: *Booker T & The MG's* Love's sweet sensation: *Bell, William & Mavis Sta ples* / Just because your love has gone: *Banks Darrell* / Chains of love: *Hughes, Jimmy* / Happy *Bell, William* / Challenge: *Staple Singers* / Soul-a lujah: *Taylor, Johnnie/Eddie Floyd/William Bell* Never, never let you go: *Floyd, Eddie & Mavis Sta ples* / Just keep on loving me: *Taylor, Johnnie & Carla Thomas* / I need you woman: *Bell, William & Carla Thomas* / I've got a feeling: *Ollie & The Night ingales* / It's time to pay for the fun (we've had) *Jeanne & The Darlings* / I could never be president *Taylor, Johnnie* / By the time I get to Phoenix: *Ma Lads (1)* / Long and lonely world: *Kelly, Colette* Midnight cowboy: *Bar-Kays* / I've fallen in love (wit you): *Thomas, Carla* / Slum baby: *Booker T & Th MG's* / Best part of a love affair: *Emotions (1)* / By th time I get to Phoenix (2): *Hayes, Isaac* / Walk on by *Hayes, Isaac* / Tupelo Part 1: *Staples, Pops/ Stev Cropper/ Albert King* / Water: *Staples, Pops/ Stev Cropper/ Albert King* / Sweeter he is part 1: *Sou Children* / You're driving me (To the arms of stranger): *Staples, Mavis* / Open up your hear *Newcomers* / Why is the wine sweeter (on the othe side): *Floyd, Eddie* / When will we be paid: *Stapl Singers* / Grinder man: *Hooker, John Lee* / Bor under a bad sign: *Bell, William* / What you gonna do *Joseph, Margie* / I'm so glad: *Hughes, Jimmy* Beautiful feelings: *Banks, Darrell* / Your love wa strange: *Dramatics* / Love bones: *Taylor, Johnnie* Hard to say goodbye: *Delaney & Bonnie* / Got to ge rid of you: *Barnes, J.J.* / Habit forming love: *Milner Reggie* / My thing is a moving thing: *T S U Torna does* / Stealing love: *Emotions (1)* / Wrapped up i love again: *King, Albert* / Do the funky chicker *Thomas, Rufus* / California girl: *Floyd, Eddie* / Tri bute to a blackwoman, Part 1: *Hayes, Bernie* / San and dance: *Bar-Kays* / Hold on I'm coming: *Sou Children* / Love's gonna tear your playhouse dow Part 1: *Brooks, Chuck* / Help me put out the flame (i my heart): *Hines, Ernie* / Black boy: *Staples, Pops* Bracing myself for a fall: *Ollie & The Nightingales* All I have to do is dream: *Bell, William & Carl Thomas* / Singing about love: *Jeanne & The Darling* / Goodies: *Chris & Shack* / Just the way you ar today: *Lewis, Barbara* / Creeper returns: *Little Sonn* / Guide me well: *Thomas, Carla* / Give a damr *Staple Singers* / Steal away: *Taylor, Johnnie* / You sweet lovin': *Joseph, Margie* / I forgot to remembe *Jones & Blumenburg* / Can't see you when I war you: *Porter, David* / Never be true: *Thomas, Carla* Can't you see what you're doing to me: *King, Albert* Sixty minute man, Part II: *Thomas, Rufus* / Preache and the bear: *Thomas, Rufus* / Something: *Booker & The MG's* / Seeing is believing: *Mad Lads (1)* You're my only temptation: *Ryan, Roz* / What I don know won't hurt me: *Thompson, Paul* / Right, tigh and out of sight: *Branding Iron* / (What's under) Th natural do: *Kasandra, John* / My girl: *Floyd, Eddie* / have learned to do without you: *Staples, Mavis* / Pla the music tornadoes: *T S U Tornadoes* / Lonel soldier: *Bell, William* / Heart association: *Emotion (1)* / I stand accused: *Hayes, Isaac* / Brand new day *Staple Singers* / Sweeter tomorrow: *Joseph, Margi* / Cool strut: *Hayes, Bernie* / You put the sunshin back in my world: *Newcomers* / Montego Bay: *Ba Kays* / Got it together parts I & II: *Robinson, Rudy The Hungry Five* / Wade in the water: *Little Sonny* You're movin' much too fast: *Nightingales* / Be year of my life: *Floyd, Eddie* / I am somebody part I *Taylor, Johnnie* / I loved you like I love my very lif *Thomas, Carla* / Soul machine: *Milner, Reggie* (Follow her) Rules and regulations: *Temprees* / (D the) Push and pull Part 1: *Thomas, Rufus* / Lov changes: *Charlene & The Soul Serenaders* / Put you world in my world (Best of two worlds): *Soul Chi dren* / Love is plentiful: *Staple Singers* / Heav makes you happy: *Staple Singers* / Who took th merry out of christmas: *Staple Singers* / Too man lovers: *Shack* / Black christmas: *Emotions (1)* Mistletoe and me: *Hayes, Isaac* / Ask the lonel *Lewis, Barbara* / Jody's got your girl and gone *Taylor, Johnnie* / Finish me off: *Soul Children* / Oh how it rained: *Floyd, Eddie* / Look of love: *Hayes Isaac* / Electrified love: *Hines, Ernie* / Melting po *Booker T & The MG's* / That's the way I like it (I like

that way): *Lewis, Barbara* / Mr. Big Stuff: *Knight, Jean* / You make me want to love you: *Emotions (1)* / Stop, In the name of love: *Joseph, Margie* / I don't wanna lose you: *Taylor, Johnnie* / (Girl) I love you: *Temprees* / World is round: *Thomas, Rufus* / Penny for your thoughts: *Bell, William* / Never can say goodbye: *Hayes, Isaac* / I don't want to be like my daddy: *Nightingales* / You've got to earn it: *Staple Singers* / Hold on to it: *Limitations* / Whatcha see is whatcha get: *Dramatics* / Born too late: *Branding Iron* / Just ain't as strong as I used to be: *Hughes, Jimmy* / That other woman got my man and gone: *Joseph, Margie* / If you think it (You may as well do it): *Emotions (1)* / Shame on the family name: *Scott, Calvin* / Blood is thicker than water: *Floyd, Eddie* / Hijackin' love: *Taylor, Johnnie* / Sweetback's theme: *Van Peebles, Melvin* / Breakdown Part I: *Thomas, Rufus* / Pin the tail on the donkey: *Newcomers* / Them hot pants: *Sain, Lee* / If that ain't a reason (for your woman to leave you): *Little Milton* / It's good to be careful (But it's better to be loved): *Shack* / Where would you be today: *Ilana* / Everybody wants to go to heaven: *King, Albert* / Got to get away from it all: *Soul Children* / Love's creepin' up on me: *United Image* / Show me how: *Emotions (1)* / If I give it up, I want it back: *Porter, David* / Woman named trouble: *Little Sonny* / Losing boy: *Giles, Eddie* / Respect yourself: *Staple Singers* / I'll kill a brick (About my man): *Hot Sauce* / You think you're hot stuff: *Knight, Jean* / All for the love of a woman: *Bell, William* / Theme from Shaft: *Hayes, Isaac* / Jamaica this morning: *MG's* / Promises of yesterday: *Mad Lads (1)* / Girl, come on home: *Lance, Major* / (Let hurt put you in the) Loser's seat: *Wilson, Joni* / My baby love: *Temprees* / How do you move a mountain: *Leaders* / Black nasty boogie part 6: *Black Nasty* / Do the funky penguin Part 1: *Thomas, Rufus* / You've got a cushion to fall on: *Thomas, Carla* / Get up and get down: *Dramatics* / Son of Shaft: *Bar-Kays* / Don't cha mess with my money, my honey or my woman: *Johnson, L.V.* / I can smell that funky music: *Mercury, Eric* / Sadness for things: *Scott, Calvin* / That's what love will make you do: *Little Milton* / Standing in for Jody: *Taylor, Johnnie*.

**CD Set** . . . . . . . . . . . . . . . . . . **9SCD 4411**
Stax / Sep '93 / Pinnacle.

## COMPLETE STAX/VOLT SOUL SINGERS, VOL.3 (1972-1975).

**Tracks:** Yum yum yum (I want some): *Floyd, Eddie* / Carry on: *Knight, Jean* / Do your thing: *Hayes, Isaac* / I've been lonely for so long: *Knight, Frederick* / Nothing is everlasting: *Thomas, Annette* / Hearsay: *Soul Children* / Angel of mercy: *King, Albert* / In the rain: *Dramatics* / She's my old lady too: *Sain, Lee* / Explain it to her Mama: *Temprees* / Right on: *Sons Of Slum* / Doing my own thing (part 1): *Taylor, Johnnie* / My honey and me: *Emotions (1)* / Let's stay together: *Hayes, Isaac* / Bring it home (amd give it to me): *Hot Sauce* / Look around you: *Black Society* / Don't do it: *Nightingales* / I'm with you: *Nightingales* / I'll take you there: *Staple Singers* / Which way: *Leaders* / Living a life without you: *Brown, Veda* / What's good for you (don't have to be good to you): *Scales, Harvey* / Let me repair your heart: *Mad Lads (1)* / What's usual seems natur'l: *Mercury, Eric* / I wanna make up (before we break up): *Lance, Major* / Ain't that loving you (for more reasons than one): *Hayes, Isaac & David Porter* / Walking the back streets and crying: *Little Milton* / Save us: *Bell, William* / 6-3-8: *Thomas, Rufus* / Starting all over again: *Mel & Tim* / Keep on loving me: *Stefan* / I'm afraid the masquerade is over: *Porter, David* / Going down slow (parts 1 & 2): *Little Sonny* / I could never be happy: *Emotions (1)* / Don't take my kindness for weakness: *Soul Children* / I'll play the blues for you (part 1): *King, Albert* / I dedicate my life for you: *Hatcher, Roger* / Do the sweetback: *March Wind* / Gettin' funky 'round here: *Black Nasty* / When the chips are down: *Porter, David* / Sugar: *Thomas, Carla* / You're good enough (to be my baby): *Floyd, Eddie* / This world: *Staple Singers* / Helping man: *Knight, Jean* / Ain't I good: *Kasandra, John* / Dance, dance, dance: *Bar-Kays* / Dedicated to the one I love: *Temprees* / Toast to the fool: *Dramatics* / Stop doggin' me: *Taylor, Johnnie* / Trouble: *Knight, Frederick* / I'm gonna cry a river: *Little Milton* / Itch and scratch (part 1): *Thomas, Rufus* / What would I do: *Hines, Ernie* / I know It's not right (to be in love with a married man): *Brown, Veda* / Holy cow: *Stefan* / What goes around (must come around): *Sons Of Slum* / Theme from the men (instrumental): *Hayes, Isaac* / Endlessly: *Staples, Mavis* / You hurt me for the last time: *Foxx, Inez* / My sweet Lord: *Williams, John Gary* / Breaking up somebody's home: *King, Albert* / How can you mistreat the one you love: *Love, Katie* / From toys to boys: *Emotions (1)* / Dryer: *Johnson, Roy Lee & The Villagers* / I may not be all you want (but I'm all you got): *Thomas, Carla* / Ain't no sweat: *Lance, Major* / Do me: *Knight, Jean* / Rainy day: *Little Milton* / It ain't what you do (it's who you let see you do it): *Soul Children* / I may not be what you want: *Mel & Tim* / Funky robot (part 1): *Thomas, Rufus* / Don't you fool with my soul (part 1): *Taylor, Johnnie* / Oh la de da: *Staple Singers* / What do you see in her: *Hot Sauce* / Thousand miles away: *Temprees* / Hey you get off my mountain: *Dramatics* / Rolling down a mountainside: *Hayes, Isaac* / You'r still my brother: *Bar-Kays* / Stop half loving these women: *Lewis, Jimmy* / Lovin' on borrowed time: *Bell, William* / Lay your loving on me: *Floyd, Eddie* / Time: *Foxx, Inez* / Heaven knows: *Mel & Tim* / I believe in you (you believe in me): *Taylor, Johnnie* / Short stopping: *Brown, Veda* / Be what you are: *Staple Singers* / I've got to love somebody's baby: *Stefan* / Playing on me: *King, Albert* / Long as you're the one somebody in the world: *Porter, David* / This is my song of love to you: *Knight, Frederick* / Sugarcane: *MG's* / Love is a hurtin' thing: *Soul Children* / Baby, lay your head down: *Floyd, Eddie* / Check me out: *Floyd, Eddie* / Running (back and forth): *Emotions (1)* / Crossing over the bridge: *Foxx, Inez* / Love's maze: *Temprees* / It aint' easy: *Bar-Kays* / Love among people: *Thomas, Carla* / What is it: *Little Milton* / I've got to go without you: *Bell, William* / Love is taking over: *Mercury, Eric* / Ruby Dean: *Hicks, Joe* / I'm so glad I fell in love with you: *Mad Lads (1)* / Fell for you: *Dramatics* / Cheaper to keep her: *Taylor, Johnnie* / I know you don't want me no more: *Thomas, Rufus* / If you're ready (come go with me): *Staple Singers* / Slipped and tripped: *Sweet Inspirations* / Peace be still: *Emotions (1)* / I'll be the other woman: *Soul Children* / Martin hop: *Newcomers* / I had a talk with my man: *Foxx, Inez* / At last: *Temprees* / Joy (part 1): *Hayes, Isaac* / Good woman turning bad: *Hot Sauce* / Mose (part 3): *Kasandra, John* / I'll be your Santa baby: *Thomas, Rufus* / I wanna do things for you: *Floyd, Eddie* / That's what the blues is all about: *King, Albert* / One way love affair: *Hurley, Carolyn* / Tin pan alley: *Little Milton* / Funky bird: *Thomas, Rufus* / We're getting careless with our love: *Taylor, Johnnie* / What do the lonely get at Christmas: *Emotions (1)* / Season's greetings: *Cix Bits* / Don't lose faith in me Lord: *Mercury, Eric* / Don't start loving me (If you're gonna stop): *Brown, Veda* / Touch a hand, make a friend: *Staple Singers* / I panicked: *Dramatics* / Change it all: *Flemming, Joy* / Gettin' what you want (losin' what you get): *Bell, William* / He's mine: *Verdell, Jackie* / My woman is good to me: *Little Sonny* / I got you and I'm glad: *Porter, David* / Put a little love away: *Emotions (1)* / Suzy: *Knight, Frederick* / Same folks: *Mel & Tim* / You make the sunshine: *Temprees* / Whole damn world is going crazy: *Williams, John Gary* / Circuit's overloaded: *Foxx, Inez* / Wonderful: *Hayes, Isaac* / Behind closed doors: *Little Milton* / Guess who: *Floyd, Eddie* / Sweet inspirations: *Dirty Tricks* / Which way did it go: *Pop Staples* / Talking to the people: *Black Nasty* / I've been born again: *Taylor, Johnnie* / Neckbone: *MG's* / Wounded woman: *Wright, Sandra* / Stop dogging me: *Hot Sauce* / Goodness gracious: *Weston, Kim* / City in the sky: *Staple Singers* / Title theme: *Hayes, Isaac* / Soul street: *Floyd, Eddie* / Flat tire: *King, Albert* / Love makes it right: *Soul Children* / Mr Cool that ain't cool: *Temprees* / Boogie ain't nuttin' (but gettin' down) (part 1): *Thomas, Rufus* / Highway to heaven: *Banks, Ron & The Dramatics* / Get it while it's hot: *Bell, William* / Passing thru: *Knight, Frederick* / Keep an eye on your close friends: *Newcomers* / My main man: *Staple Singers* / There is a God: *Staple Singers* / That's the way I want to live my life: *Mel & Tim* / Forever and a day: *Mel & Tim* / Baby, I'm through: *Emotions (1)* / It's September: *Taylor, Johnnie* / Woman to woman: *Brown, Shirley* / Did you hear yourself (part 1): *Brown, Randy* / You need a friend like mine: *Thomas, Annette* / I love, I love: *Temprees* / Let me back in: *Little Milton* / Crosscut saw: *King, Albert* / Coldblooded: *Bar-Kays* / Bump meat: *Rice, Sir Mack* / (Too little in common to be lovers) Too much going to say go: *Newcomers* / Bump and boogie (part 1): *Wrecking Crew* / What's happening baby (part 1): *Soul Children* / Who made the man: *Staple Singers* / I keep thinking to myself: *Benton, Brook* / I got a reason to smile (cause I got you): *Floyd, Eddie* / Try to leave me if you can (I bet you can't do it): *Banks, Bessie* / Burning on both ends: *Singleton, Willie* / There are more questions than answers: *Emotions (1)* / Santa Claus want some lovin': *King, Albert* / I can't let you go: *Hot Sauce* / I betcha didn't know that: *Knight, Frederick* / Lovin' you, lovin' me: *Wright, Sandra* / Do the double bump: *Thomas, Rufus* / Come and get your love: *Temprees* / Dark skin woman (part 1): *Rice, Sir Mack* / It ain't no fun: *Brown, Shirley* / If you talk in your sleep: *Little Milton* / Talk to the man: *Floyd, Eddie* / You're astounding: *Barbara & Joe* / Dy-no-mite (Did you say my love): *Green Brothers* / Boom-a-rang: *Dynamic Soul Machine* / Come what may: *Williams, John Gary* / Try me tonight: *Taylor, Johnnie* / Groovin' on my baby's love: *Waters, Freddie* / I can't shake your love (can't shake you lose): *Fiestas* / I wanna play with you: *Knight, Frederick* / I'm doing fine: *King, Albert* / No way: *Davis, Theresa* / Back road into town: *Staple Singers* / I'm so glad I met you: *Floyd, Eddie* / Packed up and took my mind: *Little Milton* / Just keep on loving me: *Taylor, Johnnie* / How can I be a witness: *Hudmon, R.B.* / Jump back '75 (part 1): *Thomas, Rufus* / I got to be myself: *Staple Singers* / It's worth a whippin': *Brown, Shirley* / Holy ghost (part 1): *Bar-Kays*.

**CD** . . . . . . . . . . . . . . . . . . . . . **10SCD 4415**
Stax / Oct '94 / Pinnacle.

## CONDITION YOUR HEART.

**Tracks:** My baby don't need changing: *Kinglets* / Pretty please: *Kinglets* / Tell me why: *Rockers* / Condition your heart: *Little Herbert & The Arabians* / Rumblin' tumblin' baby: *Emeralds* / Wham slam bam: *Green, Fred* / My love: *Turner, Ike & The Kings of Rhythm* / That's all I need: *Turner, Ike & The Kings of Rhythm* / Bye bye baby: *Love, Clayton* / Mistreated: *Love, Clayton* / I don't hurt anymore: *Bass, Fontella* / Honey bee: *Bass, Fontella* / It's alright: *Lassiter, Art* / Eastside blues: *Sain, Oliver* / Workin' again: *Smith, Robert T.*

■ **LP** . . . . . . . . . . . . . . . . . . . **RL 0069**
Red Lightnin' / Aug '89.

## COOKIN' WITH KENT.

**Tracks:** Three lonely guys: *Brilliant Corners* / I've been hurt so many times: *Davis, Larry* / New breed: *Holiday, Jimmy* / Baby take me back: *Gilliam, Johnny* / I can't stand it (I can't take it no more): *George, Brenda* / I'm lonely for you: *Adams, K. Arthur* / I've gotta get back: *Love, Mary* / No more tears: *Sweethearts* / It's been so long: *Ikettes* / All that shines is not gold: *Windjammer* / One more chance: *Four Tees* / New lease of life: *Universals* / It's crazy baby: *Turner, Ike & Tina* / What's more: *Hill, Z.Z.* / My girl is gone away: *Hammond, Clay* / Better be good: *Woods, Peggy*.

■ **LP** . . . . . . . . . . . . . . . . . . . **KENT 053**
Kent / Apr '86.

## COOL.

**Tracks:** Yeh yeh: *Santamaria, Mongo* / Money's getting cheaper: *Witherspoon, Jimmy* / Wade in the water: *Big Soul Band* / Animal farm: *Smith, Johnny "Hammond"* / Soul sauce (guachi guaro): *Tjader, Cal* / I'm ready: *Spann, Otis* / Soul roach: *Saunders, Merl* / Talking 'bout my woman: *McDuff, Brother Jack* / Pool shark: *Jackson, Willis* / Eyesight to the Blind: *Allison, Mose* / Tacos: *Santamaria, Mongo* / Step out and git it: *Nomos* / My train: *Saunders, Merl* / Canteloupe island: *Pucho & His Latin Soul Brothers* / Parchman farm: *Allison, Mose* / Peas 'n' rice: *McCoy, Freddie*.

■ **LP** . . . . . . . . . . . . . . . . . . . **KENT 077**
Kent / Apr '88.

## COVER ME SOUL.

**Tracks:** Not Advised.
**CD** . . . . . . . . . . . . . . . . . . **HIUKCD 140**
Hi / May '93 / Pinnacle.

## CREAM OF THE CROP VOL.2.

**Tracks:** Not Advised.
■ **CD** . . . . . . . . . . . . . . . . . **MOTCCD 78**
Motor City / Oct '92.

## CRY CRY CRYING.

**Tracks:** From a whisper to a scream: *Toussaint, Allen* / I just don't know what to do with myself: *Jackson, Chuck* / Invitation: *Copeland, Johnny* / Girl you turned your back on my love: *Charles, Lee* / Cry me a river: *Knight, Marie* / Put yourself in my place: *Big Maybelle* / Human: *Hunt, Tommy* / Love ain't what it used to be: *Diplomats (1)* / It hurts so good: *Love, Katie & The Four Shades Of Black* / You're in love: *Brown, Maxine* / Saving my love for you: *Franklin, Erma* / Loser again: *Moore, (Miss) Jackie* / Don't say goodnight and mean goodbye: *Shirelles* / Have you seen her: *Chi-Lites* / It's all over: *Independents*.

■ **LP** . . . . . . . . . . . . . . . . . . . **KENT 030**
Kent / Nov '84.

# D

## DANCE CLASSICS VOL. 5.

**Tracks:** Can't take my eyes off you: *Boystown Gang* / Night the lights went out: *Trammps* / Can't give you anything (but my love): *Stylistics* / Jump to the beat: *Lattisaw, Stacy* / Ain't gonna bump no more (with no big fat woman): *Tex, Joe* / Tonight, I'm alright: *Walden, Narada Michael* / Spank: *Horne, Jimmy 'Bo'* / Soul cha cha: *McCoy, Van* / I love music: *O'Jays* /

Tell everybody: *Hancock, Herbie* / Contact: *Starr, Edwin* / Get down: *Chandler, Gene* / Chic cheer: *Chic* / Keep it comin' love: *K.C. & The Sunshine Band.*
■ LP . . . . . . . . . . 01355122
MC. . . . . . . . . . 01355141
Arcade / '88 / Sony / Grapevine Distribution.

**DANCE DANCE DANCE 2 (Non-Stop Classic Soul Mix).**
**Tracks:** Check out the groove: *Thurston, Bobby* / You got the power: *War* / Funkin' for Jamaica: *Browne, Tom* / Heart's desire: *Blackman, Donald* / Unlock the funk: *Locksmith* / Expansions: *Smith, Lonnie Liston* / All I need is you: *Starship* / You're the one for me: *D-Train* / I just gotta have you (lover turn me on): *Kashif* / Meet me halfway there: *Jones, Glenn* / (Do you really love me) Tell me love: *Wycoff, Michael* / Never give you up: *Redd, Sharon* / What I got is what you need: *Unique* / Shame: *King, Evelyn 'Champagne'* / In the bush: *Musique* / Body music: *Strikers* / Everybody up: *Ohio Players.*
■ CD . . . . . . . . . . 261398
■ MC. . . . . . . . . . 411398
RCA / Jun '91.

**DANCE DIVAS.**
**Tracks:** Express: *Carroll, Dina* / U: *Clark, Loni* / Big time sensuality: *Bjork* / Give it up, turn it loose: *En Vogue* / Don't walk away: *Jade (1)* / So natural: *Stansfield, Lisa* / I wish: *Gabrielle* / You and me: *Lisa B* / Gotta get it right: *Fiagbe, Lena* / Everybody's free: *Rozalla* / My love is guaranteed: *Sybil* / Luv 4 luv: *Robin S* / Little bit more: *Sims, Kym* / Can't get enough of your love: *Dayne, Taylor* / Lost in music: *Sister Sledge* / Free love: *Roberts, Juliet* / I will always love you: *Washington, Sarah* / Born to B.R.E.E.D.: *Love, Monie* / Respect '93: *Adeva* / Alex Party: *Alex Party.*
CD. . . . . . . . . . 516652-2
MC. . . . . . . . . . 516652-4
Polygram T.V. / Jan '94 / PolyGram.

**DANCE FLOOR DISASTER.**
**Tracks:** Hard working man (Featuring Captain Beefheart on vocals.): *Nitzsche, Jack Orchestra* / You can do it: *Hudson, Al & The Partners* / Blue moon: *Bland, Bobby* / Shoo doo fu fu ooh: *Williams, Lenny* / Heart breakers: *King, B.B.* / Soul perception: *Johnson, Harold* / Sting me baby: *Garrett, Jo Ann* / Y K W: *Verdell, Jackie* / Puffin' on down the track: *Masekela, Hugh* / Hard work: *Handy, John* / Screaming please: *Ace, Buddy* / Chose it: *Smoke* / Hound dog: *Williams, Jeanette* / That's why I'm always crying: *Parker, Junior* / Don't put me down: *El Chicano* / You've got to learn: *Jones, Buster.*
■ LP . . . . . . . . . . KENT 076
Kent / May '88.

**DANCE LIKE THE DEVIL (22 Northern Soul Favourites From Pye Records).**
**Tracks:** This heart of mine: *James, Jimmy* / Love is getting stronger: *Knight, Jason* / If you knew: *Ebony Eyes* / What love brings: *Bernard, Kenny* / Ain't no soul (left in these ole shoes): *Bernard, Kenny* / Come home baby: *Powell, Keith* / Run like the devil: *Roberts, Kenny* / Gonna fix you good (everytime you're bad): *Bown, Alan Set* / Step out of line: *Cotton, Mike Sound* / (Just like) Romeo and Juliet: *Peter's Faces* / Black is black: *Sounds Orchestral* / Soul coaxing: *Sounds Orchestral* / You baby: *Trent, Jackie* / Something to give: *Rossi, Nita* / Lost Summer love: *Silver, Lorraine* / Happy faces: *Silver, Lorraine* / Bring him back: *Starr, Stella* / Nobody knows what's goin' on: *St. John, Tammy* / Real thing: *Kim D* / Number one guy: *Ferris Wheel* / Take me for a while: *Shapiro, Helen* / Just walk in my shoes: *Davis, Billie.*
CD. . . . . . . . . . NEXCD 194
Sequel / Mar '92 / Total / BMG.

**DANCE SOUND OF DETROIT VOL. 1 (Former Artists Of Motown Re-Unite).**
**Tracks:** Step into my shoes: *Reeves, Martha* / Don't burn your bridges: *Wells, Mary* / Needle in a haystack: *Velvelettes* / Emotion: *Weston, Kim* / Heaven must have sent you: *Elgins* / What goes around: *Gaye, Frankie* / All over the world: *Jackson, Chuck* / Run like a rabbit: *Johnson, Marv* / Wake me up when it's over: *Ruffin, Jimmy* / If the shoe fits: *Syreeta* / Holding on with both hands: *Marvelettes* / After dark: *Campbell, Choker.*
CD. . . . . . . . . . DSDCD 01
MC. . . . . . . . . . DSDMC 01
Nightmare / Oct '89.

**DANCE SOUND OF DETROIT VOL. 2 (Former Artists Of Motown Re-unite).**
**Tracks:** What's going on: *Gaye, Frankie* / You're the answer to my dreams: *Wells, Mary* / Angel in disguise: *Reeves, Martha* / Stop dead in my tracks: *Elgins* / Relight my fire: *Jackson, Chuck* / On the rebound: *Ruffin, Jimmy & Brenda Holloway* / By hook or by crook: *Johnson, Marv* / Let's fall in love tonight: *Starr, Edwin* / Do unto others: *Taylor, Bobby & The Vancouvers* / Restless feet: *Weston, Kim* / Love is my middle name: *Wylie, Richard 'Popcorn'* / If at first you don't succeed: *Ward, Sammy.*
CD. . . . . . . . . . DSDCD 02
MC. . . . . . . . . . DSDMC 02
Nightmare / Oct '89.

**DANCE SOUND OF DETROIT VOL. 3 (Former Artists Of Motown Re-unite).**
**Tracks:** It takes two: *Gaye, Frankie & Kim Weston* / Don't get mad get even: *Wilson, Mari* / Ain't nothing like the real thing: *Johnson, Marv & Carolyn Gill* / You made a believer out of me: *Starr, Edwin* / Helpless: *Weston, Kim* / Lightning never strikes twice: *Andantes* / Heading away from heartaches: *Elgins* / Give me a little inspiration: *Holloway, Brenda* / Down to love town: *Taylor, Bobby & The Vancouvers* / Running out of luck: *Velvelettes* / Honey from a bee: *Three Ounces Of Love* / Signal your intention: *Weston, Kim.*
CD. . . . . . . . . . DSDCD 03
MC. . . . . . . . . . DSDMC 03
Nightmare / Oct '89.

**DANCE SOUND OF DETROIT VOL. 4.**
**Tracks:** Just a little misunderstanding: *Stubbs, Joe* / Who's gonna have the last laugh: *Weston, Kim* / Major investment: *Moy, Sylvia* / Extraordinary girl: *Gaye, Frankie* / Pure energy: *Payne, Scherrie* / Timeless: *Crawford, Carolyn* / Pull my heartstrings: *Velvelettes* / Detroit City: *Van Dyke, Earl* / Destination unknown: *Stubbs, Joe* / Joke's on you: *Randolph, Barbara* / Hurry up: *Robinson, Claudette* / Cross that bridge: *Gaye, Frankie.*
CD. . . . . . . . . . DSDCD 04
MC. . . . . . . . . . DSDMC 04
Nightmare / Oct '89.

**DANCE SOUNDS OF HI.**
**Tracks:** Not Advised.
CD. . . . . . . . . . HILOCD 3
Hi / Nov '93 / Pinnacle.

**DANCE SOUNDS OF THE 70'S.**
**Tracks:** Not Advised.
CD. . . . . . . . . . JHD 105
MC. . . . . . . . . . MCJHD 105
Tring / Aug '93 / Prism Leisure PLC / Midland Records.

**DANCE TRACKS.**
**Tracks:** Not Advised.
CD. . . . . . . . . . 01372062
Compact Leisure / Jun '89.

**DANCEMASTER - VOLUME 1.**
**Tracks:** Walking on sunshine: *Rockers Revenge* / Go deh yaka (Go to the top): *Monyaka* / Candy girl: *New Edition (1)* / Love town: *Newbury, Booker* / Sun goes down (living it up) / I think I want to dance with you / Body work: *Hot Streak* / Dressing up: *Street Angels* / Tonight: *Harvey, Steve* / All my life: *Major Harris.*
■ LP . . . . . . . . . . DX 1
■ MC. . . . . . . . . . DXC 1
Decca / Dec '83.

**DANCEMASTERS - VOLUME 1.**
**Tracks:** Move to the bigband (extended club mix): *Liebrand, Ben* / Heaven: *Chimes (1)* / Boomin' system, The (The underground mix): *L.L. Cool J* / My kinda girl (LP version): *Babyface* / Right here right now (extended mix): *Western Block* / Can't do nuttin' for ya man (bass in your face: *Public Enemy* / I'll be around (after dark mix): *Nayobe* / Steppin' to the A.M. (soiree mix): *3rd Bass* / Good lovin' (Frankie Foncett mix): *Belle, Regina* / Tubular bells (extended version): *Plutonic* / Double Dutch on the sidewalk (extended mix): *Newkirk* / Flowers (wizdum mix): *Emotions (2)* / Emotions electric (Frankie Foncett mix): *Guy Called Gerald* / Get free (Eden upstairs remix): *Mwale, Anna* / Money can't buy you love: *Midnight Star* / Pianonegro (Honky Tonk remix): *Pianonegro* / Since day one (Jazzie B mix): *Marie, Teena* / Family affair (echo vox mix): *Sly & The Family Stone* / Jazz thing (video mix): *Gang Starr* / Feel it (long version): *Afros.*
■ LP . . . . . . . . . . DD 1
■ CD. . . . . . . . . . DDCD 1
■ MC. . . . . . . . . . DDC 1
Dance Division / Nov '90.

**DANCIN'.**
**Tracks:** Dancing in the street: *Reeves, Martha* / Cloud 9: *Temptations* / This old heart of mine: *Isley Brothers* / Tears of a clown: *Robinson, Smokey* / There's a ghost in my house: *Taylor, Dean* / For once in my life: *Wonder, Stevie* / I'm a roadrunner: *Walker, Junior* / War: *Starr, Edwin* / Ball of confusion: *Temptations* / Reach out and touch: *Four Tops* / Upside down: *Ross, Diana* / Signed, sealed, delivered (I'm yours): *Wonder, Stevie* / River deep, mountain high: *Supremes & Four Tops* / Love machine (part 1) / Machine gun: *Commodores* / Let's get serious: *Jackson, Jermaine* / Behind the groove: *Marie, Teena* / Papa was a rollin' stone: *Temptations* / Long hangover: *Ross, Diana* / I want you back: *Jackson Five.*
■ LP . . . . . . . . . . STAR 2225
MC. . . . . . . . . . STAC 2225
Telstar/Ronco / Nov '82 / BMG.

**DANCIN'.**
**Tracks:** Not Advised.
■ LP . . . . . . . . . . INRLP 2
MC. . . . . . . . . . INRC 2
In Recordings / Dec '86.

**DANCING 'TIL DAWN.**
**Tracks:** Woman love thief: *Stemmons Express* / I'm your yes man: *Reid, Clarence* / Lost love: *Irma & The Fascinations* / Please stay: *Ivorys* / Come back baby: *Dodds, Nella* / Show me a man: *Bradshaw, Bobby* / Livin' the nightlife: *Charts* / Out on the streets again: *Candy & The Kisses* / Last minute miracle: *Shirelles* / You busted my mind: *Clay, Judy* / Let me give you my lovin': *Brown, Maxine* / Name it and claim it: *Stewart, Darryl* / Black eyed girl: *Thompson, Billy* / Ain't that peculiar: *Tindley, George* / These chains of love (are breaking me down): *Jackson, Chuck* / Help me: *Wilson, Al.*
■ LP . . . . . . . . . . KENT 026
Kent / Oct '84.

**DANCING 'TIL DAWN.**
**Tracks:** Last minute miracle / Help me / This man / Woman lover thief / One in a million / Come back baby / Everything is everything / Marching / Out on the streets again / Love, it's getting better / Get on up / Desiree / Do you believe it / I'm your yes man / Work song / These chains of love (Are breaking me down) / Ain't that peculiar / Stop sign / Ain't no soul / Name it and claim it / Tightrope / You busted my mind / Love is a good foundation / There comes a time / I don't have a mind of my own.
CD. . . . . . . . . . CDKEND 106
Kent / Feb '94 / Pinnacle.

**DANCING ON THE FLOOR - THE 80'S REVISITED.**
**Tracks:** Dancing on the floor (hooked on love): *Third World* / Rockit: *Hancock, Herbie* / Roses: *Haywoode* / Taste of bitter love: *Knight, Gladys & The Pips* / Juicy fruit: *Mtume* / Autodrive: *Hancock, Herbie* / See the day: *Lee, Dee C.* / How 'bout us: *Champaign* / It's raining men: *Weather Girls* / I wonder if I take you home: *Lisa Lisa & Cult Jam with Full Force* / Let's hear it for the boy: *Williams, Deniece* / Give it up: *K.C. & The Sunshine Band* / Break my stride: *Wilder, Matthew* / My favourite waste of time: *Paul, Owen* / Bourgie Bourgie: *Knight, Gladys & The Pips* / Hold me tighter in the rain: *Griffin, Billy* / Amityville (the house on the hill): *Lovebug Starski* / Alice, i want you just for me: *Full Force.*
CD. . . . . . . . . . PWKS 4059
MC. . . . . . . . . . PWKMC 4059
Pickwick / Jun '91 / Pickwick.

**DEEP IN THE PHILLY GROOVE.**
**Tracks:** La-la means I love you / I need your love so bad / So long, goodbye, it's over / When times are bad / Goodbye pain / Face the future / Didn't I / One and one is five / When the bottom falls out / Follow the lamb / Not goin' to let you (Talk to me that way) / Didn't we make it / Puff puff, you're gone / Ruby Lee / You are my sun sign part 1 / Handle with care / I want to be your lover / Player / Armed and extremely dangerous / Smarty pants / Delfonics theme (How could you) / Can't go on living.
CD. . . . . . . . . . CDKEND 115
Kent / May '94 / Pinnacle.

**DEEP SOUL COLLECTION, THE.**
**Tracks:** Not Advised.
■ CD Set. . . . . . . . . . CDBOX 251
■ LP Set. . . . . . . . . . BOX 251
■ MC Set . . . . . . . . . . TCBOX 251
Charly / Nov '89.

**DEEP SOUL OF STAX.**
**Tracks:** Not Advised.
■ LP . . . . . . . . . . SXATS 1037
Stax / Nov '70.

**DEEP SOUTH MUSICAL ROOTS TOUR, THE.**
**Tracks:** Not Advised.
MC. . . . . . . . . . GVMC 228
Global Village / May '93 / A.D.A. Distribution / Topic Records / Direct Distribution.

**DEEP SOUTH, THE.**
**Tracks:** Cheaters never win: *Borders Tony* / I can't make it by myself: *Gardner, Stu* / Afflicted: *Wright, O.V.* / Gonna try: *Mike & The Censations* / Everyday will be like a holiday: *Haywood, Leon* / Something reminds me: *Carter, Melvin* / Everyday of my life:

494 ■ DELETED

Augustine Twins / I Wake Up Crying: Leroy & The Drivers / Ain't much of a home: James, Jesse / Bring It Down: Jon-Lee Group / I feel like crying: Sam & Bill / Thanks for yesterday: Eddie & Ernie / Will my baby: Lee, Little Mr. / These Arms of Mine: Matt & Robert / In return for your love: Tolliver, Kim / Keep on loving me: Bland, Bobby.
■ LP . . . . . . . . . . . . . . . . . . . . KENT 075
Kent / Mar '88.

## DEEPEST SOUL, THE.
Tracks: I'm lonely: Sanders, Nelson / You got me on a string: Freeman Brothers / You should have told me: New Yorkers / I'll be gone: Turner, Tommy / Just a little more love: Soul Commanders / Love as true as mine: Roc-kays Band / I've learned my lesson: Richardson, Donald Lee / Don't waste my time: Sinceres / Ain't gonna do you no good: Willis, Betty / These feelings: Phil & Del / Helpless girl: Staten, Little Mary / Whole lot of tears: Stuart, Jeb / Pick yourself up: Taylor, E.G. & The Sound of Soul / I'm still hurt: Little Tom / Human: Ad Libs / I worship the ground you walk on: Ad Libs / Teach me to love again: Scott, Kurtis / It won't hurt: Bogen, Richard / I'll be there: Tenderonies / Please come back: Tate, Jimmy / Make the best of what you've got: Patton, Alexander / I'm beggin' you baby: Vibra-Tones & George Johnson / Never let me go: Vibra-Tones & George Johnson.
CD . . . . . . . . . . . . . . . . . . . . GSCD 016
Goldmine / Jul '93 / Vital Distribution.

## DETROIT A-GO-GO.
Tracks: If it's all the same to you: Ingram, Luther / Cool off: Detroit Executives / Mighty lover: Ideals / Exus trek: Ingram, Luther / Get it baby: Mitchell, Stanley / Down in the dumps: Hester, Tony / Rosemary what happened: Wylie, Richard 'Popcorn' / Hanky panky: Wylie, Richard 'Popcorn' / Spaceland: Hester, Tony / Say it isn't so: Boo, Betty (1) / Frantic escape: Innocent Bystanders / Saving my love for you: People's Choice.
■ LP . . . . . . . . . . . . . . . . . . . . BURN 11
Inferno (1) / Jun '84.

## DETROIT GOLD VOL. 1.
Tracks: Not Advised.
■ LP . . . . . . . . . . . . . . . . . . . . SS 8021
Solid Smoke (USA) / Jul '84.

## DETROIT GOLD VOL. 2.
Tracks: Not Advised.
■ LP . . . . . . . . . . . . . . . . . . . . SS 8022
Solid Smoke (USA) / Jul '84.

## DETROIT SOUL FROM THE VAULTS VOL.1.
Tracks: Soul sloopy: Dynamics / Yes I love you baby (inst): Dynamics / Head and shoulders: Young, Patti / Love keeps falling away: Williams, Lloyd & Highlights / It won't matter at all: Williams, Lloyd & Highlights / Arabia (inst): Royal Playboys / What's wrong with your love (No. 2): Metros / Don't let her give you some of her love: Metros / It's real: Sanders, Nelson / Music in my soul: Milner, Reggie / Make a change: Rogers, Johnny / Soul food (inst): Rogers, Johnny / Open the door to your heart: Burdick, Doni / I have faith in you: Burdick, Doni / Give my heart a break: Turner, Sammy / Fascinating girl (inst): Lemons, George / We go to pieces (inst): Hairston, Forest / Love to a guy: Dynamics / Keep a hold on me: Lewis, Diane / Kangaroo dance: Williams, Lloyd & Highlights / Opposites attract: Swingers / I'll be on my way: Bob & Fred.
CD . . . . . . . . . . . . . . . . . . . . GSCD 019
Goldmine / Aug '93 / Vital Distribution.

## DETROIT SOUL FROM THE VAULTS VOL.2.
Tracks: Yes, I love you baby: Dynamics / Head and shoulders: Young, Patti / I've got that feelin': Garcia, Frankie / Lovin' touch: Satin Dolls / First degree love: Vaughan, Lafayette / Arabia: Royal Playboys / What's wrong with your love (No. 1): Metros / We still have time: Metros / Candle: Burdick, Doni / Whatcha gonna do: Burdick, Doni / Make a change (inst): Rogers, Johnny / Soul food: Rogers, Johnny / If you walk out of my life: Burdick, Doni / Bari track: Burdick, Doni / Merry go round: Frontera, Tommy / Fascinating girl: Lemons, George / We go to pieces: Hairston, Forest / Whenever I'm without you: Dynamics / Nobody likes me: White, Willie / Go down: Highlights / Lookin' for a woman: Brooks Brothers / I'll be on my way: Bob & Fred.
CD . . . . . . . . . . . . . . . . . . . . GSCD 020
Goldmine / Aug '93 / Vital Distribution.

## DETROIT SOUL OF POPCORN WYLIE, THE.
Tracks: Sweet darlin': Clark, Joe / Going to a deal: Neal, Tommy / Quit twistin' my arm: Mitchell, Stanley / It's OK with me: Wright, Larry / Just can't leave you: Hester, Tony / Save my lovin' for you: People's

Choice / Stone broke: Ward, Sam / With a lonely heart: 4 Voices / Such a soul stays: Third Party / Cool off: Detroit Executives / Rosemary: Popcorn Wylie / My baby ain't no plaything: New Holidays / You better go go: Lucas, Matt (2) / Say it isn't so: Boo, Betty (2) / Down in the dumps: Hester, Tony / Hold your horses: Clarke, Jimmy / I'll make you mine: Valiant Trio / Spaceland: Hester, Tony / Spellbound: Boo, Betty (2) / Angelina, Angelina: Ames, Stuart / Hanky panky: Popcorn Wylie / I'll be your champion: Hester, Tony / Hurting: Eric & The Vikings / Stop that boy: Boo, Betty (2) / King for a day: Ames, Stuart.
CD . . . . . . . . . . . . . . . . . . . . GSCD 030
Goldmine / Mar '94 / Vital Distribution.

## DIAL STORY VOL 1.
Tracks: Only girl I've ever loved: Tex, Joe / Since I found you: Kelly, Paul / You really fooled me: Harris, Chris / I've got a thing: Marchan, Bobby / Rifle man: Harris, Chris / Meet me in church: Tex, Joe / I can't help it: Kelly, Paul / I gotta sit down and cry: Marchan, Bobby / Chills and fever: Kelly, Paul / Ooo baby baby: Magnificent Seven / Get down on it: Marchan, Bobby / Don't let your left hand know: Tex, Joe / It comes and it goes: Wade, Len / Never will I make my baby cry: Magnificent Seven / Only your love: Kelly, Paul / Half a mind: Marchan, Bobby / You oughta be here with me: Snell, Annette / Can you dig it: Floyd, King / Dr. Funky: Harris, Chris / We're gonna make it: Kelly, Paul / Woman stealer: Tex, Joe / Learning to forget you: Floyd, King / Call another doctor (on the case): Kelly, Paul / Tell 'em who I am: Harris, Chris / Sad sack: Marchan, Bobby / Nine out of ten times: Kelly, Paul / I'll be your fool (once more): Snell, Annette / Save me: Holiday, Jimmy / I just want what belongs to me: Marchan, Bobby / Footprints on my mind: Snell, Annette / I need your love so bad: Kelly, Paul / Sing a song of love: Holiday, Jimmy.
CD . . . . . . . . . . . . . . . . . . . . CDCHARLY 207
Charly / Apr '90 / Charly.

## DISCO (50 Great Dancing Hits).
Tracks: Not Advised.
■ Double LP . . . . . . . . . . . . . . . . RML 101
MC Set . . . . . . . . . . . . . . . . . . RML 4C101
Ronco / Nov '83.

## DISCO BEACH PARTY.
Tracks: Not Advised.
■ Double LP . . . . . . . . . . . . . . . . SMR 8503
■ MC Set . . . . . . . . . . . . . . . . . SMC 8503
Stylus / May '86.

## DISCO DANCERS VOL.2.
Tracks: Play that funky music: Wild Cherry / Getaway / Soul city walk: Bell, Archie & The Drells / You ought to be havin' fun / Get you somebody new / From now on / Hurt: Manhattans / Message in our music: O'Jays / Lowdown: Scaggs, Boz / Git it up / Dance sister dance / More you do it / Movin' in all directions / Salty tears.
■ LP . . . . . . . . . . . . . . . . . . . . CBS 81816
CBS / Feb '77.

## DISCO DAZE.
Tracks: Not Advised.
CD . . . . . . . . . . . . . . . . . . . . MATCD 261
Castle / May '93 / BMG.
MC . . . . . . . . . . . . . . . . . . . . MATMC 261
Castle / Aug '94 / BMG.

## DISCO DAZE - DISCO NITES.
Tracks: I feel love: Summer, Donna / Contact: Starr, Edwin / And the beat goes on: Whispers / I owe you one: Shalamar / Don't push it don't force it: Haywood, Leon / Bourgie bourgie: Knight, Gladys / One nation under a groove: Funkadelic / Ain't gonna bump no more: Tex, Joe / Southern Freeez: Freeez / Rappers delight: Sugarhill Gang / Stuff like that: Jones, Quincy / Searching: Change / More, more, more: Andrea True Connection / Rapp payback: Brown, James / Intuition: Linx / Knock on wood: Stewart, Amii / Ain't no stoppin' us now: McFadden & Whitehead / Jump to the beat: Lattisaw, Stacy / Stomp: Brothers Johnson / It makes you feel like dancin': Rose Royce / Funky town: Lipps Inc. / Instant replay: Hartman, Dan / Le freak: Chic / Somebody help me out: Beggar & Co / Ring my bell: Ward, Anita / Get down: Chandler, Gene / Lady Marmalade: Labelle / Everybody get up: UK Players / Can you feel the force: Four Seasons / December '63 (oh what a night): Four Seasons.
■ Double LP . . . . . . . . . . . . . . . . RTL 2056 A/B
MC Set . . . . . . . . . . . . . . . . . . 4CRTL 2056 A/B
Ronco / Apr '81.

## DISCO DIRECTION.
Tracks: Yes sir, I can boogie: Baccara / Keep it up: Olympic Runners / Native New Yorker: Odyssey / On the road again: Rogers, D.J. / Dance and shake your funky tambourine: Inner City Express / Turn the beat

around: Robinson, Vickie Sue / Whispering: Dr. Buzzard's Original Savannah Band / Make it with you: Whispers / Shame: King, Evelyn 'Champagne' / Uptown fesitval: Shalamar / Star wars theme: Meco / Crunch: Rah Band / Who is gonna love me: Davison, Alfie / I'll play the fool: Dr. Buzzard's Original Savannah Band / Hold tight: Robinson, Vickie Sue / Shu' dig dancin' (in my hi-heeled shoes): Inner City Express / Funky tropical: Vanderbilt, Lee / Whatever it takes: Olympic Runners / Sorry I'm a lady: Baccara / Close Encounters of the Third Kind suite: Meco.
■ LP . . . . . . . . . . . . . . . . . . . . PL 42477
■ MC. . . . . . . . . . . . . . . . . . . . PK 42477
RCA / May '78.

## DISCO DYNAMITE.
Tracks: Not Advised.
MC Set . . . . . . . . . . . . . . . . . . TTMC 081
Tring / Mar '93 / Prism Leisure PLC / Midland Records.

## DISCO EXPLOSION.
Tracks: Not Advised.
CD . . . . . . . . . . . . . . . . . . . . GRF 211
MC. . . . . . . . . . . . . . . . . . . . MCGRF 211
Tring / Apr '93 / Prism Leisure PLC / Midland Records.

## DISCO FEVER.
Tracks: Get up offa that thing: Brown, James / I love the nightlife (disco round): Bridges, Alicia / Rock the boat: Hues Corporation / That's the way I like it: K.C. & The Sunshine Band / Ladies night: Kool & The Gang / Right back where we started from: Nightingale, Maxine / Hustle: McCoy, Van / I'm on fire: 5000 Volts / Yes Sir, I can boogie: Baccara / Best disco in town: Ritchie Family / I was made for dancin': Garrett, Leif / Do what you wanna do: T-Connection / If I can't have you: Elliman, Yvonne / Don't push it, don't force it: Haywood, Leon / Hang on in there baby: Bristol, Johnny / Ms. Grace: Tymes / Rock your baby: McCrae, George / Disco Queen: Hot Chocolate / More than a woman: Tavares / You're the first, the last, my everything: White, Barry.
CD . . . . . . . . . . . . . . . . . . . . CDPR 110
MC. . . . . . . . . . . . . . . . . . . . TCPR 110
MFP / Jun '93 / EMI.

## DISCO FRENZY.
Tracks: Not Advised.
■ LP . . . . . . . . . . . . . . . . . . . . SHM 978
Pickwick / '79.

## DISCO HEAT.
Tracks: Use it up and wear it out: Odyssey / Car wash: Rose Royce / More more more: Andrea True Connection / You can do it: Hudson, Al & The Partners / (Do the) Spanish hustle: Fatback Band / Shame shame shame: Shirley & Company / (You love keeps lifting me) Higher & higher: Wilson, Jackie / (Sending out an) S.O.S.: Wilson, Jackie / (You make me feel) Mighty real: Sylvester / Shaft: Hayes, Isaac / I'll take you there: Staple Singers / My man, a sweet man: Jackson, Millie / Shame: King, Evelyn 'Champagne' / Rock the boat: Hues Corporation / Disco stomp: Bohannon, Hamilton / Walking in rhythm: Blackbyrds.
CD . . . . . . . . . . . . . . . . . . . . PWKS 4148
MC. . . . . . . . . . . . . . . . . . . . PWKMC 4184
Pickwick / Oct '94 / Pickwick.

## DISCO INFERNO.
Tracks: Not Advised.
MC. . . . . . . . . . . . . . . . . . . . VCA 045
VFM Cassettes / Jan '85 / VFM Children's Entertainment Ltd. / Midland Records.

## DISCO INFERNO.
Tracks: Not Advised.
CD . . . . . . . . . . . . . . . . . . . . GRF 212
MC. . . . . . . . . . . . . . . . . . . . MCGRF 212
Tring / Mar '93 / Prism Leisure PLC / Midland Records.

## DISCO INFERNO.
Tracks: Lost in music: Sister Sledge / Le Freak: Chic / You make me feel: Sylvester / I'm every woman: Khan, Chaka / Young hearts run free: Staton, Candi / Is it love you're after: Rose Royce / Jump to the beat: Lattisaw, Stacy / Working my way back to you: Detroit Spinners / Here I go again: Bell, Archie / Supernature: Cerrone / Disco Inferno: Trammps / Dance dance dance: Chic / Nights on Broadway: Staton, Candi / Lover's holiday: Change / I shoulda loved ya: Walden, Narada Michael / Then came you: Warwick, Dionne & The Detroit Spinners / Spacer: Sheila & B Devotion / Searching: Change / We are family: Sister Sledge / Theme from Shaft: Hayes, Isaac.
CD . . . . . . . . . . . . . . . . . . . . 954831963-2
MC. . . . . . . . . . . . . . . . . . . . 954831963-4
WEA / Jun '93 / WEA.

## DISCO INFERNO 2.
**Tracks:** Shame: *King, Evelyn 'Champagne'* / Funkin' for Jamaica: *Browne, Tom* / Thinking of you: *Sister Sledge* / Native New Yorker: *Odyssey* / I'll be around: *Detroit Spinners* / Keep the fire burning: *McCrae, Gwen* / Love has come around: *Byrd, Donald* / You're a star: *Aquarian Dream* / Southern Freeez: *Freeez* / He's the greatest dancer: *Sister Sledge* / Everybody dance: *Chic* / It makes you feel like dancin': *Rose Royce* / Just a touch of love: *Slave* / Glow of love: *Change* / Ghetto child: *Detroit Spinners* / Funky nassau: *Beginning Of The End* / Get up and boogie: *Silver Convention* / Funky sensation: *McCrae, Gwen* / Forget me nots: *Rushen, Patrice.*
CD . . . . . . . . . . . . . . . . . . . . . .954832423-2
MC. . . . . . . . . . . . . . . . . . . . . . .954832423-4
East West / Dec '93 / WEA.

## DISCO MAGIC.
**Tracks:** Not Advised.
■ **Double LP.** . . . . . . . . . . . . . . . . PLD 8015
Pickwick / Oct '79.

## DISCO MIXES.
**Tracks:** Not Advised.
CD . . . . . . . . . . . . . . . . . . . . . . . .JHD 087
MC. . . . . . . . . . . . . . . . . . . . . . . .MCJHD 087
Tring / Mar '93 / Prism Leisure PLC / Midland Records.

## DISCO NIGHTS.
**Tracks:** Just an illusion: *Imagination* / I'm so excited: *Pointer Sisters* / System addict: *Five Star* / Going back to my roots: *Odyssey* / Give it up: *K.C. & The Sunshine Band* / She's strange: *Cameo (1)* / Rock the boat: *Hues Corporation* / Jumpin' Jack flash: *Franklin, Aretha* / Let the music play: *White, Barry* / Boogie wonderland: *Earth, Wind & Fire* / Can you feel it: *Jacksons* / Burn rubber on me: *Gap Band* / Love come down: *King, Evelyn 'Champagne'* / Mama used to say: *Giscombe, Junior* / Rockit: *Hancock, Herbie* / It's a disco night: *Isley Brothers* / Livin' in America: *Brown, James.*
■ MC. . . . . . . . . . . . . . . . . . . . . . . BRC 2505
Bravo / Feb '85.
CD . . . . . . . . . . . . . . . . . . . . . . . . PMP 104
Pickwick / Nov '92 / Pickwick.

## DISCO PAARRRTY.
**Tracks:** Let it flow / For the love of money / Inside America: *Jones, Juggy* / Breakaway: *Bush, Ernie* / Golden gate get down / Gotham City.
■ LP . . . . . . . . . . . . . . . . . . . . . . .CLP 540
Contempo (1) / Feb '77.

## DISCO SATURDAY NIGHT.
**Tracks:** Not Advised.
■ **MC Set** . . . . . . . . . . . . . . . . . . PLDC 8004
■ **Double LP.** . . . . . . . . . . . . . . . . PLD 8004
Pickwick / Sep '79.

## DISCO SIZZLERS.
**Tracks:** Wings of fire: *Coffey, Dennis* / Devil's gun: *CJ & Co.* / Feel the need: *Detroit Emeralds* / Bull: *Theodore, Mike Orchestra.*
■ LP . . . . . . . . . . . . . . . . . . . . . . . K 50546
Atlantic / '77.

## DISCO SPECTACULAR.
**Tracks:** Aquarius / Let the sun shine in / Where do I go / Easy to be hard / Good morning starshine.
■ LP . . . . . . . . . . . . . . . . . . . . . . . PL 13356
■ MC. . . . . . . . . . . . . . . . . . . . . . . PK 13356
RCA / May '79.

## DISCO STARTRACKS.
**Tracks:** Devils gun: *CJ & Co.* / Dance, dance, dance: *Chic* / Pinnochio theory: *Bootsy's Rubber Band* / World I a ghetto: *Benson, George* / Belfast: *Boney M* / From now on: *Clifford, Linda* / Do you believe in love at first sight: *Warwick, Dionne* / Love per hour: *Trammps* / Nights on Broadway: *Staton, Candi* / Waterbed: *Mann, Herbie* / Cosmic wind: *Theodore, Mike Orchestra* / Feel the need: *Detroit Emeralds* / Disco inferno: *Trammps* / I believe in music: *Mass Production* / I got to have your love: *Fantastic Four* / Pick up the pieces: *Average White Band* / Free spirit: *Coffey, Dennis* / Wings of fire: *Coffey, Dennis* / Rubberband man: *Detroit Spinners* / It makes you feel like dancin': *Rose Royce.*
■ LP . . . . . . . . . . . . . . . . . . . . . . K4 58041
WEA / '77.

## DISCO UK/DISCO USA.
**Tracks:** Just an illusion: *Imagination* / Rapture: *Blondie* / Gangsters of the groove: *Heatwave* / Do you feel my love: *Grant, Eddy* / I'm every woman: *Khan, Chaka* / Happy birthday: *Oxygen* / Super Casanova: *Hot Gossip* / I can't stand the rain: *Eruption (1)* / I just wanna (spend some time with you): *Edwards, Alton* / Ai no corrida: *Jones, Quincy* / So this is romance: *Linx* / Queen of the rapping scene: *Modern Romance* / I shot the sheriff: *Light Of The World* / Boogie on up: *Rokotto* / Wikka wrap: *Evasions* / British hustle: *Hi-Tension* / All American girls: *Sister Sledge* / Roller jubilee: *Di Meola, Al* / You're the one for me: *D-Train* / You bet your love: *Hancock, Herbie* / Taste of bitter love: *Knight, Gladys* / Fungi mama: *Browne, Tom* / Gonna get along without you now: *Wills, Viola* / It's a disco night (rock don't stop): *Isley Brothers* / I want your love: *Chic* / My simple heart: *Three Degrees* / I've got to learn to say no: *Fields, Richard 'Dimples'* / Sign of the times: *James, Bob* / Groove: *Franklin, Rodney* / Hold on to love: *Bristol, Johnny* / Holdin' out for love: *Bofill, Angela* / Keep on dancing: *Gary's Gang* / Light my fire: *Stewart, Amii.*
■ **Double LP.** . . . . . . . . . . . . . . .RTL 2073 A/B
Ronco / Mar '82.

## DISCO YEARS 1974-1979.
**Tracks:** Not Advised.
CD . . . . . . . . . . . . . . . . . . . . . . . . 241 677-2
■ LP . . . . . . . . . . . . . . . . . . . . . . . 241 677-1
MC. . . . . . . . . . . . . . . . . . . . . . . . 241 677-4
Atlantic / Nov '89 / WEA.

## DISTURB MY SOUL.
**Tracks:** Assassination / Nail print / Hush hush / He's a friend of mine / Our freedom song / All I need is some sunshine in my life / I don't know / All these things to me / Wade in the water / God's promise / I learned to pray / Stop laughing at your fellow man / Jesus will fix it / This is our prayer / It comes at the end of the race / He's worthy / Child of God / Till Jesus comes / Give me one more chance / Press my dying pillow / There's not a friend / Forgive these fools / Son of God / Even me.
CD . . . . . . . . . . . . . . . . . . . . . . . CDSXD 086
Stax / Feb '94 / Pinnacle.

## DIVAS.
**Tracks:** Not Advised.
■ CD . . . . . . . . . . . . . . . . . . . CDMOTCLP 51
Motor City / Jan '91.
CD . . . . . . . . . . . . . . . . . . . . . . . MOTCCD 67
Motor City / Oct '92 / Total / BMG.

## DO IT FLUID: 6 RARE GROOVES.
**Tracks:** Fantasy: *Smith, Johnny "Hammond"* / Joyous: *Pleasure (2)* / Hump: *Rushen, Patrice* / Always there: *Side Effect* / Do it fluid: *Blackbyrds* / Concrete jungle: *Three Pieces.*
■ LP . . . . . . . . . . . . . . . . . . . . . . . BGP 1002
■ MC. . . . . . . . . . . . . . . . . . . . . . . BGPC 1002
BGP / Oct '87.

## DO IT FLUID: B&G PARTY.
**Tracks:** Not Advised.
CD . . . . . . . . . . . . . . . . . . . . . . . CDBGP 1036
BGP / Apr '92 / Pinnacle.

## DO THE CROSSOVER BABY.
**Tracks:** I'll never stop loving you: *Thomas, Carla* / I got the vibes: *Armstead, Jo* / Stars: *Lewis, Barbara* / I'm the one who loves you: *Banks, Darrell* / I may not be what you want: *Mel & Tim* / Whole damned world gone crazy: *Williams, John Gary* / Be my lady: *Astors* / Since I lost my baby's love: *Lance, Major* / Bark at the moon: *Floyd, Eddie* / Catch that man: *John, Mable* / Little by little & bit by bit: *Weston, Kim* / You're my only temptation: *Ryan, Roz* / Whole world's a picture show: *Newcomers* / Special kind of woman: *Thompson, Paul* / I play for keeps: *Thomas, Carla* / Sweet sherry: *Barnes, J.J.* / Sacrifice: *Bell, William* / Loving by the pound: *Redding, Otis* / Just keep on lovin' me: *Mancha, Steve* / Man in the street: *Bell, William* / Trippin' on your love: *Staple Singers* / Did my baby call: *Mad Lads (1)* / Where would you be today: *Ilana* / One more chance: *Joseph, Margie.*
CD . . . . . . . . . . . . . . . . . . . . . . . CDKEND 105
Kent / Aug '93 / Pinnacle.

## DOIN' IT.
**Tracks:** Zaius: *Russ, Eddie* / Groove: *Franklin, Rodney* / Always there: *Bobo, Willie* / That's the way of the world: *Lewis, Ramsey* / Reach out: *Duke, George* / Doin' it: *Hancock, Herbie* / Sneaking up behind you: *Brecker Brothers* / Funkin' for America: *Browne, Tom* / Get down everybody: *Smith, Lonnie Liston* / Johannesburg: *Scott-Heron, Gil* / Hooked on young stuff: *Tempo, Nino & 5th Avenue Sax* / Streetwave: *Brothers Johnson.*
CD . . . . . . . . . . . . . . . . . . . . . . . RNBCD 104
MC. . . . . . . . . . . . . . . . . . . . . . . .RNBMC 104
Connoisseur Collection / Aug '93 / Pinnacle.

## DON'T STOP DANCING.
**Tracks:** Don't stop till you get enough: *Jackson, Michael* / It's raining men: *Weather Girls* / Doctor doctor: *Thompson Twins* / What do I do: *Fearon, Phil & Galaxy* / Your love is king: *Sade* / Just be good to me: *S.O.S. Band* / All night long: *Mary Jane Girls* / Dance hall days: *Wang Chung* / That's the way I like it: *Dead Or Alive* / Relax: *Frankie Goes To Hollywood* / Street dance: *Break Machine* / Somebody's watching me: *Rockwell* / 99 red balloons: *Nena* / Somebody else's guy: *Brown, Jocelyn* / I am what I am: *Gaynor, Gloria* / To be or not to be (the hitler rap): *Brooks, Mel* / Watching you watching me: *Grant, David* / Do it again, Billie Jean: *Club House.*
■ LP . . . . . . . . . . . . . . . . . . . . . . . STAR 2242
MC. . . . . . . . . . . . . . . . . . . . . . . . STAC 2242
Telstar/Ronco / May '84 / BMG.

## DON'T STOP THE MUSIC.
**Tracks:** Not Advised.
CD . . . . . . . . . . . . . . . . . . . . . . . . SMD 977
■ LP . . . . . . . . . . . . . . . . . . . . . . . SMR 977
MC. . . . . . . . . . . . . . . . . . . . . . . . SMC 977
Stylus / Jun '89.

## DON'T STOP THE MUSIC.
**Tracks:** Don't stop the music: *Yarbrough & Peoples* / Get down: *Chandler, Gene* / Ladies night: *Kool & The Gang* / Never can say goodbye: *Gaynor, Gloria* / Shake your groove thing: *Peaches & Herb* / You're my first my last: *White, Barry* / Candy girl: *New Edition (1)* / Get on up, get on down: *Ayers, Roy* / She's a bad mama jama: *Carlton, Carl* / Happy radio: *Starr, Edwin* / Love come down: *King, Evelyn 'Champagne'* / Ms. Grace: *Tymes* / Rock the boat: *Hues Corporation* / Jump for my love: *Pointer Sisters* / Just an illusion: *Imagination* / Going back to my roots: *Odyssey* / Stomp: *Brothers Johnson* / Razzamatazz: *Jones, Quincy* / Be thankful for what you've got: *DeVaughan, William* / I'm doing fine now: *New York City* / Swing your daddy: *Gilstrap, Jim* / Sending out an S.O.S.: *Young, Retta* / Zing went the strings of my heart: *Trammps* / You to me are everything: *Real Thing.*
CD . . . . . . . . . . . . . . . . . . . . . . . . .CD 3218
Pickwick / Sep '92 / Pickwick.

## DORADO COMPILATION 1.
**Tracks:** Scheme of things: *D Note* / Impressions: *Giant Steps NYC* / Sally's knocking: *Anderson, Jhelisa* / 13th Key: *Sunship* / Rain: *D Note* / Ain't no fun: *Monkey Business* / Circle of cruelty: *Circle in the sand.*
CD . . . . . . . . . . . . . . . . . . . . . . . DOR 008 CD
Dorado / Sep '92 / RTM / Pinnacle.

## DORADO COMPILATION 2.
**Tracks:** Not Advised.
CD . . . . . . . . . . . . . . . . . . . . . . . .DOR 016CD
LP . . . . . . . . . . . . . . . . . . . . . . . .DOR 016LP
Dorado / Oct '93 / RTM / Pinnacle.

## DORADO COMPILATION 3.
**Tracks:** Not Advised.
CD . . . . . . . . . . . . . . . . . . . . . . . . DORO 20CD
LP Set. . . . . . . . . . . . . . . . . . . . . .DORO 20LP
Dorado / May '94 / RTM / Pinnacle.

## DOUBLE DECKERS.
**Tracks:** Just an illusion: *Imagination* / Never let you go: *Savanna* / Just a little bit: *Thompson, Carroll* / Love you've been fakin': *Index (1)* / Ease your mind: *Touchdown* / Jingo: *Candido* / Feels like I'm in love: *Marie, Kelly* / Love is gonna be on your side: *Firefly* / Do it (till you're satisfied): *B.T. Express* / Lock it up: *Leprechaun* / Take your time: *Hamilton, Roy (1)* / Nice and slow: *Green, Jesse* / I like plastic: *Raven, Marsha* / I can't turn away: *Savanna* / Puerto Rico: *Decoupage* / I like what you're doing (to me): *Young & Co.* / You don't like my music: *Kid* / Nice and soft: *Wish* / It's just a groove: *Adams, Glen Affair* / Dancin' and prancin': *Candido.*
■ **Double LP.** . . . . . . . . . . . . . . . . . . .RDD 1
**MC Set** . . . . . . . . . . . . . . . . . . . . . ZCRDD 1
Red Bus / Nov '82 / Total / BMG.

## DOWN TO THE LAST HEARTBREAK.
**Tracks:** Hello heartbreaker: *Little Charles & The Sidewinders* / He's the kind of guy: *Clay, Judy* / One more time: *Scott, Benny* / Not now but later: *Johnson, Walter* / I'm down to my last heartbreak: *Pickett, Wilson* / Big mistake: *Parker, John* / It sho' ain't me: *Turner, Ike & Tina* / Can't get enough: *Thomas, Irma* / Don't stop loving me this time: *Preyer, Marvin* / I'm really thankful: *Troy, J B* / Love makes good things unwise / Lonesome guy: *Robinson, Roscoe* / Strange lips start old memories: *Traits* / Every man needs a woman: *Troy, J B* / You're gonna reap what you sow: *Copeland, Johnny.*
■ LP . . . . . . . . . . . . . . . . . . . . . . . KENT 084
Kent / Oct '88.

## DOWNTOWN DISCO PARTY.
**Tracks:** Which way is up / What you waitin' for / Put your money where your mouth is / Galaxy / Car wash / Music for gong gong / Peter Gunn / Clapping song / 1-2-3 / Drift away / Walkin' in the rain with the one I love.
■ LP . . . . . . . . . . . . . . . . . . . . . . . MCF 2866
MCA / Nov '78.



■ DELETED

# E

## EBONY.

**Tracks:** I don't wanna dance: *Grant, Eddy* / Deja vu: *Warwick, Dionne* / Ms. Grace: *Tymes* / You to me are everything: *Real Thing* / Stand by me: *King, Ben E.* / Ebony: *Williams, George* / Me and Mrs. Jones: *Paul, Billy* / Letter: *Warwick, Dionne* / I wanna get next to you: *Rose Royce* / Hurt: *Manhattans* / Tears on my pillow: *Nash, Johnny* / Make it with you: *Williams, Esther* / Sad sweet dreamer: *Sweet Sensation* / Midnight train to Georgia: *Knight, Gladys* / Lady love: *Rawls, Lou* / My simple heart: *Three Degrees* / Love is: *Brothers Johnson* / I'm stone in love with you: *Mathis, Johnny* / One in a million (girl): *O'Jays* / Don't make me over: *Houston, Thelma* / One hundred ways: *Jones, Quincy* / Float on: *Floaters* / Circles: *Atlantic Starr* / Free: *Williams, Deniece* / Drift away / Hey girl, don't bother me: *Tams* / Rescue me: *Bass, Fontella* / If you don't know me by now: *Melvin, Harold & The Bluenotes*.
■ **Double LP**. . . . . . . . . . . . . . . . . . . . **STD 6**
**MC Set** . . . . . . . . . . . . . . . . . . . . **STDK 6**
Solitaire / '83 / BMG.

## ELECTRO CLASSICS VOL.1.

**Tracks:** Let the music play: *Shannon* / Body work: *Hot* / Hip hop be bop (don't stop): *Parrsih, Man* / Feel the force: *G-Force (1)* / Boogie down: *Parrsih, Man* / Mosquito aka Hobo scratch: *West Street Mob* / Papa was a rolling stone: *Wolfer, Bill* / Girl you need a change of mind: *Fowler, Fred* / In the bottle: *C.O.D.* / Give me tonight: *Shannon*.
**CD**. . . . . . . . . . . . . . . . . . . . **DGPCD 685**
**LP** . . . . . . . . . . . . . . . . . . . . **DGPLP 685**
Deep Beats / Jun '94 / BMG.

## ENDLESS LOVE (15 Of Motown's Greatest Love Songs).

**Tracks:** Endless love: *Ross, Diana & Lionel Richie* / With you I'm born again: *Preston, Billy & Syreeta* / Touch me in the morning: *Ross, Diana* / Being with you: *Robinson, Smokey* / Cruisin': *Robinson, Smokey* / Do you know where you're going to (Theme from 'Mahogany'.): *Ross, Diana* / It's my turn: *Ross, Diana* / I've never been to me: *Charlene* / Love child: *Ross, Diana & The Supremes* / Tears of a clown: *Robinson, Smokey & The Miracles* / All this love: *Eldorados* / Three times a lady: *Commodores* / Someday we'll be together: *Ross, Diana & The Supremes* / I was made to love her: *Wonder, Stevie* / You're all I need to get by: *Terrell, Tammi*.
■ **CD** . . . . . . . . . . . . . . . . . . . . **ZD 72451**
Motown / Dec '86.

## ENDLESS LOVE (38 Romantic Love Songs).

**Tracks:** Not Advised.
**CD Set** . . . . . . . . . . . . . . . . . . . . **266 823 2**
Mainline (2) / Oct '88.

## ENDLESS LOVE.

**Tracks:** Little in love / We're all alone / Lost in love / Will you love me tomorrow / One day in your life / I wanna get next to you / You weren't in love with me / Angel of the morning / Being with you / Always on my mind / Endless love / In the air tonight / One of us / Way I want to touch you / I've never been to me / Lady of the dawn / I need you / Visions / Shine silently / After the goldrush.
■ **LP** . . . . . . . . . . . . . . . . . . . . **TVA 2**
**MC**. . . . . . . . . . . . . . . . . . . . **TVC 2**
TV / Sep '82 / Sony.

## ESSENTIAL DANCEFLOOR CLASSICS VOL. 1.

**Tracks:** Somebody else's guy: *Brown, Jocelyn* / Love fever: *Adams, Gayle* / Last night a DJ saved my life: *Indeep* / Can you handle it: *Redd, Sharon* / And the beat goes on: *Whispers* / Take that to the bank: *Shalamar* / Giving it back: *Hurtt, Phil* / Nice and soft: *Wish* / Romeo where's Juliet: *Collage* / I like (what you're doing to me): *Young & Co.* / Dancin': *Crown Heights Affair* / Let's start the dance: *Bohannon, Hamilton*.
**CD**. . . . . . . . . . . . . . . . . . . . **DGPCD 668**
Deep Beats / Mar '94 / BMG.

## ESSENTIAL DETROIT SOUL COLLECTION.

**Tracks:** Not Advised.
**CD**. . . . . . . . . . . . . . . . . . . . **GSCD 003**
**LP** . . . . . . . . . . . . . . . . . . . . **GSLP 003**
Goldmine / Mar '92 / Vital Distribution.

## ESSENTIAL DISCO VOL. 1.

**Tracks:** Penguin at the big apple - Zing went the strings of my heart: *Trammps* / Uptown festival: *Shalamar* / Come to me: *Joli, France* / Dance with you: *Lucas, Carrie* / Phoenix: *Aquarian Dream* / There but for the grace of God go I: *Machine* / In the bush: *Musique* / Feed the flame: *Johnson, Lorraine* / A-freak-a: *Lemon* / This is it: *Moore, Melba* / Baby don't change your mind: *Knight, Gladys & The Pips* / Loving you - losing you: *Hyman, Phyllis*.
**CD**. . . . . . . . . . . . . . . . . . . . **DGPCD 703**
Deep Beats / Sep '94 / BMG.

## ESSENTIAL HI-NRG CLASSICS VOL. 1.

**Tracks:** Hit'n'run love: *Jiani, Carol* / Harmony: *Suzy Q* / Last call: *Jolo* / Computer music: *Suzy Q* / One night only: *Payne, Scherrie* / Pushin' too hard: *Parker, Paul* / Cuba libra: *Modern Rocketry* / Don't leave me this way: *Tracy, Jeanie* / One look: *Moore, Jackson* / Menergy: *Cowley, Patrick* / Homosexuality: *Modern Rocketry*.
**CD**. . . . . . . . . . . . . . . . . . . . **DGPCD 664**
Deep Beats / Mar '94 / BMG.

## ESSENTIAL MELLOW GROOVE.

**Tracks:** Not Advised.
**CD**. . . . . . . . . . . . . . . . . . . . **GSCD 005**
■ **LP** . . . . . . . . . . . . . . . . . . . . **GSLP 005**
Revolver / Sep '92.

## ESSENTIAL MODERN SOUL SELECTION VOL.3, THE.

**Tracks:** For real: *Flowers* / Alone again: *Baker, Ernest* / Da da da da da (I love you): *Naturals* / I think I've got a good chance: *Barnes, J.J.* / Can this be real: *Perfections* / He's a better liar than me: *Lampkin, Tony* / I just want to do my own thing: *Reachers* / That's the way the world should be: *Up From The Bottom* / All work and no play: *Jordan, Vivalore* / Put your lovin' on me: *Fisher, Willie* / Since you said you'd be mine: *Ragland, Lou* / Can't nobody love me like you do: *Storm (1)* / I gotta make you believe in me: *BJB* / I'll do anything for you: *McDonald, Lee* / Doin' it cause it feels good: *Strong, Chuck* / All of a sudden: *Moore, Melvin* / Ain't nothing like the love: *Simmons, John* / Hungry: *Sandy's Gang* / What does the future hold: *24 Karat Gold*.
**CD**. . . . . . . . . . . . . . . . . . . . **GSCD 040**
Goldmine / Jun '94 / Vital Distribution.

## ESSENTIAL NORTHERN SOUL VOL. 1.

**Tracks:** Not Advised.
**CD**. . . . . . . . . . . . . . . . . . . . **DGPCD 704**
Deep Beats / Sep '94 / BMG.

## ESSENTIAL SLOW GROOVE DANCEFLOOR CLASSICS 1.

**Tracks:** Making love: *Todd, Pam & Love Exchange* / All I want is my baby: *Gilliam, Roberta* / In the night time: *Henderson, Michael* / Sexy mama: *Moments* / I want you: *Jones, Tamiko* / Love talk: *Gilstrap, Jim* / You are my starship: *Connors, Norman* / Valentine love: *Connors, Norman* / We both need each other: *Connors, Norman* / Be thankful for what you got: *DeVaughan, William* / You'll never know: *Hi-Gloss* / Curious: *Midnight Star*.
**CD**. . . . . . . . . . . . . . . . . . . . **DGPCD 706**
Deep Beats / Sep '94 / BMG.

## ESSENTIAL SOUL.

**Tracks:** Make it easy on yourself: *Butler, Jerry* / Land of a thousand dances: *Kenner, Chris* / Release me: *Phillips, Esther* / You're no good: *Everett, Betty* / You can make it if you try: *Allison, G* / Soulful dress: *Sugar Pie Desanto* / Here comes the judge: *Markham, Pigmeat* / In crowd: *Ramsey, Lewis Trio* / Moon river: *Butler, Jerry* / I like it like that: *Kenner, Chris* / Raindrops: *Clark, Dee* / Get out of my life woman: *Dorsey, Lee* / Down home girl: *Robinson, Alvin* / Rescue me: *Bass, Fontella*.
■ **LP** . . . . . . . . . . . . . . . . . . . . **KNLP 15003**
■ **CD** . . . . . . . . . . . . . . . . . . . . **KNCD 15003**
■ **MC**. . . . . . . . . . . . . . . . . . . . **KNMC 15003**
Replay / May '89.

## ESSENTIAL SOUL.

**Tracks:** Not Advised.
■ **CD** . . . . . . . . . . . . . . . . . . . . **3462**
■ **MC**. . . . . . . . . . . . . . . . . . . . **2462**
K-Tel / Aug '90.

## ESSENTIAL SOUL WEEKENDER.

**Tracks:** Not Advised.
■ **Double LP**. . . . . . . . . . . . . . . . . . . . **LPSD 151**
Soul Supply / Sep '90.

## ESSENTIAL UNDERGROUND DANCEFLOOR CLASSICS VOL. 1.

**Tracks:** Once I've been there: *Connors, Norman* / Mainline: *Black Ivory* / Show you my love: *Alexander, Goldie* / Feel my love: *Hudson, Laurice* / I really love you: *Heaven & Earth* / Don't send me away: *Fleming, Garfield* / We rap more mellow: *Younger Generation* / Key: *Wuf Ticket* / Bad times (I can't stand it): *Captain Rapp* / On a journey (I sing the funk electric): *Electric Funk* / (I'm just a sucker) for a pretty face: *Phillips, West* / Thanks to you: *Sinnamon*.
**CD**. . . . . . . . . . . . . . . . . . . . **DGPCD 667**
Deep Beats / Mar '94 / BMG.

## ESSENTIAL UNDERGROUND DANCEFLOOR CLASSICS VOL. 2.

**Tracks:** Go with the flow: *Weeks & Co* / Don't you love it: *Singleton, Maxine* / No news is news: *Kreamcicle* / You've reached the bottom line: *Williams, Carol (1)* / All I need is you: *Starshine* / Your love: *Satin, Silk & Lace* / I'll do anything for you: *Morgan, Denroy* / I hear music in the streets: *Unlimited Touch* / Fantastic voyage: *Lakeside* / Sweeter as the day goes by: *Shalamar* / Must be the music: *Secret Weapon* / Can't fake the feeling: *Hunt, Geraldine*.
**CD**. . . . . . . . . . . . . . . . . . . . **DGPCD 705**
Deep Beats / Sep '94 / BMG.

## EVERY GREAT MOTOWN SONG VOLS. 1 & 2 (The First 25 Years As Originally Recorded).

**Tracks:** Where did our love go: *Ross, Diana & The Supremes* / Shop around: *Robinson, Smokey & The Miracles* / Dancing in the street: *Reeves, Martha* / Reach out I'll be there: *Four Tops* / Take me in your arms (rock me a little while): *Weston, Kim* / I heard it through the grapevine: *Knight, Gladys & The Pips* / Baby love: *Ross, Diana & The Supremes* / How sweet it is (to be loved by you): *Gaye, Marvin* / Heatwave: *Reeves, Martha* / My girl: *Temptations* / You keep me hangin' on: *Ross, Diana & The Supremes* / Ooh baby: *Robinson, Smokey & The Miracles* / Please Mr. Postman: *Marvelettes* / Standing in the shadows of love: *Four Tops* / Ain't no mountain high enough: *Ross, Diana* / If I were your woman: *Knight, Gladys & The Pips* / Never can say goodbye: *Jackson Five* / Just my imagination (running away with me): *Temptations* / Touch me in the morning: *Ross, Diana* / Three times a lady: *Commodores* / Got to give it up: *Gaye, Marvin* / Sail on: *Commodores*.
■ **CD Set**. . . . . . . . . . . . . . . . . . . . **ZD 72498**
Motown / Oct '86.

## EVERY GREAT MOTOWN SONG, VOL 1: THE 60'S (The First 25 Years As Originally Recorded).

**Tracks:** Where did our love go: *Ross, Diana & The Supremes* / Shop around: *Miracles* / Dancing in the street: *Reeves, Martha* / Reach out I'll be there: *Four Tops* / Take me in your arms: *Weston, Kim* / I heard it through the grapevine: *Knight, Gladys & The Pips* / How sweet it is (to be loved by you): *Gaye, Marvin* / Heatwave: *Reeves, Martha* / My girl: *Temptations* / You keep me hangin' on: *Ross, Diana & The Supremes* / Ooo baby baby: *Miracles* / Please Mr. Postman: *Marvelettes* / Standing in the shadows of love: *Four Tops*.
■ **LP** . . . . . . . . . . . . . . . . . . . . **WL 72235**
■ **MC**. . . . . . . . . . . . . . . . . . . . **WK 72235**
Motown / Mar '88.
■ **CD** . . . . . . . . . . . . . . . . . . . . **WD 72235**
Motown / Dec '89.
**CD**. . . . . . . . . . . . . . . . . . . . **.530113-2**
**MC**. . . . . . . . . . . . . . . . . . . . **.530113-4**
Motown / Jan '93 / PolyGram.

## EVERY GREAT MOTOWN SONG, VOL 2: THE 70'S (The First 25 Years As Originally Recorded).

**Tracks:** Ain't no mountain high enough: *Ross, Diana* / If I were your woman: *Knight, Gladys & The Pips* / Never can say goodbye: *Jackson Five* / Just my imagination (running away with me): *Temptations* / Do you know where you're going to: *Ross, Diana* / Ben: *Jackson, Michael* / Touch me in the morning: *Ross, Diana* / Three times a lady: *Commodores* / Got to give it up: *Gaye, Marvin* / Love hangover: *Ross, Diana* / Sail on: *Commodores*.
■ **MC**. . . . . . . . . . . . . . . . . . . . **WK 72236**
■ **LP** . . . . . . . . . . . . . . . . . . . . **WL 72236**
Motown / Mar '88.
■ **CD** . . . . . . . . . . . . . . . . . . . . **WD 72236**
Motown / Dec '89.
**CD**. . . . . . . . . . . . . . . . . . . . **.530114-2**
Motown / Jan '93 / PolyGram.

## EXPANSION PHAT JAMS.

**Tracks:** Just let me be close to you: *Valentine Brothers* / No more tears: *Jeter, Genobia* / Beverly: *Jamariah* / You know what it's like: *Brooks, Calvin* /

Callin up (Old memories): *Haynes, Victor* / Shoulda been you: *Ware, Leon* / Didn't mean to hurt you: *Valentine, Billy* / Starlite: *Ballin, Chris* / Victory: *Baylor, Helen* / Kissing in the dark: *Rodni* / Miss you: *Fresh Air* / Love hurts: *Glaze* / Show your love: *Hutson, Leroy* / I can't stand the pain: *Lorenzo* / If you don't want my love (Soul mix): *Williams, Lewis*.
CD . . . . . . . . . . . . . . . . . . . . . . **EXCDP 3**
Expansion / Jun '94 / Pinnacle / Sony / 3MV.

### EXPANSION SOUL SAUCE VOL.1.
**Tracks:** My favourite thing: *Brooks, Calvin & Hari Paris* / Share your love: *Hutson, Leroy* / Oasis: *Baylor, Helen* / I found someone: *Gaines, Billy & Sarah* / Shine: *Aja* / Heartbeat: *Ware, Leon* / Win your love: *James, Josie* / Everybody's in a hurry: *McNeir, Ronnie* / Main squeeze: *Crook, General* / Hang on: *Robbins, Rockie* / Love is the magic: *Blu, Peggi* / We got one: *Covington, Matt* / Power to the people: *Linsey* / Friends or lovers: *Burke, Keni* / Promises: *Glaze*.
CD . . . . . . . . . . . . . . . . . . . . . . **CDEXP 1**
LP . . . . . . . . . . . . . . . . . . . . . . **LPEXP 1**
MC . . . . . . . . . . . . . . . . . . . . . . **MCEXP 1**
Expansion / Jul '93 / Pinnacle / Sony / 3MV.

### EXPANSION SOUL SAUCE VOL.2.
**Tracks:** Late night hour: *Waters, Kim* / Surrender (my soul): *Skinner, Belinda A.* / Paradise: *Tankard, Ben* / Give me all your love: *Ballin, Chris* / You are my star: *Reeves, Paulette* / Forever: *Felder, Wilton* / In can only think of you: *McCrae, Gwen* / Fool for love: *Warren, Tony* / It's up to me: *James, Josie* / One step back for love: *El Coco* / Stay with me: *Clear, Crystal* / Shame on you: *Lovesmith, Michael* / Goodbye song: *Vanesse & Carolyn* / Look of love: *Hutson, Leroy* / After affect: *Taylor, Gary*.
CD . . . . . . . . . . . . . . . . . . . . . . **CDEXP 3**
LP . . . . . . . . . . . . . . . . . . . . . . **LPEXP 3**
MC . . . . . . . . . . . . . . . . . . . . . . **MCEXP 3**
Passion/Debut/Scratch Music / May '93 / Pinnacle / 3MV.

### EXPANSION SOUL SAUCE VOL.3.
**Tracks:** Think about it: *Webb, Rick* / Ja miss me: *Valentine, Billy* / I don't know why: *White, Lynn* / One and only: *Rodni* / Take a little time: *James, Josie* / Days and nights: *Haynes, Victor* / Blind to it all: *Taylor, Gary* / Love's gonna bring you home: *Rockmelons* / All my love: *Carmichael, James* / This kind of love (so special): *Valentine Brothers* / I'd like to into you: *Kelly, Denise & Fame* / Get into your life: *Beloyd* / Losers weepers: *Blackfoot, J.* / If you don't want my love: *Williams, Lewis*.
CD . . . . . . . . . . . . . . . . . . . . . . **CDEXP 6**
LP . . . . . . . . . . . . . . . . . . . . . . **LPEXP 6**
MC . . . . . . . . . . . . . . . . . . . . . . **MCEXP 6**
Expansion / Nov '93 / Pinnacle / Sony / 3MV.

# F

### FANTASISED SOUL.
**Tracks:** Not Advised.
CD . . . . . . . . . . . . . . . . . . . . . . **K 2417032**
■ LP . . . . . . . . . . . . . . . . . . . . . **K 2417031**
MC . . . . . . . . . . . . . . . . . . . . . . **K 2417034**
Atlantic / Feb '90 / WEA.

### FAST, FUNKY & FANTASTIC (70's Soul From Fantasy).
**Tracks:** Will they miss me: *Simmons, David* / Always there: *Side Effect* / I need you girl: *Three Pieces* / Motown review: *Philly Cream* / Get your lies straight: *Coday, Bill* / Evil Ways: *Tjader, Cal* / Mr. Weatherman: *Water & Power* / Walking in rhythm: *Blackbyrds* / Take all the time you need: *Checkmates Unlimited* / S-A-T-I-S-F-A-C-T-I-O-N: *Lee, Laura* / I told you so: *Janice* / It's music: *Harris, Damon* / I don't want to be a Lone Ranger: *Watson, Johnny 'Guitar'* / Danger: *Everett, Betty*.
■ LP . . . . . . . . . . . . . . . . . . . . . **KENT 082**
Kent / Aug '88.

### FEELIN' GOOD - AMERICAN R&B HITS VOLUME 1.
**Tracks:** Not Advised.
CD . . . . . . . . . . . . . . . . . . . . . . **CDRB 11**
Charly / Nov '94 / Charly.

### FEELS SO GOOD.
**Tracks:** Free as the wind: *Crusaders* / Burnin' up the carnival: *Sample, Joe* / Young child: *Laws, Ronnie* / Hard work: *Handy, John* / Intergalactic love song: *Earland, Charles* / Running away: *Ayers, Roy* / Feels so good: *Mangione, Chuck* / Ghetto: *Hathaway, Donny* / Night crusader: *Deodato, Eumir* / Toda menina bina: *Gil, Gilberto* / Wind parade: *Byrd, Donald* / Fantasy: *Hammond, Johnny*.
CD . . . . . . . . . . . . . . . . . . . . . . **RNBCD 106**
Connoisseur Collection / Jan '94 / Pinnacle.

### FINGER SNAPPERS.
**Tracks:** You never fail to amaze me / Be that way sometime / I'm gonna love you / Give in to the power of love / Say something nice to me / Couldn't last a day without your love / It takes love / Permanent vacation / I need a love / Feel good all over / I'm doing the best I can / Shame, shame, shame / Can't live without you / You're gone.
■ LP . . . . . . . . . . . . . . . . . . . . . **LPSS 106**
Soul Supply / Jan '87.

### FLARE GROOVE.
**Tracks:** Loose booty: *Henderson, Willie* / Funky judge: *Bull & the Matadors* / Make me believe in you: *Jo, Patti* / You are the one: *AM FM* / Do bad: *Burks, Donny* / I'll bake me a man: *Acklin, Barbara* / Loose hips: *Eliminators* / Keep on dancing: *Cash, Alvin* / It's your thing: *Moorer, Betty* / If she won't (find someone who will): *Dorsey, Lee* / Wiggler (the worms don't know): *Gibson, Billy* / If it's good for you (it's good for me) (part 1): *Bo, Eddie* / Fat man: *Bohannon*.
■ LP . . . . . . . . . . . . . . . . . . . . . **KENT 078**
Kent / May '88.

### FLYIN' HIGH.
**Tracks:** Not Advised.
CD . . . . . . . . . . . . . . . . . . . . . . **RNBCD 107**
Connoisseur Collection / Jan '94 / Pinnacle.

### FOOTSTOMPERS.
**Tracks:** Like one: *Carter, Jean* / Take away the painstain: *Austin, Patti* / Ten shades of blue: *Spindles* / You should o' held on: *7th Avenue Aviators* / You don't love me anymore: *Caswell, Johnny* / Tears (nothing but tears): *Roye, Lee* / I surrender: *Holman, Eddie* / You've been away: *Parker, Rubin* / Larue: *Edmund Jr., Lada* / I'll always need you: *Barry, Len* / Playin' hide and seek: *Regan, Eddie* / Soul symphony: *Sons Of Moses* / We go together: *August & Duneen* / Cracked up over you: *White, Danny*.
■ LP . . . . . . . . . . . . . . . . . . . . . **KENT 017**
Kent / Mar '84.

### FOR COLLECTORS ONLY.
**Tracks:** Not me baby: *Silhouettes* / Hey girl (where are you going): *Topics* / Sweet magic: *Servicemen* / What a love this is (oh, oh, oh): *Revlons* / Baby I dig you: *Anderson, Gene & The Dynamic Psychedelics* / I must love you: *Timothy Wilson* / Too much of a good thing: *Ambassadors* / Something is bad: *Nomads* / Nothing can compare to you: *Velvet Satins* / I don't like to lose: *Group* / Try my love: *Sequins* / Meet me halfway: *Lillie Bryant* / My life with you: *Traditions* / You didn't have to leave: *Ellusions*.
MC . . . . . . . . . . . . . . . . . . . . . . **CLPSS 102**
Soul Supply / Dec '84 / RTM / Pinnacle.
■ LP . . . . . . . . . . . . . . . . . . . . . **LPSS 102**
Soul Supply / Jan '87 / RTM / Pinnacle.

### FOR DANCERS ALSO (For Dancers Only Vol. 2).
**Tracks:** Lay this burden down: *Love, Mary* / If I could turn back the hands of time: *Garrett, Vernon* / Beauty is just skin deep: *Turner, Ike & Tina* / My baby needs me: *Baker, Yvonne* / Good taste of love: *Monday, Danny* / Can it be me: *Williams, Mel* / Wanting you: *Bee, Jimmy* / Take your shoes off (part II): *Booker T & The MG's* / Hole in the wall: *Other Bros* / Talkin' woman: *Fulson, Lowell* / Everybody needs love: *Gauff, Willie & The Love Brothers* / Running out: *Garrett, Vernon* / Country girl: *Otis, Johnny Show* / What kind of man are you: *Day, Jackie* / I'm in your hands: *Love, Mary*.
LP . . . . . . . . . . . . . . . . . . . . . . **KENT 002**
Kent / Apr '94 / Pinnacle.

### FOR DANCERS FOREVER (25 Storming 60's Soul Sounds).
**Tracks:** You turned my bitter into sweet: *Love, Mary* / Baby, without you: *Monday, Danny* / Before it's too late: *Day, Jackie* / Your love has made me a man: *Hutch, Willie* / You just cheat and lie: *Hill, Z.Z.* / This man wants you: *Cox, Wally* / Three lonely guys: *Brilliant Corners* / My baby needs me: *Baker, Yvonne* / I don't need: *Turner, Ike & Tina* / You better be good: *Woods, Peggy* / Lay this burden down: *Love, Mary* / If I could turn back the hands of time: *Garrett, Vernon* / Can it be me: *Williams, Mel* / Dancing fast, dancing slow: *Intentions* / My jealous girl: *Hammond, Clay* / My aching back: *Fulson, Lowell* / I can't believe what you say: *Turner, Ike & Tina* / This couldn't be me: *Sweethearts* / Love is gonna get you: *Woods, Peggy* / I can feel your love: *Taylor, Felice* / Oh what heartaches: *Day, Jackie* / No puppy love: *Copeland, Johnny* / What more: *Hill, Z.Z.* / I'm so thankful: *Ikettes* / I'm in your hands: *Love, Mary*.
CD Set . . . . . . . . . . . . . . . . . . . . **CDKEND 100**
Kent / Sep '92 / Pinnacle.

### FOR DANCERS ONLY.
**Tracks:** You turned my bitter into sweet: *Love, Mary* / I can feel your love: *Taylor, Felice* / Baby, without you: *Monday, Danny* / Your love has made me a man: *Hutch, Willie* / I'm so thankful: *Ikettes* / In the sunshine: *Marvellos* / Before it's too late: *Day, Jackie* / I can't believe what you say: *Turner, Ike & Tina* / Gimme gimme: *Hill, Z.Z.* / My aching back: *Fulson, Lowell* / Come back baby: *Young, Tami* / I've been taken for a ride: *Saints* / Dancing fast, dancing slow: *Intentions* / Baby, I'm sorry: *Hill, Z.Z.* / Let me know: *Love, Mary* / If you just cheat and lie: *Hill, Z.Z.*.
LP . . . . . . . . . . . . . . . . . . . . . . **KENT 001**
Kent / Apr '94 / Pinnacle.

### FOR DANCERS ONLY/FOR DANCERS ALSO.
**Tracks:** You turned my bitter into sweet: *Love, Mary* / Let me know: *Love, Mary* / Lay this burden down: *Love, Mary* / I'm in your hands: *Love, Mary* / I can feel your love: *Taylor, Felice* / Baby, without you: *Monday, Danny* / Good taste of love: *Monday, Danny* / Your love has made me a man: *Hutch, Willie* / I'm so thankful: *Ikettes* / In the sunshine: *Marvellos* / Before it's too late: *Day, Jackie* / What kind of man are you: *Day, Jackie* / I can't believe what you say: *Turner, Ike & Tina* / Gimme gimme: *Hill, Z.Z.* / Baby I'm sorry: *Hill, Z.Z.* / You just cheat and lie: *Hill, Z.Z.* / My aching back: *Fulson, Lowell* / Talkin' woman: *Fulson, Lowell* / Come back baby: *Young, Tami* / I've been taken for a ride: *Saints* / Dancing fast, dancing slow: *Intentions* / If I could turn back the hands of time: *Garrett, Vernon* / Running out: *Garrett, Vernon* / Beauty is just skin deep: *Sweethearts* / My baby needs me: *Baker, Yvonne* / Can it be me: *Williams, Mel* / Wanting you: *Bee, Jimmy* / Take your shoes off: *Booker T Averham & The Mustangs* / Hole in the wall: *Other Brothers* / Everybody needs love: *Gauff, Willie & The Love Brothers* / Country girl: *Johnny Otis Show*.
MC . . . . . . . . . . . . . . . . . . . . . . **KENC 805**
Kent / '84 / Pinnacle.

### FORT WORTH SHUFFLE 1958-64.
**Tracks:** Not Advised.
■ LP . . . . . . . . . . . . . . . . . . . . . **KK 7426**
Krazy Kat / Dec '88.

### FRIENDS IN HIGH PLACES.
**Tracks:** More than a friend: *Baylor, Helen* / Out front: *Angel (1)* / You changed my life: *Marquis Ubu* / Thank you Jesus: *Jasper, Chris* / Call me: *Smith, Kenny* / Step by step: *Hammond, Fred* / One love one people: *Taylor, Gary* / I'll shine for you: *Austin, Dennis* / Empty promises: *Futrel* / God in you: *Dawkins & Dawkins* / Will you be ready: *Redeemed* / It's only natural: *Thomas, Keith* / Be for real: *Mitchell, Vernessa* / Love's the key: *Gaines, Billy & Sarah*.
CD . . . . . . . . . . . . . . . . . . . . . . **CDEXP 5**
LP . . . . . . . . . . . . . . . . . . . . . . **LPEXP 5**
MC . . . . . . . . . . . . . . . . . . . . . . **MCEXP 5**
Expansion / Dec '93 / Pinnacle / Sony / 3MV.

### FROM HI-TENSION TO INFINITY.
**Tracks:** Let me feel it: *Gilles, Samantha* / Love and devotion: *Bow, Michael* / Flashlight on a disconight: *Rofo* / Midnight lover: *Bianca* / I want you: *Rofo* / Love gun: *Special Touch* / One more time: *Bianca* / One shot so hot: *Bow, Michael* / You've got to move on: *Rofo* / Now is the time: *Paparazzi* / S.T.O.P.: *Gilles, Samantha* / Beach love: *Rofo*.
■ LP . . . . . . . . . . . . . . . . . . . . . **PAPX 102**
Passion (1) / Apr '88.

### FROM MOTOR CITY TO CENTRAL PARK.
**Tracks:** Tell him: *Exciters* / Cry baby: *Mimms, Garnet & Enchanters* / I love the way you love: *Johnson, Marv* / Bells: *Marcels* / Who's that lady: *Isley Brothers* / You're so fine: *Falcons (1)* / Everybody's going: *Holland, Eddie* / You got what it takes: *Johnson, Marv* / Love potion no. 9: *Clovers* / Masquerade is over, The (I'm afraid): *Pinkney, Bill & The Originals* / Wonder of it all: *Imperials* / I'll take good care of you: *Mimms, Garnet* / Till the end: *Five Satins* / Come to me: *Johnson, Marv*.
■ MC . . . . . . . . . . . . . . . . . . . . . **TCSSL 6031**
■ LP . . . . . . . . . . . . . . . . . . . . . **SSL 6031**
Stateside / Jul '87.

### FROM MOTOWN WITH LOVE.
**Tracks:** Not Advised.
■ CD . . . . . . . . . . . . . . . . . . . . . **NCD 3391**

498 ■ DELETED

■ LP ... NE 1381
■ MC. ... CE 2381
K-Tel / Oct '87.

**FROM ROUTE 66 TO THE FLAMINGO.**
**Tracks:** I can't stand it: *Soul Sisters* / Hurt by love: *Foxx, Inez & Charlie* / You can't sit down: *Upchurch, Phil Combo* / Sticks: *Adderley, Cannonball Quartet* / I got a woman: *McGriff, Jimmy* / I know: *George, Barbara* / Let the good times roll: *Shirley & Lee* / Think about the good times: *Soul Sisters* / Loop de loop: *Soul Sisters* / Little bitty pretty one: *Harris, Thurston* / Googa mooga: *Roach, Freddie* / Little bit of soap: *Mimms, Garnet* / Quiet place: *Mimms, Garnet* / Discotheque USA: *McGriff, Jimmy* / Soul serenade: *Curtis, King*.
■ MC. ... TCSSL 6034
■ LP ... SSL 6034
Stateside / May '88.

**FROM THE VAULTS.**
**Tracks:** Nobody but you: *Temptations* / Take me where you go: *Ross, Diana & The Supremes* / Cry: *Monitors (1)* / Sweeter as the days go by: *Gaye, Marvin* / I should have known better: *Marvelettes* / What more could a boy ask for: *Spinners* / It's fantastic: *Miracles* / Drop in the bucket: *Wells, Mary* / Lonely heart and lonely eyes of lonely me: *Knight, Gladys & The Pips* / Undecided lover: *Reeves, Martha*.
■ LP ... STMT 9001
Motown / May '79.
■ LP ... STMS 5080
■ MC. ... CSTMS 5080
Motown / Nov '82.

**FULLSTRENGTHSOCKITOMEKNOCK-MEOUTMAKEMEBOOGIE (I Just Love That Disco).**
**Tracks:** Time moves on / C'est la vie / My girl / Let it shine / But is it funky / Slow burnin' / Latin hustle / Gone but not forgotten / From a teacher to a preacher / Bohannon's beat / Devil's doing his work / Everybody plays the fool.
■ LP ... SOULR 2
Decca / Nov '76.

**FUNK CLASSICS VOL.1.**
**Tracks:** Everyway but loose: *Phunky* / Hypertension: *Calender* / Hustle bus stop: *Mastermind* / Water bed parts 1 & 2: *LTG Exchange* / Zone: *Rhythm Makers* / Who's got he monster: *Rimshots* / Boogie woogie: *Sound Experience* / Monster from the black tongs: *Calender* / Back it up parts 1 & 2: *Lanlords & Tenants* / Message: *Cymande* / Chance with you: *Brother to Brother* / Give me your love: *Mason, Barbara*.
CD ... DGPCD 684
LP ... DGPLP 684
Deep Beats / Jun '94 / BMG.

**FUNK IN YO FACE.**
**Tracks:** Not Advised.
CD ... 241 675-2
■ LP ... 241 675-1
MC. ... 241 675-4
Atlantic / Nov '89 / WEA.

**FUNK 'N' SOUL REVOLUTION.**
**Tracks:** Somebody touch me (in the right place): *Knight, Boobie & the Universal Lady* / Ali shuffle: *Cash, Alvin* / Give it up: *Eliminators* / (For God's sake) give more power to the people: *Chi-Lites* / Work work work: *B W & The Next Edition* / South African man: *Bohannon, Hamilton* / Foot stompin' music: *Bohannon, Hamilton* / How can you say goodbye: *Quails, Sidney Joe* / Boo on you (shakin' the baby's shoes): *Jones, Chuck & Company* / Let me down easy: *Rare Pleasure* / I ain't got nobody: *Sly & The Family Stone* / Sweeping your dirt under my rug: *Bailey, Ann* / This time around: *Soul (1)* / There it is: *Davis, Tyrone*.
■ LP ... KENT 051
Kent / Feb '86.

**FUNKY.**
**Tracks:** Not Advised.
■ LP ... 6498 141
MC. ... 7133 141
Mercury / Dec '81 / PolyGram.

**FUSION PHEW.**
**Tracks:** Sudden samba: *Larson, Neil* / Latin America: *Walton, Cedar* / Hip skip: *Williams, Tony (1)* / El bobo: *Lewis, Webster* / Hump: *Rushen, Patrice* / Rio: *Glenn, Roger* / Caveman boogie: *Wilson, Lesette* / Harlem boys: *Rollins, Sonny* / Walk tall: *Soskin, Mark* / Do it to it: *Owens, Jimmy* / Little sunflower: *Hubbard, Freddie* / On the path: *Franklin, Rodney*.
CD ... CDELV 10
LP ... LPELV 10
MC. ... MCELV 10
Passion/Debut/Scratch Music / Dec '93 / Pinnacle / 3MV.

**FUSION PHEW 2.**
**Tracks:** Ju ju: *McDuff, Jack* / He loves you: *Seawind* / Goldenwings: *Opa* / Bittersweet: *Escovedo, Pete* / Sugar loaf mountain: *Duke, George* / Happy song: *Foster, Ronnie* / Baby don't you know: *Humphrey, Bobbi* / I'm staying forever: *Henderson, Wayne* / Life is like a samba: *Benoit, David* / There are many stops along the way: *Sample, Joe* / Scapegoat: *Johnson, Al* / Slick Eddie: *Stitt, Sonny*.
CD ... CDELV 15
LP ... LPELV 15
MC. ... MCELV 15
Elevate / Jun '94 / 3MV.

**FUTURE OF SOUL.**
**Tracks:** Always: *La La* / I need your love: *England, Colin* / Flesh and blood: *Price, Louis* / Leave well enough alone: *Harvey, Dee*.
■ 12" ... ZT 45050
■ CD Single ... ZD 45050
■ MC Single ... ZK 45050
Motown / Oct '91.

# G

**GARAGE CITY.**
**Tracks:** Not Advised.
■ CD ... TCD 2584
■ LP ... STAR 2584
■ MC. ... STAC 2584
Telstar/Ronco / Sep '92.

**GARAGE CLASSICS VOL.1.**
**Tracks:** In and out of my life: *Adeva* / You don't know: *Serious Intention* / Ma foom bay: *Cultural Vibe* / Jazzy rhythm: *Wallace, Michelle* / Tee's happy: *Northend* / You're all played out: *Life (1)* / Touch me: *Rae, Fonda* / Standing right there: *Moore, Melba* / I'm caught up (in a one night love affair): *Inner Life* / What I got is what you need: *Unique*.
CD ... DGPCD 686
LP ... DGPLP 686
Deep Beats / Jun '94 / BMG.

**GARAGE CLASSIQUE.**
**Tracks:** Don't make me wait: *Peech Boys* / This time: *Private Possession* / Somebody save me (garage mix): *By All Means* / Release the tension: *Circuit* / Your life: *Konk* / Are you wid it (club mix): *Private Possession* / I will always love you: *Stockley, Eddie* / Love's got 2 be strong: *Edwards, Keyman*.
■ CD ... BRCD 528
■ LP ... BRLP 528
■ MC. ... BRCA 528
4th & Broadway / May '89.

**GARAGE GROOVES OF DETROIT.**
**Tracks:** Not Advised.
■ LP ... CDMOTCLP 52
Motor City / Jan '91.

**GARAGE SOUND OF DEEPEST NEW YORK.**
**Tracks:** Reachin': *Phase 2* / I'm a lover: *Mazelle, Kym* / You're gonna miss me: *Turntable Orchestra* / Can't win for losin': *Blaze* / I can't wait too long: *Church, Joe* / Houselights / Take some time out: *Jarvis, Arnold* / Let's work it out: *Exit* / Feel the music: *Ruff Neck*.
CD ... LICTCD 010
■ Double LP. ... LICLP 010
MC. ... LICC 010
Republic / Nov '88 / RTM / Pinnacle.

**GARAGE SOUND OF DEEPEST NEW YORK VOL.II.**
**Tracks:** Not Advised.
CD ... LICCD 020
MC. ... LICMC 020
Republic / Jul '89 / RTM / Pinnacle.
■ LP ... LICLP 020
Republic / Jun '89 / RTM / Pinnacle.

**GARAGE SOUNDS OF NEW YORK VOL.III.**
**Tracks:** Not Advised.
■ LP ... UNKNOWN
Republic / Nov '89.

**GARAGE TRAX.**
**Tracks:** Not Advised.
CD ... CDBONY 1
■ LP ... BONY 1
MC. ... CBONY 1
Indi-go (EMI) / Feb '89 / EMI.

**GARY BYRD'S SWEET INSPIRATIONS.**
**Tracks:** Not Advised.
■ LP ... REH 548
■ MC. ... ZCR 548
BBC / Nov '84.

**GEMS (Jewels From The Soul Crown).**
**Tracks:** Evil one: *Sapphires* / Hey girl don't bother me: *Tams* / Boomerang: *Tom & Jerrio* / Treat her right: *Head, Roy* / Competition ain't nothing: *Carlton, Carl* / You've been cheating: *Impressions* / Gonzo: *Booker, James* / Hey there lonely girl: *Holman, Eddie* / Tell her: *Parrish, Dean* / It's a crying shame: *Barry, Len* / Girl watcher: *Okaysions* / Homework: *Rush, Otis* / Mama didn't lie: *Fasinations*.
■ LP ... KENT 021
Kent / May '84.

**GEORGE CLINTON FAMILY SERIES PART 1.**
**Tracks:** Go for your funk: *Various* / Funk it up: *Clinton, George* / Funkin' for my momma's rent: *Clinton, George* / Send a gram: *Clinton, George* / Who in the funk do you think you are: *Clinton, George* / Better days: *Clinton, George* / Chong song: *Clinton, George* / Michelle: *Clinton, George* / Sunshine of your love: *Clinton, George* / Interview: *Clinton, George*.
CD ... ESSCD 185
■ Double LP. ... ESSLP 185
MC. ... ESSMC 185
Castle / Oct '92 / BMG.

**GEORGE CLINTON FAMILY SERIES PART 2.**
**Tracks:** May Day (S.O.S.): *Funkadelic* / These feet are made for dancin' (footstranger): *Dunbar, Ron* / Booty body ray for the plush funk: *Sterling Silver Starship* / I really envy the sunshine: *Cleaves, Jessica* / Lickety split: *Horny Horns* / Common law wife: *Flo* / Superspirit: *Morrison, Junie* / Love don't come easy: *Brides Of Funkenstein* / I can't stand it: *Lewis, Tracey & Andre Fox with Flastic Brain Flam* / Monster dance: *Ford, Ron* / We're just funkers: *Hampton, Michael* / Interview: *Clinton, George*.
CD ... ESSCD 189
MC. ... ESSMC 189
■ LP ... ESDLP 189
Castle / Jan '93.

**GEORGE CLINTON FAMILY SERIES PART 3 ("P" Is The Funk).**
**Tracks:** Clone communicado / Does disc with dat / Shove on / Rock jam / Love is something / Every booty (get on down) / Personal problems / Bubblegum gangster / She's crazy / Think right / In the cabin of my Uncle Jam (P is the funk) / My love / Interview / Commercials.
CD ... ESSCD 190
MC. ... ESSMC 190
■ LP ... ESDLP 190
Castle / May '93.

**GEORGE CLINTON FAMILY SERIES PART 4 (Testing Positive For The Funk).**
**Tracks:** Live up (to what she thinks of me): *Parliament* / Secrets: *Barnes, Sidney* / She never do's things: *Lewd, Trey* / Take my love: *Brides Of Funkenstein* / Just for play: *Brides Of Funkenstein* / Off the wall: *Cleaves, Jessica* / Get it on: *G, Jimmy* / Triune: *Morrison, Junie* / Superstar madness: *Maruga & the Soda Jerks* / One angle: *Funkadelic* / Twenty bucks: *Brides Of Funkenstein* / To care: *Four Tops* / Comin' down from your love: *Savannah, Nick & Dwarf* / Interview: *Clinton, George*.
CD ... ESSCD 198
MC. ... ESSMC 198
■ LP ... ESDLP 198
Castle / Sep '93.

**GET DANCIN' (16 Original Soul Hits).**
**Tracks:** Not Advised.
CD ... 12214
MC. ... 72214
Laserlight / Jan '94 / THE / BMG / Target.

**GET INTO THE GROOVE.**
**Tracks:** Keep that same old feeling: *Side Effect* / Jazz carnival: *Azymuth* / Rock Creeek Park: *Blackbyrds* / Do it fluid: *Blackbyrds* / Walking in rhythm: *Blackbyrds* / Joyous: *Pleasure (2)* / Beale Street: *Adams, Arthur* / Dancin': *McWilliams, Paulette* / Midnight and you: *Turrentine, Stanley* / Giving it back: *Hurtt, Phil* / I don't know what's on your mind: *Spider's Webb* / Will they miss me: *Simmons, David* / Ghettos of the mind: *Pleasure (2)* / Space bass: *Slick* / I don't

want to be alone ranger: *Watson, Johnny 'Guitar'* / Sweet Dan: *Everett, Betty* / Let your heart be free: *Rushen, Patrice*.
**CD** . . . . . . . . . . . . . . . . . . . . . . **CDSEWD 034**
South Bound / Jan '91 / Pinnacle.

## GET ON UP (16 Saturday Night Stompers).
**Tracks:** Can you feel the force: *Real Thing* / YMCA: *Village People* / Disco stomp: *Bohannon, Hamilton* / Last night a DJ saved my life: *Indeep* / White lines (don't do it): *Grandmaster Flash & Melle Mel* / This is it: *Moore, Melba* / Let the music play: *Shannon* / Girls: *Moments & Whatnauts* / Can you handle it: *Redd, Sharon* / You're the one for me: *D-Train* / Hold back the night: *Trammps* / Knock on wood: *Stewart, Amii* / More, more, more: *True, Andrea Connection* / We got the funk: *Positive Force* / Sunshine day: *Osibisa* / Feels like I'm in love: *Marie, Kelly*.
**CD** . . . . . . . . . . . . . . . . . . . . . . **MCCD 063**
**MC** . . . . . . . . . . . . . . . . . . . . . . **MCTC 063**
Music Club / '92 / Gold & Sons / THE / Video Collection / C.M. Distribution.

## GETTIN' IT OFF - WESTBOUND FUNK.
**Tracks:** Gettin' it off (Instrumental): *Haskins, Fuzzy* / Just us: *Crowd Pleasers* / Thinking single: *Counts* / Funk it down: *Frazier, Ceasar* / Super funk: *Hall, Erasmus* / In the pocket: *Boots* / Walt's first trip: *Ohio Players* / Funky world part 1 & 2: *Silky Vincent* / Get down with the get down: *Sparks, Melvin* / Super J: *Morrison, Junie* / Which way do I disco: *Haskins, Fuzzy* / Be what you is: *US Music with Funkadelic* / Funky Beethoven: *Anderson, Gene* / Crazy legs: *Austin, Donald* / What's up front that count: *Counts* / Loose booty: *Funkadelic* / Satans boogie: *Ohio Players* / Sweet thing: *Houston outlaws* / Hit it and quit it: *Bobby Franklin's insanity* / Hicky Burr: *Frazier, Ceasar*.
**CD** . . . . . . . . . . . . . . . . . . . . . . **CDSEWD 061**
**LP** . . . . . . . . . . . . . . . . . . . . . . **SEWD 061**
Westbound / Apr '93 / Pinnacle.

## GIRL GROUPS OF THE MOTORCITY.
**Tracks:** Not Advised.
■ **LP** . . . . . . . . . . . . . . . . . . . . **MOTCLP 22**
Motor City / Mar '90.

## GIRLS WITH SOUL.
**Tracks:** Woman to woman: *Brown, Shirley* / It ain't long enough: *Clay, Judy* / Keep on searching: *Alexander, Margie* / Wishes and dishes: *Sweet Inspirations* / Punish me: *Joseph, Margie* / You just don't know: *Weston, Kim* / Short stopping: *Brown, Veda* / Funny: *Hot Sauce* / Mr. Big Stuff: *Knight, Jean* / I like what you're doing (to me): *Thomas, Carla* / Don't start lovin' me (if you're gonna stop): *Brown, Veda* / Circuits overloaded: *Foxx, Inez & Charlie* / Stop in the name of love: *Joseph, Margie* / I have learned to do without you: *Staples, Mavis* / It's time to pay for the fun (we've had): *Jeanne & The Darlings* / So I can love you: *Emotions (1)*.
■ **LP** . . . . . . . . . . . . . . . . . . . . **STAXL 5003**
**MC** . . . . . . . . . . . . . . . . . . . . . . **STAXK 5003**
Stax / Aug '81 / Pinnacle.

## GIRLS WITH SOUL.
**Tracks:** Love of my man: *Kilgore, Theola* / As long as you need me: *Kilgore, Theola* / This is my prayer: *Kilgore, Theola* / Don't make me over: *Warwick, Dionne* / Wishin' and hopin': *Warwick, Dionne* / Someday: *Phillips, Esther* / Monday thru Sunday: *Phillips, Esther* / Don't let the sun catch you cryin': *Big Maybelle* / That's all: *Big Maybelle* / Same old story: *Big Maybelle* / Since I've found you: *Brown, Maxine* / Funny: *Brown, Maxine* / If you should lose me: *Lynn, Barbara* / Lonely heartache: *Lynn, Barbara*.
■ **LP** . . . . . . . . . . . . . . . . . . . . **WCS 1003**
Wand / Feb '71.

## GO GO - THE SOUND OF WASHINGTON DC.
**Tracks:** Not Advised.
■ **LP** . . . . . . . . . . . . . . . . . . . . **BOMB 1**
■ **MC** . . . . . . . . . . . . . . . . . . . . **KBOMB 1**
London / May '85.

## GO GO CRANKIN'.
**Tracks:** Meet me at the go-go: *Hot Cold Sweat* / Let's get small: *Trouble Funk* / We need some money: *Brown, Chuck & Soul Searchers* / Ohh la la la: *E.U.* / Drop the bomb / Good to go / Somebody's ringin' that door bell: *E.U.* / Say what: *Trouble Funk*.
■ **MC** . . . . . . . . . . . . . . . . . . . . **DCCA 100**
■ **LP** . . . . . . . . . . . . . . . . . . . . **DCLP 100**
4th & Broadway / Apr '85.

## GOLDEN AGE OF BLACK MUSIC (1960-70).
**Tracks:** Stand by me: *King, Ben E.* / When a man loves a woman: *Sledge, Percy* / I never loved a man (the way I love you): *Franklin, Aretha* / Sweet soul music: *Conley, Arthur* / Respect: *Franklin, Aretha* / Soul man: *Sam & Dave* / Baby I love you: *Franklin, Aretha* / (Sittin' on) The dock of the bay: *Redding, Otis* / Chain of fools: *Franklin, Aretha* / Slip away: *Carter, Clarence* / Since you've been gone (sweet sweet baby): *Franklin, Aretha* / Too weak to fight: *Carter, Clarence* / Think: *Franklin, Aretha* / Can I change my mind: *Davis, Tyrone* / I say a little prayer: *Franklin, Aretha* / Rainy night in Georgia: *Benton, Brook*.
**CD** . . . . . . . . . . . . . . . . . . . . . . **K 781 911 2**
■ **LP** . . . . . . . . . . . . . . . . . . . . **K 781 911 1**
■ **MC** . . . . . . . . . . . . . . . . . . . . **K 781 911 4**
Atlantic / Dec '88.

## GOLDEN AGE OF BLACK MUSIC (1970-75).
**Tracks:** Don't play that song: *Franklin, Aretha* / Groove me: *Floyd, King* / Precious precious: *Moore, Jackie* / Don't let the green grass fool you: *Pickett, Wilson* / Don't knock my love (part 1): *Pickett, Wilson* / First time ever I saw your face: *Flack, Roberta* / Daydreaming: *Franklin, Aretha* / Could it be I'm falling in love: *Detroit Spinners* / Killing me softly with his song: *Flack, Roberta* / Until you come back to me: *Franklin, Aretha* / Then came you: *Warwick, Dionne & Spinners* / Sideshow: *Blue Magic* / Feel like makin' love: *Flack, Roberta* / They just can't stop it (games people play): *Detroit Spinners*.
**CD** . . . . . . . . . . . . . . . . . . . . . . **781 912-2**
■ **LP** . . . . . . . . . . . . . . . . . . . . **781 912-1**
■ **MC** . . . . . . . . . . . . . . . . . . . . **781 912-4**
Atlantic / Feb '89.

## GOLDEN AGE OF BLACK MUSIC (1977-88).
**Tracks:** Dance, dance, dance: *Chic* / Closer I get to you: *Flack, Roberta & Donny Hathaway* / Le freak: *Chic* / We are family: *Sister Sledge* / Good times: *Chic* / You are in my system: *System* / (Pop pop pop) goes my mind: *Levert* / Don't disturb this groove: *System* / Come share my love: *Howard, Miki* / Casanova: *Levert* / So amazing: *Albright, Gerald*.
**CD** . . . . . . . . . . . . . . . . . . . . . . **K 781 913 2**
■ **LP** . . . . . . . . . . . . . . . . . . . . **K 781 913 1**
■ **MC** . . . . . . . . . . . . . . . . . . . . **K 781 913 4**
Atlantic / Dec '88.

## GOLDEN LADIES OF SOUL.
**Tracks:** Not Advised.
■ **MC** . . . . . . . . . . . . . . . . . . . . **SSC 3077**
Pickwick / Sep '80.

## GOLDEN SOUL.
**Tracks:** Dock of the bay / What'd I say / Feel like makin' love / In the midnight hour / Memphis soul stew / Spanish Harlem / Hold on, I'm coming / Up on the roof / I'll be around / When a man loves a woman / Show me / You make me feel like a natural woman.
■ **LP** . . . . . . . . . . . . . . . . . . . . **K 50332**
Atlantic / Apr '77.

## GOLDEN SOUL.
**Tracks:** Not Advised.
**MC** . . . . . . . . . . . . . . . . . . . . . . **AMP 021**
Ampro / Sep '81.

## GOLDEN SOUL OF THE 60'S.
**Tracks:** Not Advised.
**MC** . . . . . . . . . . . . . . . . . . . . . . **FUNC 9007**
Fun / Dec '88 / Pinnacle / Roots Records / C.M. Distribution.
**CD** . . . . . . . . . . . . . . . . . . . . . . **FCD 9007**
■ **LP** . . . . . . . . . . . . . . . . . . . . **FUN 9007**
Fun / Dec '88 / Pinnacle / Roots Records / C.M. Distribution.

## GOOD NEWS.
**Tracks:** I'm going through: *Caravan* / It's Jesus in me: *Caravan* / I'm a rollin': *Five Blind Boys Of Mississippi* / Where there's a will: *Five Blind Boys Of Mississippi* / Wade in the water: *Harmonizing Four* / Father I stretch my arms to thee: *Harmonizing Four* / Nobody knows: *Highway QC'S* / Working on the building: *Highway QC'S* / Uncloudy day: *Staple Singers* / This may be the last time: *Staple Singers* / Going away: *Staple Singers* / Good news: *Staple Singers* / Don't drive me away: *Staple Singers* / Will the circle be unbroken: *Staple Singers* / Too close: *Staple Singers* / Great day in December: *Swan Silvertones* / Oh Mary don't you weep: *Swan Silvertones* / How I got over: *Swan Silvertones* / What about you: *Swan Silvertones* / Brighter day ahead: *Swan Silvertones* / Seek, seek: *Swan Silvertones* / I'll search heaven: *Swan Silvertones*.
**CD** . . . . . . . . . . . . . . . . . . . . . . **CDCHARLY 98**
Charly / Dec '87 / Charly.

## GOOD TIMES.
**Tracks:** Memphis train: *Thomas, Rufus* / Some kind of wonderful: *Soul Brothers Six* / Memphis soul stew: *Curtis, King* / Somebody (somewhere): *Turner, Ike & Tina* / Keep looking: *Burke, Solomon* / Things get better: *Floyd, Eddie* / Three time loser: *Pickett, Wilson* / Let the good times roll: *Charles, Ray* / Looking for a fox: *Carter, Clarence* / Sweet sweet baby: *Franklin, Aretha* / Good lovin': *Olympics* / Philly dog: *Mann, Herbie* / I can't stop: *Conley, Arthur* / But it's alright: *Jackson, J.J.* / Help me: *Sharpe, Ray* / One way love: *Drifters*.
■ **LP** . . . . . . . . . . . . . . . . . . . . **KENT 094**
Kent / Oct '89.

## GOT TO GET YOUR OWN (Some Rare Grooves, Vol 1).
**Tracks:** Got to get your own: *Wilson, Reuben* / Black water gold: *African Music Machine* / Goo bah: *Continental Showstoppers* / Funky song: *Ripple* / Moon walk: *Ellis, Pee Wee* / Tropical: *African Music Machine* / You're losing me: *Sexton, Ann* / I don't know what it is but it sure is funky: *Ripple* / So much trouble in my mind: *Quatermain, Joe* / That thang: *Ellis, Pee Wee* / Dapp: *African Music Machine* / I don't dig no phony, part 2: *Scott, Moody* / Brother man, sister Ann: *Smith, Clemon*.
■ **LP** . . . . . . . . . . . . . . . . . . . . **CRM 2032**
Charly / Sep '87.
**MC** . . . . . . . . . . . . . . . . . . . . . . **TCCRM 2032**
Charly R&B / Sep '87 / Charly.
**CD Set** . . . . . . . . . . . . . . . . . . . . **INSD 5050**
Charly / Sep '91 / Charly.

## GRAMMY R & B SONGS 1960'S-1970'S.
**Tracks:** Not Advised.
■ **CD** . . . . . . . . . . . . . . . . . . . . **ZD 72297**
Motown / Feb '85.
■ **CD** . . . . . . . . . . . . . . . . . . . . **CD 72297**
Motown / Aug '89.

## GREAT DISCO DEMANDS (15 Northern Soul in-demanders).
**Tracks:** This man: *Cox, Wally* / Human jungle: *Fugitives* / Can't help loving you: *Breedlove, Jimmy* / I'm so glad: *Fuzz* / I've gotta find me somebody: *Velvets* / Can't help lovin' dat man: *Van, Ila* / Help me: *Wilson, Al* / Dance, dance, dance: *Casualeers* / If you ask me (because I love you): *Williams, Jerry* / Goodbye nothing to say: *Javells*.
■ **LP** . . . . . . . . . . . . . . . . . . . . **DDLP 5002**
Pye Disco Demand / May '75.

## GREAT SIXTIES SOUL GROUPS.
**Tracks:** Sly, the slick, and the wicked: *Lost Generation* / Woman: *Esquires* / Think twice before you walk away: *Porgy & The Monarchs* / Afraid of love: *Maestro, Johnny & The Crests* / Until you came along: *Visitors* / There's still a tomorrow: *Diplomats (1)* / Kiss and make up: *Inspirations* / Can't understand it: *Independents* / You never loved me: *Chancellors* / Lonely old world: *Artistics* / Why do you wanna make me blue: *Platters* / You have no time to lose: *Four Pennies* / Sugar (don't take away my candy): *Jive Five* / I got my own thing going: *Little Charles & The Sidewinders* / You're my one and only baby: *Intruders* / Another time, another place: *Persuaders*.
■ **LP** . . . . . . . . . . . . . . . . . . . . **KENT 083**
Kent / Aug '88.

## GREATEST GOSPEL GEMS VOLS 1 AND 2.
**Tracks:** Last mile of the way: *Cooke, Sam & The Soul Stirrers* / Touch the hem of his garment: *Cooke, Sam & The Soul Stirrers* / Search me, Lord: *May, Brother Joe* / Do you know him: *May, Brother Joe* / Mother bowed: *Pilgrim Travelers* / Straight street: *Pilgrim Travelers* / Jesus met the woman at the well: *Pilgrim Travelers* / Oh Lord, stand by me: *Five Blind Boys Of Alabama* / I'll fly away: *Five Blind Boys Of Alabama* / Too close to heaven: *Bradford, Alex* / Lord, Lord, Lord: *Bradford, Alex* / Get away Jordan: *Love Coates, Dorothy* / He's calling me: *Love Coates, Dorothy* / I'm sealed: *Love Coates, Dorothy* / My rock: *Swan Silvertones* / Jesus is a friend: *Swan Silvertones* / Let god abide: *Anderson, Robert* / Prayer for the doomed: *Chosen Gospel Singers* / Ball game: *Carr, Sister Wynona* / By and by: *Soul Stirrers* / Love of God: *Taylor, Johnnie* / I'm determined: *Meditation Singers* / Lead me, guide me: *May, Brother Joe* / Now the day is over: *Cleveland, James*.
**CD** . . . . . . . . . . . . . . . . . . . . . . **CDCHD 344**
Ace / May '91 / Pinnacle / Complete Record Co. Ltd.

## GREATEST MOMENTS IN SOUL.
**Tracks:** I'm doing fine now: *Pasadenas* / Too blind to see it: *Sims, Kym* / Something got me started: *Simply Red* / Don't lose the magic: *Christopher, Shawn* / Real love: *Driza Bone* / Change: *Stansfield, Lisa* / Tender love: *Thomas, Kenny* / Greatest love of all: *Houston, Whitney* / Make it on my own: *Limerick, Alison* / I'm every woman: *Khan, Chaka* / Don't let it show on your face: *Adeva* / Such a good feeling: *Brothers In Rhythm* / My one temptation: *Paris, Mica* / Joy and pain: *Maze Featuring Frankie Beverly* / Rhythm is a mystery: *K-Klass* / Winter in July: *Bomb*



■ DELETED

e Bass / How can we be lovers: Bolton, Michael /
fferent corner: Michael, George.

D...................................... CCD 33
LP..................................... ADD 33
MC..................................... ZDD 33
ver / Apr '92.

## REATEST SONGS WRITTEN BY ASH-ORD AND SIMPSON.

acks: Ain't no mountain high enough: Ross, Diana
/ou're all I need to get by: Gaye, Marvin & Tammi
errell / Love woke me up this morning: Temptations
/ Reach out and touch: Ross, Diana / Ain't nothing
e the real thing: Gaye, Marvin & Tammi Terrell /
dn't you Know (you'd have to cry sometime):
night, Gladys & The Pips / Remember me: Ross,
ana / Your precious love: Gaye, Marvin & Tammi
errell / Some things you never get used to: Ross,
ana & The Supremes / Destination: Anywhere:
arvelettes / Surrender: Ross, Diana / What you
ave me: Gaye, Marvin & Tammi Terrell / I can't give
ack the love I feel for you: Ross, Diana / I wouldn't
ange the man he is: Blinky / Just say, just say:
oss, Diana & Marvin Gaye / Silly wasn't it: Simp-
on, Valerie / Boss: Ross, Diana & Marvin Gaye /
ood lovin ain't easy to come by: Gaye, Marvin &
ammi Terrell / It's my house: Ross, Diana.
D...................................... ZD 72383
otown / Mar '86 / PolyGram.

## REATEST SONGS WRITTEN BY OLLAND,DOZIER,HOLLAND.

acks: You can't hurry love: Ross, Diana & The
upremes / Reach out I'll be there: Four Tops / How
weet it is (to be loved by you): Gaye, Marvin / You
eep me hangin on: Ross, Diana & The Supremes /
anding in the shadows of love: Four Tops / Heave: Reeves, Martha / Where did our love go:
oss, Diana & The Supremes / Take me in your arms
ock me a little while): Weston, Kim / Stop in the
ame of love: Ross, Diana & The Supremes / It's the
ame old song: Four Tops / Heaven must have sent
ou: Pointer, Bonnie / Baby love: Ross, Diana & The
upremes / I can't help myself: Four Tops / Reflec-
ons: Ross, Diana & The Supremes / This old heart
 mine: Isley Brothers / I hear a symphony: Ross,
ana & The Supremes / Baby I need your loving:
our Tops / My world is empty without you: Ross,
ana & The Supremes / Can I get a witness: Gaye,
arvin / Come see about me: Ross, Diana & The
upremes.
 CD................................... ZD 72380
otown / '86.
D.................................MCD 06138 MD
otown / '88 / PolyGram.

## REATEST SONGS WRITTEN BY SMOK-Y ROBINSON.

acks: Tracks of my tears: Robinson, Smokey & The
iracles / My girl: Temptations / Ooo baby baby:
obinson, Smokey & The Miracles / My guy: Wells,
ary / Shop around: Robinson, Smokey & The Mira-
es / Get ready: Temptations / You really got a hold
 me: Robinson, Smokey & The Miracles / Way you
o the things you do: Temptations / Going to a go go:
obinson, Smokey & The Miracles / Ain't that pecu-
ar: Gaye, Marvin / I second that emotion: Robinson,
mokey & The Miracles / Don't look back: Temp-
tions / More love: Robinson, Smokey & The Mira-
les / Tears of a clown: Robinson, Smokey & The
iracles / Cruisin: Robinson, Smokey / Being with
ou: Robinson, Smokey.
D...................................... ZD 72379
otown / Mar '86 / PolyGram.

## ROOVE LINE, THE - SOUL HITS '72-82.
racks: Lady Marmalade: Labelle / Boogie nights:
eatwave / I thought it was you: Hancock, Herbie /
he's a winner: Intruders / Harvest for the world:
sley Brothers / (You said) you'd gimme some more:
.C. & The Sunshine Band / Play that funky music:
Vild Cherry / Summer of '42, Theme from: Biddu
rchestra / I love to love: Charles, Tina / Groove
ne: Heatwave / You bet your love: Hancock, Herbie
 Best of my love: Emotions (2) / T.S.O.P.: MFSB /
hat lady: Isley Brothers / Kiss & say goodbye:
anhattans / Back Stabbers: O'Jays / Dr. Love:
harles, Tina / Take good care of yourself: Three
egrees.
D....................................PWKS 4062
IC...................................PWKMC 4062
ickwick / Jul '91 / Pickwick.

## ROOVESVILLE COLLECTION.
racks: No-one to love: Lewis, Pat / Stone broke:
Vard, Sam / Keep a hold on me: Barnes, J.J. /
Varning: Inst / Lovin you all of my time: Debonaires
) / Watch out: Holidays / Monday to Thursday:
ancha, Steve / Never alone: Ward, Robert / That's
hy I love you: Inst / Hit and run: Batiste, Rose /
on't be sore at me: Parliaments / Thats why I love
ou: Professionals (3) / Did my baby call: Inst / Still
 my heart: Mancha, Steve / Warning': Lewis, Pat /

I've been searchin: Hatchen, Will / Pay back (vocal):
Goode, Johnny / I love you forever: Inst.
CD...................................GSCD 056
Goldmine / Oct '94 / Vital Distribution.

## GROOVIN' - 20 SOULFUL SUMMER GROOVES.
Tracks: Regulate: Warren G. / Summertime: Jeff,
Jazzy & The Fresh Prince / Breakadawn: De La Soul
/ Set adrift on memory bliss: P.M. Dawn / Back and
forth: Aaliyah / Lover: Roberts, Joe / Your body's
calling: R. Kelly / I'm in love: Joe (2) / Long time
gone: Galliano / Joy: Soul II Soul / Connected: Stereo
MC's / People everyday: Arrested Development / It
was a good day: Ice Cube / Brother: Urban Species /
Turn on, tune in, cop out: Freak Power / Be thankful
for what you've got: Massive Attack / Apparently
nothin': Young Disciples / Still a friend of mine:
Incognito / There's nothing like this: Omar / Groovin': Tyson.
CD.................................... 5169682
MC.................................... 5169684
Polygram / Aug '94 / PolyGram.

## GROOVIN' AT THE GO-GO.
Tracks: Not only the girl knows: Victors / Hurt: Vic-
tors / Stay mine for heaven's sake: Holman, Eddie /
Eddie's my name: Holman, Eddie / I'll cry 1000 tears:
Holman, Eddie / I can't break the habit: Garrett, Lee /
One more year: United 4 / It's gonna be a false
alarm: Volcanos / Deeper than that: Preludes /
Shiggy diggy: Preludes / Groovin' at the Go-Go: 4
larks / She's puttin' you on: United 4 / I still love you:
4 larks / Another chance: 4 larks / Without you baby:
Larks (1) / For the love of money: Larks (1) / I
surrender: Holman, Eddie / Where I'm not wanted:
Holman, Eddie / Hurt (2): Holman, Eddie / She's
wanted: Clinton, Larry (1) / Focused on you: Wil-
liams, B. / It's needless to say: Williams, B..
CD...................................GSCD 026
LP...................................GSLP 026
Goldmine / Nov '93 / Vital Distribution.

## GROOVY BABY.
Tracks: Dance to the music: Sly & The Family Stone /
M'lady: Sly & The Family Stone / Give me my free-
dom: Glories / Breakin' down the walls of heartache:
Bandwagon / Baby make your own sweet music:
Bandwagon / Get ready: Elbert, Donnie / Time has
come: Chambers Brothers / Horse: Nobles, Cliff /
Make me yours: Swann, Bettye / Baby you're so
right for me: Brenda / Count the days: Foxx, Inez &
Charlie / Love is strange: Peaches & Herb / Oh how
it hurts: Mason, Barbara / Little piece of leather:
Latter, Gene / Love in them there hills: Vibrations /
Mule: James Boys.
 LP................................... 8 63452
Direction / Dec '68.

## GUYS WITH SOUL.
Tracks: Who's making love: Taylor, Johnnie / I forgot
to be your lover: Bell, William / I've never found a
girl: Floyd, Eddie / Stop half loving these woman:
Lewis, Jimmy / In the rain: Dramatics / Starting all
over again: Mel & Tim / Packed up and took my
mind: Little Milton / I like everything about you:
Hughes, Jimmy / Knock on wood: Floyd, Eddie / I've
been lonely for so long: Knight, Frederick / Cheaper
to keep her: Taylor, Johnnie / Nothing takes the
place of you: Hayes, Isaac / Nearer: Johnson, Lou /
Lovin' on borrowed time: Bell, William / What I don't
know won't hurt me: Thompson, Paul.
 LP...................................STAXL 5006
MC...................................STAXK 5006
Stax / Sep '81 / Pinnacle.

## GUYS WITH SOUL.
Tracks: Don't let the sun catch you cryin': Jackson,
Chuck / I wake up crying: Jackson, Chuck / Beg me:
Jackson, Chuck / If you need me: Burke, Solomon /
You're good for me: Burke, Solomon / Human: Hunt,
Tommy / I am a witness: Hunt, Tommy / Chain gang:
Hunt, Tommy / Pain in my heart: Redding, Otis /
These arms of mine: Redding, Otis / Gonna send you
back to Georgia: Shaw, Timmy / I'm a lonely guy:
Shaw, Timmy.
 LP....................................WCS 1002
Wand / Feb '71.

## HARLEM HEAVIES (R&B '54-62).
Tracks: Not Advised.
 LP.....................................BLP 107
Moonshine / May '85.

## HARLEM SHUFFLE (Sixties Soul Classics).
Tracks: Gimme little sign: Wood, Brenton / Dancin'
holiday: Olympics / Love makes the world go round:
Jackson, Deon / Spring: Birdlegs & Pauline / Ex-
pressway to your heart: Soul Survivors / Ooh wee
baby: Hughes, Freddie / Baby I'm yours: Lewis,
Barbara / Cool jerk: Capitols (1) / Get on up: Es-
quires / And get away: Esquires / Duck: Lee, Jackie /
I know: George, Barbara / Snake: Wilson, Al / Har-
lem shuffle: Bob & Earl / Hello stranger: Lewis,
Barbara / Oh how happy: Shades Of Blue / Oogum
boogum song: Wood, Brenton / Bounce: Olympics /
Backfield in motion: Mel & Tim / Make me your baby
/ You can make it if you try.
 LP.....................................CRB 1139
Charly R&B / Aug '86.
CD...............................CDCHARLY 85
Charly / Apr '87 / Charly.
MC...................................TCCRB 1139
Charly R&B / Apr '87 / Charly.

## HDH PRESENTS THE HITS OF HOT WAX & INVICTUS RECORDS.
Tracks: Not Advised.
CD....................................DHCD 501
HDH / Dec '86 / Pinnacle.

## HEADLINE NEWS.
Tracks: Headline news: Starr, Edwin / Stop on sight:
Starr, Edwin / Black night: Fulson, Lowell / Day
tripper: Barnes, J.J. / Harlem shuffle: Mike Cotton
Sound / I spy for the FBI: Thomas, Jano / Crazy
stockings: Josie, Marva / Substitute: Who / I'm so
thankful: Ikettes / Part 66: Jackson & Smith / Ain't
that lovin' you baby: Suzie & Big Dee / I'll love you
forever: Holidays.
 LP......................................582701
Polydor / Dec '66.

## HEART & SOUL.
Tracks: Letter: Box Tops / Kissing in the back row:
Drifters / Hang on in there baby: Bristol, Johnny /
Reunited: Peaches & Herb / Best thing that ever
happened to me: Knight / Didn't I: Delfonics / Me and
Mrs. Jones: Paul, Billy / Running away: Sly & The
Family Stone / Love train: O'Jays / What a diff'rence
a day makes: Phillips, Esther / Betcha by golly wow:
Stylistics / I'm your puppet: James & Bobby Purify /
That lady: Isley Brothers / I can see clearly now:
Nash, Johnny / L.O.D. (love on delivery): Ocean,
Billy / Can't get enough of your love babe: White,
Barry / Where did our love go: Elbert, Donnie / Get
up offa that thing: Brown, James.
CD..................................... PMP 106
Pickwick / Nov '92 / Pickwick.

## HEART & SOUL - 18 CLASSIC SOUL CUTS.
Tracks: Fine time: Yazz / Suddenly: Ocean, Billy / I
heard it through the grapevine: Gaye, Marvin /
Greatest love of all: Benson, George / One day in
your life: Jackson, Michael / Teardrops: Womack &
Womack / Midnight train to Georgia: Knight, Gladys
& The Pips / Endless love: Richie, Lionel & Diana
Ross / You're the first, the last, my everything: White,
Barry / Your love is king: Sade / Let's stay together:
Green, Al / Lovely day: Withers, Bill / Can't get by
without you: Real Thing / Cherish: Kool & The Gang /
Dreamin': Williams, Vanessa / You are everything:
Ross, Diana & Marvin Gaye / Tears of a clown:
Robinson, Smokey & The Miracles / Heaven help
me: Estus, Deon.
CD................................... 840 534 2
 LP....................................HASTV 1
MC.....................................HASTC 1
Heart & Soul (Polygram) / Aug '89.

## HEART & SOUL COLLECTION VOL 2.
Tracks: Not Advised.
CD..................................KNCD 32002
 LP.................................KNLP 32002
MC..................................KNMC 32002
Knight / May '89 / Castle Communications / BMG.

## HEART & SOUL: SOUL BALLADS.

**Tracks:** Cherish: Kool & The Gang / Till my love comes home: Vandross, Luther / Close the door: Pendergrass, Teddy / Woman in love: Three Degrees / Girls: Moments & Whatnauts / Re-united: Peaches & Herb / How many times can we say goodbye: Warwick, Dionne & Luther Vandross / Caravan of love: Isley-Jasper-Isley / All the love in the world: Warwick, Dionne / Two hearts: Mills, Stephanie & Teddy Pendergrass / Love me: Elliman, Yvonne / Don't stop the music: Yarbrough & Peoples / Like sister and brother: Drifters / Too much too little too late: Mathis, Johnny & Deniece Williams.

| | |
|---|---|
| ■ **LP** | **.KNLP 12001** |
| ■ **CD** | **KNCD 12001** |
| ■ **MC** | **KNMC 12001** |

Knight / Oct '88.

## HEART & SOUL: SOUL BALLADS VOL.2.

**Tracks:** You'll never find another love like mine: Rawls, Lou / You make me feel brand new: Stylistics / If you don't know me by now: Melvin, Harold & The Bluenotes / Have you seen her: Chi-Lites / Who'd she coo: Ohio Players / Hold back the night: Trammps / Hurt: Manhattans / Me & Mrs. Jones: Paul, Billy / Best thing that ever happened to me: Knight, Gladys / Can't help falling in love: Stylistics / Dolly my love: Moments / Don't give up: Melvin, Harold & The Bluenotes / Shine: Bar-Kays / Loving arms: Jackson, Millie.

| | |
|---|---|
| ■ **LP** | **.KNLP 12006** |
| ■ **CD** | **KNCD 12006** |
| ■ **MC** | **KNMC 12006** |

Knight / Oct '88.

## HEART & SOUL: SOUL BOYS.

**Tracks:** If you were here tonight: O'Neal, Alexander / Do what you do: Jackson, Jermaine / Shake you down: Abbott, Gregory / I really didn't mean it: Vandross, Luther / Only you: Pendergrass, Teddy / Trying to love two: Bell, William / Sanctified lady: Gaye, Marvin / Greatest love of all: Benson, George / Hold on to my love: Ruffin, Jimmy / Change: Grant, David / Gonna make you an offer you can't refuse: Helms, Jimmy / Hang on in there baby: Bristol, Johnny / Other woman: Parker, Ray Jnr. / You're the first, the last, my everything: White, Barry.

| | |
|---|---|
| ■ **LP** | **.KNLP 12002** |
| ■ **CD** | **KNCD 12002** |
| ■ **MC** | **KNMC 12002** |

Knight / Oct '88.

## HEART & SOUL: SOUL CLASSICS.

**Tracks:** My baby just cares for me: Simone, Nina / Cry like a baby: Box Tops / Wonderful world: Cooke, Sam / Natural man: Rawls, Lou / Mockingbird: Franklin, Aretha / It's in his kiss: Everett, Betty / Shout: Isley Brothers / It's a man's man's man's world: Brown, James / I can sing a rainbow: Dells / First cut is the deepest: Arnold, P.P. / Didn't I (blow your mind this time): Delphonics / Only the strong survive: Butler, Jerry / Dance to the music: Sly & The Family Stone / Reet petite: Wilson, Jackie.

| | |
|---|---|
| ■ **LP** | **.KNLP 12005** |
| ■ **CD** | **KNCD 12005** |
| ■ **MC** | **KNMC 12005** |

Knight / Oct '88.

## HEART & SOUL: SOUL DANCING.

**Tracks:** System addict: Five Star / When the going get tough the tough get going: Ocean, Billy / Livin' in America: Brown, James / My toot toot: Lasalle, Denise / Don't push it, don't force it: Haywood, Leon / Hot wild: Jackson, Millie / Use it up and wear it out: Odyssey / Ooh, la, la (let's go dancin'): Kool & The Gang / She's strange: Cameo (1) / See the day: Lee, Dee C. / Let's hear it for the boy: Williams, Deniece / Friends: Stewart, Amii / Signed, sealed, delivered: Turner, Ruby / It's a disco night (rock don't stop): Isley Brothers.

| | |
|---|---|
| ■ **LP** | **.KNLP 12015** |
| ■ **CD** | **KNCD 12015** |
| ■ **MC** | **KNMC 12015** |

Knight / Jul '89.

## HEART & SOUL: SOUL GIRLS.

**Tracks:** Another night: Franklin, Aretha / (They long to be) close to you: Guthrie, Gwen / My simple heart: Three Degrees / Best of my love: Emotions (1) / Never knew love like this before: Mills, Stephanie / What a difference a day made: Phillips, Esther / I will survive: Gaynor, Gloria / Midnight train to Georgia: Knight, Gladys / My man's a sweet man: Jackson, Millie / I'll never love this way again: Warwick, Dionne / Right time of the night: Warnes, Jennifer / It's gonna take a miracle: Williams, Deniece / If I can't have you: Elliman, Yvonne / When will I see you again: Three Degrees.

| | |
|---|---|
| ■ **LP** | **.KNLP 12004** |
| ■ **CD** | **KNCD 12004** |
| ■ **MC** | **KNMC 12004** |

Knight / Oct '88.

## HEART & SOUL: SOUL GROUPS.

**Tracks:** Native New Yorker: Odyssey / When you say you love somebody from the heart: Kool & The Gang / Summer breeze: Isley Brothers / Give it up: K.C. & The Sunshine Band / There goes my first love: Drifters / Just don't want to be lonely: Main Ingredient / When she was my girl: Four Tops / Going to the bank: Commodores / Used to be my girl: O'Jays / Ms. Grace: Tymes / Rock the boat: Hues Corporation / Kiss and say goodbye: Manhattans / You don't have to go: Chi-Lites / Day by day: Shakatak & Al Jarreau.

| | |
|---|---|
| ■ **LP** | **.KNLP 12003** |
| ■ **CD** | **KNCD 12003** |
| ■ **MC** | **KNMC 12003** |

Knight / Oct '88.

## HEART & SOUL: SOUL KISS.

**Tracks:** Joanna: Kool & The Gang / Always and forever: Heatwave / You're my latest, my greatest inspiration: Pendergrass, Teddy / Tonight I'm gonna love you all over: Four Tops / You're my angel / When the rain begins to fall: Jackson, Jermaine & Pia Zadora / What a fool believes: Franklin, Aretha / Just the way you are: White, Barry / I'd rather go blind: Turner, Ruby / (Sittin' on) the dock of the bay: Bolton, Michael / Na-na is the saddest word: Stylistics / You're a part of me: Carnes/Cotton / Lies: Butler, Jonathan / Suddenly: Ocean, Billy.

| | |
|---|---|
| ■ **LP** | **.KNLP 12013** |
| ■ **CD** | **KNCD 12013** |
| ■ **MC** | **KNMC 12013** |

Knight / Jul '89.

## HEART & SOUL: SOUL LOVE.

**Tracks:** Superstar (Don't you remember): Vandross, Luther / Can't we try: Pendergrass, Teddy / Who's zoomin' who: Franklin, Aretha / Single life: Cameo (1) / It's gonna take a miracle: Williams, Deniece / Don't walk away: Four Tops.

| | |
|---|---|
| ■ **LP** | **.KNLP 12009** |
| ■ **CD** | **KNCD 12009** |
| ■ **MC** | **KNMC 12009** |

Knight / Mar '89.

## HEART & SOUL: SOUL NIGHTS.

**Tracks:** Love come down: King, Evelyn 'Champagne' / You said you'd gimme some more: K.C. & The Sunshine Band / Harvest for the world: Isley Brothers / Get up offa that thing: Brown, James / My love is waiting: Gaye, Marvin / Let me know (I have a right): Gaynor, Gloria.

| | |
|---|---|
| ■ **LP** | **.KNLP 12007** |
| ■ **CD** | **KNCD 12007** |
| ■ **MC** | **KNMC 12007** |

Knight / Mar '89.

## HEART & SOUL: SOUL POWER.

**Tracks:** Caribbean queen (no more love on the run): Ocean, Billy / Baby we better try and get it together: White, Barry / Love train: O'Jays / Ain't no stoppin' us now: McFadden & Whitehead / What becomes of the broken hearted: Turner, Ruby / La la means I love you: Delfonics / If you're looking for: Odyssey / Lady Marmalade: Labelle / Roses: Haywoode / I can't help myself: Real Thing / Can I take you home little girl: Drifters / Never can say goodbye: Gaynor, Gloria / Runner: Three Degrees / Oops upside your head: Gap Band.

| | |
|---|---|
| ■ **LP** | **.KNLP 12014** |
| ■ **CD** | **KNCD 12014** |
| ■ **MC** | **KNMC 12014** |

Knight / Jul '89.

## HEART & SOUL: SOUL SEEKING.

**Tracks:** Down on the beach tonight: Drifters / Take good care of yourself: Three Degrees / Zing went the strings of your heart: Trammps / It's in his kiss: Lewis, Linda / Love I lost: Melvin, Harold / Let the music play: White, Barry.

| | |
|---|---|
| ■ **LP** | **.KNLP 12008** |
| ■ **CD** | **KNCD 12008** |
| ■ **MC** | **KNMC 12008** |

Knight / Mar '89.

## HEART AND SOUL.

**Tracks:** Not Advised.

| | |
|---|---|
| CD Set | **OXO 12** |

Object Enterprises / Oct '88 / Gold & Sons / THE / Midland Records.

## HEART AND SOUL.

**Tracks:** Not Advised.

| | |
|---|---|
| ■ **LP** | **EPC 32217** |

Epic / Oct '82.

## HEART AND SOUL II - BODY AND SOUL (18 Classic Soul Cuts).

**Tracks:** Miss you like crazy: Cole, Natalie / What's love got to do with it: Turner, Tina / Running with the night: Richie, Lionel / I say a little prayer: Franklin, Aretha / All of my life: Ross, Diana / Reach out I'll be there: Four Tops / My one temptation: Paris, Mica / I really didn't mean it: Vandross, Luther / If only could: Youngblood, Sydney / Sexual healing: Gaye Marvin / Being with you: Robinson, Smokey / (Sittin' on) the dock of the bay: Redding, Otis / Where is the love: Paris, Mica & Will Downing / Tonight I celebrate my love: Flack, Roberta & Peabo Bryson / When you I'm born again: Preston, Billy & Syreeta / Best thing that ever happened to me: Knight, Gladys & The Pips / One day I'll fly away: Crawford, Randy / your eyes: Benson, George.

| | |
|---|---|
| CD | **840 77** |
| ■ **LP** | **840 77** |
| MC | **840 77** |

Polydor / Feb '90 / PolyGram.

## HEART AND SOUL III.

**Tracks:** Sign your name: D'Arby, Terence Tren Easy: Commodores / Love don't live here anymo Rose Royce / Private dancer: Turner, Tina / I live your love: Cole, Natalie / Tracks of my tears: Rob son, Smokey & The Miracles / Respect: Frankl Aretha / Lovers: O'Neal, Alexander / Come into life: Sims, Joyce / Papa was a rollin' stone: Tem tations / My girl: Redding, Otis / When a man loves woman: Sledge, Percy / Tired of being alone: Gree Al / Touch me in the morning: Ross, Diana / cherie amour: Wonder, Stevie / Farewell my summ love: Jackson, Michael / Way we were: Knigh Gladys / Loving you: Riperton, Minnie.

| | |
|---|---|
| CD | **845 009** |
| LP | **845 009** |
| MC | **845 009** |

Heart & Soul (Polygram) / Jul '90.

## HEART FULL OF SOUL.

**Tracks:** Not Advised.

| | |
|---|---|
| CD | **DINCD** |
| MC | **DINMC** |

Dino / Jun '93 / Pinnacle.

## HEART OF SOUTHERN SOUL, THE.

**Tracks:** Falling in love again: Kelly Brothers / You' that great big feelin': Kelly Brothers / That's all I ca do: Anderson, Kip / Snake out of the grass (part Anderson, Roshell / Snake out of the grass (part 2 Anderson, Roshell / Soldier's sad story: Watkin Tiny / Pretty little thing: Interpreters / Your love worth the pain: Truitt, Johnny / Talk to me: Avons / Your love's so good: Webber, Lee / Somewhere o there: Matthis, Lucille / Mr Fortune teller: Dee & De / Midnight tears: Watkins, Tiny / Woman in m Mariann / Steppin' stone: Wallace Brothers / Gone need somebody: Lane, Stacy / I went off and crie Anderson, Kip / You'll never know: Brown, Shirley C C Rider: Powell, Bobby / Price is too high: Harp Slim / There goes a girl: Truitt, Johnny / Do yo thing: Whitney, Marva / Power is gone: Kem Eugene.

| | |
|---|---|
| CD | **CDCHD 5** |

Ace / Sep '94 / Pinnacle / Complete Record Co. L

## HEAT OF SOUL, VOLUME 1.

**Tracks:** Stand by me: King, Ben E. / I heard it throu the grapevine: Reeves, Martha / Patches: Carte Clarence / Rock you baby: McCae, George / Rescu me: Bass, Fontella / When a man loves a woma Sledge, Percy / Soul man: Sam & Dave / Knock o wood: Floyd, Eddie / 'In' crowd: Gray, Dobie / Ho on I'm coming: Sam & Dave.

| | |
|---|---|
| ■ **LP** | **MASL 0** |
| MC | **CMASL 0** |

Master Sound / Mar '87 / Sony.

## HI GIRLS.

**Tracks:** You gotta take the bitter with the swee Starks, Veniece / What more do you want from m Starks, Veniece / Step child: Starks, Veniece / days: Starks, Veniece / Every now & then: Stark Veniece / Trying to love my life without you: Stark Veniece / I still love you: Starks, Veniece / Without reason: Janet & The Jays / Hurting over you bo Janet & The Jays / Love what you're doing to m Janet & The Jays / Pleading for your love: Janet The Jays / When the battle is over: Joint Venture / I rather hurt you now: Joint Venture / Quiet elegenc love: Joint Venture / Mama said: Joint Venture / I nee love: Joint Venture / Love will make you feel bette Joint Venture / Your love is strange: Joint Venture Roots of love: Joint Venture / Look at the boy: Plur Jean / Here I go again: Plum, Jean / Pour on th lovin': Plum, Jean / You ask me: Plum, Jean / It's yo that I need (Part 1): Duncan Sisters / Anyway th wind blows: Coffee, Erma / You made me what I am Coffee, Erma / He's got it: Known Facts / How can believe you: Known Facts.

| | |
|---|---|
| CD | **HILOCD** |

Hi / Mar '94 / Pinnacle.

## HI RECORDS STORY, THE.

**Tracks:** Not Advised.

| | |
|---|---|
| CD | **HIUKCD 10** |

Hi / Jul '89 / Pinnacle.

■ DELETE

**II RECORDS: THE EARLY YEARS.**
**racks:** Pipleliner: *Redell, Teddy Band* / I want to old you: *Redell, Teddy Band* / There was a time: *eeder, Bill* / Till I waltz again with you again: *eeder, Bill* / Judy: *Reeder, Bill* / Secret love: *eeder, Bill* / 7.26 miles to Juliet: *Wallace, Darlene* / mokie part 2: *Bill's Black Combo* / Your true love: *immons, Gene (1)* / Teddy bear: *Simmons, Gene (1)* Shape you left me in: *Simmons, Gene (1)* / No other uy: *Simmons, Gene (1)* / Tuff: *Cannon, Ace* / Jum-in': *Simmons, Gene (1)*.
■ **Double LP.** . . . . . . . . . . . . . . **DHIUKLP 434**
i / Aug '87.
■ **LP** . . . . . . . . . . . . . . . . . . . . **HIUKLP 434**
i / May '87.

**II RECORDS: THE EARLY YEARS VOL.1.**
**racks:** Tootsie: *McVoy, Carl* / You are my sunshine / ittle John's gone / Daydreamin / Skating in the blue ght.: *Charmettes* / You made a hit.: *Fuller, Joe* / lease please: *Coburn, Kimball* / Teenage love / I'm o lonely: *Loyd, Jay B* / Going back to Memphis: *immons, Gene (1)* / Lovin Lil: *Tucker, Tommy* / Man love: *Tucker, Tommy* / Millers cave: *Tucker, ommy* / Stranger: *Tucker, Tommy* / Pipliner: *Red-ell, Teddy* / Want to hold you: *Reddell, Teddy* / here was a time: *Reeder, Bill* / Til I Waltz again with ou: *Reeder, Bill* / Judy: *Reeder, Bill* / Secret love: *eeder, Bill* / 26 Miles to Joliet: *Wallace, Darlen* / mokie: *Black, Bill Combo*.
D. . . . . . . . . . . . . . . . . . . . **HIUKCD 127**
i / Apr '92 / Pinnacle.

**II RECORDS: THE EARLY YEARS OL.2.**
**racks:** My girl Josephine: *Jayes, Jerry* / Five miles om home: *Jayes, Jerry* / Middle of nowhere: *Jayes, erry* / Long black veil: *Jayes, Jerry* / Sugar bee: *ayes, Jerry* / I'm in love again: *Jayes, Jerry* / I vashed my hands in muddy water: *Jayes, Jerry* / hackles and chains: *Tucker, Tommy* / I'm in love vith a shadow: *Tucker, Tommy* / Wild side of life: *ucker, Tommy* / Since I met you baby: *Felts, Narvel* Dee Dee: *Felts, Narvel* / 86 miles: *Felts, Narvel* / ittle bit of soap: *Felts, Narvel* / Dark shaded lasses: *Eldred, Charles* / Long tall texan: *Kellum, Aurray & Rhythm Four* / I gotta leave this town: *utton, Glenn* / Shame, shame, shame: *Tucker, ommy* / Listen to me lie: *Simmons, Gene (1)* / Vedding bells: *Simmons, Gene (1)* / Invitation to the lues: *Simmons, Gene (1)* / Time is right: *Lloyd, Jay* . / Honey babe: *Arnold, Jerry* / Son of Smokie: *lack, Bill Combo* / Crank case: *Black, Bill Combo* / D's boogie woogie: *Black, Bill Combo* / Deep elem lues: *Cannon, Ace & Bill Black's combo* / Sittin' ght: *Cannon, Ace*.
■ **Double LP.** . . . . . . . . . . . . . . **DHIUKLP 442**
i / '88.
D. . . . . . . . . . . . . . . . . . . . **HIUKCD 128**
i / Apr '92 / Pinnacle.

**II RHYTHM & BLUES.**
**racks:** That driving beat: *Mitchell, Willie & 4 Kings* / ain't easy: *Bryant, Don* / Sure looks good to me: *ryant, Don* / Clear days and stormy nights: *Bryant, on* / I will be true: *One & One* / Champion: *Mitchell, Villie* / Hey little girl: *West, Norm* / Love what you're loing to me / Without a reason: *Janet & The Jays* / ioodest man: *Miller, Gene 'Bowlegs'* / Mama's boy: *ry, James* / I've got enough: *Fry, James* / Help ourself: *Five Royales* / Roll with the punches: *Five Royales*.
■ **LP** . . . . . . . . . . . . . . . . . . . **HIUKLP 439**
i.

**IIS WAY WITH THE GIRLS.**
**racks:** Not Advised.
■ **LP** . . . . . . . . . . . . . . . . . . . . **LPSS 111**
oul Supply / Dec '86.

**IISTORY OF DANCE 1 (1959 - 1979).**
**racks:** Shout: *Isley Brothers* / Green onions: *Booker & The MG's* / Walking the dog: *Thomas, Rufus* / nock on wood: *Floyd, Eddie* / Soul finger: *Bar-Kays* Sweet soul music: *Conley, Arthur* / Chain of fools: *ranklin, Aretha* / Do the funky chicken: *Thomas, Rufus* / Family affair: *Sly & The Family Stone* / Could t be I'm falling in love: *Detroit Spinners* / Sound your unky horn: *K.C. & The Sunshine Band* / Satisfaction juaranteed: *Melvin, Harold & The Bluenotes* / Walk-ng in rhythm: *Blackbyrds* / Get up offa that thing: *Brown, James* / Funky weekend: *Stylistics* / Movin': *Brass Construction* / Can't get by without you: *Real Thing* / Car wash: *Royce, Rose* / Do what you wanna lo: *T Connection* / Darlin darlin baby: *O'Jays* / Free: *Villiams, Deniece* / If I can't have you: *Elliman, Yvonne* / I love the nightlife: *Bridges, Alicia* / Take hat to the bank: *Shalamar* / September: *Earth, Wind & Fire* / Groove line: *Heatwave* / I want your love: *Chic* / Backstrokin': *Fatback Band*.

**CD Set** . . . . . . . . . . . . . . . . . . . **DBOX 001**
Connoisseur Collection / Oct '93 / Pinnacle.

**HISTORY OF DANCE 2 (1980 - 1992).**
**Tracks:** Check out the groove: *Thurston, Bobby* / Brazilian love: *Duke, George* / Can you handle it: *Redd, Sharon* / Risin' to the top: *Burke, Keni* / You're the one for me: *D-Train* / Zoom: *Fat Larry's Band* / Last night a DJ saved my life: *Indeep* / Hold me tighter in: *Griffin, Billy* / Let the music play: *Shannon* / Trapped: *Abrams, Colonel* / Solid: *Ashford & Simpson* / Tossing & turning: *Windjammer* / Finest: *S.O.S. Band* / Love supreme: *Downing, Will* / Don't be cruel: *Brown, Bobby (1)* / Going back to my roots: *FPI Project* / Heaven: *Chimes (1)* / Wash your face in my sink: *Dream Warriors* / Don't go messing with my heart: *Mantronix* / Power: *Snap* / Finally: *Peniston, Ce Ce* / How can I love you more: *M People* / Love power: *Vandross, Luther* / Sensitivity: *Tresvant, Ralph* / Key, the secret: *Urban Cookie Collective*.
**CD Set** . . . . . . . . . . . . . . . . . . . **DBOX 002**
Connoisseur Collection / Oct '93 / Pinnacle.

**HISTORY OF HI RECORDS (Rhythm & Blues - The Glory Years).**
**Tracks:** I'm still in love with you: *Green, Al* / I die a little each day: *Clay, Otis* / Breaking up somebody's home: *Peebles, Ann* / We did it: *Johnson, Syl* / You made me what I am: *Coffee, Erma* / I can't stand the rain: *Peebles, Ann* / Call me: *Green, Al* / On the loose: *Hi-Rhythm* / Into something (Can't shake loose): *Wright, O.V.*.
■ **LP** . . . . . . . . . . . . . . . . . . . . **MCA 25227**
MCA / Mar '88.

**HISTORY OF R&B VOL. 3.**
**Tracks:** Smokey Joe's cafe: *Robins* / Devil or angel: *Clovers* / Down in the valley: *Clovers* / Corrina Corrina: *Turner, Joe* / Ruby baby: *Drifters* / Fools fall in love: *Drifters* / Since I met you baby: *Hunter, Ivory Joe* / Treasure of love: *McPhatter, Clyde* / Just to hold my hand: *McPhatter, Clyde* / Long lonely nights: *McPhatter, Clyde* / Jim Dandy: *Baker, LaVern* / Searchin': *Coasters* / Young blood: *Coasters* / C.C. rider: *Willis, Chuck*.
■ **LP** . . . . . . . . . . . . . . . . . . . . **587 096**
Atlantic / Apr '68.

**HISTORY OF R&B VOL. 4.**
**Tracks:** Yakety yak: *Coasters* / Charlie Brown: *Coasters* / Poison Ivy: *Coasters* / There goes my baby: *Drifters* / True love true love: *Drifters* / Dance with me: *Drifters* / This magic moment: *Drifters* / Save the last dance for me: *Drifters* / I count the tears: *Drifters* / Splish splash: *Darin, Bobby* / Lover's question: *McPhatter, Clyde* / I cried a tear: *Baker, LaVern* / What'd I say: *Charles, Ray* / Spanish Harlem: *King, Ben E.* / Gee whiz: *Thomas, Carla*.
■ **LP** . . . . . . . . . . . . . . . . . . . . **587 097**
Atlantic / Apr '68.

**HISTORY OF R&B VOL. 5.**
**Tracks:** Not Advised.
■ **LP** . . . . . . . . . . . . . . . . . . . . **587 140**
Atlantic / Nov '68.

**HISTORY OF R&B VOL. 6.**
**Tracks:** Not Advised.
■ **LP** . . . . . . . . . . . . . . . . . . . . **587 141**
Atlantic / Nov '68.

**HISTORY OF RHYTHM & BLUES VOCAL GROUPS.**
**Tracks:** Not Advised.
**MC.** . . . . . . . . . . . . . . . . . . . . **901 324**
Atlantic / '88 / WEA.

**HISTORY OF..,A VOL.1(1950-1958).**
**Tracks:** Let the good times roll: *Shirley & Lee* / Rockin' pneumonia and the boogie woogie flu / Lawdy Miss Clawdy: *Price, Lloyd* / Bald head: *Professor Longhair* / Later alligator: *Charles, Bobby* / Those lonely lonely nights: *King, Earl* / Walkin' with Mr.Lee: *Allen, Lee* / Ain't got no home: *Henry, Clarence 'Frogman'* / Just because: *Price, Lloyd* / Jock-a-mo: *Crawford, James'Sugarboy'& His Canecutters* / Don't you just know it: *Smith, Huey "Piano" & The Clowns* / Feel so good: *Shirley & Lee* / Things that I used to do: *Guitar Slim* / Mardis gras mambo: *Hawketts*.
■ **LP** . . . . . . . . . . . . . . . . . . . **RNLP 70076**
**MC.** . . . . . . . . . . . . . . . . . . . . **RNC 70076**
Rhino (USA) / Feb '88 / WEA.

**HISTORY OF..,A VOL.2(1959-1962).**
**Tracks:** Ooh poo pah doo(part 1): *Hill, Jessie* / Certain girl: *Doe, Ernie K.* / Fortune teller: *Spellman, Benny* / Trick bag: *King, Earl* / I know (you don't love me no more): *George, Barbara* / All these things: *Neville, Art* / It will stand: *Showmen* / Ya, ya: *Dorsey, Lee* / Mother-in-law: *Doe, Ernie K.* / Over you: *Neville, Aaron* / I like it like that (part1): *Kenner, Chris* / Sea cruise: *Ford, Frankie* / There's something on your mind (part 2): *Marchan, Bobby* / But I do: *Henry, Clarence 'Frogman'*.
■ **LP** . . . . . . . . . . . . . . . . . . . **RNLP 70077**
**MC.** . . . . . . . . . . . . . . . . . . . . **RNC 70077**
Rhino (USA) / Feb '88 / WEA.

**HISTORY OF..,A VOL.3(1962-1970).**
**Tracks:** Ride your pony: *Dorsey, Lee* / Lipstick traces: *Spellman, Benny* / Time is on my side: *Thomas, Irma* / Release me: *Adams, Johnny* / Down home girl: *Robinson, Alvin* / You'll lose a good thing: *Lynn, Barbara* / Working in a coalmine: *Dorsey, Lee* / Barefootin': *Parker, Bobby* / Get out of my life woman: *Dorsey, Lee* / Tell it like it is: *Neville, Aaron* / Something you got: *Robinson, Alvin* / Wish someone would care: *Thomas, Irma* / I won't cry: *Adams, Johnny* / Iko iko: *Dixie Cups*.
■ **LP** . . . . . . . . . . . . . . . . . . . **RNLP 70078**
**MC.** . . . . . . . . . . . . . . . . . . . . **RNC 70078**
Rhino (USA) / Feb '88 / WEA.

**HIT '67.**
**Tracks:** Funky Broadway / Groovin' / Baby I love you / Tears tears / Respect / Girl like you / Show me / etc.
■ **LP** . . . . . . . . . . . . . . . . . . . . **587 087**
Atlantic / Dec '67.

**HIT '68.**
**Tracks:** Think / I say a little prayer / She's looking good / You don't know what you mean to me / Looking for a fox / Dock of the bay / Funky St. / Skinny legs and all / Hard to handle / Don't take your love from me / Tighten up / Take time to know her.
■ **LP** . . . . . . . . . . . . . . . . . . . . **588 136**
Atlantic / Dec '68.

**HOLD BACK THE NIGHT.**
**Tracks:** Not Advised.
**CD** . . . . . . . . . . . . . . . . . . . . **DCD 5396**
Scratch / Oct '94 / Scratch Records / BMG / Grapevine Distribution.

**HOT CHILLS AND COLD THRILLS.**
**Tracks:** Something's got a hold on me: *Williams, Jeanette* / What you're puttin' me through: *Newby, Dianne* / And the band played on: *Spindles* / If that ain't loving you: *Charles, Lee* / Angel baby: *Green, Garland* / How to succeed in love: *Love, Martha Jean* / It's the little things: *Patti & The Emblems* / Something for my people: *Greatest Little Soul Band In The Land* / These kinds of blues: *Parker, Junior* / I've only got myself to blame: *Williams, Bobby* / Gonna have to show you: *Trends* / Someone's gonna cry: *Austin, Patti* / One more chance: *Lawson, Shirley* / Tell it like it is: *Marriots* / Hot thrills and cold chills: *Blue Notes* / Right to cry: *Welch, Lenny*.
■ **LP** . . . . . . . . . . . . . . . . . . . . **KENT 023**
Kent / Jun '84.

**HOT DISCO NIGHT VOL. 1.**
**Tracks:** Lust / Mondo disco / Le spank / Hot disco night / Step by step / Phenomena theme / Let's get it togetehr / Monkey see monkey do / Under construction.
■ **LP** . . . . . . . . . . . . . . . . . . . **NSPL 28271**
Pye / Oct '78.

**HOT DISCO QUEENS - VOL. 1.**
**Tracks:** Not Advised.
**CD** . . . . . . . . . . . . . . . . . . . . **.112014-2**
**MC.** . . . . . . . . . . . . . . . . . . . . **.112014-4**
Scratch / Oct '94 / Scratch Records / BMG / Grapevine Distribution.

**HOT SOUL MUSIC VOL.1.**
**Tracks:** Not Advised.
**CD** . . . . . . . . . . . . . . . . . . . . **377 161**
Arcade / Aug '89 / Sony / Grapevine Distribution.

**HOT SOUL MUSIC VOL.2.**
**Tracks:** Not Advised.
■ **LP** . . . . . . . . . . . . . . . . . . . . **377 261**
Arcade / Aug '89.

**HOT WAX GREATEST HITS.**
**Tracks:** Want ads / Stick up / Somebody's been sleeping / Too many cooks / 90 Day freeze / Mind body & soul / Westbound No. 9 / I'm not my brothers keeper / Womans' love rights / Frightened girl.
■ **LP** . . . . . . . . . . . . . . . . . . . . **SHW 5008**
Hot Wax / '72.

**HOW TO PICK A WINNER (Seahorns Soul Farm Vol. 2).**
**Tracks:** Lovely woman: *Holmes, Edward* / How to pick a winner: *Toussaint, A.* / Fairchild: *Toussaint, A.* / Just like a woman: *Lee, W.* / I love you still: *Toussaint, A.* / Man of the street: *Moore, S. & V.Toussaint* / Here comes that hurt again: *Toussaint, A.* / You got to love me: *Doe, E.K.* / Natural soul brother: *Greer, Dan* / Goodbye: *Moore, J.* / Cheatin' woman: *Holmes, Edward* / Don't set me back: *Toussaint, A.* /

■ DELETED

Did you have fun: *West, W/D.Lee/L.Delcambre* / All I want is you: *Toussaint, A.* / Sadie Mae: *Sixon, L/ J.Haywood/L.Winnifred* / You lie so much: *Doe, E.K.*.
■ LP . . . . . . . . . . . . . . . . . . . . **CRB 1124**
MC. . . . . . . . . . . . . . . . . . . . **TCCRB 1124**
Charly R&B / May '87 / Charly.

# I

## IN LOVE WITH SOUL II (The Quiet Storm).
**Tracks:** Do what you do: *Jackson, Jermaine* / Stay the night: *Parker, Ray Jnr.* / Can't we fall in love again: *Hyman, Phyllis & Michael Henderson* / Love all the hurt away: *Franklin, Aretha & George Michael* / I'm in love: *Pointer Sisters* / This time: *Kiara & Shanice Wilson* / Closer than close: *Carne, Jean* / Love changes: *Kashif* / If ever a love there was: *Four Tops & Aretha Franklin* / I just wanna be your girl: *Chapter Eight & Anita Baker* / Girl blue: *Main Ingredient* / It will be alright: *Odyssey* / Tonight I give in: *Bofill, Angela* / How many times can we say goodbye: *Warwick, Dionne & Luther Vandross* / Georgy Porgy: *Charme & Luther Van Dross*.
■ CD. . . . . . . . . . . . . . . . . . . . . **261469**
■ MC. . . . . . . . . . . . . . . . . . . . . **411469**
Ariola / Jun '91.

## IN STYLE (Rare Soul Uncovered Vol.3).
**Tracks:** You'll always be in style: *Barnes, Sidney* / Now I'm in love with you / That other place: *Flemons, Wade* / I won't stop to cry / I don't want to hurt nobody / Why don't you write: *Bates, Lee* / I can't be your part time baby / You're the dream: *Robinson, Roscoe* / Just like a yo yo: *Winters, Ruby* / My love is gone / Power of love: *Humphrey, Amanda* / I better run / My man don't think I know / But I couldn't: *Harper, Willie* / Spanish boy: *Rubies*.
■ LP . . . . . . . . . . . . . . . . . . . . **CRB 1166**
MC. . . . . . . . . . . . . . . . . . . . **TCCRB 1166**
Charly R&B / Sep '87 / Charly.

## IN THE GROOVE - THE 12 INCH DISCO PARTY.
**Tracks:** Last night a DJ saved my life: *Indeep* / Love come down: *King, Evelyn 'Champagne'* / Joy: *Band AKA* / Rappers' delight: *Sugarhill Gang* / Sexual healing: *Gaye, Marvin* / Just an illusion: *Imagination* / Taking a chance on love: *Redd, Sharon* / Twist: *Chill Fac-torr* / Rock the boat: *Forrest* / Hold me tighter in the rain: *Griffin, Billy* / Cash (cash money): *Prince Charles* / Garden party: *Mezzoforte* / Dancing on the floor: *Third World* / Message: *Flash & The Furious Five* / When boys talk: *Indeep* / Never too much: *Vandross, Luther*.
■ LP . . . . . . . . . . . . . . . . . . . . **STAR 2228**
MC. . . . . . . . . . . . . . . . . . . . **STAC 2228**
Telstar/Ronco / May '83 / BMG.

## INCREDIBLE MEDLEYS (Artists/Songs That Inspired Motown 25th Ann. TV special).
**Tracks:** Reach out I'll be there: *Temptations & Four Tops* / Get ready: *Temptations & Four Tops* / It's the same old song: *Temptations & Four Tops* / Ain't too proud to beg: *Temptations & Four Tops* / Baby I need your loving: *Temptations & Four Tops* / My girl: *Temptations & Four Tops* / I can't get next to you: *Temptations & Four Tops* / I know I'm losing you: *Temptations & Four Tops* / I can't help myself: *Temptations & Four Tops* / Nowhere to run: *Reeves, Martha* / Dancing in the street: *Reeves, Martha* / Heatwave: *Reeves, Martha* / I'm ready for love: *Reeves, Martha* / I heard it through the grapevine: *Knight, Gladys* / Friendship train: *Knight, Gladys* / You need love like I do: *Knight, Gladys* / If I were your woman: *Knight, Gladys* / Daddy could swear, I declare: *Knight, Gladys* / Neither one of us: *Knight, Gladys* / Shake me wake me: *Four Tops* / Standing in the shadows of love: *Four Tops* / Bernadette: *Four Tops* / Stop in the name of love: *Ross, Diana & The Supremes* / Back in my arms again: *Ross, Diana & The Supremes* / Come see about me: *Ross, Diana & The Supremes* / Love is like an itching in my heart: *Various original artists* / Where did our love go: *Ross, Diana & The Supremes* / I want you back: *Jackson Five* / ABC: *Jackson Five* / Love you save: *Jackson Five* / Dancing machine: *Jackson Five* / Never can say goodbye: *Jackson Five* / I'll be there: *Jackson Five*.
■ MC. . . . . . . . . . . . . . . . . . . . **CSTMS 5106**
■ LP . . . . . . . . . . . . . . . . . . . . **STMS 5106**
Motown / Oct '83.

## INFERNO PARTY.
**Tracks:** Not Advised.
■ LP . . . . . . . . . . . . . . . . . . . . **1001**
Inferno (1) / Jul '88.

## INSIDE (The Best Of British).
**Tracks:** When we're making love: *Opaz* / Be still: *French, Michelle* / Me O my: *Mid 8 Production* / Been fooled: *Caitaine, Ria* / Fight: *McKoy* / Whole thing: *Act Of Faith* / Even when you're gone: *Gems For Jem* / Mystery girl: *Green, Tee* / If I knew: *D-Swing* / Hold me closer: *Circle Of Life* / Love away: *Pearce, Mary* / Coming closer: *Feel* / Simple solution: *Dee, Jay* / Running to my baby's arms: *Ipso Facto* / Slow down: *Metropolis (1)* / Through all times: *Perfect Taste*.
CD. . . . . . . . . . . . . . . . . . . . **CDTEP 1**
LP . . . . . . . . . . . . . . . . . . . . **.LPTEP 1**
MC. . . . . . . . . . . . . . . . . . . . **MCTEP 1**
Passion/Debut/Scratch Music / Nov '92 / Pinnacle / 3MV.

## INSIDE 2.
**Tracks:** Greater love: *Nu Colours* / Reach out: *Perception* / Take me: *D-Swing* / Just don't care: *Funhill* / Visions: *Julianne* / I'll be good to you: *Green, Tee* / Time for love: *Gems For Jem* / Doing it for love: *Act Of Faith* / Get it on: *Solid State Sound* / Sunday morning blue: *Mapp, Chantel* / I know how: *Stevens, Kenni* / Calling her name: *Ipso Facto* / 2 be a friend: *Pearce, Mary* / Love when it's like this: *Antony, Joseph* / Your love my love: *Nazlyn* / Give it (this love song): *Caitaine, Ria*.
CD. . . . . . . . . . . . . . . . . . . . **CDTEP 2**
LP . . . . . . . . . . . . . . . . . . . . **.LPTEP 2**
MC. . . . . . . . . . . . . . . . . . . . **MCTEP 2**
Passion/Debut/Scratch Music / Jun '93 / Pinnacle / 3MV.

## INSIDE 3.
**Tracks:** Movin' in the right direction: *FM Inc* / Fever (rider): *D-Swing* / So much feeling: *Closer Than Close* / Gotta get it: *Index (1)* / Deeper: *Uschi* / Fallin': *Tyson* / Heaven: *Menzies, Steve* / I Luv U: *Sovereign (1)* / I like the way: *Everis* / Hurt so bad (till U like it): *Marshall, Wayne* / Learned my lesson: *Smith, Charlene* / There ain't enough love: *Zushii* / You belong to me: *Fyza* / Searching: *Robyn*.
CD. . . . . . . . . . . . . . . . . . . . **CDTEP 3**
LP . . . . . . . . . . . . . . . . . . . . **.LPTEP 3**
MC. . . . . . . . . . . . . . . . . . . . **MCTEP 3**
Passion/Debut/Scratch Music / Mar '94 / Pinnacle / 3MV.

## IS IT LOVE.
**Tracks:** Not Advised.
CD. . . . . . . . . . . . . . . . . . . . **PWKS 4133**
MC. . . . . . . . . . . . . . . . . . . . **PWKMC 4133**
Pickwick / Nov '92 / Pickwick.

## IT TAKES TWO.
**Tracks:** You're all I need to get by: *Gaye, Marvin & Tammi Terrell* / I'm your puppet: *Houston, Thelma & Jerry Butler* / You ain't livin' till you're lovin': *Houston, Thelma & Jerry Butler* / It's a lifetime thing: *Houston, Thelma & Jerry Butler* / Let's make a deal: *Syreeta & G.C. Cameron* / What good am I without you: *Gaye, Marvin & Kim Weston* / It takes two: *Supremes & Four Tops* / Love the one you're with: *Supremes & Four Tops* / River deep, mountain high: *Ross, Diana & Marvin Gaye* / You're a special part of me: *Ross, Diana & Marvin Gaye* / Stand by me: *Ruffin, David & Jimmy* / Let's make love now: *Art & Honey* / Oh how happy: *Starr, Edwin & Blinky* / I'm gonna make you love me: *Ross, Diana, The Supremes & The Temptations* / Once upon a time: *Gaye, Marvin & Mary Wells*.
■ LP . . . . . . . . . . . . . . . . . . . . **STMR 9002**
■ MC. . . . . . . . . . . . . . . . . . . . **CSTMR 9002**
Motown / Oct '81.

## IT TAKES TWO.
**Tracks:** Not Advised.
■ Double LP. . . . . . . . . . . . . . . . . . **STD 7**
MC Set . . . . . . . . . . . . . . . . . . . . **STDK 7**
Solitaire / Nov '83 / BMG.

## IT TAKES TWO.
**Tracks:** It takes two: *Gaye, Marvin & Kim Weston* / I knew you were waiting for me: *Michael, George & Aretha Franklin* / I'm back for more: *Lulu & Bobby Womack* / Would I lie to you: *Charles & Eddie* / You've lost that lovin' feeling: *Righteous Brothers* / Solid: *Ashford & Simpson* / Reunited: *Peaches & Herb* / Up where we belong: *Cocker, Joe & Jennifer Warnes* / With you I'm born again: *Preston, Billy & Syreeta* / Baby, come to me: *Austin, Patti & James Ingram* / I got you babe: *Sonny & Cher* / Senza una donna (without a woman): *Zucchero & Paul Young* / Sometimes love just ain't enough: *Henley, Don* / I'll never fall in love again: *Deacon Blue* / Don't kno much: *Ronstadt, Linda & Aaron Neville* / Where the love: *Paris, Mica & Will Downing* / Tonight celebrate my love: *Flack, Roberta & Peabo Bryson* If you were with me now: *Minogue, Kylie & Kei Washington* / At last: *Rawls, Lou & Diana Reeves*.
CD. . . . . . . . . . . . . . . . . . . . **CDEMTV 8**
MC. . . . . . . . . . . . . . . . . . . . **TCEMTV 8**
EMI / Nov '93 / EMI.

## IT'S A MAN'S MAN'S MAN'S WORLD.
**Tracks:** Walking the dog: *Thomas, Rufus* / Change gonna come: *Redding, Otis* / You don't know like know: *Sam & Dave* / I'll take good care of yo *Mimms, Garnet* / It's a man's man's world: *Brow James* / Summertime: *Stewart, Billy* / Everybo needs somebody: *Pickett, Wilson* / Gimme a litt sign: *Wood, Brenton* / I've never found a girl (to lov me like you do): *Floyd, Eddie* / I forgot to be yo lover: *Bell, William* / Walk on by: *Hayes, Isaac* / On the strong survive: *Butler, Jerry* / Your good thing about to end: *Rawls, Lou* / Drowning in a sea of lov *Simon, Joe* / I've been lonely for so long: *Knigh Frederick* / Why can't we live together: *Thoma Timmy* / Take me to the river: *Green, Al* / You & yo baby blues: *Burke, Solomon* / It's ecstasy whe you're next to me: *White, Barry* / Hang on in the baby: *Bristol, Johnny*.
CD. . . . . . . . . . . . . . . . . . . . **RNBCD 10**
MC. . . . . . . . . . . . . . . . . . . . **RNBMC 10**
Connoisseur Collection / Jul '93 / Pinnacle.

## IT'S SPELT SPECIALTY.
**Tracks:** Jesus gave me water: *Soul Stirrers* / Alor and motherless: *Five Blind Boys Of Alabama* / Fe like I'm running for the lord: *Bradford, Alex* / M hiding place: *Love Coates, Dorothy* / Playboy blue *Milton, Roy* / Daddy on my mind: *Liggins, Joe* Brown skin baby: *Liggins, Jimmy* / Please believ me: *Mayfield, Percy* / Don't miss that train: *Car Sister Wynona* / Stretch out: *Pilgrim Travelers* / It all right: *May, Brother Joe* / Until I reach my hea venly home: *Meditation Singers* / X-temporaneou boogie: *Howard, Camille* / Lucy Mae blues: *Sim Frankie Lee* / Black cat blues: *Hooker, John Lee* Born on the 13th: *Hogg, Smokey* / When the saints g marching in: *Golden Echoes* / Watch ye therefor *Chosen Gospel Singers* / Tabarin: *Hollywood Flame* / I'm a fool to care: *Neville, Art* / Short fat fanni *Williams, Larry*.
■ CD. . . . . . . . . . . . . . . . . . . . **CDSPEC**
Ace / Mar '94.

## IT'S TORTURE & 15 OTHER GREA SOUL DESTROYERS.
**Tracks:** It's torture: *Brown, Maxine* / Hey girl: *Porg & The Monarchs* / Do you love me baby: *Masque aders* / Bricks, broken bottles & sticks: *Parish, Dea* / My heart is calling: *Wilson, Jackie* / If you can't b true (find a part-time love): *Chandler, Gene* / I've go to keep movin': *Lamont, Charles & The Extremes* Killer: *Fuller, Jerry* / This man: *Cox, Wally* / Sto sign: *Wynn, Mel & The Rhythm Aces* / I'll forgive forget: *Holden, Ron* / (I need your love) your burnin touch of love: *Butler, Billy* / And get away: *Esquires* Desiree: *Charts* / You are the one I love: *Adam Apples* / I don't have a mind of my own: *Thomas B.J.*.
■ LP . . . . . . . . . . . . . . . . . . . . **KENT 04**
Kent / Sep '85.

# J

## JAMES BROWN'S FUNKY PEOPLE PART 2.
**Tracks:** I know you got soul: *Byrd, Bobby* / From the love side: *Ballard, Hank & The Midnighters* / What d I have to do to prove my love to you: *Whitney, Marva* / Soul power '74: *Parker, Maceo & The Macks* / Put i on the line: *Collins, Lyn* / You can have Watergate but gimme some bucks: *Wesley, Fred & The J.B.'s* Message from the soul sisters (parts 1 & 2): *Barnes Myra* / Hot pants..I'm coming, coming I'm coming *Byrd, Bobby* / Do you your thing: *Collins, Lyn* / I'n paying taxes, what am I buying: *Wesley, Fred & The J.B.'s* / Super good (parts 1 & 2): *Barnes, Myra* Cross the track (we better go back) (On CD only) *Parker, Maceo & The Macks* / Blow your head *Wesley, Fred & The J.B.'s*.
CD. . . . . . . . . . . . . . . . . . . . **835 857-2**

504

■ DELETED

■ LP . . . . . . . . . . . . . . . . . . . . . . . .URBLP 14
■ MC. . . . . . . . . . . . . . . . . . . . . . . . URBMC 14
Jrban / Jul '88.

## JAZZ FUSION VOLUME 1.
Tracks: Not Advised.
CD. . . . . . . . . . . . . . . . . . . . . . . . FUSIONCD 1
LP Set. . . . . . . . . . . . . . . . . . . . . . FUSIONLP 1
MC. . . . . . . . . . . . . . . . . . . . . . . . FUSIONMC 1
Jazz Fusions / Jul '94 / Total.

## JAZZ FUSIONS VOLUME II.
Tracks: Not Advised.
CD. . . . . . . . . . . . . . . . . . . . . . . . FUSIONCD 2
LP Set. . . . . . . . . . . . . . . . . . . . . . FUSIONLP 2
MC. . . . . . . . . . . . . . . . . . . . . . . . FUSIONMC 2
Jazz Fusions / Oct '94 / Total.

## JB'S FUNKY PEOPLE.
Tracks: Gimme some more: *J.B.'s* / Pass the peas: *J.B.'s* / Think (about it): *Collins, Lyn* / Givin' up food for funk (part 1): *J.B.'s* / Mama feel good: *Collins, Lyn* / Hot pants: *J.B.'s* / Rock me again & again & again...: *Collins, Lyn* / Damn right, I am somebody (part.1): *Wesley, Fred & The J.B.'s* / Take me just as I am: *Collins, Lyn* / If you don't get it the first time..: *Parker, Wesley, Fred & The J.B.'s* / Party (part 1): *Parker, Maceo & The Macks* / It's not the express it's the JBs monaurail (part 1): *Fred & The New JB's*.
■ LP . . . . . . . . . . . . . . . . . . . . . . . .URBLP 10
MC. . . . . . . . . . . . . . . . . . . . . . . . URBMC 10
Jrban / May '88 / PolyGram.

## JESUS IS THE ANSWER.
Tracks: Walk with me: *Highway QC'S* / It's me: *Highway QC'S* / How I got over: *Swan Silvertones* / That day on Calvary: *Swan Silvertones* / My religion: *Caravans (1)* / It's Jesus in me: *Caravans (1)* / I'm going through: *Caravans (1)* / I can see everybody's mother: *Five Blind Boys Of Alabama* / What he's done for me: *Five Blind Boys Of Alabama* / He has a way: *Greater Harvest Choir* / Jesus is the answer: *Argo Singers* / See how he kept me: *Argo Singers* / When tears are falling: *Harmonizing Four* / Wade in the water: *Harmonizing Four* / Uncloudy day: *Staple Singers* / Two wings: *Staple Singers*.
■ LP . . . . . . . . . . . . . . . . . . . . . . . . CRB 1083
Charly R&B / Apr '85.

## JUKE BOX SOUL.
Tracks: Not Advised.
CD Set . . . . . . . . . . . . . . . . . . . . . .WMCD 5604
Kwest / Dec '92 / THE.

## JUKE BOX STORY.
Tracks: Not Advised.
■ LP . . . . . . . . . . . . . . . . . . . . . PER 33 8606
MC. . . . . . . . . . . . . . . . . . . . . . .PER 733 8606
Perfect / Nov '87 / Pinnacle.

## JUMPING AT THE GOGO.
Tracks: I'll always need you: *Courtney, Dean* / Ain't no soul: *Paige, Ray* / Blowing up my mind: *Exciters* / Man without a woman: *Michael & Raymond* / I can't help loving you: *Anka, Paul* / You've got your mind on other things: *Beverly Ann* / Moonlight music and you: *Greene, Laura* / What's it gonna be: *Barrett, Susan* / Devil's drive: *Big Boris* / Hold on: *Freeman, Judy* / It didn't take much (for me to fall in love): *Wiggins, Percy* / Change your ways: *Kendricks, Willie* / I can't change: *Chandler, Lorraine* / Crackin' up over you: *Hamilton, Roy (1)* / Stick to me: *Walker, Robert & Soul Strings* / Honest to goodness: *Ward, Herb* / Hold on to my baby: *Cavaliers* / I can't hold on: *Chandler, Lorraine* / Happy go lucky me: *Bobbettes* / I've gotta know right now: *Valentine, Rose*.
■ LP . . . . . . . . . . . . . . . . . . . . . . . . . RS 1066
RCA / '76.

## JUST A LITTLE OVERCOME - STAX VOCAL GROUPS.
Tracks: No strings attached: *Mad Lads (1)* / These old memories: *Mad Lads (1)* / I'm so glad I fell in love with you: *Mad Lads (1)* / Highway to Heaven: *Dramatics* / Since I've been in love: *Dramatics* / Mannish boy: *Newcomers* / Girl this boy loves you: *Newcomers* / Just a little overcome: *Nightingales* / Baby, don't do it: *Nightingales* / I'm with you: *Nightingales* / Whole bit of love: *Temprees* / Your love (is all I need): *Temprees* / I refuse to be lonely: *Stingers* / Showered with love: *Ollie & The Nightingales* / Mellow way (you treat your man): *Ollie & The Nightingales* / All because of you: *Limitations* / Echo: *Epsilons* / Make this young lady mine (On CD only): *Mad Lads (1)* / Your love was strange (On CD only): *Dramatics* / Open up your heart (let me come in) (On CD only): *Newcomers* / Anyone can (On CD only): *Leaders* / Love's creeping up on me (On CD only): *United Image*.
CD. . . . . . . . . . . . . . . . . . . . . . . . . CDSXD 019
■ LP . . . . . . . . . . . . . . . . . . . . . . . . .SXD 019
Stax / Feb '89.

## JUST THE WAY.
Tracks: Not Advised.
CD. . . . . . . . . . . . . . . . . . . . . . . . . .JERVCD 1
LP . . . . . . . . . . . . . . . . . . . . . . . . . .JERVLP 1
MC. . . . . . . . . . . . . . . . . . . . . . . . . . JERVMC 1
Street Hype / Aug '93 / Total / BMG.

# K

## KEEP MOVIN' ON.
Tracks: Swingin': *Light Of The World* / Somebody help me out: *Beggar & Co* / North London boy: *Incognito* / You're lying: *Linx* / Walking into sunshine: *Central Line* / Southern Freeez: *Freeez* / Mamma used to say: *Giscombe, Junior* / Easier said than done: *Shakatak* / Wings of love: *Level 42* / Dancin' in outer space: *Atmosfear* / Time machine: *Direct Drive* / Give me: *I Level*.
CD. . . . . . . . . . . . . . . . . . . . . . . . . VSOPCD 185
MC. . . . . . . . . . . . . . . . . . . . . . . . . VSOPMC 185
Connoisseur Collection / Apr '93 / Pinnacle.

## KEEP ON DANCIN'.
Tracks: Ring my bell / That's the way I like it / It's been so long / Dance with me / What you won't do for love / Do what you wanna do / Loose caboose / Party boys / Spank / Rock your baby / Get off / Pease don't go / Dance across the floor / Calypso breakdown / Tonight is the night part 1 / On fire / Down on the third time / Do ya wanna get funky with me.
■ LP . . . . . . . . . . . . . . . . . . . . . . . TKR 54300
MC. . . . . . . . . . . . . . . . . . . . . . . . . .40 54300
TK / Nov '81 / Sony / EMI.

## KEEPIN' THE FAITH.
Tracks: Stop what you're doing: *Playthings* / Goodbye, nothing to say: *Javells* / What shall I do: *Frankie & Classicals* / If you ask me (because I love you): *Williams, Jerry* / I'm so glad: *Fuzz* / Flasher, (The): *Mistura* / Ask me: *Ecstasy, Passion & Pain* / Love light: *Jackson, Chuck* / Selfish one: *Ross, Jackie* / Landslide: *Clarke, Tony* / Breakout: *Ryder, Mitch* / Footsee: *Wigan's Chosen Few* / Love is getting strong: *Knight, Jason* / Voice your choice: *Radiants*.
■ LP . . . . . . . . . . . . . . . . . . . . . . . . PRC 5572
■ MC. . . . . . . . . . . . . . . . . . . . . . . ZCPRC 5572
PRT / Feb '84.

## KEEPIN' THE FAITH VOL 2.
Tracks: In orbit: *Lovejoy, Joy* / Burning spear: *Soulful Strings* / Hold on: *Radiants* / Emergency (dial 999): *Bown, Alan Set* / Accept my invitation: *Band Of Angels* / You get your kicks: *Ryder, Mitch & The Detroit Wheels* / Soul for sale: *Schroeder, John Orchestra* / Dance, dance, dance: *Casualeers* / Can't help lovin' dat man: *Van, Ila* / I can't help loving you: *Breedlove, Jimmy* / Ain't no more room: *Kittens* / Sevens days too long: *Wood, Chuck*.
■ LP . . . . . . . . . . . . . . . . . . . . . . . . PRC 5573
PRT / Sep '84.

## KENT 50.
Tracks: Dr. Love: *Sheen, Bobby* / Determination: *Parrish, Dean* / Hand it over: *Jackson, Chuck* / Baby without you: *Monday, Danny* / La rue: *Edmund Jr., Lada* / It's torture (instrumental): *Brown, Maxine Band* / Wrong girl: *Showmen* / Homework: *Rush, Otis* / I've lost you: *Wilson, Jackie* / Music to my heart: *Austin, Patti* / I can't believe what you say: *Turner, Ike & Tina* / Wack wack: *Young-Holt Unlimited* / Work song: *Hunt, Tommy* / I love you (yeah): *Impressions* / I'll never forget you: *O'Jays* / Time is on my side: *Thomas, Irma*.
■ LP . . . . . . . . . . . . . . . . . . . . . . . . KENT 050
Kent / Feb '86.

## KENT STOP DANCING.
Tracks: Louie Louie: *Kingsmen* / 99th floor: *Moving Sidewalks* / Sha-la-la / Killer Joe: *Rocky Fellers* / Twist and shout: *Isley Brothers* / Just a little bit: *Head, Roy* / Turn on your lovelight: *Gordon, Benny* / Oh no not my baby: *Brown, Maxine* / Washed ashore (on a lonely island in the sea): *Platters* / Your love keeps lifting me higher and higher: *Wilson, Jackie* / That's enough: *Robinson, Roscoe* / Love makes a woman: *Acklin, Barbara* / Get on up: *Esquires* / I keep forgettin': *Jackson, Chuck* / Wack wack: *Young-Holt Unlimited* / I'm gonna miss you: *Artistics*.
■ LP . . . . . . . . . . . . . . . . . . . . . . . . KENT 029
Kent / Nov '84.

## KENT STOP DANCING - THE SEQUEL.
Tracks: Ski storm: *Snowmen* / Every night a new surprise: *Moving Sidewalks* / Can you help me: *Knickerbockers* / Shake a tailfeather: *Turner, Ike & Tina* / Baby workout: *Wilson, Jackie* / Humphrey stomp: *Harrison, Earl* / Gonna send you back to Georgia: *Shaw, Timmy* / Cooking gear: *Arnold, Gear* / With this ring: *Platters* / Nothing can stop me: *Chandler, Gene* / Follow the leader: *Lance, Major* / Just a little misunderstanding: *Williams, Johnny* / (Your love keeps lifting me) higher and higher: *Wilson, Jackie* / Ain't no soul: *Milsap, Ronnie* / Come see about me: *Dodds, Nella* / Am I the same girl: *Acklin, Barbara*.
■ LP . . . . . . . . . . . . . . . . . . . . . . . . KENT 066
Kent / Mar '87.

## KENTSTAX.
Tracks: Sweet Sherry: *Barnes, J.J.* / Love's creeping up on me: *United Image* / Just keep on lovin' me: *Mancha, Steve* / I'm the one who loves you: *Banks, Darrell* / Little by little and bit by bit: *Weston, Kim* / You made me a woman: *Lewis, Barbara* / One more chance: *Joseph, Margie* / It makes me wanna cry: *Staples, Mavis* / Give 'em love: *Soul Children* / Losing boy: *Giles, Eddie* / Bet you I win: *Little Milton* / Chains of love: *Barnes, J.J.* / Since I lost my baby's love: *Lance, Major* / I don't wanna lose you: *Mancha, Steve* / It's all up to you: *Hughes, Jimmy* / Wade in the water: *Little Sonny*.
■ LP . . . . . . . . . . . . . . . . . . . . . . . . KENT 095
Kent / Nov '89.

## KING/FEDERAL SAMPLER.
Tracks: Not Advised.
CD. . . . . . . . . . . . . . . . . . . . . . . . . . CDPRO 2
Charly R&B / Oct '90 / Charly.

## KINGS OF BLACK MUSIC, THE.
Tracks: Not Advised.
CD. . . . . . . . . . . . . . . . . . . . . . . . . . .15 169
MC. . . . . . . . . . . . . . . . . . . . . . . . . . .79 043
Laserlight / Aug '91 / THE / BMG / Target.

## KINGS OF SOUL.
Tracks: Not Advised.
CD. . . . . . . . . . . . . . . . . . . . . . . . . . 100 022
Bridge (MCS Bridge) / Oct '86 / Pinnacle.

## KISSING HER AND CRYING FOR YOU.
Tracks: Kissin' her and crying for you: *Checkmates Unlimited* / What can I do: *Prophet, Billy* / Li'l lovin' sometimes: *Patton, Alexander* / Don't: *Josie, Marva* / I'm only a man: *Tee, Willie* / Drifter: *Pollard, Ray* / By yourself: *Martin J.D.* / Right on: *Delory, Al & Mandango* / I hurt on the other side: *Cook, Jerry* / Love is dangerous: *Polk, Frank* / Please keep away from me: *Parker, Elbie* / Hey girl do you love me: *Wilson, Timothy* / I still love you (from the bottom of my heart): *Four Larks* / Don't you care anymore: *Mathis, Jodi* / In your spare time: *Scott, Cindy* / He always comes back to me: *King, Clydie*.
■ LP . . . . . . . . . . . . . . . . . . . . . . . . KENT 055
Kent / Apr '86.

# L

## LADY LOVE - SWEET LOVE GROOVES.
Tracks: Not Advised.
CD. . . . . . . . . . . . . . . . . . . . . . . . . . .12 217
MC. . . . . . . . . . . . . . . . . . . . . . . . . . .72 217
Laserlight / Jul '93 / THE / BMG / Target.

## LAFAYETTE SOUL SHOW.
Tracks: Monkey in a sack: *Buck, Lil* / Got the fever child: *King Karl* / Do you like to see me cry: *King Karl* / You've got the power: *Buck, Lil* / Getting late in the evening: *Neal, Raful* / I stand accused: *Fredericks, Don* / Little bit of soap: *Fredericks, Don* / Change my way of living: *Neal, Raful* / Burghers beat: *Hart, John with Lil Bob & the lollipops* / Big boys don't cry: *Fredericks, Don* / Little red rooster: *August, Lynn* / Everybody's feeling good: *King Karl* / Blues for men: *King Karl* / I need your love: *Jewel & The Rubies* / Candy Ann: *Jewel & The Rubies* / Days go by: *Jewel & The Rubies* / Kidnapper: *Jewel & The Rubies* / Cat scream: *Buck, Lil* / Agent double o soul: *Lil' Bob & The Lollipops* / Stop: *Lil' Bob & The Lollipops* / Nobody but you: *Lil' Bob & The Lollipops* / Out of sight: *Lil' Bob & The Lollipops* / Cry, cry, cry:

■ DELETED

505

*Lil' Bob & The Lollipops* / Mule train: *Lil' Bob & The Lollipops* / I got loaded: *Lil' Bob & The Lollipops*.
■ CD. . . . . . . . . . . . . . . . . . . . CDKEND 101
Kent / Apr '93.

## LEAPERS, SLEEPERS & CREEPERS.

**Tracks:** If you were a man: *King, Clydie* / Tears keep falling: *Solo, Sam E.* / Stay with your own kind: *Holloway, Patrice* / I walked away: *Paris, Bobby* / Baby I need you: *Gee, Marsha* / Ecstacy: *Holloway, Patrice* / Walk with a winner: *McDaniels, Gene* / I'll never forget you: *O'Jays* / What are you trying to do: *Thomas, Irma* / Look at me, look at me: *Green, Garland* / Let the music play: *Preston, Billy* / Serving a sentence of life: *Douglas, Carl & Big Stampede* / What you gonna do: *Womack, Bobby* / You're on top: *Untouchables*.
■ LP . . . . . . . . . . . . . . . . . . . . . . KENT 031
Kent / Dec '84.

## LES GIRLS!.

**Tracks:** Private number: *Grimes, Carol* / Shame, shame, shame: *Thomas, Irma* / Little bell: *Dixie Cups* / Easier to say than do: *Lavette, Betty* / I'm just a down home girl: *Ad Libs* / Harper Valley PTA: *Riley, Jeannie C.* / Letter full of tears: *Knight, Gladys* / My baby specializes: *Grimes, Carol* / Piece of my heart: *Lavette, Betty* / Boy from New York City: *Ad Libs* / If you should ever leave me: *Driscoll, Julie* / I need a man: *Pittman, Barbara* / Past, present and future: *Shangri-Las* / Love me or leave me: *Simone, Nina* / Getting mighty crowded: *Everett, Betty* / Ride your pony: *Harris, Betty* / Another boy like mine: *Dixie Cups* / Lady Marmalade: *Thomas, Irma* / It's in his kiss: *Everett, Betty* / Heaven only knows: *Shangri-Las* / Little girl blue: *Simone, Nina* / Girl most likely: *Riley, Jeannie C.*.
■ Double LP. . . . . . . . . . . . . . . . . . CR 105
■ MC Set . . . . . . . . . . . . . . . . . . .CRT 105
Cambra / Aug '83.

## LET 'EM IN.

**Tracks:** Not Advised.
CD. . . . . . . . . . . . . . . . . . . . . . . . . 12 219
MC. . . . . . . . . . . . . . . . . . . . . . . . . 72 219
Laserlight / Nov '93 / THE / BMG / Target.

## LET'S GO DISCO.

**Tracks:** YMCA: *Village People* / That's the way I like it: *K.C. & The Sunshine Band* / Play that funky music: *Wild Cherry* / Lady marmalade: *Labelle* / Boogie nights: *Heatwave* / Shake your body (down to the ground): *Jacksons* / Love machine (part 1): *Miracles* / Boogie wonderland: *Earth, Wind & Fire* / Heaven must be missing an angel: *Tavares* / Let's all chant: *Zager, Michael Band* / Use it up and wear it out: *Odyssey* / Funkytown: *Lipps Inc.* / And the beat goes on: *Whispers* / Oops upside your head: *Gap Band* / Celebration: *Kool & The Gang* / It's a disco night (rock don't stop): *Isley Brothers* / Car wash: *Rose Royce* / I will survive: *Gaynor, Gloria* / Shame: *King, Evelyn 'Champagne'* / Turn the music up: *Players Association* / Shame, shame, shame: *Shirley & Company* / More, more, more: *Andrea True Connection* / Best of my love: *Emotions (1)* / Hold back the night: *Trammps* / Love I lost: *Melvin, Harold & The Bluenotes* / Hustle: *McCoy, Van* / Rock your baby: *McCrae, George* / Rock the boat: *Hues Corporation* / I love music: *O'Jays* / This is it: *Moore, Melba* / Knock on wood: *Stewart, Amii* / Red light spells danger: *Ocean, Billy* / Ain't gonna bump no more (with no big fat woman): *Tex, Joe* / In the bush: *Musique* / Boogie oogie oogie: *Taste Of Honey* / September: *Earth, Wind & Fire* / If I can't have you: *Elliman, Yvonne* / Do what you wanna do: *T-Connection* / Disco stomp: *Bohannon, Hamilton* / Girls: *Moments & Whatnauts*.
CD. . . . . . . . . . . . . . . . . . . . . . CDEMTV 78
LP . . . . . . . . . . . . . . . . . . . . . . . . EMTV 78
MC. . . . . . . . . . . . . . . . . . . . . . .TCEMTV 78
EMI / Oct '93 / EMI.

## LIBERTY BELLES.

**Tracks:** We got a good thing going: *King, Clydie* / It ain't right (lovin' to be lovin'): *Turner, Tina* / Take a look: *Thomas, Irma* / One part, two part: *King, Clydie* / Proud Mary: *Turner, Tina* / I'm on the outside looking in: *Washington, Baby* / I'm movin' on: *Yuro, Timi* / I'm moving on (part two): *Yuro, Timi* / Time is on my side: *Thomas, Irma* / Ooh poo pah doo: *Turner, Tina* / All around the world: *Washington, Baby* / Gotta travel on: *Yuro, Timi* / Wish someone would care: *Thomas, Irma* / It's all over but the crying: *Washington, Baby* / I'll never stop loving you: *King, Clydie* / I want to take you higher: *Turner, Tina*.
■ MC. . . . . . . . . . . . . . . . . . . . . EG 2604834
■ LP . . . . . . . . . . . . . . . . . . . . . EG 2604831
Stateside / Sep '85.

## LIKE SISTER & BROTHER.

**Tracks:** like sister and brother: *Drifters* / Do what you do: *Jackson, Jermaine* / Who's zoomin' who: *Franklin, Aretha* / Woman in love: *Three Degrees* / Jump (for my love): *Pointer Sisters* / We do it: *Stone, R & J* / Swing your daddy: *Gilstrap, Jim* / Body talk: *Imagination* / You've lost that lovin' feelin': *Patti & The Lovelites* / Heaven must be missing an angel: *Tavares* / Loving you: *Riperton, Minnie* / Lies: *Butler, Jonathan* / We've only just begun (the romance is not over): *Jones, Glenn* / Feelings: *Gaynor, Gloria* / So amazing: *Vandross, Luther* / Used to be my girl: *O'Jays* / If you let me stay: *D'Arby, Terence Trent* / Lady marmalade: *Labelle* / Free: *Williams, Deniece* / Signed, sealed, delivered, I'm yours: *Turner, Ruby*.
CD. . . . . . . . . . . . . . . . . . . . . . STAMCD 017
MC. . . . . . . . . . . . . . . . . . . . . . . STAMC 017
Stardust / Oct '92 / Pickwick / Conifer Records.

## LIVIN' THE NIGHTLIFE.

**Tracks:** Not Advised.
■ LP . . . . . . . . . . . . . . . . . . . . . . . SINLP 2
SMP / Mar '85.

## LIVING THE NIGHTLIFE.

**Tracks:** Carlena: *Just Brothers* / Dearly beloved: *Montgomery, Jack* / Black-eyed girl: *Thompson, Billy* / Livin' the nightlife: *Charts* / Groovy guy: *Shirelles* / It's torture: *Brown, Maxine* / Gonna give her all the love I've got: *Gordon, Benny* / I refuse to give up: *Reid, Clarence* / Send my baby back: *Hughes, Freddie* / Good things come to those who wait: *Jackson, Chuck* / Do you love me baby: *Masqueraders* / Please stay: *Ivorys* / Pretty part of you: *Hunt, Tommy* / My sweet baby: *Esquires* / Love ain't what it used to be: *Diplomats (1)* / Yesterday's kisses: *Big Maybelle* / (Happiness will cost you) One thin dime: *Lavette, Betty* / I want you: *Clay, Judy* / Since I found a love: *Hadley, Sandy* / Love keeps me crying: *Johnson, Walter* / You can't keep a good man down: *Gentlemen Four* / I don't want to lose you: *Wynn, Mel* / Look my way: *Williams, Maurice* / You must be losing your mind: *Raye, Jimmy*.
CD. . . . . . . . . . . . . . . . . . . . . CDKEND 104
Ace / Jun '93 / Pinnacle / Complete Record Co. Ltd.

## LOOKEY DOOKEY.

**Tracks:** Not Advised.
CD. . . . . . . . . . . . . . . . . . . . . EFA 11569CD
Crypt / Jun '93 / SRD.

## LOST DREAMS (New Orleans Vocal Groups).

**Tracks:** Drunk drunk drunk: *Kidds* / Why fool yourself: *Williams, Bernie* / Bluesy me: *Collis, Dave & Scubbs* / Lost dreams: *Dukes* / Sunny side of the street: *Bees* / Eternally yours: *Barons* / Cotton pickin' hands: *Dukes* / Later baby: *Matthews, Fat Man & 4 kittens* / Boom boom: *New Orleans Vocal Groups* / Teardrop eyes: *Dukes* / Ain't gonna do it: *Pelicans* / Shake the dice: *Barons* / Darling please: *Bees* / Last ride: *Dukes*.
■ MC. . . . . . . . . . . . . . . . . . . . .TCSSL 6024
■ LP . . . . . . . . . . . . . . . . . . . . . . SSL 6024
Stateside / Apr '87.

## LOST SOUL OF DETROIT, THE VOL.1.

**Tracks:** She's not everybody's girl: *Metros* / That's bad: *Lafayette* / I hold the key: *Sanders, Nelson* / I'm leaving baby: *White, Willie* / Leave me alone: *White, Willie* / I gotta know: *Hutcher, Willie* / Standing on the sideline: *Williams, Lloyd* / Can't live without you: *Milner, Reggie* / In the middle: *Reynolds, L.J.* / Stop lost over your past: *Reynolds, L.J.* / I don't mess around: *Reynolds, Jeannie* / People make the world: *Reynolds, Jeannie* / I found the right girl: *Swingers* / Alone in the chapel: *Doe & Joe* / Do you want a love: *Milner, Reggie* / She's alright: *Milner, Reggie* / Somebody help me: *Milner, Reggie* / Uphill climb to the bottom: *Lemons, George* / Nothing can seperate our love: *Turner, Sammy*.
CD. . . . . . . . . . . . . . . . . . . . . . . . GSCD 021
Goldmine / Aug '93 / Vital Distribution.

## LOUISIANA SOUTHERN SOUL.

**Tracks:** Not Advised.
■ LP . . . . . . . . . . . . . . . . . . . . . . . . KK 791
Krazy Kat / Jul '85.

## LOVE BALLADS VOL.3.

**Tracks:** Not Advised.
CD. . . . . . . . . . . . . . . . . . . . . . . . CDLVB 003
■ LP . . . . . . . . . . . . . . . . . . . . . . . LVBAL 003
MC. . . . . . . . . . . . . . . . . . . . . . . . ZCLVB 003
Street Sounds / Oct '88 / BMG / Total.

## LOVE IS A GAME.

**Tracks:** Not Advised.
■ LP . . . . . . . . . . . . . . . . . . . . . . . . CABMP 1
■ MC. . . . . . . . . . . . . . . . . . . . . . . . ZCCBM 1
Calibre / Jun '83.

## LOVE ON THE DANCE FLOOR (100 Classic Dance Floor Love Songs).

**Tracks:** Way we were: *Knight, Gladys & The Pips* / Baby, come to me: *Austin, Patti & James Ingram* / Rock me tonight: *Jackson, Freddie* / Wishing on a star: *Royce, Rose* / I still can't get over loving you: *Parker, Ray Jnr.* / I've got love on my mind: *Cole, Natalie* / Stay with me tonight: *Osborne, Jeffrey* / If you're ready: *Turner, Ruby* / Feel so real: *Arrington, Steve* / My forbidden lover: *Chic* / Joy and pain: *Maze* / Yah mo b there: *Ingram, James* / Let's go all the way: *Sly Fox* / Just an illusion: *Imagination* / Fool (If you think it's over): *Rea, Chris* / Never let her slip away: *Gold, Andrew* / All out of love: *Air Supply* / I'm not in love: *10 CC* / All by myself: *Carmen, Eric* / I can dream about you: *Hartman, Dan* / Save the last dance for me: *King, Ben E.* / We're all alone: *Coolidge, Rita* / Angel of the morning: *Mason, Mary* / You are my love: *Liverpool Express* / How 'bout us: *Champaign* / I'm stone in love with you: *Stylistics* / Where is the love: *Mills, Stephanie* / Without you: *Nilsson, Harry* / I want to know what love is: *Foreigner* / Keep on loving you: *REO Speedwagon* / Everyday hurts: *Sad Cafe* / Babe: *Styx* / Waiting for a girl like you: *Foreigner* / Wonderful tonight: *Clapton, Eric* / Sugar walls: *Easton, Sheena* / When I fall in love: *Cole, Nat King* / I wanna stay with you: *Gallagher & Lyle* / Miss you nights: *Richard, Cliff* / I can hear your heartbeat: *Rea, Chris* / For your eyes only: *Easton, Sheena* / Just the way you are: *White, Barry* / Emma: *Hot Chocolate* / Too much, too little, too late: *Mathis, Johnny* / One day I'll fly away: *Crawford, Randy* / Always and forever: *Heatwave* / Love don't live here any more: *Royce, Rose* / On the wings of love: *Osborne, Jeffrey* / Tonight I celebrate my love: *Bryson, Peabo* / You're my latest, my greatest ispiration: *Pendergrass, Teddy* / I live for your love: *Cole, Natalie* / Used ta be my girl: *O'Jays* / What a fool believes: *Franklin, Aretha* / Strange love affair: *Lanier & Co.* / Best of my love: *Emotions (2)* / When she was my girl: *Four Tops* / Lies: *Butler, Jonathan* / It's a love thing: *Whispers* / Heaven must be missing an angel: *Tavares* / Best thing that ever happened to me: *Knight, Gladys & The Pips* / Whole town's laughing at me: *Pendergrass, Teddy* / More than a woman: *Tavares* / Tonight I'm gonna love you all over: *Four Tops* / You're my angel: *Abbott, Gregory* / If I can't have you: *Elliman, Yvonne* / Reunited: *Peaches & Herb* / Just my imagination: *Turner, Ruby* / In and out of love: *Imagination* / It started with a kiss: *Hot Chocolate* / Heartbreaker: *Warwick, Dionne* / Mind blowin' decisions: *Heatwave* / I don't wanna lose you: *Kandidate* / I wanna get next to you: *Royce, Rose* / Fantasy: *Earth, Wind & Fire* / Mated: *Graham, Jaki* / Woman in love: *Three Degrees* / Body talk: *Imagination* / Take good care of me: *Butler, Jonathan* / Personal touch: *Brown, Errol* / Joanna: *Kool & The Gang* / If you're looking for a way out: *Odyssey* / You make me feel brand new: *Stylistics* / All the love in the world: *Warwick, Dionne* / Cherish: *Kool & The Gang* / When love comes calling: *Johnson, Paul* / Little bit more: *Jackson, Freddie* / Lady love: *Rawls, Lou* / I want your love: *Chic* / Twilight: *Maze* / You bet your love: *Hancock, Herbie* / I shoulda loved ya: *Walden, Narada Michael* / You sexy thing: *Hot Chocolate* / round and 'round: *Graham, Jaki* / I can make you feel good: *Shalamar* / Do what you do: *Jackson, Jermaine* / Do that to me one more time: *Captain & Tennille* / We do it: *Stone, R & J* / If you don't know me by now: *Melvin, Harold & The Bluenotes* / Baby blues: *White, Barry* / I don't want to talk about it: *Everything But The Girl* / Je t'aime...: *Birkin, Jane*.
CD Set . . . . . . . . . . . . . . . . . . . . . LOVECD 1
■ LP Set. . . . . . . . . . . . . . . . . . . . . LOVELP 1
■ MC Set . . . . . . . . . . . . . . . . . . . LOVEMC 1
Connoisseur Collection / Nov '89.

## LOVE TRAIN-THE BEST OF PHILADELPHIA.

**Tracks:** Not Advised.
■ MC. . . . . . . . . . . . . . . . . . . . . . . .40 25316
■ LP . . . . . . . . . . . . . . . . . . . . . . . PIR 25316
Philadelphia Int. / Mar '83.

## LOVE..NIGHT MOODS.

**Tracks:** Not Advised.
CD. . . . . . . . . . . . . . . . . . . . . . . . STACD 049
Stardust / Sep '94 / Pickwick / Conifer Records.

## LOVERS, THE.

**Tracks:** Lovers: *O'Neal, Alexander* / So amazing: *Vandross, Luther* / You are my lady: *Jackson, Freddie* / We're in this love together: *Jarreau, Al* / 2 a.m.: *Pendergrass, Teddy* / Sexual healing: *Gaye, Marvin* / Suddenly: *Ocean, Billy* / Sexy girl: *Thomas, Lillo* / Sign your name: *D'Arby, Terence Trent* / Rock me tonight (for old time's sake): *Jackson, Freddie* / What can I say to make ..: *O'Neal, Alexander* / Joy: *Pendergrass, Teddy* / Never too much: *Vandross, Luther* / Mornin': *Jarreau, Al*.
■ CD . . . . . . . . . . . . . . . . . . . . . . . NCD 3426
■ LP . . . . . . . . . . . . . . . . . . . . . . . . NE 1426

506

■ DELETED

**MC. . . . . . . . . . . . . . . . . . . . . . CE 2426**
-Tel / Oct '88.

# M

## IAJOR BILL'S TEXAS SOUL.
**racks:** Action: Hobbs, Willie / Dead: Robin, Ede / My
aby's back: Duncan, James / Monkey time: Mills,
lly / One woman lover: Hobbs, Willie / Mr. Pitiful:
obert & Matt / Man without a woman: Brown, Matt /
s me: Copeland, Johnny / Woman is a nice thing:
obbs, Willie / Soul of a man: Thomas, Robert /
hese arms of mine: Matt & Robert / Under the
nes: Mills, Billy / Cry, cry, cry: Hobbs, Willie / All
ese things: Mills, Billy / Evening in Paris: Milburn,
mos Jr. / Soul symphony: Sons Of Moses.
■ **LP . . . . . . . . . . . . . . . . . . . CRB 1167**
harly R&B / Apr '88.

## IAKE IT FUNKY (Connoisseur Soul Col-
ction - Volume 5).
acks: Movin': Brass Construction / Shack up: Ban-
arra / Hustle on up: Hidden Strength / Funky stuff:
ool & The Gang / Who'd she coo: Ohio Players / Put
ur body in it: Mills, Stephanie / Make it funky:
rown, James / Rigamortis: Cameo (1) / Giving up
od for funk: J.B. Allstars / Zone: Rhythm Makers /
e've got the funk: Positive Force / Hypertension:
alender / Changin': Brass Construction.
) . . . . . . . . . . . . . . . . . . . . .RNBCD 105
C. . . . . . . . . . . . . . . . . . . . . .RNBMC 105
nnoisseur Collection / Oct '93 / Pinnacle.

## ECCA MAGIC.
acks: Once I've been there: Connors, Norman /
ke me I'm yours: Henderson, Michael / Sorry, that
umber's been disconnected: Green, Marie / Without
u baby, I'm a loser: Fresh Flavour / (That's) the
ay of a woman in love: Futures / Sweet little girl of
ine: Williams, Mel / Waterfalls: Evans, Margie /
ul improvisations (part 1): McCoy, Van / Soulful
ve: Holmes, Cecil / Deeper and deeper: Wilson,
obby / I want to make love to you: Norman, Jimmy /
an't fight your love: Modulations / We can make it
tter: Scott, Rena / Living inside your love: Hyman,
yllis.
. . . . . . . . . . . . . . . . . . . KENT 090
nt / Oct '90 / Pinnacle.

## EMPHIS GOLD VOL.2.
acks: Knock on wood / Soul finger / Tramp / Hip
g her / B-a-b-y / Crosscut saw / When something
wrong with my baby / Try a little tenderness / I got
love somebody's baby / Your good thing / Every-
dy loves a winner.
■ **LP . . . . . . . . . . . . . . . . . . . .726**
ax / Apr '68.

## ENU, THE.
acks: On my mind: Big Cheese All Stars / Still
ater: Silent Majority / 8 tracks to heaven: Walk Tall
iscomulkr: Malka Family / Track Cheul: Ste / Le
eil brille: Schkoonk Heepooz / Mentira: Quintetto
/ Netour: D.J. Gilbert / Chilling: Lionel Moyst
extet / Loran's dance: Taudi Symphony / Hold it
w (CD only): Batu.
) . . . . . . . . . . . . . . . . . . . .142817
. . . . . . . . . . . . . . . . . . . . .FR 344
g Cheese / Nov '94 / Vital Distribution.

## ESSAGE, THE (Rare groove 2).
acks: I don't know if I can make it: Smith, Dawson /
ama's got the wagon: Murray, Mickey / Mr. Bump
an: Beavers, Jackie / Bra: Cymande / Keep on
ncing: Cash, Alvin / Thank you for letting me be
rself again: Parker, Maceo & All The Kings Men /
eck your bucket: Bo, Eddie / Brothers on the slide:
mande / Mr. Brown: African Music Machine / Fug:
mande.
■ **LP . . . . . . . . . . . . . . . . . . . CRB 1188**
C. . . . . . . . . . . . . . . . . . . . . TCCRB 1188
arly R&B / Apr '88 / Charly.

## D ATLANTIC SESSIONS.
acks: Not Advised.
. . . . . . . . . . . . . . . . . . . . . MMB 91
. . . . . . . . . . . . . . . . . . . . . MMB 91
. . . . . . . . . . . . . . . . . . . . . MMB 94
oonshine / Sep '94 / Pinnacle.

## MIDNIGHT MOVERS.
**Tracks:** It's a sad thing: Pollard, Ray / Hooked by
love: Banks, Homer / Hot line: Garner, Reggie / I've
got two hearts: Poets / Working on your case: O'Jays
/ Groovin' at the gogo: Four Larks / Cold wave:
Daisies / I love you baby: Scott, Cindy / Girls got 'it':
Preston, Billy / I feel strange: Wonderettes / Now I
know what love is: Wilson, Al / Trying to keep up with
the Joneses: Polk, Frank / Love slipped through my
fingers: Williams, Sam / Thumb a ride: Wright, Earl /
Wrong girl: Showmen / West Coast: Lester, Ketty.
■ **LP . . . . . . . . . . . . . . . . . . . KENT 058**
Kent / Sep '86.

## MIDNIGHT SOUL.
**Tracks:** Never too much: Vandross, Luther / Harvest
for the world: Isley Brothers / Street life: Crusaders /
Higher and higher: Wilson, Jackie / Never knew love
like this before: Mills, Stephanie / I'm your puppet:
Purify, James & Bobby / Have you seen her: Chi-
Lites / Dance to the music: Sly & The Family Stone /
Lean on me: Withers, Bill / Come into my life: Sims,
Joyce / Move on up: Mayfield, Curtis / I love music:
O'Jays / It's man's world: Brown, James / Love I lost:
Melvin, Harold / Reunited: Peaches & Herb / rescue
me: Fontella Bass / Way we were: Knight, Gladys &
The Pips / Soul city walk: Bell, Archie & The Drells.
CD. . . . . . . . . . . . . . . . . . . . . MUSCD 6
MC. . . . . . . . . . . . . . . . . . . . . MUSMC 6
Music Collection International / Nov '92 / THE / Jazz
Music.

## MIRWOOD STORY (THE SOUND OF SW-
INGIN' HOLLYWOOD).
**Tracks:** Not Advised.
CD. . . . . . . . . . . . . . . . . . . . . .GSCD 010
Goldmine / Feb '93 / Vital Distribution.

## MO' STEPPERS.
**Tracks:** Grazing in the grass: Wonder, Stevie / Use it
or lose it: Gotham / Open your door: Guinn / Brick-
house: Commodores / Bad weather: Supremes / Too
high: Brown, Norman / I can't help it: Washington,
Grover Jr. / Break the ice: Lovesmith, Michael /
Jones (12" mix): Temptations / Can I get a witness:
Randolph, Barbara / All night long: Mary Jane Girls /
Tell me tomorrow (12" mix): Robinson, Smokey / 'T'
Plays it cool: Gaye, Marvin / Love just wouldn't be
right: Marie, Teena / World of ours: Alston, Gerald /
It's a shame: Detroit Spinners.
CD. . . . . . . . . . . . . . . . . . . . .530233-2
LP Set. . . . . . . . . . . . . . . . . . .530233-1
MC. . . . . . . . . . . . . . . . . . . . .530233-4
Motown / Mar '94 / PolyGram.

## MODERN SOUL 2 - BOSS GROOVES.
**Tracks:** Show me the way: Seville / I can't get over
losing you: Butler, Sam / Take another look:
Saunders, Frankie / Try love again: Pro-fascination /
Let me give love: Empire, Freddie / Give me love:
EKG / You keep holding back on love: Sue, Carletta /
This time it's real: Nevilles, Larry / Something in-
side: Raj / What's the use: Troutman, Tony / I'll cry
over you: Sheeler, Cynthia / You're gonna wreck my
life: Guitar Ray / Where is the love: Caiton, Richard /
Very special girl: White, Earl / Man in love: Wright,
Bill / Sexy lady: Sideshow / I've got to have your
love: Robertson, Chuck.
CD. . . . . . . . . . . . . . . . . . . . .GSCD 015
LP . . . . . . . . . . . . . . . . . . . . GSLP 015
Goldmine / May '93 / Vital Distribution.

## MODERN SOUL STORY.
**Tracks:** Not Advised.
■ **Double LP. . . . . . . . . . . . . . . . . . LPSD 120**
MC. . . . . . . . . . . . . . . . . . . . CPSD 120
Soul Supply / Feb '87 / RTM / Pinnacle.

## MODERN SOUL STORY 2.
**Tracks:** Let's spend some time together: Houston,
Larry / Ain't nothing wrong with that baby: Jones,
Jimmy (1) / Don't you worry baby: Banks, F.E / You
can win: Bileo / Over the top: Dawson, Roy / 100
South of.: Philadelphia Society / Have some sym-
pathy: Wilson, Dustin / Thankful for this life: Feafe,
Marvin / No rebate on love: Dramatics / Only way is
up: Clay, Otis / I'm so happy: Lord C.M / Let the
people talk: Steptonen / I need you: Jenkins, Dianne
/ You have to lose love.: Randolph, Jimmy.
■ **Double LP. . . . . . . . . . . . . . . . . . LPSD 122**
Soul Supply / Sep '87.

## MODERN SOUL STORY 3.
**Tracks:** Not Advised.
■ **Double LP. . . . . . . . . . . . . . . . . . LPSD 133**
Soul Supply / Dec '88.

## MODERN TIMES, THE.
**Tracks:** Not Advised.
■ **LP . . . . . . . . . . . . . . . . . . . . LPSS 105**
Soul Supply / Jan '87.

## MOMENTS IN SOUL.
**Tracks:** If you were here tonight: O'Neal, Alexander /
I knew you were waiting: Michael, George & Aretha
Franklin / I still haven't found what I'm looking for:
Chimes (1) / I need lovin': Williams, Alyson / Give me
the reason: Vandross, Luther / Keep on movin': Soul
II Soul / Don't be a fool: Loose Ends / If you don't
know me by now: Simply Red / State of indepen-
dence: Summer, Donna / Ain't nobody: Khan, Chaka
/ Fantasy: Black Box / What did I do to you: Stans-
field, Lisa / Get here: Adams, Oleta / Thinking about
your love: Thomas, Kenny / Beautiful love: Adeva /
Something in red: Kaset, Angela / Carrying a torch:
Jones, Tom / Matter of fact: Innocence.
■ **LP . . . . . . . . . . . . . . . . . . . . ADD 25**
MC. . . . . . . . . . . . . . . . . . . . . ZDD 25
■ **CD . . . . . . . . . . . . . . . . . . . . CCD 25**
Dover / Aug '91.

## MONSTER SOUL.
**Tracks:** Not Advised.
■ **LP Set. . . . . . . . . . . . . . . . . . DJD 28031**
DJM / Nov '76.

## MOONLIGHTING.
**Tracks:** Divine emotions: Narada / Casanova: Levert
/ I want her: Sweat, Keith / Rain: Jones, Oran 'Juice'
/ Love is contagious: Sevelle, Taja / Gotta get you
home tonight: Wilde, Eugene / Nite and day: Sure, Al
B. / Wishing on a star: Roger / Lovers: O'Neal,
Alexander / Feel so real: Arrington, Steve / Baby
come to me: Austin, Patti & James Ingram / Moon-
lighting: Jarreau, Al / Caught up in the rapture (re-
mix): Baker, Anita / Tender love: Force MD's.
■ **LP . . . . . . . . . . . . . . . . . . . . WX 202**
■ **MC . . . . . . . . . . . . . . . . . . . WX 202C**
WEA / Sep '88.

## MORE CHRISTMAS CLASSICS.
**Tracks:** Not Advised.
■ **CD . . . . . . . . . . . . . . . . . . . .530237-2**
■ **MC . . . . . . . . . . . . . . . . . . . .530237-4**
Motown / Jan '93.

## MORE MIDNIGHT SOUL.
**Tracks:** You send me / Ha ha ha / Papa was too / My
lover's prayer / Double or nothing / Do right woman /
Use me / etc.
■ **LP . . . . . . . . . . . . . . . . . . . 588 088**
Atlantic / Dec '67.

## MORE MOTOWN MAGIC.
**Tracks:** Not Advised.
■ **LP . . . . . . . . . . . . . . . . . . . MFP 50536**
■ **MC. . . . . . . . . . . . . . . . . . .TCMFP 50536**
MFP / Sep '81.

## MORE MOTOWN MAGIC VOL 2.
**Tracks:** Not Advised.
■ **LP . . . . . . . . . . . . . . . . . . . MFP 50537**
■ **MC. . . . . . . . . . . . . . . . . . .TCMFP 50537**
MFP / Sep '81.

## MORE POWER TO YA.
**Tracks:** More power to ya / Heaven help me (I'm
falling in love with you) / Please don't break my
heart (like you did) / All I need is you / It's a man's
world / Gentle on my mind / Sweetest story / It sure
was fun / I met her in church / Mighty long way /
What the world needs now is love / Headman / Don't
let go / To make my life beautiful.
■ **LP . . . . . . . . . . . . . . . . . . . CRB 1224**
Charly R&B / Jun '89.

## MOTOR CITY - THE MUSIC OF DETROIT.
**Tracks:** Not Advised.
CD Set. . . . . . . . . . . . . . . . . . . TFP 014
MC Set. . . . . . . . . . . . . . . . . . MCTFP 014
Tring / Nov '92 / Prism Leisure PLC / Midland
Records.

## MOTOR CITY COLLECTORS ALBUM.
**Tracks:** Not Advised.
■ **CD . . . . . . . . . . . . . . . . . . CDMOTCLP 36**
Motor City / Jul '90.

## MOTOR CITY DUETS.
**Tracks:** Not Advised.
■ **CD . . . . . . . . . . . . . . . . . . CDMOTCLP 33**
Motor City / Jul '90.

## MOTOR CITY FINGER SNAPPERS.
**Tracks:** Not Advised.
■ **CD . . . . . . . . . . . . . . . . . . CDMOTCLP 34**
Motor City / Jul '90.

## MOTOR CITY FOOTSTOMPERS.
**Tracks:** Not Advised.
■ **CD . . . . . . . . . . . . . . . . . . CDMOTCLP 32**
Motor City / Jul '90.

## MOTOR CITY LOVE SONGS.
**Tracks:** Not Advised.
■ **CD** . . . . . . . . . . . . . . . . . . **CDMOTCLP 31**
Motor City / Jul '90.

## MOTOR CITY MAGIC, VOL 1.
**Tracks:** Honey baby (be mine): *Innervision* / I'm a fool, I must love you: *Falcons (1)* / Plain brown wrapper: *Rice, Larry* / Walk right on it: *Motor City Runners* / You must have been a warlock: *Third Chapter* / That's all she wrote: *King Diamond* / Message to the black women: *King Diamond* / I just want to love you: *Innervision* / God must have created love: *Bursey, Flery* / I can't help it, I'm falling: *Falcons (1)* / I'm in love again: *Innervision*.
■ **LP** . . . . . . . . . . . . . . . . . . . . **CRM 2035**
Charly / May '88.

## MOTOR CITY MAGIC, VOL 2.
**Tracks:** Standing on guard: *Falcons (1)* / Over you: *Capreez* / Second time around: *Innervision* / Watch your step now: *Motor City Runners* / I'm tempted: *Falcons (1)* / Wait a minute: *Tim Tam & The Turn Ons* / How to make a sad man glad: *Capreez* / You got the power baby: *Falcons (1)* / You must have been a warlock: *Motor City Runners* / Love, look what you made me do: *Falcons (1)* / Detroit getdown: *New Breed* / Gotta find a way to get back home: *Innervision*.
■ **LP** . . . . . . . . . . . . . . . . . . . . **CRM 2036**
Charly / May '88.

## MOTOR CITY ROOTS - THE ROOTS OF DETROIT SOUL.
**Tracks:** You've got what it takes: *Johnson, Marv & The Falcons* / You've got to move two mountains: *Johnson, Marv & The Falcons* / Happy days: *Johnson, Marv & The Falcons* / Come to me: *Johnson, Marv & The Falcons* / He gave me you: *Johnson, Marv & The Falcons* / Easier said (than done): *Johnson, Marv & The Falcons* / I need you: *Johnson, Marv & The Falcons* / All the love I've got: *Johnson, Marv & The Falcons* / You're so fine: *Johnson, Marv & The Falcons* / Pow you're in love: *Johnson, Marv & The Falcons* / You're mine: *Johnson, Marv & The Falcons* / Teacher: *Johnson, Marv & The Falcons* / Waiting for you: *Johnson, Marv & The Falcons* / Goddess of angels: *Johnson, Marv & The Falcons* / I plus love plus you: *Johnson, Marv & The Falcons* / Country shack: *Johnson, Marv & The Falcons*.
■ **LP** . . . . . . . . . . . . . . . . . . . . **SSL 6009**
Stateside / Apr '86.
■ **MC.** . . . . . . . . . . . . . . . . . . **TCSSL 6009**
Stateside / Sep '86.

## MOTOR CITY SUMMER SWINGBEATS.
**Tracks:** Not Advised.
■ **CD** . . . . . . . . . . . . . . . . . . **CDMOTCLP 35**
Motor City / Jul '90.

## MOTOR-TOWN SOUND OF DETROIT VOL.1.
**Tracks:** Not Advised.
■ **LP** . . . . . . . . . . . . . . . . . . . . **MOTCLP 1**
Motor City / Mar '90.

## MOTOR-TOWN SOUND OF DETROIT VOL.2.
**Tracks:** Not Advised.
■ **LP** . . . . . . . . . . . . . . . . . . . . **MOTCLP 2**
Motor City / Mar '90.

## MOTOR-TOWN SOUND OF DETROIT VOL.3.
**Tracks:** Not Advised.
■ **LP** . . . . . . . . . . . . . . . . . . . . **MOTCLP 3**
Motor City / Mar '90.

## MOTORCITY A GO-GO.
**Tracks:** Not Advised.
■ **CD** . . . . . . . . . . . . . . . . . . . . **MOTCCD 83**
Motor City / Oct '92.

## MOTORCITY BALLADS.
**Tracks:** Not Advised.
■ **CD** . . . . . . . . . . . . . . . . . . . . **MOTCCD 63**
Motor City / Oct '92.

## MOTORCITY BEACH PARTY.
**Tracks:** Not Advised.
■ **CD** . . . . . . . . . . . . . . . . . . . . **MOTCCD 70**
Motor City / Oct '92.

## MOTORCITY MEMORIES.
**Tracks:** Not Advised.
■ **CD** . . . . . . . . . . . . . . . . . . . . **MOTCCD 85**
Motor City / Oct '92.

## MOTORCITY SOUL SAMPLER VOL.1.
**Tracks:** Not Advised.
■ **LP** . . . . . . . . . . . . . . . . . . . . **MOTCLP 11**
Motor City / Mar '90.

## MOTORCITY SOUL SAMPLER VOL.2.
**Tracks:** Not Advised.
■ **LP** . . . . . . . . . . . . . . . . . . . . **MOTCLP 12**
Motor City / Mar '90.

## MOTORCITY SOUL SAMPLER VOL.4.
**Tracks:** Not Advised.
■ **LP** . . . . . . . . . . . . . . . . . . . . **MOTCLP 14**
Motor City / Dec '90.

## MOTORCITY SOUND OF DETROIT VOL. 6, THE.
**Tracks:** Not Advised.
■ **CD** . . . . . . . . . . . . . . . . . . . . **MOTCCD 6**
Motor City / Mar '92.

## MOTORTOWN REVUE IN PARIS.
**Tracks:** Too many fish in the sea: *Van Dyke, Earl* / Stop in the name of love: *Supremes* / Baby love: *Supremes* / Somewhere: *Supremes* / Ooh baby baby: *Miracles* / Mickey's monkey: *Miracles* / If I had a hammer: *Reeves, Martha & The Vandellas* / Nowhere to run: *Reeves, Martha & The Vandellas* / Dancing in the street: *Reeves, Martha & The Vandellas* / High heel sneakers: *Wonder, Stevie* / Funny how time slips away: *Wonder, Stevie* / Fingertips: *Wonder, Stevie*.
■ **LP** . . . . . . . . . . . . . . . . . . . . **TML 11027**
Tamla Motown / Feb '66.

## MOTORTOWN REVUE LIVE.
**Tracks:** Sing a simple song: *Originals* / I can't turn you loose: *Blinky* / I wouldn't change the man he is: *Blinky* / Who's making love: *Taylor, Bobby* / Does your mama know about me: *Taylor, Bobby* / Melinda: *Taylor, Bobby* / Cloud nine: *Temptations* / Ain't no sun since you've been gone: *Knight, Gladys & The Pips* / I wish it would rain: *Knight, Gladys & The Pips* / Monologue: *Knight, Gladys & The Pips* / Masquerade is over: *Knight, Gladys & The Pips* / I heard it through the grapevine: *Knight, Gladys & The Pips* / For once in my life: *Wonder, Stevie* / Shoo-be-doo-be-doo-da-day: *Wonder, Stevie* / Uptight: *Wonder, Stevie*.
■ **LP** . . . . . . . . . . . . . . . . . . . . **STML 11127**
Tamla Motown / Feb '70.

## MOTOWN 20TH ANNIVERSARY ALBUM.
**Tracks:** Money (that's what I want): *Strong, Barrett* / Shop around: *Miracles* / You've really got a hold on me: *Miracles* / Tears of a clown: *Robinson, Smokey* / Fingertips (part 2): *Wonder, Little Stevie* / You are the sunshine of my life: *Wonder, Stevie* / Living for the city: *Wonder, Stevie* / Uptight: *Wonder, Stevie* / For once in my life: *Wonder, Stevie* / Superstition: *Wonder, Stevie* / Heatwave: *Reeves, Martha & The Vandellas* / Dancing in the street: *Reeves, Martha & The Vandellas* / My guy: *Wells, Mary* / Baby love: *Supremes* / You keep me hangin' on: *Ross, Diana & The Supremes* / Shotgun: *Walker, Junior & The All Stars* / Ben: *Jackson, Michael* / Touch me in the morning: *Ross, Diana* / Do you know where you're going to: *Ross, Diana* / With you I'm born again: *Preston, Billy & Syreeta* / This old heart of mine: *Isley Brothers* / What becomes of the broken hearted: *Ruffin, Jimmy* / Reach out I'll be there: *Four Tops* / Bernadette: *Four Tops* / You're all I need to get by: *Gaye, Marvin & Tammi Terrell* / I heard it through the grapevine: *Gaye, Marvin* / What's going on: *Gaye, Marvin* / Cloud 9: *Temptations* / Papa was a rollin' stone: *Temptations* / I want you back: *Jackson Five* / I'll be there: *Jackson Five* / War: *Starr, Edwin* / Indiana wants me: *Taylor, R. Dean* / Help me make it through the night: *Knight, Gladys & The Pips*.
■ **Double LP.** . . . . . . . . . . . . . . . . **TMSP 6010**
■ **MC Set** . . . . . . . . . . . . . . . . . **CTMSP 6010**
Motown / Oct '81.

## MOTOWN 25 (Yesterday Today Forever).
**Tracks:** Dancing in the street / Shop around / Never can say goodbye / What's going on / Ain't no mountain high enough / You are the sunshine of my life / I can't help myself / My guy / Shotgun / Brick house / Tracks of my tears / Stop in the name of love / All this love / Billie Jean / Friendship train / Cruisin' / My girl / He's a pretender.
**VHS** . . . . . . . . . . . . . . . . . . . . **SMV 10302**
MGM/UA (Video) / '88 / MGM/UA Video / Gold & Sons / THE.
**VHS** . . . . . . . . . . . . . . . . . . . . **PES 50302**
Warner Home Video / '91 / WEA / Hollywood Nites / Gold & Sons / THE.

## MOTOWN CHARTBUSTERS.
**Tracks:** Not Advised.
■ **LP** . . . . . . . . . . . . . . . . . . . . **STAR 2283**
■ **CD** . . . . . . . . . . . . . . . . . . . . **TCD 2283**
■ **MC.** . . . . . . . . . . . . . . . . . . . **STAC 2283**
Telstar/Ronco / Nov '86.

## MOTOWN CHARTBUSTERS 80.
**Tracks:** Not Advised.
■ **LP** . . . . . . . . . . . . . . . . . . . **STML 12139**
■ **MC.** . . . . . . . . . . . . . . . . . . **CSTML 12139**
Motown / Oct '81.

## MOTOWN CHARTBUSTERS VOL.1.
**Tracks:** Blowin' in the wind: *Wonder, Stevie* / I was made to love her: *Wonder, Stevie* / You keep me hangin' on: *Supremes* / Happening: *Supremes* / Love is here and now you're gone: *Supremes* / Standing in the shadows of love: *Four Tops* / Seven rooms of gloom: *Four Tops* / It takes two: *Gaye, Marvin & Kim Weston* / When you're young and in love: *Marvelettes* / I know Im losing you: *Temptations* / What becomes of the broken hearted: *Ruffin, Jimmy* / Gonna give her all the love I've got: *Ruffin, Jimmy* / How sweet it is (to be loved by you): *Walker, Junior & The All Stars* / I'm ready for love: *Reeves, Martha* / Jimmy Mack: *Reeves, Martha* / Take me in your arms and love me: *Knight, Gladys & The Pips*.
■ **LP** . . . . . . . . . . . . . . . . . . . **STML 11055**
Motown / May '69.
**MC.** . . . . . . . . . . . . . . . . . . . . **CSTML 11055**
Motown / '81 / PolyGram.

## MOTOWN CHARTBUSTERS VOL.10.
**Tracks:** Three times a lady: *Commodores* / Easy: *Commodores* / Sail on: *Commodores* / Love hang over: *Ross, Diana* / Boss: *Ross, Diana* / Do you know where you're going to: *Ross, Diana* / Night: *Valli Frankie & Four Seasons* / Got to give it up: *Gaye Marvin* / Get it up for love: *Vega, Tata* / Big time Theme from: *Robinson, Smokey* / Your kiss is sweet *Syreeta* / I'm a sucker for your love: *Marie, Teena* Love machine: *Miracles* / It should have been me *Fair, Yvonne* / You and I: *James, Rick* / Don't leave me this way: *Houston, Thelma*.
■ **LP** . . . . . . . . . . . . . . . . . . . . **STML 1212**
**MC.** . . . . . . . . . . . . . . . . . . . . **CSTML 1212**
Motown / Oct '81 / PolyGram.

## MOTOWN CHARTBUSTERS VOL.2.
**Tracks:** Ain't nothing like the real thing baby: *Gaye Marvin & Tammi Terrell* / If I could build my whol world around you: *Gaye, Marvin & Tammi Terrell* Reflections: *Ross, Diana & The Supremes* / Som things you never get used to: *Ross, Diana & Th Supremes* / If you can want / I second that emotion You keep running away: *Four Tops* / If I were carpenter: *Four Tops* / I could never love anothe (after loving you): *Temptations* / You're my every thing: *Temptations* / I heard it through the grapevine *Knight, Gladys & The Pips* / I'm wondering: *Wonde Stevie* / Shoo-be-doo-be-doo-da-day: *Wonder, Stev* / I've passed this way before: *Ruffin, Jimmy* / Gott see Jane: *Taylor, R. Dean* / Honey chile: *Reeves Martha*.
■ **LP** . . . . . . . . . . . . . . . . . . . . **STML 110**
Motown / Nov '68.
**MC.** . . . . . . . . . . . . . . . . . . . . **CSTML 110**
Motown / Oct '81 / PolyGram.

## MOTOWN CHARTBUSTERS VOL.3.
**Tracks:** I heard it through the grapevine: *Gaye, Ma vin* / You're all I need to get by: *Gaye, Marvin Tammi Terrell* / I'm gonna make you love me: *Ros Diana & The Supremes* / My cherie amour: *Wonde Stevie* / For once in my life: *Wonder, Stevie* / N matter what sign you are: *Ross, Diana & The S premes* / Love child: *Ross, Diana & The Supremes* This old heart of mine: *Isley Brothers* / Behind th painted smile: *Isley Brothers* / I'll pick a rose for m rose: *Johnson, Marv* / I'm in a different world: *Fo Tops* / Dancing in the street: *Reeves, Martha* / G ready: *Temptations* / Stop her on sight (S.O.S): *Sta Edwin* / Road runner: *Walker, Junior & The All Sta* / Tracks of my tears: *Robinson, Smokey & T Miracles*.
■ **LP** . . . . . . . . . . . . . . . . . . . . **STML 111**
Motown / Nov '69.
**MC.** . . . . . . . . . . . . . . . . . . . . **CSTML 111**
Motown / Oct '81 / PolyGram.
■ **CD** . . . . . . . . . . . . . . . . . . . . **WD 726**
■ **LP** . . . . . . . . . . . . . . . . . . . . **WL 726**
■ **MC.** . . . . . . . . . . . . . . . . . . . **WK 726**
Motown / Jun '89 / PolyGram.

## MOTOWN CHARTBUSTERS VOL.4.
**Tracks:** I want you back: *Jackson Five* / ABC: *Jac son Five* / Onion song: *Gaye, Marvin & Tammi Te rell* / Too busy thinking about my baby: *Gaye, Mar* / I can't help myself: *Four Tops* / Do what you go do: *Four Tops* / Up the ladder to the roof: *Supreme* Someday we'll be together: *Ross, Diana & The S premes* / Cloud 9: *Temptations* / I can't get next you: *Temptations* / I second that emotion: *Tem tations with Diana Ross & The Supremes* / Yest me, yester-you, yesterday: *Wonder, Stevie* / Fa well is a lonely sound: *Ruffin, Jimmy* / What doe

e (to win your love): *Walker, Junior & The All* *rs.*
LP . . . . . . . . . . . . . . . . . . . . . STML 11162
town / Oct '70.
MC. . . . . . . . . . . . . . . . . . . . . CSTML 11162
own / Oct '81.
CD . . . . . . . . . . . . . . . . . . . . . WD 72674
LP . . . . . . . . . . . . . . . . . . . . . WL 72674
MC. . . . . . . . . . . . . . . . . . . . . WK 72674
own / Dec '89.
. . . . . . . . . . . . . . . . . . . . . . 530059-2
. . . . . . . . . . . . . . . . . . . . . . 530059-4
town / Jan '93 / PolyGram.

## )TOWN CHARTBUSTERS VOL.5.
cks: Tears of a clown: *Robinson, Smokey* / War: *r, Edwin* / Love you save: *Jackson Five* / I'll be *re: Jackson Five* / Ball of confusion: *Temptations* / all in the game: *Four Tops* / Still water (love): *r Tops* / Heaven help us all: *Wonder, Stevie* / ıed, sealed, delivered (I'm yours): *Wonder, Ste-* / I'll say forever my love: *Wonder, Stevie* / Ain't mountain high enough: *Ross, Diana* / Stoned love: *premes* / Abraham, Martin and John: *Gaye, Mar-* / Forget me not: *Reeves, Martha* / It's a shame: *own Spinners* / Never had a dream come true: *nder, Stevie* / It's wonderful: *Four Tops.*
LP . . . . . . . . . . . . . . . . . . . . . STML 11181
own / Apr '71.
MC. . . . . . . . . . . . . . . . . . . . . CSTML 11181
own / Oct '81.
CD . . . . . . . . . . . . . . . . . . . . . WD 72675
LP . . . . . . . . . . . . . . . . . . . . . WL 72675
MC. . . . . . . . . . . . . . . . . . . . . WK 72675
own / Jun '90.
. . . . . . . . . . . . . . . . . . . . . . 530060-2
. . . . . . . . . . . . . . . . . . . . . . 530060-4
own / Jan '93 / PolyGram.

## )TOWN CHARTBUSTERS VOL.6.
cks: I'm still waiting: *Ross, Diana* / Remember *Ross, Diana* / I don't blame you at all: *Robinson, okey & The Miracles* / (Come round here) I'm the you need: *Robinson, Smokey & The Miracles* / can work it out: *Wonder, Stevie* / Never can say dbye: *Jackson Five* / Mama's pearl: *Jackson Five* ese things will keep me loving you: *Velvelettes* / ana wants me: *Taylor, R. Dean* / River deep, ıntain high: *Supremes & Four Tops* / Simple ıe: *Four Tops* / Just seven numbers: *Four Tops* / ıan Jones: *Supremes* / Just my imagination (run- away with me): *Temptations* / It's Summer: *nptations* / Heaven must have sent you: *Elgins.*
LP . . . . . . . . . . . . . . . . . . . . . STML 11191
own / Oct '71.
MC. . . . . . . . . . . . . . . . . . . . . CSTML 11191
own / Oct '81.
MC. . . . . . . . . . . . . . . . . . . . . WK 72676
CD . . . . . . . . . . . . . . . . . . . . . WD 72676
LP . . . . . . . . . . . . . . . . . . . . . WL 72676
own / Jun '90.
. . . . . . . . . . . . . . . . . . . . . . 530161-4
town / Jan '93 / PolyGram.

## )TOWN CHARTBUSTERS VOL.7.
cks: Automatically sunshine: *Supremes* / Floy *Supremes* / You gotta have love in your heart: *remes & Four Tops* / Surrender: *Ross, Diana* / bedood'ndoobe, doobedood'ndoobe: *Ross, Dia-* / Just walk in my shoes: *Knight, Gladys & The s* / Rockin' robin: *Jackson, Michael* / Ain't no shine: *Jackson, Michael* / Got to be there: *Jack-, Michael* / Take a look around: *Temptations* / erstar: *Temptations* / If you really love me: *nder, Stevie* / Bless you: *Reeves, Martha* / Walk he night: *Walker, Junior & The All Stars* / Festival e: *San Remo Strings* / My guy: *Wells, Mary.*
LP . . . . . . . . . . . . . . . . . . . . . STML 11215
MC. . . . . . . . . . . . . . . . . . . . . CSTML 11215
own / Oct '81.
CD . . . . . . . . . . . . . . . . . . . . . WD 72677
LP . . . . . . . . . . . . . . . . . . . . . WL 72677
MC. . . . . . . . . . . . . . . . . . . . . WK 72677
town / Jun '90.
. . . . . . . . . . . . . . . . . . . . . . 530062-2
. . . . . . . . . . . . . . . . . . . . . . 530062-4
own / Jan '93 / PolyGram.

## )TOWN CHARTBUSTERS VOL.9.
cks: All of my life: *Ross, Diana* / Last time I saw : *Ross, Diana* / My mistake (was to love you): *ss, Diana & Marvin Gaye* / You are everything: *ss, Diana & Marvin Gaye* / Baby love: *Ross, Diana The Supremes* / High ground: *Wonder, Stevie* / s misstra know it all: *Wonder, Stevie* / Living for city: *Wonder, Stevie* / Dancing machine / Spinnin' spinnin': *Syreeta* / Keep on truckin': *Kendricks, ie* / Boogie down: *Kendricks, Eddie* / There's a st in my house: *Taylor, R. Dean* / Just my soul ponding: *Robinson, Smokey* / What becomes of broken hearted: *Robinson, Smokey* / Machine *: Commodores.*
LP . . . . . . . . . . . . . . . . . . . . . STML 11270
MC. . . . . . . . . . . . . . . . . . . . . CSTML 11270
Motown / Oct '81 / PolyGram.

## MOTOWN CRUISIN VOL 1.
**Tracks:** Not Advised.
■ **MC Set** . . . . . . . . . . . . . . . . CTMSP 6016
Motown / Sep '83.

## MOTOWN CRUISIN VOL 2.
**Tracks:** Not Advised.
■ **MC Set** . . . . . . . . . . . . . . . . CTMSP 6022
Motown / Sep '83.

## MOTOWN DANCE.
**Tracks:** Going to a go go: *Robinson, Smokey & The Miracles* / Brick house: *Commodores* / Let it whip: *Dazz Band* / Love machine: *Miracles* / Heaven must have sent you: *Pointer, Bonnie* / Dancing machine: *Jackson Five* / Love hangover: *Ross, Diana* / Dancing in the street: *Reeves, Martha & The Vandellas.*
■ **LP** . . . . . . . . . . . . . . . . . . . WL 72170
■ **MC.** . . . . . . . . . . . . . . . . . . WK 72170
Motown / May '85.

## MOTOWN DANCE PARTY.
**Tracks:** Shotgun: *Walker, Junior & The All Stars* / I can't help myself: *Four Tops* / I want you back: *Jackson Five* / You can't hurry love: *Ross, Diana & The Supremes* / Tears of a clown: *Robinson, Smokey & The Miracles* / Ain't too proud to beg: *Temptations* / Jimmy Mack: *Reeves, Martha* / Twenty five miles: *Starr, Edwin* / Uptight: *Wonder, Stevie* / I heard it through the grapevine: *Gaye, Marvin* / You keep me hangin' on: *Ross, Diana & The Supremes* / Do you love me: *Contours* / Ain't that peculiar: *Gaye, Marvin* / Way you do the things like you do: *Temptations* / Where did our love go: *Ross, Diana & The Supremes* / ABC: *Jackson Five* / Mickey's monkey / Heatwave: *Reeves, Martha* / This old heart of mine: *Isley Brothers* / It's the same old song: *Four Tops* / Going to a go go / I'm a road runner: *Walker, Junior & The All Stars* / Nowhere to run: *Reeves, Martha* / Reach out I'll be there: *Four Tops* / My guy: *Wells, Mary* / Come see about me: *Ross, Diana & The Supremes* / Get ready: *Temptations* / Needle in a haystack: *Velvelettes* / Love you save: *Jackson Five* / Love is like an itching in my heart: *Ross, Diana & The Supremes* / Heaven must have sent you: *Elgins* / Dancing in the street: *Reeves, Martha* / Standing in the shadows of love: *Four Tops* / War: *Starr, Edwin* / Stoned love: *Supremes* / I can't get next to you: *Temptations* / Brick house: *Commodores* / Superstition: *Wonder, Stevie* / Keep on truckin: *Kendricks, Eddie* / Don't leave me this way: *Houston, Thelma* / He was really saying something (Available on 12" only) / Take me in your arms (rock me a little while)*: *Weston, Kim.*
■ **CD** . . . . . . . . . . . . . . . . . . . ZD 72700
■ **LP** . . . . . . . . . . . . . . . . . . . ZL 72700
■ **MC.** . . . . . . . . . . . . . . . . . . ZK 72700
Motown / May '88.

## MOTOWN DANCE PARTY, VOL.1.
**Tracks:** Shotgun: *Walker, Junior & The All Stars* / I can't help myself: *Four Tops* / I want you back: *Jackson Five* / You can't hurry love: *Ross, Diana & The Supremes* / Tears of a clown / He was really saying something: *Velvelettes* / Get ready: *Rare Earth* / Take me in your arms (rock me a little while): *Weston, Kim* / Jimmy Mack: *Reeves, Martha* / Twenty five miles: *Starr, Edwin* / Uptight: *Wonder, Stevie* / I heard it through the grapevine: *Knight, Gladys & The Pips* / You keep me hangin' on: *Ross, Diana & The Supremes* / Do you love me: *Contours* / Too many fish in the sea: *Marvelettes* / Ain't that peculiar: *Gaye, Marvin* / Way you do the things you do: *Temptations* / Where did our love go: *Ross, Diana & The Supremes* / ABC: *Jackson Five* / Mickey's monkey: *Robinson, Smokey & The Miracles* / Heatwave: *Reeves, Martha* / This old heart of mine: *Isley Brothers* / It's the same old song: *Four Tops.*
■ **CD** . . . . . . . . . . . . . . . . . . . WD 72591
Motown / Nov '87.

## MOTOWN DANCE PARTY, VOL.2.
**Tracks:** Stop, in the name of love: *Ross, Diana & The Supremes* / Going to a go go: *Robinson, Smokey & The Temptations* / Road runner: *Walker, Junior & The All Stars* / Nowhere to run: *Reeves, Martha* / Reach out I'll be there: *Four Tops* / My guy: *Wells, Mary* / Come see about me: *Ross, Diana & The Supremes* / Get ready: *Temptations* / Needle in a haystack: *Velvelettes* / Love you save: *Jackson Five* / Love is like an itching in my heart: *Ross, Diana & The Supremes* / Heaven must have sent you: *Elgins* / Dancing in the street: *Reeves, Martha* / Standing in the shadows of love: *Four Tops* / You need love like I do: *Knight, Gladys & The Pips* / War: *Starr, Edwin* / Stoned love: *Supremes* / I can't get next to you: *Temptations* / Brick house: *Commodores* / Superstition: *Wonder, Stevie* / Got to give it up: *Gaye, Marvin* / Keep on truckin': *Kendricks, Eddie* / Dancing machine: *Jackson Five* / Don't leave me this way: *Houston, Thelma.*
■ **CD** . . . . . . . . . . . . . . . . . . . WD 72592
Motown / Nov '87.
■ **CD** . . . . . . . . . . . . . . . . . . . ZD 72703
■ **LP** . . . . . . . . . . . . . . . . . . . ZL 72703
■ **MC.** . . . . . . . . . . . . . . . . . . ZK 72703
Motown / May '90.

## MOTOWN DISCO CLASSICS VOL. 2.
**Tracks:** I'll turn to stone / Shake me, wake me / Headline news / Two can have a party / There's no stopping us now / Got to have you back / Third finger, left hand / Honey love / Take this heart of mine / Reach out I'll be there / I'm satisfied / Just look what you've done / Bird in the hand / Come see about me / Day you take one / All for you.
■ **LP** . . . . . . . . . . . . . . . . . . . STMA 8005
Tamla Motown / Aug '72.

## MOTOWN DISCOMAGIC.
**Tracks:** Not Advised.
■ **LP** . . . . . . . . . . . . . . . . . . . MFP 50448
MFP / Nov '79.

## MOTOWN GIRL GROUPS.
**Tracks:** Dancing in the street: *Reeves, Martha & The Vandellas* / My world is empty without you: *Ross, Diana & The Supremes* / Don't mess with Bill: *Marvelettes* / Heatwave: *Reeves, Martha & The Vandellas* / One who really loves you: *Wells, Mary* / I'm livin' in shame: *Ross, Diana & The Supremes* / Reflections: *Ross, Diana & The Supremes* / Nathan Jones: *Supremes* / Two lovers: *Wells, Mary* / Jimmy Mack: *Reeves, Martha & The Vandellas* / I heard through the grapevine: *Knight, Gladys & The Pips.*
■ **LP** . . . . . . . . . . . . . . . . . . . WL 72144
■ **MC.** . . . . . . . . . . . . . . . . . . WK 72144
■ **CD** . . . . . . . . . . . . . . . . . . . WD 72144
Motown / May '84.

## MOTOWN GRAMMY RHYTHM.
**Tracks:** Heatwave: *Reeves, Martha* / Ain't no mountain high enough: *Gaye, Marvin & Tammi Terrell* / For once in my life: *Wonder, Stevie* / What does it take: *Walker, Junior & The All Stars* / It's all in the game: *Four Tops* / Neither one of us: *Knight, Gladys & The Pips* / Love hangover: *Ross, Diana* / Got to give it up: *Gaye, Marvin* / Baby love: *Ross, Diana & The Supremes* / I second that emotion: *Robinson, Smokey* / Cloud 9: *Temptations* / Signed, sealed delivered I'm yours: *Wonder, Stevie* / Papa was a rollin' stone: *Temptations* / Boogie down: *Kendricks, Eddie* / Don't leave me this way: *Houston, Thelma* / Cruisin': *Robinson, Smokey.*
■ **CD** . . . . . . . . . . . . . . . . . . . WD 72297
Motown / Sep '89.

## MOTOWN HEARTBREAKERS.
**Tracks:** Not Advised.
**CD** . . . . . . . . . . . . . . . . . . . . TCD 2343
■ **LP** . . . . . . . . . . . . . . . . . . . STAR 2343
■ **MC.** . . . . . . . . . . . . . . . . . . STAC 2343
Telstar/Ronco / Sep '89.

## MOTOWN HITS OF GOLD VOL.1.
**Tracks:** My guy: *Wells, Mary* / Where did our love go: *Ross, Diana & The Supremes* / Baby love: *Ross, Diana & The Supremes* / Nowhere to run: *Reeves, Martha & The Vandellas* / Stop in the name of love: *Ross, Diana & The Supremes* / Uptight (everythings alright): *Wonder, Stevie* / Loving you is sweeter than ever: *Four Tops* / Ain't too proud to beg: *Temptations* / How sweet it is (to be loved by you): *Walker, Junior & The All Stars* / You can't hurry love: *Ross, Diana & The Supremes* / Reach out I'll be there: *Four Tops* / Beauty is only skin deep: *Temptations* / I'm ready for love: *Reeves, Martha & The Vandellas* / (I know) I'm losing you: *Temptations* / Place in the sun: *Wonder, Stevie* / Standing in the shadows of love: *Four Tops* / It takes two: *Gaye, Marvin & Kim Weston* / Love is here and now you're gone: *Ross, Diana & The Supremes.*
■ **LP** . . . . . . . . . . . . . . . . . . . WL 72401
■ **MC.** . . . . . . . . . . . . . . . . . . WK 72401
Motown / Oct '85.
■ **CD** . . . . . . . . . . . . . . . . . . . WD 72401
Motown / Jan '89.

## MOTOWN HITS OF GOLD VOL.2.
**Tracks:** Bernadette: *Four Tops* / Jimmy Mack: *Reeves, Martha & The Vandellas* / Happening: *Ross, Diana & The Supremes* / 7 rooms of gloom: *Four Tops* / Take me in your arms and love: *Knight, Gladys & The Pips* / I was made to love her: *Wonder, Stevie* / When you're young and in love: *Marvelettes* / Reflections: *Ross, Diana & The Supremes* / I'm wondering: *Wonder, Stevie* / In and out of love: *Ross, Diana & The Supremes* / Walk away Renee: *Four Tops* / Gotta see Jane: *Taylor, R. Dean* / If I were a carpenter: *Four Tops* / You're all I need to get by: *Gaye, Marvin & Tammi Terrell* / Yesterday's dreams: *Four Tops* / This old heart of mine (is weak for you): *Isley Brothers* / Love child: *Ross, Diana & The Supremes* / For once in my life: *Wonder, Stevie* / Stop

her on sight: *Starr, Edwin* / I guess I'll always love you: *Isley Brothers*.
■ LP . . . . . . . . . . . . . . . . . . . . **WL 72402**
■ MC. . . . . . . . . . . . . . . . . . . . **WK 72402**
Motown / Oct '85.
■ CD . . . . . . . . . . . . . . . . . . . . **WD 72402**
Motown / Jan '89.

## MOTOWN HITS OF GOLD VOL.3.

**Tracks:** Dancing in the street: *Reeves, Martha & The Vandellas* / You ain't livin' till you're lovin': *Gaye, Marvin & Tammi Terrell* / I'll pick a rose for my Rose: *Johnson, Marv* / I'm gonna make you love me: *Ross, Diana, The Supremes & The Temptations* / I heard it through the grapevine: *Gaye, Marvin* / Get ready: *Temptations* / Don't know why I love you: *Wonder, Stevie* / (I'm a) road runner: *Walker, Junior & The All Stars* / Behind a painted smile: *Isley Brothers* / I'm livin' in shame: *Ross, Diana & The Supremes* / Tracks of my tears: *Robinson, Smokey & The Miracles* / What is a man: *Four Tops* / My cherie amour: *Wonder, Stevie* / Too busy thinkng about my baby: *Gaye, Marvin* / Cloud 9: *Temptations* / Put yourself in my place: *Isley Brothers* / I second that emotion: *Ross, Diana & The Supremes* / Do what you gotta do: *Four Tops* / What does it take (to win your love): *Walker, Junior & The All Stars* / Yester-me, yester-you, yesterday: *Wonder, Stevie*.
■ LP . . . . . . . . . . . . . . . . . . . . **WL 72403**
■ MC. . . . . . . . . . . . . . . . . . . . **WK 72403**
Motown / Oct '85.
■ CD . . . . . . . . . . . . . . . . . . . . **WD 72403**
Motown / Jan '89.

## MOTOWN HITS OF GOLD VOL.4.

**Tracks:** Someday we'll be together: *Ross, Diana & The Supremes* / Onion song: *Gaye, Marvin & Tammi Terrell* / I can't get next to you: *Temptations* / I want you back: *Jackson Five* / Farewell is a lonely sound: *Ruffin, Jimmy* / I can't help myself: *Four Tops* / Never had a dream come true: *Wonder, Stevie* / Up the ladder to the roof: *Supremes* / Abraham, Martin and John: *Gaye, Marvin* / It's all in the game: *Four Tops* / I'll say forever my love: *Ruffin, Jimmy* / Signed, sealed, delivered, I'm yours: *Wonder, Stevie* / Love you save: *Jackson Five* / Tears of a clown: *Robinson, Smokey & The Miracles* / Ain't no moutain high enough: *Ross, Diana* / Ball of confusion (that's what the world is today): *Temptations* / Still water (love): *Four Tops* / It's wonderful (to be loved by you): *Ruffin, Jimmy* / War: *Starr, Edwin* / ABC: *Jackson Five*.
■ LP . . . . . . . . . . . . . . . . . . . . **WL 72404**
■ MC. . . . . . . . . . . . . . . . . . . . **WK 72404**
Motown / Oct '85.
■ CD . . . . . . . . . . . . . . . . . . . . **WD 72404**
Motown / Jan '89.

## MOTOWN HITS OF GOLD VOL.5.

**Tracks:** I'll be there: *Jackson Five* / It's a shame: *Detroit Spinners* / Stoned love: *Supremes* / (Come 'round here) I'm the one you need: *Robinson, Smokey & The Miracles* / Forget me not: *Reeves, Martha & The Vandellas* / Remember me: *Ross, Diana* / Indiana wants me: *Taylor, R. Dean* / Heaven must have sent you: *Elgins* / I don't blame you at all: *Robinson, Smokey & The Miracles* / Just my imagination (running away with me): *Temptations* / River deep, mountain high: *Supremes & Four Tops* / I'm still waiting: *Ross, Diana & The Supremes* / Nathan Jones: *Supremes* / Simple game: *Four Tops* / Surrender: *Ross, Diana* / If your really love me: *Wonder, Stevie* / Got to be there: *Jackson, Michael* / Floy joy: *Supremes*.
■ LP . . . . . . . . . . . . . . . . . . . . **WL 72405**
■ MC. . . . . . . . . . . . . . . . . . . . **WK 72405**
Motown / Oct '85.
■ CD . . . . . . . . . . . . . . . . . . . . **WD 72405**
Motown / Jan '89.

## MOTOWN HITS OF GOLD VOL.6.

**Tracks:** Take a look around: *Temptations* / Doobedood'ndoobe, doobedood'ndoobe, doobedood'n-doobe: *Ross, Diana* / Rockin' robin: *Jackson Five* / Walk in the night: *Walker, Junior & The All Stars* / Lookin' through the windows: *Jackson Five* / Ben: *Jackson, Michael* / Help me make it through the night / Papa was a rollin' stone: *Temptations* / Doctor my eyes: *Jackson Five* / Take me girl I'm ready: *Walker, Junior & The All Stars* / Look of love: *Knight, Gladys & The Pips* / Hallelujah day: *Jackson Five* / Touch me in the morning: *Ross, Diana* / Keep on trucking (part 1): *Kendricks, Eddie* / All of my life: *Ross, Diana* / You are everything: *Gaye, Marvin & Diana Ross*.
■ LP . . . . . . . . . . . . . . . . . . . . **WL 72406**
■ MC. . . . . . . . . . . . . . . . . . . . **WK 72406**
Motown / Oct '85.
■ CD . . . . . . . . . . . . . . . . . . . . **WD 72406**
Motown / Jan '89.

## MOTOWN HITS OF GOLD VOL.7.

**Tracks:** Machine gun: *Commodores* / There's a ghost in my house: *Taylor, R. Dean* / Your kiss is sweet: *Syreeta* / Night: *Valli, Frankie & Four Seasons* / Love machine (part 1): *Miracles* / Walk away from love: *Ruffin, David* / Do you know where you're going to: *Ross, Diana* / It shoud have been me: *Fair, Yvonne* / Love hangover: *Ross, Diana* / Don't leave me this way: *Houston, Thelma* / Easy: *Commodores* / Got to give it up (part 1): *Gaye, Marvin* / Three times a lady: *Commodores* / Gettin' ready for love: *Ross, Diana* / Sail on: *Commodores* / With you I'm born again: *Preston, Billy & Syreeta* / Still: *Commodores* / Let's get serious: *Jackson, Jermaine*.
■ LP . . . . . . . . . . . . . . . . . . . . **WL 72407**
■ MC. . . . . . . . . . . . . . . . . . . . **WK 72407**
Motown / Oct '85.
■ CD . . . . . . . . . . . . . . . . . . . . **WD 72407**
Motown / Jan '89.

## MOTOWN HITS OF GOLD VOL.8.

**Tracks:** Upside down: *Ross, Diana* / Behind the groove: *Marie, Teena* / My old piano: *Ross, Diana* / I'm coming out: *Ross, Diana* / Being with you: *Robinson, Smokey* / It's my turn: *Ross, Diana* / One day in your life: *Jackson, Michael* / I've never been to me: *Charlene* / Endless love: *Ross, Diana & Lionel Richie* / All night long: *Mary Jane Girls* / Somebody's watching me / Farewell my summer love: *Jackson, Michael* / Let it all blow: *Dazz Band* / Treat her like a lady: *Temptations* / Nightshift: *Commodores* / Rhythm of the night: *DeBarge*.
■ LP . . . . . . . . . . . . . . . . . . . . **WL 72408**
■ MC. . . . . . . . . . . . . . . . . . . . **WK 72408**
Motown / Oct '85.
■ CD . . . . . . . . . . . . . . . . . . . . **WD 72408**
Motown / Jan '89.

## MOTOWN HITS OF GOLD VOLS 1-8.

**Tracks:** Not Advised.
**CD Set** . . . . . . . . . . . . . . . . . . **WD 72401.8**
Motown / Feb '89 / PolyGram.

## MOTOWN IN MOTION.

**Tracks:** Dancin' in the street: *Reeves, Martha* / It's the same old song: *Four Tops* / You ain't livin' till you're lovin': *Gaye, Marvin & Tammi Terrell* / What does it take (to win your love): *Walker, Junior & The All Stars* / Upside down: *Ross, Diana* / All night long: *Mary Jane Girls* / Love hangover: *Ross, Diana* / Behind the groove: *James, J.* / Rhythm of the night: *DeBarge* / Little bitty pretty one: *Jackson Five* / Skywriter: *Jacksons* / Let's get serious: *Jackson, Jermaine* / Uptight: *Wonder, Stevie* / Just walk in my shoes: *Knight, Gladys & The Pips* / Rockin' robin: *Jackson, Michael* / Nathan Jones: *Supremes* / Papa was a rollin' stone: *Temptations* / Don't look any further: *Edwards, Dennis* / Somebody's watching me: *Rockwell* / Give to me baby: *James, Rick* / Let it all blow: *Dazz Band* / Too busy thinking about my baby: *Gaye, Marvin* / Keep on truckin': *Kendricks, Eddie* / Superstar: *Temptations*.
■ CD . . . . . . . . . . . . . . . . . . . . **NCD 3410**
■ LP . . . . . . . . . . . . . . . . . . . . **NE 1410**
■ MC. . . . . . . . . . . . . . . . . . . . **CE 2410**
K-Tel / Oct '88.

## MOTOWN LOVE SONGS.

**Tracks:** My cherie amour: *Wonder, Stevie* / Endless love: *Ross, Diana & Lionel Richie* / Never can say goodbye: *Jackson Five* / Being with you: *Robinson, Smokey* / Oh no: *Commodores* / How sweet it is (to be loved by you): *Gaye, Marvin* / Your precious love: *Gaye, Marvin & Tammi Terrell* / If you really love me: *Wonder, Stevie* / Still: *Commodores* / Cruisin': *Robinson, Smokey* / Three times a lady: *Commodores*.
■ LP . . . . . . . . . . . . . . . . . . . . **TMS 3509**
■ MC. . . . . . . . . . . . . . . . . . . . **TMC 3509**
Motown / '82.
■ CD . . . . . . . . . . . . . . . . . . . . **WD 72169**
■ LP . . . . . . . . . . . . . . . . . . . . **WL 72169**
■ MC. . . . . . . . . . . . . . . . . . . . **WK 72169**
Motown / May '84.

## MOTOWN MALE GROUPS.

**Tracks:** Not Advised.
■ LP . . . . . . . . . . . . . . . . . . . . **WL 72171**
■ MC. . . . . . . . . . . . . . . . . . . . **WK 72171**
Motown / Apr '84.

## MOTOWN MEMORIES.

**Tracks:** 6 by 6 / Agent double O soul / Take some time out for love / What's easy for two is so hard for one / You're not an ordinary girl / This old heart of mine / Something about you / I can't help myself / Festival time / Little darling / Helpless / Lonely lonely girl am I / Back street / Nothing's too good for my baby / Whole lot of shakin' in my heart / All turned on.
■ LP . . . . . . . . . . . . . . . . . . . . **STML 11200**
Tamla Motown / Feb '72.

## MOTOWN MEMORIES.

**Tracks:** Come and get these memories: *Reeves, Martha & The Vandellas* / Little more love: *Weston, Kim* / Jamie: *Holland, Eddie* / Please Mr. Postm *Marvelettes* / Put yourself in my place: *Elgins* / always love you: *Detroit Spinners* / I want to go b there again: *Clark, Chris* / Who wouldn't love a m like that: *John, Mable* / Do you love me: *Contou* Together till the end of time: *Holloway, Brenda* / E in the hand: *Velvelettes* / Your love is wonder *Littles, Hattie* / Function at the junction: *Long, Sho* / Come on and see me: *Terrell, Tammi* / You re got a hold on me: *Robinson, Smokey & The Mirac* / Breathtakin' guy: *Ross, Diana & The Supremes*
■ LP . . . . . . . . . . . . . . . . . . . . **TML 11**
Tamla Motown / Jan '68.

## MOTOWN MEMORIES, VOL.1 (Whe Were You When).

**Tracks:** Do you love me: *Contours* / Your standby: *Mary Wells* / He was really saying so thing: *Velvelettes* / Don't mess with Bill: *Marvele* / It takes two: *Gaye, Marvin & Kim Weston* / Jim Mack: *Reeves, Martha* / Malinda: *Taylor, Bobb The Vancouvers* / What does it take (to win y love): *Walker, Junior & The All Stars* / If I were y woman: *Knight, Gladys & The Pips* / Floy joy: *premes* / Trouble Man: *Gaye, Marvin* / Hey girl (I your style) / Do it baby: *Miracles* / Shoeshine B *Kendricks, Eddie*.
■ CD . . . . . . . . . . . . . . . . . . . . **WD 72**
Motown / Jun '88.

## MOTOWN MEMORIES, VOL.2 (Whe Were You When).

**Tracks:** What's so good about goodbye / One w really loves you: *Wells, Mary* / Come and get th memories: *Reeves, Martha* / Every little bit hu *Holloway, Brenda* / Since I lost my baby: *Ter tations* / Standing in the shadows of love: *Four To* Please return your love to me: *Temptations* / Th eyes: *Walker, Junior & The All Stars* / Bells: *Or nals* / If you really love me: *Wonder, Stevie* / I war be where you are: *Jackson, Michael* / Tell her lo has felt the need: *Kendricks, Eddie* / Walk away fr love: *Ruffin, David* / Don't leave me this way / can't turn me off (in the middle of turnin' me c *High Inergy*.
■ CD . . . . . . . . . . . . . . . . . . . . **WD 72**
Motown / Jun '88.

## MOTOWN MEMORIES, VOL.3.

**Tracks:** No love: *John, Mable* / You made a fool of me: *John, Mable* / Satan's blues: *Walker, Juni* Breadwinner: *Ward, Sam* / Part time love: *Wa Sam* / Buttered popcorn: *Vows* / Same thing: *Pa G* / That's no lie: *Parks, G* / My daily prayer: *Milbu A* / Come on home: *Darnells* / Soul stomp: *Van D Earl* / I'm walkin': *Long, Shorty* / I call it pretty mu but the old people call it the blues: *Unknown*.
■ LP . . . . . . . . . . . . . . . . . . . . **STML 11**
Tamla Motown / May '70.

## MOTOWN PRESENTS MORE CHRIS MAS CLASSICS.

**Tracks:** Santa Claus is coming to town: *Ross, Dia & The Supremes* / White Christmas: *Temptation* One little Christmas tree: *Wonder, Stevie* / Christm every day: *Robinson, Smokey & The Miracles* / dolph the red nosed reindeer: *Ross, Diana & Supremes* / Have yourself a merry little Christm *Jackson, Michael & Jackson Five* / Twinkle twin little me: *Wonder, Stevie* / My Christmas tree: *Ter tations* / Noel: *Robinson, Smokey & The Miracle* Give love on Christmas day: *Jackson, Michae Jackson Five* / Christmas song (Merry Christmas you): *Temptations* / Silver bells: *Wonder, Stevi* Little drummer boy: *Jackson Five & Michael Jacks* / Joy to the world: *Ross, Diana & The Supreme* Miracles of Christmas: *Wonder, Stevie* / Childre Christmas song: *Ross, Diana & The Supreme* Someday at Christmas: *Temptations* / Warm li home on the hill: *Wonder, Stevie* / It's Christm time: *Robinson, Smokey & The Miracles* / Sil night: *Temptations*.
CD. . . . . . . . . . . . . . . . . . . . **530 23**
MC. . . . . . . . . . . . . . . . . . . . **530 23**
Polydor / Nov '93 / PolyGram.

## MOTOWN RARE GROOVES.

**Tracks:** Scratchin': *Magic Disco Machine* / Can I a witness: *Randolph, Barbara* / Here I am ba *Marvelettes* / Mr. fix-it man: *Sisters Love* / E weather: *Supremes* / Share your love: *Ware, Leo* Heavy love affair: *Gaye, Marvin* / You can't judg book by its cover: *Wonder, Stevie* / Salsa boo *Nolen & Crossley* / Rock and roll, pop and s *Ozone* / Body talk: *Kendricks, Eddie* / Try it yo like it: *Hutch, Willie* / 'T' plays it cool (instrument *Gaye, Marvin* / Whatever you got, I want: *Jacks Michael & The Jackson Five*.
■ LP . . . . . . . . . . . . . . . . . . . . **ZL 72**
■ MC. . . . . . . . . . . . . . . . . . . . **ZK 72**
Motown / Aug '88.

## OTOWN SINGS THE BEATLES.

acks: Hard day's night: *Ross, Diana & The Su-*
*emes* / Eleanor Rigby: *Four Tops* / We can work it
t: *Wonder, Stevie* / Hey Jude: *Temptations* / Yes-
day: *Gaye, Marvin* / Long and winding road: *Ross,*
*ana* / Come together: *Supremes* / She's leaving
me: *Syreeta* / You can't do that: *Ross, Diana & The*
*premes* / Fool on the hill: *Four Tops* / You really
 a hold on me: *Robinson, Smokey & The Miracles*
lease Mr. Postman: *Marvelettes* / Michelle: *Four*
*ps* / And I love her: *Robinson, Smokey & The Mi-*
*racles* / Something: *Reeves, Martha & The Van-*
*las* / Let it be: *Temptations* / I love her: *Four Tops* /
agine: *Ross, Diana* / My love: *Walker, Junior* / We
eet lord: *Starr, Edwin* / Money (that's what I want):
ong, Barrett.

| | |
|---|---|
| MC. | WK 72348 |
| LP | WL 72348 |
| . | NSPCD 500 |
| . | NSPLP 500 |
| . | NSPMC 500 |

nnoisseur Collection / Feb '91 / Pinnacle.

## OTOWN SOLO STARS.

acks: Not Advised.

| | |
|---|---|
| LP | WL 72172 |
| MC. | WK 72172 |

town / Apr '84.

## OTOWN SONGBOOK.

cks: Not Advised.

| | |
|---|---|
| . | VSOPCD 180 |
| . | VSOPMC 180 |

nnoisseur Collection / Jan '93 / Pinnacle.

## OTOWN SOUND VOL. 1.

acks: Gotta hold on to this feeling / Doggone right /
raham, Martin and John / Breathtaking guy /
at's how heartaches are made / Bells / We'll have
made / Stay a little longer / This used to be the
ne of Johnny Mae / Touch / Whatcha gonna do /
deep within you / Cheating is telling on you /
eet darlin'.

| | |
|---|---|
| LP | STML 11217 |

mla Motown / Feb '73.

## OTOWN STORY.

cks: Not Advised.

| | |
|---|---|
| LP Set | TMSP 1130 |

mla Motown / Mar '72.

## OTOWN STORY, THE (The First 25 ars, Volumes 1 - 3).

acks: Please Mr. Postman: *Marvelettes* / Baby I'm
real: *Originals* / Keep on truckin' / Two lovers:
lls, Mary / Dancing machine: *Commodores* / Shop
und: *Robinson, Smokey & The Miracles* / You've
ally got a hold on me: *Robinson, Smokey & The*
*racles* / Tracks of my tears: *Robinson, Smokey &*
okey & The Miracles / Baby baby don't cry:
binson, Smokey & The Miracles / Super freak:
mes, Rick / Baby I need your loving: *Four Tops* / I
n't help myself: *Four Tops* / Fingertips: *Wonder,*
 I was made to love her: *Wonder, Stevie* / For
ce in my life: *Wonder, Stevie* / You're all I need to
 by: *Terrell, Tammi & Marvin Gaye* / Love ma-
ne: Miracles / Three times a lady: *Commodores* /
uisin': *Robinson, Smokey* / Heatwave: *Reeves,*
rtha / Dancing in the street: *Reeves, Martha* /
where to run: *Reeves, Martha* / Let it whip: *Dazz*
nd / Truly: *Richie, Lionel* / My girl: *Temptations* / I
sh it would rain: *Temptations* / What does it take
win your love) / Let me tickle your fancy: *Jackson,*
rmaine / Endless love: *Ross, Diana & Lionel Ri-*
e / Where did our love go: *Ross, Diana & The*
e Supremes / Love child: *Ross, Diana & The*
premes / Stop in the name of love: *Ross, Diana &*
he Supremes / I hear a symphony: *Ross, Diana &*
e Supremes / You can't hurry love: *Ross, Diana &*
e Supremes / Reflections: *Ross, Diana & The*
premes / Every little bit hurts: *Holloway, Brenda* /
n I get a witness: *Gaye, Marvin* / Stubborn kind of
ow: *Gaye, Marvin* / How sweet it is (to be loved by
u): *Gaye, Marvin* / I heard it through the grape-
e: *Gaye, Marvin* / I'm gonna make you love me:
premes and Temptations / Intro / Bad girl: *Robin-*
n, Smokey & The Miracles / Money (that's what I
nt): *Strong, Barrett* / Bye bye baby: *Wells, Mary* /
you love me: *Contours* / Way you do the things
u do: *Temptations* / My guy: *Wells, Mary* / Shot-
n: *Walker, Junior & The All Stars* / I'll be doggone:
ve, Marvin / This old heart of mine: *Isley Brothers*
eauty is only skin deep: *Temptations* / What
comes of the broken hearted: *Ruffin, Jimmy* /
ach out I'll be there: *Four Tops* / Jimmy Mack:
eves, Martha / Cloud 9: *Temptations* / My world
ded (the moment you left me): *Ruffin, Jimmy* / I
nt you back: *Jackson Five* / Up the ladder to the
f: *Supremes* / Signed, sealed, delivered (I'm

yours): *Wonder, Stevie* / War: *Starr, Edwin* / Ain't no
mountain high enough: *Ross, Diana* / I'll be there:
*Jackson Five* / What's going on: *Gaye, Marvin* / Ben:
*Jackson, Michael* / Just my imagination (running
away with me): *Temptations* / You are the sunshine
of my life: *Wonder, Stevie* / Papa was a rollin' stone:
*Temptations* / Neither one of us: *Knight, Gladys &*
*The Pips* / Let's get it on: *Gaye, Marvin* / Don't leave
me this way: *Houston, Thelma* / Sir Duke: *Wonder,*
*Stevie* / Upside down: *Ross, Diana* / With you I'm
born again: *Preston, Billy & Syreeta* / Being with
you: *Robinson, Smokey* / All night long: *Richie, Lio-*
nel / Somebody's watching me: *Rockwell* / Rhythm of
the night: *DeBarge* / In my house: *Mary Jane Girls* /
Say you, say me: *Richie, Lionel* / Do you know where
you're going to (Closing theme from 'Mahogany'):
Instrumental.

| | |
|---|---|
| ■ CD Set. | ZD 72137 |
| ■ LP Set. | ZL 72137 |
| ■ MC Set | ZK 72137 |

Motown / Feb '87.

## MOTOWN STORY, THE (The First 25 Years).

Tracks: Not Advised.

| | |
|---|---|
| ■ LP Set. | TMSP 6019 |
| MC Set | CTMSP 6019 |

Motown / Nov '83 / PolyGram.

## MOTOWN SUPERSTARS SING.

Tracks: Not Advised.

| | |
|---|---|
| ■ LP | STMS 5100 |

Motown / Nov '83.

## MOTOWN ULTIMATE HITS COLLECTION.

Tracks: Not Advised.

| | |
|---|---|
| CD. | .530465-2 |
| MC. | .530465-4 |

Motown / Nov '94 / PolyGram.

## MOTOWN'S BIGGEST POP HITS.

Tracks: I heard it through the grapevine: *Gaye, Mar-*
vin / I'll be there: *Jackson Five* / Upside down: *Ross,*
*Diana* / Baby love: *Ross, Diana & The Supremes* /
Ain't no mountain high enough: *Ross, Diana* / War:
*Starr, Edwin* / Fingertips (part 2): *Wonder, Stevie* /
Let's get it on: *Gaye, Marvin* / Three times a lady:
*Commodores* / Love child: *Ross, Diana & The Su-*
*premes* / I can't get next to you: *Temptations* / I can't
help myself: *Four Tops* / Tears of a clown: *Robinson,*
*Smokey & The Miracles* / Keep on truckin' / Where
did our love go: *Ross, Diana & The Supremes* / ABC:
*Jackson Five* / Come see about me: *Ross, Diana &*
*The Supremes* / Just my imagination (running away
with me): *Temptations*.

| | |
|---|---|
| ■ CD. | WD 72450 |

Motown / Oct '87.

## MOTOWN'S GREATEST LOVE SONGS.

Tracks: You're all I need to get by: *Gaye, Marvin &*
*Tammi Terrell* / I'm gonna make you love me: *Ross,*
*Diana & The Supremes & The Temptations* / My
cherie amour: *Wonder, Stevie* / It's all in the game:
*Four Tops* / I'll say forever my love: *Ruffin, Jimmy* /
Ain't no mountain high enough: *Ross, Diana* / Still
water (love): *Four Tops* / It's wonderful (To be loved
by you): *Ruffin, Jimmy* / I'll be there: *Jackson Five* /
Just my imagination (running away with me): *Temp-*
tations / Got to be me: *Jackson, Michael* / I second
that emotion: *Robinson, Smokey & The Miracles* /
Look of love: *Knight, Gladys & The Pips* / All of my
life: *Ross, Diana* / You are everything: *Ross, Diana &*
*Marvin Gaye* / Three times a lady: *Commodores* /
With you I'm born again: *Preston, Billy & Syreeta* /
Being with you: *Robinson, Smokey* / Endless love:
*Ross, Diana & Lionel Richie* / Let's get it on: *Gaye,*
*Marvin*.

| | |
|---|---|
| ■ LP | 530 006-1 |
| MC. | 530 006-4 |

Motown / Oct '92 / PolyGram.

## MOTOWNS GREATEST HITS.

Tracks: Not Advised.

| | |
|---|---|
| MC. | STAC 2375 |
| ■ CD. | TCD 2375 |
| ■ LP. | STAR 2375 |

Telstar/Ronco / Nov '90.

## MOVE, GROOVE & NIGHTCLUBBING.

Tracks: Not Advised.

| | |
|---|---|
| ■ Double LP. | MOVE 1 |

Polydor / Jan '83.

## MOVE INTO SOUL PART 1.

Tracks: Not Advised.

| | |
|---|---|
| ■ LP | MVLP 4 |

Move / Sep '85.

## MOVE INTO SOUL PART 2.

Tracks: Not Advised.

| | |
|---|---|
| ■ LP | MVLP 5 |

Move / Nov '85.

## MOVE INTO SOUL PART 3.

Tracks: Not Advised.

| | |
|---|---|
| ■ LP | MVLP 7 |

Move / Jan '86.

## MOVE INTO SOUL PART 4.

Tracks: Not Advised.

| | |
|---|---|
| ■ LP | MVLP 9 |

Move / Feb '86.

## MOVE INTO SOUL PART 5.

Tracks: Not Advised.

| | |
|---|---|
| ■ LP | MVLP 11 |

Move / Mar '86.

## MOVE INTO SOUL PART 6.

Tracks: Not Advised.

| | |
|---|---|
| ■ LP | MVLP 13 |

Move / Apr '86.

## MOVIN' ON.

Tracks: Introduce me to love: *Absolute (1)* / Overjoy:
*S'Mone, Guy* / It's over: *Perfect Taste* / Searching:
*China Black* / Falling by dominoes: *Music & Mystery*
/ Keep it comin': *Jullianne* / Never gonna give you
up: *Watergates* / Takes time: *Funhill* / Bring me back:
*Drakes, Anthony* / Pushin' against the flow: *Raw*
*Stylus* / Mr Magic: *Dreaming A Dream* / Reconsider:
*Bell, Melissa*.

| | |
|---|---|
| CD. | RUCD 300 |
| ■ LP. | RULP 300 |
| MC. | RUMC 300 |

Rumour / May '92 / Pinnacle / 3MV / Sony.

## MOVIN' ON 2.

Tracks: Revival: *Girault, Martine* / Love guaranteed:
*Ferrier, Robert* / Something inside: *Deep Joy* / I want
you back: *Sinclair (1)* / Got to be you: *Koo Koo* / You
turn me on: *Everis* / Call me anytime: *FM Inc* / One
girl too late: *Pure Silk* / 2.B.A.S.1: *Ballin, Chris* /
Warm love: *Law, Joanna* / Intimate connection: *Dela-*
no, Rohan / Yes, yes, yes: *Applemountain* / Higher
love: *Naked Funk*.

| | |
|---|---|
| CD. | RUCD 301 |
| ■ LP | RULP 301 |
| MC. | RUMC 301 |

Rumour / Oct '92 / Pinnacle / 3MV / Sony.

## MOVIN' ON 3.

Tracks: Don't go walking (out that door): *Watergates*
/ Keep on giving: *B.C.A.* / Turn me on: *A Certain*
*Ratio* / What you won't do for love: *Nu Visions* / Girl
overboard: *Snowboy* / It's not alright: *Stirling*
*McLean* / No man the vibe: *Vibe feat. Delroy Pinnock*
/ Poetical love: *Fyza* / Slow & easy: *Moving In The*
*Right Direction* / Coming on to me: *Mo & Beev* / No
time for change: *Outside* / Joy is free: *Think 2wice* /
Revelation: *Simon, Vannessa* / Oh happy day: *Real*
*System*.

| | |
|---|---|
| CD. | RUCD 302 |
| ■ LP | RULP 302 |
| MC. | RUMC 302 |

Rumour / Jun '91 / Pinnacle / 3MV / Sony.

## MOVIN' ON 4.

Tracks: I don't want it: *Opaz* / Rebirth: *Mighty Truth* /
Ain't gonna walk in your shadow no more: *Do'reen* /
You can depend on me: *Clarke, Rick* / So what: *Raw*
*Groove* / Mr. Beautiful: *Anuforo* / What's on your
mind: *Rose, J.B* / Love forever: *Deluxe* / One step (at
a time): *Rose, Mary* / You bring me joy: *Miss Hailey* /
Loveride: *Scott, Samantha* / Ain't no sunshine: *Fyza*.

| | |
|---|---|
| CD. | RULCD 304 |
| LP. | RULP 304 |
| MC. | RULMC 304 |

Rumour / Oct '93 / Pinnacle / 3MV / Sony.

## MOVIN' ON 5.

Tracks: Desire: *Desire* / Chill me: *Fresh N Funky* / In
the mood: *Raw To The Core* / Underhanded: *Fokus* /
Last chance: *Diplomats (1)* / Runaway love: *Serious*
*Rope* / Highwire: *Players* / Say yeah: *Izit* / Don't rush:
*Fresh Cut* / Oooh with you: *Kleeer* / Blameless:
*Malaya* / You're telling me lies: *Taylor, Justine*.

| | |
|---|---|
| CD. | RULCD 305 |
| LP. | RULP 305 |
| MC. | RULMC 305 |

Rumour / Apr '94 / Pinnacle / 3MV / Sony.

## MOVING ON UP.

Tracks: I get what I want: *Lasalle, Denise* / Choosing
you: *Williams, Lenny* / Please don't run from me:
*Clinton, George* / My life is so wonderful (when
you're around): *Dells* / Ooh baby: *Porter, Nolan* / I
got a bone to pick with you: *Andrews, Ruby* / It's all
over: *Mann, Charles* / I'll be your forever more: *Love*
*Unlimited Orchestra* / I only get this feeling: *Jackson,*
*Chuck* / I thought you were mine: *Natural Four* / Just
can't get you out of my mind: *Four Tops* / Fish ain't
bitin': *Dozier, Lamont* / When the bottom falls out:
*Perkins, Ike* / Where have you been: *Carlton, Carl*.

511

■ LP . . . . . . . . . . . . . . . . . . . . . . . . KENT 013
Kent / Mar '84.

## MR JOE'S JAMBALAYA.

**Tracks:** Beverly baby: *Allen & Allen* / Ooh poo pah doo: *Hill, Jessie* / Lottie mo: *Dorsey, Lee* / Over you: *Neville, Aaron* / Mother-in-law: *Doe, Ernie K.* / Mudd: *Montrell, Roy* / Always naggin': *Del-Royals* / I need money: *Diamond, Lee* / I like it like that: *Kenner, Chris* / All these things: *Neville, Art* / It will stand: *Showmen* / New kind of love: *Harper, Willie* / Everything happens at night: *August, Joseph 'Mr. Google Eyes'* / I'm gonna put some hurt on you: *Lewis, Raymond*.
■ Double LP. . . . . . . . . . . . . . . . . . CDX 26
■ MC. . . . . . . . . . . . . . . . . . . . . .TCCDX 26
Charly / Jun '88.

## MUSIC CITY SOUL (SUN RECORDINGS).

**Tracks:** Not Advised.
■ LP . . . . . . . . . . . . . . . . . . . . . CR 30107
Charly / Jun '76.

## MUSICAL FREEDOM - CLASSIC GARAGE VOL.2.

**Tracks:** Musical freedom (Club mix): *Adeva* / Alright: *Urban Soul* / Do you want it right now: *Degrees Of Motion* / Let the rain come down: *Intense* / Closer: *Mr. Fingers* / Follow me: *Al Y Us* / Give you: *Djaimin* / Loves got a hold on me: *Zoo Experience* / I'm the one for you: *Adeva* / Helpless: *Urbanized Featuring Silvano* / Motherland: *Tribal House* / Love itch: *Roche, Sonya* / One day: *Tyrrel Corporation* / Baby love: *Watford, Michael*.
CD. . . . . . . . . . . . . . . . . . . . . . . . CTCD 31
■ LP . . . . . . . . . . . . . . . . . . . . . . .CTLP 31
■ MC. . . . . . . . . . . . . . . . . . . . . . .CTTC 31
Cool Tempo / Nov '92.

## MUTANT DISCO.

**Tracks:** Me no pop I: *Coati Mundi* / Cowboys and gangsters / Contort yourself: *White, James* / Maladie d'amour / Wheel me out.
■ LP . . . . . . . . . . . . . . . . . . . . . .ISSP 4001
Island / May '81.

# N

## NAME OF THE GAME.

**Tracks:** Ride sally ride: *Green, Al* / Trouble is my name: *Hines, Don* / Aretha, sing one for me: *Jackson, George (1)* / Belle: *Green, Al* / Mack the knife: *Emmons, Buddy* / Patricia: *Jackson, George (1)* / Judy: *Green, Al* / Buster Browne: *Mitchell, Willie* / She's Miss Wonderful: *McClure, Bobby* / Jesus is waiting: *Green, Al* / Teenie's dream: *Mitchell, Willie* / Sunshine (isn't that your name): *Carter, Darryl* / Georgia boy: *Green, Al* / Please Mr.Foreman: *Joe L* / Amazing grace: *Green, Al* / Mimi: *Green, Al* / Miss Betty Green: *Big Lucky Carter* / Doctor love power: *Peebles, Ann* / Eli's game: *Green, Al*.
CD. . . . . . . . . . . . . . . . . . . . . . . . HILOCD 8
Demon / Mar '94 / Pinnacle / A.D.A. Distribution.

## NEVER BEFORE RELEASED MASTERS (From Motowns Brightest Stars).

**Tracks:** Not Advised.
■ LP . . . . . . . . . . . . . . . . . . . . . . WL 72425
■ MC. . . . . . . . . . . . . . . . . . . . . . WK 72425
Tamla Motown / Jun '86.

## NEW ORLEANS HIT STORY, THE (Twenty Years Of Big Easy Hits, 1950-1970).

**Tracks:** Not Advised.
CD Set . . . . . . . . . . . . . . . . . . CDINSD 5073
Charly / Jun '93 / Charly.

## NEW ORLEANS LADIES.

**Tracks:** Not Advised.
CD. . . . . . . . . . . . . . . . . . . . . . . . . CD 2078
■ LP . . . . . . . . . . . . . . . . . . . . ROUNDER 2078
MC. . . . . . . . . . . . . . . . . . . . . .ROUNDER 2078C
Rounder / '88 / Roots Records / C.M. Distribution / Topic Records / A.D.A. Distribution / Direct Distribution.

## NEW ORLEANS R'N'B 1949-67.

**Tracks:** Not Advised.
■ LP . . . . . . . . . . . . . . . . . . . . . . . KK 7403
Krazy Kat / '88.

## NEW ORLEANS RHYTHM & BLUES.

**Tracks:** Not Advised.
■ LP . . . . . . . . . . . . . . . . . . . . . . . . . . 1019
MC. . . . . . . . . . . . . . . . . . . . . . . . . . 1019 TC
Maison De Soul / '87 / Swift.

## NEW ORLEANS RHYTHM & BLUES OFFICIAL ANNIVERSARY.

**Tracks:** Not Advised.
■ LP . . . . . . . . . . . . . . . . . . . . . . . SNTF 937
Sonet / Aug '85.

## NEW ORLEANS RHYTHM KINGS.

**Tracks:** Not Advised.
CD. . . . . . . . . . . . . . . . . . . . . . . . VILCD 0042
Village Jazz / Sep '92 / Target Sales & Marketing / Jazz Music.

## NEW YORK CITY SOUL.

**Tracks:** I'm on my way: *Parrish, Dean* / Friends and lovers: *Lands, Hoagy* / Next in line: *Lands, Hoagy* / Detroit sounds: *Megatons* / You're the love of my life: *Jones, Brenda Lee* / I've gotta hear it from you: *Jackson Brothers* / I'm gone: *Sharae, Billy* / Beachcomber: *Gibson, Johnny* / Keep the boy happy: *Chiffons* / Yes I love you baby: *Dynamics* / Cover girl: *Spencer, Carl* / Beautiful music: *Fields, Lily & Hoagy Lands* / When I'm in your arms: *Casualeers* / Call on me: *Law, Johnny Four* / Silly little girl: *Dean & Jean* / Proud soul heritage: *Hebb, Bobby*.
■ LP . . . . . . . . . . . . . . . . . . . . . . . KENT 043
Kent / Aug '85.

## NEW YORK R 'N' B.

**Tracks:** Not Advised.
■ LP . . . . . . . . . . . . . . . . . . . . . . . . PY 1817
Magpie / Jul '79.

## NEW YORK ROCK & SOUL REVUE.

**Tracks:** Intro / Madison time / Knock on wood / Green flower street / Shakey ground / At last / Lonely teardrops / Drowning in the sea of love / Driftin' blues / Chain lightning / Groovin' / Minute by minute / People got to be free / Pretzel logic / Madison reprise.
■ CD. . . . . . . . . . . . . . . . . . . . . . 7599244232
■ MC. . . . . . . . . . . . . . . . . . . . . . 7599244234
WEA / Nov '91.

## NIGHT LIFE II (More Classic Soul Tracks).

**Tracks:** Fame: *Cara, Irene* / When smokey sings: *ABC* / Caravan of love: *Isley-Jasper-Isley* / Finest: *S.O.S. Band* / If you were here tonight: *O'Neal, Alexander* / Whole town's laughing at me: *Pendergrass, Teddy* / Do what you do: *Jackson, Jermaine* / Rain: *Jones, Oran 'Juice'* / Who's zoomin' who: *Franklin, Aretha* / Maniac (Not available on CD.): *Sembello, Michael* / She's strange (Not available on CD.): *Cameo (1)* / Who'd she coo (Not available on CD.): *Ohio Players* / Oops upside your head (Not available on CD.): *Gap Band* / Living in the UK (Not available on CD.): *Shakatak* / See the day: *Lee, Dee C.* / After the love has gone (Not available on CD.): *Earth, Wind & Fire* / Forever, for always, for love: *Vandross, Luther* / Broken heart can mend (Not available on CD.): *O'Neal, Alexander* / Shake you down: *Abbott, Gregory* / Summer breeze (Not available on CD.): *Isley Brothers* / Walking in the rain (with the one I love): *Love Unlimited Orchestra* / Midnight train to Georgia: *Knight, Gladys & The Pips* / Sexual healing: *Gaye, Marvin* / Lean on me: *Withers, Bill* / Saturday love: *Cherrelle & Alexander O'Neal* / Taste of bitter love (Not available on CD.): *Knight, Gladys* / Stop to love (Not available on CD.): *Vandross, Luther* / Livin' in America (Not available on CD.): *Brown, James*.
■ CD. . . . . . . . . . . . . . . . . . . . . . . .STDCD 22
■ Double LP. . . . . . . . . . . . . . . . . . . . STDLP 22
■ MC. . . . . . . . . . . . . . . . . . . . . . . STDMC 22
Masterpiece / Feb '89.

## NITEFLITE.

**Tracks:** Shiver: *Benson, George* / Shake you down: *Abbott, Gregory* / Always: *Atlantic Starr* / Sweet love: *Baker, Anita* / If you were here tonight: *O'Neal, Alexander* / Almaz: *Crawford, Randy* / Loving you / Give me the reason: *Vandross, Luther* / Criticize: *O'Neal, Alexander* / Weekend Girl: *S.O.S. Band* / So amazing: *Vandross, Luther* / How 'bout us: *Champaign* / Rock with you: *Jackson, Michael* / Show Me The Way: *Bell, Regina* / Secret Lovers: *Atlantic Starr* / One More Chance: *Jacksons*.
■ CD. . . . . . . . . . . . . . . . . . . . . . MOODCD 4
■ LP . . . . . . . . . . . . . . . . . . . . . . . . .MOOD 4
■ MC. . . . . . . . . . . . . . . . . . . . . . . . MOODC 4
Epic / Apr '88.

## NITEFLITE 2.

**Tracks:** Roses are red: *Mac Band* / Saturday lo *Cherrelle & Alexander O'Neal* / Any love: *Vandro Luther* / Come into my life: *Sims, Joyce* / Just way you like it: *S.O.S. Band* / Ain't no sunshi *Withers, Bill* / Can't stay away from you: *Estef Gloria* / Rock me tonight (for old time's sake): *Ja son, Freddie* / Stop to love: *Vandross, Luther* / Wis ing on a star: *Rose Royce* / After the love has go *Earth, Wind & Fire* / Never knew love like th *O'Neal, Alexander* / Piano in the dark: *Russell, Bre da* / Why (can't we live together): *Sade* / Tonigh celebrate my love: *Flack, Roberta & Peabo Bryso* Sexual healing: *Gaye, Marvin*.
CD. . . . . . . . . . . . . . . . . . . . . . . . . MOOD C
■ LP . . . . . . . . . . . . . . . . . . . . . . . . . .MOO
MC. . . . . . . . . . . . . . . . . . . . . . . . . . .MOOD
CBS / Apr '89 / Sony.

## NITEFLITE 3.

**Tracks:** Being with you: *Robinson, Smokey* / Just good to me: *S.O.S. Band* / I need your lovin': *W liams, Alyson* / Always and forever: *Heatwave* / H me tighter: *Griffin, Billy* / Me and Mrs. Jones: *Pa Billy* / Just my imagination: *Temptations* / Ro witcha: *Brown, Bobby (1)* / New York eyes: *Nicole Timmy Thomas* / Broken heart can mend: *O'Ne Alexander* / Juicy fruit: *Mtume* / All I want is forev *Taylor/Belle* / Never too much: *Vandross, Luthe* Between the sheets: *Isley Brothers* / Lily was he *Stewart, David A & Candy Dulfer*.
■ LP . . . . . . . . . . . . . . . . . . . . . . . . . MOOD
■ MC. . . . . . . . . . . . . . . . . . . . . . . . . MOODC
■ CD. . . . . . . . . . . . . . . . . . . . . . . . MOODCD
Epic / May '90.

## NITEFLITE/NITEFLITE 2.

**Tracks:** Not Advised.
CD Set . . . . . . . . . . . . . . . . . . . . . . . . 46625
MC. . . . . . . . . . . . . . . . . . . . . . . . . . . 46625
■ Double LP. . . . . . . . . . . . . . . . . . . . . . 46625
Epic / Dec '89.

## NITTY GRITTY.

**Tracks:** This man in love: *New Wanderers* / getting tired: *Carlettes* / Lover: *De Lites* / I need yo love: *Masters* / I know I'm in love with you: *By George 'Duke'* / That's what I want: *McGowan, Sy* / Oh oh oh what a love this is: *Revlons* / Neverth less: *Andrews, Lee & The Hearts* / You're not kind: *Durante, Paula* / You better think it over: *D Shons* / He's that way sometimes: *Wells, Bobby* She said goodbye: *Hambric, Billy* / I can't stand lose you: *Chandler, E.J.* / Elijah rockin' with so *Jacobs, Hank* / Heartbreakin' time: *Little John* You're gonna pay: *Rivingtons* / Lighten up ba *Karim, Ty* / I'm so glad: *Neal, Robert* / I was born love you: *Hunter, Herbert* / Love's like quicksa *Wynns, Sandy* / He's a flirt: *Sequins* / All of my li *Detroit Soul* / I need your love (2): *Chaumonts* / wee let it me babe: *Evans, Karl* / Cherry ba *Millionaires* / I'm standing: *Lumley, Rufus* / Try little harder: *Fi Dels* / Like a bee: *Spidells* / You g me in the palm of your hand: *Richardson, Dona Lee* / There's no you: *Occasions*.
CD. . . . . . . . . . . . . . . . . . . . . . . . . GSCD
Goldmine / Sep '93 / Vital Distribution.

## NON-STOP DISCO CHARTBUSTERS.

**Tracks:** Brazil / My way / Soul Dracula / Baby do y wanna bump / Disco hop / Rock on brother / Am amor / Chariot / Undecided love / Pretty maid / Ge together / Please love me again.
■ LP . . . . . . . . . . . . . . . . . . . . . . . . . CRLP 5
Creole / Jan '77.

## NORTHERN FLOORSHAKERS.

**Tracks:** Hide nor hair: *Grant, Earl* / Soul self satisfa tion: *Jackson, Earl* / Call me: *Bishop, Eddie* / Som thing beautiful: *Mandolph, Magaret* / Gonna be a t thing: *Sapphires* / Like Adam and Eve: *Reflectio (2)* / Up and over: *Traynor, Jay* / Darkest days: *Le Jackie* / I'm gonna love you a long long time: *Patti The Emblems* / I'm not built that way: *Hesitations* You've been a long time coming: *Braithwaite, M chell* / Pennygold: *Stevens, Lindy* / Determinatio *Parrish, Dean* / All of a sudden: *Williams, Jeanett*
■ LP . . . . . . . . . . . . . . . . . . . . . . . . . KENT 0
Kent / Oct '83.

## NORTHERN SOUL DANCE PARTY.

**Tracks:** That beatin' rhythm: *Temple, Richard* Goose pimples: *Scott, Shirley J.* / My sugar bab *Clarke, Connie* / Double cookin': *Checkerboa Squares* / Do the philly dog: *Olympics* / Not me bab *Silhouettes* / Yes I love you baby: *Dynamics* / Eddie my name: *Holman, Eddie* / Countdown: *Tempos* Going to a happening: *Neal, Tommy* / Temptati walk: *Lee, Jackie* / I'm satisfied with you: *Furys* There's nothing else to say: *Incredibles* / My lit girl: *Garrett, Bobby* / I got the fever: *Creation (3* What's the matter baby: *Reynolds, L.J.* / Let's cop

512

■ DELETE

groove: *Wells, Bobby* / Get on your knees: *Los Canarios* / I can't help myslef: *Ross, Johnny* / Earthquake: *Lynn, Bobbi* / Our love is in the pocket: *Banks, Darren* / Blowing my mind to pieces: *Relf, Bob*.
**CD** . . . . . . . . . . . . . . . . . . . . . . . . **GSCD 046**
Goldmine / Jul '94 / Vital Distribution.

## NORTHERN SOUL FEVER.

**Tracks:** Manifesto: *Case Of Tyme* / My sweet baby: *Puzzles* / No ifs, no ands, no buts: *Young, Mae* / Talking eyes: *Beatty, Pamela* / I don't want to hear it: *Exits* / Very strong on you: *Greer, Cortez* / Girl every guy should know: *Carrington, Sunny* / Bring me all your heartaches: *Beavers, Jackie* / Don't you need a boy like me: *Carlton, Carl* / Broken hearted lover: *Tojo* / I can hear you crying: *Hill, Eddie* / Try my love: *Toni & the Showmen* / In my life: *Carr, Linda* / This heart these hands: *Wells, Billy* / Just do the best you can: *Duke & Leonard* / Ain't that love enough: *Atkins, Larry* / Bad brought the good: *Turks* / Standing at a standstill: *Holmes, Sherlock* / Someone else's turn: *Clayton, Pat* / I ain't got nothing but the blues: *Friendly People* / Moments: *Bronzettes* / Sugar baby: *Holland, Jimmy* / Real nice: *Barnes, Johnny* / Beware a stranger: *Jones, Bobby* / I've got to face: *Heartbreakers* / Turn to me: *Chris Towns Unit* / Shield all around: *Holiday, Jimmy* / You better check yourself: *La'shell & the Shelletts* / I bear witness: *Apollo, Vince* / No time: *John & The Weirdest* / i got the fever: *Creation (1)* / You better believe me: *Reeder, Esque* / Love can't be modernised: *Tripps* / Take me back again: *Volcanos* / Why wonder: *And the echoes* / Lean on me: *Daye, Eddie* / Take back all these things: *Majesties* / Do what you wanna do: *Jindab, Paul* / Don't fight the feeling: *Newton, Bobby* / Airplane song: *Kerr, George* / Bok to Bach: *Father's Angels* / Oh yeah yeah yeah: *Carroll, Vivian* / Everybody's talking: *Baker, Joan* / Pretty as a picture: *Dillard, Moses* / You got it: *Dealers* / Too much of a good thing: *Ambassadors* / Ain't gonna cry no more: *Charles, Dave* / Little things: *Moore, Misty* / I only knew: *Mike & Ray* / Home town boy: *Williams, Sebastian* / Lonely lover: *McFarland, Jimmy* / One way lover: *Volumes* / Somebody help me: *Jenkins, Donald & the Delighters* / Let nobody love you: *Oakley, Virginia* / What do you think: *Lamarr, Chico* / I could see you now: *Sunny & The Sunliners* / With these eyes: *Fabulous Peps* / I want to be free *Admirations* / What can a man do: *Showstoppers*.
**CD Set** . . . . . . . . . . . . . . . . . . . . **GSCD 027**
Goldmine / Jan '94 / Vital Distribution.

## NORTHERN SOUL FEVER VOL.2.

**Tracks:** Trouble: *Agents* / Deeper: *Chequers* / Midnight brew: *Carter, Melvin* / Hey girl you've changed: *Rondells* / No one loves you: *Hot Cinnamon* / You don't need help (Part 1): *Garvin, Rex* / Hide out: *Hideaways* / Misery: *Strogin, Henry* / I'm where it's at: *Jades* / Case of love: *Renfro Bros.* / Love bound: *Studio Arts Strings* / Any way you want it: *Smith, Fred Orchestra* / Lonely eyes: *Elling, Melvin* / I can't stop you: *Performers* / Sugar pie honey: *Promatics* / Bounce: *Olympics* / Gotta get you back: *Mandolph, Bobby* / I'd best be going: *Vito & The Salutations* / Permanent vacation: *Sodd, Marion* / Seven days of loving: *Vanelli, Johnny* / All that's good: *Mills, Tico* / Send my baby back: *Hughes, Freddie* / (Oh oh oh) What a love this is: *King, Susan* / Actions speak louder than words: *Bounty, James* / You took my heart: *St.Clair, Kelly* / Crazy little things: *Soul-Jers* / Please don't go: *Splenders* / I'm coming apart at the seams: *Kittens Three* / Times gone by: *Music Track* / You'll have to wait: *Baby Sitters* / Those good times: *Lucky C* / Keep loving me like you do: *Hargraves, Sky* / Soulful jerk: *Rumblers (1)* / It was true: *Big Ben's Rebellion* / I can take care of myself: *Spyders* / Work at the top of my head: *Paris, Fred* / Stop along the way: *Taylor, Robby* / Elevator man: *Nelson, Roy* / Your love keeps drawing me closer: *Chandlers* / Baby you've got it: *Dell, Frank* / I didn't know I how *Constellations* / I must love you: *Wilson, Timothy* / I tempted: *Hollis, Sandy* / Love from the Far East: *Sister Four* / Look in the mirror: *Vondors* / I'll be there: *Collection & The Civics* / Beware, beware: *Compliments* / Stop (Don't give up your loving): *Two Fellows* / I'm losing you: *New People* / Don't leave this way: *Dynamites* / Light drivers: *Operator* / Love you from the bottom of my heart: *Buckner Brothers* / So what: *Carlton, Carl* / If you don't need : *Tyrone Wonder Boy* / Your money - my love: *Tom & Kitty* / (She keeps) Driving me out of my mind: *Mighty Lovers* / Open the door to your heart: *Burk, Doni* / Ain't gonna do you no harm: *New Wanderers* / Don't give me love: *Beery, Dorothy* / Some good in everything bad: *Fabulous Apollos*.
. . . . . . . . . . . . . . . . . . . . . . . . **GSCD 043**
Goldmine / Aug '94 / Vital Distribution.

## NORTHERN SOUL OF CHICAGO, THE.

**Tracks:** When I'm with my baby: *Magnetics* / Stubborn heart: *Mosley, Earnest* / In other words: *Fascinators* / Coming back girl: *C.O.D.'s* / No right to cry: *Galore, Mamie* / G.I. Joe we love you: *Fantasions* / Ain't no good: *Copney, Bobby* / You can't get away: *McCall, Johnny* / You've changed my whole life: *Farren, Charles* / It's mighty nice to know you: *Wood, Bobby 'Guitar'* / Your wish is my command: *Inspirations* / Have your fun: *Topics* / Lost in a city: *Majors* / She'll come back: *Britt, Mel* / Love bandit: *Collins, Barnabus & Kenya* / What you gonna do now: *Collins, Lashdown* / Two of a kind: *Flemons, Wade* / I'm gonna love you: *Age Of Bronze* / Don't say you love me until you do: *Maxwell, Holly* / I'm satisfied: *Gloria & the T-Arias* / Cheaper than one: *Hunt, Geraldine* / Heart of love: *Ventures* / Go-go gorilla: *Ideals* / Got to be your lover: *Profiles* / So much love: *Taylor, Robert* / Love now, pay later: *Williams, Lee Shot* / Is this really love: *Gardiner, Don*.
**CD** . . . . . . . . . . . . . . . . . . . . . . . . **GSCD 038**
Goldmine / May '94 / Vital Distribution.

## NORTHERN SOUL OF L.A. VOL.2.

**Tracks:** I thought you were: *Natural Four* / Rosie Brooks: *Moanin* / Crook his little finger: *Heyward, Ann* / They didn't know: *Goodnight, Terri* / Quicksand: *Osbourne, Kell* / You're welcome: *Jackson, June* / I'm a bashful guy: *Groovers* / Shy guy: *Mac, Bobby* / Closer together: *Ster, Eddie* / My faith: *Dockery, James* / Ain't that love enough: *Karim, Ty* / Ain't that right: *Oldfield, Bruce* / Sleepless nights: *Paris (1)* / Lost: *Darlettes* / Love shop: *Tate* / Try my love: *Dodds, Troy* / I'm still young: *Summers, Johnny* / Doctor of love: *Abram, J.D.* / Pyramid: *Soul Brother Inc.* / Ooh what you're doing: *Capitals* / I can't treat her bad: *Those Two* / Specially when: *Rumbold, Edwick* / To whom it amy concern: *Sands, Lola* / Faith, hope & trust: *Ross, Faye* / Girl you're so fine: *Angelle, Bobby* / Strain: *Little Stanley* / Ain't gonna: *Watson, Johnny 'Guitar'*.
**CD** . . . . . . . . . . . . . . . . . . . . . . . . **GSCD 039**
Goldmine / Jun '94 / Vital Distribution.

## NORTHERN SOUL STORY 1.

**Tracks:** I'm gonna get you: *Soulville All Stars* / Stick by me baby: *Salvadors* / Come on and live: *Fabulous Jades* / Sugar pie honey: *Promatics* / Day my heart stood still: *Jackson, Ollie* / Goose pimples: *Scott, Shirley J.* / Breakdown: *Millionaires* / Cross my heart: *Yvonne & The Violets* / Lady love: *Vontastics* / Don't wanna face the truth: *Radiants* / I'm where it's at: *Jades* / I didn't want to cry: *Gray, Pearlean & The Passengers* / Mind in a bind: *Epsilons* / I know what to do to satisfy you: *Robert, Roy* / Your wish is my command: *Inspirations* / Lonely lover: *McFarland, Jimmy* / Girl across the street: *Smith, Moses* / Another day: *Ascots* / Build your house on a strong foundation: *Gwen & Ray* / Love time: *Kelly Brothers* / Love's like a quicksand: *Wynns, Sandy* / I love my baby: *International GTO's* / Heave is in your arms: *Admirations* / Don't bring me down: *Dacosta, Rita* / Baby that's a groove: *Handy, Roy* / We must be doing something right: *Moody, Joan* / There's nothing else to say: *Incredibles* / There's that mountain: *Tripps* / You got it: *Dealers* / Never never (will I fall in love): *Herbs* / Job opening: *Del-Larks* / Wash and wear love: *Vernado, Lynne*.
■ **Double LP** . . . . . . . . . . . . . . . . . **LPSD 107**
**MC** . . . . . . . . . . . . . . . . . . . . . . **CPSD 107**
Soul Supply / Jan '87 / RTM / Pinnacle.

## NORTHERN SOUL STORY 10 (The Instrumentals).

**Tracks:** Not Advised.
■ **Double LP** . . . . . . . . . . . . . . . . . **LPSD 128**
Soul Supply / Jul '88.

## NORTHERN SOUL STORY 11 (Girl Groups).

**Tracks:** Not Advised.
■ **Double LP** . . . . . . . . . . . . . . . . . **LPSD 129**
Soul Supply / Jul '88.

## NORTHERN SOUL STORY 12.

**Tracks:** Not Advised.
■ **Double LP** . . . . . . . . . . . . . . . . . **LPSD 130**
Soul Supply / Jun '88.

## NORTHERN SOUL STORY 14.

**Tracks:** Not Advised.
■ **Double LP** . . . . . . . . . . . . . . . . . **LPSD 132**
Soul Supply / Oct '88.

## NORTHERN SOUL STORY 16.

**Tracks:** Not Advised.
■ **Double LP** . . . . . . . . . . . . . . . . . **LPSD 135**
Soul Supply / Apr '89.

## NORTHERN SOUL STORY 2.

**Tracks:** Hey little girl: *Del Capris* / Michael (the lover): *C.O.D.'s* / These windows: *Village Sound* / Sonny: *Cammotions* / I'm comin' home in the mornin': *Pride, Lou* / You got me where you want me: *Santos, Larry* / Is it all gone: *Magicians* / Barefootin' time in Chinatown: *Young, Lester* / There must be roses somewhere in this world: *Taylor, Bobby* / Lord what's happening to your people: *Smith, Kenny* / Easy baby: *Adventurers* / Make my love a hurtin' thing: *Cummings, William* / I can't take it anymore: *Persians* / Arabia: *Delcos* / Oh baby: *Creations*.
■ **Double LP** . . . . . . . . . . . . . . . . . **LPSD 118**
**MC** . . . . . . . . . . . . . . . . . . . . . . **CPSD 118**
Soul Supply / Jan '87 / RTM / Pinnacle.

## NORTHERN SOUL STORY 3.

**Tracks:** Philly dog around the world: *Raye, Jimmy* / I feel an urge coming on: *Armstead, Jo* / My baby ain't no plaything: *New Holidays* / I don't like it: *Bush, Tommy* / Try to think (what you're doing): *Davis, Court* / Do it to it: *Funky Sisters* / My life with you: *Traditions* / Sweet magic: *Servicemen* / I don't like to lose: *Washington, Cecil* / Oh oh oh what a love this is: *Revlons* / Something's bad: *Nomads* / Baby I dig you: *Anderson, Gene & The Dynamic Psychedelics* / Too much of a good thing: *Ambassadors* / Nothing can compare to you: *Velvet Satins* / If you love me (show me): *Monique (1)* / Try my love: *Sequins* / You're not my kind: *Durante, Paula* / Not me baby: *Silhouettes* / You didn't have to leave: *Ellusions* / Meet me halfway: *Bryant, Lillie* / I must love you: *Wilson, Timothy*.
■ **Double LP** . . . . . . . . . . . . . . . . . **LPSD 119**
**MC** . . . . . . . . . . . . . . . . . . . . . . **CPSD 119**
Soul Supply / Feb '87 / RTM / Pinnacle.

## NORTHERN SOUL STORY 4.

**Tracks:** No one else can take your place: *Inspirations* / Baby I'm here just to love you: *Stagemasters* / When I'm not wanted: *Holman, Eddie* / This thing called love: *Wyatt, Johnny* / Gotta draw the line: *Fletcher, Darrow* / She put the hurt on me: *Martin, Trade* / Set my heart at ease: *Farrow, Mikki* / R & B time: *Jones, E.Rodney* / Love is the only solution: *Starr, Martha* / On the run: *Accents*.
■ **Double LP** . . . . . . . . . . . . . . . . . **LPSD 121**
Soul Supply / May '87.

## NORTHERN SOUL STORY 5.

**Tracks:** Not Advised.
■ **Double LP** . . . . . . . . . . . . . . . . . **LPSD 123**
Soul Supply / Sep '87.

## NORTHERN SOUL STORY 6.

**Tracks:** Not Advised.
■ **Double LP** . . . . . . . . . . . . . . . . . **LPSD 124**
Soul Supply / Dec '87.

## NORTHERN SOUL STORY 7.

**Tracks:** Not Advised.
■ **Double LP** . . . . . . . . . . . . . . . . . **LPSD 125**
Soul Supply / Feb '88.

## NORTHERN SOUL STORY 8.

**Tracks:** Not Advised.
■ **Double LP** . . . . . . . . . . . . . . . . . **LPSD 126**
Soul Supply / Jul '88.

## NORTHERN SOUL STORY 9.

**Tracks:** Naughty boy: *Day, Jackie* / Do this for me: *Emotions (1)* / You've got a good thing: *King, Jeanie* / I'm gonna..: *Little Ben & The Cheers* / I'm gonna love you: *Hamilton, Edward* / I'm standing: *Lumley, Rufus* / I'm gonna pick up my toys: *Devonnes* / I'll always love you: *Harris, Quinn* / Love reputation: *Lasalle, Denise* / She said goodbye: *Hambrick, Billy* / I found true love: *Hambrick, Billy* / It's just a picture: *Intrepids* / She's so fine: *Topics* / Our love will grow: *Showmen* / Black power: *Coit, James* / My little cottage: *Falana, Fluffy* / I don't want a playboy: *Lynn, Barbara* / Free for all: *Mitchell, Phillip* / Pushin' and pullin': *Lovemasters*.
■ **Double LP** . . . . . . . . . . . . . . . . . **LPSD 127**
Soul Supply / Jun '88.

# O

## OH NO IT'S THE SEVENTIES.

**Tracks:** Kung Fu fighting: *Douglas, Carl* / More, more, more: *True, Andrea Connection* / What's your name, what's your number: *True, Andrea Connection* / Hold back the night: *Trammps* / Sad sweet dreamer: *Sweet Sensation* / Can you feel the force: *Real Thing* / You to me are everything: *Real Thing* / This is it: *Moore, Melba* / Shame, shame, shame: *Shirley & Company* / Zing went the strings of my

heart: *Trammps* / Theme from Shaft: *Holmes, Cecil* / We got the funk: *Positive Force* / 7-6-5-4-3-2-1 (Blow your whistle): *Rimshots* / Sending out an S.O.S.: *Young, Retta* / It's a better than good time: *Knight, Gladys*.
**CD** . . . . . . . . . . . . . . . . . . . . . . **NEMCD 627**
Sequel / Feb '93 / Total / BMG.

## OKEH RHYTHM AND BLUES.
**Tracks:** Not Advised.
■ **Double LP** . . . . . . . . . . . . . . . . **EPC 22125**
**MC** . . . . . . . . . . . . . . . . . . . . . . **40 22125**
Epic / May '82 / Sony.

## OKEH SOUL.
**Tracks:** Delilah: *Lance, Major* / Monkey time: *Lance, Major* / Um, um, um, um, um, um.: *Lance, Major* / Hey little girl: *Lance, Major* / You'll want me back: *Lance, Major* / Think nothing about it: *Lance, Major* / Does it matter: *Opals* / Patty cake: *Artistics* / Get my hands on some lovin': *Artistics* / This heart of mine: *Artistics* / Misty: *Vibrations* / Forgive and forget: *Vibrations* / Welcome home: *Jackson, Walter* / That's what Mama say: *Jackson, Walter* / What would you do: *Jackson, Walter* / My ship is coming in: *Jackson, Walter* / It's an uphill climb (to the bottom): *Jackson, Walter* / Matador: *Lance, Major* / Rhythm: *Lance, Major* / Found true love: *Butler, Billy & The Enchanters* / (You make me think) You ain't ready: *Butler, Billy & The Enchanters* / Gotta get away: *Butler, Billy & The Enchanters* / I can't work no longer: *Butler, Billy & The Enchanters*.
■ **Double LP** . . . . . . . . . . . . . . . . **EPC 22126**
**MC** . . . . . . . . . . . . . . . . . . . . . . **40 22126**
Epic / May '82 / Sony.

## OLD TOWN & BARRY SOUL STIRRERS.
**Tracks:** Think smart: *Fiestas* / I'm so glad: *Howard, Frank* / Oh, oh here comes the heartbreak: *Jones, Thelma* / Try love one more time: *Sparkels* / If I had known: *Houston, Freddie* / You can't trust your best friend: *Height, Donald* / My foolish heart: *Coleman, David* / Gotta find a way: *Jones, Thelma* / We're gonna make it: *Reid, Irene* / Stop, take another look: *Divine Men* / Could this be love: *Rosco & Barbara* / Jerk it: *Gypsies* / Cross my heart: *Yvonne & The Violets* / Baby I need: *Lorraine & The Delights* / Left out: *Johnson, Jesse* / My heart's on fire: *Bland, Billy* / Chills & fever: *Houston, Freddie* / Drown my heart: *Coleman, David* / Barefootin' time in Chinatown: *Young, Lester* / I want a chance for romance: *Rivera, Hector* / It's a woman's world (you better believe it): *Gypsies* / Soul stirrer: *Bobby & Betty Lou* / Gypsy said: *Fiestas* / Things have more meaning now: *Scott, Peggy*.
**CD** . . . . . . . . . . . . . . . . . . . . . . **CDKEND 111**
Ace / Jun '94 / Pinnacle / Complete Record Co. Ltd.

## OLDIES BUT GOODIES VOL.2.
**Tracks:** Not Advised.
**CD** . . . . . . . . . . . . . . . . . . . . . . **100 041**
Bridge (MCS Bridge) / '86 / Pinnacle.

## ON THE REAL SIDE.
**Tracks:** I've got the need: *Jackson, Chuck* / Where did our love go: *Elbert, Donnie* / Sweet baby: *Elbert, Donnie* / Shine shine shine: *Elbert, Donnie* / Hotline: *Jackson, Chuck* / You made me love you: *Wynne, Philippe* / All the way: *Wynne, Philippe* / You ain't going anywhere but gone: *Wynne, Philippe* / Let me go love: *Wynne, Philippe* / Beautiful woman: *Martin, Derek* / On the real side: *Saunders, Larry* / Love is strange: *Elbert, Donnie*.
**CD** . . . . . . . . . . . . . . . . . . . . . . **NEMCD 615**
Sequel / Jul '91 / Total / BMG.

## ON THE SOUL SIDE.
**Tracks:** Love and desire: *Holloway, Patrice* / Gonna fix you good (every time you're bad): *Imperials* / Dr. Love: *Sheen, Bobby* / Ready, willing and able: *Holiday, Jimmy & Clydie King* / Lot of love: *Banks, Homer* / Lipstick traces: *O'Jays* / Record: *Barnum, H.B.* / It was easier to hurt her: *Mimms, Garnet* / Fortune teller: *Spellman, Benny* / It will stand: *Showmen* / Boy watcher: *Thompson, Ginger* / Do wah diddy diddy: *Exciters* / I want you to be my baby: *Greenwich, Ellie* / Point of no return: *McDaniels, Gene* / Baby, I love you: *Holiday, Jimmy* / What's a matter, baby: *Yuro, Timi*.
■ **LP** . . . . . . . . . . . . . . . . . . . . **KENT 006**
Kent / Sep '83.

## ON THE UP BEAT.
**Tracks:** Shing a ling: *Cooperettes* / Raining teardrops: *Demures* / I've lost you: *Wilson, Jackie* / Oh Linda: *Taylor, Linda* / You are / Just ain't no love: *Young-Holt Unlimited* / Have more time: *Smith, Marvin* / California montage: *Young-Holt Unlimited* / Don't take it out on this world: *Adam's Apples* / I'm so glad: *Johnson, Herb & The Impacts* / Purple haze: *Jones, Johnny & The King Casuals* / Gotta find me a lover: *Franklin, Erma* / Nothing but blue skies: *Wilson, Jackie* / Chase is on: *Artistics* / I'll bet you: *Butler, Billy* / What goes up (must come down): *Davis, Tyrone*.
■ **LP** . . . . . . . . . . . . . . . . . . . . **KENT 020**
Kent / Aug '84.

## ON THE UP BEAT.
**Tracks:** Serious: *Allen, Donna* / Fake: *O'Neal, Alexander* / No lies: *S.O.S. Band* / See me: *Vandross, Luther* / Thigh ride: *Tawatha* / Shake you down: *Abbott, Gregory* / Happy: *Surface* / After loving you: *Juicy* / Rain: *Jones, Oran 'Juice'* / My favourite person: *O'Jays*.
■ **LP** . . . . . . . . . . . . . . . . . . . . **ONUP 1**
■ **MC** . . . . . . . . . . . . . . . . . . . . **ONUP C1**
Epic / Jul '87.

## ONE MINIT AT A TIME.
**Tracks:** Well: *Jimmie & Vella* / Lot of love: *Banks, Homer* / Take me: *Womack, Bobby* / I'm gonna do all I can to do right by my man: *Turner, Ike & Tina* / Girls from Texas: *Lewis, Jimmy* / Working on your case: *O'Jays* / Party in the woods: *Persuasions* / Funky Broadway: *Dozier, Gene* / Gonna get that boat: *Turner, Ike & Tina* / I wanna be free: *Players* / Give me your love: *Holiday, Jimmy* / I know you know I know: *Banks, Homer* / Hunk of funk: *Dozier, Gene* / I can't stand the pain: *Irwin, Dee* / Shing a ling: *King, Clydie*.
■ **MC** . . . . . . . . . . . . . . . . . . . . **TCSSL 6002**
■ **LP** . . . . . . . . . . . . . . . . . . . . **SSL 6002**
Stateside / Apr '86.

## OOH POO PAH DOO (Early Sixties Soul 1960/1965).
**Tracks:** Fool in love: *Turner, Ike & Tina* / Ooh poo pah doo: *Hill, Jessie* / Cry baby: *Mimms, Garnet & Enchanters* / That's how heartaches are made: *Washington, Baby* / Hurt so bad: *Imperials* / I know: *George, Barbara* / Over you: *Neville, Aaron* / It's gonna work out fine: *Turner, Ike & Tina* / Mother-in-law: *Doe, Ernie K.* / I love the way you love: *Johnson, Mary* / Lipstick traces: *O'Jays* / Mockingbird: *Foxx, Inez & Charlie* / Think: *McCracklin, Jimmy* / Wish someone would care: *Thomas, Irma* / Certain girl: *Doe, Ernie K.* / She's with her other love: *Hayward, Leon*.
■ **LP** . . . . . . . . . . . . . . . . . . . . **CGB 1012**
**MC** . . . . . . . . . . . . . . . . . . . . . . **C CGB 1012**
Capitol / Nov '81 / EMI.

## ORIGINAL SOUL CLASSICS.
**Tracks:** Not Advised.
■ **CD** . . . . . . . . . . . . . . . . . . . . **NCD 5153**
K-Tel / '89.

## ORIGINAL SOUND OF DETROIT.
**Tracks:** He's so fine: *Corvells* / Lonely nights: *Falcons (1)* / My baby / You're on my mind / What's my destiny / That's what I aim to do / Tell it to my face / Witchcraft in the air / Baby I'm coming home / I don't want to part time love / You killed my love / Has it happened to you yet / I'm depending on you / Keep on loving me / Baby sitting / You must know I love you.
■ **LP** . . . . . . . . . . . . . . . . . . . . **SPE 6602**
Ember / Dec '67.

## ORIGINALS.
**Tracks:** Wonderful world: *Cooke, Sam* / I heard it through the grapevine: *Gaye, Marvin* / Stand by me: *King, Ben E.* / When a man loves a woman: *Sledge, Percy* / C'mon everybody: *Cochran, Eddie* / Mannish boy: *Waters, Muddy* / Ain't nobody home: *King, B.B.* / Can't get enough: *Bad Company* / Joker: *Miller, Steve Band* / Should I stay or should I go: *Clash* / 20th century boy: *T. Rex* / Mad about the boy: *Washington, Dinah* / (Take a little) piece of my heart: *Franklin, Erma* / Heart attack and vine: *Hawkins, Screamin' Jay*.
**CD** . . . . . . . . . . . . . . . . . . . . . . **MOODCD 29**
**LP** . . . . . . . . . . . . . . . . . . . . . . **MOOD 29**
**MC** . . . . . . . . . . . . . . . . . . . . . . **MOODC 29**
Columbia / May '93 / Sony.

## ORIGINALS 2.
**Tracks:** Up on the roof: *Drifters* / It takes two: *Gaye, Marvin & Kim Weston* / (Sittin' on) the dock of the bay: *Redding, Otis* / 'In' crowd: *Gray, Dobie* / La bamba: *Los Lobos* / All right now: *Free (1)* / Move on up: *Mayfield, Curtis* / I get the sweetest feeling: *Wilson, Jackie* / Hey Joe: *Hendrix, Jimi* / Papa's got a brand new bag: *Brown, James* / No particular place to go: *Berry, Chuck* / (Love is like a) heatwave: *Reeves, Martha & The Vandellas* / Bad moon rising: *Creedence Clearwater Revival* / Let's work together: *Canned Heat* / Wanderer: *Dion* / My baby just cares for me: *Simone, Nina* / Stella Mae: *Hooker, John Lee*.
**CD** . . . . . . . . . . . . . . . . . . . . . . **MOODCD 31**
**LP** . . . . . . . . . . . . . . . . . . . . . . **MOOD 31**
**MC** . . . . . . . . . . . . . . . . . . . . . . **MOODC 31**
Columbia / Mar '94 / Sony.

## ORIGINALS, THE.
**Tracks:** I'll be there: *Jackson Five* / It only takes a minute: *Tavares* / Hang on in there baby: *Bristol, Johnny* / Rock your baby: *McCrae, George* / Now that we've found love: *Third World* / Show you the way to go: *Jacksons* / Tired of being alone: *Green, Al* / Summer breeze: *Isley Brothers* / You to me are everything: *Real Thing* / Play that funky music: *Wild Cherry* / It takes two: *Gaye, Marvin & Kim Weston* / Fantasy: *Earth, Wind & Fire* / I believe in miracles: *Jackson Sisters* / Don't leave me this way: *Melvin, Harold & The Bluenotes* / Shame, shame, shame: *Shirley & Company* / Give me just a little more time: *Chairmen Of The Board* / Respect yourself: *Staple Singers* / Tender love: *Force MD's* / Please don't go: *K.C. & The Sunshine Band*.
**CD** . . . . . . . . . . . . . . . . . . . . . . **DINTVCD 43**
**LP** . . . . . . . . . . . . . . . . . . . . . . **DINTV 43**
**MC** . . . . . . . . . . . . . . . . . . . . . . **DINTVMC 43**
Dino / Aug '92 / Pinnacle.

## OUT OF THE BLUE.
**Tracks:** I'll make the living if you make the loving worthwhile: *Chandler, Gene* / It's cool: *Jackson, Walter* / L.A. nights: *Agawa, Yasuko* / Oh darlin': *Brothers By Choice* / Share my love with you: *Magnum Force* / I'll never love the same way twice: *Mason, Barbara* / Rose of Sharon: *Bridges, Calvin* / One more time: *Dante (1)*.
■ **LP** . . . . . . . . . . . . . . . . . . . . **AN 03**
**MC** . . . . . . . . . . . . . . . . . . . . . . **ANC 03**
Rounder / '88 / Roots Records / C.M. Distribution / Topic Records / A.D.A. Distribution / Direct Distribution.

## OUT ON THE FLOOR TONIGHT.
**Tracks:** Out on the floor: *Gray, Dobie* / I'll hold you: *Frankie & Johnny* / Tainted love: *Jones, Gloria* / Love factory: *Laws, Eloise* / You been gone too long: *Sexton, Ann* / Good thing going: *Coulter, Phil Orchestra* / I'm not strong enough: *Four Perfections* / Gotta get closer to my love: *Show Stoppers* / New York in the dark: *Ad Libs* / If that's what you wanted: *Beverly, Frankie* / You don't mean me no good: *Jelly Beans* / Your autumn of tomorrow: *Crow (1)* / It really hurts me girl: *Carstairs* / Queen of fools: *Mills, Barbara* / Touch of venus: *Wynns, Sandy*.
■ **LP** . . . . . . . . . . . . . . . . . . . . **INFERNO 00**
Inferno (1) / Apr '80.

# P

## P.FUNK.
**Tracks:** Not Advised.
■ **LP** . . . . . . . . . . . . . . . . . . . . **PFUNK**
**MC** . . . . . . . . . . . . . . . . . . . . . . **ZCFUNK**
Street Sounds / Jul '86 / BMG / Total.

## PAYING OUR DUES.
**Tracks:** You hit me where it hurt me: *Clark, Alice* / Something's burnin': *Marvellos* / Go for yourse[lf] / *Laster, Larry* / You gotta pay your dues: *Drifters* / Both ends against the middle: *Moore, Jackie* / Tak[e] your love and run: *Lynn, Barbara* / My heart needs [a] break: *Jones, Linda* / I'll be loving you: *Soul Brothe[rs] Six* / Something new to do: *Sheen, Bobby* / Tell m[e] why: *Life (1)* / Since you said you'd be mine: *Ra[g]land, Lou* / Angel baby: *Banks, Darrell* / Where di[d] go wrong: *Embers* / That's when the tears sta[rt]: *Blossoms* / Just say goodbye: *Phillips, Esther*.
■ **LP** . . . . . . . . . . . . . . . . . . . . **KENT 0**
Kent / Aug '89.

## PEACOCK CHICKS & DUCHESSES SIN[G] THE BLUES.
**Tracks:** Mr. Thrill: *Jones, mildred* / New orlean[s]: *Johnson, Gwen* / Bettye Jean: *Washington, Bett[ye] Jean* / Why oh why: *Washington, Bettye Jean* / He['s] my kind of man: *Ford, Valli* / No you can't..: *Brow[n], Jewel* / Don't touch my bowl: *Hill, Gladys* / B[...] shape blues: *Mitchell, Joe Ann* / Trumpet blo[w] away: *Johnson, Gwen* / Young Boy: *Johnson, Gwe[n]* / Roll like a big wheel: *Brown, Olive* / Letter to [m]y girlfriend: *Brown, Olive* / Looking for a home: *Brow[n], Olive* / Bonita's blues: *Cole, Bonita* / Life is like th[...] *Cole, Bonita*.
■ **LP** . . . . . . . . . . . . . . . . . . . . **CHD 2**
Ace / Feb '88.

**PEPPER HOT BABY (Baton R&B).**
**Tracks:** Not Advised.
■ LP . . . . . . . . . . . . . . . . . . . . . . . . KK 7449
Krazy Kat / Mar '89.

**PHILADELPHIA CLASSICS.**
**Tracks:** Love is the message: *MFSB* / Sound of Philadelphia: *MFSB & Three Degrees* / Dirty ol' man: *Three Degrees* / I love music: *O'Jays* / Don't leave me this way: *Melvin, Harold & The Bluenotes* / Love train: *O'Jays* / I'll always love my mama: *Intruders* / Bad luck: *Melvin, Harold & The Bluenotes*.
■ Double LP. . . . . . . . . . . . . . . . . . . . PIR 88274
Philadelphia Int. / Feb '78.
■ CD. . . . . . . . . . . . . . . . . . . . . . . . 4689912
■ MC. . . . . . . . . . . . . . . . . . . . . . . . 4689914
Philadelphia Int. / Oct '91.
CD. . . . . . . . . . . . . . . . . . . . . . . . .983337 2
MC. . . . . . . . . . . . . . . . . . . . . . . . .983337 4
Pickwick/Sony Collector's Choice / Oct '93 / Pickwick / Pinnacle.

**PHILADELPHIA GOLD.**
**Tracks:** Love train / Your song / If you don't know me by now / Take good care of yourself / You'll never find another love like me / TSOP / Soul city walk / Love epidemic / Year of decision / Don't leave me this way / When will I see you again / Back stabbers / Wake up everybody / Let 'em in / Whole town's laughing at me / She's a winner / Do it anyway you wanna / Darlin' darlin' baby / Me and Mrs. Jones / Let's clean up the ghetto.
■ LP . . . . . . . . . . . . . . . . . . . . . . . . PIR 86049
Philadelphia / Jan '78.

**PHILADELPHIA STORY, THE.**
**Tracks:** Not Advised.
■ LP . . . . . . . . . . . . . . . . . . . . . . . . PHST 1986
MC. . . . . . . . . . . . . . . . . . . . . . . . ZCPHS 1986
Street Sounds / Nov '86 / BMG / Total.

**PHILADELPHIA YEARS (8 CD BOX SET).**
**Tracks:** Not Advised.
■ CD Set. . . . . . . . . . . . . . . . . . . . KNCD 82001
Knight / Jul '91.

**PHILIDELPHIA SOUL CLASSICS VOL.1.**
**Tracks:** Not Advised.
CD. . . . . . . . . . . . . . . . . . . . . . . . STCD 1000
Disky / Jun '93 / THE.

**PHILLYBUSTERS VOL.IV.**
**Tracks:** I love music: *O'Jays* / Soul city walk: *Bell, Archie* / Love is everywhere: *Unknown artist/s* / I'm not in love: *Unknown artist/s* / Wake up everybody: *Melvin, Harold & The Bluenotes* / Philadelphia freedom: *Unknown artist/s* / Let's make a baby: *Paul, Billy* / You'll never find another love like mine: *Rawls, Lou* / No tell motel: *Unknown artist/s* / Float like a butterfly: *Unknown artist/s* / Round 1: *Unknown artist/s* / Love epidemic: *Unknown artist/s* / Summertime and I'm feeling mellow: *Unknown artist/s* / Here we go again: *People's Choice* / Message in our music: *O'Jays*.
■ LP . . . . . . . . . . . . . . . . . . . . . . . . PIR 81658
Philadelphia Int. / Feb '77.

**PLATFORM SOUL.**
**Tracks:** Not Advised.
■ CD . . . . . . . . . . . . . . . . . . . . . . . . ONCD 3456
■ LP . . . . . . . . . . . . . . . . . . . . . . . . CE 2456
K-Tel / Apr '90.

**POPS, WE LOVE YOU - THE ALBUM.**
**Tracks:** Not Advised.
LP . . . . . . . . . . . . . . . . . . . . . . . . .STML 12114
Motown / '79.

**POWER & SOUL.**
**Tracks:** Perfect year: *Carroll, Dina* / Come in out of the rain: *Moten, Wendy* / Get here: *Adams, Oleta* / No more tears (enough is enough): *Mazelle, Kym & Jocelyn Brown* / I will survive: *Gaynor, Gloria* / Ain't no mountain high enough: *Ross, Diana* / River deep mountain high: *Turner, Tina* / Respect: *Franklin, Aretha* / (Take a little) Piece of my heart: *Franklin, Erma* / Help me make it through the night: *Knight, Gladys* / And I'm telling you I'm not going: *Holiday, Jennifer* / All woman: *Stansfield, Lisa* / Save the best for last: *Williams, Vanessa* / Sweet love: *Baker, Anita* / It should have been me: *Fair, Yvonne* / Stay with me baby: *Turner, Ruby* / Piano in the dark: *Russell, Brenda* / I will: *Winters, Ruby* / Superwoman: *White, Karyn* / Power of love: *Rush, Jennifer*.
CD. . . . . . . . . . . . . . . . . . . . . . . . .516896-2
MC. . . . . . . . . . . . . . . . . . . . . . . . .516896-4
Polygram T.V. / Aug '94 / PolyGram.

**PRECIOUS STONE: IN THE STUDIO WITH SLY STONE 1963-65.**
**Tracks:** Swim: *Sly & Rose* / Scat swim: *Stone, Sly* / I taught him: *Scott, Gloria* / Don't say I didn't warn you: *Scott, Gloria* / Help me with my broken heart: *Stone, Sly* / Out of sight: *Stone, Sly* / Nerve of you: *O'Connor, Emile* / Every dog has his day: *O'Connor, Emile* / On Broadway: *Stone, Sly* / Searchin': *Stone, Sly* / Lord, Lord: *Stone, Sly* / Seventh son: *Stone, Sly* / Jerk: *Sly & Sal* / That little old heartbreaker: *Freeman, Bobby* / I'll never fall in love again: *Freeman, Bobby* / Ain't that lovin' you baby: *Preston, Billy* / Buttermilk: *Stone, Sly* / Fake it: *George & Teddy* / Laugh: *George & Teddy* / Little Latin lupe lu: *Preston, Billy* / Dance all night: *Sly & Freddie* / Temptation walk: *Stone, Sly* / Underdog: *Stone, Sly* / Radio spot: *Stone, Sly* / Can't you tell I love her: *Preston, Billy* / Life of fortune & fame: *Preston, Billy* / Take my advice: *Preston, Billy* / As I get older: *Preston, Billy*.
CD. . . . . . . . . . . . . . . . . . . . . . . . CDCHD 539
Ace / Aug '94 / Pinnacle / Complete Record Co. Ltd.

**PRELUDE - DEEP GROOVES.**
**Tracks:** Come on dance, dance: *Saturday Night Band* / In the bush: *Musique* / Just let me do my thing: *Sine (1)* / Check out the groove: *Thurston, Bobby* / Can you handle it: *Redd, Sharon* / You'll never know: *Hi-Gloss* / You're the one for me: *D-Train* / Body music: *Strikers* / Never give you up: *Redd, Sharon* / What I got is what you need: *Unique* / Love how you feel: *Redd, Sharon* / Music: *D-Train*.
CD. . . . . . . . . . . . . . . . . . . . . . . . NEDCD 263
LP . . . . . . . . . . . . . . . . . . . . . . . . NEDLP 263
MC. . . . . . . . . . . . . . . . . . . . . . . . .NEDMC 263
Sequel / Oct '93 / Total / BMG.

**PURE SOUL.**
**Tracks:** I got caught: *Carter, Clarence* / Ask me 'bout nothing (but the blues): *Bland, Bobby* / Mirror, mirror on the wall: *Saints* / Doomed by jealousy: *Montre El, Jackie* / No cookies in my bag: *Britton, Aldora* / You played on a player: *Green, Garland* / Check my tears: *Trends* / Mr. Soft touch: *Williams, Jeanette* / Court of love: *Unifics* / Drop by my place: *Carlton, Carl* / This time will be different: *Blue Notes* / Mr. Independent: *Soul Twins* / Do you love me: *Rayons* / I still love you: *Stanback, Jean* / Your baby doesn't love you anymore: *Ruby & The Romantics*.
■ LP . . . . . . . . . . . . . . . . . . . . . . . . KENT 019
Kent / Apr '84.

**PYE INTERNATIONAL STORY, THE.**
**Tracks:** Come on let's go: *Valens, Ritchie* / I'll be with you in apple blossom time: *June, Rosemary* / I shot Mr. Lee: *Bobbettes* / Model girl: *Jones, Davy* / Blue moon: *Jones, Davy* / (I don't know why) But I do: *Henry, Clarence 'Frogman'* / At last: *James, Etta* / You always hurt the one you love: *Henry, Clarence 'Frogman'* / Daddy's home: *Shep & The Limelites* / Goodbye cruel world: *Darren, James* / If you gotta make a fool of somebody: *Ray, James (2)* / Let me in: *Sensations (1)* / Something's got a hold on me: *James, Etta* / Johnny Angel: *Fabares, Shelly* / I wish that we were married: *Ronnie & The Hi-Lites* / Cindy's birthday: *Crawford, Johnny* / Rinky dink: *Cortez, Dave 'Baby'* / My Dad: *Petersen, Pete* / Every day I have to cry: *Alaimo, Steve* / My colouring book: *Stewart, Sandy* / Mama didn't lie: *Bradley, Jan* / Little band of gold: *Gilreath, James* / Help me: *Williamson, Sonny Boy (1)* / Country line special: *Davis, Cyril & The All Stars* / Let it rock: *Berry, Chuck* / Pretty thing: *Diddley, Bo* / Memphis, Tennessee: *Berry, Chuck* / Louie Louie: *Kingsmen* / Tonight you're gonna fall in love with me: *Shirelles* / High heel sneakers: *Tucker, Tommy* / Gonna send you back to Georgia (A city slick): *Shaw, Timmy* / No particular place to go: *Berry, Chuck* / Smokestack lightnin': *Howlin' Wolf* / Soulful dress: *Desanto, Sugar Pie* / My babe: *Little Walter* / Oh no not my baby: *Brown, Maxine* / Shakin' all over: *Guess Who* / Just a little bit: *Head, Roy* / Daydream: *Lovin' Spoonful* / Psychotic reaction: *Count Five* / Harlem shuffle: *Traits* / Talk talk: *Music Machine* / Funky Broadway: *Dyke & The Blazers* / Incense & peppermints: *Strawberry Alarm Clock* / As long as you're here: *Yanosky, Zal* / Yellow brick road: *Captain Beefheart & His Magic Band* / Green tambourine: *Lemon Pipers* / Simon says: *1910 Fruitgum Company* / Yummy yummy yummy: *Ohio Express* / Telephone man: *Wilson, Mari*.
CD. . . . . . . . . . . . . . . . . . . . . . . . NEDCD 239
Sequel / Jul '93 / Total / BMG.

# Q

**QUARTET OF SOUL.**
**Tracks:** I love you 1000 times: *Platters* / With this ring: *Platters* / Shing-a-ling-a-loo: *Platters* / Tightrope: *Foxx, Inez & Charlie* / Come by here: *Foxx, Inez & Charlie* / Baby take it all: *Foxx, Inez & Charlie* / Biggest man: *Hunt, Tommy* / Never love a robin: *Hunt, Tommy* / If I'm hurt you'll feel the pain: *Barbara & Brenda* / Too young to be fooled: *Barbara & Brenda*.
■ LP . . . . . . . . . . . . . . . . . . . . . . . . SSL 10209
Stateside / Feb '68.

# R

**RADIO'S NO 1 HITS (Most Requested Music of our Time).**
**Tracks:** Dancing in the street: *Reeves, Martha & The Vandellas* / Stop, in the name of love: *Supremes* / My cherie amour: *Wonder, Stevie* / You can't hurry love: *Supremes* / How sweet it is (to be loved by you): *Gaye, Marvin* / Please Mr. Postman: *Marvelettes* / Heatwave: *Reeves, Martha & The Vandellas* / I heard it through the grapevine: *Gaye, Marvin* / Baby, I need your loving: *Four Tops* / You've made me so very happy: *Holloway, Brenda* / I can't help myself: *Four Tops* / Where did our love go: *Supremes* / Someday we'll be together: *Ross, Diana & The Supremes*.
■ CD. . . . . . . . . . . . . . . . . . . . . . . . WD 72602
Motown / Feb '88.

**RAINBOW ROAD - SOUTH CAMP.**
**Tracks:** Tearstained face: *Varner, Don* / When it's over: *Varner, Don* / Let me be a woman: *Varner, Brenda* / You made your bed: *Bradford, Eddie* / Self preservation: *Brandon, Bill* / What kind of spell: *Borders Tony* / You ain't woman enough (to take my man): *Lynn, Loretta* / You better believe it: *Borders Tony* / Masquerade: *Varner, Don* / Home just ain't home at suppertime: *Hill, Z.Z.* / Strangest feeling: *Brandon, Bill* / Cheaters never win: *Borders Tony* / Heaven help me (I'm falling in love): *Edwards, June* / All I need is you: *Brandon, Bill* / It's a mans world: *Causey, Buddy* / It sure was fun: *Bradford, Eddie* / One woman man: *Varner, Don* / Rainbow road: *Brandon, Bill* / You left the water running: *Varner, Don* / Think I'll go somewhere and cry myself to sleep: *Perkins, Joe* / Love and a friend: *Borders Tony* / I'll be your baby tonight: *Brandon, Bill* / Movin' in the groove: *Brandon, Bill* / Don't give up on me: *Varner, Brenda* / Your big chance: *Brandon, Bill* / Close to me / Sugar makes everything sweeter: *Sledge, Percy Jnr*.
CD. . . . . . . . . . . . . . . . . . . . . . . . CDCHARLY 200
■ LP . . . . . . . . . . . . . . . . . . . . . . . . CRB 1225
Charly R&B / Sep '89.

**RARE.**
**Tracks:** Action speaks louder than words: *Chocolate Milk* / Ain't no change: *New Birth* / If you've got it ..: *Headhunters* / Turn off the lights: *Larry Young's Fuel* / Haboglabotribin': *Wright, Bernard* / Walk that walk: *Irvine, Weldon* / 2 win u back: *Jones Girls* / Let it go: *Broom, Bobby* / Elevate our minds: *Williams, Linda* / Looking up for you: *Wycoff, Michael* / I love you: *Irvine, Weldon* / Holding you, loving you: *Blackman, Donald* / How about love: *Chocolate Milk*.
MC. . . . . . . . . . . . . . . . . . . . . . . . NK 90070
■ CD. . . . . . . . . . . . . . . . . . . . . . . . ND 90070
■ LP . . . . . . . . . . . . . . . . . . . . . . . . NL 90070
RCA / Aug '90.

**RARE 2.**
**Tracks:** Pop: *Limit* / Spoiled: *Main Ingredient, featuring Cuba Golding* / April lady: *Wax (1)* / Will you take my love: *Mason, Harvey* / How's your love life, baby: *Perry, Greg* / Since I found you: *Bowman, Candy* /

I've quit running the streets: *Green, Garland* / Tropical love: *Bofill, Angela* / When and if I fall in love: *Wax (1)* / We've got the love: *Plush* / Evening of love: *Main Ingredient, featuring Cuba Golding* / I've got to see you right away: *Perry, Jeff* / Never (gonna let you go): *Charme*.
■ LP . . . . . . . . . . . . . . . . . . . . . PL 71681
■ MC. . . . . . . . . . . . . . . . . . . . . PK 71681
RCA / Apr '88.
■ LP . . . . . . . . . . . . . . . . . . . . . NL 74704
■ CD. . . . . . . . . . . . . . . . . . . . . ND 74704
■ MC. . . . . . . . . . . . . . . . . . . . . NK 74704
RCA / Aug '90.

### RARE 3.
**Tracks:** Ain't no time for nothing / I'm always dancin' to the music: *Golson, Benny* / Rough out there: *Modulations* / Miss Cheryl: *Banda Black Rio* / We're getting down: *Irvine, Weldon* / Shake it up: *Vibrations* / Passion play: *Sugarhill Gang* / Love me like this: *Real To Reel* / Work to do: *Main Ingredient* / Yellow sunshine: *Yellow Sunshine* / Am I cold, am I hot: *Harris, Bill*.
■ LP . . . . . . . . . . . . . . . . . . . . . 209.498
■ MC. . . . . . . . . . . . . . . . . . . . . 409.498
Ariola / Dec '88.
■ CD . . . . . . . . . . . . . . . . . . . . . .260935
MC. . . . . . . . . . . . . . . . . . . . . . .410935
■ LP . . . . . . . . . . . . . . . . . . . . . .210935
Ariola / Aug '90.

### RARE 4.
**Tracks:** Sweet power your embrace: *Mason, James (1)* / Evil vibrations: *Mighty Riders* / Grand theft: *Chocolate Milk* / All that matters: *Michigan Avenue* / La la for love: *Serenade* / Let me be your pacifier: *Green, Garland* / Oops here I go again: *Wright, Edna* / Renaissance: *Smith, Lonnie Liston* / Under the skin: *Brothers* / Stick by me: *Serenade* / Dance the night away: *Kruz*.
■ LP . . . . . . . . . . . . . . . . . . . . . 210.007
■ MC. . . . . . . . . . . . . . . . . . . . . 410.007
Ariola / Sep '89.
■ LP . . . . . . . . . . . . . . . . . . . . . .210936
MC. . . . . . . . . . . . . . . . . . . . . . .410936
■ CD . . . . . . . . . . . . . . . . . . . . . .260936
Ariola / Aug '90.

### RARE 5.
**Tracks:** Disco nights: *G.Q.* / To midnight lovers: *Passion (1)* / Betcha by golly wow: *Patti & The Lovelites* / I just wanna be your girl: *Chapter 8* / I wanna be with you: *Beverly & Duane* / You got me dreaming: *Evans, Linda* / Got to be there: *Patti & The Lovelites* / Soft and tender touch: *Watson, Fred* / Expansions: *Smith, Lonnie Liston* / Delerium: *McGee, Francine*.
■ LP . . . . . . . . . . . . . . . . . . . . . .210928
■ MC. . . . . . . . . . . . . . . . . . . . . .410928
■ CD . . . . . . . . . . . . . . . . . . . . . .260928
Ariola / Aug '90.

### RARE GROOVE.
**Tracks:** Boogie wonderland: *Earth, Wind & Fire & The Emotions* / Shake your body: *Jacksons* / Thats the way i like it: *K.C. & The Sunshine Band* / Use it up and wear it out: *Odyssey* / And the beat goes on: *Whispers* / Contact: *Starr, Edwin* / More than a woman: *Tavares* / If i can't have you: *Elliman, Yvonne* / I will survive: *Gaynor, Gloria* / Ring my bell: *Ward, Anita* / Hang on in there baby: *Bristol, Johnny* / Rock your baby: *McCrae, George* / You bet your love: *Hancock, Herbie* / Now that we've found love: *Third World* / Play that funky music: *Wild Cherry* / It's a disco night: *Isley Brothers* / Le freak: *Chic* / We are family: *Sister Sledge* / Boogie nights: *Heatwave* / You make me feel (mighty real): *Sylvester* / Don't stop the music: *Yarbrough & Peoples* / Working my way back to you: *Detroit Spinners* / Rock the boat: *Hues Corporation* / Funky town: *Lipps Inc.* / Love come down: *King, Evelyn 'Champagne'* / I can make you feel good: *Shalamar* / Celebration: *Kool & The Gang* / Haven't stopped dancing yet: *Gonzales* / Right back where we started from: *Nightingale, Maxine* / Get along without you now: *Wills, Viola* / Jump to the beat: *Lattisaw, Stacy* / Searching: *Change*.
CD . . . . . . . . . . . . . . . . . . . . . QTVCD 016
LP . . . . . . . . . . . . . . . . . . . . . . .QTV 016
MC. . . . . . . . . . . . . . . . . . . . . . QTVC 016
Quality / Nov '92 / Pinnacle.

### RARE GROOVE 2.
**Tracks:** It's all right now: *Harris, Eddie* / London express: *Sain, Oliver* / I wouldn't change a thing: *Escovedo, Coke* / Atmosphere strut: *Cloud One* / Four play: *Wesley & Horny Horns* / Funky music is the..: *Dynamic Corvettes* / Get me back on time: *Pickett, Wilson* / Bus stop: *Sain, Oliver* / Bye bye baby: *Bay City Rollers* / Bump: *Kenny* / Baker Street: *Rafferty, Gerry* / Love is in the air: *Young, John Paul* / Tiger feet: *Mud* / My Sharona: *Knack (1)* / Now is the time: *James, Jimmy* / Jack in the box: *Moments* / Heaven must be missing an angel: *Tavares* / You're my first..: *White, Barry* / I love America: *Juvet, Patrick* / Girls: *Moments & Whatnauts* / Rock the boat: *Hues Corporation* / You sexy thing: *Hot Chocolate*.
CD . . . . . . . . . . . . . . . . . . . . . CDRARE 2
■ LP . . . . . . . . . . . . . . . . . . . . .RARELP 2
MC. . . . . . . . . . . . . . . . . . . . . . ZCRARE 2
Street Sounds / Jun '88 / BMG / Total.

### RARE GROOVES.
**Tracks:** Not Advised.
■ LP . . . . . . . . . . . . . . . . . . . . . CHILLP 1
MC. . . . . . . . . . . . . . . . . . . . . . ZCCHIL 1
Jam Today / May '87 / Jetstar.

### RARE NORTHERN SOUL VOL.2.
**Tracks:** What more do you want: *Toones, Gene* / Can't we talk it over: *Allen, L* / You can't mean it: *Chapter Five* / Cheatin' kind: *Gardner, Don* / Lady in green: *Magnetics* / Dream my heart: *Edwards, Shirley* / Showstopper: *Cashmeres* / Love you just can't walk away: *Courtney, Dean* / I'm catching on: *Lloyd, Betty* / I've arrived: *Flanagan, Steve* / Fireman: *Reegan, Vala & The Valarons* / Chasing my dream all over town: *Wren, Jenny* / Baby I don't need your love: *Chants* / To the ends of the earth: *Middleton, Tony* / There's room for me: *Davis, Jesse* / Breakaway: *Basil, Toni* / It's just love: *Andrews, John*.
■ LP . . . . . . . . . . . . . . . . . . . . . .RNS 002
RNS / Apr '89.

### RARE PRELUDES VOL.1.
**Tracks:** C'mon stop: *Black Gold* / Your love: *Satin, Silk & Lace* / Music got me: *Visual* / I don't wanna hear it: *Adams, Gayle* / You are the one: *Pilot* / On a journey (I sing the funk electric): *Electrik Funk* / Some how some way: *Visual* / All I need is you: *Starshine* / Don't stop my love: *Passion (2)*.
■ LP . . . . . . . . . . . . . . . . . . . . . 210.008
■ CD . . . . . . . . . . . . . . . . . . . . . 260.008
■ MC. . . . . . . . . . . . . . . . . . . . . 410.008
Ariola / Sep '89.

### RARE SOUL FROM DETROIT.
**Tracks:** That's why I love you: *Professionals (1)* / Lady in green: *Magnetics* / I have a girl: *Magnetics* / I need my baby: *Beavers, Jackie* / Keep loving me: *Hargraves, Silky* / Johnny on the spot: *Edwards, Dennis* / I can't stand it: *Sophisticates* / I am nothing: *Williams, Al* / My dear beloved: *Montgomery, Jack* / Rat race: *Washington, Gino* / I'm catching on: *Lloyd, Betty* / Not a chance in a million: *Mitchell, Jock* / I don't like to lose: *Group featuring Cecil Washington* / Geni: *Bryant, Terri*.
LP . . . . . . . . . . . . . . . . . . . . . . . SPE 23
Specialty / Sep '90 / Pinnacle.

### RARE SOUL ON CD.
**Tracks:** Not Advised.
CD . . . . . . . . . . . . . . . . . . . . . . . SSCD 1
Soul Supply / Mar '88 / RTM / Pinnacle.

### RARE SOUL UNCOVERED.
**Tracks:** Hung up on your love: *Montclairs* / I can't see your love: *Ballads* / Nothing takes the place of you: *Toussaint, Allen* / That's enough: *Robinson, Roscoe* / I hurt the other side: *Barnes, Sidney* / Don't talk like that: *Murray, Clarence* / You gotta pay the price: *Taylor, Gloria* / Medley of soul: *Downing, Big Al* / Breakaway: *Valentines* / Come on train: *Thomas, Don* / I need you more than ever: *Montclairs* / Would you believe: *Lee, Jacky* / Getting mighty crowded: *Everett, Betty* / Don't let me down: *Hughes, Freddie* / Just another heartbreak: *Little Richie* / You've been gone long: *Sexton, Ann* / Let's go baby (where the action is): *Parker, Robert* / Soul shake: *Scott, Peggy*.
■ LP . . . . . . . . . . . . . . . . . . . . . CRB 1085
MC. . . . . . . . . . . . . . . . . . . . . . TCCRB 1085
Charly R&B / May '84 / Charly.

### RARE SOUL UNCOVERED VOL.2.
**Tracks:** Lonely for you baby: *Dees, Sam* / I'm your love man: *Lost Souls* / Don't ever leave me: *Williams, Maurice* / Nothing worse than being alone: *Ad Libs* / Unwanted love: *Montclairs* / Gonna take a journey: *Strong, Barrett* / What can a man do: *Williams, Maurice* / Night the angels cried: *Dynamite, Johnny* / Touch me, hold me, kiss me: *Inspirations* / I'd think it over: *Fletcher, Sam* / Being without you: *Williams, Maurice* / You're gonna need me: *Ford, Ted* / I keep tryin': *Hughes, Freddie* / I'm a teardrop: *Jerms* / Running for my life: *Shelton, Roscoe* / Til I get it right: *Hobbs, Willie* / Sweet and easy: *McCoy, Van* / Make up your mind: *Strong, Barrett*.
■ LP . . . . . . . . . . . . . . . . . . . . . CRB 1109
MC. . . . . . . . . . . . . . . . . . . . . . TCCRB 1109
Charly R&B / '86 / Charly.

### RARE SOUL: BEACH MUSIC CLASSICS VOL.1.
**Tracks:** Not Advised.
CD. . . . . . . . . . . . . . . . . . . . . . . R2 70277
Rhino (USA) / Apr '92 / WEA.

### RARE SOUL: BEACH MUSIC CLASSIC VOL.2.
**Tracks:** Not Advised.
CD . . . . . . . . . . . . . . . . . . . . . . R2 7027
Rhino (USA) / Apr '92 / WEA.

### RARE SOUL: BEACH MUSIC CLASSIC VOL.3.
**Tracks:** Not Advised.
CD . . . . . . . . . . . . . . . . . . . . . . R2 7027
Rhino (USA) / Apr '92 / WEA.

### RAREST UK 45'S OF THE 60'S.
**Tracks:** To the ends of the earth: *Middleton, Tony* Fireman: *Reegan, Vala & The Valarons* / Ever, eve *Clements, Soul Joe* / You can't mean it: *Chapter Fiv* / Next in line: *Lands, Hoagy* / Better use your hea *D'Ell, Dennis* / Open the door to your heart: *Bank Darrell* / I need you: *Martin, Shane* / Stranger in m arms: *Randell, Lynne* / One in a million: *Chapte Five* / It's rough out there: *Jackson, Jerry (1)* / Touc of Venus: *Wynns, Sandy* / Looky looky: *Brothe Grimm* / You just don't know: *Checker, Chubby* You've got me where you want me: *Ford, Jon* / Pan is on: *Hamilton, Roy (1)* / Got to find a way: *Ha Cajun* / Don't pity me: *Lynne, Sue* / You turned m bitter into sweet: *Love, Mary* / Drifter: *Pollard, Ray* Tears of joy: *Merrell, Ray* / Per-so-nal-ly: *Pari Bobby* / Soulful jerk: *Rumblers (1)* / Evil one: *Sa phires* / It's just love: *Andrews, John* / Not too lor ago: *Uniques* / Walk with a winner: *McDaniels, Ger* / 81: *Candy & The Kisses* / Gotta have your lov *Sapphires* / Baby I don't need your love: *Chants* / feel so good: *Manchester's Playboys* / It's a sa thing: *Pollard, Ray* / Closer she gets: *Drevar, John* Wanting you: *Stevens, April* / Queen of fools: *Mil Barbara* / I just can't help myself: *Volumes* / I su render: *Holman, Eddie* / On a magic carpet rid *Dee, Kiki*.
MC. . . . . . . . . . . . . . . . . . . . . . BRMC 0
Beatin' Rhythm / Mar '91.

### REBIRTH OF COOL.
**Tracks:** Not Advised.
CD . . . . . . . . . . . . . . . . . . . . . . .BRCD 5
■ LP . . . . . . . . . . . . . . . . . . . . . .BRLP 5
MC. . . . . . . . . . . . . . . . . . . . . . .BRCA 5
4th & Broadway / Feb '91 / PolyGram.

### REBIRTH OF COOL III.
**Tracks:** Not Advised.
CD . . . . . . . . . . . . . . . . . . . . . . .BRCD 5
LP Set. . . . . . . . . . . . . . . . . . . . . BRLPD 5
MC. . . . . . . . . . . . . . . . . . . . . . .BRCA 5
4th & Broadway / Apr '93 / PolyGram.

### REBIRTH OF COOL IV.
**Tracks:** Just wanna touch her: *D.J. Krush* / Play m funk: *Simple E* / Rent strike: *Groove collective* / R conscious: *Buchanan, Courtney* / My favouri things: *Jordan, Ronny* / Otha fish: *Pharcyde* / Cant milla: *Tranquility Bass* / Aftermath: *Tricky* / Eart song: *Batu* / Cool like the blues: *Warfield, Justin* Straight plays: *F Mob* / Crazy: *Outside* / Spock with beard: *Palmskin Productions* / World mutation *Tone Productions* / Tree, air & rain on Earth: *Monc Grosso* / Great men's dub: *Burning Spear* / Soul the people: *Bread & Butter*.
CD . . . . . . . . . . . . . . . . . . . . . . .BRCD 6
LP . . . . . . . . . . . . . . . . . . . . . . .BRLP 6
MC. . . . . . . . . . . . . . . . . . . . . . .BRCA 6
4th & Broadway / Jun '94 / PolyGram.

### REBIRTH OF COOL, TOO.
**Tracks:** I've lost my ignorance (and don't kno where to find it): *Dream Warriors* / La raza: *Kid Fro* / Senga abele (lion roar): *Dibango, Manu & M Mello* / Cool and funky: *Jordan, Ronny* / I should'v known better: *Paris, Mica* / All for one: *Brand Nubia* / One to grow on: *UMC's* / Family: *McKoy* / Try m love: *Washburn, Lalomie* / Kickin' jazz: *Outlaw* Looking at the front door: *Main Source* / Free yo feelings: *Slam Slam* / Go with the flow: *Rock, Pete C.L. Smooth* / Set me free: *Bygraves* / Black whi *Chapter & Verse* / Slow jam: *Dodge City Production*
CD . . . . . . . . . . . . . . . . . . . . . . .BRCD 5
■ LP . . . . . . . . . . . . . . . . . . . . . BRLPD 5
MC. . . . . . . . . . . . . . . . . . . . . . . 51208
4th & Broadway / Feb '92 / PolyGram.

### RECORD COLLECTOR, VOL 1.
**Tracks:** I can't hide it: *Appreciations* / Silent trea ment: *Demain, Arin* / Little togetherness: *Your Hearts* / Joker: *Mylestones* / Love on a rampag *Kerr, George Orchestra* / So in luv: *Robinson, Othe lo* / There is nothing else to say: *George, Cassietta* Looking for you: *Echoes* / You won't say nothin *Lewis, Tamala* / Bok to Bach: *Father's Angels* Stronger than her love: *Flirtations* / I never kne *Foster, Eddie* / These things will keep me loving yo *Blue Sharks*.

■ LP . . . . . . . . . . . . . . . . . . . . .DS 100001
Destiny (Northern Soul) / May '80.

**RED BIRD STORY VOL.2, THE.**
**Tracks:** Paradise: *Shangri-Las* / He cried: *Shangri-Las* / Dressed in black: *Shangri-Las* / I wonder: *Butterflys* / Gee baby gee: *Butterflys* / Dum dum ditty: *Goodees* / If there's anything else you want (let me know): *Joy, Roddie* / Welcome to my heart: *Bouquets* / Big bad world: *Saint, Cathy* / It sounds like my baby: *Banks, Bessie* / Searchin': *Robinson, Alvin* / How can I get over you: *Robinson, Alvin* / I'm gonna put some hurt on you: *Robinson, Alvin* / Bottom of my soul: *Robinson, Alvin* / Keep it up: *Soul Brothers* / Fugitive from love: *Jones, Linda* / It was a lie: *Bobby Moore & The Fourmosts* / You don't know: *Greenwich, Ellie* / Baby: *Greenwich, Ellie* / Another boy like mine: *Greenwich, Ellie* / Our love can still be saved: *Barry, Jeff* / I'll still love you: *Barry, Jeff* / Talk to me baby: *Mann, Barry* / Amy: *Mann, Barry* / Baby be mine: *Jelly Beans* / Kind of boy you can't forget: *Jelly Beans* / Chapel of love: *Jelly Beans* / Here she comes: *Jelly Beans* / Ain't love a funny thing: *Jelly Beans* / Whisper sweet things: *Jelly Beans* / Goodnight baby: *Jelly Beans* / Do wah diddy diddy: *Jelly Beans*.
■ MC Set . . . . . . . . . . . . . . . . . .TCCDX 19
Charly / Aug '88.
■ Double LP. . . . . . . . . . . . . . . . . . CDX 19
Charly / Jan '88.

**RED HOT 'N' BLUE.**
**Tracks:** Not Advised.
■ LP . . . . . . . . . . . . . . . . . . . . . CRB 1061
Charly R&B / Sep '83.

**REGAL RECORDS IN NEW ORLEANS.**
**Tracks:** I'll never be free: *Gayten, Paul* / Yeah, yeah, yeah: *Gayten, Paul* / You ought to know: *Gayten, Paul* / You shouldn't: *Gayten, Paul* / Confused: *Gayten, Paul* / Bear hug: *Gayten, Paul* / Oooh la la: *Gayten, Paul* / My last goodbye: *Gayten, Paul* / I ain't gonna let you in: *Gayten, Paul* / Kickapoo juice: *Gayten, Paul* / Each time: *Gayten, Paul* / Fishtails: *Gayten, Paul* / Suzette: *Gayten, Paul* / Happy birthday to you: *Gayten, Paul* / For you my love: *Gayten, Paul* / Back trackin' aka Dr. Daddy-o: *Gayten, Paul* / Gold ain't everything: *Gayten, Paul* / Baby what's new: *Laurie, Annie* / My rough and ready man: *Laurie, Annie* / Low down feeling: *Laurie, Annie* / 3x7=21: *Laurie, Annie* / I don't marry to soon: *Laurie, Annie* / Messy Bessy: *Bartholomew, Dave* / Nickel wine: *Bartholomew, Dave* / Riding high: *Brown, Roy* / Brand new baby: *Brown, Roy*.
CD. . . . . . . . . . . . . . . . . . . . . .CDCHD 362
Ace / Jan '92 / Pinnacle / Complete Record Co. Ltd.

**RETURN OF SUPERBAD.**
**Tracks:** Not Advised.
■ CD. . . . . . . . . . . . . . . . . . . . . NCD 3421
■ LP . . . . . . . . . . . . . . . . . . . . . NE 1421
■ MC. . . . . . . . . . . . . . . . . . . . . CE 2421
K-Tel / Sep '88.

**REVIVAL 70'S, VOL.5 (Soft Soul Ballad Hits Of The 70's).**
**Tracks:** Hustle: *McCoy, Van* / Betcha by golly wow: *Stylistics* / Float on: *Floaters* / Drift away: *Gray, Dobie* / La la means I love you: *Delfonics* / Jack & Jill: *Raydio* / Loving you: *Riperton, Minnie* / Love's theme: *Love Unlimited Orchestra* / Just the way you are: *White, Barry* / Native New Yorker: *Odyssey* / Summer breeze: *Isley Brothers* / Wake up everybody: *Melvin, Harold & The Bluenotes* / Whole town's laughing at me: *Pendergrass, Teddy* / Greatest love of all: *Benson, George*.
■ LP . . . . . . . . . . . . . . . . . . . . . .OG 1019
■ MC. . . . . . . . . . . . . . . . . . . . . .OG 2019
Old Gold / Sep '87.

**REVIVAL 70'S, VOL.6 (Late 70's dance treats).**
**Tracks:** Don't leave me this way / Ain't no stoppin' us now: *McFadden & Whitehead* / September: *Earth, Wind & Fire* / Boogie nights: *Heatwave* / Boogie oogie oogie: *Taste Of Honey* / Ain't gonna bump no more: *Tex, Joe* / I will survive: *Gaynor, Gloria* / Best of my love: *Emotions (1)* / Heaven must be missing an angel: *Tavares* / Love really hurts without you: *Ocean, Billy* / Contact: *Starr, Edwin* / Get down: *Chandler, Gene* / Que sera mi vida: *Gibson Brothers* / I feel love: *Summer, Donna*.
LP . . . . . . . . . . . . . . . . . . . . . .OG 1020
MC. . . . . . . . . . . . . . . . . . . . . .OG 2020
Old Gold / Sep '87.

**RHYTHM & BLUE EYED SOUL.**
**Tracks:** Need your loving: *Flirtations* / Whose little girl: *Williams, Danny* / Ask the lonely: *Fantastics* / I wanna know: *Paul, John E* / Bert's apple crumble: *Quick* / I want you to be: *Davis, Billie* / Crawling up a hill: *Mayall, John* / Air travel: *Farlowe, Chris* / Name it you got it: *Moonshine, Micky* / Only a fool: *McPhatter, Clyde* / Don't change it: *Fearns Brass Foundry* / Girl don't make me wait: *Timebox* / Blue beat: *Beazers* / Looking back: *Williams, Larry & Johnny Watson* / Keep you hand out: *Spann, Otis* / Can't let her go: *Hipster Image*.
■ LP . . . . . . . . . . . . . . . . . . . . .KENT 086
Kent / Mar '89.

**RHYTHM AND BLUES HOUSEPARTY.**
**Tracks:** Let the doorbell ring: *Dale, Larry* / I'll never let you go (boo-hoo-hoo): *Little Richard* / Stranded in the jungle: *Cadets (1)* / Harbour lights: *Beasley, Jimmy* / Who's been fooling you: *Myles, Big Boy* / Chop chop: *Chimes (2)* / Hey fine mama: *Five Notes* / How long she's been gone: *Phillips, Marvin* / Ay la bah: *Cooper, Dolly* / Pretty soon: *Young Jessie* / Great pretender: *Fran, Carol* / These golden rings: *Jive Five* / Hole in the wall: *Dixon, Floyd* / Drag race: *Houston, Joe* / W-O-M-A-N: *James, Etta* / Ooh-Bop-She-Bop: *Dukes* / Come on little children: *Gaddy, Bob* / Every time I hear that mellow saxophone: *Montrell, Roy*.
CD. . . . . . . . . . . . . . . . . . . . . .CDCH 179
Ace / Jul '86 / Pinnacle / Complete Record Co. Ltd.
■ LP . . . . . . . . . . . . . . . . . . . . . . CH 179
■ MC. . . . . . . . . . . . . . . . . . . . . .CHC 179
Ace / Sep '86 / Pinnacle / Complete Record Co. Ltd.

**RHYTHM AND BLUES VOL.2.**
**Tracks:** Not Advised.
VHS . . . . . . . . . . . . . . . . . . . . .MMGV 044
Magnum / Jun '93 / THE.

**RHYTHM DIVINE VOL.2.**
**Tracks:** Dance to the music: *Stone, Sly* / Shake your body down to the ground: *Jacksons* / That lady: *Isley Brothers* / Best of my love: *Emotions (1)* / Backstabbers: *O'Jays* / Rock your baby: *McCrae, George* / That's the way I like it: *K.C. & The Sunshine Band* / Boogie oogie oogie: *Taste Of Honey* / Car wash: *Rose Royce* / I will survive: *Gaynor, Gloria* / When will see you again: *Three Degrees* / Contact: *Starr, Edwin* / This is it: *Moore, Melba* / More more more: *Andrea True Connection* / Heaven must be missing an angel: *Tavares* / Rock the boat: *Hues Corporation* / Right back where we started from: *Nightingale, Maxine* / Celebration: *Kool & The Gang* / Don't stop the music: *Yarbrough & Peoples* / Use it up wear it out: *Odyssey* / Shame: *King, Evelyn 'Champagne'* / Swing your Daddy: *Gilstrap, Jim* / Don't take away the music: *Tavares* / Be thankful for what you got: *DeVaughan, William* / Respect yourself: *Staple Singers* / Beat goes on: *Whispers* / Love town: *Newbury, Booker* / Somebody else's guy: *Brown, Jocelyn* / Change of heart: *Change* / Burn rubber on me: *Gap Band* / You gave me love: *Crown Heights Affair* / Message: *Grandmaster Flash* / I found lovin: *Fatback Band* / Hang on in there baby: *Bristol, Johnny*.
CD. . . . . . . . . . . . . . . . . . . . . . DINCD 27
MC. . . . . . . . . . . . . . . . . . . . . . DINMC 27
Dino / Oct '91 / Pinnacle.

**RHYTHM DIVINE, THE.**
**Tracks:** Blame it on the boogie: *Jacksons* / Love train: *O'Jays* / Harvest for the world: *Isley Brothers* / Boogie nights: *Heatwave* / Love really hurts without you: *Ocean, Billy* / Lady Marmalade: *Labelle* / Don't leave me this way: *Melvin, Harold* / Play that funky music: *Wild Cherry* / Family affair: *Stone, Sly* / Ladies night: *Kool & The Gang* / First, last, everything: *White, Barry* / Never can say goobye: *Gaynor, Gloria* / Funky town: *Lipps Inc.* / I feel love: *Summer, Donna* / Hustle: *McCoy, Van* / Oops up side your head: *Gap Band* / Young hearts run free: *Staton, Candi* / Le freak: *Chic* / Lost in music: *Sister Sledge* / Funky nassau: *Beginning Of The End* / Ain't nobody: *Khan, Chaka* / Southern freeze: *Freeze* / Move on up: *Mayfield, Curtis* / Baby don't change your mind: *Knight, Gladys* / You to me are everything: *Real Thing* / We are family: *Sister Sledge* / Now that we've found love: *Third World* / Mighty real: *Sylvester* / Walkin' in rhythm: *Blackbyrds* / Shaft: *Hayes, Isaac* / Feel the need in me: *Detroit Emeralds* / Suspicious minds: *Staton, Candi*.
LP . . . . . . . . . . . . . . . . . . . . . . DINTV 22
MC. . . . . . . . . . . . . . . . . . . . . . DINMC 22
■ CD. . . . . . . . . . . . . . . . . . . . . . DINCD 22
Dino / Jun '91.

**RHYTHM IN RHYTHM & BLUES, THE (1951-62).**
**Tracks:** I hear you knockin': *Lewis, Smiley* / Snag-a-tooth Jeanie: *Smith, Huey* / That's how you got killed before: *Bartholomew, Dave* / Domino stomp: *Domino, Fats* / I've been walkin': *Eaglin, Ford* / Bobby sox ramble: *Houston, Joe* / Deacon rides again: *McNeely, Big Jay* / Blue Monday: *Domino, Fats* / Shufflin' fox: *Bartholomew, Dave* / Bumpity bump: *Lewis, Smiley* / Sleepwalking woman: *Smilin' Joe* / Great big eyes: *Archibald* / Come on: *King, Earl*.
■ MC. . . . . . . . . . . . . . . . . . . . .TCSSL 6030
■ LP . . . . . . . . . . . . . . . . . . . . . SSL 6030
Stateside / Jul '87.

**RHYTHM IN SOUL.**
**Tracks:** Not Advised.
MC. . . . . . . . . . . . . . . . . . . . . . . ASK 782
Autograph / Apr '85.

**RHYTHM IN SOUL - VOL.2.**
**Tracks:** Not Advised.
MC. . . . . . . . . . . . . . . . . . . . . . . ASK 793
Autograph / Apr '85.

**RHYTHM OF THE NIGHT.**
**Tracks:** Single life: *Cameo (1)* / Freeway of love: *Franklin, Aretha* / Nightshift: *Commodores* / If you were here tonight: *O'Neal, Alexander* / Gotta get you home tonight: *Wilde, Eugene* / Treat her like a lady: *Temptations* / Love can turn around: *Farley 'Jackmaster' Funk* / Pull up to the bumper: *Jones, Grace* / Finest: *S.O.S. Band* / Mine all mine: *Cashflow* / Cherish: *Kool & The Gang* / Your love is king: *Sade* / Ain't nothin' goin' on but the rent: *Guthrie, Gwen* / Rhythm of the night: *DeBarge* / Loco in Acapulco: *Four Tops* / Wishing well: *D'Arby, Terence Trent* / Jump for my love: *Pointer Sisters* / Who's zoomin' who: *Franklin, Aretha* / Get outta my dreams get into my car: *Ocean, Billy* / Star: *Earth, Wind & Fire* / Can't wait another minute: *Five Star* / Best of my love: *Emotions (2)* / Always & Forever: *Heatwave* / Lies: *Butler, Jonathan* / Caravan of love: *Isley-Jasper-Isley* / Why (Can't we live together): *Sade* / I won't cry: *Goldsmith, Glen* / I'd rather go blind: *Turner, Ruby* / On the wings of love: *Osborne, Jeffrey* / Sweetest Sweetest: *Jackson, Jermaine* / Hurt: *Manhattans* / Never too much: *Vandross, Luther*.
■ CD. . . . . . . . . . . . . . . . . . . . . . NCD 3348
■ LP . . . . . . . . . . . . . . . . . . . . . . NE 1348
■ MC. . . . . . . . . . . . . . . . . . . . . . CE 2348
K-Tel / Feb '87.

**RIGHT BACK WHERE WE STARTED FROM.**
**Tracks:** Right back where we started from: *Nightingale, Maxine* / Snake: *Wilson, Al* / Better use your head: *Imperials* / City lights: *Naylor, Jerry* / Baby mine: *Houston, Thelma* / This beautiful day: *Jackson, Levi* / Nobody but me: *Human Beinz* / Leap frog: *Nelson, Sandy* / So is the sun: *World Column* / Looking for you: *Mimms, Garnet* / End of our love: *Wilson, Nancy* / Number one in your heart: *Goins, Herbie & The Nightimers* / In the midnight hour: *Preston, Billy* / Got hung up along the way: *Jay & The Americans* / Time won't let me: *Outsiders (2)*.
■ LP . . . . . . . . . . . . . . . . . . . . . KENT 039
Kent / May '85.

**RIGHT TRACK, THE.**
**Tracks:** Right track: *Butler, Billy* / Angel baby: *Carrow, George* / You don't want me no more: *Lance, Major* / Where have all the flowers gone: *Jackson, Walter* / Counting on you baby: *McNeil, Landy* / I still love you: *Seven Souls* / Call me tomorrow: *Harris, Major* / Danse a la musique: *French Fries* / Talkin' 'bout poor folks: *Edwards, Lou* / I worship you baby: *Glories* / I'm in a world of trouble: *Sweet Things* / I need you: *Martin, Shane* / Too late: *Williams, Larry & Johnny Watson* / Chain reaction: *Spellbinders* / I don't want to discuss it: *Little Richard*.
■ LP . . . . . . . . . . . . . . . . . . . . . . SINLP 3
SMP / '86.

# S

**S.O.U.L. AGENTS.**
**Tracks:** I don't want to lose you: *Wilson, Jackie* / Girl I need you: *Artistics* / Everything's wrong: *Cooperettes* / I'm the one to do it: *Baker, LaVern* / After you: *Acklin, Barbara* / Keep your chin up: *Ross, Jackie* / Love ain't nothin' but pain: *Smith, Marvin* / Ain't there something money can't buy: *Young-Holt Unlimited* / I get the sweetest feeling: *Franklin, Erma* / One monkey don't stop no show: *Baker, LaVern* / From the teacher to the preacher: *Chandler, Gene & Barbara Acklin* / Thank you baby: *Butler, Billy* / There goes the lover: *Chandler, Gene* / That's what you are to me: *Robbins, Tracie* / To change my love: *Chi-Lites* / You left me: *Artistics*.
■ LP . . . . . . . . . . . . . . . . . . . . . KENT 025
Kent / Sep '84.

### S.O.U.L. SAMPLER 1993.
**Tracks:** I'll be your winner: *Clark, Jimmy Soul* / Oh my darlin': *Lee, Jackie* / Pizza pie man: *Grier, Roosevelt* / Hide out: *Hideaways* / Girl across the street: *Smith, Moses* / Lady love: *Vontastics* / I've been trying: *Chants* / I need your love: *Woods, Ella* / This love: *Joytones* / Streets got my lady: *Brandon, Bill* / Girl I love you: *Fisher, Shelley* / Given up on love: *Thompson, Johnny* / Searching for soul: *Wade, Jake & the soul searchers* / Everything's gonna be alright: *Moore, Robert* / You: *Wilson, Spanky*.
■ **CD** . . . . . . . . . . . . . . . . . . . . **GSCD 013**
Goldmine / Apr '93.

### SAFE SOUL VOL.1.
**Tracks:** Just loving you: *Green, Garland* / Once you fall in love: *McLoyd, Eddie* / I'll see you in hell first: *Mitchell, Phillip* / Rising cost of love: *Jackson, Millie* / it takes both of us: *Act One* / If I can't have your love: *Brown, Jocelyn* / Plenty of love: *C-Brand* / Stay with me: *Martin, Daltrey* / Still in love with you: *Bailey, J.R.* / My shining star: *Fatback Band* / Sweet music, soft lights and you: *Jackson, Millie & Isaac Hayes* / I'll see you in hell first (alternative take) (Available on CD only): *Mitchell, Phillip* / Feed me your love (Available on CD only): *Fatback Band*.
**CD** . . . . . . . . . . . . . . . . . . . . **CDSEW 020**
■ **LP** . . . . . . . . . . . . . . . . . . . . **SEW 020**
South Bound / Jan '90.

### SAFE SOUL VOL.2.
**Tracks:** Never like this: *Two Tons* / Hooked on you: *Simmons, David* / I think I love you: *Shock* / It's way too late: *Watson, Johnny 'Guitar'* / Love starved: *Brown, Shirley* / Whatcha see is whatcha get: *Dramatics* / Lovin': *Hurtt, Phil* / Shouting out love: *Emotions (2)* / Ghettos of the mind: *Pleasure (2)* / Always there: *Side Effect* / Everybody's singin' love songs (Available on CD format only.): *Sweet Thunder* / Ladies night out (Available on CD format only.): *Pleasure (2)*.
**CD** . . . . . . . . . . . . . . . . . . . . **CDSEWD 022**
**LP** . . . . . . . . . . . . . . . . . . . . **SEWD 022**
South Bound / Aug '90 / Pinnacle.

### SALSOUL 1.
**Tracks:** All of my lovin': *Williams, Jimmy* / Are you single: *Aurra* / All about the paper: *Holloway, Loleatta* / Can you see where I'm coming from: *Instant Funk* / Ten per cent: *Double Exposure* / Take some time: *Salsoul Orchestra* / Step out of my dream: *Stranglers* / Falling in love: *Surface*.
■ **LP** . . . . . . . . . . . . . . . . . . . . **LIPS 1**
Graphic / Jun '88.
■ **MC** . . . . . . . . . . . . . . . . . . . . **TCLIPS 1**
Kiss / Jun '88.

### SALSOUL MASTERCUTS CLASSICS VOL.1.
**Tracks:** Not Advised.
**CD** . . . . . . . . . . . . . . . . . . . . **CUTSCD 10**
Beechwood / Feb '93 / Pinnacle.
**Double LP** . . . . . . . . . . . . . . . . **CUTSLP 10**
**MC** . . . . . . . . . . . . . . . . . . . . **CUTSMC 10**
Salsoul / Feb '93 / BMG.

### SALSOUL MASTERCUTS CLASSICS VOL.2.
**Tracks:** First choice: *Dr. Love* / My love is free: *Double Exposure* / Ain't no mountain high enough: *Inner Life* / This will be a night to remember: *Holman, Eddie* / Just as long as I got you: *Love Committee* / Helplessly: *Moment Of Truth* / Spring rain: *Silvetti* / Moment of my life: *Inner Life* / Sing sing: *Gaz* / Hit and run: *Holloway, Loleatta* / Ooh, I love it (love break): *Salsoul Orchestra* / Dancin' and prancin': *Candido*.
**CD** . . . . . . . . . . . . . . . . . . . . **CUTSCD 13**
**LP** . . . . . . . . . . . . . . . . . . . . **CUTSLP 13**
**MC** . . . . . . . . . . . . . . . . . . . . **CUTSMC 13**
Beechwood / Jun '93 / Pinnacle.

### SAMPLER 1994, THE.
**Tracks:** Your love makes me lonely: *Chandlers* / I don't want to hear it: *Exits* / Give in to the power of love: *Committee* / Ain't gonna do you no harm: *Willis, Betty* / Lighten up baby: *Karim, Ty* / Dontcha tell nobody: *Vont Claires* / Candle: *Durdick, Doni* / I don't mess around: *Reynolds, Jeannie* / What have I got now: *Fletcher, Darrow* / All of a sudden: *Incredibles* / I found out: *Lacour, Bobby* / I'll cry over you: *Sheeler, Cynthia* / I'll cry 1000 tears: *Holman, Eddie* / Let's get together: *George, Cassietta* / Crumbs off the table: *Young Disciples* / Breakdown: *Memphians* / Cool off: *Detroit Executives*.
**CD** . . . . . . . . . . . . . . . . . . . . **GSCD 034**
Goldmine / Apr '94 / Vital Distribution.

### SANCTIFIED SOUL.
**Tracks:** Not Advised.
**CD** . . . . . . . . . . . . . . . . . . . . **241 704 2**
Atlantic / '88 / WEA.
■ **LP** . . . . . . . . . . . . . . . . . . . . **241 703 1**
**MC** . . . . . . . . . . . . . . . . . . . . **241 703 4**
Atlantic / Nov '89 / WEA.

### SATISFYING OUR SOULS.
**Tracks:** Don't pity me: *Sommers, Joanie* / Mr. Creator: *Apollas* / I remember the feeling: *Lewis, Barbara* / Contact: *Three Degrees* / Love don't you go through no changes on me: *Sister Sledge* / Afternoon of the rhino: *Post, Mike Coalition* / Feels good: *Wilson, Bobby* / Don't you even care: *Uggams, Leslie* / I just can't live my life (without you babe): *Jones, Linda* / Thank you baby for loving me: *Soul Brothers Six* / Crazy baby: *Coasters* / Satisfied: *Aiken, Ben* / Catch me I'm falling: *Phillips, Esther* / Bring your love back to me: *Lyndell, Linda* / Stirrin' up some soul: *Markett's* / (I love her so much) it hurts me: *David & Rueben*.
■ **LP** . . . . . . . . . . . . . . . . . . . . **KENT 092**
Kent / Jun '89.

### SATURDAY NIGHT DISCO PARTY.
**Tracks:** You should be dancing / Beat goes on and on / Doctor Love / Hit and run / Night fever / Ten per cent / Stayin' alive / Dance a little bit closer.
■ **LP** . . . . . . . . . . . . . . . . . . . . **SSLM 4001**
Salsoul / Sep '78.

### SEHORN'S SOUL FARM.
**Tracks:** Star revue: *Lee, Warren* / Why you wanna do it: *Harper, Willie* / Blues, tears and sorrow: *Williams, John (2)* / Sinner girl: *Spellman, Benny* / Love affair: *Holmes, Eldridge* / Let's make it: *Haywood, Joe* / Get low down: *Moore, Curley* / Hercules: *Neville, Aaron* / Struttin' on Sunday: *Neville, Aaron* / Climb the ladder: *Lee, Warren* / Don't pity me: *Moore, Curley* / Oh love, this is Sonny: *Fisher, Sonny* / All my love: *King, Earl* / That's what you need: *Harper, Willie* / Gossip, gossip: *Diamond Joe* / Hotcha mama: *Doe, Ernie K.*.
■ **LP** . . . . . . . . . . . . . . . . . . . . **CRB 1032**
Charly R&B / Feb '82.

### SEXUAL HEALING.
**Tracks:** Sexual healing: *Gaye, Marvin* / Never too much: *Vandross, Luther* / There's nothing like this: *Omar* / Baby come to me: *Austin, Patti & James Ingram* / Get here: *Adams, Oleta* / If you were here tonight: *O'Neal, Alexander* / Joy and pain: *Maze Featuring Frankie Beverly* / When a man loves a woman: *Sledge, Percy* / If you don't know me by now: *Melvin, Harold & The Bluenotes* / Rock me tonight (for old times sake): *Jackson, Freddie* / Solid: *Ashford & Simpson* / Rock your baby: *McCrae, George* / Hang on in there baby: *Bristol, Johnny* / I want your sex: *Michael, George* / I'm gonna love you just a little more babe: *White, Barry* / Love won't let me wait: *Harris, Major* / Tonight I celebrate my love: *Flack, Roberta & Peabo Bryson* / I want to wake up with you: *Gardiner, Boris*.
**CD** . . . . . . . . . . . . . . . . . . . . **CDEMTV 60**
■ **LP** . . . . . . . . . . . . . . . . . . . . **EMTV 60**
■ **MC** . . . . . . . . . . . . . . . . . . . . **TCEMTV 60**
EMI / Oct '91.

### SHEER ECSTASY.
**Tracks:** Doctor's orders: *Maegan* / I've got you where I want you, babe: *Stereo Fun Inc.* / Trouble in Paradise: *Sylvester* / Dancing through the night: *Alikia* / Love me real: *Gaynor, Gloria* / Ready or not: *Miller, Cat* / Pillow talk: *Lusst* / My man must be American: *Simone* / Too late: *Sylvester* / Go go gorilla: *Gazuzu*.
■ **LP** . . . . . . . . . . . . . . . . . . . . **XTLP 4**
**MC** . . . . . . . . . . . . . . . . . . . . **XTCC 4**
Ecstasy / Nov '84.

### SHEER ECSTASY (VOL. 2).
**Tracks:** Rhythm of your love (Re-mix): *Roberts, Isabel* / Living for the city: *Sylvester* / Sizzlin': *Mitchell, Brenda* / With you I could have it all: *Houston, Cissy* / I don't wanna fall in love again: *Silver, Karen* / AM-FM: *King, Natasha* / So shy: *Mac Mac - Jammolott kingdom* / Love is like an itching in my heart: *Cijay* / Big time operator: *Coulson, Julie* / Spotlite of love: *Juice*.
■ **LP** . . . . . . . . . . . . . . . . . . . . **XTLP 5**
**MC** . . . . . . . . . . . . . . . . . . . . **XTCC 5**
Ecstasy / May '86.

### SHOVE IT.
**Tracks:** My man, a sweet man: *Jackson, Millie* / Night fever: *Fatback Band* / Can you get to that: *Funkadelic* / Pain: *Ohio Players* / Baby let me take you (in my arms): *Detroit Emeralds* / Man size job: *Lasalle, Denise* / Keep on stepping: *Fatback Band* / Get down, get down (get on the floor): *Simon, Joe* / Pleasure: *Ohio Players* / It's all over but the shouting: *Jackson, Millie* / Funky dollar bill: *Funkadelic*.
**CD** . . . . . . . . . . . . . . . . . . . . **CDSEWX 015**
**MC** . . . . . . . . . . . . . . . . . . . . **SEWCX 015**
■ **LP** . . . . . . . . . . . . . . . . . . . . **SEWX 015**
Westbound / Oct '89.

### SHRINE - THE RAREST SOUL LABEL.
**Tracks:** Don't let him hurt you: *Les Chansonettes* / Guess who loves you: *Daye, Eddie & Four Bars* / No other way: *Cautions* / Dream my heart: *Edwards, Shirley* / No more like me: *Pollard, Ray* / I'm a lover: *Hall, Sidney*.
**LP** . . . . . . . . . . . . . . . . . . . . **HRH 1 LP**
Horaces / May '90.

### SILKY SOUL HITS OF THE 70'S (OLD GOLD).
**Tracks:** Not Advised.
■ **LP** . . . . . . . . . . . . . . . . . . . . **OG 1004**
■ **MC** . . . . . . . . . . . . . . . . . . . . **OG 2004**
Old Gold / Jun '85.

### SING A SONG OF SOUL.
**Tracks:** Soul of the man: *Fontella Bass* / Don't mess up a good thing: *Fontella Bass* / We're gonna make it: *Little Milton* / Voice the choice: *Maurice & The Radiants* / Take me for a little while: *Ross, Jackie* / Love ain't nothin': *Nash, Johnny* / Wang dang doodle: *Taylor, Koko* / I had to talk with my man: *Collier, Mitty* / Searching for my love: *Moore, Bob* / Temptation 'bout to get me: *Knight Brothers* / Love is a five letter word: *Phelps, James* / only time will tell: *James, Etta* / I do love you: *Stewart, Billy*.
■ **LP** . . . . . . . . . . . . . . . . . . . . **CRL 4519**
Chess / Dec '66.

### SIXTIES SOUL STARS.
**Tracks:** Not Advised.
■ **CD Set** . . . . . . . . . . . . . . . . . . **CDBOX 253**
■ **LP Set** . . . . . . . . . . . . . . . . . . **BOX 253**
■ **MC Set** . . . . . . . . . . . . . . . . . . **TCBOX 253**
Charly / Nov '89.

### SIXTIES, THE (Motown Time Capsule).
**Tracks:** Not Advised.
**VHS** . . . . . . . . . . . . . . . . . . . . **VHR 1220**
CIC Video / Mar '87 / Sony / Pickwick / THE / Gold & Sons.

### SLIDE GUITAR GOSPEL 1944-64.
**Tracks:** Not Advised.
**CD** . . . . . . . . . . . . . . . . . . . . **DOCD 5222**
Document / Apr '94 / Vital Distribution / Hot Shot / Jazz Music.

### SLIPPIN' AROUND.
**Tracks:** Not Advised.
**CD** . . . . . . . . . . . . . . . . . . . . **HDH CD 010**
■ **LP** . . . . . . . . . . . . . . . . . . . . **HDH LP 010**
HDH / Oct '89.

### SLIPSTREAM - THE BEST OF BRITISH JAZZ FUNK.
**Tracks:** London Town: *Light Of The World* / Girl / Feels like the right time: *Shakatak* / Southern Freeez: *Freeez* / Turn it on: *Level 42* / Locomoto Inversions / You know you can do it: *Central Line* / Slipstream: *Morrissey-Mullen* / Shaping up: *Hipnosis* / W.T.L.D.L.T.W.: *Multivision* / Roberto Who Cayenne / Incognito: *Incognito*.
■ **LP** . . . . . . . . . . . . . . . . . . . . **BEGA 3**
■ **MC** . . . . . . . . . . . . . . . . . . . . **BEGC 3**
Beggars Banquet / Nov '81.

### SLOW JAM 2.
**Tracks:** Not Advised.
■ **LP** . . . . . . . . . . . . . . . . . . . . **SLJAM 2**
■ **MC** . . . . . . . . . . . . . . . . . . . . **ZCJAM 2**
Street Sounds.

### SLOW JAM 3.
**Tracks:** Not Advised.
■ **LP** . . . . . . . . . . . . . . . . . . . . **SLJAM 3**
**MC** . . . . . . . . . . . . . . . . . . . . **ZCJAM 3**
Street Sounds / Jul '87 / BMG / Total.

### SLOW MOTION (14 Urban Contemporary Love Ballads).
**Tracks:** Your body's calling: *R. Kelly* / Let me do U: *P.O.V.* / All night: *Me 2 U* / Please tell me tonight: *Motiv* / Don't go nowhere: *Riff (2)* / Always: *Mint Condition* / When I need somebody: *Tresvant, Ralph* / I got a thang 4 ya: *Low Key* / La la love: *Avila Bobby Ross* / Make love 2 me: *Lorenzo* / Baby it' real: *Serenade* / I'll be there for you: *M.L.* / Wait fo me: *Chalant* / Gangsta lean: *D.R.S.*.
**CD** . . . . . . . . . . . . . . . . . . . . **CDELV 1**
**LP** . . . . . . . . . . . . . . . . . . . . **LPELV 1**
**MC** . . . . . . . . . . . . . . . . . . . . **MCELV 1**
Elevate / Jun '94 / 3MV.

### SLOW 'N' MOODY, BLACK 'N' BLUESY
**Tracks:** Nothing can change this love: *Hill, Z.Z.* / Yo messed up my mind: *Hammond, Clay* / I can't stan it: *Holiday, Jimmy* / Directly from my heart: *Littl Richard* / I don't need: *Turner, Ike & Tina* / Let's g together: *Arthur & Mary* / Darling I'm standing b you: *Jones, Jeanette* / Baby i'll come right awa

Love, Mary / If i'd lose you: Day, Jackie / I don't wanna lose you: Young, Tami / (Baby) come to me: Little Henry & The Shamrocks / Ain't nobody's business: King, B.B. / Every dog has his day: Copeland, Johnny / Baby what you want me to do: Little Richard / Baby I'll come: Love, Mary / Everybody needs somebody: Love, Mary / Weep no more: Terry & The Tyrants / It's real (part 1): Robbins, Jimmy / Can't count the days: Robbins, Jimmy / Whenever I can't sleep: Gauff, Willie & The Love Brothers / Last one to know: Haywood, Joe / Mr. President: Haywood, Joe / Woman needs a man: Baker, Yvonne / Farewell: Gauff, Willie & The Love Brothers / Why should I be the one: Gauff, Willie & The Love Brothers / I'll come back to you: Mighty Hannibal / Consider yourself: Johnson, Stacey.
■ LP . . . . . . . . . . . . . . . . . . . . KENT 003
Kent / Jul '83.
CD . . . . . . . . . . . . . . . . . . . . CDKEND 003
Kent / Nov '94 / Pinnacle.

**SMART.**
**Tracks:** My little red book: *Middleton, Tony* / Mellow moonlight: *Haywood, Leon* / Take me for a little while: *Mirettes* / Skate: *Parrish, Dean* / One wonderful moment: *Shakers* / Stand by me: *Grant, Earl* / Great googa mooga: *Tom & Jerrio* / You better move on: *Alexander, Arthur* / Two ways to skin a cat: *Reed, Jimmy* / Love love love: *Barry, Len* / I don't know: *Alaimo, Steve* / Turn on your lovelight: *Bland, Bobby* / Can't satisfy: *Impressions* / Night life: *King, B.B.* / Someone out there: *Candy & The Kisses*.
■ LP . . . . . . . . . . . . . . . . . . . . KENT 052
Kent / Mar '86.

**SOLAR GALAXY OF STARS.**
**Tracks:** Lady: *Whispers* / Song for Donnie: *Whispers* / And the beat goes on: *Whispers* / Right in the socket: *Shalamar* / I owe you one: *Shalamar* / Take that to the bank: *Shalamar* / Second time around: *Shalamar* / Givin' in to love: *Lakeside* / All the way live: *Lakeside* / Rock: *Dynasty* / I've just begun to love you: *Dynasty* / I don't wanna be a freak: *Dynasty*.
■ Double LP . . . . . . . . . . . . . . . . SOLA 4
MC Set . . . . . . . . . . . . . . . . . . SOLC 4
Solar / Oct '80 / Sony.

**SOLAR SYSTEM, THE.**
**Tracks:** Midas touch: *Midnight Star* / And the beat goes on: *Whispers* / Take that to the bank: *Shalamar* / Romeo where's Juliet: *Collage* / Wet my whistle: *Midnight Star* / It's a love thing: *Whispers* / There it is: *Shalamar* / Get in touch with me: *Collage* / Headlines: *Midnight Star* / Night to remember: *Shalamar* / Sweet sensation: *Whispers* / Operator (edited version): *Midnight Star* / Over and over: *Shalamar* / Some kinda lover: *Whispers*.
■ LP . . . . . . . . . . . . . . . . . . . . MCG 3338
■ CD . . . . . . . . . . . . . . . . . . . . DMCG 3338
■ MC . . . . . . . . . . . . . . . . . . . . MCGC 3338
MCA / May '87.

**SOLD ON SOUL.**
**Tracks:** Be careful girl: *Turner, Betty* / Serving a sentence of life: *Douglas, Carl* / Drifter: *Pollard, Ray* / Your eyes may shine: *Short Kuts* / I lost a true love: *Wagner, Danny* / Walk with a winner: *lcDaniels, Gene* / Hold on: *O'Jays* / Find me love: *eShannon, Jackie* / Surrounded by a ray of sunshine: *Jones, Samantha* / My dear heart: *Robinson, Shawn* / Better use your head: *Imperials* / Nothing's too good for my baby: *Nelson, Sandy*.
■ LP . . . . . . . . . . . . . . . . . . . . LBR 1007
United Artists / May '80.

**SOLID GOLD SOUL.**
**Tracks:** Got to get you off my mind: *Burke, Solomon* / Just out of reach: *Burke, Solomon* / Don't fight it: *Pickett, Wilson* / In the midnight hour: *Pickett, Wilson* / I want to do everything for you: *Tex, Joe* / Hold what you've got: *Tex, Joe* / See-saw: *Covay, Don* / Mercy: *Covay, Don* / Don't play that song: *King, Ben E.* / I've been loving you too long: *Redding, Otis* / Mr. Pitiful: *Redding, Otis*.
■ LP . . . . . . . . . . . . . . . . . . . . 588 037
Atlantic / Dec '66.

**SOLID HITBOUND STORY, THE (A Collection Of Rare Detroit 60's Soul).**
**Tracks:** I must love you: *Davis, Melvin* / That's why I love you: *Professionals (1)* / Hit and run: *Owens, Gwen* / Watch out: *Inst* / Friday night: *Mancha, Steve* / Just can't leave you: *Hester, Tony* / Baby baby: *Pokays* / Still in my heart: *Davis, Melvin* / Just like my baby: *Inst* / Deeper in love: *Mancha, Steve* / Headache in my heart: *DeBarge, Bunny* / I lost you: *Holidays* / Look what I almost missed: *Lewis, Pat* / Heartbreaker: *Gilford, Jimmy* / Never alone: *Inst*.
CD . . . . . . . . . . . . . . . . . . . . GSCD 053
Goldmine / Oct '94 / Vital Distribution.

**SOLID SOUL.**
**Tracks:** Stand by me: *King, Ben E.* / Soul man: *Sam & Dave* / Knock on wood: *Floyd, Eddie* / My guy: *Wells, Mary* / Hey there lonely girl: *Holman, Eddie* / Patches: *Carter, Clarence* / Rescue me: *Bass, Fontella* / Mr. Big Stuff: *Knight, Jean* / Backfield in motion: *Mel & Tim* / Tighten up: *Bell, Archie & The Drells* / Harry hippie: *Womack, Bobby* / Satisfaction guaranteed: *Melvin, Harold & The Bluenotes* / In crowd: *Gray, Dobie* / When a man loves a woman: *Sledge, Percy*.
■ CD . . . . . . . . . . . . . . . . . . . . ONCD 5123
K-Tel / May '87.

**SOLID SOUL (2).**
**Tracks:** You're the first, the last, my everything: *White, Barry* / Hang on in there girl: *Bristol, Johnny* / Wonderful world: *Cooke, Sam* / Don't leave me this way: *Melvin, Harold & The Bluenotes* / Papa was a rollin' stone: *Temptations* / Family affair: *Sly & The Family Stone* / Didn't I (blow your mind this time): *Delfonics* / Working in a coalmine: *Dorsey, Lee* / Harlem shuffle: *Bob & Earl* / You make me feel brand new: *Stylistics* / Tired of being alone: *Green, Al* / I heard it through the grapevine: *Gaye, Marvin* / How sweet it is (to be loved by you): *Walker, Junior & The All Stars* / Papa's got a brand new bag: *Brown, James* / Barefootin': *Parker, Robert* / Love train: *O'Jays* / Reet petite: *Wilson, Jackie*.
CD . . . . . . . . . . . . . . . . . . . . TCD 2304
■ LP . . . . . . . . . . . . . . . . . . . . STAR 2304
MC . . . . . . . . . . . . . . . . . . . . STAC 2304
Telstar/Ronco / Nov '87 / BMG.

**SOLID SOUL SENSATIONS.**
**Tracks:** Not Advised.
■ LP . . . . . . . . . . . . . . . . . . . . DDLP 5001
Pye Disco Demand / Jun '75.

**SOME 'MODERN' SOUL (The Buddah Collection).**
**Tracks:** Oh lovin' you: *Paragons* / Dance and free your mind Pt. 1: *Sins of Satan* / Sharing: *Vitamin E* / Midnight lady: *Morris, David Jnr.* / Deeper and deeper: *Wilson, Bobby* / Makin' love ain't no fun (without the one you love): *Ebonys* / I wanna make love to you: *Norman, Jimmy* / I can't fight your love: *Modulations* / You and I: *Anderson, Joe* / Everybody stand and clap your hands (for the entertainer): *Black Satin & Fred Parris*.
CD . . . . . . . . . . . . . . . . . . . . NEXCD 154
■ Double LP . . . . . . . . . . . . . . . . NEXLP 154
Sequel / Feb '91.

**SON OF STAX FUNK.**
**Tracks:** Title theme (Tough guys): *Hayes, Isaac* / Type thang: *Hayes, Isaac* / Steppin' out: *Sho Nuff* / Mix match man: *Sho Nuff* / What does it take: *Sons Of Slum* / Man: *Sons Of Slum* / Getting funky round here: *Black Nasty* / Nasty soul: *Black Nasty* / Watch the dog: *Shack* / Patch it up: *Johnson, Roy Lee* / Funky hot grits: *Thomas, Rufus* / Soul town: *Forevers* / Shake your big hips: *Tolbert, Israel* / Bump meat: *Rice, Sir Mack* / Do me: *Knight, Jean* / In the hole: *Bar-Kays* / Watch me do it (On CD only): *Sho Nuff* / Right on (On CD only): *Sons Of Slum* / Talkin' to the people (On CD only): *Black Nasty* / I'd kill a brick for my man (On CD only): *Hot Sauce* / Carry on (On CD only): *Knight, Jean* / Sang & dance (On CD only): *Bar-Kays* / Do the funky chicken (On CD only): *Thomas, Rufus* / Devil is dope (On CD only): *Dramatics*.
CD . . . . . . . . . . . . . . . . . . . . CDSXD 075
LP . . . . . . . . . . . . . . . . . . . . SXD 075
Stax / Feb '93 / Pinnacle.

**SOPHISTICATED SOUNDS (Soul For The Connoisseur).**
**Tracks:** Since I found love: *Hadley, Sandy* / You could be my remedy / Call on Billy: *Soul, Billy T.* / I'm a lover: *Carter, Chuck* / Hurt: *North, Freddie* / I wouldn't change a thing about you: *Wyatt, Johnny* / You say: *Esquires* / You must be losing: *Raye, Jimmy* / Love is a good foundation: *Uggams, Leslie* / I don't want to lose you: *Wynn, Mel* / Change: *Eady, Ernestine* / Yesterday's kisses: *Big Maybelle* / You got my love: *Wells, Donnie* / I'm gonna have a party: *Bruce, Ed* / Lover: *Hunt, Tommy*.
■ LP . . . . . . . . . . . . . . . . . . . . KENT 079
Kent / Jun '88.

**SOUL - IN THE BEGINNING.**
**Tracks:** December 7th / 1941 / Mojo hand / Tell me where you stayed last night / Down & out / Line on your body / Trouble in mind / Be my chauffeur / Please come back to me / Treat your daddy well.
■ LP . . . . . . . . . . . . . . . . . . . . 6467251
Avco-Embassy / '72.

**SOUL AFFAIR.**
**Tracks:** What becomes of the broken hearted: *Ruffin, Jimmy* / Hey girl don't bother me: *Tams* / If you don't know me by now: *Melvin, Harold* / Everlasting love: *Knight, Robert* / Hey there lonely girl: *Holman, Eddie* / Save the last dance for me: *Drifters* / Stand by me: *King, Ben E.* / I will: *Winters, Ruby* / When a man loves a woman: *Sledge, Percy* / Do it anyway you wanna: *People's Choice* / Backfield in motion: *Mel & Tim* / Love on a mountain top: *Knight, Robert* / Mr. Big Stuff: *Carne, Jean* / Love I lost: *Melvin, Harold & The Bluenotes* / Knock on wood: *Floyd, Eddie* / Show and tell: *Wilson, Al* / I've passed this way before: *Ruffin, Jimmy* / Something old, something new: *Fantastics* / Tighten up: *Bell, Archie* / Harlem shuffle: *Bob & Earl*.
CD . . . . . . . . . . . . . . . . . . . . CRXCD 14
■ LP . . . . . . . . . . . . . . . . . . . . CRX 14
MC . . . . . . . . . . . . . . . . . . . . CRXC 14
Creole / Jun '88 / THE / BMG.

**SOUL AND THEN SOME.**
**Tracks:** Not Advised.
■ LP . . . . . . . . . . . . . . . . . . . . BLUE LP 1
Blue Chip / Jul '89.

**SOUL BALLADS.**
**Tracks:** Fresh: *Kool & The Gang* / Let the music play: *White, Barry* / Don't walk away: *Four Tops* / Hold on to my love: *Ruffin, Jimmy* / Hot pants: *Brown, James* / I really didn't mean it: *Vandross, Luther* / Harvest for the world: *Isley Brothers* / Shake you down: *Abbott, Gregory* / Sexual healing: *Gaye, Marvin* / Hurt: *Manhattans* / Hold me tight: *Nash, Johnny* / Use it up and wear it out: *Odyssey* / Freeway of love: *Franklin, Aretha* / Rock the boat: *Hues Corporation* / System addict: *Five Star* / In the midnight hour: *Reeves, Martha* / If you feel it: *Houston, Thelma* / (They long to be) close to you: *Guthrie, Gwen* / Girls are more fun: *Parker, Ray Jnr.* / Goin' to the bank: *Commodores*.
CD . . . . . . . . . . . . . . . . . . . . STAMCD 018
MC . . . . . . . . . . . . . . . . . . . . STAMC 018
Stardust / Oct '92 / Pickwick / Conifer Records.

**SOUL BALLADS.**
**Tracks:** Not Advised.
CD . . . . . . . . . . . . . . . . . . . . MPV 5550
MC . . . . . . . . . . . . . . . . . . . . MPV 45550
Movieplay / Apr '94 / Target / Midland Records / BMG.

**SOUL BEAT.**
**Tracks:** Going nowhere: *Gabrielle* / How can I love you more: *M People* / Don't walk away: *Jade (1)* / Right here: *S.W.V.* / I love your smile: *Shanice* / Tom's diner: *DNA (1)* / When I'm good and ready: *Sybil* / Please don't go: *KWS* / Now that we've found love: *Heavy D & The Boyz* / I'm doing fine now: *Pasadenas* / Love I lost: *West End Featuring Sybil* / I wanna sex you up: *Color Me Badd* / Gypsy woman: *Waters, Crystal* / Ain't no Cassanova: *Sinclair (1)* / Things that make you go hmmm: *C & C Music Factory* / I will survive: *Gaynor, Gloria* / Best of my love: *Lovestation* / Everybody dance: *Evolution* / U got 2 let the music: *Cappella* / Motownphilly: *Boyz II Men*.
CD . . . . . . . . . . . . . . . . . . . . JARCD 9
MC . . . . . . . . . . . . . . . . . . . . JARTC 9
Cookie Jar / Nov '93.

**SOUL BY THE SEA.**
**Tracks:** Not Advised.
CD . . . . . . . . . . . . . . . . . . . . BBCCD 857
LP . . . . . . . . . . . . . . . . . . . . REB 857
MC . . . . . . . . . . . . . . . . . . . . ZCF 857
BBC / Jul '91 / Pinnacle / Bond Street Music / THE.

**SOUL CHASERS.**
**Tracks:** Got to get away: *Brown, Sheree* / Be for real: *Miller, Cat* / Do it any way you want: *Winters, Robert* / Trying to get to you: *Carter, Valerie* / (A case of) Too much love makin': *Scott, Gloria* / Top of the stairs: *Collins and Collins* / I want to be your everything: *High Fashion* / Would you believe in me: *Lucien, John* / All of my love: *Jeter, Genobia* / Looking up to you: *Wycoff, Michael* / And so it begins: *Syreeta* / Never stopped loving you: *Davis, Tyrone* / Hold tight: *Magic Lady* / Call me: *Reynolds, L.J.*.
CD . . . . . . . . . . . . . . . . . . . . CD EXP4
■ LP . . . . . . . . . . . . . . . . . . . . LP EXP4
MC . . . . . . . . . . . . . . . . . . . . MC EXP4
Expansion / Nov '92 / Pinnacle / Sony / 3MV.

**SOUL CHRISTMAS.**
**Tracks:** Not Advised.
■ LP . . . . . . . . . . . . . . . . . . . . SD 33269
Atco / Jun '88.

**SOUL CITIES.**
**Tracks:** Stop shovin' me around: *Delicates* / First date: *Doods, Nella* / Why why why: *Leavill, Otis* / Hang up the phone: *Wyatt, Johnny* / She broke his heart: *Just Brothers* / I refuse to give up: *Reid, Clarence* / Look my way: *Williams, Maurice* / One who really loves you: *Sugar Pie Desanto* / Get a hold

of yourself: *Platters* / Midsummer night in Harlem: *Thomas, Charlie* / Send my baby back: *Hughes, Freddie* / Dedicated to the greatest: *Copeland, Johnny* / Fall guy: *Cautions* / Gonna give her all the love I've got: *Gordon, Benny* / My arms aren't strong enough: *Clay, Judy* / I've got love for you: *Intruders*.
■ LP . . . . . . . . . . . . KENT 089
Kent / Mar '89.

**SOUL CITY USA.**
**Tracks:** Not Advised.
■ LP . . . . . . . . . . . . BLUESTLP 1
Blue Chip / Dec '89.

**SOUL CLASS OF '66.**
**Tracks:** You've been leading me on: *Steinways* / Give up girl: *Questel, Connie* / Take your time: *Austin, Patti* / I can feel it: *Carlton, Carl* / Girl I love you: *Green, Garland* / Little girl lost: *Sheppards* / Do it: *Marvellos* / Walkin' uptown: *Prince Arthur & His Knights Of The Round Table* / Baby baby: *Crampton Sisters* / Love ain't love: *Ballard, Florence* / Once upon a time: *Orlons* / Baby baby take a chance on me: *Montgomery, Jack* / I'll try: *Sam & Bill* / Gotta get to know you: *Band, Bobby* / I've never loved nobody (like I love you): *Barnes, Ortheia* / I cry alone: *Ruby & The Romantics*.
■ LP . . . . . . . . . . . . KENT 011
Kent / Jan '84.

**SOUL CLASSICS.**
**Tracks:** When a man loves a woman: *Sledge, Percy* / Saturday night at the movies: *Drifters* / Walking the dog: *Thomas, Rufus* / Just one look: *Troy, Doris* / Tonight's the night: *Burke, Solomon* / Knock on wood: *Floyd, Eddie* / Under the boardwalk: *Drifters* / If you need me: *Burke, Solomon* / Patches: *Carter, Clarence* / Stand by me: *King, Ben E.* / Hold on I'm coming: *Sam & Dave* / Soul man: *Sam & Dave* / Dance to the music: *Sly & The Family Stone* / Baby I'm yours: *Lewis, Barbara* / Warm and tender love: *Sledge, Percy* / Save the last dance for me: *Drifters*.
CD . . . . . . . . . . . . OCN 2002WD
■ LP . . . . . . . . . . . . OCN 2002WL
MC . . . . . . . . . . . . OCN 2002WK
Ocean (2) / Mar '89.

**SOUL CLASSICS.**
**Tracks:** Cry like a baby: *Box Tops* / Didn't I (blow your mind this time): *Delfonics* / Ms. Grace: *Tymes* / Kissin' in the back row of the movies: *Drifters* / Aquarius (let the sunshine in): *5th Dimension* / Woman needs love, A (just like you do): *Parker, Ray Jnr.* / Givin' up givin' in: *Three Degrees* / Highwire: *Carr, Linda* / I am what I am: *Gaynor, Gloria* / I can't help myself: *Real Thing* / Caribbean queen (no more love on the run): *Ocean, Billy* / Hot wild unrestricted crazy love: *Jackson, Millie* / I'd rather go blind: *Turner, Ruby* / Hang on in there baby: *Bristol, Johnny* / Can't give you anything: *Stylistics* / I'm your puppet: *Purify, James & Bobby* / It's in his kiss: *Everett, Betty* / I can sing a rainbow/love is bluie: *Dells* / My baby just cares for me: *Simone, Nina* / She's the one: *Brown, James*.
CD . . . . . . . . . . . . STAMCD 016
MC . . . . . . . . . . . . STAMC 016
Stardust / Oct '92 / Pickwick / Conifer Records.

**SOUL CLASSICS.**
**Tracks:** Not Advised.
CD . . . . . . . . . . . . 7567948132
WEA / Dec '91 / WEA.

**SOUL CLASSICS (2).**
**Tracks:** Not Advised.
CD . . . . . . . . . . . . 100 050
Bridge (MCS Bridge) / Jun '87 / Pinnacle.

**SOUL CLASSICS - CHESS MASTERS.**
**Tracks:** Not Advised.
■ LP . . . . . . . . . . . . CHXL 106
MC . . . . . . . . . . . . CHXT 106
Chess Masters / Dec '88 / EMI.

**SOUL CLASSICS VOL.1.**
**Tracks:** Not Advised.
MC Set . . . . . . . . . . . . TTMC 011
Tring / Jun '92 / Prism Leisure PLC / Midland Records.

**SOUL CLASSICS VOL.2.**
**Tracks:** Not Advised.
MC Set . . . . . . . . . . . . TTMC 012
Tring / Jun '92 / Prism Leisure PLC / Midland Records.

**SOUL COLLECTION.**
**Tracks:** Not Advised.
CD . . . . . . . . . . . . DRIVE 3014
In-Market / Dec '87.

**SOUL COLLECTION (EP).**
**Tracks:** Oh girl: *Jones, Glenn* / Let me show you: *Jackson, Millie* / Love zone: *Ocean, Billy* / You bring out the best in me: *Armstrong, Vanessa*.
■ 12" . . . . . . . . . . . . JSOUL 2
Jive / Mar '88.

**SOUL COLLECTION 1.**
**Tracks:** Not Advised.
CD . . . . . . . . . . . . ONN 14
Object Enterprises / May '89 / Gold & Sons / THE / Midland Records.

**SOUL COLLECTION 2.**
**Tracks:** Not Advised.
CD . . . . . . . . . . . . ONN 15
Object Enterprises / May '89 / Gold & Sons / THE / Midland Records.

**SOUL COLLECTION VOL 1.**
**Tracks:** Not Advised.
CD Set . . . . . . . . . . . . 353792
MC Set . . . . . . . . . . . . 503792
■ Double LP. . . . . . . . . . . . 303792
RCA / Oct '90.

**SOUL COLLECTION VOL 2.**
**Tracks:** Not Advised.
CD Set . . . . . . . . . . . . 353838
MC Set . . . . . . . . . . . . 503838
■ Double LP. . . . . . . . . . . . 303838
RCA / Oct '90.

**SOUL DANCE.**
**Tracks:** Not Advised.
CD . . . . . . . . . . . . 4717322
MC . . . . . . . . . . . . 4717324
Epic / Jun '92 / Sony.

**SOUL DANCE.**
**Tracks:** Not Advised.
CD . . . . . . . . . . . . STACD 058
Wisepack / Sep '94 / THE / Conifer Records.

**SOUL DAZE/SOUL NITES.**
**Tracks:** Not Advised.
■ Double LP. . . . . . . . . . . . RTL 2080 AB
Ronco / Aug '82.

**SOUL DECADE.**
**Tracks:** Not Advised.
■ LP . . . . . . . . . . . . 240807 1
■ MC . . . . . . . . . . . . 240807 4
WEA / Mar '86.

**SOUL DECADE - THE 60'S.**
**Tracks:** Not Advised.
■ Double LP. . . . . . . . . . . . ZL 74816
■ MC Set . . . . . . . . . . . . ZK 74816
■ CD Set. . . . . . . . . . . . ZD 74816
Motown / Sep '90.

**SOUL DECADE - THE SIXTIES (30 Years Of Tamla Motown & Atlantic).**
**Tracks:** I heard it through the grapevine: *Gaye, Marvin* / Stand by me: *King, Ben E.* / What becomes of the broken hearted: *Ruffin, Jimmy* / When a man loves a woman: *Sledge, Percy* / Tracks of my tears: *Robinson, Smokey* / (Sittin' on) The dock of the bay: *Redding, Otis* / My guy: *Wells, Mary* / Save the last dance for me: *Drifters* / Sweet soul music: *Conley, Arthur* / Get ready: *Temptations* / Knock on wood: *Floyd, Eddie* / Baby love: *Supremes* / Respect: *Franklin, Aretha* / It takes two: *Weston, Kim & Marvin Gaye* / Baby: *Thomas, Carla* / Reach out: *Four Tops* / Green onions: *Booker T & The MG's* / Shot gun: *Jr. Walker & The All Stars* / Walking the dog: *Thomas, Rufus* / Do you love me: *Contours* / Just one look: *Troy, Doris* / When you're young and in love: *Marvelettes* / Tramp: *Redding, Otis & Carla Thomas* / Take me in your arms: *Knight, Gladys & The Pips* / Yester me yester you yesterday: *Wonder, Stevie* / Soul man: *Sam & Dave* / I'm gonna make you love me: *Ross, Diana, The Supremes & The Temptations* / You're all I need to get by: *Gaye, Marvin & Tammi Terrell* / Soul finger: *Bar-Kays* / Tighten up: *Bell, Archie & The Drells* / Dancing in the street: *Reeves, Martha & The Vandellas* / In the midnight hour: *Pickett, Wilson*.
■ CD . . . . . . . . . . . . ZD 748162
■ LP . . . . . . . . . . . . ZL 748162
■ MC . . . . . . . . . . . . ZK 748162
Motown / Oct '91.

**SOUL DEEP.**
**Tracks:** Love of my man / Sad shade of blue / Let me down easy / I don't know what you got but it's got me / Faithful and true / Every little bit hurts / Hymn no. 5 / Ashes to ashes / Either way I lose / I love you / It's too late / Giving up / Nothing takes the place of you / What was I supposed to do / Long cold winter / Corn bread row.
■ CD . . . . . . . . . . . . CDCHARLY 42
Charly / Jan '87.

**SOUL DEEP VOL. 2.**
**Tracks:** Not Advised.
■ LP . . . . . . . . . . . . CLP 606
Contempo (1) / Apr '78.

**SOUL DESIRE.**
**Tracks:** Sexual healing: *Gaye, Marvin* / Sign your name: *D'Arby, Terence Trent* / Shake you down: *Abbott, Gregory* / Rock me tonight (for old time's sake): *Jackson, Freddie* / After the love has gone: *Earth, Wind & Fire* / Loving you: *Riperton, Minnie* / Give me the reason: *Vandross, Luther* / How 'bout us: *Champaign* / I still haven't found what I'm looking for: *Chimes (1)* / Smooth operator: *Sade* / Ain't no sunshine (eclipse mix): *Withers, Bill* / I need your lovin': *Williams, Alyson* / Mated: *Graham, Jaki & David Grant* / Always and forever: *Heatwave* / Tonight I celebrate my love to you: *Bryson, Peabo & Roberta Flack* / If you don't know me by now: *Melvin, Harold & The Bluenotes*.
CD . . . . . . . . . . . . 4717322
MC . . . . . . . . . . . . 4717324
Columbia / Jun '92 / Sony.

**SOUL DESIRE VOL.2.**
**Tracks:** On the wings of love: *Osborne, Jeffrey* / So amazing: *Vandross, Luther* / Soul provider: *Bryson, Peabo* / Wind beneath my wings: *Knight, Gladys* / Cherish: *Kool & The Gang* / Secret Lovers: *Atlantic Starr* / Winter in July: *Bomb The Bass* / Come into my life: *Sims, Joyce* / Hang on to your love: *Sade* / See the day: *Lee, Dee C.* / Show me the way: *Belle, Regina* / Free: *Williams, Deniece* / Reunited: *Peaches & Herb* / Just the way you are: *White, Barry* / Me & Mrs. Jones: *Paul, Billy* / Don't leave me this way: *Melvin, Harold*.
CD . . . . . . . . . . . . 472416-2
MC . . . . . . . . . . . . 472416-4
Columbia / Nov '92 / Sony.

**SOUL DESIRE VOL.3.**
**Tracks:** Love supreme: *Downing, Will* / My one temptation: *Paris, Mica* / Sweetest taboo: *Sade* / Never too much: *Vandross, Luther* / I can make you feel good: *Shalamar* / Finest: *S.O.S. Band* / Juicy fruit: *Mtume* / I'm doing fine now: *Pasadenas* / Piano in the dark: *Russell, Brenda* / Feel so high: *Des'ree* / Wishing on a star: *Cover Girls* / Baby come to me: *Belle, Regina* / My love is waiting: *Gaye, Marvin* / Shining star: *Manhattans* / Mind blowing decisions: *Heatwave* / Caravan of love: *Isley-Jasper-Isley*.
CD . . . . . . . . . . . . 473932 2
MC . . . . . . . . . . . . 473932 4
Columbia / Jun '93 / Sony.

**SOUL DESIRE VOLS. 1-3.**
**Tracks:** Sexual healing: *Gaye, Marvin* / Sign your name: *D'Arby, Terence Trent* / Shake you down: *Abbott, Gregory* / Rock me tonight (For old time's sake): *Jackson, Freddie* / After the love has gone: *Earth, Wind & Fire* / Lovin' you: *Riperton, Minnie* / Give me the reason: *Vandross, Luther* / How 'bout us: *Champaign* / I still haven't found what I'm looking for: *Chimes (1)* / Smooth operator: *Sade* / Ain't no sunshine: *Withers, Bill* / I need your lovin': *Williams, Alyson* / Mated: *Graham, Jaki & David Grant* / Always and forever: *Heatwave* / Tonight, I celebrate my love for you: *Bryson, Peabo & Roberta Flack* / If you don't know me by know: *Melvin, Harold & The Bluenotes* / On the wings of love: *Osborne, Jeffrey* / So amazing: *Vandross, Luther* / Soul provider: *Bryson, Peabo* / Wind beneath my wings: *Knight, Gladys* / Cherish: *Kool & The Gang* / Secret lovers: *Atlantic Starr* / Winter in July: *Bomb The Bass* / Come into my life: *Sims, Joyce* / Hang onto your love: *Sade* / See the day: *Lee, Dee C.* / Show me the way: *Belle Regina* / Free: *Williams, Deniece* / Reunited: *Peaches & Herb* / Just the way you are: *White, Barry* / Me & Mrs. Jones: *Paul, Billy* / Don't leave me this way: *Melvin, Harold* / Love supreme: *Downing, Will* / My one temptation: *Paris, Mica* / Sweetest taboo: *Sade* / Never too much: *Vandross, Luther* / I can make you feel good: *Shalamar* / Finest: *S.O.S. Band* / Juicy fruit: *Mtume* / I'm doing fine now: *Pasadenas* / Piano in the dark: *Russell, Brenda* / Feel so high: *Des'ree* / Wishing on a star: *Cover Girls* / Baby come to me: *Belle, Regina* / My love is waiting: *Gaye Marvin* / Shining star: *Manhattans* / Mind blowing decisions: *Heatwave* / Caravan of love: *Isley-Jasper-Isley*.
CD Set . . . . . . . . . . . . 474121-2
Columbia / Oct '94 / Sony.

**SOUL DEVOTION - THE VERY BEST OF HEART & SOUL.**
**Tracks:** Don't be a stranger: *Carroll, Dina* / My destiny: *Richie, Lionel* / One moment in time: *Houston, Whitney* / Going nowhere: *Gabrielle* / Change: *Stansfield, Lisa* / Sign your name: *D'Arby, Terence Trent* / Save the best for last: *Williams, Vanessa* / My one

520 ■ DELETED

temptation: *Paris, Mica* / Stay with me baby: *Turner, Ruby* / Sexual healing: *Gaye, Marvin* / Three times a lady: *Commodores* / Being with you: *Robinson, Smokey* / My cherie armour: *Wonder, Stevie* / What becomes of the broken hearted: *Ruffin, Jimmy* / You are everything: *Ross, Diana & Marvin Gaye* / With you I'm born again: *Preston, Billy & Syreeta* / Best thing that ever happened to me: *Knight, Gladys & The Pips* / One day in your life: *Jackson, Michael* / Touch me in the morning: *Ross, Diana* / I say a little prayer: *Franklin, Aretha* / Tired of being alone: *Green, Al* / (Sittin' on) The dock of the bay: *Redding, Otis* / When a man loves a woman: *Sledge, Percy* / Hey there lonely girl: *Holman, Eddie* / After the love has gone: *Earth, Wind & Fire* / If you don't know me by now: *Melvin, Harold & The Bluenotes* / Have you seen her: *Chi-Lites* / Lovely day: *Withers, Bill* / Teardrops: *Womack & Womack* / It's too late: *Quartz (1)* / If you're looking for a way out: *Odyssey* / Wishing on a star: *Rose Royce* / One day I'll fly away: *Crawford, Randy* / Always: *Atlantic Starr* / Slow hand: *Pointer Sisters* / Your love is king: *Sade*.
**CD** . . . . . . . . . . . . . . . . . . . . . . . . . . . **516624-2**
**MC** . . . . . . . . . . . . . . . . . . . . . . . . . . . **516624-4**
Polygram T.V. / Mar '94 / PolyGram.

## SOUL DREAMING.
**Tracks:** Like sister and brother: *Drifters* / Didn't I (blow your mind this time): *Delfonics* / Love come down: *King, Evelyn 'Champagne'* / Native New Yorker: *Odyssey* / Woman in love: *Three Degrees* / You make me feel brand new: *Stylistics* / Hold to my love: *Ruffin, Jimmy* / When she was my girl: *Four Tops* / Livin' in America: *Brown, James* / You're the first, my last, my everything: *White, Barry* / Joanna: *Kool & The Gang* / Summer breeze: *Isley Brothers* / I really didn't mean it: *Vandross, Luther* / Never knew love like this: *O'Neal, Alexander* / Sexual healing: *Gaye, Marvin* / Let's hear it for the boy: *Williams, Deniece* / Come back and finish what you started: *Knight, Gladys & The Pips* / Kiss and say goodbye: *Manhattans*.
**CD** . . . . . . . . . . . . . . . . . . . . . . . . . **STACD 006**
**MC** . . . . . . . . . . . . . . . . . . . . . . . . . **STAMC 006**
Wisepack / Nov '92 / THE / Conifer Records.

## SOUL EMOTION.
**Tracks:** If you don't know me by now: *Simply Red* / Mercy, mercy me/I want you: *Palmer, Robert* / Wherever I lay my hat: *Young, Paul* / Let's stay together: *Turner, Tina* / Change: *Stansfield, Lisa* / One moment in time: *Houston, Whitney* / Walk on by: *Warwick, Dionne* / Thinking about your love: *Thomas, Kenny* / Too many walls: *Dennis, Cathy* / It's too late: *Quartz (2)* / Never knew love like this before: *Mills, Stephanie* / There's nothing like this: *Omar* / Move closer: *Nelson, Phyllis* / It's a man's man's man's world: *Brown, James* / In the midnight hour: *Pickett, Wilson* / Can't get enough of your love: *White, Barry* / After the love has gone: *Earth, Wind & Fire* / Solid: *Ashford & Simpson*.
**CD** . . . . . . . . . . . . . . . . . . . . . . . . . . **5151882**
**MC** . . . . . . . . . . . . . . . . . . . . . . . . . . **5151884**
Polygram T.V. / Mar '92 / PolyGram.

## SOUL EXPERIENCE, THE.
**Tracks:** Not Advised.
**CD** . . . . . . . . . . . . . . . . . . . . . . . . . . **BOXD 28**
Pickwick / Nov '92 / Pickwick.

## SOUL FEVER.
**Tracks:** Not Advised.
**MC** . . . . . . . . . . . . . . . . . . . . . . . . . . **GM 0216**
K-Tel Goldmasters / Aug '84 / C.M. Distribution / Arabesque Ltd. / Ross Records / PolyGram.

## SOUL FOOD.
**Tracks:** Lots of love / Somebody special / You won't get away / Baby I can't stand it / Bent out of shape / I need you baby / Gonna move to the city / 60 minutes of your love / I wanna be free / How you like your love / Anything for you / My mistakes of yesterday / Swish fish / Ready, willing and able.
■ **LP** . . . . . . . . . . . . . . . . . . . . . . . . **MLS 40011**
Minit / Jan '69.

## SOUL FOR LOVERS.
**Tracks:** Not Advised.
**CD** . . . . . . . . . . . . . . . . . . . . . . . . . **DCD 5274**
Denwest Records / Nov '92.

## SOUL FROM THE VAULTS.
**Tracks:** Don't be jealous / Set me free / Come on & love me / Now that you've gone / Pony time / Please love me / Let it live / Baby I can't take it / Stranded in the jungle / Cherry pie / Soulville express / Rock everybody / Ain't that right / Out her / Hey little sister.
■ **LP** . . . . . . . . . . . . . . . . . . . . . . . . . **SPE 6606**
Umber / '72.

## SOUL HITS.
**Tracks:** Not Advised.
**CD Set** . . . . . . . . . . . . . . . . . . . . . . **44-1724-2**
Pilz / Oct '92 / BMG.

## SOUL HITS DANCE PARTY.
**Tracks:** Not Advised.
**CD** . . . . . . . . . . . . . . . . . . . . . . . . **QSCD 6005**
Quality (Charly) / Apr '92 / Charly.

## SOUL IN DARKNESS.
**Tracks:** Not Advised.
**CD** . . . . . . . . . . . . . . . . . . . . . . . . . **BRCD 536**
■ **MC** . . . . . . . . . . . . . . . . . . . . . . . . **BRCA 536**
■ **LP** . . . . . . . . . . . . . . . . . . . . . . . . **BRLP 536**
4th & Broadway / Aug '89.

## SOUL INSPIRATION.
**Tracks:** My destiny: *Richie, Lionel* / I love your smile: *Shanice* / looking through patient eyes: *P.M. Dawn* / I never felt like this before: *Paris, Mica* / Drift away: *Gray, Dobie* / What's going on: *Gaye, Marvin* / Got to be there: *Jackson, Michael* / Sweet love: *Baker, Anita* / Save the best for last: *Williams, Vanessa* / Have you seen her: *Chi-Lites* / What becomes of the broken hearted: *Ruffin, Jimmy* / Hey there lonely girl: *Holman, Eddie* / Me and Mrs. Jones: *Jackson, Freddie* / Piano in the dark: *Russell, Brenda* / Wake up everybody: *Melvin, Harold* / Feel so high: *Des'ree* / Until you come back to me: *Franklin, Aretha* / Love makes the world go round: *Don-E*.
**CD** . . . . . . . . . . . . . . . . . . . . . . . . . **516 226-2**
**MC** . . . . . . . . . . . . . . . . . . . . . . . . . **516 226-4**
Polygram T.V. / Jun '93 / PolyGram.

## SOUL INSPIRATION (54 Soul Classics From The 70's And 80's).
**Tracks:** Just an illusion: *Imagination* / I'm so excited: *Pointer Sisters* / System addict: *Five Star* / Going back to my roots: *Odyssey* / Give it up: *K.C. & The Sunshine Band* / She's strange: *Cameo (1)* / Rock the boat: *Hues Corporation* / Jumpin' Jack flash: *Franklin, Aretha* / Let the music play: *White, Barry* / Boogie wonderland: *Earth, Wind & Fire* / Can you feel it: *Jacksons* / Burn rubber on me: *Gap Band* / Love come down: *King, Evelyn 'Champagne'* / Mama used to say: *Giscombe, Junior* / Rockit: *Hancock, Herbie* / It's a disco night: *Isley Brothers* / Livin' in America: *Brown, James* / Do what you do: *Jackson, Jermaine* / All the love in the world: *Warwick, Dionne* / Joanna: *Kool & The Gang* / Night to remember: *Shalamar* / Your love is king: *Sade* / Never knew love like this before: *Mills, Stephanie* / Secret lovers: *Atlantic Starr* / Stay with me tonight: *Osbourne, Jeffrey* / There goes my first love: *Drifters* / Reach out I'll be there: *Gaynor, Gloria* / One hundred ways: *Jones, Quincy & James Ingram* / You make me feel brand new: *Stylistics* / Never, never gonna give you up: *White, Barry* / Woman in love: *Three Degrees* / Summer breeze: *Isley Brothers* / My love is waiting: *Gaye, Marvin* / Lovely day (remix): *Withers, Bill* / What a fool believes: *Franklin, Aretha* / Letter: *Box Tops* / Kissing in the back row: *Drifters* / Hang on in there baby: *Bristol, Johnny* / Reunited: *Peaches & Herb* / Best thing that ever happened to me: *Knight, Gladys & The Pips* / Didn't I: *Delfonics* / Me and Mrs. Jones: *Paul, Billy* / Running away: *Sly & The Family Stone* / Love train: *O'Jays* / What a diff'rence a day makes: *Phillips, Esther* / Betcha by golly wow: *Stylistics* / I'm your puppet: *Purify, James & Bobby* / That lady: *Isley Brothers* / I can see clearly now: *Nash, Johnny* / L.O.D. (Love on delivery): *Ocean, Billy* / Can't get enough of your love babe: *White, Barry* / Where did our love go: *Elbert, Donnie* / Get up offa that thing: *Brown, James*.
**CD Set** . . . . . . . . . . . . . . . . . . . . . . . **BOXD 43**
Pickwick / Jan '94 / Pickwick.

## SOUL JAZZ LOVE STRATA-EAST.
**Tracks:** Peace go with you, brother: *Scott-Heron, Gil* / Well you needn't: *Ridley, Larry* / Prince of peace: *Sanders, Pharoah* / Changa chikuyo: *Ridley, Larry* / John Coltrane: *Jordan, Clifford* / Hopscotch: *Rouse, Charlie* / Bottle: *Scott-Heron, Gil* / Travelling man: *Cowell, Stanley* / First impressions: *Farrah, Shamek* / Dance of the little children: *Parker, Billy* / Eddie Harris: *Jordan, Clifford* / Smiling Billy suite Pt.2: *Heath Brothers*.
**CD** . . . . . . . . . . . . . . . . . . . . . . . . **SJRCD 019**
**LP Set** . . . . . . . . . . . . . . . . . . . . . . . **SJRLP 019**
Soul Jazz / Oct '94 / New Note.

## SOUL JAZZ VOL.1.
**Tracks:** Honky tonk: *Butler, Billy* / Return of the prodigal son: *Green, Byrdie* / I've got the blues: *Moody, James* / Mom and dad: *Earland, Charles* / 322 wow: *Lytle, Johnny* / Up to date: *Smith, Johnny "Hammond"* / Dat dere: *Adderley, Cannonball Quartet* / Light: *Ammons, Gene*.
**CD** . . . . . . . . . . . . . . . . . . . . . . . . **CDBGP 1028**
■ **LP** . . . . . . . . . . . . . . . . . . . . . . . . **BGP 1028**
BGP / Jun '89.

## SOUL JEWELS VOL.1 (Let's Do It Over).
**Tracks:** Our love: *Powell, Bobby* / How do you walk away from fear: *Taylor, Ted (1)* / I can't stand to see you go: *Valentine, Joe* / I stayed away too long: *Wallace Brothers* / In time: *Powell, Bobby* / To be free: *Bass, Fontella* / Strangest feeling: *Taylor, Ted (1)* / Nothing takes the place of you: *McCall, Toussaint* / Woman's love: *Valentine, Joe* / I'm not going to cry over spilt milk: *Powell, Bobby* / I want everyone to know: *Bass, Fontella* / Friendship only goes so far: *Taylor, Ted (1)* / Hold my hand: *Powell, Bobby* / My baby's gone: *Wallace Brothers* / Let's do it over: *McCall, Toussaint*.
■ **LP** . . . . . . . . . . . . . . . . . . . . . . . . . **CRB 1192**
Charly R&B / Dec '88.
**MC** . . . . . . . . . . . . . . . . . . . . . . . . . **TCCRB 192**
Charly R&B / Nov '90 / Charly.

## SOUL JEWELS VOL.3.
**Tracks:** I need some lovin': *Taylor, Little Johnny* / Take time to know the truth: *Patterson, Bobby* / I had my heart set on you: *Young, Billy Joe* / I'm asking forgiveness: *Ridgley, Tommy* / Something strange is going on in my house: *Taylor, Ted (1)* / Until you were gone: *Perkins, Joe* / What would I do without you: *Taylor, Little Johnny* / I pledge: *Lonnie & Floyd* / One ounce of prevention: *Patterson, Bobby* / Let's call the whole thing off: *Taylor, Ted (1)* / I'm not going to leave: *Perkins, Joe* / I ask myself a question: *Taylor, Little Johnny* / Give this fool another chance: *Young, Billy Joe* / I'm in the wrong: *Patterson, Bobby* / I want to be a part of you: *Taylor, Ted (1)* / How are you fixed for love: *Taylor, Little Johnny*.
■ **LP** . . . . . . . . . . . . . . . . . . . . . . . . . **CRB 1194**
Charly R&B / Apr '89.

## SOUL JUKE BOX HITS.
**Tracks:** Not Advised.
**CD Set** . . . . . . . . . . . . . . . . . . . . . . . **DCD 5064**
■ **Double LP** . . . . . . . . . . . . . . . . . . . . . **DLP 2064**
**MC Set** . . . . . . . . . . . . . . . . . . . . . . . **DMC 4064**
Disky / Jul '89 / THE.

## SOUL LOVE.
**Tracks:** Not Advised.
**CD** . . . . . . . . . . . . . . . . . . . . . . . . . **STACD 055**
Stardust / Aug '93 / Pickwick / Conifer Records.

## SOUL MAN.
**Tracks:** Soul man / Evolution / Outside / Love and affection / Eek-ah-bo-static automatic / Bang bang bang (who's on the phone?) / Totally academic / Suddenly it's magic / Black girls / Sweet Sarah.
■ **CD** . . . . . . . . . . . . . . . . . . . . . . . . . **11073**
Delta (1) / Apr '87.

## SOUL MATE.
**Tracks:** Not Advised.
**CD** . . . . . . . . . . . . . . . . . . . . . . . . . **DINCD 82**
**MC** . . . . . . . . . . . . . . . . . . . . . . . . . **DINMC 82**
Dino / Feb '94 / Pinnacle.

## SOUL MEETING.
**Tracks:** Spring / Just a little bit / Honest I do / Dimples / Hands off / Big boss man / Baby what you want me to do / No more doggin' / Little wheel / You can make it if you try / Mess around / Boom boom.
■ **LP** . . . . . . . . . . . . . . . . . . . . . . . . . **JOY 122**
Joy / Oct '68.

## SOUL MINING.
**Tracks:** Soul Man: *Sam & Dave* / Knock on Wood: *Floyd, Eddie* / Patches: *Carter, Clarence* / Walking the dog: *Thomas, Rufus* / Rescue Me: *Bass, Fontella* / In crowd / Love wont let me wait: *Harris, Major* / Duck: *Lee, Jacky* / Western movies: *Olympics* / I Know: *George, Barbara* / Rainy night in Georgia / Get on up: *Esquires*.
■ **LP** . . . . . . . . . . . . . . . . . . . . . . . . . **TOP 149**
**MC** . . . . . . . . . . . . . . . . . . . . . . . . . **KTOP 149**
Topline / Sep '86 / Charly.

## SOUL MUSIC SET FREE.
**Tracks:** Not Advised.
■ **CD** . . . . . . . . . . . . . . . . . . . . . . . . . **CDTR 7**
Timeless (Soul) / Jan '90.

## SOUL NIGHTS.
**Tracks:** Searching: *China Black* / Just a step from heaven: *Eternal (1)* / Don't be a stranger: *Carroll, Dina* / End of the road: *Boyz II Men* / Let's get it on: *Gaye, Marvin* / Night shift: *Commodores* / Rainy night in Georgia: *Crawford, Randy* / Where is the love: *Paris, Mica & Will Downing* / Just another day: *Secada, Jon* / So close to love: *Moten, Wendy* / Now I know what made Otis blue: *Young, Paul* / Stop loving me, stop loving you: *Hall, Daryl* / Because of you: *Gabrielle* / Let's stay together: *Pasadenas* / So amazing: *Vandross, Luther* / Shake you down: *Abbott, Gregory* / Everybody's gotta learn sometime: *Yazz* / Drift away: *Gray, Dobie* / Tonight, I cxelebrate

my love: Bryson, Peabo & Roberta Flack / Midnight at the Oasis: Muldaur, Maria.

| | |
|---|---|
| CD | .525005-2 |
| MC | .525005-4 |

Polygram T.V. / Aug '94 / PolyGram.

### SOUL OF A MAN.
Tracks: Not Advised.
■ LP . . . . . . . . . . . . . . . . . . . KENT 038
Kent / May '85.

### SOUL OF BLACK MUSIC - GOSPEL SCENE.
Tracks: Not Advised.
■ Double LP . . . . . . . . . . . . . . . .426001
Vogue / Jun '84.

### SOUL OF BLACK MUSIC VOL 1.
Tracks: Borrowed time / Gamblin' man / Jesus you've been good / Going home to get my crown / I'm going to serve Jesus / Grandma's hands / I'll be satisfied / Lord I've done what you told me to do / I'm holding on / What am I going to do / Won't it be grand / My soul / I've already been to the water / Sleep on mother.
■ LP . . . . . . . . . . . . . . . . . . . SNTF 795
Sonet / Sep '79.

### SOUL OF BLACK MUSIC VOL 2.
Tracks: Ezekiel / Nobody's fault but mine / Stop by / He's working it out / May the work I've done speak for me / What about me / New walk / When we get to heaven / I love to praise Him / Stand by me / Everyday will be Sunday / Through it all / How much do I owe / Walk through the valley.
■ LP . . . . . . . . . . . . . . . . . . . SNTF 796
Sonet / Sep '79.

### SOUL OF BRITISH R'N'B 1962-1968.
Tracks: Stop stop stop (or honey I'll be gone): Gouldman, Graham / Time it takes: Dean, Alan & His Problems / Midnight confession: Kelly, Pete Solution / Mary open the door: Duffy's Nucleus / Get on the right track baby: Money, Zoot Big Roll Band / Little girl: Bond, Graham Organisation / My love: Jones, Ronnie / Precious words: Cocker, Joe / Strut around: Bond, Graham Organisation / Sugar baby (part 1): Powell, Jimmy / Cross my heart: Exotics / If your love don't swing: Kelly, Pete Solution / I need your lovin': Jones, Ronnie & The Nightimers / Night time is the right time: Korner, Alexis & Blues Inc / Walking the dog: Money, Zoot Big Roll Band / Can you hear me: Powerhouse (1) / Love is a beautiful thing: Quick / Ooh-la-la: Exotics / Sugar baby (part 2): Powell, Jimmy / Chain gang: Powerhouse (1).
■ LP . . . . . . . . . . . . . . . . . . . SEE 67
See For Miles / Apr '86.

### SOUL OF DETROIT.
Tracks: Not Advised.
| | |
|---|---|
| CD | .CDSD 136 |
| ■ Double LP | .LPSD 136 |
Soul Supply / Apr '89.

### SOUL OF LA, THE.
Tracks: Sweet magic: Servicemen / Wonders of love: Soul Gents / You should have told me: New Yorkers / Under your spell: Paramounts / This is the way I feel: Four Tempos / There's that mountain: Trips / Do this for me: Emotions (1) / It was wrong: Shades Of Jade / Anything for you: Furys / Jealous of you: Mystics / Don't let love get you down: Phonetics / You're good enough for me: Versatiles / (Down in) East LA: Angelenos / You'll never make the grade: Sun Lovers / Sad sad memories: Tempos / No one else can take your place: Inspirations / (I love her so much) it hurts me: Majestics / Hey hey girls: Vines / Is the feeling still there: Remarkables / Save your love: Soul Patrol / Girl, I love you: Sinceres / Just a little: Prominents / Love is a hurting game: Four Sights / My poor heart: Sun Lovers / Beginning of the end: Young Hearts.
CD . . . . . . . . . . . . . . . . . . . .GSCD 032
Goldmine / Mar '94 / Vital Distribution.

### SOUL OF NEW ORLEANS, THE.
Tracks: Not Advised.
■ CD . . . . . . . . . . . . . . . . . CDCHARLY 16
Charly / '88.

### SOUL OF NEW YORK.
Tracks: Not Advised.
■ LP . . . . . . . . . . . . . . . . . . . BLUETTLP 1
Blue Chip / Nov '89.

### SOUL OF RHYTHM 'N' BLUES REVUE (Live At The Lone Star Roadhouse).
Tracks: Not Advised.
| | |
|---|---|
| CD | SHAN 9005CD |
| MC | SHAN 9005C |
Shanachie / Oct '93 / A.D.A. Distribution / Jazz Music / C.M. Distribution / Koch International.

### SOUL OF THE 80'S.
Tracks: Not Advised.
MC . . . . . . . . . . . . . . . . . . MCJHD 042
Tring / Jun '92 / Prism Leisure PLC / Midland Records.

### SOUL OF THE 80'S VOL. 2.
Tracks: Not Advised.
| | |
|---|---|
| CD | .JHD 043 |
| MC | MCJHD 043 |
Tring / Jun '92 / Prism Leisure PLC / Midland Records.

### SOUL ON SOUND NO 33.
Tracks: Not Advised.
■ MC . . . . . . . . . . . . . . . . . . SOSS 032
Soul On Sound / Jul '84.

### SOUL ON THE STREETS VOL. 1.
Tracks: Take care of yourself: Dan-Elle / Love and devotion: Marshall, Wayne / 24/7 Love: Irini / Save your love: S.L.O. / Hooked on you: Everis / Don't let them know: Irini / Fire & desire: Dan-Elle / You turn me on: Everis / Sexual thing: Marshall, Wayne / Sweet lovin': 3rd Zone / Fire & desire (remix): Dan-Elle / Everybody's gotta rave: Marshall, Wayne / Don't let them know (remix): Irini / She want's a 24/7: Hyper Man.
| | |
|---|---|
| CD | .SCGCD 201 |
| LP | .SCGLP 201 |
| MC | .SCGMC 201 |
SCG Records / May '94 / Jetstar.

### SOUL PARTY.
Tracks: Grits and cornbread: Soul-runners / Spreadin' honey: Soul-runners / Headline news: Starr, Edwin / In between the heartaches: Elbert, Donnie / Too far gone: Elbert, Donnie / Ain't that loving you baby: Irwin, Suzie & Big Dee / I like what I'm trying to do: Ellis, Waygood / Stone free: Hendrix, Jimi / Hey Joe: Hendrix, Jimi / I spy: Thomas, Jano / Judy in disguise: Amboy Dukes / Don't feel sorry for me: Ikettes.
■ LP . . . . . . . . . . . . . . . . . . . 236 213
Polydor / Apr '68.

### SOUL PASSION.
Tracks: Not Advised.
| | |
|---|---|
| ■ LP | .CN 2055 |
| ■ MC | .CN4 2055 |
Contour / '82.

### SOUL POWER.
Tracks: Sign your name: D'Arby, Terence Trent / Paradise: Sade / Never too much: Vandross, Luther / Can you feel it: Jacksons / Let's hear it for the boy: Williams, Deniece / That lady: Isley Brothers / Ain't no sunshine: Withers, Bill / Crazy: Manhattans / Sweet understanding love: Four Tops / Something old, something new: Fantastics / Wedding bell blues: 5th Dimension / Slightest touch: Five Star / Ain't nothin' goin' on but the rent: Guthrie, Gwen / Livin' in America: Brown, James / Come into my life: Sims, Joyce / Down on the street: Shakatak / Secret lovers: Atlantic Starr / What a difference a day makes: Phillips, Esther / Gonna get along without you: Wills, Viola.
| | |
|---|---|
| CD | .STACD 015 |
| MC | .STAMC 015 |
Telstar/Ronco / Oct '92 / BMG.

### SOUL POWER VOL.1.
Tracks: Not Advised.
VHS . . . . . . . . . . . . . . . . . . . VC 4087
Video Collection / Feb '90 / Gold & Sons / Video Collection / THE.

### SOUL POWER VOL.2.
Tracks: Not Advised.
VHS . . . . . . . . . . . . . . . . . . . VC 4088
Video Collection / Feb '90 / Gold & Sons / Video Collection / THE.

### SOUL QUEENS, THE.
Tracks: Not Advised.
| | |
|---|---|
| CD | .15 168 |
| MC | .79 042 |
Laserlight / Aug '91 / THE / BMG / Target.

### SOUL REFLECTION.
Tracks: Three times a lady: Commodores / I don't wanna lose you: Turner, Tina / Have you seen her: M.C. Hammer / Stop to love: Vandross, Luther / Criticize: O'Neal, Alexander / Yah mo B there: Ingram, James & Michael McDonald / There'll be sad songs (to make you cry): Ocean, Billy / Almaz: Crawford, Randy / If you don't know me by now: Melvin, Harold & The Bluenotes / Just my imagination (running away with me): Temptations / I second that emotion: Robinson, Smokey & The Miracles / Too busy thinking about my baby: Gaye, Marvin / Hold back the night: Trammps / Just the way you are:

White, Barry / You sexy thing: Hot Chocolate / Always: Atlantic Starr / Baby, come to me: Austin, Patti & James Ingram.
| | |
|---|---|
| CD | 845 334 |
| ■ LP | 845 334 |
| MC | 845 334 |
Polygram T.V. / Feb '91 / PolyGram.

### SOUL SAUCE SAMPLER.
Tracks: Not Advised.
■ 12" . . . . . . . . . . . . . . . . . . EXPAND 3
Expansion / Jul '92.

### SOUL SEARCHING.
Tracks: Could it be I'm falling in love: Detroit Spinners / Used to be my girl: O'Jays / I can see clearly now: Cliff, Jimmy / Don't let love get you down: Bell / Archie & The Drells / Let's get it on: Gaye, Marvin / Reunited: Peaches & Herb / Me & Mrs Jones: Paul, Billy / Right here (Human nature radio mix): S.W.V. / I still haven't' found what I'm looking for: Chimes (1) / Special kind of love (Radio edit): Carroll, Dina / Stay / Eternal (1) / I miss you: Haddaway / Walk on by: Warwick, Dionne / Almaz: Crawford, Randy / Feel so high: Des'ree / Lovely day: Withers, Bill / Night to remember: Shalamar / Don't let it go to your head: Carne, Jean / (You make me feel) Like a natural woman: Franklin, Aretha / Delicate: D'Arby, Terence Trent / I love your smile: Shanice / These arms of mine: Redding, Otis / On the wings of love: Osborne, Jeffrey / Your body's calling (LP version): R. Kelly / Hearts run free: Staton, Candi / Whole town's laughing at me: Pendergrass, Teddy / Show me the way: Bell, Regina / Private number: Clay, Judy & William Bell / I want your love: Chic / Sweet love: Baker, Anita / Woman to woman: Brown, Shirley / I'm doing fine now: New York City / Winter in July: Bomb The Bass / Misty blue: Moore, Dorothy.
| | |
|---|---|
| CD Set | MOODCD 3 |
| MC Set | MOODC 3 |
Columbia / Jul '94 / Sony.

### SOUL SEARCHING VOL. 1.
Tracks: Show me: Jones, Glenn / Imitation of love: Jackson, Millie / Give a little more: Butler, Jonathan / Hurting inside: Turner, Ruby / Children of the ghetto: Real Thing / I'm in love: Turner, Ruby / I need to be by myself: Jackson, Millie / It's never too late to try: Ocean, Billy / Letter: Wilson, Precious / Don't turn your back: Bell Armstrong, Vanessa.
| | |
|---|---|
| ■ LP | .HOP 21 |
| ■ MC | .HOPC 21 |
| ■ CD | .CDHOP 21 |
Jive / Jul '87.

### SOUL SEARCHING VOL. 2.
Tracks: Not Advised.
| | |
|---|---|
| ■ CD | .CDHOP 21 |
| ■ LP | .HOP 21 |
| ■ MC | .HOPC 21 |
Jive / Aug '88.

### SOUL SELLER.
Tracks: That's life / Tears of joy / If you love me / I work it out / Funky soul / Which way should I turn / Please please please / What kind of man / Stone fox / If you don't give me what I want / Funky soul train.
■ LP . . . . . . . . . . . . . . . . . . . .23655
Polydor / Feb '69.

### SOUL SENSATION.
Tracks: Not Advised.
MC . . . . . . . . . . . . . . . . . . . DY 1
Dynamic (Cassettes) / Sep '81.

### SOUL SENSATION.
Tracks: Not Advised.
| | |
|---|---|
| CD | MATCD 20 |
| MC | MATMC 20 |
Castle / Dec '92 / BMG.

### SOUL SENSATION.
Tracks: Confusion: Foxx, Inez & Charlie / La de dah love you: Foxx, Inez & Charlie / My momma told me: Foxx, Inez & Charlie / Jaybirds: Foxx, Inez & Charlie / I'm jealous: Turner, Ike & Tina / Real me: Turner, Ike & Tina / You're everything to me: Turner, Ike & Tina / Wake up: Turner, Ike & Tina / Tango: Isley Brothers / Love is a wonderful thing: Isley Brothers / Gotta get back to Georgia: Willis, Timmy / Mr Soul: Willis, Timmy / Satisfaction: Willis, Timmy / You get 'em beat: Soul Sisters / I'm a happy man: Jive Five / Who was that: Britt, Tina / She blew a good thing: American Poets.
■ LP . . . . . . . . . . . . . . . . . . . UAL/S 290
United Artists / Jul '69.

### SOUL SENSATION.
Tracks: Mockingbird / Stop, in the name of love / Way you do the things you do / My cherie amour / I heard it through the grapevine / I can't myself / Just to be with you / It's gonna work out fine / I can't have you loose / I ain't got nobody / Barefootin' / In the

■ DELETE

Midnight hour / Knock on wood / Boy from New York City / It's in his kiss / What's going on / Every beat of my heart / Iko iko / Cool jerk. / Poison ivy.
■ LP . . . . . . . . . . . . . . . . . . . . PLE 7012
Pickwick / Dec '78.

**SOUL SERENADE.**
**Tracks:** Not Advised.
■ LP . . . . . . . . . . . . . . . . . . . . KENT 041
Kent / Jun '85.

**SOUL SHAKIN'.**
**Tracks:** Not Advised.
■ LP . . . . . . . . . . . . . . . . . . . . SHM 3108
■ MC. . . . . . . . . . . . . . . . . . . . HSC 3108
Hallmark / '82.

**SOUL SHOTS.**
**Tracks:** Not Advised.
CD. . . . . . . . . . . . . . . . . . . . R 21575774
Rhino (USA) / Mar '88 / WEA.

**SOUL SHOTS VOL. 1 (We Got More Soul).**
**Tracks:** But it's alright: *Jackson, J.J.* / Two for the price of one: *Williams, Larry & Johnny Watson* / Your love keeps lifting me higher and higher: *Wilson, Jackie* / Ain't nothing but a house party: *Show Stoppers* / Duck: *Lee, Jacky* / I take what I want: *Purify, James & Bobby* / Harlem shuffle: *Bob & Earl* / Funky broadway (part 1): *Dyke & The Blazers* / Boogaloo down Broadway: *Fantastic Johnny C* / Barefootin': *Parker, Robert* / I got you (I feel good): *Brown, James & The Famous Flames* / We got more soul: *Dyke & The Blazers* / Summertime: *Stewart, Billy.*
■ LP . . . . . . . . . . . . . . . . . . . . RNLP 70037
MC. . . . . . . . . . . . . . . . . . . . RNC 70037
Rhino (USA) / Oct '87 / WEA.

**SOUL SHOTS VOL. 2 (The In Crowd).**
**Tracks:** Get on up: *Esquires* / It's got to be mellow: *Haywood, Leon* / Love makes the world go round: *Jackson, Deon* / Sunny: *Hebb, Bobby* / Cowboys to girls: *Intruders* / Gimme little sign: *Wood, Brenton* / Black pearl: *Checkmates Unlimited* / In crowd / My pledge of love: *Jeffrey, Joe Group* / Backfield in motion: *Mel & Tim* / She shot a hole in my soul: *Curry, Clifford* / Jerk: *Larks (2)* / Oogum boogum song: *Wood, Brenton* / Mercy, mercy, mercy: *Williams, Larry & Johnny Watson.*
■ LP . . . . . . . . . . . . . . . . . . . . RNLP 70038
MC. . . . . . . . . . . . . . . . . . . . RNC 70038
Rhino (USA) / Oct '87 / WEA.

**SOUL SHOTS VOL. 3 (Soul Twist - Instrumentals).**
**Tracks:** Night train: *Brown, James & The Famous Flames* / Last night: *Mar-Keys* / Soul twist: *Curtis, King & The Noble Knights* / Groovin': *Booker T & The MG's* / Wack wack: *Young-Holt Unlimited* / Grazing in the grass: *Masekela, Hugh* / Soul serenade: *Curtis, King* / Twine time: *Cash, Alvin & The Crawlers* / Time is tight: *Booker T & The MG's* / In crowd: *Lewis, Ramsey* / Soul finger: *Bar-Kays* / Horse: *Nobles, Cliff* / Soulful strut: *Young-Holt Unlimited* / Harlem nocturne: *Viscounts.*
■ LP . . . . . . . . . . . . . . . . . . . . RNLP 70039
MC. . . . . . . . . . . . . . . . . . . . RNC 70039
Rhino (USA) / Oct '87 / WEA.

**SOUL SHOTS VOL. 4 (Tell Mama - Screamin' Soul Sisters).**
**Tracks:** Nitty gritty: *Ellis, Shirley* / Tell mama: *James, Etta* / Hard to handle: *Drew, Patti* / Bold soul sister: *Turner, Ike & Tina* / Lee Cross: *Franklin, Aretha* / Heartbeat: *Jones, Gloria* / Stay with me: *Ellison, Lorraine* / Wang dang doodle: *Taylor, Koko* / I know (you don't love me no more): *George, Barbara* / Rescue me: *Bass, Fontella* / Hypnotised: *Jones, Linda* / Why (am I treated so bad): *Sweet Inspiration* / Ask me: *Brown, Maxine* / You send me: *Franklin, Aretha.*
■ LP . . . . . . . . . . . . . . . . . . . . RNLP 70040
MC. . . . . . . . . . . . . . . . . . . . RNC 70040
Rhino (USA) / Oct '87 / WEA.

**SOUL SHOTS VOL.5 (La La Means I love you - Soul Ballads).**
**Tracks:** Tell it like it is: *Neville, Aaron* / Sitting in the park: *Stewart, Billy* / Hey there lonely girl: *Holman, Eddie* / La la means I love you: *Delfonics* / That's all: *Midniters* / Yes I'm ready: *Mason, Barbara* / Oh what a night: *Dells* / I do love you: *Stewart, Billy* / I'm your puppet: *James & Bobby Purify* / Funny: *Hinton, Joe* / Love is a hurtin' thing: *Rawls, Lou* / Cry baby: *Mimms, Garnet & Enchanters* / Dark end of the street: *Carr, James* / People get ready: *Impressions.*
■ LP . . . . . . . . . . . . . . . . . . . . RNLP 70041
MC. . . . . . . . . . . . . . . . . . . . RNC 70041
Rhino (USA) / Oct '87 / WEA.

**SOUL SISTER, BLUES BROTHER.**
**Tracks:** Not Advised.
CD. . . . . . . . . . . . . . . . . . . . DINCD 61
MC. . . . . . . . . . . . . . . . . . . . DINMC 61
■ LP . . . . . . . . . . . . . . . . . . . . DINTV 61
Dino / May '93.

**SOUL SISTERS EP.**
**Tracks:** I want to know / Take me for a little while / Mama don't lie / In orbit.
■ 7" . . . . . . . . . . . . . . . . . . . . CHES 4009
Chess (PRT) / Jul '85.

**SOUL SOLDIERS.**
**Tracks:** I'm the one who loves you: *Banks, Darrell* / No one blinder (than a man who won't see): *Banks, Darrell* / Just because your love has gone: *Banks, Darrell* / Only the strong survive: *Banks, Darrell* / Got to get rid of you: *Barnes, J.J.* / Snowflakes: *Barnes, J.J.* / I like everything about you: *Hughes, Jimmy* / I'm so glad: *Hughes, Jimmy* / Did you forget: *Hughes, Jimmy* / Chains of love: *Hughes, Jimmy* / Just ain't strong as , used to be: *Hughes, Jimmy* / Since I lost my baby's love: *Lance, Major* / I wanna make up (before we break up): *Lance, Major* / That's the story of my life: *Lance, Major* / Girl come on home: *Lance, Major* / Ain't no sweat: *Lance, Major* / Beautiful feeling (On CD only): *Banks, Darrell* / When a man loves a woman (On CD only): *Banks, Darrell* / Let 'em down baby (On CD only): *Hughes, Jimmy* / I'm not ashamed to beg or plead (On CD only): *Hughes, Jimmy* / Sweet Sherry (On CD only): *Barnes, J.J.* / Baby please come back home (On CD only): *Barnes, J.J..*
CD. . . . . . . . . . . . . . . . . . . . CDSX 012
■ MC. . . . . . . . . . . . . . . . . . . . SXC 012
■ LP . . . . . . . . . . . . . . . . . . . . SX 012
Stax / Aug '88.

**SOUL SOURCE (The Soul Era Vol.1).**
**Tracks:** Emergency (dial 999): *Bown, Alan* / (Accept my) invitation: *Band Of Angels* / Hallelujah: *Revolution* / Questions: *Barry, Sandra* / Hey diddley dee dum dum: *James, Jimmy* / Neighbour, neighbour: *Spectres* / Down home girl: *Felders Orioles* / When you move you lose: *Keith & Billie* / Soul sauce: *Timebox* / Nevertheless: *Riot Squad* / You beat me to the punch: *Jackson, Tony (2)* / Parchment farm: *Jay, Peter* / Every little bit hurts: *Clark, Petula* / Ain't no soul: *Bernard, Kenny* / I can't believe what you say: *McKenna, Val* / Michael: *Washington, Geno* / Ain't love good (CD bonus track.): *Cotton, Mike* / It was easier to hurt her (CD bonus track.): *Powell, Keith & The Valets* / Stay with me baby (CD bonus track.): *Baldry, Long John* / Build me up buttercup (CD bonus track.): *Foundations* / Agent double o soul (CD bonus track.): *Schroeder, John Orchestra* / Ain't that peculiar (CD bonus track.): *Sounds Orchestral.*
CD. . . . . . . . . . . . . . . . . . . . NEXCD 109
■ LP . . . . . . . . . . . . . . . . . . . . NEXLP 109
Sequel / Feb '90.

**SOUL SOUVENIRS.**
**Tracks:** I'm in need of love: *Courtney, Lou* / Hip to your ways: *Ujima* / Love is here: *Messina, Jim* / Just a kiss away: *Miles, Buddy* / You make me a believer: *Dozier, Lamont* / Good life: *Humphrey, Bobbi* / Loves to hot to hide: *Coulter, Clifford* / Crazy: *Gaines, Rosie* / I'm back for more (album version): *Johnson, Al* / How can I be sure: *Jackson, Randy* / Look at me, look at you (we're flying): *Shaw, Marlena* / You know you want to be loved: *Barrow, Keith.*
CD. . . . . . . . . . . . . . . . . . . . 4678782
■ MC. . . . . . . . . . . . . . . . . . . . 4678784
■ LP . . . . . . . . . . . . . . . . . . . . 4678781
Columbia / Jan '91.

**SOUL SOUVENIRS 2.**
**Tracks:** It's alright with me: *La Belle, Patti* / Give me some emotion: *Lewis, Webster* / Call on me: *Perry, Jeff* / Trust your heart: *Womack, Bobby* / What do you want me to do: *Courtney, Lou* / You're messin' up a good thing: *Cash, Heywood* / Hey baby: *White, Anthony* / This love is for real: *Banks, Ron* / Good times: *Gaines, Rosie* / Prime time: *Robinson, William* / What about you: *Hall, Carl* / It's all over now: *Snell, Annette* / Make me love the rain: *Wright, Betty* / Do you ever think about me: *Mangione, Chuck* / Here we go again (Only on CD single): *Isley Brothers* / Tonight's the night for love (Only on CD single): *Johnson, Al* / Space talk (Only on CD single): *Puthli, Asha.*
■ CD. . . . . . . . . . . . . . . . . . . . 4688242
■ LP . . . . . . . . . . . . . . . . . . . . 4688241
■ MC. . . . . . . . . . . . . . . . . . . . 4688244
Columbia / Oct '91.

**SOUL SPECTACULAR VOLUME III.**
**Tracks:** Band of gold / Still water (love) / Patches / You've got me dangling on a string / My cherie amour / It's all in the game / Signed, sealed, delivered I'm yours / I'll say forever my love / Gimme a little sign / Behind a painted smile / Walk away Rene / I'll be there.
■ LP . . . . . . . . . . . . . . . . . . . . MALS 1397
Marble Arch / Jun '71.

**SOUL SPIN.**
**Tracks:** That's no way to treat a girl: *Knight, Marie* / I got my heart set on you: *Toys (1)* / You'll fall in love: *Jive Five* / On top of the world: *Soul (1)* / Don't cry (sing along with the music): *Moore, Melba* / My heart cries for you: *Porgy & The Monarchs* / I love you a thousand times: *Platters* / Long after tonight is all over: *Radcliffe, Jimmy* / Hole in the wall: *Stone, George* / This diamond ring: *Ambrose, Sammy* / Try some soul: *Crossen, Ray* / You lie so well: *Knight, Marie* / You got it baby: *Toys (1)* / Sweet sweet lovin': *Platters* / Live on: *Troy, J B* / Run run roadrunner: *Williams, Jerry.*
■ LP . . . . . . . . . . . . . . . . . . . . KENT 024
Kent / Aug '84.

**SOUL STARTRACKS.**
**Tracks:** Living a little laughing a little: *Detroit Spinners* / I say a little prayer: *Franklin, Aretha* / Killing me softly with his song: *Flack, Roberta* / When a man loves a woman: *Sledge, Percy* / In the midnight hour: *Pickett, Wilson* / Saturday night at the movies: *Drifters* / I've been loving you too long: *Redding, Otis* / Dark end of the street: *Carter, Clarence* / Show must go on: *Dees, Sam* / Move on up: *Mayfield, Curtis* / New York City life: *Wilson, Tony* / Ghetto: *Hathaway, Donny* / What am I going to do about you girl: *Dozier, Lamont* / Star in the ghetto: *Average White Band* / 634 5789: *Pickett, Wilson* / Try a little tenderness: *Redding, Otis* / Sweet soul music: *Conley, Arthur* / Knock on wood: *Floyd, Eddie* / Hold on I'm coming: *Sam & Dave* / Green onions: *Booker T & The MG's.*
■ LP . . . . . . . . . . . . . . . . . . . . K4 58042
WEA / '77.

**SOUL STIRRERS: A TRIBUTE TO SAM COOKE.**
**Tracks:** My loved ones / Striving / Hello sunshine / That's heaven to me / Farther along / Slow train / Don't move that mountain / God is standing by / Peace in the valley / Son / Heaven is my home.
■ LP . . . . . . . . . . . . . . . . . . . . GCH 8086
■ MC. . . . . . . . . . . . . . . . . . . . GCHK 78086
Chess (Charly) / Jul '88.

**SOUL STIRRINGS - THE NU INSPIRATIONAL.**
**Tracks:** Not Advised.
CD. . . . . . . . . . . . . . . . . . . . BRCD 599
LP . . . . . . . . . . . . . . . . . . . . BRLP 599
MC. . . . . . . . . . . . . . . . . . . . BRCA 599
4th & Broadway / Oct '93 / PolyGram.

**SOUL SUPERBOWL-THE SIXTIES V THE SEVENTIES.**
**Tracks:** Please give me one more chance / Thanks for a little lovin' / Baby boy / She won't come back / Skate a while baby / Keep her guessing / Hey it's love / Where does that leave me / Katrina / Love's the only way to survive / What kind of love / Spread love / Look up with your mind / I fooled you this time.
■ LP . . . . . . . . . . . . . . . . . . . . KENT 060
Kent / Nov '86.

**SOUL SURVIVORS.**
**Tracks:** Troglodyte: *Soul Survivors* / Snake / Girl watcher / Got to get you off my mind / Only the strong survive / Slipaway / Tonights the night / Show and tell / Supernatural thing / Looking for a love / Can I change my mind / Groovy situation.
■ LP . . . . . . . . . . . . . . . . . . . . TOP 151
Topline / Jan '87.

**SOUL TIME.**
**Tracks:** Soul time: *Ellis, Shirley* / Beat: *Lance, Major* / Quitter never wins: *Williams, Larry & Johnny Watson* / I'm coming to your rescue: *Triumphs* / Love trap: *Valentine, T D* / More today than yesterday: *Spiral Staircase* / Little bit of something: *Little Richard* / He who picks a Rose: *Carstairs* / This heart of mine: *Artistics* / There's a pain in my heart: *Poppies* / Help me: *Spellbinders* / Walk like a man: *Moore, Johnny* / Lot of love: *Taj Mahal* / It's all over me: *Blackwell, Otis* / I need your love so desperately: *Peaches & Herb* / Stranger in my arms: *Randell, Lynne* / Seven the loser: *Lomax, Eric* / Country roads: *High Voltage.*
■ LP . . . . . . . . . . . . . . . . . . . . SINLP 4
SMP / Apr '86.

**SOUL TIME.**
**Tracks:** Not Advised.
CD. . . . . . . . . . . . . . . . . . . . 100 037
Bridge (MCS Bridge) / '86 / Pinnacle.

## SOUL TO SOUL.

**Tracks:** You make me feel brand new: *Stylistics* / You're the first, the last, my everything: *White, Barry* / More: *Gaye, Marvin* / Reunited: *Peaches & Herb* / One and only: *Knight, Gladys & The Pips* / Hang on in there baby: *Bristol, Johnny* / Crazy about your love: *Manhattans* / Stop me from starting this feeling: *Rawls, Lou* / Day by day: *Shakatak* / Never can say goodbye: *Gaynor, Gloria* / Without you: *Three Degrees* / Nightlife: *Stewart, Verdi* / Hustle: *McCoy, Van & Soul City Symphony* / Native New Yorker: *Odyssey* / Sex machine (Only available on CD.): *Brown, James* / Hold on to my love (Only available on CD.): *Ruffin, Jimmy* / Part time lover (Only available on CD.): *Helms, Jimmy* / Can't give you anything but my love (Only available on CD.): *Stylistics* / Make it with you (Only available on CD.): *Williams, Esther* / Help me make it through the night (Only available on CD.): *Knight, Gladys & The Pips* / Close the door: *Pendergrass, Teddy* / Best of my love: *Emotions (1)* / All the love in the world: *Warwick, Dionne* / Kiss and say goodbye (Not available on CD.): *Manhattans* / Love train: *O'Jays* / Never knew love like this before: *Mills, Stephanie* / Living inside your love (Not available on CD.): *Hyman, Phyllis* / If you don't know me by now: *Melvin, Harold.*

■ **Double LP.** . . . . . . . . . . . . . . . . **STDLP 21**
■ **CD.** . . . . . . . . . . . . . . . . . . . . **STDCD 21**
■ **MC.** . . . . . . . . . . . . . . . . . . . . **STDMC 21**
Masterpiece / Feb '89.

## SOUL TO SOUL VOL.1.

**Tracks:** Not Advised.
**MC.** . . . . . . . . . . . . . . . . . . . . . **SSC 1**
Dynamic / Mar '89 / Jetstar.

## SOUL TOGETHER.

**Tracks:** Not Advised.
■ **LP** . . . . . . . . . . . . . . . . . . . . **218 005**
Atlantic / Feb '70.

## SOUL TRACKS.

**Tracks:** Not Advised.
**CD.** . . . . . . . . . . . . . . . . . . . . **CDSR 046**
**MC.** . . . . . . . . . . . . . . . . . . . . **TCSR 046**
Telstar/Ronco / May '94 / BMG.

## SOUL TRAIN.

**Tracks:** Do the whoopee: *Desanto, Sugar Pie* / Soul poppin': *Jones, Johnny & The King Casuals* / Soul bossa nova: *Sattin, Lonnie* / 3 days, 1 hour, 30 minutes: *Wilson, Jackie* / Watermelon man: *Sattin, Lonnie* / Batman to the rescue: *Baker, LaVern* / Little girl lost: *Brown, Maxine* / So fine: *Turner, Ike & Tina & The Ikettes* / We need an understanding: *Turner, Ike & Tina & The Ikettes* / Bad night: *Ambrose, Sammy* / Damelo baby: *Aztecs* / Jerkin' time: *Diplomats (1)* / Soul train: *Little Richard* / Smokey Joe's: *Candy & The Kisses* / Come see about me: *Dodds, Nella* / Just a little bit of your soul: *Jackson, Chuck Orchestra.*

■ **LP** . . . . . . . . . . . . . . . . . . . . **KENT 080**
Kent / Jun '88.

## SOUL UPRISING.

**Tracks:** Not Advised.
■ **LP** . . . . . . . . . . . . . . . . . . . . **KENT 034**
Kent / Feb '85.

## SOUL VOL.2.

**Tracks:** Not Advised.
**VHS** . . . . . . . . . . . . . . . . . . . . **MMGV 038**
MMG Video / Jan '93 / THE.

## SOUL YEARS 1966, THE.

**Tracks:** Not Advised.
**CD.** . . . . . . . . . . . . . . . . . . . . **CYSRCD 66**
Connoisseur Collection / Aug '89 / Pinnacle.

## SOUL YEARS 1970, THE.

**Tracks:** Not Advised.
■ **CD.** . . . . . . . . . . . . . . . . . . **KNCD 22070**
■ **MC.** . . . . . . . . . . . . . . . . . . **KNMC 22070**
Knight / Sep '90.

## SOUL YEARS 1971, THE.

**Tracks:** Not Advised.
■ **CD.** . . . . . . . . . . . . . . . . . . **KNCD 22071**
■ **MC.** . . . . . . . . . . . . . . . . . . **KNMC 22071**
Knight / Sep '90.

## SOUL YEARS 1972, THE.

**Tracks:** Not Advised.
■ **CD.** . . . . . . . . . . . . . . . . . . **KNCD 22072**
■ **MC.** . . . . . . . . . . . . . . . . . . **KNMC 22072**
Knight / Sep '90.

## SOUL YEARS 1973, THE.

**Tracks:** Not Advised.
■ **CD.** . . . . . . . . . . . . . . . . . . **KNCD 22073**
■ **MC.** . . . . . . . . . . . . . . . . . . **KNMC 22073**
Knight / Sep '90.

## SOUL YEARS 1974, THE.

**Tracks:** Not Advised.
■ **CD.** . . . . . . . . . . . . . . . . . . **KNCD 22074**
■ **MC.** . . . . . . . . . . . . . . . . . . **KNMC 22074**
Knight / Sep '90.

## SOUL YEARS 1975, THE.

**Tracks:** Can't give you anything but my love: *Stylistics* / Right back where we started from: *Nightingale, Maxine* / Walkin' in rhythm: *Blackbyrds* / Hold back the night: *Trammps* / What am I gonna do with you: *White, Barry* / This will be: *Cole, Natalie* / Can I take you home little girl: *Drifters* / What a diff'rence a day makes: *Phillips, Esther* / Take good care: *Three Degrees* / Ride a wild horse: *Clark, Dee* / Do it anyway you wanna: *People's Choice* / Swing your daddy: *Gilstrap, Jim* / Reach out: *Gaynor, Gloria* / Girls: *Moments & Whatnauts* / There goes my first love: *Drifters* / I love music: *O'Jays* / Lady Marmalade: *Labelle* / Try to remember: *Knight, Gladys & The Pips* / Shining star: *Earth, Wind & Fire* / Wake up everybody: *Melvin, Harold & The Bluenotes* / You sexy thing: *Hot Chocolate* / Pick up the pieces: *Average White Band* / Fire: *Ohio Players* / Hustle: *McCoy, Van* / That's the way I like it: *K.C. & The Sunshine Band* / I wanna dance: *Disco Tex & The Sexolettes* / (Are you ready) do the bus stop: *Fatback Band* / Loving you: *Riperton, Minnie.*

■ **Double LP.** . . . . . . . . . . . . . . **KNLP 22075**
■ **CD Set.** . . . . . . . . . . . . . . . . **KNCD 22075**
■ **MC Set** . . . . . . . . . . . . . . . . **KNMC 22075**
Knight / Oct '89.

## SOUL YEARS 1976, THE.

**Tracks:** Love really hurts (without you): *Ocean, Billy* / Midnight train to Georgia: *Knight, Gladys & The Pips* / I'm your puppet: *Purify, James & Bobby* / Hurt: *Manhattans* / Misty blue: *Moore, Dorothy* / Get up offa that thing: *Brown, James* / Don't stop it now: *Hot Chocolate* / You'll never find: *Rawls, Lou* / Sophisticated lady: *Cole, Natalie* / Love ballad: *L.T.D.* / This is it: *Moore, Melba* / Kiss and say goodbye: *Manhattans* / Movin': *Brass Construction* / Play that funky music: *Wild Cherry* / You see the trouble: *White, Barry* / Shake your booty: *K.C. & The Sunshine Band* / Spanish hustle: *Fatback Band* / Can't help falling in love: *Stylistics* / I'll be good to you: *Brothers Johnson* / Who'd she coo: *Ohio Players* / Harvest for the world: *Isley Brothers* / Now is the time: *James, Jimmy & The Vagabonds* / Disco lady: *Taylor, Johnnie* / Funky weekend: *Stylistics* / You to me are everything: *Real Thing* / Darlin' darlin' baby: *O'Jays* / Soul city walk: *Bell, Archie* / Heaven must be missing an angel: *Tavares.*

■ **Double LP.** . . . . . . . . . . . . . . **KNLP 22076**
■ **CD Set.** . . . . . . . . . . . . . . . . **KNCD 22076**
■ **MC Set** . . . . . . . . . . . . . . . . **KNMC 22076**
Knight / Oct '89.

## SOUL YEARS 1977, THE.

**Tracks:** Show you the way to go: *Jacksons* / Baby don't change your mind: *Knight, Gladys & The Pips* / I believe you: *Moore, Dorothy* / Lovely day: *Withers, Bill* / Free: *Williams, Deniece* / Strawberry letter 23: *Brothers Johnson* / It's ecstasy when you lay down next to me: *White, Barry* / Boogie nights: *Heatwave* / Love hit me: *Nightingale, Maxine* / Saturday nite: *Earth, Wind & Fire* / Shuffle: *McCoy, Van* / That's what friends are for: *Williams, Deniece* / Baby come back: *Player* / Too hot to handle: *Heatwave* / red light spells danger: *Ocean, Billy* / Whodunnit: *Tavares* / Greatest love of all: *Benson, George* / So you win again: *Hot Chocolate* / Keep it comin' love: *K.C. & The Sunshine Band* / Everytime I turn around: *L.T.D.* / Ain't gonna bump no more: *Tex, Joe* / Best of my love: *Emotions (2)* / Let's clean up the ghetto: *Philadelphia All Stars* / I will: *Winters, Ruby* / Don't leave me this way: *Melvin, Harold & The Bluenotes* / Jack & Jill: *Parker, Ray Jnr.& Raydio* / Real mother: *Watson, Johnny 'Guitar'* / Native New Yorker: *Odyssey.*

■ **Double LP.** . . . . . . . . . . . . . . **KNLP 22077**
■ **CD Set.** . . . . . . . . . . . . . . . . **KNCD 22077**
■ **MC Set** . . . . . . . . . . . . . . . . **KNMC 22077**
Knight / Oct '89.

## SOUL YEARS 1978, THE.

**Tracks:** September: *Earth, Wind & Fire* / I thought it was you: *Hancock, Herbie* / Shame: *King, Evelyn 'Champagne'* / Blame it on the boogie: *Jacksons* / More than a woman: *Tavares* / Dance (disco heat): *Sylvester* / If I can't have you: *Elliman, Yvonne* / Boogie oogie oogie: *Taste Of Honey* / Is this a love thing: *Parker, Ray Jnr.& Raydio* / Holding on (when love): *L.T.D.* / Used to be my girl: *O'Jays* / Fantasy: *Earth, Wind & Fire* / Our love: *Cole, Natalie* / Get down: *Chandler, Gene* / Always and forever: *Heatwave* / Close the door: *Pendergrass, Teddy* / Whenever you want my love: *Real Thing* / Too much too little too late: *Mathis, Johnny & Deniece Williams* / Shake and dance with me: *Con Funk Shun* / Don't hold back: *Chanson* / Stuff like that: *Jones, Quincy* / Every one's a winner: *Hot Chocolate* / Come back and finish what you started: *Knight, Gladys & The Pips* / Come to me: *Winters, Ruby* / You make me feel: *Sylvester* / Your sweetness is my ..: *White, Barry* / Flashlight: *Parliament* / Givin' up, givin' in: *Three Degrees.*

■ **Double LP.** . . . . . . . . . . . . . . **KNLP 22078**
■ **CD Set.** . . . . . . . . . . . . . . . . **KNCD 22078**
■ **MC Set** . . . . . . . . . . . . . . . . **KNMC 22078**
Knight / Oct '89.

## SOUL YEARS 1979, THE.

**Tracks:** After the love has gone: *Earth, Wind & Fire* / I will survive: *Gaynor, Gloria* / Ladies night: *Kool & The Gang* / Ain't no stoppin' us now: *McFadden & Whitehead* / H.A.P.P.Y. radio: *Starr, Edwin* / Ring my bell: *Ward, Anita* / Reunited: *Peaches & Herb* / My simple heart: *Three Degrees.*

■ **Double LP.** . . . . . . . . . . . . . . **KNLP 22079**
■ **CD Set.** . . . . . . . . . . . . . . . . **KNCD 22079**
■ **MC Set** . . . . . . . . . . . . . . . . **KNMC 22079**
Knight / Oct '89.

## SOUL YEARS 1980, THE.

**Tracks:** Not Advised.
■ **MC.** . . . . . . . . . . . . . . . . . . **KNMC 22080**
■ **CD** . . . . . . . . . . . . . . . . . . . **KNCD 22080**
Knight / Jul '91.

## SOUL YEARS 1981, THE.

**Tracks:** Not Advised.
**CD.** . . . . . . . . . . . . . . . . . . . . **KNCD 22081**
■ **MC.** . . . . . . . . . . . . . . . . . . **KNMC 22081**
Knight / Jul '91.

## SOUL YEARS 1982, THE.

**Tracks:** Not Advised.
**CD.** . . . . . . . . . . . . . . . . . . . . **KNCD 22082**
■ **MC.** . . . . . . . . . . . . . . . . . . **KNMC 22082**
Knight / Jul '91.

## SOUL YEARS 1983, THE.

**Tracks:** Not Advised.
**CD.** . . . . . . . . . . . . . . . . . . . . **KNCD 22083**
■ **MC.** . . . . . . . . . . . . . . . . . . **KNMC 22083**
Knight / Jul '91.

## SOUL YEARS 1984, THE.

**Tracks:** Not Advised.
■ **MC.** . . . . . . . . . . . . . . . . . . **KNMC 22084**
■ **CD** . . . . . . . . . . . . . . . . . . . **KNCD 22084**
Knight / Jul '91.

## SOUL YEARS OF MINIT RECORDS (Struttin' & Flirtin' 1966-1969).

**Tracks:** What is this: *Womack, Bobby* / 60 minutes of your love: *Banks, Homer* / Working on your case: *O'Jays* / Hunk of funk: *Dozier, Gene & The Brotherhood* / Baby I love you: *Holiday, Jimmy* / I know you don't want me no more: *Jones, Gloria* / Fly me to the moon: *Womack, Bobby* / How I miss you baby: *Womack, Bobby & D. Carter* / Get right: *Players* / I wish it would rain: *Turner, Ike & Tina* / Worried life blues: *Parker, Little Jr.* / My heart is in danger: *Ray, Alder* / I've got love for my baby: *Young Hearts* / I'm gonna do all I can to do right by my man: *Turner, Ike & Tina.*

■ **MC.** . . . . . . . . . . . . . . . . . . **TCSSL 6028**
■ **LP** . . . . . . . . . . . . . . . . . . . . **SSL 6028**
Stateside / Jul '87.

## SOUL YEARS, THE.

**Tracks:** Strong as death: *Green, Al* / Back for a taste of your love: *Johnson, Syl* / I don't do windows: *Wright, O.V.* / She's my woman: *Bobo Mr. Soul* / Teenies dream: *Mitchell, Willie* / After you: *Quiet Elegance* / You got my mind messed up: *Quiet Elegance* / Trying to live my life without you: *Clay, Otis* / I've been there before: *Peebles, Ann* / Turning over the ground: *Mitchell, Phillip* / Wake up fool: *Masqueraders* / When the battle is over: *Joint Venture* / Let them know you care: *Jackson, George (1)* / Aretha, sing one for me: *Jackson, George (1).*

■ **LP** . . . . . . . . . . . . . . . . . . . . **HIUKLP 440**
Hi / '88.

## SOUL'D TOGETHER.

**Tracks:** I want a little bit: *CJ's Uptown Crew* / You're so cold: *Cotton, Tony* / First love last love: *Edwards, Janice* / My baby: *Harris, J.* / That's the way I feel: *Main Attraction* / Open up your heart: *Bilal, Thurston* / Deliverance: *Mason, Laverna* / Flashback: *Mathis, Diane* / Come take my love: *Harris, J.* / It's true: *Nash, Kevin* / I wanna share my world: *Alstin, Frank* / Style (I like yours too): *CJ's Uptown Crew* / Heart like a stone: *Gaines, Rosie* / Gone: *Cotton, Tony* / I got the love: *Riley, Walter* / Eyes: *Edwards, Janice.*

**CD.** . . . . . . . . . . . . . . . . . . . . **ATCD 015**
■ **LP** . . . . . . . . . . . . . . . . . . . . **ATLP 015**
About Time / Mar '92.

## SOUL'D TOGETHER VOL.2.

**Tracks:** Not Advised.
**CD.** . . . . . . . . . . . . . . . . . . . . **ATCD 016**
About Time / Nov '92 / BMG.

### OUL'D TOGETHER VOL.3.
racks: Close to you: *Bush, Charles* / I want you: *mith, Antoine* / Second go around: *Cornelious, Eve* House my love: *Blount, Carlton* / Never go back: *edford, Kenne* / G.o.o.d. times: *DeBarge* / I knew I ould always count on you: *Brown, Shirley* / Thank ou lady: *Brittan, James* / 9 to 5 (who said it): *Floyd, eff* / Reaching for the sky: *Riley, Walter* / Drug free ociety: *Mozie B* / Never give up: *Mathis, Diane* / ne more night: *Gaines, Rosie* / Let me kiss you here it hurts: *Burris, Warren* / Girl I miss you: *roup life* / If you need it: *Bush, Charles.*
D . . . . . . . . . . . . . . . . . . . . . . . . . **ATCD 017**
bout Time / Aug '93 / BMG.

### OULFUL KINDA MUSIC.
racks: Do what you gotta do: *Contenders* / Oh baby: *rown, Phyllis* / Can't lose my head: *Blackwell, eorge* / Ain't got nothing but the blues: *Friendly eople* / You don't love me: *Epitome Of Sound* / eep pushing on: *Carpettes* / Just do the best you an: *Duke & Leonard* / I don't want to lose you: *Bell oys* / I love her so much it hurts: *Majestics* / Prove ourself a lady: *Bounty, James.*
■ LP . . . . . . . . . . . . . . . . . . . . . . . . **LPSS 103**
oul Supply / Jan '87.

### OULFUL LOVE.
racks: Misty blue: *Simon, Joe* / If you don't want my ove (give it back): *Womack, Bobby* / I do love you: *tewart, Billy* / Tell it like it is: *Neville, Aaron* / othing takes the place of you: *McCall, Toussaint* / I ad a talk with my man: *Collier, Mitty* / Stand by me: *ittle Milton* / Love is blue: *Dells* / Release me: *hillips, Esther* / When a man loves a woman: *ledge, Percy* / At last: *James, Etta* / Sweet woman ke you: *Tex, Joe* / Ruler of my heart: *Thomas, Irma* / itting in the park: *Stewart, Billy.*
D . . . . . . . . . . . . . . . . . . . . . . . . **CDINS 5006**
■ LP . . . . . . . . . . . . . . . . . . . . . . . . **INS 5006**
IC . . . . . . . . . . . . . . . . . . . . . . . . **TCINS 5006**
nstant (2) / Jul '89 / Charly.

### OULFUL STUFF.
racks: Am I the same girl: *Acklin, Barbara* / Love akes a woman: *Acklin, Barbara* / Oh no not my aby: *Brown, Maxine* / Since I found you: *Brown, laxine* / Baby it's you: *Shirelles* / I'm gonna miss ou: *Artistics* / Saving my love for you: *Franklin, rma* / Just don't know what to do with myself: *Hunt, ommy* / Just as long as you need me: *Independents* Love uprising: *Leavill, Otis* / I'm the one to do it: *aker, LaVern* / I keep forgettin': *Jackson, Chuck* / ny day now: *Jackson, Chuck* / Turn back the hands f time: *Davis, Tyrone* / Lonely teardrops: *Wilson, ackie* / Can't get enough: *Thomas, Irma* / Can't get ou off my mind: *Diplomats (1)* / Put yourself in my lace: *Big Maybelle* / Make the night a little longer: *unt, Tommy* / Girl don't care: *Chandler, Gene* / ave you seen her: *Chi-Lites* / Sly, the slick and the icked: *Lost Generation* / Soulful strut: *Young-Holt nlimited.*
D . . . . . . . . . . . . . . . . . . . . . . . . **CDKEN 919**
IC . . . . . . . . . . . . . . . . . . . . . . . . **KENC 919**
ent / Nov '88 / Pinnacle.

### OULIN' VOL 1.
racks: Not Advised.
■ LP . . . . . . . . . . . . . . . . . . . . . . . . **BLP 501**
loonshine / Dec '85.

### OULIN' VOL 2.
racks: Not Advised.
■ LP . . . . . . . . . . . . . . . . . . . . . . . . **BLP 502**
loonshine / May '86.

### OULIN' VOL 3.
racks: Not Advised.
■ LP . . . . . . . . . . . . . . . . . . . . . . . . **BLP 503**
loonshine / Nov '86.

### OULIN' VOL 4.
racks: Not Advised.
■ LP . . . . . . . . . . . . . . . . . . . . . . . . **BLP 504**
loonshine / '88.

### OULMATES.
racks: Rainy night in Georgia: *Benton, Brook* / nock on wood: *Floyd, Eddie* / Tighten up: *Bell, rchie* / Tonight's the night / Soul man: *Sam & Dave* Walking the dog: *Thomas, Rufus* / Warm and tender ove / Patches: *Carter, Clarence* / Stand by me: *King, Ben E.* / Hold on I'm coming: *Sam & Dave* / Goin' out of my head: *Imperials* / Shoop shoop song: *Everett, Betty.*
■ LP . . . . . . . . . . . . . . . . . . . . . . . . **SPR 8526**
MC . . . . . . . . . . . . . . . . . . . . . . . . **SPC 8526**
pot / Feb '83.

### OUND OF ALABAMA SOUL.
racks: My love looks good: *Knight, Frederick* / I'm alling in love: *Knight, Frederick* / My love is real: *Controllers* / When did you stop / Its only a matter of time: *True Image* / Fool and his money: *True Image* / Take another look: *Saunders, Frankie* / I won't stop loving you: *Ward, Anita* / I'm ready for your love: *Ward, Anita* / It ain't fair: *True Image.*
■ LP . . . . . . . . . . . . . . . . . . . . . . . . **TRLP 113**
Timeless (Soul) / Jan '87.
■ CD . . . . . . . . . . . . . . . . . . . . . . . . **TLCD 411**
■ LP . . . . . . . . . . . . . . . . . . . . . . . . **TRPL 113**
Timeless (Soul) / Jan '90.

### SOUND OF COOLTEMPO, VOL. 2.
**Tracks:** Ring my bell: *Love, Monie Vs Adeva* / Outstanding: *Thomas, Kenny* / Lovesick: *Gang Starr* / Keep the dream alive: *Light Of The World* / Matter of fact: *Innocence* / Alright: *Urban Soul* / (Won't you) shelter me: *Circuit Featuring Koffi* / Pure (energy): *G.T.O.* / My heart: *Beat* / D-shake: *Mainline.*
CD . . . . . . . . . . . . . . . . . . . . . . . . **CCD 1867**
■ LP . . . . . . . . . . . . . . . . . . . . . . . . **CTLP 23**
■ MC . . . . . . . . . . . . . . . . . . . . . . . . **ZCTLP 23**
Cool Tempo / Jun '91.

### SOUND OF DETROIT/RARE STAMPS/ HERE TO STAY (Don Davis Presents).
**Tracks:** Baby, please come back home: *Barnes, J.J.* / Chains of love: *Barnes, J.J.* / Now that I got you back: *Barnes, J.J.* / Easy living: *Barnes, J.J.* / Sweet Sherry: *Barnes, J.J.* / Don't make me a storyteller: *Mancha, Steve* / Love like yours: *Mancha, Steve* / Keep the faith: *Mancha, Steve* / I don't wanna lose you: *Mancha, Steve* / Hate yourself in the morning: *Mancha, Steve* / Just keep on loving me: *Mancha, Steve* / Just because your love has gone: *Banks, Darrell* / Forgive me: *Banks, Darrell* / Only the strong survive: *Banks, Darrell* / Don't know what to do: *Banks, Darrell* / When a man loves a woman: *Banks, Darrell* / We'll get over: *Banks, Darrell* / Beautiful feeling: *Banks, Darrell* / I could never hate her: *Banks, Darrell* / Never alone: *Banks, Darrell* / No one blinder (than a man who won't see): *Banks, Darrell* / My love is strictly reserved: *Banks, Darrell.*
CD . . . . . . . . . . . . . . . . . . . . . . . . **CDSXD 061**
Stax / Jul '92 / Pinnacle.

### SOUND OF FUNK VOL 1.
**Tracks:** Damph F'aint: *Johnson, Herb Settlement* / Sad chicken: *Leroy & The Drivers* / How long shall I wait: *Fields, James Lewis* / Hector: *Village Callers* / Let the groove move you: *Lewis, Gus 'The Groove'* / Groovy world: *Fabulous Caprices* / Jan jan: *Unknown artist/s* / Iron leg: *Mickey & The Soul Generation* / You got to be a man: *Williams, Frank* / Searching for soul: *Unknown artist/s* / Push & pull: *Sons Of Slum* / Take this woman off the corner: *Spencer, James* / Everything gonna be alright: *Unknown artist/s* / Tramp Part 1: *Showmen Inc.* / I'm the man: *Showmen Inc.* / Whip, The Part 1: *Brown, Al* / You: *Wilson, Spanky* / Brother Brown: *Bob, Camille* / Happy soul: *Cortez, Dave & The Moon People* / Let my people go: *Darondo* / Nefertiti: *Wysdom.*
CD . . . . . . . . . . . . . . . . . . . . . . . . **GSCD 007**
LP . . . . . . . . . . . . . . . . . . . . . . . . **GSLP 007**
Goldmine / Nov '92 / Vital Distribution.

### SOUND OF FUNK VOL.3.
**Tracks:** Got a thing for you baby: *Mr Percolator* / Funky funky hot pants: *Mason, Wee Willie* / J.B's latin: *Spittin' Image* / New bump & twist: *Kats* / Hit drop: *Explosions* / Africana: *Propositions* / Got a gig on my back: *Kelly & The Soul Explosion* / Soul drippin's: *Interns* / Let's get together: *George, Cassietta* / Baby I've got it: *King George & The Fabulous Souls* / Fon-kin love: *Love International* / Campbell lock: *Campbell, Don* / Funky soul shake: *White, E.T. & The Potential Band* / Hot pants (part 1): *20th Century* / Closed mind: *Different Bags* / Give a damn: *Gordon, Benny* / Stop (what'cha doing to me): *Roberts, Roy* / Gimme some tonight: *Holmes Justice, Marvin* / How you get higher: *Hunter & His Games.*
CD . . . . . . . . . . . . . . . . . . . . . . . . **GSCD 023**
LP . . . . . . . . . . . . . . . . . . . . . . . . **GSLP 023**
Goldmine / Sep '93 / Vital Distribution.

### SOUND OF FUNK VOL.4.
**Tracks:** Funky buzzard: *Little Oscar* / Fun in your thang: *Phelps, Bootsey & The Soul Invaders* / Funky fat man: *Bynum, Burnett & The Soul Invaders* / Keep on brother keep on: *Fatback Band* / Crumbs for the table: *Young Disciples & Co.* / Moon walk: *King Solomon* / Bumping: *Chestnut, Tyrone* / Open up your heart: *Raw Soul & Frankie Beverly* / Get some: *Wee Willie & The Winners* / (Ride on) iron horse: *Marlboro Men* / Funky funk: *Big Al & The Star Treks* / Funky moon meditation: *Moonlighters* / Wait a minute: *Xplosions* / Do the funky donkey: *Turner, Otis & The Mighty Kingpins* / Funky line part 1: *Fabulous Shalimars* / Hold tight: *McNutt, Bobby* / Funky hump: *Cook, Little Joe* / Be black baby: *Tate, Grady* / Can you dig it: *Chico & Buddy.*
CD . . . . . . . . . . . . . . . . . . . . . . . . **GSCD 028**
LP . . . . . . . . . . . . . . . . . . . . . . . . **GSLP 028**
Goldmine / Jan '94 / Vital Distribution.

### SOUND OF FUNK VOL.5.
**Tracks:** Dynamite: *Colt, Steve* / Crazy legs: *Soul Tornadoes* / Breakdown: *Memphians* / Revolution rap (Part 1): *Green, Cal* / Wait a minute: *Xplosions* / Funkie moon: *Johnson, Smokey & Company* / Soul combination: *Soul Combination* / Afro bush: *Gaunichaux, E. & the Skeptics* / Football: *Mickey & The Soul Generation* / Whip (Part 1): *Simpkins, Darnell & the Family Tree* / Give a man a break: *Mintz, Charles* / I laugh & talk (but I don't play): *Strong, Zeke & the Ladyetts* / Kuri kuri: *Diety* / Hot pants: *Bee, Jimmy* / Bear funk: *Revolution Funk* / (Do the) yum yum man: *Contributors Of Soul* / Whip (Part 2): *Simpkins, Darnell & the Family Tree* / I laugh & talk (instrumental): *Strong, Zeke & the Ladyetts* / Revolution rap (Part 2): *Green, Cal.*
CD . . . . . . . . . . . . . . . . . . . . . . . . **GSCD 036**
LP . . . . . . . . . . . . . . . . . . . . . . . . **GSLP 036**
Goldmine / Apr '94 / Vital Distribution.

### SOUND OF FUNK VOL.6.
**Tracks:** Gigolo: *Anderson, Gene* / You did it: *Robinson, Ann* / Foxy little Mama: *Stone, Bob & His Band* / Oof (Do anything I want): *Colbert, Chuck* / Sweet thing: *Campbell, Milton & The R-D-M Band* / Rerun: *King Hannibal* / Atlanta boogaloo: *Inclines* / Rough nut: *Zodiacs* / Fussin & cussin (Part 1): *Four Wheel Drive* / (Get ready for ) Changes: *Marva & Melvin* / Funky John: *Cameron, Johnny & The Camerons* / Soul chills: *Soul, Dede & The Spidels* / Loneliest one: *Anderson, Gene* / Life is like a puzzle: *Village Soul Choir* / Sunshine (Part 1): *Scacy & The Sound Service* / Take it where you found it: *Jackson, Lorraine* / Fussin & Cussin (Part (2): *Four Wheel Drive* / Soul chills (Part 2): *Soul, Dede & The Spidels* / Boogie man: *Jones, Rufus R.*
CD . . . . . . . . . . . . . . . . . . . . . . . . **GSCD 045**
LP . . . . . . . . . . . . . . . . . . . . . . . . **GSLP 045**
Goldmine / Aug '94 / Vital Distribution.

### SOUND OF NEW ORLEANS, THE.
**Tracks:** Not Advised.
■ CD Set . . . . . . . . . . . . . . . . . . . . . . **CDBOX 254**
■ LP Set . . . . . . . . . . . . . . . . . . . . . . **BOX 254**
■ MC Set . . . . . . . . . . . . . . . . . . . . . . **TCBOX 254**
Charly / Nov '89.

### SOUND OF PHILADELPHIA.
**Tracks:** Me and Mrs. Jones: *Paul, Billy* / I love music: *O'Jays* / Don't leave me this way: *Melvin, Harold & The Bluenotes* / Nights over Egypt: *Jones Girls* / Year of decision: *Three Degrees* / Love train: *O'Jays* / Love TKO: *Pendergrass, Teddy* / When will I see you again: *Three Degrees* / Show me the way to go: *Jacksons* / If you don't know me by now: *Melvin, Harold & The Bluenotes* / Backstabbers: *O'Jays* / You'll never find another love like mine: *Rawls, Lou* / Wake up everybody: *Melvin, Harold & The Bluenotes* / TSOP: *MFSB* / Soul City walk: *Bell, Archie & The Drells* / Love I lost: *Melvin, Harold & The Bluenotes.*
CD . . . . . . . . . . . . . . . . . . . . . . . . **PWKS 588**
LP . . . . . . . . . . . . . . . . . . . . . . . . **SHM 3309**
MC . . . . . . . . . . . . . . . . . . . . . . . . **HSC 3309**
Pickwick / Jul '90 / Pickwick.

### SOUND OF PHILADELPHIA VOL.1.
**Tracks:** Not Advised.
CD . . . . . . . . . . . . . . . . . . . . . . . . **312 161**
Arcade / Aug '89 / Sony / Grapevine Distribution.

### SOUND OF PHILADELPHIA VOL.2.
**Tracks:** Not Advised.
CD . . . . . . . . . . . . . . . . . . . . . . . . **312 261**
Arcade / Aug '89 / Sony / Grapevine Distribution.

### SOUND OF SOUL.
**Tracks:** Dogging me around: *Washington, Albert* / These arms of mine: *Washington, Albert* / Lasting love: *Clay, Otis* / Tired of falling: *Clay, Otis* / I've got a claim on you: *Everett, Betty* / Can't stand it no longer: *Kelly Brothers* / You're that great big feeling: *Kelly Brothers* / Lost without the love of my guy: *Wills, Viola* / I've got to have all of you: *Wills, Viola* / Fire still burns: *Shelton, Roscoe* / Whole lot of lovin': *Soul Merchants* / This thing called love: *Wyatt, Johnny.*
■ LP . . . . . . . . . . . . . . . . . . . . . . . . **PTL 1008**
President / May '68.

### SOUND OF St. LOUIS SOUL.
**Tracks:** Got to forget you: *Beverley, Charles* / Good women go bad: *Carr, Barbara* / Taking a chance: *Beverley, Charles* / You've been doing wrong: *Carr, Barbara* / Hollywood: *Beverley, Charles* / Sweet loving baby: *Dee, Dave* / Don't you wanna man: *Hunter/Ross* / Good times are gone: *Hunter/Ross* / I'd love you tomorrow: *Hunter/Ross* / Rose bush: *Hunter/Ross.*
■ LP . . . . . . . . . . . . . . . . . . . . . . . . **TRLP 108**
Timeless (Soul) / Dec '87.
■ CD . . . . . . . . . . . . . . . . . . . . . . . . **TLCD 367**

■ DELETED

■ LP . . . . . . . . . . . . . . . . . . . . . . . . . . TRPL 108
Timeless (Soul) / Jan '90.

## SOUND OF THE FUNK VOLUME 2.

**Tracks:** Gat or bat / Humpty dumpty: *Vibrettes* / I've got reasons: *Hooper, Mary Jane* / Got to get me a job: *Alford, Ann* / Love got a piece of your mind: *5 Ounces of earth* / African strut: *Westbrook, Lynn* / Spin-II jug: *Brooks, Smokey* / Girl chooses the boy: *Collins, Lashdown* / Funk I-Tus: *Warm excursion* / Chocolate sugar: *Six Feet Under* / Screwdriver: *Austin, Lee* / Skin II black: *Bush, Tommy* / Communication is where it's at: *Billy the baron* / World: *1619 Bab* / Fun & funk: *Fantastic epics* / Marvin's groove: *B.W. Souls* / Hot butter 'n' all: *Darondo*.
CD . . . . . . . . . . . . . . . . . . . . . . . . . . GSCD 012
LP . . . . . . . . . . . . . . . . . . . . . . . . . . GSLP 012
Goldmine / Apr '93 / Vital Distribution.

## SOUND OF THE GULF COAST.

**Tracks:** Schoolday blues: *Johnny & The Jammers* / Let me come your way: *Boykin, Burl* / Sweet Lilly: *Roy 'Boogie Boy'* / True love: *Roy 'Boogie Boy'* / Good lovin': *Chas & Gene* / Baby don't go: *Charles, Andy & The Blues Kings* / Woke up this morning: *Canfil, Chase* / I had a dream: *Canfil, Chase* / No one else will do: *Mitchell, Joey* / Penalty of love: *Velvetones*.
■ LP . . . . . . . . . . . . . . . . . . . . . . . . . . CH 20
Ace / May '80.

## SOUNDS OF MOTOWN, THE (Ready Steady Go Special).

**Tracks:** Not Advised.
■ VHS . . . . . . . . . . . . . . . . . . . . . . . MVP 99 1071 2
PMI / Feb '85.

## SOUNDWAVE NO.7.

**Tracks:** Not Advised.
■ MC. . . . . . . . . . . . . . . . . . . . . . . . . . SW 07
Soul On Sound / Jul '84.

## SOUTHERN FRIED SOUL.

**Tracks:** You're so good to me baby: *Spencer, Eddie* / It takes a whole lotta woman: *Gauff, Willie & The Love Brothers* / When she touches me: *Martin, Rodge* / Good man is hard to find: *Martin, Rodge* / Can you handle it: *Allison, Levert* / You can get it now: *Middleton, Gene* / Man who will do anything: *Middleton, Gene* / So many times: *Lewis, Levina* / Look a little higher: *Up Tights* / Just a dream: *Up Tights* / Sad sad song: *Crawford, Charles* / Fa fa fa fa fa (sad song): *McDade, Joe* / My girl's a soul girl: *Rogers, Lon* / Too good to be true: *Rogers, Lon* / You're being unfair to me: *Sample, Hank* / So in love with you: *Sample, Hank* / I'll always love you: *Moultrie, Sam* / I found what I wanted: *Lacour, Bobby* / Cry like a baby: *Lacour, Bobby* / Love waits for no man: *Curlee, Bobby & The Preachers* / Why is it taking so long: *Baxter, Tony* / I'm surprised: *Vann, Paul*.
CD . . . . . . . . . . . . . . . . . . . . . . . . . . GSCD 025
Goldmine / Nov '93 / Vital Distribution.

## SOUTHERN GROOVES.

**Tracks:** Not Advised.
CD . . . . . . . . . . . . . . . . . . . . . . . . . . CPCD 8067
Charly / Nov '94 / Charly.

## SOUTHERN SANCTIFIED SINGERS.

**Tracks:** Not Advised.
■ LP . . . . . . . . . . . . . . . . . . . . . . . . . . RL 328
Roots (Germany) / Oct '88.

## SOUTHERN SOUL BELLES.

**Tracks:** Love of my man: *West, Barbara* / I'm in love: *Lavette, Betty* / That's all a part of lovin' him: *Young, Tommie* / Every little bit hurts: *Scott, Peggy* / Fight fire with fire: *Holiday, Shay* / Easier to say (than do): *Lavette, Betty* / Do you still feel the same: *Young, Tommie* / Shell of a woman: *Allen, Doris* / Nearer to you: *Lavette, Betty* / Anyone but you: *West, Barbara* / Giving up: *Ad Libs* / Gonna make a change: *Montgomery, Carolyn* / Hanging heavy in my mind: *Allen, Doris* / You brought it all on yourself: *Young, Tommie* / Let me down easy: *Lavette, Betty* / Give me back the man I love: *West, Barbara*.
■ LP . . . . . . . . . . . . . . . . . . . . . . . . . . CRB 1035
Charly R&B / Feb '82.
CD . . . . . . . . . . . . . . . . . . . . . . . . . . CDINS 5018
LP . . . . . . . . . . . . . . . . . . . . . . . . . . INS 5018
MC. . . . . . . . . . . . . . . . . . . . . . . . . . TCINS 5018
Instant (2) / Feb '90 / Charly.

## SOUTHERN SOUL BROTHERS.

**Tracks:** Easy going fellow: *Mills, Billy* / Just the touch of your hand: *Vann, Paul* / One of these days: *Brown, Piney* / Wife you save (maybe your own): *Little Richie* / Loving her was easier: *Gaines, Earl* / I'll find my sunshine: *Scott, Moody* / Hey girl: *Beavers, Jackie* / Mojo blues: *John R* / You made your bed so hard: *Davis, Geator* / That's all I want from you: *Baker, Sam* / Sad memories: *Mills, Billy* / I wish I was a baby: *Little Richie* / Wedding cake: *Shelton, Roscoe* / Nashville women: *Brown, Piney* / Woman's touch: *Scott, Moody* / V.C. blues: *Orange, Allen*.
■ LP . . . . . . . . . . . . . . . . . . . . . . . . . . CRB 1156
Charly R&B / Jul '87.

## SOUTHERN STATES SOUND.

**Tracks:** Not Advised.
CD . . . . . . . . . . . . . . . . . . . . . . . . . . MCCD 135
Music Club / Jan '92 / Gold & Sons / THE / Video Collection / C.M. Distribution.

## SPECIAL MOTOWN DISCO ALBUM.

**Tracks:** Not Advised.
■ LP . . . . . . . . . . . . . . . . . . . . . . . . . . STML 12059
Tamla Motown / May '77.

## SPECIAL MOTOWN DISCO ALBUM, VOL. 2.

**Tracks:** I love to dance: *Finished Touch* / Why do you wanna see my bad side: *Robinson, Smokey* / Brick house: *Commodores* / You & I: *James, Rick* / Lovin livin & givin: *Ross, Diana* / Standin' on the verge of gettin it on: *Platinum Hook* / After the dance: *21st Creation* / Love masterpiece: *Houston, Thelma*.
■ LP . . . . . . . . . . . . . . . . . . . . . . . . . . STML 12102
Motown / Feb '79.

## SPECIALTY STORY, THE.

**Tracks:** Boogie number one: *Sepia-Tones* / Voo-it voo-it: *Blues Woman* / Milton's boogie: *Milton, Roy* / R.M.Blues: *Milton, Roy* / Rainy day blues: *Jump Jackson Band* / Ice Cream Freezer: *Blues Man* / True blues: *Milton, Roy* / Rockin' boogie: *Lutcher, Joe & His Society Cats* / Thrill me: *Milton, Roy* / Tear drop blues: *Liggins, Jimmy* / Cadillac boogie: *Liggins, Jimmy* / Keep a dollar in your pocket: *Milton, Roy & His Solid Senders* / X-Temporaneous boogie: *Howard, Camille* / You don't love me: *Howard, Camille* / Fat meat: *Wynn, Big Jim* / Everything I do is wrong: *Milton, Roy* / Hop, skip, jump: *Milton, Roy* / Careful love: *Liggins, Jimmy* / Big city blues: *Maceo, Big* / I want a roller: *Hogg, Smokey* / Huckle-buck: *Milton, Roy & His Solid Senders* / Fiesta on old Mexico: *Howard, Camille* / Honeydripper: *Liggins, Joe* / Don't put me down: *Liggins, Joe* / Information blues: *Milton, Roy* / Rag mop: *Liggins, Joe* / Pink champagne: *Liggins, Joe* / Junior jives: *Milton, Roy* / Where there is no love: *Milton, Roy* / Everything gonna be alright: *King, Perry & His Pied Pipers* / Please send me someone to love: *Mayfield, Percy* / Strange things happening: *Mayfield, Percy* / Little Joe's boogie: *Liggins, Joe* / Oh Babe: *Milton, Roy* / Lost love: *Mayfield, Percy* / Frankie Lee: *Liggins, Joe* / What a fool I was: *Mayfield, Percy* / Money blues: *Howard, Camille* / It's later than you think: *Milton, Roy* / T-twist twist: *Milton, Roy* / I have news for you: *Milton, Roy* / Prayin' for your return: *Mayfield, Percy* / Strange angel: *Easton, Amos* / Best wishes: *Milton, Roy* / Cry baby: *Mayfield, Percy* / Love will make you a slave: *Greenwood, Lil* / I can't lose with the stuff I use: *Williams, Lester* / Wheel of fortune: *Four Flames* / Big question: *Mayfield, Percy* / Lawdy Miss Clawdy: *Price, Lloyd* / So tired: *Milton, Roy* / Night and day (I miss you so): *Milton, Roy* / Oooh oooh oooh: *Price, Lloyd* / Restless heart: *Price, Lloyd* / Dream girl: *Jesse & Marvin* / Tell me pretty baby: *Price, Lloyd* / Ain't it a shame: *Price, Lloyd* / Frantic: *Crawford, Jimmy & Frank Motley* / Too close to heaven: *Bradford, Alex* / I'm coming home: *Swan Silvertones* / I've got a new home: *Pilgrim Travelers* / One room country shack: *Walton, Mercy Dee* / Lucy Mae blues: *Sims, Frankie Lee* / Early in the morning: *Milton, Roy* / She's been gone: *H-Bomb Ferguson* / Hard living alone: *Dixon, Floyd* / Drunk: *Liggins, Jimmy* / I ate the wrong part: *Temple Little & His 88* / Blood stains on the wall: *Honey Boy* / Baby doll: *Marvin & Johnny* / Things that I used to do: *Guitar Slim* / I'm your best bet baby: *King, Earl* / No room in the hotel: *Chosen Gospel Singers* / I'm mad: *Hooker, John Lee* / Sopmething's going on in my room: *Cleanhead, Daddy* / Zindy Lou: *Chimes (1)* / One more river: *Soul Stirrers* / Where's my girl: *Belvin, Jesse* / Nite owl: *Allen, Tony & The Champs* / Tutti frutti: *Little Richard* / Eternity: *Kador, Ernest* / Rich woman: *Millet, Lil* / Squeeze box boogie: *Chenier, Clifton* / Touch the hem of his garment: *Soul Stirrers* / Long tall Sally: *Little Richard* / Slippin' & slidin' (peepin' & hidin'): *Little Richard* / Oh-Rooba-Lee: *Maye, Arthur Lee & The Crowns* / Gloria: *Maye, Arthur Lee & The Crowns* / Cherokee dance: *Landers, Bob & Willie Joe & His Unitar* / Rip it up: *Little Richard* / Ready teddy: *Little Richard* / Sweet breeze: *Green, Vernon & The Phantoms* / (Everytime I hear that) Mellow saxophone: *Montrell, Roy* / She's got it: *Little Richard* / Heeby-jeebies: *Little Richard* / Should I ever love again: *Carr, Wynona & The Bumps Blackwell Band* / Just hold my hand: *Myles, Big Boy and the Sha-Weez* / Girl can't help it: *Little Richard* / All around the world: *Little Richard* / Oooh-whee baby: *Neville, Art* / Just because: *Williams, Larry* / Lucille: *Little Richard* / Send me some livin': *Little Richard* / Open up your heart: *Church, Eugene* / Our romance: *King, Clydie* / Jenny Jenny: *Little Richard* / Miss Ann: *Litt Richard* / Short fat fannie: *Williams, Larry* / Leavin' all up to you: *Don & Dewey* / Keep a-knockin': *Litt Richard* / Bony moronie: *Williams, Larry* / Twitch *Hall, Rene Orchestra & Willie Joe* / I'll come runnin back to you: *Cooke, Sam* / Good golly, Miss Moll *Little Richard* / Slow down: *Williams, Larry* / Dizz Miss Lizzy: *Williams, Larry* / Justine: *Don & Dewey* True fine mama: *Little Richard* / Ooh my soul: *Litt Richard* / Lights out: *Byrne, Jerry* / Love of god: *So Stirrers* / Koko Joe: *Don & Dewey* / Baby face: *Litt Richard* / There's a moose on the loose: *Jackso Roddy* / Haunted house: *Fuller, Johnny* / She sai yeah: *Williams, Larry* / Bad boy: *Williams, Larry* Farmer John: *Don & Dewey* / Big boy Pete: *Don Dewey* / Bama lama bama loo: *Little Richard*.
CD Set . . . . . . . . . . . . . . . . . . . . . . . . . . 5 SPCD 441
Fantasy / Mar '94 / Pinnacle / Jazz Music.

## SPOTLIGHT ON SOUL.

**Tracks:** Not Advised.
■ LP . . . . . . . . . . . . . . . . . . . . . . . . . . SPOT 103
■ MC. . . . . . . . . . . . . . . . . . . . . . . . . . ZCSPT 103
PRT / Oct '83.

## SPOTLIGHT ON SOUL.

**Tracks:** Soul man: *Sam & Dave* / Knock on woo *Floyd, Eddie* / Harlem shuffle: *Bob & Earl* / My gu *Wells, Mary* / Stay: *Williams, Maurice & The Zodiac* / Stagger Lee: *Price, Lloyd* / Tell it like it is: *Neville Aaron* / Every beat of my heart: *Knight, Gladys & Th Pips* / So fine: *Turner, Ike & Tina* / Mockingbir *Foxx, Inez* / Oh no, not my baby: *Brown, Maxine* Precious & few: *Climax Blues Band* / Show & te *Wilson, Al* / Seems like I gotta do wrong: *Whispers* Stand by me: *King, Ben E.* / When a man loves woman: *Sledge, Percy*.
CD. . . . . . . . . . . . . . . . . . . . . . . . . . HADCD 14
MC. . . . . . . . . . . . . . . . . . . . . . . . . . HADMC 14
Javelin / Feb '94 / THE.

## SSS SOUL SURVEY.

**Tracks:** Cryin' in the streets: *Perkins, George* / Lo nely room: *Murray, Mickey* / Game of love: *Hobbs Willie* / I have no one: *Hamilton, Big John* / Actio speaks louder than words: *Bell, Reuben* / That's how strong my love is: *Giles, Eddie* / How much can man take: *Hamilton, Big John* / Them changes: *Ha milton, Big John & Doris Allen* / Baby you got i *Murray, Clarence* / One way love affair: *White Danny* / Lift me up: *Hamilton, Big John* / If I could se you one more time: *Adams, Johnny* / Lonely man *Soul, Johnny* / Too late: *Bell, Reuben* / Some leavin alone: *Bush, Tommy* / Take this hurt off me: *Hami ton, Big John*.
■ LP . . . . . . . . . . . . . . . . . . . . . . . . . . CRB 103
Charly R&B / Feb '82.

## STAND BY ME.

**Tracks:** Not Advised.
CD . . . . . . . . . . . . . . . . . . . . . . . . . . YDG 7460
MC. . . . . . . . . . . . . . . . . . . . . . . . . . YDG 4571
Yesterday's Gold / Feb '93 / Target / Midland Re cords / Target Sales & Marketing.

## STAND IN FOR LOVE.

**Tracks:** It's starting to get to me now: *Thomas, Irma* Underneath my make up: *Thrills* / No, no, I can't hel you: *McKay, Beverley* / I'm through trying to prove my love for you: *Womack, Bobby* / I found a nev love: *Holiday, Jimmy* / Let's live: *Neville, Aaron* / Ge out of my life: *Little Anthony/Imperials/101 Strings* Quiet place: *Mimms, Garnet & Enchanters* / I can' wait until I see my baby's face: *Washington/King* Missin' my baby: *King, Clydie* / Anyone who knows what love is (will understand): *Thomas, Irma* / That's how much I love you: *Houston, Eddie* / Everyday *Neville, Aaron* / Workin' on a groovy thing: *Drew Patti*.
■ LP . . . . . . . . . . . . . . . . . . . . . . . . . . KENT 05
Kent / Apr '86.

## STAN'S SOUL SHOP.

**Tracks:** No more ghettos in America: *Winston, Stan ley* / Man in love: *Perkins, George* / Losing boy *Giles, Eddie* / What was I supposed to do: *Carter Clarence* / You're gonna miss me: *Bell, Reuben* You got me tamed: *Hammond, Clay* / Lord will make a way: *Robinson, Roscoe* / That's enough: *Robinson Roscoe* / Prelude to a heartbreak: *Montclairs* / wake up crying: *Camille, Bob* / Cry to me: *Powell Bobby* / I get my groove from you: *Patterson, Bobby* Stand by me: *Soul Stirrers* / I still love you: *Steele Eddie* / Good thing: *Jones, Casey* / Going home to Georgia: *Gilliam, Johnny*.
■ LP . . . . . . . . . . . . . . . . . . . . . . . . . . CRB 1033
Charly R&B / Feb '82.

## STAX (BOXED SET) 811-820.

**Tracks:** Not Advised.
■ 7" Set . . . . . . . . . . . . . . . . . . . . . . . . . . STAXBOX 2
Stax / Nov '87.



■ DELETED

**STAX 20 GOLDEN GREATS.**
**Tracks:** Shaft / Private number / Respect yourself / Who's making love / Starting all over again / Soul limbo / Shortstopping / I've been lonely for so long / I'll be the other woman / Dedicated to the one I love / Time is tight / I'll take you there / My baby specializes / Knock on wood / Woman to woman / In the rain.
**LP** . . . . . . . . . . **STX 3013**
Stax / Mar '79.

**STAX CLASSICS.**
**Tracks:** Shaft: *Hayes, Isaac* / Who's making love: *Taylor, Johnnie* / Private number: *Clay, Judy & William Bell* / Time is tight: *Booker T & The MG's.*
■ **EP** . . . . . . . . . . **BD 109**
Bye Big Deal / Jun '77.

**STAX FUNK - GET UP AND GET DOWN.**
**Tracks:** Shaft, Theme from: *Hayes, Isaac* / Castle of joy: *Fat Larry's Band* / What goes around (must come around): *Sons Of Slum* / Dark skin woman (On CD/MC only): *Rice, Sir Mack* / Whatcha see is whatcha get: *Dramatics* / Son of Shaft: *Bar-Kays* / Dryer part 1: *Johnson, Roy Lee & The Villagers* / Cool strut part one (On CD/MC only): *Hayes, Bernie* / Mr. Big Stuff: *Knight, Jean* / Funkasize you: *Sho Nuff* / Holy ghost: *Bar-Kays* / Men, The (Theme from) (On CD/MC only): *Hayes, Isaac* / Circuits overloaded: *Foxx, Inez & Charlie* / FLB: *Fat Larry's Band* / Black: *Mar-Keys* / Get up and get down: *Dramatics* / Moving on: *Dynamic Soul Machine* / You chose me (On CD/MC only): *Sho Nuff* / Dryer part 2 (On CD/MC only): *Johnson, Roy Lee & The Villagers* / Cool strut part 1 (On CD/MC only): *Hayes, Bernie.*
**CD** . . . . . . . . . . **CDSX 020**
■ **LP** . . . . . . . . . . **SX 020**
**MC** . . . . . . . . . . **SXC 020**
Stax / May '89 / Pinnacle.

**STAX GOLD (Hits 1968-1974).**
**Tracks:** Soul limbo: *Booker T & The MG's* / Time is tight: *Booker T & The MG's* / Private number: *Clay, Judy & William Bell* / Who's making love: *Taylor, Johnnie* / Bring it on home to me: *Floyd, Eddie* / I forgot to be your lover: *Bell, William* / I like what you're doing (to me): *Thomas, Carla* / Do the push and pull part 1: *Thomas, Rufus* / Mr. Big Stuff: *Knight, Jean* / Whatcha see is whatcha get: *Dramatics* / Respect yourself: *Staple Singers* / I'll take you there: *Staple Singers* / Theme from Shaft: *Hayes, Isaac* / Son of Shaft: *Bar-Kays* / I've been lonely for so long: *Knight, Frederick* / Starting all over again: *Mel & Tim* / Woman to woman: *Brown, Shirley* / I'll be the other woman: *Soul Children* / So I can love you (Not on LP): *Emotions (2)* / I have learned to do without you (Not on LP): *Staples, Mavis* / In the rain (Not on LP): *Dramatics* / Dedicated to the one I love (Not on LP): *Temprees* / Short stoppin' (Not on LP): *Brown, Veda* / Cheaper to keep her (Not on LP): *Taylor, Johnnie.*
**CD** . . . . . . . . . . **CDSXD 043**
**LP** . . . . . . . . . . **SXD 043**
■ **MC** . . . . . . . . . . **SXDC 043**
Stax / Sep '91.

**STAX GREATEST HITS.**
**Tracks:** In the rain: *Dramatics* / I'll take you there: *Staple Singers* / Who's making love: *Taylor, Johnnie* / Do the funky chicken: *Thomas, Rufus* / Hearsay: *Soul Children* / Dedicated to the one I love: *Temprees* / I could never be president: *Taylor, Johnnie* / Woman to woman: *Brown, Shirley* / Good woman turning bad / Respect yourself: *Staple Singers* / I've been lonely for so long: *Knight, Frederick* / Shaft, Theme from: *Hayes, Isaac* / Mr. Big Stuff: *Knight, Jean* / Private number: *Clay, Judy & William Bell* / So I can love you: *Emotions (1)* / Starting all over again: *Mel & Tim* / That's what love will make us do: *Little Milton* / Whatcha see is whatcha get: *Dramatics.*
**CD** . . . . . . . . . . **JCD 7021110**
Stax / Mar '87 / Pinnacle.

**STAX O' SOUL: SAMPLER OF STAX TRAX.**
**Tracks:** Will you love me tomorrow: *Bell, William* / Stolen angel: *Tonettes* / Zip-a-dee-doo-dah: *Booker T & The MG's* / Little boy: *Thomas, Carla* / Last clean shirt: *Thomas, Rufus* / Cupid: *Redding, Otis* / Sweet devil: *John, Mable* / Need your love so bad: *Johnson, Ruby* / I've never found a girl: *Floyd, Eddie* / I could never be president: *Taylor, Johnnie* / What side of the door: *Hughes, Jimmy* / Open the door to your heart: *Little Milton* / I can't break away (from your love): *Lewis, Barbara* / When something is wrong with my baby: *Weston, Kim* / I finally got you: *McCracklin, Jimmy* / Takin' all the love I can: *Joseph, Margie* / Wade in the water: *Little Sonny* / I've been lonely for so long: *Knight, Frederick* / Respect yourself: *Staple Singers* / Getting funky round here: *Black Nasty* / Flat tire: *King, Albert* / We need each other, girl: *Hayes, Isaac* / Move me move me: *Brown, Shirley.*
**CD** . . . . . . . . . . **CDSXX 100**
Stax / Oct '93 / Pinnacle.

**STAX REVUE LIVE AT THE 54 BALLROOM.**
**Tracks:** Green onions: *Booker T & The MG's* / You can't sit down: *Booker T & The MG's* / Summertime: *Booker T & The MG's* / Soul twist: *Booker T & The MG's* / Boot-leg: *Booker T & The MG's* / Don't have to shop around: *Mad Lads (1)* / Candy: *Astors* / Last night: *Mar-Keys* / Any other way: *Bell, William* / You don't miss your water: *Bell, William* / Every ounce of strength: *Thomas, Carla* / Do the dog: *Thomas, Rufus* / Walking the dog: *Thomas, Rufus.*
**CD** . . . . . . . . . . **CDSXD 040**
Stax / Sep '91 / Pinnacle.

**STAX SIRENS AND VOLT VAMPS.**
**Tracks:** Try a little tenderness: *Sweet Inspirations* / I've got to go on without you: *Brown, Shirley* / Take it off her (and put it on me): *Brown, Veda* / Love slave: *Alexander, Margie* / Shouldn't I love him: *John, Mable* / Got to be the man: *Emotions (2)* / Save the last kiss for me: *Knight, Jean* / Nobody: *Joseph, Margie* / Who could be loving you: *Ross, Jackie* / Standing in the need of your love: *Jeanne & The Darlings* / I'll never grow old: *Charmells* / Give love to save love: *Clay, Judy* / You hurt me for the last time: *Foxx, Inez & Charlie* / I like what you're doing (to me): *Thomas, Carla* / If I had it my way: *Weston, Kim* / How can you mistreat the one you love (Available on CD only): *Love, Katie* / Love changes (Available on CD only): *Charlene & The Soul Serenaders* / What happened to our good thing (Available on CD only): *Haywood, Kitty* / Where would you be today (Available on CD only): *Ilana.*
**CD** . . . . . . . . . . **CDSX 013**
■ **LP** . . . . . . . . . . **SX 013**
■ **MC** . . . . . . . . . . **SXC 013**
Stax / Jun '88.

**STAX TRAX: 18 CLASSIC SOUL HITS.**
**Tracks:** I'll take you there: *Staple Singers* / Time is tight: *Booker T & The MG's* / Knock on wood: *Floyd, Eddie* / Stay with me, baby: *Brown, Shirley* / I've been lonely for so long: *Knight, Frederick* / Private number: *Clay, Judy & William Bell* / Long walk to D.C.: *Staple Singers* / Sixty minutes man: *Thomas, Rufus* / Why I keep living these memories (end s1): *Knight, Jean* / Shaft, Theme from: *Hayes, Isaac* / Bring it on home to me: *Floyd, Eddie* / Woman to woman: *Brown, Shirley* / Respect yourself: *Staple Singers* / Soul limbo: *Booker T & The MG's* / Mr. Big Stuff: *Knight, Jean* / My girl: *Floyd, Eddie* / (Sittin' on) the dock of the bay: *Staple Singers* / Funky chicken: *Thomas, Rufus.*
■ **LP** . . . . . . . . . . **CBR 1023**
**MC** . . . . . . . . . . **KCBR 1023**
Premier (Sony) / '84 / Sony / Pinnacle.

**STAX/VOLT REVUE, VOL 1: LIVE IN LONDON.**
**Tracks:** Not Advised.
■ **LP** . . . . . . . . . . **SD7721**
Atlantic / Jun '88.

**STAX/VOLT REVUE, VOL 2: LIVE IN PARIS.**
**Tracks:** Not Advised.
■ **LP** . . . . . . . . . . **SD7722**
Atlantic / Jun '88.

**STAX/VOLT REVUE, VOL 3: LIVE IN EUROPE.**
**Tracks:** Introduction (London): *Emperor Rosko* / Red beans and rice: *Booker T & The MG's* / Booker-loo: *Booker T & The MG's* / Green onions: *Booker T & The MG's* / Hip-hug-her: *Booker T & The MG's* / Introduction (Paris): *Hubert* / Let me be good to you: *Thomas, Carla* / Yesterday: *Thomas, Carla* / Something good (is going to happen): *Thomas, Carla* / B-A-B-Y: *Thomas, Carla* / Introduction (London) 2: *Emperor Rosko* / I don't want to cry: *Floyd, Eddie* / Raise your hand: *Floyd, Eddie* / Knock on wood: *Floyd, Eddie* / Introduction (London) 3: *Emperor Rosko* / Respect: *Redding, Otis* / My girl: *Redding, Otis* / Shake: *Redding, Otis* / Day tripper: *Redding, Otis* / Introduction: *Redding, Otis* / Fa-fa-fa-fa-fa (Sad song): *Redding, Otis* / Introdcution: *Redding, Otis* / Try a little tenderness: *Redding, Otis.*
**CD** . . . . . . . . . . **CDSXD 044**
Stax / May '92 / Pinnacle.

**STAY WITH ME.**
**Tracks:** Do what you do: *Jackson, Jermaine* / All the love in the world: *Warwick, Dionne* / Joanna: *Kool & The Gang* / Night to remember: *Shalamar* / Your love is king: *Sade* / Never knew love like this before: *Mills, Stephanie* / Secret lovers: *Atlantic Starr* / Stay with me tonight: *Osborne, Jeffrey* / There goes my first love: *Drifters* / Reach out I'll be there: *Gaynor, Gloria* / One hundred ways: *Jones, Quincy* / You make me feel brand new: *Stylistics* / Never, never gonna give you up: *White, Barry* / Woman in love: *Three Degrees* / Summer breeze: *Isley Brothers* / My love is waiting: *Marvin Gaye* / Lovely day (remix): *Withers, Bill* / What a fool believes: *Franklin, Aretha.*
**CD** . . . . . . . . . . **PMP 105**
Pickwick / Nov '92 / Pickwick.

**STILL GROOVE JUMPING.**
**Tracks:** High low Jack: *Lucas, Buddy* / Mr. Bear comes to town: *Mr. Bear* / I'm gonna keep my good eye on you: *Mr. Bear* / Peek-a-boo: *Mr. Bear* / Bear hug: *Mr. Bear* / When I get married: *Dupree, Champion Jack* / Rockin with red (she knows how to rock me): *Piano Red* / Jump man jump: *Piano Red* / She's got no hair: *Crudup, Arthur* / Country boy: *Kennedy, Tiny* / You better heed my warning: *Dale, Larry* / Down in the bottom: *Dale, Larry* / Midnight hours: *Dale, Larry* / Right now baby: *Gaines, Roy* / All my life: *Gaines, Roy* / Drink up: *Du-Droppers.*
■ **LP** . . . . . . . . . . **DT 33006**
Detour / Jul '87.

**STONED ALCHEMY.**
**Tracks:** Come on: *Berry, Chuck* / Red rooster: *Howlin' Wolf* / Fortune teller: *Spellman, Benny* / I just want to make love to you: *Waters, Muddy* / Road runner: *Diddley, Bo* / Down home girl: *Robinson, Alvin* / Bright lights, big city: *Reed, Jimmy* / Down the road apiece: *Berry, Chuck* / Around and around: *Berry, Chuck* / Ruler of my heart: *Thomas, Irma* / I can't be satisfied: *Waters, Muddy* / Fannie Mae: *Brown, Buster* / Cops & robbers: *Diddley, Bo* / Down in the bottom: *Howlin' Wolf* / You can't catch me: *Berry, Chuck* / Diddley daddy: *Diddley, Bo* / I'm your hoochie coochie man: *Waters, Muddy* / Honest I do: *Reed, Jimmy* / How many more years: *Howlin' Wolf* / You can make it if you try: *Allison, Gene* / Route 66: *Berry, Chuck* / Carol: *Berry, Chuck* / I need you baby: *Diddley, Bo* / Susie Q: *Hawkins, Dale* / Pretty thing: *Diddley, Bo* / Got my mojo working: *Waters, Muddy* / It's all over now: *Womack, Bobby.*
**CD Set** . . . . . . . . . . **CDINS 5016**
■ **Double LP** . . . . . . . . . . **INSD 5016**
**MC Set** . . . . . . . . . . **TCINSD 5016**
Instant (2) / Sep '89 / Charly.

**STORY OF GOLDBAND RECORDS, THE.**
**Tracks:** Stormy weather: *Phillips, Phil* / Let's boogie: *Bonner, Juke Boy* / Sugar Bee: *Cleveland Crochet* / Let's go boppin' tonight: *Ferrier, Al* / Crawl: *Guitar Junior* / So what: *Duhan, Johnny* / Cindy Lou: *Terry, Gene* / You're lonesome now: *Perrywell, Charles* / Boogie in the mud: *James, Danny* / Going crazy baby: *Guitar Junior* / Rooster strut: *Savoy, Ashton* / No future: *Rockin' Sidney* / You're so fine: *Kershaw, Pee Wee* / Frosty: *James, Danny* / San Antonio: *Big Walter* / Please accept my love: *Wilson, Jimmy* / Blue bayou shuffle: *Cookie & The Cupcakes* / Teenage baby: *Herman, Sticks* / Secret of love: *Anderson, Elton* / Chicken stuff: *Wilson, Hop* / Teardrops in my eyes: *Terry, Gene* / Puppy love: *Parton, Dolly* / Don't leave me: *Phillips, Phil.*
**CD** . . . . . . . . . . **CDCHD 424**
Ace / Nov '92 / Pinnacle / Complete Record Co. Ltd.

**STORY SO FAR - SPECIAL PRICE SAMPLER, THE (Essential Argo/Cadet Grooves).**
**Tracks:** Not Advised.
**CD** . . . . . . . . . . **ARCD 517**
**LP** . . . . . . . . . . **ARC 517**
Charly / Feb '94 / Charly.

**STREET JAZZ VOL.1.**
**Tracks:** Natasha: *Like Young* / Klute: *F.R.I.S.K.* / Theme from the underground bowling alley: *T.U.B.A.* / West by South West: *As One* / Be bop breakdance: *Little Eye* / Candyfloss: *Forest Mighty Black* / A.W.O.L.: *British Underground Productions* / Get up, get down: *Fishbelly Black* / London kills me: *Groove Nation* / Don't rub another man's rhubard: *Innuendo* / You know what it's like: *Duverney, Ondrea* / Free your mind: *Action People* / Seasons of my mind: *Batu* / Apple strudle: *Up Bustle & Out.*
**CD** . . . . . . . . . . **CDTEP 4**
**LP** . . . . . . . . . . **LPTEP 4**
**MC** . . . . . . . . . . **MCTEP 4**
Step 2 / Jun '94 / 3MV / Sony.

**STREET SOUNDS ANTHEMS.**
**Tracks:** I found lovin': *Fatback Band* / What's missing: *O'Neal, Alexander* / Bring the family back: *Paul, Billy* / Ain't no stoppin' us now: *McFadden & Whitehead* / Dominoes (Live): *Byrd, Donald* / Movin': *Brass Construction* / Encore: *Lynn, Cheryl* / Hard work / Groove: *Franklin, Rodney* / Prance on: *Henderson, Eddie.*
■ **LP** . . . . . . . . . . **MUSIC 5**
**MC** . . . . . . . . . . **ZCMUS 5**
Street Sounds / Jan '87 / BMG / Total.

## STREET SOUNDS ANTHEMS 2.
**Tracks:** Not Advised.
■ LP . . . . . . . . . . . . . . . . . . . . MUSIC 10
MC. . . . . . . . . . . . . . . . . . . . ZCMUS 10
Street Sounds / Jun '87 / BMG / Total.

## STREET SOUNDS ANTHEMS 3.
**Tracks:** Not Advised.
■ LP . . . . . . . . . . . . . . . . . . . . MUSIC 11
MC. . . . . . . . . . . . . . . . . . . . ZCMUS 11
Street Sounds / Jul '87 / BMG / Total.

## STREET SOUNDS ANTHEMS 4.
**Tracks:** Not Advised.
■ CD. . . . . . . . . . . . . . . . . . . . CDMUS 12
■ LP . . . . . . . . . . . . . . . . . . . . MUSIC 12
MC. . . . . . . . . . . . . . . . . . . . ZCMUS 12
Street Sounds / Sep '87 / BMG / Total.

## STREET SOUNDS ANTHEMS 5.
**Tracks:** Not Advised.
■ CD. . . . . . . . . . . . . . . . . . . . CDMUS 13
■ LP . . . . . . . . . . . . . . . . . . . . MUSIC 13
■ MC. . . . . . . . . . . . . . . . . . . . ZCMUS 13
Street Sounds / Mar '88.

## STREET SOUNDS ANTHEMS 6.
**Tracks:** Dance, dance, dance: *Chic* / Contact: *Starr, Edwin* / Young hearts run free: *Staton, Candi* / Hi tension: *Hi-Tension* / Get down: *Chandler, Gene* / Keep your body working: *Kleeer* / Dancer: *Soccio, Gino* / Tuch me: *Rae, Fonda.*
■ CD. . . . . . . . . . . . . . . . . . . . CDMUS 14
■ LP . . . . . . . . . . . . . . . . . . . . MUSIC 14
MC. . . . . . . . . . . . . . . . . . . . ZCMUS 14
Street Sounds / Jun '88 / BMG / Total.

## STREET SUITE.
**Tracks:** Groovin' (that's what we're doin'): *S.O.S. Band* / Enuff is enuff: *Franklin, Rodney* / Spunky: *James, Bob* / Phone home: *Chingas, Johnny* / Chou chow: *Square* / Ride on: *Watanabe, Sadao* / Positive energy: *Duke, George* / What's going on / Hannibal: *Tyner, McCoy* / Give it all your heart: *Hancock, Herbie* / I'll never see you smile again: *James, Bob & Earl Klugh* / Portuguese love: *Ferguson, Maynard* / Patamar: *Montarroyos, Marcio* / Steppin' out: *Mangione, Chuck* / Only one: *Earland, Charles.*
■ LP . . . . . . . . . . . . . . . . . . . . CBS 22226
MC. . . . . . . . . . . . . . . . . . . . 40 22226
CBS / May '83 / Sony.

## STRICTLY SWING.
**Tracks:** I'm still waiting: *Jodeci* / Sweet thing: *Blige, Mary J.* / Lovin' you: *Johnson, Crystal J.* / Personality: *Velasquez, Nesto* / Truthful: *Heavy D & The Boyz* / Affair: *Mahogany Blue* / Get a little freaky with me: *Hall, Aaron* / Above the rim: *Bell Biv Devoe* / Next stop uptown: *Father M.C.* / My cutie: *Wreckx N Effect* / Every little thing U do: *Williams, Christopher* / Taste your love: *Brown, Horace.*
CD. . . . . . . . . . . . . . . . . . . . MCD 10987
MC. . . . . . . . . . . . . . . . . . . . MCC 10987
■ LP . . . . . . . . . . . . . . . . . . . . MCA 10987
MCA / Dec '93.

## STRUT YOUR FUNKY STUFF.
**Tracks:** Not Advised.
CD. . . . . . . . . . . . . . . . . . . . DCD 5394
Scratch / Oct '94 / Scratch Records / BMG / Grapevine Distribution.

## SUE BOX, THE.
**Tracks:** Vengeance (Will bw mine): *Matadors* / Itchy twichy feeling: *Hendricks, Bobby* / Thousand dreams: *Hendricks, Bobby* / Psycho: *Hendricks, Bobby* / Written in the stars: *Four Jokers* / Believe it or not: *Covay, Don* / Betty Jean: *Covay, Don* / I feel like a million: *Bradley, Mamie* / Chicken scratch: *Commandos* / Hand in hand: *Darrow, Johnny* / Don't start me talking: *Darrow, Johnny* / Don't leave: *Adams, Bobby* / Fool in love: *Turner, Ike & Tina* / I idolize you: *Turner, Ike & Tina* / I'm jealous: *Turner, Ike & Tina* / It's gonna work out fine: *Turner, Ike & Tina* / Poor fool: *Turner, Ike & Tina* / Tra la la la la: *Turner, Ike & Tina* / You should'a treated me right: *Turner, Ike & Tina* / Worried and hurtin' inside: *Turner, Ike & Tina* / Two is a couple: *Turner, Ike & Tina* / Stagger Lee and Billy: *Turner, Ike & Tina* / Night ridin': *Night Riders* / That's all I need: *Turner, Ike & The Kings of Rhythm* / Trouble up the road: *Brenston, Jackie* / You ain't the one: *Brenston, Jackie* / I wanna marry you: *Jimmy & Jean* / I can't believe it: *Jimmy & Jean* / My man Rockhead: *Carter, Eloise* / My love: *Turner, Ike & The Kings of Rhythm* / Keep your business to yourself: *Woods, Pearl* / Stick shift: *Duals* / She put the hurt on me: *Prince la la* / Gettin' married soon: *Prince la la* / Come back to me: *Prince la la* / I know (You don't love me no more): *George, Barbara* / You talk about love: *George, Barbara* / Send for me (If you need some lovin'): *George, Barbara* / She's got everything: *George, Barbara* / May I have this dance: *Senors* / Graveyard: *Blenders* / I've got a woman (Part 1): *McGriff, Jimmy* / All about my girl: *McGriff, Jimmy* / Last minute (Part 1): *McGriff, Jimmy* / Handful of memories: *Washington, Baby* / That's how heartaches are made: *Washington, Baby* / Leave me alone: *Washington, Baby* / I can't wait until I see my baby: *Washington, Baby* / Only those in love: *Washington, Baby* / Come on let me try: *Linda & The Del Rios* / Prancing: *Ike & Tina's Kings of Rhythm* / It seemed like heaven to me: *Morris, Elmore* / Let's shimmy: *Coleman, King* / Hitch hike (Part 1): *Byrd, Russell* / Any other way: *Shane, Jackie* / In my tenement: *Shane, Jackie* / Hold on baby: *Hockadays* / Summer's love: *Barrett, Richie* / Mockingbird: *Foxx, Inez* / Ask me: *Foxx, Inez* / I see you my love: *Foxx, Inez* / Hurt by love: *Foxx, Inez* / La de da I love you: *Foxx, Inez* / Daddy rollin' stone: *Martin, Derek* / Don't put me down like this: *Martin, Derek* / Count to ten: *Martin, Derek* / If you go: *Martin, Derek* / I can't stand it: *Soul Sisters* / Good time tonight: *Soul Sisters* / Loop de loop: *Soul Sisters* / Think about the good times: *Soul Sisters* / So far away: *Jacobs, Hank* / Monkey hips and rice: *Jacobs, Hank* / Everybody but me: *Smith, O.C.* / You're mine you: *Helms, Jimmy* / I can't tell you: *Robbins, Sylvia* / Dreams: *Watkins, Lovelace* / Limbo Lucy: *Everglades* / Yesterday: *Glenn, Tyree Jr.* / Ain't that bad: *Villa, Pancho & The Bandits* / You succeeded: *Phillips, Sandra* / World without sunshine: *Phillips, Sandra* / Time waits for no-one: *Eddie & Ernie* / Outcast: *Eddie & Ernie* / I'm going for myself: *Eddie & Ernie* / I can't do it: *Eddie & Ernie* / Fat back: *Doggett, Bill* / Real thing: *Britt, True* / Annie don't love me no more: *Hollywood Flames* / I'm gonna stand by you: *Hollywood Flames* / One more hurt: *Black, Marjorie* / Love in my heart: *Entertainers* / What can I do: *Prophet, Billy* / New breed: *Turner, Ike* / She blew a good thing: *Poets* / So young (And so innocent): *Poets* / I was born a loser: *Lee, Bobby* / If you've ever loved someone: *Wells, Jean* / She's called a woman: *Magnificent Seven* / Soul at sunrise: *Juggy.*
CD Set . . . . . . . . . . . . . . . . . . . . SUEBOX 1
EMI / Jun '94 / EMI.

## SUE STORY,THE.
**Tracks:** Not Advised.
■ LP . . . . . . . . . . . . . . . . . . . . OLLP 8022
Line / Feb '84.

## SULTRY SOUL SISTERS - WONDER WOMAN VOL.3.
**Tracks:** Not Advised.
■ LP . . . . . . . . . . . . . . . . . . . . RNLP 065
Rhino (USA) / Feb '85.

## SUMMER DAYS - BOOGIE NIGHTS.
**Tracks:** Love train: *O'Jays* / Best of my love: *Emotions (1)* / Boogie wonderland: *Earth, Wind & Fire & The Emotions* / Don't let love let you down: *Bell, Archie & The Drells* / Summer breeze: *Isley Brothers* / Only the strong survive: *Paul, Billy* / Young hearts run free: *Staton, Candi* / Can't get by without you: *Real Thing* / Show you the way to go: *Jacksons* / Me and Mrs. Jones: *Jacksons* / Always and forever: *Heatwave* / If you don't know me by know: *Melvin, Harold & The Bluenotes* / You make me feel like a natural woman: *Franklin, Aretha* / Love TKO: *Pendergrass, Teddy* / You'll never find another love like mine: *Rawls, Lou* / Heaven must be missing an angel: *Tavares.*
■ LP . . . . . . . . . . . . . . . . . . . . PRT 10052
Portrait / Jan '86.

## SUNSET SOUND OF LA.
**Tracks:** Roses are red: *Mac Band* / Don't be cruel: *Brown, Bobby (1)* / If it isn't love: *New Edition (1)* / Sleepless weekend: *Huntsberry, Howard* / You're puttin' a rush on me: *Mills, S* / Middles of the night: *Body* / I'm the one: *Perri* / I'll give you love: *Sue Ann* / Girlfriend: *Pebbles* / Some kind of lover: *Watley, Jody* / Lovin' on next to nothin': *Knight, Gladys* / Passion and pain: *McClain, Janice* / Intimacy: *St. Paul* / Slow starter: *Hall, Randy* / One track mind: *Pettus, Giorge.*
■ LP . . . . . . . . . . . . . . . . . . . . DEAL 1
■ CD. . . . . . . . . . . . . . . . . . . . DDEAL 1
■ MC. . . . . . . . . . . . . . . . . . . . DEALC 1
MCA / Oct '88.

## SUPER RHYTHM 'N' BLUES.
**Tracks:** Keep on knowin' / I found my baby there: *Charles, Ray* / Letter: *King, B.B.* / Could this be love: *Tex, Joe* / I thank God: *Cooke, Sam* / Big fine woman: *Hooker, John Lee* / Lovin' woman: *Simone, Nina* / Blues are bluer: *Holiday, Billie* / Cry baby cry: *Angels (1)* / Need him / Wild child: *Phillips, Esther* / Walkin' and talkin': *Charles, Ray* / Please love me: *King, B.B.* / I'm tramping / Porgy: *Simone, Nina* / Deep river: *Cooke, Sam* / My man (mon homme): *Holiday, Billie* / See what you have done: *Charles, Ray* / Blues for Christmas: *Hooker, John Lee* / That's heaven to me: *Cooke, Sam* / Feel like I wanna cry: *Phillips, Esther* / I just can't take it: *Tex, Joe* / I'm wondering: *Charles, Ray* / Milky white way / Maybellene: *Berry, Chuck* / Memphis: *Berry, Chuck* / Lover come back to me: *Holiday, Billie* / Did you cry the blues: *Charles, Ray* / Peace breaker: *Pickett, Wilson* / Why don't you love me: *Hendrix, Jimi & Little Richard* / Long tall Sally / Baby call on me: *Pickett, Wilson* / Let the good times roll: *Shirley & Lee* / My prayer: *Platters* / Goodnight Irene: *Hendrix, Jimi & Little Richard* / Sweet little sixteen: *Berry, Chuck.*
■ LP . . . . . . . . . . . . . . . . . . . . 2M 126 54315/16/17
Pathe Marconi (France) / Dec '85.

## SUPER SOUL.
**Tracks:** Beg me: *Jackson, Chuck* / I wake up crying: *Jackson, Chuck* / You're good for me: *Burke, Solomon* / If you need me: *Burke, Solomon* / I am a witness: *Hunt, Tommy* / Human: *Hunt, Tommy* / These arms of mine: *Redding, Otis* / Pain in my heart: *Redding, Otis* / Gonna send you back to Georgia: *Shaw, Timmy* / If you need me (2): *Pickett, Wilson* / Baby don't weep: *Pickett, Wilson* / That's enough: *Robinson, Roscoe* / 1000 rivers: *Robinson, Roscoe* / Just one more time: *Barnes, J.J.* / Hideaway: *Wood, Brenton* / I love Mary: *Hebb, Bobby.*
■ LP . . . . . . . . . . . . . . . . . . . . NPL 28107
Pye / Mar '68.

## SUPERFUNK.
**Tracks:** Not Advised.
CD. . . . . . . . . . . . . . . . . . . . VTCD 30
MC. . . . . . . . . . . . . . . . . . . . VTDMC 30
Virgin / Jun '94 / EMI.

## SURE SHOTS.
**Tracks:** Not Advised.
■ LP . . . . . . . . . . . . . . . . . . . . KENT 074
Kent / Feb '88.

## SWAMPLAND SOUL.
**Tracks:** Not Advised.
■ LP . . . . . . . . . . . . . . . . . . . . GRLP 7754
Goldband / Feb '79.

## SWAMPLANDS BEAT.
**Tracks:** Rock a way blues / Who's baby are you baby / Freight train / I'm just a mender / Let's go boppin' tonight / Thought I found love / Girl left alone / Never had the blues / Feels so good / What is that thing you call love / Honey baby / Oh, baby / Too tired to rock / Wrapped around your finger.
■ LP . . . . . . . . . . . . . . . . . . . . GCL 117
Goldband / Sep '84.

## SWEET BLACK MUSIC.
**Tracks:** This magic moment / Warm and tender love / We need understanding / Sweet lovin' woman / You broke your promise / Smoke gets in your eyes / Beautiful world outside / Stand by me / Shake a tailfeather / Win your love for me / He's so fine / Love really hurts without you.
MC. . . . . . . . . . . . . . . . . . . . 510479.3
Magnum Music / Dec '88 / Magnum Music Group / THE.

## SWEET SOUL DREAMS.
**Tracks:** Not Advised.
CD. . . . . . . . . . . . . . . . . . . . 290426
MC. . . . . . . . . . . . . . . . . . . . 490426
Ariola / Dec '92 / BMG.

## SWEET SOUL HARMONIES.
**Tracks:** My lovin' (Radio edit): *En Vogue* / Stay: *Eternal (1)* / I wanna sex you up: *Color Me Badd* / Right here (Human nature radio mix): *S.W.V.* / Motownphilly: *Boyz II Men* / I'm doing fine now: *Pasadenas* / Love train: *O'Jays* / My girl: *Temptations* / If you don't know me by now: *Melvin, Harold & The Bluenotes* / Best thing that ever happend to me: *Knight, Gladys & The Pips* / Back ot life (Accapella): *Soul II Soul & Caron Wheeler* / Apparently nothin' (Edit): *Young Disciples* / Ghetto heaven (Remix edit): *Family Stand* / (Sexual) Healing: *Gaye, Marvin* / After the love has gone: *Earth, Wind & Fire* / There's nothing like this: *Omar* / Ghetto child: *Detroit Spinners* / Casanova: *Levert* / Don't walk away: *Jade (1)* / Thinking of you (Rampo radio remix): *Sister Sledge.*
CD. . . . . . . . . . . . . . . . . . . . VTCD 20
Virgin / Jan '94 / EMI.

## SWEET SOUL HARMONIES 2.
**Tracks:** Could it be I'm falling in love: *Detroit Spinners* / Summer breeze: *Isley Brothers* / I love music: *O'Jays* / Save our love: *Eternal (1)* / Crazy: *Seal (1)* / Zoom: *Fat Larry's Band* / Downtown (1994): *S.W.V.* / Would I lie to you: *Charles & Eddie* / What's going on: *Gaye, Marvin* / Don't look any further: *M People* / Hold on: *En Vogue* / Slowhand: *Pointer Sisters* / Keep on moving: *Soul II Soul* / We are family (Original version): *Sister Sledge* / You can't hurry love: *Supremes* / Tribute (Right on): *Pasadenas* / Ain't no sunshine: *Withers, Bill* / Everything must change:

528
■ DELETED

Young, Paul / Too young to die: *Jamiroquai* / Let's stay together: *Green, Al.*
CD . . . . . . . . . . VTCD 31
MC. . . . . . . . . . VTMC 31
Virgin / Aug '94 / EMI.

**SWEET SOUL MUSIC.**
**Tracks:** Time is tight: *Booker T & The MG's* / Private number: *Clay, Judy & William Bell* / I'll take you there: *Staple Singers* / Shoutin' out love: *Emotions (1)* / To the push and pull (Part 1): *Thomas, Rufus* / Come tomorrow: *Joseph, Margie* / Lonely for your love: *Bell, William* / Shaft, Theme from: *Hayes, Isaac* / Watcha see is watcha get: *Dramatics* / I had a talk with my man: *Foxx, Inez & Charlie* / Take care of your homework: *Taylor, Johnnie* / Why is the wine sweeter: *Floyd, Eddie* / Holy cow: *Anderson, Stephan* / Mr. Big Stuff: *Knight, Jean* / Soul clap '69: *Booker T & The MG's* / I've been lonely for so long: *Knight, Frederick* / Slipped, tripped and fell in love: *Sweet Inspirations* / Baby that's a no no: *Lewis, Barbara* / Starting all over again: *Mel & Tim* / Son of Shaft: *Bar-Kays* / Dedicated to the one I love: *Temprees* / Respect yourself: *Staple Singers* / When something is wrong with my baby: *Weston, Kim* / I wake up wanting you: *Thomas, Carla* / Who's making love: *Taylor, Johnnie* / I've never found a girl: *Floyd, Eddie* / Sweeter he is: *Soul Children* / Pin the tail on the donkey: *Newcomers.*
■ Double LP. . . . . . . . . . CR 049
■ MC Set . . . . . . . . . . CRT 049
Cambra / '83.

**SWEET SOUL MUSIC.**
**Tracks:** Not Advised.
CD. . . . . . . . . . SETCD 083
Stardust / Sep '94 / Pickwick / Conifer Records.

**SWEET SOUL MUSIC (2).**
**Tracks:** If you don't know me by now: *Melvin, Harold* / Dancing in the street: *Reeves, Martha* / What becomes of the broken hearted: *Ruffin, Jimmy* / My guy: *Wells, Mary* / Rescue me: *Bass, Fontella* / Rock your baby: *McCrae, George* / Spanish harlem: *King, Ben E.* / Sweet soul music: *Sam & Dave.*
CD. . . . . . . . . . OCN 2001WD
■ LP . . . . . . . . . . OCN 2001WL
MC. . . . . . . . . . OCN 2001WK
Ocean (2) / Mar '89.

**SWEET SOUL SOUNDS.**
**Tracks:** Into something fine: *Raelettes* / I'm gettin' long alright: *Raelettes* / Let no one hold you: *Hendrix, Margie* / Lover's blues: *Hendrix, Margie* / For the love of a woman: *Tams* / Little more soul: *Tams* / How can I get over a fox like you: *Icemen* / Dedicate my song to you: *Impressions* / I made a mistake: *Impressions* / I can't say: *Everett, Betty* / My baby loving my best friend: *Everett, Betty* / Goin' goin' gone: *Griffith, Emile* / Keep me in mind: *Samson & Delilah* / No sad songs: *Keyes, Troy* / I never knew how good I had it: *Trends* / Take your time: *Reed, Lula.*
■ LP . . . . . . . . . . SSL 10243
Stateside / Sep '68.

**SWEET SOULFUL CHICAGO.**
**Tracks:** Wrapped, tied and tangled: *Baker, LaVern* / Love song: *Artistics* / Help yourself: *Butler, Billy* / I'm in danger: *Visitors* / Feeling's gone: *Esquires* / Hold on: *Smith, Marvin* / It's all over between us: *Charles, Lee* / Getting nowhere fast: *Smith, Floyd* / I love you: *Leavill, Otis* / It could have been me: *Franklin, Erma* / Fool, fool, fool (look in the mirror): *Acklin, Barbara* / Sweeter as the days go by: *Lance, Major* / No easy way down: *Jackson, Walter* / You can't keep a good man down: *Davis, Tyrone* / My baby's gone: *Chandler, Gene* / You got me walking: *Blake, Cicero.*
■ LP . . . . . . . . . . KENT 070
Kent / Jun '87.

**SWEET SOUND OF SUCCESS.**
**Tracks:** You've got the power: *Esquires* / If I had you: *O'Dell, Brooks* / There's still tomorrow: *Diplomats (1)* / Same old story: *Big Maybelle* / Don't say goodnight and mean goodbye: *Shirelles* / Invisible: *Miles, Lenny* / That's enough: *Robinson, Roscoe* / Baby take me: *Jackson, Chuck* / Keep on searchin': *Candy & The Kisses* / Finders keepers, losers weepers: *Dodds, Nella* / If I catch you: *Shaw, Timmy* / Hand it over: *Jackson, Chuck* / He's no good: *Hughes, Freddie* / Love of my man: *Kilgore, Theola* / Look over your shoulder: *Jackson, Chuck* / One step at a time: *Brown, Maxine* / Door is open: *Hunt, Tommy* / It's mine: *Montgomery, Tammy* / Lonely people do foolish things: *Clay, Judy* / How much pressure: *Robinson, Roscoe* / Come see about me: *Dodds, Nella* / Half a man: *Cooke, L.C.* / This world's in a hell of a shape: *Ross, Jackie* / Do it now: *Banks, Bessie* / Ask me: *Brown, Maxine* / Can't let you out of my sight: *Jackson, Chuck & Maxine Brown* / Gonna send you back to Georgia: *Shaw, Timmy* / Don't believe him Donna: *Miles, Lenny.*
CD. . . . . . . . . . CDKEND 112
Ace / Jun '94 / Pinnacle / Complete Record Co. Ltd.

**SWEET STUFF.**
**Tracks:** I'll erase away: *Whatnauts* / I dig your act: *Whatnauts* / Friends by day (lovers by night): *Whatnauts* / Blues flyaway: *Whatnauts* / You forgot too easy: *Whatnauts* / I just can't lose your love: *Whatnauts* / Please make love go away: *Whatnauts* / Tweedly dum-dum: *Whatnauts* / In the bottle: *Brother to Brother* / Hurry sundown: *Staton, Candi* / Count on me: *Staton, Candi* / Suspicious minds: *Staton, Candi* / Me and my gemini this is it: *First Class* / Sweet stuff: *Sylvia (3)* / Love is God almighty: *Optimystic* / Where were you: *Mills, Eleonore* / Peace: *O'Jays* / Soul je t'aime: *Sylvia & Ralfi Pagan.*
CD. . . . . . . . . . NEMCD 616
Sequel / Jul '91 / Total / BMG.

**SWEETER THAN THE DAY BEFORE (28 Classic Cuts From The Chess Stable).**
**Tracks:** Strange change: *Ward, Herb* / Baby you've got it: *McAllister, Maurice & the Radiants* / Such a pretty thing: *Chandler, Gene* / Chained to your heart: *Moore, Bobby & The Rhythm Aces* / Love reputation: *Lasalle, Denise* / Let's wade in the water: *Shaw, Marlena* / Make sure (you have someone who loves you): *Dells* / What can I do: *Kirby, George* / Lucky boy: *Hutton, Harold* / Later than you think: *Mack, Andy* / Sweeter than the day before: *Valentinos* / If I would marry you: *Montgomery, Tammy* / Is it a sin: *Timiko* / Whole new plan: *Garrett, Joan* / Look at me now: *Callier, Terry* / Strange feeling: *Nash, Johnny* / Mighty good lover: *Vashonettes* / My baby's good: *Williams, Johnny* / Sometimes: *Little Milton* / Can't you hear the beat: *Carltons* / I can't stand it: *Seminoles* / I just kept on dancing: *Banks, Doug* / Pay back: *James, Etta* / Pain: *Collier, Mitty* / Landslide: *Clarke, Tony* / Thinkin' about you: *Dells* / Ain't got no problems: *Sunday* / Count me out: *Stewart, Billy.*
CD. . . . . . . . . . CDARC 515
LP . . . . . . . . . . ARC 515
Charly / Jun '91 / Charly.

# T

**T.S.O.P - THE SOUND OF PHILADELPHIA.**
**Tracks:** T.S.O.P: *MFSB* / I love music: *O'Jays* / Love I lost: *Melvin, Harold & The Bluenotes* / Let 'em in: *Paul, Billy* / You'll never find another love like mine: *Rawls, Lou* / I'll always love my mama: *Intruders* / Show you the way to go: *Jacksons* / Ain't no stoppin' us now: *McFadden & Whitehead* / Let's groove: *Bell, Archie & The Drells* / What's your name: *Stylistics* / Love train: *O'Jays* / Lady love: *Rawls, Lou* / Whole town's laughing at me: *Pendergrass, Teddy* / If you don't know me by now: *Melvin, Harold & The Bluenotes* / Me & Mrs. Jones: *Paul, Billy* / Love TKO: *Pendergrass, Teddy* / Holdin' on: *Wansel, Dexter* / Nights over Egypt: *Jones Girls* / Was that all it was: *Carne, Jean* / Turn off the lights: *Pendergrass, Teddy* / Wake up everybody: *Melvin, Harold & The Bluenotes* / Backstabbers: *O'Jays* / Life on Mars: *Wansel, Dexter* / Sexy: *MFSB* / When will I see you again: *Three Degrees* / Close the door: *Pendergrass, Teddy* / See you when I get there: *Rawls, Lou* / Let's clean up the ghetto: *Philadelphia All Stars.*
■ CD. . . . . . . . . . NCD 3406
■ Double LP. . . . . . . . . . NE 1406
■ MC Set . . . . . . . . . . CE 2406
K-Tel / Apr '88.

**TABASKO - THE SALSOUL REMIX PROJECT.**
**Tracks:** Not Advised.
CD. . . . . . . . . . SALSARCD 1
LP Set. . . . . . . . . . SALSARLP 1
MC. . . . . . . . . . SALSARMC 1
Beechwood / Nov '93 / Pinnacle.

**TAKIN' YOU THERE.**
**Tracks:** Not Advised.
■ LP . . . . . . . . . . XSTAX 10
Stax / Nov '72.

**TALKIN' LOUD SAMPLER 1.**
**Tracks:** Young Disciples Theme: *Young Disciples & MC Mello* / Get it: *Steps Ahead* / Mean machine 90: *Jalal* / Step right on: *Young Disciples & Outlaw Posse* / Glide: *Incognito* / Tribal knight: *Ace Of Clubs* / Wild and peaceful: *Bassic* / Little ghetto boy: *Galliano.*
CD. . . . . . . . . . 8467922
■ LP . . . . . . . . . . 8467921
■ MC. . . . . . . . . . 8467924
Talkin' Loud / Sep '90.

**TALKIN' LOUD SAMPLER 2.**
**Tracks:** Hide and seek: *Urban Species* / Hungry like a baby: *Galliano* / Colibri: *Incognito* / You've got to move: *Omar* / Back to the real world: *K-Creative* / All I have in me: *Young Disciples* / Theme from Marx: *Marxman* / Qui semme le vente recolte le tempo: *M.C. Solaar* / Serious love: *Perception* / I commit: *Powell, Bryan* / Take me now: *Payne, Tammy* / Apparently nothing: *Young Disciples* / There's nothing like this: *Omar* / Prince of peace: *Galliano* / Always there: *Incognito.*
CD. . . . . . . . . . 5159362
MC. . . . . . . . . . 5159364
■ LP . . . . . . . . . . 5159361
Talkin' Loud / Jan '93.

**TEAR STAINED SOUL (The Quinvy Broadway Sound Vol 1).**
**Tracks:** Tearstained face: *Varner, Don* / Push Mr.Pride aside: *Bradford, Eddie* / Mojo mama: *Varner, Don* / Hand shaking: *Braswell, Jimmy* / Little bit of love: *Bradford, Eddie* / When it's over: *Varner, Don* / You made your bed: *Bradford, Eddie* / Bless your sweet little soul: *Johnson, Al* / Meet me in church: *Varner, Don* / Home for the summer: *Braswell, Jimmy* / Don't give up on me: *Varner, Brenda* / Love waits for no man: *Johnson, Al* / Down in Texas: *Varner, Don* / Let me be a woman: *Varner, Brenda.*
■ LP . . . . . . . . . . CRB 1219
Charly R&B / Feb '89.

**TEARING UP THE DANCEFLOOR.**
**Tracks:** Not Advised.
■ CD. . . . . . . . . . MOTCCD 81
Motor City / Oct '92.

**TEARS IN MY EYES.**
**Tracks:** Should I let him go: *Parker, Paulette* / I don't want to go: *Lee, Little Mr.* / I ain't myself anymore: *Bland, Bobby* / He made woman for man: *Wright, O.V.* / It's private tonight: *Adams, Arthur* / First love: *Mirettes* / I wanna make you happy: *Mandolph, Magaret* / Beginning of my end: *Unifics* / Shopping for love: *Mike and The Censations* / I need your love to comfort me: *Sam & Bill* / Let me hear it from you: *McLean, Chuck* / Inside story: *Ace, Buddy* / Long walk on a short pier: *Davis, Rhonda* / Thrill is gone (The): *King, B.B.* / Tears in my eyes: *Fascinations* / This must end: *Impressions.*
■ LP . . . . . . . . . . KENT 045
Kent / Oct '85.

**TESTIFYIN'.**
**Tracks:** My great loss (ashes to ashes): *Smith, Charles* / Glad to be home: *Smith, Charles* / I'm useless: *Smith, Charles* / Why can't I cry: *Smith, Charles* / The only time you say you love me: *Smith, Charles* / Stand up and take it like a man: *Smith, Charles* / Pull me out of the water: *Smith, Charles* / Two pillows: *Smith, Charles* / Why does it hurt so bad: *Armstrong, Chuck* / How sweet it is (to be loved by you): *Armstrong, Chuck* / I'm gonna forget about you: *Armstrong, Chuck* / Keep your mind on me: *Armstrong, Chuck* / She's gonna come back: *Ford, Ted* / Pretty girls everywhere: *Ford, Ted* / You're gonna need me: *Ford, Ted* / Please give me another chance: *Ford, Ted.*
■ LP . . . . . . . . . . CRB 1155
Charly R&B / '89.

**TEXAS RHYTHM AND BLUES.**
**Tracks:** Love me, pretty baby: *Booker, Connie Mack* / All alone: *Booker, Connie Mack* / Whoopin' and hollerin': *Stevens, Preacher* / Blue memories: *Kimble, Quinn* / Feel my broom: *Kimble, Quinn* / I'll be there: *Daniels, Melvin & The King Curtis Orchestra* / If you don't want my lovin': *Daniels, Melvin & The King Curtis Orchestra* / Boogie in the moonlight: *Daniels, Melvin & The King Curtis Orchestra* / Hey hey little girl: *Daniels, Melvin & The King Curtis Orchestra* / Craw fishin': *Garlow, Clarence Bonton* / Route 90: *Garlow, Clarence Bonton.*
■ LP . . . . . . . . . . CH 29
Ace / Dec '88.

**THAT BEATIN' RHYTHM.**
**Tracks:** Don't pretend: *Belles* / Words can't explain: *Belles* / My sugar baby: *Matthews, Sherlie* / My little girl: *Garrett, Bobby* / Oh my darlin': *Lee, Jacky* / I can't get away: *Garrett, Bobby* / Cigarette ashes: *Conwell, Jimmy* / That beatin' rhythm: *Temple, Richard* / Baby do the philly dog: *Olympics.*
■ LP . . . . . . . . . . BURN 1
Inferno (1) / May '84.

## THAT DRIVING BEAT.
Tracks: Not Advised.
| | |
|---|---|
| ■ LP | LPSS 101 |
| MC | CLPSS 101 |
Soul Supply / Dec '84 / RTM / Pinnacle.

## THAT'S FUNK, VOL.2.
Tracks: Not Advised.
| | |
|---|---|
| ■ LP | 6 25635 |
| MC | 425635 |
Teldec (1) / Sep '84 / Pinnacle / C.M. Distribution / Swift.

## THAT'S SOUL (20 Original Hits).
Tracks: Not Advised.
| | |
|---|---|
| ■ CD | 19435 |
Delta (1) / May '87.

## THELMA RECORD CO STORY, THE (Legendary Detroit Soul).
Tracks: Love is the only solution: Star, Martha / I'm a peace loving man: Laskey, Emanuel / Lucky to be loved by you: Hargreaves, Silky / I just can't leave you: Inst / You got the best of me: Hill, Eddie / I just cant leave you: Batiste, Rose / Sorry ain't good enough: Matthews, Joe / I love you: Inst / Gonna cry a river: Ward, Robert / I've got to run for my life: Laskey, Emanuel / Someday: Batiste, Rose / Whirlpool: Inst / You better mend your ways: Matthews, Joe / No part time love for me: Star, Martha / Nobody loves me like my baby: Gilford, Jimmy.
| | |
|---|---|
| CD | GSCD 055 |
Goldmine / Nov '94 / Vital Distribution.

## THEN THAT'S WHAT THEY CALL DISCO.
Tracks: We got the funk: Positive Force / Lookin' for love tonight: Fat Larry's Band / Hi-tension: Hi-Tension / Can you feel the force: Real Thing / You can do it: One Way Featuring Al Hudson / Shake your groove thing: Peaches & Herb / Sir Dancealot: Olympic Runners / You make me feel (mighty real): Sylvester / Space bass: Slick / Get down: Chandler, Gene / Everything is great: Inner Circle / White lines (don't do it): Grandmaster Flash.
| | |
|---|---|
| CD | CDELV 05 |
| LP | LPELV 05 |
| MC | MCELV 05 |
Passion/Debut/Scratch Music / May '93 / Pinnacle / 3MV.

## THESE ARMS OF MINE.
Tracks: Not Advised.
| | |
|---|---|
| CD | YDG 74633 |
| MC | YDG 45812 |
Yesterday's Gold / Feb '93 / Target / Midland Records / Target Sales & Marketing.

## THESE KIND OF BLUES VOL.1 (Duke-Peacock compilation).
Tracks: Tennessee woman: Robinson, Fenton / Little boy blue: Bland, Bobby / Okie dokie stomp: Brown, Clarence 'Gatemouth' / Texas flood: Davis, Larry / These kind of blues part 1: Parker, Junior / These kind of blues part 2: Parker, Junior / She's gone: McCracklin, Jimmy / You've got to pass this way again: Robinson, Fenton / Bobby's blues: Bland, Bobby / Just before dawn: Brown, Clarence 'Gatemouth' / That's alright: Parker, Junior / Keep on doggin': Gordon, Roscoe / Stormy Monday blues: Bland, Bobby.
| | |
|---|---|
| ■ LP | ACLP 6009 |
Action / '69.

## THEY WROTE THE SONGS.
Tracks: Walk on by: Warwick, Dionne / I say a little prayer: Franklin, Aretha / I just don't know what to do with myself: Springfield, Dusty / Make it easy on yourself: Walker Brothers / Do you know the way to San Jose: Warwick, Dionne / House is not a home: Vandross, Luther / There's always something there to remind me: Shaw, Sandie / What the world needs now is love: De Shannon, Jackie / Windows of the world: Pretenders (1) / I'll never fall in love again: Gentry, Bobbie / You'll never get to Heaven if you break my heart: Stylistics / Look of love: Springfield, Dusty / Trains and boats and planes: Kramer, Billy J. & The Dakotas / Reach out for me: Warwick, Dionne / (They long to be) Close to you: Hayes, Isaac / Anyone who had a heart: Vandross, Luther / Arthur's theme: Cross, Christopher / This guy's in love with you: Bacharach, Burt.
| | |
|---|---|
| CD | DINCD 16 |
| LP | DINTV 16 |
| MC | DINMC 16 |
Dino / Dec '90 / Pinnacle.

## THINK SMART SOUL STIRRERS JERK IT AT THE PARTY I.
Tracks: It's a woman's world (you better believe it): Gypsies / Think smart: Fiestas / Left out: Johnson, Jesse / Baby I need you: Lorraine & The Delights / Jerk it: Gypsies / Barefootin' time in Chinatown:

Young, Lester / I want a chance for romance: Rivera, Hector / My foolish heart: Coleman, David / If I had known: Houston, Freddie / You can't trust your best friend: Height, Freddie / We're gonna make it: Reid, Irene / Souvenirs of heartbreak: Jones, Thelma / Cross my heart: Yvonne & The Violets / At the party: Young, Lester / Soul stirrer: Lou, Bobby & Betty / You better believe me: McKay, Beverley.
| | |
|---|---|
| ■ LP | KENT 064 |
Kent / Jan '87.

## THIS IS CHARLY RHYTHM AND BLUES.
Tracks: Look at little sister (live): Ballard, Hank & The Midnighters / Lovin' machine: Harris, Wynonie / It's in his kiss: Everett, Betty / Need your love so bad: Little Willie John / All these things: Neville, Aaron / That's what you're doing to me: Dominoes / Hide away: King, Freddie / Howlin' for my baby: Howlin' Wolf / Dimples: Hooker, John Lee / It hurts me too: James, Elmore / Shame, shame, shame: Reed, Jimmy / Think: Five Royales / Look ka py py: Meters / Holy cow: Dorsey, Lee / Your friends: Clark, Dee / I'm gonna forget about you: Cray Band, Robert / Cuttin' in: Watson, Johnny 'Guitar' / Make it easy on yourself: Butler, Jerry / Sad shade of blue: Davis, Geator / Rainbow: Chandler, Gene / Aged and mellow blues: Phillips, Esther.
| | |
|---|---|
| ■ LP | SAM 2 |
| ■ MC | TCSAM 2 |
Charly / Aug '87.
| | |
|---|---|
| ■ CD | CDSAM 101 |
Charly / Oct '87.

## THIS IS CHARLY SOUL (Charly R & B sampler).
Tracks: Coming to bring you some soul: Baker, Sam / Nothing can stop me: Chandler, Gene / Working in a coalmine: Dorsey, Lee / Tippi toes: Meters / He called me baby: Washington, Ella / Lover's holiday: Scott, Peggy & Jo Jo Benson / He will break your heart: Butler, Jerry with Curtis Mayfield / Somebody shot my eagle: Blast, C.L. / Land of a thousand dances: Kenner, Chris / All these things: Neville, Aaron / United: Holman, Eddie / Sidewalks, fences and walls: Burke, Solomon / When something is wrong with my baby: Williams, Charles with Johnny Otis Band / I'm his wife, you're just a friend: Sexton, Ann / I'm useless: Smith, Charles / Turn on your lovelight: Gaines, Earl.
| | |
|---|---|
| ■ LP | SAM 1 |
| ■ MC | TCSAM 1 |
Charly / Aug '87.

## THIS IS HOW IT ALL BEGAN - SPECIALTY RECORDS VOL. 1 & 2.
Tracks: Not Advised.
| | |
|---|---|
| ■ LP Set | SNTF 5002/3 |
Specialty / '72.

## THIS IS MOTOWN.
Tracks: Not Advised.
| | |
|---|---|
| ■ LP | WL 72204 |
| ■ MC | WK 72204 |
Motown / May '84.

## THIS IS NORTHERN SOUL.
Tracks: I've got something good: Sam & Kitty / To the ends of the earth: Middleton, Tony / My little cottage: Falana, Fluffy / People that's why: Idle Few / I am nothing: Williams, Al / Exus trek: Ingram, Luther / How to make a sad man glad: Capreez / Eddie's my name: Holman, Eddie / Love slipped thru my fingers: Williams, Sam / Baby don't you weep: Hamilton, Edward / Rules: Blanding, Gil / Lover: Delites / Trouble: Agents / If it's all the same to you babe: Ingram, Luther / Such misery: Precisions / This won't change: Tipton, Lester / This man in love: New Wanderers.
| | |
|---|---|
| ■ LP | GRAL 1002 |
Grapevine (Northern Soul) / Jul '80.

## THIS IS NORTHERN SOUL.
Tracks: Silent treatment: Demain, Arin / My sugar baby: Clark, Connie / Double cookin': Checkerboard Squares / I've got to get myself together: Turner, Spyder / Love makes me lonely: Chandlers / Walk with me heart: Smith, Bobby / Emperor of my baby's heart: Harris, Kurt / Nobody knows: Wonder, Diane / You're on top girl: Empires / Are you angry: Servicemen / No right to cry: Galore, Mamie / So sweet so satisfying: Treetop, Bobby / Not me baby: Silhouettes / Love's just begun: Grayson, Calvin / Falling in love with you baby: Cook, Little Joe / Those lonely nights: Soul Communicators / Bar track: Burdock, Doni / He broke your game wide open: Dell, Frank / I've had it: Andrews, Lee / I'll always love you: Moultrie, Sam / Sister lee: Ward, Sam / Prove yourself a lady: Bounty, James / Psychedelic soul: Russell, Saxie.
| | |
|---|---|
| CD | GSCD 014 |
| MC | GSMC 014X |
Goldmine / Jun '93 / Vital Distribution.

## THIS IS SOUL.
Tracks: Dancing in the street: Reeves, Martha / Warm and tender love: Sledge, Percy / Under the boardwalk: Drifters / What becomes of the broken hearted: Ruffin, Jimmy / Stand by me: King, Ben E. / Drift away: Gray, Dobie / Spanish Harlem: King, Ben E. / Jimmy Mack: Reeves, Martha / Knock on wood: Floyd, Eddy / Take time to know her: Sledge, Percy / Hey girl don't bother me: Tams / Rescue me: Bass, Fontella / If you don't know me by now: Melvin, Harold & The Bluenotes / What is soul: King, Ben E. / In the midnight hour: Pickett, Wilson / You don know like I know: Sam & Dave / Sysljfm (the letter song): Tex, Joe / Green onions: Booker T & The MG's / Everybody needs somebody to love: Burke, Solomon / B.A.B.Y. / When a man loves a woman: Sledge, Percy / I say a little prayer: Franklin, Aretha / Tribute to a king: Bell, William / (Sittin' on) the dock of the bay: Redding, Otis.
| | |
|---|---|
| CD | OS 001 |
Music Collection International / Aug '87 / THE / Jazz Music.

## THIS IS SOUL.
Tracks: Not Advised.
| | |
|---|---|
| CD | AVC 50 |
| MC | AVM 50 |
Avid / Dec '92 / ACD Trading Ltd. / BMG.

## THIS IS SOUL.
Tracks: Mustang Sally: Pickett, Wilson / Land of 1,000 dances: Pickett, Wilson / B-a-b-y: Thomas, Carla / Sweet soul music: Conley, Arthur / When a man loves a woman: Sledge, Percy / Warm and tender: Sledge, Percy / Everything I need: Sam & Dave / What is soul: King, Ben E. / I never loved a man: Franklin, Aretha / Fa fa fa fa fa: Redding, Otis / Knock on wood: Floyd, Eddie / Keep looking: Burke, Solomon.
| | |
|---|---|
| ■ LP | 643 301 |
Atlantic / Apr '68.

## THIS IS SOUL.
Tracks: Not Advised.
| | |
|---|---|
| LP | SOUL 1 |
| MC | SOULK 1 |
Starblend / Jan '85.

## THIS IS SOUL.
Tracks: Not Advised.
| | |
|---|---|
| ■ LP | 780168-1 |
| MC | 780168-4 |
Atlantic / Jul '84 / WEA.

## THIS IS SOUL (3).
Tracks: Mustang Sally: Pickett, Wilson / B-A-B-Y: Thomas, Carla / Sweet soul music: Conley, Arthur / When a man loves a woman: Sledge, Percy / I got everything I need: Sam & Dave / What is soul: King, Ben E. / Fa fa fa fa fa (sad song): Redding, Otis / Knock on wood: Floyd, Eddie / Keep looking: Burke, Solomon / I never loved a man (the way I loved you): Franklin, Aretha / Warm and tender love: Sledge, Percy / Land of a thousand dances: Pickett, Wilson.
| | |
|---|---|
| ■ LP | K 20023 |
Elektra / Apr '80.

## THIS IS SOUL (4 CD PACK).
Tracks: Not Advised.
| | |
|---|---|
| CD Set | OX 0003 |
Music Collection International / Dec '87 / THE / Jazz Music.

## THIS IS SOUL II.
Tracks: Soul sister brown sugar: Sam & Dave / There goes my baby: Drifters / Heatwave: Reeves, Martha / Rock your baby: McCrae, George / Only the strong survive: Butler, Jerry / Love I lost: Melvin, Harold & The Bluenotes / In the midnight hour: Reeves, Martha / Save the last dance for me: Drifters / Soul man: Sam & Dave / Rainy night in Georgia: Benton, Brook / It's been so long: McCrae, George / Wake up everybody: Melvin, Harold & The Bluenotes / When a man loves a woman: Sledge, Percy / Get ready: Reeves, Martha / Baby (you've got what it takes): Benton, Brook.
| | |
|---|---|
| CD | OS 0012 |
Music Collection International / Aug '87 / THE / Jazz Music.

## THIS IS SOUL II.
Tracks: Not Advised.
| | |
|---|---|
| CD | AVC 516 |
| MC | AVM 516 |
Avid / Dec '92 / ACD Trading Ltd. / BMG.

## THIS IS SOUL, VOL 2.
Tracks: Not Advised.
| | |
|---|---|
| CD | CDCD 1176 |
Charly / Apr '94 / Charly.

■ DELETED

## HREE TIMES A LADY (Motown's reatest Love Songs).

acks: Love child: Ross, Diana & The Supremes / th you I'm born again: Preston, Billy & Syreeta / ree times a lady: Commodores / I've never been me: Charlene / It's my turn: Ross, Diana / Touch e in the morning: Ross, Diana / Being with you: obinson, Smokey / Endless love: Ross, Diana & onel Richie / All this love: DeBarge.

| CD | WD 72603 |
| otown / Nov '87. | |
| LP | WL 72603 |
| MC. | WK 72603 |
| otown / Mar '88. | |

## HREE TIMES A LADY - LADIES OF OUL.

acks: Not Advised.

| CD | KNCD 15015 |
| MC | KNMC 15015 |
| night / Sep '91. | |

## IME IS RIGHT, THE.

acks: Not Advised.

| LP | TIRLP 001 |
| reeway / Nov '88. | |

## IMELESS SOUL COLLECTION.

acks: Not Advised.

| CD | CDTR 3 |
| meless (Soul) / Jan '90. | |

## OGETHER WE ARE BEAUTIFUL.

acks: Not Advised.

| LP | MALP 002 |
| alaco / '88. | |

## OO GOOD TO BE FORGOTTEN MORE OUL CLASSICS.

acks: Whispers: Wilson, Jackie / Oh no not my aby / Have you seen her: Chi-Lites / There was a ne: Chandler, Gene / I just don't know what to do ith myself: Hunt, Tommy / Love of my man: Kilgore, heola / Washed ashore (on a lonely island in the n): Platters / Hook and sling: Bo, Eddie / No pity (in e naked city): Wilson, Jackie / To good to be rgotten: Chi-Lites / Love makes a woman: Acklin, arbara / I'm gonna miss you: Artistics / Tell him I'm ot home: Jackson, Chuck / Long after tonight is all ver: Radcliffe, Jimmy / With this ring: Platters / idsummer night in Harlem: Thomas, Charlie & The rifters.

| LP | CRB 1161 |
| C. | TCCRB 1161 |
| harly R&B / Jul '87 / Charly. | |

## OUGH STUFF.

acks: Not Advised.

| LP | CR 30186 |
| harly / May '80. | |

## RACKS OF MY TEARS.

acks: Tracks of my tears: Robinson, Smokey & The emptations / I'm not in love: 10 CC / Jealous guy: oxy Music / (I just) died in your arms: Cutting Crew See the day: Lee, Dee C. / After the love has gone: arth, Wind & Fire / Farewell is a lonely sound: uffin, Jimmy / Desperado: Eagles (1) / Can't be with ou tonight: Boucher, Judy / I guess thats why they all it the blues: John, Elton / All cried out: Moyet, lison / Only when you leave: Spandau Ballet / Love ant live here anymore: Rose Royce / On my own: abelle, Patti & Michael McDonald / I'm still waiting: oss, Diana / Hold me now: Logan, Johnny.

| LP | STAR 2295 |
| MC | STAC 2295 |
| elstar/Ronco / Sep '87. | |

## RIPPIN' ON YOUR SOUL.

acks: Special kind of woman: Thompson, Paul / I ay not be what you want: Mel & Tim / Sea shells: harmels / Did my baby call: Mad Lads (1) / Whole orld's a picture show: Newcomers / Yes Sir rother: Brown, Shirley / Come what may: Williams, ohn Gary / I've been born again: Taylor, Johnny / lind Alley: Emotions (2) / Baby that's a no no: ewis, Barbara / Trippin' on your love: Staple ingers / If it's love that you want: Brown, Randy / aking all the love I can: Joseph, Margie / Ain't no eed of crying: Allen, Rance Group.

| P | KENT 096 |
| ent / May '90 / Pinnacle. | |

## ROUBLE, HEARTACHES & SADNESS.

acks: Trouble, heartaches & sadness: Peebles, nn / What more do you want from me: Starks, eniece / Lonely soldier: Bryant, Don / That's just y luck: Johnson, Syl / Ain't no love in my life: itchell, Phillip / I must be losin' you: Clayton, Willie

/ I can't let you go: Peebles, Ann / I've been hurt: Big Lucky Carter / Can't hide the hurt: Bryant, Don / I can't take it: Clay, Otis / Heartaches, heartaches: Peebles, Ann / Love you left behind: Johnson, Syl / Trying to live my life without you: Clay, Otis / 'Bout to make me leave home: Johnson, Syl / You're gonna make me cry: Peebles, Ann / I die a little each day: Clay, Otis / I'm leavin' you: Peebles, Ann / Please don't give up on me: Johnson, Syl / Everytime I think about you I get the blues: One Plus One / Won't you try me: Peebles, Ann / Please don't leave: One Plus One.

| CD | HILOCD 10 |
| Hi / Mar '94 / Pinnacle. | |

## TWIST AND SHOUT.

Tracks: Not Advised.

| CD | 241 690-2 |
| LP | 241 690-1 |
| MC. | 241 690-4 |
| Atlantic / Nov '89 / WEA. | |

## TWIST AND SHOUT AT THE CAMDEN PALACE.

Tracks: Your love is lifting..: Wilson, Jackie / 1-2-3: Barry, Len / One fine day: Chiffons / Clapping song: Ellis, Shirley / Little bit of soul: Music Explosion / Treat her right: Head, Roy / Wipe out: Surfaris / Twist and shout: Isley Brothers / Wanderer: Dion / Reet petite: Wilson, Jackie / Tequila: Champs / Louie Louie: Kingsmen / Peaches and cream: Ikettes / When the boy's happy (the girl's happy too): Four Pennies / Little bit of soap: Jarmels / Baby it's you: Shirelles.

| LP | ACT 005 |
| MC | ACTC 005 |
| Impact (Ace) / May '87. | |

## ULTIMATE GIRL GROUPS.

Tracks: Not Advised.

| CD | GSCD 006 |
| LP | GSLP 006 |
| Goldmine / Sep '92. | |

## UNCUT FUNK.

Tracks: Not Advised.

| LP | 5158711 |
| CD | 5158712 |
| MC | 5158714 |
| Phonogram / '92. | |

## UNTOUCHABLES.

Tracks: What goes up (must come down) / I need a helping hand: Servicemen / Darling, darling / I'm gonna hurt you / I'm getting tired: Carlettes / You can forget it: Sisters Three / Standing at a standstill / I want to be free / Talking eyes / You got me in the palm of your hand: Richardson, Donald Lee / You left me / This time you're wrong / This heart, these hands / Where were you: Epitome Of Sound.

| LP | LPSS 110 |
| Soul Supply / '86. | |

## UP ALL NIGHT (30 Northern Soul Classics).

Tracks: Nothing can stop me: Chandler, Gene / Getting mighty crowded: Everett, Betty / Nothing worse than being alone: Ad Libs / That other place: Flemons, Wade / I keep tryin': Hughes, Freddie / You're the dream: Shelton, Roscoe / I hurt on the other side: Barnes, Sidney / Lonely for you baby: Dee, Sonny / Come on train: Thomas, Don / Breakaway: Valentines / You're gonna need me: Ford, Ted / Being without you: Williams, Maurice / Why don't you write: Bates, Lee / But I couldn't: Harper, Willie / Just another heartache: Little Richie / Touch me, hold me, kiss me: Inspirations / Tear stained face: Varner, Don / Hung up on your love: Montclairs / Running for my life: Shelton, Roscoe / My man don't think I know: Davies, Gwen / Hold on: Beavers, Jackie / You've been gone too long: Sexton, Ann / That's enough: Robinson, Roscoe / I'd think it over twice (if I were you): Fletcher, Sam / You'll always be in style:

Barnes, Sidney / Don't let me down: Hughes, Freddie / Sweet and easy: McCoy, Van / Power of love: Humphrey, Amanda / Now I'm in love with you: Sims, Marvin L. / I'm a fool, I must love you: Falcons (1).

| CD Set | CDINS 5028 |
| MC Set | TCINSD 5028 |
| Charly / Apr '90 / Charly. | |

## UP ALL NIGHT VOL 2 (30 Hits From The Original Soul Underground).

Tracks: Not Advised.

| CD | CDGRM 500 |
| LP | LPGRM 500 |
| Charly / Jun '93 / Charly. | |

## UPTIGHT.

Tracks: Not Advised.

| CD | MOTCCD 64 |
| Motor City / Oct '92. | |

## UPTOWN MTV UNPLUGGED.

Tracks: Forever my lady: Jodeci / Come & talk to me: Jodeci / Stay (Not available on LP): Jodeci / Lately: Jodeci / One nite stand: Father / Sweet thing: Blige, Mary J. / Reminisce: Blige, Mary J. / I don't want to do anything: Blige, Mary J. / All I see: Williams, Christopher / Come go with me: Williams, Christopher / Is it good to you: Heavy D & The Boyz / Interlude: Heavy D & The Boyz / Blue funk: Heavy D & The Boyz / Next stop uptown (studio version): Father.

| CD | MCD 10858 |
| LP | MCA 10858 |
| MC. | MCC 10858 |
| MCA / Jun '93. | |

## URBAN 88.

Tracks: Payback mix: Brown, James / Everybody (get loose): Phoenix (1) / Why did you do it: Groove Train / I'm so happy: Beasley, Walter / It's a choice: Visions (1) / Theme from P.O.P.: Perfectly Ordinary People / It began in Africa: Cook, Norman / Starsky and Hutch, Theme from: Taylor, James Quartet / It's your thing: Rockaway Three / Got to have a mother for me: Brown, James / Ace of clubs: Ace Of Clubs / Running away: Ayers, Roy.

| CD | 837 664-2 |
| LP | 837 664-1 |
| MC | 837 664-4 |
| Urban / Nov '88. | |

## URBAN BLACK VOL. 1.

Tracks: Not Advised.

| CD | SOUNDSCD 1 |
| LP | SOUNDSLP 1 |
| MC. | SOUNDSMC 1 |
| Street Sounds / Oct '94 / BMG / Total. | |

## URBAN CLASSICS.

Tracks: Cross the track (we better go back): Parker, Maceo & The Macks / I believe in miracles: Jackson Sisters / I know you got soul: Byrd, Bobby.

| LP | URBLP 4 |
| MC. | URBMC 4 |
| Urban / Nov '87 / PolyGram. | |
| CD | 833 915-2 |
| Urban / Sep '88 / PolyGram. | |

## URBAN CLASSICS VOL 2.

Tracks: She's the one: Brown, James / You're the song I've always wanted to sing: Thomas, Timmy / Soul, soul, soul, (somebody): Wild Magnolias / Pass the peas: J.B.'s / Funky stuff: Kool & The Gang / Misdemeanor: Sylvers, Foster / Never get enough: Byrd, Bobby / Mr. Big Stuff: Collins, Lyn / I dig everything about you: Mob (1) / Brother green: Ayers, Roy / Yes, it's you: Sherell, Charles.

| LP | URBLP 5 |
| MC. | URBMC 5 |
| Urban / May '88 / PolyGram. | |
| CD | 816 715-2 |
| Urban / Sep '88 / PolyGram. | |

## URBAN CLASSICS VOL 3.

Tracks: Making my daydream real: We Are The People / You and I: Bristol, Johnny / I have learned to do without you: Taylor, Debbie / Funky luvah: Creative Source / Shake her loose: Jackson Sisters / Let me in your life: Cofield, Pat / Power of love: McClain, Alton & Destiny / Tell me what you want: Ruffin, Jimmy / Grandma's hands: Blossoms / You're hardly gone: Thomas, Tyrone / Moonlight lovin': Hayes, Isaac.

| CD | 841 515 2 |
| LP | 841 515 1 |
| MC. | 841 515 4 |
| Urban / Feb '90 / PolyGram. | |

## VIBE (THE SOUND OF SWING).
**Tracks:** Love no limit: Blige, Mary J. / Realize: Wilson, Charlie / That's the way love is: Brown, Bobby (1) / If you feel the need: Shomari / I like your style: Bubba / Don't keep me waiting: Rhythm Within / Real love: Lorenzo / One night stand: Father / Do you wanna chill with me: Solid State Sound / Yo - that's a lot of body: Ready For The World / Baby, baby, baby: TLC / Right here: S.W.V. / Helluva: Brotherhood Creed / I dream, I dream: Jackson, Jermaine.
| | |
|---|---|
| CD | CDELV 07 |
| LP | LPELV 07 |
| MC | MCELV 07 |
Passion/Debut/Scratch Music / Jul '93 / Pinnacle / 3MV.

## VIBE 2.
**Tracks:** Not Advised.
| | |
|---|---|
| CD | CDELV 17 |
| LP | LPELV 17 |
| MC | MCELV 17 |
Elevate / Jun '94 / 3MV.

## WAY DOWN DEEP IN MY SOUL.
**Tracks:** Not Advised.
■ LP . . . . . . . . . . . . . . . . . . . SH 9103
Sugarhill / '88.

## WAY WITH THE GIRLS (30 Female Soul Rarities From The 1960's).
**Tracks:** You will never get away: Maye, Cholli / Here come the heartaches: Lovells / I'm a sad girl: Johnson, Deena / If you can stand me: Lewis, Tamala / Thrills and chills: Smith, Helene / I feel strange: Wonderettes / Lost without your love: Carlettes / Now that I found you baby: Mirettes / It's over: Lindsay, Terry / It's all over: Gee's / Why weren't you there: Lindsay, Thelma / Step aside baby: Lollipops / It happens everyday: Persianettes / Source of love: Marie, Gina / Sweet, sweet: Durettes / Pretty boy: Hall, Dora / Big man: Starr, Karen / Ain't gonna hurt my pride: Judi & The Affections / You're the guy: Argie & The Arketts / There's something the matter (with your heart): Cynthia & The Imaginations / Wonderful one: Lindsey, Theresa / My, my sweet love: Lee, Barbara / If you love me, show me: Monique (2) / Sugar boy: Charmettes / Don't cha tell nobody: Vont Claires / Don't cry: Irma & The Larks / My fault: Passionettes / Try my love: Sequins / How can I get to you: Soul, Sharon / His way with the girls: Lornettes.
CD . . . . . . . . . . . . . . . . . . . GSCD 029
Goldmine / Mar '94 / Vital Distribution.

## WE FUNK THE BEST.
**Tracks:** First time around / We funk the best / Love thang / Sing sing / Burning spear / Got my mind made up / Showdown / I'm funkin' you tonight / Jingo / Ice cold love.
■ LP . . . . . . . . . . . . . . . . . . . SSLM 4002
Salsoul / Dec '79.

## WEEKENDER (12 Extended Dance Classics).
**Tracks:** Not Advised.
| | |
|---|---|
| CD | MUSCD 10 |
| MC | MUSMC 10 |
Music Club / Sep '93 / Gold & Sons / THE / Video Collection / C.M. Distribution.

## WE'RE LEAVIN' IT UP TO YOU.
**Tracks:** Anyone who had a heart: Warwick, Dionne / Wishin' and hopin': Warwick, Dionne / Up on the roof: Drifters / I don't want to cry: Jackson, Chuck / I

---

wake up crying: Jackson, Chuck / Two people in the world: Imperials / He's so fine: Chiffons / Boys: Shirelles / Will you still love me tomorrow: Shirelles / Spanish Harlem: King, Ben E. / Louie, Louie: Kingsmen / Money: Kingsmen / I'm leaving it up to you: Dale & Grace / Mama didn't lie: Bradley, Jan.
■ LP . . . . . . . . . . . . . . . . . . . WCS 1004
Wand / Feb '71.

## WEST 25TH.
**Tracks:** Not Advised.
| | |
|---|---|
| CD | CHIP 151 |
| LP Set | HIP 151 |
| MC | HIPC 151 |
Jive / Aug '94 / BMG.

## WEST 25TH CLASSICS.
**Tracks:** Not Advised.
| | |
|---|---|
| CD | CHIP 152 |
| LP | HIP 152 |
| MC | HIPC 152 |
Jive / Oct '94 / BMG.

## WEST COAST WINNERS (R & B 1953-67).
**Tracks:** Not Advised.
■ LP . . . . . . . . . . . . . . . . . . . BLP 103
Moonshine / Feb '85.

## WEST END STORY VOL.1.
**Tracks:** Heartbeat: Gardner, Taana / Let's go dancin': Sparque / Heat you up (melt you down): Lites, Shirley / Do it to the music: Raw Silk / Can't you feel it: Michelle / Rescue me: Thomas, Sybil / Time: Stone (1) / You can't have your cake: Taylor, Brenda.
| | |
|---|---|
| CD | 110652 |
| LP | 110651 |
| MC | 110654 |
Musidisc / Jun '93 / Vital Distribution / Discovery / A.D.A. Distribution / Harmonia Mundi (UK).

## WEST END STORY VOL.2.
**Tracks:** Work that body: Gardner, Taana / It's all over my face: Loose Joints / Another man: Mason, Barbara / Give your body up to music: Nichols, Billy / Ride on the rhythm: Mahogany / Girl I like the way you move: Stone (1) / Do'in the best that I can: Lavette, Betty / Just in time: Rawsilk.
| | |
|---|---|
| CD | 110692 |
| LP | 110691 |
| MC | 110694 |
Musidisc / Aug '93 / Vital Distribution / Discovery / A.D.A. Distribution / Harmonia Mundi (UK).

## WEST END STORY VOL.3.
**Tracks:** When you touch me: Gardner, Taana / Let me feel your heartbeat: Glass / Music turns me on: Sparque / When the shit hits the fan: Master Boogie's song & dance / Disco dance: Michele / Chillin' out: Brooks, Inez / Speak well: Philly U.S.A. / Keep on dancin': Phrase II.
| | |
|---|---|
| CD | 110942 |
| MC | 110491 |
Musidisc / Nov '93 / Vital Distribution / Discovery / A.D.A. Distribution / Harmonia Mundi (UK).

## WEST END STORY VOL.4.
**Tracks:** No frills: Gardner, Taana / Take some time: Sparque / Searchin' for some lovin': Trusty, Debbie / I get lifted: Sweet Life / Hot summer nights: Love Club / Don't I ever cross your mind: Mason, Barbara / Hold me, squeeze me: Michele / People come dance: Holt, Ednah & Starluv.
| | |
|---|---|
| CD | 111872 |
| LP | 111871 |
Musidisc / Jan '94 / Vital Distribution / Discovery / A.D.A. Distribution / Harmonia Mundi (UK).

## WESTBOUND SOUND OF DETROIT.
**Tracks:** Gonna spread the news: Unique Blend / Yes I'm in love: Unique Blend / Does he treat you better: Unique Blend / Monny & Daddy: Unique Blend / Old fashioned woman: Unique Blend / Lonely in a crowd: Superlatives / I don't know how (to say I love you) don't walk away: Superlatives / Things are looking up: Detroit Emeralds / Rosetta Stone: Detroit Emeralds / That's all I got: Detroit Emeralds / If you need me, call me (and I'll come running): Fantastic Four / I'm falling in love (I feel good all over): Fantastic Four / What's it all about: Counts / Happy days: Magictones / Everything's gonna be alright: Magictones / I've changed: Magictones / I'll make it up to you: Magictones / Trying real hard (to make the grade): Magictones / I don't what it is but it sho is funky: Mighty Elegant / I find myself falling in love with you: Mighty Elegant / What am I gonna do: Houston outlaws / I'm loving you, you're leaving me: Motivations / I love you: Motivations / My baby ain't no plaything: New Holidays / When I'm back on my feet: Unknown artist/s.
CD . . . . . . . . . . . . . . . . . . . CDSEWD 065
Westbound / Aug '94 / Pinnacle.

---

## WHAT IS FUNK (12 Funk Classics).
**Tracks:** Do it ('til you're satisfied): B T Express / What is funk: Rare Gems Odyssey / Get the funk ou[t] my face: Brothers Johnson / Take your time (do i[t] right): S.O.S. Band / Spirit of the boogie: Kool & The Gang / Don't stop the music: Yarbrough & Peoples / Funky nassau: Beginning Of The End / Love injec[-] tion: Trussel / U + Me = Love: Undisputed Truth / Yum yum gimme some: Fatback Band / Finders keepers: Chairmen Of The Board / Express: B T Express.
CD . . . . . . . . . . . . . . . . . . . RNBCD 10[8]
Connoisseur Collection / Apr '94 / Pinnacle.

## WHAT'S HAPPENING..STATESIDE.
**Tracks:** Ready, willing and able: Holiday, Jimmy & Clydie King / Dead end street: Rawls, Lou / Working on your case: O'Jays / Lookin' for a love: Womack, Bobby / Girls from Texas: Lewis, Jimmy / As long as I have you: Mimms, Garnet / I'm waitin' at the station: Neville, Aaron / Tell it like it is: Swan, Bettye / Nutbush City Limits: Turner, Ike & Tina / Better use your head: Imperials / Mockingbird: Foxx, Inez & Charlie / Who's that lady: Isley Brothers / Mardi gras in: Professor Longhair / Ain't nothing you can do: Hill, Z.Z. / Lot of love: Banks, Homer.
| | |
|---|---|
| ■ LP | SSLX 1 |
| ■ MC | TCSSLX 1 |
Stateside / Mar '87.

## WHAT'S THE QUESTION VOL.2.
**Tracks:** Is that asking too much: Bryant, Don / Wha[t] have you done to my heart: Imported Moods / Wha[t] is this feeling: Green, Al / What made you change: McGee, Eddie / Will you be my man (in the morning): Quiet Elegance / How can you mend a broken heart: Green, Al / How can I believe in you: Known Facts [/] How's your lovelife: Quiet Elegance / Hello, how have you been: Clayton, Willie / Baby, what's wrong with you: Green, Al / How strong is a woman: Peebles, Ann / Did you ever have the blues: Bryant, Don / Who's gonna love you: Johnson, Syl / Baby please: West, Norm.
CD . . . . . . . . . . . . . . . . . . . HILOCD 9[
Hi / Mar '94 / Pinnacle.

## WHEN A MAN LOVES A WOMAN.
**Tracks:** Young girl: Puckett, Gary & The Union Gap / I've got you under my skin: Torme, Mel / Time for love: Bennett, Tony / Way we were: Hill, Vince / Most beautiful girl: Rich, Charlie / Tears on my pillow: Nash, Johnny / Nearness of you: Torme, Mel / Very special love song: Rich, Charlie / Misty blue: Hill, Vince / Together: Smith, O.C. / Cupid: Nash, Johnny [/] (I left my heart) in: Bennett, Tony / Lady Willpower: Puckett, Gary & The Union Gap / Behind closed doors: Rich, Charlie / Folks who live on the hill: Torme, Mel / Stranger in paradise: Bennett, Tony / When I fall in love: Hill, Vince / Little green apples: Smith, O.C. / Woman woman: Puckett, Gary & The Union Gap / Hold me tight.
MC Set . . . . . . . . . . . . . . . . . . . DTOL 1028[2]
Ditto / Feb '90 / Pickwick.

## WHEN A MAN LOVES A WOMAN.
**Tracks:** Not Advised.
■ LP . . . . . . . . . . . . . . . . . . . PER 33 860[7]
Perfect / Nov '87.

## WHEN A MAN LOVES A WOMAN.
**Tracks:** Not Advised.
CD . . . . . . . . . . . . . . . . . . . HRCD 8053[
Disky / May '94 / THE.

## WHEN A MAN LOVES A WOMAN.
**Tracks:** Not Advised.
| | |
|---|---|
| CD | DINCD 88 |
| MC | DINMC 88 |
Dino / Aug '94 / Pinnacle.

## WHEN A MAN LOVES A WOMAN (16 Love Songs With Soul).
**Tracks:** When a man loves a woman: Sledge, Percy / (Your love keeps lifting me) Higher and higher: Wilson, Jackie / Have you seen her: Chi-Lites / So in love: Mayfield, Curtis / I'd rather go blind: James, Etta / That's the way I feel about cha: Womack, Bobby / Shoop shoop song (It's in his kiss): Everett, Betty / Gimme little sign: Wood, Brenton / Rescue me: Bass, Fontella / Ruler of my heart: Thomas, Irma / Tell it like it is: Neville, Aaron / I had a talk with my man: Collier, Mitty / (If loving you is wrong) I don't want to be right: Ingram, Luther / Every beat of my heart: Knight, Gladys & The Pips / You send me: Cooke, Sam / Hold what you've got: Tex, Joe.
CD . . . . . . . . . . . . . . . . . . . CPCD 8057
Charly / Sep '94 / Charly.

## WHOLE LOT OF SOUL IS HERE.
**Tracks:** Not too old to cry: Trends / Your little sister: Marvelows / For crying out loud: Sigler, Bunny / I

■ DELETED

alkin' bout you babe: *Little Charles & The Sidewders* / Baby I need your love: *Williams, Bobby* / I eed you: *Impressions* / Are you trying to cross over: *Virettes* / Life of the party: *Craig, Anna* / Satisfaction uaranteed: *Burkes, Donnie* / Changing by the minute: *Fletcher, Darrow* / Get off my back: *Sims, Marvin L.* / Yum yum tree: *Bland, Bobby* / Whole lot f soul is gone: *Conerly, Bobby* / Paying the cost to be the boss: *King, B.B.* / It rained 40 days and nights: ꞇꞇeen, Garland* / Young lover: *Lee, Little Mr.*.
  **LP** . . . . . . . . . . . . . . . . . . . . . . **KENT 048**
ent / Jan '86.

## VIGAN CASINO STORY, THE.
**Tracks:** Flasher: *Mistura* / Long after tonight is all ꞷver: *Radcliffe, Jimmy* / We go together: *August & ꞷueen* / Tears: *Roye, Lee* / You've been away: ꞷoye, Lee* / Take away the pain stain: *Autin, Patty* / ꞷve Adam & Eve: *Reflections (2)* / Dance, dance, ꞷance: *Casualeers* / If you ask me: *Williams, Jerry* / ꞷetter use your head: *Imperials* / Joker: *Myslestones* / Ski-ing in the snow: *Invitations* / Time will pass you ꞷy: *Legend, Tobi* / I can't help lovin' you: *Anka, Paul* / I'll always need you: *Courtney, Dean* / Stick by me ꞷaby: *Salvadors* / You dont' love me: *Epitome Of ꞷound* / I never knew: *Foster, Eddie* / Put your arms ꞷround me: *Sherry's* / I really love you: *Tomangoes* / ꞷm on my way: *Parrish, Dean.*
  **D** . . . . . . . . . . . . . . . . . . . . . . . **GSCD 051**
ꞷoldmine / Sep '94 / Vital Distribution.

## WIND DOWN ZONE.
**Tracks:** Happy: *Surface* / Stay: *Controllers* / Curious: ꞷidnight Star* / Something in the way you make me ꞷeel: *Mills, Stephanie* / Gotta get you home tonight: ꞷilde, Eugene* / Oasis: *Baylor, Helen* / It never rains ꞷ Southern California: *Tony Toni Tone* / Portugese ꞷve: *Marie, Teena* / Everybody loves the sunshine: ꞷyers, Roy* / Why people fall in love: *McNeir, Ronnie* / Heaven sent you: *Clarke, Stanley* / Tik tok: *Lorenzo* / Don't be so distant: *Taylor, Gary* / Buttercup: *Anderson, Carl.*
  **D** . . . . . . . . . . . . . . . . . . . . . **CDELV 04**
  **P** . . . . . . . . . . . . . . . . . . . . . **LPELV 04**
  **C.** . . . . . . . . . . . . . . . . . . . **MCELV 04**
ꞷassion (1) / Feb '93 / Pinnacle.

## VIND DOWN ZONE VOL.2.
**Tracks:** Between the sheets: *Isley Brothers* / No ꞷs gonna love you: *S.O.S. Band* / New York eyes: ꞷicole (1)* / Woman to Woman: *Brown, Shirley* / In the ꞷick of it: *Russell, Brenda* / Stay away from you: ꞷallin, Chris* / Fool's paradise: *Morgan, Meli'sa* / ꞷover to lover: *Anderson, Maxi* / Silver shadow: ꞷtlantic Starr* / Roses are red: *Mac Band* / Babyface: ꞷerc & Monk* / Heaven: *Winans, Bebe & Cece* / Rock ꞷreek park: *Blackbyrds* / Sugar free: *Juicy.*
  **D** . . . . . . . . . . . . . . . . . . . . . **CDELV 06**
  **P** . . . . . . . . . . . . . . . . . . . . . **LPELV 06**
  **C.** . . . . . . . . . . . . . . . . . . . **MCELV 06**
ꞷassion/Debut/Scratch Music / May '93 / Pinnacle / ꞷMV.

## VIND DOWN ZONE VOL.3.
**Tracks:** Sexy girl: *Thomas, Lillo* / Ev'ry little bit: ꞷcott, Millie* / Genie: *B B & Q Band* / There ain't ꞷothin' (like your lovin'): *Laurence, Paul* / I'm the one ꞷor you: *Whispers* / Get in touch with me: *Collage* / ꞷour smile: *Rene & Angela* / I need your lovin: ꞷilliams, Alyson* / My sensitivity: *Vandross, Luther* / ꞷddictive love: *Winans, Bebe & Cece* / Never say ꞷoodbye to love: *Moore, Rene* / Can't wait: *Payne, ꞷreda* / When we're making love: *Lasalle, Denise* / ꞷre you ready: *Robbins, Rockie.*
  **D** . . . . . . . . . . . . . . . . . . . . . **CDELV 11**
  **P** . . . . . . . . . . . . . . . . . . . . . **LPELV 11**
  **C.** . . . . . . . . . . . . . . . . . . . **MCELV 11**
ꞷassion/Debut/Scratch Music / Dec '93 / Pinnacle / ꞷMV.

## VIND DOWN ZONE VOL.4.
**Tracks:** Make it last forever: *Sweat, Keith* / Games: ꞷooker, Chuckii* / Please be mine: *Belle, Regina* / ꞷet's start love over: *Jaye, Miles* / Nite & day: *Sure, ꞷ B.* / You can't turn me away: *Striplin, Sylvia* / I ꞷelieve in love: *Harris, Major* / Rockin' you eternally: ꞷare, Leon* / Don't stop doin' what cha' do: *Mills, ꞷtephanie* / In the mood: *Davis, Tyrone* / Warm ꞷeather: *Pieces Of A Dream* / Feels like I'm falling in

love: *Bar-Kays* / Strung out for your love: *Four Tops* / Lovers everywhere: *L.T.D.*.
  **CD** . . . . . . . . . . . . . . . . . . . . **CDELV 14**
  **LP** . . . . . . . . . . . . . . . . . . . . **LPELV 14**
  **MC** . . . . . . . . . . . . . . . . . . . **MCELV 14**
Elevate / Apr '94 / 3MV.

## WINDY CITY SOUL.
**Tracks:** Lay it on me: *Maurice & Mac* / Lean on me: *Maurice & Mac* / You left the water running: *Maurice & Mac* / So much love: *Maurice & Mac* / Temptation: *Brothers, Knight* / 'Bout to get me: *Brothers, Knight* / Sinkin' low: *Brothers, Knight* / She's A1: *Brothers, Knight* / Searchin' for my love: *Moore, Bobby & The Rhythm Aces* / How can you do it baby: *Moore, Bobby & The Rhythm Aces* / Hey Mr. DJ: *Moore, Bobby & The Rhythm Aces* / Promise is a promise: *Lasalle, Denise* / Love reputation: *Lasalle, Denise* / Countdown: *Lasalle, Denise* / Love is a five letter word: *Phelps, James* / Wasting time: *Phelps, James* / Oh what a feeling: *Phelps, James.*
  **LP** . . . . . . . . . . . . . . . . . . . . **GCH 8117**
Chess (Charly) / '89.

## WINDY CITY SOUL VOLUME 2.
**Tracks:** Have pity on me: *Young, Billy* / Left the water running: *Young, Billy* / Can you be a one man woman: *Dees, Sam* / Put you back in your place: *Dees, Sam* / Maryanna: *Dees, Sam* / Love starvation: *Dees, Sam* / I'm gonna start a war: *Barbara & The Browns* / I don't want to have to wait: *Barbara & The Browns* / Plenty of room: *Barbara & The Browns* / To know I can't touch: *Barbara & The Browns* / Too much / I tried to tell you / Tell him tonight: *Bollinger, William* / You can lead your woman to the altar: *Bollinger, William.*
  **LP** . . . . . . . . . . . . . . . . . . . . **GCH 8118**
Chess (Charly) / '89.

## WINNER TAKES ALL.
**Tracks:** Not Advised.
  **LP** . . . . . . . . . . . . . . . . . . . . **KENT 035**
Kent / Apr '85.

## WINNERS CIRCLE.
**Tracks:** Love was never: *Meadows, Marion* / If I had to live my life without you: *Harp, Everette* / All over you, all over me: *Germaine, Nikita* / Somebody's been sleeping in my bed: *Brown, Gary* / Say you'll never leave me: *By All Means* / Want to be loved: *Ferrell, Rachelle* / Let's get smooth: *Calloway* / Just an illusion: *Najee* / I've just begun to love you: *Grant, Tom* / Luxury of love: *Peaston, David* / With this heart: *Hiroshima* / Good things: *Abrams, Colonel* / Trilogy of love: *Prince Markie Dee.*
  **CD** . . . . . . . . . . . . . . . . . . . . **CDEXP 2**
  **LP** . . . . . . . . . . . . . . . . . . . . **LPEXP 2**
  **MC** . . . . . . . . . . . . . . . . . . . **MCEXP 2**
Passion/Debut/Scratch Music / Apr '93 / Pinnacle / 3MV.

## WINNERS CIRCLE 2.
**Tracks:** Romantically inspired: *Tashan* / Light of love: *Angie & Debbie* / Wanna make love 2U: *Mansfield, Rodney* / You can't go wrong: *Vertical Hold (1)* / Come a little closer: *Rice, Gene* / Quiet time: *Belle, Regina* / Love tonight: *Walker, Chris* / Where do we go from here: *Steele, Jevetta* / I wanna love: *Moore, Chante* / If you ever loved someone and lost: *Beasley, Walter* / Never too late: *Goodman, Gabrielle* / Wait a minute: *Mahogany Blue* / More today than yesterday: *Company (1)* / Wonderin': *Moten, Wendy.*
  **CD** . . . . . . . . . . . . . . . . . . . . **CDEXP 7**
  **LP** . . . . . . . . . . . . . . . . . . . . **LPEXP 7**
  **MC** . . . . . . . . . . . . . . . . . . . **MCEXP 7**
Expansion / Dec '93 / Pinnacle / Sony / 3MV.

## WOMAN TO WOMAN.
**Tracks:** Woman to woman: *Brown, Shirley* / I've never loved a man the way I loved you: *Franklin, Aretha* / Rescue me: *Bass, Fontella* / I can't stand the rain: *Peebles, Ann* / Oh no not my baby: *Brown, Maxine* / I'd rather go blind: *James, Etta* / Dirty man: *Lee, Laura* / Mockingbird: *Foxx, Inez & Charlie* /

When something is wrong with my baby: *Weston, Kim* / B.A.B.Y.: *Thomas, Carla* / Misty blue: *Moore, Dorothy* / Time is on my side: *Thomas, Irma* / Whatcha gonna do about it: *Troy, Doris* / Fire: *Taylor, Koko* / Greatest love: *Clay, Judy* / Mr. Bigstuff: *Knight, Jean* / Let me down easy: *Lavette, Betty* / Clean up woman: *Wright, Betty* / If loving you is wrong I don't want to be right: *Jackson, Millie* / Stay with me baby: *Ellison, Lorraine.*
  **CD** . . . . . . . . . . . . . . . . . . **VSOPCD 184**
  **CD** . . . . . . . . . . . . . . . . . . . **RNBCD 101**
  **MC** . . . . . . . . . . . . . . . . . . **VSOPMC 184**
  **MC** . . . . . . . . . . . . . . . . . . . **RNBMC 101**
Connoisseur Collection / Apr '93 / Pinnacle.

## YOU BETTER BELIEVE IT.
**Tracks:** You better believe it: *Borders Tony* / I think I'd do it: *Hill, Z.Z.* / Since I fell for you: *Brandon, Bill* / Living high on the hog: *Borders Tony* / He kept on talking: *Varner, Don* / Faithful and true: *Hill, Z.Z.* / Cornbread woman: *Borders Tony* / Masquerade: *Varner, Don* / When you get what you want: *Brandon, Bill* / Cheaters never win: *Borders Tony* / Handshaking: *Varner, Don* / Home just ain't home (at suppertime): *Hill, Z.Z.* / Lonely weekends: *Borders Tony* / Strangest feeling: *Brandon, Bill* / I'm still in love with you: *Varner, Don* / It's a hang up baby: *Hill, Z.Z.*.
  **LP** . . . . . . . . . . . . . . . . . . . . **CRB 1223**
Charly R&B / Apr '89.

## YOU THRILL MY SOUL (Female & Girl Groups From The Early Stax Sessions).
**Tracks:** Same thing: *Thomas, Carla* / Here it comes again: *Thomas, Carla* / I can't stay: *Thomas, Carla* / Heavenly angel: *Tonettes* / Stolen angel: *Tonettes* / Unhand that man: *Tonettes* / Gone for good: *Rene, Wendy* / Same guy: *Rene, Wendy* / Love at first sight: *Stephens, Barbara* / Heartbreaker: *Parker, Deanie* / Ask him: *Parker, Deanie* / Love is like a flower: *Stephens, Barbara* / Just one touch: *Parker, Deanie* / Ain't enough hours in the day: *Thomas, Carla* / Gosh I'm lucky: *Thomas, Carla* / He hasn't failed me yet: *Rene, Wendy* / Crying all by myself: *Rene, Wendy* / Last love: *Rene, Wendy* / Crowded park: *Rene, Wendy* / Can't stay away: *Rene, Wendy* / Tell me: *Tonettes* / Come to me: *Tonettes* / Do boys keep diaries: *Thomas, Carla.*
  **CD** . . . . . . . . . . . . . . . . . . . **CDSXD 088**
Stax / Sep '93 / Pinnacle.

## ZOMBA SOUL COMPILATION.
**Tracks:** Not Advised.
  **CD** . . . . . . . . . . . . . . . . . . . **EMPRCD 548**
  **MC** . . . . . . . . . . . . . . . . . . . **EMPRMC 548**
Emporio / Nov '94 / THE / C.M. Distribution.

534

# USEFUL ADDRESSES

## PERIODICALS

**Blues & Soul**
153 Praed Street
London W2 1RL
Tel: 0171-402 6869
Fax: 0171-723 1362

**Echoes**
7 - 9 Charlotte Street
London W1 1HD
Tel: 0171-436 4540
Fax: 0171-436 4573

**Soul Buyer**
63A Bruce Grove
London
N17 6RN
Tel: 0181-808 4554
Fax: 0181-365 0143

**Touch Magazine**
Studio 606
8 Nursery Road
London
SW9 8BP
Tel: 0171-738 7308

## MERCHANDISE

**Right Track**
P.O. Box 251
Northampton
Northants
NN5 6RT
Tel: 0850 286374

## RETAILERS

**Black Note Records**
262 London Road
Westcliff-on-Sea
Essex
SS0 7LB
Tel/Fax: 01702 431219

**Crazy Beat**
87A Corbots Tey Road
Upminster
Essex
RM14 2AH
Tel: 01708 228678
Fax: 01708 640946

**Expansion**
56 Swan Street
Manchester
M4 5JU
Tel: 0161-832 1364

**Groove Shelter Music**
12 Kentish Town Road
London NW1
Tel: 0171-267 8532

**Hot Biscuit Records**
P.O. Box 18
St Leonards on Sea
East Sussex
TN37 6XS
Tel: 01424 427174

**Jaffa Spins (Mail Order)**
43B Crowborough Road
Southend-on-Sea
Essex
SS2 6LW
Tel: 01702 611761
Fax: 01702 611761

**Jumbo Records**
5 - 6 St Johns Centre
Leeds
West Yorkshire
LS2 8LQ
Tel: 01532 455570
Fax: 01532 425019

**Record Corner**
27 Bedford Hill
London SW12 9EX
Tel: 0181-673 1066
Fax: 0181-675 6665

**Red Records**
500 Brixton Road
London
SW9 8EQ
Tel: 0171-274 4476
Fax: 0171-274 5896

**Rhythm 'N' Bass**
1 Witney Chambers
Longbridge Road
Barking
Essex
Tel: 0181-507 3378
Fax: 0181-507 3378

**Soul Bowl Records**
P.O. Box 3
Kings Lynn
Norfolk
Tel: 01553 840895
Fax: 01553 841033

**Soul Brother Records**
1 Keswick Road
London
SW15 2HL
Tel: 0181-875 1018
Fax: 0181-871 0180

**Soul Explosion (Mail Order)**
Capel Mair Farm
Nantyffin
Brechfa
Carmarthen
Dyfed
SA32 7RE
Tel: 01267 202322
Fax: 01267 202322

**Souled Out CD's**
Broadway Studios
28 Tooting High Street
Wandsworth
London
SW17 0RG
Tel: 0181-402 9525
Fax: 0181-659 4427

**Soul-Utions (Mail Order)**
P.O. Box 22
Grantham
Lincs
NG31 6AA
Tel: 01400 281876
Fax: 01400 282193

**Time Is Right Records**
27 Goldhawk Road
London
W12 8QQ
Tel: 0181-748 2792

**Voices From The Shadows**
Unit 2D
Hull Road
Withernsea
East Yorkshire
HU19 2EQ
Tel: 01964 614873

536

# MAIN DISTRIBUTORS

## 3MV

2A/B Hillgate Place
London
SW12 9ER
Tel: 0181-675 9947
Fax: 0181-675 9948/8125

## ACD

Unit 2
Chapman's Park Ind Estate
377/378 High Road
London
NW10 9LF
Tel: 0181-451 4494
Fax: 0181-451 5555

## BMG

Bedford House
69-79 Fulham High Street
London
SW6 3JW
Tel: 0171-973 0011
Fax: 0171-973 0354

## Charly

156 - 166 Ilderton Road
London
SE15 1NT
Tel: 0171-639 8603
Fax: 0171-639 2532

## Complete

12 Pepys Court
84 The Chase
Clapham Common
London
SW4 0NF
Tel: 0171-498 9666
Fax: 0171-498 1828

## Direct Distribution

50 Stroud Green Road
London
N4 3EF
Tel: 0171-263 1240
Fax: 0171-281 5671

## EMI Records

20 Manchester Square
London
W1A 1ES
Tel: 0171-486 4488
Fax: 0171-465 0743

## Empire

6 Chestnut Avenue
Wallderslade
Chatham
Kent
ME4 9AJ
Tel: 01634 200967
Fax: 01634 672214

## Jazz Music

Glenview
Moylegrove
Cardigan
Dyfed
SA43 3BW
Tel: 01239 86278
Fax: 01239 86296

## Jetstar

155 Acton Lane
London
NW10 7NG
Tel: 0181-961 5818
Fax: 0181-965 7008

## Koch International

24 Concord Road
London
N1 9BE
Tel: 0181-992 7177
Fax: 0181-896 0817

## Pickwick

The Waterfront
Elstree Road
Elstree
Hertfordshire
Tel: 0181-207 6207
Fax: 0181-207 5789

## Pinnacle/New Note

Electron House
Cray Avenue
St Mary Cray
Orpington
Kent
BR5 3PN
Tel: (01689) 870622
Fax: (01689) 878269

## PolyGram

Clyde Works
Grove Road
Romford
Essex
RM6 4QR
Tel: (01708) 755888
Fax: (01708) 736990

## Sony

10 Great Marlborough Street
London
W1V 2LP
Tel: 0171-911 8200
Fax: 0171-911 8600

## Soul Trader

Unit 43
Abbey Business Centre
Ingate Place
London
SW8 3NS
Tel: 0171-498 0732

## SRD

70 Lawrence Road
London
N15 4EG
Tel: 0181-802 3000
Fax: 0181-802 2222

## Timewarp

80 St John's Hill
London
SW11 1SF
Tel: 0171-738 9488
Fax: 0171-738 2278

## Total

Unit 7
Pepys Court
84 The Chase
London SW4 0NF
Tel: 0171-978 2300

## Vital

Portland House
22/24 Portland Square
Bristol BS2 8RZ
Tel: (01272) 446777
Fax: (01272) 446888

## Warner Brothers/WEA

The Warner Building
28 Kensington Church Street
London W8 4EP
Tel: 0171-937 8844
Fax: 0171-938 3901

## Word Records

9 Holdom Avenue
Bletchley
Milton Keynes
Bucks MK1 1QR
Tel: 01908 648440
Fax: 01908 648592